RHS

Inspiring everyone to grow

Plant Finder 2019

Devised by Chris Philip and Realised by Tony Lord

Editor-in-Chief
Janet Cubey

RHS Editors
Dawn Edwards Kálmán Könyves
Neil Lancaster Rosalyn Marshall

Compiler
Lindsay Durrant

British Library Cataloguing Publication Data
A catalogue record for this book is available from the British Library

ISBN 9781907057946

RHS Publisher – Rae Spencer-Jones

RHS Art Editor – Mark Timothy

RHS Prepress Designer – Anthony Masi

RHS Head of Editorial – Chris Young

Designer – Peter Cooling

Printed and bound by CPI WILLIAM CLOWES, Copland Way, Ellough, Beccles, Suffolk, NR34 7TL

The compiler and editors of the RHS Plant Finder have taken every care, in the time available, to check all the information supplied to them by the nurseries concerned. Nevertheless, in a work of this kind containing as it does hundreds of thousands of separate computer encodings, errors and omissions will inevitably occur. The RHS, the Publisher and Editors, cannot accept responsibility for any consequences that may arise from such errors.

If you find any mistakes, we hope that you will let us know so that the matter can be corrected in the next edition.

Front cover photograph: *Pulsatilla vulgaris* (RHS / Neil Hepworth)

Back cover photographs from top left:
Callicarpa bodinieri var. *giraldii* 'Profusion' (RHS / Clive Nichols)
Symphyotrichum novae-angliae 'Brunswick' (RHS / Joanna Kossak)
Prunus domestica 'Czar' (C) AGM (RHS / Tim Sandall)
Daucus carota 'Cosmic Purple' (RHS / Tim Sandall)

The Royal Horticultural Society is the UK's leading gardening charity dedicated to advancing horticulture and promoting good gardening. Its charitable work includes providing expert advice and information, training the next generation of gardeners, creating hands-on opportunities for children to grow plants and conducting research into plants, pests and environmental issues affecting gardeners.

For more information visit www.rhs.org.uk or call 020 3176 5800.

Contents

New Plant Highlights
Janet Cubey *page 7*

Plant Health Threats to our Gardens
Dr Melanie Tuffen *page 25*

General Information *page 33*

Introduction *page 34*
New in this Edition
List of nurseries for plants with more than 30 suppliers
Plants last listed in earlier editions
RHS Online
Application for entry
Acknowledgements *page 35*
Symbols and Abbreviations *page 36*

Extended Glossary *page 37*

Conservation and the Environment *page 42*

Supplementary Keys to the Directory *page 45*
Collectors' References *page 45*
Nomenclatural Notes *page 49*
Classification of Genera *page 50*

How to Use the Plant Directory *page 55*

Using the Plant Directory *page 56*

Plants *page 57*

The Plant Directory *page 58*

AGM Fruit *page 823*

AGM Vegetables *page 835*

RHS Plants for Pollinators *page 853*

Nurseries *page 861*

Using the Nursery Listings *page 863*

How to Use the Nursery Listings *page 864*

Nursery Details by Code *page 866*

Nursery Index by Name *page 950*

Display Advertisements *page 956*

Index of Advertisers *page 958*

Take the RHS home with you
Discover a world of gifts, accessories, home ware, foods and RHS Exclusive collections in our gift shops, along with one of the largest selections of horticultural books available in the UK.
Buy in confidence at our plant centres with the RHS 5 year guarantee on all hardy plants and friendly experts on hand to help answer your questions.
EVERY SALE SUPPORTS
EVERY SALE HELPS
CHARITABLE WORK OF THE
RHS
Inspiring everyone to grow
You can also shop online at **rhsshop.co.uk** and **rhsplants.co.uk**
RHS Registered Charity No. 222879/SC038262

New plant highlights

A celebration of some of the diverse array of plants that are new to the *RHS Plant Finder 2019*. We were delighted to receive more suggestions of significant new plants from our Plant Finder nurseries, some of which are included within my selection together with their thoughts about these plants. Happy browsing!

Author: **Janet Cubey,** Editor-in-Chief

JOHN CULLEN GARDENS LTD

Achillea Moon Dust ('Novaachdus')

Suggested by John Cullen Gardens, which holds a Plant Heritage National Plant Collection of *Achillea*, this compact cultivar with pale yellow flowers is proving "much more popular than the taller ones" and "great for keeping in pots and containers or for the front of the border".

It was raised in the USA by Darwin Perennials from open-pollinated seed of *Achillea* 'Moonshine'. The lacy yarrow foliage is silvery-grey-green, it grows to not much more than 30cm in height, favours full sun and is popular with pollinating insects.

***Ajuga tenorii* Princess Nadia ('Piotrek01')**

Raised by Piotr Szczęsny of Nadia Plants in the Netherlands, and marketed by Plantipp B.V., Princess Nadia has a lot going for her. There's her compact creeping habit, variegated grey-green leaves with cream margins and the dramatic purple-pink overlay to her young leaves and shoots. Then, as you'd expect from a bugle, she has plenty of intense deep blue flowers in spring, producing a high-impact display, and the bonus is that she's said to be repeat flowering too.

This bugle is very hardy and suitable for both sun and shade, provided the soil is well-draining.

Andropogon gerardii 'Red Arrow'

Andropogon is described by Camolin Potting Shed nursery as a "tough and resilient clump-forming grass with deep fibrous roots that allow it to endure drought, neglect and poor soil. New introduction 'Red Arrow' has abundant inflorescences that stay erect. Both stems and leaves have spectacular autumn colouration. It flowers July to October and reaches 1.8m high."

Another new *Andropogon gerardii* cultivar sits alongside European-raised 'Red Arrow' in this year's Plant Directory. Bred in the USA, 'Red October' has red hues on the green leaves in spring, intensifying to burgundy leaves in autumn. One day I hope to see them planted alongside one another too.

CAMOLIN POTTING SHED

CAMOLIN POTTING SHED

Aruncus 'Sparkles'

Shorter than your average goat's beard, this compact hybrid cultivar caught my eye. I've not yet traced its origins but it may possibly be from Sweden – it certainly seems popular there. Frothy plumes of creamy-white flowers in late spring and early summer are followed later in the season by fine yellow-orange autumn colour. This very hardy, moisture-loving plant only grows to 40cm in height, opening up the planting possibilities for this great genus.

Beschorneria yuccoides
FLAMINGO GLOW 'Besys'

Striking, golden-variegated *Beschorneria yuccoides* FLAMINGO GLOW is a mutation that was found by landscape designer Graeme Burton in 2005, in a garden in Hamilton, New Zealand. It has proven to be completely stable when vegetatively reproduced.

The leaves are the typical dark grey-green colour of *Beschorneria yuccoides* at the margins but a prominent, wide, central yellow stripe extends along their full length. The majestic, dark flamingo-pink flowering spikes, produced after several years, give a riotous trio of colours.

Buddleja Berries and Cream 'Pmoore14'

UK breeder Peter Moore of Longstock Park Nursery believes this is the first *Buddleja* with "variegated flowers", with "bicoloured purple and white flowers and a few flowers on each raceme wholly white and a few wholly purple". With an upright habit, it flowers profusely from late July to early September, producing 15–20cm-long spikes. Removing dead flower spikes encourages secondary shoots to develop more flowers. In six years of Peter's trials, "more butterflies were attracted to this one than other cultivars in my garden".

Also new on the scene this year in the butterfly bush world is the Rocketstar Series – cultivars with a low-growing, compact habit but still producing big flowers, this year in pink, indigo or purple.

PROVEN WINNER

VISIONS BV, NETHERLANDS

Carex morrowii 'Everglow' (EverColor Series)

Developed in Ireland by Patrick FitzGerald of FitzGerald Nurseries, this is the first EverColor Series cultivar from *Carex morrowii* (rather than *C. oshimensis*), having arisen from *C. morrowii* 'Fisher's Form'.

The intense orange leaf margins drew me to this cultivar. The leaves have a dark green central stripe but the outer margins change from cream in spring, when new growth emerges, to orange by the end of summer until the end of the year when the colour becomes more bronzed and fades in its intensity.

Great for ground cover or for containers, it forms a neat, tidy mound with mature plants reaching 60cm tall by 50cm wide.

THE BETH CHATTO GARDENS

Corydalis 'Korn's Purple'

Bred by alpine nurseryman Peter Korn in Sweden, 'Korn's Purple' is of hybrid origin, a selected seedling derived from *Corydalis flexuosa*, *C. elata* and *C. capitata*.

Large clusters of deep purple-blue flowers with small white centres are held above ferny green foliage in late spring to early summer. Deciduous and fully hardy, it favours a rich, fertile soil where it can then reach up to 50cm tall.

If paler electric-blue flowers and bronzed foliage are more your preference, 'Porcelain Blue', another new cultivar this year, might be the one for you.

Distylium Blue Cascade 'Piidist-ii'

Bred in the USA by plantsman Michael Dirr, this hybrid in the *Hamamelis* family has parentage involving *Distylium myricoides* and *D. racemosum*.

While the clusters of small dark red flowers in each leaf axil in spring bring joy to the heart, this plant is really grown for its foliage characters. It offers a compact, spreading layered growth habit (up to 75cm tall), dark blue-green mature foliage and maroon purple new growth. It should be hardy in most of the British Isles.

SAPHO

Crocosmia Firestars Series ('Firestarter', 'Hotspot' and 'Scorchio')

The *Crocosmia* Firestars Series has been produced by amateur breeder Paul Lewis from the Isle of Wight, and I'm delighted that three of the five (so far) in the series appear in *RHS Plant Finder* this year. For more than 25 years he's been breeding and selecting *Crocosmia* with the aim of producing ones that thrive, overwinter and flower reliably well.

'Hotspot' is golden yellow with red stripes through the centre of the petals and grows to 75cm tall. 'Firestarter' (pictured), also to 75cm tall, has golden- yellow flowers with a striking orange edge and a central stripe coming out of the red centre. 'Scorchio' is taller, to 90cm, with larger, more orange flowers that still have the central petal stripe. All grow best in full sun with well-drained but moisture-retentive soil.

SEIONT

Dryopteris wallichiana Jurassic Gold 'Hollasic'

Launched by Seiont Nurseries at the Four Oaks Trade Show in 2018, where it won the hardy nursery stock Best New Plant Introduction, Jurassic Gold was discovered by nurseryman Bob Hollister on the Jurassic Coast of Dorset.

It's a hardy fern with rose-bronze new fronds at the start of the season that age to a golden hue before fading to yellow and ultimately turning to green. I can see this make a brightening splash of colour in shady corners of our gardens for years to come.

Eucalyptus gunnii France Bleu ('Rengun')

A dwarf seedling was spotted by a French nurseryman in 2009 and now, after years of trialling, we have France Bleu. With the same silvery-blue-green foliage colour and lovely scent you'd expect from the species, the difference is in the height – it grows to 2m (or 3m) tall. However, if you cut it back once a year it'll stay small enough for container cultivation and retain the smaller juvenile foliage. Or you can plant it out and allow it to become a multi-stemmed shrub, which, without a haircut, will develop the typical adult foliage in subsequent years.

SAPHO

Eryngium × *zabelii* 'Blue Waves'

'Blue Waves' was bred in the UK at Dove Cottage Nursery and grown there for 10 years before being taken up by Hillier Nurseries Ltd and propagated by tissue culture. It was selected for its short, strong, upright, branched stems with numerous flowerheads. The showy bracts are in scale with the height of the stem and the flowers are long-lasting and known to repeat (hence the name), as well as looking good during winter months. While it will grow in a range of soil types, other than wet or waterlogged ones, it does like full sun.

This stunning cultivar was runner-up in the 2018 RHS Chelsea Plant of the Year competition.

Fuchsia Sparkling Silver ('Lowssil')

Selected by Lowaters Nursery of Hampshire, Sparkling Silver is a variegated-leaved fuchsia; the silvery-grey-green leaves have a creamy-white margin. Its large, semi-double flowers have scarlet, slightly swept-back sepals and a purple-mauve, rippled skirt of petals beneath. This bushy cultivar is said to be hardy and, like all fuchsias, does best in full sun or lightly dappled shade, with a moist, fertile soil, in a container or planted out.

Gaillardia 'Apricot Honey'

This new *Gaillardia* was raised by Rosy Hardy of Hardy's Cottage Garden Plants in Hampshire, where she has has been evaluating and propagating it for more than two years. Rosy says: "As its names suggests, 'Apricot Honey' produces large, soft apricot flowers throughout the summer with a height and spread of 70cm x 80cm."

Grown in a sunny spot, in a container or planted out, this is a popular plant for pollinating insects, with its long flowering period through to the first frosts.

Hydrangea Runaway Bride Snow White ('Ushyd0405')

The clear winner of the 2018 RHS Chelsea Plant of the Year, Runaway Bride Snow White was bred by Ushio Sakazaki (who also created the Surfinia petunias). It's an interspecific hybrid with unusual qualities that we're not yet used to seeing in hydrangeas, such as a graceful weeping habit and flowering from both terminal and lateral buds. This gives a profusion of creamy-white lacecap flowers in late spring and summer, reblooming until autumn. I expect we'll see more in this breeding line.

Lonicera japonica var. *repens* Pink Aperitif ('Crowthlon')

Pink Aperitif is an apt name for this stable mutation of creeping Japanese honeysuckle, *Lonicera japonica* var. *repens*, which was selected in the UK. The young foliage is first pink then cream when it appears in spring before fading to green in summer. Scented, red-flushed flowers appear while the foliage is still flushed with pink and cream; a combination to delight two senses at once.

Primula 'Tregor Truffle'

Barnhaven Primroses describe their cultivar 'Tregor Truffle': "This eye-catching double primrose was introduced in 2018 by Barnhaven – the latest in a long line of beautiful double primroses from our nursery's breeding programme, which started in the 1930s. From early–late spring, it produces abundant, luscious rich purple blooms, generously frothed with white, and nicely centred in crisp green foliage. Hardy to -20°C, it appreciates a semi-shady position with rich soil and being divided every few years."

ORANGEPIPPINTREES.CO.UK

ORANGEPIPPINTREES.CO.UK

Prunus avium 'Black Oliver'

'Black Oliver' is a traditional English mid-season black cherry that originated in Herefordshire in the early 20th century. It's not been readily available until now – this year six nurseries are listing it in the Plant Directory. It isn't self-fertile but it's in Flowering group 3 and flowers in midseason, so you'll easily find a pollination partner. The well-sized black fruit has sweet, juicy, dark red flesh. It also has some resistance to canker and is not prone to cracking.

MILLAIS NURSERIES

Rhododendron 'Jessica de Rothschild'

Millais Nurseries says: "Although bred by Edmund de Rothschild in 1966, 'Jessica de Rothschild' was not registered with the RHS until 1996, and we are the first nursery to propagate it from Exbury Gardens. Perfect for the smaller garden, it has a neat compact habit, and flowers profusely from a young age. We are launching it at the 2019 RHS Chelsea Flower Show, to mark the Centenary of Lionel de Rothschild starting his gardens at Exbury. Opening a light greenish-yellow, flushed yellowish-pink at the edges, with a glowing deeper yellow centre, the strong flowers sit in a neat rounded truss above a compact plant with good foliage. It grows to 100–125cm in 10 years, and requires moist acid soil."

Rosa TOTTERING-BY-GENTLY 'Auscartoon'

After not selecting a rose for my shortlist in 2018, I felt I should this year and TOTTERING-BY-GENTLY is just one of many I could have chosen. The graceful purity and simplicity of the single yellow flowers with golden stamens, held in large open sprays, drew me to this rose. Its light musky scent (a scent is a must for me in a rose) is described as having "fresh notes of orange peel" and it's also a repeat flowerer.

Bred by David Austin Roses, this English shrub rose was named in 2018 for the 25th anniversary of the cartoon of the same name.

DAVID AUSTIN ROSES

MIDDLETON NURSERIES

Salvia 'Amethyst Lips'

Already proving popular, one of the latest "lips" salvia enters this year's book with the highest number of nurseries supplying it.

Bred in Norfolk by a keen amateur breeder, 'Amethyst Lips' has white flowers edged with dark purple – a great new colour to sit alongside original 'Hot Lips' (white edged with red) and more recent Pink Lips ('Jeremy'; white edged with pink). With all of them, at different points in the season, with different temperatures, you can also get pure colour flowers or pure white flowers, or all three at once.

'Cherry Lips' (white edged with cherry red), seemingly from the same breeder, also appears for the first time. With four colours, from three different origins, are there any more on the horizon?

HARDY'S COTTAGE GARDEN PLANTS

Salvia 'Kisses and Wishes'

Different origins are true for the "wish" salvias too. 'Wendy's Wish' (purple-pink) arose in Australia in 2005, 'Ember's Wish' (bright orange-red) and 'Love and Wishes' (dark purple-red) also hailed from Australia as a sport and a hybrid respectively. Then last year 'Kisses and Wishes' was launched, another sport of 'Wendy's Wish' that was found in a garden of a plantswoman in West Sussex.

It grows to 75cm tall and, like all salvia, does best in a warm, sunny position. This one is only hardy to 0°C, so needs winter protection. It flowers continuously from early summer to autumn, with vibrant pink flowers and green-flushed-red calyxes.

Silene Sparkling Rose 'Insilsparo'

Bred by nurserywoman Silvia Hofmann, this sterile interspecific hybrid of *Silene asterias* and *S. noctiflora* is marketed by Innovaplant. Packed heads of intense campion-pink flowers have an impactful flowering period from early summer to autumn. Final flowering height is up to 45cm and it is described as being "cold resistant but not fully hardy". It suits a container or border planting in sun or light shade.

HAYLOFT PLANTS

LISA WESLEY @ GROWILD NURSERY

Synurus excelsus

And last but by no means least, a species that should be better known. It was submitted by Growild, one of our new *RHS Plant Finder* nurseries, with this description: "A majestic thistle relative from the sunny mountain slopes and forest edges of Japan, it makes an excellent architectural focal point. The large, nodding heads of deepest burgundy with a sugar-frosting of snow-white pollen are a magnet for bees and produced from September well into October, extending the season of interest in the garden. Even when not in flower, the bristly flower buds, which look like they're intricately wound with spider's webs, are carried on stems up to a stately 1.8m tall and really make an impact at the back of the border for weeks on end.

It prefers a sunny position in moist soil, but performs well even on heavy clay."

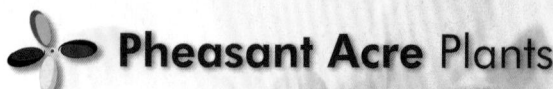

Traditional rose gardens are endangered by exotic pathogens, such as rose rosette virus, arriving on imported plants

Plant health threats to our gardens

Plant pests and diseases invading the UK are on the increase – and many first arrive here on imported plants. By making informed choices about where they source their plants, gardeners can play an important role in protecting the UK's plant health

Author: **Dr Melanie Tuffen,** RHS Biosecurity Coordinator

Xylella has caused devastation in Italian olive groves (right), and outbreaks have also been reported from several other European countries (see map, far right)

Pests and diseases are a normal part of gardening, and there are ways we can control them to limit impacts. Pests and diseases arriving from overseas on imported plants, seeds and timber can be more damaging than native pests. Our garden plants may have no natural defences against them, having never been exposed to them before, and natural enemies that help control our garden pests may not be able to attack these exotic invaders.

Xylella fastidiosa in Europe

Many new pests and diseases have entered Europe in recent years, but one of the biggest threats to plant health in Europe in decades is the arrival of the bacterial pathogen *Xylella fastidiosa*. Native to the Americas, this pathogen was first recorded in Europe in 2013 in Italy. Since then, outbreaks have been detected in France, Spain, Portugal and Germany.

Xylella causes a disease called bacterial leaf scorch – because infected leaves of plants look scorched and dry, similar to the symptoms of drought.

The host range of *Xylella* is huge: more than 350 different plant species have been recorded as hosts. Some plants are more susceptible to the disease than others: olives are dying in their tens of thousands in Italy, but hosts such as lavender and rosemary show very few symptoms – but can act as an unseen source of the disease.

In Europe, *Xylella* is spread by the common froghopper, also called meadow spittle bug, owing to the "cuckoo spit" produced by its immature stage on plants.

Impacts of *Xylella* in Europe have been huge – not only from the bacteria killing hosts, but also from the implementation of measures to try to control the disease, which has led to the destruction of many additional plants.

The spread of *Xylella* in Europe

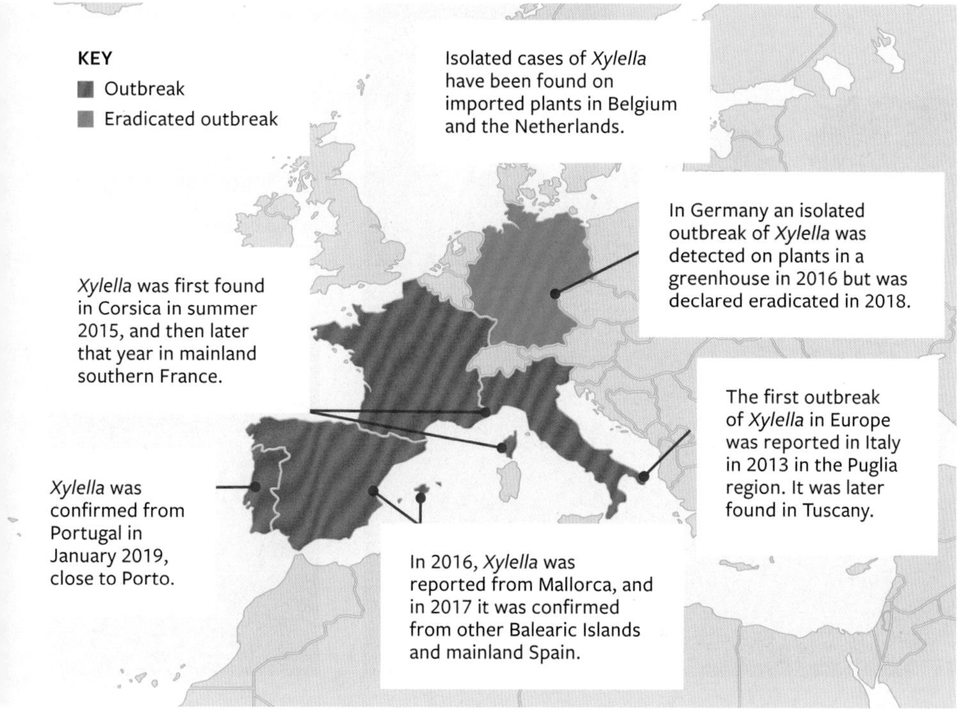

KEY
Outbreak
Eradicated outbreak
Isolated cases of *Xylella* have been found on imported plants in Belgium and the Netherlands.
In Germany an isolated outbreak of *Xylella* was detected on plants in a greenhouse in 2016 but was declared eradicated in 2018.
Xylella was first found in Corsica in summer 2015, and then later that year in mainland southern France.
The first outbreak of *Xylella* in Europe was reported in Italy in 2013 in the Puglia region. It was later found in Tuscany.
Xylella was confirmed from Portugal in January 2019, close to Porto.
In 2016, *Xylella* was reported from Mallorca, and in 2017 it was confirmed from other Balearic Islands and mainland Spain.

Plant health regulations

Regulations on the import of plants into the UK help reduce the risk of pests and diseases being introduced. The rules are different if you are importing from the European Union (EU) compared to outside of the EU. Plants fall into three categories when imported: prohibited, controlled and uncontrolled.

Prohibited – plants that are so high risk they are prohibited from being imported from certain regions.

Controlled – plants that can be imported, but have to meet certain criteria and be accompanied by official documentation.

All plants from outside the EU, and certain plants from within the EU, are controlled.

Uncontrolled – plants that have no specific criteria for their import – this only applies to certain plant species from the EU.

Before importing any plants, you should check with the Animal and Plant Health Agency (APHA) whether there are any requirements. The UK has a scheme where the APHA must be informed before certain tree species are imported from the EU because of the pests or diseases they could carry (see p29 for more information).

Some USA rose gardens have been completely wiped out (left) by the deadly rose rosette virus (below)

When an infected plant is found, all *Xylella* hosts within 100 metres of it have to be destroyed by law. Therefore, because the pathogen has such a wide host range, a single infected plant in a garden can lead to huge losses.

The threat of rose rosette

The USA is facing a deadly threat to rose plants. Rose rosette virus is a fatal disease that has been spreading rapidly, completely destroying some rose gardens.

Infected roses show various symptoms including stunted growth, excessive thorn production and the appearance of many succulent, red shoots. The plants become highly sensitive to frost damage and are often killed over winter.

The virus is spread by minuscule mites, too small to be seen with the naked eye, which could be easily imported with dormant bare-rooted roses or budwood.

What gardeners can do

The message is simple when it comes to importing plants: wherever possible, use British-sourced and -grown plants. Because the UK is located off the coast of mainland Europe, most pests that arrive here come on traded material, with imported plants being a major source of new pests and diseases.

By favouring home-grown material, and understanding and adhering to plant health regulations when importing from abroad, we can help ensure healthy gardens for many more generations to come.

High-risk plants

The following plants are susceptible to different pests and diseases, and the Animal and Plant Health Agency (APHA) must be informed prior to their importation to the UK. Email: planthealth.info@apha.gsi.gov.uk Phone: 01904 405138

1 Ash (*Fraxinus excelsior*)

At the time of press, to help prevent the spread of the deadly ash dieback disease, importation of ash trees is prohibited. If this prohibition is lifted, ash trees will be subject to importation pre-notification.

2 Elm (*Ulmus minor* var. *vulgaris*)

Elms are returning to the British landscape as new cultivars become available that are resistant to Dutch elm disease, which wiped out many elms in the 1970s. But sadly there are also new threats, such as elm yellows disease and the recently introduced elm zig zag sawfly.

3 Oak (*Quercus robur*)

Our iconic British oak trees are threatened by a range of pests that are currently absent from the UK. In 2005, oak processionary moth was introduced to London, and measures are in place to try to stop its spread. The tiny hairs of its caterpillars can irritate the human skin.

© CROWN

4 Olive (*Olea europaea*)

Olive is a major host of *Xylella* and despite measures to control its spread, infected olives have still been found moving in trade. These imported olives are at high risk of introducing *Xylella* to the UK.

5 Pine (*Pinus*)

In Europe, pine processionary moth is a serious pest of pine trees. Like the oak processionary moth, its caterpillar hairs can also cause skin rashes, eye problems and sore throats.

6 Plane (*Platanus*)

Plane trees line many streets in the UK, but sadly in Europe they are succumbing to plane wilt fungus. Introduction of this disease could negatively affect our city streets, resulting in the removal of often historic trees. Another threat is the plane lace bug, which can also give a nasty bite!

7 *Prunus*

All types of *Prunus* (those grown for fruit and flowers) are included within the pre-notification scheme. *Prunus* is a host of *Xylella* in Europe, and a shot hole disease of cherry laurel, currently absent from the UK, could also be introduced on imported plants.

8 Sweet chestnut (*Castanea sativa*)

Two pests of sweet chestnut have recently entered the UK. The oriental chestnut gall wasp can cause aesthetic damage to plants, but the fungal disease sweet chestnut blight is more serious, with potential to kill trees, especially younger ones.

Peter Beales
World Leaders in Classic Roses
Mail Order Free Catalogue
Plant Centre Display Gardens
www.classicroses.co.uk
01953 454707

I
GENERAL INFORMATION

INTRODUCTION

The *RHS Plant Finder* exists to put enthusiastic gardeners in touch with suppliers of plants. It is comprehensively updated every year.

The book is divided into two related sections: **PLANTS** and **NURSERIES**.

PLANTS includes an A-Z Directory of around 78,000 plant names, against which are listed a series of nursery codes. These codes point the reader to the full nursery details contained in the **NURSERIES** section towards the back of the book.

It is important to remember when ordering plants that many of the nurseries listed in the book are small, family-run businesses that propagate their own material. They cannot, therefore, guarantee to hold large stocks of the plants they list. Some will, however, propagate to order.

Nurseries appearing in the *RHS Plant Finder* for the first time or re-entering after an absence are printed in bold type in the **Nursery Index by Name** (pp.950-954).

NEW IN THIS EDITION

For our third colour section we've an article on Plant Health Threats to our Gardens. Alongside this is the second Editor's choice of new plant highlights, illustrating 25 of the plants that are appearing in the book for the first time in this edition.

The plant names used in the 2019 edition reflect the decisions made by the RHS Nomenclature and Taxonomy Advisory Group (NATAG). Nomenclatural Notes (p.49) gives a brief overview of these changes made since the compilation of the previous edition of the book.

One of the significant edits this year is the move of *Saintpaulia*, or the African violets, to within *Streptocarpus*. The reasons behind this move are explained by Dawn Edwards in the December 2018 edition of *The Plantsman*. At the same time we've added the horticultural classification (AV), so that the African violets, or saintpaulias, can be easily identified within *Streptocarpus*.

LISTS OF NURSERIES FOR PLANTS WITH MORE THAN 30 SUPPLIERS

To prevent the book from becoming too big, we do not print nursery codes where more than 30 nurseries offer the same plant. The plant is then listed as being "widely available". See **How to Use the Plant Directory** (p.55).

A full list of all the nurseries held on file as current suppliers can be found by searching the RHS website Find a Plant facility or can be made available in printed form by post from the Compiler at the address below. For the latter, please ensure you include the full name of the plant (as given in the *RHS Plant Finder*) and enclose a stamped addressed envelope.

PLANTS LAST LISTED IN EARLIER EDITIONS

Plants cease to be listed for a variety of reasons. For more information, turn to **How to Use the Plant Directory** (p.55). A listing of more than 60,000 plants listed in earlier editions but for which we have no current suppliers will be made available on the RHS website.

RHS ONLINE

The plant data from the *RHS Plant Finder* is available on the Royal Horticultural Society's website at www.rhs.org.uk/plants under the Find a Plant section.

APPLICATION FOR ENTRY

If you would like your nursery to be considered for inclusion in the next edition of the *RHS Plant Finder*, please contact the Compiler. Entries to the book are free.

Contact details

Lindsay Durrant
Compiler, *RHS Plant Finder*
RHS Garden Wisley
Woking
Surrey
GU23 6QB
Ⓣ (01483) 226577
Ⓔ plantfinder@rhs.org.uk

ACKNOWLEDGEMENTS

This edition was compiled by Lindsay Durrant with Jane Rowlands, assisted by Sam Webster, Olivia Pavey and Isabelle David. Richard Sanford managed the editing of the plant names in the database and Julia Barclay and Rupert Wilson administered the RHS Horticultural Database using the BGBase™ Collection Management Software.

RHS botanists Dawn Edwards, Kálmán Könyves, Neil Lancaster and Rosalyn Marshall undertook the task of editing the new plant names for this edition of the book.

RHS Book Publisher Rae Spencer-Jones collated the colour section and we acknowledge the contribution of Louise Bowering, Louise Tee, Sarah Carrington, Mark Timothy, Marina Jordan-Rugg, John David and Gill Skilton. We would also like to thank those who have kindly provided plant images, especially our nurseries featuring in the book this year.

Special thanks go to Melanie Tuffen, RHS Biosecurity Co-ordinator for the article on Plant Health Threats to our Gardens, and also to Gerard Clover (Head of Plant Health) and Rebekah Robinson (Senior Scientist, Plant Pathology) for their advice and contribution.

We say thank you and farewell to Dr Alan Leslie, our RHS registrar for *Dianthus* and *Rhododendron*, who retired in June after 39 years with the RHS. The high quality of the RHS Registers is a reflection of his high standards and attention to detail.

He served as Chairman of NATAG, Secretary of the ISHS Special Commission for Cultivar Registration and has been an active member of the International Commission for the Nomenclature of Cultivated Plants for many years. With Chris Brickell, he was instrumental in the reconciliation of the then new classification of *Rhododendron* species with the needs of gardeners and horticulturalists, establishing the system of Groups under the Cultivated Plant Code (ICNCP) to accommodate the species no longer accepted in the generic classification. His knowledge, experience and pragmatism made him an invaluable resource to all within and outside of the RHS.

As ever, we are grateful for the professional support of Kerry Walter of BG-Base (UK) Ltd and Max Phillips of Strange Software Ltd. Finally, we are greatly indebted to Peter Cooling for his skill in turning our data into a publishable form.

Our colleagues on the RHS Nomenclature and Taxonomy Advisory Group, along with the RHS International Cultivar Registrars, have all provided valuable guidance and information. Many nurseries have supplied useful details on new plants and have suggested corrections to existing entries. Some of these remain to be checked and will be entered in the next edition, although those that contravene the Codes of Nomenclature may have to be rejected. We appreciate your patience while these checks are made. We are also grateful to our regular correspondents and to all those readers who have made helpful comments.

Clematis	D.R. Donald, Int. Cultivar Registrar
Chrysanthemum	J. Barker
Conifers	S. McDonald, Int. Cultivar Registrar
Dahlia	S. McDonald, Int. Cultivar Registrar
Dianthus	S. MacDonald, Int. Cultivar Registrar
Delphinium	M.R. Underwood, Int. Cultivar Registrar
Ilex	S. Andrews
Lilium	D.R. Donald, Int. Cultivar Registrar
Narcissus	M.R. Underwood, Int. Cultivar Registrar
Nerine	Dr J.C. David
Orchids	J.M.H. Shaw, Int. Cultivar Registrar
Rhododendron	S. McDonald, Int. Cultivar Registrar
Sorbus	Dr H. McAllister
Thymus	M. Easter, Int. Cultivar Registrar

Janet Cubey
RHS Editor-in-Chief
February 2019

Symbols and Abbreviations

Symbols Appearing to the Left of the Name

*	Name not validated. Not listed in the appropriate International Registration Authority checklist nor in works cited in the Bibliography. For fuller discussion see p.37
I	Invalid name. See *International Code of Botanical Nomenclature 2018* and *International Code of Nomenclature for Cultivated Plants 2016*. For fuller discussion see p.37
§	Plant listed elsewhere in the Plant Directory under a synonym
×	Hybrid genus
+	Graft hybrid genus

Symbols Appearing to the Right of the Name

✿	Plant Heritage National Plant Collection® exists for all or part of this genus. Further details can be found by searching the National Plant Collections online or in the Plant Heritage Directory available from www.plantheritage.org.uk or by phone (01483) 447540.
♈H4	The Royal Horticultural Society's Award of Garden Merit, see p.37
(d)	double-flowered
(F)	Fruit
(f)	female
(m)	male
(v)	variegated plant, see p.41
PBR	Plant Breeders' Rights see p.39
new	New plant entry in this edition

For abbreviations relating to individual genera see **Classification of Genera p.50**

For **Collectors' References** see p.45

For symbols used in the **Nurseries** section see p.863

Symbols and Abbreviations used as Part of the Name

×	hybrid species
aff.	affinis (akin to)
agg.	aggregate, a single name used to cover a group of very similar plants, regarded by some as separate species
ambig.	ambiguous, a name used by two authors for different plants and where it is unclear which is being offered
cf.	compare to
cl.	clone
f.	forma (botanical form)
gx	grex
sensu stricto	in the narrow sense
sp.	species
subsp.	subspecies
subvar.	subvarietas (botanical subvariety)
var.	varietas (botanical variety)

It is not within the remit of this book to check that nurseries are applying the right names to the right plants or to ensure nurseries selling plants with Plant Breeders' Rights are licensed to do so.

We recommend that you use the latest edition of the *RHS Plant Finder*

EXTENDED GLOSSARY

This glossary combines some of the helpful introductory sections from older editions in an alphabetical listing. A fuller, more discursive account of plant names, *Guide to Plant Names*, and a detailed guide to the typography of plant names, *Recommended Style for Printing Plant Names*, are both available as leaflets. To request a copy of either please send an A4 sae to The Compiler at the contact address given on page 34.

ADVISORY COMMITTEE ON NOMENCLATURE AND TAXONOMY

See **Nomenclature and Taxonomy Advisory Group**

AUTHORITIES

In order that plant names can be used with precision throughout the scientific world, the name of the person who coined the name of a plant species (its author, or authority) is added to the plant name. Usually this information is of little consequence to gardeners, except in cases where the same name has been given to two different plants or a name is commonly misapplied. Although only one usage is correct, both may be encountered in books, so indicating the author is the only way to be certain about which plant is being referred to. This can happen equally with cultivars. Authors' names, where it is appropriate to cite them, appear in a smaller typeface after the species or cultivar name to which they refer and are abbreviated following Brummitt and Powell's *Authors of Plant Names*.

🏆 AWARD OF GARDEN MERIT

The Award of Garden Merit (AGM) is intended as a practical guide for the gardener and is therefore awarded only after a period of assessment by the RHS Standing and Joint Committees. The AGM is awarded only to plants that are:

- excellent for ordinary use in appropriate conditions
- available
- of good constitution
- essentially stable in form and colour
- reasonably resistant to pests and diseases

The AGM symbol is cited in conjunction with the **hardiness** rating. A full list of AGM plants may be found on the RHS website at www.rhs.org.uk/agmplants.

The AGM list was originally reviewed every ten years, to ensure that every plant still merited the award. The last review took place in 2012; since 2013, the list has been subject to a "rolling review", and AGMs may now be rescinded at any time.

BOTANICAL NAMES

The aim of the botanical naming system is to provide each different plant with a single, unique, universal name. The basic unit of plant classification is the species. Species that share a number of significant characteristics are grouped together to form a genus (plural **genera**). The name of a species is made up of two elements; the name of the genus followed by the specific epithet, for example, *Narcissus romieuxii*.

Variation within a species can be recognised by division into subspecies (usually abbreviated to subsp.), varietas (or variety abbreviated to var.) and forma (or form abbreviated to f.). Whilst it is unusual for a plant to have all of these, it is possible, as in this example, *Narcissus romieuxii* subsp. *albidus* var. *zaianicus* f. *lutescens*.

The botanical elements are always given in italics, with only the genus taking an initial capital letter. The rank indications are never in italics. In instances where the rank is not known it is necessary to form an invalid construction by quoting a second epithet without a rank. This is an unsatisfactory situation, but requires considerable research to resolve.

In some genera, such as *Hosta*, we list the cultivar names alphabetically with the species or **hybrid** to which they are attributed afterwards in parentheses. For example, *Hosta* 'Reversed' (*sieboldiana*). In other situations where the aim is not to create a list alphabetically by cultivar name we would recommend styling this as *Hosta sieboldiana* 'Reversed'.

CLASSIFICATION OF GENERA

Genera that include a large number of species or with many cultivars are often subdivided into informal horticultural classifications or more formal Cultivar Groups, each based on a particular characteristic or combination of characteristics. Colour of flower or fruit and shape of flower are common examples and, with fruit, whether a cultivar is grown for culinary or dessert purposes. How such groups are named differs from genus to genus.

To help users of the *RHS Plant Finder* find the plants they want, the classifications used within cultivated genera are listed using codes and plants are marked with the appropriate code in brackets after its name in the Plant Directory. To find the explanation of each code, simply look it up under the genus concerned in the **Classification of Genera** starting on p.50. The codes relating to edible fruits are also listed here, but these apply across several genera.

Collectors' References

Abbreviations (usually with numbers) following a plant name refer to the collector(s) of the plant. These abbreviations are expanded, with a collector's name or expedition title, in the section **Collectors' References** starting on p.45.

A collector's reference may indicate a new, as yet unnamed range of variation within a species. The inclusion of collectors' references in the *RHS Plant Finder* supports the book's role in sourcing unusual plants.

The Convention on Biological Diversity calls for conservation of biodiversity, its sustainable use and the fair and equitable sharing of any derived benefits. Since its adoption in 1993, collectors are required to have prior informed consent from the country of origin for the acquisition and commercialisation of collected material.

Common Names

In a work such as this, it is necessary to refer to plants by their botanical names for the sake of universal comprehension and clarity. However, at the same time we recognise that with fruit and vegetables most people are more familiar with their common names than their botanical ones. Cross-references are therefore given from common to botanical names for fruit, vegetables and the commoner culinary herbs throughout the Plant Directory.

Cultivar

Literally meaning cultivated variety, cultivar names are given to denote variation within species and that generated by hybridisation, in cultivation. To make them easily distinguishable from botanical names, they are not printed in italics and are enclosed in single quotation marks. Cultivar names coined since 1959 should follow the rules of the International Code of Nomenclature for Cultivated Plants (**ICNCP**).

Descriptive Terms

Terms that appear after the main part of the plant name are shown in a smaller font to distinguish them. These descriptive elements give extra information about the plant and may include the **collector's reference**, **authority**, or what colour it is. For example, *Clematis henryi* B&SWJ 3402, *Penstemon* 'Sour Grapes' M. Fish, *Akebia quinata* cream-flowered.

Families

Genera are grouped into larger groups of related plants called families. Most family names, with the exception of eight familiar names, end with the same group of letters, *-aceae*. While it is still acceptable to use these eight exceptions, the modern trend adopted in the *RHS Plant Finder* is to use alternative names with *–aceae* endings. The families concerned are *Compositae* (*Asteraceae*), *Cruciferae* (*Brassicaceae*), *Gramineae* (*Poaceae*), *Guttiferae* (*Clusiaceae*), *Labiatae* (*Lamiaceae*), *Leguminosae* (*Fabaceae*), *Palmae* (*Arecaceae*) and *Umbelliferae* (*Apiaceae*).

Apart from these exceptions we now follow (from 2010) *Mabberley's Plant-book* (3rd edition).

Genus (plural – genera)

Genera used in the *RHS Plant Finder* were originally based on Brummitt's *Vascular Plant Families and Genera* but are now based on a range of sources. For spellings and genders of generic names, Greuter's *Names in Current Use for Extant Plant Genera* has also been consulted. See **Botanical Names**.

Grex

Within orchids, hybrids of the same parentage, regardless of how alike they are, are given a grex name. Individuals can be selected, given cultivar names and propagated vegetatively. For example, *Pleione* Versailles gx 'Bucklebury', where Versailles is the grex name and 'Bucklebury' is a selected **cultivar**.

Group

This is a collective name for a group of cultivars within a genus with similar characteristics. The word Group is always included and, where cited with a cultivar name, it is enclosed in brackets, for example, *Actaea simplex* (Atropurpurea Group) 'Brunette', where 'Brunette' is a distinct cultivar in a group of purple-leaved cultivars.

Another example of a Group is *Rhododendron polycladum* Scintillans Group. In this case *Rhododendron scintillans* was a species that is now botanically 'sunk' within *R. polycladum*, but it is still recognised horticulturally as a Group.

Group names are also used for swarms of hybrids with the same parentage, for example, *Rhododendron* Polar Bear Group. These were formerly treated as **grex** names, a term now used only for orchids. A single clone from the Group may be given the same cultivar name, for example, *Rhododendron* 'Polar Bear'.

HARDINESS

Hardiness ratings are shown for **Award of Garden Merit** plants. To assist gardeners to determine more clearly which plants are hardy in their local area, the RHS introduced a new, enhanced, hardiness rating scheme in 2013, to coincide with the publication of the new **Award of Garden Merit** plant list. The categories now used are as follows:
Temperature ranges given are intended to be absolute minimum winter temperatures (°C).
H1a = Heated greenhouse – tropical >15
H1b = Heated greenhouse – subtropical 10 to 15
H1c = Heated greenhouse – warm temperate 5 to 10
H2 = Tender – cool or frost-free greenhouse 1 to 5
H3 = Half-hardy – unheated greenhouse/mild winter -5 to 1
H4 = Hardy – average winter -10 to -5
H5 = Hardy – cold winter -15 to -10
H6 = Hardy – very cold winter -20 to -15
H7 = Very hardy <-20

Further definition of these categories can be found on the RHS website, in the Feb 2013 edition of *The Garden* and in the *RHS Plant Finder 2013* essay.

HYBRIDS

Some species, when grown together, in the wild or in cultivation, are found to interbreed and form hybrids. In some instances a hybrid name is coined, for example hybrids between *Primula hirsuta* and *P. minima* are given the name *Primula* × *forsteri*, the multiplication sign indicating hybrid origin. Hybrid formulae that quote the parentage of the hybrid are used where a unique name has not been coined, for example *Eucryphia cordifolia* × *E. lucida*. In hybrid formulae you will find parents in alphabetical order, with the male (m) and female (f) parent indicated where known. Hybrids between different genera are also possible, for example × *Mahoberberis* is the name given to hybrids between *Mahonia* and *Berberis*.

There are also a few special-case hybrids called graft hybrids, where the tissues of two plants are physically rather than genetically mixed. These are indicated by an addition rather than a multiplication sign, so *Laburnum* + *Cytisus* becomes + *Laburnocytisus*.

ICNCP

The ICNCP is the International Code of Nomenclature for Cultivated Plants. First published in 1959, the 9th edition was published in 2016.

Cultivar names that do not conform to this Code, and for which there is no valid alternative, are flagged I (for invalid). This code states that the minimum requirement is for a cultivar name to be given in conjunction with the name of the genus. However, in the *RHS Plant Finder* we choose to give as full a name as possible to give the gardener and botanist more information about the plant, following the Recommendation in the Code.

NOMENCLATURE AND TAXONOMY ADVISORY GROUP

This Group advises the RHS on individual problems of nomenclature regarding plants in cultivation and, in particular, use of names in the *RHS Horticultural Database*, reflected in the annual publication of the *RHS Plant Finder*.

The aim is always to make the plant names in the *RHS Plant Finder* as consistent, reliable and stable as possible and acceptable to gardeners and botanists alike, not only in the British Isles but around the world. Recent proposals to change or correct names are examined with the aim of creating a balance between the stability of well-known names and botanical and taxonomic correctness. In some cases the conflicting views on the names of some groups of plants will not easily be resolved. The Group's policy is then to wait and review the situation once a more obvious consensus is reached, rather than rush to rename plants only to have to change them again when opinions have shifted.

As we start 2019, Dr John David (attending RHS staff member) is Acting Chairman of the Group. The Group also includes Susyn Andrews, James Armitage, Chris Brickell, Dr James Compton, Dr John Grimshaw, Dr Stephen Jury, Dr Alan Leslie, Dr Tony Lord, Chris Sanders, with Björn Aldén, Dr Crinan Alexander, Dr Janet Cubey, Dr Marco Hoffman, Prof David Mabberley, Svengunnar Ryman and Julian Sutton (corresponding members) and Mike Grant and Julian Shaw (attending RHS staff) and Dr Dawn Edwards as Secretary.

NOTES ON NOMENCLATURE AND IDENTIFICATION

The **Notes on Nomenclature and Identification**, p.49, give further information for names that are complex or may be confusing. See also **Nomenclature and Taxonomy Advisory Group**.

PLANT BREEDERS' RIGHTS

Plants covered by an *active* grant of Plant Breeders' Rights (PBR) are indicated throughout the Plant Directory. Grants indicated are those awarded by both UK and EU Plant Variety Rights offices. Because grants can both come into force and lapse at any time, this book can only aim to represent the situation at one point in time, but it is hoped that this will act as a useful guide to growers and gardeners. UK and EU grants represent the published position as of the end of December 2018. We do not give any indication where PBR grants may be pending.

To obtain PBR protection, a new plant must be registered and pass tests for distinctness, uniformity and stability under an approved name. This approved name, under the rules of the **ICNCP**, established by a legal process, has to be regarded as the cultivar name. Increasingly however, these approved names are a code or "nonsense" name and are therefore often unpronounceable and meaningless, so the plants are given other names designed to attract sales when they are released. These secondary names are often referred to as selling names but are officially termed **trade designations**. We do our best to link PBR names to their trade descriptions but if you spot any we've missed, do let us know.

On the odd occasion the name for a plant with Plant Breeders' Rights in the EU differs from the name by which it is known outside of the EU and indeed may be different to that given in the relevant International Cultivar Registration Authority (ICRA) register. As the *RHS Plant Finder* has to use the correct name for the plant within the EU, on these occasions this may not be the same name given as the accepted name in the relevant RHS Cultivar Register and Checklist which, being international provides the name that complies with the **ICNCP**.

For further information on UK PBR contact:
Plant Variety Rights Office,
Animal and Plant Health Agency,
Eastbrook,
Shaftesbury Road,
Cambridge CB2 8DR
Ⓣ **(0208) 026 5993**
Ⓔ **pvs.helpdesk@apha.gsi.gov.uk**
Ⓦ **www.gov.uk/plant-breeders-rights**

For details of plants covered by EU Community Rights contact:
Community Plant Variety Office (CPVO)
3 Boulevard Maréchal Foch, CS 10121
49101 Angers Cedex 2, France
Ⓣ **00 33 (02) 41 25 64 00**
Ⓔ **cpvo@cpvo.europa.eu**
Ⓦ **www.cpvo.europa.eu**

The *RHS Plant Finder* takes no responsibility for ensuring that nurseries selling plants with PBR are licensed to do so.

Reverse Synonyms

It is likely that users of this book will come across names in certain genera that they did not expect to find. This may be because species have been transferred from another genus (or **genera**).

Selling Names

See **Trade Designations**

Series

With seed-raised plants and some popular vegetatively propagated plants, especially bedding plants and pot plants such as *Petunia* or *Glandularia*, Series have become increasingly popular. A Series contains a number of similar cultivars, but differs from a **Group** in that it is a marketing device, with cultivars added to create a range of flower colours in plants of similar habit. Individual colour elements within a Series may be represented by slightly different cultivars over the years.

The word Series is always included and, where cited with a cultivar name it is enclosed in brackets, for example *Aquilegia* 'Robin' (Songbird Series). The Series name usually follows the rest of the plant name, but sometimes in this book we list it before the cultivar name in order to group members of a Series together when they occur next to one another on the page.

Species

See under **Botanical Names**

Subspecies

See under **Botanical Names**

Synonyms

Although the ideal is for each species or cultivar to have only one name, anyone dealing with plants soon comes across a situation where one plant has received two or more names, or two plants have received the same name. In each case, only one name and application, for reasons of precision and stability, can be regarded as correct. Additional names are known as synonyms. Further information on synonyms and why plants change names is available in *Guide to Plant Names*. See the introduction to this glossary for details of how to request a copy.

See also **Reverse Synonyms**.

Trade Designations

A **trade designation** is the name used to market a plant when the cultivar name is considered unsuitable for selling purposes. It is distinguished typographically (see below) from a cultivar name, and is not enclosed in single quotation marks.

In the case of **Plant Breeders' Rights** it is a legal requirement for the cultivar name to appear with the trade designation on a label at the point of sale. Most plants are sold under only one trade designation, but some, especially roses, are sold under a number of names, particularly when cultivars are introduced from other countries. Usually, the correct cultivar name is the only way to ensure that the same plant is not bought unwittingly under two or more different trade designations. The *RHS Plant Finder* follows the recommendations of the **ICNCP** when dealing with trade designations and PBR. These are always to quote the cultivar name and trade designation together and to style the trade designation in small capitals, for example *Choisya* × *dewitteana* GOLDFINGERS ('Limo'PBR). Here GOLDFINGERS is the trade designation and 'Limo' is the cultivar name that has been granted **Plant Breeders' Rights**.

TRANSLATIONS

When a cultivar name is translated from the language of first publication, the translation is regarded as a **trade designation** and styled accordingly. We endeavour to recognise the original cultivar name in every case and to give an English translation where it is in general use.

VARIEGATED PLANTS

Following a suggestion from the Variegated Plant Group of the Hardy Plant Society, a (v) is cited after those plants which are "variegated". The dividing line between variegation and less distinct colour marking is necessarily arbitrary and plants with light veins, pale, silver or dark zones, or leaves flushed in paler colours, are not shown as being variegated unless there is an absolutely sharp distinction between paler and darker zones.

Further details of the Variegated Plant Group can be found at www.hardy-plant.org.uk.

VARIETY

See under **Botanical Names** and **Cultivar**

CONSERVATION AND THE ENVIRONMENT

Invasive Plants

As the *RHS Plant Finder* demonstrates, gardens in Britain have been greatly enriched by the diversity of plants introduced to cultivation from abroad. While the vast majority of those introduced have enhanced our gardens, a few have proved to be highly invasive and to threaten native habitats. Once such plants are established it is very difficult, costly and potentially damaging to native ecosystems to eradicate or control the invasive "alien" species. Gardeners can help by choosing not to buy or distribute non-native invasive plants and by taking steps to prevent them escaping into the wild and by disposing of them in a responsible way.

Ten of the most serious invasive non-native species are no longer listed in the *RHS Plant Finder*. Any cultivars or varieties of them that are listed are believed to be less invasive than the species. These 10 plants are:

**Azolla filiculoides* – fairy fern
**Crassula helmsii* – New Zealand pygmy weed
†‡*Elodea nuttallii* – Nuttall's waterweed
Fallopia japonica – Japanese knotweed
†‡*Heracleum mantegazzianum* – giant hogweed
†**Hydrocotyle ranunculoides* – floating pennywort
†‡*Impatiens glandulifera* – Himalayan balsam
†*Lagarosiphon major* – curly waterweed
†**Ludwigia grandiflora* – water primrose
†**Myriophyllum aquaticum* – parrot's feather

From April 2014 the five aquatic species indicated by a * above have been banned from sale in the UK. Anyone trading in these species is liable to a fine of up to £5000 or a six months prison sentence.

The EU Regulation on Invasive Alien Species, which became law early in 2015, has a provision for a list of species of EU-wide (Union) concern. Species that are included in the list attract the strictest measures of control, including a ban on keeping, growing or cultivating, transporting or trading, use or exchange, as well as release into the wider environment. These controls will apply to individuals as well as organisations and businesses that own or hold any of these species. There are now 23 plants on this list, many of which are of marginal importance to gardeners, or are already banned from sale in the UK or excluded from Plant Finder (marked with † in the above list), but four widely grown species, *Eichhornia crassipes, Gunnera tinctoria, Lysichiton americanus* and *Pennisetum setaceum* are included. The species marked with a ‡ were banned from the beginning of August 2018.

The species affected are:

‡*Asclepias syriaca* – milkweed
Baccharis halmifolia – tree groundsel
Cabomba caroliniana – Carolina fanwort
Eichhornia crassipes – water hyacinth
‡*Gunnera tinctoria* – Chilean rhubarb
Ludwigia peploides – water primrose
Lysichiton americanus – American skunk cabbage
‡*Myriophyllum heterophyllum* – broadleaf watermilfoil
Parthenium hysterophorus – Parthenium weed
‡*Pennisetum setaceum* – crimson fountaingrass
Pueraria montana var. *lobata* – Kudzu

Gardeners who already have these species in their gardens are not at risk of prosecution for possession as the Regulation is not retrospective, but will be required to meet the other requirements of the Regulation to ensure that they control the species effectively on their property and do not allow it to spread.

Species control provisions

The UK Government introduced new provisions in the Infrastructure Act (2015) to control invasive non-native species in England and Wales. There are two levels of control: a species control agreement and a species control order. In the former the owner of land where an invasive non-native species is present, when approached by the relevant environmental authority, agrees to take action to limit or remove the species. If the landowner fails to do so, or does not agree, or where it is not known who the landowner is, then the environment authority can take action to enforce the control of the species. This may involve entry of the property by the authority to carry out the control if the owner fails to comply. In the case of an emergency then a species control order may be issued without going through the previous steps. Only those species listed on Schedule 9 of the Wildlife & Countryside Act can be subject to these control measures. For the purposes of the Act, Defra, Natural England, the Environment Agency and the Forestry Commission are defined as Environmental Authorities in England. For Wales it is Natural Resources Wales.

Bringing plants back from abroad

Travelling can be a great source of inspiration for gardeners and often provides an opportunity to encounter new and interesting plants. Anyone wishing to bring plants back into Britain from overseas must realise, however, that this is a complex matter. Various regulations are in force that apply to amateur gardeners as well as to commercial nurseries. The penalties for breaking these can be serious.

Most countries have regulations concerning the collection of plants from the wild, including seed. These regulations are likely to ban collection from certain protected places, such as national parks, ban the collection of rare or endangered species, and require permits to collect where special protection measures are not in place. In addition there is likely to be an additional permit to export any collected plant material. Travellers are frequently reminded of regulations in force at airports and other points of entry to a country. Anyone wishing to collect wild plants, for whatever purpose, will need to contact the country concerned well in advance of travel to seek the relevant permits. Breach of the regulations will result, as a minimum, in the confiscation of plant material if discovered. Any such material brought back to the UK is illegal.

The situation with plants in cultivation in another country is less clear and travellers are advised to check with the authorities in the country, particularly with regard to any Access and Benefit Sharing requirements (see **Nagoya Protocol** below), export permits or phytosanitary certificates that might be needed.

Plant Health regulations are in place to control the spread of pests and diseases. Plants are divided into the categories of prohibited, controlled and unrestricted, but there are also limits that vary according to the part of the world you are travelling from.
Ⓦ https://planthealthportal.defra.gov.uk

The Convention on International Trade in Endangered Species (CITES) affects the transport of animal and plant material across international boundaries. Its aim is to prevent exploitative trade and thereby to prevent harm and the ultimate extinction of wild populations. A tighter regime on trade in species of wild fauna and flora exists in the EU that requires export permits for any plants listed in Appendices A, B & C and import permits for Appendices A & B. There is a further Appendix D for non-CITES listed species that the EU consider to be endangered. A broad range of plants is covered in these Appendices, including *Cactaceae* and *Orchidaceae* and, although species are mentioned in the convention title, the restrictions cover all cultivars and hybrids of listed species too, except for specific exclusions, where there are annotations in the Appendices.
Ⓦ www.gov.uk/cites-imports-and-exports#cites-species

The Convention on Biological Diversity (CBD or the "Rio Convention") recognises the property rights of individual countries in relation to their own biodiversity. It exists to enable access to that biodiversity, but equally to ensure the sharing of any benefit derived from it. In principle it is possible to collect plant material from other countries that have asserted their rights under the CBD, by ensuring that you have obtained documentary evidence of prior informed consent on the basis of mutually agreed terms for any uses that the material will be put to in the future. In practice the legal requirements for collecting plant material vary from country to country and it is advisable to contact the National Focal Point for further information.
Ⓦ www.cbd.int

The **Nagoya Protocol**, is a supplementary agreement of the CBD which entered into force in 2015, and provides a framework for Access and Benefit Sharing. In the UK this is implemented by the European Union Regulation which is effective from 12 October 2014, and requires anyone utilising genetic resources from another country which is a signatory of the Nagoya Protocol, collected after 12 October 2014, to carry out due diligence to ensure that the material was collected in accordance with the Protocol and the CBD. While the most likely examples of utilisation are the development of new products or medicines from plants, breeding programmes to raise new plants for horticulture would also be covered. Although the burden to prove legitimate use of the genetic resource lies with the person or organisation utilising the genetic resource, anyone providing the source of the genetic resource (such as wild collected plants) will need to be able to provide the relevant paperwork, such as a Material Transfer Agreement and Prior Informed Consent.
Ⓦ http://www.cbd.int/abs/about/

In March 2015 the UK Government put in place the scheme of penalties for failure to comply with the EU Regulation which includes a range of both civil and criminal penalties, with the ultimate sanction of a two-year prison sentence. This legislation also formally appointed the Office for Product Safety and Standards (formerly Regulatory Delivery, and previously National Measurement and Regulation Office) as the authority to enforce compliance in the UK, effective from June 2015.
Ⓦ https://www.gov.uk/guidance/abs

European Habitats Directive. The full implementation of this Directive into UK law in 2007 extended protection to all of the European Protected Species (EPS) listed in the Appendices of that Directive (these are Appendices II(b) and IV(b) for plants) whether they are native to the UK or not. This requires a licence for material of any of these species collected in the wild after 1994. These are issued by Natural England (for England), Natural Resources Wales (in Wales) and Scottish Natural Heritage (for Scotland).
Ⓦ www.gov.uk/guidance/wild-plants-sell-them-legally

Contact addresses

The UK authorities issue licences for UK plants. For other EU states a collector would need to contact the relevant national authorities.

Department for Environment, Food & Rural Affairs (Defra)
Nobel House
17 Smith Square
London
SW1P 3JR
For biodiversity queries:
Ⓔ biodiversity@defra.gsi.gov.uk

Plant Health
Room 11G02
Animal and Plant Health Agency
The National Agri-food Innovation Campus
Sand Hutton,
York
YO41 1LZ
Ⓣ 01904 405 138
Ⓔ planthealth.info@apha.gov.uk

CITES
Animal & Plant Health Agency (APHA)
Centre for International Trade – Bristol
1/17 Temple Quay House
2 The Square
Temple Quay
Bristol
BS1 6EB
Ⓣ 0117 372 8774
Ⓕ 0117 372 8206
Ⓔ wildlife.licensing@apha.gov.uk
Ⓦ www.gov.uk/plant-health-controls

Invasive Species
Natural England
Wildlife Management & Licensing
Horizon House
Deanery Road
Bristol
BS1 5AH
Ⓣ 020 8026 1089
Ⓔ wildlife@naturalengland.org.uk

Non-Native Species Secretariat
Animal and Plant Health Agency
Sand Hutton
York
YO41 1LZ
Ⓦ www.nonnativespecies.org

Nagoya Protocol
Office for Product Safety and Standards (OPSS)
Stanton Avenue
Teddington
TW110JZ
Ⓣ 020 8943 7272

The information provided on these pages is correct at the time of going to press, but current uncertainties over the nature of the UK's departure from the European Union mean that provisions concerning the movement of plants out of the UK into the EU, and from the EU into the UK, could be subject to significant change. Should this occur, the RHS will seek to provide relevant updates on our website.

Supplementary Keys to the Directory

Collectors' References

Abbreviations following a plant name, refer to the collector(s) of the plant. These abbreviations are expanded below, with a collector's name or expedition title. For a fuller explanation, see p.38.

A&JW Watson, A. & J.
A&L Ala, A. & Lancaster, Roy
AB&S Archibald, James; Blanchard, John W. & Salmon, M.
AC Clark, Alan J.
AC&H Apold, J.; Cox, Peter & Hutchison, Peter
AC&W Albury; Cheese, M. & Watson, J.M.
ACE AGS Expedition to China (1994)
ACL Leslie, Alan C.
AER Robinson, Allan
AGS/ES AGS Expedition to Sikkim (1983)
AGSJ AGS Expedition to Japan (1988)
AH Hoog, A.
AIM Avent, Tony Mexico (1994)
Airth Airth, Murray
Akagi Akagi Botanical Garden
AL&JS Sharman, Joseph L. & Leslie, Alan C.
APA Cox, K.; Hootman, S.; Hudson, T.; et al, Expedition to Arunchal Pradesh (2005)
ARG Argent, G.C.G.
ARGS Alaska Rock Garden Society trip to China
ARJA Ruksans, J. & Siesums, A.
B Blanchard, John
B&F MA Brown, Robert & Fisher, Rif & Middle Atlas (2007)
B L. Beer, Len
B&L Brickell, Christopher D. & Leslie, Alan C.
B&M & BM Brickell, Christopher D. & Mathew, Brian
B&S Bird P. & Salmon M.
B&SWJ Wynn-Jones, Bleddyn & Susan
B&V Burras, K. & Vosa, C.G.
BB Bartholomew, B.
BBJMT Boland, Brownless, Jamieson & McNamara
BC Chudziak, W.
BC&W Beckett; Cheese, M. & Watson, J.M.
Beavis Beavis, Derek S.
Berry Berry, P.
Berry & Brako Berry, P. & Brako, Lois
BKBlount Blount, B.K.
BKN Bis, J., Kupčák, P. & Novak, H.
BL&M University of Bangor Expedition to NE Nepal
BM Mathew, Brian F.
BM&W Binns, David L.; Mason, M. & Wright, A.
BO Olsen, Bjornar
BOA Boardman, P.
Breedlove Breedlove, D.
BR Rushbrooke, Ben
BS Smith, Basil
BSBE Bowles Scholarship Botanical Expedition (1963)
BSSS Crûg Expedition, Jordan (1991)
Bu Bubert, S.
Burtt Burtt, Brian L.
BWJ Wynn-Jones, Bleddyn
C Cole, Desmond T.
C&C Cox, P.A. & Cox, K.N.E.
C&Cu Cox, K.N.E. & Cubey, J.
C&H Cox, Peter & Hutchison, Peter
C&K Chamberlain & Knott
C&R Christian & Roderick
C&S Clark, Alan & Sinclair, Ian W.J.
C&V K.N.E. Cox & Vergera, S.
C&W Cheese, M. & Watson, J.M.
CC Chadwell, Christopher
CC&H Chamberlain, David F.; Cox, Peter & Hutchison, P.
CC&McK Chadwell, Christopher & McKelvie, A.
CC&MR Chadwell, Christopher & Ramsay
CCH&H Chamberlain, D.F.; Cox, P.; Hutchison, P. & Hootman, S.
CD&R Compton, J.; D'Arcy, J. & Rix, E.M.
CDB Brickell, Christopher D.
CDC Coode, Mark J.E.; Dockrill, Alexander
CDC&C Compton; D'Arcy; Christopher & Coke
CDPR Compton; D'Arcy; Pope & Rix
CE&H Christian, P.J.; Elliott & Hoog
CEE Chengdu Edinburgh Expedition China (1991)

CGG Glendoick Gardens Expedition to Guizou (2009)
CGV Vosa, Canio
CGW Grey-Wilson, Christopher
CH Christian, P. & Hoog, A.
CH&M Cox, P.; Hutchison, P. & Maxwell-MacDonald, D.
CHB Boulanger, Charles
CHP&W Kashmir Botanical Expedition
CL Lovell, Chris
CLD Chungtien, Lijiang & Dali Exped. China (1990)
CM&W Cheese M.; Mitchel J. & Watson, J.
CN&W Clark; Neilson & Wilson
CNDS Nelson, C. & Sayers D.
COLA Costin, J.J. & Lancaster, R., Japan (1990)
Cooper Cooper, R.E.
Cox Cox, Peter A.
CPC Cobblewood Plant Collection
CPN Compton, James
CS Stapleton, Christopher
CSE Cyclamen Society Expedition (1990)
CT Teune, Carla
CW&T Clark, A., Wilson, H. & Taggart, J., North Vietnam
CWJ Colley, Finlay; Wynn-Jones, Bleddyn, Taiwan (2007)
Dahl Dahl, Sally
DBG Denver Botanic Garden, Colorado
DC Cheshire, David
DF Fox, D.
DG Green, D.
DHTU Hinkley, D., Turkey (2000)
DJF Ferguson, Dave
DJH Hinkley, Dan
DJHC Hinkley D., China
DJHS Hinkley, D., Sichuan
DJHT Hinkley, Dan in Taipingshan, Taiwan
DJHV Hinkley, D., Vietnam
DM Millais, David
Doleshy Doleshy, F.L.
DS&T Drake, Sharman J. & Thompson
DWD Rose, D.
DZ Zummell, D.
ECN Nelson, E. Charles
EDHCH Hammond, Eric D.
EGM Millais, T.
EKB Balls, Edward K.
EM East Malling Research Station
EMAK Edinburgh Makalu Expedition (1991)
EMR Rix, E.Martyn
EN Needham, Edward F.
ENF Fuller, E. Nigel
ETE Edinburgh Taiwan Expedition (1993)
ETOT Kirkham, T.S.; Flanagan, Mark
F Forrest, G.
F&M Fernandez & Mendoza, Mexico
F&W Watson, J. & Flores, A.
Farrer Farrer, Reginald
FK Kinmonth, Fergus W.
FMB Bailey, F.M.
FO Otiery, Felix
G Gardner, Martin F.
G&K Gardner, Martin F. & Knees, Sabina G.
G&P Gardner, Martin F. & Page, Christopher N.
GDJ Dumont, Gerard
GG Gusman, G.
GS Sherriff, George
Green Green, D.
Guitt Guittoneau, G.G.
Guiz Guizhou Expedition (1985)
GWJ Goddard, Sally; Wynne-Jones, Bleddyn & Susan
G-W&P Grey-Wilson, Christopher & Phillips
H Huggins, Paul
H&B Hilliard, Olive M. & Burtt, Brian L.
H&D Howick, C. & Darby
H&M Howick, Charles & McNamara, William A.
H&W Hedge, Ian C. & Wendelbo, Per W.
Harry Smith Smith, K.A.Harry
Hartside Hartside Nursery
HCM Heronswood Expedition to Chile (1998)
HECC Hutchison; Evans; Cox, P.; Cox, K.
HEHEHE Zetterlund, H. et al, Gothenburg Botanic Gardens Expedition to northern China
Hird Hird
HH&K Hannay, S & S & Kingsbury, N.
HK Kuenzler, Horst
HLMS Springate, L.S.
HM&S Halliwell, B.; Mason, D. & Smallcombe
HOA Hoog, Anton
HOLUB Holubec, V.
HRS Hers, J.
Hummel Hummel, D.
HW&E Wendelbo, Per; Hedge, I. & Ekberg, L.
HWEL Hirst, J.Michael; Webster, D.
HWJ Crûg Heronswood Joint Expedition
HWJCM Crûg Heronswood Expedition
HWJK Crûg Heronswood Expedition, East Nepal (2002)
HZ Zetterlund, Henrik
ICE Instituto de Investigaciónes Ecológicas Chiloé & RBGE
IDS International Dendrological Society
ISI Int. Succulent Introductions
J&JA Archibald, James & Jennifer
J. Jurasek Jurasek, J.
JCA Archibald, James
JE Jack Elliott
JJ Jackson, J.
JJ&JH Halda, J. & Halda, J.
JJH Halda, Joseph J.
JL Lode, Joel
JLS Sharman, J.L.

JMH	Hoog, J. & M.
JM-MK	Mahr, J.; Kammerlander, M.
JMT	Mann Taylor, J.
JN	Nielson, Jens
JR	Russell, J.
JRM	Marr, John
JW	Watson, J.M.
K	Kirkpatrick, George
K&LG	Gillanders, Kenneth & Gillanders, L.
K&Mc	Kirkpatrick, George & McBeath, Ronald J.D.
K&P	Josef Kopec & Milan Prasil
K&T	Kurashige, Y. & Tsukie, S.
KC	Cox, Kenneth
KEKE	Kew/Edinburgh Kanchenjunga Expedition (1989)
KGB	Kunming/Gothenburg Botanical Expedition (1993)
KM	Marsh, K.
KMR	Kupčák, M.
KR	Rushforth, K.D.
KRW	Wooster, K.R. (distributed after his death by Kath Dryden)
KW	Kingdon-Ward, F.
KWJ	Crûg-World of Ferns Joint Expedition, Vietnam (2007)
L	Lancaster, C. Roy
L&S	Ludlow, Francis & Sherriff, George
LA	Long Ashton Research Station clonal selection scheme
LB	Bercht, L. (*Cactaceae*)
LB	Bird P.; Salmon, M.
LEG	Lesotho Edinburgh/Gothenburg Expedition (1997)
Lismore	Lismore Nursery, Breeder's Number
LM&S	Leslie, Mattern & Sharman
LP	Palmer, W.J.L.
LS&E	Ludlow, Frank; Sherriff, George & Elliott, E. E.
LS&H	Ludlow, Frank; Sherriff, George & Hicks, J. H.
LS&T	Ludlow, Frank; Sherriff, George & Taylor, George
LZ	Lutz, Eberhard
M&PS	Mike & Polly Stone
M&T	Mathew & Tomlinson
Mac&W	McPhail & Watson
McB	McBeath, R.J.D.
McLaren	McLaren, H.D.
MDM	Myers, Michael D.
MECC	Scottish Rock Garden Club, Nepal (1997)
MESE	Alpine Garden Society Expedition, Greece (1999)
MF	Foster, Maurice
MH	Heasman, Matthew T.
MK	Kammerlander, Michael
MP	Pavelka, Mojmir
MPF	Frankis, M.P.
MS	Salmon, M.
MS&CL	Salmon, M. & Lovell, C.
MSF	Fillan, M.S.
MUG	Uhlig, M.
NAPE	Expedition to Naglaland and Arunachal Pradesh (2003)
NICE	North India Expedition (1997)
NJM	Macer, N.J.
NMWJ	Taiwan National Museum of Natural Science; Wynn-Jones, B. & S.
NN	Nielsen & Nielsen (2009)
NNS	Ratko, Ron
NS	Turland, Nick
NVD	Expedition to Vietnam
NVFDE	Northern Vietnam First Darwin Expedition
Og	Ogisu, Mikinori
ORO	Oron, Peri
OS	Sonderhousen, O.
P. Bon	Bonavia, P.
P&C	Paterson, David S. & Clarke, Sidney
P&W	Polastri & Watson, J. M.
PAB	Barney, P.A.
PB	Bird, Peter
PBR	Bruggeman, P.
PC&H	Pattison, G.; Catt, P. & Hickson, M.
PD	Davis, Peter H.
PDM	Purdom, William
PF	Furse, Paul
PG	Pichler, G.
PJC	Christian, Paul J.
PJC&AH	P.J. Christian & A. Hogg
PNMK	Nicholls, P.; Kammerlander, M.
Polunin	Polunin, Oleg
Pras	Prasil, M.
PS&W	Polunin, Oleg; Sykes, William & Williams, John
PW	Wharton, Peter
R	Rock, J.F.C.
RB	Brown, R.
RBS	Brown, Ray, Sakharin Island
RCB AM	Brown, Robert, Expedition to Armenia
RCB/Arg	Brown, Robert, Argentina, (2002)
RCB E	Brown, Robert, Expedition to Spain (Andalucia)
RCB/Eq	Brown, Robert, Ecuador, (1988)
RCB RA	Brown, Robert
RCB RL	Brown, Robert, Expedition to Lebanon
RCB/TQ	Brown, Robert, Turkey (2001)
RE	Evans, Ron
RH	Hancock, R.
RJN	Neilsen, R.
RKMP	Ruksans, J.; Krumins, A.; Kitts, M.; Paivel, A.
RM	Ruksans, J. & Kitts, M.
RMRP	Rocky Mountain Rare Plants, Denver, Colorado

RS	Suckow, Reinhart
RSC	Richard Somer Cocks
RV	Richard Valder
RWJ	Crûg Farm-Rickards Ferns Expedition to Taiwan (2003)
S&B	Blanchard, J.W. & Salmon, M.
S&F	Salmon, M. & Fillan, M.
S&L	Sinclair, Ian W.J. & Long, David G.
S&SH	Sheilah & Spencer Hannay
Sandham	Sandham, John
SB	Brack, Steven
SB&L	Salmon, Bird & Lovell
SBEC	Sino-British Expedition to Cangshan
SBEL	Sino-British Lijiang Expedition
SBQE	Sino-British Expedition to Quinghai
Sch	Schilling, Anthony D.
SD	Sashal Dayal
SDR	Rankin, Stella & David
SEH	Hootman, Steve
SEP	Swedish Expedition to Pakistan
SF	Forde, P.
SG	Salmon, M. & Guy, P.
SH	Hannay, Spencer
Sich	Simmons, Erskine, Howick & Mcnamara
SJ	Johansson, Stellan
SLIZE	Swedish-Latvian-Iranian Zagros Expedition to Iran (May 1988)
SOJA	Kew/Quarryhill Expedition to Southern Japan
SS&W	Stainton, J.D. Adam; Sykes, William & Williams, John
SSNY	Sino-Scottish Expedition to NW Yunnan (1992)
T	Taylor, Nigel P.
T&K	Taylor, Nigel P. & Knees, Sabina
TCM	Mitchell, Thomas Carly
TG	Thomas, H-P. & Gilmer, K.
TH	Hudson, T.
TJR	Roberts, Tim
TS&BC	Smythe, T. & Cherry, B.
TSS	Spring Smyth, T.L.M.
TW	Weston, Tony
USDAPI	US Department of Agriculture Plant Index Number
USDAPQ	US Dept. of Agriculture Plant Quarantine Number
USNA	United States National Arboretum
VdL	Van de Laar, Harry
VHH	Vernon H. Heywood
VV	Victor, David
W	Wilson, Ernest H.
W&B	Watkins, D. & Brown, R., Bulgaria (2012)
W&O	Wu, August & Olsen, Bjornar
WJC	Wynn-Jones, B. & S. & Colley, F.
WM	McLewin, William
Woods	Woods, Patrick J.B.
Wr	Wraight, David & Anke
WWJ	Wharton, Peter; Wynn-Jones, Bleddyn & Susan
Yu	Yu, Tse-tsun
ZE&S	Zetterlund, H., Eriksson, A-I. & Strid, A.

NOMENCLATURAL NOTES

The following changes have been made during 2018 to the names used in the *RHS Plant Finder* based upon decisions of the RHS Nomenclature and Taxonomy Advisory Group (NATAG). If you have any suggestions for other plant name changes within the *RHS Plant Finder*, then please write, stating your reasons in full to:

The Secretary
Dr Dawn Edwards
Nomenclature and Taxonomy Advisory Group
Royal Horticultural Society
RHS Garden Wisley
Woking
Surrey
GU23 6QB

- *Ajania* moved into *Chrysanthemum*
- *Altingia* moved into *Liquidambar*
- Transferring *Alyssum spinosum* & *A. pyrenaicum* to *Hormathophylla*
- *Anaphalioides* corrected to *Anaphaloides*
- Identifyable hybrids previously in *Argyranthemum* moved into × *Argyrimelia* and × *Glebianthemum*
- *Betonica* resurrected out of *Stachys*
- Updating the family of *Desfontainia* to *Columelliaceae*
- Incorporating *Dryandra* R.Br. into *Banksia*
- Changes to the species recognised within *Echeveria*
- Moving *Hacquetia epipactis* into *Sanicula*
- *Halimodendron* to within *Caragana*
- *Helosciadium* as distinct from *Apium*
- *Humata tyermannii* corrected to *H. tyermanii*
- Changes of the generic boundary of *Iochroma*; incorporating *Acnistus* but separating out *Eriolarynx* and *Trozelia*
- Combining the three legume families (*Caesalpiniaceae*, *Mimosaceae*, *Papilionaceae*) into one, the *Fabaceae*
- *Morus* 'Waisei-kirishima-shikinari' as the correct name, in accordance with the raiser's wishes and the Japanese Plant Variety Rights application, for *Morus* 'Matsunaga', also known as CHARLOTTE RUSSE and MOJO BERRY
- *Ophiopogon planiscapus* 'Nigrescens' to the earlier epithet 'Kokuryū'
- Identification of material in circulation as *Nepeta recta* as *Stachys recta*
- Updating *Paeonia* to reflect many of the names used by Hong in *Peonies of the World*
- Recognising *Pennisetum advena* as a species rather than a hybrid
- Including *Quisqualis* within *Combretum*
- *Rosularia sedoides* to *Sedum sedoides*
- *Sedum* 'Little Missy' as a synonym of *Crassula pellucida* subsp. *marginalis* 'Variegata'
- A revision of *Gesneriaceae* including:
  - *Alsobia* separated out from *Episcia*
  - *Ancylostemon*, × *Brigandra* and *Opithandra* included within *Oreocharis*
  - *Chirita* disbanded into various genera including *Primulina, Deinostigma, Henckelia* and *Microchirita*
  - *Seemannia* separated out from *Gloxinia*
  - *Saintpaulia* incorporated within *Streptocarpus*, identifiable by the horticultural classification (AV)

This is not intended to be an exhaustive list of the changes made to the RHS Horticultural Database, reflected in the *RHS Plant Finder*; many more changes are made during the year by the RHS botanical team. This list just highlights some of the NATAG changes.

You'll find some of these have had explanatory articles, or will have been mentioned on the new Plant Bulletin feature, in *The Plantsman* in the last 12 months. Watch out for articles in the coming year on future changes.

As part of its consideration of the family *Rosaceae*, NATAG is currently looking into the *Sorbus* issue with the aim of agreeing a practical approach.

CLASSIFICATION OF GENERA

Genera including a large number of species, or with many cultivars, are often subdivided into informal horticultural classifications, or formal cultivar groups in the case of *Clematis* and *Tulipa*. The breeding of new cultivars is sometimes limited to hybrids between closely related species, thus for *Saxifraga* and *Primula*, the cultivars are allocated to the sections given in the infrageneric treatments cited. Please turn to p.37 for a fuller explanation.

ACER PALMATUM

(A) Amoenum Group
(D) Dissectum Group
(Dw) Dwarf Group
(L) Linearilobum Group
(M) Matsumurae Group
(P) Palmatum Group

ACTINIDIA

(s-p) Self-pollinating

BEGONIA

(C) Cane-like
(R) Rex Cultorum
(S) Semperflorens Cultorum
(T) × *tuberhybrida* (Tuberous)

CHRYSANTHEMUM

(By the National Chrysanthemum Society)
(1) Indoor Large (Exhibition)
(2) Indoor Medium (Exhibition)
(3a) Indoor Incurved: Large-flowered
(3b) Indoor Incurved: Medium-flowered
(3c) Indoor Incurved: Small-flowered
(4a) Indoor Reflexed: Large-flowered
(4b) Indoor Reflexed: Medium-flowered
(4c) Indoor Reflexed: Small-flowered
(5a) Indoor Intermediate: Large-flowered
(5b) Indoor Intermediate: Medium-flowered
(5c) Indoor Intermediate: Small-flowered
(6a) Indoor Anemone: Large-flowered
(6b) Indoor Anemone: Medium-flowered
(6c) Indoor Anemone: Small-flowered
(7a) Indoor Single: Large-flowered
(7b) Indoor Single: Medium-flowered
(7c) Indoor Single: Small-flowered
(8a) Indoor True Pompon
(8b) Indoor Semi-pompon
(9a) Indoor Spray: Anemone
(9b) Indoor Spray: Pompon
(9c) Indoor Spray: Reflexed
(9d) Indoor Spray: Single
(9e) Indoor Spray: Intermediate
(9f) Indoor Spray: Spider, Quill, Spoon or Any Other Type
(10a) Indoor, Spider
(10b) Indoor, Quill
(10c) Indoor, Spoon
(11) Any Other Indoor Type
(12a) Indoor, Charm
(12b) Indoor, Cascade
(13a) October-flowering Incurved: Large-flowered
(13b) October-flowering Incurved: Medium-flowered
(13c) October-flowering Incurved: Small-flowered
(14a) October-flowering Reflexed: Large-flowered
(14b) October-flowering Reflexed: Medium-flowered
(14c) October-flowering Reflexed: Small-flowered
(15a) October-flowering Intermediate: Large-flowered
(15b) October-flowering Intermediate: Medium-flowered
(15c) October-flowered Intermediate: Small-flowered
(16) October-flowering Large
(17a) October-flowering Single: Large-flowered
(17b) October-flowering Single: Medium-flowered
(17c) October-flowering Single: Small-flowered
(18a) October-flowering Pompon: True Pompon
(18b) October-flowering Pompon: Semi-pompon
(19a) October-flowering Spray: Anemone
(19b) October-flowering Spray: Pompon
(19c) October-flowering Spray: Reflexed
(19d) October-flowering Spray: Single
(19e) October-flowering Spray: Intermediate
(19f) October-flowering Spray: Spider, Quill, Spoon or Any Other Type
(20) Any Other October-flowering Type
(21a) Korean: Anemone
(21b) Korean: Pompon
(21c) Korean: Reflexed
(21d) Korean: Single
(21e) Korean: Intermediate
(21f) Korean: Spider, Quill, Spoon, or any other type
(22a) Charm: Anemone

(22b)	Charm: Pompon
(22c)	Charm: Reflexed
(22d)	Charm: Single
(22e)	Charm: Intermediate
(22f)	Charm: Spider, Quill, Spoon or Any Other Type
(23a)	Early-flowering Outdoor Incurved: Large-flowered
(23b)	Early-flowering Outdoor Incurved: Medium-flowered
(23c)	Early-flowering Outdoor Incurved: Small-flowered
(24a)	Early-flowering Outdoor Reflexed: Large-flowered
(24b)	Early-flowering Outdoor Reflexed: Medium-flowered
(24c)	Early-flowering Outdoor Reflexed: Small-flowered
(25a)	Early-flowering Outdoor Intermediate: Large-flowered
(25b)	Early-flowering Outdoor Intermediate: Medium-flowered
(25c)	Early-flowering Outdoor Intermediate: Small-flowered
(26a)	Early-flowering Outdoor Anemone: Large-flowered
(26b)	Early-flowering Outdoor Anemone: Medium-flowered
(27a)	Early-flowering Outdoor Single: Large-flowered
(27b)	Early-flowering Outdoor Single: Medium-flowered
(28a)	Early-flowering Outdoor Pompon: True Pompon
(28b)	Early-flowering Outdoor Pompon: Semi-pompon
(29a)	Early-flowering Outdoor Spray: Anemone
(29b)	Early-flowering Outdoor Spray: Pompon
(29c)	Early-flowering Outdoor Spray: Reflexed
(29d)	Early-flowering Outdoor Spray: Single
(29e)	Early-flowering Outdoor Spray: Intermediate
(29f)	Early-flowering Outdoor Spray: Spider, Quill, Spoon or Any Other Type
(29Rub)	Early-flowering Outdoor Spray: Rubellum
(30)	Any Other Early-flowering Outdoor Type

CLEMATIS

(Cultivar Groups as per Matthews, V. (2002) *The International Clematis Register & Checklist 2002*, RHS, London.)

(A)	Atragene Group
(Ar)	Armandii Group
(C)	Cirrhosa Group
(EL)	Early Large-flowered Group
(F)	Flammula Group
(Fo)	Forsteri Group
(H)	Heracleifolia Group
(I)	Integrifolia Group
(LL)	Late Large-flowered Group
(M)	Montana Group
(T)	Texensis Group
(Ta)	Tangutica Group
(V)	Viorna Group
(Vb)	Vitalba Group
(Vt)	Viticella Group

DAHLIA

(Classification according to The International Dahlia Register (1969), 22nd Supp. (2012) formed through consultation with national dahlia societies.)

(Sin)	1 Single
(Anem)	2 Anemone-flowered
(Col)	3 Collerette
(WL)	4 Waterlily
(D)	5 Decorative
(Ba)	6 Ball
(Pom)	7 Pompon
(C)	8 Cactus
(S-c)	9 Semi-cactus
(Misc)	10 Miscellaneous
(Fim)	11 Fimbriated
(SinO)	12 Single Orchid (Star)
(DblO)	13 Double Orchid
(P)	14 Peony-flowered
(B)	Botanical
(DwB)	Dwarf Bedding
(Lil)	Lilliput

DIANTHUS

(By the RHS)

(b)	Carnation, border
(M)	Carnation, Malmaison
(p)	Pink
(p,a)	Pink, annual
(pf)	Carnation, perpetual-flowering
(pt)	Carnation, pot

FRUIT

(B)	Black (*Vitis*), Blackberry (*Rubus*), Blackcurrant (*Ribes*)
(Ball)	Ballerina (*Malus*)
(C)	Culinary (*Malus, Prunus, Pyrus, Ribes*)
(Cider)	Cider (*Malus*)
(D)	Dessert (*Malus, Prunus, Pyrus, Ribes*)
(F)	Fruit
(G)	Glasshouse (*Vitis*)
(O)	Outdoor (*Vitis*)
(P)	Pinkcurrant (*Ribes*)
(Perry)	Perry (*Pyrus*)

(R) Red (*Vitis*), Redcurrant (*Ribes*)
(S) Seedless (*Citrus*, *Vitis*)
(s-p) Self-pollinating
(W) White (*Vitis*), Whitecurrant (*Ribes*)

FUCHSIA

(E) Encliandra
(T) Variants and hybrids of *F. triphylla*

GLADIOLUS

(B) Butterfly
(E) Exotic
(G) Giant
(L) Large
(M) Medium
(Min) Miniature
(N) Nanus
(P) Primulinus
(S) Small
(Tub) Tubergenii

HEPATICA NOBILIS

(Adapted from the International Hepatica Society classification for *Hepatica nobilis*)
(1) Hyoujun (normal)
(2) (degenerated anther)
(3) Otome (degenerated stamen)
(4) Henka (petal deformity)
(5/d) Herashibe (semi-double, primitive)
(5A/d) Choji (semi-double, primitive)
(6/d) Nidan (semi-double, advanced)
(7/d) Sandan (double, primitive)
(8/d) Karako (double, advanced)
(9/d) Sene-e (double, completed)

HYDRANGEA MACROPHYLLA

(H) Hortensia
(L) Lacecap

IMPATIENS

(NG) New Guinea Group

IRIS

(Adapted from the American Iris Society Classification)
(AB) Arilbred
(BB) Border Bearded
(Cal-Sib) Series *Californicae* × Series *Sibiricae*
(CH) Californian Hybrid
(DB) Dwarf Bearded (not assigned)
(Dut) Dutch (can be assigned to *I.* × *hollandica*)
(IB) Intermediate Bearded
(J) Juno (subgenus *Scorpiris*)
(La) Louisiana Hybrid
(MDB) Miniature Dwarf Bearded
(MTB) Miniature Tall Bearded
(Rc) Regeliocyclus (Section *Regelia* × Section *Oncocyclus*)
(Reticulata)
(SDB) Standard Dwarf Bearded
(Sib) Siberian
(Sino-Sib) Series *Sibiricae*, chromosome number 2n=40
(SpH) Species Hybrid
(Spuria) Spuria
(TB) Tall Bearded

LILIUM

(Classification according to *The International Lily Register* (ed. 4, 2007))
(I) Asiatic hybrids derived from *L. amabile*, *L. bulbiferum*, *L. callosum*, *L. cernuum*, *L. concolor*, *L. dauricum*, *L. davidii*, *L.* × *hollandicum*, *L. lancifolium*, *L. lankongense*, *L. leichtlinii*, *L.* × *maculatum* and *L. pumilum*, *L.* × *scottiae*, *L. wardii* and *L. wilsonii*.
(II) Martagon hybrids derived from *L. dalhansonii*, *L. hansonii*, *L. martagon*, *L. medeoloides and L. tsingtauense*
(III) Euro-Caucasian hybrids derived from *L. candidum*, *L. chalcedonicum*, *L. kesselringianum*, *L. monadelphum*, *L. pomponium*, *L. pyrenaicum* and *L.* × *testaceum*.
(IV) American hybrids derived from *L. bolanderi*, *L.* × *burbankii*, *L. canadense*, *L. columbianum*, *L. grayi*, *L. humboldtii*, *L. kelleyanum*, *L. kelloggii*, *L. maritimum*, *L. michauxii*, *L. michiganense*, *L. occidentale*, *L.* × *pardaboldtii*, *L. pardalinum*, *L. parryi*, *L. parvum*, *L. philadelphicum*, *L. pitkinense*, *L. superbum*, *L. vollmeri*, *L. washingtonianum* and *L. wigginsii*.
(V) Longiflorum lilies derived from *L. formosanum*, *L. longiflorum*, *L. philippinense and L. wallichianum*.
(VI) Trumpet and Aurelian hybrids derived from *L.* × *aurelianense*, *L. brownii*, *L.* × *centigale*, *L. henryi*, *L.* × *imperiale*, *L.* × *kewense*, *L. leucantheum*, *L. regale*, *L. rosthornii*, *L. sargentiae*, *L. sulphureum* and *L. sulphurgale* (but excluding hybrids of *L. henryi* with all species listed in Division VII).
(VII) Oriental hybrids derived from *L. auratum*, *L. japonicum*, *L. nobilissimum*, *L.* × *parkmanii*, *L rubellum* and *L. speciosum* (but excl. all hybrids of these with *L. henryi*).
(VIII) Other hybrids not covered by any of the previous divisions (I-VII)
(IX) Species and cultivars of species
a/ upward-facing flowers
b/ outward-facing flowers
c/ downward-facing flowers

/a	trumpet-shaped flowers
/b	bowl-shaped flowers
/c	flat flowers (or with only tepal tips recurved)
/d	recurved flowers

MALUS *SEE* FRUIT

NARCISSUS

(By the RHS, revised 1998)

(1)	Trumpet
(2)	Large-cupped
(3)	Small-cupped
(4)	Double
(5)	Triandrus
(6)	Cyclamineus
(7)	Jonquilla and Apodanthus
(8)	Tazetta
(9)	Poeticus
(10)	Bulbocodium
(11a)	Split-corona: Collar
(11b)	Split-corona: Papillon
(12)	Miscellaneous
(13)	Species

NYMPHAEA

(H)	Hardy
(D)	Day-blooming
(N)	Night-blooming
(T)	Tropical

PAEONIA

(S)	Shrubby

PELARGONIUM

(A)	Angel
(C)	Coloured Foliage (in combination)
(Ca)	Cactus (in combination)
(d)	Double (in combination)
(Dec)	Decorative
(Dw)	Dwarf
(DwI)	Dwarf Ivy-leaved
(Fr)	Frutetorum
(I)	Ivy-leaved
(Min)	Miniature
(MinI)	Miniature Ivy-leaved
(R)	Regal
(Sc)	Scented-leaved
(St)	Stellar (in combination)
(T)	Tulip (in combination)
(U)	Unique
(Z)	Zonal
(Za)	Zonartic

PRIMULA

(Classification by Section as per Richards. J. (2002) *Primula* (2nd edition). Batsford, London)

(Ag)	*Auganthus*
(Al)	*Aleuritia*
(Am)	*Amethystinae*
(Ar)	*Armerina*
(Au)	*Auricula*
(A)	Alpine Auricula
(B)	Border Auricula
(S)	Show Auricula
(St)	Striped Auricula
(Bu)	*Bullatae*
(Ca)	*Capitatae*
(Cf)	*Cordifoliae*
(Ch)	*Chartaceae*
(Co)	*Cortusoides*
(Cr)	*Carolinella*
(Cu)	*Cuneifoliae*
(Cy)	*Crystallophlomis*
(Da)	*Davidii*
(De)	*Denticulatae*
(Dr)	*Dryadifoliae*
(F)	*Fedtschenkoanae*
(G)	*Glabrae*
(Ma)	*Malvaceae*
(Mi)	*Minutissimae*
(Mo)	*Monocarpicae*
(Mu)	*Muscarioides*
(Ob)	*Obconicolisteri*
(Or)	*Oreophlomis*
(Pa)	*Parryi*
(Pe)	*Petiolares*
(Pf)	*Proliferae*
(Pi)	*Pinnatae*
(Pr)	*Primula*
(Poly)	Polyanthus (can be assigned to *P.* × *polyantha*)
(Prim)	Primrose
(Pu)	*Pulchellae*
(Py)	*Pycnoloba*
(R)	*Reinii*
(Si)	*Sikkimenses*
(So)	*Soldanelloides*
(Sp)	*Sphondylia*
(Sr)	*Sredinskya*
(Su)	*Suffrutescentes*
(Y)	*Yunnanenses*

PRUNUS *SEE* FRUIT

PYRUS *SEE* FRUIT

RHODODENDRON

(A)	Azalea (deciduous, species or unclassified hybrid)
(Ad)	Azaleodendron
(EA)	Evergreen azalea
(G)	Ghent azalea (deciduous)
(K)	Knap Hill or Exbury azalea (deciduous)
(M)	Mollis azalea (deciduous)
(O)	Occidentalis azalea (deciduous)

(R) Rustica azalea (deciduous)
(V) Vireya rhododendron
(Vs) Viscosa azalea (deciduous)

RIBES *SEE* FRUIT

ROSA

(A) Alba
(Bb) Bourbon
(Bs) Boursault
(Ce) Centifolia
(Ch) China
(Cl) Climbing (in combination)
(D) Damask
(DPo) Damask Portland
(F) Floribunda or Cluster-flowered
(G) Gallica
(Ga) Garnette
(GC) Ground Cover
(HM) Hybrid Musk
(HP) Hybrid Perpetual
(HT) Hybrid Tea or Large-flowered
(Min) Miniature
(Mo) Moss (in combination)
(N) Noisette
(Patio) Patio, Miniature Floribunda or Dwarf Cluster-flowered
(Poly) Polyantha
(Ra) Rambler
(RH) Rubiginosa hybrid (Hybrid Sweet Briar)
(Ru) Rugosa
(S) Shrub
(SpH) Spinosissima Hybrid
(T) Tea

RUBUS *SEE* FRUIT

SAXIFRAGA

(Classification by Section from Gornall, R.J. (1987). *Botanical Journal of the Linnean Society,* 95(4): 273-292)

(1) *Ciliatae*
(2) *Cymbalaria*
(3) *Merkianae*
(4) *Micranthes*
(5) *Irregulares*
(6) *Heterisia*
(7) *Porphyrion*
(8) *Ligulatae*
(9) *Xanthizoon*
(10) *Trachyphyllum*
(11) *Gymnopera*
(12) *Cotylea*
(13) *Odontophyllae*
(14) *Mesogyne*
(15) *Saxifraga*

STREPTOCARPUS

(AV) African violets (previously in the genus *Saintpaulia*)

TULIPA

(Classification by Cultivar Group from *Classified List and International Register of Tulip Names* by Koninklijke Algemeene Vereniging voor Bloembollencultuur 1996)

(1) Single Early Group
(2) Double Early Group
(3) Triumph Group
(4) Darwin Hybrid Group
(5) Single Late Group (including Darwin Group and Cottage Group)
(6) Lily-flowered Group
(7) Fringed Group
(8) Viridiflora Group
(9) Rembrandt Group
(10) Parrot Group
(11) Double Late Group
(12) Kaufmanniana Group
(13) Fosteriana Group
(14) Greigii Group
(15) Miscellaneous

VIOLA

(C) Cornuta Hybrid
(dVt) Double Violet
(ExVa) Exhibition Viola
(FP) Fancy Pansy
(P) Pansy
(PVt) Parma Violet
(SP) Show Pansy
(T) Tricolor
(Va) Viola
(Vt) Violet
(Vtta) Violetta

VITIS *SEE* FRUIT

How to Use the Plant Directory

Nursery Codes

Look up the plant you require in the alphabetical Plant Directory. Against each plant you will find one or more four or five letter codes, for example WCru, each code represents one nursery offering that plant. The first letter of each code indicates the main area of the country in which the nursery is situated. For this geographical key, refer to the **Nursery Codes and Symbols** on p.862.

Turn to the **Nursery Details by Code** starting on p.866 where, in alphabetical order of codes, you will find details of each nursery which offers the plant in question. For a fuller explanation of how to use the nursery listings please turn to p.863. **Always check that the nursery you select has the plant in stock before you set out.**

Plants with more than 30 Suppliers

In some cases, against the plant name you will see the term 'Widely available' instead of a nursery code. If we were to include every plant listed by all nurseries, the *RHS Plant Finder* would become unmanageably bulky. We therefore ask nurseries to restrict their entries to those plants that are not already well represented. As a result, if more than 30 nurseries offer any plant the Directory gives no nursery codes and the plant is listed instead as being 'Widely available'.

You should not have difficulty in locating these in local nurseries or garden centres. If, however, you are unable to find such plants, a list of all the current suppliers we have on file is available by post or online. See the Introduction (p.34).

Finding Fruit, Vegetables and Herbs

You will need to search for these by their botanical names. Common names are cross-referenced to their botanical names in the Plant Directory.

If you have Difficulty Finding your Plant

If you cannot immediately find the plant you seek, look through the various species of the genus. You may be using an incomplete name. The problem is most likely to arise in very large genera such as *Phlox* where there are a number of possible species, each with a large number of cultivars. A search through the whole genus may well bring success. For space reasons, we are not able to list in the Plant Directory annuals, orchids or cacti (except hardy terrestrial orchids and hardy cacti), or non-ornamental vegetables. For fruit and vegetables with an RHS Award of Garden Merit please see the relevant sections on p.824 and p.836.

Cross-references

It may be that the plant name you seek is a synonym. Our intention is to list nursery codes only against the correct botanical name. Where you find a synonym you will be cross-referred to the correct name.

Plants Last Listed in Earlier Editions

It may be that the plant you are seeking has no known suppliers and is thus not listed.

The loss of a plant name from the Directory may arise for a number of reasons – the supplier may have gone out of business, or may not have responded to our latest questionnaire and has therefore been removed from the book. Such plants may well be available but we have no knowledge of current suppliers. Alternatively, some plants may have been misnamed by nurseries in previous editions and are now appearing under their correct name.

For further information on plants last listed in earlier editions please see the Introduction (p.34).

We recommend that you use the latest edition of the *RHS Plant Finder*

USING THE PLANT DIRECTORY

The purpose of the Plant Directory is to help the reader correctly identify the plant they seek and find stockists. Each nursery has a unique code which appears to the right of the plant name. **Nursery Details by Code** (p.866) gives details about each nursery. The first letter in each code denotes its geographical region. Turn to the **Nursery Codes and Symbols** (p.862) to find the correct code for an area.

The Plant Directory provides information about plants through symbols and notes. For example: if a plant has an alternative name; is new to the book; or has received the RHS Award of Garden Merit.

Rudbeckia (Asteraceae)

	AUTUMN SUN	see *R. laciniata* 'Herbstsonne'
	'Berlin'	EBee ECtt LRHS NRHS
	californica	EHyd
	- B&SWJ 14105	WCru
	deamii	see *R. fulgida* var. *deamii*
	'Dublin'	ECtt MBNS
	fulgida	SWvt WFar
	- 'City Garden'	ECtt GBin LRHS NLar SRms WFar
§	- var. ***deamii*** ♀H6	Widely available
	- 'Early Bird Gold'	CWGN EBee ECtt EHyd EPfP GBin GMaP LCro LRHS MHol NLar NRHS SAko SCob WCAu WFar
	- - 'Forever Gold' new	SEdd SMad
	- var. ***fulgida***	CMea EBee EPfP LEdu SPhx SPoG
	- 'Little Goldstar' PBR	CBod CKno CRos EBee ECtt EHyd ELan EPfP LCro LOPS LRHS MAsh MPri MTin NDov NLar NRHS SCob SCoo SLon SPoG SRms WFar WHil
§	- var. ***speciosa*** ♀H6	EBee ECha ECtt EHyd ELan ELon EPfP GAbr GBin GWyn LRHS MMuc NRHS SEND SEdd SHar SPlb SPtp SRms SWvt WFar XLum
	- var. ***sullivantii***	CDoC
	- - 'Goldsturm' ♀H6	Widely available
	- - 'Pot of Gold'	NLar SCob
	- VIETTE'S LITTLE SUZY ('Blovi')	CBod EHyd LRHS LSou NRHS SRms WFar
	grandiflora	EHyd
	- 'Sundance'	SPhx
§	***hirta***	SIvy
	- AUTUMN COLORS (mixed)	EHyd ELan LCro LOPS LRHS NRHS
	- 'Cappuccino'	EHyd ELan EPfP LRHS NRHS
	- CHEROKEE SUNSET (mixed) (d)	CSpe
	- 'Cherry Brandy'	CSpe LRHS MNHC NGBl SPhx
	- CHIM CHIMINEE (mixed)	NGBl SCoo
	- 'Goldilocks'	SVic
	- 'Indian Summer' ♀H3	CRos EHyd EPfP LRHS MNHC NRHS SPhx
	- 'Irish Eyes'	SPhx SSal SVic
	- 'Marmalade'	EHyd EPfP SPhx SVic
	- 'Prairie Sun'	CRos EHyd EPfP LRHS MBros NGBl NRHS SPhx
	- 'Sonora'	NGBl
	- (Sunbeckia Series) SUNBECKIA ALICIA	LRHS
	- - SUNBECKIA OLIVIA	LRHS
	- (Toto Series) 'Toto Lemon'	LRHS
	- - 'Toto Rustic'	LRHS
	- - 'Toto' ♀H3	LCro LOPS LRHS SWvt
	JULY GOLD	see *R. laciniata* 'Juligold'
	laciniata	CKno CMac CSpe EBee EHyd ELan EPPr GQue LEdu MNrw NDov NGBl NLar SMHy SPeP SPhx SRms

DESCRIPTIVE TERM (B&SWJ 14105)
See p.38.

NEW (new)
Plant new to this edition.

SYMBOLS TO THE LEFT OF THE NAME (§)
Provides information about the name of the plant. See p.36 for the key.

TRADE DESIGNATION (VIETTE'S LITTLE SUZY)
See p.40.

SYMBOLS TO THE RIGHT OF THE NAME ((d))
Tells you more about the plant itself, e.g. (d) *indicates that the plant is double-flowered,* (F) *= fruit. See p.36 for the key.*

ABBREVIATIONS (- 'Sonora')
To save space a dash indicates that the previous heading is repeated. If written out in full the name would be Rudbeckia hirta *'Sonora'.*

CROSS-REFERENCES (see *R. laciniata* 'Herbstsonne')
Directs you to the correct name of the plant and the nursery codes. See p.55.

♀H6
This plant has received the RHS Award of Garden Merit. See p.37.

PBR
Plant Breeders' Rights. See p.39.

WIDELY AVAILABLE
Indicates that more than 30 Plant Finder nurseries supply the plant, and it may be available locally. See p.55.

NURSERY CODE
A unique code identifying each nursery. Turn to p.866 for details of the nurseries.

II
PLANTS

THE PLANT DIRECTORY

A

Abelia (*Caprifoliaceae*)

	chinensis misapplied	see *A.* × *grandiflora* 'Lake Maggiore'
§	***chinensis*** R. Br.	CBcs CExl CKel CMCN CMac EBee EHyd ELan EPfP LRHS MGil MMuc SEND SPer SRms WGrn WLov
	'Edward Goucher' ♀H5	Widely available
	engleriana	CExl CRos EHyd EPfP LRHS MAsh MBlu MGil NLar SBrt SLon WLov
	floribunda	see *Vesalea floribunda*
§	× ***grandiflora***	CBod CBrac CCVT CDoC CEme CKel CRos CSBt CTri CTsd EPfP ERom GArf LCro LOPS LPar LRHS NLar SCob SDix SEdd SGBe SGbt SGsty SWeb WAvo WLov XSen
	- 'Aurea'	see *A.* × *grandiflora* 'Gold Spot'
	- 'Brockhill Allgold'	CKel EMil EPfP LRHS SPoG
	- common clone	see *A.* × *grandiflora* 'Lake Maggiore'
	- 'Compacta'	WFar
	- CONFETTI ('Conti'PBR) (v)	CBcs CBod CDoC CEme CKel CMac CRos CSBt EHyd ELan EPfP ERom LPar LRHS LSRN MGos MRav NLar SEle SGbt SGol SGsty SPer SPoG SWvt WFar
	- dwarf	MSwo
§	- 'Francis Mason' (v)	Widely available
§	- 'Gold Spot' (v)	CBod CDoC EPfP NLar SPer
	- 'Gold Strike'	see *A.* × *grandiflora* 'Gold Spot'
	- 'Goldsport'	see *A.* × *grandiflora* 'Gold Spot'
	- 'Hopleys'PBR (v) ♀H5	CBcs CMac CRos CSBt CTri EHed EHyd ELan EPfP LRHS MAsh MGos NLar SCoo SGBe SGol SLon SPoG SRms SWvt WGrn WLov
	- 'Kaleidoscope'PBR (v)	Widely available
	- LADY LIBERTY ('Keylib')	SGBe
§	- 'Lake Maggiore' ♀H5	CBar CMac CSBt MBlu MGil MGos MMuc MRav MSwo SEND SPer SPoG SRms SSta
	- LUCKY LOTS ('Wevo2') (v)	EBee NLar SCob SEdd SGol
	- MAGIC DAYDREAM ('Opstal103')	CBod CWGN LCro LOPS MGos NEoE SCoo
	- MYSTIC DAYDREAM ('Opstal40')	EBee
	- 'Panache' (v)	WCot
	- 'Prostrate White'	GKev NLar SPoG
	- 'Radiance' (v)	CBod EBee NEoE SCob SEdd
	- 'Semperflorens'	LRHS WFar
	- 'Sherwoodii'	MAsh MGil MGos SEdd
	- 'Sparkling Silver' (v)	CKel EMil LRHS SEdd SGsty
	- SUNNY CHARMS ('Mindu01'PBR)	CBcs
	- 'Sunrise' (v)	NLar
	- SUNSHINE DAYDREAM ('Abelops'PBR) (v)	CBod CEnd EBee LCro LOPS MGos MMrt MPkF NLar SCob SEdd SGBe SGbt SGol SPad SRms WFar
	- 'Tanya'	WAvo
	- 'Variegata'	see *A.* × *grandiflora* 'Francis Mason'
§	'Lynn'PBR	MGos SPoG XSte
	mosanensis	CBod CMCN CRos EHed EHyd ELan EPfP LRHS MBlu MGil NQui SCoo SLon WCot WGob WLov
	- BRIDAL BOUQUET ('Monia')	SChF
	parvifolia	CBcs CBod CEme CExl CKel CMCN CMac CSBt CTri EHyd LRHS MGil NLar SLon SPer SPoG SWvt WGrn WLov
	- 'Bumblebee'	CRos LCro LOPS MAsh MGos NLar SPoG SRms XSte
	PASTEL CHARM ('Minduo2')	LRHS
	PETITE GARDEN ('Minedward'PBR)	CBod CDoC CEme CKel SGol
	PINKY BELLS	see *A.* 'Lynn'
	rupestris misapplied	see *A.* × *grandiflora*
	rupestris Lindl.	see *A. chinensis* R. Br.
	triflora	see *Zabelia triflora*
	umbellata	see *Zabelia umbellata*

Abeliophyllum (*Oleaceae*)

distichum	CBcs CEnd CRos CSde EBee EHed EHyd ELan ELon EPfP IDee LPar LRHS MAsh MBlu MSwo NRHS SGol SGsty SPer SWvt WCFE WCot WFar
- Roseum Group	CBcs CBod CExl CRos EHyd ELan ELon EPfP EShb LCro LOPS LRHS MAsh MGil MHtn MMuc MRav NQui SLon SPoG WCot

Abelmoschus (*Malvaceae*)

esculentus	SVic

Abies ✿ (*Pinaceae*)

alba	CAco MMuc NWea
- 'Barabits' Star' **new**	CAco
- 'Bystricka'	NLar
- 'Chmel W.B.' **new**	CKen
- 'Green Spiral'	CAco NLar
- 'Münsterland'	CKen
- 'Nana' misapplied	see *Picea glauca* 'Nana'
- 'Pendula'	CAco CKen
- 'Pyramidalis'	CAco
- 'Scarabantia' **new**	CAco
- 'Schwarzwald'	CKen
amabilis	CAco LRHS NWea
- 'Spreading Star'	SLim
arizonica	see *A. lasiocarpa* var. *arizonica*
× ***arnoldiana***	CAco
balsamea	CAco MMuc NWea
- 'Bruce's Variegated' (v) **new**	NLar
- 'Cook's Blue'	CKen
- 'Eugene Gold'	NLar
- Hudsonia Group	CKen GArf LRHS
- - 'Nana'	CAco CKen ELan LPar LRHS MGil NLar
- 'Jamie'	CKen

	- 'Kiwi'	NLar
	- 'Le Feber'	CKen
	- var. ***phanerolepis*** 'Bear Swamp'	CKen NHol NLar
	- 'Piccolo'	CAco CKen LRHS MGil NLar
	- 'Renswoude'	CKen NLar
	- 'Sky Meadow'	NLar
	- 'Tyler Blue'	CKen
	- 'Verkade's Prostrate'	CKen
	borisii-regis	CAco
*	- 'Pendula'	CKen
	- 'Spring Delight'	NLar
	brachyphylla dwarf	see *A. homolepis* 'Prostrata'
	bracteata	CAco
	cephalonica	CAco CMCN LRHS
	- 'Barabits' Gold'	CAco
	- 'Greg's Broom'	CKen NLar
§	- 'Meyer's Dwarf'	CAco NLar SLim WLea
	- 'Nana'	see *A. cephalonica* 'Meyer's Dwarf'
	cephalonica* × *nordmanniana	MHtn
	chensiensis	CAco LRHS
	cilicica	CAco
	- 'Spring Grove'	CKen
	concolor	CAco CBcs CBod IPap LMaj LPar MMuc NWea SEND
	- 'Archer's Dwarf'	CAco CKen NLar SLim
	- 'Bedoń' **new**	CAco
	- 'Birthday Broom'	CKen
	- 'Blue Cloak'	CKen
	- 'Blue Sapphire'	CKen
§	- 'Compacta' ♀H7	CAco CKen MGos NHol SLim WLea
	- 'Fagerhult'	CKen
	- 'Gable's Weeping'	CKen
	- 'Glauca'	see *A. concolor* 'Violacea'
	- 'Glauca Compacta'	see *A. concolor* 'Compacta'
	- 'Globosa' **new**	CAco
	- 'Hillier Broom'	see *A. concolor* 'Hillier's Dwarf'
§	- 'Hillier's Dwarf'	CKen
	- 'Husky Pup'	CKen
	- 'La Veta'	CKen
	- Lowiana Group	CAco
	- - 'Creamy'	CKen NLar
	- 'Masonic Broom'	CKen
	- 'Mike Stearn'	CKen
	- 'Mora'	CKen
	- 'Piggelmee'	CKen MAsh
	- 'Pygmy'	CKen
	- 'Scooter'	CKen
	- 'Sherwood's Blue'	CAco
	- Violacea Group	CKen LRHS
§	- - 'Violacea' ♀H7	CAco
	- - 'Violacea Prostrate' ♀H7	CAco NHol NLar SAko
	- 'Wattez Prostrate'	SLim
	- 'Wattezii'	CKen
	- 'Wintergold'	CAco CKen MAsh MBlu NHol NLar SLim
	delavayi	CMCN EPfP LEdu SAko WPGP
	- var. ***delavayi***	CExl
	- - Fabri Group	see *A. fabri*
	- 'Gold Splash' **new**	LRHS
	- 'Major Neishe'	CKen
	- 'Midnight Blue' **new**	CAco
	durangensis	CAco
	var. ***coahuilensis*** **new**	
§	***fabri***	CAco CKen LRHS
	fanjingshanensis **new**	CAco
	fargesii	CKen
	- var. ***faxoniana***	CAco
	firma	CAco
	forrestii	CKen
	- var. ***georgei***	NWea
	fraseri	CAco CBcs EWhm MMuc NWea WTSh
	- 'Blue Bonnet'	CAco CKen NLar
	- 'Franklin'	NLar
	- 'Kline's Nest'	SLim
	- 'Palmeri'	NLar
	- 'Raul's Dwarf'	CKen
	grandis	CAco CJun CMCN CMac EPfP IPap MMuc NWea WMou WTSh
	- 'Compacta'	CKen
	- 'Van Dedem's Dwarf'	CKen SLim
	guatemalensis **new**	CAco
	holophylla	CAco
	homolepis	CAco CKen
	- 'F.R. Newman'	SLim
§	- 'Prostrata'	CKen
	- var. ***umbellata*** **new**	CAco
	× ***insignis*** **new**	CAco
	kawakamii	CAco
	koreana ♀H7	CAco CBcs CBrac CCVT CEme CJun CLnd CMCN CMac ELan EPfP GKin IPap LMaj LPar LRHS MBlu MGos MMuc MPri NHol NPoe NWea SCob SGol SLim SWvt WMat WMou WTSh
	- 'Alpin Star'	CKen MAsh NLar
	- 'Aurea'	see *A. koreana* 'Flava'
	- 'Blaue Zwo'	CKen
	- 'Blauer Eskimo' ♀H7	CKen MAsh NLar SLim
	- 'Blauer Pfiff'	CAco CKen NLar
	- 'Blinsham Gold'	CKen
	- 'Blue Emperor'	CAco MBlu NLar
	- 'Blue Magic'	CAco CKen NLar
	- blue-leaved	CDoC
	- 'Brilliant'	CKen LRHS SCoo
	- 'Cis' ♀H7	CKen MGil NHol NLar SLim
	- 'Compact Dwarf'	CAco LPar
	- CRYSTAL GLOBE	see *A. koreana* 'Kristallkugel'
	- 'Dark Hill'	NLar
	- 'Discus'	CAco NLar
	- 'Doni-tajuso'	CKen NLar
	- 'Eisregen'	CKen SAko
	- 'Festival'	NHol
§	- 'Flava'	CAco
	- 'Frosty'	NLar SLim
	- 'Gait'	CKen NLar
	- 'Golden Glow'	SLim
	- 'Goldener Traum'	CKen NLar
	- 'Green Carpet'	CAco CKen NLar SLim
	- 'Green 'n' Cream'	CAco LRHS
	- 'Grüne Spinne'	MBlu
	- 'Horstmann'	CKen
	- 'Inge'	NLar
	- 'Inverleith'	CKen
	- 'Kleiner Prinz'	NLar
	- 'Kohout'	CAco CKen
	- 'Kohout's Ice Breaker'PBR ♀H7	CAco CKen LRHS MAsh MGos NLar SAko SLim
§	- 'Kristallkugel'	CKen LRHS MAsh MBlu MGil NLar
	- 'Lippetal'	CKen
	- 'Luminetta'	CAco CKen NHol
	- 'May' **new**	CAco
	- 'Nadelkissen'	CKen NHol
	- 'Nisbet'	CAco LRHS NHol
	- 'Oberon'	CAco CKen MAsh MGil NHol NLar SLim
	- 'Piccolo'	CKen
	- 'Pinocchio'	CKen MGil NHol
	- 'Prostrata'	see *A. koreana* 'Prostrate Beauty'
§	- 'Prostrate Beauty'	CKen
	- 'Ry'	MGil NLar
	- 'Schneestern'	NLar

	- 'Schwedenkönig'	NLar SLim
	- 'Sherwood Compact'	CKen
	- 'Shorty'	CKen NLar
	- 'Silberkugel'	CKen LRHS SLim
	- 'Silberlocke' ♀H7	CAco CCVT CKen MAsh MBlu MGos NLar NOrn SCoo SLim SMad WHwl WMat
	- 'Silbermavers'	CAco CKen
	- 'Silberperl'	CKen LRHS NLar SLim
	- 'Silver Show'	CAco MGil NHol NLar SAko SLim WLea
	- 'Threave'	CKen NHol
	- 'Tundra'	CAco NLar SLim
	- 'Verdener Dom'	NLar
	- 'Wellenseind'	CKen NLar
	- 'Winter Goldtip'	SLim
	koreana	CAco
	× ***lasiocarpa*** new	
	lasiocarpa	CAco NWea
	- 'Alpine Beauty'	CKen
§	- var. ***arizonica***	CAco
	- - 'Compacta' Hornibr. ♀H7	CCVT CKen LMaj MAsh MGos NHol NLar SLim SPoG WMat
	- - 'Kenwith Blue'	CAco CKen SLim
	- 'Beano Broom'	CKen NLar
	- 'Chikov'	CKen
	- 'Day Creek'	CKen
	- 'Duflon'	CKen NLar
	- 'Elaine'	CKen
	- 'Green Globe'	CAco CKen NLar SLim WLea
	- 'Hurricane Ridge'	CKen
	- 'Joe's Alpine'	CKen
	- 'Kyle's Alpine'	CKen
	- var. ***lasiocarpa***	CAco
	- 'Logan Pass'	CKen
	- 'Lopalpun'	CKen
	- 'Mulligan's Dwarf'	CKen
	- 'Prickly Pete'	CKen
	- 'Rhumpa'	SAko
	- 'Stevens Blue'	CKen
	- 'Toenisvorst'	CKen
	- 'Utah'	CKen
	magnifica	CAco IPap
	- 'Glauca' new	CAco
	- 'Mount Si'	CKen
I	- 'Nana'	CKen
	- var. ***shastensis*** new	CAco
	- witches' broom	CKen
	marocana	see *A. pinsapo* var. *marocana*
	nebrodensis	CAco CKen
	- 'Sicilian Gold'	NLar
	nephrolepis	CAco
	nobilis	see *A. procera*
	nordmanniana	CAco CBcs CBrac CCVT CJun CMCN CMac ELan EWhm IPap LBuc LMaj LPar MMuc NLar NWea SCob SGsty SPoG SWeb WMou WTSh
	- 'Arne's Dwarf'	CKen
	- 'Barabits' Compact'	CAco NLar
	- 'Barabits' Spreader'	CKen
	- 'Dobřichovice'	NLar
	- subsp. ***equi-trojani***	CAco
	- - 'Archer'	CKen
	- - 'Franke'	NLar
	- 'Filip's Gold Heart'	NLar
	- 'Golden Spreader' ♀H7	CAco CKen LRHS MAsh MBlu MGos NLar SCoo SLim
	- 'Hasselt'	see *A. nordmanniana* 'Pévé Hasselt'
	- 'Jakobsen'	CKen
	- 'Midwinter Gold'	NLar
	- 'Münsterland'	CAco NLar
	- subsp. ***nordmanniana***	LRHS
	'Aurea' new	
	- 'Peli'	NLar
	- 'Pendula'	CAco MBlu MGil SMad
§	- 'Pévé Hasselt'	CKen NLar
	- 'Reginac' new	NLar
	- 'Saerling'	NLar
	- 'Silberspitze'	CKen
	numidica	CAco CKen
	- 'Delicado' new	CAco
	- 'Glauca'	CAco CKen
	pindrow	CAco
	var. ***brevifolia*** new	
	pinsapo	CAco LRHS WMou WThu
	- 'Atlas'	CKen
	- 'Aurea' ♀H6	CAco CCVT CKen ELan LMaj NHol NLar SLim WHwl
I	- 'Aurea Nana'	CKen
	- 'Fastigiata'	CAco SAko SGol
	- 'Fatima'	CKen
	- 'Glauca' ♀H6	CAco CCVT CKen ELan LMaj LRHS MBlu NLar SEND SLim WLea
	- 'Hamondii'	CKen
I	- 'Horstmann'	CAco CKen NHol NLar SLim
	- 'Kelleriis'	NLar
§	- var. ***marocana***	CAco LRHS
	- 'Marokko'	CKen
	- 'Pendula'	CAco CKen
	- var. ***pinsapo***	CAco
	- 'Quicksilver'	CKen
	- 'San Pedro'	CKen
	- var. ***tazaotana*** new	CAco
	- 'Ubrique'	NLar
§	***procera***	CAco CBcs CMCN EPfP IPap MGil NWea WMou WTSh
	- 'Blaue Hexe'	CKen SLim
	- 'Delbar Cascade'	CAco CKen
	- Glauca Group	EPfP GKin MBlu NHol
	- - 'Glauca' ♀H7	CAco ELan LMaj SAko SCoo
	- - 'Glauca Prostrata' ♀H7	CKen LRHS MAsh SLim
I	- 'Glauca Pendula' new	CAco
	- 'Hupp's Dwarf'	CAco CKen NLar
	- 'Hupp's Single Snake' new	CAco
	- 'Jeddeloh'	CKen
	- 'La Graciosa'	CAco NLar
	- 'Noble's Dwarf'	SLim
	- 'Pospíšil'	CKen
	- 'Rat Tail'	CAco NLar
	- 'Rick's Foxtail' new	CAco
	- 'Seattle Mount'	CKen
	- 'Sherwoodii'	CKen NLar SLim
	recurvata	CAco
	Rosemoor hybrid	CKen
	sachalinensis	CAco CKen
	sibirica	CAco EPfP
	spectabilis	EPfP
	veitchii	CAco NWea WTSh
	- 'Glauca' new	CAco
	- 'Heddergott'	CKen NHol SLim
	- 'Heine'	CKen LRHS
	- 'Kramer'	CAco CKen
I	- 'Pendula'	CAco CKen
	- 'Rumburk'	CKen MAsh SLim
	- 'Secrest'	NLar
	- 'Syców'	CKen
	vejarii	CAco
	× ***vilmorinii*** new	CAco

Abromeitiella see *Deuterocohnia*

Abutilon ✿ (Malvaceae)

'Apfelsine' new	SPad
'Aphrodite'	CTsd EHed MMrt SPad
'Ashford Red'	CBcs CCCN ELan EMil LRHS SPalm WKif
'Bartley Schwarz'	MSCN
Bella Series	CDoC
'Buttercup' new	SPad
'Canary Bird' ♀H2	CBcs CCCN WKif
'Cannington Carol' (v) ♀H2	CCCN CEme LSRN SEND
'Cannington Peter' (v) ♀H2	CCCN
'Cloth of Gold'	CMac
'Color Sensation' new	SPad
'Cynthia Pike' (v)	CRos EHyd LRHS NRHS
'Fairy Tales' new	SPad
'Feuerwerk' new	SPad
'Flamenco'	CCCN CWGN
'Giant Orange' new	SPad
'Golden Terracotta' new	SPad
'Himbeere' new	SPad
'Hinton Seedling'	CCCN CRHN LSRN SPad
indicum	EBtc
'Isabella' new	SPad
'Jacqueline Morris'	LRHS
'John Thompson'	CBcs CCCN CKel CWGN
'Kentish Belle' ♀H3	Widely available
'Kleine Schönheit' new	SPad
'Lachskönigin' new	SPad
'Leila Jackson'	EBee EHed EShb SPad
'Lilac Jewel' new	SPad
'Lilac Wonder' new	SPad
'Lilli' new	SPad
'Lillian' new	SPad
'Lisa Roja' new	SVen
'Marion' ♀H1b	CCCN CRHN CRos EHyd LRHS LSRN NRHS SPlb
'Master Michael'	CMac
megapotamicum ♀H3	CBcs CBod CCCN CChe CDoC CKel CMac CPla CRHN CTri ELan ELon EPfP LRHS MGos MRav MSCN SCob SCoo SDix SEND SEle SPer SPoG SRms WSHC XSen
- 'Big Bell'	CCCN ECre MSCN WFar WGob
- 'Ines'	ELon SPad WPGP
- 'Pink Charm'	CCCN EHed ELon EShb SPad
- 'Variegatum' (v) ♀H3	CBcs CCCN CDoC CKel CMac ELon EPfP LRHS MGil SEle SLon SMad SPer SPoG SWvt WGob
- 'Wisley Red'	CCCN CKel CRHN EHed ELon LRHS SCob WGob
× ***milleri*** hort. ♀H3	CCCN CMac CRHN EHed ELon WCot WGob
- 'Variegatum' (v)	CCCN CKel CMac EBee LRHS WCot
'Moonlight Shadow' new	SPad
'Nabob' ♀H2	CBcs CCCN CDow CExl CKel CRHN CSde EBee ELan EPfP EShb SAko SEND SIvy SPalm WCot WFar
'Orange Hot Lava'	CExl EBee ECre WPGP
'Paddy's Nephew'	EBee
'Patrick Synge'	CBcs CCCN CDow EBee SChF SPhx WPGP
pictum 'Thompsonii' (v) ♀H2	CCCN MGil SEND
'Pink Lady'	CCCN
'Red Bells'	SVen
'Red Tiger'	LRHS SPad WKif XSte
RED TRUMPET ('Oostredtrump'PBR)	MMrt
'Rosela' new	SPad
'Roter Vulkan' new	SPad
'Russels Dwarf'	CCCN
'Savitzii' (v) ♀H2	MSCN
'Schneeflocke' new	SPad
'Silver Belle'	CCCN
'Simcox White'	CCCN
'Sonnenkind' new	SPad
'Souvenir de Bonn' (v) ♀H2	CCCN EShb WCot
'Sunny' new	SPad
× ***suntense***	CBcs CCCN CSBt EHyd LRHS LShi MSCN NPer NRHS
- 'Gorer's White' new	LRHS
- 'Jermyns' ♀H4	CExl EPfP LSRN MGos SCob SPoG SWvt
- 'Violetta'	WSpi
'Tango'	CCCN CRos CWGN LRHS MSCN SIvy SMad SPad WCot WGob
'Versicolor' new	SPad
'Victorian Lady' (d)	SPad
'Victory'	CCCN CWGN MSCN
vitifolium	CBcs CCCN CDTJ EBee LShi MGil SPad SPer SPoG WCot WFar WKif WSpi
- 'Album'	CBcs CCCN CExl WSpi
- 'Buckland'	CCCN
- 'Chalk Blues'	SPer
- 'Tennant's White' ♀H4	CCCN CExl CRos EHyd EPfP LRHS NRHS SAko WCot
- 'Veronica Tennant' ♀H4	CExl EBee EPfP SChF
'Waltz'	CCCN CWGN EBee ELan EShb SIvy SPad WBor WCot WGob
YELLOW TRUMPET ('Oosttrump'PBR)	EHed

Acacia (Fabaceae)

acinacea	SPlb
adunca	SPlb
angustissima	SPlb
axillaris	SPlb
baileyana ♀H3	CBcs CBod CCCN CDoC CEme CMac CSBt EHed EPfP LSRN MGos SCoo SEdd SPlb SWvt WFar
- var. ***aurea***	SPlb
- 'Purpurea' ♀H3	CBcs CBod CCCN CDoC CEme CEnd CExl CMac CSBt CSpe CTsd CWit EHed ELan EPfP EShb LSRN MGos MTrO SCoo SIvy SMad SPer SPlb SPoG SWvt WLov WPGP XSte
- 'Songlines'	CRos MGos NRHS
boormanii	CDoC CTsd EGrI GBin IDee SEdd SGBe SPlb WPGP
cognata 'Limelight'PBR new	XSte
cultriformis	CTsd ESwi
dealbata ♀H3	Widely available
- 'Gaulois Astier'	CDoC CKel CSBt EPfP LRHS LSRN MGos NRHS SPoG SWeb SWvt WCot
'Exeter Hybrid'	CSBt
glaucoptera	SPlb
gregorii	SPlb
jibberdingensis	SPlb
julibrissin	see *Albizia julibrissin*
karroo	see *Vachellia karroo*
longifolia	CDTJ CMac XSte
macradenia	SPlb
mearnsii	EBee SEdd
melanoxylon	CBcs CBod CDTJ CMCN SPlb XSte
nanodealbata	SPad
obliquinervia	XSte
pataczekii	CSBt WPGP
pendula	SPlb
podalyriifolia	SPlb
pravissima ♀H3	CBcs CBod CChe CDoC CEme CExl CMac CTsd EHed ELan EPfP GBin

	IDee ILea LRHS LSRN SArc SEdd SGBe SPlb SWvt
retinodes ♀H2	CBcs CCCN CCht CDTJ CTsd ILea SEND SEdd SPad SWvt XSte
- 'Lisette'	MGos XSte
riceana	CTsd SVen
rubida	SPlb
sentis	see *A. victoriae*
spectabilis	SPlb
suaveolens	SPlb
truncata	SPlb
verticillata	CBcs CBod CDTJ CDoC ELan EPfP
- riverine form	CCCN CExl EPfP LRHS SEND
§ ***victoriae***	SPlb

Acaena (*Rosaceae*)

adscendens misapplied	see *A. affinis*, *A. saccaticupula* 'Blue Haze'
adscendens ambig. 'Glauca'	NBir
§ ***affinis***	EBee ECha
anserinifolia misapplied	see *A. novae-zelandiae*
buchananii	EBee EPPr GAbr GBin GKev GWyn NLar SCob SRms XLum
caerulea hort.	see *A. caesiiglauca*
§ ***caesiiglauca***	CTri EPPr GAbr GMaP GQue
inermis	NWad SPlb
- 'Purpurea'	EBee ECha ECtt ELan EShb GAbr GArf GKev GMaP GQue MACG MMuc NDov NHol NHpl NLar NWad SLee SPlb WCav
magellanica	GAbr GKev XLum
microphylla	CBod GArf GQue MBel NLar SCob SLee SPlb SRms XLum
- Copper Carpet	see *A. microphylla* 'Kupferteppich'
- 'Glauca'	see *A. caesiiglauca*
- 'Grüner Zwerg'	NLar
§ - 'Kupferteppich'	ECtt ELan EPPr GAbr GKev GLog GMaP LEdu MRav NBir NBro NLar SEdd SLee SMHy SRms
minor var. ***antarctica***	GBin
myriophylla	EBee
§ ***novae-zelandiae***	CTri EBee GAbr GKev SDix
ovalifolia	GKev
'Pewter'	see *A. saccaticupula* 'Blue Haze'
'Purple Carpet'	see *A. microphylla* 'Kupferteppich'
'Purple Haze'	CSpe
saccaticupula	EBee GKev LShi MMuc
§ - 'Blue Haze'	CRos EBee ECha EHyd GWyn LRHS MACG MRav NBir NFav NLar NRHS SPlb SRms
tesca	GBin GQue

Acalypha (*Euphorbiaceae*)

§ ***herzogiana***	CCCN EShb

Acanthocalyx see *Morina*

Acantholimon (*Plumbaginaceae*)

armenum	XSen

Acanthopanax see *Eleutherococcus*

ricinifolius	see *Kalopanax septemlobus*

Acanthus ✿ (*Acanthaceae*)

balcanicus misapplied	see *A. hungaricus*
caroli-alexandri	see *A. spinosus* L.
dioscoridis	CDor LRHS
- var. ***perringii***	CDor EBee ECha MNrw NLar WCot WFar XLum
eminens	WCot XLum
greuterianus	WHil
hirsutus	CDor CFis EPri WCot WHil
- JCA 106.700	WHil
- subsp. ***syriacus***	ECha LShi
'Hollande du Nort'	CRos EBee LRHS NRHS XLum
§ ***hungaricus***	CBod CDoC CDor CMac CRos EBee ELan EMor ILea LCro LOPS LRHS MACG MBel MRav NLar NRHS SCob SDix SPer WCot WFar WHil
- MESE 561	EPPr
- 'White Lips'	EBee MNrw MThu NLar WCot WFar WHil XLum
longifolius Host	see *A. hungaricus*
mollis	Widely available
- 'Fielding Gold'	see *A. mollis* 'Hollard's Gold'
- free-flowering	ESwi MAvo SChr XLum
§ - 'Hollard's Gold'	Widely available
- 'Jefalba'	see *A. mollis* (Latifolius Group) 'Rue Ledan'
- Latifolius Group	CDor MRav SRms XLum
§ - - 'Rue Ledan' ♀H6	EBee ECtt EPPr EWTr LRHS MAvo MNrw NGdn NLar NSti SMHy SPhx WCAu WCot WHil XLum
- - 'Sjaak'	MAvo WHil
- 'Long Spike'	WHil
- 'Niger'	EBee
- 'Tasmanian Angel' (v)	CAbb CDor CWGN ECtt ELan LRHS NFav NHpl SEdd SPoG WCot WFar WSMil
'Morning's Candle'	CBod EBee ECtt ELan MNrw NGdn NLar WFar WHil XLum
§ ***polystachius***	WHil XLum
pubescens	see *A. polystachius*
sennii	EBee ECha ESwi LRHS SMad SPhx WAvo WCot WHil WSHC XLum
spinosus misapplied	see *A. spinosus* Spinosissimus Group
§ ***spinosus*** L.	Widely available
- Ferguson's form	EBee WCot
- 'Lady Moore' (v)	CDor NLar
- 'Royal Haughty'	MAvo XLum
§ - Spinosissimus Group	CBct CDor EBee GBin LEdu LPot MGos MRav NChi NLar WCot WFar WHil XLum
'Summer Beauty'	EBee ECtt EWes LRHS NLar WCot WFar WHil XLum
'Whitewater' (v)	CBcs CBct CDor CWGN EBee ECtt ELan GKin MPri NLar NSti SCob SPad SPeP SPer SPoG SRms WBor WCot WHil XLum XSte

Acca (*Myrtaceae*)

sellowiana (F)	Widely available
- 'Gemini' (F)	SGol
- 'Mammoth' (F)	CBcs CCCN
- 'Triumph' (F)	CBcs CCCN LPar LShi
- 'Variegata' (F/v)	CCCN CWit EBee

Acer ✿ (*Sapindaceae*)

acuminatum	CMCN
albopurpurascens NMWJ 14455	WCru
amoenum B&SWJ 10916	WCru
- B&SWJ 10977	WCru
- 'Firecracker'	see *A. palmatum* 'Firecracker'
'Ample Surprise'PBR	MBlu
'Asian Queen'	CJun
buergerianum	CMen EBee IPap MMuc MPkF NLar SBrt SGol SGsty WHwl WPGP
- B&SWJ 12676 from South Korea	WCru
- var. ***formosanum*** CWJ 12477	WCru

- 'Integrifolium'	see *A. buergerianum* 'Subintegrum'
- 'Naruto'	CMCN MPkF
§ - 'Subintegrum'	CMCN
campbellii	MBlu
- subsp. ***campbellii***	WPGP
- - GWJ 9360	WCru
- - PAB 13.071	LEdu
- 'Exuberance'	CJun
campestre ♀H6	Widely available
- 'Anny's Globe'	MBlu
- 'Carnival' (v) ♀H6	CEnd ELan ELon MAsh MBlu MTrO NOra NOrn NPoe SPer SPoG SWvt
- 'Elegant'	see *A. campestre* 'Huibers Elegant'
- 'Elsrijk'	CCVT CLnd IPap LMaj LPar MNic NOrn NRog SCob SCoo SGsty WHwl
- 'Evelyn'	see *A. campestre* 'Queen Elizabeth'
- 'Evenley Red'	EBee EPfP ESwi MBlu SEdd SMad WMou WPGP
- 'Green Column'	LRHS
§ - 'Huibers Elegant'	WHwl
- 'Louisa Red Shine'	CLnd SCob
- 'Nanum'	MBlu SGsty
- 'Pendulum'	CEnd
- 'Postelense'	ELan MBlu
§ - 'Queen Elizabeth'	MGos SGol
- 'Red Shine'	CBod EBar LMaj MMuc SGol WHwl
- 'Royal Ruby'	MGos
- 'Ruby Glow' ♀H6	CEnd
- 'William Caldwell'	CEnd LRHS MBlu SEdd SPer
capillipes	CBcs CLnd CMCN EBee ELan LMaj LPar MMuc MTrO NOrn NRog SCob SGbt SPlb SPtp WMat WTSh
- 'Antoine'	CJun LRHS MBlu
- 'Candy Stripe'	see *A.* × *conspicuum* 'Candy Stripe'
- 'Honey Dew'	SSta
aff. ***capillipes***	NWea
cappadocicum	CCVT CEnd CMCN LPar NWea
- 'Aureum' ♀H6	CBcs CEnd CLnd CMCN EBee ELan EPfP GKin IArd LPar MAsh MBlu MRav MTrO NLar NOra NOrn NWea SCob SGbt SGol SPer SWvt WFar WMat WMou WTSh
- var. ***mono***	see *A. pictum*
- 'Rubrum' ♀H6	CArg CBcs CLnd CMCN EBee ELan EPfP GKin LMaj LPar MBlu MMuc MRav MTrO NOra NOrn SEND SGol SPer WFar WMat
- subsp. ***sinicum***	SPtp
cappadocicum × (× ***conspicuum***) 'Phoenix'	MTrO
carpinifolium	CMCN EBee EPfP EWTr LRHS MBlu MMuc NLar WPGP
- B&SWJ 10955	WCru
- B&SWJ 11124	WCru
§ ***caudatifolium*** CWJ 12403	WCru
- NMWJ 14459	WCru
- RWJ 9843	WCru
§ ***caudatum*** GWJ 9279	WCru
- GWJ 9317	WCru
- HWJK 2240	WCru
- HWJK 2338	WCru
- subsp. ***ukurunduense***	MPkF
- - B&SWJ 12602	WCru
- - B&SWJ 8658	WCru
cinnamomifolium	see *A. coriaceifolium*
circinatum	CBcs CCVT CJun CMCN EGrl MBlu MMuc NLar NWea SEND SPlb
- B&SWJ 9565	WCru
- 'Burgundy Jewel'	CJun LCro LOPS LRHS MPkF NLar WHwl
- 'Monroe'	CJun CMCN
- 'Pacific Fire'	CJun NLar
- 'Whitney Broom'	NLar WHwl
cissifolium	CMCN EPfP NLar
- B&SWJ 10801	WCru
§ × ***conspicuum*** 'Candy Stripe'	CJun
- 'Elephant's Ear'	CJun MBlu NLar
- 'Phoenix'	CEnd CJun CMCN EBee EPfP GKin LRHS MBlu NLar NOra SPoG WPGP
- 'Silver Ghost'	SWvt
§ - 'Silver Vein'	CEnd CJun CMCN EPfP MTrO NLar SGol SSta SWvt
§ ***coriaceifolium***	CMCN
crataegifolium	CMCN SSta
- B&SWJ 11036	WCru
- 'Ittai-san-nishiki'	SSta
- 'Meuri-no-ōfu' (v)	SSta
- 'Veitchii' (v)	CMCN EBee EPfP LRHS MBlu SSta
creticum misapplied	see *A. sempervirens*
dasycarpum	see *A. saccharinum*
davidii	CBcs CExl CTsd EGrl EHed IPap LCro LMaj LOPS LPar MBlu MGos MMuc MRav NOrn NRog SCob SGol SGsty SSta XSte
§ - 'Canton'	CJun SSta
- 'Cantonspark'	see *A. davidii* 'Canton'
- 'Cascade'	MBlu
- 'George Forrest' ♀H5	CBcs CExl CMCN CMac EBee ELan EPfP GBin IArd LRHS MGos MMuc NLar NOra NOrn NWea SGbt SPoG SSta SWvt WMat
- 'Hagelunie'	SSta
- 'Hansu-suru' (v)	SSta
- 'Karmen'	CJun EPfP SSta
- 'Purple Bark'	CExl CJun SSta
- 'Rosalie'	CJun EPfP MAsh MBlu SSta WHwl
- 'Sekka'	SSta
- 'Serpentine'	CBcs CJun CMCN EPfP IArd MAsh MBlu NLar NOrn SSta
- 'Silver Vein'	see *A.* × *conspicuum* 'Silver Vein'
- VIPER ('Mindavi')	EBee EPfP IArd LRHS MAsh MNic NOra NOrn SGsty SPer SPoG WMat
diabolicum	CMCN
duplicatoserratum NMWJ 14599	WCru
elegantulum	CExl CJun GBin SPtp
erythranthum FMWJ 13157	WCru
fabri	CExl
- WWJ 11614	WCru
flabellatum	CJun
- var. ***yunnanense***	CBcs CMCN MMuc SPtp
forrestii	CExl CMCN MMuc SPtp WPGP
- BWJ 7515	WCru
- 'Alice'	CEnd CJun SSta
- 'Inoense'	SSta
- 'Sirene'	SSta
- 'Sparkling'	CJun
× ***freemanii***	CMCN LMaj LPar
- 'Armstrong'	LSRN MMuc SGol
- AUTUMN BLAZE ('Jeffersred') ♀H6	CBcs CCVT CDoC CLnd CMCN EPfP IArd IPap LMaj LPar LRHS MBlu MGos MMuc MTrO NOra NOrn SCob SCoo SGol SGsty SPer SPoG WHwl WMat WMou
- CELEBRATION ('Celzam')	CArg CCVT EBee IPap MGos SGol
§ - 'Morgan'	LRHS
ginnala	see *A. tataricum* subsp. *ginnala*
glabrum B&SWJ 14119	WCru
globosum	see *A. platanoides* 'Globosum'

grandidentatum	see *A. saccharum* subsp. *grandidentatum*
griseum ♀^{H5}	Widely available
grosseri	CMCN CTri SGol
- var. ***hersii***	CBcs CDoC CLnd EBee EGrI ELan EPfP LSRN MMuc NOra NOrn NRog NWea SSta SWvt WMat
- 'Leiden'	EPfP LRHS
heldreichii	CMCN
henryi	CBcs NLar
heptaphlebium B&SWJ 11695	WCru
- B&SWJ 11713	WCru
- FMWJ 13369	WCru
japonicum	CMCN SEWo SavN
- B&SWJ 12847	WCru
- CWJ 12840	WCru
§ - 'Aconitifolium' ♀^{H6}	Widely available
- 'Ao-jutan'	CJun
- 'Attaryi'	CMen WHwl WLea
- 'Aureum'	see *A. shirasawanum* 'Aureum'
- 'Emmit's Pumpkins'	CJun
- 'Ezo-no-momiji'	see *A. shirasawanum* 'Ezo-no-momiji'
- 'Fairy Lights'	WHwl
- 'Filicifolium'	see *A. japonicum* 'Aconitifolium'
- 'Green Cascade' ♀^{H6}	CEnd CJun CMCN CMac CMen MGos MPkF NLar SJap WHwl
- 'King's Copse'	CJun
- 'Kujaku-bato'	WHwl
- 'Laciniatum'	see *A. japonicum* 'Aconitifolium'
- f. ***microphyllum***	see *A. shirasawanum* 'Microphyllum'
- 'Ogurayama'	see *A. shirasawanum* 'Ogurayama'
- 'Ō-taki'	CJun
- 'Ruby'	MPkF NLar
- 'Vitifolium' ♀^{H6}	CDoC CEnd CJun CMCN CMac EGrI ELan EPfP LMaj LPar LRHS MBlu MGos MPkF NLar SPer SPoG SSta WHwl WLea WLov WTSh
kawakamii	see *A. caudatifolium*
laevigatum	IArd
- FMWJ 13378	WCru
- FMWJ 13439	WCru
§ - var. ***reticulatum*** B&SWJ 11698	WCru
laurinum FMWJ 13412	WCru
laxiflorum	SSta
§ ***longipes***	SPtp
macrophyllum	CMCN EPfP MBlu MMuc
- B&SWJ 13183	WCru
mandshuricum	LRHS
- B&SWJ 12592	WCru
§ ***maximowiczianum***	MPkF
maximowiczii	MPkF
micranthum ♀^{H6}	EPfP LRHS MBlu WPGP
- CWJ 12843	WCru
mono	see *A. pictum*
monspessulanum	CMCN LEdu LMaj SEND XSen
morifolium B&SWJ 11473	WCru
morrisonense Hayata	see *A. caudatifolium*
negundo	CMCN LPar NRog NWea SCob SWvt
- B&SWJ 14060	WCru
- 'Auratum'	CMCN SGol
- 'Aureomarginatum' (v)	CCVT LPar SGol
§ - 'Elegans' (v)	CEnd CMCN ELan SCoo
- 'Elegantissimum'	see *A. negundo* 'Elegans'
- 'Flamingo' (v)	CAco CBcs CCVT CEnd CMCN CMac ELan EPfP IPap LPar MAsh NLar NOra NWea SCob SGol SGsty SPer SPoG SWvt WMat

- 'Kelly's Gold'	CBcs CBod CCVT CEnd ELan MTrO NLar NWea SGol SPoG WMat
- 'Sensation'	NLar
- 'Variegatum' (v)	LPar SCob SGol
- var. ***violaceum*** ♀^{H6}	CEnd ELan EPfP SVen
- 'Winter Lightning' ♀^{H6}	NLar
nikoense misapplied	see *A. maximowiczianum*
nipponicum	SPtp
'Norwegian Sunset'	CBod CCVT
oliverianum	CExl MBlu
- subsp. ***formosanum*** NMWJ 14460	WCru
- - NMWJ 14514	WCru
- - NMWJ 14521	WCru
opalus	CMCN LMaj SEND WMou
orientale misapplied	see *A. sempervirens*
ORIENTALIA ('Minorient')	EHed MMrt NOrn WFar
orizabense	EBee
PACIFIC SUNSET ('Warrenred')	LMaj NLar SEWo
palmatum	CAco CBcs CCVT CDoC CLnd CMCN CMen CSBt CTri EGrI GKin IPap LCro LMaj LPar MBlu MGos NWea SArc SCob SEWo SGol SGsty SPlb SWvt SavN WFar WLea WLov WTSh
- (D)	CAco CBcs CCVT CEnd CJun CMac CTri LCro LMaj LMil LOPS LRHS LSRN MAsh MGos MRav NHol NLar NRHS SCob SCoo SGol SSta SWvt WCFE WFar WHCr WMat
- 'Akane' (P)	CMen LRHS MPkF NLar WHwl
§ - 'Aka-shigitatsu-sawa' (M)	CDoC CJun CMCN CMac CMen ESMi LRHS MGos MPkF NLar WHwl
- 'Akegarasu' (M)	CJun CMCN CMen NLar
- 'Alpenweiss' (P)	CJun
- 'Alpine Surprise'	SAko
- 'Amagi-shigure' (M)	CJun LCro LOPS MPkF NLar WHwl
- 'Amber Ghost' (M)	CJun NLar WHwl
- 'Anne Irene'^{PBR} (P)	LRHS MPkF NLar WHwl
- 'Aoba-jo' (Dw)	CJun CMen MPkF WHwl WLea
- 'Ao-kanzashi' (P/v)	MPkF
- 'Ao-shidare' (D)	CJun
- 'Aoshime-no-uchi'	see *A. palmatum* 'Shinobuga-oka'
- 'Aoyagi' (P)	CEnd CJun CMCN CMen EMac ESMi GKin LRHS MGos MPkF NLar NRHS SCoo WHwl WLea
- 'Aoyagi-gawa'	CJun
§ - 'Arakawa' (P)	CEnd CMCN CMen ESMi MPkF NLar WHwl
- 'Arakawa-ukon'	CJun
- 'Aratama' (Dw)	CJun CMCN CMen EMac WHwl WLea XSte
- 'Ariadne' (M/v) ♀^{H6}	CDoC CEnd CJun EGrI MGos MPkF NLar SCoo SPoG WHwl
- 'Ariake-nomura' (A)	CMen MPkF
- 'Asahi-zuru' (P/v)	CJun CMCN CMen LRHS MGos NLar NRHS SPer WHwl WMat
- 'Atrolineare' (L)	CMen MPkF NLar WHwl
- 'Atropurpureum' (A)	Widely available
- 'Attraction' (P)	CMac CMen
- 'Aureum' (P)	CMCN CMen CTri ELan EPfP LMil LRHS MAsh MBlu MGos MPkF NLar NRHS SPoG WFar WHwl
- 'Autumn Fire' (D)	CJun
- 'Autumn Glory' (M)	CEnd CJun CMen
- 'Autumn Red' (M)	CMen ESMi WLea
* - 'Autumn Showers'	CEnd CJun
- 'Azuma-murasaki' (M)	CJun CMen MPkF
- 'Baby Lace' (Dw)	CWGN SAko
- 'Baldsmith' (D)	CJun EMac ESMi MPkF WHwl
- 'Barrie Bergman' (D)	CJun NLar

	- 'Beni-chidori' (P)	CMen ESMi WHwl
	- 'Beni-fushigi' (P)	MPkF
	- 'Beni-gasa' (M)	CJun MPkF WHwl
	- 'Beni-hime' (Dw)	MPkF WHwl
	- 'Beni-hoshi' (Dw)	MPkF WHwl
	- 'Beni-kagami' (M)	CEnd CJun CMCN IDee MPkF NLar WHwl
	- 'Beni-kawa' (P)	CJun CMCN CMen ESMi LRHS MPkF NOrn WHwl
	- 'Beni-komachi' (P)	CDoC CEnd CMCN CMen ELon EPfP ESMi MGos MPkF NOrn WHwl
	- 'Beni-kosode' (v)	MPkF NLar
	- 'Beni-maiko' (P) ♀H6	CBod CDoC CEnd CJun CMCN CMen CRos EGrI EPfP ESMi IDee LRHS MGos MPkF NLar NOrn NRHS SCoo SGsty SWeb SWvt WHwl WLov
	- 'Beni-otake' (L)	CBcs CJun CMen EPfP ESMi MGos MPkF NLar SAko WHwl WLea
	- 'Beni-otome'	MPkF WHwl
	- 'Beni-schichi-henge' (P/v)	CBcs CDoC CEnd CJun CMCN CMen CRos CWGN ESMi LRHS MAsh MGos MPkF NHol NLar NOra NOrn NRHS SAko SCoo SLau SPer SSta WHwl WMat
	- 'Beni-shidare' (D)	LRHS WHwl
	- 'Beni-shidare Tricolor'	see *A. palmatum* 'Toyama-nishiki'
	- 'Beni-shidare Variegated'	see *A. palmatum* 'Toyama-nishiki'
	- 'Beni-shi-en' (P)	CJun MPkF
	- 'Beni-shigitatsu-sawa'	see *A. palmatum* 'Aka-shigitatsu-sawa'
	- 'Beni-tsukasa' (P/v) ♀H6	CEnd CJun CMCN CMen ESMi LMaj SSta WHwl
	- 'Beni-tsuru'	MPkF
	- 'Beni-yubi-gohon' (P)	CJun MPkF WHwl
	- 'Berrima Bridge' (D)	CJun
	- 'Berry Broom'	MPkF NLar
	- 'Berry Dwarf' (Dw)	CJun MPkF
	- 'Bewley's Red' (D)	CJun
	- 'Bi Hō' (P)	CJun CRos ELan EPfP LCro LMil LOPS LRHS MAsh MPkF NLar NRHS SAko SGol WHwl
	- 'Black Lace' (M)	LRHS MAsh MGos MPkF NLar NRHS WHwl
	- 'Bloodgood' (A) ♀H6	Widely available
	- 'Bonfire' misapplied	see *A. palmatum* 'Seigai'
	- 'Bonfire' ambig.	CJun
	- 'Bonfire' (v) **new**	LRHS
	- 'Bonnie Bergman'	CJun
	- 'Boskoop Glory' (A)	GKin
	- 'Brocade' (D)	CJun MPkF NLar
	- 'Bronzewing' (D)	CJun
	- 'Bultinck' (M)	MPkF
	- 'Burgundy Lace' (M) ♀H6	CEnd CJun CMCN CMen ELan EMac EPfP ESMi GKin LMil LRHS LSRN MAsh MGos MPkF NRHS SCoo SGol SPoG SSta WHwl
	- 'Butterfly' (P/v)	CAco CEnd CJun CMCN CMac CMen CWGN EHed ELan ESMi LCro LOPS LPar LRHS LSRN MAsh MBlu MGos MPkF NLar NOrn SCoo SGol SWeb SWvt WFar WHwl WLea
	- 'Calico' (P)	CJun NLar WHwl
	- 'Candy Kitchen'	see *A. palmatum* 'Kandy Kitchen'
	- 'Caperci Dwarf' (Dw)	MPkF
	- 'Carminium'	see *A. palmatum* 'Corallinum'
	- 'Caroline' (v)	NLar
	- 'Cascade'	LRHS NOrn
	- 'Cascade Gold' (P)	LRHS MPkF NLar
	- 'Chantilly Lace' (D)	CJun
	- 'Chikuma-no' (A)	CMen MPkF
	- 'Chi-otome' (P)	WHwl
	- 'Chirimen-nishiki' (P/v)	MPkF
	- 'Chishio' (P)	CMCN CMen ESMi LMil MPkF NLar WHwl
	- 'Chishio Improved' (P)	CDoC CEnd CJun CMCN CMac CMen EPfP LRHS MGos NHol NLar NOrn NRHS SWvt WHwl
	- 'Chitose-yama' (M) ♀H6	CJun CMCN CMen EGrI EPfP GKin LPar LRHS MAsh MGos MPkF NLar NRHS SGsty SSta WHwl WLea
§	- 'Chiyo-hime'	CBod ESMi LCro LOPS LPar LRHS WFar WHwl
	- 'Coonara Pygmy' (Dw)	CJun CMCN CMac CMen EMac ESMi GKin MPkF SCoo
	- 'Coral Pink' (Dw)	CJun CMen ESMi MPkF SSta
§	- 'Corallinum' (P) ♀H6	CBcs CEnd CJun CMCN CMen EPfP ESMi NLar SPoG WHwl
	- var. ***coreanum*** B&SWJ 8606	WCru
	- 'Crimson Carol' (M)	CJun NLar WHwl
	- 'Crimson Prince'	CJun NLar SCoo
	- 'Crimson Princess' (D)	CBcs CDoC CRos EPfP LMaj LRHS NOrn NRHS SWeb WMat
	- 'Crimson Queen' (D) ♀H6	CBcs CBrac CCVT CEnd CJun CMCN CMac CMen CRos CSBt EHed ELan EMac EPfP GKin LMaj LPar LRHS MAsh MGos MTrO NLar NOrn NRHS SCob SJap SPer SSta WFar WMat
	- 'Crippsii' (D)	CMac CMen MPkF SCoo SLau XSte
	- 'Deshōjō' (P)	CMCN CMen ELon ESMi LMaj LPar MBlu MGos NLar NPoe SCoo SGsty WHwl WMat XSte
	- 'Diana' (Dw)	CJun CMen
	- 'Dissectum' (D)	CBod CDoC CEme CTri EGrI ELon EWTr LBuc LOPS LPar LRHS MTrO NOra NOrn NWea WCFE WFar WHwl WTSh
	- 'Dissectum Atropurpureum' (D)	CRos EGrI LMil NWea SGsty WHwl
	- 'Dissectum Flavescens' (D)	CBcs CEnd CJun CMac CMen EMac LPar MBlu MGos MPkF SGsty SJap WHwl WMat
§	- 'Dissectum Nigrum' (D)	CJun CMac CMen MAsh MPkF NOrn WHwl WLea
	- 'Dissectum Palmatifidum' (D)	CMen EMac MPkF SCoo SJap SPer WHwl
	- 'Dissectum Rubrifolium' (D)	MPkF
§	- 'Dissectum Variegatum' (Dw/v)	CJun MPkF WHwl
	- Dissectum Viride Group	Widely available
	- 'Doctor Tilt' (P)	WHwl
	- 'Donzuru-bo'	CJun
	- 'Dormansland'	CEnd
	- 'Dr Seuss' (L)	NLar
	- 'Dragon's Fire'	CJun
	- 'Dwarf Shishi' (Dw)	NLar
	- 'Earthfire'	MPkF
I	- 'Ebbingei'	CMac
	- 'Eddisbury' (P) ♀H6	CJun CMen CSBt MBlu NLar SSta WHwl
	- 'Edna Bergman' (M)	CJun
	- 'Effegi'	see *A. palmatum* 'Fireglow'
	- 'Eimini' (Dw)	MPkF NLar
§	- 'Elegans' (M) ♀H6	CMen EPfP LRHS NRHS
	- 'Elizabeth' (Dw)	CJun
	- 'Ellen' (D)	CJun MPkF
	- 'Elmwood' (v)	WHwl
	- 'Emerald Lace' (D) ♀H6	CBod CDoC CJun CRos EBee EHed EMac GKin IPap LBuc LCro LOPS LPar LRHS MGos MPkF NLar NOrn

		NRHS SGsty SJap SPoG SSta WFar WHwl WLea
§	- 'Emperor 1' (A)	CBcs CJun EMac LPar MAsh MPkF SJap SPer WMat XSte
	- 'Englishtown' (Dw)	MPkF NLar
	- 'Enkan' (L)	CBod CDoC CEnd CJun CMen CWGN EHed EPfP LMil LRHS MGos MPkF MTrO NLar NOra SPoG WHwl WLea WLov WMat
	- 'Eono-momiji'	CMen
	- 'Ever Red'	see *A. palmatum* 'Dissectum Nigrum'
	- 'Fairy Hair' (L)	CJun
	- 'Fall's Fire' (P)	CJun
	- 'Fascination' (M)	CJun
	- 'Felice' (D)	CJun MPkF WHwl
	- 'Festival'	NLar SGsty
	- 'Filigree' (Dw/v)	CJun CMCN CMen EPfP MAsh MGos MPkF NLar WHwl
	- 'Fior d'Arancio' (M)	CJun MPkF NLar WHwl
	- 'Fireball'	CJun
§	- 'Firecracker'^{PBR} (D)	CBod CDoC CRos EHed LRHS MAsh MPkF NLar NRHS SWeb WHwl
§	- 'Fireglow' (A)	CBcs CBod CDoC CEnd CJun CMCN CMen CRos CSBt ESMi LMaj LMil LPar LRHS LSRN MGos MPkF NLar NRHS SAko SCoo SGol SGsty SJap SPer SWeb WHwl XSte
	- 'First Ghost' (M/v)	CJun
	- 'Frederici Guglielmi'	see *A. palmatum* 'Dissectum Variegatum'
	- 'Garnet' (D) ♀^{H6}	Widely available
	- 'Garnet Tower' (D)	LRHS MPkF NLar
	- 'Garyū' (Dw)	MPkF
	- 'Geisha Gone Wild' (P/v)	CJun NLar
	- 'Gentaku'	CJun
	- 'Germaine's Gyration' (D)	CJun
	- 'Gibbsii'	CMen
	- 'Glowing Embers' (P)	CJun WHwl
	- GOING GREEN ('Sonkootgre'^{PBR})	CAco CRos LCro LOPS LRHS MPkF NLar NRHS SCoo WHwl
	- 'Going Red'	LRHS NLar
	- 'Golden Hornet'	NLar
	- 'Golden Pond' (A)	CJun
	- 'Goshiki-kotohime' (Dw/v)	CMCN NLar
	- 'Goshiki-shidare'	see *A. palmatum* 'Toyama-nishiki'
	- 'Grandma Ghost' (M)	CJun
	- 'Green Fingers' (D)	NLar
	- 'Green Flag'	CJun
	- 'Green Globe' (D)	CJun WHwl
	- 'Green Hornet' (D)	CJun
	- 'Green Lace' (D)	CMen LMaj MPkF
	- 'Green Mist' (D)	CJun
	- 'Green Trompenburg' (M)	CJun CMen MPkF
§	- 'Hagoromo'	CMac CMen ESMi SCoo WHwl
	- 'Hamaotome' (A)	WHwl
	- 'Hana-matoi'^{PBR} (v)	CMCN MPkF
	- 'Hanami-nishiki' (Dw)	CMen MPkF
	- 'Hanzel' (D)	NLar
	- 'Happy Corallinum' (A)	CJun
	- 'Haru-iro'	CJun
	- 'Harusame' (P/v)	MPkF NLar
	- 'Hazeroino' (v)	CMen MPkF
	- 'Heartbeat' (D)	CDoC CJun MPkF
	- 'Heffner's Red'	CJun
	- 'Helena'	see *A. shirasawanum* 'Helena'
	- var. ***heptalobum***	CMCN
	- 'Heptalobum Elegans Purpureum'	see *A. palmatum* 'Hessei'
	- 'Herbstfeuer' (P)	CJun NLar
§	- 'Hessei' (M)	CEnd CMen MPkF
	- 'Higasa-yama' (P/v)	CEnd CJun CMCN CMen CWGN ESMi LRHS
	- 'Highland Sunset' **new**	CEnd
	- 'Hino-tori-nishiki'	CMen WHwl
	- 'Hogyōku' (A)	CJun CMCN CMen ESMi MPkF
	- 'Hoshi-kuzu' (Dw)	MPkF
	- 'Hupp's Dwarf' (Dw)	CJun MPkF
	- 'Hupp's Red Willow'	MPkF NLar WMat
	- 'Ibo-nishiki' (P)	CMen ESMi MPkF
	- 'Ichigyōji' (A)	CEnd CJun CMen MAsh WHwl WLea
	- 'Ightham Gold'	SSta
	- 'Iijima-sunago' (M)	CMen MPkF
	- 'Inaba-shidare' (D) ♀^{H6}	Widely available
	- 'Inazuma' (M)	CJun CMCN CMen EGrI MPkF SCoo SLau WHwl
	- 'Irish Lace'	CJun
	- 'Irish Lace' × ***palmatum*** 'Yasemin'	CJun
	- 'Isobel'	NLar
	- 'Iso-chidori' (Dw)	MPkF WHwl
	- 'Issai-nishiki'	CMen MPkF
*	- 'Issai-nishiki-kawazu'	MPkF
	- 'Jane'	CJun MPkF
	- 'Japanese Sunrise' (P)	CBcs CJun MPkF NLar WHwl WLea WMat
	- 'Jerre Schwartz' (Dw)	CBod CDoC CEnd CRos EPfP LCro LOPS LRHS MGos MPkF NLar NRHS WHwl WLea
	- 'Jirō-shidare' (P)	CJun MPkF NLar
	- 'JJ'	CJun
	- 'Johnnie's Pink' (P)	MPkF
	- 'Julia D.'	CJun
	- 'Kaba' (Dw)	CMen MPkF SPoG
	- 'Kagero' (A/v)	MPkF
§	- 'Kagiri-nishiki' (P/v)	CJun CMCN CMac CMen CWGN MPkF SPer WHwl XSte
	- 'Kamagata' (Dw)	CEnd CJun CMCN CMen ESMi LRHS MAsh MGos MPkF NLar SCoo WHwl XSte
§	- 'Kandy Kitchen' (Dw)	CMen MPkF WHwl XSte
	- 'Karaori-nishiki' (P/v)	CMen MPkF NLar
	- 'Karasu-gawa' (P/v)	CJun CMen CWGN MPkF
	- 'Kasagiyama' (M)	CEnd CJun CMen MPkF
	- 'Kasen-nishiki' (P)	CMen MPkF
	- 'Kashima' (Dw)	CEnd CJun CMCN CMen ESMi MBlu MPkF NLar WHwl WLea
	- 'Katja'	CJun CMen MPkF
	- 'Katsura' (P) ♀^{H6}	Widely available
	- 'Katsura-nishiki'	MPkF
	- 'Kawahara Rose'	MPkF NLar
I	- 'Kawaii' (D)	CJun
	- 'Ki-hachijō' (M)	CJun CMCN CMen LRHS MPkF SWeb
	- 'Killarney' (M)	CJun
	- 'Kinky Krinkle' (P)	CJun LRHS NLar
	- 'Kinran' (M)	CJun CMen ESMi MPkF WHwl
	- 'Kinshi' (L) ♀^{H6}	CEnd CJun CMCN CMen EPfP LRHS MPkF MTrO NLar NOra NOrn SAko WHwl WLea WLov WMat
	- 'Kiri-nishiki' (D)	CJun CMen MPkF NLar
	- 'Ki-shuzan' (M)	CJun WHwl
	- 'Kiyohime' (Dw) ♀^{H6}	CMCN CMen ESMi MPkF WHwl
	- 'Koba-shōjō' (M)	MPkF
	- 'Kogane-nishiki' (P)	CMen LPar NLar WHwl
	- 'Kogane-sakae' (A)	CJun MPkF
	- 'Koko' (M)	WHwl
	- 'Kokobunji-nishiki' (v)	MPkF
	- 'Komachi-hime' (Dw)	CJun CMen MPkF WLov

	- 'Komon-nishiki' (P/v)	CJun CMen ESMi MPkF WHwl
	- 'Korean Gem' (M)	CJun CMen MPkF
	- 'Koriba' (P)	CJun MPkF NLar
	- 'Koshibori-nishiki' (P)	MPkF
	- 'Kotohime' (Dw)	CJun CMCN CMen LRHS MGos MPkF NLar SCoo SPoG WHwl
	- 'Koto-ito-komachi' (Dw/L)	CJun CMen ESMi MPkF WHwl
	- 'Koto-maru' (Dw)	NLar
	- 'Koto-no-ito' (L)	CMCN LBuc LRHS MAsh MBlu MGos MPkF NLar SAko SPoG WHwl WLea
	- 'Koya-san' (Dw)	CMen MPkF
	- 'Kurabu-yama' (M)	CMen MPkF
	- 'Kuro-hime' (Dw)	MPkF
	- 'Kurui-jishi' (Dw)	MPkF
	- 'Kyōryū'	MPkF
	- 'Kyra'	CMen MPkF
	- 'Lace Lady' (D)	NOrn
	- 'Limelight' (P)	CDoC NLar
§	- 'Linearilobum' (L)	CBcs CDoC CMen EPfP MGos MPkF MTrO NLar NOra SCoo SLau WHwl WMat
	- 'Linearilobum Atropurpureum' (L)	WHwl
*	- 'Lionheart' (D)	CBcs CJun CMen CWGN ESMi MGos MPkF NLar SCoo WHwl
	- 'Little Princess'	see *A. palmatum* 'Chiyo-hime'
	- 'Lozita' (P)	NLar
	- 'Lutescens' (A)	CMen MPkF
	- 'Lydia'	MPkF
	- 'Maiko' (P)	CMen MPkF
	- 'Mallet'	NLar
	- 'Mama' (P)	CMen
	- 'Manyō-no-sato' (P/v)	LCro LRHS MPkF NLar WHwl
	- 'Mapi-no-machi-hime' (Dw)	CEnd CJun CMCN CMen LRHS MPkF NHol NRHS
	- 'Marakumo' (P)	MPkF
	- 'Marasaki-yama'	MPkF
	- 'Mardi Gras'	CJun
	- 'Margaret'	MPkF
	- 'Margaret Bee' (A)	CJun NLar
	- 'Marjan' (M)	CJun MPkF NLar
	- 'Marlo'[PBR] (D)	CRos LRHS MAsh MGos NLar NRHS WHwl
	- 'Masamurasaki'	CMen MPkF
	- 'Masukagami' (P/v)	CEnd CJun LMaj MPkF NLar
	- 'Matsu-ga-e' (P/v)	CMen MPkF
	- 'Matsukaze'	CJun CMCN CMen LRHS
	- var. ***matsumurae*** B&SWJ 11100	WCru
	- - B&SWJ 11195	WCru
	- 'Matsuyoi' (A)	CJun MPkF
	- 'Meihō-nishiki' (A/v)	CJun
	- 'Melanie'	CJun
	- 'Mendip Fantasy'	CMen
	- 'Meoto'	CJun
	- METAMORPHOSA ('Arjos1') **new**	CBcs
	- 'Midori-no-teiboku' (Dw)	CJun MPkF
	- 'Mika' (P)	LRHS MPkF
	- 'Mikawa-yatsubusa' (Dw)	CJun CMCN CMac CMen EMac ESMi MGos MPkF NLar SAko WHwl WLea
	- 'Mikazuki' (M/v)	CJun LRHS MPkF WLea
	- 'Mimaye'	CJun
	- 'Mini Mondo'	MPkF
	- 'Mirte' (M)	CJun CMen MPkF NLar
	- 'Mischa'	MPkF
	- 'Mizuho-beni' (P)	CJun CMen NLar
	- 'Mizu-kuguri' (A)	CJun MPkF
	- 'Momoiro-koya-san' (Dw)	CJun LRHS MPkF NLar WHwl
	- 'Mon Papa' (M)	CJun CMen MPkF NLar
	- 'Monzukushi' (A)	CJun MPkF
	- 'Moonfire' (M)	CJun CMCN EMac EPfP LRHS MAsh MPkF NLar WHwl WLea
	- 'Moonglow' **new**	CJun
	- 'Murasaki-hime' (Dw)	MPkF
	- 'Murasaki-kiyohime' (Dw)	CEnd CJun CMCN CMen ESMi MPkF WHwl
	- 'Mure-hibari' (M)	CJun CMen MPkF
	- 'Murogawa' (A)	CJun CMen
	- 'Musashino' (M)	CJun
	- 'Mutsu-beni-shidare' (D)	NLar
	- 'Mystic Jewel' (P)	MPkF WHwl
	- 'Nakata'	NLar
	- 'Nanase-gawa' (A)	MPkF NLar
	- 'Nicholsonii' (M)	CMen MPkF NLar WHwl
	- 'Nigrum' (A)	CMCN CTri NOra WHwl
	- 'Nishiki-gasane' (P/v)	CMen MPkF
§	- 'Nishiki-gawa' (P)	CJun CMen ESMi MPkF WHwl
	- 'Nishiki-momiji' (P)	CMen WLea
	- 'Nomura'	CJun CMen
	- 'Nomura-nishiki' (Dw/v)	CMen
	- 'Nomurishidare' misapplied	see *A. palmatum* 'Shōjō-shidare'
	- 'Nuresagi' (M)	CEnd CJun MPkF
	- 'Octopus' (D)	CJun MPkF NLar
	- 'Ōgi-nagashi' (P/v)	MPkF NLar
	- 'Ōgon-sarasa' (A)	CJun MPkF
	- 'Ojishi' (Dw)	CMen MPkF
	- 'Ō-kagami' (P)	CBcs CEnd CJun CMac CMen EPfP ESMi MAsh MGos MPkF NLar SCoo WHwl WLea
	- 'Okukuji-nishiki' (P)	CJun
	- 'Okushimo' (P)	CEnd CJun CMCN CMen EHed ESMi LRHS MPkF NLar WHwl
	- 'Olsen's Frosted Strawberry' (P)	MPkF
	- 'Omato' (A)	CJun MPkF WHwl
	- 'Omure-yama' (M)	CBcs CDoC CEnd CJun CMCN CMen EPfP ESMi MGos MPkF SCoo SGol SJap WHwl
	- 'Orange Dream' (P) ♀H6	Widely available
	- 'Orange Flame' (D) **new**	NLar
	- 'Orangeola' (D) ♀H6	CBod CEnd CJun CMen CSBt CTri EHed LRHS MAsh MGos MPkF NHol NLar NOrn NRHS SCoo SJap SLau SPoG SWeb WHwl WMat
	- 'Oranges and Lemons' (M)	CJun
	- 'Oregon Sunset' (M)	CJun MPkF WHwl WMat
	- 'Oridono-nishiki' (P/v)	CBod CEnd CJun CMCN CMac CMen CWGN ELan ELon EPfP ESMi IArd LPar MBlu MGos MPkF SGsty SPoG SSta SWeb
	- 'Oriental Mystery'	CJun
	- 'Ornatum' (D) ♀H6	CMCN CMen EPfP LMaj LSRN MAsh MGos MPkF MRav NLar NOrn SCoo SJap WCFE
	- 'Ōsakazuki' (A) ♀H6	Widely available
	- 'Osakii' **new**	LRHS
	- 'Ōshio-beni' (A)	CJun CMen EGrI
	- 'Ōshu-beni' (M)	CJun
	- 'Ōshu-shidare' (M)	CJun CMen ESMi MPkF
	- 'Oto-hime' (Dw)	CJun CMen MPkF
	- 'Otome-zakura' (P)	CJun CMen MPkF WHwl
	- 'Otto's Dissectum' (D)	CJun
	- 'Patricia'	WHwl
	- 'Peaches and Cream' (M/v)	CJun CMen ESMi MPkF NLar WHwl
	- 'Pendulum Julian' (D)	CMCN MPkF
	- 'Pévé Chameleon'	MPkF NLar
	- 'Pévé Dave'	CEnd CRos LRHS LSRN MAsh MPkF NLar NRHS WHwl
	- 'Pévé Multicolor'	CJun NLar
	- 'Pévé Ollie'[PBR]	MPkF NLar

- 'Pévé Stanley' MPkF NLar
- 'Pévé Starfish' NLar
- 'Phoenix' (P) CBcs CBod CJun IPap LRHS MGos MPkF NLar SCoo WHwl
- 'Pine Bark Maple' see *A. palmatum* 'Nishiki-gawa'
- 'Pink Ballerina' (Dw/v) CJun NLar
- 'Pink Filigree' (D) CJun CMen
- 'Pink Passion' (v) ELon LPar LRHS LSRN
- 'Pixie' (Dw) CMen CSBt ESMi LBuc MGos MPkF MTrO NOra SAko SWeb WHwl WLea WMat XSte
- 'Princetown Gold' CCVT
- 'Pung-kil' MPkF SAko WHwl WLea
- 'Purple Ghost' (M) CJun NLar
- 'Raraflora' (D) CJun
- 'Red Autumn Lace' (D) CJun LMaj
- 'Red Baron' (A) CJun
- 'Red Cloud' (L) CJun MPkF
- 'Red Dragon' (D) CJun CMen CWGN MAsh MPkF SAko WHwl
- RED EMPEROR see *A. palmatum* 'Emperor 1'
- 'Red Feather' (D) CJun MPkF NLar
- 'Red Filigree Lace' (D) CEnd CJun CMCN CMen CWGN MPkF
- 'Red Flame' NLar
- 'Red Flash' (A) CJun CMen MPkF NLar
- 'Red Jonas' MPkF NLar
- 'Red Pygmy' (L) ♀H6 CEnd CJun CMCN CMac CMen CRos CWGN ELan EPfP GKin LMil LPar LRHS MAsh MBlu MGos MPri NHol NLar NRHS SAko SCoo SGol SGsty SLau SPer SPoG SWvt WHwl XSte
- 'Red Select' (D) MPkF
- 'Red Spider' (L) CJun WHwl
- 'Red Wood' (P) CJun SGol SLau
- 'Redwine'PBR (P) CRos EPfP LRHS MPkF NLar NRHS WHwl
- 'Renjaku-maru' MPkF
- 'Reticulatum' see *A. palmatum* 'Shigi-tatsu-sawa'
- 'Ribesifolium' see *A. palmatum* 'Shish geshira'
- 'Rilas Red' (D) NLar
- 'Rising Sun' CJun
- 'Roseomarginatum' see *A. palmatum* 'Kagiri-nishiki'
- 'Rough Bark Maple' see *A. palmatum* 'Arakawa'
- 'Rubrum' (A) CMen

I - 'Rubrum Kaiser' CJun
- 'Ruby' (P) MPkF
- 'Ruby Ridge' (M) CJun
- 'Ruby Star' CJun MPkF
- 'Rufescens' (P) MPkF
- 'Ruslyn-in-the-Pink' (Dw) NLar
- 'Ryokū-ryū' (P) CMen MPkF
- 'Ryusen' LRHS MBlu MPkF NLar SGsty WHwl
- 'Ryuzu' (Dw) CJun MPkF NLar
- 'Sagara-nishiki' (v) CEnd CMen ESMi MPkF
- 'Sai-ho' MPkF
- 'Saint Jean' MPkF
- 'Samidare' (A) CJun MPkF NLar
- 'Sandra' (Dw) CMen MPkF
- 'Sango-kaku' (P) ♀H6 Widely available
- 'Saoshika' (A) CJun CMen MPkF NLar
- 'Sa-otome' (P) CMen MPkF
- 'Satsuki-beni' (M) CJun CMen EGrI ESMi MPkF WHwl
- 'Sawa-chidori' (M) MPkF WHwl
- 'Sazanami' (M) CEnd CJun CMen LRHS MPkF WHwl WLea
- 'Scolopendriifolium' see *A. palmatum* 'Linearilobum'

§ - 'Seigai' (M) CJun
- 'Seigen' (Dw) CEnd CJun CMCN CMen ESMi MBlu MPkF
- 'Seiryū' (D) ♀H6 Widely available
- 'Seiun-kaku' (P) CJun CMen LRHS MPkF WHwl
- 'Sekimori' (D) CJun NLar
- 'Sekka-yatsubusa' (P) CMCN CMen MPkF NLar WHwl
- 'Semi-no-hane' (M) CJun WHwl
- 'Senkaki' see *A. palmatum* 'Sango-kaku'
- 'Septemlobum Elegans' see *A. palmatum* 'Elegans'
- 'Septemlobum Purpureum' see *A. palmatum* 'Hessei'
- 'Sessilifolium' dwarf see *A. palmatum* 'Hagoromo'
- 'Shaina' (P) Widely available
- 'Sharp's Pygmy' (P) CJun CMen MPkF XSte
- 'Sherwood Flame' (M) CJun CMen EGrI MAsh MBlu MGos MPkF NLar SCoo SJap WHwl
- 'Shichihenge' (P) MTrO NLar
- 'Shidava Gold' (Dw) CJun EMac MPkF
- 'Shigarami' (P) CJun CMen MPkF

§ - 'Shigi-tatsu-sawa' (A/v) CEnd CJun CMCN CMac CMen LRHS MGos MPkF NLar NRHS SWeb WHwl
- 'Shigure-bato' (M) CJun MPkF NLar
- 'Shigurezome' (M) MPkF WHwl
- 'Shikageori-nishiki' (P) CJun CMen MPkF
- 'Shime-no-uchi' (L) CJun CMen
- 'Shin Nyo'PBR MBlu
- 'Shin-chishio' (P) CJun
- 'Shin-deshōjō' (P) ♀H6 CBcs CEnd CJun CMCN CMac CMen CRos CSBt CWGN EMac EPfP LMil LRHS LSRN MAsh MGos MPkF MPri NLar NOrn NRHS SCoo SJap SLau SPer SPoG SSta WHwl

§ - 'Shinobuga-oka' (L) CJun CMCN CMen MPkF NLar SLau SWeb
- 'Shinonome' (M) CJun CMen MPkF
- 'Shirazz' (P/v) CBcs CDoC CEnd CWGN EMac ESMi LMil LPar LRHS LSRN MGos MPkF NLar NOra NRHS SJap SPer SWvt WHwl WMat XSte

§ - 'Shish geshira' (P) ♀H6 CJun CMCN CMac CMen ESMi LMaj LPar LRHS MBlu MGos MPkF NLar SCoo SJap SWeb WHwl
- 'Shishio-hime' (Dw) MPkF
- 'Shishi-yatsubusa' CJun MPkF
- 'Shōjō' (A) CJun CMCN WHwl
- 'Shōjō-no-mai' (P) CJun
- 'Shōjō-nomura' (A) CEnd CMen MPkF SWeb

§ - 'Shōjō-shidare' (D) CEnd CJun CMen MPkF NOra WHwl WMat
- 'Shu-shidare' (D) CJun
- 'Silhouette'PBR GBin LCro LOPS LRHS MPkF WLov
- 'Sister Ghost' (M) CJun
- 'Skeeter's Broom' (Dw) CBcs CJun CMen CSBt EBee ELan EPfP ESMi IArd LRHS MAsh MGos MPkF NLar NRHS SCoo SJap SPoG WHwl WLea WLov

* - 'Sode-nishiki' (P) CJun MPkF
- 'Spreading Star' NOrn
- 'Spring Delight' (D) CJun MPkF SAko
- 'Stanley's Jewel' (Dw) MPkF NLar
- 'Starfish'PBR LBuc LCro LOPS LRHS MPkF
- 'Stella Rossa' (D) CEnd CJun LMaj MPkF NLar
- 'Suisei' (Dw/v) MPkF
- 'Sumi-nagashi' (M) CBcs CCVT CDoC CJun CMen CRos ESMi LRHS MAsh MGos MPkF MTrO NLar NOra NOrn NRHS SCoo SJap WMat
- 'Sumi-shidare' (D) NLar

I - 'Summer Gold' (P) CJun CRos LMaj LRHS MPkF NLar NRHS SGsty SJap SWvt
- 'Sunset' (D) CJun MPkF
- 'Sunshine' (D) MPkF
- 'Super Nigrum' (D) LMaj

- 'Super Ruby' (L)	NLar
- 'Susan'	MPkF
- 'Takao' (P)	CMen
- 'Tama-hime' (Dw)	CJun CMen ESMi MPkF WHwl
- 'Tamukeyama' (D)	CBcs CJun CMCN CMen IDee LBuc LRHS MAsh MGos MPkF MTrO NLar NOra NOrn SAko SCoo SJap SLau WHwl WMat XSte
- 'Tana' (A)	CJun CMCN CMen MPkF
- 'Tarō-yama' (Dw)	CJun MPkF
- 'Tatsuta'	CMen MPkF
- 'Taylor'PBR (P/v)	CEnd CRos CWGN EPfP LPar LRHS LSRN MAsh MGos MPkF NLar NRHS SCoo SPoG
- 'Tennyo-no-hoshi' (P)	CMen ESMi MPkF NLar WHwl
- 'The Bishop' (A)	NLar
- 'Tiger Rose' (M)	CJun
- 'Tiny Tim'	CJun
- 'Tobiosho' (P)	CJun
- 'Tochi-no-hikari' **new**	LRHS
§ - 'Toyama-nishiki' (Dw/v)	CJun CMCN CMen CWGN ESMi MPkF
- 'Trompenburg' (M) 🏆H6	Widely available
- 'Trompenson' **new**	NLar
- 'Tsuchigumo' (P)	CJun CMen MPkF NLar
- 'Tsukubane' (A)	WHwl
- 'Tsukuma-no'	MPkF
- 'Tsukushigata' (A)	MPkF
- 'Tsuma-gaki' (A)	CJun CMCN CMen LRHS MGos MPkF NLar SJap
- 'Tsuri-nishiki' (M)	CJun CMen MPkF
- 'Twombly's Red Sentinel'	CJun LRHS MBlu MPkF NLar
- 'Ueno-homare' (P)	CMen
- 'Ueno-yama'	CBcs CJun LPar SPer
- 'Uki-gumo' (P/v)	CEnd CJun CMCN CMac CMen ESMi LRHS MGos MPkF NHol SCoo SPer SPoG SSta
- 'Umegae' (A)	CJun
- 'Uncle Ghost' (M)	CJun
- 'Usu-midori'	CJun
- 'Utsu-semi' (A)	CJun MPkF WHwl
- 'Van der Akker'	CJun
- 'Versicolor' (P/v)	CMCN MPkF
- 'Vic Pink' (D)	CJun
- 'Villa Taranto' (L) 🏆H6	CEnd CJun CMCN CMen EPfP ESMi MBlu MGos MPkF MTrO NLar NOra SCoo SGol SJap WMat XSte
- 'Volubile' (P)	CMCN CMen ESMi MPkF WHwl
- 'Wabito' (P)	CJun CMen MPkF
- 'Waka-midori'	CMen WHwl
- 'Waka-momiji' (P/v)	CJun
- 'Wakehurst Pink' (M/v)	CMCN LRHS NOra NOrn
- 'Waterfall' (D)	CJun CMCN
- 'Watnong' (D)	CJun MPkF
- 'Wendy' (P)	CJun CMen MPkF NLar WHwl
- 'Westonbirt Orange' (A)	LRHS NOrn WHwl
- 'Westonbirt Red' (M)	NOrn
- 'Wetumpka Red'	CJun NLar
- 'Whitney Red' (A)	CMen
- 'Wild Goose' (P)	MAsh MPkF WLea
- 'Will's Devine'	CJun MPkF
- 'Wilson's Pink Dwarf' (Dw)	CEnd CJun CMen CRos EHed LRHS MAsh MGos MPkF NLar NRHS SAko SCoo SPoG WFar
- 'Winter Flame' (P)	CJun LRHS MPkF NHol NOrn WHwl XSte
- 'Wou-nishiki'	CMCN CMen MPkF
- 'Yana-gawa'	CMen
- 'Yasemin' (M)	CDoC CJun CMen CWGN LRHS MPkF NLar NOrn
- 'Yashio'	MPkF
- 'Yatsubusa' (Dw)	MPkF
- 'Yezo-nishiki' (A/v)	CMen MBlu MPkF WHwl
- 'Yūba-e' (M)	MPkF NOra NOrn
- 'Yūgure' (M)	LRHS MPkF
- 'Zaaling' (D)	CMen WHwl
- 'Zoë' (Dw)	MPkF NLar
papilio	see *A. caudatum*
pauciflorum 'Blaze Away'	CJun
pectinatum	GKev MMuc WPGP
- GWJ 9354	WCru
- 'Mozart'	CJun LPar LRHS MBlu NLar NWea SSta
- subsp. ***pectinatum*** HWJ 569	WCru
- - HWJ 944	WCru
pensylvanicum	CBcs CLnd CMCN EBee EPfP MGos MMuc MRav NRog SCob SPtp SSta
- 'Erythrocladum'	CBcs CEnd CJun CMCN EPfP MAsh NHol NLar NOrn
pentaphyllum	CMCN WPGP
§ ***pictum***	CMCN
- B&SWJ 12737	WCru
- subsp. ***macropterum*** **new**	WPGP
- 'Mallet Court'	CMCN
- subsp. ***okamotoanum***	CMCN
- - B&SWJ 12623	WCru
- subsp. ***pictum*** f. ***ambiguum*** B&SWJ 8806	WCru
- 'Shufu-nishiki'	CMCN
platanoides	CBcs CBrac CCVT CLnd CMCN CMac CSBt CTri EPfP GQue IPap LPar MGos MSwo MTrO NOrn NRog NWea SCob SEWo SPer SavN WMat WMou WTSh
- 'Cleveland'	LPar
- 'Columnare'	CLnd CMCN LMaj LPar SCob SCoo
- 'Crimson King' 🏆H7	Widely available
- 'Crimson Sentry'	CArg CBod CCVT CEme CEnd CLnd CMac CTri EBee ELan LCro LMaj LPar LRHS LSRN MAsh MGos MNic MRav NOrn SGol SGsty SPer SWvt
- 'Deborah'	CLnd EPfP LMaj LPar SCob SPer
- 'Dissectum'	CAco IArd NRog
- 'Drummondii' (v)	Widely available
- 'Emerald Queen'	LMaj LPar SCob
- 'Faassen's Black'	NWea
§ - 'Globosum'	CMCN LMaj LPar MNic NLar SArc SCob SGsty SWvt
- 'Laciniatum'	CMCN EBtc EPfP GBin
- PRINCETON GOLD ('Prigo'PBR) 🏆H7	CBcs CCVT CDoC CEnd CLnd EBee ELan IPap LBuc LMaj LPar LRHS MAsh MGos MTrO NLar NOra NOrn NWea SCob SCoo SEWo SLim SPer SPoG SWvt WMat
- 'Royal Red'	EPfP LMaj LPar MRav NLar SCoo SEWo SGsty
- 'Schwedleri' 🏆H7	CMCN NWea WTSh
- SENSATION	see *A. platanoides* 'Ulmers Sensation'
- subsp. ***turkestanicum***	CMCN SSta
- 'Ulmers Select'	WMat
§ - 'Ulmers Sensation'PBR (v)	SPoG
pseudoplatanus	CBcs CBrac CCVT CLnd CMCN CTri GDam LPar MGos MTrO NRog NWea SCob SPer SavN WMou WTSh
§ - 'Atropurpureum'	SCob SEND SEWo
- 'Brilliantissimum' 🏆H7	Widely available
- f. ***erythrocarpum*** 'Erythrocarpum'	CMac

	- 'Gadsby'	CAco
	- 'Leopoldii' misapplied	see *A. pseudoplatanus* f. *variegatum*
	- 'Negenia'	LPar
	- 'Prinz Handjéry'	CEnd CMCN CTri MGos MTrO NHol NLar NOra NOrn NWea SGol WMat
	- f. ***purpureum***	NRog NWea
	- 'Spaethii' misapplied	see *A. pseudoplatanus* 'Atropurpureum'
§	- f. ***variegatum*** (v)	LPar NRog
	- - 'Esk Sunset' (v)	CLnd EBee ELan LSRN MGos MTrO NOra SPoG WMat
	- - 'Leopoldii' ambig. (v)	CCVT CMCN SEND SWvt
	- - 'Simon-Louis Frères' (v)	CBcs CCVT CDoC CLnd CMCN LRHS MAsh MGos MTrO NLar NOra NOrn NRog SPer SWvt WMat
	- 'Worley'	CDoC CMCN CMac LMaj MRav NRog NWea SEND SLim SPer
	pseudosieboldianum	CMCN LRHS MBlu MPkF
	- B&SWJ 8468	WCru
	- B&SWJ 8746	WCru
	- B&SWJ 8769	WCru
	- var. ***microsieboldianum*** B&SWJ 8766	WCru
	- subsp. ***takesimense***	MBlu
	- - B&SWJ 8500	WCru
	- - B&SWJ 8540	WCru
	'Red Flamingo' (v)	CBcs CJun CMac CRos EPfP LRHS MAsh MBlu MTrO NOra SGol SGsty SPoG WMat
	'Red Wings'	see *A.* 'Red Wings' (A. palmatum hybrid)
§	'Red Wings' (*A. palmatum* hybrid)	CJun
	reticulatum	see *A. laevigatum* var. *reticulatum*
	rubescens CWJ 12438	WCru
	- NMWJ 14525	WCru
	rubrum	CAco CAgr CBcs CLnd CMCN CSBt CTri EBee EGrl EPfP IPap LCro LMaj LOPS MGos MTrO NRog NWea SCoo SEWo SGol WCFE WMat WTSh
	- 'Autumn Flame'	CCVT WMat
	- 'Autumn Spire'	CJun
	- 'Brandywine'	CEnd CJun CMac EPfP LRHS LSRN MAsh MBlu MTrO NLar NOra NOrn NWea SCoo SPoG WHwl WMat
	- 'Embers'	CJun
	- FAIRVIEW FLAME	see *A. rubrum* 'Pete's Fairview'
	- 'Firedance'	CJun
	- 'Florida Flame'	CMCN
	- 'Joseph'	NLar
	- 'New World'	SCoo
	- 'October Glory' 🏆H6	Widely available
§	- 'Pete's Fairview'	CJun SPer
	- 'Red King'	CJun
	- 'Red Rocket'	MTrO
	- RED SUNSET ('Franksred') 🏆H6	CAco CBcs CEnd CMCN EBee ELan EPfP EWTr IArd LMaj LPar NLar SCoo SGol SLim SPer SPoG WHwl WMat
	- 'Scanlon'	CBcs CEnd CJun CMCN EBee ELan EPfP LRHS MTrO NOra SLim SPer WHCr WMat
	- 'Schlesingeri'	CEnd CJun CMac
I	- 'Sekka'	MBlu
	- 'Somerset'	CJun SCoo WMat
	- SUMMER RED ('Hosr')	EBee LRHS SCoo SMad WMat
	- 'Sun Valley'	CJun CMac IArd MAsh MTrO NOra NOrn NWea WMat WMou
	- 'Tilford'	CJun
§	***rufinerve***	CBcs CLnd CMCN EBee EGrl EPfP EWTr LPar MMuc NLar NOra NOrn NWea SCob SCoo SGol SPtp SSta SWvt WLov WMat WTSh
	- 'Albolimbatum' (v)	CJun CMCN LRHS
	- 'Erythrocladum'	CJun MBlu
	- 'Ko-fuji-nishiki'	SSta
I	- 'Sunshine'	SSta
	- 'Winter Gold'	CJun NLar SSta
	- 'Yellow Ribbon'	LRHS
§	***saccharinum***	CAco CBcs CCVT CLnd CMCN EBee EGrl EPfP LPar MGos MTrO NOra NRog NWea SCoo SGol SPer WMat WTSh
	- 'Born's Gracious'	CJun
	- 'Fastigiatum'	see *A. saccharinum* 'Pyramidale'
	- f. ***laciniatum***	EBee MBlu MMuc SPer
	- - 'Laciniatum Wieri'	CMCN IPap NLar SCob
§	- 'Pyramidale'	CLnd IArd IPap LMaj SPer
	saccharum	CAco CAgr CBcs CLnd CMCN EBee EPfP IArd IPap LMaj MBlu MTrO NWea WTSh
	- 'Fiddlers Creek'	CJun
§	- subsp. ***grandidentatum***	CMCN
§	***sempervirens***	EBee EPfP IArd SEND
	'Sensu'	CJun MPkF NLar WHwl
	'Serendipity'	SSta
	serrulatum CWJ 12437	WCru
	- hybrid NMWJ 14548	WCru
	shenkanense	CExl
	shirasawanum	LRHS SavN
§	- 'Aureum' 🏆H6	Widely available
	- 'Autumn Moon'	CBcs CBrac CJun CMCN CMen CWGN EGrl EMac EPfP IDee LPar MAsh MPkF MTrO NLar NOra SCoo SGol SPer SPoG WHwl WLea WMat XSte
§	- 'Ezo-no-momiji'	CMen MPkF WHwl
	- 'Gloria'	CJun MPkF WHwl
	- 'Green Snowflake'	MPkF NLar
§	- 'Helena'	WHwl
	- 'Johin'	MPkF
	- 'Jordan'	CBcs CBod CDoC CEme CEnd CMCN CMac CRos CWGN EBee ELan EPfP IArd LBuc LMil LRHS LSRN MAsh MGos MPkF MThu NLar NOrn NRHS SMad SPoG SWvt WHwl WLea
	- 'Kakure-gasa'	CJun
	- 'Lovett'	CJun
§	- 'Microphyllum'	NLar
	- MOONRISE ('Munn 001'[PBR])	EPfP LCro LOPS LRHS MPkF NLar SCoo SGsty SMad WHwl
	- 'Mr Sun'	CJun
§	- 'Ogurayama'	CJun CMen WHwl
	- 'Palmatifolium'	CJun
	- 'Red Dawn'	CJun MPkF WHwl
	- 'Sonya Marie' (v)	MPkF
	- 'Susanne'	CJun CMen NLar
	- var. ***tenuifolium*** B&SWJ 11073	WCru
	sieboldianum 🏆H6	CMCN CMen MAsh MBlu MMuc NOra SEND SGol
	- B&SWJ 10849	WCru
	- B&SWJ 11049	WCru
	- B&SWJ 11090	WCru
	- 'Sode-no-uchi'	CJun CMen
	- var. ***tsushimense*** B&SWJ 10962	WCru
	sikkimense B&SWJ 11689	WCru

	- B&SWJ 11703	WCru
	- FMWJ 13166 from northern Vietnam	WCru
	- WJC 13674 from Sikkim	WCru
	- WWJ 11601	WCru
	- WWJ 11613	WCru
	- WWJ 11853	WCru
	- subsp. ***sikkimense***	WLov
	'Silver Cardinal' (v)	CEnd CJun CMCN EPfP MBlu NLar SSta
	'Silver Vein'	see *A.* × *conspicuum* 'Silver Vein'
	sinense	CMCN
	- 'Rogou'	CJun
	spicatum	CMCN NLar WLov
§	***sterculiaceum***	EBee
	- PAB 13.135	LEdu
	- subsp. ***franchetii***	CMCN
	- subsp. ***sterculiaceum*** NJM 13.087	WPGP
	- subsp. ***franchetii***	WPGP
	tataricum	CMCN SPtp
§	- subsp. ***ginnala***	CArg CBcs CMCN EGrI IPap LPar MBlu MGos NLar NWea SGol SPer
	- - 'Flame'	CAco CCVT CJun EBee EPfP MGos MMuc NWea SGbt SPoG
	- subsp. ***semenovii***	SPtp WLov
	tegmentosum ♀H5	CJun CMCN EPfP MBlu
	- 'Cobhay Ghost'	CJun
	- subsp. ***glaucorufinerve***	see *A. rufinerve*
	tonkinense subsp. ***liquidambarifolium*** DJHV 06173	WCru
	triflorum ♀H7	CBcs CCVT CJun CMCN EBee EPfP LMaj LRHS MBlu NLar NOra WMat WMou
	truncatum	MPkF
	- 'Akikaze-nishiki' (v)	MPkF
	tschonoskii	GKin
	- subsp. ***koreanum***	MPkF
	- - B&SWJ 12596	WCru
	- - B&SWJ 12603	WCru
	turkestanicum from Kyrgyzstan	WPGP
	velutinum	CMCN
	villosum	see *A. sterculiaceum*
	wardii	WPGP
	'White Tigress'	CJun EBee EPfP NLar SSta WMat
	× ***zoeschense***	MPkF
	- 'Annae'	LPar MMuc

Aceriphyllum see *Mukdenia*

Achillea (Asteraceae)

	ageratifolia ♀H5	ELan GWyn SRms XSen
§	***ageratum***	CBod CCBP CLau ENfk EWhm GPoy GQue LEdu MHer MNHC SEdi SRms SVic WFar WGwG WJek WTre
	'Alabaster'	EBee LRHS NRHS
	ANTHEA ('Anblo')	CDoC EBee ECtt EShb GMaP GQue LRHS LSRN MBriF MCot MRav NRHS SHar SRms SWvt WFar
§	'Apfelblüte' (Galaxy Series)	CBod EBee ECha ECtt ECul ELan EPfP EShb EWTr LEdu LRHS LSRN MHer MMuc MRav NGdn NHol NRHS NSti SEND SPad SPer SRms WCAu WFar
	APPLEBLOSSOM	see *A.* 'Apfelblüte'
	'Apricot Beauty'	ECul WSpi
	'Apricot Delight' (Tutti Frutti Series)	EBee ECul ELan GBee LRHS NRHS SCoo WTor
	'Apricot Seduction' (Seduction Series)	ECul WFar
	argentea misapplied	see *A. clavennae*, *A. umbellata*
	aurea	see *A. chrysocoma*
	'Bahama'	EPPr GQue
	'Belle Epoque'	WSpi
	biebersteinii	XLum
	'Breckland Ruby'	EWes
	'Carmina Burana'	CMea
§	***chrysocoma***	WIce XLum
	- 'Grandiflora'	ECha MBel MMuc NGdn WBrk WFar
§	***clavennae***	GKev NBir SPlb SRms WAbe
	clypeolata Sibth. & Sm.	EHyd SPlb SRms
	coarctata	CKel NBir XSen
	Colorado Group	CBod ECul EHyd LRHS NRHS
	'Coronation Gold' ♀H7	CEme CRos EBee ECtt ECul ELan EPfP LRHS MAsh MRav NChi NDov NRHS SCob SGbt SPer SRms SWvt WCAu WCot WSpi XSen
	'Credo' ♀H7	Widely available
	crithmifolia	CKel XLum XSen
	decolorans	see *A. ageratum*
	(Desert Eve Series) DESERT EVE CREAM ('Deseve')	ECul
	- DESERT EVE DEEP ROSE ('Desderos')	EBee ECul LRHS
	- DESERT EVE LIGHT YELLOW	ECul LRHS SRms
	- DESERT EVE RED ('Desred'PBR)	EBee ECul LRHS
	- DESERT EVE TERRACOTTA ('Dester') new	LPot
	- DESERT EVE YELLOW ('Desyel'PBR)	EBee LRHS
§	'Fanal'	CBod CCBP CEme CPla CRos EBee ECha ECtt ECul ELan EPfP GWyn LRHS MACG MRav NBir NHol NRHS SCoo SGbt SPer SWvt WCAu
	'Faust'	CDor ELon MACG
	'Feuerland'	EBee ECha ECtt ELon EPfP LRHS MRav NBir NDov NGdn NRHS SPer SPoG WFar WSpi XSen
	filipendulina	XSen
	- 'Cloth of Gold' ♀H7	Widely available
	- 'Gold Plate' ♀H7	Widely available
	- 'Hymne'	EBee ECha XLum
	- 'Parker's Variety'	CBod EBee GQue XLum
	'Fleur van Zonneveld'	NDov WGoo
	FLOWERS OF SULPHUR	see *A.* 'Schwefelblüte'
	(Forncett Series) 'Forncett Beauty'	SWvt
	- 'Forncett Bride'	EBee
	- 'Forncett Citrus'	ECtt WFar
	- 'Forncett Fletton'	ECtt ECul EPfP MACG MBel MCot MRav NDov NGdn NHol WFar
	- 'Forncett Ivory'	MAvo
	'Gloria Jean'	SHar
	'Golden Fleece'	GWyn LRHS
	grandifolia misapplied	see *Tanacetum macrophyllum* (Waldst. & Kit.) Sch.Bip.
§	***grandifolia*** Friv.	CBod GGro MArl MHol NBro SSal WFar
	'Great Expectations'	see *A.* 'Hoffnung'
	'Hannelore Pahl'	XLum
	'Heidi' ♀H7	MRav
	'Heinrich Vogeler'	ELon NLar XLum
	'Hella Glashoff' ♀H7	CMea CRos EBee EBlo ETod LRHS MACG NLar NRHS SPhx WGoo
§	'Hoffnung'	NLar NRHS

× ***huteri***	EDAr MMuc NGdn NHpl NRya SEND SRms SWvt WCav WFar
'Inca Gold'	CBcs ECha ECtt ECul EPPr LRHS MCot MRav NDov NHol NRHS SPer SRms SWvt WFar WHoo WSpi
× ***kellereri***	XLum XSen
'King Alfred'	CMea NHpl SRms
× ***kolbiana***	EWes SRms WFar XSen
§ 'Lachsschönheit' (Galaxy Series) ♀H7	CDor CEme CRos EBee ECha ECtt ELan EPfP GMaP LRHS MAsh MBNS MCot MRav NBir NDov NHol NLar NRHS NSti SCob SPer SRms WCAu WFar WHil
× ***lewisii*** 'King Edward' ♀H5	EBou EDAr ELan NBir SLee SRms WAbe WFar WIce
'Lucky Break' ♀H7	EBee ECha ECtt EWes MACG WCot
macrophylla	MBNS
'Marie Ann'	CWCL LSRN
'Marmalade'	CDor MRav NDov SMrm
'Martina' ♀H7	ECtt EWoo LRHS MBNS MBel MRav NDov NGdn NHol NRHS WBrk WCot WGwG WHoo
'McVities'	CWCL
millefolium	CCBP CHab ECul ENfk GPoy GQue LCro LOPS LShi MBow MNHC NAts NGrd NMir SRms SVic WHer WJek WSFF WSpi WWild
- 'Angie' (Song Siren Series) **new**	ECul
- 'Bloodstone'	ECtt EWes MRav
- 'Carla Hussey'	WFar
- 'Cassis'	CBod CSpe ECul EHyd EPfP LRHS MCot NChi NGBl NLar NRHS SBls WFar WHil
§ - 'Cerise Queen'	Widely available
- 'Chamois'	MNrw
- 'Cherry King'	NBir
- 'Circus'	ECul XLum
- 'Dark Lilac Beauty'	CWCL
- Kirschkönigin	see *A. millefolium* 'Cerise Queen'
- 'Lansdorferglut' ♀H7	CRos EBee ECha EPPr LRHS NDov NRHS SPhx
- 'Laura' (Song Siren Series)	CWGN ECtt ECul EPfP MNrw NLar WFar
- 'Lavender Beauty'	see *A. millefolium* 'Lilac Beauty'
§ - 'Lilac Beauty'	CBod EBee ECha ELon EPPr EPfP EWTr EWoo GBin GMaP GWyn LCro LOPS LSRN MMuc MRav NBir NHol NLar SBut SCob SCoo SGBe SRms WBrk WCAu WCav WFar WSpi XLum
* - 'Lilac Queen'	MArl
- Little Moonshine ('Acbz0002'PBR) **new**	ECul
- 'Little Susie' (Song Siren Series)	CWGN ECtt ECul NLar WFar
- Milly Rock Rose ('Florachro1') **new**	CBod
- (New Vintage Series) New Vintage Lilac	see *A. millefolium* (New Vintage Series) New Vintage Violet
- - New Vintage Red ('Balvinred')	CBod LRHS SCob SCoo WHil
- - New Vintage Rose ('Balvinrose')	ECul LRHS NFav SCob SCoo
§ - - New Vintage Violet ('Balvinviolet')	CBod ECul LRHS MHol SCob SCoo
- - New Vintage White ('Balvinwite')	CBod ECul LRHS NFav SCob SMrm
- 'Old Brocade'	EShb NDov
- Pastel Shades	WFar
- 'Peggy Sue'	CWGN ECtt EWes LRHS WFar
- 'Pomegranate' (Tutti Frutti Series)	CRos CWGN EAJP ECul EPfP EWTr IPot LCro LOPS LRHS MNrw NLar NRHS WCot WTor XLum
- 'Pretty Woman' (Song Siren Series)	CWGN EBee ECul
- 'Raspberry Ripple'	ECul GBin GWyn
- 'Red Beauty'	CWCL EBee EPfP MBNS SRms XLum
- 'Red Velvet' ♀H7	Widely available
- (Ritzy Series) 'Ritzy Rose' **new**	ECul
- - 'Ritzy Ruby' **new**	ECul
- 'Rose Madder'	CBod CWCL ECtt ECul EPfP EWTr GMaP LRHS MMuc MNrw MPie NBir NGdn NHol NLar NRHS SMrm SPer SPoG SWvt WCot WFar WGwG WSpi XLum
- 'Ruby Port'	WFar
- 'Salmon Queen'	NHol WFar
- 'Sammetriese'	EBee ELon MNrw
- 'Schneetaler'	MNrw
- 'Sue's Pink'	ECul
- (Summer Fruits Series) 'Summer Fruits Carmine'	EBee ECul ELan SCoo
- - 'Summer Fruits Lemon'	EBee ECul ELan EMor LRHS NRHS WFar WSpi
- - 'Summer Fruits Salmon'	EBee ECul ELan LRHS WFar
- 'Summertime'	WFar
- 'White Beauty'	ECul WCAu
- 'Wonderful Wampee'	EBee ECul EHyd ELan EWes LRHS MNrw NRHS SCob SCoo SPoG
'Mondpagode' ♀H7	ECtt EPfP MBNS MRav NGdn SWvt
Moon Dust ('Novaachdus') **new**	CBod ECul
* 'Moonbeam'	SEND
'Moonshine' ♀H7	Widely available
'Moonwalker'	CBod ECul EPfP MACG SCoo WCot XLum
nobilis	XSen
- subsp. ***neilreichii***	CBod ECha LRHS MBNS NSti SWvt WFar WGwG
* ***odilis***	EWTr
'Paprika' (Galaxy Series)	Widely available
'Petra'	EBee IPot MMrt MNrw NLar XLum
pindicola subsp. ***integrifolia***	EWes
'Pineapple Mango'PBR	NLar
'Pink Grapefruit' (Tutti Frutti Series)	CRos EBee GWyn IPot LRHS NLar NRHS SCoo WCAu
'Pretty Belinda'	CDor CRos EBee ECtt EHyd EPfP ETod EWhm GWyn LRHS LSRN MAvo MBel MSpe NLar NRHS SAko SCob SPoG SRms WCAu WFar
'Prospero'	WCot
ptarmica	CBod EMor MHer NAts NMir SRms
* - 'Ballerina'	NDov
- 'Nana Compacta'	CMac EHyd GBin MACG NBir SPlb SPoG WFar
- 'Noblessa'	MACG MBNS NLar
- 'Perry's White' (d)	ECha MNrw WCot
- 'Stephanie Cohen'	see *A. sibirica* 'Stephanie Cohen'
- The Pearl Group seed-raised (d)	CTri ECul ELan GWyn MACG MMuc SBls SBut SGbt SPlb WFar
- - 'Boule de Neige' (clonal) (d)	ELan MRav NPer SHar SPer WFar WSpi XLum
- - 'The Pearl' (clonal) (d)	CMac CSBt EBee ECha EHyd EPfP GDam GQue LCro LPot LRHS LSRN MBel MRav NBid NBir NBro NLar NRHS SCob SRms WBor WBrk WCAu WCot WFar WHil
pyrenaica	XLum
'Rougham Salmon'	CDor

	'Ruby Wine'	SHar WFar
	'Safran'	EBee ECul NLar XLum
	salicifolia 'Silver Spray'	NLar SDix
	'Sally'	EPPr
	SALMON BEAUTY	see *A.* 'Lachsschönheit'
	'Sandra Wagg'	ECtt
	'Sandstone'	see *A.* 'Wesersandstein'
	'Saucy Seduction' (Seduction Series)	CWCL ECul ELan ELon IPot LRHS MACG NBid NLar SCob
	'Saucy Sensation'	ECul SCob
§	'Schwefelblüte'	MRav NBir
	'Schwellenburg'	ECha WCot WFar
	sibirica	GGro
	subsp. ***camschatica***	
	- - 'Love Parade'	CBod EBee GQue MNrw NLar SBut SGbt SPer WFar XLum
§	- 'Stephanie Cohen'	SMrm
	Song Siren Series **new**	CBod
	'Stephanie'	EWes LSRN
	SUMMER BERRIES (mixed)	CRos ECul EHyd LPot LRHS NGrd NRHS WFar
	Summer Pastels Group	CBod EHyd EPfP GKev LRHS NGrd NLar NRHS SRms WFar
	- 'Peachy Seduction'PBR (Seduction Series)	ECul NLar WCAu
	- 'Strawberry Seduction' (Seduction Series)	ECtt ECul LRHS NLar
	'Summerwine' ♀H7	Widely available
	'Sunny Seduction' (Seduction Series)	ECtt ELon LRHS NLar
I	'Taygetea'	EBee ECul ELan GWyn LCro LOPS MBNS SPoG SRkn WCAu WCot WFar WHil WSpi
	'Terracotta'	Widely available
	'The Beacon'	see *A.* 'Fanal'
	'Tissington Old Rose'	MNrw
	tomentosa ♀H5	CKel CTri EBou ECha GPSL LCro LOPS WFar
§	- 'Aurea'	LPar LShi NBro
	- 'Goldie'	WFar
	- 'Maynard's Gold'	see *A. tomentosa* 'Aurea'
	'Tri-colour'	CBod EWTr MBNS NGdn
§	***umbellata***	LCro LOPS NSla XSen
	'W.B. Childs'	ELan MNrw MRav NDov SHar
	'Walther Funcke'	Widely available
§	'Wesersandstein'	CWCL GMaP IPot MNrw NBir SGbt
	'Wilczekii'	SRms

× *Achimenantha* (*Gesneriaceae*)

'Cool Inferno'	WDib
'Golden Jubilee'	WDib
'Himalayan Sunrise'	WDib
'Inferno' ♀H1b	WDib
'Pisces'	WDib
'Star of Stars' **new**	WDib

Achimenes (*Gesneriaceae*)

admirabilis	WDib
'Aimee Saliba' **new**	WDib
'Ambroise Verschaffelt' ♀H1c	SDir WDib
'Apricot Glow'	WDib
'Aquamarine'	WDib
'Aurora Charm'	WDib
'Ballerina'	WDib
'Beautiful Fire'	WDib
'Big Weiss'	WDib
'Blue Sparks'	SDeJ
'Caligula'	WDib
'Cameo Rose'	WDib
'Candy Shop'	WDib
'Caprice' **new**	WDib
(Cascade Series) 'Cascade Fairy Pink'	WDib
- 'Cascade Fashionable Pink'	WDib
- 'Cascade Rose Red'	WDib
'Cattleya'	SDir
cettoana	WDib
'Charm'	SDeJ WDib
'Claret'	WDib
'Crummock Water'	WDib
'Dale Martens'	WDib
'Dot'	WDib
'Double Picotee Rose' (d)	WDib
'Double Pink Rose' (d)	WDib
erecta	WDib
'Erlkönig'	WDib
'Extravaganza'	WDib
'Femme Fatale' **new**	WDib
'Firefly'	WDib
'Flamenco'	WDib
'Forget Me Not' **new**	WDib
'George Houche' **new**	WDib
'Glory'	WDib
'Golden Butterfly'	WDib
'Golden Lady' **new**	WDib
'Harry Williams'	SDir WDib
'Hilda Michelssen' ♀H1c	WDib
'Himalayan Mandarin' (Himalayan Series)	SDir WDib
'Hugues Aufray'	WDib
'Ice Tea'	WDib
'Imperial Light' **new**	WDib
'Jay Dee Large White' (Jay Dee Series)	WDib
'Jennifer Goode'	WDib
'Johanna Michelssen'	WDib
'Just Divine'	WDib
'Kim Blue'	WDib
'Lady in Black'	WDib
'Lavender Fancy'	WDib
'Light Lilac'	WDib
'Little Beauty'	WDib
'Little Lulu' **new**	WDib
longiflora var. ***alba*** 'Snow Queen'	SDir
- 'Major'	WDib
'Madame Bovary' **new**	WDib
'Magnificent'	WDib
'Mauve Delight' **new**	WDib
'Melon Ice Cream'	WDib
mexicana	SDeJ
misera	WDib
'Nocturne'	WDib
'Old Rose Pink'	WDib
'Opal'	WDib
'Orange Delight'	WDib
'Orange Orchard'	WDib
'Pally'	WDib
'Patens Major'	WDib
'Peach Blossom'	SDeJ WDib
'Peach Cascade' (Cascade Series)	WDib
'Peach Glow'	WDib
pedunculata	WDib
'Petite Fadette'	WDib
'Poil de Carotte'	WDib
'Primadonna'	SDeJ WDib
'Pulcherrima'	SDeJ
'Purple King'	WDib
'Queen of Queens'	WDib
'Rai'	WDib

'Rainbow' WDib
'Rainbow Warrior' WDib
'Rozi Roza' WDib
'Santa Claus' WDib
'Schneewittchen' WDib
'Serge Saliba' WDib
'Serge's Fantasy' WDib
'Show-off' WDib
'Shy Sun' WDib
skinneri WDib
'Snow Princess' SDeJ
'Stan's Delight' (d) ♀H1c WDib
'Sterntaler' WDib
'Sugarland' WDib
'Sun Dance' WDib
'Sun Wind' WDib
'Sweet and Sour' WDib
'Tango' WDib
'Tarantella' WDib
'Tetra Himalayan Purple' (Tetra Series) WDib
'Tiger Eye' WDib
'Valse Bleu' WDib
'Veronika Gotmanova' new WDib
'Violacea Semiplena' (d) WDib
'Vivid' WDib
'Weinrot Elfe' WDib
'Wetterlow's Triumph' WDib
'Yellow Beauty' WDib
'Yellow English Rose' (d) new WDib

Achimenes × *Smithiantha* see × *Achimenantha*

Achlys (*Berberidaceae*)

triphylla WCru
– B&SWJ 13541 WCru

Achnatherum see *Stipa*

Achyranthes (*Amaranthaceae*)

bidentata var. ***longifolia*** PAB 8037 LEdu

Acidanthera see *Gladiolus*

Aciphylla (*Apiaceae*)

aurea GKev SPlb
glaucescens CBrP SPlb
montana CMen
scott-thomsonii GKev
squarrosa GKev

Acis (*Amaryllidaceae*)

§ ***autumnalis*** ♀H5 CAvo CBor CBro CSpe CTri CTtf EAJP ECha EDAr EHyd ELan EPot EWes GArf GKev LEdu NBir NHpl NRHS NRog SMHy SRms SRot WAbe WFar WHoo WPGP WSHC WShi
– var. ***autumnalis*** NRog
– var. ***oporantha*** CMiW CWCL EPri GKev NRog
– – f. ***dispathacea*** GEdr GKev NRog
– var. ***pulchella*** CElw GKev NRog
– 'September Snow' ELan EPri GKev NLar NRog
ionica NRog
I – subsp. ***vlorensis*** GKev
§ ***longifolia*** GKev
nicaeensis CTtf EHyd EPot GKev NRHS NWad WCot WThu
§ ***rosea*** CTtf GKev NRog WAbe
§ ***tingitana*** CBro
§ ***trichophylla*** GKev
– pink-flowered EPri
– f. ***purpurascens*** WCot
§ ***valentina*** CTtf NRog WCot

Acmella (*Asteraceae*)

§ ***oleracea*** CLau

Acnistus (*Solanaceae*)

australis see *Eriolarynx australis*

Aconitum (*Ranunculaceae*)

ACE EPPr
'Album' WWtn
altissimum see *A. lycoctonum* subsp. *vulparia*
anglicum see *A. napellus* subsp. *napellus* Anglicum Group
§ ***anthora*** CSpe EBee EPfP GKev SPeP WCot
arcuatum see *A. fischeri* var. *arcuatum*
austroyunnanense WSHC
– BWJ 7902 WCru
autumnale misapplied see *A. carmichaelii* Wilsonii Group
autumnale Rchb. see *A. fischeri* Rchb.
× ***bicolor*** see *A.* × *cammarum* 'Bicolor'
'Blue Lagoon'PBR CBod CWGN EBee MSCN NLar SCob WHil WWtn
'Blue Opal' EBee EWes
'Blue Sceptre' NLar SRms
§ 'Blue Sparrow' EBee IPot LSou MHol WTor
'Bressingham Spire' ♀H7 ECtt EHyd ELan EPfP GKin LRHS MAvo MCot NDov NGdn NPer NRHS SRms SSut WFar WSpi
bulbilliferum HWJK 2120 WSHC
× ***cammarum*** NChi
§ – 'Bicolor' ♀H7 CBod CExl CWGN EBee ECtt ELan ELon EMor EPfP GAbr GKev GMaP MNrw MSCN NBro NHol NPer NRHS NWad SPer SPoG SRms WCAu WCot WFar WPnP WSHC WSpi
– 'Eleanora' CBod ECtt EMor EPfP EWld MHol NLar SRms
– 'Grandiflorum Album' EMor LPla MNrw WGoo
– 'Pink Sensation'PBR GKev NLar
§ ***carmichaelii*** CBod EHyd ELan EPfP GKin LRHS MMuc MNrw NBro NChi NGdn NRHS SEND SMrm SRms WCot WFar WSpi
– B&SWJ 8809 ESwi
– Arendsii Group EBee ECtt GKev LEdu WCAu WCFE
– – 'Arendsii' ♀H7 Widely available
– – 'Cloudy'PBR CWGN EBee ECtt ELon EMor ITim LEdu LPla MAvo MBel MBriF NGdn NLar NRHS SEdd SPer WCot WSpi
– 'Moody Blues' EBee
– 'Redleaf' see *A. carmichaelii* 'Royal Flush'
– 'River Finn' WCot
– 'River Lugg' WCot
– 'River Medway' WCot
– 'River Nene' WCot
– 'River Ouse' WCot
– 'River Spey' WCot
– 'River Teifi' WCot
– 'River Trent' WCot
– 'River Welland' WCot
§ – 'Royal Flush'PBR CWGN EBee ECha ECtt LSun MBNS MCot MNrw NLar SPeP SPoG WCot
– var. ***truppelianum*** WCot
§ – Wilsonii Group CMac EBee EGrI LEdu MCot MRav NDov WHoo

	- - 'Autumn Amethyst'	SMHy
	- - 'Barker's Variety'	CKno EBee ELon NGdn NLar NSti SRms WCot WSpi
	- - 'Kelmscott' 🏆H7	ELon MCot MRav SDix SMHy WCot WFar WSpi
	- - 'Spätlese'	CDor CWGN EBee ECtt ELon EWoo LEdu LRHS MCot NBir NGdn NLar SPer SPoG WCAu WCot XLum
§	***chasmanthum***	CRos EBee LRHS NRHS
	- GWJ 9393	WCru
	chiisanense	ESwi
	- B&SWJ 4446	WCru
	cilicicum	see *Eranthis hyemalis* Cilicica Group
	compactum	see *A. napellus* subsp. *vulgare*
	confertiflorum	see *A. anthora*
	delphinifolium	CExl
	elwesii	LEdu
	episcopale	WCru
	ferox	EBee
	- GWJ 9333 from Sikkim	WCru
	- GWJ 9403	WCru
	fischeri misapplied	see *A. carmichaelii*
§	***fischeri*** Rchb.	NBid NLar WCot
	- B&SWJ 8809	WCru
§	- var. ***arcuatum*** B&SWJ 774	WCru
	formosanum B&SWJ 3057	WCru
	fukutomei B&SWJ 337	MRav WCru
	gammiei GWJ 9418	WCru
	grossedentatum	LPla NLar
	- subsp. ***paniculatum***	see *A. variegatum* subsp. *paniculatum*
§	***hemsleyanum***	CExl CRHN CWGN ECtt GKev GLog MBel NBid WCru
	- dark blue-flowered	WSpi
	- 'Red Wine'	CBcs CBod EWld MBNS NLar NSti SMad
	- var. ***unguiculatum***	GKev
	hyemale	see *Eranthis hyemalis*
	'Ivorine'	CEme CRos EBee ECha EHyd EMor GMaP ILea LEdu LRHS LShi MCot MHol NGdn NLar NRHS NSti SPer WFar WPnP
	jaluense B&SWJ 8741	WCru
	japonicum	EBee GQue NLar WCot
	- var. ***hakonense***	CExl
	- var. ***montanum*** B&SWJ 5507	WCru
§	- subsp. ***napiforme***	EWes
	- - B&SWJ 943	EBee ELon WCru
§	- subsp. ***subcuneatum*** B&SWJ 6228	WCru
	kitadakense B&SWJ 11173	WCru
	laciniatum GWJ 9254	WCru
	- GWJ 9324	WCru
	lamarckii	see *A. lycoctonum* subsp. *neapolitanum*
	lasianthum	see *A. lycoctonum* subsp. *vulparia*
	leucostomum	EBee
	loczyanum	WCot
	- B&SWJ 11529	WCru WSHC
	lycoctonum	GBin NGrd NLar NSti WSpi
	- 'Darkeyes'	WCot
§	- subsp. ***lycoctonum***	SRms
§	- subsp. ***moldavicum***	SBrt WCot
§	- subsp. ***neapolitanum***	CDor EBee GMaP MMuc NLar SEND WBor WSpi
	- 'Russian Yellow'	ESwi EWld
§	- subsp. ***vulparia***	GKev GPoy ILea LEdu MHol MRav NGdn SRms
	mairei	see *A. vilmorinianum*

	moldavicum	see *A. lycoctonum* subsp. *moldavicum*
	nagarum	GKev LEdu WCot
	- KR 7589	EBee
	napellus	CBod CCBP ECtt EPfP GAbr GPoy ILea MBel MBros MCot MHol MMuc MNHC NAts NGrd SPoG SRms WCot WFar WHoo WPnP WShi
	- 'Bergfürst'	LRHS
	- 'Blue Valley'	EPfP
	- 'Gletschereis'	EBee
§	- subsp. ***napellus*** Anglicum Group	MCot MHol MMuc SEND WCot
	- - - 'Spring Yellow'	WCot
	- 'Rubellum'	EMor GKev MACG NBro NLar NSti WFar
	- 'Schneewittchen'	CSpe EMor EWes MBel SCob
§	- subsp. ***vulgare***	GKev
	- - 'Albidum'	CBod EGrI ELon EMor EPfP EWoo GMaP LEdu LPla MBel MHol NBid NHol NLar NRHS SPer SPoG
	- - 'Carneum'	EBee EPfP NGrd WHer
	- 'William Turner'	NGrd
	napiforme	see *A. japonicum* subsp. *napiforme*
	nasutum	WCot
	- white-flowered	WCot
	neapolitanum	see *A. lycoctonum* subsp. *neapolitanum*
	'Newry Blue'	CRos EBee ECtt ELan LRHS MArl MBNS MHol MRav NBir NRHS NWad SBls SRms WSpi
	orientale misapplied	see *A. lycoctonum* subsp. *vulparia*
	paniculatum misapplied	see *A. variegatum* subsp. *paniculatum*
	piepunense	EBee GKev
	proliferum	WCot
	- B&SWJ 4107	WCru
	pseudohuiliense	CExl
	pseudolaeve var. ***erectum*** B&SWJ 8466	WCru
	pterocaule new	GGro
	pulchellum new	GKev
	'Purple Sparrow'	see *A.* 'Blue Sparrow'
	pyramidale	see *A. napellus* subsp. *vulgare*
	pyrenaicum misapplied	see *A. lycoctonum* subsp. *neapolitanum*
	ranunculifolium	see *A. lycoctonum* subsp. *neapolitanum*
	sachalinense	WCot
	- subsp. ***yezoense***	EBee NLar WCot
	scaposum	GKev
	senanense var. ***incisum*** B&SWJ 11032	WCru
	- subsp. ***paludicola*** B&SWJ 10866	WCru
	seoulense	EBee SBls
	- B&SWJ 694	WCru
	- B&SWJ 864	WCru
	'Spark's Variety' 🏆H7	Widely available
	spicatum GWJ 9394	WCru
	'Stainless Steel' 🏆H7	CBcs CBod CExl ECtt EMor EPfP EWTr EWoo GMaP GQue LEdu LRHS NBro NDov NGdn NLar SAko SCob SPhx SPoG WCAu WCot WFar WPnP WSHC WSpi
	subcuneatum	see *A. japonicum* subsp. *subcuneatum*
	'Surprise'	WCot
	× ***tubergenii***	see *Eranthis hyemalis* Tubergenii Group

	uchiyamae	SBls
	- B&SWJ 1005	WCru
	- B&SWJ 1216	ECha WCru
	- B&SWJ 4446	NLar
	variegatum	EBee
§	- subsp. ***paniculatum***	LPla WCot
	- - 'Roseum'	WFar
§	***vilmorinianum*** BWJ 8055	WCru
	violaceum var. ***robustum***	see *A. chasmanthum*
	volubile misapplied	see *A. hemsleyanum*
	vulparia	see *A. lycoctonum* subsp. *vulparia*
	yamazakii	WCru
	zigzag var. ***ryohakuense*** B&SWJ 8906	WCru

Aconogonon see *Persicaria*

Acorus ✿ (*Acoraceae*)

	calamus	CBen CKno CLau CPud CWat GPoy MNHC NPer WMAq
	- subsp. ***angustatus***	GPoy
	- 'Argenteostriatus' (v)	CBen CWat ECha MMuc SEND SRms WMAq
*	***christophii***	ELon EPPr
	gramineus	GPoy NPer
	- 'Golden Delight'	CBod LRHS SRms
	- 'Golden Edge' (v)	ELon LLWG NRHS NWad
	- 'Hakuro-nishiki' (v)	GWyn NWad SRms SWvt WFar XLum
	- 'Licorice'	LPla MSCN WBrk WGrn
	- 'Masamune' (v)	EWes
	- 'Ōborozuki' misapplied	see *A. gramineus* 'Ogon'
§	- 'Ōgon' (v)	Widely available
	- var. ***pusillus***	NBro
	- 'Variegatus' (v)	CBcs CBen CBod CChe CEme CExl CRos CWat ELan EMor GMaP LPar LPot LRHS LSun MGos MMuc MRav NBid NBro NFav NRHS SArc SCoo SEND SPoG SRms SWvt
	'Intermedius'	NPer

Acradenia (*Rutaceae*)

	frankliniae	CBcs CCCN CMac CTsd EPfP IArd IDee MBlu MHtn SPlb WPGP

Actaea (*Ranunculaceae*)

	alba misapplied	see *A. pachypoda, A. rubra* f. *neglecta*
	arizonica	CRos EBee LPla LRHS NLar NRHS WCru
	asiatica B&SWJ 616	WCru
	- B&SWJ 6351 from Japan	WCru
	- B&SWJ 8694 from Korea	WCru
	- BWJ 8174 from China	WCru
	biternata B&SWJ 8917	WCru
	- B&SWJ 11190	NLar WCru
	'Chocoholic'	CBod CWGN EBee ECtt ELan ELon EMor GEdr ILea IPot LRHS LSou MAvo MHol MMrt MNHC MNrw MPri NLar NRHS SPVi WCav
§	***cimicifuga***	GPoy
	aff. ***cimicifuga*** WJC 13720	WCru
§	***cordifolia***	EBee GBin GMaP LPla LRHS MBros NLar SWvt
	- 'Blickfang'	SPVi
	dahurica	EWTr GBin LPla
	- B&SWJ 8426	WCru
	- B&SWJ 8573	WCru
	- tall	NBid
	'Dark Chocoholic' **new**	IPot
	erythrocarpa	see *A. rubra*
§	***japonica***	NLar
	- B&SWJ 5828	WCru
	- B&SWJ 11136	WCru
	- B&SWJ 11526	WCru
	- from Jejudo, South Korea	EBee MNrw
	- var. ***acutiloba*** B&SWJ 6257	WCru
	- 'Cheju-Do'	IPot LPla LRHS MHol MMrt NLar SPVi
	- compact B&SWJ 8758A	WCot WCru
	- 'Silver Dance'	NLar
	mairei BWJ 7635	WCru
	- BWJ 7939	WCru
§	***matsumurae***	CExl NLar
	- B&SWJ 11187	WCru
	- B&SWJ 11528	WCru
	- 'Elstead Variety' ♀H7	CExl MRav
	- 'White Pearl' ♀H7	CBcs CDor CExl CRos EBee ECha ECtt ELan EPfP GMaP GQue ILea LRHS MBel MCot MNrw MRav NBid NLar NRHS NSti SCob SPVi SPer SPoG SRms SWvt WPGP XLum
§	***pachypoda***	CBro CExl EBee EPfP EWTr GLog GPoy LShi MBel NBid NLar WCru
	- MISTY BLUE ('Lk05'PBR)	CAvo CBcs CBod CBro CDor CSpe CWGN EBee ECha ECtt EHed ELan ESwi GEdr LPla LRHS MNrw NLar SEdd SPeP SPoG WCot WNPC XSte
	- 'Silver Leaf'	CSpe WSHC
§	***podocarpa***	EBee LPla NLar SPlb SRms WCru
	'Queen of Sheba'PBR	CWGN EBee EMor IPot MBel NDov NLar SPVi
	racemosa ♀H7	CBod CMac EBee ELan EPfP GBin GPoy NBid NGdn NLar NSti SEdd SWvt WFar WWtn XLum
§	***rubra***	CSpe EBee ECha ELan MMrt NBid NLar NWad SMad SPoG WCru
	- B&SWJ 9555	WCru
	- ***alba***	see *A. pachypoda, A. rubra* f. *neglecta*
§	- f. ***neglecta***	GLog WCot WCru
	simplex	EBee GLog WCot
	- B&SWJ 8653	WCru
	- B&SWJ 8664	WCru
	- B&SWJ 10957	WCru
	- B&SWJ 11133	WCru
§	- Atropurpurea Group	CBod EBee ECha EGrI ELan ELon EMor GMaP ILea LCro LOPS LRHS MACG MGos MNHC MRav NBir NChi NGdn NLar SPeP SPer SRms SWvt WCAu WFar WPnP WSHC
	- - 'Black Negligee'	Widely available
	- - 'Brunette' ♀H7	Widely available
	- - 'Carbonella'	CWGN EBee ECtt ELan EMor MNrw NLar SPVi WFar WHil
	- - 'Hillside Black Beauty' ♀H7	CDor CTtf EBee ECtt EMor GKin GMaP LRHS NBir NLar
	- - 'James Compton' ♀H7	CDor CExl CKel CPar EBee ECha EMor EWoo GBee GBin GKin GMaP GWyn ILea IPot LRHS MAvo MBel MCot NDov NGBl NGdn NLar NRHS SWvt WCAu WCot WFar
	- - 'Mountain Wave'	ECtt NDov SPVi
	- 'Cally Dappled' (v)	MBriF
	- 'Pink Spike'	Widely available
§	- 'Prichard's Giant'	ECha ELon EMor MACG MBros MNrw MRav NLar WFar
	- ***ramosa***	see *A. simplex* 'Prichard's Giant'
	- variegated (v)	WCot
	spicata	CSpe GBin GPoy WCru
	taiwanensis B&SWJ 3413	WCru

- RWJ 9996	WCru
yesoensis	LPla NLar
- B&SWJ 6355	WCru
- B&SWJ 10860	WCru

Actinella see *Tetraneuris*

Actinidia (*Actinidiaceae*)

sp.	CCCN
BWJ 8161 from China	WCru
arguta	CRHN EBee MGil
- (f/F)	CAgr LRHS
- B&SWJ 4455 from Jejudo, South Korea	WCru
- B&SWJ 4823 from Japan	WCru
- B&SWJ 8529 from Ulleungdo, South Korea	WCru
- 'Ambrosia Grande'	NLar
- 'Ananasnaya' (f/F)	CAgr WPGP
- 'Bayern' (f/F)	CAgr CCCN
- 'Geneva 2' (f/F)	CAgr
- 'Honigbeere' (m)	NLar
- 'Issai' (s-p/F)	CAgr CBcs CBod CCCN CMac EPom LBuc LEdu MBlu SVic WKor WPGP
- 'Jumbo' (f/F)	CAgr LEdu SVic
- 'Ken's Red' (f/F)	CAgr CCCN CDoC LEdu SVic SWeb WPGP
- 'Kokuwa' (s-p/F)	CAgr
- 'Meader' (m)	CAgr
- var. ***purpurea*** 'Hardy Red' (f/F) **new**	CAgr
- 'Purpurna Sadowa' (f/F)	NLar
- 'Rogow' (f/F) **new**	CAgr
- SCARLET SEPTEMBER KIWI ('Mirzan') (f/F)	CAgr
- 'Shoko' (f/F)	WCru
- 'Unchae' (m)	WCru
- 'Weiki' (m)	CAgr CCCN LEdu SVic WPGP
chinensis Planch. var. ***setosa*** H.L. Li B&SWJ 3563	WCru
coriacea WWJ 11895	WCru
§ ***deliciosa***	CCCN MRav
- 'Atlas' (m)	NLar
- 'Hayward' (f/F)	CBcs CCCN EPfP LSRN SCob SWvt WFar
- 'Jenny' (s-p/F)	CAgr CBod CEnd CMac CRos CTri ELan EPfP EPom LBuc LRHS MBros MGos NLar SPoG SPre SSFr SVic WFar
- 'Oriental Delight' (s-p/F)	CRHN
- SOLISSIMO ('Renact'PBR) (s-p/F)	CDoC CRos EHyd LRHS MCoo MTrO NRHS SSFr
- 'Solo' (s-p/F)	CCCN CMac CRHN CRos EPfP LRHS LSRN NLar SPer SWvt
- 'Tomuri' (m)	CBcs CCCN EBee EPfP LSRN SWvt
hypoleuca B&SWJ 5942	WCru
'Kiwai Bee'	CCCN
kolomikta ♀H5	Widely available
- B&SWJ 4243	LSRN WCru
- (m)	CDoC MBlu
- 'Adam' (m)	ETho
- 'Doctor Szymanowski' (s-p/F)	CAgr
- 'Sentyabraskaya' (f/F)	NLar
- 'Tomoko' (f/F)	WCru
- 'Yazuaki' (m)	WCru
melanandra	SPlb
petelotii FMWJ 13137	WCru
- HWJ 628	WCru
pilosula misapplied	see *A. tetramera* var. *maloides*
pilosula (Finet & Gagnep.) Stapf ex Hand.-Mazz.	CDoC CRos EHyd ELan IArd IDee LRHS MBNS NRHS SPoG SRms WKif
polygama B&SWJ 5444	WCru
- B&SWJ 8525 from Korea	WCru
- B&SWJ 8923 from Japan	WCru
- B&SWJ 12564 from Korea	WCru
rufa B&SWJ 3525	WCru
strigosa WJC 13662	WCru
- WJC 13807	WCru
aff. ***strigosa*** HWJK 2367	WCru
§ ***tetramera*** var. ***maloides*** ♀H5	CBcs CExl CKel CWGN EBee EPfP MGil NLar SBrt SCoo WBor WCru WLov WPGP WSHC

Adansonia (*Malvaceae*)

grandidieri	SPlb
madagascariensis	SPlb
rubrostipa	SPlb
za	SPlb

Adelocaryum see *Lindelofia*

Adenanthos (*Proteaceae*)

sericeus	SPlb

Adenium (*Apocynaceae*)

obesum ♀H1a	CCCN CDoC
- 'Olivia'	LCro LOPS

Adenocarpus (*Fabaceae*)

decorticans	SPlb

Adenophora (*Campanulaceae*)

sp.	MHol WCot
'Afterglow'	see *Campanula rapunculoides* 'Afterglow'
'Amethyst'	SSal
aurita	WHil
bulleyana	ELan NBid NLar SBls SPlb WCot WFar
* ***campanulata***	WCav
capillaris	NLar
subsp. ***leptosepala***	
- - BWJ 7986	WCru
coelestis	CExl GKev MACG NBid
- B&SWJ 7998	WCru
divaricata B&SWJ 11018	WCru
FAIRY BELLS	see *A.* 'Gaudi Violet'
§ 'Gaudi Violet'	CBod EMor LRHS MAvo MBriF MHol NCou SCoo SPad SPoG WCot
grandiflora B&SWJ 8555	WCru
khasiana	CExl GKev NLar XLum
kurilensis	GArf
lamarkii B&SWJ 8738	WCru
latifolia misapplied	see *A. pereskiifolia*
liliifolia	CMea EBee EPfP GJos GKev NPer WFar
maximowicziana B&SWJ 11008	WCru
morrisonensis RWJ 10008	MHol WCru
- subsp. ***uehatae***	GEdr GKev XLum
- - B&SWJ 126	WCru
§ ***nikoensis***	EBee GEdr GJos NBid WCot
- B&SWJ 11201	WCru
- f. ***linearifolia***	EWld
§ ***pereskiifolia***	EWes SBut SHar SPlb WCot
- 'Alba'	SRms
- 'White Blaze'	LCro LOPS
polyantha	NLar SRms
polymorpha	see *A. nikoensis*

potaninii	CPla EBee MACG MMuc SEND WFar WHal
- pale-flowered	WHal
remotiflora	EBee MHol
- B&SWJ 8714	WCru
- B&SWJ 11016	WCru
stricta subsp. ***confusa***	EBee
- subsp. ***sessilifolia***	EBee
takedae	EBee GArf SBrt
- B&SWJ 11424	WCru
taquetii	GEdr
taquetii × ***waldensteinia***	EPot
tashiroi	CPla EBee GKev XLum
triphylla	GKev
- B&SWJ 10916	WCru
- var. ***japonica*** B&SWJ 10933	WCru

Adenostyles (*Asteraceae*)

alpina	SBrt

Adesmia (*Fabaceae*)

longipes	SPlb

Adiantum (*Pteridaceae*)

sp.	CMac
§ ***aleuticum*** ♀H6	CLAP CMiW LCro LOPS NBro NLar SPlb WFib
- 'Imbricatum'	Widely available
§ - 'Japonicum'	WFar
- 'Miss Sharples'	CDTJ CLAP GEdr LEdu LRHS NLar NRHS SRms
§ - 'Subpumilum' ♀H5	CLAP NBro WCot WFib
- 'Tasselatum'	WCot
bonatianum	CExl
capillus-veneris	EBee NBro WFib
- 'Mairisii'	see *A.* × *mairisii*
caudatum	CDoC EShb
cuneatum	see *A. raddianum*
fulvum	CDoC
hispidulum ♀H4	CBdn CCCN CDoC EBee EHed EPfP LEdu LRHS MAsh NRHS
- 'Bronze Venus'	CCCN CDoC CRos EShb LRHS NRHS SRms
§ × ***mairisii*** ♀H5	CLAP CRos EShb LEdu LRHS MAsh NRHS
pedatum misapplied	see *A. aleuticum*
pedatum ambig.	CBod CTsd EWld SEdd
pedatum L.	CBcs CBct CDor CLAP EFer ELon GAbr GMaP LEdu NBro NLar SPlb WCot WFar
- var. ***subpumilum***	see *A. aleuticum* 'Subpumilum'
poiretii	LEdu
§ ***raddianum***	CDoC
§ - 'Fragrantissimum'	EShb LCro LOPS
- 'Fritz Lüthi'	CDoC EShb
- 'Lisa'	EShb
- 'Misty Cloud' **new**	CBdn
reniforme	WCot
× ***tracyi***	LEdu WPGP
venustum ♀H7	Widely available
- 'Texas'	LEdu

Adlumia (*Papaveraceae*)

fungosa	CSpe

Adonis (*Ranunculaceae*)

aestivalis	CKel
amurensis misapplied	see *A.* 'Fukujukai'
amurensis ambig.	CMea EBee EMor GEdr LEdu
- 'Pleniflora'	see *A. multiflora* 'Sandanzaki'
- 'Ryokuho'	GEdr
- 'Sakhalin'	EBee
annua	CKel SPhx
brevistyla	GEdr WAbe
'Chichibu-beni'	GEdr
§ 'Fukujukai'	ECha GEdr MBel
multiflora 'Beni-nadeshiko'	GEdr
- 'Hakuju'	GEdr
- 'Hanazono' (d)	GEdr
§ - 'Sandanzaki' (d)	EBee EMor GBin GEdr LEdu
pyrenaica	CSpe
ramosa	GEdr
'Sado-no-maboroshi' (d)	GEdr
vernalis	EMor GPoy

Adoxa (*Adoxaceae*)

moschatellina	EBee EWld LEdu MNrw NGrd NRya WHer WSFF WShi WWtn

Adromischus (*Crassulaceae*)

cooperi ♀H2	CDoC SIvy
filicaulis	SIvy
leucophyllus **new**	SIvy
maculatus ♀H2	CDoC
schuldtianus	CDoC

Aechmea ✿ (*Bromeliaceae*)

'Blue Rain'PBR	CDoC
fasciata	WSFF
filicaulis	NCft
'Nigre' ambig. **new**	NCft
recurvata	NCft
- var. ***benrathii***	NCft
'Red Bands' **new**	NCft

Aegle (*Rutaceae*)

sepiaria	see *Citrus trifoliata*

Aegopodium (*Apiaceae*)

podagraria	CNat
'Dangerous' (v)	
- gold-margined (v)	EPPr
- 'Variegatum' (v)	CEme EBee ECha EPPr EShb GGro GKev GMaP GQue LRHS MBel MRav NBid NRHS NSti SEND SPer WCot WFar WHil XLum

Aeonium (*Crassulaceae*)

appendiculatum **new**	SIvy
arboreum	CDTJ CDoC CKno CPbh CPla ELan EShb GBin NCft SChr SEND SIvy SMrm WABo
- 'Atropurpureum'	CAbb CCCN CDTJ CPla CSde ELan EShb NCft NPer SEND SIvy
- var. ***holochrysum***	NCft
I - 'Magnificum'	NCft SArc SIvy
- 'Tip Top' **new**	CBod CSpe ELan SEdd
- 'Variegatum' (v)	CPbh CPla NPer
'Ballecerina'	SAll
balsamiferum	CCCN CDTJ CDoC CPbh NCft SChr SIvy SSim WCot
'Black Cap'	CCCN
'Blush'	CKno
'Blushing Beauty' ♀H1c	CAbb EGrl NCft SEdd SIvy SSim WCot
canariense	CCCN CDTJ CTsd SIvy SVen
- var. ***palmense***	SIvy SVen
castello-paivae	SChr SIvy
ciliatum	SPlb
'Copper Kettle'	WAvo
'Cornish Tribute'	CCCN CPbh SEdd SIvy SSim

	'Cristata Sunburst'	CDTJ WCot
	cuneatum	CDTJ CPbh CSde NCft SEND
	- blue-leaved	SChr
	'Cyclops'	CAbb CPbh NCft
	davidbramwellii	CTsd
*	***decorum*** 'Variegatum' (v)	WCot
	'Dinner Plate'	CDTJ CPbh
	diplocyclum	CPbh
	'Du Rozzen'	CPbh
*	***escobarii***	SPlb
	'Firecracker'	CAbb
	glandulosum	SVen
	gomerense	CPla
	goochiae	SIvy
	- 'Ballerina' (v)	NCft SGro SIvy SSim WABo
	gorgonium	NCft
	haworthii 🏆H1c	CDTJ CDoC NCft SEND SEdd SSim SVen
	- 'Kiwi'	CCCN EGrI SEdd SIvy SSim WCot
	- 'Variegatum' (v) 🏆H1c	CDTJ CPbh EShb MHer SIvy SVen
	hierrense	CPbh SPlb
	holochrysum Webb & Berth.	CAbb
	lancerottense	SIvy
	'Lemon-Lime' (v)	WOld
	leucoblepharum	EShb NCft SAll SIvy
	lindleyi	NCft SChr
	× ***loartei*** **new**	SEdd SIvy
	'Logan Rock'	CPbh SEdd WCot
	'Marnier-Lapostolle' **new**	NCft
	'Maximus' **new**	NCft
	'Merry Maiden'	CPbh
*	***multiflorum*** 'Variegatum' (v)	CDTJ
	'Pen-du'	WABo
	'Poldark'	CCCN CPbh
	'Pomegranate'	CCCN
	rubrolineatum	SEdd WCot
	sedifolium	CPbh CPla NCft SIvy SSim
	'Simply Misty'	SSim
	'Simply Scarlet'	SSim
	simsii	CDTJ CPbh CTsd NCft
	- variegated (v)	EShb
	simsii × 'Zwartkop'	CBod CCCN CDoC CPbh CPla ELan ETod MHer NCft SChr SEdd WCot
	spathulatum	CDTJ CPbh EDAr WCot
	'Sunburst' (v) 🏆H1c	CPbh SIvy WCot
	tabuliforme 🏆H1c	CCCN CDTJ CDoC CPbh NCft SBls SMad SPlb SSim WCot
	'Torchbearer'	CPbh
	'Trewidden'	WCot
	undulatum	SPlb
	urbicum	EShb SIvy
	'Velour'	CCCN CDTJ CDoC CPbh EPfP NCft NPer SIvy SSim
	'Voodoo'	CAbb EGrI ELan SIvy SMad SSim WCot
	'Zwartkop' 🏆H1c	Widely available

Aeschynanthus ✿ (*Gesneriaceae*)

	sp.	CDoC
	Black Pagoda Group	WDib
	'Fire Wheel'	WDib
	'Hot Flash'	WDib
	'Little Tiger'	WDib
	longicalyx	see *A. rhododendron*
§	***longicaulis*** 🏆H1a	CDoC WDib
	marmoratus	see *A. longicaulis*
	radicans 🏆H1a	WDib
§	***rhododendron***	WDib
	'Scooby Doo'	WDib
	speciosus 🏆H1a	WDib

Aesculus ✿ (*Sapindaceae*)

	arguta	see *A. glabra* var. *arguta*
	assamica WWJ 11886	WCru
§	× ***bushii***	MBlu
	californica	CBcs CMCN EPfP SBrt WPGP
	- 'Canyon Pink'	CMCN
	× ***carnea***	CAco NRog SCob SGol
	- 'Briotii'	CAco CBcs CCVT CDoC CEnd CMac CSBt EBee ELan EPfP IPap LMaj LPar LRHS MGos MMuc MTrO NLar NOrn NRog NWea SCob SEND SEWo SGbt SPer SWeb WMat WTSh
*	- 'Variegata' (v)	CMCN
	chinensis	CBcs CMCN
	flava 🏆H5	CAco CMCN EBee ELan EPfP IArd LMaj MMuc SEND
	- f. ***vestita***	EPfP MBlu
	georgiana	see *A. sylvatica*
	glabra	CMCN MMuc
§	- var. ***arguta***	NLar
	- 'October Red'	EPfP
	glaucescens	see *A.* × *neglecta*
	hippocastanum	CAco CBcs CCVT CMac CSBt CTri EBee ELan IPap LPar LRHS MGos MMuc MSwo MTrO NLar NOra NRog NWea SCob SEWo SPer WFar WMat WTSh
	- 'Aureomarginata' (v)	CMac
§	- 'Baumannii' (d)	CMCN ELan LPar MGos MSwo NRog NWea SPer
	- 'Digitata'	CMCN IPap
	- 'Flore Pleno'	see *A. hippocastanum* 'Baumannii'
	- 'Hampton Court Gold'	CMCN CMac
	- f. ***laciniata***	CMCN NLar
	- 'Pyramidalis'	LPar
	- 'Wisselink'	CMCN
	indica	CLnd CMCN ELan EPfP EWTr MMuc MTrO SEND SGol SPtp WMou WTSh
	- 'Sydney Pearce' 🏆H5	CAco CBcs CEnd CMCN EPfP IArd MBlu MGos MTrO NLar NOra WMat
	× ***mississippiensis***	see *A.* × *bushii*
	× ***mutabilis*** 'Induta'	CAco CMCN EPfP MTrO NOra WMat
§	× ***neglecta***	CMCN
	- 'Autumn Fire'	EPfP MTrO NLar NOrn WMat
	- 'Erythroblastos' 🏆H5	CBcs CEnd CMCN EPfP MBlu SCoo SPer WCot WMat
	parviflora 🏆H5	CBcs CMCN CTri EBee ELan EPfP EWTr GKin IDee LMaj MBlu MGos MMuc MRav MTrO NLar NOra NWea SEND SMad SPer SWvt WMat
	pavia	CBcs CMCN MMuc
	- 'Atrosanguinea'	CEnd CMCN EPfP
	- var. ***discolor*** 'Koehnei'	CMCN ELan EPfP MTrO NLar NOra SPoG WMat
	- northern	SBrt
	- 'Purple Spring'	EPfP
§	- Splendens Group	CMCN EPfP
	splendens	see *A. pavia* Splendens Group
§	***sylvatica***	CMCN
	turbinata	CBcs MMuc WMou
	wilsonii	CBcs CExl MBlu

Aethionema (*Brassicaceae*)

	sp. **new**	GArf
	armenum	GKev
§	***grandiflorum*** 🏆H5	CBod EPot GJos GKev MCot MHol SRms

- Pulchellum Group ♀H5	CSpe
* ***kotschyi*** hort.	WAbe
pulchellum	see *A. grandiflorum*
schistosum	SPlb
'Warley Rose' ♀H5	CRos EHyd ELan EPot EWTr LRHS MAsh NBir NRHS SRms WIce WThu WTor XSen
'Warley Ruber'	CMea EPot WAbe

Agapanthus ✿ (*Agapanthaceae*)

'Adonis'	IBlr
'African Moon'	CPrp IBal
'African Skies' ♀H3	CAbb CPrp IBal LBuc LRHS SFai SGBe WABo XSte
africanus misapplied	see *A. praecox*
africanus 'Albus' misapplied	see *A. praecox* 'Albiflorus'
africanus hybrid	CBod
'Aimee'	CBro IBal
'Alan Street' ♀H4	CAvo IBal
'Albus' ambig.	GMaP
I 'Albus Nanus'	IBal
I 'Albus Roseus'	IBal
'Alice Double' (d)	CPbh
'Allisio'	IBal
'Amsterdam'	EBee EWTr IBal
'Angela'	CPrp ELon IBal
'Ankara'	IBal
'Anneke'	IBal
'Antibe'	IBal
'Aphrodite'	IBlr
'Aquamarine'	CAvo EPri IBal
'Arctic Star' ♀H4	CAvo CCCN CDoC CExl CKno CMac CPar CWCL EBee ELan ELon EPfP IBal LRHS LSRN LSou MAvo NHoy NLar SCoo SDys SFai SGBe SPoG WABo XSte
'Ardernei'	IBal
'Ardernei Hybrid'	CAvo CExl ECha ECtt EWes GAbr IBal IBlr WCot WGwG
§ 'Argenteus Vittatus' (v)	WSHC
'Ascona'	IBal
'Atlas'	IBlr
'Aureovittatus' (v)	IBal
'Autumn Mist'	IBal
§ 'B in B'PBR	CBro CCCN CExl ECha ELan IBal MBNS MRav NBid NLar SCob WCot WFar
'Baby Blue'	see *A.* 'Blue Baby' Rom.
'Baby Pete'PBR	EWoo IBal NHoy
BACK IN BLACK	see *A.* 'B in B'
'Ballerina' ♀H3	CPne IBal
'Ballyrogan'	IBlr
'Bangor Blue'	IBlr
'Barnfield Blue'	CPrp EBee IBal
'Beatrice'	CPrp
'Becky'	IBal
'Beeches Dwarf'	IBal
'Ben Hope'	CBro IBal IBlr XLum
'Berlin'	IBal
'Beth Chatto'	see *A. campanulatus* 'Albovittatus'
'Bethlehem Star'	EPri
'Bicton Bell'	IBal IBlr
'Bicton Bride'	IBal
'Big Ben'	IBal
'Big Blue'	CBod CCCN CChe CEnd CMac CPrp CSde CWCL EBee SEND SRkn WABo WSMil WSpi
'Big Dutch Blue' new	IBal
'Black Beauty'	CPrp EBee EPfP IBal LSou WSpi
'Black Buddhist'	CCCN EBee ECtt EPfP EPri GKev IBal IPot NGdn NHoy NSti XSen
'Black Magic'	CAbb CBod CPar CPrp CWCL EBee ELan IBal IPot LSou NHoy NSti SCob SFai SMad SPad SPoG WABo WFar
'Black Pantha'PBR	Widely available
BLITZ PRESTIGE ('Allprestige'PBR) new	IBal IPot LRHS
'Blitzza'	IBal
'Bloemfontein'	IBal
§ 'Blue Baby' Rom.	CCCN EHyd ELan ELon IBal LRHS
'Blue Bird'	CPrp
'Blue Brush'	CPrp EPfP SCoo
'Blue Cascade'	IBlr
'Blue Companion'	CPrp IBlr
'Blue Dot'	CBod CPrp EPfP LSou SDys
'Blue Formality'	IBal IBlr
'Blue Giant'	CBro CCCN CChe CDor CPrp EBee EGrl ELan EPfP ETod IBal LRHS MGos WAvo WSpi
'Blue Globe'	CBod EBee EPri GMaP IBal MSCN
'Blue Heaven'PBR	CPne CWGN EWes EWoo IBal ILea NHoy
'Blue Horizons'PBR (v)	CCCN IBal
'Blue Ice' ♀H4	CPrp EBee EWoo IBal NHoy SAko SEdd WABo WTyc XSte
'Blue Imp'	CBro IBal IBlr NWad
'Blue Jay'	IBal
'Blue Magic' ♀H5	EBee IBal NHoy
'Blue Moon'	CBro CPrp EBee ECha ECtt EPri GAbr IBal IBlr MAvo MHol SEND WCot
'Blue Nile'	CBdn CPne CPrp IBal
'Blue Pixie'	IBal
'Blue Prince'	ELon
'Blue Rinse'	IBal
'Blue Skies' ambig.	SDir
I 'Blue Skies' Dunlop	IBlr
'Blue Sparkler'	CPrp
'Blue Spear'	CRos
'Blue Steel'	IBal
BLUE STORM ('Atiblu'PBR) (Storm Series)	CPrp EHyd EPfP ERom IBal LBuc LRHS SArc SCoo SGBe
'Blue Triumphator'	CDor EPfP GKev GMaP IBal ILea MACG NHoy SCob WSpi
'Blue Umbrella'	CDor CPrp ELan SGsty SRkn WSpi
blue-flowered	WAvo WCFE
'Bluety'PBR	IBal
'Boleyn Blue'	ECha
'Bray Valley'	CPne CPrp
'Bressingham Blue'	CAbb CBro CDoC CTri EBee EBlo EPfP EWes IBal IBlr LRHS LSou MAvo MRav NHoy SFai SMHy WABo WSpi
'Bressingham Bounty'	EBee EBlo IBal LRHS
'Bressingham White'	CDoC CPrp EPfP LRHS MRav
'Bridal Bouquet'	EBee EPfP IBal LBuc LRHS LSRN LSou NHoy SAko SFai SGBe WABo
'Bright Blue'	IBal
BRILLIANT BLUE ('Aga0451')	CEnd CKno EBee IBal LRHS LSou MHol SCoo SFai WABo WHoo XSte
'Bristol'	IBal
'Broadleigh Babe'	CBro
'Buckingham Palace'	CBro EBee ECha ELon EWes GAbr IBal IBlr NChi WCot
'Calimero'	IBal
'Cally Blue'	GAbr IBal
'Cally Large White'	GAbr
'Cally Longstem'	EBee
'Cally Pale Blue'	IBal
campanulatus	CBod CMac CPbh CPrp ELan ELon EPfP EWTr GKin IBal IBlr MRav NChi SGbt WAvo WFar WKif WSpi

– var. ***albidus***	CBod CPrp ECha ELan EPfP GKin IBlr LRHS MHer MMuc NBid NGdn NHoy SEND SPer WGwG WHoo WSHC WSpi
§ – 'Albovittatus' (v)	CTtf IBal
– bright blue-flowered	IBal
– 'Cobalt Blue'	CBod CPrp ECha EGrl ELan EPri GKin IBal LSou MAsh MMuc NGdn SMrm WHoo
– dark blue-flowered	CPrp
– 'Oxford Blue'	GDam IBlr LRHS
– subsp. ***patens***	CEme EPfP GKev IBal LRHS MRav
– – deep blue-flowered	IBlr LRHS
– 'Profusion'	CBro ECha EPri IBal IBlr LRHS NHoy
– 'Ultramarine'	CPrp IBal
– variegated (v)	EBee ECha NPer
– 'Wedgwood Blue'	CPrp EBee IBal IBlr
– 'Wendy'	EBee EPfP IBlr LRHS
– 'White Hope'	IBal IBlr LRHS
'Carefree'	CPrp
'Castle of Mey'	CAvo CBro CExl CPrp EBee ELon GAbr IBal IBlr LCro LOPS LRHS LSou MAvo NHoy SFai WABo WCAu WSpi
'Catharina'	IBal
§ ***caulescens***	CBdn CPne CPrp IBal IBlr LRHS
– subsp. ***angustifolius***	ELon IBal IBlr SEND
– subsp. ***caulescens***	IBlr
'Cedric Morris'	EPri IBal IBlr
'Celebration'	CPne CPrp IBal SFai
'Chandra'	IBal IBlr
'Charlotte' PBR	CMac CRos EBee ELan EPfP IBal LRHS LSou MHol SCoo SEdd SFai SPoG WABo WTor
'Cherbours'	IBal
'Cherry Holley'	ELon IBal WSpi
'Chika's Blue'	EBee IBal MAvo
'Clarence House'	CBro IBal
'Cloudy Days'	IBal
coddii	CExl CPbh CPrp EPri IBal IBlr MHer WCot
'Columba'	CPrp EBee ELon IBal MAvo NBid XSen
comptonii	see *A. praecox* subsp. *minimus*
'Connie's Delight' **new**	ETod
'Cool Blue'	CPrp
'Corina'	EBee
'Croft's Pearl' **new**	IBal
DANUBE	see *A.* 'Donau'
'Dart Valley'	CPrp IBal
'Dawn Star'	ECha
'Debbie'	IBal
'Delft'	CPrp EBee IBal IBlr
'Delft Blue'	EPau GBee IBal NLar
'Density'	IBlr
'Dnjepr'	CBro EBee IBal
'Dokkum'	IBal
'Dokter Brouwer'	EWTr GKev ILea LSRN MCot MPtr SDir
§ 'Donau'	CBro EBee EPri EShb GKev IBal MPtr NBir
DOUBLE DIAMOND ('Rfdd' PBR) ♀H3	EBee EHyd EPfP EPri EWes IBal LRHS LSRN LSou NHoy NWad SAko SCob SCoo SEdd SFai SGBe SPoG WFar WSpi
'Dublin'	IBal
'Duivenbrugge Blue'	IBal
'Durban'	IBal
'Dutch Seaside' **new**	IBal
dwarf blue	IBal NHoy

dyeri	see *A. inapertus* subsp. *intermedius*
'Early Blue'	ELon EWoo IBal
'Eggesford Sky'	CPne CPrp EBee IBal
'Elaine'	IBal
'Elisa'	IBal
'Elizabeth Salisbury'	IBal
'Ellamae'	IBal
'Elsie's Sunshine'	WFar
'Enigma'	Widely available
'Enigma Variations'	EBee
'Ethel's Joy'	EPri IBal
'Eve'	IBlr
'Evening Eclipse'	ELan EPfP IBal LRHS
'Evening Star'	CPrp ECha EPri WABo
EVER BLUE	IBal
EVER SAPPHIRE ('Andbin') **new**	LRHS SFai
EVER WHITE ('Wp001') ♀H3 **new**	LRHS SFai
'Exmoor' ♀H4	CPrp IBal MAvo WABo
'Findlay's Blue'	SMHy
'Finnline' (v)	SRms
'Fiona' **new**	IBal
FIREWORKS ('Mdb001') ♀H3 **new**	SFai XSte
'Flore Pleno' (d)	CExl CMac CPrp ECha ECtt ELan GAbr GKin IBal IBlr LSou MHer MHol NGdn NHoy SMrm WCot WFar WSHC
'Flower of Love' ♀H4	CAvo CPne CPrp EPfP IBal LCro LOPS LRHS LSou NLar SFai SPoG WABo XSte
I 'Forma'	IBal
§ 'Franni'	WCav
'Full Moon'	IBal SFai
'Fulsome'	IBlr
'Gail's Purple'	IBal
'Gayle's Lilac'	CBcs CBod CCCN CElw CExl CPrp ELan ELon EPfP EWTr GKin LSou MPie MRav NGdn WGwG
'Gem'	CPrp ELon MAvo
'Genua'	IBal
'Getty White'	ELan
'Glacier'	IBal
'Glacier Stream'	CBro CDor EPri IBal NLar SEdd XSen
'Glen Avon'	CAbb CCCN CExl EBee EPfP EWoo IBal LRHS SCoo SFai SLon WABo
'Gold Strike' PBR (v)	IBal LSou NHoy SFai SPoG WABo WCot
'Golden Drop' PBR (v)	CBcs EHyd IBal LRHS LSou NHoy NSti SFai SPad SPeP SRms WABo
'Golden Rule' (v)	IBlr
'Gothenburg'	IBal
'Greenfield'	EBee IBal
'Hamar'	IBal
'Hanneke'	IBal SFai
'Hannover'	IBal
'Happy Blue' ♀H4	IBal
'Harvest Blue'	CPne IBal
§ Headbourne hybrids	Widely available
– dark blue-flowered	LPot LRHS
'Headbourne White'	EPri
'Heavenly Blue'	CCCN
'Helen'	IBlr
'Helsinki'	IBal
'His Majesty'	CBod IBal
'Hole Park Blue'	NHoy WMal
'Hoyland Blue' ♀H3	CPrp IBal NHoy WFar
'Hoyland Chelsea Blue'	NHoy

	'Ice Blue Star' ♀H5	CBro CPrp IBal
	'Ice Lolly'	CBro IBal
	ICICLES ('Duivenbrugge White')	CKno GKev IBal LSou MHol NSti SFai WABo
	inapertus	CAvo CBro CPbh CPrp EWes IBal WBrk WPGP WSHC
	- 'Avalanche' ♀H4	IBal WSpi
	- 'Cascade Crystal'	IBal
	- 'Cascade Diamond'	IBal
	- 'Crystal Drop'	CAbb CExl CPrp EPri EWoo IBal LSou SFai WABo
	- dwarf	IBlr
	- subsp. ***hollandii***	IBal IBlr
	- - 'Sky' ♀H4	CAbb CDor EBee EMor EPri EWTr EWoo IBal IBlr LRHS NBid SRms WABo
	- - 'Zealot'	IBlr
	- 'Ice Cascade'	CCCN EBee IBal
	- 'Icicle'	CSpe SPoG
	- subsp. ***inapertus***	IBlr
I	- - 'Albus'	IBlr
	- - 'Cyan'	IBlr
	- - 'White'	CPrp IBal
§	- subsp. ***intermedius***	CPrp IBal IBlr NHoy
*	- - 'August Bells' ♀H5 **new**	CBro
	- - 'Long Tom'	CExl EBee EPri
	- 'Margaret'	CCCN
	- 'Midnight Cascade'	CCCN CExl CPar CPrp CSpe EBee ECtt IPot LEdu NBid NHoy SEdd SRms WFar WTyc
	- 'Mood Indigo'	EBee EPri IBal NHoy
	- subsp. ***parviflorus***	IBlr
	- subsp. ***pendulus***	IBal IBlr
	- - 'Black Magic'	IBal SPeP WTyc XSte
	- - 'Graskop'	CBcs CCCN CExl CPrp EBee EHyd EPfP EPri EWoo IBal IBlr MNrw NHoy NSti SEdd SFai SMHy SRms WTyc
	- - 'Violet Dusk'	IBlr
	- 'Sapphire Cascade'	LSRN
	- tall pale blue-flowered	WPGP
	- 'Tempest'	WPGP
	- 'White Cloud'	IBal
	'Indigo Dreams'	CBdn CKno CPar CPne CPrp EBee IBal LPla LRHS MAvo MHol NHoy SFai WABo XSte
	'Inkspots'	CCCN CMac CPrp EHyd EPfP IBal LSou NHoy SEdd SPoG
	'Intermedius' Leichtlin	IBal LEdu
I	'Intermedius' van Tubergen	IBal MACG NBid
	'Isabella' **new**	IBal
	'Isis'	CAvo CBro CPrp CSde ECha ELon EPfP EPri IBal IBlr LRHS
	'Jacaranda' ♀H3	CMac EWoo IBal LRHS LSou NHoy SCoo SEdd SFai SGBe WABo
	'Jack Elliott'	MAvo
	'Jack's Blue'	CBro CDor CJun EBee ECtt ELan ELon EMor EPri GMaP IBal LSRN MHol MNrw NGdn NHoy NLar SCoo WCot WFar WSpi
	'Jersey Giant'	CPrp
	'Jessica' **new**	LSou SFai
	'Jodie'	CPrp ELon MAvo
	'Johanna'	IBal
	'Johannesburg'	IBal
	Johannesburg hybrids	ECha
	'Jolanda'	CPrp IBal
	'Jonie'	IBal
	'Jonny's White' ♀H4	IBal
	'Kalmthout Blue'	IBal
	'Kew White'	SMHy
	'Kilmurry Blue'	IBal
	'Kilmurry White'	IBal
	'Kingston Blue'	ECha IBlr MAvo NBid NHoy WSHC
	'Kobold'	CBro IBal WFar
§	'Lady Grey'	IBlr
	'Lady Moore'	SMHy
	L'AMOUR D'ÉTÉ BLEU ('Corag02bl'PBR) **new**	IBal
§	'Lapis'	CBod CDoC CMac CPrp CSde EBee EPfP EPri EWoo IBal LRHS LSou MHol MPri NHoy NLar SCoo SEdd SFai SGBe WABo XSte
	'Lapis Lazuli'	see *A.* 'Lapis'
	'Latent Blue'	IBlr
	'Lavender Haze'	CCCN CDoC CMac EBee EHyd EPfP EWoo IBal LRHS NHoy SCoo SEdd SFai SGBe WABo WSMil WSpi
	'Leanne'	IBal
	'Leicester' ♀H4	IBal
	'Liam's Lilac'	CBdn CCCN CDoC CExl CPrp ELon IBal LCro LOPS LSou MAvo NHoy NLar SFai WABo WFar
	'Lilac Flash'	CPbh CPne IBal
	'Lilac Lullaby'	IBal
	'Lilac Time'	CExl CPrp IBal IBlr
	'Lilliput'	CBcs CBro CCCN CMac CMea CPrp CSpe EBlo ECha ECtt ELan ELon EPfP EShb GArf GKev GMaP IBal LRHS LSou MRav NGdn SPer SRms WCFE WFar XSen
	'Lissabon'	IBal
	'Lisse'	IBal
	'Little Dutch Blue'	EWoo IBal MHol WCot
	'Little Dutch White'PBR	IBal LEdu MHol SEdd WCot
	'Little Frank'	NHoy
	'Little Sebastian'	NHoy
	'Little White'	IBal
	'Littlecourt'	CBro IBal MAvo
	'Loch Hope' ♀H6	CAvo CBro CPrp EBee EBlo ECtt ELon EPfP IBal LPla LRHS MAvo MHol MRav SDix WCot WSpi
	'Lorna'	CPrp
	'Los Angeles'	IBal
	'Luly' ♀H4	IBal MGos WFar
	'Luna'	EBee IBal
	'Lydenburg'	EPri IBal IBlr LEdu MAvo WPGP
	'Lyn Valley'	CBdn CPne CPrp EBee IBal
	'Mabel Grey'	see *A.* 'Lady Grey'
	'Madurodam'	IBal
	'Magnifico'	CPrp IBlr
	'Malaga'	IBal
	'Malmo'	IBal
	'Marchants Midnight Blue'	SMHy
	'Marcus'	IBal SDir
	'Margaret'	GKev IBal LSRN NHoy WFar
	'Marianne'	IBal
	'Marijke'	IBal
	'Marjorie' ♀H5	CBdn CPne WABo
	'Martine'	IBal MAvo
	'Maureen' ♀H5	CPrp EBee IBal LSRN
	'Maurice'	IBal
	'May Snow' (v)	WCot
	'Medan'	IBal
	'Medusa'	IBal
	'Megan's Mauve' ♀H3	CBro CPne EBee ELon EPri IBal LCro LOPS LSRN NSti SFai WABo XSte
	'Meibont' (v)	IBal WCot
	'Melbourne'	MHtn
	'Mercury'	IBlr
	'Messina'	IBal
	MI CASA ('Aaopr017')	IBal SPad

	'Michelle'	IBal
	'Middleburg'	IBal
	MIDKNIGHT BLUE ('Monmid')	EWes WSHC
	'Midnight'	EWes IBal
	'Midnight Blue' ambig.	CDoC ELan EPfP EShb GKev IBal MCot NLar NWad SMHy WFar
	'Midnight Blue' P.Wood	IBlr
	'Midnight Dream'	EBee ECtt EPot IBal LEdu NHoy STPC WFar
§	'Midnight Star' ♀H5	Widely available
	'Mini Blue'	IBal
	'Misty Dawn' (v)	CBcs CPrp CWGN EBee ECtt ELon EWhm IBal LSou MHol SPeP WCot WSMil
	'Mole Valley'	IBal
	'Molly Howick'	EBee EBlo LRHS
	'Monique' ♀H4	IBal
	'Montreal'	IBal
	'Moody Blue' **new**	IBal
	'Moonlight Star'	EBee IBal IPot LRHS MHol NHoy SFai WABo WFar
	'Moonshine'	IBal WFar
I	'Mooreanus' misapplied	EBee EPfP IBal NBid
	'Morning Star'	IBal
	'Mount Stewart'	IBal IBlr
	'Nancy'	IBal
	'Napoli'	IBal
	'Navy Blue'	see *A.* 'Midnight Star'
	'Newa'	EBee
	'Newcastle'	IBal
	'Night Sky'	MHol SFai
	'Nikki'	CMea CPne IBal
	'Norman Hadden'	IBlr
	'Northern Light'	IBal
	'Northern Star'PBR ♀H4	Widely available
	nutans	see *A. caulescens*
	'Nyx'	IBlr
	'Odessa'	IBal
	'Oslo'	IBal
I	'Ovatus' **new**	ERom
	'Oxbridge'	IBlr
	'Oxford'	IBal
	'Pacific Blue'PBR	CDoC IBal
	Palmer's hybrids	see *A.* Headbourne hybrids
	'Patent Blue'	CPrp IBal IBlr
	'Pavlova'	IBal
	'Penelope Palmer'	CPrp IBal IBlr
	'Peter Franklin'	IBal
	'Peter Pan' ambig.	Widely available
	'Peter Pan American'	GKev NHoy
	'Phantom'	CPrp EBee IBal IBlr MAvo NLar SAko SFai WABo WCot WFar
	'Picton Blue'	WFar
	'Pinocchio'	IBal SDeJ
	'Pirame'	IBal
	PITCHOUNE BLUE ('Scrarey09'PBR)	IBal
	'Plas Merdyn Blue'	CPrp
	'Plas Merdyn White'	IBal IBlr
	'Podge Mill'	IBal IBlr
	'Polar Ice'	EBee ELon EPfP EPri IBal ILea LSRN MBow MNrw MPtr NHoy SDir WCAu WFar WSpi
	'Polar Star'	IBal SCoo
	'Porcelain'	IBal IBlr
§	***praecox***	Widely available
§	- 'Albiflorus'	Widely available
	- 'Maximus Albus'	IBal IBlr
§	- subsp. ***minimus***	CElw IBal IBlr SEND
	- - 'Adelaide'	CPrp IBal

	- 'Neptune'	IBlr
§	- subsp. ***orientalis***	CBro CCCN IBlr
	- - 'Mount Thomas'	CPrp
	- - 'Silver Star' (v)	IBal
	- subsp. ***praecox***	IBlr
	- - 'Variegatus'	see *A.* 'Argenteus Variegatus'
	- 'Saturn'	IBlr
	- Slieve Donard form	IBlr
	- 'Storms River'	IBal
	- 'Uranus'	IBlr
	- 'Venus'	IBlr
	'Premier'	IBlr
	'Pretty Heidy'	LSou MHol SFai
	'Pretty Wendy'	IBal
	'Prince of the Night' **new**	SMHy
	'Princess Margaret'	CPrp IBal
§	'Purple Cloud'	Widely available
	'Purple Delight' ♀H3	CPar CPbh CPrp EBee EPfP IBal LCro LOPS LRHS SAko SCoo SFai SGBe WABo WFar XSte
	'Purple Emperor'	IBal MHol SFai
	'Purple Fountain'	IBal SRms
	'Purple Haze'	IBal
	'Purple Heart'	SFai
	'Purple Magic'	IBal
	'Purple Ripple'	IBal
	'Purple Star'	CCCN
	'Queen Anne'	IBal
	'Queen Mother'	CPrp IBal WSpi
	QUEEN MUM ('Pmn06'PBR)	Widely available
	'Queen of the Ocean'	IBal
	'Radiant Star'	IBal LRHS
	'Regal Beauty'	CBro CSBt EBee EWoo IBal LSRN NBid SAko SFai WABo
	'Rhapsody in Blue'	CPne CPrp
	'Rhone'	CBro IBal IBlr
	'Robin'	IBal
	'Rosewarne'	CBcs CBod CCCN CDoC CExl IBal IBlr
	'Rotterdam'	IBal XSen
	'Roxanne'	EBee IBal
	'Royal Blue' ♀H5	CBro CPrp GMaP IBal WCot WSpi
	'Royal Knight'	IBal
	'Royal Velvet' ♀H4	CKno EPfP IBal LCro LOPS MAvo MHol SFai WFar XSte
	'Ruan Vean'	CPrp
	'Ruthie's Sunshine'	WFar
	'Sabang'	IBal
	'Sally Anne'	CBdn CPne CPrp WABo
	'San Remo'	IBal
	'Sandringham' ♀H5	CBcs CBod CPrp EBee ELon EPfP EPri ETod EWes IBal LSRN NBid NHoy SEdd SFai WABo WFar
	'Sandy'PBR ♀H4	CKno IBal IPot LSou MHol SFai
	'Sapphire'	CPrp IBlr
	'Sarah'PBR	CCCN EBee IBal LSRN MTin NLar SFai
	'Saville Blue'	CPrp MCot
	'Sea Coral'	CBod CCCN CMac CPne CPrp EBee ECtt EMor EPri ETod IBal LPla MAvo MPie NSti
	'Sea Foam'	CMac XLum
	'Sea Mist'	CCCN CPne CPrp
	'Sea Spray'	CCCN EBee EPri IBal WFar
	'Sea Storm' (Storm Series)	CBod
	'Selma Bock'	CPbh
	'Semarang'	IBal
	'Senna'PBR	CCCN CExl EBee EPot GKev IBal SIvy
	'Septemberhemel'	IBal
	'Shooting Stars'	GBee IBal

'Silberpfeil'	IBal MPtr
'Silver Anniversary'	IBal NHoy
'Silver Baby' ♀H3	CAbb CAvo CBod CDoC CKno CPrp CWGN EBee EHyd EPfP EPri ETod IBal LEdu LRHS LSou NHoy SFai SRms WABo WTyc
'Silver Jubilee'	IBal
'Silver Lining'	CPne ECtt EMor IBal LRHS SFai
'Silver Mist'	CDor CPne IBal IBlr
SILVER MOON ('Notfred'PBR) (v) ♀H5	CAvo CBcs CBod CBro CCCN EBee EHyd ELan EPfP ETod GKev IBal LLWG LRHS LSou MCot MGos MHol NHoy NLar NSti SCob SEdd SFai SGsty SPoG WABo WCot
'Silver Sceptre'	IBlr
'Silver Stream'	NHoy
'Silver Suzy'	IBal
'Sky Rocket'	CPrp IBal IBlr WMal
'Sky Star'	IBal
'Skyscraper'	IBal
'Slieve Donard'	IBlr
'Snow Cloud' ♀H4	CAbb CBro CExl CPne EBee EHyd EPfP LCro LOPS LRHS NLar SAko SEND SEdd SFai SLon WABo WSpi
'Snow Crystal' ♀H3	IBal LRHS SFai XSte
'Snow Pixie'	CSpe EBee EWoo IBal LSRN LSou NHoy SFai WABo WSpi
'Snow Princess'	ELon IBal
'Snow Shadows'	CBro IBal
'Snowball'	CExl WSpi
'Snowdrops'	CCCN EBee
'Snowstorm'PBR (Storm Series)	EBee ERom IBal LRHS SArc SCoo SGBe
'Sofie'PBR	EBee IBal STPC
'Sorento'	IBal
'Southern Cross'	EBee IBal NHoy SFai SGsty
'Southern Star'	CPrp IBal
'Star Quality'	IBal LRHS LSRN LSou MNrw SCoo SFai WABo
'Starburst'	IBlr
'Starburst Blue'	IBal
'Starburst White'	IBal
'Stardust'	EPfP IBal SCoo
'Stargazer'	IBal LRHS
'Stars and Stripes'	IBal
'Stellenbosch'	LEdu WPGP
'Stéphanie Charm'	IBal
'Stockholm'	GAbr IBal
'Storm Cloud' Reads	see *A.* 'Purple Cloud'
'Storm Cloud' (d)	CBro IBal
'Strawberry Ice'	CBro EBee IBal SEdd SFai WABo WSpi
'Streamline'	CBcs CBod CElw CEnd CKno CMea CPla CPrp CSde EBee ECtt EGrl EHyd ELon EMor EPfP EShb GAbr GKin GMaP IBal LRHS MACG MRav NHoy SDys SEND WSHC
'Su Casa'	IBal
'Summer Blue'	IBal
'Summer Clouds'	CPrp ELan
'Summer Days' ♀H4	CPne IBal WABo
'Summer Delight'	IBal
'Summer Skies'	CPne CPrp ELon IBal
'Summer Snow'	IBal
'Sunfield'	CDor CPrp EPfP IBal ILea LRHS MNrw MPtr NLar NPer
'Super Star'	CBro CPrp IBal
'Susan Elizabeth'	CPrp
'Sweet Surprise'	IBal LBuc LRHS SFai SGBe
'Sylvia'PBR	IBal
'Sylvine'	CPrp IBal
'Tall Boy'	IBlr
'Tarka'	CBdn CExl CPne CPrp ELon EPfP EPri EWoo IBal LSou NHoy SDys WABo
'Taw Valley'	CKno CPrp ELon IBal LCro LOPS MGos NHoy SEdd SMad WABo
'Thorn'	IBal
'Thumbelina'	CBro CMac EBee IBal LSou NHoy
THUNDER STORM ('Dunaga02') (Storm Series) (v)	CWGN IBal SPeP
'Timaru'	CBro CElw CPrp EBee ECha ECtt ELan ELon EPfP GMaP IBal MHol NGdn WCot XSte
'Tinkerbell' (v)	CBcs CBdn CBor CBro CCCN CEme CPne CTtf EBee EBlo ELan EPfP EPri EShb IBal LRHS MGos MHol MRav NHoy NPer SPoG SRms SWvt
'Tiny White'	EPri
'Titan'	IBlr
'Titch'	IBal
'Tom Thumb'PBR	CBod CDoC CExl CPrp CSde CTsd ECtt EHyd EPau EPfP GBin IBal LRHS NHoy
'Top Slice' (v)	WCot
'Torbay'	CBod CElw CPrp ECtt ELon EMor EPfP EShb GAbr GKev GKin IBal MAvo MNrw NHol NLar SGbt WAvo WHoo
'Tornado'	CPrp EBee ECtt ELon ETod IBal ILea LRHS NLar STPC
'Triangle'	CPbh IBal
'Tsolo'	IBal
'Twilight Zone'	EBee IBal LRHS SCoo
TWISTER ('Ambic001'PBR) ♀H4	Widely available
umbellatus Redouté	see *A. praecox* subsp. *orientalis*
'Underway'	EWes GKev IBal
'Vallée Blanche'	IBal
'Vallée de la Loire'	IBal
'Vallée de la Sarthe'	IBal
'Vallée de l'Authion'	IBal
Ventnor hybrid	SVen
'Volendam'	IBal
'Washington'	IBal
'Wavy Navy'	IBal
'Wedding Day'	CPne EBee IBal
'Wembworthy'	CBdn CPne CPrp EBee IBal
'White Baby'	IBal
'White Dwarf'	see *A.* white-flowered, dwarf
'White Flash'	IBal
'White Giant'	CSBt EGrl WSpi
'White Heaven'PBR	EBee ECtt ELon EPfP EWoo GAbr IBal IPot LCro LEdu LOPS LRHS LSun MAvo MHol NHoy NSti SCob SDix SEND SEdd SFai WCot WSpi
'White Ice'	CPbh IBal
'White Pixie'	IBal
'White Smile'	EPri
'White Superior'	CBod EBee EPfP GMaP MNHC MSCN
'White Umbrella'	EHyd ELan LRHS
'White Wings'	IBal
white-flowered	WAvo WCFE
§ - dwarf	CBro ECha EPfP EShb IBal MAsh NBir NGdn NHol SGbt
'Whitney'PBR	IBal IBlr
'Windlebrooke'	CCCN EAJP ECha EPot EPri IBal MAvo NLar SDeJ WCot
'Windsor Castle'	IBlr

'Windsor Grey'	Widely available
'Winsome'	IBlr
'Winter Sky'	IBal
'Wolga'	CBro EBee IBal
'Wolkberg' Kirstenbosch	CPrp IBal IBlr
'Yellow Tips'	IBal
'Yves Klein'	IBlr WABo
'Zachary'	CPrp EBee ELon EPri WABo
'Zeal Thomas'	IBal
'Zigzag White'	WCot

Agapetes (*Ericaceae*)

'Ludgvan Cross' 🏆H2	CBcs CCCN CTsd LRHS MGil
serpens 🏆H2	CBcs CCCN CTsd SLon
- 'Scarlet Elf'	CCCN CTsd

Agastache (*Lamiaceae*)

'After Eight'	CDor ECha ECtt ETod EWTr LRHS MBel
anethiodora	see *A. foeniculum* (Pursh) Kuntze
anisata	see *A. foeniculum* (Pursh) Kuntze
'Astello Indigo'	MNHC SPhx XLum
aurantiaca	SPhx SPlb
- 'Apricot Sprite'	CSpe LShi MHol NGdn NRHS SCoo SRkn WCav WKif
'Ayala'	EBee
'Blackadder'	Widely available
'Blaue Sangria'	NDov
'Blue Boa'[PBR]	CBod CDor CKno CWGN EBee ECha ECtt ETod GWyn LCro LOPS MAvo MBel MNHC NCou NDov NLar NSti SEdd SGBe SIvy SMad SPoG SRms WCAu WSpi WTor
* 'Blue Bonnet'	CSpe
'Blue Fortune' 🏆H6	CBcs CRos ECha EHyd EPfP EWoo GBee GWyn LCro LOPS LPla LRHS MCot MRav NDov NLar NRHS SCob SCoo SEdd SMad SMrm SPer SPhx SRms SWvt WCAu WNPC WSpi XSen
'Bolero'	CSpe LRHS MPie SPhx
§ ***cana***	SPhx
- 'Heatwave'[PBR]	EBee EPfP NDov WNPC
'Cotton Candy'[PBR]	EBee LCro LOPS
'Firebird'	CWGN EBee ECtt ELan EPfP LRHS SRms SWvt
'Fleur'	ECtt WGoo
foeniculum misapplied	see *A. rugosa*
§ ***foeniculum*** (Pursh) Kuntze	CBee CCBP CLau EBee ELan ENfk GPoy LRHS MHer MNHC SPhx SRms WJek WTre XAbr
- 'Alabaster'	CBcs EBee EWes GWyn LCro LOPS NLar
'Globetrotter'	EAJP SPhx
'Kolibri'	ECtt ILea WGoo
(Kudos Series) 'Kudos Ambrosia'[PBR]	ECtt ELan LRHS NRHS SGBe SPoG WCot
- 'Kudos Coral'[PBR]	CKno CPla ELan EPfP LRHS MBros MHol NRHS SGBe SRkn WNPC
- 'Kudos Gold'[PBR]	CKno ELan EPfP MHol NSti SCoo SGBe SPoG SRkn WNPC
- 'Kudos Mandarin'[PBR]	ELan EPfP LRHS NLar NRHS SGBe SPoG
- 'Kudos Red' **new**	NLar
- 'Kudos Silver Blue'	ECtt ELan LRHS NLar NRHS
- 'Kudos Yellow'[PBR]	ELan LRHS
'Linda'	CWGN NDov WCot WMal
§ ***mexicana***	WFar
- 'Red Fortune'[PBR]	CBcs CWGN EBee ECtt EHyd ELan EPfP LCro LOPS LRHS MHol MPie NRHS SPoG WCot WMal
- 'Sangria'	CWGN ILea NGdn SBut SPhx SRms XLum XSen
'Morello' **new**	SPad
nepetoides	EPPr NDov
ORANGE NECTAR (Nectar Series)	EBee MPie WCot
'Painted Lady'	ECtt
pallidiflora	SPlb
var. ***neomexicana***	
- - 'Rose Mint'	CDor CSpe
'Pink Pop'	ELan EPfP
'Purple Haze'	CDoC EAJP EBee LRHS MAvo NDov NRHS
'Raspberry Summer'[PBR]	CWGN EBee ECtt EPfP LRHS MHtn NRHS
§ ***rugosa***	CBod ECha GPoy MNHC NAts SPhx SPlb SRms WJek
- f. ***albiflora***	WCAu
- - 'Alabaster'	CDor NDov
- - 'Liquorice White'	CBod ECha ELan EPfP GWyn LRHS MArl MBel NGBl SBls SGbt SMrm SPer SPlb SPoG SRms
- BEELICIOUS PURPLE ('Agapd') **new**	CBod LRHS LSou MMrt
- 'Golden Jubilee'	CBod CRos CSpe EBee EBou ECha ELan EPfP LRHS MAsh MAvo MHol NGdn NLar NRHS NSti SBls SGbt SRms SWvt WJek WSMil
- 'Heronswood Mist'	EBee
- 'Korean Zest'	WCru
- 'Liquorice Blue'	CBod CDor EGrl ELan EPfP GKev LRHS MAsh MBel MSpe NAts NGBl NGdn SBls SGbt SMrm SPer SPoG SRms SSut SWvt WHoo
- 'Little Adder'	CBcs CBod LRHS MHol MTin NDov WGwG WNPC
rupestris	CSpe SPhx XSen
- 'Apache Sunset'	SPlb XSen
'Serpentine'	EBee EWes NLar WGoo
'Spicy'	NDov
'Summer Fiesta'[PBR]	EBee
'Summer Glow'[PBR]	CDor CWGN ECtt EPfP LRHS NDov NLar NRHS SDys SPoG WCot
'Summer Love'[PBR]	ECtt NLar
'Summer Sunset'[PBR]	CDor CWGN EBee LCro LOPS LRHS NRHS
'Tangerine Dreams'	ECtt EPfP LRHS MPie NRHS SCoo
'Tango'	SBls
'Tutti-frutti'	ECtt
'Violet Vision'[PBR]	CWGN ECtt EPfP LCro LOPS MBel MMrt

Agathaea see *Felicia*

Agathis (*Araucariaceae*)

australis	SMad

Agathosma (*Rutaceae*)

capensis **new**	LRHS
ovata	CCCN
- 'Glentana' **new**	LRHS
serpyllacea	CCCN

Agave ✿ (*Asparagaceae*)

sp.	EOli
albomarginata	CDTJ
americana 🏆H2	CAbb CBcs CBen CDow CPla ELan EPfP EShb LPar LSun SArc SChr SCob SEND SEdd SGsty SPalm SPlb SPre SSim SVen SWeb SWvt WCot WGrn

	- 'Marginata' (v) 🏆H2	CAco CBrP CDTJ NQui SEND SVen WCot WSFF WSMil
	- 'Mediopicta' misapplied	see *A. americana* 'Mediopicta Alba'
	- 'Mediopicta' (v) 🏆H2	CDTJ SArc WGrn
§	- 'Mediopicta Alba' (v) 🏆H2	CAbb CBrP CCCN CDTJ CJun CPbh ELan EOli NCft SPalm SPlb WCot WGrn WSMil
	- 'Mediopicta Aurea' (v)	CTtf WCot
	- subsp. ***protamericana***	CDTJ EOli NCft
	- - blue	SPlb
	- 'Striata' (v)	CDTJ EShb WCot
	- 'Variegata' (v) 🏆H2	CAbb CBcs CBen CBod CDow CEme CPbh CSde ELan EOli EPfP EShb LSun NCft NPer SArc SChr SCob SGsty SPalm SPlb SSim SWeb SWvt WBor
	angustifolia	see *A. vivipara* var. *vivipara*
	- var. ***marginata*** hort.	SSim WCot
	applanata	CJun SPlb
	asperrima	CDTJ
§	- subsp. ***maderensis***	SPlb
	atrovirens	WCot
	- var. ***mirabilis***	CDTJ
	attenuata	CDTJ SPalm SPlb
	beauleriana	SPalm
	'Bloodspot'	WCot
	'Blue Brian'	SArc
	boldinghiana	WCot
	bovicornuta	WCot
	bracteosa	CAco CCCN CDTJ WCot
	celsii	see *A. mitis* var. *mitis*
	cerulata subsp. ***nelsonii***	CDTJ
	chrysantha	CAco CCCN CDTJ WCot
	- 'Black Canyon'	WCot
	chrysoglossa	CDTJ
	colimana	see *A. ortgiesiana*
	colorata	CCCN CDTJ CJun WCot
	'Cornelius'	WCot WGrn
	cupreata	CDTJ
	decipiens	SPlb
	deserti	CAco CDTJ CJun WCot
	- var. ***simplex***	WCot
	difformis	CDTJ
	durangensis	SPlb
	elongata	see *A. vivipara* var. *vivipara*
	ensifera	CJun
	felgeri	CDTJ
	ferdinandi-regis	see *A. victoriae-reginae*
	ferox	see *A. salmiana* var. *ferox*
	filifera 🏆H2	CCCN CDTJ CDoC CJun CPbh NCft SChr SPlb SSim WCot
	flexispina	SPlb
	garciae-mendozae	CDTJ
	geminiflora	CCCN CDTJ CJun CPbh EShb
	gentryi	CDTJ SPlb WCot
	ghiesbreghtii	CPbh
	guadalajarana	CDTJ CPbh
	guttata	WCot
	havardiana	CDTJ SPalm XSen
	horrida	CDTJ CJun
	- subsp. ***horrida***	SPlb
	- 'Perotensis'	CDTJ EShb
	hurteri	CDTJ
	impressa	CDTJ WCot
	isthmensis	SPlb
	kerchovei	WCot
	lechuguilla	CDTJ WCot XSen
	lophantha	see *A. univittata*
	- var. ***caerulescens***	see *A. univittata*
	'Macha Mocha'	WCot
	macroacantha 🏆H1c	CDTJ SPalm
	maculosa	SBrt WCot
	marmorata	CJun
	maximilliana	SPlb
	mckelveyana	WCot
	- DJF 1575 from Bagdad, Arizona	WCot
	mitis	CDoC
§	- var. ***mitis***	CDTJ SPlb SSim
	- var. ***mitis* × *variegata***	WCot
	montana	CDTJ CTsd EOli SChr SPlb SPtp XSen
	multifilifera	XSen
§	***obscura***	CDTJ WCot
§	***ortgiesiana***	WCot
	ovatifolia	CDTJ CJun EOli SMad SPalm SPlb WCot XSen
	palmeri	CCCN CDTJ SPlb WCot XSen
	panamana	see *A. vivipara* var. *vivipara*
	parrasana 🏆H2	CDTJ SSim WCot
	parryi 🏆H2	CBod CDTJ CPbh GKev SPlb SPtp SSim WCot XSen
	- var. ***couesii***	CDTJ XSen
	- 'Cream Spike' (v)	CBcs CBod CTsd NCft SEdd SMad SMrm SPad SPalm WCot WGrn WSMil
	- var. ***huachucensis***	CDTJ WCot
	- subsp. ***neomexicana***	CCCN CDTJ SPlb WCot XSen
	- - SB 948 from W of Artesia, New Mexico	WCot
	- 'Ohi-kissho-ten-nishiki' (v)	WCot
	- subsp. ***parryi***	CDTJ WCot WPGP
	- var. ***truncata***	CDTJ SPlb
	- - variegated (v)	WCot
	parviflora 🏆H2	WCot
	polyacantha	see *A. obscura* var. ***xalapensis***
	potatorum 🏆H2	WCot
	- 'Gary Fisher'	WCot
	salmiana	CDTJ SPlb
	- subsp. ***crassispina***	SPlb
§	- var. ***ferox***	CDTJ SArc SChr SPalm SPlb
	scabra	CCCN WCot
	- subsp. ***maderensis***	see *A. asperrima* subsp. *maderensis*
	schidigera	WCot
	- 'Shira-ito-no-ohi' (v)	WCot
	schottii	CDTJ WCot
	'Sharkskin Shoes'	WCot
	shrevei subsp. ***magna***	SPlb
	sileri	WCot
	sisalana	CDTJ
	stictata	WCot
	striata subsp. ***falcata***	WCot
*	- 'Rubra'	CDTJ SPlb WCot
	stricta 🏆H2	CCCN CDTJ NCft WCot
	- 'Nana'	CDTJ NCft SMad
	- 'Rubra'	WCot
	tenuifolia	CPla
	titanota 🏆H1c	SPlb
	toumeyana 🏆H2	CPbh SPlb WCot
	- var. ***bella***	CDTJ
	triangularis	CDTJ
	undulata	WCot
	- 'Chocolate Chips'	WCot
§	***univittata***	CDTJ CJun WCot
	- 'Quadricolor' (v) 🏆H2	CDTJ CPbh NCft SMad SPlb SSim WCot
I	- 'Splendida' (v) **new**	NCft
	utahensis 🏆H3	CDTJ EOli SEND SPlb WCot XSen
	- DJF 1521 from Peach Springs, Arizona	WCot
	- var. ***eborispina***	WCot
	- subsp. ***kaibabensis***	WCot
	variegata	WCot

- B&SWJ 10234 WCru
§ ***victoriae-reginae*** ♀H2 CCCN CDTJ CJun CPbh EOli EShb NCft SChr SPalm SPlb SSim WCot XSen
- dwarf WCot
- variegated (v) CTtf
virginica WCot
§ ***vivipara*** var. ***vivipara*** WCot
wocomahi WCot
xylonacantha CDTJ SChr SPlb WCot
zebra CDTJ

Ageratina (*Asteraceae*)

§ ***altissima*** CDor CMac SMrm
- 'Braunlaub' EBee NBir NLar SHar WCAu
- 'Chocolate' Widely available
- LUCKY MELODY ('Allmelody') CBod LRHS SMad
§ ***aromatica*** SBut
§ ***ligustrina*** CBcs CBod CCht CDoC CExl CKel CMCN CRHN CSde CTri EBee ECha EHed ELan EWoo LRHS MBlu NAts SDix SEND SPer SPoG SRkn SRms WLov WMal WSFF

Ageratum (*Asteraceae*)

'Blue Champion' MPri SCob
corymbosum CSpe EShb
houstonianum 'Blue Danube' ♀H2 LCro LOPS
- 'High Tide Blue' MPri
petiolatum LRHS SGBe SHar WFar

Aglaonema (*Araceae*)

'Jubilee Compacta'[PBR] LCro LOPS

Agrimonia (*Rosaceae*)

eupatoria CBod CHab ENfk GPoy MHer MNHC NAts NMir SRms WHer WWild
* - var. ***alba*** NLar SBut
- 'Cambridge Lace' (v) MAvo WCot

Agropyron (*Poaceae*)

glaucum see *Elymus hispidus*
magellanicum see *Elymus magellanicus*
pubiflorum see *Elymus magellanicus*

Agrostemma (*Caryophyllaceae*)

coronaria see *Lychnis coronaria*
githago CHab LCro LOPS MBow MNHC NBir SRms SVic
- 'Ocean Pearl' CSpe SPhx
- 'Purple Queen' CSpe

Agrostis (*Poaceae*)

calamagrostis see *Stipa calamagrostis*
capillaris CHab SPhx SVic
nebulosa SPhx WCot
stolonifera 'Julia Ann' (v) WCot

Aichryson (*Crassulaceae*)

× ***aizoides*** var. ***domesticum*** 'Variegatum' (v) ♀H1c CDTJ CPbh EBak SIvy SSim WCot
bethencourtianum variegated (v) **new** SEdd

Ailanthus (*Simaroubaceae*)

§ ***altissima*** CBcs CCVT CExl IPap LPar NWea SCob SEND SPlb SWvt
§ - 'Hongye' MBlu
- 'Purple Dragon' see *A. altissima* 'Hongye'
- var. ***tanakae*** CWJ 12452 WCru
- - NMWJ 14522 WCru
glandulosa see *A. altissima*

Ainsliaea (*Asteraceae*)

apiculata MAsh
chapaensis B&SWJ 11732 WCru
latifolia FMWJ 13426 WCru
nervosa B&SWJ 11344 WCru
petelotii FMWJ 13427 WCru
tonkinensis B&SWJ 11819 WCru

Ajania see *Chrysanthemum*

Ajuga (*Lamiaceae*)

genevensis GBin GEdr GWyn LRHS SPhx
incisa EWld
- 'Bikun' (v) CBct EBee NEoE SPoG WCot WFar
- 'Blue Enigma' CExl NLar WFar
- 'Blue Ensign' EHed WSHC
'Little Court Pink' see *A. reptans* 'Purple Torch'
lupulina GEdr
- BO 15-009 **new** GGro
metallica hort. see *A. pyramidalis*
'Pink Lightning' (v) ELan EWTr LRHS NHpl NRHS SRms WCot WFar WHil
'Pink Spires' WFar
§ ***pyramidalis*** EGrI
- 'Metallica Crispa' EBee ELan EWes GBin GJos GKev GWyn NBir NEoE NHol NHpl NLar SRms SWvt WCav WFar WTor XLum
reptans CHab ECtt ENfk GDam GKev GPoy LCro LOPS MBel MHer MNHC NAts SRms
- f. ***albiflora*** CDor WFar
- - 'Alba' CBod EBee EGrI ELon GWyn MBel MRav NBro SRms WFar
- 'Arctic Fox' (v) GEdr NBro SWvt
- 'Argentea' see *A. reptans* 'Variegata'
§ - 'Atropurpurea' CTri ECha EGrI EHyd ELan EPfP GAbr GWyn LCro LOPS MGos MMuc NFav NWad SEND SGol SPlb SRms SWvt WBrk XLum
- BLACK SCALLOP ('Binblasca'[PBR]) Widely available
- 'Blueberry Muffin' ECtt LCro LOPS NHpl
- 'Braunherz' Widely available
- 'Burgundy Glow' (v) Widely available
§ - 'Catlin's Giant' ♀H7 Widely available
- 'Choc Ice' EWTr
- 'Chocolate Chip' see *A. tenorii* 'Valfredda'
- 'Ebony' LSRN
- 'Evening Glow' EBee GJos LRHS WIce
- 'Golden Beauty' (v) LPar SRms WFar
- 'Golden Glow' (v) ELan LRHS NRHS WFar
- 'Harlequin' (v) SWvt
- 'John Pierpoint' SHar
§ - 'Jungle Beauty' MRav
- 'Macrophylla' see *A. reptans* 'Catlin's Giant'
- 'Mahogany' EMor NLar SRms
§ - 'Multicolor' (v) CEme ELan LRHS MAsh MPri NRHS SCob SPlb SPoG SRms SWvt WFar
- 'Pink Elf' CDor GQue MRav NBro
- 'Pink Surprise' MHer NRya WFar
- 'Purple Brocade' NLar
§ - 'Purple Torch' ELon MPie NLar SHar SRms SWvt
- 'Purpurea' see *A. reptans* 'Atropurpurea'
- 'Rainbow' see *A. reptans* 'Multicolor'
- 'Rosea' CBod GWyn MBel SBut WFar XLum
- 'Rowden Amethyst' EBtc WHil

- 'Rowden Royal Purple'	WBrk
- 'Tricolor'	see *A. reptans* 'Multicolor'
§ - 'Variegata' (v)	ECtt LRHS NHpl SPoG SRms WFar WTor
'Rose Glow'	NHpl
'Sparkler' (v)	EMor NHpl WFar
SUGAR PLUM ('Binsugplu'^{PBR}) (v)	ECul ELan EMor MCot
tenorii 'Dixie Chip'	WFar
- PRINCESS NADIA ('Piotrek01') (v) **new**	EMor NLar WNPC
§ - 'Valfredda'	EBee EHyd EPfP EShb EWoo GAbr GBin GKev GQue GWyn LLWG LRHS NLar NRHS SLee SRms SWvt WBrk WFar XLum

Akebia ✿ (*Lardizabalaceae*)

longeracemosa	CRHN EBee LRHS MGil SChF
- B&SWJ 3606	CExl LEdu WCot WCru WPGP
× ***pentaphylla***	CBcs CKel EBee EHyd ELan EPfP LRHS MAsh MGil MRav NChi SPer
quinata	Widely available
- B&SWJ 4425	WCru
- 'Amethyst Glow'	CDoC CKel CRos CWCL EHyd ELon EMil EPfP LRHS MHtn NLar SEle SMad SMrm SPer SPoG
- cream-flowered	CCCN CKel CRHN EBee EHyd EMil EPfP LCro LOPS LPar LRHS MGil MGos MHtn MRav NLar SCob SGsty SMrm SPer SRms SSta SWvt WCru WLov WPGP
- 'Shirobana'	CBcs CWGN MBlu MGil
- 'Silver Bells'	EBee
- 'White Chocolate' 🏆H6	ESwi WCru WSHC
trifoliata	CBcs CRHN EBee EHyd ELan EPfP LRHS MGil MGos SLon
- B&SWJ 5063	WCru
- B&SWJ 14570	WCru

Alangium (*Cornaceae*)

platanifolium	CBcs CExl WPGP
- var. ***macrophyllum***	CCCN EPfP MGil WBor

Albizia (*Fabaceae*)

chinensis	EPfP
distachya	see *Paraserianthes lophantha*
§ ***julibrissin***	CDTJ CGrG CTsd EBee EGrI EHed EPfP IDee IPap LPar LRHS MGil MVil
- NJM 13.018	WPGP
- CHOCOLATE FOUNTAIN ('Ncaj1')	ELan LPar LRHS MTrO NOra WHwl WMat
- 'Evy's Pride' **new**	MTrO WMat
- 'Evy's Purple'	ELan
- OMBRELLA ('Boubri'^{PBR})	ELan MTrO NOra WHwl WMat WPGP
- f. ***rosea*** 🏆H4	CBcs CEme CExl CKel CMCN CWGN CWit ELan EPfP MGil SArc SEND SEdd SEle SIvy SLim SMad SPad SPlb SPoG WLov WPGP
I - 'Rouge Selection'	CKel EPfP SPoG
- 'Shidare'	ELan LRHS MTrO NOra WHwl WMat
- 'Summer Chocolate'^{PBR} 🏆H3	CRos CWGN EHed EHyd ELan EPfP IDee LRHS LSRN MAsh MTrO NOra NRHS SCoo SPoG WHwl WMat
kalkora	SPlb
lophantha	see *Paraserianthes lophantha*

Albuca ✿ (*Asparagaceae*)

sp.	WHil
JCA 15856	WHil
canadensis (L.) F.M. Leight.	EPri NFav WHil
corymbosa **new**	WHil
'Dirk Wallace'	CExl
fastigiata	WHil
glauca	EBee MPie
humilis	CExl CPla EPot MHer WHil
nelsonii	CAvo CPrp EBee MPie
polyphylla **new**	WHil
shawii	CAvo CBod CBor CBro CPrp EAJP EBee EPri ERCP EWld GBin LRHS MACG MHer MHol MPie NSla SChr SCoo SPoG SRms WAvo WGwG WHil WKif
spiralis	GKev
- 'Frizzle Sizzle'	CDoC
wakefieldii	WHil

× *Alcalthaea* (*Malvaceae*)

suffrutescens 'Freedom'	ELan WFar
- 'Parkallee' (d)	CCBP CDor EBee ECha ECtt ELan EPPr GMaP GWyn LPla LRHS MAvo MCot MHol MNrw MPie NLar SPhx WCot WMal XLum
- 'Parkfrieden' (d)	CSpe ECha ECtt MAvo MNrw NLar SPhx XLum
- 'Parkrondell' (d)	CDor ECha ECtt ELan LRHS MAvo MNrw MPie SHar SPhx WCot XLum
- 'Poetry'	ECtt ELan LRHS

Alcea (*Malvaceae*)

ficifolia	LShi MHer WFar WSpi
- pink-flowered **new**	LShi
- yellow-flowered **new**	LShi
froloviana	GGro
'Las Vegas'	WFar
nudiflora	GGro
pallida	XSen
§ ***rosea***	SSal WFar
- 'Blacknight' (Spotlight Series)	CBod ELan EPfP LRHS MHer NLar SCoo SGBe
- Chater's Double Group (d)	EPfP GKev SCob SPoG SRms SVic WFar
- - chamois (d)	EPfP
- - chestnut-brown-flowered (d)	EPfP
- - maroon-flowered (d)	EPfP LRHS SPoG
- - pink-flowered (d)	ELan EPfP
- - red-flowered (d)	ELan EPfP SCob SPoG
- - rose-pink-flowered (d)	LRHS
- - salmon-pink-flowered (d)	EPfP
- - scarlet-flowered (d)	EPfP LRHS SPoG
- - violet-flowered (d)	EPfP
- - white-flowered (d)	ELan EPfP LCro LOPS LRHS SPoG
- - yellow-flowered (d)	EPfP LRHS SPoG SRms
- 'Crème de Cassis'	ELan EPfP
- double scarlet-flowered (d)	LRHS
- Halo Series	WFar WHil
- - 'Halo Apricot'	CRos EHyd EPfP LRHS NRHS SPoG WHoo
- - 'Halo Blush'	CRos EHyd EPfP LRHS NRHS SPoG
- - 'Halo Cerise'	CRos EHyd EPfP LRHS NRHS SPoG WHil
- - 'Halo Cream'	CRos EHyd EPfP LRHS NRHS SPoG
- - 'Halo Red'	EPfP LRHS NRHS SCoo SPoG
- - 'Halo White'	EHyd EPfP LRHS NRHS SPoG
- 'Mars Magic' (Spotlight Series)	CBod EBee ELan EPfP LRHS MHer NLar SCoo SGBe
- 'Nigra'	CKel CSpe ELan EPfP EWoo LCro LOPS LRHS LSRN LShi NFav NGdn SCob SPer SRms WCAu

	- 'Polarstar' (Spotlight Series)	CBod EBee ELan LRHS NLar SCoo SGBe
	- 'Radiant Rose' (Spotlight Series)	CBod ELan EPfP LRHS MHer SCoo SGBe
	- single-flowered	MMuc SRms
	- - pink-flowered	EWoo
	- (Spring Celebrities Series) 'Spring Celebrities Apricot' (d) new	CBod
	- - 'Spring Celebrities Crimson' (d)	CBod
	- - 'Spring Celebrities Lemon' (d)	CBod NRHS
	- - 'Spring Celebrities Pink' (d)	CBod
	- - 'Spring Celebrities White' (d)	NRHS
	- Summer Carnival Group	GQue SRms
	- 'Sunshine' (Spotlight Series)	CBod EBee EPfP LRHS NLar SGBe
	- 'The Watchman'	WHil
§	***rugosa***	CBod EBee LEdu MCot XSen

Alcea × *Althaea* see × *Alcalthaea*

Alchemilla ✿ (*Rosaceae*)

	abyssinica	EBee
	alpina misapplied	see *A. conjuncta*, *A. plicatula*
	alpina ambig.	EGrI EMor MCot
	alpina L.	EBee ELan EMor EPfP GPoy GQue LEdu LRHS MBel MMuc MRav NBir NChi SEND SRms WFar WPGP WSHC
§	***conjuncta***	CDor CMac CSpe EBee ECha EGrI ELan EPfP GAbr GKev GLog GMaP GWyn LEdu MHer MRav NBid NGrd NRya NSti SPer SPlb SRms SRot WCAu WHoo
	ellenbeckii	EGrI NChi WTor
	epipsila	EBee ELan EPfP EShb LRHS NLar SPhx
	erythropoda ♀H7	Widely available
	- 'Alba'	LRHS
	- (Cepa Group) 'Alma'	LSun
	- from Turkish	ECha
	faeroensis	EGrI XLum
	- var. ***pumila***	EBee WAbe
	fissa	EBee
	glaucescens	CNat
	hoppeana misapplied	see *A. plicatula*
	iniquiformis	EBee EGrI
	'Irish Silk'	CBod
	mollis ♀H7	Widely available
I	- 'Auslese'	SWvt
	- 'Robustica'	GQue LSun MMuc SEND SPlb WFar
	- 'Thriller'	CBod EHyd EPfP LRHS NRHS WFar
	- 'Variegata' (v)	CNat
	'Mr Poland's Variety'	see *A. venosa*
	pedata	NChi
§	***plicatula***	NLar WCav
	saxatilis	CBod EBou MACG NLar SHar
	sericata 'Gold Strike'	CBod EBee ECtt ELan EMor EPfP GLog LRHS NRHS SCoo SHar SWvt
	straminea	EBee MRav
	valdehirsuta	EBee
§	***venosa***	EBee SHar SMHy
	vetteri	EBee NFav WHrl
	vulgaris agg.	GQue
	vulgaris misapplied	see *A.xanthochlora*
§	***xanthochlora***	GPoy NLar SRms WHer

alecost see *Tanacetum balsamita*

Alectryon (*Sapindaceae*)

excelsus	CBcs

Alisma (*Alismataceae*)

lanceolatum	LLWG
plantago-aquatica	CBen CHab CPud CWat MWts NPer WMAq WWtn
- var. ***parviflorum***	LLWG SPlb WWtn

Allagoptera (*Arecaceae*)

arenaria	SPalm

Allamanda (*Apocynaceae*)

cathartica	CCCN

Alliaria (*Brassicaceae*)

petiolata	CCBP GPoy MNHC SPhx WHer WSFF

Allium ✿ (*Alliaceae*)

	RCB AM 21	WCot
	SSSE 250	GEdr
§	***acuminatum***	GKev NRog
	acutiflorum	GKev LHWs NRog
	aflatunense misapplied	see *A. hollandicum*
	aflatunense ambig.	ECha EGrI LRHS LSRN NRog SCob SDeJ
	akaka	NRog
	albidum	see *A. denudatum*
	albopilosum	see *A. cristophii*
	alexeianum	NRog
	altissimum	NRog
	- 'Album' new	GKev
	- 'Goliath'	GKev LRHS NRHS NRog WCot
	amabile	see *A. mairei* var. *amabile*
	'Ambassador' ♀H5	CAvo CMea CRos ECul ERCP GKev ILea LCro LHWs LOPS LRHS MPtr NRHS NRog SDir SDix SPer WCot WFar WPhe
	amethystinum	GKev NRog
	- 'Red Mohican'PBR	EBee ERCP LEdu LHWs MBriF MNrw MPtr SDeJ WCot WHoo WPhe
	ampeloprasum	ECha GKev SDix SPlb WHer WShi
	- var. ***babingtonii***	CAgr GKev GPoy LEdu NRog SRms WHer WKor WPGP WShi
	- - 'Green Drops'	GKev LHWs
§	- 'Elephant'	LCro LEdu LOPS WCot
	- 'Hairy Friend' new	LHWs
	- 'Pink Lady'	GKev LHWs
	- 'Purple Mystery'	GKev LHWs WCot
	- 'Rose Picture' new	LHWs
	- 'White Cloud'	EBee ELan GKev LHWs
	amphibolum	GKev NRog
	amplectens	NRog
	- 'Graceful Beauty'	EBee ELan EPot ERCP LCro LOPS MBow NLar SDeJ SDir SPer
§	***angulosum***	CAvo CMiW GKev LEdu MHol MPtr NHpl NRog SDix WCot WMal XSen
	aschersonianum	SDeJ WCot
	atropurpureum	EBee ECha ECul ELan ERCP EWoo GBin GKev GWyn LCro LHWs LOPS LRHS NRHS NRog SDeJ SDir SPhx WCot
	atropurpureum × ***schubertii***	SGBe
	atroviolaceum W&B BG A-5	WCot
	austroiranicum new	NRog
	azureum	see *A. caeruleum*

	backhousianum	NRog
	- 'Green Craze'	GKev LHWs
	barsczewskii 'Aman Kutan' **new**	NRog
	'Beau Regard' 🏆H7	CWCL EBee ELan ERCP GKev LCro LOPS LRHS NLar NRog SDir
	beesianum misapplied	see *A. cyaneum*
	beesianum W.W. Sm.	CMiW CTtf EBee GRum LEdu NBir NHpl
	- from Sichuan, China	CMiW
	bisceptrum	NRog
	bodeanum	see *A. cristophii*
	bolanderi	GKev
	- var. ***mirabile*** **new**	NRog
	'Bolero'	NRog
	brevicaule	GKev
	brevistylum	GKev
	bulgaricum	see *Nectaroscordum siculum* subsp. *bulgaricum*
§	***caeruleum***	CAvo CBor CDor EBee EGrI EPfP EPot ERCP EWoo GKev LCro LHWs LOPS LRHS MGos MNrw NBir NLar NPer NRHS NRog NRya SDeJ SDir SDix SPhx WCot
	- ***azureum***	see *A. caeruleum*
	caesium 🏆H5	ERCP GKev NRog WCot
	- AQUAMARINE	see *A. caesium* 'Pskem's Beauty'
§	- 'Pskem's Beauty'	NRog WCot
	- 'Summer Sky' **new**	GKev
	- 'Wine' **new**	GKev
	- 'Zaamin' **new**	NRog
	callimischon subsp. ***callimischon***	GKev NRog
	- subsp. ***haemostictum***	NRog WCot
	'Caméléon'	EBee ERCP GKev IPot LCro LHWs LOPS LRHS NRHS NRog WCot
	campanulatum	NRog
	canadense	CAvo SHar WKor
	candolleanum	GKev NRog
§	***carinatum***	WHer
§	- subsp. ***pulchellum*** 🏆H5	CBro CSpe CTtf ECha EGrI EPot GKev MHer MMuc MNrw NBir NRog SDeJ SPhx WThu
	- - f. ***album*** 🏆H5	CBro CSpe CTtf ECha EGrI GKev LEdu LSun MNrw NBir SPhx
§	***carolinianum***	WCav
	caspium subsp. ***baissunense*** **new**	NRog
	cepa	CBod SVic
	- Aggregatum Group	CLau GPoy SRms
	- Proliferum Group	CAgr CLau EWhm GPoy LEdu MHer MNHC SRms WHer WJek WKor XAbr
	- var. ***viviparum***	GKev LHWs
	cernuum	Widely available
§	- 'Hidcote' 🏆H6	EBee EDAr WKif XSen
	- 'Major'	see *A. cernuum* 'Hidcote'
	- pink-flowered	CLau
I	- 'Purple King'	GKev
	- 'White Dwarf'	CBor CMea ELan EPot GKev LHWs
	- 'White Master'	CAvo GKev LHWs
	- 'White Max'	LHWs
	- white-flowered	LEdu
	chinense	CAgr GPoy LEdu WFar
	- 'October Mist'	LEdu
	cirrhosum	see *A. carinatum* subsp. *pulchellum*
	colchicifolium	NRog
	convallarioides	GKev NRog
	cowanii	see *A. neapolitanum* Cowanii Group
	crenulatum	NRog
	crispum	NRog
§	***cristophii*** 🏆H5	Widely available
	cupanii	GKev NRog
	cupuliferum	GKev NRog
	curtum RCB RL 13	WCot
§	***cyaneum*** 🏆H5	CMiW CTtf EBlo EPot GArf GEdr GKev LBee MHer NHpl NRog NRya WCot WFar
	cyathophorum	CBor CSpe
§	- var. ***farreri***	CBro CMiW CTtf EPPr EPot GKev LEdu LHWs MHer MNrw NHpl NRya WCot WThu
	cyrilli	GKev
	daghestanicum	GKev
	darwasicum	WCot
	- 'Darwas Wonder' **new**	NRog
	decipiens	GKev
	- subsp. ***decipiens*** **new**	NRog
	- subsp. ***quercetorum*** **new**	NRog
§	***denudatum***	GKev
	diabaloense	NRog
	dolichostylum	GKev
§	***drummondii***	LRHS NRHS
	'Dutchman' **new**	GKev
	egorovae **new**	NRog
	elatum	see *A. macleanii*
	elburzense	NRog
	'Emir'	GKev
	ericetorum	GKev WCot
	- PAB 1009	LEdu
	eriocoleum **new**	GKev
	'Eros'	CBor CTtf EBee LCro LOPS SDir
	falcifolium	LHWs NRog WCot
	farreri	see *A. cyathophorum* var. *farreri*
	fetisowii	NRog
	fimbriatum	NRog
	'Firmament'	ECha ERCP GKev SDeJ WCot
	fistulosum	CAgr CHby CLau ENfk EWhm GKev GPoy LCro LHWs LOPS MHer MNHC MPri NRog SRms SVic WCot WGwG WJek
	- red-flowered	WHil
	fistulosum × ***pskemense***	GKev LHWs
	flavum 🏆H5	CBor CBro CTtf ECha EPPr EPot ERCP NHpl SDeJ SPhx WThu XSen
	- subsp. ***flavum***	GKev NRog SPhx
	- - var. ***minus***	MMuc NRog SEND
	- subsp. ***tauricum***	GKev SPhx WCot
	'Forelock'	ERCP GBin GKev LHWs MNrw NRog WCot
	forrestii	WCot
	geyeri	EBee GKev
	giganteum	Widely available
	- 'Twinkling Stars'	ERCP GKev
	'Gimli' **new**	NRog
	'Gladiator' 🏆H6	CAvo CRos CWCL EBee ERCP EShb EWoo GKev GMaP ILea LCro LHWs LOPS LRHS LSun MACG MPtr NRHS NRog SDeJ SDir SGBe WPhe
	glandulosum **new**	GKev
	glaucum	see *A. senescens* subsp. *glaucum*
	'Globemaster' 🏆H6	Widely available
	'Globus'	EBee GKev NRog
	grande **new**	NRog
	guttatum subsp. ***dalmaticum***	GKev
	- subsp. ***sardoum***	GKev
	gypsaceum	NRog
	haemanthoides	WCot
	'Hair'	see *A. vineale* 'Hair'
	heldreichii	NRog
*	***hirtifolium*** var. ***album***	EBee GKev NRog

	Name	Suppliers
§	***hollandicum***	CArg CAvo ECha GKev LCro LOPS NRog SCob SPlb WFar XLum
	- 'Purple Sensation' 🏆H6	Widely available
	- 'Purple Surprise'	NBir WCot
	hookeri	GGro GKev LEdu
	- ACE 2430	LEdu WCot
	- var. ***muliense***	GEdr LEdu SPhx
	- 'Zorami'	CAgr ELan LEdu WMal WPGP
	huber-morathii	CBor EBee
	humile	GEdr
	hyalinum	CAvo GKev LHWs
	- pink-flowered	WCot
	'In Orbit'	LPla LSou WNPC
§	***insubricum*** 🏆H5	CMea CSpe EDAr GBin GEdr LRHS MNrw NBir NHpl NRHS NRya
	'Jackpot'	CWCL EBee ERCP MPtr NRog
	jajlae	see *A. rotundum* subsp. *jajlae*
	jesdianum	GKev
	- 'Akbulak' 🏆H5	EBee LHWs NRog
	- 'Early Emperor' 🏆H5	CAvo CWCL EBee ERCP GKev LRHS NRHS NRog
	- 'Michael Hoog'	see *A. rosenorum* 'Michael H. Hoog'
	- 'Pendjikent' **new**	NRog
	- 'Per Wendelbo' **new**	GKev NRog
	- 'Purple King'	LRHS NRHS NRog
	- 'Shing'	GKev
	- 'White Empress' PBR	EBee
	- white-flowered	NRog
	jodanthum **new**	NRog
	'Judith'	WCot
	'Judith's Findling'	WCot
	kansuense	see *A. sikkimense*
	karataviense	EBee ECha ELan EPot EWTr EWoo GAbr GKev LCro LOPS LRHS MBow NBir NHpl NLar NRHS NRog SCob SDeJ SWvt WCAu
	- subsp. ***henrikii***	NRog
	- 'Ivory Queen'	CAvo EBee ECha ERCP GKev LCro LOPS LRHS LSRN NHpl NLar NRHS NRog SDeJ SDir SPlb XSte
	- pink-flowered	GKev
	- 'Red Giant' **new**	NRog
	kharputense	NRog
	kokanicum	GRum
	komarovianum	see *A. thunbergii*
	komarovii	NRog
	kwakense **new**	NRog
	lacunosum var. ***davisiae***	NRog
	ledebourianum	GKev
	lemmonii	GKev NRog
	lenkoranicum	CAvo WCot
	lipskyanum **new**	GKev NRog
	litvinovii	EBee GKev NRog SPhx WCot WFar
	longifolium	GKev
	loratum	EBee
	'Lucy Ball'	ERCP GKev LRHS NBir NLar NRHS NRog SDeJ
§	***lusitanicum***	CBro CCBP CLau CSpe ECha ERCP EShb GKev GMaP IPot LEdu LHWs MBros MHol NDov SDix SMHy SRms WGoo XLum XSen XSte
	- 'Lisa Blue'	GKev LEdu LHWs
	- 'Lisa Green' **new**	LEdu LPla
	luteolum **new**	GKev
§	***macleanii***	EBee GKev LRHS NRHS NRog
	- 'His Excellency'	CAvo EBee ERCP GKev LRHS NRog
	macranthum	CSpe EBee GKev NHpl NRog SBrt
	- S&L 5369 **new**	GGro
	macrostemon var. ***uratense***	GKev
	mairei	EHyd LRHS MMuc NRHS NRya
§	- var. ***amabile***	GEdr LEdu NRya NSla WThu
	- - dark-flowered	CBor
	maximowiczii	GKev LHWs NHpl NRog
	- white-flowered	GKev
	'Mercurius' PBR	EBee GKev LRHS NRHS NRog SDeJ SPhx WCot
	'Metallic Shine'	GKev SDir SPhx
	meteoricum	CTtf GKev WCot
	'Miami'	CRos EBee ECul ERCP GKev LHWs LRHS NRHS NRog SDeJ SPhx
	'Millennium'	CBod GMaP LCro LOPS LPla LRHS LSou MHol NDov SHar WCot WGoo WHoo WMal WNPC
	minutiflorum **new**	NRog
	moly	CAgr CWCL EWld GKev GQue LCro LOPS MBow MRav NRya SDeJ SIvy SRms WCav XLum
	- 'Jeannine' 🏆H6	EBee EPot GBin GKev LRHS NRHS NRog SDix
	'Mont Blanc'	CRos EBee ELan ERCP GBin GKev ILea LRHS MACG NLar NRHS NRog SDir
	monticola **new**	NRog
	moschatum	GKev
	multibulbosum	see *A. nigrum*
	murrayanum misapplied	see *A. unifolium*
	murrayanum Regel	see *A. acuminatum*
	narcissiflorum misapplied	see *A. insubricum*
§	***narcissiflorum*** Vill.	CSpe LEdu MNrw NSla
	neapolitanum	CAgr GKev LRHS NRHS NRog SRms WKor XLum
§	- Cowanii Group	GKev LCro LOPS LRHS NRHS NRog SDeJ SPhx WCot
§	***neriniflorum***	NSla
	'Nevsar' **new**	NRog
	nevskianum	EPot GKev LHWs NRog
§	***nigrum***	CArg CAvo CBro CKel ECha EPfP EPot ERCP EWoo GKev GWyn LCro LHWs LOPS LRHS MCot MPtr NBir NPer NRHS NRog SDeJ SDir SPhx WCot WPhe
	- f. ***roseum***	CBro
	nutans	EWhm GKev LEdu LHWs MHer SRms WHal WJek
	- 'Caroline'	LEdu LHWs WGoo
	- 'Esmee' **new**	GKev LEdu LHWs
§	***obliquum***	CAvo CBor CBro CSpe ECha EGrI EPri ERCP GEdr GKev LCro LOPS LPla MBriF MMuc NRog SDeJ SPhx WCot WMal
	ochotense	GKev LPla WCot
	odorum L.	see *A. ramosum* L.
	'Okra' **new**	GKev
	oleraceum	WHer
	olympicum	GKev
	opacum **new**	GKev
§	***oreophilum***	CRos ECha GJos GKev LCro LOPS LRHS NRHS NRog SRms
	- 'Agalik Giant'	NRog
	- 'Kusavli Curl' **new**	NRog
	- 'Purple Gem' **new**	NRog
	- 'Samur'	WCot
	- 'Sulev's Dwarf' **new**	NRog
	- 'Zwanenburg' 🏆H6	EPot
	orientale	GKev
	'Ostara'	ERCP GKev MPtr
	ostrowskianum	see *A. oreophilum*
	ovalifolium var. ***leuconeurum***	GEdr
	pallens	NBir
§	***paniculatum***	GKev NRog WCot

* - var. ***minor***	GKev
paradoxum	LEdu NBir
- var. ***normale*** ♀H5	CBro EPot EWld GKev NBir WCot
parciflorum	GKev
parvum	NRog
pedemontanum	see *A. narcissiflorum* Vill.
pendulinum	GKev
'Pinball Wizard'	CAvo EBee ECul EHyd ERCP GKev LCro LHWs LOPS LRHS MPtr NLar NRHS NRog
'Ping Pong'	ECul GKev MPtr NLar
'Pink Jewel'	CAvo ERCP GKev IPot SDeJ WCot
platycaule	WCot
plummerae	EBee GKev
'Powder Puff' ♀H5	CAvo GKev MMrt
prattii	EBee WCot
protensum	NRog
przewalskianum	SGro
psebaicum new	GKev
pseudowinklerianum new	NRog
pskemense	GKev LEdu NLar WCot
pulchellum	see *A. carinatum* subsp. *pulchellum*
'Purple Rain' ♀H5	CAvo CBro CWCL ECha ELan ERCP LCro LHWs LOPS LRHS MPtr NRHS NRog SDeJ SGBe WCot WHoo WPhe
'Purple Suze'	GKev IPot LHWs
pyrenaicum misapplied	see *A. angulosum*
pyrenaicum Costa & Vayr.	XSen
ramosum Jacq.	see *A. obliquum*
§ ***ramosum*** L.	GKev LEdu
'Red Eye'	LCro LOPS
'Rien Poortvliet'	GKev
roborowskianum	GKev
robustum	NRog
rosenbachianum misapplied	see *A. stipitatum*
rosenbachianum Regel	CBro LRHS NRHS NRog
- 'Album'	CRos GKev NRHS WCot
- 'Michael Hoog'	see *A. rosenorum* 'Michael H. Hoog'
§ ***rosenorum*** 'Michael H. Hoog' ♀H5	EPot NRog
roseum	CMea CRos GKev LCro LOPS LRHS MBow NRHS NRog SDeJ XLum
rotundum	GKev
§ - subsp. ***jajlae***	NRog
'Round 'n' Purple' ♀H5	CAvo ERCP GKev LCro LOPS NRog
rupestre	GKev
saralicum new	NRog
sarawschanicum	NRog
- 'Chinoro'	NRog
sativum	ENfk LOPS MPri SPoG SRms
- 'Elephant'	see *A. ampeloprasum* 'Elephant'
- var. ***ophioscorodon***	GPoy SPlb WKor
saxatile	GKev WCot
scabriflorum new	NRog
schmitzii	GKev LEdu WPGP
schoenoprasum	Widely available
- f. ***albiflorum***	CCBP CLau ECha EWhm GKev LEdu LHWs MHer NBir SRms XLum
- 'Black Isle Blush'	GPoy LEdu LPla MBriF MHer WGoo
- 'Cha Cha'	MBriF WHil WJek
- 'Colesbourne Giant'	EBee LEdu
- 'Corsican White'	EBee LEdu XSen
- dwarf, white-flowered	SRms
- 'Elbe'	LEdu
- 'Evergreen'	CLau
- fine-leaved	CLau
- 'Forescate'	ECha EWhm EWoo GKev LEdu LHWs LRHS LSou MHer MRav NBir NRHS SRms WJek XLum
- 'Glowing Amethyst'	GKev
- 'Grande'	CLau
- medium-leaved	CLau MPri
- 'Pink Bere'	LEdu WPGP
- 'Pink Perfection'	GPoy LEdu MHer
- 'Polar Bere'	LEdu WPGP
- 'Polyvert'	CLau
- 'Profusion'	see *A. schoenoprasum* 'Sterile'
- 'Rising Star'	XSen
- 'Shining Silver'	LEdu
- var. ***sibiricum***	SDix WShi
- 'Silver Chimes'	CBor EWhm MRav
- 'Staro'	CLau
§ - 'Sterile'	LEdu
- thick-leaved	CLau SRms
schubertii	CAvo CBod CSpe EGrI EHyd ELan EPfP EPot ERCP EShb EWTr GKev LCro LHWs LOPS LRHS MPtr NRHS NRog SCoo SDeJ SPer SPhx WCot WFar WPhe
- 'Magic'	EWhm
scorodoprasum 'Art'	CRos ERCP GKev LRHS NRHS
- subsp. ***jajlae***	see *A. rotundum* subsp. *jajlae*
- 'Passion'	CRos LRHS NRHS NRog
- 'Purple Caila'	GKev
- subsp. ***scorodoprasum***	NRog
senescens ♀H6	CBod CBro CTri EBee EPot LEdu LHWs LRHS MBel MRav NRHS SPtp SRms WBrk WCAu XSen
§ - subsp. ***glaucum***	CAvo CMea CMiW CSpe EBlo ECha EDAr EWTr GKev LEdu LPla LRHS MACG MHer MHol NDov NGdn NLar NRya SEND WCot WHoo XSen
- subsp. ***senescens***	EGrI GKev LEdu WPGP
shelkovnikovii	NRog
sibthorpianum	see *A. paniculatum*
siculum	see *Nectaroscordum siculum*
§ ***sikkimense***	CBor CSpe EDAr EWTr GArf GEdr GKev GQue MHer MMuc NHpl NSla WCot WFar
'Silver Spring'	EPot ERCP GKev LCro LOPS SDeJ
siskiyouense	NRog
sivasicum new	GKev NRog
sphaerocephalon ♀H6	Widely available
- subsp. ***arvense***	NRog WCot
'Spider'	EPot ERCP GKev NRog SPhx WCot WHoo
I ***splendens*** var. ***kurilense***	GEdr
stamineum W&B BGF-2	WCot
staticiforme	GKev
'Statos'	EBee GKev LRHS MPtr NRHS NRog WCot WPhe
stellatum	LRHS NRHS WGwG
stellerianum	GKev
- var. ***kurilense***	NRya WAbe WThu
'Stipineva' new	NRog
§ ***stipitatum***	GKev NRog WCot
- 'Album'	NRog
- 'Glory of Pamir'	NRog
- 'Mars'	EBee LRHS NRHS NRog SDix
- 'Mount Everest' ♀H5	CAvo CBod CBro CRos ECul EPfP EPot ERCP EShb EWoo GBin GKev GMaP GWyn ILea LCro LHWs LOPS LRHS LSRN MPtr NLar NRHS NRog SDeJ SDir SDix SPer SPhx WPhe
- 'Pink Ball' new	NRog
- 'Pink Globe' new	NRog
- 'Titan' new	NRog
- 'Violet Beauty' ♀H5	CAvo CRos CWCL EWhm LCro LHWs LOPS LRHS MHtn NLar NRHS WCot WPhe

- 'White Giant'	CRos CWCL EBee GKev LEdu LHWs LRHS MPtr NRHS NRog SArc
stracheyi	WCot
strictum Schrad.	ITim
struzlianum new	NRog
suaveolens	MMuc
subhirsutum	GKev
subvillosum	GKev
'Sugar Melt' new	GKev
'Summer Beauty'	see *A. lusitanicum*
'Summer Drummer'	ECha EPfP ERCP GKev LHWs LRHS MBros NRog SDeJ SDir WCot
'Sweet Discovery'	NRog
taquetii	see *A. thunbergii*
tardans	GKev
tauricola	GKev
texanum	GKev
§ ***thunbergii*** ♀H5	CTtf MHer NBir NRya WAbe
- PAB 3821	LEdu
- 'Album'	LEdu NRya WAbe
- 'Ozawa'	GEdr SMHy SRms WCot WFar
tibeticum	see *A. sikkimense*
tolmiei var. ***platyphyllum***	NRog
trifoliatum new	GKev
tripedale	CAvo CBro EPot ERCP GKev
triquetrum	ELan EPot GKev LEdu MBow NBir SEND WCot WFar WHer
* ***tschikatschevii*** new	NRog
tschimganicum	EBee
tuberosum	Widely available
- B&SWJ 8881	WCru
- purple/mauve-flowered	CHby CLau
- 'White Dwarf'	SPhx WCot
tuncelianum	GKev LHWs NRog WCot
'Turkish Delight' new	NRog
ubipetrense new	NRog
§ ***unifolium*** ♀H5	CAvo CWCL EBee EPot ERCP EWoo GKev GWyn LCro LOPS MRav NBir NPer NQui NRog SDeJ SPhx SRms WCot WGwG
ursinum	CHab CHby CLau CTtf ENfk EWhm GKev GPoy LCro LEdu LOPS MHer MNHC MPri NAts NPoe NRog SMad SPlb SRms SVic WFar WKor WSFF WShi XAbr XLum
- 'Golden Fleece'	CTtf WCot
validum NNS 06-41	WCot
victorialis	NRog
- 'Cantabria'	EBee GKev
vineale	GQue WHer WJek
- 'Dready'	ERCP GKev
§ - 'Hair'	CRos ELan ERCP LRHS NBir NPer NRHS NRog SDeJ
violaceum	see *A. carinatum*
virgunculae	CMea EDAr GEdr
- f. ***albiflorum***	GEdr
wallichii	CSpe EBee EWes GArf GGro GKev LEdu NBir NChi WCot
- CLD 1500	LEdu NBid
- PAB 2976	LEdu WPGP
- PAB 9191	LEdu
- dark-flowered	CTtf GBin WCot WFar
winklerianum	GKev
woronowii	NRog
zaprjagajevii	WCot
zebdanense	EWoo GKev NRog

almond see *Prunus dulcis*

Alniphyllum (*Styracaceae*)

eberhardtii FMWJ 13121	WCru
fortunei FMWJ 13013	WCru

Alnus ✿ (*Betulaceae*)

cordata ♀H6	CBcs CBod CCVT CLnd CMCN CMac CSBt CTri ELan EPfP LBuc LMaj LPar MGos MMuc MVil NRog NWea SCob SEND SEWo SPer SPlb WMat WMou WTSh
cremastogyne	EBtc
fauriei	GKev
firma	CSto
glutinosa	CArg CBcs CCVT CHab CLnd CMac CSBt CTri EPfP GBin GDam IPap LBuc LMaj LPar MGos NRog NWea SCob SEWo SPer WMat WMou WSFF WTSh
- 'Aurea'	CEnd MGos MTrO NLar WCot
- 'Imperialis' ♀H7	CCVT CDoC CEnd CLnd CMac EBee ELan EPfP EWTr IDee IPap LRHS MBlu MMuc MTrO NLar NOra NOrn NWea SCob SEND SGol SMad SPer WMat WMou WTSh
- 'Laciniata'	CCVT GKev IPap MGos NLar NWea SCob
- 'Pyramidalis'	MBlu
hirsuta	GKev
incana	CAco CBcs CCVT CLnd CMCN LBuc LMaj LPar MGos NLar NRog NWea SCob SPer WMat WTSh
- 'Aurea' ♀H7	CBcs CCVT CEnd CLnd CMac EBee ELan EPfP GBin IArd IPap LMaj LPar LRHS MBlu MGos MRav NLar NOra NOrn NPoe NRog NWea SCob SEWo SGol SPer SPoG WMat
- 'Laciniata'	LPar NLar NOrn NWea SCoo WFar WMou
- 'Pendula'	WMou
japonica	MBlu
maximowiczii	CSto GKev MVil
- from Ulleungdo, South Korea	WCru
nitida	EBtc
oregana	see *A. rubra*
pendula B&SWJ 10895	WCru
rhombifolia	EBtc
§ ***rubra***	CMCN ELan MCoo NWea WMat WTSh
- f. ***pinnatisecta***	CMCN MBlu NRog
serrulata	CMCN GKev
sieboldiana	GKev LRHS MVil WCru
× ***spaethii***	LMaj LPar MBlu
subcordata NJM 13.009	EBee WPGP
viridis	CAgr CSto MCoo NWea WTSh
- subsp. ***sinuata***	CAgr

Alocasia (*Araceae*)

× ***amazonica*** 'Bambino Arrow'	CDoC
- 'Polly'	CDoC LCro LOPS
'Calidora'	CDTJ
'Dragon Scale'	LCro LOPS
lauterbachiana	LCro LOPS
macrorrhizos	CDTJ CTsd
'Portodora'	CDTJ
wentii	CDTJ

Aloe ✿ (*Asphodelaceae*)

arborescens	CDTJ CDoC CPbh EShb NCft SEND SIvy SPlb SSim WABo
- 'Variegata' (v) ♀H1c	CPbh EShb SRms

aristata ♀H3	CBcs CBen CBod CCht CDoC NCft SArc SBls SChr SEND SEdd SIvy SPad SPalm SPlb SSim WABo XLum
- 'Cathedral Peak'	SChr
- COSMO ('Green Pearl'PBR)	EPfP SMad SPad
barbadensis	see *A. vera*
barberae	CCCN CPbh
'Bedford's Beau'	NCft
'Brass Hat' **new**	NCft
brevifolia ♀H2	EShb SArc SIvy SSim
broomii	CCCN CPbh SPlb
buettneri	EShb
camperi 'Maculata'	SEND
ciliaris	EShb SChr
'Cleopatra'	LSun SEdd WCot
cooperi	CCCN CDTJ WSMil
deltoideodonta	NCft
dichotoma	CAbb SPlb
ecklonis	CCCN SPlb
ferox	CAbb CBod CCCN CDTJ CPbh CTrC
fosteri	CDTJ
greatheadii var. ***davyana***	SChr SPlb WHil
haworthioides ♀H1c	SIvy
humilis	CDoC SChr
jucunda	NCft
juvenna	SRms
maculata	CDTJ
marlothii	CAbb CCCN SPlb
microstigma	CCCN
'Midnight Exchange'	NCft
mitriformis	NGBl SChr SEND SPalm
mutabilis	SEND
peglerae	NCft SRms
petricola	CAbb
plicatilis ♀H2	CCCN CDTJ EShb
polyphylla ♀H3	CCCN CDTJ CPbh
pratensis	CCCN CDTJ
rauhii ♀H1b	CPbh SIvy SSim
reitzii	CAbb CPbh NCft SPlb
'Snowflake'	EShb
somaliensis ♀H1b	NCft
squarrosa	CDoC NCft
striata	CBcs CCCN CPbh EShb SPlb SSim
striatula ♀H3	CBrP CDTJ CSde CTrC ETod IBlr IKel LEdu SArc SChr SEND SPlb SVen WABo WCot WMal WSMil
- var. ***caesia***	WPGP
succotrina	CAbb
tenuior	EShb
variegata (v) ♀H1c	CBen EShb LSun SSim
§ ***vera*** ♀H1c	CBod CCBP CCCN CCht CDoC ELan GPoy LCro LOPS LPar MBros MHer MNHC MPri NPer SChr SEND SEdd SMad SMrm SPalm SPlb SPre SRms SSim SVic WSFF XAbr
'White Beauty'	EShb SPad
wickensii	SPlb
yavellana	SPlb

Aloe × *Haworthia* see × *Alworthia*

Aloinopsis (*Aizoaceae*)

lueckhoffii	SSim
rosulata	SSim
spathulata	GEdr

Alonsoa (*Scrophulariaceae*)

'Bright Spark'	CSpe
incisifolia	CCCN CSpe
meridionalis	CBod CCCN
- 'Rebel'	SCoo SRkn
- 'Shell Pink'	CBod
'Pink Beauty'	CSpe
warscewiczii	CCCN
- 'Peachy-keen'	CSpe

Alopecurus (*Poaceae*)

§ ***magellanicus***	GBin
pratensis	CHab
- 'Aureovariegatus' (v)	CTri EShb GMaP NBid SPer SRms
- 'Aureus'	NBro SPlb

Alophia (*Iridaceae*)

lahue	see *Herbertia lahue*

Aloysia (*Verbenaceae*)

chamaedryfolia	EPfP
citriodora	see *A. citrodora*
§ ***citrodora*** ♀H3	Widely available
- 'Spilsbury Mint'	CRos ELan EPfP LRHS MHer
gratissima	WJek
triphylla	see *A. citrodora*

Alpinia (*Zingiberaceae*)

japonica	CExl LEdu XSte
- B&SWJ 8889	ESwi WCru
- PAB 6441	LEdu
zerumbet 'Variegata' (v)	XSte

Alsobia (*Gesneriaceae*)

§ ***dianthiflora***	WDib
§ 'San Miguel'	WDib

Alstroemeria ✿ (*Alstroemeriaceae*)

'Adonis'PBR	SAlS WViv
'Aimi'	CTtf EGrI MNrw SAlS SWvt WViv
'Alexis'PBR	SAlS WViv
'Amarillo'	WViv
'Andez Rose' **new**	CDor
'Andez Vanilla' **new**	CDor
'Angelina'	SWvt
'Apollo' ♀H4	EHyd ELan MNrw NBir NRHS SAlS SWvt WViv
'Arthur' (Maxi Series)	SAlS
'Athena'	WViv
aurantiaca	see *A. aurea*
§ ***aurea***	GWyn MRav SRms XLum
- 'Cally Apricot'	WMal
- 'Lutea'	GKev NLar SDeJ SPlb WPav
- 'Orange King'	EGrI ELan EPfP GKev NLar SDeJ
'Authion' (Garden Series)	SAlS
'Avanti'	EHyd ELan LRHS NRHS SAlS WViv
'Avrillé' (Garden Series)	SAlS
'Baugé' (Garden Series)	SAlS
'Béatrice' (Midi Series)	SAlS
'Blushing Bride'	SAlS SWvt WMal WViv
'Bodega'PBR	WViv
'Bolero'	WViv
'Bonanza'	SAlS WViv
brasiliensis	WCot WSHC WViv XLum
- 'Cally Star' (v)	EBee EPPr NLar
'Briançon' (Garden Series)	SAlS
'Cahors' (Planet Series) ♀H4	LCro LOPS
'Candy'	SAlS WViv
'Caroline' (Midi Series)	EGrI
'Catherine' (Little Miss Series)	WViv
'Charles' (Maxi Series)	SAlS
'Charlotte' (Mini Series)	EGrI
'Charm'	SAlS SWvt WSpi WViv
'Chi Chi'	WCot
'Chinon' (Garden Series)	SAlS

§ 'Christina'[PBR] (Little Miss Series)	EGrI ELan LRHS NRHS SAlS SWvt WViv
'Christine' (Midi Series)	SAlS
'Christine Marsh'	WViv
'Cindy'	WViv
'Coronet' ♀H4	WViv
'Dandy Candy'	EHyd MACG MHol NGdn NLar WCot
'Davina'[PBR] (Little Miss Series)	EHyd LRHS NLar NRHS WViv
'Dayspring Delight' (v)	MNrw
§ DIANA, PRINCESS OF WALES ('Stablaco')	EHyd LRHS NRHS
'Diane' (Midi Series)	SAlS
Doctor Salter's hybrids	SRms
Duchesses d'Anjou Series	see *A.* Midi Series
Ducs d'Anjou Series	see *A.* Maxi Series
'Eleanor'	WViv
'Eleanor' (Little Miss Series)	EHyd LRHS NRHS WViv
ELIZABETH ('Stamutro') **new**	EGrI
'Elvira'	SAlS WViv
'Emily'[PBR] (Little Miss Series)	LRHS SAlS WViv
'Etna'[PBR]	SAlS WViv
'Evening Song'	EHyd SAlS SWvt WViv
exserens	WCot
'Flaming Star'	LSvl SAlS WViv
'Flirt'	LOPS
'Fougeré' (Garden Series)	CTtf SAlS
'Frances' (v)	CAvo CBro WFar
'François' (Maxi Series)	SAlS
'Freedom'	CWGN ECtt ELon EWoo MHol NLar NSti SCob SCoo SPoG WCot
'Friendship' ♀H5	EHyd ELan LRHS NRHS SAlS SWvt WMal WViv
'Gaspard' (Mini Series)	SAlS
'Georges' (Maxi Series)	SAlS
'Gina'[PBR] (Little Miss Series)	EGrI ELan LRHS NRHS WViv
'Gloria'	ELan LRHS NRHS SWvt WViv
'Glory of the Andes' (v)	CWGN NLar
'Golden Delight'	EHyd ELan LRHS NRHS SAlS WViv
§ H.R.H. PRINCESS ALICE ('Staverpi')	LRHS NRHS
'Hawera'	GBin
'Henri' (Maxi Series)	CBod MHol SAlS
§ HOLIDAY VALLEY ('Tessumholid') (Summer Paradise Series) **new**	LHWs LRHS SAlS
hookeri	WFar
(Inca Series) INCA ADORE ('Koadore')	CExl MThu WViv
- INCA AVANTI ('Koncavanti'[PBR])	CWGN WViv
- INCA AZURE ('Konazur'[PBR])	WViv
- INCA BANDIT ('Koncaband')	SAlS SGBe WViv
- INCA BATTLE	SAlS SGBe WViv
- INCA BLUE HEAVEN	WViv
- INCA CLASSIC ('Konclassic')	WViv
- INCA CORAL ('Konocoral')	WViv
- INCA DEVOTION ('Konevotio'[PBR])	NLar
- INCA DREAM ('Kodream')	WViv
- INCA EXOTICA ('Koexotica')	SAlS WViv
- INCA FIRE	WViv
- INCA FLAMINGO	WViv
- INCA GLOW ('Koglow')	CExl CWGN EGrI EHyd ELon MHol NLar SDeJ SRms WViv
- INCA GOAL ('Koncagoal')	CBcs CBod SCoo WViv
- INCA HUSKY ('Koncahusky'[PBR])	CBcs CBod CWGN LHWs LRHS MHol SCoo SEdd WViv
- INCA ICE ('Koice')	CWGN NLar WViv
- INCA JOLI ('Koncajoli'[PBR])	WViv
- INCA LAKE ('Koncalake')	CWGN WViv
- INCA LOLLY ('Koncalolly'[PBR])	WViv
- INCA LUCKY ('Koncalucky'[PBR]) **new**	LHWs SAlS
- INCA MAMBO ('Koncamambo'[PBR])	WViv
- INCA MILK ('Koncamilk')	WViv
- INCA MOONLIGHT ('Komolight')	NLar
- INCA MYSTIC ('Koncamystic'[PBR]) **new**	SAlS
- INCA NOBLE ('Koncanoble')	WViv
- INCA OBSESSION ('Koobsion')	WViv
- INCA PRETTY	WViv
- INCA PULSE ('Konpulse'[PBR])	CWGN ELon NLar SDeJ WViv
- INCA RIO **new**	WViv
- INCA ROCKY ('Konyrock')	WViv
- INCA SERIN ('Koserin'[PBR])	CWGN WViv
- INCA SMILE ('Koncasmile'[PBR])	CWGN WViv
- INCA SUNDANCE ('Koncasuna')	CBod CPla LHWs SCoo SEdd SGBe SPad
- INCA SWEETY ('Koncasweet'[PBR])	CPla LHWs WViv
- INCA TOTO ('Koncatoto'[PBR])	WViv
- INCA TROPIC ('Kotrop')	CExl CWGN WViv
- INCA VITO ('Koncavito'[PBR])	CBcs CBod CPla CWGN LHWs MHol NLar SCoo SEdd SPad SPoG
- INCA YUKO ('Koncayuko'[PBR])	CBod CWGN ELon LBuc MHol WSpi WViv
INDIAN SUMMER ('Tesronto'[PBR]) (Summer Paradise Series)	CBod CRos CWCL CWGN ECtt EHyd EPfP LCro LHWs LOPS LRHS LSou MAsh MHol MPri NHpl NRHS NSti SAlS SCoo SEdd SMad SPoG SWvt WCot WFar WHil WViv WWFP XSte
(Inticancha Series) INTICANCHA ANTARCTICA ('Tesantarc'[PBR])	WViv
- INTICANCHA BRYCE ('Tesbryce'[PBR])	LHWs LRHS LSou MHol NLar SAlS SCob SCoo WFar WViv
- INTICANCHA CABANA ('Tescaban')	CBod CRos EHyd LHWs LRHS LSou MHol NRHS SAlS SCob
- INTICANCHA CREAMY DARK PINK ('Tescreda')	SDeJ WViv
- INTICANCHA DARK PURPLE ('Tesdarklin'[PBR])	CRos LHWs LRHS MSCN NLar NRHS SAlS WFar WViv
- INTICANCHA DOBA ('Tesdoba'[PBR]) **new**	LHWs
- INTICANCHA IMALA ('Tesima'[PBR])	EHyd
- INTICANCHA INDIGO ('Tesindig'[PBR])	CBod LHWs SAlS SCoo
- INTICANCHA KANIKA ('Tesikani')	EHyd SAlS
- INTICANCHA MACHU ('Tesmach'[PBR])	SAlS WFar WViv
- INTICANCHA MAGIC WHITE ('Tesmaghwi')	CBod LHWs LSou MHol SAlS SCoo
- INTICANCHA MAYA ('Tesmaya'[PBR])	CRos CWGN ECtt EHyd LHWs LRHS NRHS SAlS SCob SCoo WFar WViv

- INTICANCHA MOONLIGHT ('Tesmoonli')	LHWs SAlS
- INTICANCHA NAVAYO ('Tesnava'^{PBR})	ECtt LHWs LRHS LSou MHol SAlS SCoo WFar
- INTICANCHA PASSION ('Tespassion'^{PBR})	ECtt EHyd LHWs LSou SAlS SCoo WViv
- INTICANCHA PURPLE ('Tespurplin'^{PBR})	CWGN WFar WViv
- INTICANCHA RED ('Tesrobin'^{PBR})	CBod CRos CWGN LRHS MHol NRHS SAlS SCoo WFar WViv
- INTICANCHA SUNDAY ('Tessunday'^{PBR})	SAlS WViv
- INTICANCHA SUNLIGHT ('Tessunlight'^{PBR})	ECtt NLar WFar WViv
- INTICANCHA SUNSHINE ('Tesshine'^{PBR})	CBod LHWs LRHS LSou MHol SAlS
- INTICANCHA VALENTINO ('Tesvalen'^{PBR})	LRHS
- INTICANCHA WHITE PINK BLUSH ('Tesblushin'^{PBR})	EHyd LRHS NRHS WFar WViv
- INTICANCHA WHITE PINK HEART ('Tesheartin')	NLar SAlS SCoo
'Isabel' (Little Miss Series)	LRHS WFar WViv
ISABELLA ('Stalis')	LSRN
§ ***isabellana***	SBrt WCru WMal
'Isabelle' (Midi Series)	SAlS
'Jessica'^{PBR} (Little Miss Series)	LRHS SAlS WViv
'Joséphine' (Midi Series)	SAlS
'Junon' (Planet Series)	LCro LOPS
'Laguna'	SAlS WViv
LAURA ('Stalauli'^{PBR})	ECtt
'Layon' (Garden Series)	SAlS
'Léo' (Mini Series)	SAlS
'Leonie'	SAlS
ligtu hybrids	CAvo ECha EPfP GKev LCro LOPS MNrw NPer SDeJ SRms SWvt WBrk
'Lilac Bush' (Garden Jewels Series) **new**	WViv
'Liré' (Garden Series)	CTtf MHol SAlS
'Little Miss Natalie'	see *A.* 'Natalie'
'Louis' (Maxi Series)	CBod SAlS
'Louise' (Midi Series)	LSRN SAlS
'Lucas' (Mini Series)	SAlS
'Lucca'	SAlS WViv
'Lucinda'	SWvt WViv
'Lucy' (Little Miss Series)	SAlS WViv
'Maestro'^{PBR}	WViv
Majestic Series	see *A.* Garden Series
'Marcé' (Garden Series)	SAlS
'Marguerite' (Midi Series)	SAlS
'Marie' (Midi Series)	SAlS
'Marissa'	GMaP
'Mars' (Planet Series)	CTsd EHyd LRHS MThu
'Mathilde' (Midi Series)	NLar SAlS
'Matilda' (Little Miss Series)	WViv
'Mauve Majesty'	ELon LRHS MACG NLar SPoG WCot WHoo WViv
'Mazé' (Garden Series)	SAlS
'Miranda' (Little Miss Series)	LRHS WViv
'Montsoreau' (Garden Series)	SAlS
'Moulin Rouge'	WViv
§ 'Natalie'^{PBR} (Little Miss Series)	EHyd LRHS NRHS SAlS WViv
'Neptune'	LCro LOPS
'Nicolas' (Maxi Series)	SAlS
'Noah' (Mini Series)	SAlS
'Océane' (Mini Series)	SAlS
'Orange Glory' 🏆^{H4}	EHyd ELon MNrw SWvt WMal WViv
'Orange Supreme'	EHyd LRHS NRHS SAlS WViv
'Oriana' 🏆^{H4}	SWvt WViv
pallida	SPlb
'Pandora'^{PBR}	LRHS NRHS SAlS WViv
'Peaches' (Garden Jewels Series) **new**	WViv
'Perfect Orange'	WViv
'Phoenix' (v) 🏆^{H4}	SWvt WViv
'Pink' (Garden Jewels Series) **new**	WViv
'Pink Lady'	SAlS WViv
'Pink Perfection'	NLar
'Pink Sensation'	LRHS NRHS SAlS WViv
Pitchounes Series	see *A.* Mini Series
Planet Series **new**	EGrl
'Polka'	WViv
presliana RB 94103	WCot
PRINCESS DIANA	see *A.* DIANA, PRINCESS OF WALES ('Stablaco'), *A.* (Princess Series) PRINCESS DIANA ('Zapridapal')
(Princess Series) PRINCESS AMINA ('Zapriamin'^{PBR})	CBcs SPoG WViv
- PRINCESS ANOUSKA ('Zaprinous'^{PBR})	NLar WViv
- PRINCESS ARIANE ('Zapriari'^{PBR})	WViv
- PRINCESS BEATRIX ('Stadoran')	SChr
- PRINCESS CAMILLA ('Stapricamil')	SPoG
- PRINCESS CLAIRE ('Zapriclair'^{PBR})	CBcs CRos CWGN EHyd EPfP LRHS NRHS SAlS
- PRINCESS DANIELA ('Stapridani')	SCoo
§ - PRINCESS DIANA ('Zapridapal'^{PBR})	CWGN EPfP WViv
- PRINCESS ELIANE ('Zaprielia'^{PBR})	CBcs CRos EHyd LRHS NRHS SAlS WViv
- PRINCESS FABIANA ('Zaprifabi'^{PBR})	CRos CWGN EHyd LRHS NLar NRHS SAlS SPoG WViv
- PRINCESS ISABELLA ('Zapribel'^{PBR})	EHyd LSRN SAlS WViv
- PRINCESS IVANA ('Staprivane'^{PBR})	SPoG
- PRINCESS JULIETA ('Zapriju'^{PBR})	NLar
- PRINCESS KATE ('Zaprikate'^{PBR})	CBcs CRos CWGN EHyd EPfP LRHS NRHS SAlS WViv
- PRINCESS LAUREN **new**	LRHS SAlS
- PRINCESS LETIZIA ('Zaprilet')	EHyd EPfP SPoG
- PRINCESS LILIAN ('Zaprilian'^{PBR})	CRos EHyd EPfP LRHS NRHS SAlS WViv
- PRINCESS LISA ('Zaprilisa')	CWGN LRHS SAlS
- PRINCESS LOUISE ('Zaprilou'^{PBR})	CBcs EHyd LSRN WViv
- PRINCESS MARGARET ('Staprimar')	NLar
- PRINCESS MARY ('Zaprimary'^{PBR})	NLar
- PRINCESS MATHILDE ('Zaprimat'^{PBR})	WViv
- PRINCESS PAOLA ('Stapripal'^{PBR})	CBcs CRos CWGN EHyd LRHS NRHS SCoo SPoG WViv
- PRINCESS SARA ('Staprisara'^{PBR})	CRos EHyd EPfP LRHS NRHS SAlS SPoG
- PRINCESS SUSANA ('Staprisusa')	SCoo
- PRINCESS TAMARA ('Zapritama')	CBcs CWGN LRHS

- Princess Theresa ('Zapriteres'PBR) EPfP NLar SAlS
- Princess Victoria see *A.* 'Victoria'
- Princess Zavina ('Staprivina'PBR) NLar SPoG
pseudospathulata WCot
§ ***psittacina*** CBro CMea ECha EPPr EPfP GBin MCot MHer SHar SMHy SRms WAvo WFar WViv
- 'Mona Lisa' CBod XLum
- 'Royal Star' (v) CBod CBro CExl CWCL EHyd EPPr EPfP EPri EWTr EWoo LRHS MHol NRHS SBea SHar SPoG SRms WCot WFar WHoo WSHC WSpi XLum
pulchella Sims see *A. psittacina*
'Purple Rain' SWvt WViv
'Querré' (Garden Series) SAlS
'Red Beauty' (v) see *A.* 'Spitfire'
'Red Beauty' EHyd ELan GMaP LRHS NRHS SWvt WViv
'Red Elf' ♀H4 SAlS SMHy SWvt WViv
'Regina' see *A.* 'Victoria'
'Rhubarb and Custard' ELan
Rock 'n' Roll ('Alsdun01'PBR) (v) CDor CTtf EBee ELan LCro LOPS LSou MHol MHtn MNrw MSCN NHpl SMad SPoG SRms WCot WFar WViv
'Rosanna' (Little Miss Series) WViv
§ 'Roselind' (Little Miss Series) EGrI ELan LRHS NRHS SAlS SWvt WViv
'Rosie' (Mini Series) SAlS
'Saturne' (Planet Series) CDor LCro LOPS
'Segré' (Garden Series) SAlS
'Selina' EHyd MNrw WViv
'Serenade' WViv
'Sirius' (Planet Series) ♀H4 LCro LOPS
'Sonata' ♀H4 WViv
§ 'Sophie'PBR (Little Miss Series) ELan LRHS SWvt WViv
§ 'Spitfire' (v) ♀H4 EHyd LCro LOPS SWvt WCot WViv
Summer Paradise Series MHol
- Summer Break ('Tessumbreak') CBod ECtt EPfP LHWs LRHS LSou MHol SAlS SCoo SMrm
- Summer Breeze ('Teshunte'PBR) CRos ECtt EHyd LHWs LRHS NRHS SAlS SCoo SPoG WFar WViv
- Summer Holiday see *A.* Holiday Valley
- Summer Party ('Tessumpar') CRos ECtt EHyd LRHS NRHS WFar
- Summer Red ('Tessumred') **new** LHWs
- Summer Relieve ('Gasumrelie') **new** LHWs LRHS MHol
- Summer Saint ('Tessumsaint') CBod ECtt EPfP LHWs LRHS LSou MHol MHtn SCoo SMrm WViv
- Summer Sky ('Tessumsky') CBod EPfP LHWs LRHS MHol SAlS SCoo
- Summer Snow ('Gasumsnow') LHWs LSou SAlS SCoo
'Summertime' LRHS NRHS WViv
'Sunstar' GMaP
'Sweet Laura'PBR CBod ECtt ELan ELon EWoo LRHS LSRN MHol MNrw NGdn NLar NSti SMad SPoG WCot WSpi WViv
'Tangerine Tango' WViv
'Tanya' MNrw SAlS WViv
§ 'Tara'PBR (Little Miss Series) ELan LRHS NLar NRHS SAlS SWvt WViv
'Tessa' ♀H4 EHyd SAlS WViv
'Thorigné' (Garden Series) SAlS
'Tiercé' (Garden Series) SAlS
Time Valley (Summer Paradise Series) **new** LHWs
'Uranus' LCro LOPS
'Valley Girl' **new** LHWs
'Vanessa' (Little Miss Series) **new** EGrI LRHS
'Ventura' WViv
'Venus' (Planet Series) LCro LOPS WViv
'Veronica' (Little Miss Series) WViv
§ 'Victoria' EGrI
'William' (Maxi Series) SAlS
'Yellow Friendship' ♀H4 MNrw NLar SWvt WViv
'Yellow' (Garden Jewels Series) **new** WViv

Althaea (*Malvaceae*)

armeniaca WCot
cannabina CCBP CDor CFis CSpe CTtf ECha ELan EPPr EPri GGro MAvo MBel MHer MNrw MPie NGBl SBls SBut SHar SPhx SPtp WBor WCot WHal WHil WSHC
officinalis CBee CBod CCBP CGrG CHab CTsd ELan ENfk EPPr GPoy MAvo MBow MHer MMuc MNHC NLar SRms SVic WHer WJek WSpi XAbr XSen
§ - 'Romney Marsh' MAvo MRav WMal
rosea see *Alcea rosea*
rugosostellulata see *Alcea rugosa*

Altingia see *Liquidambar*

Alvesia (*Lamiaceae*)

rosmarinifolia **new** WHil

× *Alworthia* (*Asphodelaceae*)

'Black Gem' EBee EShb NCft SIvy SRms SSim

Alyogyne (*Malvaceae*)

§ ***huegelii*** CCCN EShb SEND SEle SIvy SPlb
- 'Santa Cruz' CCCN
Magic Moments ('Hutwow'PBR) CCCN ELan SMad SPad SPoG

Alyssum (*Brassicaceae*)

caespitosum WAbe
cuneifolium GJos
montanum ECha MAsh SPlb SRms
§ - 'Berggold' EBou ELan EPfP LRHS WIce
- Mountain Gold see *A. montanum* 'Berggold'
- subsp. ***pluscanescens*** **new** WCot
oxycarpum EPot
saxatile see *Aurinia saxatilis*
- 'Summit' EPfP GJos LRHS NSla SRms
spinosa see *Hormathophylla spinosa*
'Takara Yellow' GWyn
tortuosum SEND
wulfenianum WIce

Amaranthus (*Amaranthaceae*)

'Autumn Palette' CSpe
caudatus LCro LOPS SVic
cruentus CLau
- 'Hot Biscuits' **new** SPhx
- 'Velvet Curtains' ♀H2 LCro LOPS
hypochondriacus 'Pygmy Torch' ♀H2 CSpe
tricolor CLau SRms

× *Amarcrinum* (*Amaryllidaceae*)

'Dorothy Hannibal' WCot
memoria-corsii CPrp

- 'Howardii'	EPri GKev LEdu MPie NRog SDeJ WCot

× *Amarine* (*Amaryllidaceae*)

tubergenii	CAvo
- Belladiva Series	CBro CSpe EBee ELan ERCP GKev LCro LOPS LRHS NHoy SDir
- - 'Anastasia'PBR	CBro ELan ERCP GKev NHoy SEdd SMad
- - 'Aphrodite'PBR	CBro GKev NHoy SDir SMad WFar
- - 'Elvi'	NHoy
- - 'Emanuelle'PBR	CAvo CBro ELan ERCP GKev NHoy
- - 'Paris' **new**	CBro
- - 'Smilla'	CBro GKev NHoy SEdd
- - 'Tomoka'PBR	CBro GKev
- 'Fletcheri'	WCot
- 'Zwanenburg'	CSpe GKev MPie NRog WCot

× *Amarygia* (*Amaryllidaceae*)

§ ***bidwillii*** 'Alba'	CAvo CBro CPrp
- 'Rosea'	WCot

Amaryllis (*Amaryllidaceae*)

§ ***belladonna*** ♀H4	CBcs CBro CPbh CPrp CTri CTsd EBee EGrl EPfP ERCP EShb GKev LCro LOPS MPie NRog SDeJ SDir SEND SEdd SPeP WCot
- 'Hathor'	CBro SMHy
- 'Johannesburg'	CBro WCot
- 'Major'	SChr
- 'Parkeri Alba'	see × *Amarygia bidwillii* 'Alba'
- 'Purpurea'	WCot
- white-flowered	NRog SDeJ

Amaryllis × *Brunsvigia* see × *Amarygia*

Amaryllis × *Crinum* see × *Amarcrinum*

Amaryllis × *Nerine* see × *Amarine*

Ambrosina (*Araceae*)

bassii	WCot

Amelanchier ✿ (*Rosaceae*)

alnifolia	MGil NGrd WKor
- 'Forestburg'	MBlu NLar
- 'Honeywood'	CAgr MBlu MCoo NLar NOra
- 'Jb30' (F)	CAgr MCoo NOra
- 'Martin' (F)	CAgr NOra
- 'Northline' (F)	CAgr LCro LOPS LRHS MCoo NLar NOra
- 'Obelisk'PBR	CAgr CDoC CRos EBee EHyd ELan EPfP GKin LBuc LPar LRHS LSRN MAsh MCoo MGos MRav MSwo MTrO NLar NOra NOrn SCoo SGsty SMad SPer SPoG WHwl WMat
- pink-fruited	NLar
§ - var. ***pumila***	MMrt WCot
- 'Regent' (F)	CAgr
- 'Smokey'	CAgr MBlu MCoo NLar NOra SPoG WKor
- 'Thiessen'	MCoo NLar NOra
arborea TRADITION ('Trazam')	NLar SAko
bartramiana	SSta
- 'Eskimo'	NLar
canadensis K. Koch	see *A. lamarckii*
canadensis ambig.	CAco CDoC EGrl ILea IPap LMaj LPot LShi MMuc MPri NOra NWea SEND SEWo SPoG WFar WHwl WKor WLov
canadensis (L.) Medik.	CAgr CLnd CMac CSBt CTri EBee ELan EPfP LEdu LRHS MGos MRav MSwo SArc SPer WMat
§ - 'Glenn Form'	CEnd EBee EPfP LMaj LPar LRHS MGos MTrO NLar NOra SEWo SGol SLim SPer SPoG WTSh
- 'Prince William'	CAgr MBlu MCoo SGol
- RAINBOW PILLAR	see *A. canadensis* 'Glenn Form'
× ***grandiflora***	SCob
- 'Autumn Brilliance'	CEnd CJun EPfP MBlu NHol NLar NOrn NRHS SGol
- 'Ballerina'	Widely available
- 'Cole's Select'	EBee EMil LRHS NLar SWvt
- 'Princess Diana' ♀H7	NLar SCoo
§ - 'Robin Hill' ♀H7	Widely available
- 'Rubescens'	CEnd CJun EBee NLar SLon SWvt
'La Paloma' ♀H6	EBee EPfP LRHS LSRN MAsh MGos MTrO NOra NOrn SCoo SLim WHwl WMat WMou
laevis	CBcs CTri EPfP
- 'Prince Charles'	NLar
- 'R.J. Hilton' ♀H7	CDoC EBee EPfP EWTr LRHS MAsh MTrO NOra SCoo WHwl WMat WMou
- 'Snow Cloud'	CCVT
- 'Snowflakes'	CBod CEnd CSBt EBee EPfP LPar LRHS LSRN MAsh MNic MTrO NLar NOra NOrn SCob SEWo SLim SPer SPoG SWvt WHwl WMat
§ ***lamarckii*** ♀H7	Widely available
ovalis misapplied	see *A. spicata* (Lam.) K. Koch
ovalis Medik.	SPlb
- 'Edelweiss'	EPfP EWTr IArd LRHS MGos MRav MTrO NLar SCoo
- 'Helvetia'	NLar
pumila	see *A. alnifolia* var. *pumila*
rotundifolia ambig.	CAgr MCoo
sanguinea 'Chimney Rock'	NLar
§ ***spicata*** (Lam.) K. Koch	CAgr MCoo
stolonifera	CTri

Amelanchier × *Sorbus* see × *Amelasorbus*

× *Amelasorbus* (*Rosaceae*)

raciborskiana	MBlu NLar

Amellus (*Asteraceae*)

asteroides	MAsh

Amicia (*Fabaceae*)

zygomeris	CDTJ CDow CMCN CSde CSpe EBee EPfP EShb EWes IPot LEdu LRHS MGil SChF SDix SEle SMrm SPoG WCot WPGP WSHC XSte
- 'John's Big Splash' (v)	WCot

Ammi (*Apiaceae*)

majus ♀H6	CBod CKel CSpe EWoo LCro LEdu LOPS LRHS MAvo MNHC SDix SPhx
visnaga	see *Visnaga daucoides*

Ammobium (*Asteraceae*)

calyceroides	GBin

Ammocharis (*Amaryllidaceae*)

coranica	WCot

Ammophila (*Poaceae*)

arenaria	CKno EBee WABo XLum XSen
breviligulata	EBee XLum

Amomum (*Zingiberaceae*)

sp.	SDir
subulatum	SDir SPre

Amomyrtus (*Myrtaceae*)

§ ***luma***	CBcs CTri CTsd EBee ELon IDee LEdu MMuc SEND SPoG WJek WPGP WPav
meli	WPGP

Amorpha (*Fabaceae*)

canescens	CSpe EBee SBls SPlb
fruticosa	MBlu MGil MMuc SEND SPlb

Amorphophallus ✿ (*Araceae*)

albus	CDTJ LEdu SPlb WCot
bulbifer	CDTJ ESwi SDeJ SDir SPlb
dunnii	CDTJ LEdu
henryi	WCot
kerrii	CExl WCot
kiusianus B&SWJ 4845	WCru
konjac	CDTJ CExl LEdu NGKo SChF SChr SDeJ SPlb WCot
- 'Tattered Umbrella' <u>**new**</u>	SPlb
napalensis	SDir WCot XLum
ongsakulii	WCot
stipitatus	LEdu WCot
yuloensis	WCot

Ampelocissus (*Vitaceae*)

sikkimensis HWJK 2066	WCru

Ampelodesmos (*Poaceae*)

mauritanicus 🏆H3	CKno ECha EShb EWes MAvo SDix SEND SPlb SPtp WCot

Ampelopsis (*Vitaceae*)

aconitifolia	NLar WCru
- 'Chinese Lace'	EBee EShb ESwi EWTr MRav NLar SMad WBor WCot
arborea	WCru
brevipedunculata	ELan LShi MGil SCoo SPer SSal WAvo
- 'Elegans' (v)	CBcs CBod CDoC CMac EBee ELan ELon EPfP EShb LRHS MGil MGos MHtn MRav SNig SPer SPoG SWvt WAvo WCot WLov
delavayana	EShb MGil MMuc
glandulosa var. ***hancei*** B&SWJ 1793	WCru
henryana	see *Parthenocissus henryana*
megalophylla	EShb NLar
sempervirens hort. ex Veitch	see *Cissus striata*
tricuspidata 'Veitchii'	see *Parthenocissus tricuspidata* 'Veitchii'

Amphicome see *Incarvillea*

Amsonia (*Apocynaceae*)

'Blue Ice'	Widely available
ciliata	EMor LEdu MCot MMrt NLar SHar WPGP XLum
§ ***elliptica***	EBee EMor EPPr WFar
'Ernst Pagels'	EBee ECha EMor EPPr LEdu MAvo SHar SMHy WCot WGoo
hubrichtii	CBod CDor CEme CFoA CSpe EBee ECha EMor EPPr EPfP IPot LEdu LRHS LSun MBel NFav NLar NRHS SBls SBut SDix SEdd SMHy SPhx SWvt WCAu WPGP WSHC
illustris	CSpe EBee EBlo EMor EPPr LEdu LRHS NLar NRHS SBls SBut SHar SMHy SPhx WHoo
§ ***orientalis***	CMea CPla CSpe CTri EBee ECha EGrI ELan EMor GBin GWyn LEdu LPla LRHS LShi MAvo MCot MRav NDov NLar NRHS SBut SPhx SVen SWvt WCot WFar WKif XLum
- from Turkey	LEdu SMHy
- 'Cally Dark Stem'	LPla
sinensis	see *A. elliptica*
tabernaemontana	Widely available
* - ***galacticifolia***	EGrI
- 'Montana'	SPer SWvt
- var. ***salicifolia***	EBee EBlo EMor LCro LEdu LOPS LPla LRHS MCot NDov NRHS SCob WCAu WPGP
- 'Stella Azul'	EBee MNrw
- 'Storm Cloud'	EMor IPot
tomentosa	EBee
var. ***stenophylla***	

Amygdalus see *Prunus*

Anacampseros (*Portulacaceae*)

telephiastrum <u>**new**</u>	CPla

Anacamptis (*Orchidaceae*)

§ ***laxiflora***	NLAp
§ ***morio***	NLAp
pyramidalis	NLAp

Anacyclus (*Asteraceae*)

pyrethrum	GPoy
- var. ***depressus*** 🏆H4	EBee EBou ELan EPfP GKev MAsh MMuc NSla SPlb SRot
- - 'Garden Gnome'	CTri SRms
- - 'Silberkissen'	CMea CPla EDAr

Anagallis (*Primulaceae*)

arvensis	SPhx
monellii 'Gentian Blue' 🏆H3	LCro LOPS
- subsp. ***linifolia*** 'Blue Light'	CSpe
- 'Skylover'	CCCN LCro LOPS
tenella	CWat LLWG
- 'Studland'	WAbe

Ananas (*Bromeliaceae*)

comosus (F)	CCCN SPre
- 'Champaca' (F) 🏆H1a	CCCN LCro LOPS SPre

Anaphalis (*Asteraceae*)

alpicola	EBee
margaritacea	CBcs ECha GMaP NBid NLar SRms WCAu WFar
§ - 'Neuschnee'	EBee GJos LPla MACG NLar SBls WFar
- NEW SNOW	see *A. margaritacea* 'Neuschnee'
- var. ***yedoensis***	CTri SDix
§ ***nepalensis*** var. ***monocephala***	EBee MCot NSti SRms
nubigena	see *A. nepalensis* var. *monocephala*
transnokoensis	EWes MACG
§ ***trinervis***	CExl
triplinervis 🏆H7	EBee ELan EPfP EShb EWld EWoo GAbr GKev GMaP LRHS MRav NBid NLar NRHS SBls SBut SCob SMrm SPer SSal WCAu WFar XLum
- CC 1620	EPPr NBir

- 'Silberregen'	SAko
§ - 'Sommerschnee' ♀H7	CBod CMac CTtf ECha ECtt EPfP GWyn LPot LRHS MCot MHol MRav NLar NRHS NWad SCob SGbt SPer WGwG WHoo WTre WWtn
- SUMMER SNOW	see *A. triplinervis* 'Sommerschnee'

Anaphaloides (*Asteraceae*)

§ ***bellidioides***	CTri ECha

Anchusa (*Boraginaceae*)

sp.	CHab
§ ***azurea***	CBod NLar
- 'Dropmore'	CDor EBee EBou EPfP LCro LOPS LRHS MRav NLar SAng SCob SRms
- 'Feltham Pride'	EBee ELan LRHS NRHS SRms SWvt WHoo
- 'Little John'	SRms
- 'Loddon Royalist'	Widely available
- 'Opal'	CBod CNor ECtt EWoo LRHS NRHS WCAu WGwG
capensis 'Blue Angel'	SWvt
cespitosa	ELan EWes WAbe WIce
italica	see *A. azurea*
laxiflora	see *Borago pygmaea*
myosotidiflora	see *Brunnera macrophylla*
officinalis	MNHC SRms
sempervirens	see *Pentaglottis sempervirens*

Ancylostemon see *Oreocharis*

Andrachne (*Phyllanthaceae*)

colchica	see *Leptopus chinensis*

Andromeda (*Ericaceae*)

polifolia	LPar SavN SPlb
- 'Alba'	EHyd LRHS MAsh SPer SWvt
- 'Alisa'	GKev
- 'Blue Ice'	CDoC EHyd ELan GArf GBin IDee LRHS LSRN MAsh NBir NLar SPer SPoG WAbe WFar XSte
- 'Blue Lagoon'	CDoC NLar
- 'Compacta' ♀H6	CDoC EHyd ELan LRHS LSRN MAsh NLar NWad SWvt WFar
- 'Grandiflora'	GKev
- 'Kirigamine'	GArf LRHS MAsh
- 'Macrophylla' ♀H6	WThu
- 'Nikko'	CMac NLar
- 'Shibutsu'	GArf

Andropogon (*Poaceae*)

gerardii	NWsh XLum
- 'Prairie Sommer'	NDov
- 'Red Arrow' new	IPot
- 'Red October' new	LPla
- 'Weinheim Burgundy'	IPot MNrw
ischaemum	see *Bothriochloa ischaemum*
'JS Purple Konza'	IPot MNrw
scoparius	see *Schizachyrium scoparium*

Androsace (*Primulaceae*)

sp.	MAsh
adenocephala	GKev
albana	GKev
alpina	WAbe
bisulca var. ***aurata***	GKev
- var. ***bisulca*** new	GKev
brachystegia	GKev
bulleyana	WAbe
carnea	GEdr
- subsp. ***brigantiaca***	GKev NHar NHpl NSla
- var. ***halleri***	see *A. carnea* subsp. *rosea*
- subsp. ***laggeri*** ♀H5	NHar NSla WAbe
- - 'Andorra'	GArf
§ - subsp. ***rosea***	NHpl NSla
carnea* × *pyrenaica	ELan EPot WIce
cylindrica	CRos EPot GKev LRHS NRHS
cylindrica* × *hirtella	CRos EHyd EPot LRHS NRHS
dasyphylla	GKev
delavayi	WAbe
- ACE 1786	WAbe
geraniifolia	CPla EBee ECha GKev SRms
globifera	EPot WAbe
halleri	see *A. carnea* subsp. *rosea*
hedraeantha	NSla WAbe
himalaica	EPot GEdr WAbe
hirtella	GKev WAbe
idahoensis	WAbe
idahoensis* × *laevigata	WAbe
jacquemontii	see *A. villosa* var. *jacquemontii*
kosopoljanskii	EPot
lactea	GKev WAbe
laevigata	CPla GArf
- 'Gothenburg'	WFar
- 'Saddle Mount'	GKev
lanuginosa ♀H5	CBod CMea CSpe EBou EDAr EPot GBin GKev NHol NHpl SBut SGro SLee SRms SRot WAbe WIce
limprichtii	see *A. sarmentosa* var. *watkinsii*
× ***marpensis***	EPot WAbe
mathildae	NSla WAbe
microphylla	see *A. mucronifolia* G.Watt
montana	WAbe
mucronifolia misapplied	see *A. sempervivoides*
§ ***mucronifolia*** G.Watt	EPot WAbe
mucronifolia G.Watt × ***sempervivoides***	EPot
muscoidea	GKev WAbe
- 'Dolpo Lilac'	WAbe
- Schacht's form	EPot WAbe
nivalis	SPlb
obtusifolia	GKev
ochotensis	WAbe
primuloides	see *A. studiosorum*
pubescens	CRos EHyd EPot LRHS NRHS
pyrenaica	CRos EHyd EPot ITim LRHS NRHS SPlb WAbe
rigida	WAbe
robusta	GKev
- subsp. ***purpurea***	GKev WAbe
- - 'Dolpo Dwarf'	WAbe
rotundifolia	CTtf GArf GKev
sarmentosa misapplied	see *A. studiosorum*
sarmentosa ambig.	NHpl SPlb
sarmentosa Wall.	EBou SRms WHoo
- from Namche, Nepal	EPot WAbe
- Galmont's form	see *A. studiosorum* 'Salmon's Variety'
- 'Sherriffii'	MMuc SRms WIce
§ - var. ***watkinsii***	EPot
- var. ***yunnanensis*** misapplied	see *A. studiosorum*
selago	WAbe
- 'Red Eye'	WAbe
§ ***sempervivoides***	CRos EBou EDAr EHyd ELan EPot GArf GBin GKev GMaP LRHS MAsh MBel NFav NHol NRHS NSla SGro SLee SPlb SRms WIce
- 'Susan Joan'	EPot GKev NHar WAbe
septentrionalis	CSpe
- 'Stardust'	ELan LRHS
strigillosa	GKev NHpl

§	***studiosorum*** ♀H5	EPot GAbr GKev WAbe
	- 'Chumbyi'	CBor EPot NHpl SRms WIce WThu
	- 'Conwy Gem'	WAbe
	- 'Conwy Jewel'	WAbe
	- 'Doksa' ♀H5	EPot WAbe WIce
§	- 'Salmon's Variety'	CMea CTri EDAr
	tangulashanensis	GKev
	vandellii	ITim NSla WAbe
	villosa	GArf GKev WAbe
§	- var. ***jacquemontii***	CTtf WThu
	- - lilac-flowered	EPot
	- - pink-flowered	EPot WAbe
	vitaliana	see *Vitaliana primuliflora*
	watkinsii	see *A. sarmentosa* var. *watkinsii*

Andryala (*Asteraceae*)

	agardhii	GKev
	glandulosa	WCot
	lanata	see *Hieracium lanatum*

Anemanthele (*Poaceae*)

§	***lessoniana*** ♀H4	Widely available
	- 'Buffalo Gold'	LRHS LSun SGBe
	- 'Gold Hue'	ELon
	- 'Sirocco'	CBod LRHS MACG WCot WFar

Anemarrhena (*Asparagaceae*)

	asphodeloides	SBrt WCot

Anemia (*Schizaeaceae*)

	tomentosa	LEdu

Anemone ✿ (*Ranunculaceae*)

	aconitifolia Michx.	see *A. narcissiflora*
	altaica	GKev NLar SRms
	amurensis	CExl
	'Annerose' **new**	NLar
	apennina ♀H6	CAvo GEdr LEdu WShi
	- var. ***albiflora***	ECha EMor EPot GKev MAvo
	- double-flowered (d)	CTtf ECha MAvo
	- 'Petrovac'	CBor EMor EPot LEdu NRog
	baldensis	SRms
	barbulata	CExl EBee EWes GKev GPSL LEdu
	blanda ♀H6	CRos EPfP LCro LOPS LRHS MACG MAsh MBow NLar NRHS NRog SEND SRms WCav WFar WShi
I	- 'Alba'	CRos EHyd LRHS NRHS
	- blue-flowered	CAvo CMea CRos CTri CTtf EHyd ELan EPfP EPot ERCP EShb GAbr GKev GMaP ILea LCro LOPS LRHS NRHS NRog SCob SDeJ SDir SPer SPhx SPoG SRms WCot
	- 'Charmer'	EPot GKev ILea NHpl NRog SDeJ WCot
	- 'Ingramii'	EPot WCot
	- 'Pink Star' **new**	NRog
	- pink-flowered	EShb
	- var. ***rosea***	CRos EHyd LRHS NRHS NRog SDeJ SPoG
	- - 'Pink Star'	CAvo ERCP GKev NBir
	- - 'Radar'	CBor EPot ERCP GKev MNrw NBir NHpl NRog SDeJ
	- 'Violet Star'	GKev NRog SDeJ WHil
	- 'White Splendour' ♀H6	CAvo CBor CMea CTri CTtf ELan EPfP EPot ERCP EShb EWTr GAbr GKev ILea LCro LEdu LOPS NBir NLar NRog SDeJ SDir SPhx SPoG SRms WCot WHil
	- white-flowered	CRos LRHS NRHS
	'Bowles's Mauve'	GEdr
	caerulea	LEdu
	canadensis	EPPr GEdr LEdu WCot
	chapaensis HWJ 631	WCru
	'Cinderella'PBR (Fantasy Series)	EHyd LRHS SCoo WSpi
	coelestina var. ***linearis***	GKev
	coronaria	EPfP SVic
	- De Caen Group	CCBP CRos EHyd EPfP GKev LOPS LRHS MACG NRHS SPoG
	- - 'Bicolor'	GKev SDeJ WCot
	- - blue-flowered	CRos LRHS NRHS
	- - 'Bordeaux'	LCro LOPS
§	- - 'Die Braut'	CCBP ERCP GKev LCro LOPS NBir SDeJ
	- - 'His Excellency'	see *A. coronaria* (De Caen Group) 'Hollandia'
§	- - 'Hollandia'	EGrI GKev SDeJ
	- - 'Mister Fokker'	EGrI ERCP GBin GKev LCro LOPS SDeJ
	- - pink-flowered	CRos LRHS NRHS
	- - red-flowered	CRos LRHS NRHS
	- - THE BRIDE	see *A. coronaria* (De Caen Group) 'Die Braut'
	- - 'The Governor'	ERCP GKev ILea SDeJ
	- (Harmony Series) 'Harmony Blue' **new**	LRHS
	- - 'Harmony Orchid'	EHyd EPfP LRHS NRHS
	- - 'Harmony Pearl'	EHyd LRHS NRHS
	- - 'Harmony Scarlet'	CRos EHyd LRHS NRHS
	- - 'Harmony White' **new**	LRHS
	- Saint Bridgid Group (d)	EHyd GKev LRHS NRHS
	- - 'Lord Lieutenant' (d)	ERCP GKev NBir SDeJ
	- - 'Mount Everest' (d)	ERCP GKev ILea NBir SDeJ
	- - 'The Admiral' (d)	GKev NBir SDeJ
	- 'Sylphide' (Mona Lisa Series)	EGrI ERCP GKev ILea LCro LOPS NBir SDeJ
	cylindrica	CElw EPPr GAbr GEdr NDov
	'Dainty Swan'	CWGN EBee IPot MNrw MPri NLar WTor
	'Danish White'	MNrw WCot
	decapetala	MHer
	demissa var. ***major***	EBee
	DREAMING SWAN ('Macane004'PBR)	CMiW CPar CWGN EBee ELan EMor EPfP GBin GEdr GMaP LRHS LSou MBNS MBel MNrw MPri NLar NSti SCoo SEdd SHar SPoG SWvt WFar WNPC
	drummondii	CWCL EBee GKev
	'Elfin Swan'	CPar CWGN EMor EPfP GEdr LRHS MBel MHol MNrw NLar NRHS SPoG WCot
	fasciculata	see *A. narcissiflora*
	filisecta	CBod EBee MBel MHol WCot
	flaccida	CBor CBro EHyd EPPr GEdr LEdu LRHS MAvo MNrw NRHS SHar WCot WHal WSHC
	- 'Futabazuru' (d)	GEdr WFar
	- 'Ginpai' (d)	GEdr WFar
	× ***fulgens*** 'Multipetala'	XLum
	globosa	see *A. multifida* Poir.
	'Guernica'	EWes
	'Hatakeyama Double' (d)	LPla WSHC
	'Hatakeyama Single'	LPla
	hepatica L.	see *Hepatica nobilis*
§	***hortensis***	EBee
§	***hupehensis***	CExl EBee EBou GMaP LSun NDov XLum
	- BWJ 8190	WCru
	- f. ***alba***	CExl CSpe
§	- 'Bowles's Pink' ♀H7	CDor CExl EBee LCro LOPS NLar
	- 'Crispa'	see *A.* × *hybrida* 'Lady Gilmour' Wolley-Dod

	- 'Eugenie'	ECtt EPfP NBir
	- 'Hadspen Abundance' 🏆H7	Widely available
	- var. ***hupehensis***	WFar
§	- var. ***japonica***	SRms
	- - B&SWJ 4886	WCru
	- - PAB 8884	LEdu
	- - 'Bodnant Burgundy'	EBee LRHS SWvt
§	- - 'Bressingham Glow'	CExl CMac EBee ECtt ELan EPfP EPot EShb GKev GKin NBir NLar SPer WBrk WCAu WFar WHil
§	- - 'Pamina' 🏆H7	Widely available
	- - 'Pink Saucer'	CBod WFar WHil
	- - PRINCE HENRY	see *A. hupehensis* var. *japonica* 'Prinz Heinrich'
§	- - 'Prinz Heinrich'	Widely available
§	- - 'Rotkäppchen' 🏆H7	CDor ECtt EShb GKin LSun NHol NLar NSti SPad SWvt WCot
	- - 'Splendens'	CMea CRos EHyd ELan EPfP LCro LOPS LRHS NLar NRHS SCob SCoo SPer SPoG SRms SWvt WHal WSpi XLum
	- - 'Tiki Sensation'^{PBR}	CWGN LCro LOPS NLar WHil
	- 'Little Princess'^{PBR}	EBee ECtt EShb MNrw NLar
	- 'Ouvertüre'	ECtt
	- 'Pocahontas'^{PBR} (Fantasy Series)	ECtt EHyd EPfP GBin GEdr LRHS MNrw NLar NRHS SCoo
	- 'Praecox'	CBod CMea CRos EPfP LRHS MBNS MBros NBir NRHS SGbt SRms SWvt WCAu WGwG WHoo
	- 'Red Riding Hood' (Fantasy Series)	GEdr LRHS NLar NRHS WSpi
	- 'September Charm'	see *A.* × *hybrida* 'September Charm'
	- 'Superba'	WSpi
§	× ***hybrida***	NChi
	- 'Alba' misapplied (UK)	see *A.* × *hybrida* 'Honorine Jobert'
	- 'Albert Schweitzer'	see *A.* × *hybrida* 'Elegans'
	- 'Andrea Atkinson'	CCBP CDor EBee EBou ECtt ELan EMor EPfP GAbr GWyn LRHS LSRN LSun MPie NBid NGdn NLar NRHS NSti SGbt SPad SPoG SRms SWvt WBor WCot WGwG WHoo WSpi XLum
	- 'Bowles's Pink'	see *A. hupehensis* 'Bowles's Pink'
	- 'Bressingham Glow'	see *A. hupehensis* var. *japonica* 'Bressingham Glow'
	- 'Carmen'	LPla LSou MHol MNrw NLar
	- 'Cloudy Abundance' **new**	MNrw
	- 'Coupe d'Argent'	EBee ECtt MBel NLar SHar XLum
§	- 'Elegans' 🏆H7	ECtt GMaP LCro LOPS LRHS MMuc NBir SEND SWvt WFar
	- 'Frau Marie Maushardt'	WBrk
§	- 'Géante des Blanches'	SMrm
§	- 'Honorine Jobert' 🏆H7	Widely available
	- 'Josephine'	WFar
§	- 'Königin Charlotte' 🏆H7	Widely available
	- 'Kriemhilde'	EBee
	- 'Lady Gilmour' misapplied	see *A.* × *hybrida* 'Montrose'
	- 'Lady Gilmour' ambig.	GWyn SGbt SMrm XLum
§	- 'Lady Gilmour' Wolley-Dod	CBod EBee ECtt EPfP LRHS MRav NBir NChi NRHS SRms WSpi
	- 'Loreley'	CDor EPfP LPla MBNS MCot NDov NLar SWvt WCot
	- 'Märchenfee'	MNrw
§	- 'Margarete' Kayser & Seibert	CExl ECtt ELan EPfP NDov SHar WHil
	- 'Max Vogel'	see *A.* × *hybrida* 'Elegans'
	- 'Monterosa'	see *A.* × *hybrida* 'Montrose'
§	- 'Montrose'	EBee ECha ELan EWes GMaP LCro LOPS LPla NBir NLar SPeP SRms WCAu
	- 'Pamina'	see *A. hupehensis* var. *japonica* 'Pamina'
	- PINK KISS ('Pkan'^{PBR})	EBee LPla
	- Pretty Lady Series	SCob
	- - 'Pretty Lady Diana'^{PBR}	EBee ECtt LBuc LCro LRHS NLar SCob SCoo SGBe SWvt WTyc
	- - 'Pretty Lady Emily'^{PBR}	EPfP LBuc LRHS NLar SCob SCoo SGBe SWvt WHil
	- - 'Pretty Lady Julia'^{PBR}	EBee NLar WHil
	- - 'Pretty Lady Maria'	EBee LRHS NLar SCob SCoo SGBe
	- - 'Pretty Lady Susan'	CWGN EBee LBuc LCro LOPS LRHS NLar SGBe SWvt WHil
	- PRINCE HENRY	see *A. hupehensis* var. *japonica* 'Prinz Heinrich'
	- 'Profusion'	CTri EBee LBuc WHal
	- QUEEN CHARLOTTE	see *A.* × *hybrida* 'Königin Charlotte'
	- 'Richard Ahrens'	CRos ECtt EPfP EShb EWoo GBee GMaP LRHS LSRN MGos NGdn NLar NRHS SCoo SWvt WGwG
§	- 'Robustissima'	CBod CRos EBee EMor EPfP GMaP LRHS LSRN MCot MHol MMuc MNrw NBir NGdn NLar NRHS NSti SEND SPer SRms SWvt WAvo WCAu WFar
	- 'Rosea'	LRHS
	- 'Rosenschale'	EWes LRHS MNrw NRHS SHar
	- 'Rotkäppchen'	see *A. hupehensis* var. *japonica* 'Rotkäppchen'
§	- 'September Charm' 🏆H7	Widely available
	- 'Serenade'	ECtt ELan EPfP LRHS LSRN MRav NBir NLar NRHS SMrm SPoG WCAu XLum
	- TOURBILLON	see *A.* × *hybrida* 'Whirlwind'
§	- 'Whirlwind'	Widely available
	- 'White Queen'	see *A.* × *hybrida* 'Géante des Blanches'
	- WIRBELWIND	see *A.* × *hybrida* 'Whirlwind'
	japonica	see *A. hupehensis*, *A. hupehensis* var. *japonica*, *A.* × *hybrida*
	- 'Crustata'	CMac
§	× ***lesseri***	CSpe ECha GEdr GKev MBel SRms
	leveillei	Widely available
	- BWJ 7919	WCru
§	× ***lipsiensis***	CBro CTtf EBee ECtt EPot GAbr GEdr GKev GMaP LEdu MBel MCot MNrw NHpl NLar NRog WCru WFar WHal WHoo WSHC WSpi
	- 'Pallida' 🏆H5	CBor CElw CMiW CSpe ELon GEdr GKev LEdu MCot NLar NRog WCot WFar WIce WShi
	- 'Schwefelfeuer'	LEdu MAvo NDry
	- 'Sioux' **new**	EPPr
	- 'Stiby'	NDry
	- 'Vindobonensis'	GEdr MAvo WCot
	lithophila	GEdr GKev
	magellanica hort. ex Wehrh.	see *A. multifida* Poir.
	'Margarette'	see *A.* × *hybrida* 'Margarete' Kayser & Seibert
	matsudae B&SWJ 1452	WCru
	- NMWJ 14517	WCru
	multifida misapplied red-flowered	see *A.* × *lesseri*
§	***multifida*** Poir.	CTsd ECha EGrI EHyd EPPr EPfP GKev LRHS LSun NBir NRHS NSti SPer WFar WHoo
	- Annabella Series	GKev
	- - 'Annabella Deep Rose'	GJos WHil
	- - 'Annabella White'	GJos
	- 'Major'	CMea CSpe EPfP GPSL SPhx WIce
	- 'Rubra'	ECtt EHed EPPr EPfP GBin GEdr GKev GWyn LRHS MPie MSCN

		NBir NFav NLar NRHS SPoG WBor WFar WGwG
	- white-flowered	EHed
	- yellow-flowered	GArf GEdr
§	***narcissiflora***	CSpe EBee GKev LPla NBir NChi
	- subsp. ***crinata*** **new**	NLar
§	- var. ***protracta***	GKev
	nemorosa	Widely available
	- 'Alba'	CCBP CMiW EGrI WFar
	- 'Alba Plena' (d)	ECha ECtt EPPr EPfP GKev MAvo NGdn NLar NRog WFar WSHC
	- 'Allenii' ♀H5	CBor CBro CElw CMiW CRos ELon EPPr EPfP EPot GEdr GKev GMaP ITim LRHS MAvo MBel MRav NRHS NRog NRya WFar WShi
	- 'Amy Doncaster'	CLAP
	- 'Apuseni'	LEdu
	- 'Atley'	EBee GEdr MAvo NRog WCot WFar
	- 'Atrocaerulea'	GArf NLar
	- 'Atrorosea'	EPPr
	- 'Axel' **new**	EPPr
	- 'Ballyrogan Blue'	MAvo
	- 'Behemoth Blue'	LEdu
	- 'Big Blush' **new**	SPVi
	- 'Bill Baker's Pink'	CLAP LEdu
	- 'Birka' **new**	SPVi
	- 'Blue Beauty'	CMiW EBee ELon GMaP MAvo
	- 'Blue Bonnet'	EPot ITim LEdu MAvo
	- 'Blue Eyes' (d)	CBor CElw CLAP CWCL EMor EPPr GBin GEdr GKev GMaP IPot ITim LEdu LShi MAvo NBir NHpl NLar SMHy SPVi WFar WHoo WPnP WSHC WTyc
	- 'Blue Queen'	ELon NRog
	- blue-backed double (d)	CBro
	- 'Blush'	LEdu
	- 'Bowles's Purple'	CBor CMiW EBee EMor EPot GEdr GMaP LRHS NBid NHar NHpl NRog NRya WCot WFar WSHC
	- 'Bracteata'	CBro CMiW GEdr GKev MMrt NRog NSla SDir SPVi
	- 'Bracteata Pleniflora' (d)	CLAP CMiW CTtf EBee ELon EPot GKev GMaP LEdu LShi MAvo MNrw NBir SDeJ WCot WHal WShi
	- 'Buckland'	EPfP EPot SPVi
	- 'Caerulea'	EPot ITim
	- 'Cedric's Pink'	CMiW ECha EPPr MAvo WFar
	- 'Celestial'	EPPr MAvo
	- 'Dark Leaf'	MAvo
	- 'Dee Day'	EPPr LEdu MAvo
	- 'Dell Garden'	EPPr
	- 'Evelyn Meadows'	MAvo WSHC
	- 'Explosion' (d)	NDry
	- 'Flash'	NDry
	- 'Flore Pleno' (d)	CBor CPla EBee LShi NBir WFar
	- 'Flushing'	GEdr MAvo WFar
	- 'Frenzy'	MAvo WCot
	- 'Frühlingsfee'	EPPr MAvo
	- 'Gerda Ramusen'	CBro ELan ELon EPot EShb EWes LEdu WHoo
	- 'Gerry'	MAvo
I	- 'Gigantea Rubra'	WCot
	- 'Glyncoch Gold'	WCot
	- 'Green Dream'	WSHC
	- 'Green Fingers'	EPPr GEdr GKev GMaP MMrt NHar NRog WSHC
	- 'Hakumane Senjuizaki'	WCot
	- 'Hannah Gubbay'	EPot
	- 'Helsinki'	MAvo
	- 'Hilda'	EBee ECtt GEdr GKev IPot LEdu NBir NLar NRog NRya WPnP
	- 'Ice and Fire'	EPot GKev LEdu
	- 'Jack Brownless'	LEdu
	- 'Kentish Pink'	GBin GMaP SPVi
	- 'Knightshayes Vestal' (d)	CExl CLAP CMiW MRav WSHC
	- 'La Rochanne'	MNrw
	- 'Lady Doneraile'	EPot LEdu NBir WFar WSHC
	- 'Lapis'	NDry
	- 'Latvian Pink'	EPot GEdr LEdu MAvo WFar
	- 'Leeds' Variety'	CMiW EPot GMaP LEdu SPVi
	- 'Lionel Bacon'	LEdu MAvo
	- 'Lismore Blue'	EBee EPPr EPot MAvo
	- 'Lismore Pink'	GEdr LEdu
	- 'Lucia'	EPot GEdr GKev LEdu MAvo WCot WFar
	- 'Lychette'	CBor ECha EPPr EPot ERCP GAbr GEdr GKev MAvo NRog WSHC
	- 'Maret' (d)	NDry
	- 'Marie Rose'	EPot WFar
	- 'Mart's Blue'	CBor EPfP GKev WCot WFar
	- 'Monstrosa'	EPot MAvo NRog
	- 'Multiplicity' **new**	EPPr
	- 'Parlez Vous'	CExl EPPr GEdr LEdu MNrw NHpl NRog WFar WPnP WSHC
	- 'Pentre Pink'	EPot MAvo
	- 'Pink Carpet'	GEdr LEdu
	- 'Pink Delight'	LEdu
	- 'Ploeger's Plena' (d)	MAvo
	- 'Robinsoniana' ♀H5	Widely available
	- 'Rosea'	CBor LEdu NLar
I	- 'Rotkäppchen' **new**	SPVi
	- 'Royal Blue'	CBro CMiW EBee ECtt EMor EPPr GAbr GEdr GKev GMaP IPot LEdu MAvo NDov NHpl NLar NRog SDir WCot WFar WHoo WPnP
	- 'Salt and Pepper'	LEdu NDry
	- 'Slack Top Pink'	MAvo
	- 'Slenaken'	MAvo
§	- 'Stammerberg' (d)	EPPr MAvo
	- 'Stammheim'	see *A. nemorosa* 'Stammerberg'
	- 'Tage Lundell' (d) **new**	SPVi
	- 'Tilo'	MAvo
	- 'Tinney's Blush'	CLAP
	- 'Tomas'	CLAP EAJP ELon EPot GEdr LEdu NHpl NRya WFar
	- 'Tups'	LEdu NDry
	- 'Vestal' (d) ♀H5	Widely available
	- 'Virescens' ♀H5	CAvo CMiW CTtf CWCL EBee EGrI ELon EMor EPPr GEdr GKev GMaP LEdu LShi MAvo NBir NHar NLar NRog WShi
	- 'Viridiflora'	CExl CLAP EPfP GAbr GBin MAvo MNrw NBir WCot WSHC
	- 'Westwell Pink'	EPPr MNrw SPVi WCot WFar WSHC WShi
	- white-flowered	CRos LRHS NRHS
	- 'Wilks' Giant'	MAvo NRog
	- 'Wilks' White'	ELon EPPr GEdr MAvo
	- 'Wisley Pink'	EPot LEdu MAvo WFar
I	- 'Wisley White Form'	MAvo NLar
	- 'Wyatt's Pink'	ELon EPot GKev LEdu SPVi
	- 'Yerda Ramusem'	EPPr LEdu MAvo MNrw WSHC
	multifida × ***ranunculoides***	see *A.* × *lipsiensis*
	obtusiloba	GBin GEdr NHpl WAbe WHal
	- CLD 1549	GEdr
	- 'Alba'	GEdr WAbe
	- Harperley selection **new**	NHpl
	- 'Large Blue'	EPot GEdr LEdu NSla WAbe
	- 'Pradesh'	GEdr NHar NHpl WFar
I	- 'Sulphurea'	GEdr WAbe
	palmata	GEdr LEdu WKif

	parviflora	GKev
	pavonina	CMea CMiW CSpe ECha MHol SLon SMHy SPoG WFar
	polyanthes	CRos EBee EBlo EHed EPfP GEdr GKev LRHS NRHS
	prattii	CExl GEdr LEdu NHpl
	protracta	see *A. narcissiflora* var. *protracta*
	pseudoaltaica	LEdu
	- pink-flowered	WFar
	- 'Yuki-no-sei' (d)	GEdr WFar
	pulsatilla	see *Pulsatilla vulgaris*
	raddeana	NRog
*	- f. ***rosea***	GEdr
	ranunculoides 🏆H6	CBro CMiW CTtf CWCL EBee ELon EMor EPot GAbr GArf GEdr GMaP LEdu LRHS MAvo MBel NBid NFav NHar NHol NHpl NLar NRog NRya NSti SDeJ WFar WPnP WSHC WShi
	- 'Anne' (d)	NDry
	- 'Ants' (d)	NDry
	- 'Aureus' (d)	NDry
	- 'Bill Baker'	LEdu MAvo
	- 'Crazy Vienna'	EPPr WCot
	- 'Dagerort' (d)	NDry
	- 'Dagö' (d)	NDry
	- 'Ellen' (d)	NDry
	- 'Ferguson's Fancy'	EPPr
	- 'Frank Waley'	MAvo WCot
	- 'Fuchsis Traum'	LEdu MAvo WCot WSHC
	- 'Golden Dream' (d)	NDry
	- 'Grandiflora'	MAvo
	- 'Hiiumaa' (d)	NDry
	- 'Kahar' (d)	NDry
	- 'Kreet' (d)	NDry
*	- ***laciniata***	MAvo WCot
	- 'Leena' (d)	NDry
	- 'Leida' (d)	NDry
	- 'Linda' (d)	NDry
I	- 'Linearis'	NDry
	- 'Orange'	NDry
	- 'Orjaku' (d)	NDry
	- 'Papa' (d)	NDry
	- 'Pisi' (d)	NDry
	- 'Pleniflora' (d) 🏆H6	CAvo EPPr GKev LRHS NLar NRHS NRog WFar
	- subsp. ***ranunculoides***	GKev
	- 'Sääre' (d)	NDry
	- 'Semi-Plena'	CTtf GEdr LEdu NRog
	- 'Siil' (d)	NDry
	- 'Sirje' (d)	NDry
	- 'Star 1' (d)	NDry
	- 'Tafka' (d)	NDry
	- 'Tapio' (d)	NDry
	- 'Virve' (d)	NDry
	- 'Vulkaan' (d)	NDry
	- subsp. ***wockeana***	EBee LEdu MAvo
	reflexa	EBee
	rivularis	Widely available
	- B&SWJ 13944	WCru
	- BWJ 7611	WCru
	- CC 4588	CExl
	- 'Glacier'	CCBP EBee EMor MHol SBls SBut WHil
	aff. ***rivularis***	WSpi
	RUFFLED SWAN ('Macane007'PBR)	CBod CPar CWGN EBee EHed EMor EWTr GBin GPSL LEdu LRHS MBNS MNrw NLar NRHS NSti SCoo SEdd SHar SLon SPoG WTyc
	rupicola	GEdr NBir WCot
	× ***seemannii***	see *A.* × *lipsiensis*
	stolonifera double-flowered (d)	EBee LEdu LShi WCot WSHC
	sulphurea misapplied	see *Pulsatilla alpina* subsp. *apiifolia*
	sumatrana B&SWJ 11265	WCru
	sylvestris	Widely available
	- 'Elise Fellmann' (d)	EBee WHal
	- 'Madonna'	LSun
	tenuifolia	NHpl
	tetrasepala	WCot
§	***tomentosa***	CBod LRHS NRHS SDix SRms
§	- 'Albadura'	EBee GKev
	- 'Robustissima'	see *A.* × *hybrida* 'Robustissima'
	- 'September Glanz'	EBee
	trifolia L.	CMiW EBee EPPr EPot GEdr LEdu NBid NLar WCot
	trullifolia	GArf GBin GEdr NHar NQui WAbe
	- 'Alba'	GEdr
	- var. ***linearis***	GEdr WAbe
	udensis	GEdr WCot
	vernalis	see *Pulsatilla vernalis*
	virginiana	EBee LEdu LPla MNrw WHrl
	vitifolia misapplied	see *A. tomentosa*
	vitifolia Buch.-Ham. ex DC.	LEdu WPGP
	WILD SWAN ('Macane001'PBR)	Widely available

Anemonella (*Ranunculaceae*)

thalictroides	CBor CElw CTtf EMor EPot GEdr GKev MAvo MBel NHpl NLar NRya SPVi WAbe WFar WPnP WSHC WSpi XLum
- 'Alba Plena' (d)	WSHC
- 'Amelia'	CElw GEdr MAvo NBro NHpl
- 'Babe'	WCot
- 'Betty Blake' (d)	CBor CElw EBee GEdr GKev MAvo MMrt NBro NHpl NRya NSla SDir SPVi WCot WFar
- 'Blushing Bride' (d)	GEdr NBro WCot
- 'Cameo'	CBor GEdr GKev MNrw NHpl NRya SDir WCot WFar
- 'Charlotte'	GEdr
- 'Dark Pink'	EBee GBin MAvo NHpl
- 'Diamante'	CElw LPla WCot
- 'Double Diamante' (d)	WCot
- 'Full Double White' (d)	NHpl
- 'Green Hurricane' (d)	CBor GEdr GKev MAvo NRya SDir SPVi WCot WFar
- 'Hakikomi-fu' (v)	GEdr
- 'Kikuzaki Pink' (d)	CBor GEdr GKev WFar
- 'Kikuzaki White' (d)	CBor GEdr GKev WFar
- 'Pink Fairy'	SMHy
- 'Pink Flash' (d) **new**	SPVi
- f. ***rosea***	CElw ELan EMor NLar WAbe
- - 'Oscar Schoaf' (d)	CElw EPot GArf GEdr GKev MAvo NHpl SPVi WCot WFar
- - semi-double pink-flowered (d)	CElw MAvo
- 'Rosea Plena' (d)	CBor EMor GArf SDir
- semi-double white-flowered (d)	CElw
- 'Shiozaki' (d)	GEdr
- 'Spring Nymph'	SMHy
- 'Tairin'	CBor GEdr NHpl WCot WFar

Anemonopsis (*Ranunculaceae*)

macrophylla	CExl CMiW CSpe EBee EHed EPfP EWes EWld GArf GEdr GKev LEdu LRHS MNrw MRav NFav NHpl NLar WCru WFar WPGP WSHC
- 'Alba'	GKev

- double-flowered (d) GEdr WSHC
- 'White Swan' CMiW EWld GEdr SBls WCru WSHC

Anemopsis (*Saururaceae*)

californica CPud EWat LCro LLWG LOPS MWts SBrt WCot

Anethum (*Apiaceae*)

graveolens CArg ENfk GPoy LCro LOPS MBow MBros MHer MNHC MPri SPhx SRms SVic XAbr
- 'Dukat' CLau LCro LOPS

angelica see *Angelica archangelica*

Angelica (*Apiaceae*)

sp. SEdi WCru
acutiloba WFar
- var. ***iwatensis*** B&SWJ 11197 WCru
anomala WFar
- B&SWJ 10886 ESwi WCru
archangelica Widely available
- subsp. ***decurrens*** LEdu WPGP
arguta B&SWJ 14115 WCru
- B&SWJ 14162 WCru
atropurpurea EPfP LRHS MNrw MRav SWvt
brevicaulis GGro LEdu
breweri B&SWJ 14083 WCru
cartilaginomarginata B&SWJ 12663 WCru
cyclocarpa WJC 13658 WCru
dahurica EWTr GGro LRHS SPhx WFar WHil
decursiva B&SWJ 5746 WCru
edulis WHer
- B&SWJ 10968 WCru
genuflexa B&SWJ 14109 WCru
gigas Widely available
- B&SWJ 4170 WCru
- 'Atropurpurea' NLar
hendersoni SPhx
hispanica see *A. pachycarpa*
japonica B&SWJ 11480 WCru
montana see *A. sylvestris*
morii RWJ 9802 WCru
nubigena WJC 13763 WCru
§ ***pachycarpa*** CBod CRos EBee EPPr GBin GGro GMaP LRHS MHer MRav NBir NGBl NLar NRHS SPhx WCot WFar
pubescens NDov
- B&SWJ 5593 LEdu WCru
sachalinensis GBin GGro
sinensis GGro LEdu
'Summer Delight' see *Ligusticum scoticum*
§ ***sylvestris*** CHab LLWG NAts
- B&SWJ 15332 **new** WCru
- 'Burgundy' NGBl
- 'Ebony' ♀H5 CBct CBod CCBP CPla CSpe CTtf CWCL ECha ECtt GAbr GJos LEdu LRHS MAvo MBNS MHer MHol NLar NSti SEdd SPad SPoG WCot
* - 'Purpurea' CBod CDor EWes MAsh
- 'Vicar's Mead' EBee ECha ELan GGro GJos LRHS NBir NDov SCoo SPhx SWvt WCAu WHil
taiwaniana CDTJ EBee ELan ESwi GGro MMuc NLar SSal
triquinata B&SWJ 15429 **new** WCru
ursina WCru

Angelonia (*Plantaginaceae*)

ADESSA BLUE BICOLOR **new** LSou
(Angelface Series) ANGELFACE PINK IMPROVED ('Anpinkim'^{PBR}) **new** MHol
- ANGELFACE WEDGWOOD BLUE ('Anwedg') MHol
ARCHANGEL DEEP ROSE ('Balarcrose') CRos EHyd LRHS NRHS

Anigozanthos (*Haemodoraceae*)

sp. CDoC
'Bush Ranger' (Bush Gems Series) CCCN
flavidus SPlb
- 'Ember' CCCN
- 'Illusion' CCCN
- 'Opal' CCCN
- 'Pearl' CCCN
- red-flowered SPlb
- 'Splendour' CCCN
- 'Yellow Gem' CCCN
manglesii SPlb
rufus SEle

anise see *Pimpinella anisum*

Anisodontea (*Malvaceae*)

§ ***capensis*** ♀H2 CCCN ELan EPri MACG SChF SEle SPlb SRkn SRms SVen SWvt WABo WHil WLov
- 'Elegans Princess' CCCN WHil
'Crystal Rose' EPfP MGos
'El Rayo' CSde CWGN EBee ECtt ELan ELon LPla MHol MNrw MPie SCob SDys SEdd SIvy SMad SPad SPoG SRkn WAvo WBor WBrk WCot WFar WLov WMal WSHC WTre XLum
'Elegant Lady' SEle
huegelii see *Alyogyne huegelii*
× ***hypomadara*** misapplied see *A. capensis*
§ ***hypomadara*** (Sprague) D.M. Bates MAvo WCot
julii SVen
LADY IN PINK ('Nuanilaninp') CBod MBNS MBros MHol NCou SEdd SEle
'Large Magenta' CMac EBee EPfP ILea LRHS MBNS SEdd SGBe SWvt

Anisodus (*Solanaceae*)

carnioliciodes BWJ 7501 WCru

Anisotome (*Apiaceae*)

imbricata var. ***imbricata*** WAbe
lyallii IKel

Annona (*Annonaceae*)

cherimola (F) CCCN
squamosa (F) SPlb

Anoda (*Malvaceae*)

cristata 'Candy Cups' **new** CSpe

Anoiganthus see *Cyrtanthus*

Anomalesia see *Gladiolus*

Anomatheca (*Iridaceae*)

cruenta see *Freesia laxa*

Anredera (*Basellaceae*)

§ ***cordifolia*** CRHN EShb GKev LEdu

Antennaria (*Asteraceae*)

aprica see *A. parvifolia*
dioica CTri ECtt GAbr GBin GPoy MACG SPlb SRms WAbe XLum
- 'Alba' GQue MCot
- 'Alex Duguid' GPSL NWad
- 'Aprica' see *A. parvifolia*
- 'Bright Rose' new LRHS
- 'Minima' EPot GMaP NBro NSla WAbe
- 'Nyewoods Variety' SRms
- var. ***rosea*** see *A. rosea*
- 'Rotes Wunder' CMea ECha NSla WAbe WHoo
* - 'Rubra' ECha ECtt EDAr NBir SRms WCav WIce XLum
'Joy' WAbe
§ ***parvifolia*** CTri SRms
- 'Alba' EDAr
§ ***rosea*** ♀H5 CRos EHyd EPfP GArf GKev GMaP LRHS MAsh NRHS SPlb SRms WHoo WIce

Antenoron see *Persicaria*

Anthemis ✿ (*Asteraceae*)

from Turkey ECtt EWes
arvensis CHab MBow MNHC SRms
- subsp. ***sphacelata*** WCot
§ 'Beauty of Grallagh' WSpi
'Cally Cream' ELon GWyn LPla LRHS SDix SMrm SPhx WMal
'Cally White' GAbr GBin LPla WBrk
carpatica NBro
- 'Karpatenschnee' EHyd EPfP LRHS NRHS SAko SRms
cretica subsp. ***leucanthemoides*** WAbe
- subsp. ***tenuiloba*** EWes
frutescens Voss see *Argyranthemum frutescens*
'Grallagh Gold' misapplied, orange-yellow see *A.* 'Beauty of Grallagh'
'Grallagh Gold' ECha ECtt NPer SPhx WFar
§ ***marschalliana*** CBor EBou EDAr GKev LRHS NHpl NRHS SMrm SPlb SRms WAbe WCot WKif
nobilis see *Chamaemelum nobile*
'Orange Dream' CBcs
punctata subsp. ***cupaniana*** ♀H4 Widely available
- - 'Nana' NBir NPer SEdd SHar WCot
rudolphiana see *A. marschalliana*
sancti-johannis EPfP LRHS MACG NPer NRHS SAko SMrm SRms
SUSANNA MITCHELL ('Blomit') CDor CRos CTtf EBee ECtt ELon GAbr GMaP LRHS LSRN MAvo MBel MHol MNrw NDov NLar NRHS SMrm SWvt WMal WSHC XLum
'Tetworth' ECha ELan EPfP LRHS SAko
tinctoria CBod CHby CMac ENfk GPoy MHer MNHC MRav NAts NPer SRms SWvt WSFF
- 'Alba' EBee LRHS NRHS WFar
- 'Charme' PBR LRHS NLar SPoG SRms SWvt
- 'Compacta' EWes XLum
- 'E.C. Buxton' ♀H6 Widely available
- 'Eva' NDov NFav
- 'Hall Farm Frilly' ECtt ELon
- 'Kelwayi' CRos EBee EBou EPfP GLog GQue GWyn LRHS MACG NLar NPer NRHS SPer SRms WFar
- 'Lemon Ice' EBee EWoo GBin GWyn MBel NLar
- 'Lemon Maid' ECtt ELon SMrm
- 'Sauce Hollandaise' Widely available
- subsp. ***tinctoria*** SMrm
- 'Wargrave Variety' CBod CElw CMac ECha ECtt ELan EPfP GBin GWyn LRHS MAvo MHol NBir NGdn NRHS SDix SPhx SWvt WCAu WFar
'Tinpenny Sparkle' EBee ECtt EWes EWhm GWyn MACG MHol NLar WFar WHoo
triumfettii EBee NDov NPer
tuberculata NChi

Anthericum (*Asparagaceae*)

algeriense see *A. liliago*
* ***bovei*** CBro
§ ***liliago*** CSpe ELan EWTr EWoo GKev GMaP MCot MRav NLar SMad SPer
- 'Major' ♀H5 CAvo CBro ECha MHol SPhx
plumosum see *Trichopetalum plumosum*
ramosum CFis CSpe EBee ECha EPPr EPot EPri EWes GKev LEdu LRHS MBrN NBid NBir NLar NSla SPhx WCot WSHC

Antholyza (*Iridaceae*)

coccinea see *Crocosmia paniculata*
paniculata see *Crocosmia paniculata*

Anthoxanthum (*Poaceae*)

odoratum CHab GPoy GQue SPhx

Anthriscus (*Apiaceae*)

cerefolium CHby CLau ENfk GPoy LCro LOPS MBow MHer MNHC SEdi SPhx SRms SVic WSFF XAbr
nemorosa LEdu
sylvestris CHab GQue LCro LOPS LRHS NMir SPhx WFar WSFF
- 'Going for Gold' CTtf EPPr EWes MHol MNrw NChi WCot WHil WMal
- 'Golden Fleece' ECha GGro LShi SPad
- 'Kabir' LRHS
- 'Ravenswing' Widely available
- yellow-leaved GBin

Anthurium (*Araceae*)

PINK CHAMPION ('Antinkeles' PBR) LCro LOPS
RED CHAMPION ('Anthbnena' PBR) LCro LOPS

Anthyllis (*Fabaceae*)

hermanniae 'Compacta' see *A. hermanniae* 'Minor'
§ - 'Minor' ELan EPot ITim WAbe
montana XSen
- subsp. ***atropurpurea*** LRHS NRHS
- 'Rubra' ♀H5 CSpe EDAr EPot LShi SPhx WAbe
vulneraria CHab GJos NAts NMir NRya SPhx WSFF
- var. ***coccinea*** CBod CBor CKel EAJP ELan EWld GJos GKev LCro LOPS MACG MBel NAts NSla SPhx WIce
- dark red-flowered CSpe SPhx

Antirrhinum (*Plantaginaceae*)

asarina see *Asarina procumbens*
barrelieri SEND

braun-blanquetii	CBod WCot
charidemi	EBee
'Defiance' **new**	SSal
'Eva Grey' **new**	CKel LRHS
hispanicum 'Avalanche'	ECtt
§ - subsp. ***hispanicum***	CSpe
latifolium	EBee
majus 'Admiral White'	LCro LOPS
- APPEAL BICOLOUR MIX	LOPS SCob
- 'Black Prince'	CSpe ECtt ELan LPla
- 'Night and Day'	CSpe EWTr
- 'Rocket White' (Rocket Series)	CSpe
- Sonnet Series, formula mixed	MBros MPri
molle	CSpe EBee GKev MCot NPer SChF
- pink-flowered	MCot SBut
- white-flowered	EBee SBut
PRETTY IN PINK ('Pmoore07'PBR)	CBod CSBt IPot LCro LOPS LRHS LSou MBros MHol SLon SPeP WHil WNPC
pulverulentum	GKev
sempervirens	CFis WAbe XLum
siculum	EBee

añu see *Tropaeolum tuberosum*

Aphelandra (*Acanthaceae*)

squarrosa	EShb

Aphyllanthes (*Asparagaceae*)

monspeliensis	XLum XSen

Apios (*Fabaceae*)

§ ***americana***	EWes LEdu NBir SBrt WCot WCru WKor WSHC
- 'Nutty'	CAgr MCoo
tuberosa	see *A. americana*

Apium (*Apiaceae*)

graveolens	CHab CLau CTsd ENfk GPoy MHer MNHC SRms SVic WJek
- var. ***dulce*** 'Aurora'	LOPS
- - 'Brydon's Prize Red'	SVic
- - 'Celebrity' ♀H2	LRHS MCtn NRHS
- - 'Golden Self-blanching'	LCro LOPS SVic
- - 'Victoria' ♀H2	EDel EKin MBros
- 'Giant Pink' - Mammoth Pink ♀H4	NRob
- var. ***rapaceum*** 'Prinz' ♀H4	CHby EDel EKin LCro LOPS MCtn SVic
§ - (Secalinum Group) 'Par-cel'	MHer SRms
- - 'Zwolsche Krul'	MBow
nodiflorum	see *Helosciadium nodiflorum*

Apium × *Petroselinum* (*Apiaceae*)

hybrid, misapplied	see *A. graveolens* Secalinum Group

Apocynum (*Apocynaceae*)

cannabinum	GPoy

Apodasmia (*Restionaceae*)

similis **new**	XSte

Aponogeton (*Aponogetonaceae*)

desertorum	EWat LLWG
distachyos	CBen CPud CWat EWat LCro LLWG LOPS MWts NPer SVic WMAq XLum

apple see *Malus domestica*; see also AGM Fruit Section

apricot see *Prunus armeniaca*

Aptenia (*Aizoaceae*)

cordifolia	CCCN NPer SChr SPlb SVen
- 'Variegata' (v)	CCCN

Aquilegia (*Ranunculaceae*)

akitensis misapplied	see *A. flabellata* var. *pumila*
'Alaska' (State Series)	EBee EMor NRHS
alpina	CMea EBee EBou ECha EPfP LCro LOPS LRHS MAsh MNHC NGdn SCob SPer SRms SSal WHoo WSpi XLum
amaliae	see *A. ottonis* subsp. *amaliae*
'Apple Blossom'	NBir
aragonensis	see *A. pyrenaica*
§ ***atrata***	CKel EBee GKev GQue LRHS
atrovinosa from Kazakhstan **new**	GGro
aurea Janka	GKev
bertolonii ♀H5	CMea GKev LRHS NRHS NSla SRms
Biedermeier Group	CRos EPfP GJos LRHS NGdn NRHS
'Blue Star' (Star Series)	CWCL EAJP ELan EPfP GMaP GWyn LRHS NRHS SBls SCoo SGbt SPer SPtp
'Bluebird' (Songbird Series)	LBuc NBir NPer SCoo SGBe WFar
buergeriana	GKev
- 'Calimero'	GKev MBNS NLar
- var. ***oxysepala***	see *A. oxysepala*
'Bunting' (Songbird Series)	SGbt
canadensis	CSpe EBou ELan GAbr GKev GLog NBir NBro SBls SPhx SRms WFar WSpi
- 'Corbett'	SBls
- 'Little Lanterns'	EAJP EDAr NHpl NLar
- 'Nana'	GKev
- 'Pink Lanterns'	EDAr
'Cardinal' (Songbird Series)	LBuc SCoo SGBe
chaplinei	GKev NBir
chrysantha	GJos GKev GWyn MCot SRms SWvt WKif XSen
- 'Denver Gold'	EShb MACG SPhx WHil
- 'Yellow Queen'	CExl CKel CWCL EMor EPPr EPfP EWoo GBin GMaP LCro LOPS LRHS MBel NGdn SGbt SPhx SWvt WCFE WHil WTor
clematiflora	see *A. vulgaris* var. *stellata*
Clementine Series	LRHS
coerulea	GKev SRms
- var. ***coerulea***	SPhx
- 'Rotstern'	CBod
'Colorado' (State Series)	NRHS
'Crimson Star'	CRos CWCL ELan EMor EPfP EShb LRHS MBel NRHS SCoo SPoG
desertorum	GKev
discolor	WThu
'Dove' (Songbird Series)	LBuc MHer SGBe SGbt SHar
I 'Dragonfly'	CBcs CRos EAJP ELan EPfP LRHS NRHS SPoG
ecalcarata	see *Semiaquilegia ecalcarata*
elegantula	GKev
flabellata 'Blackcurrant Ice'	CWCL
- Cameo Series	SRot
- - 'Cameo Blue and White'	SRms
- - 'Cameo Rose and White'	MHer
- 'Georgia' (State Series)	LRHS NRHS
- 'Ministar'	EDAr GWyn
- 'Nana Alba'	see *A. flabellata* var. *pumila* f. *alba*
§ - var. ***pumila*** ♀H5	EAJP ECha EDAr EPfP GEdr GKev LRHS LSun NGdn NRHS SRms

§	- - f. ***alba***	ECha GKev LRHS NRHS
	- - 'Atlantis'	LRHS
I	- - f. ***kurilensis*** 'Rosea'	WAbe
	- 'Vermont' (State Series)	EBee EMor
	flavescens	GKev
	'Florida' (State Series)	EMor LRHS NRHS WHil
	formosa	GKev GQue NChi
§	***fragrans***	EBee GArf GKev
	'Fruit and Nut Chocolate'	EBee WCot WMal
	glandulosa	GWyn
	glauca	see *A. fragrans*
	'Goldfinch' (Songbird Series)	LBuc NBir SCoo SGBe SGbt
	grahamii	EWTr
	'Heavenly Blue'	CBod CDor EBee GWyn
	'Hensol Harebell'	MBriF SHar SPtp SRms WSpi
	'Honeydew'	GWyn
	japonica	see *A. flabellata* var. *pumila*
	jonesii	GEdr GKev SPlb
	jonesii × saximontana	GKev
	'Kansas' (State Series)	LRHS
	karelinii	GKev
	'Koralle'	CBod CDor GWyn SBls WHil
	'Kristall'	CBod EShb EWTr LEdu MBel
*	***kuhistanica***	CBor EBee GKev GWyn
	laramiensis	GKev
	'Leprechaun Gold' (v)	EMor EPfP MACG NGdn SBls SDix
	'Lime Sorbet'	LRHS SRms
	longissima	CPla LEdu MHer SHar WCav WHoo WPGP
	'Louisiana' (State Series)	LRHS NRHS
	'Magpie'	see *A. vulgaris* 'William Guiness'
	× ***maruyamana***	EBee
	McKana Group	CBod CTri ELan EPfP GAbr GJos MGos NGdn NHol NLar SCob SPer SPlb SPoG SRms SVic SWvt WCav WFar
	'Montana' (State Series)	LRHS
	Mrs Scott-Elliot hybrids	CBod CSBt EPfP SCoo
	Music Series	SRms
	'Nightingale' (Songbird Series)	SGbt
	nigricans	see *A. atrata*
	olympica	LSun
	'Oregon' (State Series)	LRHS
	'Origami Yellow' (Origami Series)	WHil
§	***ottonis*** subsp. ***amaliae***	WAbe
§	***oxysepala***	CExl GGro GLog
	- var. ***kansuensis***	GKev
	Perfumed Garden Group	GAbr WFar
§	***pyrenaica***	GKev
	- dwarf	WAbe
	'Red Hobbit'	CSpe CTsd ELan EPfP LRHS MBros NGdn NHpl NLar SCoo WFar
	'Red Star' (Star Series)	CWCL EAJP EPfP EShb LRHS SGbt SPer SPoG
	'Robin' (Songbird Series)	SGbt
	rockii	GKev
	'Rose Queen'	CDor EPfP EShb GWyn SPtp
	'Roundway Chocolate'	SBls
	saximontana	GKev NSla
§	'Schneekönigin'	LRHS NRHS WCFE
	scopulorum	GKev
	- hybrid new	EPot
	- subsp. ***perplexans***	GKev
	sibirica	EBee
	'Silver Queen'	EMor EWoo GBin
	skinneri	CExl GLog
	- 'Tequila Sunrise'	CSpe ELan EMor LRHS MACG MHer NRHS
	SNOW QUEEN	see *A.* 'Schneekönigin'
	Spring Magic Series	MPri WCav
	- SPRING MAGIC BLUE AND WHITE	LRHS SCob
	- SPRING MAGIC ROSE AND WHITE	LRHS
	- SPRING MAGIC WHITE	NRHS SCob
	- SPRING MAGIC YELLOW	LRHS
	stellata	see *A. vulgaris* var. *stellata*
	'Sunburst Ruby'	CWCL
	(Swan Series) 'Swan Lavender'	SCob WFar
	- 'Swan Pink and Yellow'	CBod SCob
	- 'Swan Red and White'	CBod SCob WFar
	- 'Swan Violet and White'	SCob WFar
	triternata	GWyn
	'Virginia' (State Series)	CBod LRHS MSCN NRHS
	viridiflora	CBod CBor EMor GGro GKev LRHS WAbe WCot
	- 'Chocolate Soldier'	CSpe EMor SBls SPeP
	(Volcano! Group) 'Volcano!' (mixed)	GQue
	vulgaris	CBod CHab EPfP GBin GKev GPoy GQue GWyn LCro LOPS MBow MHer MNHC NBro NGdn NGrd SCob SPlb WCAu WShi XSen
	- 'Adelaide Addison'	ECha
	- var. ***alba***	CBod CMea EPfP LRHS MMuc NRHS SCob SEdd
	- 'Altrosa'	GWyn
	- 'Aureovariegata'	see *A. vulgaris* Vervaeneana Group
	- ***clematiflora***	see *A. vulgaris* var. *stellata*
	- (Clementine Series) 'Clementine Blue' (d)	CRos EPfP NRHS SPoG WCot
	- - 'Clementine Dark Purple' (d)	CRos EPfP NRHS SPoG
	- - 'Clementine Red' (d)	EPfP LRHS NRHS
	- - 'Clementine Rose' (d)	CRos GQue LRHS NRHS SPoG
	- - 'Clementine Salmon Rose' (d)	CRos EPfP LRHS NRHS SPoG
	- - 'Clementine White' (d)	CRos CWCL EPfP LRHS NRHS SPoG WSpi
	- 'Crystal Star'	EPfP LRHS NRHS
	- 'Eyecatcher'	WCot
	- var. ***flore-pleno*** bicoloured (d)	XAbr
	- - black-flowered (d)	MMuc SEND WCot
	- - 'Dorothy Rose' (Dorothy Series) (d)	SPtp
	- - purple-flowered (d)	WSpi
*	- - 'White Bonnet' (d)	CWCL
	- 'Heidi'	GWyn WSpi XSen
	- 'Mellow Yellow'	GPSL SDix
	- MUNSTEAD WHITE	see *A. vulgaris* 'Nivea'
§	- 'Nivea'	CDor CSpe EBee ECha ELan EPfP EWoo LCro LOPS NChi SEND SPoG SPtp WCot WSpi
	- Pom Pom Series	WSpi
	- - 'Pom Pom Crimson'	WCot
§	- var. ***stellata***	CDor GWyn NBir NBro
	- - (Barlow Series) 'Black Barlow' (d)	Widely available
	- - - 'Blue Barlow' (d)	CBod CDor CRos CSpe EBee ECtt EMor EPfP GMaP ILea LCro LOPS LRHS LSRN MPri NRHS SCob SCoo SEdd SPer STPC SWvt WCot WSpi
	- - - 'Bordeaux Barlow' (d)	CBod LRHS NRHS STPC
	- - - 'Christa Barlow' (d)	CRos EBee EPfP LRHS NLar NRHS
	- - - 'Nora Barlow' (d)	Widely available
	- - - 'Rose Barlow' (d)	CBod EPfP LRHS LSRN NRHS SCob WSpi
	- - - 'White Barlow' (d)	CDor CRos EPfP GMaP LCro LOPS LRHS MBel MPri NRHS SCob SPer STPC SWvt

- - blue-flowered	MMuc NBir SEND
- - 'Greenapples' (d)	CDor EAJP EMor EPfP EWhm GQue LRHS MACG MBros SBls SCob WHoo
* - - 'Iceberg'	WSpi
- - 'Royal Purple' (d)	NBro
- - 'Ruby Port' (d)	CBcs CBod CDor ECha ELan EMor EPfP EWoo GMaP GWyn ILea LCro LOPS LRHS LSRN MACG MNrw NChi NGdn NLar NRHS SBls SCob SEdd SGbt SPer SPhx WCAu WTyc
- - white-flowered	CSpe NBir NBro
- variegated foliage	see *A. vulgaris* Vervaeneana Group
§ - Vervaeneana Group (v)	CDor CSpe EPfP GAbr LRHS MBow NBir NPer SPlb SRms WHoo
- - 'Woodside White' (v)	NBir WBrk
§ - 'William Guiness'	Widely available
- 'William Guiness Doubles' (d)	GWyn
'White Star' (Star Series)	CDor EBee ELan EPfP GMaP LRHS SCoo SGbt SPoG
'White Swan'	WFar
Winky Series	GJos GQue LRHS SWvt WFar
- 'Winky Blue-White'	CRos GBin LRHS NLar NRHS
- 'Winky Purple-White'	LRHS NRHS
- 'Winky Red-White'	LRHS NRHS SWvt
- 'Winky Rose-Rose'	CRos LRHS NRHS
yabeana	GKev LRHS SPhx
'Yellow Star' (Star Series)	CBcs CBod CDor CWCL ECtt EPfP LRHS MHol NRHS SGbt SPer

Aquilegia × Semiaquilegia (*Ranunculaceae*)

hybrid, blue-flowered	NGdn

Arabis (*Brassicaceae*)

albida	see *A. alpina* subsp. *caucasica*
alpina	SPlb
§ - subsp. ***caucasica***	GDam GKev
- - 'Arctic Joy' (v)	NWad WCot WHoo
- - 'Corfe Castle'	ECtt
- - 'Douler Angevine' (v)	CBod ECtt NHpl SPoG SRms WIce
- - 'Flore Pleno' (d) ♀H6	CElw CTri ECtt ELan EWld GAbr GMaP SGro SRms WBrk WHoo XLum
- - LITTLE TREASURE DEEP ROSE ('Ararosa') **new**	LRHS
- - LITTLE TREASURE WHITE ('Aralba')	GWyn LRHS
- - 'Lotti Deep Rose'	CBod
- - 'Lotti White'	CBod
- - 'Pink Pearl'	WFar
- - 'Pinkie'	SBut
- - 'Pixie Cream'	ECtt NGdn SRms
- - 'Rosea'	EPfP GJos NBir SRms
§ - - 'Schneehaube' ♀H6	CTri EPfP GMaP GWyn NBir NGdn SPoG SRms
- - SNOWCAP	see *A. alpina* subsp. *caucasica* 'Schneehaube'
- - 'Snowdrop'	WFar
- - 'Variegata' (v)	ELan SPoG SRms
androsacea	GKev SRms
× ***arendsii*** 'Compinkie'	GJos SPlb SRms
blepharophylla	MPri
§ - 'Frühlingszauber' ♀H5	CTri EAJP ELan EPfP GJos MAsh NBir NGdn SPoG SRms WCav
- 'Rose Delight'	EPfP GJos LRHS NRHS
- 'Rote Sensation'	ELan NGdn
- SPRING CHARM	see *A. blepharophylla* 'Frühlingszauber'
carduchorum	XLum
caucasica	see *A. alpina* subsp. *caucasica*
§ ***collina*** subsp. ***rosea***	GJos NFav
cypria	GJos
ferdinandi-coburgi	NHol SRms WCav
- 'Aureovariegata' (v)	CMea CTri ECtt ELan SWvt
- 'Old Gold' (v)	CBod EBou EPfP GQue GWyn LPot LRHS MAsh MHer NBir NFav NHol NRya SLee SPoG SRms SRot SWvt WCFE WCav WFar XLum
- 'Variegata'	see *A. procurrens* 'Variegata'
koehleri	GJos
procurrens	WCot XSen
§ - 'Variegata' (v) ♀H6	CTri ECtt ELan EPfP EWes GAbr GPSL LRHS MAsh MBrN MHer SLee SPlb SRms WCot WFar XLum
pumila	GKev
purpurea	GJos
rosea	see *A. collina* subsp. *rosea*
SNOW CAP	see *A. alpina* subsp. *caucasica* 'Schneehaube'
soyeri subsp. ***subcoriacea***	GKev
× ***suendermannii***	XLum

Arachniodes (*Dryopteridaceae*)

aristata	CTsd LEdu MBel SAko
davalliaeformis	CLAP EBee LRHS MAsh NRHS SPlb WCot WPGP
rhomboidea	CLAP
simplicior	CBdn CCCN CLAP EBee EHed EShb ESwi LBuc LEdu LLWG LRHS MAsh NRHS SPlb WCot WPGP
standishii	CLAP CRos EBee EHed EShb LEdu LRHS MAsh NRHS SPlb WCot WPGP

Araiostegia (*Davalliaceae*)

faberiana	CExl
hymenophylloides	WCot
parvipinnata	see *A. perdurans*
§ ***perdurans***	LEdu WPGP
- B&SWJ 1608	EBee WCru
pulchra HWJ 1007	ESwi WCru

Aralia ✿ (*Araliaceae*)

NJM 13.033	EBee
apioides EDHCH 9720	WCru
armata B&SWJ 6916	WCru
bipinnata Blanco CWJ 12407	WCru
- RWJ 10101	WCru
cachemirica	CDTJ ESwi EWld NBid SDix SMad SPlb WCru
californica	ESwi GPoy LEdu NLar WCru
castanopsidicola CWJ 12411	WCru
chapaensis B&SWJ 11812	WCru
- HWJ 1013	WCru
chinensis misapplied	see *A. elata*
chinensis L. BWJ 8102	WCru
continentalis	LEdu NLar WHoo
- pink-flowered B&SWJ 8437	WCru
cordata Thunb.	CAgr GPoy LEdu
- B&SWJ 5596	WCru
- B&SWJ 8524 from Ulleungdo, South Korea	WCru
- var. ***sachalinensis*** B&SWJ 4773	WCru
- 'Sun King'	CBod CKel EBee ECtt EPfP ESwi GBin LCro LOPS LRHS LSou MGil MHol MNrw NBid NEoE NLar SDix SPad SPeP SPoG SWvt WBor WFar WHil WLov XSte
dasyphylla	LEdu
decaisneana NMWJ 14531	WCru
- NMWJ 14542	WCru
- RWJ 9910	WCru

§ ***elata***	CBcs CDoC CExl CMac EBee ELan EPfP IPap LMaj LPar LRHS MBlu MGos MHtn MMuc SArc SGol SPoG SWvt WFar WSpi
- B&SWJ 5480	WCru
- 'Albomarginata'	see *A. elata* 'Variegata'
- 'Aureo-marginata' (v)	WSpi
- 'Aureovariegata' (v) 🏆H5	CBcs EWes NLar
- 'Golden Umbrella' (v)	NLar
- 'Silver Umbrella' (v)	NLar WSpi
§ - 'Variegata' (v) 🏆H5	CBcs NLar SWvt
foliolosa B&SWJ 8360	WCru
- NJM 13.033	WPGP
- NJM 13.061	WPGP
kansuensis B&SWJ 9515	ESwi
- BWJ 7650	WCru
leschenaultii B&SWJ 11789	WCru
- B&SWJ 9515	WCru
nudicaulis L.	GPoy
papyrifera	see *Tetrapanax papyrifer*
racemosa	GPoy LEdu SBls SPhx SRms WJek
- B&SWJ 9570	WCru
searelliana B&SWJ 11736	WCru
sieboldii de Vriese	see *Fatsia japonica*
spinosa L.	MBlu NChi SPlb
subcordata HWJK 2385	WCru
verticillata B&SWJ 11797	WCru
vietnamensis B&SWJ 12349E	WCru

Araucaria (*Araucariaceae*)

sp.	GDam MAsh
angustifolia	CAco CDTJ IKel WPGP
§ ***araucana***	Widely available
bidwillii	CAco MMuc SEND
columnaris	CAco
cunninghamii	CAco
excelsa misapplied	see *A. heterophylla*
§ ***heterophylla*** 🏆H2	CAco CCCN CDoC ERom LCro SEND
imbricata	see *A. araucana*
laubenfelsii new	CAco
luxurians new	CAco

Araujia (*Apocynaceae*)

sericifera	CBcs CRHN EShb SVen WSHC

Arbutus ✿ (*Ericaceae*)

andrachne	CDow CKel LRHS WHwl XSte
× ***andrachnoides*** 🏆H4	CBrP CRos ELan EPfP LRHS LSRN MAsh MRav NRHS SPoG WPGP WSpi
× ***androsterilis***	WPGP
menziesii	CMCN MBlu MGil MHid
× ***reyorum*** 'Marina'	CJun EBee ELan EPfP LRHS MAsh MBlu MPkF SMad SPoG WPGP
× ***thuretiana***	WPGP
unedo	Widely available
- 'Atlantic' 🏆H5	CCCN CDoC CJun EBee EPfP LRHS LSRN MAsh MGos MPkF SCob SGbt SGol SWvt WHwl XSte
- 'Compacta'	CBcs CCCN CRos EBee ELan EPfP LRHS MAsh NLar SCob SGol SLon SWvt WFar WTyc
- 'Elfin King'	ELan EPfP LRHS MAsh SLon SPoG SWvt
- 'Quercifolia'	CCCN CJun EBee ELan LEdu LRHS MAsh NLar SMad
- ROSELILY ('Minlily'PBR)	CDoC CKel EBee EHed EMil LRHS LSRN MPkF SGsty XSte
- f. ***rubra*** 🏆H5	Widely available
xalapensis	SPlb

Archontophoenix (*Arecaceae*)

cunninghamiana	SPalm

Arctanthemum (*Asteraceae*)

§ ***arcticum***	ECha NLar XLum
- 'Polarstern'	EBee MNrw WFar
- 'Roseum'	EBee ELon WFar
- 'Schwefelglanz'	WFar

Arcterica see *Pieris*

Arctium (*Asteraceae*)

lappa	GPoy SEdi SRms SVic WHer WSFF
minus	GQue NMir

Arctostaphylos (*Ericaceae*)

uva-ursi	GArf GQue NLar SPlb
- 'Snowcap'	MAsh
- 'Vancouver Jade'	CMac CRos ELan GArf GKin LRHS LSRN MAsh NRHS SCoo SPer SPoG SSta SWvt

Arctotheca (*Asteraceae*)

calendula	EBee WMal WSHC

Arctotis (*Asteraceae*)

acaulis	WSMil
HAYLEY ('Archley'PBR)	CCCN CCht ECtt MBNS
'Heidi'	CCht MBNS
'Holly'	CCht CPla MHol
'Hope'	CCht
× ***hybrida*** hort. 'Apricot'	CCCN ECtt
- 'Flame' 🏆H2	CCCN CCht ECtt MBNS SCoo SMrm WABo
- 'Harlequin'	XAbr
- 'Red Devil'	CCCN CCht EWoo MBNS MBow SCoo SMrm WABo
- 'Wine'	CCCN CCht MBNS SCoo SMrm SRkn WABo
(Opera Series) OPERA FIRE ('Kleat12611') new	LRHS
- OPERA ORANGE ('Kleat12609') new	LRHS
- OPERA ROSE ('Kleat12610'PBR) new	LRHS
(The Ravers Series) BUMBLEBEE ('Arc406') new	LRHS
- CHERRY FROST ('Arc245') new	LRHS
§ - HANNAH ('Archnah'PBR)	CCht ECtt LRHS MBNS
- 'Pink Sugar'	LRHS
- PUMPKIN PIE	see *A.* (The Ravers Series) HANNAH

Ardisia (*Primulaceae*)

§ ***crenata*** 'Queen Star'PBR	LCro LOPS
japonica	WCot
- B&SWJ 1032	WCru
- var. ***angusta***	WCot
- 'Houkan' (v)	CDTJ SMad WPGP
- 'Ito Fukurin' (v)	CBct CDTJ EBee WPGP
- var. ***minor***	GEdr
- - B&SWJ 1841	WCru
- - B&SWJ 3809	WCru
- variegated (v) new	CBct

Arecastrum see *Syagrus*

Arenaria (*Caryophyllaceae*)

§ ***alfacarensis***	EPot NLar SPlb WAbe XLum

balearica	EWes LLWG MAsh NAts NSla SPlb SRms WFar WIce XLum
capillaris	CTri
festucoides	GKev
hookeri	WAbe
subsp. ***desertorum***	
kansuensis	NLar
ledebouriana	MACG NLar SBrt
montana ♀H5	CMea CTri ECha EDAr EPfP EWoo LCro LOPS LRHS MBel MGos NBir NRHS NSla SEdd SPlb SRms SRot WAbe WCav WFar WIce WKif
- 'Avalanche'	CBod ECtt LSun MACG
- 'Lemon Ice' **new**	CMea
pulvinata	see *A. alfacarensis*
purpurascens	EPot EWes LLWG NLar SRms WAbe
* ***scopolina***	EWes
tetraquetra subsp. ***amabilis***	EPot

Argania (*Sapotaceae*)

spinosa	WPGP XAbr

Argemone (*Papaveraceae*)

grandiflora	CSpe EPPr WHil
mexicana	LRHS
platyceras	CSpe WFar

Argyranthemum ✿ (*Asteraceae*)

Aramis Series	see × *Argyrimelia* Aramis Series
CHERRY LOVE ('Supacher') (Daisy Crazy Series) (d) ♀H2	CCCN
'Citronelle'	CBcs
'Cornish Gold' ♀H2	CBcs CCCN ECtt EShb MCot
double pink-flowered (d)	SVen
'Everest'	NRHS SPoG
foeniculaceum misapplied, pink-flowered	see *A.* 'Petite Pink'
§ ***foeniculaceum*** (Willd.) Webb & Sch.Bip.	MCot
- 'Royal Haze' ♀H2	CCCN NPer
§ ***frutescens***	LCro LOPS WKif XLum
§ - subsp. ***canariae*** ♀H2	CCCN
gracile 'Chelsea Girl' ♀H2	CCCN CSpe MBNS MCot WABo WKif
Grandaisy Series	see × *Argyrimelia* Grandaisy Series
- GRANDAISY YELLOW	see × *Glebianthemum* GRANDAISY YELLOW
GYPSY ROSE ('M9/18d')	CCCN
'Jamaica Primrose' ♀H2	CSpe CTri SDix SSal WABo
aff. 'Jamaica Primrose'	CDow
LARITA BANANA SPLIT ('Kleaf10067') (LaRita Series) ♀H2	NRHS SPoG WHil
'Levada Cream' ♀H2	CSpe
'Lolly'	CWCL
(Madeira Series) MADEIRA CRESTED HOT PINK ('Bonmad 11277')	LSou
- MADEIRA CRESTED IVORY ('Bonmadcivy') (d)	SPoG
- MADEIRA CRESTED MERLOT ('Bonmadmerlo'[PBR]) (d)	LSou WHil
- MADEIRA CRESTED PINK ('Bonmadcink'[PBR])	SPoG
- MADEIRA CRESTED YELLOW ('Bonmadcrel'[PBR])	SPoG
- MADEIRA RED ('Bonmadre'[PBR])	SPoG
- MADEIRA WHITE ('Ohmadleva')	MBros
- MADEIRA WHITE IMPROVED ('Bonmadwitim'[PBR])	MBros SPoG
'Mary Wootton' (d)	ECtt
METEOR RED ('Supa742') (Daisy Crazy Series)	CBcs CWGN MBNS
MOLIMBA XL PASTEL YELLOW ('Argyrayesi'[PBR]) (Molimba Series)	SPoG
PACIFIC GOLD ('Pacargone'[PBR]) (d)	CWGN
§ 'Petite Pink' ♀H2	CCCN
PING-PONG ('Innping'[PBR]) (d)	CCCN
POLLY ('Innpolly')	CBcs
'Powder Puff' (d)	ECtt
'Raspberry Ruffles' (d)	CBcs CPla MCot WHil
SOLE MIO ('Supa3047') (d)	CWCL
'Sugar and Ice' (d)	CCCN
'Sugar Baby' (d)	CCCN
'Summer Melody' (d)	CCCN
'Summer Pink'	CCCN
'Vancouver' (d) ♀H2	CCCN ECtt
'Vera'	CCCN
'White Spider'	CCCN

Argyranthemum × *Glebionis* see × *Glebianthemum*

Argyranthemum × *Ismelia* see × *Argyrimelia*

× *Argyrimelia* (*Asteraceae*)

§ (Aramis Series) 'Aramis Apricot' **new**	LRHS LSou
- 'Aramis Deep Rose' **new**	LSou
- 'Aramis Double Primrose' (d) **new**	LRHS
- 'Aramis Ice'	LRHS
- 'Aramis Lemon'	LSou
- 'Aramis Pink Eye' **new**	LRHS
- 'Aramis Rose'	LRHS LSou
- 'Aramis Wine Red'	LRHS
- 'Aramis Yellow' **new**	LRHS
§ Grandaisy Series	SCob
- GRANDAISY PINK HALO ('Bonmax 9163') ♀H3	MBros SCob
- GRANDAISY RED ('Bonmax 1472')	CWCL MBros SCob

Argyrocytisus (*Fabaceae*)

§ ***battandieri***	Widely available
- 'Yellow Tail' ♀H5	ELan EPfP LRHS MGos MTrO NLar NOrn SPoG SSta WAvo WMat XSte

Arisaema (*Araceae*)

CC 4904	CExl
CC 5511	CExl
amurense	CBor CElw WThu
angustatum var. ***peninsulae*** B&SWJ 8639	WCru
brachyspathum	see *A. heterophyllum*
brevipes	CExl
candidissimum ♀H4	CBor CDor ECha ELon EPPr EPfP EPot EWld GEdr GKev LRHS MRav NLar NRHS NSla SDeJ SDir WAbe WCot WHal WPnP
- pink-flowered	NGKo
- white-flowered	GEdr
ciliatum ♀H4	CPla CWCL EBee EPot GEdr NLar WTyc

- var. ***liubaense*** EPfP GEdr GKev ITim WCot
- - CT 369 CExl SDys WSHC
concinnum GKev NGKo WPnP XLum
consanguineum CBcs CExl EBee EPfP GBin GEdr GKev SMrm SPtp WCot WFar WMal WPnP XLum
- subsp. ***kelung-insulare*** B&SWJ 256 WCru
- 'The Perfect Wave' WCot
- variegated (v) GKev WCot
costatum CCCN EBee EPfP EPot GKev NGKo SDir WCot WFar WPGP XLum
exappendiculatum CExl WPnP WTyc
fargesii CExl EPot GKev
flavum CMiW CWCL EBee EPfP ESwi GArf GBin GKev NGKo SDir SPlb SPtp WHil WTyc
- CC 6303 ITim
- subsp. ***abbreviatum*** GKev MBel
- - CC 6300 ITim
§ ***franchetianum*** CExl GKev
galeatum WCot
§ ***griffithii*** EMor GKev NBid NLar SDeJ SDir
- var. ***pradhanii*** GKev
- - WJC 13660 WCru
aff. ***griffithii*** SDir
helleborifolium see *A. tortuosum*
§ ***heterophyllum*** GKev ITim
intermedium MNrw XLum
jacquemontii GKev GLog NLar SDir
- CC 5184 ITim
japonicum Blume see *A. serratum* var. *mayebarae*
japonicum Komarov see *A. serratum*
jinshajiangense CExl
kishidae GEdr
kiushianum GKev SDir WCot
§ ***lobatum*** CExl
§ ***nepenthoides*** EGrI EPot GKev SDir WPnP WTyc
ochraceum see *A. nepenthoides*
ovale SDir
propinquum GKev
purpureogaleatum see *A. franchetianum*
quinatum GKev
ringens ambig. CDTJ EPfP GEdr GKev
ringens (Thunberg) Schott green-flowered GKev SDir
aff. ***ringens*** NHpl
sazensoo GEdr
§ ***serratum*** GKev
- B&SWJ 14607 WCru
§ - var. ***mayebarae*** GEdr GKev
sikokianum CMiW EPot EWld GEdr GKev LRHS NHpl NLar SDir WPnP WTyc
- variegated (v) GEdr NHpl
speciosum CExl EGrI GEdr GKev NGKo SDeJ SPlb WCot WPnP XLum
* - var. ***magnificum*** CBcs GKev NLar XLum
- var. ***mirabile*** GKev
taiwanense GEdr GKev
- B&SWJ 269 WCru
- NMWJ 14541 WCru
- f. ***cinereum*** WMal
- - NMWJ 14530 WCru
- silver-leaved WFar
thunbergii GEdr
- subsp. ***urashima*** GKev SDir WTyc
§ ***tortuosum*** CExl ECha EPfP GKev LEdu NGKo NLar SDir WFar WPnP XLum
- var. ***helleborifolium*** NBid XLum
triphyllum CElw CExl EMor GKev GPoy NLar SPlb

§ ***utile*** EPot GKev
verrucosum see *A. griffithii*
- var. ***utile*** see *A. utile*

Arisarum (*Araceae*)

proboscideum Widely available
vulgare GKev
- subsp. ***simorrhinum*** GKev

Aristea (*Iridaceae*)

§ ***capitata*** CDoC CPla
ecklonii CBcs CBod CExl CPbh CTsd EBee EPri EShb EWld GBin LRHS MHer MHol
- GWJ 9469 CDoC MHol WCru
thyrsiflora see *A. capitata*

Aristolochia (*Aristolochiaceae*)

argentina new SBrt
baetica CExl SBrt WCru
- B&SWJ 15071 new WCru
californica LEdu
chilensis CCCN SPlb
clematitis GPoy LEdu
contorta EBee EPfP WPGP
cucurbitifolia B&SWJ 7043 WCru
debilis SBrt
durior see *A. macrophylla*
fimbriata CPla SBrt
- B&SWJ 13612 WCru
gigantea ♀H1b CCCN
grandiflora CCCN
griffithii B&SWJ 2118 WCru
kaempferi CCCN
- B&SWJ 14674 WCru
- NMWJ 14565 WCru
kanukuensis NMWJ 14577 WCru
× ***kewensis*** CCCN
§ ***macrophylla*** CBcs CCCN LPar MRav WPGP WSpi
manshuriensis EBee EWld
- B&SWJ 12557 WCru
paucinervis GKev
sempervirens CPla GGro LEdu SBrt WCru WSHC
- B&SWJ 13600 ESwi WCru
- from Carqueirame, Toulon new SBrt
sipho see *A. macrophylla*
trilobata SBrt

Aristotelia (*Elaeocarpaceae*)

§ ***chilensis*** LEdu MGil WKor WPav
- 'Variegata' (v) CCCN CMCN CMac
macqui see *A. chilensis*
peduncularis CExl
serrata CTsd ESwi GBin MGil SVen

Armeria (*Plumbaginaceae*)

'Abbey Deep Rose' (Abbey Series) new CBod
§ ***alliacea*** (Cav.) Hoffmanns. & Link ECha
- f. ***leucantha*** SRms
alpina GKev
Bees' hybrids SBut
'Brutus' MAvo MHCG
caespitosa see *A. juniperifolia*
- 'Bevan's Variety' see *A. juniperifolia* 'Bevan's Variety'
§ ***curvifolia*** GKev
(Joystick Series) 'Joystick Lilac Shades' EBee ELan EPfP NRHS SPoG
- 'Joystick Red' ELan EPfP NRHS SPoG

- 'Joystick White' ELan EPfP NRHS SPoG

§ ***juniperifolia*** 🏆H5 CMea EGrI ELan EPfP GArf GJos LRHS MAsh MHer NRHS NSla SGro SLee SPlb SRms WAbe WIce XLum

- 'Alba' ELan EPfP EPot GBin GJos GMaP MHer NHpl SLee SRms SRot WHoo

- 'Babi Lom' **new** NLar

§ - 'Bevan's Variety' 🏆H5 EBou ECha EGrI ELan EPfP EPot GEdr GKev GMaP MMuc NLar NRya SIvy SPoG SRms SRot WCav WHoo

- dark-flowered WAbe

- 'New Zealand Form' see *A. juniperifolia* 'Sugar Baby'

- spiny, dwarf EPot

§ - 'Sugar Baby' NLar SRms

juniperifolia* × *maritima SRms

§ ***maritima*** CHab CSde ECtt ELan EPfP GJos LPot LRHS MBel MBow NAts NRHS SRot SWvt WBrk WWild

§ - 'A Little in the Red' EPot WFar

- 'Alba' CBcs CTri ECha ELan EPfP EWoo GJos LPot LRHS MAsh MBel MCot MMuc NHpl NRHS NRya SEND SLee SPlb SPoG SRms WBrk WCFE WCav

- subsp. ***andina*** see *A. curvifolia*

- (Armada Series) 'Armada Deep Rose' **new** LRHS

- - 'Armada Rose' EPfP LRHS NRHS SRms

- - 'Armada White' **new** LRHS

- 'Bloodstone' CTri ELan

- 'Corsica' CMea CTri NBir NRya

- DÜSSELDORF PRIDE see *A. maritima* 'Düsseldorfer Stolz'

§ - 'Düsseldorfer Stolz' CBod CElw CPbh CSde EBou ECha ECtt EDAr ELan EPfP GKev GMaP LRHS MACG MBros NDov NLar NRHS SPoG SWvt WIce XLum

§ - 'In the Red' CBod CMea ECha ELon EShb GMaP LPot LRHS MAvo MBel MHer MMuc NHol NHpl NLar NRya SEND SEdd SLee SPad SRms SRot SWvt WCav WFar WHoo WIce WSMil

- 'Laucheana' WCav WHoo

- 'Morning Star Deep Rose' LSun NFav

- 'Morning Star White' CBod CMea CPbh CPla GKev

- 'Nifty Thrifty' (v) CTri ECtt ELan MACG MHer SPoG SRms WFar WSMil

- 'Rubrifolia' see *A. maritima* 'In the Red'

- 'Rubrifolia Compacta' see *A. maritima* 'A Little in the Red'

- 'Ruby Glow' CTri

- 'Splendens' CBcs CTri EDAr EPfP EWoo LRHS MAsh MBros MMuc NHpl NMir NRHS NRya SLee SPoG SSut

- 'Vindictive' 🏆H5 CMea

pseudarmeria EPfP WMal

- (Ballerina Series) 'Ballerina' MACG NBir

- - 'Ballerina Lilac' CBod CRos EPfP LRHS MPri NRHS SLee WBrk WFar

- - 'Ballerina Pink' **new** CRos LRHS

- - 'Ballerina Red' CBod CRos EPfP EShb LRHS LShi NFav NRHS SLee SPeP SRms WFar WTor

- - 'Ballerina White' CRos EPfP LRHS LShi NRHS WBrk WFar

splendens 'Perfecta' NRHS

tweedyi GKev

'Vesuvius' XLum

vulgaris see *A. maritima*

Armoracia (*Brassicaceae*)

§ ***rusticana*** CBod CCBP CHby CLau CTri ELan ENfk GAbr GPoy LOPS MHer MNHC NPer SPoG SRms SVic WHer WHrl WSpi XAbr XLum

- 'Horwood' LCro

- 'Variegata' (v) ELan LEdu NSti SRms WHer

Arnica (*Asteraceae*)

angustifolia subsp. ***iljinii*** NBir

chamissonis Less. CBod CCBP CHby ENfk MNHC NLar SRms

lessingii GArf

montana CPla GPoy MHer MNHC SRms

Arnoglossum (*Asteraceae*)

§ ***plantagineum*** SPhx

Aronia (*Rosaceae*)

arbutifolia EPfP LSRN MBlu SGol SLon SPlb

- 'Erecta' CBod CCVT EBee EHed ELan EPfP LRHS MBlu MGil MMuc SPoG SRms SWvt

melanocarpa CCVT CMCN CPla CRos CSpe EGrI ELan EPfP EWld GKin LRHS MAsh NRHS NWea WKor

- var. ***grandifolia*** CJun

- 'Hugin' CAgr CJun IDee LEdu LPar MCoo MMuc MPkF NLar SVic WPGP XSte

* - 'Red Viking' NOra

× ***prunifolia*** WKor

- 'Aron' (F) CAgr CJun MCoo WPGP

- 'Autumn Magic' CBcs CJun EBee ELan MAsh

- 'Brilliant' CBcs CDoC CKel EBee ELan EPfP MGil SGol SPer WMat

- 'Karhumäki' (F) NLar

- 'Nero' (F) CAgr CBcs CBod GBin LEdu MCoo MGil NLar WMat WPGP

- 'Serina' (F) CJun

- 'Viking' (F) CAgr CCVT CDoC CJun CKel EBee EPfP EPom GBin IDee LBuc LCro LEdu LOPS LRHS MBlu MMuc MTrO NLar SGol WFar WHwl WPGP

Aronia × *Sorbus* see × *Sorbaronia*

Arrhenatherum (*Poaceae*)

elatius CHab

- var. ***bulbosum*** 'Variegatum' (v) ELan EPPr GBin GMaP GQue MMuc NBid NWad SEND

Artemisia ✿ (*Asteraceae*)

RBS 0207 CExl

from Taiwan WHer

§ ***abrotanum*** Widely available

- 'Courson' ECha XSen

absinthium CBod CEls CHab CLau ELan ENfk GJos GPoy GQue MGil MHer MNHC NLar SRms SVic WHer XSen

- 'Lambrook Mist' CEls CFis CKel CMac ECtt ELan EPfP EWoo GQue LRHS MRav SCob SMrm WCAu

- 'Lambrook Silver' CDor CEls CExl EBee ECha ELan EPfP EWoo GMaP LSRN MHer MRav NBro NLar SCob SEdd SPer SRms SWvt

- 'Persian Lace' CEls

- 'Silver Ghost' CEls

afra CEls XSen

§ ***alba*** CBod CEls GPoy SRms WJek XAbr XSen

§ - 'Canescens' 🏆H5 CEls EBee ECha EGrI EPfP GMaP MAsh MHer MRav NLar SMrm XLum XSen

	annua	CEls
	anomala	CEls
§	***arborescens*** 🏆H4	CEls CKel GAbr SPer SRms SSal
	- 'Brass Band'	see *A.* 'Powis Castle'
	- 'Faith Raven' 🏆H3	CEls GBin MBNS NLar WLov
	arbuscula	CEls
	argentea misapplied	see *A. arborescens*
	argentea L'Hér.	CEls
	argyi	CEls
§	***armeniaca***	CEls WHer
	assoana	see *A. caucasica*
	atrata	CEls
	barrelieri	CEls
	caerulescens	CEls WCot
	subsp. ***cretacea***	
	- subsp. ***gallica***	CEls
	californica	CEls WHer
	- 'Canyon Gray'	CEls
	- 'Montara'	CEls
	campestris	XSen
	- subsp. ***borealis***	CEls
	- subsp. ***campestris***	CEls
	- subsp. ***maritima***	CEls XLum
	- - from Wales	CEls
	camphorata	see *A. alba*
	cana	CEls
	canescens misapplied	see *A. alba* 'Canescens'
	canescens Willd.	see *A. armeniaca*
	capillaris	CEls XLum
	carruthii	CEls
§	***caucasica*** 🏆H7	CEls CKel EWes MHer SPhx SRms
	- var. ***caucasica***	EBou
	chamaemelifolia	CBod CEls SRms XLum XSen
	douglasiana	CEls
	- 'Valerie Finnis'	see *A. ludoviciana* 'Valerie Finnis'
	dracunculus	ECha EWTr GQue LCro LOPS MNHC MRav SDix SPhx SPlb SRms SVic WBrk XAbr XSen
	- French	CBod CCBP CEls CHby CLau CTsd EBou ENfk EWhm GJos GPoy LCro LEdu LOPS MBow MBros MHer MPri NGrd SEND WCav WFar WGwG WJek
	- Russian	CEls EBou ENfk LCro LOPS SVic
	ferganensis	CEls
	filifolia	CEls
	fragrans	CEls
	frigida	CEls
	genipi	CEls GJos XAbr
	glacialis	CEls
	gmelinii	CEls
	gnaphalodes	see *A. ludoviciana*
	gorgonum	CEls SEND
	herba-alba	CEls XSen
	indica var. ***momiyamae***	CEls ECha WCot
	japonica	CEls
	kitadakensis 'Guizhou'	see *A. lactiflora* Guizhou Group
	laciniata	CEls
	lactiflora 🏆H7	CEls CElw EBee ECha GMaP MRav NDov NGdn SBls SDix SMrm SPer SRms WTre WWtn
	- NJM 11.010	CEls
	- 'Elfenbein'	CEls EPPr LPla MNrw MRav NDov SMHy
§	- Guizhou Group	Widely available
	- - 'Dark Delight'	CEls EBee ECtt EWes LEdu SPhx WMal
	- 'Jim Russell'	CDor CEls CElw EBee EWes LEdu SPhx
	- ***purpurea***	see *A. lactiflora* Guizhou Group
	- 'Weisse Dame'	CEls MNrw

	- 'Weisses Wunder'	CEls EBee
	lanata Willd.	see *A. caucasica*
	lanata Lam.	XSen
	laxa	see *A. umbelliformis*
	'Little Mice'	CEls NLar
§	***ludoviciana***	CEls GBee NLar NPer SBls SRms WFar XLum
	- subsp. ***ludoviciana*** var. ***incompta***	CEls
	- - var. ***latiloba***	CEls NBro SWvt
	- subsp. ***mexicana*** var. ***albula***	CEls
	- 'Silver Queen'	Widely available
	- 'Valerie Finnis' 🏆H6	Widely available
	MAKANA SILVER ('Tnartms') **new**	WTor
	maritima	XSen
	- 'Coca-Cola'	CEls EBee LCro LOPS SRms
	- var. ***maritima***	CEls
	mauiensis	CEls
§	***michauxiana***	CEls EBee
	molinieri	CEls XLum
	mutellina	see *A. umbelliformis*
	niitakayamensis	CEls
	nova	CEls
§	***nutans***	CEls MRav
	ORIENTAL LIMELIGHT ('Janlim') (v)	CEls CEme EBee NLar SDix SWvt WHrl
	palmeri hort.	see *A. ludoviciana*
	aff. ***parviflora*** CLD 1531	CEls
	pedemontana	see *A. caucasica*
	pontica	CEls EBee ECha EGrI GMaP GPoy GQue MNHC MRav NBro NLar NSti SEND SRms WFar WHoo WPGP
§	'Powis Castle' 🏆H3	Widely available
	princeps	CEls EBee GPoy
	procera Willd.	see *A. abrotanum*
	purshiana	see *A. ludoviciana*
	pycnocephala	CEls
	- 'David's Choice'	CEls
	ramosa	CEls
	'Rosenschleier'	CEls EPPr GQue WWtn
	schmidtiana 🏆H5	CEls ECha SDix SRms
	- 'Nana' 🏆H5	Widely available
	- 'Nana Attraction'	EPot GJos SRot
	selengensis	CEls
	somai var. ***batakensis*** NMWJ 14559	WCru
	splendens misapplied	see *A. alba* 'Canescens'
	stelleriana	CEls CTri ECha GKev MACG MHol NBro NLar SRms
	- RBS 0207	CEls
	- from Alaska	WCot
	- 'Boughton Silver'	CDor CEls CMea CRos EBee ECtt EPfP EWoo GMaP LRHS MAsh MAvo MHer NLar NRHS NSti SCob SPer SRms SWvt
	- 'Mori'	see *A. stelleriana* 'Boughton Silver'
	- 'Nana'	CEls SWvt
	- 'Prostrata'	see *A. stelleriana* 'Boughton Silver'
	- 'Shemya'	CEls
	- 'Silver Brocade'	see *A. stelleriana* 'Boughton Silver'
	suksdorfii	CEls
	taurica	CEls
§	***thuscula***	CEls
	tridentata	WHer
	- subsp. ***tridentata***	CEls
	- subsp. ***wyomingensis***	CEls
§	***umbelliformis***	CEls EWes
	vallesiaca	CEls
	verlotiorum	CEls

vulgaris	CBod CEls GJos GPoy MGil MNHC WHer
– 'Variegata' (v)	ELan SRms
× ***wurzellii***	CEls

Arthropodium (*Asparagaceae*)

candidum 'Capri'	LPot
– 'Little Lilia' (v)	CBct WCot
– 'Maculatum'	MPie NHpl SPlb
– 'Purpureum'	CTtf ECha GEdr NWsh
cirratum	CSpe CTsd EWld MHer MPie SVen WCFE WFar WSMil
– bronze **new**	CPla
– 'Matapouri Bay'	CBcs LRHS SEND
minus	CExl

artichoke, globe see *Cynara cardunculus* Scolymus Group

artichoke, Jerusalem see *Helianthus tuberosus*

Arum (*Araceae*)

sp. **new**	GArf
byzantinum	GKev
'Chameleon' ♀H7	CDor EPri GRum LEdu MAvo NBir NLar SEND SMad SPer WBrk WCot
§ ***concinnatum***	GKev
– 'Mount Ida'	LEdu
concinnatum* × *cyrenaicum	GKev
cornutum	see *Sauromatum venosum*
creticum	CBro EBee EPot GKev MNrw MRav WBor
– 'Karpathos'	CExl EBee GKev WAbe WCot
– 'Marmaris White'	EBee MAvo SBrt WCot
– white-flowered	CMea
– white-spotted	EWes
cyrenaicum	GKev
dioscoridis	EBee GKev NRog
§ – var. ***dioscoridis***	GKev
– var. ***liepoldtii***	see *A. dioscoridis* var. *dioscoridis*
– var. ***smithii***	see *A. dioscoridis* var. *dioscoridis*
– var. ***syriacum***	GKev
dracunculus	see *Dracunculus vulgaris*
gratum	GKev
hygrophilum	GKev LEdu
– B&SWJ 15277 **new**	WCru
– subsp. ***euxinum***	GKev
italicum	CTri GWyn LCro LOPS MHol NRog SDeJ WCot WShi
– 'Angelique'	WCot
– 'Edward Dougal'	WCot WFar
– 'Green Marble'	LEdu MAvo WFar
– subsp. ***italicum***	GKev MHer WBrk
§ – – 'Marmoratum' ♀H6	Widely available
– – 'Spotted Jack'	WCot
– – 'Tiny'	CExl SMHy SWvt
– – 'Uniquity'	WCot
§ – – 'White Winter' ♀H6	LEdu WBrk WCot
– subsp. ***neglectum***	SChr
– – 'Miss Janay Hall' (v)	MAvo WCot
– 'Pictum'	see *A. italicum* subsp. *italicum* 'Marmoratum'
– 'Sandy McNabb'	WCot
– 'Yarnells'	LEdu WCot
aff. ***italicum***	CMiW SDir
italicum* × *maculatum	WHer
korolkowii	WCot
maculatum	EPot GKev GPoy MBow MHer MRav NLar NRog WHer WShi
– 'Painted Lady' (v)	WCot
– 'Pleddel'	MRav
– Tar Spot Group	SEND
***megobrebi* new**	GKev
nickelii	see *A. concinnatum*
§ ***nigrum***	GKev LEdu
orientale subsp. ***orientale***	GKev
petteri misapplied	see *A. nigrum*
pictum	CExl CMac EWes GKev LEdu
– B&SWJ 15276 **new**	WCru
– 'Taff's Form'	see *A. italicum* subsp. *italicum* 'White Winter'
purpureospathum	GKev LEdu
rupicola var. ***rupicola***	GKev
– var. ***virescens***	LEdu
'Streaked Spectre'	LEdu
'The Patch'	WCot

Aruncus ✿ (*Rosaceae*)

aethusifolius ♀H7	Widely available
– 'Filigran'	EBee GBin
– 'Little Gem'	WCru
– 'Porzellan'	EBee
asiaticus B&SWJ 8624	WCru
dioicus	Widely available
– (f) **new**	EMor
§ – (m) ♀H6	CBar CBen CMac ELan MBNS MRav MWts NBro NSti SMad SPer SRms
– CHILD OF TWO WORLDS	see *A. dioicus* 'Zweiweltenkind'
– 'Glasnevin'	ECtt MRav NHol WFar
– var. ***kamtschaticus***	CPla EWes LSun NLar NWad WHrl
– – RBS 0208	NGdn
– 'Kneiffii'	CBod CEme CRos CTtf EBee ECha ECtt ELan EMor EPfP GKin GMaP LRHS MAvo MCot MHol MPnt MRav NChi NRHS SCob SPad SPer SPlb SPoG SRms SWvt WCAu WFar WKif
– 'Whirlwind'	EWhm LPla
§ – 'Zweiweltenkind'	EWTr LPla LRHS NLar SBls SMad WCot
'Guinea Fowl'	CBod CKel ECtt ELon EMor GKev GQue LLWG MCot MHol NBid NBir NGdn NLar WCAu WWtn
'Horatio'	Widely available
'Johannifest'	EBee ECtt MAvo MCot WCot
'Misty Lace'	CBod EBee ECtt ELan NGdn NLar SAko SMrm
'Noble Spirit'	LSun NGdn NLar
'Perlehuhn'	EBee
plumosus	see *A. dioicus*
'Sparkles' **new**	IPot
sylvestris	see *A. dioicus*
'Woldemar Meier'	ILea MAvo MCot NLar WCot

Arundinaria (*Poaceae*)

anceps	see *Yushania anceps*
auricoma	see *Pleioblastus viridistriatus*
falconeri	see *Himalayacalamus falconeri*
fargesii	see *Bashania fargesii*
fastuosa	see *Semiarundinaria fastuosa*
fortunei	see *Pleioblastus variegatus*
§ ***gigantea***	CDTJ
– subsp. ***tecta***	CBcs
hookeriana Munro	see *Himalayacalamus hookerianus*
japonica	see *Pseudosasa japonica*
jaunsarensis	see *Yushania anceps*
marmorea	see *Chimonobambusa marmorea*
murielae	see *Fargesia murielae*
nitida	see *Fargesia nitida*
oedogonata	see *Oligostachyum oedogonatum*
palmata	see *Sasa palmata*

pumila	see *Pleioblastus argenteostriatus* f. *pumilus*
pygmaea	see *Pleioblastus pygmaeus*
quadrangularis	see *Chimonobambusa quadrangularis*
simonii	see *Pleioblastus simonii*
vagans	see *Sasaella ramosa*
variegata	see *Pleioblastus variegatus*
veitchii	see *Sasa veitchii*
viridistriata	see *Pleioblastus viridistriatus*

Arundo (*Poaceae*)

donax	CAbb CKno EBee ELan ELon EWes IDee LRHS MAvo MBlu MNrw MRav SArc SCob SDix SEND SMad SPlb SPoG SSut WHal
- 'Golden Chain' (v)	CKno EPPr EWes SMad SSal WSMil
- 'Macrophylla'	CExl CKno EBlo EPPr EWes LEdu WPGP WSMil
- 'Peppermint Stick' (v)	SSal
- 'Variegata'	see *A. donax* var. *versicolor*
§ - var. ***versicolor*** (v)	CBcs CBen CEme CKel CKno CPla EBee ELan ELon EWes GBin LRHS MRav NRHS NWsh SArc SCob SDix SEND SMad SPer SPlb SPoG SSta WSMil XLum
I - - 'Aureovariegata' (v)	CBod CDTJ SEND
formosana	CKno EPPr
- 'Golden Showers'	ESwi

Asarina (*Plantaginaceae*)

barclayana	see *Maurandya barclayana*
erubescens	see *Lophospermum erubescens*
§ ***procumbens***	CTri GAbr GKev NBir NRya SBut SLee SPhx SRms WBrk WKif XAbr

Asarum (*Aristolochiaceae*)

arifolium	EBee EPPr MBriF
- 'The Giant'	EBee EMor NLar XSte
- white-flowered	EBee
canadense	CDor EBee EMor GEdr GKev GPoy LEdu MBriF
caudatum	EBee ECha ELan EMor ESwi GEdr GKev LEdu LPla MBriF NBro NLar SRms WCot WSpi
- 'Little Murphy'	WCot
- white-flowered	GGro
caulescens	EPPr GGro
- green-flowered **new**	WFar
- near-white-flowered **new**	GGro
Chen Yi 5 **new**	ESwi
delavayi	WCot
- giant	EBee
epigynum	CDTJ CDor EBee EMor ESwi MNrw NLar WCot XLum
- 'Silver Web'	GGro NSti WCot
europaeum ♀H6	Widely available
- PAB 4377	LEdu WPGP
- Pontic	WPGP
fauriei	GGro
'Koton' **new**	EMor
lemmonii	LEdu
longirhizomatosum	GEdr WCru
maculatum	GKev
- B&SWJ 1114	WCru
maximum	CBor GKev
- 'Green Panda'	CDTJ
- 'Ling Ling' **new**	EHed
- 'Silver Panda'	CBct CDTJ CExl EHed EMor ESwi MNrw NGBl SMad WCot
pulchellum	ESwi
savatieri	SHar
sieboldii	WCru
- green-flowered **new**	GGro WFar
splendens	CBct CBor CBro CDTJ EBee ELan EMor EPfP GKev ILea LEdu MBriF MHol MNrw NGKo NLar NSti SDir SDix SPlb SPoG WCot WFar XLum
wulingense	CExl

Asclepias ✿ (*Apocynaceae*)

'Cinderella'	EShb
curassavica	CCCN EShb SRkn
- 'Silky Gold'	EShb
exaltata	EBee
fruticosa	see *Gomphocarpus fruticosus*
hallii	EBee
incarnata	CPla CSpe ECha MRav SBrt SPlb SSal WTre XLum
- 'Ice Ballet'	CBod EBee MACG NLar SPer
- 'Soulmate'	CBod EBee EPfP GQue MHol MSCN SBls SPer
physocarpa	see *Gomphocarpus physocarpus*
speciosa	CBod GGro MMuc SBea SBls SBrt SBut
tuberosa	CBcs CBod CBor CSpe EBee EShb GJos GPoy LRHS MBel MHer MNHC MPie MSCN NRHS SMad SPad SPer SPoG SRms WGwG WHil XLum XSen
- subsp. ***interior***	EPPr MHol SBls

Asimina (*Annonaceae*)

triloba (F)	CBcs CCCN CDTJ IBal LPar MBlu NLar SGol SPlb WKor
- 'Sunflowers'	CCCN IDee SAko

asparagus see also AGM Vegetables Section

Asparagus (*Asparagaceae*)

acutifolius	XSen
asparagoides ♀H3	EShb
densiflorus	WCot
- 'Mazeppa'	EShb
- 'Myersii' ♀H1c	EShb LCro LOPS SEND
- 'Myriocladus'	EShb
- Sprengeri Group ♀H1c	EShb LCro LOPS NGBl SEND
falcatus	CDoC EShb SEND
filicinus NJM 12.024	WPGP
- var. ***giraldii***	WCot
aff. ***meioclados***	WFar
- B&SWJ 8309	WCot WCru
plumosus	see *A. setaceus*
pseudoscaber	EBee SDix WCot
'Spitzenschleier'	
retrofractus	WCot
scandens	EShb WCot
schoberioides	LEdu
- B&SWJ 8814	WCru
§ ***setaceus*** ♀H2	CDoC EShb LCro LOPS SPlb WCot
- 'Pyramidalis' ♀H1c	CDoC
tenuifolius	WPGP
virgatus	EBee EShb LEdu SPlb WPGP

Asperula (*Rubiaceae*)

§ ***arcadiensis*** ♀H3	EPot SPlb
aristata subsp. ***scabra***	ECha MMuc WCot
- subsp. ***thessala***	see *A. sintenisii*
boissieri	EPot SPlb WAbe
daphneola	ELan EPot EWes
gussonei	ELan EPot WAbe WHoo
lilaciflora var. ***caespitosa***	see *A. lilaciflora* subsp. *lilaciflora*

§	– subsp. ***lilaciflora***	EBou ELan
	nitida	ELan EPot WIce
	– subsp. ***puberula***	see *A. sintenisii*
	odorata	see *Galium odoratum*
§	***sintenisii***	CMea EPot WAbe WHoo
	suberosa misapplied	see *A. arcadiensis*
	taurina	EBee
	– subsp. ***caucasica***	NLar WBor
	tinctoria	GPoy MHer SRms

Asphodeline (*Asphodelaceae*)

	liburnica	CBro CFis CMea CPla ECha EPri LCro LOPS MMuc SEND SPhx SSal XSen
§	***lutea***	Widely available
§	– 'Gelbkerze'	EBee SBls WAvo
	– YELLOW CANDLE	see *A. lutea* 'Gelbkerze'
	taurica	SBrt

Asphodelus (*Asphodelaceae*)

	acaulis	WCot WMal
§	***aestivus***	CKel EBee EWes MBel WCot
	albus	CBro CKel CMea CSpe EBee ECha EGrI EPPr EPfP GAbr GBin NBid NGBl SBls SPlb SRms XLum XSen
	cerasiferus	see *A. ramosus*
	fistulosus	CBro CKel EBee LEdu SVen XSen
	lusitanicus	see *A. ramosus*
	luteus	see *Asphodeline lutea*
	microcarpus	see *A. aestivus*
§	***ramosus***	CPar MCot WCot

Aspidistra ✿ (*Asparagaceae*)

	B&SWJ 6645 from Thailand	WCru
	Chen Yi 135	WCot
	attenuata B&SWJ 377	WCru
	– B&SWJ 2001	WCru
	– B&SWJ 3727	WCru
	– 'Dungpu Dazzler'	WCru
	– 'Small 'n' Smart'	WCru
	– 'Xitou Starlet'	WCru
	caespitosa 'Jade Ribbons'	see *A. hainanensis* 'Jade Ribbons'
	Chen Yi 135	ESwi
	daibuensis B&SWJ 312b	ESwi WCru
	– B&SWJ 1949	WCru
	– B&SWJ 3236	WCru
	– B&SWJ 6863	WCru
	– B&SWJ 6866	WCru
	– 'Taiwan Stars'	ESwi WCru
	– 'Tidy Trim'	ESwi WCru
	– 'Totally Dotty' (v)	ESwi WCru
	– 'Yuli Yummy'	ESwi WCru
	elatior 🏆H3	CBct CDTJ CTsd EBak EBee EShb ESwi LCro LEdu LOPS MRav SAko SEND SMad SPlb WCot XLum
	– 'Akebono' (v)	WCot
	– 'Asahi' (v)	ESwi WCot
	– 'Hoshi-zora' (v)	WCot
	– 'Lennon's Song' (v)	ESwi SEND WCot
	– 'Milky Way' (v)	EBee EShb ESwi SEND XLum
	– 'Okame' (v)	WCot
	– 'Variegata' (v) 🏆H3	CPla EShb
	aff. ***elatior*** 'Mystery Man' **new**	WCru
	fasciaria	WCru
	fungilliformis 'China Star' (v)	ESwi SMad WCot WCru
	aff. ***geastrum*** 'Opium Hit'	WCru
§	***hainanensis*** 'Jade Ribbons'	EShb ESwi WCot WCru
	linearifolia	WCru
	– 'Leopard' (v)	ESwi WCot WCru
	– 'Skinny Dippin''	WCru
	lurida	EShb
	– 'Ginga'	see *A. sichuanensis* 'Ginga'
	– 'Ginga Giant' (v)	ESwi WCot WCru
	minutiflora	ESwi WCot
	– 'Spangled Ribbons'	WCru
	mushaensis B&SWJ 315	WCru
	– B&SWJ 1953	WCru
	– 'Purple Picket'	WCru
	– 'Wushe Wacky'	WCru
	aff. ***mushaensis*** 'Spotty Dotty' (v)	ESwi WCru
	omeiensis	WCot
	punctata	WCru
	retusa 'Nanjing Green'	WCru
	saxicola 'Uan Fat Lady'	see *A. zongbayi* 'Uan Fat Lady'
	sichuanensis	WCru
	– 'Beauty Spot' **new**	WCru
§	– 'Ginga' (v)	ESwi WCot
	– 'Misty Spot' **new**	WCru
	– 'Rarely Spotted' **new**	WCru
	– 'Spotty' **new**	WCru
	– 'Well Spotted' **new**	WCru
	sutepensis B&SWJ 5216	WCru
	– B&SWJ 6645	WCru
	– 'Chiang-dao Chace'	WCru
	– 'Pha-Hom Pok-adot'	WCru
	tonkinensis	ESwi WCot WCru
	typica 'China Sun'	ESwi WCot
	vietnamensis	WCru
	zongbayi	WCot
§	– 'Uan Fat Lady'	EBee ESwi WCot WCru

Asplenium ✿ (*Aspleniaceae*)

	antiquum 🏆H3	EShb
	bulbiferum ambig. 'Suze'	IKel
	bulbiferum Forst.f.	EShb ESwi GBin SPlb
§	***ceterach***	CLAP NHar SMad WCot WHer WHoo
	daucifolium	NWad WCot
	× ***ebenoides*** 🏆H4	EMor LEdu NBro NHar SPlb
§	× ***lucrosum*** 🏆H1c	EShb ESwi
	'Maori Princess' 🏆H2	GBin WFib
	nidus 🏆H1b	IKel LCro LOPS
	– 'Crispy Wave'PBR	CDoC EShb LCro LOPS
	nitidum **new**	SPlb
	'Parvati'	CDoC
§	***scolopendrium*** 🏆H6	Widely available
	– 'Angustatum' 🏆H6	Widely available
	– Crispum Group 🏆H6	CLAP EFer ELan NBid SRms WAbe WFar WFib
	– – 'Crispum Bolton's Nobile'	WFib
	– – 'Golden Queen'	CDor MAvo
	– Crispum Cristatum Group	SCob
	– Crispum Fimbriatum Group	CLAP
	– – 'Drummondiae'	CLAP
	– Cristatum Group	CBdn CDor CLAP CRos EBee ECtt ELan ELon EMor EPfP LRHS MGos MRav NBro NLar NRHS SPer SRms SRot WFib
	– Fimbriatum Group	MHost
	– 'Fimbriatum Cristatum'	CLAP
	– 'Furcatum'	CDTJ EBee EHed ELan ELon EMor NLar SPad
	– 'Kaye's Lacerated' 🏆H5	EFer WFib
	– Marginatum Group	CBdn EFer
	– 'Muricatum'	ELan MRav NBid WFib
	– 'Sagittatocristatum'	CLAP
	– 'Sagittatoprojectum Sclater'	WFib

- Undulatum Group	CDTJ CRos EBee ECha EPfP GBin GQue LRHS MAsh NBir NLar NRHS SRms WCot WFar WGwG XLum
trichomanes 🏆H6	Widely available
- Cristatum Group	CLAP CRos LRHS NRHS
- Incisum Group 🏆H6	CLAP EFer WAbe

Astelia (*Asteliaceae*)

banksii	CBcs CBct CBod CPbh CPla CRos CTrC CTsd EPfP IBal LRHS LSRN MCot MGos NCou NRHS SCoo SEdd SGBe
§ ***chathamica*** 🏆H3	CAbb CCCN CCht CSpe CTrC CTsd ELan EPfP EWld GDam LPar LRHS LSRN MGos MHol SAko SArc SCob SCoo SPer SPlb SPoG SWvt WCot WSpi
- 'Silver Spear'	see *A. chathamica*
fragrans	LEdu
grandis	LEdu WPGP
nervosa	LSRN SArc
- 'Westland'	CBcs CBct CBod CCCN CPla CRos CTrC CTsd ELan GBin GWyn ILea LPar LRHS LSRN MGos NRHS SCob SGBe SWvt
'Red Devil'	CBcs CBct CBod CPla CTrC GWyn MGos MHol SCob SEdd SGBe SPeP SPoG WHer WPav XSte
'Red Shadow'	XSte
'Silver Shadow'PBR	CBcs CBod CRos EPfP LCro LOPS LRHS MMrt NRHS SCob SGBe SMad SPad SWvt WFar WSpi XSte

Aster ✿ (*Asteraceae*)

acris	see *Galatella sedifolia*
ageratoides	WCot
- 'Ashvi'	CKno CMil ECtt EShb EWoo GBin MBel MHol NDov NSti SDix SEdd SPoG WCAu WCot WFar WSHC
- 'Asran'	ECtt EPPr EWes EWhm LEdu MACG MHer MHol MMuc MPie NLar SEND WBor WBrk WCAu WCot WFar XLum
- 'Ezo Murasaki'	CDor CSpe ECha ELon GBin LEdu LPla MAvo MNrw NDov SAko SPoG WCot XLum
- var. ***firmus***	WPGP
- 'Harry Smith'	NDov NSti SAko SEdd SPoG WCot WFar WHil
- 'Little Theo'	CKno
- 'Stardust'	WHoo
- 'Starshine'	CBcs CBod CKno CWGN EBee ECtt EPfP EWoo MAvo WCot
alpinus 🏆H5	EBou EPfP GArf GKev LCro LOPS MAsh MHol SRms WFar
- var. ***albus***	EDAr ELan EPfP GKev LRHS WCot XLum XSen
- 'Antje'	MNrw
- DARK BEAUTY	see *A. alpinus* 'Dunkle Schöne'
§ - 'Dunkle Schöne'	CCBP EDAr MACG MBel SRms WFar XLum XSen
- 'Goliath'	EDAr ELan EPfP SPlb WFar
- 'Happy End'	CRos EPfP LRHS NRHS SRms WCAu XLum XSen
- 'Pinkie'	EBou EDAr ELan EPfP ITim MACG
- 'Trimix'	LPot NBir NFav SRms
- violet-flowered	LRHS
- 'White Beauty'	MACG
amelloides	see *Felicia amelloides*
amellus	ELon
- 'Blue King'	EWes IPot NLar SWvt WFar WSpi
- 'Breslau'	ELon
- 'Brilliant'	CBod ECha ECtt ELon EPPr LPla LRHS LSou MBNS MRav NLar NRHS NSti NWsh SAko SGbt SPer SPhx SRms WCAu WHoo WSpi
- 'Butzemann'	ELon NLar WCot WFar
- 'Danzig'	NDov NLar
- 'Doktor Otto Petschek'	ELon NLar WCot
- 'Forncett Flourish' 🏆H7	ECtt MHCG WCot WHoo
- 'Framfieldii' 🏆H7	SMHy WCot WFar
§ - 'Glücksfund'	SAko XSen
- 'Gründer'	MAvo MHCG WCot
- 'Jacqueline Genebrier' 🏆H7	MHCG
- 'King George' 🏆H7	Widely available
- 'Kobold' 🏆H7	LPla
- 'Lac de Genève'	LPla WCot XLum
- 'Lady Hindlip'	ELon MMrt WCot
- 'Louise'	MBrN MHCG
- 'Mira'	ELon GBin SAko
- 'Moerheim Gem'	ECtt WCot
- 'Nocturne'	ELon WCot
- 'Peach Blossom'	CBod
- PINK ZENITH	see *A. amellus* 'Rosa Erfüllung'
§ - 'Rosa Erfüllung' 🏆H7	CBod CDor CMac EBee ECtt ELan ELon EPPr EPfP EWes GMaP LPla LRHS MACG MAvo MNrw MRav NLar NRHS SCob SGbt SPhx SPoG SWvt WCAu WSpi
- 'Rotfeuer'	ELon WSpi
- 'Rudolph Goethe'	CBod EBee ECtt ELan ELon EMil EPfP LRHS MACG NLar NRHS SCob WCAu WSpi
- 'September Glow'	SHar
- 'Silbersee' 🏆H7	ELon SAko
- 'Sonia'	ECtt ELon LRHS NRHS SWvt
- 'Sonora' 🏆H7	CMea LPla MNrw SHar SPhx WKif WTor
- 'Sternkugel'	ELon
§ - 'Veilchenkönigin' 🏆H7	Widely available
- VIOLET QUEEN	see *A. amellus* 'Veilchenkönigin'
- 'Weltfriede'	ECtt
× ***amethystinus***	see *Symphyotrichum* × *amethystinum*
asperulus misapplied	see *A. peduncularis*
batangensis W/O 7057 **new**	GGro
'Betel Nut'	ECha SDix
capensis 'Variegatus'	see *Felicia amelloides* variegated
'Carmen'	XLum
'Cheavers'	LRHS NRHS
'Chilly Fingers'	MAvo MNrw
ciliolatus	see *Symphyotrichum ciliolatum*
'Climax' misapplied	see *Symphyotrichum laeve* 'Arcturus', *S. laeve* 'Calliope'
coelestis	see *Felicia amelloides*
coloradoensis	see *Xanthisma coloradoense*
'Connecticut Snow Flurry'	see *Symphyotrichum ericoides* var. *prostratum* 'Snow Flurry'
corymbosus	see *Eurybia divaricata*
'Cotswold Gem'	LRHS MHCG MNrw WCot
diplostephioides	EWhm GArf GEdr GLog MMrt SPlb
divaricatus	see *Eurybia divaricata*
'Dwarf Barbados'	EPfP LRHS NRHS
'Dwarf Blue'	LRHS
'Eleven Purple'PBR	MNrw NDov
falcatus	see *Symphyotrichum falcatum*
'Fanny's Fall'	see *Symphyotrichum oblongifolium* 'Fanny's'
'Fingers and Thumbs'	MAvo
× ***frikartii***	CBod CMac EPfP LRHS MRav SGbt SWvt WSHC
- 'Flora's Delight'	CBod CMea CRos EBlo ECtt ELon EMor EPfP LRHS MRav NLar NRHS SPoG SRms WCAu WHoo WSpi

- 'Jungfrau'	CWGN EBee ELan EPPr GBee GMaP LRHS MRav NLar NRHS SPhx SRms WSHC
- 'Mönch' 🏆H7	Widely available
- WONDER OF STAFA	see *A.* × *frikartii* 'Wunder von Stäfa'
§ - 'Wunder von Stäfa' 🏆H7	CEnd CExl CKno EBee ECtt ELon EPPr EPfP GBin GMaP LCro LOPS LRHS MBNS MBel MCot NBir NLar SRGP SWvt WCAu WCot WFar WHoo WSpi
furcatus	see *Eurybia furcata*
glehnii	WCAu
- 'Aglenii'	MNrw NDov
× ***herveyi***	see *Eurybia* × *herveyi*
himalaicus	GArf NSla WFar
hybridus luteus	see *Solidago* × *luteus*
'Ice Cool Pink'	IPot SMHy
'Ivy House'	ECtt
'JS El Macho' **new**	MNrw
* ***kotarimus***	MHol MMrt XLum
laevis	see *Symphyotrichum laeve*
laterifolius 'Snow Flurry'	see *Symphyotrichum ericoides* var. *prostratum* 'Snow Flurry'
limonifolius	GKev
linosyris	see *Galatella linosyris*
macrophyllus	see *Eurybia macrophylla*
mongolicus	see *Kalimeris mongolica*
'Moody Blue'	MAvo
'Mrs Dean'	ECtt
natalensis	see *Felicia rosulata*
'Natasha'	LSRN
novi-belgii	see *Symphyotrichum novi-belgii*
oblongifolius	see *Symphyotrichum oblongifolium*
OCTOBERLIGHT	see *Symphyotrichum* 'Oktoberlicht'
pappei	see *Felicia amoena*
§ ***peduncularis***	CKno EBee ECha EMor EPPr EShb GBee MAvo MHol NCou NSti SMad WCot WFar WMal
petiolatus	see *Felicia petiolata*
pilosus	see *Symphyotrichum pilosum*
ptarmicoides	see *Solidago ptarmicoides*
puniceus	see *Symphyotrichum puniceum*
pyrenaeus 'Lutetia'	CBod CKno ECha EPPr EPfP EShb GMaP LRHS MAvo MBow MNrw NLar NRHS SBut SEdd SPhx SRGP SRms WCAu WCot WFar WKif XLum
radula	see *Eurybia radula*
rotundifolius 'Variegatus'	see *Felicia amelloides* variegated
rugulosus 'Asrugo'	CKno
§ ***scaber***	WCot
- 'Ki Hakikomi-fu' **new**	GGro
schreberi	see *Eurybia schreberi*
sedifolius	see *Galatella sedifolia*
sibiricus	see *Eurybia sibirica*
'Small-Ness'	EShb GBin GKev LRHS MAvo NWad
'Snow Flurry'	see *Symphyotrichum ericoides* var. *prostratum* 'Snow Flurry'
souliei	EBee GArf
spathulifolius	WCot XLum
spectabilis	see *Eurybia spectabilis*
subcaeruleus	see *A. tongolensis*
tataricus 'Jindai'	EBee SPeP SSal WCAu
thomsonii	GBin SHar WCot WSpi
- 'Nanus'	EBee EShb GBin GMaP LRHS MCot MRav SPoG WSHC WSpi
§ ***tongolensis***	GKev NHpl
- 'Berggarten'	CWCL LRHS MHol MNrw NRHS WHil
- 'Wartburgstern'	CBod EMor EPfP LRHS SGbt WHil XLum
tradescantii misapplied	see *Symphyotrichum pilosum* var. *pringlei*
tradescantii L.	see *Symphyotrichum tradescantii*
trinervius var. ***harae***	WFar
tripolium	see *Tripolium pannonicum*
'Triumph'	WCot
turbinellus	see *Symphyotrichum turbinellum*
vimineus 'Ptarmicoides'	see *Solidago ptarmicoides*

Asteranthera (*Gesneriaceae*)

ovata	CExl GGGa SLon WAbe WPGP

Asteromoea (*Asteraceae*)

mongolica	see *Kalimeris mongolica*
pinnatifida	see *Kalimeris pinnatifida*

Asteropyrum (*Ranunculaceae*)

cavaleriei	GEdr
peltatum	GEdr

Asterotrichion (*Malvaceae*)

discolor	CTsd EBee SPlb SVen

Astilbe ✿ (*Saxifragaceae*)

CC 5201	CExl
'Alive and Kicking'	LRHS LSou
'Amerika' (× *arendsii*)	CSBt SRms
'Amethyst' (× *arendsii*)	CMHG CMac EPfP LBuc MBel MRav NBir NHol SPer WFar
'Angel Wings' (× *arendsii*)	CMHG NEoE
'Anita Pfeifer' (× *arendsii*)	CMHG NLar XLum
'Aphrodite' (*simplicifolia* hybrid)	CBcs XLum
× ***arendsii***	EPfP LBuc XLum
(Astary Series) 'Astary Pink' (× *arendsii*)	LRHS NRHS
- 'Astary Red' (× *arendsii*)	LRHS NRHS
- 'Astary White' (× *arendsii*)	CRos LRHS NRHS
astilboides	SWvt
'Avalanche'	NEoE NHol WBrk WSpi
§ 'Beauty of Ernst' (× *arendsii*)	CBod CMHG EBee ELon EMor EPfP LRHS MNrw SRms XSte
§ 'Beauty of Lisse' (× *arendsii*)	CBod ELon MNrw SPad
'Bergkristall' (× *arendsii*)	CMHG
'Betsy Cuperus' (*thunbergii* hybrid)	CMHG WCAu
'Bonn' (*japonica* hybrid)	CMHG CWCL CWat NLar SCoo SRms
§ 'Brautschleier' (× *arendsii*) 🏆H7	CBod CExl CMHG CMac ECtt EPfP GBin GKev GWyn LCro LOPS LRHS LSRN NGdn NLar NQui NRHS WPnP XLum
'Bremen' (*japonica* hybrid)	CMHG
'Bressingham Beauty' (× *arendsii*) 🏆H7	CExl CRos CWCL EBee ECtt ELan EPfP EWoo GBin GKev GMaP ILea LCro LOPS LRHS MRav NEoE NHol NRHS SEdd SRms SWvt WFar
BRIDAL VEIL (× *arendsii*)	see *A.* 'Brautschleier'
§ 'Bronce Elegans' (*simplicifolia* hybrid) 🏆H7	ECha EMor GLog GMaP GWyn MBow NHol NLar SRms WFar WSpi
'Bronze Sprite' (*simplicifolia* hybrid)	WFar
'Bronzelaub' (× *arendsii*)	CMHG
* ***bumalda*** 'Bronze Pygmy'	NHol
'Bumalda' (× *arendsii*)	CSBt EGrI EMor GBin GLog GMaP NChi NGdn NRHS SPlb WFar WWtn
'Bunter Zauber' (× *arendsii*)	XLum
'Burgunderrot' (× *arendsii*)	MNrw NLar SRms
'Cappuccino' (× *arendsii*)	EMor ILea LRHS MBros MSCN SPad WWtn
'Catherine Deneuve'	see *A.* 'Federsee'

	Name	Suppliers
	'Cattleya Dunkel' (× *arendsii*)	CMHG
	'Cattleya' (× *arendsii*)	CMHG GWyn LRHS NLar NRHS SAko WSpi XLum
	'Ceres' (× *arendsii*)	CMHG
	'Cherry Ripe'	see *A.* 'Feuer'
	chinensis	GBin MBros WSHC
	- B&SWJ 8178	WCru
	- 'Brokat'	CMHG GBin
	- var. ***davidii***	GBin XLum
	- - B&SWJ 8583	WCru
	- - B&SWJ 8645	WCru
	- 'Diamonds and Pearls'[PBR]	CWGN ECtt LRHS LSou WFar WSpi
	- 'Finale'	NHol
	- 'Intermezzo'	GBin GMaP NLar
	- 'Little Vision in Pink'[PBR]	EPfP WFar
	- 'Milk and Honey'[PBR]	CWGN ECtt EWTr LRHS MBNS WFar WSpi
§	- var. ***pumila*** ♀H7	Widely available
	- - 'Serenade'	CMHG CMac NGdn
I	- - 'Tiny Form'	GRum
	- 'Purple Glory'	ECtt
	- 'Spätsommer'	CMHG
	- var. ***taquetii***	CMac ELan EPfP NSti SRms XLum
	- - PURPLE LANCE	see *A. chinensis* var. *taquetii* 'Purpurlanze'
§	- - 'Purpurlanze' ♀H7	CKno EBee ECha ECtt EMor EShb GBin GMaP LSRN MCot MRav NBir NBro NChi NDov NGdn NHol NLar SCob SPoG SWvt WBor WFar WHoo WSpi WWtn
§	- - 'Superba' ♀H7	CMac ECha LRHS NBro NWad SDix SEdd SPer SRms WFar
	- 'Troll'	GBin
	- 'Veronika Klose'	CMHG GBin LRHS NLar WHoo
	- 'Vision in Pink'[PBR]	CMHG CWCL ELan EPfP MBNS MNrw NDov SCob SMrm WFar
	- 'Vision in Red'[PBR]	CMHG CWCL CWat ECtt EGrI ELan EPfP LRHS MBNS MNrw NDov NLar SCob SGbt SMrm SPoG WCAu WFar
	- 'Vision in White'	EPfP LCro LOPS MBros NEoE NLar SAko SCob SMrm SPoG WFar
	- 'Visions'	CMac ELan EPfP LRHS MBNS NBro NEoE NGdn NRHS SCob WSMil
	- 'White Cloud'	NQui
	'Chocolate Shogun'	CBcs CMil CSpe CWGN EBee EMor LPla LRHS LSou LSun MAvo MBNS MHol MNrw MThu NCou NSti SPad SPoG WCot WFar WTor XSte
	COLOGNE	see *A.* 'Köln'
	COLOR FLASH	see *A.* 'Beauty of Ernst'
	COLOR FLASH LIME	see *A.* 'Beauty of Lisse'
	'Country and Western'[PBR] (× *arendsii*)	NEoE
	'Crimson Feather'	see *A.* 'Gloria Purpurea'
	× ***crispa*** 'Lilliput'	ECtt NBir NEoE NLar NRya NWad
§	- 'Perkeo' ♀H5	CBcs ECtt GMaP LRHS NBir NEoE NHpl NLar NRHS SRms WFar
	- 'Peter Pan'	see *A.* × *crispa* 'Perkeo'
	- 'Red Rog'	NEoE
	- 'Snow Queen'	NBir NEoE
	'Darwin's Dream'	CMHG MBros MNrw NEoE NLar WFar
	'Darwin's Favourite' (× *arendsii*)	CWCL
	'Delft Lace'	CAbb CBod CMHG EBee EWoo LBuc LRHS MBel MMrt MSCN NRHS SRms
	'Deutschland' (*japonica* hybrid) ♀H7	CBcs CMHG EBee ECtt EMor EPfP EWoo GBin GKev GLog GMaP ILea LRHS LSRN MACG MBNS MGos MRav NBir NEoE NHol NLar NRHS SAko SCob SPer SPoG SRms WSpi
§	'Diamant' (× *arendsii*)	CMHG LSRN MMuc MNrw NBir NFav NGdn NHol WFar
	DIAMOND	see *A.* 'Diamant'
	'Drayton Glory' (× *arendsii*)	see *A.* × *rosea* 'Peach Blossom'
	'Drum and Bass'[PBR]	LSou NLar
	'Dunkelachs' (*simplicifolia* hybrid)	EBee
	'Dusseldorf' (*japonica* hybrid)	CMHG CWCL EBee LRHS NRHS
	'Eden's Odysseus'	NHol NWad
	'Eden's Twinkle'	EBee EMor
	'Elegans' (*simplicifolia* hybrid)	CMac
	'Elisabeth' van Veen (× *arendsii*)	CBod CMHG
	ELIZABETH BLOOM ('Eliblo'[PBR]) (× *arendsii*)	EBlo EMor LLWG LRHS MAsh MRav NGdn NHol NRHS
	'Ellie' (× *arendsii*)	CMHG CMac CWCL ECtt ELan EPfP EShb GBee GQue LLWG LSRN MBNS MBel NGdn NHol NLar SPoG WFar
	'Else Schluck' (× *arendsii*)	ECha
	'Erica' (× *arendsii*)	CExl CMHG CTri EGrI EMor EWTr GBin GLog NEoE NLar WBrk WFar
	'Etna' (*japonica* hybrid)	CBcs CMHG CPud ECtt LRHS NGdn NLar NRHS SRms WFar WHoo
	'Europa' (*japonica* hybrid)	CMHG CMac ECtt EMor GBin GWyn LRHS MGos NGdn NLar NRHS SCoo SPoG SRms WCAu WFar
	'Fanal' (× *arendsii*) ♀H7	Widely available
	'Fata Morgana' (× *arendsii* hybrid)	CMHG
§	'Federsee' (× *arendsii*)	CBcs CMHG CWCL EBee EBlo ECha ECtt LRHS MBNS NBro NEoE NGdn NRHS WFar WWtn XLum
§	'Feuer' (× *arendsii*)	CMHG CMac ECtt NEoE NGdn NHol NLar WFar
	FIRE	see *A.* 'Feuer'
	'Fireberry'[PBR] (Short 'n' Sweet Series)	EBee MSCN NLar
	'Flamingo'[PBR] (× *arendsii*)	ECtt MBNS MBel NLar
§	***formosa*** B&SWJ 10946	WCru
	'Freya' (× *arendsii*)	MAsh
	'Gertrud Brix' (× *arendsii*)	CMHG CWat MMuc NBir NGdn XLum
§	***glaberrima***	NBid
§	- var. ***saxatilis*** ♀H5	GArf GBin GEdr NFav WAbe WFar
	- - 'Candy Floss'	NEoE
	- ***saxosa***	see *A. glaberrima* var. *saxatilis*
§	'Gloria Purpurea' (× *arendsii*)	CMHG NQui
	'Gloria' (× *arendsii*)	CMHG CMac CTri ECtt LRHS
	GLOW	see *A.* 'Glut'
§	'Glut' (× *arendsii*)	CMHG CWCL ECtt MMuc NGdn NHol SAko SGbt SRms WFar WWtn
	'Granat' (× *arendsii*)	CMHG CMac NBir NGdn NHol NLar
	grandis	WHer
	- BWJ 8076A	NLar
	'Grete Püngel' (× *arendsii*)	ECha GBin SRms WFar
	'Happy Spirit'	CBod EPfP LLWG MHol NLar
	'Harmony' (× *arendsii*)	CMHG
	'Heart and Soul'[PBR]	CWGN EPfP LRHS LSou
	'Hennie Graafland' (*simplicifolia* hybrid)	CBcs CMHG CWCL LSun NLar WFar
	'Holden Clough' (*japonica* hybrid)	NHol
	HYACINTH	see *A.* 'Hyazinth'

§	'Hyazinth' (× *arendsii*)	CExl CMHG CRos EBee GBin GMaP LRHS NBir NHol NRHS
	'Icecream' (× *arendsii*)	CBod
	'Inshriach Pink' (*simplicifolia* hybrid)	CBcs CMHG GBee LRHS NBir NHol NLar NRHS SGro SRms
	'Irrlicht' (× *arendsii*)	CMHG CMac CMea EBee EPfP EShb MHol NWad SRms WHoo WPnP WWtn
	'Isa Hall'	CMHG NEoE NFav NWad
	japonica	CExl
*	- 'Catherine Gladstone'	LRHS
*	- 'Pumila'	NBir NGdn
	'Jo Ophorst' (*davidii* hybrid)	NGdn NLar
	'Jump and Jive'[PBR]	LLWG WFar
	'Juno'	XLum
	'Koblenz' (*japonica* hybrid)	CMHG
§	'Köln' (*japonica* hybrid)	CMHG CRos LRHS NRHS
	koreana	WCot
	- B&SWJ 8611	WCru
	- B&SWJ 8680	WCru
	'Kvěle' (× *arendsii*)	CMHG CRos LRHS NRHS WFar
	'Lilli Goos' (× *arendsii*)	CMHG GBin
	'Little Vision in Purple'[PBR]	CBod
	'Lollipop'	CMHG ECtt MBNS NEoE SRms
	longicarpa B&SWJ 6711	WCru
	'Look at Me'[PBR] (× *arendsii*)	CWGN ECtt EPfP LCro LOPS LSou MBel MNrw SPoG
	'Maggie Daley'	CMHG NBro NEoE SRms
	'Mainz' (*japonica* hybrid)	CMHG EBee ECtt LRHS NRHS
	'Mars' (× *arendsii*)	CMHG
	microphylla	CMHG
	- B&SWJ 11085	WCru
	- pink-flowered	GKev
	'Midnight Arrow' (*davidii* hybrid)	CMHG
	'Mighty Chocolate Cherry'	EMor ILea LCro LOPS NLar SEdd SPeP
	'Mighty Pip' (× *arendsii*)	CBod SPeP
	MIGHTY RED QUIN	see *A.* 'Red Quin'
	'Moerheim Glory' (× *arendsii*)	GBin NGdn NLar
	'Moerheimii' (*thunbergii* hybrid)	CMHG
	'Mont Blanc' (× *arendsii*)	CMHG
	'Montgomery' (*japonica* hybrid) ♀H7	CRos CWCL EBee EMor EPfP EShb GAbr ILea LRHS LSRN LSou MBNS MBel MNrw NGdn NHol NLar NRHS SPoG WBor
	'Nemo'	MAsh
	'New Wave'	LLWG
	'Nikki'	CMHG NEoE NLar
§	***okuyamae*** B&SWJ 10975	WCru
	'Opal'	CMHG
	OSTRICH PLUME	see *A.* 'Straussenfeder'
	'Peaches and Cream'	NBro NLar
	'Peter Barrow' (*glaberrima* hybrid)	SRms
	'Pink Lightning'[PBR] (*simplicifolia* hybrid)	CBod CWCL EShb LLWG MBNS NLar WFar
	PINK PEARL (× *arendsii*)	see *A.* 'Rosa Perle'
	'Poschka'	NEoE
	'Professor van der Wielen' (*thunbergii* hybrid)	CMHG ECha GBin MACG NHol NLar NWad SAko SRms WSpi
	pumila	see *A. chinensis* var. *pumila*
	'Purple Rain'[PBR] (× *arendsii*)	ILea MAsh
	'Radius'	CBod CMHG EGrI ELon NGdn NLar WPnP
	'Raspberry' (Short 'n' Sweet Series)	CBod
	'Red Baron'	NEoE SPad WBrk
§	RED LIGHT	see *A.* 'Rotlicht'

§	'Red Quin'[PBR] **new**	NLar
	'Red Sentinel' (*japonica* hybrid)	CBcs CPud CWCL CWat EMor EPfP EWoo GMaP GWyn LSun MBros MHol NBro NEoE NGdn NHol NLar NWad WFar WWtn
	'Rheinland' (*japonica* hybrid) ♀H7	CBcs CPud CWCL GWyn LRHS MAsh NGdn NLar NRHS SCob SEND WPnP
	'Rhythm and Blues'[PBR]	ECtt NLar
	rivularis	SDix WCot
	- CC 5201	GKev
	- GWJ 9366	WCru
	- PAB 9763	LEdu
I	- 'Grandiflora'	GBin
§	- var. ***myriantha***	EBee WPGP
	- - BWJ 8076a	WCru
	- - SICH 757	CExl
	'Robinson's Pink'	NGdn
	'Rock and Roll'[PBR]	LSRN
§	'Rosa Perle' (× *arendsii*)	CMHG NHol
§	× ***rosea*** 'Peach Blossom'	CBcs CMHG EMor EPfP ILea LLWG NBir NEoE NGdn SBls SCob SCoo SPoG SWvt WFar WHoo WWtn
	- 'Queen Alexandra'	CMHG XLum
	'Rosea' (*simplicifolia* hybrid)	NHol
§	'Rotlicht' (× *arendsii*)	CMHG CMac CRos GBin LRHS NEoE NGdn NHol NLar NRHS
	'Salmonea' (*simplicifolia* hybrid)	CMHG
	'Saxosa'	see *A. glaberrima* var. *saxatilis*
	'Sheila Haxton' (*chinensis*)	CMHG
	Showstar Group (× *arendsii*)	CSBt SRms WWtn
	simplicifolia ♀H5	GArf WFar
	- BRONZE ELEGANCE	see *A.* 'Bronce Elegans'
	- 'Darwin's Snow Sprite'	CMac NHol NLar SCob WFar
	- 'Jacqueline'	CMHG NHol
*	- 'Nana Alba'	NEoE
	- 'Rose of Cimarron'	CMHG NEoE NWad
	- 'White Sensation'[PBR]	ELan LRHS NLar NRHS
	'Snowdrift' (× *arendsii*)	CPud CRos CWat GMaP LRHS MBNS MMuc NBir NEoE NRHS
	'Solferino' (× *arendsii*)	CMHG
	'Spartan' (× *arendsii*)	see *A.* 'Rotlicht'
	'Spinell' (× *arendsii*)	MACG WFar WPnP
	'Spotlight'[PBR]	CBod GBin LRHS MSCN
	'Sprite' (*simplicifolia* hybrid) ♀H7	Widely available
§	'Straussenfeder' (*thunbergii* hybrid) ♀H7	CBod CMac ECtt EPfP GBin GMaP GQue LRHS NBir NBro NGdn NHol NLar NRHS SPer SPoG SRms WCAu WWtn
	'Sugar Plum' (*simplicifolia* hybrid)	NGdn
	'Sugarberry'[PBR] (Short 'n' Sweet Series)	NLar
	'Superba'	see *A. chinensis* var. *taquetii* 'Superba'
	thunbergii	CExl LRHS NRHS
	- var. ***congesta*** B&SWJ 10961	WCru
	- var. ***formosa***	see *A. formosa*
	- var. ***hachijoensis***	EBee
	- - B&SWJ 5622	WCru
	- var. ***okuyamae***	see *A. okuyamae*
	- var. ***sikokumontanum*** B&SWJ 11164	WCru
	- - B&SWJ 11534	WCru
	- var. ***terrestris*** B&SWJ 6125	WCru
	'Thunder and Lightning' (*chinensis* hybrid)	NEoE

'To Have and To Hold' — MNrw
'Venus' (× *arendsii*) — ECtt GMaP MBNS MCot MMuc NGdn NHol SEND WFar
'Vesuvius' (*japonica* hybrid) — CBcs ECtt NBro NLar
virescens — see *A. rivularis* var. *myriantha*
'Vision Inferno'PBR (× *arendsii*) — NDov
§ 'W.E. Gladstone' (*japonica* hybrid) — EMor EWoo
'Walküre' (× *arendsii*) — CMHG
'Walter Bitner' — GBin NHol NRHS
'Washington' (*japonica* hybrid) — EMor LRHS NGdn WPnP
§ 'Weisse Gloria' (× *arendsii*) — CMHG CMac ECha EMor EWTr GBin LRHS NBro NHol NRHS SCoo SEdd SGbt WCAu WFar WWtn
'White Diamond' (× *arendsii*) — WFar
WHITE GLORIA — see *A.* 'Weisse Gloria'
'White Wings'PBR (*simplicifolia* hybrid) — NLar
'Whiteberry' (Short 'n' Sweet Series) — MBros NLar
'William Reeves' (× *arendsii*) — CMHG NHol NWad
'Willie Buchanan' (*simplicifolia* hybrid) — CBcs CMHG CRos GAbr GBin GKev GMaP LRHS NHol NHpl NRHS NWad SLee SRms WAbe WCFE WFar WHoo
(Younique Series) YOUNIQUE CARMINE ('Verscarmine'PBR) — ILea LLWG LRHS LSou
- YOUNIQUE CERISE ('Verscerise'PBR) — ILea LRHS
- YOUNIQUE LILAC ('Verslilac'PBR) — EGrI LRHS
- YOUNIQUE PINK ('Verspink'PBR) — LRHS
- YOUNIQUE RASPBERRY ('Versraspberry') **new** — LRHS
- YOUNIQUE RUBY RED — see *A.* (Younique Series) YOUNIQUE RED
§ - YOUNIQUE RED ('Versred'PBR) — ILea LRHS
- YOUNIQUE SALMON ('Verssalmon'PBR) **new** — ILea LRHS
- YOUNIQUE SILVERY PINK ('Versilverypink'PBR) — EWTr LRHS WFar
- YOUNIQUE WHITE ('Verswhite'PBR) — ILea LRHS
'Zuster Theresa' (× *arendsii*) — CMHG LRHS MBNS MNrw NLar NRHS

Astilboides (*Saxifragaceae*)

§ ***tabularis*** — Widely available

Astragalus (*Fabaceae*)

canadensis — LRHS NRHS
glycyphyllos — GJos NAts SPhx WCot
macrocarpus — SPhx

Astrantia ✿ (*Apiaceae*)

'Atomic Sunburst' — GQue
bavarica — GKev WFar
'Berendien Stam' — CElw MAvo MNrw NLar WFar
'Bloody Mary' — EBee GLet LEdu MNrw NGdn NLar
'Bright and Breezy' — MAvo
'Buckland' — Widely available
'Burgundy Manor' — CBod CWCL EMor MAvo MHol NLar SHar
'Bury Court' — MAvo NDov
carniolica major — see *A. major*
- 'Rubra' — CBcs GMaP WSpi
- 'Variegata' — see *A. major* 'Sunningdale Variegated'
'Censation Milano' — CWGN EMor LRHS NLar
'Clear Pink' — NDov
'Dark Shiny Eyes' — CExl CWCL ECtt GLet MAvo NLar NSti SWvt
'Hadspen Blood' — Widely available
'Harvington Adrian's Choice Pink' — NRHS
'Harvington Selected Red' — NRHS
'Helen' — NLar
helleborifolia — see *A. maxima*
'Larch Cottage Clear Pink' — NLar WFar
'Larch Cottage Magic' — WFar
'Madeleine' — see *A. major* 'Madeleine van Bennekom'
§ ***major*** — Widely available
- 'Abbey Road'PBR — CEme CExl CWCL ECtt EMor EPfP EShb EWTr EWoo LRHS LSou MHol MPnt MidI NLar NRHS SRkn SRms
I - 'Alba' — CBcs GKev GLet LRHS MCot MRav NBir NGdn NPer SCob SPer WPnP WSpi
- 'April Love' — CBod GLet
- 'Berdien' — EBee
- subsp. ***biebersteinii*** — NBir
- 'Bo-Ann' — CWCL NLar WFar
- 'Can Candy' — MNrw
- 'Celtic Star' — SWvt
- 'Claret' — Widely available
- 'Côte d'Azur' — WSpi
- 'Cottage Herbery' — MNrw
- 'Dark Desire' — GLet MAvo NDov WGoo
- 'Elaine's Pink' — WHoo
- 'Elmblut' — WFar
- 'Florence'PBR — CAvo CBct CBod CBor CKno CRos CWCL CWGN EBee ECtt EMor EPfP GLet LRHS MHol MNrw MPri MidI NDov NLar NRHS SPeP SPoG SWvt WFar WSpi
- Gill Richardson Group — Widely available
- 'Gracilis' — CBod EBee EPfP WFar
- 'Green Tapestry' (v) — WCot
- 'Gwaun Valley' — WFar
- subsp. ***involucrata*** — CElw WGoo
- - 'Barrister' — MAvo NLar
- - 'Canneman' — MNrw NLar SMHy WCot
- - 'Jumble Hole' — MAvo NDov WFar WGoo
- - 'Margery Fish' — see *A. major* subsp. *involucrata* 'Shaggy'
- - 'Moira Reid' — CExl CWCL ECtt GLet GMaP MRav SHar WGoo
- - 'Orlando' — MAvo MNrw WFar
§ - - 'Shaggy' — Widely available
- - 'Snape Cottage' — MAvo WFar
- 'Jade Lady' — WFar
- 'Jitse' — WFar
- 'Large White' — LCro LOPS SRms
- 'Lars' — CExl ECtt EMor EWTr GLet LRHS MNrw NGdn NLar SPer SPoG SRms SWvt WCAu
- 'Little Snowstar' — CWCL
- 'Lola' — CDor EBee GLet NLar
§ - 'Madeleine van Bennekom' — CWCL ECha ECtt GLet WFar
- 'Midnight Owl' — ECtt EMor MNrw NSti
- 'Penny's Pink' — EBee EWTr EWhm EWoo GLet LCro LOPS LRHS MNrw MidI WSpi
- 'Pink Crush' — CRos EBlo EPfP LRHS NRHS
- 'Pink Pride' — GLet GWyn MidI WCAu WFar

- 'Pink Sensation'	EBee GLet
- 'Pink Surprise'	GLet MNrw NLar
- 'Primadonna'	CBod CRos EBee EBlo EBou EPfP EPri GLet GMaP LRHS NLar NRHS SBls SPlb SRms
- 'Princesse Sturdza'	CWCL WFar
- 'Red Joyce'	EBee EMor NLar WCAu
- 'Reverse Sunningdale Variegated' (v)	MAvo WFar
- 'Rosa Lee'	CElw CWCL NLar WGoo
- var. ***rosea***	CRos CWCL EPfP GKev GLet GWyn LRHS MRav NGdn NRHS SHar WCAu WFar XLum
- - George's form	EPPr LSRN
- 'Rosensinfonie'	CWCL EBee EHed GJos GLet GMaP GWyn NBro SBls WPnP
§ - 'Rubra'	CRos CWCL EMor EPfP GKev GKin LCro LOPS LPot LRHS MCot MGos NBir NChi NPer NRHS SRms WBor WCAu WHal
- 'Ruby Cloud'	CBod ECtt EMor EPfP EPri GLet LSou NBro NGdn NLar NRHS SPad WFar WSpi
- 'Ruby Giant'	EBee EWTr GKin
- 'Ruby Wedding'	Widely available
- 'Silver Glow'	EBee ECtt
- 'Sparkling Stars'	CWCL MBros
- 'Star of Beauty'PBR (Sparkling Stars Series)	CKno CRos CWCL ECtt ELan EMor EPfP GLet GWyn LEdu LRHS MNrw MPri NDov NLar NRHS NSti SCob SCoo SGBe SPoG SRms SWvt WSpi
- 'Star of Billion'PBR	EBee ECtt ELan EPfP GLet LRHS MBros MHol MNrw MidI NLar NRHS SCob SCoo SEdd SPoG SWvt WCAu WCot
- 'Star of Fire'PBR	CWGN ECtt GLet LRHS MAsh MBel MBros MNrw NLar SCob WFar WHil
- 'Star of Love'	CKno EPfP GLet LRHS LSou MHol NDov WSpi
- 'Star of Magic'PBR (v)	GLet MAvo MNrw SPoG WCAu WCot
- 'Star of Royals'PBR	CWCL ECtt GLet LRHS MidI NRHS SPoG WFar
- 'Star of Summer'	EBee
- 'Starburst'	MNrw WFar
- 'Sue Barnes' (v)	MNrw NLar
§ - 'Sunningdale Variegated' (v) ♀H7	Widely available
- 'Titoki Point'	WCot
- 'Venice'PBR	Widely available
§ ***maxima*** ♀H7	Widely available
- 'Mark Fenwick'	MNrw NBir
I - 'Rosea'	CDor ECtt MNrw NBir NGdn
'Millwood Crimson'	CMiW
minor	LRHS
'Moulin Rouge'PBR	Widely available
§ 'Mrs MacGregor'	MAvo MNrw MPie WFar
'Old Warwickshire Pink'	see *A.* 'Mrs MacGregor'
'Orion' **new**	EMor
'Queen's Children'	CDor GLet
'Rainbow'	NLar
'Roma'PBR ♀H7	Widely available
rubra	see *A. major* 'Rubra'
'Ruby Star'PBR ♀H7	Widely available
'Sheila's Red'	MNrw
'Snow Star'PBR	CRos CWCL EBee ELan EPfP EShb EWoo GLet LRHS MACG MBNS MMrt MNrw NLar NRHS
(Sparkling Stars Series) 'Sparkling Stars Pink'	CBod GLet MHol MNrw
- 'Sparkling Stars Red' **new**	NLar
'Star of Heaven'	NLar
'Star of Passion'PBR	EBee ECtt ELan EPfP GLet LRHS NRHS SCob
'Star of Treasure'PBR	EBee ELan EMor EPfP GLet IPot LRHS NLar NRHS
'Superstar'PBR	CAvo CBod CDor CWCL EBee ECtt ELan ELon EMor EPfP EWTr GLet IPot LRHS MBNS MHol MNrw MRav NDov NLar NSti SCoo SEdd SWvt WCot WFar WSpi
'Warren Hills'	EBee GMaP MNrw MPie NLar WFar
'Washfield'	CWCL EGrI MMrt NDov
'White Angel' **new**	CKno CMea

Astrodaucus (*Apiaceae*)

littoralis	LEdu SPhx WPGP
orientalis	SPhx

Astrolepis (*Pteridaceae*)

sinuata	SPlb

Astroloba ✿ (*Liliaceae*)

spiralis **new**	NCft

Astrophytum (*Cactaceae*)

myriostigma ♀H2	SPad

Asyneuma (*Campanulaceae*)

campanuloides	SGro
limonifolium	GKev
§ ***prenanthoides***	SMrm
pulvinatum	GKev WAbe

Athamanta (*Apiaceae*)

cretensis	SPhx SPtp
macedonica	SPhx
turbith	CSpe MNrw SBrt
- subsp. ***haynaldii***	MACG SPhx
vestina	LRHS SBrt SPhx

Athanasia (*Asteraceae*)

§ ***parviflora***	SPlb

Athrotaxis (*Cupressaceae*)

cupressoides	CBcs LRHS
laxifolia	SMad
selaginoides	CAco

Athyrium ✿ (*Woodsiaceae*)

auriculatum	CBdn
'Branford Beauty'	CLAP CRos LEdu LRHS NRHS
'Branford Rambler'	CBdn CLAP EBee LEdu NBro
filix-femina	Widely available
§ - subsp. ***angustum*** ♀H6	EMor LRHS MRav NGdn NRHS
- - f. ***rubellum*** 'Lady in Red' ♀H6	CBdn CBod CDor CLAP CRos CSta CWCL EBee EGrI EHed ELan EPfP ESwi IBal LCro LEdu LRHS LSRN MAsh MAvo MGos NFav NLar NRHS SCoo SPoG WCot WLov
- 'Clarissimum Jones'	WCot
- 'Crispum Grandiceps Kaye'	NGdn
- Cristatum Group	CLAP EFer ELan LSRN NGdn SMHy WCot WFib
- 'Dre's Dagger'	CBdn CBod CLAP CMiW EMor LEdu NBro NFav SPoG WPGP
- 'Fieldii'	CLAP EFer
- 'Frizelliae' ♀H6	Widely available
- 'Frizelliae Capitatum'	CLAP WFib
- 'Frizelliae Cristatum'	CLAP
- 'Howardii'	NBro

- 'Lady-in-Lace' ♀H6	EBee
- 'Minutissimum'	EBee ELan LRHS NRHS WCot
- Plumosum Group	MRav WFib XLum
- 'Plumosum Axminster'	CLAP EFer EShb WCot WFar
- 'Plumosum Cristatum Drueryi'	WCot
- 'Plumosum Drueryi'	EFer
- 'Plumosum Percristatum'	WCot
- RED STEM	see *A. filix-femina* 'Rotstiel'
§ - 'Rotstiel'	CDTJ CLAP EBee EMor NBro NLar
- 'Setigerum Cristatum'	WFar
- 'Vernoniae' ♀H6	CLAP MRav
- 'Vernoniae Cristatum'	CLAP WFib
- 'Victoriae'	CDTJ CDor CRos CWCL EBee ECtt EFer ELan EPfP GMaP IBal LEdu LLWG LRHS MHtn NBid NLar NRHS WFar WSpi XLum
- aff. 'Victoriae'	CBod CLAP CSta MACG MAsh WFar
'Ghost' ♀H5	CBdn CLAP CRos EBee EHed EMor ESwi LEdu LRHS MAsh MGos NBro NLar NRHS NSti SPlb SPoG WCot
goeringianum 'Pictum'	see *A. niponicum* var. *pictum*
minimum	CBdn CLAP EMor LEdu NBro NLar WCot WPGP
niponicum	CLAP CPud
- 'Godzilla'	CLAP EBee EHed LEdu NBro
- f. ***metallicum***	see *A. niponicum* var. *pictum*
§ - var. ***pictum*** ♀H5	Widely available
- - 'Apple Court'	CBdn CLAP CRos EBee EHed ESwi LEdu LRHS MAsh NBro NRHS
- - 'Burgundy Lace'	CLAP CMiW EBee ECtt EGrI EHed ESwi MPnt NBro NLar SEdd WCot
* - - 'Cristatoflabellatum'	CLAP EBlo
- - 'Pearly White'	CBdn CLAP MAsh NBro
- - 'Pewter Lace'	CLAP CMiW EBee ECtt EMor EWoo LEdu MACG NBro NLar SMad SPad SPeP WSpi
- - 'Red Beauty'	Widely available
- - 'Regal Red'	CLAP EBee LRHS MAsh NRHS
- - 'Silver Falls' ♀H5	CBcs CBdn CLAP CRos EBee EShb ESwi LEdu LLWG LRHS MAsh NBro NRHS SCoo SPoG WCot
- - 'Soul Mate'	CLAP
- - 'Ursula's Red'	CBod CLAP CMiW CSta EBee EGrI ELan ELon EMor EPot EShb LCro LLWG LOPS LRHS LSun MHol NBid NHpl NLar SCob SEdd SPoG WCot WFar WPGP
'Ocean's Fury'	CLAP EBee ECtt EShb ESwi LPla SPoG WCot
otophorum ♀H4	MRav NBid WPGP
- var. ***okanum*** ♀H4	Widely available
vidalii	CBdn CBod CLAP CRos EGrI EHed EMor IBal LEdu LLWG LRHS NBro NLar NRHS SCob SMad WFar WFib XLum

Atractylodes (*Asteraceae*)

japonica	LEdu

Atragene see *Clematis*

Atriplex (*Amaranthaceae*)

canescens	CAgr
halimus	CAgr CBcs CCoa CLau CSde EBee ECha EPPr MRav NLar SLon SPer SPlb WCot XAbr
- 'Cascais'	WCot
- 'Limelight' (v)	ECha EPPr
hortensis	ENfk
- var. ***rubra***	CKel CSpe ELan MNHC SMrm SRms

Atropa (*Solanaceae*)

belladonna	GPoy SEND
mandragora	see *Mandragora officinarum*

aubergine see AGM Vegetables Section

Aubrieta (*Brassicaceae*)

'Agnetta'	ECtt
'Alba'	see *A.* 'Fiona'
'Alix Brett'	CMea
§ 'Argenteovariegata' (v) ♀H6	CRos LRHS NRHS
'Audrey Blue' (Audrey Series)	GDam GWyn
§ 'Aureovariegata' (v) ♀H6	CMea NPer XLum
Axcent Series	MPri
- AXCENT BURGUNDY	EPfP LRHS
- AXCENT DARK RED ('Audeldare')	WIce
- AXCENT DEEP RED ('Abrz0001'PBR)	SRms
- AXCENT GLACIER LIGHT BLUE	SEE *A.* Axcent Series AXCENT LIGHT BLUE
§ - AXCENT LIGHT BLUE ('Abrz0002'PBR)	CRos EPfP LRHS NRHS
- AXCENT LILAC ('Audelip'PBR)	CRos EPfP LRHS NRHS
bicoloured	CBod CMea
BLAUE SCHÖNHEIT	see *A.* 'Blue Beauty'
'Blaumeise'	CBod EBou MHol
§ 'Blue Beauty'	CMea EBou ECtt EPfP GBin GMaP NHpl NLar WHoo
'Blue Emperor'	ECtt
'Blue Whale'	ECtt GAbr LBuc NLar SRms SWvt
§ 'Bob Saunders' (d)	CMea ECtt
'Boundary Haze'	EBou
'Boundary Purple'	EBou
'Bressingham Pink' (d) ♀H6	ECtt SRms
'Bressingham Red'	ECtt EPfP GMaP GRum SRms
canescens subsp. ***cilicica***	GKev
Cascade Series	SPoG
- 'Blue Cascade'	CTri EBou EGrI EPfP GMaP MBNS SPlb SPoG SRms
- 'Lilac Cascade'	SPoG SRms
- 'Purple Cascade'	CTri EBou LCro LOPS LSRN MAsh MBNS SPlb SPoG SRms
- 'Red Cascade' ♀H6	CTri EBou ECtt EGrI ELan EPfP LSRN MBNS SPlb SPoG
× ***cultorum***	CKel LSun SVic XSen
deltoidea Variegata Group (v)	CBod MAsh MHol WFar
- - 'Nana Variegata' (v)	CMea GRum
'Doctor Mules' ♀H6	ECtt SRms WCav
'Doctor Mules Variegata' (v)	CBod ECtt ELan EPfP GDam GMaP GWyn LRHS MHer NLar SPoG SRot SWvt WHoo WIce
double pink-flowered (d)	CBod ELan GAbr GMaP MBros MHol
'Elsa Lancaster'	EPot NHpl
§ 'Fiona'	CMea EWes
'Florado Rose Red' **new**	CBod LRHS
glabrescens	CMea EPot NHpl WAbe
'Gloria'	CMea ECtt NHpl NLar WHoo WIce
'Golden King'	see *A.* 'Aureovariegata'
gracilis 'Kitte'	CBod CSma EBou ECtt ELan EPfP MHer NLar SPoG SRms
- 'Kitte Blue'	CRos ELan EPfP LBuc LRHS MPri NRHS SPoG SRms WIce
- 'Kitte Blue Blush Bicolour' **new**	ELan
- 'Kitte Purple'	ELan EPfP GKev SPoG
- 'Kitte Rose'	CRos EPfP LBuc LRHS NRHS

– 'Kitte Rose Blush Bicolour' new	ELan
– 'Kitte Rose Red' new	ELan
– 'Kitte White'	CRos EPfP LRHS MHer NRHS
'Greencourt Purple' ♀H6	ECtt MHer
'Hamburger Stadtpark'	CWCL ECtt ELan EPfP EWoo GMaP SRms XLum
'Hürth'	GBin
'Ida'	ECtt WIce
'Kati'	GMaP
'Lime Variegated' (v)	NHpl WCav
'Oakington Lavender'	ECtt
pinardii	GKev WAbe
'Pink Beauty'	ECtt
'Pixie Pearls' new	LRHS
'Purple Charm'	SRms
'Red Carpet'	MAsh MHer SRms
'Regado White' new	CBod
'Rose Queen'	CMea ECtt
Royal Series ♀H6	LCro LOPS
– 'Royal Blue'	CBod CTri ELan EPfP GKev MBros NLar SRms WFar
– 'Royal Lilac'	CTri WFar
– 'Royal Red'	CBod CTri ELan EPfP GBin GWyn SRms WCav
– 'Royal Violet'	ELan EPfP SBut WFar
'Schofield's Double'	see *A.* 'Bob Saunders'
'Silberrand' (v)	ECha LBuc
§ 'Snow Maiden'PBR	NHpl
'Somerfield Silver'	ELan
'Somerford Lime' (v)	ELan EPfP SRms WIce
'Swan Red' (v)	EBou ECtt NHpl NSla WTor
'Valerie' (v)	EWes GRum
'Westacre Gold' (v)	CBod ECtt EWes MHol
'Winterberg'	ECtt

Aucuba ✿ (*Garryaceae*)

chlorascens B&SWJ 11815	WCru
himalaica	CDTJ GBin SBrt
var. ***dolichophylla***	
– – Og 95038	WCru
japonica	CCVT CDoC CEme LPar NLar SEWo WCru WFar
– B&SWJ 14602	WCru
– var. ***borealis*** (f) CWJ 12898	WCru
– 'Clent Wortley Hall' (m)	WCFE
– 'Crassifolia' (m)	SArc
– 'Crotonifolia' (f/v) ♀H5	Widely available
– 'Crotonifolia' (m/v)	CMac MAsh SDix SGsty SRms
– 'Dentata' (f)	SRms WAvo WCru
– 'February Star' (f/v)	ESwi SDix
– 'Golden Girl' (v)	CBod CEnd LRHS MAsh NRHS SLon
– 'Golden King' (m/v) ♀H5	CBod CDoC CEme CMac CSBt EBee ELan ELon EPfP LRHS MAsh MGos NLar NRHS SCob SGsty SLim SMad WFar
– 'Golden Spangles' (f/v)	CBcs CKel EMil EPfP LRHS SWvt
– 'Leucocarpa' (f)	SPer
– f. ***longifolia***	CMac EPfP SArc SDix WCru
– – 'Salicifolia' (f) ♀H5	CEme EBee ELon ESwi MRav WCru WFar WPGP
– 'Maculata' misapplied	see *A. japonica* 'Variegata'
– 'Marmorata' (v)	LRHS MAsh NRHS
– 'Mr Goldstrike' (m/v)	CBod CEnd CRos EPfP LRHS MAsh SCoo SGBe SGbt
– PEPPER POT ('Shilpot') (m/v) ♀H5	CRos EPfP LRHS MAsh SLon WCFE
– 'Picturata' (m/v)	CBod CEme CMac ELan ELon ESwi MAsh NLar SEND WFar
– 'Rozannie' (f/m) ♀H5	Widely available
– 'Sulphurea Marginata' (f/v)	CKel CMCN CMac CTri EShb ESwi LRHS NLar NRHS SPer WFar
§ – 'Variegata' (f/v)	CBod CBrac CCVT CChe CEme CMac CRos CSBt CTri EBee ELan ELon EPfP LBuc LRHS MAsh MGos MSCN NHol NRHS NWea SCob SGbt SLim SLon SNig SPer SRms SWeb WAvo
– 'Variegata' white-flowered (m/v)	SGbt
omeiensis	CBcs CDTJ CExl CMCN IDee
– B&SWJ 2864	ESwi WCru
– BWJ 8048	WCru
– L 614	WPGP

Aulax (*Proteaceae*)

cancellata	CCCN SPlb

Aurinia (*Brassicaceae*)

§ ***saxatilis*** ♀H5	ELan EPfP MMuc SPlb WFar XSen
– 'Citrina' ♀H5	ECha EGrI SRms
– 'Compacta'	GJos WIce
– 'Dudley Nevill'	WFar
– 'Dudley Nevill Variegated' (v)	ECha EWes
– GOLD BALL	see *A. saxatilis* 'Goldkugel'
– 'Gold Cushion' new	LRHS
– 'Gold Dust'	GJos SRms
§ – 'Goldkugel'	CBod CMea EPfP GJos GWyn NFav SPoG SRms WFar
– 'Variegata' (v)	SPoG SRms WHoo

Austrocedrus (*Cupressaceae*)

§ ***chilensis***	CAco CKen SLim

Avena (*Poaceae*)

candida	see *Helictotrichon sempervirens*

Avenula see *Helictotrichon*

Averrhoa (*Oxalidaceae*)

carambola (F)	CCCN SVic

avocado see *Persea americana*

Azadirachta (*Meliaceae*)

indica	MVil XAbr

Azalea see *Rhododendron*

Azara ✿ (*Salicaceae*)

dentata	CBcs CMac CTrC WFar WPav
– 'Variegata'	see *A. integrifolia* 'Variegata'
integrifolia	CCCN IDee MGil WPav
– 'Uarie'	CCCN
§ – 'Variegata' (v)	CCCN CKel
lanceolata	CBcs CExl CTri CTsd LEdu NSti SPer WPav
microphylla ♀H4	CBcs CCCN CDoC CEme CExl CKel CMac CTri EBee ELan ELon EPfP LRHS LSRN MAsh MGil MMuc NQui SArc SEND SPer SPlb WFar WPGP WPav WSpi
* – 'Albovariegata' (v)	CTri WPav
– 'Gold Edge' (v)	CEme WFar WPav
– 'Variegata' (v)	CBcs CExl CKel CMac EBee ELan EPfP LRHS MAsh MGil NFav NLar SEND SPer SPoG WAvo WFar WPav
* ***patagonica***	MBlu WPav
petiolaris	CTri MGil WPav
serrata ♀H4	CBcs CBrac CCCN CEnd CKel CMCN CTsd CWit ELan EPfP EShb

	GBin LRHS MGil NLar SDix SEND SGol SPer SPoG SRms SVen WBor WFar WKif WPav WSpi
- 'Maurice Mason'	EBee IArd
uruguayensis	CCCN CExl CTsd GBin IDee WPav

Azorella (*Apiaceae*)

filamentosa	EPot GEdr WAbe
glebaria misapplied	see *A. trifurcata*
glebaria A. Gray	see *Bolax gummifer*
gummifer	see *Bolax gummifer*
lycopodioides	SPlb
patagonica	SPlb
§ ***trifurcata***	CPar CSpe CTri GAbr GKev MMuc NBir NFav SPlb WAbe
- 'Nana'	GArf GEdr GMaP XLum

Azorina (*Campanulaceae*)

§ ***vidalii***	EShb NWad SPlb

B

Babiana (*Iridaceae*)

angustifolia	NRog
disticha	see *B. fragrans*
§ ***fragrans***	CPbh NRog
nana	MBros
- 'Claudia'	GKev
- 'Halley'	GBin
- subsp. ***maculata*** new	NRog
- 'The Bride' new	GKev
odorata	CPla NRog
patersoniae	NRog SPlb
plicata	see *B. fragrans*
pygmaea	NRog
rubrocyanea	CPla
sambucina	NRog
stricta ♀H2	CCCN NRog SDeJ
- Kew hybrids	NRog
- 'Purple Star'	CBor CExl NRog
thunbergii	CPbh
tubulosa	NRog
vanzyliae	NRog
villosa	NRog
villosula	NRog
'Zwanenburg's Glory'	CPrp

Baccharis (*Asteraceae*)

genistelloides	MPkF XSte
patagonica	EHyd MMuc SArc SVen

Backhousia (*Myrtaceae*)

citriodora	GPoy MHer

Bacopa (*Plantaginaceae*)

misapplied	see *Chaenostoma cordatum*

Baeckea (*Myrtaceae*)

gunniana	CExl
linifolia	SPlb
virgata	SPlb

Baeometra (*Colchicaceae*)

uniflora new	CPla

Balbisia (*Ledocarpaceae*)

peduncularis	CCCN

Baldellia (*Alismataceae*)

ranunculoides	EWat WMAq
- f. ***repens***	LLWG

Ballota (*Lamiaceae*)

acetabulosa	ECha EWes WCot
'All Hallow's Green'	see *Marrubium bourgaei* var. *bourgaei* 'All Hallows Green'
hirsuta	XSen
nigra	GPoy NMir SRms
pseudodictamnus ♀H4	CBcs CBod CCBP CMac CTtf EBee ECha EHyd ELan EPfP EWld EWoo GMaP IDee LRHS LSRN MPie MRav NPer NRHS SCob SDix SEND SLon SMrm SPer WSHC XLum XSen
- B&M 8119	WCot WPGP
- from Crete	ECha
- 'Candia'	SHar
- compact	CBct SPer XSen
rupestris 'Frogswell Carolyn' (v)	XSen

Baloskion (*Restionaceae*)

§ ***tetraphyllum***	CPbh GBin LRHS SPlb SPoG WSMil XSte
§ - 'Cornish Gold' (v)	CPbh

Balsamita see *Tanacetum*

Balsamorhiza (*Asteraceae*)

rosea	GEdr

banana see *Ensete*, *Musa*

Banksia ✿ (*Proteaceae*)

blechnifolia new	CPbh
canei	SPlb
ericifolia	CPbh
- var. ***ericifolia***	CCCN CTsd
- var. ***macrantha***	SPlb
formosa	CPbh SPlb
'Giant Candles'	CPbh CTrC LRHS XSte
grandis	CCCN CPbh
§ ***heliantha***	SPlb
integrifolia	CBcs CCCN CDTJ CPbh CTrC CTsd IArd IDee LRHS SPlb XSte
marginata	CTrC CTsd SPlb
media	SPlb
menziesii	CPbh CTsd
- shrubby	CCCN
oblongifolia	SPlb
occidentalis	CTsd
paludosa	CTrC SPlb
praemorsa	CCCN CTsd XSte
- yellow-flowered	CCCN CTsd
prionotes	CCCN
robur	CCCN SPlb
serrata	CCCN SPlb XSte
speciosa	SPlb
spinulosa	CPbh CTrC LRHS
- 'Birthday Candles'	CPbh
- var. ***collina***	SPlb
- var. ***spinulosa***	CCCN
violacea	SPlb

Baptisia (*Fabaceae*)

§ ***alba***	EWTr LPla MBel MNrw NSti SBls SCob SPhx
- var. ***alba***	WCAu
§ - var. ***macrophylla***	EHyd EWes LRHS MNrw NRHS SPhx

australis 🏆H7	Widely available
- 'Blueberry Sundae'	CSpe CWGN EBee EWTr ILea MSCN SPer WHil
- 'Caspian Blue'	CExl GMaP LEdu SBls
- 'Exaltata' 🏆H7	EBee ECtt EPau LPla MBNS MSCN NLar WCot
- var. ***minor***	CSpe MMrt SPhx
× ***bicolor*** 'Starlite' (Prairieblues Series)	MNrw SMHy
bracteata var. ***leucophaea***	SPhx
'Carolina Moonlight'	EBee ECtt EWes GBin LRHS MNrw NSti SCob SHar SPer XLum
'Cherries Jubilee'	CWGN EBee ILea LCro LOPS LRHS MSCN WCot WHil
'Chocolate Chip'	MCot SHar
'Dutch Chocolate' (Decadence Series)	CBcs CWGN EBee ECtt ELan EWes ILea IPot LCro LOPS NDov NSti SPad SPer SPoG WCot WTyc
'Grape Taffy'	EWTr LCro LOPS MSCN
'Indigo Spires'	EBee ILea MBel
lactea	see *B. alba* var. *macrophylla*
'Lemon Meringue'	CBod EBee ECha ELan LCro LOPS MNrw MSCN NDov SPoG WCot
leucantha	see *B. alba* var. *macrophylla*
pendula	see *B. alba*
'Pink Lemonade'	EWTr LCro LOPS WHil
'Pink Truffles' (Decadence Series)	EBee IPot LCro LOPS NSti SHar WCot WHil
'Purple Smoke'	CBcs CExl CSpe EBee ECtt ILea LCro LEdu LOPS LRHS MBel SMHy SPhx WHil WPGP WSHC XSte
'Solar Flare' (Prairieblues Series)	ILea MBel
'Sparkling Sapphires' (Decadence Series)	IPot WHil
sphaerocarpa	LPla SPhx SPlb
tinctoria	SPhx
'Vanilla Cream'	EWTr IPot LCro LOPS LRHS MMrt NSti WCot WHil
× ***variicolor*** 'Twilite' (Prairieblues Series)	CPla EBee ILea IPot LRHS SCob

Barbarea (*Brassicaceae*)

praecox	see *B. verna*
rupicola 'Sunnyola'	CBor
§ ***verna***	GPoy MHer SRms SVic
vulgaris 'Variegata' (v)	NBro
- 'Variegated Winter Cream' (v)	EPfP

Barleria (*Acanthaceae*)

obtusa	EShb
oenotheroides	CCCN
suberecta	see *Dicliptera sericea*

Barnardia (*Asparagaceae*)

japonica white-flowered **new**	NRog

Barosma see *Agathosma*

Bartlettina (*Asteraceae*)

§ ***sordida***	CCCN

Basella (*Basellaceae*)

rubra	CLau SPre

Bashania (*Poaceae*)

§ ***fargesii***	MMuc MRav MWht SEND
I ***qingchengshanensis***	MWht

basil see *Ocimum basilicum*

Bauhinia (*Fabaceae*)

alba hort.	see *B. variegata*
* ***lutea***	CCCN
natalensis	SPlb
purpurea L.	CCCN SPlb
tomentosa	CCCN
§ ***variegata***	CAco
'White Lady'	CCCN
yunnanensis	SBrt SPlb

Baumea see *Machaerina*

bay see *Laurus nobilis*

beans see AGM Vegetables Section

Beaucarnea (*Asparagaceae*)

recurvata 🏆H1c	CDoC LCro LOPS SPad SPlb

Beaufortia (*Myrtaceae*)

sparsa	CTrC
squarrosa	SPlb

Beaumontia (*Apocynaceae*)

grandiflora	EShb

Bedfordia (*Asteraceae*)

linearis	SPlb

Beesia (*Ranunculaceae*)

§ ***calthifolia***	CBct CDTJ CDor EBee EPfP ESwi EWld GEdr LEdu SChF SMad WCot WCru WPGP WSHC
- DJHC 98447	CExl
deltophylla misapplied	see *B. calthifolia*

beetroot see AGM Vegetables Section

Begonia ✿ (*Begoniaceae*)

U614 **new**	GGro
from Siam	GGro
from Taiwan	GGro
'Abel Carrière' (R)	WDib
aconitifolia (C)	EShb
albopicta (C)	EBak
- 'Rosea' (C)	EShb WDib
AMOUR ('Yamour') (Million Kisses Series)	MBros
'Angela Jane' (T)	WFib
aff. ***angularis***	SPlb
§ ***annulata*** 🏆H1b	GGro LEdu
- HWJK 2424	ESwi WCru WFar
- 'Karma Khonoma' **new**	WPGP
'Apricot Delight' (Fragrant Falls Improved Series) (T)	WFib
'Apricot Nectar' (Fragrant Falls Improved Series) (T)	EHyd NRHS
I 'Apricot Shades Improved'	SDeJ
'Argentea' (R)	EBak
'Argenteo-guttata'	EShb
'Aya' (C)	WDib
balansana	CBct
'Beatrice Haddrell'	CBct
BELEAF INCA NIGHT ('Krbelin02'PBR) (R)	SCob
'Benitochiba' (R) 🏆H1b	CAbb CBcs CBct CBod CDTJ CExl CSpe ECtt ESwi GBin SPoG WCot WDib

	'Beryl Rhodes' (T)	WFib
	'Bethlehem Star'	NWad WDib
	'Billy Langdon' (T)	WFib
	'Black Fang' ♀H1b	WDib
	'Black Knight' (R)	WDib
	'Blackberry Swirl' (R)	WDib
	'Blazing Star' (T)	LCro LOPS
	'Blue Sky Appleblossom'	MBros
	'Blushing Star' (T)	LCro LOPS
	'Bokit' × ***imperialis***	WDib
	boliviensis (T)	ESwi
	- 'Firecracker'	WDib
	BONFIRE ('Nzcone'PBR) ♀H1b	SPoG
	'Bouton de Rose' (T)	SDeJ
	burkillii **new**	GGro
	'Buttermilk' (T)	WFib
	'Can-can' (T)	WFib
	carolineifolia ♀H1b	WDib
	'Cascade Florence'	SDeJ
	'Cascade Sunray'	SDeJ
	'Casey Corwin' (R)	WDib
	cathayana	EBee
	- B&SWJ 8315 **new**	WCru
	'Champagne'	LCro LOPS
	'Chantilly Lace'	NWad
I	***chapaensis*** HWJ 642	WCru
	'China Curl' (R) ♀H1b	WDib
	chitoensis B&SWJ 1954	WCru
	'Christmas Candy'	WFar
	× ***chungii*** DJHT 99168 **new**	GGro
	chuyunshanensis PB 07-1111 **new**	GGro
	'Cleopatra' ♀H1b	WDib
	coccinea (C)	WPav
	'Comte de Lesseps' (C)	WDib
	'Connee Boswell' ♀H1b	WDib
§	***corallina*** (C)	EBak
	'Crestabruchii'	WCot
	cucullata var. ***arenosicola*** (S)	ECtt ESwi LRHS
	'Curly Fireflush' (R) ♀H1b	WDib
	'Daisy Trinder' (T) **new**	WFib
	'David Blais' (R) ♀H1b	WDib
	'Dawnal Meyer' (C)	WDib
I	'De Elegans'	WDib
	Devil Series (S)	SCob
	- 'Devil White' (S)	SCob
	- DEVIL'S DELIGHT (mixed) (S)	LCro LOPS MBros SCob
	'Dewdrop' (R) ♀H1b	WDib
	'Dibleys Pink Showers' ♀H1b	WDib
	discolor	see *B. grandis* subsp. *evansiana*
	'Down Home' (C)	WDib
	DRAGON WING RED ('Bepared'PBR) ♀H1b	EShb MBros
§	***dregei*** (T) ♀H1b	CSpe EShb
	ELEGANCE ('Yagance'PBR) (Million Kisses Series) ♀H1b	MBros
	emeiensis	CAbb CBct EPPr GGro WFar WPGP
	'Emerald Giant' (R)	WDib
	'Erythrophylla' ♀H1b	EShb
	'Escargot' (R) ♀H1b	WDib
	'Fairy Lights' (T)	WFib
	Fimbriata Group (T)	SDeJ
	'Fireworks' (R) ♀H1b	WDib
	'Flo'Belle Moseley' (C)	WDib
§	***foliosa*** var. ***miniata*** ♀H1b	CTsd EBak EShb MArl SDix SIvy WCot WDib
	- - pink-flowered	CCCN SIvy
	formosana f. ***albo-maculata*** B&SWJ 6881	WCru
	Fragrant Falls Improved Series (T)	SCob SPoG
	fuchsioides	see *B. foliosa* var. *miniata*
	'Funky Pink' (Funky Series) (T/d)	LSou SCob
	fusca	WMal WPGP
	'Garden Angel Blush' (Garden Angel Series)	CAbb CBct CBod EHed WCot
	'Gay Gordon' (T)	WFib
	'George McCormick' (T) **new**	WFib
	'Glowing Embers' ♀H1b	CRos ECtt LBuc MBros NWad SCob SPoG
	grandis (T)	IDee
§	- subsp. ***evansiana*** ♀H2	CBct CMiW CTsd ELan EPPr EShb LEdu LRHS SDix SEND SPlb WCot WCru WFar XLum
	- - B&SWJ 11188	WCru
	- - var. ***alba*** hort. ♀H2	CMiW EBee EPPr EShb ESwi EWld LEdu SDix SGro WCot WPGP XLum
	- - 'Claret Jug'	CExl EBee ECtt EPPr ESwi MSCN WGrn WSMil
	- - 'Pink Parasol'	ESwi WCru
	- - pink-flowered	WFar
	- - 'Simsii'	EBee WFar
	- - 'Sublime'	LEdu
	- 'Heron's Pirouette'	EPPr WFar
	- subsp. ***holostyla*** 'Nanjiang Silver'	EPPr GGro
	- 'Sapporo'	EBee EPPr ESwi GGro SChr WCru WFar
§	- subsp. ***sinensis*** (T)	NWad WFar
	- - BWJ 8011A	GGro
I	- - 'Red Undies'	ESwi GGro WCru WFar
	- - 'Snowpop'	WFar WPGP
	- aff. subsp. ***sinensis*** (T)	GGro
	- - BWJ 8133 **new**	WCru WFar
	'Green Gold' (R) ♀H1b	WDib
	'Green Sparkles' (R) **new**	WDib
	'Green Valleyleaf'	NWad
	griffithii	see *B. annulata*
	guaniana 'Pink Lady'	GGro WCru WFar
	haageana hort. ex W. Watson	see *B. scharffii*
	(Hanging Basket Series) 'Hanging Basket Orange' (T)	SDir
	- 'Hanging Basket Pink' (T)	SDir
	- 'Hanging Basket Red' (T)	SDir
	- 'Hanging Basket Salmon' (T)	SDir
	- 'Hanging Basket White' (T)	SDir
	hatacoa	LEdu
	- silver-leaved	WDib
	Heaven Series (S)	SCob
	- HEAVEN DELIGHT (mixed)	LCro LOPS
	- 'Heaven Red' (S)	SCob
	- 'Heaven White' (S)	MBros
	'Helen Teupel' (R)	WDib
	'Helena Hall' (T)	WFib
	'Hilo Holiday' (R) ♀H1b	WDib
	HONEYMOON ('Yamoon'PBR) (Million Kisses Series)	MBros
	Illumination Series (T/d)	LCro LOPS MBros
	- 'Illumination Apricot' (T/d)	SCoo
	- 'Illumination Rose' (T/d)	SCoo
	- 'Illumination Salmon Pink' (T/d) ♀H2	SCoo
	- 'Illumination White' (T/d)	SCoo

× ***intermedia*** 'Bertinii' (T) LCro LOPS SDeJ
'Jennifer Wilson' (T) WFib
'Jessie Cruickshank' (T) WFib
'John Smith' (T) WFib
'Jolly Noel' **new** WDib
'Joyful Blaze' (R) **new** WDib
* ***koelzii*** CDTJ ESwi
– NJM 12.077 WPGP
'La Paloma' (C) WDib
labordei 'Candy Floss' WCru WFar
Large-flowered Double Group (T/d) SDeJ
'Lianne' (T) WFib
'Lime Green' GGro
'Limeade' 🏆H1b WDib
'Linda Jackson' (T) WFib
listada 🏆H1b WDib
'Little Brother Montgomery' (C) 🏆H1b NWad WDib
'Lois Burks' (C) WDib
'Lucerna' (C) EBak ELan EShb WDib
luxurians 🏆H1b CAbb CBct CBod CDTJ CSpe EBee ECtt ELan ESwi GBin SDix SIvy SMad SPlb WCot WPGP WSMil
macduffieana see *B. corallina*
maculata (C) LCro LOPS
– 'Wightii' (C) CSpe WDib
'Madame Butterfly' (C) NWad
(Majestic Series) 'Majestic Pink' (T) SCob
– 'Majestic Red' (T) SCob
– 'Majestic Sunburst' (T) SCob
– 'Majestic Yellow' (T) SCob
'Majesty' (T) WFib
Marginata Group (T) SDeJ
* 'Marginata Crispa White' SDeJ
'Marmaduke' 🏆H1b WDib
'Marmorata' (T) SDeJ
'Martin Johnson' (R) 🏆H1b WDib
masoniana 🏆H1b ESwi WDib WSFF
I 'Matador' (T) WFib
'Matisse' (Impressionist Series) EHyd NRHS
'Melissa' (T) WFib
'Merry Christmas' (R) WDib
'Metallic Mist'PBR ESwi
§ ***metallica*** 🏆H1b EShb
'Midnight Magic' (R) 🏆H1b WDib
Million Kisses Series LBuc MPri
'Mishmi Silver' CBct GGro LEdu WPGP
'Monet' (Impressionist Series) EHyd NRHS
'Mother's Day' (T) LCro LOPS
'Mrs E. McLaughlan' (T) WFib
'Mrs Peters' (T) WFib
'Munchkin' 🏆H1b WDib
'My Best Friend' WDib
'Namur' (R) 🏆H1b WDib
'Nick Woodfield' WFib
Nonstop Series (T/d) MBros SCob SDeJ
– 'Nonstop Pink' (T/d) SDeJ
– 'Nonstop Red' (T/d) MBros SDeJ
– 'Nonstop Rose Petticoat' (T/d) MBros
– 'Nonstop Salmon' (T/d) SDeJ
– 'Nonstop White' (T/d) MBros SCob SDeJ
– 'Nonstop Yellow' (T/d) MBros SCob SDeJ
(Northern Lights Series) 'Northern Lights' (T) SCob
– 'Northern Lights Pink' (T) MBros SCob
– 'Northern Lights Scarlet Burst' (T) SCob

'Odorosa' SDeJ
'Ollykey' (T) WFib
'Orange Rubra' (C) WDib
'Orangeade' (C) NWad
'Organdy' (mixed) MBros
palmata CBct CDTJ CExl GGro WFar
– 'Dark Star' **new** GGro
– 'Snow Splash' **new** GGro
panchtharensis GGro SPlb WFar
– B&SWJ 2692 WCot WCru
'Peardrop'PBR MBros
pedatifida GGro
– DJHC 98473 ESwi EWld WCru WFar
– 'Apalala' WFar WPGP
Pendula Group (T) SDeJ
– 'Pink Giant' (T) LCro LOPS
– 'Red Giant' (T) LCro LOPS
– 'White Giant' (T) LCro LOPS
'Picasso' (Impressionist Series) EHyd NRHS
'Picotee' (T) SDeJ
'Pink Cascade' SDeJ
'Pink Champagne' (R) 🏆H1b WDib
'Pink Flamingo' (T) LCro LOPS
'Pink Gin' (R) WDib
'Pink Spirit' (R) WDib
'Pink Twist' WDib
'Pollux' 🏆H1b WDib
'Powder Puff' (T) WFib
'Président Carnot' (C) 🏆H1b NWad
'Preston Guild' (T) **new** WFib
'Princess Alice' (T) WFib
'Princess of Hanover' (R) 🏆H1b WDib
putii B&SWJ 7245 WCru
'Queen Olympus' WDib
'Raspberry Swirl' (R) WDib
ravenii (T) CDTJ
'Ray Peters' WFib
'Red Admiral' (T) WFib
'Red Glory' (T) LCro LOPS
'Red Robin' (R) 🏆H1b WDib
'Red Tempest' WDib
'Red Undies' (*grandis*) see *B. grandis* subsp. *sinensis* 'Red Undies'
'Regal Minuet' (R) 🏆H1b WDib
'Renoir' (Impressionist Series) EHyd NRHS
rex (R) WCot
'Richmondensis' (S) EShb
'Rocheart' (R) 🏆H1b WDib
'Rosy Jewel' (R) WDib
'Roy Hartley' (T/d) WFib
'Sal's Comet' (R) 🏆H1b WDib
'Sandra Haynes' (T) WFib
'Satin Starburst' (R) WDib
'Sceptre' (T) WFib
'Sceptre Cross' (T) WFib
§ ***scharffii*** EBak SDix
'Scherzo' WDib
'Sea Urchin' WDib
§ Semperflorens Cultorum Group (S) SCob
'Senator White' (Senator Series) MBros
serratipetala 🏆H1b EBak WDib
'Shamus' WDib
* ***shepherdii*** WDib
sikkimensis ESwi GGro
– var. ***kamengensis*** **new** GGro
silletensis WCot

- subsp. ***mengyangensis*** WCot
'Silver Cloud' (R) ♀H1b WDib
'Silver Jewell' ♀H1b WDib
'Silver Lace' WDib
'Silver Spirit' (R) WDib
'Silver Splendor' CSpe ECtt ESwi
sinensis see *B. grandis* subsp. *sinensis*
sizemoreae WDib WMal
'Snow Storm' WDib
I 'Snowcap' (C) ♀H1b EShb WDib
solananthera A. DC. ♀H1b WDib
'Solid Silver' (R) WDib
soli-mutata ♀H1b WDib
'Stained Glass' WDib
'Star Bright' WDib
'Star Light' WDib
STARSHINE MIXED LSou
'Sugar Candy' (T/d) WFib
'Sugar Plum' MAsh
SUMMERWINGS CRos SPoG
DARK ELEGANCE ('Insumdaele'PBR) (Summerwings Series)
'Sunset Yellow Champagne' LCro LOPS
'Susan' (T) WFib
sutherlandii (T) ♀H2 CAvo CCCN CExl EBak EBee EShb ESwi EWld GQue NPer SAdn SDix SGro SIvy WCot WDib WHer WMal WPGP
- 'Papaya' (T) CSpe
'Sweet Dreams' (T/d) WFib
(Sweet Spice Series) SWEET SPICE CITRUS ('Kerbespicit') (T/d) LSou MPri SCob
- SWEET SPICE ENGLISH ROSE ('Kerbespiros'PBR) (T/d) LSou MPri SCob
'Switzerland' (T) SDeJ
'Tahiti' (T) WFib
taliensis GGro
- EDHCH 042 WCot WCru WFar
tapatia (T) F&M 337 WPGP
'Tapestry' NWad
tengchiana PB 07-1110 **new** GGro
'Tessa Robinson' (T) WFib
'Thurstonii' ♀H1b EShb
'Tiger Paws' ♀H1b EShb
'Tiny Gem' WDib
'Torsa' **new** GGro WFar
* ***tripartita*** (T) WDib
'Truffle Cream' MBros
'Two Face' WDib
'Tye Dye' CBct WFar
'Van Gogh' (Impressionist Series) EHyd NRHS
'Vera Coates' (T) WFib
'Vesuvius' (R) WDib
'Vibrant Star' (T) LCro LOPS
'Wavy Green' CBct EBee ESwi GGro
'Whispers' (T) WFib
'Wild Swan' GGro WCru WFar
'Ziggy' (T) WFib

Belamcanda see *Iris*

chinensis see *Iris domestica*

Bellevalia (*Asparagaceae*)

sp. GArf
'Cream Pearl' WCot
cyanopoda **new** GKev
desertorum JCA 0.227.690 WCot
dubia GKev NRog WCot WSHC
forniculata WCot
hyacinthoides WCot
longistyla GKev
§ ***paradoxa*** CBor CMea ERCP GBin GKev MNrw NRog SDeJ WCot
pycnantha misapplied see *B. paradoxa*
pycnantha ambig. SDeJ
pycnantha (K. Koch) Losinsk. 'Green Pearl' ERCP GKev SDeJ
romana ERCP GKev NRog SDeJ WCot
sarmatica GKev
tabriziana WCot
trifoliata GKev

Bellis (*Asteraceae*)

§ ***caerulescens*** CMiW ECtt GAbr
perennis SPhx WWild
- 'Alice' ECtt
- Bellissima Series LCro LOPS MBros
- 'Big Bob' (d) ECtt WCot
- HEN AND CHICKENS see *B. perennis* 'Prolifera' single-flowered
- 'Miss Mason' CMiW WCot
- old strain WCot
- 'Prolifera' double-flowered (d) WCot
§ - 'Prolifera' single-flowered CFis ECtt
- Rusher Series LRHS
- 'Single Blue' see *B. caerulescens*
- Tasso Series (d) **new** GQue
- 'The Pearl' WCot
rotundifolia 'Caerulescens' see *B. caerulescens*

Bellium (*Asteraceae*)

bellidioides GQue

Belloa (*Asteraceae*)

chilensis SPlb

Beloperone see *Justicia*

Bensoniella (*Saxifragaceae*)

oregona CExl

Benthamiella (*Solanaceae*)

patagonica EPot SPlb WAbe
- F&W 9345 WAbe
- white-flowered WAbe
- yellow-flowered WAbe

Berberidopsis (*Berberidopsidaceae*)

corallina CBcs CDoC CMac CRHN CRos EBee EGrI ELan EPfP IArd LRHS MGil MGos MRav NLar SCob SDix SLim SPoG SWvt WPav WSHC

Berberis (*Berberidaceae*)

CC 4730 CExl
CC 7810 CMCN
aggregata GKev NBir SRms WKor
amurensis var. ***latifolia*** B&SWJ 8539 WCru
aquifolium see *Mahonia aquifolium*
- 'Fascicularis' see *Mahonia* × *wagneri* 'Pinnacle'
asiatica CExl WPGP
bealei see *Mahonia bealei*
buxifolia 'Nana' misapplied see *B. microphylla* 'Pygmaea'
calliantha WFar
candidula C.K. Schneid. LRHS MMuc MSwo NLar SEND
× ***carminea*** 'Buccaneer' WSpi

	- 'Pirate King'	CSBt EBee EHyd EPfP LRHS MAsh SPer SPoG SWvt WAvo
	chilensis	WPav
	darwinii ♀H5	Widely available
I	- 'Compacta'	CBod CDoC CEme CMac CPla CRos CSBt EBee ELan EPfP LBuc LRHS MAsh MGos NLar NRHS SCob SLim SNig SPad SPoG SWvt WCot WFar WPav
	densa B&SWJ 14873	WCru
	aff. ***densa*** B&SWJ 14880	WCru
	dictyophylla	ELan EPfP LRHS MMuc NLar WSpi
	dulcis 'Nana'	see *B. microphylla* 'Pygmaea'
	empetrifolia	WPav WSpi
	× ***frikartii*** 'Amstelveen' ♀H5	CCVT CDoC CEme CEnd EPfP LPar MBNS MMuc MRav SCob
	- 'Telstar'	SCob
	gagnepainii misapplied	see *B. gagnepainii* var. *lanceifolia*
	gagnepainii C.K. Schneid.	CMac NWea
§	- var. ***lanceifolia***	MMuc NLar SEND
	- - 'Fernspray'	EBee EPfP MRav SRms
	- 'Purpurea'	see *B.* × *interposita* 'Wallich's Purple'
	'Georgei' ♀H6	EPfP LRHS SPtp
§	***glaucocarpa***	SPtp
	'Goldilocks'	CKel EBee EPfP MBlu SPoG
	goudotii B&SWJ 10769	WCru
	- B&SWJ 14721	WCru
	- B&SWJ 14892	WCru
	hamiltoniana H&M 1919	EBee GKev SPtp
	hypokerina	CMac IDee SPtp WPGP
	insignis	IDee
	- subsp. ***insignis*** var. ***insignis*** B&SWJ 2432	WCru
§	× ***interposita*** 'Wallich's Purple'	CCVT EPfP LRHS MRav MSwo SGol SPer
	jamesiana	SPtp
	julianae	CArg CBcs CBrac CEme CEnd CMac ELan EPfP MGos MMuc MSwo NWea SCob SEND SGsty SPer SRms SWvt WFar WSpi
§	'Jytte'	EBee
	koehneana	SPtp
	koreana	EPfP NLar
	linearifolia 'Orange King'	see *B. trigona* 'Orange King'
	'Little Favourite'	see *B. thunbergii* f. *atropurpurea* 'Atropurpurea Nana'
	× ***lologensis*** 'Apricot Queen' ♀H5	CBcs CMac CRos EPfP LRHS MAsh MGos NLar SPer SPoG SWvt
	- 'Mystery Fire'	IArd MAsh MGos NLar SWvt
	- 'Stapehill'	CBrac CMac CRos EHyd ELan EPfP LRHS MAsh SPoG
	malipoensis	GRum
§	× ***media*** 'Parkjuweel'	MRav SRms
	- 'Red Jewel' ♀H6	CDoC CMac EPfP EWoo LRHS MAsh MGos MMuc MRav SPoG WCFE WFar
	microphylla	GKev WCFE
	- SDR 7027	GKev
§	- 'Pygmaea'	CBod EBee EHyd EPfP LRHS MRav SPer WPav
	× ***ottawensis*** 'Auricoma'	SGol SWvt
	- f. ***purpurea***	CCVT CMac
§	- - 'Silver Miles' (v)	MRav WFar WLov
§	- - 'Superba'	CBar CBcs CBod CDoC CEnd CSBt CTri CTsd EBee ELan ELon EPfP ERom EWoo LPar MGos MMuc MRav MSwo NLar NWea SCob SEND SGsty SPer SRms SWvt WFar
	poiretii	CExl
	polyantha var. ***polyantha***	CTri
	'Red Tears'	MAsh MRav SPer WFar
	× ***rubrostilla*** 'Cherry Ripe'	CMac
	- 'Wisley'	EHyd

	sibirica	GBin
	sieboldii	LEdu MAsh MRav WCFE WLov WPav WSpi
§	***soulieana***	CEme NWea
	stenophylla Hance	see *B. soulieana*
	× ***stenophylla*** Lindl. ♀H5	CBod CCVT CMac CSBt CTri EPfP GBin LBuc MMuc MRav SPer SRms
	- 'Claret Cascade'	EBee ELan MRav SPer SPoG
	- 'Corallina Compacta' ♀H5	CMac CRos EHyd ELan EPfP EPot GKev LRHS MAsh MHer SPer SPoG SRms
	- 'Cornish Cream'	see *B.* × *stenophylla* 'Lemon Queen'
	- 'Crawley Gem'	GAbr NWea
	- 'Cream Showers'	see *B.* × *stenophylla* 'Lemon Queen'
	- 'Etna'	CTsd EHyd ELan LRHS MAsh SCoo SPoG
	- 'Irwinii'	CKel CMac LRHS SPer
	- 'Lemon Queen'	WSpi
	- 'Nana'	EHyd
	subacuminata FMWJ 13290	WCru
	sublevis PAB 8943	LEdu
	taliensis	CExl
	temolaica ♀H5	EPfP EWes IArd IDee NLar NWea WAvo WSpi
	thunbergii	CArg CBcs CEnd CMac EPfP LBuc LPar NWea SCob SPer SWvt WFar
	- 'Anna' PBR	GBin
	- f. ***atropurpurea***	CBcs CBod CBrac CCVT CDoC CMac CSBt CTri EBee ELan EPfP LBuc LCro LOPS MGos MRav MSwo NLar NWea SCob SGol SPer SPlb SRms WAvo WTSh
	- - 'Admiration' PBR ♀H7	CBcs CDoC CRos CSBt EHyd ELan EPfP GKev LBuc LCro LOPS LPar LRHS LSRN MAsh MGos MRav NHol NLar NRHS SCob SCoo SGbt SLon SPer SPoG SWvt WFar WLov
§	- - 'Atropurpurea Nana' ♀H7	Widely available
	- - 'Bagatelle'	CDoC CEme CRos EGrI ELan EPfP IArd LRHS LSRN MAsh MGos MRav NLar SCob SPer SWvt WLov
	- - 'Concorde' ♀H7	CRos EHyd ELan EPfP LPar LRHS MAsh NRHS SCob
	- - 'Dart's Red Lady' ♀H7	CDoC CExl CRos CSBt EHyd ELan EPfP EWoo LRHS MAsh NLar NRHS SCob SPer SWvt WAvo WFar
	- - 'Golden Ring' (v) ♀H7	CBcs CDoC CEme CMac CRos EHyd ELan EPfP LRHS MAsh MGos MRav NRHS SGbt SPer SPoG SWvt WAvo WFar
	- - 'Harlequin' (v) ♀H7	CBrac CChe CDoC CEme CEnd CKel CRos EHyd ELan EPfP LCro LOPS LPar LRHS LSRN MAsh MGos NRHS SGol SPer SPoG SRms SWvt WFar
	- - 'Helmond Pillar'	CBod CDoC CEme CMac CRos CSBt EBee EHyd ELan ELon EPfP LCro LOPS LRHS LSRN MAsh MGos MRav NHol NLar NRHS SCob SGol SPer SPoG SWvt WLov
	- - 'Maja' PBR	CBod
	- - 'Pink Queen' (v)	CKel ELan EPfP LRHS MAsh WFar
	- - 'Red Chief'	CBcs CBod CMac ELan EPfP EWoo LPar LRHS MAsh MGos MSwo NRHS SGol SLon SPoG SRms SWvt WFar
	- - 'Red Pillar'	CChe CDoC CMac ELan EPfP MAsh MGos SGbt SNig SWvt WFar WLov
	- - 'Red Rocket'	EBee EGrI LPar LRHS NLar NRHS SCob SCoo
	- - 'Rose Glow' (v) ♀H7	Widely available

	- - 'Rosy Rocket'PBR (v)	CKel CWGN EBee ELan EPfP LRHS MRav NHol NLar SPad SPer SPoG WFar
	- 'Atropurpurea Superba'	see *B.* × *ottawensis* f. *purpurea* 'Superba'
	- 'Aurea'	CBcs CBrac CDoC CMac EGrI EHyd ELan EPfP LRHS LSRN MBlu MGos MRav NLar NRHS SCob SGbt SPlb SRms SWvt
	- BONANZA GOLD ('Bogozam'PBR)	CBcs CRos EHyd ELan EPfP LRHS MAsh NLar
	- 'Crimson Pygmy'	see *B. thunbergii* f. *atropurpurea* 'Atropurpurea Nana'
	- 'Diabolic'	CBod EGrI EHyd MAsh NHol NRHS SPer SPoG
	- 'Erecta'	CMac EPfP MRav SPer WCFE
	- 'Fireball'PBR 🏆H7	CRos EHyd EPfP LRHS MAsh
	- FLAMINGO ('Hoho 1'PBR)	NLar SGol
	- 'Golden Dream'PBR	MGos
	- GOLDEN HORIZON ('Hoho 2'PBR) **new**	CBod
	- 'Golden Rocket'PBR	CBod CRos EBee EHyd ELan EPfP GArf LRHS MAsh MGos MRav NLar NRHS SCoo SPer SPoG WFar
	- GOLDEN RUBY ('Goruzam') (v)	LCro LOPS
	- 'Golden Torch'	CDoC CSBt EHyd ELan EPfP LPar LRHS MAsh MRav NHol NRHS SWvt WLov
	- 'Green Carpet'	CMac EGrI LRHS MBlu NLar SGol SPoG SWvt
	- 'Green Ornament'	NHol
§	- 'Kelleriis' (v)	EHyd LRHS MRav
	- 'Kobold'	CMac EHyd EPfP MGos NLar SPer
	- 'Lutin Rouge'PBR	LCro LOPS
	- 'Maria'PBR 🏆H7	CWGN EGrI EHyd ELon EPfP LRHS MGos MRav NLar NRHS SCob SGol SPoG WGrn WLov
	- 'Natasza'PBR **new**	LRHS
	- 'Orange Dream'PBR	CDoC EBee LPar MGos SCoo
	- 'Orange Ice'PBR **new**	LRHS XSte
	- 'Orange Rocket'PBR	CBod CDoC CRos EBee EGrI EHyd ELan EPfP LCro LOPS LPar LRHS MAsh MGos MRav NHol NRHS SCob SCoo SPer SPoG WFar WLov
	- 'Orange Sunrise'PBR (v)	CBod LCro LOPS LRHS SPad
	- 'Orange Torch' **new**	LRHS SCoo
	- 'Pow-wow'	EHyd ELan LPar MGos NLar NRHS SCoo SGol SPoG SWvt WLov
	- 'Redtorch'PBR	CRos EHyd LRHS NRHS
	- 'Ruby Star'PBR **new**	LRHS
	- 'Silver Mile'	see *B.* × *ottawensis* f. *purpurea* 'Silver Miles'
	- 'Silver Pillar'PBR **new**	NLar
	- 'Smaragd'	WFar
	- 'Somerset'	CMac
	- 'Starburst'PBR (v)	CBod CSBt EBee EHyd EPfP LRHS MGos NEoE NHol NRHS SCoo SLon SRms SWvt
	- 'Tiny Gold'PBR	EHyd ELan GKev LCro LOPS LRHS MAsh SLim SLon SWvt WFar
*	- 'Tricolor' (v)	CMac MRav WFar
	triacanthophora 'Cally Rose'	EPfP GBin WPGP
§	***trigona*** 'Orange King'	CBcs CMac ELan EPfP GBin LRHS MAsh MGos NLar SPer SPoG
*	***tsinglingensis*** **new**	WPGP
	valdiviana 🏆H5	CBcs CExl CJun EPfP GBin IArd IDee IKel MBlu SChF SMad WPGP
	verruculosa 🏆H5	CBcs CBrac CDoC LRHS MBlu MGos SPer SRms SWvt WFar
	aff. ***verticillata*** B&SWJ 10672	WCru
	virescens B&SWJ 2646D	WCru
	vulgaris	CAgr CNat GPoy MCoo NWea WKor XSen
	- 'Atropurpurea'	NWea
	wallichiana DC.	GArf
	wilsoniae	CBcs CBod CMac CTri ELan ELon EPfP GLog NWea SPer SRms WAvo WFar WSpi
	- blue-leaved	WFar
	- var. ***guhtzunica***	EWes
	aff. ***wilsoniae***	CBrac

Berberis × *Mahonia* see × *Mahoberberis*

Berchemia (*Rhamnaceae*)

racemosa	NLar

bergamot see *Citrus* × *limon* Bergamot Group

Bergbambos (*Poaceae*)

§	***tessellata***	MMuc SEND

Bergenia ✿ (*Saxifragaceae*)

	'Abendglocken'	CMac ECha ECtt EGrI EPfP NSti WCot WFar
§	'Abendglut'	Widely available
	'Admiral'	CBct CMac ECha EGrI EPri WCot
	afghanica	XLum
*	***agavifolia***	CBct XLum
	'Andrea'	WCot
	'Angel Kiss' (Dragonfly Series)	CMil CWCL ECtt ELan GBin LCro LOPS LRHS MNrw NLar SCob SWvt WCot
	'Apple Blossom'	CRos EHyd EPfP LRHS MAsh NRHS
	'Apple Court White'	CBct
	'Autumn Magic'	CBct CBod EGrI ELon EPfP LRHS MBow NCou SCoo WFar
	'Baby Doll'	Widely available
	'Bach'	CBct CDor CRos EBee ECtt EHyd EPfP GAbr LPla LRHS LSun MBel MCot MMuc NGBl NLar NRHS NSti SCob SGbt SRms SWvt WCAu WCot WFar WWtn
§	'Ballawley' clonal	CRos ECha EHyd LRHS MRav NRHS WCot XLum
	'Ballawley' seed-raised	see *B.* Ballawley hybrids
	'Ballawley Guardsman'	CBct
§	Ballawley hybrids	CMac SWvt WSpi
	'Bartók'	CBct ECtt GAbr NRHS WCAu WCot WPGP
	beesiana	see *B. purpurascens*
	'Beethoven'	CBct ECha EGrI GBin NBir WCAu WCot
	'Biedermeier' 🏆H7	ECha
	'Bizet'	CBct XLum
	'Borodin'	CBct
	'Brahms'	CBct
	'Bressingham Bountiful'	CBct
	'Bressingham Ruby'	CBct CRos CWCL EBee EBlo ECha ECtt ELon EPfP LRHS LSRN MGos MRav NBir NLar NRHS SPer SWvt WCAu WCot WHoo WSpi
	'Bressingham Salmon'	CBct EBee ECha ECtt ELon GMaP MRav NLar SRms WCot
	'Bressingham White' 🏆H6	Widely available
	'Britten' 🏆H7	CBct CMac GBin
	ciliata	CBct CDor CMac ECha EGrI EPri EShb ETod GMaP LEdu LRHS MBriF

		MRav NHol NLar SPer WAvo WFar WPGP WSHC WSpi XLum
	- 'Dumbo'	CAbb CBct GBin IBal LEdu NLar WCAu
	- f. ***ligulata***	see *B. pacumbis*
	- 'Wilton'	CBct EWld LEdu MAvo SHar WCot WPGP WSHC
	ciliata* × *crassifolia	see *B.* × *schmidtii*
	'Claire Maxine' 🏆H7	CBct ECtt EPPr GBin GQue LRHS MPie NFav NLar NWad SRms WCAu WCot WSHC
	cordifolia	CBar CMac CSBt CTri EBee EHyd ELan EPfP GDam GKev GMaP LPot LRHS MBel MBros MGos MMuc MSwo NGrd NLar NRHS SCob SEND SPer SPlb SRms SWvt WWtn XSen
	- 'Flore Pleno' (d)	CBct
	- 'Jelle'	CBct CBod EBee NLar WCAu
	- 'Lunar Glow'	ECtt EPfP SRms WFar
	- 'Purpurea'	CBcs CBod CMac CRos CWCL EBee ECha EGrI EHyd ELan EPfP GBin GQue LBuc LCro LOPS LRHS NBir NRHS SCob SMrm SPer SRms SWvt WFar XLum
	- 'Rosa Schwester'	CBct ECha
	- 'Rosa Zeiten' 🏆H7	CBct GBin
	- 'Tubby Andrews' (v)	CBct CMac CTtf ECha EShb LEdu LRHS MAvo NEoE NLar SRms WHil WHrl
	- 'Vinterglöd'	CBod EBou ELon EPfP GMaP LSun MBel MGos NLar SBls SRms SWvt XLum
	crassifolia	EPfP SRms XLum
	- DF 90028	CBct GBin
	- 'Autumn Red'	CBct ECha
	- 'Orbicularis'	see *B.* × *schmidtii*
	'Croesus'	GBin
*	***cyanea***	WCot
	'Dark Damsel'	CBct IBal
	'David'	CBct EBee ECha
	'Delbees'	see *B.* 'Ballawley' clonal
	'Diamond Drops'	CBod IBal SMrm
	'Eden's Dark Margin'	CBct CBod ECtt ELan ELon GBin MHol MNrw NLar WCot
	'Eden's Magic Giant' 🏆H7	CBct ECtt ELan ELon EShb GBin GQue LRHS MHol MMrt MPie NLar SDix SRms WCot WFar XSen
	emeiensis	CBct CDor LEdu LSun WCot WSHC
	'Eric Smith' 🏆H7	ECha EGrI SWvt WCAu
	'Eroica' 🏆H7	Widely available
	'Evening Glow'	see *B.* 'Abendglut'
	'Flirt' PBR **new**	LRHS SPad
§	'Glockenturm'	CBct
	'Godfrey Owen'	EBee WSHC
	'Harzkristall'	CBct CBod CChe CDor CMac CMea CPla CRos EHyd ELan EPfP GBin GKev GWyn LRHS NCou NRHS SCob SCoo SHar SPoG SWvt WSpi
	'Hellen Dillon'	see *B. purpurascens* 'Irish Crimson'
	'Herbstblute'	EBee EPfP GBin WCAu
	'Ice Queen'	EBee ELan EWoo GBin LCro LOPS LRHS NLar SWvt WCAu WCot
	'Jo Watanabe'	CBct ECha MRav
	'Kashmir'	XLum
	'Little Pine'	WCot
§	'Margery Fish'	CBct CFis ECha
	'Memelinks Pride' **new**	NLar
	milesii	see *B. stracheyi*
§	'Morgenröte' 🏆H6	CBcs CBct CBod CMac CRos ECha EGrI ELon EPfP EWoo GMaP LRHS LSRN MRav NHol NLar NSti SAko SPer SRms SWvt WCAu WCot XSen
	MORNING RED	see *B.* 'Morgenröte'
	'Mrs Crawford'	ECha
	'Oeschberg'	CBct EPPr GBin
	'Opal'	CBct EBee GBin
	'Overture'	Widely available
§	***pacumbis***	EBee EWld GBin NBid NSti XLum
	- B&SWJ 2693	WCru
	- CC	GGro
	- CC 1793	SGro WCot
	- CC 3616	CBct WSHC
	'Pink Dragonfly'	CBct CMac CRos ECtt EHyd ELon EPfP LPla LRHS MAsh NLar NRHS SCob SWvt WCAu WCot WFar
	'Pink Ice'	CBct CDor WSHC
	'Pinneberg'	CBct
	'Pugsley's Pink' 🏆H7	CBct ECha MAvo
§	***purpurascens*** 🏆H5	CEme CMac EBee EPfP GMaP LPot SCoo SPer WPGP WSpi
	- SDR 4548	GKev
	- var. ***delavayi*** 🏆H5	EBee EHyd LRHS NLar NRHS SRms
§	- 'Irish Crimson' 🏆H7	ECha EGrI GBin WCot
	aff. ***purpurascens***	NGdn
	'Purpurglocken'	ECtt WCAu
	'Rietheim'	CBct EBee GBin
	'Rosenkristall'	CRos EHyd EPfP LRHS NRHS
	'Rosi Klose'	CBct CDor CRos ECha ECtt EGrI EHyd ELon EPfP EWes GBin LRHS MAsh MHol NGdn NRHS SCoo WCot WFar WHoo
	'Rosi Ruffles'	EBee
	'Rotblum'	CBct ELon EPfP GMaP LBuc NBir NGdn NGrd NRHS SRkn SRms
	'Sakura' (Dragonfly Series)	CMil CWCL EBee GBin MNrw NHar SCob
§	× ***schmidtii***	CBct CMac GBin MRav NBir NLar
	'Schneekissen'	CBct CMac ECtt EHyd EPri MCot WCAu WGwG
§	'Schneekoenigin'	CBct ECha EGrI SWvt WCot
§	'Silberlicht' 🏆H6	Widely available
	SILVERLIGHT	see *B.* 'Silberlicht'
	'Simply Sweet'	WCot
	SNOW QUEEN	see *B.* 'Schneekoenigin'
	'Spring Fling' PBR (Dragonfly Series)	GBin LRHS
§	***stracheyi***	CExl ECha GBin GKev NBid NLar WCot
	- Alba Group	ECha EGrI
	'Sunningdale' 🏆H7	CBcs CBct CMac ECha EHyd EPfP GMaP LRHS MRav NBir NGdn NRHS SPer SWvt WCAu
	'Walter Kienli'	GBin
	WINTER FAIRY TALES	see *B.* 'Wintermärchen'
§	'Wintermärchen' 🏆H7	CBct CChe CRos ECha EGrI ELan ELon EPfP EPri EShb GWyn LRHS MCot MMuc MRav NHol NRHS SEND SPoG SRms SWvt WCot
	'XXL'	WCot

Bergenia × *Mukdenia* see × *Mukgenia*

Bergera (*Rutaceae*)

§	***koenigii***	EOHP GPoy SCit SPre SVen WJek WSFF

Bergeranthus (*Aizoaceae*)

	scapiger	SRot
	vespertinus	XLum

Berkheya (*Asteraceae*)

	cirsiifolia	EBee GGro NFav SPhx
	macrocephala	SPlb

multijuga	EHyd GGro SPlb
purpurea	CBcs CBod CDor CFoA CRos CSpe EBlo ECha EHyd ELon EPfP GGro LRHS NRHS SBls SPhx SPlb SRms SSal WCot WKif WSHC
- 'Silver Spike'	EGrl EPfP MSCN NGdn
- 'Zulu Warrior'	CGrG CMac EGrl LShi MHer SMrm
radula	EBee GGro

Berlandiera (*Asteraceae*)

lyrata	CBod EHyd GEdr

Berula (*Apiaceae*)

erecta	NPer

Berzelia (*Bruniaceae*)

galpinii	SPlb
intermedia	LRHS

Beschorneria (*Asparagaceae*)

albiflora	LRHS WCot XSte
calcicola	WCot
'Red Bells'	WCot
rigida	WCot
septentrionalis	CBcs CBod CDTJ EBee GAbr GBin LRHS MBNS MHol NGBl SEdd SPad SPeP WCot WGrn XSte
- variegated (v)	WCot
tubiflora	CDTJ WSMil
wrightii	WCot
yuccoides 🏆H3	CAbb CExl CPla EBee SChr SEND SPlb
- FLAMINGO GLOW ('Besys'PBR) (v) **new**	MBNS SPad
- 'Quicksilver'	CCCN CEnd CExl EPfP LRHS MHtn SPoG WGrn WPav

Bessera (*Asparagaceae*)

elegans	CPla EPot GKev SDeJ SDir WCot WHil

Besseya (*Plantaginaceae*)

alpina	GEdr
wyomingensis	EBee GKev

Beta (*Amaranthaceae*)

vulgaris	WHer
- subsp. ***maritima***	CAgr

Betonica (*Lamiaceae*)

§ ***macrantha***	CDor CMac CTri EBee ECha EDAr EGrl EHyd GJos GKev GLog LEdu LRHS NBir NChi NFav NLar NRHS NSti SPhx SRms WCAu WCFE WCot
* - 'Alba'	EBee ECha MSpe WCAu
- 'Ben' (v)	LEdu
- 'Morning Blush'	SPhx WCot WFar
* - 'Nivea'	EBee
- 'Robusta' 🏆H7	ELan ELon GAbr LEdu MAvo MMuc NBro NGdn WCot
- 'Rosea'	CElw EHyd ELan GBee GMaP LRHS MAvo NRHS SPlb WCAu
- 'Superba' 🏆H7	CSpe EBee ECtt EPfP GKev GMaP LEdu MAvo MHol MRav NDov NLar SAng SCob SMad SPer SRms SWvt WBor WCAu WCot WFar XLum
- 'Violacea' 🏆H7	EBee GKev NChi WCot
§ ***nivea***	CFis CMea EWes LRHS NLar SWvt WCAu WCot
§ - subsp. ***ossetica***	GEdr
§ ***officinalis***	CBee CCBP CHab EGrl EMor GJos GKev GPoy GQue ILea MBow MHer MNHC NAts NGrd NMir NRya SRms WCot WHer WShi WTre WWild
- 'Alba'	LEdu MArl MAvo NBro SMHy WCAu
- 'Cally Bicolor'	GBin
- dark-flowered	WHoo
- dwarf, white-flowered	GRum NFav
§ - 'Hummelo' 🏆H7	Widely available
- 'Marchant's Pink'	SMHy
- 'Pink Cotton Candy'	EBee SCob SPhx
- 'Rosea'	EAJP EGrl NBro WFar
- 'Rosea Superba'	CTtf ECha GWyn WCot
- 'Saharan Pink'	EBee EPfP LSRN MHol NLar
- 'Spitzenberg'	LPla
- 'Wisley White'	CRos ECtt EHyd GKev LBuc LEdu LRHS MHol NGrd NHpl NRHS SCob SRms WCot WFar

Betula ✿ (*Betulaceae*)

alba	see *B. pendula*, *B. pubescens*
albosinensis misapplied	see *B. utilis*
albosinensis Burkill	CBrP CLnd CMCN MMuc
- 'Bowling Green'	CExl CJun EBee MBlu WPGP
§ - 'China Rose' 🏆H7	CBcs CJun CSto EBee EPfP MTrO WMat WPGP
- 'China Ruby' K.Ashburner	see *B. albosinensis* 'China Rose'
- 'China Ruby' ambig.	CJun CLnd EPfP MTrO NOra
- 'China Ruby' B. Humphrey 🏆H7	MTrO
- 'Chinese Garden'	CJun CSto EBee MBlu WPGP
- 'Chris Lane'	CJun WPGP
- 'Chris Sanders'	WPGP
- clone F	see *B. albosinensis* 'Ness'
- 'Joseph Rock'	CJun
- 'K.Ashburner'	CAco CJun
§ - 'Ness'	CJun
- 'Pink Champagne'	CBcs CJun CSto EPfP LRHS MBlu MGos MTrO WMat WPGP
- 'Red Panda' 🏆H7	CAco CJun CSto EBee LRHS MTrO WHwl WMat WPGP
- 'Rhinegold'	MBlu
- var. ***septentrionalis***	CAco CCVT CEnd CLnd CMac EBee ELan ELon EPfP GBin IPap MBlu MGos MRav MSwo NOrn NRog NWea SCob SGol SLim SPer WHwl WPGP WSpi
- - PDM 752	WPGP
- - 'Kansu'	CJun EBee MAsh MBlu MTrO NLar NOra NWea WMat
- - 'Purdom'	CJun CLnd
§ ***alleghaniensis***	CBcs CMCN CSto EPfP GKev MMuc NLar WCru
ashburneri	WPGP
bomiensis	GKev
borealis	see *B. pumila*
chichibuensis	CJun GKev MMrt MVil SPtp
chinensis	GKev MVil
'Cobhay Cream Spire'	CJun
'Cobhay Snow Spire'	CJun
'Conyngham'	CJun MBlu SLau
costata misapplied	see *B. ermanii* 'Grayswood Hill'
costata ambig.	CMCN LMaj SGol
costata Trautv.	MSwo
- 'Daleside'	EBee MTrO NDal NOra WMat
- 'Fincham Cream'	see *B. ermanii* 'Fincham Cream'
'Crimson Frost'	CDoC EBee GBin
cylindrostachya	WPGP
dahurica Pall.	CBrP MVil
- 'Maurice Foster'	CJun CSto EBee MBlu WPGP

- 'Stone Farm'	CJun
ermanii	CBcs CCVT CMCN CMac CSto EGrI ELan GBin IPap LMaj LPar MBlu MGos MMuc MRav NOrn NRog NWea SGol
- B&SWJ 8801 from South Korea	WCru
- B&SWJ 10852 from Aomori, Japan	WCru
- B&SWJ 12600 from South Korea	WCru
- from Hokkaido, Japan	CAco
- 'Blush'	CJun EPfP MBlu SCoo WMou
§ - 'Fincham Cream'	CJun
§ - 'Grayswood Hill' ♀H7	CEnd CJun CLnd CMCN CSBt EBee EPfP LRHS MBlu MVil SCob SCoo SWvt WHwl WPGP
- 'Hakkoda Orange'	CJun CSto EBee SCoo WPGP
- 'Holland'	IArd LMaj
- 'Kwanak Weeping'	CJun MAsh MBlu
- 'Mount Zao'	CJun CSto EBee EPfP NOrn WMou WPGP
- 'Polar Bear'	CJun CLnd EBee EPfP MBlu MTrO NLar NOrn SCoo WMat
'Fascination' ♀H6	CBcs CCVT CDoC CJun CMCN CMac EBar EBee EPfP IArd LMaj LPar LRHS LSRN MBlu MGos MNic MTrO MVil NOra NOrn NWea SCoo SGol SLim SPer WHwl WMat WMou WSpi
'Fetisowii'	CJun EBee MBlu MTrO NOra WMat
globispica	CJun MVil
gmelinii	see *B. ovalifolia*
'Hergest' ♀H6	CJun EBee EPfP MGos MTrO NOra WHCr WHwl WMat
insignis	CJun WPGP
- subsp. ***fansipanensis***	IArd IDee MVil SAko
- - B&SWJ 11751	WCru
- - FMWJ 13149	WCru
- subsp. ***insignis*** **new**	GKev
jacquemontii	see *B. utilis* var. *jacquemontii*
'Kerscott Charm' **new**	CSto
lenta	CMCN IDee MBlu MMuc
luminifera	EBee IArd WPGP
lutea	see *B. alleghaniensis*
maximowicziana	CMCN EWTr GKev MBlu NLar SGol WSpi
medwediewii	CAco CJun CMCN CSto EBee EPfP GKev MVil NLar WPGP
- 'Gold Bark' ♀H7	CJun CMCN EPfP MBlu
megrelica	CSto GKev
michauxii	MVil NLar WCru
'Mount Apoi'	CJun LRHS MTrO WMat
nana	NWea
- 'Glengarry'	EPot GEdr
nigra	CAco CBcs CCVT CEnd CLnd CMCN EBee ELan IPap LMaj LPar NLar NRog NWea SArc SCob SEWo SGol SGsty WMou WTSh
- 'Black Star'	EBee NOra NOrn WMat
§ - 'Cully'	CMCN EBee LRHS MBlu MTrO NOra NOrn NWea SGol WMat
- HERITAGE	see *B. nigra* 'Cully'
- 'Little King'	CMCN
- 'Peter Collinson'	CJun
- 'Shiloh Splash'	LPar SSta
- 'Summer Cascade'PBR	EBee LPar LSRN MAsh NOra NOrn SLon WHwl WMat
- Wakehurst form	EPfP SPer SPoG WPGP WSpi
§ ***ovalifolia*** MF 357	GKev
papyrifera	CAco CBcs CCVT CMCN CMac CSto EBee ELan EPfP GQue IPap LBuc LPar MGos MMuc MSwo MTrO NOra NRog NWea SGol SPer WMat WTSh
- 'Belle Vue'	EBee
- var. ***cordifolia*** 'Clarenville'	CJun
- 'Saint George'	CAco CJun EBee WMat
§ ***pendula***	Widely available
- f. ***crispa***	see *B. pendula* 'Laciniata'
- 'Dalecarlica' misapplied	see *B. pendula* 'Laciniata'
- 'Dalecarlica' ambig.	LRHS MRav NOra SWvt WFar WHCr WMat WTSh
- 'Dark Prince'	NOrn
- 'Fastigiata'	CCVT CJun CLnd CSBt EBee ELan IPap LPar LRHS MGos NOrn NWea SCoo SGol SPer WHwl
- FASTIGIATA JOES ('Jolep 1')	EBee ELan LPar MAsh MNic MTrO NOra NOrn SEWo SPoG WMat
- 'Golden Beauty'	CEnd CJun CMac MAsh MGos MTrO NOra NOrn NRog NWea SGol SLim SPer WMat
- 'Golden Cloud'	EWTr
- 'Golden Fountain' **new**	MTrO WMat
- 'Golden Obelisk' **new**	NOrn
§ - 'Laciniata' ♀H7	CBcs CMCN CMac EBee ELan LMaj LPar MBlu MGos MSwo MTrO NOra NOrn NRog NWea SCob SCoo SGol SPer WMou WTSh
- 'Long Trunk'	CBrac EBee MBlu NOrn SGol SLim
- 'Obelisk'	LMaj
- 'Purpurea'	CCVT CMCN CMac CSBt ELan GKin IDee IPap LPar LSRN MGos MSwo NOrn NRog NWea SCoo SGol SPer WFar WTSh
- 'Silver Grace'	CJun LSRN MBlu
§ - 'Spider Alley'PBR	EBee EHed ELan GBin LPar LRHS MTrO NOra SLon WHwl WMat
- 'Swiss Glory'	LMaj
- 'Tristis' ♀H7	CBcs CCVT CEnd CLnd CMCN CMac CTri EBee EPfP IPap LMaj LPar LRHS LSRN MGos MNic MRav MSwo MTrO NOra NOrn NRog NWea SCob SGol SLim SPer WFar WMat
- 'Youngii'	Widely available
- 'Zwitsers Glorie'	CJun WHwl
pendula* × *utilis **new**	LPar
platyphylla Sukaczev DAKOTA PINNACLE ('Fargo')	NOra SCoo WMat
× ***plettkei*** 'Golden Treasure'PBR **new**	GKev
populifolia	EBtc
potaninii	GKev MVil
§ ***pubescens***	CCVT CHab CTri EBee IPap LMaj LPar MMuc NRog NWea SCob WTSh
- 'Armenian Gold'	CLnd NRog
§ ***pumila***	CSto
× ***purpusii***	GKev MVil
raddeana	EBtc GKev
'Royal Frost'	CBcs EBee GQue LMaj LRHS LSRN MBlu MTrO NLar NOra NWea SGol WHwl WMat
'Silver Trestles'	see *B. pendula* 'Spider Alley'
szechuanica 'Liuba White'	CJun MBlu
tianschanica	WPGP
§ ***utilis***	CMCN LMaj LRHS NWea SSta
- GWJ 9259	WCru
- HWJK 2250	WCru
- HWJK 2345	WCru
- Sch 2168	EBee
- S&L from Nepal **new**	CAco

- 'Bhutan Sienna'	CJun CSto EBee WPGP
- 'Buddha'	CJun EBee MBlu WPGP
- 'China Bronze'	CSto MBlu WPGP
- 'Cobhay Amber'	CJun
- 'Cobhay Sentinel'	CJun
- 'Dark-Ness'	CJun MBlu MTrO NOra SLon WMat WPGP
* - 'Fastigiata'	CJun CLnd NOrn SSta
- 'Forest Blush' ♀H7	CJun CSto EBee EPfP WPGP
- 'Himalayan Pink'	CJun WSpi
§ - var. ***jacquemontii***	Widely available
- - Polunin	WPGP
§ - - 'Doorenbos' ♀H7	Widely available
- - 'Grayswood Ghost' ♀H7	Widely available
§ - - 'Inverleith'	CJun CSto SCoo WPGP
- - 'Jermyns' ♀H7	CBcs CEnd CJun CLnd EBee EPfP LRHS LSRN MBlu MTrO NOra NOrn SCob SCoo SLim SPer SSta SWvt WHCr WMat WPGP
- - 'McBeath'	MGos MTrO
- - 'Moonbeam'	CJun CLnd CSBt EBee EHyd LRHS MAsh MNic MTrO NOrn NWea SCoo SEWo SLim SPer SPoG SWeb WHCr WMat
- - 'Silver Shadow' ♀H7	CEnd CJun CLnd CMCN EBee ELan EPfP LRHS LSRN MAsh MBlu MTrO NOra NOrn NRHS NRog NWea SCob SCoo SGbt SLau SLim SPer SPoG SSta WHCr WMat WSpi
- - 'Snow Leopard'	CJun CSto WPGP
- - 'Snow Queen'	see *B. utilis* var. *jacquemontii* 'Doorenbos'
- - 'Trinity College'	CJun EBee ELan LRHS MGos MSwo MTrO NOrn SCoo WHwl WLov WMat WPGP
- 'Jim Russell'	WPGP
- 'Knightshayes'	CJun EBee WPGP
- 'Mount Luoji'	CJun CSto EBee EPfP WPGP
- 'Nepalese Orange'	CJun CSto EBee EPfP MTrO NOrn SGol WMat WMou WPGP
- var. ***occidentalis***	WPGP
- - 'Kyelang'	CJun
- 'Park Wood' ♀H7	CAco CJun EPfP WPGP
- 'Polar Bear'	MBlu
- var. ***prattii***	CJun MBlu MVil
- 'Ramdana River'	CJun MBlu WPGP
- 'Schilling'	CJun
- 'Sichuan Red'	CJun CSto
- 'Silver Queen'	CTri WSpi
- subsp. ***utilis*** 'Edinburgh'	CJun CLnd LRHS MBlu MTrO NOra WMat
- 'Wakehurst Place Chocolate' ♀H7	CJun CSBt EBee GBin MBlu MGos MTrO NLar NOra NWea SCoo SGbt SLim WMat WSpi
- 'White-Ness'	EBee MBlu MNic MTrO WMat
cf. ***utilis***	SGol
verrucosa	see *B. pendula*

Biarum (*Araceae*)

S&L 604	WCot
SB&L 597	WCot
carratracense from Spain	WCot
davisii	EPot WCot
ditschianum from Turkey	WCot
marmarisense	NRog WCot
tenuifolium	WCot
- LB 295	WCot
- PB 357	WCot
- S&L 174	WCot
- subsp. ***abbreviatum***	SBrt
- - MS 974	WCot
- subsp. ***arundanum***	GKev WCot
- - from Spain **new**	NRog
- subsp. ***galianii*** PB 435	WCot
- subsp. ***tenuifolium***	GKev
- subsp. ***zelebori***	WCot
- - CRL 502	WCot
- - LB 300	WCot

Bidens (*Asteraceae*)

atrosanguinea	see *Cosmos atrosanguineus*
§ ***aurea***	CCBP ECtt EMor EPPr EWes LEdu MAsh MCot MHol MRav MSpe NPer SBut SIvy SMrm WBor WFar WHal WMal WPGP XLum
- 'Hannay's Lemon Drop'	CFis CKno CTtf EAJP ECtt ELan ELon EMor EPPr EPfP EWTr ILea LEdu LPot LShi MAsh MHol MSpe SDix SGbt SPeP SPoG SPtp SRms WBor WFar WMal WPGP
* - 'Lemon Queen'	SBls
- 'Mellow Yellow'	WCot
- 'Rising Sun'	ECtt EWes
- 'Super Nova'	EPPr
- white-flowered	EBee ELon EMor EPPr GPSL NSti WFar
'Compact Bicolour Star' (Hawaiian Flare Series)	LSou
ferulifolia	NPer
- 'Bee Alive' (Bee Series)	MBros WHil
- BEEDANCE PAINTED RED ('Sunbidevb 2'PBR)	SPoG
- BEEDANCE PAINTED YELLOW ('Sunbidevb4'PBR)	SPoG
- 'Golden Eye'	ECtt MBros SPoG
- SUN DROP ('Danbid7346')	LSou
'Firelight'	WHil
'Giant Yellow Red Tip' (Hawaiian Flare Series)	LSou
heterophylla Ortega	see *B. aurea*
integrifolia	SSal
'Rockstar'	CPla
triplinervia 'Sunny Days' **new**	WCru
'Yellow Red Star' (Hawaiian Flare Series)	LSou

Bigelowia (*Asteraceae*)

nuttallii **new**	CSpe

Bignonia (*Bignoniaceae*)

capreolata	CCCN CRHN WSHC XSen
lindleyana	see *Clytostoma calystegioides*
tweedieana	see *Dolichandra unguis-cati*
unguis-cati	see *Dolichandra unguis-cati*

Bijlia (*Aizoaceae*)

tugwelliae	SSim

Bilderdykia see *Fallopia*

Billardiera (*Pittosporaceae*)

longiflora ♀H3	CBcs CKel CRos CSBt CTri EBee EHyd ELan EPfP GKev IArd LRHS MAsh MGil MGos MRav SCob SCoo SPer SPoG SWvt
- 'Cherry Berry'	CBcs CRos EHyd ELan EPfP LRHS SMad SNig SPer SPoG SRms SWvt
- 'Fructu-albo'	CBcs EHyd ELan EPfP EWes LRHS NLar SLon SPer SPoG SWvt

Billbergia ✿ (*Bromeliaceae*)

nutans	CCCN EBak EShb LEdu NGBl SChr SEND SPlb SSal WSFF
- var. ***schimperiana***	EShb
* - 'Variegata' (v)	CCCN CPla ELan EShb NCft SChr SSal WCot
'Santa Barbara' (v)	SChr
× ***windii*** 🏆H1b	EBak NCft

Biophytum (*Oxalidaceae*)

sensitivum	CDoC WSFF

Biscutella (*Brassicaceae*)

laevigata new	MACG

Biserrula (*Fabaceae*)

pelecinus	LShi

Bismarckia (*Arecaceae*)

nobilis	CCCN SPalm

Bistorta see *Persicaria*

Bituminaria (*Fabaceae*)

bituminosa	CKel WCot

blackberry see *Rubus fruticosus*; see also AGM Fruit Section

blackcurrant see *Ribes nigrum*; see also AGM Fruit Section

Blechnum (*Blechnaceae*)

alpinum	see *B. penna-marina* subsp. *alpinum*
appendiculatum new	CBdn
brasiliense 🏆H1a	EShb ESwi SPlb
- 'Volcano'	CBcs CBdn CBod CBrP CCht CMiW CTsd LBuc LCro LLWG LOPS LRHS SIvy SPad SPalm SPoG
cartilagineum	CDTJ
§ ***chilense*** 🏆H4	CBdn CDTJ CKel CLAP CTsd EBee EHyd EPfP EShb ETod EWes GAbr GBin GKev IBal IKel LEdu LRHS NBro NRHS SArc SMad SPlb SRms WCru WSMil XSte
cycadifolium	CDTJ CTsd IKel
discolor	IKel XSte
- 'Silver Lady'	CDoC
fluviatile	CDTJ IKel
gibbum 🏆H1a	CDoC CKel EShb ETod IKel LRHS SPlb
- 'Silver Lady'	EShb
longicauda new	ETod IKel
magellanicum misapplied	see *B. chilense*
magellanicum (Desv.) Mett.	IKel SPlb
minus	ETod IKel
montanum new	ETod IKel
§ ***niponicum***	GEdr
novae-zelandiae	CTrC CTsd ETod IKel XSte
nudum	CBdn CDTJ ETod IKel
palmiforme	ETod IKel
penna-marina	Widely available
§ - subsp. ***alpinum***	EBee ECha EPfP GEdr GKev NWad
- - BR 68	GEdr
- 'Cristatum'	CLAP GAbr GEdr GWyn NBro NHar NWad
spicant 🏆H6	Widely available
- ***incisum***	see *B. spicant* 'Rickard's Serrate'
§ - 'Rickard's Serrate'	CLAP
- Serratum Group	WAbe
tabulare misapplied	see *B. chilense*
tabulare (Thunb.) Kuhn	CBcs CBdn CDTJ CKel CTsd IKel WCot
vulcanicum	CPla
wattsii	EBee ETod

Blepharocalyx (*Myrtaceae*)

§ ***cruckshanksii***	CCCN CExl CMCN CSde CTsd ELon IDee MGil SEND SVen WLov WPGP
- 'Heaven Scent'	see *B. cruckshanksii*

Blephilia (*Lamiaceae*)

ciliata	SPhx

Bletilla (*Orchidaceae*)

sp.	NDav
Brigantes gx	NLAp
Coritani gx	NLAp
formosana	NLAp
hyacinthina	see *B. striata*
ochracea	CExl NLAp SDir
Penway Dragon gx	NLAp
sinensis	CExl
§ ***striata*** 🏆H4	CBct CDoC CExl CTri CTsd EBee EMor EPot GAbr GKev LCro LEdu LOPS LRHS MBel MHer MNrw MSCN NRHS SDeJ SDir SIvy SPer SPlb WCot WFar WSMil XLum
- ***alba***	see *B. striata* f. *gebina*
- 'Albostriata'	CBct CExl ELan EMor WCot XLum
- BLUE DRAGON	see *B. striata* 'Soryu'
- blue-flowered	NLAp
§ - f. ***gebina***	CBod CExl CTri EBee ELan EMor GKev LCro LEdu LOPS LRHS MACG NLAp NRHS SDeJ SDir SIvy SPeP SPer WCot XLum
- - variegated (v)	EBee GKev LEdu
- 'Kuchi-beni'	EBee GKev LRHS NLAp XSte
- 'Lips'	GKev NLAp SDir
- purple-flowered	GKev
- 'Shi-ran'	EBee LRHS MSCN XSte
§ - 'Soryu'	CBor GKev LRHS MHol MSCN SDir SPeP WTyc
- variegated (v)	CTtf GKev
- yellow-flowered	GKev
Yokohama gx 'Sweet Lips'	GKev

Bloomeria (*Asparagaceae*)

crocea var. ***aurea***	NRog
humilis new	NRog

blueberry see *Vaccinium corymbosum*; see also AGM Fruit Section

Blumea (*Asteraceae*)

balsamifera	CHab

Bocconia (*Papaveraceae*)

cordata	see *Macleaya cordata* (Willd.) R. Br.
frutescens B&SWJ 10654	WCru

Boehmeria (*Urticaceae*)

nivea	LEdu LPla WCot WPGP
platanifolia	MNrw
aff. ***platanifolia*** new	GGro
sieboldiana	EBee EPPr LPla WFar
tricuspis PB 96.976 new	WPGP
- var. ***unicuspis*** new	GGro

virgata var. ***rotundifolia*** PB 02.530 new — WPGP

Boenninghausenia (*Rutaceae*)

albiflora B&SWJ 1479 — WCru

Bolax (*Apiaceae*)

glebaria — see *B. gummifer*
§ ***gummifer*** — GEdr GKev SPlb WAbe WFar

Boltonia (*Asteraceae*)

asteroides — CCBP GQue NGrd NWsh SMrm SPer XLum
- var. ***latisquama*** — CMea GMaP MACG MHol MRav NLar SHar SSal XLum
- - JIM CROCKETT ('Masbolimket'PBR) — EBee
- - 'Nana' — EWTr MACG
- - 'Snowbank' — WCAu WGoo
decurrens — CBod EPPr
incisa — see *Kalimeris incisa*

Bomarea (*Alstroemeriaceae*)

acuminata — see *B. andreana*
acutifolia — EBee WCot
- B&SWJ 14291 — WCru
- F&M 104 — WPGP
§ ***andreana*** B&SWJ 14310 — WCru
- B&SWJ 14376 — WCru
aff. ***andreana*** B&SWJ 10617 — WCru
boliviensis misapplied — see *Alstroemeria isabellana*
aff. ***bredemeyerana*** B&SWJ 14706 — WCru
- B&SWJ 14725 — WCru
caldasii — see *B. multiflora*
costaricensis — EBee
- B&SWJ 10467 — WCru
distichifolia — CExl WCru
§ ***edulis*** 🏆H3 — CAvo CPla CRHN MGil SBrt WAvo WCot WPav
- B&SWJ 9017 — WCru
- F&M 104 — CExl
'Fiesta' — WCot
frondea — see *B. multiflora*
hirsuta — CPla
- B&SWJ 14442 — WCru
- B&SWJ 14902 — WCru
hirtella — see *B. edulis*
§ ***multiflora*** 🏆H2 — CCCN CExl CTsd EBee SBrt WCot WCru WFar WPGP WSHC
- B&SWJ 14347 — WCru
- B&SWJ 14354 — WCru
- B&SWJ 14406 — WCru
- B&SWJ 14419 — WCru
- B&SWJ 14847 — WCru
aff. ***multiflora*** B&SWJ 14730 — WCru
- B&SWJ 14946 — WCru
ovallei — CCCN
patacocensis JCA 13987 — WCot
patinii B&SWJ 14213 — WCru
- B&SWJ 14310 — WCru
- B&SWJ 14895 — WCru
puracensis B&SWJ 14705 — WCru
- B&SWJ 14729 — WCru
salsilla 🏆H3 — CAvo CCCN SBrt
setacea B&SWJ 10681 — WCru
- B&SWJ 14875 — WCru

Bombax (*Malvaceae*)

ceiba — SPlb

Bongardia (*Berberidaceae*)

chrysogonum — CAvo EHyd EPot GKev NRHS

Bonia (*Poaceae*)

§ ***solida*** — MMuc MWht SEND

Boquila (*Lardizabalaceae*)

trifoliolata — WCru

borage see *Borago officinalis*

Borago (*Boraginaceae*)

laxiflora — see *B. pygmaea*
officinalis — CCBP CHby CLau ENfk EPfP GPoy LCro LOPS MBow MHer MNHC MPri NBir SEdi SPhx SRms SVic XAbr
- 'Alba' — CLau ENfk LCro LOPS LRHS MBow SEdi SPhx SRms WJek
- 'Bill Archer' (v) — CNat
§ ***pygmaea*** — CExl CSpe EWld MHer MNrw NBir NChi NSti SRms WHer WJek XAbr

borecole see AGM Vegetables Section

Borinda (*Poaceae*)

KR 5287 — MWht
KR 5600 — MWht
KR 6438 — MWht
KR 6439 — MWht
KR 7346 — MWht
KR 7613 — MWht
KR 7662 — MWht
albocerea 🏆H4 — EPfP MWht
- Yunnan 2 — CDTJ
- Yunnan 3a — CDTJ
- Yunnan 4 — see *B. lushuiensis* Yunnan 4
angustissima — CDTJ CExl EPfP LPar MMuc MWht NLar XSte
boliana — SSut
frigida — CDTJ
- KR 4059 — MWht
grossa — CDTJ
- KR 5931 — MWht
'Harlequin' new — WCot
lushuiensis — WCot
§ - Yunnan 4 — CDTJ MWht
macclureana KR 5051 — MWht
- KR 5177 from Gyala, Nepal — MWht
aff. ***macclureana*** KR 6900 — MWht
nujiangensis — CDTJ WPGP
papyrifera — MWht WCot WPGP XSte
- CS 1046 — CBdn CJun MWht
- KR 3968 new — MWht
perlonga Yunnan 6 — MWht
scabrida misapplied — see *Fargesia robusta*
Yunnan 4 — see *B. lushuiensis* Yunnan 4

Boronia (*Rutaceae*)

anemonifolia 'Pink Star' — LCro LOPS
crenulata — CBcs CCCN
heterophylla — CAbb CBcs CBod CCCN CSde CTsd ECre EGrl EPfP EShb MPkF SEle WCot XSte
- 'Ice Charlotte' — CCCN CTsd EShb SEle

Bossiaea (*Fabaceae*)

riparia — SPlb
scolopendria — SPlb

Bothriochloa (*Poaceae*)

§ ***bladhii*** — CKno EBee EPPr SRms
caucasica — see *B. bladhii*
§ ***ischaemum*** — EPPr

Bougainvillea (*Nyctaginaceae*)

sp. — CDoC
'Alexandra' — CCCN SPre SWeb
§ × ***buttiana*** 'Raspberry Ice' (v) — EShb
glabra ♀H2 — EShb SPre
§ - 'Sanderiana' — SWeb
'Sentimento' — CCCN
Vera Series — CCCN

Boussingaultia (*Basellaceae*)

baselloides Hook. — see *Anredera cordifolia*

Bouteloua (*Poaceae*)

curtipendula — CBod LPla
§ ***gracilis*** — CBod EHyd SBls

Bouvardia (*Rubiaceae*)

× ***domestica*** — EShb
ternifolia — EBee ESwi WCot

Bowiea (*Asparagaceae*)

volubilis — GKev SPlb

Bowkeria (*Stilbaceae*)

sp. — CCCN
cymosa — SPlb SVen

Boykinia (*Saxifragaceae*)

aconitifolia — CElw CMac GEdr GLog MACG NRya SMad WCru
elata — see *B. occidentalis*
heucheriformis — see *B. jamesii*
§ ***jamesii*** — CPla EPot GKev
lycoctonifolia — LEdu NLar
§ ***occidentalis*** — MBriF WCru
rotundifolia — EPPr NBir WCru
tellimoides — see *Peltoboykinia tellimoides*

boysenberry see *Rubus* 'Boysenberry'

Brachychilum see *Hedychium*

Brachychiton (*Malvaceae*)

acerifolius — SPlb
bidwillii — EShb
populneus — SPlb
§ ***rupestris*** — EShb

Brachyglottis (*Asteraceae*)

§ ***bidwillii*** — WCot WPGP
- 'Basil Fox' — WAbe
§ ***compacta*** — EHyd EPfP LRHS MAsh SPer
- 'Drysdale' — CRos EHyd ELan EPfP ILea LRHS NRHS SCoo SEdd SGBe SGsty SLon SWvt
§ - 'Moira Reid' (v) — CExl
§ - 'Sunshine' ♀H4 — CAgr CBar CBod CRos CSBt CTri EBee EHyd ELan EPfP GArf LCro LOPS LRHS MGos MMuc MRav MSwo NPer NRHS SCob SEND SPer SPlb SRms SWvt WAvo
'Frosty' — CBod
greyi misapplied — see *B. compacta* 'Sunshine'
§ ***greyi*** (Hook. f.) B. Nord. — CMac
greyi × ***repanda*** — GDam
huntii — SVen
laxifolia misapplied — see *B. compacta* 'Sunshine'
'Menthe Glaciale' — ILea
§ ***monroi*** — CBcs CMac CSBt EHyd ELan EPfP LRHS MAsh MRav SLon SVen WFar
repanda 'Purpurea' — CBcs
§ ***rotundifolia*** — CCCN EBee ELan
'Silver Waves' — CBod
I 'Sunshine Improved' — CBcs CBrac MAsh MPri SGbt
WALBERTON'S SILVER DORMOUSE ('Walbrach'PBR) ♀H4 — CBcs CBod CEme CRos CSBt EBee EHyd ELan EPfP GBin LRHS MGos MRav NCou NRHS NSti SCob SCoo SEdd SPoG SWvt WNPC

Brachypodium (*Poaceae*)

pinnatum — EPPr
sylvaticum — CHab MMuc SEND

Brachyscome (*Asteraceae*)

angustifolia 'Billabong Mauve Delight'PBR **new** — LSou
'Magenta Delight' — LSou

Bracteantha see *Xerochrysum*

Brahea (*Arecaceae*)

armata ♀H1c — CBrP CDTJ CPHo CTsd SPalm SPlb WSMil
dulcis — SPalm
edulis — CCCN CPHo SChr SPalm WSMil
'Super Silver' — CPHo

Brassaia see *Schefflera*

Brassica (*Brassicaceae*)

japonica — see *B. juncea* var. *crispifolia*
juncea — SVic
§ - var. ***crispifolia*** — MNHC
- f. ***juncea*** — MBros
oleracea — CAgr CLau SVic WHer
- var. ***ramosa*** — LEdu NGrd
- - 'Cotswold Cream' (v) — WCot
- - 'D'Aubenton Panaché' (v) — WCot
rapa — SVic
* - var. ***japonica*** — MNHC
- subsp. ***nipposinica*** var. ***laciniata*** — LCro LOPS SVic

Briggsia see *Oreocharis*

× *Brigandra* see *Oreocharis*

calliantha — see *Oreocharis* 'Calliantha'

Brighamia (*Campanulaceae*)

insignis — CCCN SPad

Brillantaisia (*Acanthaceae*)

kirungae — CCCN EShb

Brimeura (*Asparagaceae*)

§ ***amethystina*** ♀H5 — CExl EGrI GBin LEdu SDeJ SPhx WPGP WThu
- 'Alba' — EGrI SDeJ SPhx

Briza (*Poaceae*)

maxima — CTtf LPot NGdn NSti NWad SHar SPhx SSal
media — Widely available
- 'Golden Bee' — CKno CRos EHyd EPPr EPfP EWes LEdu LRHS MMrt NRHS SMad SPhx WMal

- 'Limouzi' CBod CElw CKno CWCL EHyd ELon EPPr GBin LEdu LRHS MACG MAvo NLar NSti SMHy SMad SMea SPoG WPnP XLum
- 'Romany Silver' LEdu
- 'Russells'PBR CBod CDor CKno CTtf EBee EHyd ELan ELon EPfP LEdu MGos NLar NRHS NWsh SCob SMea SPer SPoG SRms SWvt XLum

subaristata EPPr
triloba EAJP EHyd NWsh SPhx

broccoli see AGM Vegetables Section

Brodiaea (*Asparagaceae*)

§ ***californica*** CSpe EBee ERCP GKev WCot
- NNS 00-109 WCot
- 'Babylon' ERCP GKev
- lavender-flowered **new** NRog
- var. ***leptandra*** NRog
- violet-flowered **new** NRog

'Corrina' see *Triteleia* 'Corrina'
elegans NRog
filifolia **new** NRog
ida-maia see *Dichelostemma ida-maia*
jolonensis NRog
kinkiensis **new** NRog
laxa see *Triteleia laxa*
§ ***minor*** NRog
pallida NRog
peduncularis see *Triteleia peduncularis*
purdyi see *B. minor*
stellaris NRog

Bromus (*Poaceae*)

erectus CHab
- W&B BG B-5 WCot

inermis 'Skinner's Gold' (v) EPPr WCot

Broussonetia (*Moraceae*)

papyrifera CBcs CMCN ELan ESwi LMaj MGil WAvo WBor WCot WKor WLov
- 'Golden Shadow' **new** LRHS XSte
- 'Laciniata' SMad

Browallia (*Solanaceae*)

from Sikkim CSpe
americana SPhx

Bruckenthalia see *Erica*

Brugmansia (*Solanaceae*)

'Angels Exotic' (d) NGKo
'Angels Phenomenal' (d) NGKo
'Apricot Queen' NGKo
§ ***arborea*** ♀H1c CBcs CDTJ NGKo
- 'Rosea' variegated (v) ELan
- variegated (v) ELan

aurea CCCN SAdn
aurea* × *suaveolens **new** SAdn
× ***candida*** CCCN
- 'Angels Sunbeam' (d) ♀H1c ELan
- 'Chartreuse' CDow
- 'Creamsickle' (d) ♀H1c NGKo
- double-flowered (d) SAdn
- § - 'Grand Marnier' ♀H1c NGKo
- 'Knightii' (d) ♀H1c CDTJ CDow
- 'Pink Perfektion' (d) NGKo
- 'Plena' see *B.* × *candida* 'Knightii'
- § - 'Variegata' (v) CCCN CDTJ NGKo

× ***cubensis*** 'Charles Grimaldi' NGKo
× ***insignis*** 'Pink' NGKo
'Jamie' (v) NGKo
'Madame Foster' NGKo
'Miner's Claim' (v) NGKo
§ ***sanguinea*** ♀H1c CCCN CDow SAdn SPlb
§ ***suaveolens*** ♀H1c CBcs
- 'Variegata' (v) EShb
- yellow-flowered EShb

'Variegata Sunset' see *B.* × *candida* 'Variegata'
versicolor misapplied see *B. arborea*
§ ***versicolor*** Lagerh. CCCN SAdn
'Vulcsa Red' NGKo
* 'Yellow Trumpet' ELan

Brunfelsia (*Solanaceae*)

americana CCCN WFib
australis WFib
calycina see *B. pauciflora*
lactea CCCN
§ ***pauciflora*** ♀H1c CCCN EShb SPer

Brunia (*Bruniaceae*)

albiflora SPlb

Brunnera ✿ (*Boraginaceae*)

§ ***macrophylla*** Widely available
- 'Alba' see *B. macrophylla* 'Betty Bowring'
- 'Alexanders Great'PBR Widely available
- § - 'Betty Bowring' Widely available
- 'Blaukuppel' CBod EWes NBir
- 'Dawson's White' (v) CBcs CDor CRos CWCL ECha ECtt EHed ELan ELon EMor EPfP GKev GMaP LRHS MBel MRav NBid NBir NHpl NLar NRHS SPer SRms SWvt WBor WCAu WCot WFar WTyc
- 'Diane's Gold'PBR EBee ECha ECtt MGos MHol MNrw NLar SHeu
- 'Emerald Mist'PBR (v) EBee ECtt LPla MBel MGos MTin NLar SWvt WSpi
- 'Golden Jack Frost' CBcs CBct CBod MPnt
- 'Gordano Gold' (v) WCot
- 'Green Gold' (v) EMor NLar WFar
- 'Hadspen Cream' (v) ♀H6 Widely available
- 'Henry's Eyes' EBee EPfP
- 'Inspector Morse' WCav
- 'Jack Frost'PBR ♀H6 Widely available
- 'Jack's Gold' ILea MSCN NSti SMrm
- 'Jennifer' EMor MBel NSti WCAu
- 'Joanna' NSum
- 'King's Ransom'PBR (v) CBct CWGN ECtt EMor GPSL NLar NSti SCob WFar
- 'Langford Hewitt' (v) MNrw
- 'Langtrees' CBct CMac EBee ECha EHyd GBin MCot MMuc NBir NGdn SEND SPer WSpi
- 'Little Jack' (v) CRos EBee EHyd EMor EPfP LRHS LSou NRHS SPoG
- 'Looking Glass'PBR ♀H6 Widely available
- § - 'Mister Morse'PBR (v) ♀H6 CExl CWGN ECtt EHed EMor EPau GDam GMaP GWyn LEdu LSun MACG MAvo MBel MNrw MPnt NBir NGBl NGdn NLar NSti NWad SCob SPer SWvt WCAu WCot WFar WSpi
- 'Sea Heart'PBR CMea CSpe EBee ECtt EHed EPfP IPot LEdu LRHS LSou MBel NLar NSti SCob SHeu WCAu WPnP
- 'Silver Heart'PBR CBct CWGN ECtt EHed EMor LRHS LSou MCot SCob SCoo SHeu SMad SPad WBor

- 'Silver Spear' CDor EBee LRHS MGos MSCN NGBl NLar WCAu WCav WCot WHoo
- 'Silver Wings' CElw EBee ECtt EHyd EPfP GKev MBel MGos NBir NGdn NLar NSti NWad WCAu WFar
- 'Spring Yellow' ECtt WCAu
- 'Starry Eyes' IPot MACG MBel MCot
- 'Sterling Silver' **new** WTor
'Mrs Morse' see *B. macrophylla* 'Mister Morse'
sibirica CElw EBee EPPr EWes NBid NLar WCAu

Brunsvigia (*Amaryllidaceae*)

bosmaniae WCot
elandsmontana WCot
josephinae WCot
- LAV 30394 WCot
marginata WCot
multiflora see *B. orientalis*
§ ***orientalis*** WCot
pulchra WCot
radulosa WCot
rosea 'Minor' see *Amaryllis belladonna*

Brussels sprouts see AGM Vegetables Section

Bryonia (*Cucurbitaceae*)

dioica GGro GPoy

Bryophyllum see *Kalanchoe*

Bucinellina see *Columnea*

Buddleja ✿ (*Scrophulariaceae*)

BO 15-043 **new** GGro
W/O 7061 **new** GGro
agathosma CExl SLon WCFE WLav WSHC
albiflora SLon WLav
- BO 15-041 **new** GGro
alternifolia ♀H6 Widely available
- 'Argentea' CBcs CDoC EHyd ELan EPfP LRHS MBNS MRav NLar SLon SPer SPoG SWvt WCot WLav XSen
asiatica ♀H3 EShb SLon WLav
- B&SWJ 11278 WCru
asiatica* × *lindleyana WSpi
auriculata CBcs CExl CMCN CSde CTrC ELan EPPr EPfP IArd IDee MGil NSti SDix SLon SPlb SVen WGwG WLav
'Autumn Surprise' SLon
'Bel Argent' EBee WPGP
BERRIES AND CREAM ('Pmoore14') **new** SGBe SLon
'Blue Chip'PBR (Lo and Behold Series) EHyd EPfP LBuc LPar LSou MAsh MGos NLar SGol SLon SRms SWvt WCot WFar WLav
'Blue Chip Junior' (Lo and Behold Series) SLon SPoG
* 'Blue Trerice' CExl
caryopteridifolia EBtc SEND SLon
colvilei CBcs CCCN CKel ELan EPfP GBin GKin IArd LRHS SLon SWvt WBor WSpi
- B&SWJ 2121 WCru
- GWJ 9399 WCru
- WJC 13760 WCru
- 'Kewensis' CBod CExl CRHN CWit ELan EPfP EWes MGil NLar SLon SMad SVen WCFE WLav WLov WSHC
- large-leaved SBrt
- pink-flowered EHed EPPr GBin MGil NLar WSpi
- 'Tregye' **new** WPGP
cordata LRHS SLon SVen
- B&SWJ 10433 WCru
coriacea SLon
CRAN RAZZ ('Boseranz') CBod
§ ***crispa*** CBct CDoC CDow CExl CKel EBee ECha EHyd ELan EPfP LRHS SLon SPer SVen SWvt WFar WKif WPGP WSHC WSpi
- var. ***farreri*** MGil SLon SPoG
- 'Stone House Cottage' CKel SLon WSHC
crotonoides subsp. ***amplexicaulis*** SLon
davidii CCVT CDoC NPol NWea WTSh
- B&SWJ 8083 WCru
- ADONIS BLUE ('Adokeep'PBR) CBcs CSBt EHyd MAsh SCob SLon SPoG WLav
- 'African Queen' CRos SLon WLav
- 'Apollonaria' WLav
§ - 'Autumn Beauty' SLon WLav
- 'Autumn Delight' LRHS SLon
- 'Beijing' see *B. davidii* 'Autumn Beauty'
- 'Billy's Blue' WLav
- 'Black Knight' ♀H6 Widely available
- 'Blue Eyes' WLav
- 'Blue Horizon' ♀H6 LRHS NLar SLon SRGP WCot WLav
- 'Border Beauty' CRos LRHS SLon WLav
- 'Butterfly Heaven'PBR WLav
- Buzz Series LBuc NHol SLon
- - BUZZ CANDY PINK ('Tobudsopin') CDoC CNor CPla CRos EHyd ELan GJos LRHS NRHS SLon SPad SPoG WHil WLav
- - BUZZ HOT RASPBERRY CMea ELan GJos LRHS NPer SCoo SGBe SLon WHil WLav
- - BUZZ INDIGO CDoC CRos CSBt EHyd ELan EPfP LRHS NRHS SGBe WHil WLav
- - BUZZ IVORY ('Tobudivory'PBR) CEnd CMac CRos EBee EHyd ELan EPfP LRHS LSRN MGos NHol NLar NRHS SCob SLon SPer SPoG WCot WHil WLav WSpi
- - BUZZ LILAC ELan MGos NHol SLon
- - BUZZ MAGENTA IMPROVED ('Tobudmagen') MBros
- - BUZZ MAGENTA ('Tobudpipur'PBR) CChe CDoC CEnd CMac CMea EHyd ELan LRHS LSRN MGos NHol NLar NRHS SCob SCoo SGBe SLon SPoG SRms SWvt WFar WLav WSpi
- - BUZZ SKY BLUE ('Tobudskybl'PBR) CDoC CMac CRos EGrl EHyd EPfP GJos LRHS MBros MGos NHol NLar NRHS SCoo SGBe SLon SPer SPoG SRms WFar WHil WLav
- - BUZZ VELVET ('Tobudvelve'PBR) CRos EGrl ELan LRHS NRHS SLon SPer WCav
- - BUZZ VIOLET ('Tobudviole') CDoC EGrl EHyd ELan GJos LRHS MGos NHol NLar NRHS SCob SLon SPoG SWvt WLav
- CAMBERWELL BEAUTY ('Camkeep') (English Butterfly Series) ♀H6 SLon WLav
- 'Castle Blue' CRos LRHS SLon
- 'Castle School' WLav
- 'Clive Farrell' see *B. davidii* 'Autumn Beauty'
- 'Corinne Tremaine' WHer
- 'Cotswold Blue' WLav
- 'Cotswold Twilight' WLav
- 'Darent Valley' ♀H6 SLon
- 'Dartmoor' ♀H6 Widely available
- 'Dart's Ornamental White' MRav SLon WLav
- 'Dart's Papillon Blue' LRHS SLon WLav

- 'Dart's Purple Rain'	LRHS SLon WLav
- 'Dubonnet'	SLon WLav
- 'Ecolonia'	SLon WLav
- 'Empire Blue'	CBcs CDoC CSBt ECtt EHyd EPfP GKin LRHS LSRN MGos NBir NPer NRHS NWea SCoo SGBe SPer SPlb SPoG SRms SWvt XSen
- 'Fair Lady'	WLav
- 'Fascinating'	MRav NBir SLon WLav
- 'Flaming Violet'	SLon WLav
- FLORENCE ('Watflor')	NLar SCob SLon WFar
- 'Foxtail'	WLav
- 'Glasnevin Hybrid'	LRHS NLar SLon WLav
- 'Gonglepod'	CRos LRHS SLon WLav
- 'Greenway's River Dart'	LRHS SLon
- 'Grey Dawn'	WLav
- 'Griffin Blue'	MAsh WLav
- 'Gulliver'PBR	CBod EHyd LRHS NLar NRHS SCob SGol SLon WFar WLav
- 'Harlequin' (v)	CBcs CBod CMac CTsd EHed ELan EPfP LRHS MAsh MGos MSwo NLar NRHS NWea SEND SGBe SGol SPer SPlb SPoG SRms SWvt WFar WLov XSen
- 'Île de France'	LPar NLar NWea SLon SRms WLav
- 'Leela Kapila'	LRHS SLon
- 'Les Kneale'	SLon WLav
- 'Lilac Moon'	WLav
- 'Loganberry Jam'	WLav
- MARBLED WHITE ('Markeep') (English Butterfly Series)	CBod EHyd EShb NEoE SLon WLav
- MASQUERADE ('Notbud') (v)	MRav SLon
- MOONSHINE ('Buddma'PBR)	CBod MTin NEoE WFar
§ - NANHO BLUE ('Mongo')	CBcs CBrac CMac CRos CSBt EBee EPfP GBin GKev GKin LPar LRHS MAsh MGos MRav MSwo NBir NLar NRHS SCoo SGol WSpi XSen
- 'Nanho Petite Indigo'	see *B. davidii* NANHO BLUE
- 'Nanho Petite Plum'	see *B. davidii* NANHO PURPLE
§ - NANHO PURPLE ('Monum') ♀H6	CBcs CMac CRos CTri EPfP LRHS LSRN MGos MRav NLar NRHS SGol SLon SPer SPlb SRms XSen
- NANHO WHITE ('Monite') ♀H6	CMac CRos EPfP GKev LRHS SGol SLon SRms XSen
- var. ***nanhoensis***	SGol WFar WLav
- - blue-flowered	EPfP NWad SLon SPer
- 'Orchid Beauty'	LRHS SLon WLav
- 'Orpheus'	CRos LRHS SLon WLav
- 'Panache'	CRos EHyd EPfP LRHS MAsh NRHS SLon WLav
- 'Party Girl'	SLon
- 'Peace'	CMac CTri LSRN MRav NLar SLon SPoG WLav
- PEACOCK ('Peakeep'PBR) (English Butterfly Series)	CSBt MAsh SCob WLav
- 'Persephone'	SLon WLav
- 'Petite Indigo'	see *B. davidii* NANHO BLUE
- 'Pink Beauty'	LSRN MBlu SRGP WFar
- 'Pink Pearl'	SLon WLav
- 'Pink Spreader'	LRHS SLon WLav
- 'Pixie Blue'	LBuc MAsh WLav
- 'Pixie Red'	LBuc MAsh NLar WLav
- 'Pixie White'	LBuc MAsh SCob SGol WLav
- PURPLE EMPEROR ('Pyrkeep') (English Butterfly Series)	NBir SLon WLav
- 'Purple Friend'	LRHS SLon WLav
- 'Red Admiral'	SLon
- RÊVE DE PAPILLON BLUE ('Minpap3')	WLav
- RÊVE DE PAPILLON ('Minpap')	CRos EHyd LRHS MAsh NRHS SCoo WLav
- 'Royal Purple'	SWvt
- 'Royal Red' ♀H6	Widely available
- 'Saith Ffynnon Early'	WSFF
- 'Santana' (v)	CBod CMac EHyd ELon EPfP EWes LRHS MGos MRav MSCN NHol NLar NRHS NWad SCob SGol SPoG SRms SWvt WAvo WSpi XSen
- 'Shire Blue'	WLav
- 'Son of Orpheus'	WLav
- 'Sophie' **new**	NLar
- 'Southcombe Splendour'	CRos LRHS
- 'Summer Beauty'	MBlu SLon WLav
- 'Summer House Blue'	SLon WLav
- 'Twotones'	WLav
- 'Variegata' (v)	MAsh SLon SWvt WLav
- 'White Ball'	ELan NLar SLon WLav
- 'White Bouquet'	CBod CCVT CSBt EPfP GKin MSwo NLar NWea SEND SPer SRGP SWvt WLav XSen
- 'White Cloud'	EPfP LRHS SLon SRms WGwG
- 'White Harlequin' (v)	SLon WCFE
- 'White Profusion' ♀H6	Widely available
- 'White Wings'	CRos LRHS SLon WLav
- 'Wisteria Lane'	CBod LCro LOPS SMad WNPC
davidii* × *fallowiana	WSpi
§ ***delavayi***	CExl ECre GBin SEND WCru
DREAMING LAVENDER ('Hinebud1'PBR)	CBod SLon WNPC
DREAMING ORANGE	SLon
DREAMING PURPLE ('Hinebud4')	LSou WNPC
DREAMING WHITE ('Hinebud3'PBR)	LSou WNPC
'Ellen's Blue'	CExl CRos EPfP LRHS NLar WLav
fallowiana misapplied	see *B.* 'West Hill'
fallowiana Balf. f. & W.W. Sm.	CRos LRHS WLav
- ACE 2481	LRHS
- BWJ 7803	WCru
- var. ***alba*** ♀H5	CMac CRos EHyd ELan EPPr EPfP LRHS MBNS MRav NLar NRHS SDix SLon SPer WLov
- 'Bishop's Violet'	CTsd
'Flower Power'	see *B.* × *weyeriana* 'Bicolor'
(Flutterby Flow Series) FLUTTERBY FLOW LAVENDER ('Podaras 12'PBR)	LCro LOPS
- FLUTTERBY PEACE ('Podaras 6'PBR)	LBuc
(Flutterby Petite Series) FLUTTERBY PETITE BLUE HEAVEN ('Podaras 8'PBR)	CBod LCro LOPS MThu NLar SLon
- FLUTTERBY PETITE DARK PINK ('Podaras 10'PBR)	CBod LCro LOPS NLar SNig
- FLUTTERBY PETITE SNOW WHITE ('Podaras 15'PBR)	CBod LCro LOPS NLar SLon SNig
- FLUTTERBY PETITE TUTTI FRUITTI PINK ('Podaras 13'PBR)	CBod LBuc LCro LOPS SLon SNig SRms
(Flutterby Series) FLUTTERBY LAVENDER ('Podaras 11'PBR)	CSBt
forrestii	WCru
- BWJ 8020	EBee WCru
globosa ♀H5	Widely available
- RCB/Arg C-11	WCot

- 'Cally Orange'	GBin WGwG
- cream-flowered HCM 98.017	WPGP
- 'Lemon Ball'	LRHS MBlu NPer SLon WLav
glomerata	EShb MGil SLon SPlb
- 'Silver Service'	CDow CKel CPla EPfP LRHS
heliophila	see *B. delavayi*
indica	SLon WLav
INSPIRED PINK	see *B.* × *weyeriana* 'Pink Pagoda'
japonica	SLon
- B&SWJ 8912	WCru
× ***lewisiana*** 'Margaret Pike'	SLon
'Lilac Chip' (Lo and Behold Series)	CDoC LPar NLar SGol
limitanea	SLon SPtp
- from Cangshan, Yunnan, China	SBrt
lindleyana	Widely available
- 'Little Treasure'	NEoE SLon
- 'Miss Vicie'	LRHS
aff. ***lindleyana***	GWyn WLov WSpi
- B&SWJ 11478	WCru
'Lochinch' ♀H5	Widely available
longifolia	EBee SLon
'Longstock Gem'	SGBe SLon
'Longstock Silver'	LRHS SLon
loricata	CExl CMCN EHyd EPPr EPfP GBin GWyn IDee LRHS LShi MGil SEdd SLon SPlb WLav WSpi
macrostachya	WCot
- HWJ 602	WCru
- WWJ 12016	WCru
§ ***madagascariensis*** ♀H2	CRHN EShb NLar SLon SPlb SVen
megalocephala B&SWJ 9106	WCru WPGP
'Miss Ruby' PBR ♀H5	CDoC EBee EPfP LBuc LPar LRHS LSRN MAsh NRHS SLon WLav
§ 'Morning Mist' PBR	CBod CDoC CExl CKel CMac CSBt CWGN EPfP GBin LCro LOPS LPar LRHS LSRN NHol NRHS SGBe SLon SRms SWvt WCot WFar XSte
myriantha	CExl SLon WPGP
nappii	SLon
nicodemia	see *B. madagascariensis*
nivea	CExl MGil SLon WLav WSpi XSen
- B&SWJ 2679	WCru
- pink-flowered	SLon
aff. ***nivea***	WSpi
officinalis ♀H3	CExl CSde SLon WLav
paniculata	SLon
- GWJ 9286 from Sikkim	WCru
parvifolia	SLon
- MPF 148	WLav
× ***pikei*** 'Hever'	SRms XSen
- UNIQUE ('Pmoore12' PBR)	CDoC CMac LCro LOPS SLon SPoG XSte
'Pink Delight' ♀H5	Widely available
'Pink Micro Chip' (Lo and Behold Series)	SLon SPoG
'Pink Perfection'	WFar
'Pride of Hever'	SDys
'Pride of Longstock'	SLon SPoG
pterocaulis	EBee
'Purple Chip' (Lo and Behold Series)	LPar
'Red Chip' (Lo and Behold Series)	SGol
(Rocketstar Series) ROCKETSTAR FLAMINGO ('Smnbdpt') **new**	SLon
- ROCKETSTAR INDIGO ('Smnbdbt') **new**	SLon
- ROCKETSTAR ORCHID ('Smnbdo') **new**	SLon
saligna	SLon
'Salmon Spheres'	SLon WLav
salviifolia	CBcs CBct CCCN CExl CMac CSde CTrC CTsd EBee IDee LRHS MBlu MGil NLar SBrt SEND SPlb SVen WAvo WCFE WGwG WKif WLav WLov WPGP
- white-flowered	EBee SLon WPGP
SILVER ANNIVERSARY	see *B.* 'Morning Mist'
speciosissima	WPGP
stachyoides	WLav
stenostachya	CExl SLon
sterniana	see *B. crispa*
SUGAR PLUM ('Lonplum' PBR)	CBod CKel CSBt EGrl EHyd EMil EPfP LBuc LCro LOPS LRHS MAsh NRHS SGBe SLon SPoG WNPC
tibetica	see *B. crispa*
TRUE BLUE ('Bostulu' PBR) **new**	NLar
tubiflora	SLon WLav
venenifera	SLon
- B&SWJ 895	EBee
- B&SWJ 6036	WCru
× ***wardii***	WCFE
- KR 4881	WPGP
§ 'West Hill' ♀H5	CRos EHyd EPfP LRHS NRHS SLon WLav
× ***weyeriana***	CMac ECtt EPPr EWTr GJos MBNS MGil MNrw MSwo NBir SIvy SPlb SWvt WAvo WBor
§ - 'Bicolor'	EBee EPPr EPfP LCro LOPS LSRN MNrw NLar NQui SCob SCoo SLon SRms WLav WMal XSte
- 'Boy Blue'	SLon WLav
- 'Golden Glow'	GBin GWyn LRHS LSRN NLar SLon SWvt WLav WSFF
- 'Honeycomb'	CBod EHed EShb MGos MMrt NLar SPad
- 'Lady de Ramsey'	NLar SEND
- 'Moonlight'	CDoC CExl ELan EPPr GBin GWyn LRHS SLon SPer WCot WLav WMal WSpi XSen
§ - 'Pink Pagoda' PBR	CBcs CEme CSBt EPfP NLar SGBe SLon SPoG
- pink-flowered	XSen
- 'Sungold' ♀H6	Widely available
'White Chip' (Lo and Behold Series)	LPar LSou SGol
'Winter Sun'	SLon
yunnanensis	CBcs GGro NLar SBrt SLon
- B&SWJ 8146	WCru

Buglossoides (*Boraginaceae*)

§ ***purpurocaerulea***	ECha EWld LPla MNrw NBid WCot WFar

Bukiniczia (*Plumbaginaceae*)

cabulica	GKev WIce

Bulbine (*Asphodelaceae*)

caulescens	see *B. frutescens*
§ ***frutescens***	CBod CCBP LRHS MHer MNHC NChi SRms SSal SVen WSMil XLum
- 'Hallmark'	CCCN CKel LRHS
latifolia	CCCN
§ ***semibarbata***	CCCN

Bulbinella (*Asphodelaceae*)

angustifolia	GKev MHer

gibbsii var. ***balanifera*** GKev
hookeri CExl EBee EHyd GBee GBin GEdr GKev ITim SMad SRms WCot WHal
latifolia subsp. ***latifolia*** IBlr
nutans EBee

Bulbinopsis see *Bulbine*

Bulbocodium (*Colchicaceae*)

vernum EPot GKev NRog SDeJ

bullace see *Prunus insititia*

Bunias (*Brassicaceae*)

orientalis CAgr LEdu

Bunium (*Apiaceae*)

bulbocastanum CAgr LEdu LRHS SPhx SSal WPGP XLum
ferulaceum CCBP MHol MPie SEdd SHar SMad WBrk
- W&B BG B-10 WCot

Buphthalmum (*Asteraceae*)

salicifolium EBee ELan EPfP MMuc NBro NGdn SPer SRms WCot WFar WHil
- 'Alpengold' ECha GMaP NLar
- 'Dora' ECtt WCot WFar
- 'Sunwheel' CBod SRms
speciosum see *Telekia speciosa*

Bupleurum (*Apiaceae*)

angulosum NBir
- copper-leaved see *B. longifolium*
candollei LEdu SAng WPGP WSHC
falcatum CSpe ECha LRHS NDov SDix SPhx WCot WKif
- short **new** CSpe
- tall **new** CSpe
fruticescens XSen
fruticosum CBcs CBod CCCN CKel CSpe EBee ECre EHyd ELan EPfP EShb EWes GBin LRHS MNrw NRHS SCob SDix SEND SEdd SLon SMad SPer SPoG SPtp WCot WLov WSHC XLum XSen
gibraltaricum XSen
griffithii 'Decor' CSpe
§ ***longifolium*** CElw CSpe EBee ECre EWes LEdu MNrw NAts NBir WBor WFar WPGP
- subsp. ***aureum*** LPla LRHS SPhx
- 'Bronze Beauty' CPla GEdr MBriF MMrt SPtp
- subsp. ***longifolium*** **new** WPGP
ranunculoides CSpe LPla SPhx XLum
rotundifolium CSpe LEdu SAng SPhx WCot
- 'Copper' NDov

Bursaria (*Pittosporaceae*)

spinosa CCCN

Butia (*Arecaceae*)

capitata 🏆H1c CCCN CDTJ CPHo ETod LPar SArc SPalm
§ - var. ***odorata*** SPlb
eriospatha CPHo SPalm
odorata see *B. capitata* var. *odorata*

Butomus (*Butomaceae*)

umbellatus CBen CPud CSpe CWat ECha EWat GBin MNrw MRav MWts NBir NPer WMAq WWtn
- f. ***albiflorus*** ECha
- 'Rosenrot' EWat LLWG
- 'Schneeweisschen' EWat LLWG MWts

butternut see *Juglans cinerea*

butternut squash see AGM Vegetables Section

Buxus (*Buxaceae*)

aurea 'Marginata' see *B. sempervirens* 'Marginata'
balearica CJun EBtc WSpi
bodinieri LTop
'Green Gem' NWad
harlandii misapplied CMen SRiv
macowanii LTop
macrophylla NWea WSpi
§ ***microphylla*** NWad SGol
§ - 'Compacta' CMen MHer WCot
- 'Faulkner' 🏆H6 CBod ELan EPfP LBuc MGos SCob SGol SGsty SPer SRiv SRms SWeb WSpi
- 'Golden Triumph'PBR NLar
- 'Green Pillow' MHer SRiv WSpi
- 'Herrenhausen' WSpi
- var. ***insularis*** see *B. sinica* var. *insularis*
- var. ***japonica*** SGol
- - 'National' WSpi
§ - - 'Winter Gem' MRav
- 'John Baldwin' SRiv
- var. ***sinica*** LTop WSpi
sempervirens Widely available
§ - 'Angustifolia' MRav NWad SMad
- 'Arborescens' LMaj
- 'Argenteo-variegata' (v) SGol WFar
- 'Aurea' see *B. sempervirens* 'Aureovariegata'
- 'Aurea Maculata' see *B. sempervirens* 'Aureovariegata'
- 'Aurea Marginata' see *B. sempervirens* 'Marginata'
§ - 'Aureovariegata' (v) CBod EPfP EShb LTop MGos MRav NLar NWad SRiv SRms
- 'Bentley Blue' LTop NWea
- 'Blauer Heinz' CBod ELan GQue LTop MRav NWea SRiv WAvo WSpi
- 'Bowles's Blue' WCFE
- 'Bullata' LMaj
- clipped ball CEme EPfP GDam LSRN LTop MGos NLar SRiv SRms
- clipped bird LTop SRiv
- clipped cone CEme GDam LSRN LTop SRiv SRms
- clipped pyramid EPfP LSRN LTop MGos NLar SRiv SRms
- clipped spiral LSRN LTop NLar SRiv SRms
- 'Elegans' LTop
§ - 'Elegantissima' (v) 🏆H6 Widely available
- 'Fiesta' SRms
- 'Gold Tip' see *B. sempervirens* 'Notata'
§ - 'Graham Blandy' 🏆H6 MHer SAko SGol SRiv WSpi
- 'Green Balloon' LBuc
- 'Greenpeace' see *B. sempervirens* 'Graham Blandy'
- 'Handsworthensis' LTop NWea SEND SRms WCFE WSpi
- 'Ickworth Giant' WSpi
- 'Japonica Aurea' see *B. sempervirens* 'Latifolia Maculata'
- 'Kensington Gardens' WSpi
- 'King Midas' SAko
- 'Kingsville' see *B. microphylla* 'Compacta'
- 'Kingsville Dwarf' see *B. microphylla* 'Compacta'
- 'Latifolia' WMou
§ - 'Latifolia Maculata' (v) 🏆H6 EPfP LTop MMuc NPer SEND SPoG SRiv WSpi
§ - 'Marginata' (v) LTop SGol WSpi

	– 'Memorial'	LTop NWad SRiv WSpi
	– 'Myosotidifolia'	SRiv WCot WSpi
	– 'Myrtifolia'	WSpi
§	– 'Notata' (v)	WSpi
	– 'Pendula'	WSpi
	– 'Prostrata'	NWad WSpi
	– 'Pylewell'	WSpi
	– 'Raket'	NWea SGsty
	– 'Rosmarinifolia'	MRav
	– 'Rotundifolia'	ELan LTop MMuc SEND WSpi
	– 'Silver Beauty' (v)	CBod
	– 'Silver Variegated'	see *B. sempervirens* 'Elegantissima'
	– 'Suffruticosa'	CArg CBrac CKel CSBt CTri ELan EPfP EShb GPoy LSRN LTop MGos MHed MRav MSwo NHol NLar NWea SCob SEND SGol SPer SRiv SRms SWvt WCFE WSpi
	– 'Suffruticosa Variegata' (v)	SRms SWvt
	– 'Twisty'	WFar
	– 'Vardar Valley'	NWad SRiv WSpi
	– 'Variegata' (v)	CBrac CPla MSwo SArc
	– 'Wisley Blue'	LTop WSpi
§	***sinica*** var. ***insularis***	LTop
	– – 'Filigree'	NWad WSpi
	– – 'Justin Brouwers'	LPla SRiv WSpi
	– – 'Tide Hill'	LTop SRiv WFar WSpi
	wallichiana	LTop

C

cabbages see AGM Vegetables Section

Cacalia (*Asteraceae*)

suaveolens	see *Hasteola suaveolens*

Cachrys (*Apiaceae*)

alpina	LEdu SPhx WHil

Caesalpinia (*Fabaceae*)

gilliesii ♀H3	CBcs EBee LRHS SPlb WCot
pulcherrima ♀H3	CCCN
spinosa	SPlb WPav

Caiophora (*Loasaceae*)

coronata	GEdr

calabrese see AGM Vegetables Section

Caladium (*Araceae*)

'Aaron' (v)	SDir
'Candidum' (v)	SDeJ SDir
'Carolyn Whorton'	SDeJ
'Florida Cardinal' (v)	SDeJ
'Frieda Hempel'	SDeJ SDir
'White Christmas' (v)	SDeJ

Calamagrostis (*Poaceae*)

	× ***acutiflora***	XLum
	– 'Avalanche'	CEme CKno EBee EBou ECha ECtt EHyd ELon EPPr EPfP EShb ETod EWes EWoo GQue GWyn LRHS MAsh MAvo NDov NRHS NWsh SGbt SPoG
	– 'Eldorado' (v)	CKno ECha EPPr LRHS MAvo MMuc WCot
	– 'England' (v)	EPPr GBin MNrw
	– 'Karl Foerster' ♀H6	Widely available
	– 'Overdam' (v)	Widely available
	– 'Stricta'	EPPr GMaP
	– 'Waldenbuch'	CKno EPPr SMea
	argentea	see *Stipa calamagrostis*
	arundinacea	CExl CMac SPlb XSen
§	***brachytricha*** ♀H6	Widely available
	– 'Mona'	NDov
	canadensis	SPhx
	emodensis	CMea CSpe EAJP EWoo LRHS MBel NBid SBls WChS WGrn
	epigejos	WPGP
	'Glenorchy Fireworks'	EPPr
	'Kyrgyz Giant'	WPGP
	ophitidis	SPlb
	splendens misapplied	see *Stipa calamagrostis*
	splendens Trin.	LPla
	varia	CKno ELon GBin LPla SMrm

Calamintha (*Lamiaceae*)

	alpina	see *Clinopodium alpinum*
§	***ascendens***	EBee
	clinopodium	see *Clinopodium vulgare*
	cretica	SPhx
§	***grandiflora***	CBod CCBP ECha EGrI GJos GPoy MNHC MNrw MRav NBir NLar NPer SPer SPhx SPlb SRms WCAu WCav XSen
	– 'Elfin Purple'	EBee ELan SBut
	– 'Variegata' (v)	EBee ELan ELon ENfk EPfP SRms WCAu
	'Harrogate'	WGoo
§	***nepeta***	Widely available
	– subsp. ***glandulosa***	SBut
	– – ACL 1050/90	WHoo
	– – 'White Cloud'	CFoA EBee ECtt ELan EPfP MBel MBriF MPie MRav NBir SBut SRms WCAu XSen
	– 'Gottfried Kuehn'	MRav
	– 'Lila Riese' **new**	NDov
	– 'Marvelette Blue' **new**	NLar
§	– subsp. ***nepeta***	ELan ELon EPfP GMaP MHer MMuc MRav NDov SPer WFar WHal XLum
	– – 'Blue Cloud'	CCBP CSpe EBee EBou ECha ECtt EMor EPfP EPri GMaP GWyn MBel MBriF MRav NBir NDov SPhx SPoG SPtp SRms WCAu WFar
	– 'Triumphator'	WGoo
	– 'Weisse Riese'	CMea EBee NDov
	nepetoides	see *C. nepeta* subsp. *nepeta*
	sylvatica	see *Clinopodium menthifolium*
I	– 'Menthe'	LRHS WHil
	vulgaris	see *Clinopodium vulgare*

calamondin see *Citrus* × *microcarpa*

Calandrinia (*Portulacaceae*)

sibirica	see *Claytonia sibirica*
skottsbergii **new**	WAbe
umbellata	EDAr WIce

Calanthe (*Orchidaceae*)

aristulifera	WFar
bicolor	see *C. striata*
Chiseki gx **new**	NLAp
discolor	EBee GKev NLAp SDir
– var. ***flava***	see *C. striata*
discolor × ***hancockii*** **new**	NLAp
Fuji gx **new**	NLAp
hancockii × **Kozu gx** red-flowered **new**	NLAp
hancockii × ***striata***	NLAp
Higo gx	NLAp
Kazusa gx **new**	NLAp

Kozu gx	GKev LEdu NLAp WPGP
light green-flowered **new**	NLAp
reflexa	NLAp SDir
sieboldii	see *C. striata*
§ ***striata***	EBee NLAp SDir
striata* × *yueana **new**	NLAp
Takane gx × ***yueana***	NLAp
tricarinata	NLAp SDir WFar

Calathea (*Marantaceae*)

crocata	see *Goeppertia crocata*
leopardina	see *Goeppertia concinna*
makoyana	see *Goeppertia makoyana*
oppenheimiana	see *Ctenanthe oppenheimiana*
orbiculata	see *Goeppertia truncata*
stromata	see *Ctenanthe burle-marxii*
zebrina	see *Goeppertia zebrina*

Calceolaria (*Calceolariaceae*)

andina	EDAr
arachnoidea	EDAr EWes GEdr SPlb WPav
§ ***biflora***	EDAr EWes GKev LShi
- 'Goldcrest Amber'	SPlb
'Camden Hero'	CBcs EPPr EShb
cavanillesii	SPlb
corymbosa	CTsd EBee GKev
- subsp. ***floccosa***	GKev
falklandica	GKev
filicaulis	EBee GKev
- subsp. ***luxurians***	GKev
fothergillii	WAbe
integrifolia ♀H2	CAbb CBcs CDTJ CExl CFis CTri ECtt ELan MGil MSCN SAdn SPer SPoG SRms
- bronze-flowered	MSCN SPer
- 'Gaines' Yellow'	EPPr
'John Innes'	GKev
'Kentish Hero'	EDAr ELan LShi MGil MHer NHpl SDys WAbe WMal
pavonii	MGil
aff. ***pavonii***	CRHN
perfoliata B&SWJ 14722	WCru
plantaginea	see *C. biflora*
rugosa	see *C. integrifolia*
tenella	NSla WAbe
thyrsiflora **new**	LShi
aff. ***tomentosa*** B&SWJ 14896	WCru
uniflora var. ***darwinii***	GKev NHpl WAbe
'Walter Shrimpton'	WAbe

Caldcluvia (*Cunoniaceae*)

paniculata	IArd

Calendula ✿ (*Asteraceae*)

arvensis	CCCN
'Bronze Beauty'	CSpe
officinalis	CCBP CLau ENfk GPoy LCro LOPS MHer MNHC SRms SVic SWvt WSFF XAbr
- 'Apricot Twist'	LSou
- Fiesta Gitana Group ♀H5	LCro LOPS SCob
- 'Indian Prince' (Prince Series)	LCro LOPS SPhx
PowerDaisy Series	LRHS
- POWERDAISY TANGO ('Kercaltan')	MHol
'Tarifa'	SEND
(Winter Wonders Series) WINTER WONDERS AMBER ARCTIC ('212372D')	LCro LOPS
- WINTER WONDERS BANANA BLIZZARD ('2012357d'PBR)	LCro LOPS
- WINTER WONDERS GOLDEN GLAZE ('2012329d')	LCro LOPS
- WINTER WONDERS PEACH POLAR ('2012391D'PBR)	LCro LOPS

Calibrachoa (*Solanaceae*)

Cabaret Series	SCob
- CABARET BRIGHT RED ('Balcabrite'PBR) ♀H2	MBros
- CABARET DEEP BLUE ('Balcabdebu'PBR)	MBros SCob
- CABARET DEEP YELLOW ('Balcabdepy'PBR)	MBros
- CABARET HOT PINK ('Balcabhopi')	MBros
- CABARET LEMON YELLOW ('Balcablemy') **new**	LSou
- CABARET PURPLE ('Balcabpurp')	LSou
- CABARET WHITE ('Balcabwit')	MBros
(Can-can Series) CAN-CAN BLACK CHERRY	LSou MBros
- CAN-CAN CHERRY BLOSSOM	LSou
- CAN-CAN CORAL REEF ('Balcanoree')	LSou MBros
- CAN-CAN DOUBLE BLUE (d)	MBros
- CAN-CAN DOUBLE DARK YELLOW (d)	MBros
- CAN-CAN DOUBLE PINKMANIA (d) **new**	LSou
- CAN-CAN DOUBLE PROVENCE BLUE (d)	LSou
- CAN-CAN NEON PINK ('Balcaneoni')	LSou
- CAN-CAN SUNLIGHT **new**	LSou
Kabloom Series	MBros
- KABLOOM DEEP PINK ('Pas1020305')	MBros
- KABLOOM WHITE ('Pas1020307')	MBros
SUPERBELLS STRAWBERRY PUNCH ('Uscal58205') (Superbells Series)	MBros
TRIXI EARLY SODA (mixed) **new**	MPri
TRIXI EARLY SUNSET (mixed)	MPri
TRIXI EARLY TRICOLORE (mixed) **new**	MPri
TRIXI HOT PETTICOAT (mixed) (d) **new**	MPri
TRIXI LOLLIPOP (mixed) **new**	MPri
TRIXI SPIRIT (mixed) **new**	MPri

Calla (*Araceae*)

aethiopica	see *Zantedeschia aethiopica*
palustris	CPud CWat EWat LLWG NPer SRms WMAq

Callerya (*Fabaceae*)

§ ***reticulata***	CExl

Calliandra (*Fabaceae*)

'Dixie Pink'	CCCN
portoricensis	CCCN
surinamensis	CCCN SMad

tweediei 🏆H1b	CCCN

Callianthemum (*Ranunculaceae*)

alatavicum new	GKev
anemonoides	GEdr WAbe WCot
coriandrifolium	GEdr
kernerianum	EPot GEdr WAbe

Callicarpa (*Lamiaceae*)

CW&T 6228	CMCN
americana	CExl
- var. ***lactea***	CMCN
bodinieri	CChe EGrI ILea SavN
- var. ***giraldii***	CBrac LMaj MRav NLar SGol
- - 'Profusion' 🏆H6	Widely available
- 'Imperial Pearl'	EPfP LRHS
'Cardinal'	CJun
cathayana	NLar
dichotoma	CBcs CExl NLar
- f. ***albifructa***	NLar
- 'Issai'	EBee EPfP ILea MBlu NLar
formosana NMWJ 14553	WCru
japonica	CExl CMen NLar SBrt
- B&SWJ 12621	WCru
- f. ***albibacca***	NLar
- 'Heavy Berry'	CBod NLar
- 'Koshima-no-homate'	NLar
- 'Leucocarpa'	CBcs CBod CExl CMac EBee ELan EPfP NLar SPer SPoG WGob WLov
- var. ***luxurians*** B&SWJ 8521	WCru
kwangtungensis	CBcs NLar
mollis	CExl
psilocalyx NJM 13.057	WPGP
shikokiana	NLar
× ***shirasawana***	NLar
aff. ***tikusikensis*** B&SWJ 7127	WCru
Van den Broek selection	NLar
yunnanensis	NLar

Callirhoe (*Malvaceae*)

bushii	EBee WSHC
involucrata	CTsd WSHC XLum
- var. ***tenuissima***	EBee

Callisia (*Commelinaceae*)

elegans	EShb
fragrans	EOHP EShb
- 'Melnickoff' (v)	EShb
§ ***navicularis***	SSim
repens	EShb
'Turtle'	CDoC

Callistemon (*Myrtaceae*)

acuminatus	CCCN
brachyandrus	SVen
citrinus	CTri EGrI EPfP SEle SGBe SPlb WGrn
- 'Albus'	see *C. citrinus* 'White Anzac'
- 'Firebrand'	LRHS
- 'Splendens' 🏆H3	Widely available
§ - 'White Anzac'	CBrac CDoC CKel CMac CSBt CSde ELan EMil EPfP LRHS SEND SIvy SPoG
comboynensis	CCCN
* 'Country Park'	CTrC
glaucus	see *C. speciosus*
'Honey Maker' new	CTsd
'Inferno'	CTrC EGrI SPad
laevis hort.	see *C. rugulosus*
linearifolius	LSRN
linearis 🏆H2	CBrac CKel CMac CSde CTrC CTri ELan EPfP LRHS LSRN MGos SCob SEND SIvy SLon SPlb SWvt
macropunctatus	SPlb SVen
'Masotti' PBR	EGrI EHyd SPoG
'Mauve Mist'	CAbb CBod CCCN CDoC ELan EPfP EWTr LRHS SAko SPad SPoG SVen WGrn
pallidus	CBcs CBrac CCCN CDoC CKel CMac CTrC CTsd EGrI EHyd ELan EPfP LRHS MRav NRHS SAko SEND SEle SGBe SIvy SPer SPlb SVen
paludosus	see *C. sieberi* DC.
pearsonii 'Rocky Rambler'	CTrC
'Perth Pink'	CAbb CBcs CBod CCCN CDoC CKel CSBt CSde EGrI ELan EPfP LRHS MPkF SEle SIvy SPad SVen WGrn XSte
pinifolius	SPlb SVen
§ ***pityoides***	CCCN CExl CTsd EGrI ELan EWTr NLar SEle SGBe SIvy SVen
'Red Clusters'	CBcs CBod CBrac CDoC CKel CMac CSde CTrC ELan EPfP LRHS MAsh MMrt SCoo SWvt WFar
rigidus	CBcs CBod CChe CDoC CRos CTri CTsd CWit EHyd ELan EPfP IArd LRHS LSRN MGos MMuc MRav NLar NRHS SAko SCoo SPer SVen SWvt
§ ***rugulosus***	CBrac CCCN CTrC LPar MPri SGbt SVen SWvt
salignus 🏆H2	CBcs CBod CCCN CEme CMac CTrC CTri EPfP MRav NLar SEle SVen
sieberi misapplied	see *C. pityoides*
§ ***sieberi*** DC.	CBcs CDoC CMCN CTsd EBee ELan EPfP LRHS MGil MMuc NLar SPlb
§ ***speciosus***	NLar SEND SPlb
subulatus	SArc SPlb
- 'Crimson Tail'	CTrC MGil MMuc SPtp
viminalis	CCCN SPlb
- 'Captain Cook'	CMac SVen SWvt WFar
- 'Endeavour'	CCCN
- 'Hannah Ray'	WFar
- HOT PINK ('Kkho1' PBR)	CTrC EGrI LRHS MGos SCob SCoo
- 'Little John'	CBcs CBod CBrac CSde SEND SPad SWvt
'Violaceus'	NLar SPlb SVen
viridiflorus	CTrC CTsd SEND SPlb SPtp WGwG
'White Anzac'	see *C. citrinus* 'White Anzac'

Callistephus (*Asteraceae*)

chinensis	SVic

Callitriche (*Plantaginaceae*)

sp.	WSFF
brutia subsp. ***hamulata***	LLWG
§ ***palustris***	CBen CPud
stagnalis	EWat WMAq
verna	see *C. palustris*

Callitris (*Cupressaceae*)

endlicheri	CBrP
rhomboidea	WPav

Callitropsis see *Chamaecyparis*

× ***leylandii***	see × *Cuprocyparis leylandii*
nootkatensis	see *Xanthocyparis nootkatensis*

Calluna ✿ (*Ericaceae*)

vulgaris	NAts
- 'Alba Elongata'	see *C. vulgaris* 'Mair's Variety'

§	– 'Alba Plena' (d)	GPer
§	– 'Alba Rigida'	CFst GPer
	– 'Alex Warwick'	GPer
	– 'Alexandra'PBR (Garden Girls Series)	SCoo SPoG
	– 'Alicia'PBR (Garden Girls Series) 🏆H7	SCoo SPoG
	– 'Allegro'	GPer SCoo
	– 'Alportii'	GPer
	– 'Amethyst'PBR (Garden Girls Series)	SPoG
	– 'Amilto'	CFst SPer
	– 'Anette'PBR (Garden Girls Series)	SCoo
	– 'Angie' (Garden Girls Series)	CFst
	– 'Annegret'	see *C. vulgaris* 'Marlies'
	– 'Annemarie' (d) 🏆H7	CFst GPer SCoo SPlb
	– 'Anne's Goldzwerg'	CFst
	– 'Anne's Zwerg'	CFst
	– 'Arina'	GPer SCoo
	– 'Athene'PBR (Garden Girls Series)	CFst
	– 'Atholl Gold'	CFst
	– 'August Beauty'	GPer
	– 'Baby Ben'	CFst
	– 'Beoley Crimson'	GPer SCoo
	– 'Beoley Gold' 🏆H7	CTri GPer MAsh NHol SCoo
	– 'Beoley Silver'	SCoo
	– 'Blazeaway'	CTri GPer MAsh SCoo
	– 'Bonfire Brilliance'	GPer NHol
	– 'Boskoop'	GPer MAsh NHol
	– 'C.W. Nix'	GPer
	– 'Caerketton White'	GPer
	– 'Con Brio'	GPer SCoo
	– 'Corrie's White'	GJos GPer
	– 'Cottswood Gold'	GJos GPer SCoo
	– 'County Wicklow' (d) 🏆H7	CTri ELan GPer NHol SCoo WTyc
	– 'Cramond' (d)	GPer
	– 'Cuprea'	SCoo
	– 'Dark Beauty'PBR (d) 🏆H7	CBcs CFst ELan GPer LCro LOPS MAsh NHol SCoo WTyc
	– 'Dark Star' (d) 🏆H7	CFst GJos GPer MAsh NHol SCoo
	– 'Darkness' 🏆H7	CBcs CFst CTri GPer SCoo WTyc
	– 'David Hagenaars'	CFst
	– 'Disco Queen'	GPer
	– 'Drum-ra'	GPer
	– 'Dunnet Lime'	SPlb
	– 'Easter-bonfire'	SCoo
	– 'Elsie Purnell' (d) 🏆H7	CFst ELan GPer NHol SCoo SPlb
	– 'Feuerwerk'	SCoo
	– 'Firefly' 🏆H7	CFst GPer NHol SCoo SPer
	– 'Flamingo'	GPer SCoo
	– 'Forest Fire'	CFst
	– 'Foxii Nana'	NHol
	– 'Fred J. Chapple'	GPer
	– 'Galaxy'PBR	CFst
	– 'Glenfiddich'	GPer
	– 'Gold Flame'	GPer
	– 'Gold Haze'	CTri MAsh NHol SCoo
	– 'Gold Knight'	SCoo
	– 'Golden Angie' (Garden Girls Series)	CFst
	– 'Golden Carpet'	GJos GPer MAsh NHol
	– 'Grey Carpet'	CFst
	– 'Guinea Gold'	GPer
§	– 'H.E. Beale' (d)	CTri GPer MAsh NHol SCoo
	– 'Hammondii Aureifolia'	GPer SPlb
	– 'Hannover'	CFst
	– 'Highland Rose'	SPlb
	– 'Hilda'PBR (Garden Girls Series)	CFst
§	– 'Hugh Nicholson'	GPer
	– 'J.H. Hamilton' (d)	CTri ELan GPer MAsh NHol SCoo
	– 'Jan Dekker'	GPer
	– 'Jana' (d)	CFst
	– 'Johnson's Variety'	SCoo
	– 'Joy Vanstone'	GJos GPer
	– 'Kerstin' 🏆H7	CFst GPer NHol SCoo SPer SPlb
	– 'Kinlochruel' (d) 🏆H7	CBcs CFst CTri GJos GPer MAsh NHol SPlb WTyc
	– 'Kiran'	CFst
	– 'Kirby White'	MAsh SPlb
	– 'Klaudine'PBR (Garden Girls Series)	CFst
	– 'Leslie Slinger'	SCoo
	– 'Loch Turret'	GPer
§	– 'Mair's Variety'	GPer SCoo
§	– 'Marlies'	MNHC
	– 'Melanie' (Garden Girls Series)	NHol SCoo
	– 'Mrs Pat'	MAsh
	– 'Multicolor'	MAsh NHol
§	– 'My Dream' (d)	SCoo
	– 'Nana Compacta'	GPer
	– 'Orange Max'	GPer
	– 'Peter Sparkes' (d) 🏆H7	CBcs CFst GPer MAsh NHol SCoo
	– 'Pink Beale'	see *C. vulgaris* 'H.E. Beale'
	– 'Purple Passion'	SCoo
	– 'Radnor' (d)	GPer
	– 'Ralph Purnell'	ELan SCoo
	– 'Red Beauty'	CBcs CFst SPer
	– 'Red Favorit' (d)	CFst GJos GPer
	– 'Red Fred'	SCoo
	– 'Red Haze'	GPer NHol SCoo
	– 'Red Pimpernel'	ELan SCoo
	– 'Red Star' (d)	NHol
	– 'Robert Chapman' 🏆H7	CFst CTri MAsh NHol
	– 'Rosalind, Underwood's'	NHol
	– 'Rosita'PBR (Garden Girls Series)	CFst
	– 'Ruby Slinger'	NHol
	– 'Ruth Sparkes' (d)	NHol
	– 'Salmon Leap'	GPer
	– 'Sandy'PBR (Garden Girls Series)	SPoG
	– 'Silvana'PBR (Garden Girls Series)	CFst
	– 'Silver Fox'	CBcs CFst
	– 'Silver Knight'	ELan GJos GPer MAsh NHol SCoo SPlb
	– 'Silver Queen' 🏆H7	GPer MAsh NHol
	– 'Sir John Charrington'	GPer NHol
	– 'Sister Anne' 🏆H7	GPer SCoo
	– 'Snowball'	see *C. vulgaris* 'My Dream'
	– 'Spitfire'	GPer
	– 'Spring Cream' 🏆H7	GPer MAsh NHol SCoo
	– 'Spring Torch'	GPer MAsh NHol SCoo
	– 'Stefanie'	MNHC
	– 'Strawberry Delight' (d)	SCoo
	– 'Summer Orange'	GJos GPer
	– 'Sun Sprinkles'	CFst
	– 'Sunset'	GJos GPer
	– 'Tib' (d) 🏆H7	GPer MAsh SPer WTyc
	– 'Tricolorifolia'	SCoo
	– 'Velvet Fascination' 🏆H7	GPer SCoo
	– 'White Coral' (d) 🏆H7	ELan SCoo
	– 'White Lawn'	CFst GPer NHol
	– 'Wickwar Flame' 🏆H7	CBcs CFst ELan GPer MAsh NHol SCoo SPlb
	– 'Winter Chocolate'	MAsh NHol SCoo
	– 'Yellow Beauty'PBR	CFst
	– 'Yvette's Gold'	CFst

Calocedrus (*Cupressaceae*)

§ ***decurrens*** 🏆H7	CAco CBcs CLnd EPfP IPap LPar MBlu MGil NWea SPtp WTSh
- 'Aureovariegata' (v) 🏆H7	CAco CBcs LPar
- 'Berrima Gold' 🏆H7	CAco NLar
- 'Columnaris'	CAco
§ - 'Depressa'	CKen
- 'Maupin Glow' (v)	CAco NLar SLim
- 'Nana'	see *C. decurrens* 'Depressa'
- 'Pillar'	CKen NLar

Calocephalus (*Asteraceae*)

brownii	see *Leucophyta brownii*

Calochortus (*Liliaceae*)

'Cupido'PBR	CExl EPot GKev NRog SDeJ
luteus 'Golden Orb'PBR	CExl NRog SDeJ
splendens 'Violet Queen'	NRog SDeJ
superbus	NRog SDeJ
'Symphony'PBR	CExl SDeJ
venustus	NRog SDeJ
- 'Burgundy'	SDeJ

Calomeria (*Asteraceae*)

§ ***amaranthoides***	WJek

Calonyction see *Ipomoea*

Calopogon (*Orchidaceae*)

tuberosus	NLAp
- f. ***albiflorus***	NLAp

Caloscordum see *Allium*

Calothamnus (*Myrtaceae*)

quadrifidus	XSte
validus	SPlb
villosus	SPlb

Calpurnia (*Fabaceae*)

aurea	SPlb

Caltha (*Ranunculaceae*)

howellii	see *C. leptosepala* subsp. *howellii*
laeta	see *C. palustris* var. *palustris*
leptosepala	EBee GArf GEdr GKev GMaP LLWG NLar
- SDR 8134	GKev
§ - subsp. ***howellii*** NNS 07-87	GKev
natans	LLWG
palustris	Widely available
- var. ***alba***	Widely available
- 'Auengold'	LLWG
- 'Auenwald'	LLWG
- var. ***barthei***	GEdr
- 'Bronze Age' **new**	CDor
- 'Flore Pleno' (d) 🏆H7	CBen CEme CMac CMea CTtf EBee ECha ELan EWat GAbr GKin GMaP MMuc MRav NBir NChi NFav NGdn NHol NLar NPer NRya SEND SPer SPlb SRms WFar WPnP XLum
- 'Himalayan Snow'	EBee LLWG WFar
- 'Honeydew'	CDor ELon LLWG MNrw WCot WSHC
- var. ***laeta***	LLWG
- 'Marilyn'	LLWG
- 'Multiplex' (d)	CDor ECtt EMor
- Newlake hybrid	LLWG
§ - var. ***palustris***	CBen ECha LLWG WWtn
- - 'Plena' (d)	CPud CRos CWat EHyd EWat LRHS MTin NRHS
- var. ***radicans***	EWat GEdr
- - 'Flore Pleno' (d)	WWtn
- 'Stagnalis'	MWts
polypetala Hochst.	CDor CPud CWat MSCN NPer SMad
ex Lorent	WMAq
sagittata	GEdr WSHC
scaposa	GKev

Calycanthus (*Calycanthaceae*)

'Aphrodite'	CBcs CJun CMCN EHed ELan EPfP LPar LRHS MGos MTrO SHor WMat
chinensis	CBcs CCCN CJun CMCN EBee EGrI EHed EHyd EPfP IDee LRHS MBlu MGil MPkF NLar SPtp
floridus	CAgr CBcs CBod CEme CJun CMCN CTsd CWit EBee EHyd EPfP GKev LEdu MBNS MBlu MGil MMuc NLar SEND SGsty SIvy SPad SPer SPlb SPoG SWvt SavN WFar WLov
- 'Athens'	CJun NLar WPGP
- var. ***glaucus*** 'Purpureus'	CJun EGrI MBlu NLar
- 'Michael Lindsay'	CJun NLar WPGP
mohrii	NLar
occidentalis	CBcs CMCN CPla MAsh MBlu MGil SBrt
× ***raulstonii*** 'Hartlage Wine' 🏆H5	CBcs CDoC CJun CMCN CRos EGrI EHed EHyd ELan ELon EPfP GKin IArd IDee LCro LOPS LPar LRHS LSRN MAsh MBlu MGos MPkF NLar SCoo SMad SPoG SavN WKif XSte
'Venus'	CBcs CJun CMCN EHed ELan ELon EPfP IDee LCro LOPS LPar LRHS MAsh MBlu MPkF NLar SHor SavN XSte
'White Dress' **new**	NLar

Calystegia (*Convolvulaceae*)

§ ***hederacea*** 'Flore Pleno' (d)	SMad
soldanella	CPla
- NNS 99-85	WCot

Calytrix (*Myrtaceae*)

tetragona	SPlb

Camassia ✿ (*Asparagaceae*)

'Blue Candle'	CAvo EPfP EPot NHsp SPhx
'Blue Heaven'	CAvo CMea CRos ELan EPfP ERCP GKev LRHS LSun NHsp NLar NRHS NRog SDeJ SPhx
Broadleigh Belle Group	CBro
cusickii	CBro CExl CRos CTri CWCL EBee ECtt EGrI EHyd ELan EPfP EPot ERCP EWhm GKev LCro LOPS LRHS MACG MCot MPtr NBir NLar NRHS NRog SCoo SDeJ SDix WPnP
- 'Crystal Star'	NHsp NRog
- 'Zwanenburg'	CRos EHyd ERCP GKev IPot LRHS NHpl NHsp NRHS NRog WCot
esculenta Lindl.	see *C. quamash*
leichtlinii misapplied	see *C. leichtlinii* subsp. *suksdorfii*
leichtlinii (Baker) S.Watson	see *C. leichtlinii* subsp. *leichtlinii*
'Alba' misapplied	
* - 'Alba Plena'	LSun MHol MNrw MPtr NBir NHpl
- Avon's Stellar Group	CAvo
- 'Blue Wave'	NHsp NWad
- 'Harlequin' (v)	NHsp
§ - subsp. ***leichtlinii***	Widely available
- 'Magdalen'	MAvo

– pale pink-flowered	GKev NHsp
– 'Plena' (d)	ECha
– 'Sacajawea' (v)	CAvo CBor CMea CRos CTtf ECha EHyd EPfP ERCP GKev GPSL LRHS MAvo NHsp NRHS NRog SDeJ WCot WFar WTor
– 'Semiplena' (d)	CAvo CBro CRos CTtf EBee ECtt EHyd EPfP EPot ERCP GKev IPot LRHS MBel MBriF MNrw NRHS NRog NSti SPhx WBor WCot WPnP WShi
§ – subsp. ***suksdorfii***	EGrI LCro LOPS MBriF NPoe WCot
– – 'Alba'	CAvo CBod CRos EGrI EHyd EPot EWoo GBin GMaP LCro LOPS LRHS NRHS NSti SCob SEdd SPtp WBor
§ – – 'Blauwe Donau'	ILea
– – Caerulea Group	Widely available
– – – 'Maybelle'	CAvo CMea ERCP LRHS MBriF MPri NHsp
– – 'Electra'	CAvo CMea ECha MAvo WCot
– – 'Lady Eve Price'	MAvo WCot
§ ***quamash***	Widely available
– 'Blue Melody' (v)	CMea CRos EBee EHyd EPot ERCP GMaP LEdu LRHS NHsp NRHS NRog SDeJ
– 'Orion'	CRos EBee EHyd ERCP GKev LEdu LRHS NHsp NRHS NRog WCot
– var. ***quamash***	CBcs MHol

Camellia ✿ (*Theaceae*)

'Admiral Spry' **new**	CSgt
'Adorable' (*pitardii* hybrid)	LRHS LSRN XSte
'April Blush'	WFar
'Autumn Jewel' **new**	XSte
azalea	SavN
'Baby Bear'	XSte
'Barbara Clark' (*reticulata* × *saluenensis*)	CSgt MAsh NRHS SRot
'Black Lace' ♀H5	CBod CDoC CSgt CTrh CTri EGrI EPfP LCro LMaj LMil LOPS LPar LRHS LSRN MAsh MPri NRHS SArc SGol SGsty SRot SWeb SWvt XSte
'Blissful Dawn'	CTrh
'Bonnie Marie'	CBcs SCam
'Canterbury'	EGrI LRHS SCam XSte
'Christmas Daffodil' (*japonica* hybrid)	CBcs LRHS XSte
'Cinnamon Cindy'	LRHS SCam SRot XSte
'Cinnamon Scentsation'	LRHS XSte
'Congratulations'	CSBt LSRN
'Contessa Lavinia Maggi'	see *C. japonica* 'Lavinia Maggi'
'Cornish Snow' (*cuspidata* × *saluenensis*) ♀H4	CDoC CEnd CMac CTri CTsd SRot SWvt WFar
'Cornish Spring' (*cuspidata* × *japonica*) ♀H4	CBcs CCCN CDoC CSBt CSgt CTrh EGrI MAsh NRHS SCam
'Crimson Candles' ♀H5	LRHS XSte
'Debut' (*japonica* × *reticulata*)	XSte
'Delia Williams'	see *C.* × *williamsii* 'Citation'
'Den Burton' (*japonica* × *reticulata*)	XSte
'Diamond Head' (*japonica* × *reticulata*)	CBcs LSRN
'Doctor Clifford Parks' (*japonica* × *reticulata*) ♀H4	XSte
'Donckelaeri'	see *C. japonica* 'Masayoshi'
edithae	XSte
'Extravaganza' (*japonica* hybrid) ♀H5	CTrh IArd SCoo
'Fairy Blush'	LRHS MGos XSte
'Fairy Wand'	LRHS XSte
'Fascination'	SWvt
'Felice Harris' (*reticulata* × *sasanqua*)	SCoo
'Fiesta Grande'	XSte
forrestii	GKev WPGP
'Forty-niner' (*japonica* × *reticulata*)	CBcs CSgt LRHS NRHS
'Fragrant Pink'	SCam
'Francie L' ♀H4	CMac XSte
fraterna	CBcs
'Frau Minna Seidel'	see *C. japonica* subsp. *rusticana* 'Otome'
'Free Spirit'	CTrh
'Freedom Bell' ♀H5	CDoC CSgt CTrh EGrI EPfP GKin MPri NRHS SCam SCob SGol XSte
'Frosted Star'	LRHS XSte
'Gay Baby'	CDoC LRHS XSte
'Golden Anniversary'	see *C. japonica* 'Dahlohnega'
grijsii	CBcs CExl CTrh XSte
handelii	CExl
'Happy Anniversary'	CSBt LSRN SWvt
§ ***hiemalis*** 'Bonanza'	CTrh LRHS XSte
– 'Chansonette'	CDoC CSgt LRHS SCam
§ – 'Dazzler'	CBcs NRHS SCam SRot
– 'Elfin Rose'	LRHS
– 'Kanjirō'	MHtn SCam SRot SWeb
I – 'Maiden's Blush' **new**	SRot
– 'Shishigashira'	CTrh
– 'Shōwa-no-sakae'	LRHS MHtn XSte
'High Fragrance'	LRHS XSte
'Hooker'	CSgt NRHS
'Imbricata Rubra'	see *C. japonica* 'Imbricata'
'Innovation'	CDoC CSgt LRHS
'Inspiration' (*reticulata* × *saluenensis*) ♀H5	CBcs CDoC CMac CSgt CTrh EPfP LRHS LSRN MGos NLar SCam XSte
japonica	LMaj SEWo SPre
– 'Aaron's Ruby'	ELon NRHS
– 'Ace of Hearts'	SCoo
– 'ACS Jubilee'	LRHS XSte
– 'Ada Pieper'	CTrh
– 'Adelina Patti' ♀H5	CDoC CTrh SCam
– 'Adeyaka'	CSgt LRHS NRHS SGol
– 'Adolphe Audusson' ♀H5	Widely available
§ – 'Akashigata' ♀H5	CBcs ELon EPfP LSRN NRHS SCam
– 'Alba Plena' (d) ♀H5	CBod CSBt CTrh LRHS SCob SWvt WFar XSte
– 'Alba Simplex'	CMac CTrh ELan EPfP LMaj MPri SSta
§ – 'Albertii'	XSte
– 'Alexander Hunter' ♀H5	NRHS
§ – 'Althaeiflora'	ELon NRHS SCam
– 'Anemoniflora'	CBcs EPfP NRHS
– 'Angel'	LSRN
– 'Angela Cocchi'	LPar
– 'Angello'	NRHS
– 'Annie Wylam' ♀H5	CBcs CTrh LRHS SCoo
– 'Apollo' ambig.	CBcs LRHS NRHS
§ – 'Apollo' Paul, 1911	MSwo SCam
§ – 'Apple Blossom'	CSgt NRHS
– 'April Blush'	CSgt
– 'April Kiss'	CSgt
– 'April Remembered'	CSgt WFar
– 'April Rose'	CSgt WFar
– 'April Tryst' **new**	EGrI
– 'Arajishi' misapplied	see *C. japonica* subsp. *rusticana* 'Beni-arajishi'
– 'Augustine Supreme'	CMac
– 'Australis' ♀H5	LPar
– 'Ave Maria' ♀H5	CTrh LMaj MGos NRHS XSte
– 'Baby Pearl'	LSRN SCam

	Cultivar	Suppliers
	- 'Baby Sis'	NRHS
	- 'Baby Sis Pink' **new**	XSte
	- 'Ballet Dancer' ♀H5	LSRN SCam
	- 'Baron Gomer'	see *C. japonica* 'Comte de Gomer'
	- 'Baronne Leguay'	SCam
	- 'Beau Harp'	NRHS
	- 'Bella Romana'	SCam XSte
	- 'Berenice Boddy' ♀H5	CTrh LRHS NRHS
	- 'Betty Foy Sanders'	CTrh LRHS
	- 'Betty Robinson'	NRHS
	- 'Betty Sheffield'	LRHS NRHS
	- 'Betty Sheffield Pink'	LMil NRHS SCam
	- 'Betty Sheffield Supreme'	CBcs
	- 'Betty's Beauty'	XSte
	- 'Billie McCaskill'	SCam
	- 'Binda' **new**	CSgt
	- 'Black Magic'	CDoC CSgt CTrh LRHS MAsh NRHS
	- 'Black Tie'	CDoC CEnd CTrh ELon LRHS MGos NRHS SCam WFar
	- 'Blackburnia'	see *C. japonica* 'Althaeiflora'
§	- 'Blood of China'	CBcs CSBt LRHS LSRN MGos NLar NRHS SCam SCoo SEdd SGol SWvt
	- 'Blush Tinsie'	NRHS
	- 'Bob Hope' ♀H5	CBcs CDoC CTrh CTri NRHS SCam
	- 'Bob's Tinsie' ♀H5	CSBt ELon EPfP LSRN MGos NRHS SPoG XSte
§	- 'Bokuhan' ♀H5	SCam XSte
	- 'Bonomiana'	EGrI LRHS SGol SGsty
	- 'Bright Buoy'	NRHS
	- 'Brushfield's Yellow'	CBcs CBod CDoC CRos CSBt CSgt CTrh CTsd EGrI ELan ELon EPfP IArd LRHS LSRN MAsh MGos NLar NRHS SCam SCoo SGol SPer SRot SSta
	- 'Bush Hill Beauty'	see *C. japonica* 'Lady de Saumarez'
§	- 'C.M. Hovey' ♀H5	CMac CSgt NRHS
	- 'C.M. Wilson'	CMac
	- 'Campari' **new**	XSte
	- 'Campsii Alba'	EGrI SCam SCoo
	- 'Can Can'	CDoC ELon
	- 'Candy Apple'	CBcs
	- 'Cara Mia'	NRHS SCam SCoo
	- 'Carolyn Tuttle'	CSgt NRHS
	- 'Carter's Sunburst' ♀H5	ELon
	- 'Chandleri Elegans'	see *C. japonica* 'Elegans'
	- 'Charlotte de Rothschild'	CTrh CTri
	- 'Cinderella'	NRHS
	- CLASSIQUE ('Kerguelen'PBR) (v)	LRHS SRot WFar XSte
	- 'Colonel Firey'	see *C. japonica* 'C.M. Hovey'
	- 'Commander Mulroy' ♀H5	SCoo
	- 'Compacta Alba' **new**	LPar
§	- 'Comte de Gomer'	ELon EPfP LPar MPri NRHS SCam SGol
	- 'Conspicua'	CBcs
§	- 'Coquettii' ♀H5	CSgt LRHS MAsh NRHS XSte
	- 'Curly Lady'PBR	MPri WFar
§	- 'Dahlohnega'	CBcs CBod CRos CSBt CTrh ELon EPfP LMil LRHS LSRN MGos NRHS SEdd SGol WFar XSte
	- 'Daitairin'	see *C. japonica* 'Dewatairin'
	- 'Daphne du Maurier'	CDoC CSgt NRHS
	- 'Dark of the Moon'	NRHS
	- 'Dear Jenny'	CBcs CSgt
	- 'Debutante'	CBcs CMac ELon LMaj SCam SGsty
	- 'Desire' ♀H5	CBcs CBod CDoC CEnd CSBt CSgt CTrh EPfP LCro LMil LOPS LRHS LSRN MAsh MGos NRHS SCam SGol SPoG SRot WFar XSte
	- 'Devonia'	CBcs
§	- 'Dewatairin' (Higo)	CBcs SCam XSte
	- 'Diddy's Pink Organdie'	NRHS
	- 'Dixie Knight'	NRHS SCam
	- 'Dobreei'	CMac
	- 'Doctor Burnside'	CBcs CTrh LPar SCam SGsty SWeb
	- 'Doctor King'	CDoC CEnd CSgt EPfP LMil LRHS MAsh MPri NRHS SCob SCoo SEdd SGol SPoG WFar
	- 'Doctor Tinsley' ♀H5	CDoC CRos CSgt EPfP LRHS MAsh MPri NRHS SCam SWeb
	- 'Dona Herzilia de Freitas Magalhães'	CBcs
	- 'Donckelaeri'	see *C. japonica* 'Masayoshi'
	- 'Donnan's Dream'	CTrh
	- 'Drama Girl' ♀H5	CBcs NRHS SCam
	- 'Duchesse Decazes'	CBcs
	- 'Edelweiss'	SCam
§	- 'Elegans'	CBcs CPla CSgt EGrI ELon EPfP LCro LMil LOPS LPar LRHS MGos NRHS SCam SGol SLim SPer SPoG SRot SWvt
	- 'Elegans Champagne'	CSgt
	- 'Elegans Supreme'	CSgt
	- 'Elisabeth'	LRHS NRHS
	- 'Elizabeth Cooper'	CTrh LSRN
	- 'Elizabeth Hawkins'	CSgt CTrh LRHS NRHS
	- 'Elizabeth Weaver'	CTrh
	- 'Emmett Pfingstl'	SCam
	- 'Emperor of Russia'	CBcs NRHS
	- 'Eric Baker'	SCam
	- 'Eugène Lizé'	SCam
	- 'Eximia'	NRHS
	- 'Faith'	CBcs CSgt
	- 'Fanny'	MHtn
§	- 'Faustina'	NRHS
	- 'Fimbriata'	XSte
	- 'Finlandia Variegated' (v)	ELon SCam
	- 'Firebird'	CBcs CTsd
	- 'Flashlight'	EPfP NRHS
§	- 'Fleur Dipater'	CRos LRHS NRHS SCam XSte
	- 'Flowerwood'	SGsty
	- 'Forest Green'	SRot
	- 'Frans van Damme'	CBcs
	- 'Fred Sander'	NRHS
§	- 'Gigantea'	ELon NRHS
	- 'Giuditta Rosani'	CDoC NRHS
	- 'Glen 40'	see *C. japonica* 'Coquettii'
	- 'Gloire de Nantes' ♀H5	CTrh EGrI XSte
	- 'Gold Tone'	ELon SCam
	- 'Goshozakura'	XSte
	- 'Grace Albritton' (d)	XSte
	- 'Grace Bunton'	CBcs ELon
	- 'Grand Prix' ♀H5	ELon LSRN NLar SWeb
	- 'Grand Slam' ♀H5	CBcs SCam
	- 'Grandiflora Alba'	CBcs
	- 'Guest of Honor'	EGrI NRHS
	- 'Guilio Nuccio' ♀H5	CBcs CTri ELon LSRN MPri NRHS SCam SLim SWeb
	- 'Gus Menard'	SCam
	- 'H.A. Downing'	SCam
§	- 'Hagoromo' ♀H5	CBcs CSBt CTrh LMaj LPar NRHS SWeb XSte
§	- 'Hakurakuten' ♀H5	CTrh CTri SCam SCoo SRot
	- 'Hanafūki'	NRHS SCam
	- 'Happy Birthday'	EGrI LSRN
	- 'Happy Higo'	SCam
	- 'Haru-no-utena'	CTrh
	- 'Hatsuzakura'	see *C. japonica* 'Dewatairin'
	- 'Hawaii'	CMac CSBt CTrh ELon NRHS SCam
	- 'High Hat'	CBcs
§	- 'Hikarugenji'	NRHS
	- 'Hinomaru'	CMac

	- 'Holly Bright'	CTrh LRHS XSte
	- 'Honeyglow'	XSte
§	- 'Imbricata'	CTrh LRHS MAsh NRHS SGol
	- 'In the Pink'	CSgt
	- 'Italiana Vera'	CDoC CSgt LRHS MAsh NRHS
	- 'J.J. Whitfield'	CMac
	- 'Janet Waterhouse'	CBcs LRHS XSte
§	- 'Japonica Variegata' (v)	NRHS
	- 'Jiuqu' **new**	LMaj
	- 'Joseph Pfingstl' ♀H5	CSgt CTri EPfP LRHS NLar NRHS SCam
	- 'Jovey Carlyon'	CBcs CDoC CSgt MAsh NRHS
	- 'Joy Sander'	see *C. japonica* 'Apple Blossom'
	- 'Juno'	NRHS
	- 'Jupiter' Paul, 1904 ♀H5	CMac CSgt CTri EGrI EPfP LRHS LSRN SCam
	- 'Kenny'	CBcs
	- 'Kentucky'	LRHS NRHS
	- 'Kick-off'	CSgt CTrh LRHS SCam
	- 'Kimberley'	CBcs CTsd EGrI LSRN SCam SGol SRot
	- 'King Size'	CDoC
	- 'King's Ransom'	CSgt LRHS NRHS
	- 'Kingyoba-shiro-wabisuke'	SCam
	- 'Kingyo-tsubaki'	LPar SCam SSta
	- 'Kitty Berry'	CTrh
	- 'Kokinran'	SCam
§	- 'Konronkoku' ♀H5	CSgt LRHS NRHS
	- 'Kouron-jura'	see *C. japonica* 'Konronkoku'
	- 'Kramer's Beauty'	CBcs
	- 'Kramer's Supreme' ♀H5	CBod CCCN CDoC CSgt ELon LSRN MGos NRHS SCam SCob SCoo SGol XSte
§	- 'Kumasaka'	CDoC CSgt CTri LRHS NRHS
	- 'L.T. Dees' (d)	XSte
	- 'La Pace Rubra'	SCam
	- 'Lady Campbell'	CBod CTri EGrI EPfP LPar LRHS MPri SCam SCoo SGol WFar
	- 'Lady Clare'	see *C. japonica* 'Akashigata'
§	- 'Lady de Saumarez'	CBcs CMac CSgt CTsd
	- 'Lady Loch'	CTrh
	- 'Lady Marion'	see *C. japonica* 'Kumasaka'
	- 'Lady McCulloch'	NRHS
	- 'Lady Vansittart'	CBod CDoC CRos CSgt CTrh EPfP LCro LMil LOPS LRHS LSRN MAsh MGos NRHS SCam SCob SGol SLim SPoG SSta XSte
§	- 'Lady Vansittart Pink'	CMac
	- 'Lady Vansittart Red'	see *C. japonica* 'Lady Vansittart Pink'
	- 'Lady Vansittart Shell'	see *C. japonica* 'Yours Truly'
	- 'Latifolia'	SCam
	- 'Laurie Bray'	SCoo SGsty SRot SWeb
§	- 'Lavinia Maggi' ♀H5	CBcs CDoC CSgt CTri EPfP LMaj LRHS LSRN MGos MPri NRHS SCam SCob SCoo SGol SPoG SRms SSta XSte
	- 'Lavinia Maggi Rosea'	LMaj XSte
	- 'Lemon Drop'	CBcs CTrh
	- 'Lily Pons'	CTrh
	- 'Lipstick'	LRHS XSte
	- 'Little Bit'	ELon SSta
	- 'Little Man'	NRHS
	- 'Lovelight' ♀H5	CTrh NRHS
	- 'Ludgvan Red'	NRHS
	- 'Lulu Belle'	CBcs
	- 'Mabel Blackwell'	SCam
	- 'Madame de Strekaloff'	CMac CSBt SCam
	- 'Madame Lourmand'	XSte
	- 'Madge Miller'	NRHS
	- 'Magnoliiflora'	see *C. japonica* 'Hagoromo'
	- 'Maiden's Blush'	CMac
	- 'Manuroa Road'	XSte
	- 'Margaret Davis' ♀H5	CBod CCCN CDoC CPla CRos CSBt CSgt CTrh ELan ELon EPfP LCro LOPS LRHS LSRN MAsh MGos NRHS SCam SCoo SGol SLim WFar XSte
	- 'Margaret Davis Picotee'	CBcs SPer
	- 'Margaret Rose'	SCam
	- 'Margaret Wells' **new**	LMaj
	- 'Margherita Coleoni'	CBcs XSte
	- 'Marian Mitchell'	SCam
	- 'Mariana'	ELon
	- 'Marie Bracey'	SGol
	- 'Mariottii Rubra'	CMac
	- 'Marjorie Magnificent'	CSgt MAsh
	- 'Mark Alan'	LSRN SCam
	- 'Maroon and Gold'	NRHS
	- 'Mars' ♀H5	SCam
	- 'Marshmallow'	LRHS XSte
	- 'Mary Costa'	CBcs CTrh SCam
	- 'Mary J. Wheeler'	LSRN
§	- 'Masayoshi' ♀H5	CSBt CSgt NRHS XSte
	- 'Mathotiana Alba'	CBcs CMac CTri EPfP LSRN MGos SCam WSpi
§	- 'Mathotiana Rosea'	CBcs CMac NLar
	- 'Mathotiana Supreme'	SCam
	- 'Matilija Poppy'	SCam
	- 'Matterhorn'	CTrh
	- 'Mercury' ♀H5	CMac EPfP
	- 'Mermaid'	NRHS
	- 'Midnight'	CBcs CDoC CSgt CTsd EGrI LRHS NRHS
	- 'Midnight Magic'	CBcs CSgt CTrh CTri LRHS NRHS
	- 'Midnight Serenade'	NRHS
	- 'Midnight Variegated' (v)	LRHS XSte
§	- 'Mikenjaku'	CSgt EPfP LRHS MAsh NRHS SGol SRot
	- 'Mikuni-no-homare' (Higo) **new**	XSte
	- 'Miriam Stevenson'	SCam
	- 'Miss Charleston'	CBcs
	- 'Monte Carlo'	SCam
	- 'Montironi' **new**	XSte
	- 'Moshe Dayan'	CDoC CSgt CTsd LMil LRHS MAsh NRHS
§	- 'Mrs Bertha A. Harms'	NRHS
	- 'Mrs D.W. Davis'	CBcs EPfP
	- 'Mrs Tingley' (d)	SGol
	- 'Mrs William Thompson'	NRHS SCam
	- 'Nagasaki'	see *C. japonica* 'Mikenjaku'
	- 'Nancy Bird'	SCam
	- 'Nigra'	see *C. japonica* 'Konronkoku'
	- 'Nina Avery'	SCam
	- 'Nobilissima' ♀H5	CBcs CBod CMac CSgt CTrh CTri LCro LMil LOPS MBlu SCam SCob SGol SPer SPoG SRot WFar XSte
	- 'Nuccio's Cameo' ♀H5	CBcs CDoC CSgt CTrh EPfP LRHS MAsh MPri NRHS SCob
	- 'Nuccio's Gem' ♀H5	CDoC CSgt LCro LOPS LPar LRHS NRHS SGol SGsty SWeb XSte
	- 'Nuccio's Jewel' ♀H5	CBcs CDoC CSBt CSgt EPfP LMaj LMil LPar LRHS LSRN MAsh NRHS SCam SGol SWeb XSte
	- 'Nuccio's Pearl' ♀H5	CBod CEnd EPfP LPar LRHS LSRN MPri NRHS SArc SRot SWeb XSte
	- 'Nuccio's Pink Lace'	CBcs CDoC CSgt CTri LRHS NRHS
§	- 'Odoratissima'	SGol
	- 'Okan' (Higo)	XSte
	- 'Oki-no-nami'	LPar
	- 'Onetia Holland'	LSRN SCam SLim SRot WFar
	- 'Oo-La-La'	CTrh LRHS

- 'Optima'	ELon NRHS SCam
- 'Orandakō'	SCob
- 'Paulette Goddard'	SCam
- 'Paul's Apollo'	see *C. japonica* 'Apollo' Paul, 1911
- 'Peachblossom'	see *C. japonica* 'Fleur Dipater'
- 'Pearl Harbor'	SCam
- 'Pearl Maxwell'	EGrI
- 'Pensacola Red'	CDoC
- 'Pink Chiffon'	NRHS
- 'Pink Clouds'	CBcs
- 'Pink Perfection'	see *C. japonica* subsp. *rusticana* 'Ōtome'
- 'Pope John Paul XXIII'	SCam
- 'Powder Puff'	LRHS
- 'Primavera'	CTrh LRHS SCam
- 'Prince Albert'	see *C. japonica* 'Albertii'
- 'Prince Murat'	NRHS
- 'Princess Baciocchi'	ELan SCam
- 'Princess du Mahe'	CMac
- 'R.L. Wheeler' ♀H5	CBcs CDoC CSBt CSgt CTri EPfP LPar LRHS MGos MPri NRHS SCam SCoo SGol SRot
- 'Red Dandy'	SCam
- 'Red Red Rose'	NRHS XSte
- 'Robert Lasson'	XSte
- 'Roger Hall'	CBcs CDoC CSgt CTrh LRHS LSRN NRHS SGol SPoG
- 'Rōgetsu'	CBcs
- 'Rosularis'	ELon
- 'Royal Velvet'	CTrh
- 'Rubens' **new**	MAsh
- 'Rubescens Major'	CBcs
- 'Ruddigore'	CTrh
- subsp. ***rusticana*** 'Arajishi' misapplied	see *C. japonica* subsp. *rusticana* 'Beni-arajishi'
- - 'Arajishi' Ko'emon	SCam
§ - - 'Beni-arajishi'	CBcs CSgt NRHS
- - 'Botanyuki'	XSte
§ - - 'Ōtome'	SCam SGsty
- 'Sabiniana'	NRHS XSte
- 'Sacco Nova'	LPar XSte
- 'Saint André'	CMac CSgt LRHS MAsh NRHS
- 'San Dimas' ♀H5	CDoC CTrh NRHS SCam SWeb XSte
- 'Sanpei-tsubaki'	XSte
- 'Sarah Frost'	LPar
- 'Satsuma' **new**	XSte
- 'Saturnia'	CDoC CRos CSgt ELon LMil LRHS NRHS
- 'Scentsation' ♀H5	CTri LRHS NRHS
- 'Sea Foam'	NRHS SCam
- 'Sea Gull'	SCam
- 'Shikibu'	CTrh SCam XSte
- 'Shiro Chan'	ELon SCam
- 'Shirobotan'	ELon NRHS SCam
- 'Shūgetsu'	LRHS
- 'Silver Anniversary' ♀H5	CBcs CBod CDoC CEnd CRos CSBt CTri ELon EPfP LCro LMil LOPS LRHS LSRN MAsh MGos MHtn MPri NLar NRHS SCob SCoo SEdd SGol SLim SPoG SRot SWvt WFar
- 'Silver Chalice'	CSgt
- 'Silver Ruffles'	CTrh ELon NRHS SCam
- 'Silver Waves'	XSte
- 'Snowball' **new**	LMaj SGsty
- 'Something Beautiful'	SCam
- 'Souvenir de Bahuaud-Litou' ♀H5	CBcs CSgt MAsh SCam
- 'Splendens Carlyon'	CSgt LRHS MAsh NRHS
- 'Spring Fever'	SCam
- 'Spring Fling'	CTrh LRHS SPoG XSte
- 'Spring Formal'	CTrh LRHS XSte
- 'Spring Frill'	SCam
- 'Stacy Susan'	XSte
- 'Strawberry Parfait'	CBcs
- 'Sugar Babe'	CTrh NRHS SCam
- 'Sundae'	CBcs
- 'Sunny Side' **new**	XSte
- 'Sweet Dreams' **new**	XSte
- 'Sylva' ♀H5	GGGa
- 'Sylvia'	CMac
- 'Takanini'	CBcs CTrh SCam XSte
- 'Tammia'	LRHS NRHS
- 'Teresa Ragland'	SCam
- 'The Mikado'	NRHS SRot
- 'Tiffany'	EGrI ELon NRHS SCam
- 'Tiki'	SCoo
- 'Tinker Bell'	ELon
- 'Tom Pouce'	XSte
- 'Tom Thumb' ♀H5	CTrh ELon NRHS SRms
- 'Tomorrow'	EGrI SCam
- 'Tomorrow's Dawn'	SCam
- 'Tregye'	CBcs
- 'Trewithen White'	CDoC NRHS
§ - 'Tricolor' ♀H5	CBcs CMac CSBt CTrh ELon MGos NRHS SCam SRot
- 'Tricolor Red'	see *C. japonica* 'Lady de Saumarez'
- 'Triphosa'	LPar SWeb
- 'Triumphans' **new**	XSte
- 'Valtevareda'	XSte
- 'Vergine di Collebeato'	XSte
- 'Victor Emmanuel'	see *C. japonica* 'Blood of China'
- 'Ville de Nantes'	CSgt MAsh NRHS XSte
- 'Ville du Havre' **new**	XSte
- 'Virginia Carlyon'	CBcs CSgt
- 'Virginia Robinson'	SCam XSte
- 'Visconti Nova'	NRHS
- 'Vittorio Emanuele II'	CSgt CTrh LRHS MAsh NRHS
- 'Volcano'	XSte
- 'Volunteer'	LCro LOPS LRHS MGos XSte
- 'Wheel of Fortune'	NRHS
- 'White Nun'	LMaj LPar
- 'White Swan'	CDoC CMac CSBt CSgt LRHS MAsh NRHS
- 'Wildfire'	NRHS
- 'William Bartlett'	CBcs CTrh SCoo
- 'William Honey'	CTrh
- 'Wisley White'	see *C. japonica* 'Hakurakuten'
- 'Witman Yellow'	CTrh
§ - 'Yours Truly'	CDoC CMac CSgt CTrh CTsd LSRN MAsh NRHS
- 'Yukimi-guruma'	LPar
'Jury's Yellow'	see *C.* × *williamsii* 'Jury's Yellow'
'Koto-no-kaori' (*lutchuensis* hybrid)	LRHS XSte
'Larry Piet' (*reticulata* hybrid)	XSte
'Lasca Beauty' (*japonica* × *reticulata*)	XSte
'Lavender Queen'	see *C. sasanqua* 'Lavender Queen'
'Leonard Messel' (*reticulata* × (× *williamsii*)) ♀H5	CDoC CMac CTrh CTri EPfP MGos NLar NRHS SCam SPer XSte
'Lila Naff' (*reticulata* hybrid)	XSte
'Lovely Lady' **new**	XSte
lutchuensis	MPkF
'Magic Mum'	LSRN
'Maud Messel' (*reticulata* × (× *williamsii*))	SCam
'Mimosa Jury'	LRHS XSte
'Nicky Crisp' (*japonica* × *pitardii*)	CTrh LRHS NRHS SPoG XSte
oleifera	CBcs CExl CTrh
'Paddy's Perfumed' **new**	XSte

	'Paolina Guichardini'	XSte
	'Paper Dolls' **new**	EGrI
	'Pink Goddess' (*hiemalis* hybrid)	LRHS MPkF XSte
	'Pink Icicle' (*oleifera* hybrid)	SCam SGol
	'Pink Spangles'	see *C. japonica* 'Mathotiana Rosea'
	pitardii WWJ 11925 from Vietnam	WCru
	'Quintessence' (*japonica* × *lutchuensis*)	LRHS XSte
	reticulata 'Arch of Triumph'	XSte
	- 'Captain Rawes'	XSte
	- 'Jean Morel'	XSte
	- 'Kerdalo' **new**	XSte
	- 'Mary Williams'	EGrI LRHS SCob SGol SPoG
	- 'Miss Tulare'	XSte
	- 'Nuccio's Ruby'	XSte
	rosthorniana CUPIDO	see *C. rosthorniana* 'Elina'
§	- 'Elina' PBR	ELan EPfP IDee LCro LOPS LRHS MGos NRHS SPoG XSte
	'Royalty' (*japonica* × *reticulata*) ♀H5	CBcs
	sasanqua Thunb.	LMaj MHid
I	- 'Alba'	CMac CSgt CTri LMil
	- 'Baronesa de Soutelinho'	CSgt ELon
	- 'Ben'	CSgt
	- 'Bonanza'	see *C. hiemalis* 'Bonanza'
	- 'Cleopatra'	CSgt EGrI EPfP LPar SCob SEWo SGsty
	- 'Crimson King' ♀H4	CSgt CTrh NRHS
	- 'Dazzler'	see *C. hiemalis* 'Dazzler'
	- 'Dwarf Shishi'	CTrh
	- 'Early Pearly'	LRHS SCam XSte
	- 'Fragrans'	ELon
	- 'Fuji-no-mine'	ELon SCam
	- 'Fuji-no-yuki'	XSte
§	- 'Fukuzutsumi'	SRot
	- 'Gay Sue'	CTrh EGrI SCam
	- 'Hinode-gumo'	SEWo SGsty
	- 'Hiryū'	EGrI LRHS MHtn NRHS SCam SEWo XSte
	- 'Hugh Evans' ♀H4	CBcs CSgt CTrh EGrI ELan ELon EPfP LMil LRHS NRHS SCam SRot SSta
	- 'Jean May' ♀H4	ELon EPfP NRHS WCot
	- 'Jennifer Susan'	CTrh CTri LPar
	- 'Kenkyō'	ELon SCam SSta
§	- 'Lavender Queen'	SCam
	- 'Maiden's Blush'	CSgt EGrI NRHS SCam WCot
	- 'Mignonne'	CSgt CTrh
	- 'Mine-no-yuki'	CTrh
	- 'Narumigata' ♀H4	CBcs CDoC CMac CTrh CTsd EGrI EPfP LCro LOPS LRHS MBlu MGos NRHS SCam SPoG SSta XSte
	- 'Navajo'	CTrh
	- 'New Dawn'	SRot
	- 'Nyewoods'	CMac
	- 'Papaver'	SCam
	- 'Paradise Audrey'	LMil LSRN SPoG
	- 'Paradise Belinda'	EPfP LMil SPoG
	- 'Paradise Blush'	CBcs SWvt
	- 'Paradise Helen'	LSRN
	- 'Paradise Pearl'	CBcs EPfP LMil
	- 'Paradise Venessa'	EPfP SCam
	- 'Peach Blossom'	EGrI
	- 'Plantation Pink'	CSgt CTrh EGrI LCro LMil LOPS LRHS NRHS SCob SPer SRkn SWvt WCot
	- 'Rainbow'	CBcs CDoC CSgt CTrh EGrI ELan ELon EPfP LRHS NRHS SCoo SPer SRot SSta
	- 'Rosea'	CMac CSgt ELon NRHS SCam
	- 'Sasanqua Rubra'	CMac SCam
	- 'Sasanqua Variegata' (v)	CTrh SCam
	- 'Sekiyō'	LRHS XSte
	- 'Snowflake'	SCam
	- 'Sparkling Burgundy'	see *C.* 'Sparkling Burgundy'
	- 'Tanya'	CTrh SCam
	- 'Versicolor'	CSgt LCro LOPS LRHS NRHS XSte
	- 'Winter's Joy'	CBcs SCam
	- 'Winter's Snowman'	CDoC LCro LOPS LRHS NLar NRHS SGol
	'Satan's Robe' (*reticulata* hybrid)	CBcs CDoC
	'Scented Sun'	CTrh
	'Show Girl' (*reticulata* × *sasanqua*) ♀H4	SCam
§	***sinensis***	CBcs CCCN CTrh CTsd GPoy MHtn NLar NRHS SPlb SPre SWeb SWvt WPGP XSte
	- var. ***assamica***	CCCN CDoC SPre
	- var. ***sinensis***	CCCN CSgt LCro LOPS
	'Snow Flurry'	CBcs CTrh NRHS SGol
§	'Sparkling Burgundy' ♀H4	LCro LOPS MGos NRHS SRot
	'Spring Daze' **new**	XSte
	'Spring Festival' (*cuspidata* hybrid) ♀H4	CBcs CEnd CSBt CTrh EGrI EPfP LCro LMil LOPS LRHS MGos MPri NRHS SCam SGol XSte
	'Spring Mist' (*japonica* × *lutchuensis*)	CTrh
	'Sugar Dream'	CTrh SCam
	'Superscent'	CTrh
	'Survivor'	LRHS
	'Swan Lake'	EPfP LMil MGos MPri NRHS SGol
	'Sweet Emily Kate' (*japonica* × *lutchuensis*)	LRHS XSte
	'Sweet Jane'	LRHS SCam
	'Sweet Olive' (d)	XSte
	'Tamzin Coull' (d)	XSte
	'Tarōkaja' (wabisuke)	SCam
	thea	see *C. sinensis*
	'Tinsie'	see *C. japonica* 'Bokuhan'
	'Tom Knudsen' (*japonica* × *reticulata*) ♀H4	NRHS SCam XSte
	transarisanensis **new**	WAbe
	transnokoensis ♀H4	CExl CTrh LRHS XSte
	'Transtasman'	LRHS
	'Tricolor Sieboldii'	see *C. japonica* 'Tricolor'
	'Tristrem Carlyon' (*reticulata* hybrid)	CDoC CSgt CTri CTsd EPfP LRHS MAsh MPri NRHS
	tsaii	IDee XSte
	'Usu-ōtome'	see *C. japonica* subsp. *rusticana* 'Otome'
	'Valley Knudsen' (*reticulata* × *saluenensis*)	XSte
	× ***vernalis*** 'Yuletide'	CBcs CDoC CRos CSgt CTrh EGrI LCro LMil LOPS LRHS LSRN MGos NRHS SCob SWeb XSte
	'Volcano'	LRHS
	'White Retic' (*japonica* × *reticulata*)	XSte
§	× ***williamsii***	SWeb
	- 'Angel Wings'	NRHS
	- 'Anticipation' ♀H5	CBcs CBod CDoC CEme CEnd CMac CRos CSBt CSgt CTrh EGrI EPfP GKin LCro LMil LOPS LRHS MAsh MGos MSwo NRHS SCob SGol SLim SPer SPoG SRot SWvt WFar XSte
	- 'Anticipation Variegated' (v)	CBcs NRHS
	- 'Ballet Queen'	CBcs CSBt SCam

– 'Ballet Queen Variegated' (v)	ELon
– 'Bartley Number Five'	CMac
– 'Beatrice Michael'	CBcs CMac
– 'Blue Danube'	CBcs SCoo
– 'Bow Bells'	CTri
– 'Bowen Bryant' ♀H5	CSgt CTrh EPfP LRHS NRHS SGol
– 'Brigadoon' ♀H5	CBcs CDoC CSgt CTrh CTri EPfP GGGa MAsh NRHS SCam XSte
– 'Burncoose'	CBcs
– 'Buttons 'n' Bows'	XSte
– 'C.F. Coates'	SCam
– 'Caerhays'	CBcs
– 'Celebration'	CSBt LSRN
– 'Charles Colbert'	XSte
– 'Charles Michael'	CBcs
– 'China Clay' ♀H5	CBcs CDoC CSgt LSRN MAsh NRHS
§ – 'Citation'	CBcs CMac LMaj
– 'Contribution'	CTrh LRHS MAsh
– 'Crinkles'	SCam
– 'Daintiness' ♀H5	XSte
– 'Debbie' ♀H5	Widely available
– 'Debbie's Carnation'	NRHS
– 'Donation' ♀H5	Widely available
– 'Dream Boat'	LRHS XSte
– 'E.G. Waterhouse'	CBod CSBt CSgt CTrh CTri EGrl ELan EPfP GKin LRHS MGos NRHS SCam SGol SSta WFar XSte
– 'E.G. Waterhouse' variegated (v) **new**	XSte
– 'E.T.R. Carlyon' ♀H5	CBcs CBod CDoC CRos CSgt CTrh CTri EPfP LMil LRHS MAsh MGos NLar NRHS SGol SLim SRot XSte
– 'Edward Carlyon'	CSgt
– 'Elegant Beauty' ♀H5	CBcs CDoC CSgt CTrh ELon LRHS MAsh NLar NRHS SCam SRot
– 'Elizabeth Anderson'	CTrh
– 'Elsie Jury' ♀H5	CDoC CMac CSgt CTri ELon GKin LRHS MAsh MGos NLar NRHS SCam SGol
– 'Exaltation'	SCam
– 'Francis Hanger'	CDoC CTrh NRHS SRot
– 'Galaxie'	CBcs SCam
– 'Gay Time'	CSgt LRHS MAsh NRHS
– 'George Blandford' ♀H5	CBcs CMac
– 'Glenn's Orbit' ♀H5	NLar SCam
– 'Golden Spangles' (v)	CMac EPfP MGos MMuc NRHS SPer SPoG SRot
– 'Grand Jury'	ELon NRHS
– 'Gwavas'	CBcs CCCN CSgt CTrh LRHS MAsh NRHS SCam
– 'Hilo'	SCam
– 'J.C. Williams' ♀H5	CBcs CMac CTri SRot
– 'Jamie'	LRHS XSte
– 'Jenefer Carlyon'	CBcs
– 'Jennifer Trehane'	CTrh
– 'Jill Totty'	CTrh
– 'John Pickthorn'	CBcs
– 'Julia Hamiter' ♀H5	CBcs CDoC CSgt LRHS MAsh NRHS
§ – 'Jury's Yellow' ♀H5	CBcs CBod CCCN CDoC CPla CRos CSBt CSgt CTrh CTri EGrl EPfP GGGa LCro LMil LOPS LRHS LSRN MAsh MGos MPri SCam SCob SGol SLim SPoG SRot SSta SWvt XSte
– 'Laura Boscawen'	CBcs CTrh SCam
– 'Les Jury' ♀H5	CBcs CDoC CSBt CTrh LMil LSRN MGos NRHS SGol SLim SPer SRot WFar XSte
– 'Lucky Star' (d)	XSte
– 'Margaret Waterhouse'	CDoC CSgt SCam
– 'Marjorie Waldegrave'	CSgt MAsh NRHS
– 'Mary Jobson'	CBcs
– 'Mary Larcom'	CBcs
– 'Mary Phoebe Taylor' ♀H5	CBcs LMaj NLar SCam SLim
– 'Mildred Veitch'	CSBt
– 'Mirage'	CTrh
– 'Monica Dance'	CBcs
– 'Muskoka' ♀H5	CBcs EPfP
– 'Night Rider'	WPGP XSte
– 'November Pink'	CBcs SCam
– 'Philippa Forward'	CBcs CMac
– 'Pink Wave'	CSgt NRHS
– 'Red Dahlia'	CBcs
– 'Rendezvous'	CSgt CTrh SCam
– 'Rose Parade'	CDoC CSgt
– 'Rose Quartz'	CDoC CSgt LRHS
– 'Rosemary Williams'	CBcs CMac
– 'Ruby Wedding' (d) ♀H5	CBcs CBod CDoC CEme CPla CRos CSBt CSgt CTrh EGrl EPfP LMil LRHS LSRN MAsh MGos MHtn MPri NRHS SCam SCoo SLim SPoG SWvt WFar
– 'Saint Ewe' ♀H5	CBcs CSBt CSgt CTrh CTri EPfP MGos NRHS SCam XSte
– 'Saint Michael'	CBcs
– 'Senorita' ♀H5	CSgt EGrl ELon LRHS NLar NRHS SCam SGol SRot
– 'Shocking Pink'	CSgt NRHS
– 'The Duchess of Cornwall'	CSgt LRHS NRHS
– 'Tiptoe'	CTrh SCoo
– 'Toni Finlay's Fragrant'	CTrh
– 'Tulip Time'	XSte
– 'Twinkle Star'	CSgt NRHS
– 'Water Lily' ♀H5	CBcs CSgt CTri ELon LRHS MAsh NLar NRHS SCam SRot
– 'Wilber Foss'	CBcs CSgt LRHS NRHS SCam
– 'William Carlyon'	CSgt NRHS
– 'Winter Gem'	LRHS XSte
'Winter's Charm'	CDoC CSgt LRHS NRHS
'Winter's Interlude'	CBcs CDoC CSgt LRHS MAsh NRHS
'Winter's Star' **new**	SGol
'Winter's Toughie'	CDoC CSgt MAsh NRHS SCam
'Winton' (*cuspidata* × *saluenensis*)	CBcs
'Yoimachi' (*fraterna* × *sasanqua*)	CTrh LRHS XSte
'Yume'	LRHS XSte
yunnanensis	IDee

Camissonia (*Onagraceae*)

bistorta 'Sunflakes'	CSpe

Campanula (*Campanulaceae*)

RCB AM 13	WCot
alata	CCBP GJos
'Albert Kirkham'	EBee WCot
§ ***alliariifolia***	CBod CDor CEme EBee ECha ECtt EHyd ELan EPfP EWoo GKev GLog LRHS MRav NBro NGdn NRHS NSti SBut SEND SPer SRms WCAu WCot WFar WGwG WSpi
– DHTU 0126	WCru
– 'Ivory Bells'	see *C. alliariifolia*
– 'Ivory Towers'	EBee
americana	WFar
ardonensis	GKev
armena	GJos
arvatica	EACa EHyd EPot LRHS NRHS NSla SRms WAbe WFar
aucheri	see *C. bellidifolia* subsp. *aucheri*
'Barbara Valentine'	EBee EWTr WCAu
barbata	EACa EBee EPfP GKev
bayerniana	GJos GKev

'Belinda'	EPot
bellidifolia	NSla
§ - subsp. ***aucheri***	EPot GEdr
§ - subsp. ***besenginica***	GEdr
- subsp. ***saxifraga***	GEdr
§ ***betulifolia*** ♀H5	GEdr GKev NSla WCot WFar
biebersteiniana	GEdr ITim NSla
'Birch Hybrid'	EACa ECtt EHyd ELan ELon EPot GBee LRHS NRHS SAko SRms WFar
'Blue Moon' **new**	LRHS
'Blue Octopus'	CWGN EHyd ELon EMor LSou MPnt SRms WSpi
'Blue Pearl'	WAbe
bononiensis	SRms
'Burghaltii'	GKev MACG NLar
calaminthifolia	ITim
* ***campanulata***	MCot
carpatica ♀H5	EPfP GQue LRHS NGdn SPlb SRms WFar
- f. ***alba***	EHyd LRHS NGdn NRHS SEdd SPlb
§ - - 'Weisse Clips'	EHyd EPfP GDam GJos GMaP LCro LOPS LRHS NGdn NHol NRHS SPer SPoG SRms SWvt WFar
§ - 'Blaue Clips'	CBcs ECtt EHyd EPfP GDam GJos GMaP LCro LPar LRHS MGos NFav NGdn NRHS SPer SPoG SRms SRot SWvt WFar
- BLUE CLIPS	see *C. carpatica* 'Blaue Clips'
- 'Blue Moonlight'	EACa EHyd LRHS NRHS
- 'Blue Uniform'	LRHS
- 'Chewton Joy'	EACa EHyd LRHS NRHS
- 'Kathy'	EPot
- 'Pearl Deep Blue'	MTin
- 'Rapido Blue'	MACG MHol
- 'Rapido White'	MACG
- var. ***turbinata***	SRms
- - 'Foerster'	EHyd NRHS
- - 'Isabel'	EHyd NRHS
- - 'Jewel'	EHyd LRHS NRHS
- WHITE CLIPS	see *C. carpatica* f. *alba* 'Weisse Clips'
- white-flowered **new**	LRHS
§ ***cashmeriana***	WAbe
cephallenica	see *C. garganica* subsp. *cephallenica*
§ ***chamissonis***	EPot GArf GEdr NWad
- 'Alba'	WFar
- 'Major'	EWes
- 'Oyobeni'	EACa
§ - 'Superba' ♀H5	CBor EACa NHpl WAbe WIce
'Chloe'	EBee EWTr WFar WHil
choruhensis	EWes GEdr SPlb
ciliata	GEdr
Clockwise Series **new**	LRHS SRot
§ ***cochlearifolia*** ♀H5	CMea EBee EBou EHyd EPfP GAbr GJos GKev GMaP LRHS MMuc NHpl NRHS NWad SPoG WCav WFar WHoo
- var. ***alba***	EBou EDAr ELan LShi NHpl NRya SRms WAbe WFar
- - 'Advance White'	WFar
- - double white-flowered (d)	WFar
- - 'White Baby' (Baby Series)	EACa EHyd EPfP EPot NRHS NWad SPoG SRms WFar
- 'Bavaria Blue'	NHol
- 'Blue Baby' (Baby Series)	EPfP LRHS NHpl SPoG SRms SRot WIce
- 'Blue Wonder'	ECtt
- 'Elizabeth Oliver' (d) ♀H5	CMea EACa ECtt EDAr EHyd ELan GArf GEdr GMaP LRHS MHer MSCN NBir NHar NHpl NRHS SEdd SPlb SRms WAbe WFar WHoo WIce WSHC
- 'Flore Pleno' (d)	WFar
- 'R.B. Loder' (d)	EHyd LRHS MHer NRHS
- 'Silver Bells'	ECha LSou
- 'Tubby'	EACa EHyd EPot MHer SGro SRms
collina	EACa EHyd GEdr GPSL LRHS NRHS
'Constellation'	EACa
'Covadonga'	CMea EACa EHyd LRHS NRHS WAbe WThu
'Cremewit'	EPot
'Crystal'	ECtt MAvo MCot MHol MSpe NLar WCot WFar
cymbalaria	GKev
dasyantha	see *C. chamissonis*
dolomitica	EACa GJos
'E.K. Toogood'	CElw EACa EBou ECtt EPot SRms WFar
erinus	MHol
'Faichem Lilac'	WCot
fenestrellata	EACa EPot SLee
§ - subsp. ***istriaca***	GKev
finitima	see *C. betulifolia*
fragilis subsp. ***cavolinii***	GArf
garganica ♀H5	EACa EBou EDAr EHyd EPfP GMaP GWyn MRav NFav NRHS SRms SVic SWvt WFar
- 'Aurea'	see *C. garganica* 'Dickson's Gold'
- 'Blue Diamond'	EACa EBou ELon NLar
§ - subsp. ***cephallenica***	EACa
§ - 'Dickson's Gold'	Widely available
- 'Erinus Major'	EACa
- 'Filigree'	WBrk WCot WFar
- subsp. ***istriaca***	see *C. fenestrellata* subsp. *istriaca*
- 'Major'	SPoG WFar
- 'Mrs Resholt'	CTri ECtt EPau EWoo NBir NLar SEdd SRms SWvt WBrk WFar WIce
- 'W.H. Paine' ♀H5	EACa ECtt NFav NLar NSla WAbe WBrk WFar WHoo
'Glandore'	EACa SAko XLum
glomerata	CBee CExl GAbr GEdr GJos GKev LSRN LShi MHer NAts NBir NGBl NGrd NMir WFar
- var. ***acaulis*** hort.	EPfP NGrd NLar SCob SRms WFar
- var. ***alba***	CBcs CBod CDor CNor CRos CSpe EACa ECtt EHyd ELan EMor EPfP GJos GMaP LRHS MBel NRHS SAng SCob SGbt SPer SPlb SPoG WCAu WGwG
§ - - 'Schneekrone'	ECha LCro LOPS WFar
- BELLEFLEUR WHITE (Bellefleur Series)	EWTr
- 'Caroline' ♀H7	CDor CWGN EACa EBee ECha ECtt EHyd EMor EPfP EPri GWyn LEdu LRHS LSRN MACG MBel MBriF MHol MNrw MRav NLar NRHS NSti SEdd SPer WCAu WCot WFar WMal
- var. ***dahurica***	CSpe EAJP EBee EHyd EMor NLar SHar
- 'Emerald'	CBod EBee EHyd EPfP LRHS MHer MSCN NLar NRHS SCob SPad SRms WFar XSen
- 'Freya'^{PBR} ♀H7	CBod EACa EBee ECtt EPfP LPla MNrw SPad WCot WFar WMal
- (Genti Series) GENTI BLUE ('Allgentibl'^{PBR})	LRHS MPri WFar
- - GENTI TWISTERBELL ('Allgentitwist'^{PBR})	CBod EHed EMor MHol MSCN NEoE SCob
- - GENTI WHITE ('Allgentiw'^{PBR})	CWGN LRHS MPri NLar SCoo WFar
- 'Joan Elliott'	EBee ECha ECtt EPfP LEdu LRHS MHol MPie SGbt WGwG XSen

- 'Purple Pixie'	SRms
- 'Stevie's Wonder'	LRHS
- 'Superba' ♀^{H7}	Widely available
grossekii	EBee EHyd GJos
'Hannah'	EHyd EPot NRHS
× ***haylodgensis*** misapplied	see *C.* × *haylodgensis* 'Plena'
§ × ***haylodgensis*** W. Brockbank 'Marion Fisher' (d)	WAbe WFar
§ - 'Plena' (d)	EACa ECtt EHyd EPot LRHS NRHS SRms WAbe WFar
- 'Yvonne'	ECtt ELan EPot NHpl WFar
hercegovina 'Nana'	WAbe
'Hilltop Snow'	EPot
hofmannii	GJos GKev NWad
hypopolia	WAbe
§ ***incurva***	CSpe EACa GArf GEdr GJos GKev WAbe
- 'Blue Ice'	GArf
IRIDESCENT BELLS ('Iribella'^{PBR})	CWGN EACa EBee EMor EWes LCro LSou MBel MHol MNrw MSCN NSti SCob SPad SPer WCAu WHil WPnP WTyc
isophylla ♀^{H2}	CPla EPot
- 'Alba' ♀^{H2}	EPot
- 'Pamela'	EPot
JENNY ('Harjen'^{PBR})	CWGN SHar
'Joan Beeston'	WAbe
'Joe Elliott'	WAbe
kemulariae	EDAr GJos WCot XLum
'Kent Belle' ♀^{H7}	Widely available
kirpicznikovii	EBee GEdr GKev
kolenatiana	GJos
komarovii	WCot
lactiflora	CElw CMac CSpe EACa EBee ECha EHyd EPfP GAbr GJos LRHS MCot MNrw NRHS SPer WCAu WFar WSpi WWtn
- ***alba***	see *C. lactiflora* white-flowered
- 'Alba' ♀^{H7}	EBee ECha EPfP GBin GMaP MAvo MBel MMuc SEND WBrk WCAu WCot WSpi
- 'Assendon Pearl' ♀^{H7}	LPla LRHS MHol SHar SPhx WCot
- AVALANCHE ('Camblo')	EACa EBee ECtt LCro LOPS
- 'Border Blues'	ECtt ELon EPfP MHol MNrw NDov NLar WFar
- 'Dixter Presence'	LPla SMHy
- dwarf pink-flowered	EAJP EPfP GAbr NLar WFar
- 'Favourite' ♀^{H7}	ECtt EWoo NGdn SHar
- 'Loddon Anna' ♀^{H7}	Widely available
- 'Marchants Nimbus'	GBin
- 'Monica's Dream' **new**	EACa ECtt WWtn
- 'Platinum' ♀^{H7}	LPla
- 'Pouffe'	CRos EACa EBee ECtt EHyd EPfP GMaP GWyn LRHS MNrw NGdn NRHS SGbt SPer SWvt
- 'Prichard's Variety' ♀^{H7}	Widely available
- 'Superba' ♀^{H7}	EACa ECtt
- 'Violet'	EPfP WSpi
- 'White Pouffe'	CBod EACa ECtt EHyd EPfP EWoo GMaP LRHS NChi NDov NLar NRHS NSti SCob SGbt SPer SPoG WFar
§ - white-flowered	ECha NBir SEdd SPer WCAu WCav
lasiocarpa	EPot
latifolia	EACa GJos GQue LShi MCot NBid NChi NMir SPer SRms WCAu WSpi
- var. ***alba***	CRos EBee EHyd EPfP EWTr GJos GWyn LRHS MBel NRHS SPer SRms WHal WSpi
* - 'Amethyst'	SBls WSpi
- - blue-flowered	SEND
- 'Brantwood'	EHyd EPfP MRav WSpi
- 'Gloaming'	EBee ECtt EHyd WSpi
- var. ***macrantha***	EBee EHyd ELan EPfP GMaP LRHS NFav NRHS NSti SWvt
- - 'Alba'	GLog GMaP MRav NFav NLar NWad WCAu
latiloba	WCot WKif
§ - 'Alba'	EBee MCot MNrw NLar WBrk
- 'Hidcote Amethyst'	CDor CWGN ECtt EHyd ELan ELon LRHS MBriF MCot NBid NBir NGdn NLar SPer WCAu WCot WKif WSpi
- 'Highcliffe Variety' ♀^{H7}	EACa EBee ECtt EHyd EPfP LRHS MACG MBriF MPie NLar NRHS SPer SPoG WCAu WCot WSpi WWtn
- 'Percy Piper' ♀^{H7}	CKel CRos EACa EBee EHyd LRHS MAsh MPie MRav NLar NRHS WCAu WSpi
- 'Splash'	MNrw
'Linda'	IPot
'Lynchmere'	CMea EPot WAbe WMal
makaschvilii	CPla EACa EWhm GArf GKev GWyn SPtp
makaschvilii × ***trachelium***	WCot
'Margaret Brine'	WAbe
'Marion Fisher'	see *C.* × *haylodgensis* W. Brockbank 'Marion Fisher'
medium 'Alba'	CBod
- 'Caerula'	CBod
§ - var. ***calycanthema*** hort.	WSpi
- 'Cup and Saucer'	see *C. medium* var. *calycanthema* hort.
- 'Rosea'	CBod
'Mevr. V. Vollenhove'	EBee ECtt MAvo MHol
'Misty Dawn' ♀^{H7}	NLar WCot
moesiaca	GKev
muralis	see *C. portenschlagiana*
myrtifolia	WAbe
- 'Helmi' **new**	WAbe
nitida	see *C. persicifolia* var. *planiflora*
'Norman Grove'	EPot
ochroleuca	CMea EBee GBin WCot XLum
odontosepala	NWad WFar
- from Iran	EMor EPPr NLar
olympica misapplied	see *C. rotundifolia* 'Olympica'
ossetica	EBee ECtt WBor
pallida subsp. ***tibetica***	see *C. cashmeriana*
patula	CSpe EACa WKif
§ - subsp. ***abietina***	CSpe
'Paul Furse'	ECtt NSti SHar WCot
'Pearlescent Pink'	EWes LSou
'Pearlescent White'	EWes LSou
pelia	CPla
pendula	LRHS SBls SGBe
persicifolia	Widely available
- var. ***alba***	Widely available
§ - 'Alba Coronata' (d)	GAbr LShi SRms XLum
- 'Alba Flore-Pleno' (d)	SGbt
- 'Alba Plena'	see *C. persicifolia* 'Alba Coronata'
- 'Azure Beauty'	EBee ECtt NLar WCot WSpi XSen
- 'Beau Belle'	EWld NLar
§ - 'Bennett's Blue' (d)	MRav
- blue and white-flowered	SRms
- 'Blue Bell'	GWyn MACG
- 'Blue Bloomers' (d)	CDor EACa EHyd EPri EWes MRav MSCN NQui NWad SRms WCFE WCot WHal XLum
- 'Blue-eyed Blonde'^{PBR} (v)	NLar
- blue-flowered	EWoo MBow SPlb SRms
- 'Boule de Neige' (d)	CDor WSpi

§	- 'Chettle Charm'	CDor CTri CWCL ECtt EHyd EPfP EShb GAbr LRHS MBriF MCot MRav NBir NLar NRHS SCob SRms SWvt WCot WFar
	- 'Cornish Mist'	CDor CExl EBee EPfP GBin MPie NLar WCAu WSpi
	- 'Fleur de Neige' (d)	MRav
	- 'Frances' (d)	WCot
	- 'Gawen'	CMac ECtt EHyd SGbt WCAu WCot
	- 'George Chiswell'	see *C. persicifolia* 'Chettle Charm'
	- 'Grandiflora'	CDor EAJP
	- 'Grandiflora Alba'	EAJP GBin NLar NWad SDix
	- 'Hampstead White' (d)	WSpi
	- 'Kelly's Gold'	SRms
	- 'La Belle' (d)	EBee EHyd MNrw NLar
	- 'La Bello'PBR	EBee EHyd MNrw NLar
	- 'La Bonne Amie' (d)	EBee EPfP MNrw NLar SPoG
	- 'Moerheimii' (d)	WSpi
	- 'Perry's Boy Blue'	NPer
§	- var. ***planiflora***	WAbe
	- - f. ***alba***	NHpl WAbe WCot
	- 'Powder Puff' (d)	EPfP GBin GWyn NLar
	- 'Pride of Exmouth' (d) ♀H7	CDor CMiW MHer MRav WSpi
	- subsp. ***sessiliflora*** 'Alba'	see *C. latiloba* 'Alba'
	- 'Snowdrift'	SRms
	- (Takion Series) 'Takion Blue'	EHyd ELan GWyn LRHS MNHC NRHS SCoo SPoG SRms
	- - 'Takion White'	CSpe EHyd ELan EPfP GQue GWyn LRHS NRHS SCoo SPoG SRms
	- 'Telham Beauty' ambig.	CBod EWTr MACG MCot SCob SGbt SMrm SWvt WCFE WSpi XLum
	- 'Telham Beauty' misapplied	CSBt EBee EHyd ELan EPfP LRHS MRav NRHS SPer SRms SWvt
	- 'Telham Beauty' D.Thurston	MBow NFav NLar
	- 'Tinpenny Blue'	WCot
	- 'White Bell'	MACG
	- 'Wortham Belle' ambig.	LPot MHol MRav SGbt SMrm WCAu
	- 'Wortham Belle' Blooms	ECtt EHyd LRHS NRHS WGwG
	'Peter Nix'	EACa
	petrophila	WAbe
	pilosa	see *C. chamissonis*
	- 'Superba'	see *C. chamissonis* 'Superba'
	'Pink Octopus'PBR	CBor CRos CSpe CTtf CWGN ECtt EHyd ELan ELon EMor EPfP EWoo LPot LRHS LSou MBNS MHol MSCN NGdn NLar NRHS SCob SEle SPad SPoG SRkn SRms STPC WSpi XLum
	planiflora	see *C. persicifolia* var. *planiflora*
	pollinensis	WCot
§	***portenschlagiana*** ♀H5	Widely available
	- 'Alba'	WFar
	- 'Blue Sky'	LRHS
	- 'Catharina'	EACa ECtt EHyd EPPr EShb LRHS MBros NRHS SPoG SRms
	- CLOCKWISE DEEP BLUE (Clockwise Series) <u>**new**</u>	NBir
	- 'Lieselotte'	CMea EACa ECtt EPot SAko WFar
	- 'Major'	EACa NCou
	- 'Resholdt's Variety'	CBar CMea CTri EACa EAJP EBou ECtt EDAr EHyd ELan EPfP GKev LRHS MBel MRav NRHS SAko SLee SRms WAbe WCot XLum XSen
	- 'Sago'	CBod MHol
	poscharskyana	Widely available
	- 'Blauranke'	EACa EWes SAko WFar
	- 'Blue Gown'	EACa ECtt SAko
	- 'Blue Rivulet'PBR	ECtt
	- BLUE WATERFALL ('Camgood')	CWCL CWGN EACa ECtt LRHS MBNS NDov SPoG WBrk WCot
	- 'E.H. Frost'	CElw EACa ECtt ELan EPPr EPfP EShb EWTr GBin GKev GMaP LPot MACG MCot MMuc NLar NRya SAko SEND SLee SPer SRms SWvt WBrk WFar WSpi
	- 'Erich G. Arends'	SAko
I	- 'Freya'	EACa SAko
	- 'Frühlingszauber'	WCot
	- 'Garden Star'	CBod MHol
	- 'Hirsch Blue'	LRHS SRms SRot
	- 'Lilacina'	EACa EPPr
	- 'Lisduggan Variety'	CElw EACa EBee ECtt EPPr EWes GMaP MACG MHer NLar SAko SLee SRms WFar WIce XSen
	- 'Nana Alba'	EACa EPPr MACG SAko WBrk
	- 'Pinkins'PBR	CSma EACa ECtt
	- 'Schneeranke'	XSen
	- 'Silberregen'	SAko
	- 'Stella' ♀H5	EACa ECha ECtt EGrI EHyd ELan EPfP GBin GMaP IPot LRHS LSRN MRav NDov NRHS SAko SPer SWvt WBrk WCav WCot WHoo XLum
	- 'Trollkind'	EACa EPPr SAko WFar
	- variegated (v)	EBee EPPr
	- 'Weissranke'	WFar
	- white-flowered	CTri WFar
	prenanthoides	see *Asyneuma prenanthoides*
	× ***pseudoraineri*** hort.	EACa EHyd EWes NRHS
	pulla	EACa EBou ECtt EHyd ELan GEdr LRHS NHpl NRHS NSla SCob SPoG SRms WAbe WIce
	- 'Alba'	EACa EHyd LRHS NRHS NSla WAbe WIce
	× ***pulloides*** hort. 'G.F.Wilson' ♀H5	EACa ECtt GEdr GMaP IPot NLar SRkn WFar
	- 'Jelly Bells'PBR	NLar
	punctata	GArf GJos MCot NBro NSti WCAu WFar
	- f. ***albiflora***	WFar
	- 'Alina's Double' (d)	NLar
	- 'Folies Bergère'	CBor
	- var. ***hondoensis***	GKev
	- 'Hot Lips'	CMac SLee
*	- var. ***howozana***	GKev
	- 'Kurokawa'	WFar
	- var. ***microdonta*** B&SWJ 5553	WCru
	- 'Milky Way'	EMor LSou NEoE WHil
*	- 'Nana'	WFar
	- 'Pantaloons' (d)	CDor CMac CWGN EMor EWes NLar SCob SRms
	- 'Pink Chimes'	CBod CDor NLar SEle
	- 'Plum Wine'	NWad
	- purple-flowered	EHyd ELan EPfP LRHS
	- f. ***rubriflora***	CBod CDor CRos CSde CSpe EBee EBou ECtt EGrI EHyd ELan EMor EPfP LRHS MBel MCot MNrw NRHS SBls SCob SPer SRms WCAu
	- - 'Beetroot'	CWCL EBee EMor GBee GBin GKev GWyn MHer MHol NLar NWad WFar
	- - 'Bowl of Cherries'	EHyd NLar SRms
	- - 'Cherry Bells'	EHyd EMor EPfP LRHS LSRN NRHS
	- - 'Vienna Festival'	CSBt
	- - 'Wine 'n' Rubies'	EBee EMor
I	- 'Silver Bells'	ECtt EHyd EMor EPfP MBel NLar NSti SRms WFar WHil
	- 'Wedding Bells'	CDor EACa EBou EHyd EMor EPfP EPri LPot LRHS LSRN MACG MBel MBriF MBros MSpe NLar NRHS SCob SRms WCAu WHil

I	– 'White Bells'	MHol
	– white hose-in-hose (d)	XLum
	'Purple Sensation'PBR	CWGN EBee EPfP LSou MBel MNrw MSCN NLar WCot
	pusilla	see *C. cochlearifolia*
	pyramidalis	CCBP CSpe EACa EBee EGrI ELan EPfP GJos MMuc NGBl SDix SPlb WBor
	– 'Alba'	CSpe EACa ELan EPfP GJos NGBl SCoo SDix SPlb
	– variegated (v)	LRHS
	raddeana	EACa GKev SBrt WBrk
	raineri	EPot NSla WAbe
	– 'Nettleton Gold'	EACa EHyd LRHS NRHS
§	***rapunculoides***	SRms WCFE
§	– 'Afterglow'	MAvo WFar
	– 'Alba'	MAvo WFar
	– 'Campbell Blue' **new**	WBrk
	rapunculus	MNHC
	recurva	see *C. incurva*
	rhomboidalis Gorter	see *C. rapunculoides*
	rhomboidalis L.	WCot
	rigidipila	GJos WHer
	(Ringsabell Series) 'Ringsabell Indigo Blue'	CBod EBee ELan EMor EPfP SPoG
	– 'Ringsabell Mulberry Rose'	CBod ELan EPfP SRms WCAu
	– 'Ringsabell Opal White'	ELan
	rotundifolia	CMac EACa EBou EHyd ELan EPfP GAbr GJos GLog MBow MHer MNHC NMir SPhx SPlb SRms WBrk WWild
	– var. ***albiflora***	CElw EWes
	– 'Jotunheimen'	EACa WAbe
§	– 'Olympica'	EACa EBee WHoo
	– 'White Gem'	CBod EACa EBee EHyd ELan EPfP GKev LRHS NRHS WHoo
	'Royal Wave'	ECtt IPot NLar
	'Samantha'	EACa ECtt GKev LRHS LSRN NHpl SEdd SGBe SHar WFar
	'Sarastro'	Widely available
	sarmatica	EACa EBee EPfP SGro SRms WFar
	– 'Hemelstraling'	MAvo MCot MHer MHol
	– subsp. ***woronowii***	ITim
	sartorii	GEdr WAbe
	scheuchzeri	WAbe
	'Senior'	EACa ECtt EPPr SAko WCot WGoo
§	***sibirica***	GJos
	– 'Royal Wedding'	EMor
	'Snow Dune'	WCAu
	'Stansfieldii'	EACa EHyd EPot LRHS NRHS
	stevenii	see *C. stevenii* subsp. *beauverdiana*
§	– subsp. ***beauverdiana***	SBrt
	subramulosa	see *C. cochlearifolia*
	'Summer Pearl'	ECtt LLWG SGBe
	'Summertime Blues'PBR	EBee EHyd ELan EMor LRHS MHol NLar NRHS WCot WMal
§	'Swannables'	EHyd EShb MAvo MRav WFar
	takesimana	CSpe CTtf ECtt EHyd ELan EPfP GKev GKin LEdu LRHS NGrd NLar NRHS SPer SRms SWvt
I	– 'Alba'	EMor WFar XLum
	– 'Beautiful Trust'	CDor MHol
	– 'Bellringers'	SBls
	– 'Elizabeth'	CBod CRos EACa EBee ECtt EGrI EHyd EMor EPPr EPfP GMaP GWyn LRHS LSRN MBel MHol MSpe NGdn NRHS SCob SCoo SGbt SPer SPlb SWvt WCAu WFar WHil XLum
	– 'Elizabeth II' (d)	EPPr SHar WFar
	– 'Feenrock JP'	XLum
	– 'White Giant'	SHar
	thyrsoides	CSpe EBee GJos SBls
	'Timsbury Chimes'	WAbe
	'Timsbury Perfection'	WAbe
	tommasiniana 🏆H6	GJos SBrt WAbe
	trachelium	EACa EBee EHyd ELon EMor GJos GKev MBow MHer MNHC MRav NAts NGrd NMir WCot WFar WHer WShi WSpi
	– f. ***alba***	EBee EHyd ELan GJos NLar SGbt WCot WFar
	– – 'Alba Flore Pleno' (d)	LEdu LPla SMHy
	– 'Bernice' (d)	CDor EACa EBee ECtt ELan EMor EPfP EWTr GMaP LRHS MAvo MCot MHol MNrw MPie MTin NLar NSti SCob SPer WBor WCAu WCot WFar WSpi XSen
	– 'Purple Break'	EBee MHol WCot
	– 'Snowball'	CMac
	'Van-Houttei'	CDor NLar WCot
	versicolor	CDoC SRms
	vidalii	see *Azorina vidalii*
	'Viking'PBR	EHyd SPad SRms
	waldsteiniana	EPot GKev WAbe
	wanneri	CPla EDAr GJos
	'White Octopus'	ECtt LSou SEle
	× ***wockei*** 'Puck'	EACa ECtt EHyd EPot LRHS NRHS WAbe
	zangezura	EACa EBou EDAr ELan GJos GKev SBut SGbt
	zoysii	WAbe

Campanula × *Symphyandra* see *Campanula*

Campanumoea see *Codonopsis*

Campsis (*Bignoniaceae*)

	grandiflora	CBcs CWGN EHyd ELan EPfP LRHS LSRN SPer SWvt WCFE
	radicans	CBcs CBod CMac CRHN CWCL EGrI EHyd ELan EPfP LPar LRHS MGil MHtn MSwo NRHS SCoo SLon SNig SPer SPlb
	– 'Atrosanguinea'	SVen
	– 'Flamenco'	CBcs CDoC CKel CMac CWCL EBee EHyd ELan EPfP EWTr LRHS LSRN MGil SAdn SCob SCoo SNig SPoG SVen SWvt WLov
§	– f. ***flava*** 🏆H4	CBcs CMac CRos CTri CWCL EBee EHyd ELan EPfP EWTr LRHS MBlu MGil MGos MHtn NRHS SCob SCoo SGbt SPer SPoG SVen SWvt
	– 'Stromboli'	EPfP SGsty
	– 'Yellow Trumpet'	see *C. radicans* f. *flava*
	× ***tagliabuana*** DANCING FLAME ('Huidan'PBR)	CWCL CWGN EHyd EPfP LRHS
	– INDIAN SUMMER ('Kudian'PBR)	CBcs CDoC CKel CRos CWCL CWGN EHyd ELon EPfP LRHS LSRN MGil MGos NRHS SCoo
	– 'Madame Galen' 🏆H4	CBcs CDoC CKel CRos CTri CWCL CWGN EBee EHyd ELan ELon EPfP LPar LRHS LSRN MAsh MBlu MGos SCob SEND SGbt SPer SPoG SRms SSta SVen SWvt WSHC
	– 'Takarazuka Yellow'PBR (Summer Jazz Series)	EHyd LRHS NRHS
	– 'Takarazuka Zujin'PBR (Summer Jazz Series)	EHyd LRHS NRHS

Camptosorus see *Asplenium*

Campylandra see *Tupistra*

Campylotropis (*Fabaceae*)

macrocarpa	WSHC

Canarina (*Campanulaceae*)

canariensis ♀H2	CCCN CMCN CTsd SBrt SVen
- from Los Silos, Tenerife	WCot

Candollea see *Hibbertia*

Canna ✿ (*Cannaceae*)

	sp. **new**	WHil
	'Alberich'	SHaC
	altensteinii	CDTJ SHaC SPlb
	'Ambassador'	SDeJ
	'Ambassadour'	SHaC
	'Annaeei' ♀H3	SHaC SPlb
	'Anthony and Cleopatra' (v)	WCot
I	'Aphrodite' van Klaveren	MBros
	'Argentina'	SHaC
	'Assaut'	SHaC
	'Australia'	CBen CDTJ ETod SHaC
	'Baron Seguier'	XLum
	'Bird of Paradise'	SHaC
	'Black Knight'	CBod LSvl SCob SDeJ SHaC
	'Bonfire'	CDTJ CTsd
	brasiliensis	CPla EShb SHaC SSal WSMil
	'Brillant'	SDeJ SHaC
	'Burbank'	CDTJ
	'Caballero'	SHaC XLum
	'Caliméro'	SHaC
	'Carnaval'	SHaC
	'Centenaire de Rozain-Boucharlat'	SDeJ SHaC XLum
	'Champion'	SHaC
	'Chocolate Sunrise'	LCro LOPS
	'Chouchou'	SHaC
§	'City of Portland'	SDeJ SHaC
§	'Cleopatra'	CCCN SDeJ SHaC
	coccinea	SArc SSal
	compacta	SHaC
	'Corail'	SHaC
	'Corsica' (Island Series)	SHaC
	'Durban' Hiley, orange-flowered	see *C.* 'Phasion'
	'Durban' ambig.	CBen CWGN ETod SArc SEdd SHaC WSMil
	'E. Neubert'	ELan ETod SHaC
	edulis	CDTJ XLum XSte
§	× ***ehemanii*** ♀H3	CAvo CDTJ SBrt SHaC
	'Emblème'	SHaC
	'En Avant'	SHaC SPlb
	'Endeavour'	SHaC
	'Erebus' ♀H3	SHaC SSal
	'Ermine'	SHaC
	'Extase'	SHaC
	'Fatamorgana'	SHaC
	'Feuerzauber'	SHaC
	'Fiesta'	SHaC
	FIREBIRD	see *C.* 'Oiseau de Feu'
	'Firebird'	SHaC
	flaccida	SHaC
	'General Eisenhower' ♀H3	SHaC
	× ***generalis*** Cannova Series	SHaC
	- - CANNOVA BRONZE ORANGE ('Fcaa33')	CCht SHaC
	- - CANNOVA BRONZE SCARLET ('Fcaa35') ♀H2	CCht MPri SHaC
	- - CANNOVA LEMON ('Fcaa02')	SHaC
	- - CANNOVA MANGO ('Fcaa10')	CCht SHaC
	- - CANNOVA ORANGE SHADES ('Fcaa17')	MPri SHaC
	- - CANNOVA RED SHADES ('Fcaa23') ♀H2	CCht SHaC
	- - CANNOVA ROSE ('Fcaa05') ♀H2	SHaC
	- - CANNOVA YELLOW ('Fcaa02') ♀H2	CCht SHaC
	× ***generalis*** × ***indica***	SHaC
	glauca	SHaC
	'Gnom'	SDeJ
	'Golden Girl'	MBros
	'Golden Lucifer'	SDeJ
	'Golden Orb'	SHaC
	'Grand Duc'	SHaC
	'Grande'	ESwi SHaC SPlb SSal
	'Grandiose'	SHaC
	'Happy Carmen' (CannaSol Series)	SHaC
	'Happy Cleo' (CannaSol Series)	SHaC
	'Happy Emily' (CannaSol Series)	CBod MSCN SHaC
	'Happy Isabel' (CannaSol Series)	SHaC
	'Happy Julia' (CannaSol Series)	SHaC
	'Happy Wilma' (CannaSol Series)	SHaC
	Henlade hybrids	CDTJ
	'Herman'	SHaC
	'Hossegor'	XLum
	'Indiana'	SHaC
	indica	CAbb CDTJ CPla CTsd EWld NGKo SArc SHaC SPlb WSMil
	- 'Purpurea'	CDTJ SHaC SIvy SPlb
	- 'Red King Rupert'	CCCN
	- 'Russian Red' ♀H3	SHaC
	- TROPICANNA GOLD ('Mactro'PBR)	CBcs CCCN CRos ELan LCro LOPS LRHS MPie SPeP
	'Intrigue'	SHaC
	iridiflora misapplied	see *C.* × ***ehemanii***
	iridiflora Ruiz & Pav.	CDTJ SArc
	'Italia'	CDTJ
	jacobiniflora	SHaC
	jaegeriana	SHaC
	'Jivago'	SHaC
	'Julie' **new**	ETod
	'Kalimpong'	CDTJ
I	'King Humbert' (blood-red)	CBcs CDTJ SDeJ
	KING HUMBERT (orange-red)	see *C.* 'Roi Humbert'
	'King Midas'	see *C.* 'Richard Wallace'
§	'Königin Charlotte'	SDeJ SHaC
	latifolia	SHaC
I	'Leopoldii' **new**	SHaC
	'Lesotho Lil'	SHaC
	'Libération'	XLum
	'Liberté'	see *C.* 'Wyoming'
	'Lion Rouge'	XLum
	'Lolita'	SHaC
	'Louis Cayeux' ♀H3	SHaC
	'Louis Cottin'	CCCN CDTJ
	'Lucifer'	CCCN MBros NPer SDeJ XLum
	'Lucy Steele'	SHaC
	lutea	SHaC
	'Madame Paul Casaneuve'	SHaC
	'Madeira' (Island Series)	SHaC

	'Malawiensis Variegata'	see *C.*'Striata'
	'Marlena'	SHaC
	'Marshmallow'	SHaC
	'Montaigne'	SHaC
	'Moonshine'	CCCN LCro LOPS
	'Mrs Oklahoma'	SDeJ
	'Musifolia' ♀H3	CDTJ ESwi ETod EWes NGKo SHaC SIvy
	'Mystique' ♀H3	SHaC
§	'Oiseau de Feu'	XLum
	'Oiseau d'Or'	SHaC
	'Orange Chocolate'	SHaC
	'Orange Punch'	SHaC
	'Orchid'	see *C.*'City of Portland'
	'Panache'	CDTJ SHaC
	'Panama'	SHaC
	paniculata	SHaC
	'Perkeo'	SHaC
§	'Phasion' (v) ♀H3	CAbb CCCN CSpe ELan LCro LOPS LRHS NPer SHaC SPad SPalm SPeP SPoG WCot WSMil XLum
	'Picasso' ♀H3	CBcs CCCN CDTJ CExl SHaC
	'Pink Futurity' (Futurity Series)	CCCN
	'Pink Perfection'	SHaC
	'President'	ETod SDeJ SHaC WSMil XLum
	'Pretoria'	see *C.*'Striata'
	'Pretoria Variegata'	see *C.*'Striata'
	'Prince Charmant'	SHaC
	'Professor Lorentz'	see *C.*'Wyoming'
	'Queen Charlotte'	see *C.*'Königin Charlotte'
	'Ra' ♀H3	SHaC
	'Red Cherry'	SDeJ
§	'Richard Wallace'	CBod CExl SDeJ SHaC SPlb
	'Robert Kemp'	SHaC
§	'Roi Humbert'	ETod SHaC
	'Roi Soleil'	SHaC
	'Roma'	SHaC
	'Rosa Fuerta' **new**	SHaC
	'Rosemond Coles'	SDeJ SHaC
	'Saladin'	SHaC
	'Salsa'	SHaC
	'Sémaphore'	SHaC WCot
	'Shenandoah' ♀H3	SHaC
	'Singapore Girl'	SHaC
	'Society Belle' ♀H3	SHaC
	'Soudan'	CDTJ
	'South Pacific'	SHaC
	'South Pacific Ivory' **new**	SHaC
	speciosa	CDTJ SPlb
	'Strasbourg'	NPer XLum
	'Striata' misapplied	see *C.*'Stuttgart'
§	'Striata' (v) ♀H3	CBcs CBen CCCN CDTJ CTsd CWGN ETod SEND SEdd SHaC SIvy SPalm WCot XLum
	'Striped Beauty' (v)	CCCN CDTJ CTsd SHaC
§	'Stuttgart' (v)	CBod CDTJ ESwi EWes SHaC SSal
	'Sunset'	WCot
	'Tali'	ETod SHaC
	'Taney'	SHaC
	'Taroudant'	SHaC
	'Tenerife' (Island Series)	ETod
	'Triomphe'	SHaC
	(Tropical Series) 'Tropical Bronze Scarlet'	SHaC
	- 'Tropical Red'	SHaC
	- 'Tropical Rose'	SHaC
	- 'Tropical Salmon'	SHaC
	- 'Tropical White'	SHaC
	- 'Tropical Yellow'	SHaC
	TROPICANNA	see *C.*'Phasion'
	TROPICANNA BLACK ('Lon01'PBR)	CAbb CBcs CPla CRos ELan EPfP ETod LCro LOPS LRHS SIvy SPeP SPoG
	tuerckheimii	SHaC
	'Valentine'	WCot
	'Vanilla Cream'	SDeJ
*	'Variegata' (v)	SPalm
	'Velvet Red'	ETod
	'Verdi' ♀H3	SHaC
	warscewiczii	CDTJ CExl EShb SHaC
	'Weymouth'	CDTJ
	'Whithelm Pride' ♀H3	SDeJ SHaC
	'Wilma' **new**	ETod
	'Wintzer's Colossal'	SHaC
§	'Wyoming' ♀H3	CBcs CBod CCCN CDTJ LCro LOPS SCob SDeJ SEND SHaC SSal
	'Yara'	SDeJ SHaC
	'Yellow Humbert' misapplied	see *C.*'Cleopatra', *C.*'Richard Wallace'
	'Yellow Humbert'	SDeJ

Cannomois (*Restionaceae*)

	grandis	CPbh LRHS SPlb

Cantua (*Polemoniaceae*)

	buxifolia ♀H3	CBcs CCCN CExl CTsd ECre EShb MGil SIvy
	- 'Alba'	CBcs CCCN EShb
	- 'Dancing Oaks'	SVen

Cape gooseberry see *Physalis peruviana*

Capanea see *Kohleria*

Capeochloa (*Poaceae*)

§	***cincta***	WCot

Capnoides see *Corydalis*

Capparis (*Capparaceae*)

	spinosa	CCCN SBrt WJek
	- subsp. ***rupestris***	SPlb

Capsicum (*Solanaceae*)

	annuum	CCCN SVic
	- 'Ancho'	SVic
	- var. ***annuum*** 'Blondy'	LRHS NRHS
	- - (Cerasiforme Group) 'Piccante Calabresé'	SVic
	- - (Conioides Group) 'Super Chili' ♀H1c	EDel SPre SVic
	- - 'Demetra' ♀H1c	EKin
	- - (Grossum Group) 'Almapaprika'	SVic
	- - - 'Bell Boy'	LCro LOPS LRHS NRHS
	- - - 'Bendigo'	MBros
	- - - 'Corno di Toro Rosso' ♀H1c	CHby LCro LOPS MCtn
	- - - 'Friggitello' ♀H1c	MCtn
	- - - 'Mini Bell Red'	SVic
	- - - 'Mini Bell Yellow'	SVic
	- - - 'Mohawk' ♀H1c	CRos EHyd EKin LRHS MBros NRHS
	- - - 'Redskin' ♀H1c	CRos EHyd EKin LCro LOPS LRHS NRHS
	- - - 'Thor'	LRHS
	- - - 'Topepo Rosso' ♀H1c	MCtn
	- - (Longum Group) 'Bolivian Rainbow' ♀H1c	SVic
	- - - cayenne	CCCN LCro LOPS

- - - 'Filius Blue' ♀H1c	NRob
- - - 'Fish'	SVic
- - - 'Golden Cayenne'	SVic
- - - jalapeño	EHyd LCro LOPS LRHS NRHS SVic
- - - 'Hot Thai' ♀H1c	CRos EHyd LRHS NRHS
- - - 'Joe's Long Cayenne'	SVic
- - - 'Loco' ♀H1c	CRos EHyd LRHS NRHS
- - - 'Piccante Di Cayenna'	LCro LOPS
- - - 'Ring of Fire'	SEdi SVic
- - - 'Serrano'	SVic
- - - 'Tokyo Hot'	SVic
- - 'Marconi Rosso'	LOPS SVic
- - 'Prairie Fire' ♀H1c	CCCN CRos EHyd LCro LOPS LRHS NRHS NRob SVic
- - 'Purple Mavros'	LRHS NRHS
- - 'Red King' **new**	EKin
- - SWEETONIA MIX **new**	EKin
- 'Apache' ♀H1c	CCCN CRos EHyd EKin LRHS MBros MPri NRHS NRob SPre
- 'Basket of Fire' ♀H1c	CRos EDel EHyd EKin NRHS SPre SVic
- 'Britney'	LRHS
- 'Bulgarian Carrot'	SVic
- 'Cayenne Purple' **new**	SVic
- 'Cayenne Red'	SEdi SPre SVic
- 'Cayenne Sweet'	SVic
- 'Cheyenne'	CRos EHyd LRHS NRHS
- 'Cow Horn'	SVic
- 'Cozumel' **new**	SVic
- 'Demon Red' ♀H1c	CRos EHyd EKin LRHS MCtn NRHS SPre SVic
- 'Etna' ♀H1c	CRos EHyd LRHS MCtn NRHS
- 'Explosive Ember'	SVic
- 'Fat Bird' **new**	SVic
- 'Fresno' ♀H1c	LRHS NRHS
- var. ***glabriusculum***	SVic
- 'Holy Mole'	SVic
- 'Hungarian Hot Wax' ♀H1c	CHby EKin LCro LOPS MCtn NRob SVic
- 'Hungarian Yellow Wax'	SVic
- 'Jalapeño Farmer's Market Potato' **new**	SVic
- 'Jalapeno Fooled You'	SVic
- 'Jericho'	CRos EHyd LRHS NRHS
- 'Jigsaw' **new**	SVic
- 'Krakatoa' ♀H1c	CRos EHyd LRHS NRHS
- 'Las Cruces Cayenne'	SVic
- 'Masquerade'	CRos EHyd LRHS NRHS
- 'Medina'	LRHS
- 'Medusa'	CRos EHyd LRHS NRHS
- 'Nosferatu'	SVic
- 'Numex April Fools' Day' **new**	SVic
- 'Numex Garnet'	SVic
- 'Numex Heritage Big Jim' **new**	SVic
- 'Numex Lemon Spice' **new**	SVic
- 'Numex Orange Spice' **new**	SVic
- 'Numex Piñata'	SVic
- 'Numex Primavera'	SVic
- 'Numex Sweet' **new**	SVic
- 'Numex Twilight'	CRos EHyd LRHS NRHS SPre SVic
- 'Padron'	LCro LOPS SVic
- 'Paper Lantern'	CRos EHyd LRHS NRHS
- 'Pasilla Bajio'	SVic
- 'Peter Pepper'	SVic
- 'Pinocchio's Nose'	SVic
- 'Pot Black' ♀H1c	EDel SVic
- 'Razzamatazz'	CRos EHyd NRHS
- 'Red Cherry Small'	SEdi
- 'Serrano Purple' **new**	SVic
- 'Treasure's Red' ♀H1c **new**	LRHS
- 'Tricolor Variegatum' (v) ♀H1c	NRob
- 'Trinidad Perfume'	LRHS
- 'Vampire'	SVic
baccatum 'Aji Limon'	SVic
- 'Aji Omnicolor'	SVic
- 'Brazilian Starfish'	SVic
- 'Christmas Bell'	SVic
chinense 'Bhut Jolokia'	LRHS SVic
- 'Carolina Reaper'	SVic
- 'Cheiro Roxa'	SVic
- Habanero Group	EKin NRob
- - 'Habanero Caribbean Red'	SVic
- - 'Naga Morrich'	SVic
- - 'Caribbean Antillais' ♀H1c	SVic
- 'Habenero Mustard' **new**	SVic
- 'Hot Paper Lantern'	SVic
- 'Numex Suave Orange'	SVic
- 'Numex Suave Red'	SVic
- 'Peito de Moca'	SVic
- 'Scotch Bonnet'	CRos EHyd LRHS MBros NRHS SPre
- 'Seven Pod Brain Strain Yellow'	SVic
- 'Shabu Shabu' **new**	SVic
- 'Trinidad Moruga Scorpion'	LRHS SVic
frutescens 'Adorno'	LCro LOPS
- Tabasco Group	LRHS SVic
'Rodeo'	SVic

Caputia (*Asteraceae*)

§ ***scaposa***	EShb WSMil
§ ***tomentosa*** ♀H1c	EShb SEdd SIvy

Caragana (*Fabaceae*)

CC 3945	CExl
arborescens	CAgr CMCN ELan EPfP NLar NWea SPer SPlb
- PAB 13.376	LEdu
- 'Lorbergii'	MBlu NLar SPer
- 'Pendula'	CMac ELan GBin MBlu NLar SCoo SPer WSpi
- 'Walker'	ELan LPar MAsh MBlu MGos NHol NLar NWea SCoo SPer
aurantiaca	NLar SBrt
halodendron	CBcs LPar MBlu SPer

carambola see *Averrhoa carambola*

caraway see *Carum carvi*

Cardamine (*Brassicaceae*)

asarifolia misapplied	see *Pachyphragma macrophyllum*
bipinnata	WCot
bulbifera	EBee ELon EPPr ESwi GBin GEdr GGro GQue LEdu MAvo NAts NRya WCru
californica	EBee EPPr LEdu MAvo NRya WCot WCru
concatenata	WCru
digitata	EBee EMor
diphylla	EBee WCot WCru
- 'American Sweetheart'	CExl
- 'Eco Cut Leaf'	CExl EBee LEdu MAvo WCru
- 'Eco Moonlight'	WCru
enneaphylla	GWyn NBid NLar

glanduligera	CElw CTtf EBee ECha ELon EPPr EPri GEdr LEdu MAvo MNrw NLar NSla SBrt WCot WCru WFar
§ ***heptaphylla***	CMiW ECha ELon GEdr GKev ILea LEdu MBel WCru WSHC
- from the Pyrenees	NLar
- 'Big White'	EBee EPPr GAbr GBin MAvo MNrw NLar WFar
- Guincho form	EPPr GEdr MAvo WCot
- 'Helen Myers'	GEdr
§ ***kitaibelii***	CMiW EMor EPPr EWld LEdu MNrw NLar SBrt WCot WCru WFar
latifolia Vahl	see *C. raphanifolia*
macrophylla	CTtf EBee EWld GEdr LEdu WCot WSHC
- 'Bright and Bronzy'	CExl EPPr MAvo WCru
maxima	SHar WCru
microphylla	GKev
pentaphylla ♀^{H5}	CBor CSpe EBee EPPr EWld GAbr GBin GKev GMaP LEdu MCot NHpl NLar SPhx WCru WSHC
* - 'Alba'	EPPr
pratensis	CBcs CDor CPud CTtf CWat GAbr GJos LCro LOPS LRHS MACG MBow MHer MNHC NAts NMir SPhx SRms WHer WSFF WShi
- 'Diane's Petticoat'	MAvo
- 'Edith' (d)	LPot
- 'Flore Pleno' (d)	CDor CSpe CTtf ECha GArf GQue LEdu MHer NBid NBir NBro NLar NRya WSFF
- 'Flore Pleno' white-flowered (d)	LEdu
- white-flowered	CDor
- 'William' (d)	LEdu
quinquefolia	CElw CMiW CTtf ECha EHed EHyd ELon EPfP ILea LEdu MBel MNrw MPie NLar SDix SDys WBrk WCot WCru WFar
- PAB 9992	LEdu
§ ***raphanifolia***	CExl EBee ECha GAbr LLWG NBid NBro NRya SHar WBor WFar
- PAB 204	LEdu
trifolia	CElw CMac EBee ECha ELon EMor EPPr EWld GBin GEdr GMaP ILea LEdu MAvo MNrw MRav NBir NBro NLar NRya SBut WCot WCru WFar
waldsteinii	CElw CExl EBee EPPr GArf GEdr ILea LEdu NBro NLar SMHy WCru WFar WSHC
yezoensis	ESwi GBin
- B&SWJ 4659	EBee EPPr WCru

cardamon see *Elettaria cardamomum*

Cardiandra (*Hydrangeaceae*)

alternifolia B&SWJ 5719	WCru
- B&SWJ 5845	WCru
- B&SWJ 6177	WCru
- B&SWJ 6354	WCru
- subsp. ***moellendorffii***	CExl WPGP
- 'Pink Geisha'	WCru
amamiohshimensis	WCru
formosana	CExl IArd IDee WPGP
- B&SWJ 2005	WCru
- 'Crûg's Abundant'	WCru
- 'Hsitou'	WCru
- 'Hsitou Splendour'	WCru

Cardiocrinum ✿ (*Liliaceae*)

cordatum B&SWJ 2812	WCru
- B&SWJ 4841	WCru
- B&SWJ 5427	WCru
- B&SWJ 6336	WCru
- B&SWJ 11069	WCru
- var. ***glehnii***	CCCN GEdr GKev
- - B&SWJ 10827	WCru
- - B&SWJ 10843	WCru
- red-veined	SBrt
giganteum	CBcs CBor CCCN EBee EHyd GAbr GBin GEdr GKev LRHS MNrw NBid NHpl NLar NRHS SBea SDir SMad WCru WPnP WTyc
- B&SWJ 2419	WCru
- GWJ 9219 from Sikkim	WCru
- HWJK 2158 from Nepal	WCru
- WJC 13661 from Sikkim	WCru
- WJC 13698 from Sikkim	WCru
- 'Big and Pink' **new**	WCru
- var. ***giganteum***	CSpe
- var. ***yunnanense***	CBct EBee EPfP GEdr IKel ITim NBid WCru WPGP
- - PAB 8347	LEdu
- - NJM 11.023 from Guizhou	WPGP
aff. ***giganteum*** NJM 12.060 from Nagaland, India	WPGP

cardoon see *Cynara cardunculus*

Carduus (*Asteraceae*)

nutans	GGro

Carex (*Cyperaceae*)

from Kyoto, Japan	EPPr GGro
acuta	CHab CPud
- 'Variegata' (v)	CBen CMac EShb GMaP LLWG NBro
acutiformis	NMir
alba	WCot
'Amazon Mist'	CBod CRos EPfP LRHS MACG NLar NRHS SCob SRms SWvt WFar
arenaria	CKno
§ ***atrata*** subsp. ***pullata*** KEKE 494	EBee
aurea	CBod GWyn WChS
baccans	CExl SBrt
berggrenii	CSde NFav SPlb
boottiana	MHost
brunnea	CMac
- 'Jenneke' (v)	CBod EBee EHyd SWvt
- 'Jubilo'^{PBR}	EBee
- 'Lady Sunshine' **new**	CKno
- 'Variegata' (v)	LPot WHoo WSpi
buchananii	Widely available
- 'Firefox'	CBod CEme LRHS
- 'Green Twist'	CBod EHyd EShb LRHS NRHS
- 'Red Rooster'	EBee EWoo LBuc LSun MACG NLar NWsh SCob
- 'Viridis'	CBod XLum
chathamica	LRHS SVen WABo WCot
ciliatomarginata 'Treasure Island' (v)	EBee
comans	EPfP NBro
- 'Bronze Perfection'	CBod
- bronze-leaved	CBod CDoC CPla CRos CSBt EHyd ELan EPfP GArf GDam LPot LRHS MAsh MHost NBir NRHS NSti NWad NWsh SCob SCoo SPer SRms SWvt WCAu WSMil XLum
- 'Bronzita'	LRHS WFar
- 'Dancing Flame'	CWCL ELon
- 'Frosted Curls'	Widely available

- 'Phoenix Green' NWsh
- red-leaved NLar SRms
- 'Small Red' see *C. comans* 'Taranaki'
§ - 'Taranaki' SCoo
conica 'Hime-kan-suge' see *C. conica* 'Snowline'
§ - 'Snowline' (v) CMac ELan EShb GGro GMaP LEdu NBro NLar NWsh SWvt XLum
davalliana EBee
dioica LLWG
dipsacea CKno CMac CRos CWCL EBlo EHyd EShb GMaP LRHS MHost NLar NRHS NWad WHal
- 'Dark Horse' MMuc
divulsa CKno
- subsp. ***leersii*** EPPr
§ ***dolichostachya*** 'Kaga-nishiki' (v) CSBt EPPr GKev LRHS SGBe
§ ***elata*** 'Aurea' ♀H6 Widely available
- 'Bowles's Golden' see *C. elata* 'Aurea'
- 'Knightshayes' CKno WCot WFar
elongata CHab
'Evergold' see *C. oshimensis* 'Evergold'
firma 'Green Dragon' GEdr
- 'Variegata' (v) EPot GEdr WAbe
flacca CHab CKno EPPr
- 'Blue Zinger' CBod CKno ELan NLar SCoo WFar XSen
§ - subsp. ***flacca*** EBee NSti
flagellifera CBcs CBod CMac CRos CSpe CTri CWCL EBee EBlo EHyd ELan ELon EPPr EPfP EShb GMaP LRHS MHost MMuc NBir NRHS SCob SDix SEND SPlb SPoG WSMil
- 'Kiwi' EHyd NRHS
folliculata EPPr
glauca Scop. see *C. flacca* subsp. *flacca*
'Gold Fountains' see *C. dolichostachya* 'Kaga-nishiki'
grayi EHyd GBin LEdu LRHS MACG MBlu NLar NRHS SBls SPlb WHoo WSHC
'Ice Dance' (v) Widely available
laxiculmis 'Bunny Blue'PBR CBod CKno NLar XLum
limosa LLWG
MILK CHOCOLATE ('Milchoc'PBR) (v) CBod ECtt ELan EPfP LRHS LSou MAsh SGbt SRms
morrowii misapplied see *C. oshimensis*
morrowii Boott 'Everglow' (EverColor Series) (v) **new** CBod CKno XSte
I - 'Fisher's Form' (v) CBrac CTri ELan EPPr MRav SWvt WBrk
- 'Gilt' (v) EPPr NWad
- 'Irish Green' CBod WFar
- 'Nana Variegata' (v) CTri
- 'Pinkie' CDoC MHost
- VANILLA ICE ('Vanice'PBR) (v) CKno SCoo
- 'Variegata' (v) CBod ELan EPPr EWoo GMaP LRHS MMuc NBir NSti SRms WAvo XLum
* ***multifida*** EGrI
muskingumensis CExl CKel CKno CWCL ELan EPPr EPfP EShb GBin LEdu LLWG LRHS MACG MHost NBro NLar SCob SDix SSal WChS WPnP WSMil
- 'Little Midge' CKno CMac EShb GBin LPla NLar
- 'Oehme' (v) CKno CWCL EHyd EPPr LLWG NBid NHol NWad
- 'Silberstreif' (v) CKno EPPr EShb GBin LEdu MMuc XLum
nigra (L.) Reichard WAvo
§ - 'On-line' (v) EPPr
- 'Variegata' see *C. nigra* 'On-line'
No 4, Nanking (Greg's thin leaf) EPPr

obnupta CKno
ornithopoda 'Aurea' see *C. ornithopoda* 'Variegata'
§ - 'Variegata' (v) GBin NHol NWsh
§ ***oshimensis*** EPPr WCot
- (EverColor Series) 'Everillo'PBR CBcs CBct CBod CKel CKno EBee EMor EPfP LBuc LRHS MAsh NGBl NLar NWad NWsh SCob SCoo SGBe SPeP SPoG SRms WCot
- - 'Everlime'PBR CBct CBod CKno LRHS MAsh SCoo SGBe XSte
- - 'Everlite' (v) CKno LCro LOPS LRHS
- - 'Everoro' (v) CKno LRHS LSun MHol WCot
- - 'Eversheen'PBR (v) LRHS SCoo SGBe XSte
- EVERCREAM ('Ficre'PBR) (v) XSte
- EVEREST ('Fiwhite'PBR) (v) Widely available
§ - 'Evergold' (v) ♀H7 Widely available
- 'Evergreen' SCob
- 'Variegata' (v) NBir
otrubae CHab CPud
panicea CPud CWCL CWat EBee EPPr EShb LLWG XLum
pendula CHab CKno CPud CTri ECha ELan EPfP GMaP LRHS MHost MMuc NBro NLar NMir SCob SEND SMad XLum XSen
- 'Cool Jazz' (v) EPPr
- 'Moonraker' (v) ESwi MHost WCot
petriei EBee ECha ELon
phyllocephala EShb
- 'Spark Plug'PBR (v) **new** SPad
- 'Sparkler' (v) ELon LRHS SCob SPad SPoG SWvt
plantaginea EPPr EShb GBin LEdu WPGP WSHC XLum
praegracilis CKno
pseudocyperus CPud GBin NPer NWsh WPnP
remota CKno EPPr EShb LPla
RIBBON FALLS ('Et Crx02'PBR) **new** CBod
riparia CHab CPud MWts NPer
- 'Bowles's Golden' see *C. elata* 'Aurea'
sabynensis see *C. umbrosa* subsp. *sabynensis*
scaposa ESwi WCot
- KWJ 12304 LEdu WCru
secta CKno CRos EHyd EPPr EPfP GMaP LPla LRHS NRHS SRms
- from Dunedin, New Zealand EPPr
siderosticta WSHC
- 'Banana Boat' see *C. siderosticta* 'Golden Falls'
§ - 'Golden Falls' (v) MNrw SMad
- 'Kisokaido' (v) EShb
- 'Shima-nishiki' (v) EBee
- 'Variegata' (v) CPla CTri CTsd ELan EShb LEdu MACG NBir NLar NSti NWsh
'Silver Sceptre' (v) CBod CBrac EBlo EHyd EMor EShb GKev GMaP LPar LRHS MBNS MBel MGos NRHS NSti NWad NWsh SIvy SPlb SWvt WBrk WFar XLum
solandri CKno
spicata CHab
spissa MNrw
stricta Gooden. 'Bowles's Golden' see *C. elata* 'Aurea'
stricta Lam. MMuc SEND
sylvatica CHab CKel
tenuiculmis CWCL EBee EHyd LRHS NRHS NSti NWad SPtp WCot
testacea Widely available
- 'Limeshine' WFar

- 'Old Gold'	SPlb
- 'Prairie Fire'	CSpe EBou EPfP GMaP LBuc LCro LOPS LRHS MACG NLar NRHS SBls SCob SCoo SGBe SPtp SRms WGrn WSMil XLum
texensis	EPPr
'The Beatles'	LRHS NBir
'Triffid'	MHost
trifida	CKno MACG MHost
- 'Chatham Blue'	MMuc SIvy
- 'Rekohu Sunrise'[PBR] (v)	CBod CKel CKno EBee ELon EPfP LRHS LSun MMuc NSti SGBe SLon WCot
§ ***umbrosa*** subsp. ***sabynensis*** 'Thinny Thin' (v)	EShb
vulpina	MHost

Carica (*Caricaceae*)

papaya (F)	SPre SVic
- 'Babaco'	CCCN
pubescens	see *Vasconcellea pubescens*

Carissa (*Apocynaceae*)

grandiflora	see *C. macrocarpa*
§ ***macrocarpa*** (F)	CCCN SVic WKor

Carlina (*Asteraceae*)

acaulis	ELan SPlb
§ - subsp. ***simplex***	ECha EHyd ELon LRHS NRHS
- - bronze-leaved	GGro SPhx
vulgaris	GKev GPoy
- 'Silver Star'	SPhx

Carmichaelia (*Fabaceae*)

odorata	CExl
petriei	SMad
stevensonii	CBcs CCCN EBee IArd MBlu NLar WPGP
williamsii	CTsd

× *Carmispartium* see *Carmichaelia*

Carpenteria (*Hydrangeaceae*)

californica	CCCN CEme CKel CSBt CTri EBee EHyd ELan EPfP ESwi GBin IDee LCro LOPS LRHS MGil MGos NLar NRHS SCob SPer SWvt WFar WHwl WSpi XSte
- 'Bodnant' ♀H4	CBcs CBod CCCN EBee EHed EHyd ELan LRHS LSRN MAsh MGos NLar NRHS SGBe SWvt WFar WGob WPGP WSpi
- 'Elizabeth' ♀H4	CSBt CWGN EPfP LSRN MAsh MGil NLar SPoG
- 'Eskimo'	CBcs CCCN CDoC CKel EBee EMil SWvt WSpi
- 'Ladhams' Variety'	CBcs CMac EHyd EPfP LRHS MRav SGBe SMad SWvt WHwl WKif WSpi

Carpinus ✿ (*Betulaceae*)

betulus ♀H7	Widely available
* - 'A. Beeckman'	CLnd
- 'Columnaris'	CLnd EBee
* - 'Columnaris Nana'	MPkF WLov
§ - 'Fastigiata' ♀H7	Widely available
I - 'Folis Argenteovariegatis Pendula' (v)	MBlu
- 'Frans Fontaine'	CCVT CEnd CLnd CMCN CMac EBee EPfP EWTr IArd IPap LMaj LPar LSRN MBlu MGos MTrO NLar NOra NWea SCob SCoo SEWo SGol SGsty SLim SPer SPoG WLov WMat WMou
- 'Globus'	MBlu
- 'Lucas'	CCVT EBee LPar MBlu MNic MTrO NOra SGol WMat
- 'Monument'	MPkF
I - 'Monumentalis'	LMaj NLar
- 'Pendula'	CAco CEnd EBee LPar MBlu SWvt WMou
- 'Purpurea'	CEnd CLnd MBlu
- 'Pyramidalis'	see *C. betulus* 'Fastigiata'
- ROCKHAMPTON RED ('Lochglow')	EWTr LRHS MBlu MNic MSwo MTrO NOra NOrn SGol WMat WMou
- 'Rockingham Red' **new**	MSwo
- 'Stegemanns Primus'[PBR]	EBee
caroliniana	CLnd CMCN EPfP LMaj
- from Mexico	WPGP
- 'Red Fall'	EPfP LRHS MBlu WMou
- 'Sentinel Dries'	LRHS MBlu MMrt WMou
cordata	MBlu SSta
coreana	LMaj
fangiana	CBcs CEnd CExl CJun CLnd EBee EPfP MBlu WPGP
fargesiana	EBee WPGP
- KR 8780	WPGP
fargesii	see *C. viminea*
henryana	CExl CMen EBtc
- var. ***simplicidentata***	CMCN MBlu
japonica ♀H6	CAco CBcs CEnd CLnd CMCN CMen EBee EPfP EWTr IPap LPar MBlu NOra SAko SCoo SEWo SSta WMat WMou
- B&SWJ 10803	WCru
- B&SWJ 11072	WCru
- 'Chinese Lantern'	MTrO WMat
kawakamii	CMCN
- CWJ 12412	WCru
- CWJ 12449	WCru
laxiflora	CExl CMen
- B&SWJ 10809	WCru
- B&SWJ 11035	WCru
- var. ***longispica*** B&SWJ 8772	WCru
- var. ***macrostachya***	see *C. viminea*
omeiensis	EBee
- KR 280	WPGP
orientalis	CMCN
- 'Perdika' **new**	LRHS
polyneura	CMCN EBee MBlu SSta WPGP
pubescens	WPGP
rankanensis	SSta
- NMWJ 14544	WCru
- RWJ 9839	WCru
× ***schuschaensis***	EBtc LRHS
shensiensis	EBee WPGP
tschonoskii B&SWJ 10800	WCru
- BBJMT 297	WPGP
turczaninowii	CBcs CMCN CMen IPap MBlu NLar SSta
- var. ***turczaninowii***	WPGP
§ ***viminea***	CEnd CExl SSta WCot

Carpobrotus (*Aizoaceae*)

acinaciformis	SVen
§ ***edulis***	CCCN CDTJ CSde SArc SEND SVen XLum
- 'Gugh Dawn' (v)	SVen
- var. ***rubescens***	CCCN
- white-flowered	CCCN

muirii	CCCN SVen
sauerae	CCCN

Carrierea (*Salicaceae*)

calycina	CBcs IArd WPGP

carrot see *Daucus carota* for species; also AGM Vegetables Section for cultivars

Carthamus (*Asteraceae*)

dianius	SBrt
mitissimus	GEdr
tinctorius	MNHC SRms SVen SVic
- 'Kinko' **new**	CSpe

Carum (*Apiaceae*)

carvi	CBod CLau ENfk GPoy MHer MNHC SRms SVic WJek XAbr
petroselinum	see *Petroselinum crispum*

Carya ✿ (*Juglandaceae*)

cordiformis	CMCN MBlu
glabra	CBcs
illinoinensis (F)	CAgr CBcs CLnd MBlu
- 'Carlson No 3' seedling (F)	CAgr
- 'Colby' seedling (F)	CAgr
- 'Cornfield' (F)	CAgr
- 'Lucas' (F)	CAgr
laciniosa (F)	EPfP
- 'Henry' (F)	CAgr
- 'Keystone' seedling (F)	CAgr
ovata (F)	CAgr CBcs EPfP MBlu WPGP
- 'Grainger' seedling (F)	CAgr
- 'Neilson' seedling (F)	CAgr
- 'Weschcke' seedling (F)	CAgr
- 'Yoder No 1' seedling (F)	CAgr
tomentosa	WPGP

Caryophyllus see *Syzygium*

Caryopteris (*Lamiaceae*)

× ***clandonensis***	CMac ECtt MGil NBir
- 'Arthur Simmonds' ♀H4	ECha
- BLUE BALLOON ('Korball')	NLar SGol
- BLUE EMPIRE ('Elst33'PBR) **new**	CTsd
- 'Dark Knight'	CBod CDoC CKel CRos CSpe EBee EGrI EHed EHyd ELan EPfP LBuc LCro LOPS LRHS MAsh MCot NRHS SCob SCoo SEdd SEle SPer SPoG STPC SWvt WFar WHil WHoo
- 'Ferndown'	EHed NLar SEND SRms
- 'First Choice' ♀H4	CBrac CRos EHyd ELan EPfP LRHS LSRN MAsh MGil NRHS SPer SRkn SWvt
- 'Gold Giant'	CRos EHyd EPfP LRHS MAsh NRHS
- GRAND BLEU ('Inoveris'PBR)	CMac EBee EHed EHyd ELan EPfP LRHS LSRN MGil MGos MHtn NLar SGbt SGol SGsty SWvt SavN WLov
- 'Heavenly Baby' ♀H4	CRos EHyd EPfP LRHS MAsh SLon
- 'Heavenly Blue'	Widely available
- 'Hint of Blue'	SGol
- HINT OF GOLD ('Lisaura'PBR) ♀H4	CRos CSBt EHyd ELan EPfP LCro LOPS LRHS MAsh NLar NRHS SCob
- 'Kew Blue'	CBcs CRos CSBt EBee EHyd ELan EPfP EShb LRHS LSRN MAsh MGos MHer MSwo NLar NRHS SCoo SGbt SGol SLon SPer SRms SSta SWvt XSen
- 'Longwood Blue'	CRos EPfP LRHS
- 'Pershore'	WAvo
- PETIT BLEU ('Minbleu'PBR)	EBee LRHS
- PINK PERFECTION ('Lisspin')	CBod CRos EHyd ELan LRHS NEoE NRHS SEle SPoG
- STEPHI ('Lissteph'PBR)	CBcs CRos EHyd ELan EPfP LRHS NRHS SPoG WNPC
- STERLING SILVER ('Lissilv'PBR) ♀H4	CKel CMac CRos EBee EHyd EPfP LPar LRHS LSRN MAsh NEoE NRHS SCob SPer SPoG SRkn SRms SSta WHil
- 'Summer Gold'	CMac MAsh
- 'Summer Sorbet'PBR (v) ♀H4	CEme CMac CRos CWGN EBee ELan EPfP EWes LRHS MAsh MGos NLar SCob SCoo SGbt SGol SNig SPer SRms SWvt WCot WFar
- weeping	ELan EPPr WFar
- 'White Surprise'PBR	CBod CEme CMac CWGN EHed EHyd ELan EMil EPfP LRHS NRHS SCob SGol SGsty SPer SPoG WFar WHil
- 'Worcester Gold' ♀H4	CBcs CMac CSBt CTri ECha EHyd ELan EPfP LRHS MAsh MGos MHer MRav MSwo NRHS SEND SGol SNig SPer SPlb SRms SWvt WAvo WFar
- aff. 'Ferndown'	CBrac
divaricata	CMCN LPla SBrt WFar
- 'Electrum'	WCot WFar WSHC
- 'Jade Shades'	WSHC
- pink-flowered	WFar
- 'Snow Fairy' (v)	MGil
§ ***incana***	SPer
- 'Blue Cascade'	CKel ELan EPfP LRHS MRav NLar SRms WAvo WGrn
- 'Delft Blue'	CKel EBee
§ - 'Jason'PBR	CBcs CBrac EGrI NLar SPoG WFar
- SUNSHINE BLUE	see *C. incana* 'Jason'
mastacanthus	see *C. incana*

Caryota (*Arecaceae*)

mitis	CCCN

Cassandra see *Chamaedaphne*

Cassia (*Fabaceae*)

corymbosa Lam.	see *Senna corymbosa*
fistula	CDow
marilandica	see *Senna marilandica*
nemophila	SPlb

Cassinia (*Asteraceae*)

fulvida	SVen
leptophylla	CBcs
vauvilliersii	SVen
'Ward Silver'	XSte

Cassinia × *Helichrysum* (*Asteraceae*)

hybrid	WKif

Cassiope ✿ (*Ericaceae*)

'Askival Snowbird'	EPot
'Askival Snow-wreath'	see *C.* Snow-wreath Group
'Edinburgh'	EPot ITim WThu
lycopodioides	ITim
- 'Beatrice Lilley' ♀H5	EPot GArf GKev GRum ITim WThu
- 'Jim Lever'	WAbe
- 'Rokujō'	ITim
mertensiana	GArf
- 'California Pink'	GKev
- subsp. ***californica***	ITim
- var. ***gracilis***	GArf ITim WThu
'Muirhead'	WThu
'Randle Cooke'	EPot
selaginoides	GArf

– LS&E 13284	EPot WAbe WThu
§ Snow-wreath Group	EPot
tetragona var. ***saximontana***	GKev
wardii	EPot

Castanea ✿ (*Fagaceae*)

'Bouche de Bétizac' (F)	CAgr
crenata	CAgr
henryi	CMCN
– CBS 0755.04 new	WPGP
'Maraval' (F)	CAgr WMat
'Maridonne' (F)	CAgr
'Marigoule' (F)	CAgr EPom NRog WMat
'Marsol' (F)	CAgr NRog WMat
'Précoce Migoule' (F)	CAgr
sativa	CAco CBrac CCVT CDoC CLnd CSBt CTri ELan EPfP EPom IPap MAsh MGos MMuc MNic MTrO NOra NOrn NRog NWea SCob SEWo SGol SLim SPer WBor WFar WMat WMou WTSh
§ – 'Albomarginata' (v) ♀H6	CEnd EPfP NOra SPoG WMat
– 'Anny's Summer Red'	SPer
– 'Argenteovariegata'	see *C. sativa* 'Albomarginata'
– 'Aureomarginata'	see *C. sativa* 'Variegata'
– 'Belle Epine' (F)	CAgr
– 'Bournette' (F)	CAgr
* – 'Doré de Lyon'	CAgr
– 'Marlhac' (F)	CAgr NOra NRog WMat
– 'Marron Comballe' (F)	CAgr
– 'Marron de Goujounac' (F)	CAgr
– 'Marron de Lyon' (F)	CAgr CEnd CHab EPfP EPom NRog NWea SVic
– 'Regal' (F)	EPom
§ – 'Variegata' (v)	CAco CMCN ELan SCob
seguinii	WPGP

Castilleja (*Orobanchaceae*)

applegatei subsp. ***pinetorum***	GKev
integra	SPlb
latifolia	GKev
miniata	LShi SPlb WAbe
revealii new	GKev
sessiliflora	SPlb
sulphurea	GKev

Casuarina (*Casuarinaceae*)

cunninghamiana	CAco EBtc SPlb
glauca	SVen

Catalpa ✿ (*Bignoniaceae*)

bignonioides ♀H6	Widely available
– B&SWJ 15090	WCru
– 'Aurea' ♀H6	Widely available
* – 'Aurea Nana'	LPar
– 'Nana'	ELan ERom MNic SGsty WLov
– 'Purpurea'	see *C.* × *erubescens* 'Purpurea'
– 'Variegata' (v)	EBee ELon EPfP WLov
bungei	CCVT CMCN MBlu SArc
§ × ***erubescens*** 'Purpurea' ♀H6	CBcs CBod CCVT CEnd CMCN CMac EBee EHed ELan ELon EPfP LMaj LRHS MBlu MGil MRav MSwo MTrO NLar NOra NOrn SPer SPoG SWvt WHwl WLov WMat WPGP
fargesii f. ***duclouxii*** ♀H6	CBcs CEnd CLnd EBee EPfP MBlu SAko SChF WLov WPGP
ovata	CMCN EGrl EHed
speciosa ♀H6	CAco CMCN GBin SVen
– 'Frederik'	NLar
– 'Pulverulenta' (v)	CAco EBee EHed MBlu SMad WLov

Catalpa × *Chilopsis* see × *Chitalpa*

Catananche (*Asteraceae*)

caerulea	Widely available
– 'Alba'	CMea CRos CSpe EBee ECha EHyd ELan EPfP EWoo LRHS MBel MNrw NRHS SCob SEdd SGbt SPer SPoG SWvt WCAu WSHC XLum XSen
– 'Amor Blue'	CRos EHyd EPfP LRHS MACG NRHS SPoG
– 'Amor White'	SPeP
– 'Major' ♀H5	CRos EHyd LCro LOPS LRHS NRHS SEdd SRms

Catha (*Celastraceae*)

edulis	GPoy

Catharanthus (*Apocynaceae*)

roseus (Roseus Group) 'Mediterranean Lilac' new	LShi

Cathcartia (*Papaveraceae*)

chelidoniifolia	EHyd NBid

Catopsis (*Bromeliaceae*)

morreniana	NCft

cauliflower see AGM Vegetables Section

Caulokaempferia (*Zingiberaceae*)

petelotii B&SWJ 11818	WCru
– HWJ 541	WCru

Caulophyllum (*Berberidaceae*)

thalictroides	EBee EMor EPPr GKev LEdu MMrt WCru WHil WPGP WPnP WSHC
– subsp. ***robustum***	EBee WCru

Cautleya ✿ (*Zingiberaceae*)

cathcartii	CExl LEdu
– 'Tenzing's Gold'	EBee ESwi EWld LEdu WCru WPGP WSHC
§ ***gracilis***	CDTJ CExl CSpe GKev
– BWJ 7843	WCru
– from Manipur, India	WPGP
– 'Crûg Gold'	WCru WPGP
– 'Dzoukou'	LEdu
lutea	see *C. gracilis*
spicata	CBct CCCN CDTJ CSpe MHid NGKo XLum
– CC 3676	CExl
– 'Arun Flame'	CBct ESwi LEdu MNrw WCru WPGP
– 'Bleddyn's Beacon'	ESwi WCru WSHC
– 'Crûg Canary'	LEdu MHid WCru WPGP
– 'Crûg Compact'	WCru
* – var. ***lutea***	CBct CDTJ LEdu MHid WPGP
– 'Robusta'	CAvo CBcs CExl EBee EBlo ELan EPPr EPfP LEdu LRHS MMrt MNrw SMad WCot WCru WPGP XSte

Cayratia (*Vitaceae*)

japonica B&SWJ 6636	WCru
§ ***thomsonii*** BWJ 8123	EPPr

Ceanothus ✿ (*Rhamnaceae*)

'A.T. Johnson'	EPfP SEdd SGol SPer SRms

	arboreus	SArc
	- 'Trewithen Blue' ♀H4	Widely available
	'Autumnal Blue' ♀H4	CBcs CBod CBrac CDoC CEnd CExl CKel CMac CSBt CTri EBee EHyd ELan EPfP LCro LOPS LRHS MGos MRav MSwo NLar NRHS SCob SGbt SGol SPer SRms SSta SWvt WAvo
	'Blue Cushion'	CTri EPfP LRHS MGos NLar NRHS SLon SWvt
	'Blue Diamond'PBR	LSRN
	'Blue Jeans'	NLar
	'Blue Mound' ♀H4	Widely available
	'Blue Sapphire'PBR	CBod CWGN ELan EPfP LRHS LSRN SPoG SRms SWvt WTyc
	'Blue Sensation'	NLar
	'Burkwoodii' ♀H4	CBcs CEnd CKel CRos ELan EPfP LRHS MAsh MGos MRav SCob SCoo SPer SRms SWvt
	'Cascade' ♀H4	CBcs LPar LSRN SPlb WAvo
	'Concha' ♀H4	Widely available
	'Cynthia Postan'	CBod EHyd EPfP MHer NLar
	'Dark Star' ♀H4	CBcs CBod CChe CRos CSBt CTri CWGN EHyd ELan ELon EPfP LRHS LSRN MAsh NHol NRHS SPoG SSta SWvt
	'Delight'	CBcs
	× ***delileanus*** 'Gloire de Versailles' ♀H4	CBcs CKel ELan EPfP EWTr ILea MGos MRav MSwo NLar SCoo SGol SPer SPoG SWvt WKif WSpi
	- 'Henri Desfossé'	CKel ELan EPfP LSRN MHtn MRav MSwo NLar SPer SPoG WKif WSpi
	- 'Topaze' ♀H4	CKel CTsd ELan EPfP LRHS MRav NLar SLon WKif WSpi
	dentatus Torr. & A. Gray	SPlb
	'Diamond Heights'	see *C. griseus* var. *horizontalis* 'Diamond Heights'
	EL DORADO ('Perado') (v)	CBod CKel CSBt ELan SGol WAvo
	gloriosus 'Emily Brown'	CBcs CBrac ELan MRav NLar
§	***griseus*** var. ***horizontalis*** 'Diamond Heights' (v)	LRHS LSRN NLar SCob SPer
	- - 'Silver Surprise'PBR (v)	LBuc LSRN NLar SRms
	- - 'Yankee Point'	CBcs CBod CDoC CMac CRos CSBt EHyd EPfP EShb LPar LRHS LSRN MGos MRav MSwo NLar NRHS SCob SCoo SEND SEdd SGol SGsty SPlb SPoG SWvt
	impressus	CTri MAsh SPer SWvt WFar
	'Italian Skies'	CBcs CBod CBrac CEme CEnd CKel CRos CSBt EHyd ELan EPfP GDam LRHS LSRN MGos MSwo NLar NRHS SCob SCoo SEdd SGol SGsty SLon SPer SPlb SPoG SWvt
	'Julia Phelps'	WAvo
	'Lemon and Lime'PBR	CKel LBuc SCoo
	'Madagascar'	SCoo SEdd SPoG
	MARIE-ROSE ('Minmarose')	CKel EMil EPfP
	× ***pallidus*** 'Marie Simon'	EGrl EHyd ELan EPfP LPar LSRN MGos SPer SPoG SRms SWvt WCFE WKif WSpi
	- 'Perle de Jade'	ILea
	- 'Perle Rose' ♀H4	CBcs EPfP MGos MHtn NLar SPer WKif WSpi
	papillosus	IArd WPav
§	'Pershore Zanzibar'PBR (v)	CBcs CEme CMac CRos CTri EHyd LRHS MGos MRav MSwo NRHS SCoo SGbt SPer SPoG SRms WAvo
	'Pin Cushion'	CDoC EHyd EPfP LRHS
	'Point Millerton'	see *C. thyrsiflorus* 'Millerton Point'
	'Popcorn'	LRHS
	prostratus	SMad
	'Puget Blue' ♀H4	Widely available
	'Puget Blue' × ***thyrsiflorus*** var. ***repens***	LOPS LPar
	'Ray Hartman'	NLar
	repens	see *C. thyrsiflorus* var. *repens*
	'Skylark' ♀H4	Widely available
	'Snow Flurries'	see *C. thyrsiflorus* 'Snow Flurry'
	'Snow Showers'	CBcs
	'Southmead' ♀H4	CRos CTri EHyd ELan EPfP LRHS MGos MSwo NRHS
	thyrsiflorus	CTri SRms SWvt
§	- 'Millerton Point'	CBod CCCN ELan EPfP NLar SGol
	- 'Mystery Blue' ♀H4	EHyd LRHS NRHS SWvt
§	- var. ***repens*** ♀H4	Widely available
§	- 'Snow Flurry'	ELan MSwo NFav SCob
	'Tilden Park'	CRos EHyd LRHS
	'Tuxedo'PBR	MRav NLar SCob SGol
	× ***veitchianus***	CSBt EPfP SPer
	'Victoria'	CEnd EBee LPar LRHS LSRN MPri MSwo NLar SGol SGsty SRms
	'Zanzibar'	see *C.* 'Pershore Zanzibar'

Cedrela (*Meliaceae*)

	sinensis	see *Toona sinensis*

Cedronella (*Lamiaceae*)

§	***canariensis***	CBod CCBP ENfk GPoy MNHC SRms WJek XAbr
	triphylla	see *C. canariensis*

Cedrus (*Pinaceae*)

	atlantica	CAco CBod LMaj LRHS NWea SCob SGol WMat WTSh
	- 'Aurea' ♀H6	CAco NLar SLim
	- 'Fastigiata'	CAco LRHS NLar SLim
	- Glauca Group	CCVT CMac CMen EBee ELan EPfP EWTr IPap MBlu MGos MNic NLar SCob SEWo SGol SPer SPlb SPoG SWeb WMat WMou
	- - 'Glauca' ♀H6	CAco CLnd LMaj LPar MAsh MTrO NOra NOrn NWea SAko SGsty WTSh
	- - 'Glauca Pendula' ♀H6	CAco CCVT CLnd LPar LRHS MBlu MGos NLar NOra NWea SGol SGsty SLim WMat
	- - 'Silberspitz'	CKen NLar
	- 'Pendula'	CBod NOra NOrn
	- 'Sapphire Nymph'	CKen MAsh NLar SLim
	brevifolia	CAco EBtc LMaj LRHS NLar
	- 'Epstein'	CAco
	- 'Hillier Compact'	CKen NLar
	- 'Jade Medusa'	CAco
	- 'Kenwith'	CKen NLar
	deodara ♀H6	Widely available
	- 'Albospica' (v)	SWvt
	- 'Aurea' ♀H6	CCVT CKen EPfP LMaj MGos NHol NOra NOrn SGol SGsty WFar WMat
I	- 'Aurea Pendula'	CAco
	- 'Blue Dwarf'	CKen
*	- 'Blue Mountain Broom'	CKen
	- 'Blue Snake'	CKen
	- 'Blue Surprise'	CAco SLim
	- 'Bush's Electra'	MBlu NLar
	- 'Cream Puff'	CAco
	- 'Deep Cove'	SLim
	- 'Devinely Blue'	CKen
	- 'Feelin' Blue' ♀H6	CAco CKen ELan LMaj LRHS MAsh MTrO NLar SGsty SLim SWeb SWvt WFar WMat
	- 'Gold Cascade'	SLim
	- 'Golden Horizon'	CAco CKen CMen ELan MAsh MTrO NLar SCob SLim SPoG WFar WMat

– 'Karl Fuchs'	CAco LMaj LRHS NLar
– 'Kelly Gold'	EBee
– 'Klondyke'	CAco MAsh
– 'Lime Glow'	CAco CKen SLim
– 'Mr Blue'	SPoG
– 'Nana'	CKen
– 'Pendula' ♀H6	CKen LRHS NWea SLim
– 'Pygmy'	CKen
– 'Robusta'	CAco LMaj WPGP
– 'Roman Candle'	CAco
– 'Scott'	CKen
– 'Silver Mist'	CKen
– 'Silver Spring'	CAco
libani ♀H6	CAco CBrac CCVT CEme CLnd CMCN CMac ELan EPfP IPap LMaj LPar LRHS MBlu MMuc NLar NOra NOrn NWea SCob SEND SGol SGsty SPlb SWvt WFar WMou WTSh
– 'Blue Angel'	SLim
– 'Blue Fountain'	NLar
– 'Comte de Dijon'	NLar
– 'Fontaine'	NLar
– 'Glauca'	CAco
– 'Golden Dwarf'	CKen
– 'Green Prince'	NLar
– 'Hedgehog'	CKen NLar
– 'Home Park'	CKen NLar
– 'Italie'	NLar
– 'May'	LRHS NLar SLim
– 'Minitaur'	CAco NLar
– Nana Group	CKen ELan
– 'Pendula'	CAco CKen NLar
– 'Sargentii'	MBlu NLar

Ceiba (*Malvaceae*)

pentandra	SPlb

Celastrus (*Celastraceae*)

dependens CWJ 12478	WCru
– NMWJ 14556	WCru
flagellaris B&SWJ 8572	WCru
hookeri B&SWJ 11667	WCru
kusanoi CWJ 12445	WCru
orbiculatus	CBcs MRav SLon WHer
– Hermaphrodite Group ♀H6	MGil SDix
– var. ***papillosus*** B&SWJ 591	WCru
– var. ***punctatus*** CWJ 12439	WCru
scandens	CMac SPhx SPlb
stephanotiifolius B&SWJ 4727	WCru
stylosus WJC 13746	WCru

celeriac see AGM Vegetables Section

celery see AGM Vegetables Section

Celmisia (*Asteraceae*)

allanii	GArf GKev WAbe
argentea	EPot GArf NHar WAbe
bellidioides	GAbr GArf GKev NSla WAbe
coriacea misapplied	see *C. semicordata*
coriacea Raoul	see *C. mackaui*
'Eggleston Silver'	NBir
gracilenta	GKev WAbe
haastii* × *viscosa	NSla
hectorii	GArf GBin WAbe
§ ***mackaui***	GArf
ramulosa	ITim NHar WAbe
– var. ***tuberculata***	NSla
§ ***semicordata***	GKev NHar NHpl
sessiliflora	EPot GArf WAbe
§ ***walkeri***	GKev
webbiana	see *C. walkeri*
I 'Wooley Hybrid'	EPot

Celosia (*Amaranthaceae*)

argentea var. ***cristata*** (Plumosa Group) 'Dragon's Breath' ♀H2	CRos LSou
– – – Kimono Series	MBros SPoG
KELOS FIRE RED **new**	MBros
KELOS FIRE YELLOW **new**	MBros

Celsia see *Verbascum*

× *Celsioverbascum* see *Verbascum*

Celtica see *Stipa*

Celtis (*Cannabaceae*)

australis	CBcs CMCN EBee IPap LEdu LPar MBlu WKor
– var. ***eriocarpa*** **new**	MVil
biondii	NLar
choseniana B&SWJ 12774	WCru
occidentalis	EBtc EWTr IPap WKor
sinensis	CMen

Cenolophium (*Apiaceae*)

denudatum ♀H6	Widely available

Centaurea ✿ (*Asteraceae*)

HH&K 271	NBid
RCB AM 6	WCot
W&B BGB-1	WCot
alpestris	NLar SPhx
'Amethyst on Ice'	ELan LBuc SRms WCav
§ ***atropurpurea***	CBod CSpe EBee EGrI EHyd ELan EWTr EWes LPot LRHS MBNS MBel MHol NBid NGBl NLar NSti SBls SHar SMad SPhx SPlb WCot WMal
babylonica RCB/TQ 18	WCot
bagadensis	GKev
bella	CBod EBee ECtt EHyd ELon EWTr EWoo LRHS MBel MRav MSpe NBro NGrd NRHS NSti SBut SMHy SPhx WFar WKif XLum XSen
benoistii misapplied	see *C. atropurpurea*
benoistii ambig.	MRav
benoistii ambig. × ***orientalis***	SPhx
candidissima misapplied	see *C. cineraria*
candidissima Lam.	see *C. rutifolia*
'Caramia'	CBcs CBod EBee ECtt EHyd ELan EPfP LEdu LRHS MHol MNrw MSpe NBid NHpl NLar NRHS WCAu
carniolica	SHar
– SDR 5443	EBee
cheiranthifolia	CFis EPPr MHol MNrw NBid NBir NLar SBut SHar
§ ***cineraria***	CSpe ECre WSpi
– subsp. ***cineraria*** ♀H3	SEND SSal WCot WMal
clementei	XSen
I 'Copper Hybrid'	CPla
cyanoides	LRHS
cyanus	CHab CSpe GArf LCro LOPS MBow MHer MNHC MPri SVic
– 'Black Ball'	CSpe LCro LOPS LRHS MNHC SPhx
– 'Blue Ball'	CSpe
– 'Blue Diadem'	SPhx

- 'Florence Blue' (d) LRHS SPhx
- 'Mauve Ball' **new** CSpe
- 'Pinkie' (d) MNHC SPhx
- 'Snowman' LRHS SPhx

cynaroides Link see *Rhaponticum centaureoides*
dealbata CBod CMac EAJP EBee EHyd EPfP LRHS MBel MHol MMuc NBro NGrd NLar NMir NRHS SCob SEND SRms STPC
- 'Steenbergii' CMac LRHS NBid NBir NGdn NPer NSti SPer SPoG WCAu WCot

declinata RCB UA 18 WCot
gigantea WHer
glastifolia EBee
gymnocarpa see *C. cineraria*
jacea ELon GAbr GWyn NBid NLar SBut SPhx SSal WCot WPGP XLum
- PAB 8821 LEdu

'John Coutts' CBod CRos EBee ECha ECtt EHyd ELan EPfP GLog GMaP LEdu LRHS MBel MMuc MRav NBid NBir NLar NRHS NSti SEND SGbt SPer SPoG SRms WCAu WCot WHil WHoo
'Jordy' Widely available
karabaghensis EBee GKev MSpe
macrocephala ECha ECtt EHyd ELan ELon EPfP EShb EWTr GAbr LEdu LRHS MBel NBid NBro NChi NGBl NLar NRHS SBls SDix SPer SPoG SRms WCAu
mollis NBid
montana Widely available
- 'Alba' Widely available
- 'Amethyst Dream'[PBR] CRos EBee EHed EHyd EMor EPfP LRHS MNrw NLar NRHS SCoo SPoG WCAu
- 'Amethyst in Snow' CElw CRos EAJP EBee ECtt EHyd EMor EPfP LEdu LRHS MBNS MHol NHol NLar NRHS NWad SCob SPoG WBor WCAu WTor
- 'Black Sprite' CBod CSpe CWGN EAJP EBee ECtt EHyd ELon EPfP GMaP LRHS MBNS MNrw NFav NLar NRHS NSti SPoG WBor WBrk WFar WHil
- 'Blewit' EBee NLar WCAu
§ - 'Carnea' CElw ELon EPPr GMaP LRHS MBel MCot NBir NChi NLar SHar SPhx WBrk WCAu WFar
- 'Elworthy Glacier' CElw WMal
- 'Gold Bullion' CBod CSpe CWGN EBee ECtt EHyd EWes GMaP LRHS MRav NBid NRHS SMad SMrm WSHC
- 'Grandiflora' CCBP EBee ELon MPie
- 'Joyce' CElw NBid NLar SCob SHar WCAu WSHC
- 'Lady Flora Hastings' CElw CSpe EPPr NBid WBrk
- 'Lavender Mist' CBod NRHS
- lilac-flowered NBid NLar
- 'Ochroleuca' CElw NBid
- 'Parham' CBod CElw CRos ECtt EHyd ELon GAbr GQue LRHS MNrw MRav NLar NRHS NSti SPer SPlb WSHC
- 'Purple Heart' Widely available
- 'Purple Prose' CElw EPPr LPla
- 'Purpurea' CElw
- 'Rosea' see *C. montana* 'Carnea'
I - 'Violacea' NBid
- 'Violetta' CElw EBee ELon LCro LOPS MSpe NBid NBir WBrk WCAu

nervosa NBid NBro
nigra CBod CDor CHab EBee ELan ELon EPfP EWTr GJos GQue LCro LOPS MBow NLar NMir SPhx SRms SVic WSFF WWild
- var. ***alba*** NBid
- 'Mardi Gras' (v) ECtt
- subsp. ***rivularis*** NBid
- 'Waterfall White' MAvo MHol

orientalis CBod CSpe EHyd EWes LRHS LSou MHol MSpe NGBl SGbt SPhx WHoo
pannonica EPPr
- subsp. ***pannonica*** HH&K 259 NBid

Phoenix hybrids **new** LRHS
phrygia CBod MMuc NLar SPhx WCot
pulcherrima MNrw
'Pulchra Major' see *Rhaponticum centaureoides*
pullata EHyd
rigidifolia EBee
rupestris EBee SPhx
ruthenica CFis EWTr SPhx SPlb WGoo
§ ***rutifolia*** WMal
salicifolia NBir
scabiosa CBod CCBP CDor CHab GQue LCro LOPS MHer MNHC MSpe NBid NBir NGrd NMir SPhx SRms SVic WShi
'Silver Feather' CBcs CBod CKno EHyd LRHS MHol NRHS NSti SBut SGBe SPoG SRms WNPC
simplicicaulis EBee ELon MAsh NBir NChi NHpl SHar SRms WCav WHoo XLum XSen
thracica WCot
triumfettii 'Hoar Frost' EBee ELon NDov
- subsp. ***stricta*** LPla SHar

Centaurium (*Gentianaceae*)

erythraea GKev GPoy
scilloides GKev NSla WAbe

Centella (*Apiaceae*)

§ ***asiatica*** GPoy LCro LEdu LOPS WJek XAbr

Centradenia (*Melastomataceae*)

inaequilateralis CCCN
- 'Cascade' ♀H2 MBros

Centranthus (*Caprifoliaceae*)

§ ***lecoqii*** ECha ECtt EPPr EWes GBin LRHS NDov SPhx WCot WGoo
macrosiphon CMac
§ ***ruber*** Widely available
* - 'Alba Pura' GAbr
§ - 'Albus' Widely available
- 'Atrococcineus' ECha MMuc SGbt
- var. ***coccineus*** CBcs CBod CRos EAJP EBee EHyd ELan EPfP EWoo GAbr GBin GJos GKin GMaP LPot LRHS LSun MRav NRHS SBut SCob SEND SPer SPhx SSut WCot WFar XLum XSen
- mauve-flowered misapplied see *C. lecoqii*
- 'Roseus' EHyd EPfP
- 'Rosy Red' CBod
- 'Ruby Red' LSun
- 'Snowcloud' EBee ECtt EHyd ENfk EPfP MBow MNHC NFav SBut SRms WHil

Centratherum (*Asteraceae*)

punctatum CSpe

Centropogon (*Campanulaceae*)

ferrugineus B&SWJ 10665 WCru

Cephalanthus (*Rubiaceae*)

'Magical Moonlight'	LCro LOPS LRHS NLar
occidentalis	CBod EBee MAsh MBNS MBlu NLar NQui SPhx SPoG
- SUGAR SHACK ('Smcoss')	LRHS

Cephalaria (*Caprifoliaceae*)

§ ***alpina***	CBod CDor EHyd EMor EPPr EPfP LRHS MAsh MNrw NRHS SDix SHar SPhx SRms WBrk WFar XLum
caucasica	see *C. gigantea*
dipsacoides	LRHS MSpe SPhx SRms SSal WGoo
§ ***flava***	EHyd
galpiniana	SPlb
§ ***gigantea***	Widely available
leucantha	CFis MMuc NLar SEND SPhx WBrk
litvinovii	SPhx
radiata	CFoA NDov SPhx
tatarica hort.	see *C. gigantea*
tchihatchewii	ILea NLar WCot
transsylvanica	SPhx
- W&B BGJ-1	CSpe WCot

Cephalotaxus (*Taxaceae*)

fortunei	CAco LEdu WCru
- var. ***fortunei*** <u>**new**</u>	CAco
harringtonia	CMCN LEdu
- var. ***drupacea***	CAco
- 'Fastigiata'	CAco IArd IDee LPar LRHS MAsh MGil MGos SLim SPoG
- 'Gimborn's Pillow'	CAco MAsh
- 'Korean Gold'	LRHS SLim
sinensis	CAco

Cephalotus (*Cephalotaceae*)

follicularis 🏆H2	CHew SHmp

Cerastium (*Caryophyllaceae*)

alpinum	SRms
- var. ***lanatum***	EWes
biebersteinii	XLum
candidissimum	EWes
fontanum	CHab
tomentosum	CBar CBod CKel CSBt CTri CWCL EBee ELan EPfP EWTr GKev GWyn LPot LRHS MHol MMuc NBir SEND SLee SPer SPlb SPoG WFar
- var. ***columnae***	ECha EWes GMaP WIce XLum XSen

Ceratonia (*Fabaceae*)

siliqua	SEND SPlb SVic

Ceratophyllum (*Ceratophyllaceae*)

demersum	CBen CPud CWat EWat LCro LOPS MWts SVic WMAq WSFF
submersum	LLWG

Ceratostigma (*Plumbaginaceae*)

abyssinicum	CBcs EGrI ELan ESwi EWTr SIvy
asperrimum B&SWJ 7260	WCru
capensis	CMac
griffithii	Widely available
§ ***plumbaginoides*** 🏆H5	Widely available
willmottianum 🏆H4	Widely available
- BWJ 8140	WCru
- DESERT SKIES ('Palmgold'PBR)	CMac EPfP NLar SCob SWvt
- FOREST BLUE ('Lice'PBR) 🏆H4	CBrac CDoC CEnd CKel CMac CRos CSBt EHyd ELan EPfP LCro LOPS LRHS LSRN MAsh MGos MPri MRav NRHS SAko SCoo SGBe SPer SPoG SSta SWvt XSte
- SAPPHIRE RING ('Lissbrill'PBR)	CBcs CCCN CDoC CPla CRos EBee EHyd ELan EPfP LRHS LSRN MAsh MGos NRHS SCoo SPoG WFar WHil

Cercidiphyllum ✿ (*Cercidiphyllaceae*)

japonicum 🏆H5	Widely available
- 'Boyd's Dwarf'	CDoC CJun CRos EHyd ELan EPfP LRHS MBlu NLar SPoG SSta
- 'Chameleon' (v)	MBlu NLar
- GLOWBALL ('Jww4'PBR)	IArd MBlu
- 'Herkenrode Dwarf'	MBlu NLar
- 'Heronswood Globe' 🏆H5	CJun CMCN EPfP MBlu NLar SSta WHwl
- 'Kreukenberg Dwarf'	CJun NLar SSta
- 'Morioka Weeping'	CJun EBee MPkF NLar SChF SSta
- 'Peach'	CJun NLar
§ - f. ***pendulum*** 🏆H5	Widely available
- - 'Amazing Grace'	MBlu SGbt SSta
- RA ('Jww3'PBR) <u>**new**</u>	NLar
- 'Raspberry'	CJun MBlu NLar
- RED FOX	see *C. japonicum* 'Rotfuchs'
§ - 'Rotfuchs'	CBcs CEme CEnd CJun CMCN CMac CRos EBee EHyd ELan EPfP LRHS MBlu MGos NLar SAko SChF SGol SGsty SPoG SSta WFar WHwl WMat
- 'Ruby'	CJun EBee MBlu
- 'Strawberry'	CBcs CJun MBlu NLar SSta
- 'Tidal Wave'	CJun LRHS MBlu NLar SSta
- 'Titania'	NLar SSta
magnificum	CEnd CExl CMCN EBee MBlu MMrt NLar
- f. ***pendulum***	see *C. japonicum* f. *pendulum*

Cercis ✿ (*Fabaceae*)

canadensis	CAgr CMCN CTsd CWGN LMaj LPar MGil MGos MTrO NLar NWea SCob SavN XSen
- f. ***alba***	CBcs CMCN LSRN
- - 'Royal White'	EPfP MBlu SPer
- 'Alley Cat' (v)	MTrO WMat
- 'Appalachian Red'	MBlu MGos WMou
- CAROLINA SWEETHEART ('Nccc1')	LRHS MTrO WMat
- 'Cascading Hearts'	EHyd NRHS
- 'Flame'	CJun SSta
- 'Forest Pansy' 🏆H5	Widely available
- 'Hearts of Gold'PBR	CMac CWGN EBee LPar LRHS MGos MRav MTrO NLar NOra NOrn SLon SPoG WHwl WMat XSte
- LAVENDER TWIST ('Covey')	CMac EBee EHyd ELan EPfP LCro LMaj LOPS LPar LRHS LSRN MBlu MGos MTrO NLar NOra NOrn NRHS SGol SLon SPoG SRms WHwl WMat
- LITTLE WOODY ('Litwo'PBR)	MGos NLar SGol
- 'Melon Beauty'	MBlu NLar WHwl
- 'Merlot'	ELan MGos NLar NWea SGsty WHwl WMat
- 'Pauline Lily'	NLar
- 'Pink Heartbreaker'	SGol
- 'Pink Pom Poms'	EBee MTrO NLar WHwl WMat
- RED FORCE ('Minrouge3'PBR)	CDoC EHed LRHS LSRN NLar SGsty WCot XSte
- 'Ruby Falls'PBR 🏆H5	CBcs CMac CTri EBee EHyd ELan EPfP EWTr LCro LMaj LOPS LPar LRHS LSRN MGos MTrO NOra NRHS SMad SPoG WHwl WMat
- 'Rubye Atkinson'	NLar

- var. ***texensis*** 'Oklahoma' EBee ELan EPfP MGos MTrO WMat WPGP
- - 'Texas White' CEnd CMac EBee EPfP LRHS MTrO NLar NOrn WMat
- - 'Traveller' LPar SGol
- 'The Rising Sun' MGos
- 'Vanilla Twist'PBR CMac EBee LPar MTrO NLar SPoG WHwl WMat

chinensis CAco EGrI EWTr GKev LMaj NLar SavN WMou
- B&SWJ 12665 WCru
- f. ***alba*** MGos
- 'Avondale' ♀H5 CBcs CEnd CJun CMac EBee EGrI EHed EHyd ELan EPfP EWes LCro LMaj LOPS LPar LRHS LSRN MAsh MBlu MGos MTrO NLar NOra NOrn SCoo SPoG SWvt WHwl WMat WMou
- 'Diane' SSta
- 'Don Egolf' ♀H5 CJun MBlu MGos NLar SGol
- 'Shirobana' LMaj LPar WMat

chingii CExl WPGP
griffithii CMCN LEdu NLar SSta WPGP
occidentalis SSta
racemosa CExl WPGP XSen
siliquastrum Widely available
- f. ***albida*** EHyd ELan EPfP EWes GKev SSta
- 'Bodnant' ♀H5 CMac EPfP EWes LRHS LSRN MBlu MGos NLar NOra SSta WHwl WMat
- 'White Swan' CJun

Cerinthe (*Boraginaceae*)

major SWvt
- 'Purpurascens' CSpe EBee ELan EPfP LCro LOPS MNHC SMrm SPhx SPoG WCav WKif

Ceropegia (*Apocynaceae*)

§ ***linearis*** subsp. ***woodii*** ♀H1c CDoC EShb
sandersonii ♀H1c CCCN CDoC ELan EShb
woodii see *C. linearis* subsp. *woodii*

Cestrum (*Solanaceae*)

aurantiacum EShb SEND
buxifolium B&SWJ 14395 WCru
× ***cultum*** 'Cretan Pink' CCCN
- 'Cretan Purple' CBcs CCCN EBee EGrI EHyd ELan ELon EPfP EShb IDee LRHS MGil SWvt WKif
diurnum × ***nocturnum*** EShb
§ ***elegans*** CEme CExl CKel CSde CTsd CWit EBee ELon EPfP EWld IDee LRHS MGil NQui SEND SIvy SLon SPad SWvt WCFE
fasciculatum SDix
'Newellii' ♀H3 CBcs CCCN CExl CKel EBak EBee EGrI EHyd ELan ELon EPfP LRHS SIvy SPlb SVen SWvt WKif
nocturnum CBcs CCCN EBak EShb WCFE
parqui ♀H3 CBcs CCCN CEme CKel CMCN CTsd EBee EGrI ELan EPfP IDee MGil SDix SEND SIvy SLon SMad SWvt WKif WSHC
- purple-tinged SBrt
psittacinum CExl
purpureum misapplied see *Iochroma cyaneum* 'Trebah'
purpureum (Lindl.) Standl. see *C. elegans*
roseum CExl
- B&SWJ 10255 from Oaxaca State, Mexico WCru
- 'Ilnacullin' CCCN CSde EBee
violaceum misapplied see *Iochroma cyaneum* 'Trebah'

Ceterach see *Asplenium*

officinarum see *Asplenium ceterach*

Chaenomeles (*Rosaceae*)

cathayensis CAgr EPfP EWTr LEdu NLar WCru WFar WHer WKor WPGP
§ ***japonica*** CAco CCCN MMuc SCob SEND SPre WKor
- 'Chojubai' CMen
- 'Cido' CAgr LEdu MCoo
- 'Orange Beauty' NHol SCob
- 'Rising Sun' NLar
- 'Sargentii' MBlu NLar SGol
MADAME BUTTERFLY ('Whitice') CBod EBee EHyd ELan EPfP LRHS LSRN MAsh MRav NRHS SCob SGol SPoG SRms
maulei see *C. japonica*
'Orange Star' CEme CEnd SGol
sinensis see *Pseudocydonia sinensis*
§ ***speciosa*** NWea
- 'Apple Blossom' see *C. speciosa* 'Moerloosei'
- 'Contorta' MAsh WFar
- 'Eximia' LRHS NLar SGsty
- 'Falconnet Charlet' (d) EHyd LRHS MRav NRHS SGol SRms
- 'Flocon Rose' EPfP SGol
- 'Friesdorfer' CDoC LRHS SGsty
- 'Geisha Girl' (d) ♀H6 Widely available
- 'Grayshott Salmon' WSpi
- HOT FIRE ('Minvesu') CDoC CRos EPfP LRHS SGsty WCot WSpi
- 'Kinshiden' CEme CKel EMil EPfP LRHS LSRN NLar SGol SGsty WSpi
- MANGO STORM ('Mincha01'PBR) CRos EPfP LRHS NLar SGol SGsty
§ - 'Moerloosei' ♀H6 Widely available
- 'Nivalis' Widely available
- 'Orange Storm'PBR CRos EBee LCro LOPS LRHS LSRN SGol
- 'Pink Storm'PBR CRos EPfP LCro LOPS LRHS NLar SGol
- RED KIMONO ('Ainoomoi'PBR) LRHS NLar SGol
- 'Rubra Grandiflora' SGsty WSpi
- 'Scarlet Storm'PBR CRos EBee EPfP LRHS NLar SGol
- 'Simonii' (d) CBcs MRav NWea WSpi
- 'Snow' MAsh MSwo SRms
- 'Umbilicata' MBlu SPer SRms
- 'Yukigotan' (d) CDoC LEdu NLar SGol SWvt WSpi
× ***superba*** 'Boule de Feu' CTri MCoo
- 'Cameo' (d) CBrac CEnd ELon EPfP IArd LEdu LPar LRHS MBNS MMrt MRav NLar SCob SGbt SGol SIvy SPer SRms WCot WFar
- 'Coquelicot' NLar
- 'Crimson and Gold' ♀H6 Widely available
- 'Elly Mossel' CMac SGol SRms WFar
- 'Etna' WFar
- 'Fire Dance' CAco CTsd MSwo SGol SPer WCot WLov WSpi
- 'Fusion' CAgr
- 'Hollandia' SRms
- 'Issai White' MRav
- 'Jet Trail' CBcs CMac CRos CSBt EHyd ELan EPfP EWoo GDam LPar LRHS MAsh MGos MRav MSwo NLar NRHS SCob SGbt SGol SNig SRms SWvt WFar
- 'Knap Hill Scarlet' CBod CRos EBee EHyd ELan EPfP LRHS MAsh MGos MNHC NRHS

SCob SCoo SPer SPoG SRms SWvt WCot
- 'Lemon and Lime' — CBcs CBod CEme CMac ELan LRHS MAsh MGos MRav NLar SLon SPer SRms WLov WSpi
- 'Nicoline' ♀H6 — CBcs CKel LRHS MGos
- 'Pink Lady' ♀H6 — Widely available
- 'Pink Trail' — NLar SGbt SRms
- 'Red Joy' — CKel EPfP LRHS MRav NLar SRms
- 'Red Trail' — CKel MRav
- 'Rowallane' ♀H6 — CBod MRav
- 'Salmon Horizon' — IArd NLar SGol
- 'Texas Scarlet' — CKel SRms WMou
- 'Tortuosa' — CBod MBNS NLar WCot WGrn

'Toyo-nishiki' — MBlu

Chaenorhinum (*Plantaginaceae*)

'Bon Bini' **new** — LRHS
glareosum — GKev NHpl
§ ***origanifolium*** — GArf GKev SPlb
- 'Blue Dream' — CSpe EBou EPfP EWTr GKev LRHS LShi MAsh SBls SBut SPoG SWvt WFar WHoo WIce

Chaenostoma (*Scrophulariaceae*)

§ ***cordatum*** (Abunda Series) ABUNDA COLOSSAL BLUE ('Balabolue') — LSou MBros
- - ABUNDA COLOSSAL PINK — MBros
- - ABUNDA COLOSSAL WHITE ('Balabowite'PBR) — LSou MPri
- 'Olympic Gold' (v) — SCoo
- (Scopia Series) SCOPIA DOUBLE BALLERINA SNOWBALL (d) **new** — LSou
- - SCOPIA GOLDEN LEAVES WHITE ('Dancop15') — MBros
- 'Snowflake' — MBow MBros NPer SCoo SPoG SWvt

Chaerophyllum (*Apiaceae*)

aromaticum — LEdu
aureum — NAts
azoricum — LEdu LPla LShi MAvo
coloratum — SPtp
creticum — SPtp
hirsutum 'Roseum' — Widely available

Chaetanthera (*Asteraceae*)

villosa **new** — SPlb

Chamaecrista (*Fabaceae*)

fasciculata — SPhx

Chamaecyparis ✿ (*Cupressaceae*)

funebris — see *Cupressus funebris*
lawsoniana — CAco CBrac GDam IPap LMaj NWea SCob WTSh
- 'Allumii Aurea' — see *C. lawsoniana* 'Alumigold'
- 'Allumii Magnificent' — MAsh
§ - 'Alumigold' — LPar LRHS MAsh NOrn
- 'Alumii' — CBrac NOrn
- 'Aurea' — CBrac
- 'Aurea Densa' ♀H6 — CKen CSBt MGos
- 'Aurea Nana' — see *C. lawsoniana* 'Aurea Densa', *C. lawsoniana* 'Minima Aurea'
- 'Bleu Nantais' ♀H6 — CKen LBee LRHS MGos SCoo SPoG WCFE
- 'Blom' — CKen
- 'Blue Surprise' — CKen
- 'Brégéon' — CKen NLar
- 'Broomhill Gold' ♀H6 — CSBt LBee MGos NOrn SCoo SPoG SVic
- 'Caudata' — CKen
§ - 'Chilworth Silver' ♀H6 — CBod CBrac CSBt LBee MAsh
- 'Columnaris' — EPfP LBee LPar SCoo SPoG
- 'Columnaris Glauca' — CBrac CMac MGos NOrn NWea SCob SCoo SGsty SPer
- 'Cream Glow' — CKen CSBt LRHS
- 'Dik's Weeping' ♀H6 — CAco NLar NWea
- 'Drooping Solo' — CKen NLar
- 'Dutch Gold' — MAsh
- 'Dwarf Blue' — see *C. lawsoniana* 'Pick's Dwarf Blue'
- 'Eclipse' — CKen
- 'Elegantissima' ambig. — CMac
- 'Ellwoodii' ♀H6 — CBod CBrac CMac CSBt CTri ELan EPfP LPar LRHS MAsh MGil MGos MPri NLar NWea SCob SCoo SGsty SLim SPer
- 'Ellwood's Gold' ♀H6 — CBcs CBod CBrac CEme CMac CSBt ELan EPfP LBee LPar LRHS MAsh MGos MPri NOrn NWea SCob SGsty SLim SPer SPlb SPoG SVic
- 'Ellwood's Gold Pillar' ♀H6 — LBee LRHS MAsh NHol NLar SLim
§ - 'Ellwood's Nymph' — CKen
- ELLWOOD'S PILLAR ('Flolar') ♀H6 — CMac LBee LRHS MAsh MGos NLar NOrn SCoo SLim
- 'Ellwood's Pygmy' — CMac
- 'Ellwood's Silver Threads' — CMac LBee
- 'Ellwood's Variegata' — see *C. lawsoniana* 'Ellwood's White'
§ - 'Ellwood's White' (v) — CMac SPoG
- 'Emerald Spire' — MAsh
- 'Erecta Viridis' — CBrac CMac NWea
- 'Filip's Golden Tears' — ELan NLar
- 'Fleckellwood' — MAsh NOrn
- 'Fletcheri' ♀H6 — CBrac CMac NWea
- 'Fletcheri Aurea' — see *C. lawsoniana* 'Yellow Transparent'
- 'Forsteckensis' — NWea
- 'Fraseri' — NWea
- 'Gimbornii' ♀H6 — NLar
- 'Glauca Pendula' — CAco
- 'Gnome' — CKen CMac NHol SCoo SPoG
- 'Golden King' — NWea
§ - 'Golden Pot' — CBod CSBt LBee
- 'Golden Wonder' ♀H6 — MAsh NWea SCoo
- 'Grayswood Feather' ♀H6 — LBee MAsh SCob
- 'Green Globe' ♀H6 — CKen CMen CSBt LBee MAsh MGil
§ - 'Green Hedger' — CSBt
§ - 'Green Pillar' — EPfP LBee NWea
- 'Green Spire' — see *C. lawsoniana* 'Green Pillar'
- 'Imbricata Pendula' ♀H6 — CAco CKen IDee MBlu NLar SLim SMad WPGP
- 'Intertexta' — SLim
- 'Ivonne' ♀H6 — EPfP GDam LPar MAsh MGos NWea SCoo SLim SPoG
- 'Jackman's Variety' — see *C. lawsoniana* 'Green Pillar'
- 'Jeanette' — CKen
- 'Karaca' **new** — NLar
- 'Kilmacurragh' ♀H6 — CAco MAsh
- 'Kilworth Column' — LRHS NLar NWea
- 'Knowefieldensis' — CMac
- 'Lane' den Ouden — CBrac
§ - 'Lanei Aurea' ♀H6 — NWea
- 'Little Spire' ♀H6 — CAco LRHS NLar WLea
§ - 'Lutea Nana' — CBrac CMac
- 'Luteocompacta' — LBee

	- 'Mason's Pillar'	CKen
	- 'Minima Argentea'	see *C. lawsoniana* 'Nana Argentea'
	- 'Minima Aurea' ♀H6	CBrac CKen CMac CSBt EPfP LBee MAsh MGil MGos NWea SCoo SLim SPoG
	- 'Minima Glauca' ♀H6	CBrac CMac NWea SCoo SLim WFar
	- 'Moonsprite' ♀H6	CKen MAsh NLar SCoo SLim SPoG
	- 'Nana'	CBrac
	- 'Nana Albospica' (v)	LBee
§	- 'Nana Argentea'	CKen EPfP SPoG
	- 'Nana Lutea'	see *C. lawsoniana* 'Lutea Nana'
	- 'Nicole'	MAsh NWea SCoo
	- 'Nyewoods'	see *C. lawsoniana* 'Chilworth Silver'
	- 'Nymph'	see *C. lawsoniana* 'Ellwood's Nymph'
	- 'Pearly Swirls' (v)	NLar SCoo SPoG
§	- 'Pelt's Blue'	CSBt NLar
	- 'Pembury Blue' ♀H6	CBod CBrac EPfP LBee MGos NLar NOrn NWea SCob SCoo SLim SPoG
§	- 'Pick's Dwarf Blue'	CBrac
	- 'Pina Colada'PBR	LRHS
	- 'Pitt Lane'	CKen
	- Pot of Gold	see *C. lawsoniana* 'Golden Pot'
	- 'Pottenii'	CBrac LBee NLar NOrn NWea
	- 'Pygmaea Argentea' (v) ♀H6	CBrac CEme CKen CMac CSBt ELan MAsh MGos SCoo SLim SPoG
	- 'Pygmy'	CMen NWea
	- 'Rijnhof'	LBee
	- 'Rimpelaar'	CKen MGil NWad
	- 'Silver Queen' (v)	CKen
	- 'Silver Threads' (v)	ELan LBee SCoo SPoG
	- 'Silver Tip' (v)	LRHS
	- 'Snow Flurry' (v)	CKen
	- 'Snow White' (v) ♀H6	LBee LRHS MAsh MGos NHol SCoo SLim SPoG SVic
	- 'Somerset'	CMac
	- 'Springtime'PBR	CSBt LBee
	- 'Stardust' ♀H6	CBcs CSBt ELan MAsh MGos MPri NOrn SCob
	- 'Stewartii'	NWea
	- 'Sulphur Spire'PBR **new**	LRHS
	- 'Summer Snow' (v) ♀H6	NHol SCoo
	- 'Sunkist'	SLim
	- 'Sunny Smile'PBR **new**	SCoo
	- 'Tharandtensis Caesia'	NLar
	- 'Treasure' (v)	MAsh
	- 'Van Pelt'	see *C. lawsoniana* 'Pelt's Blue'
	- 'Waterfall'	CAco
	- 'Winston Churchill'	CMac NOrn NWea
	- 'Wisselii' ♀H6	CAco CKen LRHS MGos NLar NWea SCoo SLim
	- 'Wisselii Nana'	CKen
	- 'Wissel's Saguaro' ♀H6	CAco CKen LRHS NLar SLim
	- 'Yellow Spire'	SLim
§	- 'Yellow Transparent'	CMac
	× ***leylandii***	see × *Cuprocyparis leylandii*
	nootkatensis	see *Xanthocyparis nootkatensis*
	obtusa 'Albovariegata' (v)	CKen
	- 'Arneson's Compact'	CKen
	- 'Aurea'	CAco
	- 'Aurora' ♀H7	CKen ELan LRHS SCoo SLim SPoG
	- 'Bambi'	CKen CMen WAbe
	- 'Barkenny'	CKen NLar
	- 'Bartley'	CKen
	- 'Bassett'	CKen
	- 'Bess'	CKen
	- 'Blizzard' (v)	NLar
	- 'Brigitt'	CKen
	- 'Butterball'	CKen CMen LRHS
	- 'Caespitosa'	WAbe
	- 'Chabo-yadori'	NLar
	- 'Chilworth'	CKen NWad
	- 'Chima-anihiba'	CKen
	- 'Chirimen'	CAco CKen CMen MGil NLar
	- 'Clarke's Seedling'	CKen
	- 'Confucius'	LRHS LSRN
	- 'Contorta'	MGil
§	- 'Coralliformis'	CBod CMac NLar
§	- 'Crippsii' ♀H7	CMac
	- 'Crippsii Aurea'	see *C. obtusa* 'Crippsii'
	- 'Dainty Doll'	CKen NHol NWad
	- 'Densa'	see *C. obtusa* 'Nana Densa'
	- 'Draht'	CAco LRHS
	- 'Draht Hexe'	CKen
	- 'Elf'	CKen NLar
	- 'Ellie B'	CKen CMen
	- 'Ericoides'	CKen
	- 'Fernspray Gold' ♀H7	CAco CCVT EPfP LRHS MGos MMrt SCoo SPoG WLea
	- 'Filiformis Aurea' **new**	CAco
	- 'Flabelliformis'	CKen NWad
	- 'Gitte'	CAco SLim
	- 'Gnome'	CKen CMen
	- 'Gold Fern'	CKen
	- 'Golden Fairy'	CKen
	- 'Golden Filament' (v)	CKen
	- 'Golden Nymph'	CKen
	- 'Golden Sprite'	CKen WAbe
	- 'Gracilis Aurea'	CMen
	- 'Green Cushion'	CKen
	- 'Green Diamond'	CKen
	- 'Hage'	CKen
	- 'Hannah'	NLar
	- 'Hypnoides Nana'	CKen
	- 'Intermedia'	CKen WAbe
	- 'Junior'	CKen
	- 'Juniperoides'	CKen LRHS
	- 'Juniperoides Compacta'	WAbe
	- 'Kamarachiba' ♀H7	CAco CKen CSBt LBee LSRN MAsh NLar NOrn SCoo SLim SPoG
	- 'Kerdalo'	CAco LRHS NLar
	- 'Kosteri' ♀H7	CAco CKen CMac ELan LBee NHol SCoo
	- 'Leprechaun'	WAbe
	- 'Limerick'	CKen
	- 'Little Markey'	CKen CMen
	- 'Lucas'PBR	CAco LRHS
	- 'Lutea Nova'	CAco
	- 'Lycopodioides Aurea'	CAco NLar
	- 'Marian'	CKen
§	- 'Mariesii' (v)	CKen
	- 'Melody'	CKen NLar
	- 'Meroke'	CAco MGil
	- 'Minima'	CKen
	- 'Nana' ♀H7	CKen CMac CMen LBee LPar NHol NWad
	- 'Nana Aurea' ♀H7	CBrac CMac CSBt EPfP MAsh NHol
§	- 'Nana Densa'	CKen CMac
	- 'Nana Gracilis' ♀H7	CAco CBrac CKen CMen CSBt ELan EPfP LRHS MAsh MGil MGos NWad NWea SCob SCoo SLim SMad SPoG WLea
I	- 'Nana Gracilis Aurea'	CMen
I	- 'Nana Lutea' ♀H7	CKen CMen ELan LBee LRHS MAsh MGos NHol NWad NWea SLim
	- 'Nana Rigida'	see *C. obtusa* 'Rigid Dwarf'
	- 'Nana Variegata'	see *C. obtusa* 'Mariesii'
	- 'Oregon Crested'	LRHS MGil NLar
	- 'Pagoda' **new**	CAco
	- 'Petite Minorette' **new**	CAco
	- 'Pillnitz'	NLar

– 'Pygmaea' CBrac CSBt SCoo SLim
– 'Rashahiba' LRHS
– 'Rezek Dwarf' CKen CMen
§ – 'Rigid Dwarf' CKen LBee LRHS
– 'Saffron Spray' LRHS NLar SLim
– 'Snowflake' (v) CKen ELan NWad
– 'Snowkist' (v) CKen
– 'Spiralis' CKen
– 'Spirited' **new** CAco
– 'Stoneham' CKen CMen
– 'Strangman' CKen
– 'Suiroya-hiba' SLim
– 'Tempelhof' CAco CKen SCoo SLim
– 'Tetragona Aurea' CAco CMac NWad
– 'Timothy' CMac
– 'Tonia' (v) CKen MAsh SLim
– 'Torulosa' see *C. obtusa* 'Coralliformis'
– 'Tsatsumi Gold' ♀H7 CAco CKen CMen ELan EPfP LRHS SCoo SLim SPoG
– 'Villa Marie' LRHS
– 'Wiels Baby' NLar
– 'Wyckoff' CKen
– 'Yellowtip' (v) CKen EPfP MAsh
pisifera CAco
– 'Baby Blue' CKen ELan EPfP LRHS SCoo SPoG
– 'Blue Bun' CKen
– 'Blue Globe' CKen
– 'Blue Moon'PBR LCro LOPS LRHS MGos
– 'Boulevard' ♀H7 CBcs CBod CBrac CEme CMac CSBt ELan EPfP LBee LPar LRHS MAsh MGos NWea SCob SCoo SLim WBor
– 'Compacta' LRHS
– 'Curly Top' ♀H7 EPfP LRHS MAsh NHol SCoo SLim SPoG
– 'Filifera' CMac CSBt
– 'Filifera Aurea' ♀H7 CEme CKen CMac ELan EPfP LBee LPar MAsh MGos NHol NWea SCob SCoo WCFE
– 'Filifera Nana' EPfP LRHS SLim
– 'Filifera Nana Aurea' see *C. pisifera* 'Golden Mop'
– 'Filifera Sungold' see *C. pisifera* 'Sungold'
– 'Fuiri-tsukomo' CKen
– 'Gold Cushion' CKen
– 'Gold Dust' see *C. pisifera* 'Plumosa Aurea'
– 'Gold Spangle' CBrac CKen
§ – 'Golden Mop' CBrac CKen
– 'Green Pincushion' CKen CMen
– 'Hime-himuro' CKen
– 'Hime-sawara' CKen CMen
– 'Lime Pie' CKen
– 'Nana' CBrac CKen CMen LRHS NHol
– 'Nana Aureovariegata' (v) CSBt LBee
– 'Nana Aurescens' **new** LRHS
I – 'Nana Compacta' CMac
– 'Nana Variegata' (v) CMac LBee
I – 'Parslorii' CKen
– 'Pici' CKen
§ – 'Plumosa Aurea' CKen LPar MAsh
– 'Plumosa Aurea Compacta' CKen NWad
– 'Plumosa Aurea Nana' MAsh
I – 'Plumosa Aurea Nana Compacta' CMac
– 'Plumosa Aurescens' CMac
§ – 'Plumosa Compressa' ♀H7 CBrac CKen NWad
– 'Plumosa Densa' see *C. pisifera* 'Plumosa Compressa'
I – 'Plumosa Juniperoides' CKen
– 'Pygmy' see *C. pisifera* 'Tsukumo'
– 'Silver Lode' (v) CKen
– 'Silver Surprise' **new** LRHS
– 'Snow' (v) CKen LRHS
– 'Snowflake' CKen
– 'Spaan's Cannon Ball' CKen CMen
– 'Squarrosa Dumosa' CKen
I – 'Squarrosa Lombarts' CMac CSBt
– 'Squarrosa Lutea' CKen
– 'Squarrosa Sulphurea' CSBt ELan LRHS SCoo
§ – 'Sungold' ♀H7 CBod CKen CSBt ELan EPfP LRHS MAsh MGos NWea SCoo SLim SPoG SRms
– 'Tama-himuro' CKen
– 'Teddy Bear' CAco SMad
– 'True Blue' CKen ELan LRHS MAsh NWea
§ – 'Tsukumo' CKen
thyoides 'Andelyensis' CMac CSBt
– 'Blue Rock' SLim
– 'Conica' MAsh
– 'Ericoides' LBee SPlb
– 'Little Jamie' CKen
– 'Red Star' see *C. thyoides* 'Rubicon'
§ – 'Rubicon' CBod CEme CMac CSBt EPfP LBee MAsh SCoo SPoG
– 'Top Point' LBee MAsh SCoo SLim SPoG

Chamaecytisus see *Cytisus*

Chamaedaphne (*Ericaceae*)

calyculata CBcs

Chamaedorea (*Arecaceae*)

metallica misapplied see *C. microspadix*
§ ***microspadix*** ♀H1a CPHo SPalm
radicalis CBrP CPHo SArc SPalm

Chamaemelum (*Asteraceae*)

§ ***nobile*** CBod CHby CLau CTri EBou ENfk EPfP GPoy LCro LOPS LRHS MBow MHer MNHC MPri NGdn SPlb SRms SVic WSpi WTre XAbr
– dwarf SMor SVic
– dwarf, double-flowered (d) LEdu
– 'Flore Pleno' (d) CBod CElw CLau CMea CPrp CTri ECha ENfk EPfP MHer MNHC MRav NBro NGdn NGrd SGro SRms WFar WHal WJek WTre
– 'Treneague' CBod CCBP CPrp CTri EBou ECha EHyd ELan ENfk EPfP EWhm GAbr GPoy GQue LRHS MBow MCot MHer MNHC NRHS SAng SMor SPer SPlb SRms WFar WHal WHer WJek WTre

Chamaenerion (*Onagraceae*)

§ ***angustifolium*** WSFF
§ – 'Album' Widely available
– 'Hullavington Fire' CNat
– 'Isobel' CTtf MRav WCot
– 'Stahl Rose' CMea EWes LEdu LRHS MBel MBriF NSti SGbt SMad SMrm SPhx WCot WHrl
§ ***dodonaei*** EWes MHer SBut SPhx WCot

Chamaepericlymenum see *Cornus*

Chamaerops (*Arecaceae*)

excelsa misapplied see *Trachycarpus fortunei*
excelsa Thunb. see *Rhapis excelsa*
humilis ♀H4 CAbb CAco CBcs CBod CBrP CDoC ELan EPfP ETod LPar MGos SArc SChr SEND SGsty SIvy SPlb SPoG SWeb WLov
§ – var. ***argentea*** CBrP CDTJ CPHo EOli LPar MGos SChr SPalm SPlb SWeb WCot
– var. ***cerifera*** see *C. humilis* var. *argentea*

- var. ***humilis*** EOli SPalm
- 'Vulcano' CDTJ LPar SArc SChr SGsty SPalm WLea

Chamaespartium see *Genista*

Chamaesphacos (*Lamiaceae*)
ilicifolius misapplied see *Siphocranion macranthum*

Chamelaucium (*Myrtaceae*)
uncinatum CCCN EShb
- 'Snowflake' CCCN

Chamerion see *Chamaenerion*

chard see AGM Vegetables Section

Charybdis (*Asparagaceae*)
§ ***maritima*** CBod MHol NRog WCot

Chasmanthe (*Iridaceae*)
aethiopica CPbh EPri SBrt SChr
bicolor CExl EPri EWld
floribunda EPri GKev SDeJ XSte
- var. ***duckittii*** GKev SDeJ SPeP
- - 'Golden Wave' GKev
- 'Saturnus' EGrI GKev SPeP WABo WCFE

Chasmanthium (*Poaceae*)
§ ***latifolium*** CBod CEme CKno CRos CSde CSpe EBee ECha EHyd ELan ELon EPPr EPfP EShb LEdu LRHS MBel NRHS SCob SDix SMad SPad SPoG SRms SSal WBor WCot WPnP XLum
- 'Little Tickler' SBls
- 'River Mist' (v) ELan SPoG XLum

Chasmatophyllum (*Aizoaceae*)
sp. EDAr

Cheilanthes (*Pteridaceae*)
distans WCot
eckloniana WCot
farinosa LEdu
grisea WCot
lanosa CBdn CBod CCCN CCht CDoC CMiW CSpe CTsd EBee EHyd EWes LBuc LRHS NRHS SPlb SPoG SRot XLum XSte
lindheimeri WCot
myriophylla WCot
tomentosa CBod CCCN CRos CTsd EHyd LEdu LRHS MAsh NRHS
wootonii WCot

Cheiranthus see *Erysimum*

Cheirolophus (*Asteraceae*)
benoistii misapplied see *Centaurea atropurpurea*
benoistii (Humb.) Holub MRav
sempervirens B&SWJ 15321 **new** WCru

Chelidonium (*Papaveraceae*)
hylomeconoides GEdr
japonicum see *Hylomecon japonica*
majus GPSL GPoy NBir NMir WHer WHil WSFF XAbr
- 'Flore Pleno' (d) GJos NBid NBir NBro
- var. ***grandiflorum*** W/O 7061 **new** GGro
- var. ***laciniatum*** LShi WCot

Chelone (*Plantaginaceae*)
barbata see *Penstemon barbatus*
§ ***glabra*** CBod CMac EBee ECha ELan GMaP GWyn LRHS MHol MMuc MPie NBid NBro NGdn NHol NLar SPeP SPer SPlb SRms WFar WNPC WPnP WSHC WWtn
lyonii EBee NLar WShi
- 'Hot Lips' WHil WPnP
- 'Pink Temptation' EBee GEdr SBls
- TINY TORTUGA ('Armitpp02') SPad
obliqua Widely available
- var. ***alba*** see *C. glabra*
- 'Pink Sensation' WFar
- PINK TURTLE ('Arturtle'PBR) MBros MHol

Chelonopsis (*Lamiaceae*)
moschata EBee EGrI EWld LEdu MBel SPlb WHil
- white-flowered **new** GGro WFar
yagiharana CMea WFar WTre

Chengiopanax (*Araliaceae*)
sciadophylloides WCru

Chenopodium (*Amaranthaceae*)
ambrosioides SEdi SVic
bonus-henricus CAgr CHab CHby ENfk EWhm GPoy GQue MCoo MHer MNHC SRms SVic WHer WJek WKor XAbr
capitatum CSpe SVic
giganteum CLau MNHC SRms WJek

cherimoya see *Annona cherimola*

cherry, Duke see *Prunus* × *gondouinii*

cherry, sour or morello see *Prunus cerasus*; see also AGM Fruit Section

cherry, sweet see *Prunus avium*; see also AGM Fruit Section

chervil see *Anthriscus cerefolium*

chestnut, sweet see *Castanea sativa*

Chiastophyllum see *Umbilicus*
simplicifolium see *Umbilicus oppositifolius*

chicory see *Cichorium intybus*; also AGM Vegetables Section

Chiliotrichum (*Asteraceae*)
diffusum CCCN GAbr GArf MMuc
- 'Siska' CBcs GBin

chilli pepper see *Capsicum*; also AGM Vegetables Section

Chimaphila (*Ericaceae*)
umbellata GJos

Chimonanthus ✿ (*Calycanthaceae*)
fragrans see *C. praecox*
nitens CMCN NLar
§ ***praecox*** Widely available

- 'Brockhill Goldleaf' NLar
- 'Diane' **new** EPfP
- 'Grandiflorus' ♀H5 CJun CRos EHyd ELan EPfP EWTr LRHS MAsh MPkF SPer SPoG WCot XSte
- 'Luteus' ♀H5 CJun CRos EHyd ELan EPfP LEdu LRHS MAsh MGos NLar SChF SPer SPoG WCot
- 'Moonlight' **new** EPfP
- 'Red Heart' NLar
- 'Trenython' ♀H5 CJun

yunnanensis W.W.Sm. **new** NLar

Chimonobambusa (*Poaceae*)

KR 7592 MWht

§ ***marmorea*** CDTJ LPar MMuc
- 'Variegata' (v) CDTJ ESwi

§ ***quadrangularis*** CBcs CDTJ EPfP ESwi MWht
- 'Suow' (v) CDTJ

tumidissinoda CBcs CDTJ ESwi MWht WFar

Chinese cabbage see AGM Vegetables Section

Chinese chives see *Allium tuberosum*

Chiogenes see *Gaultheria*

Chionanthus (*Oleaceae*)

retusus CBcs CCCN CEme EHed EHyd EPfP EWTr LMaj MPkF NLar SBrt

virginicus CBcs CCCN CMCN EHyd ELan EPfP EWTr GBin LPar MBlu MGil MMuc MRav NLar SPer SPlb WSpi

Chionochloa (*Poaceae*)

conspicua CBod CElw EBee EPfP GAbr GBee GBin GKev MAvo NBid NBir NFav WPGP
- subsp. ***conspicua*** WCot
- 'Rubra' see *C. rubra*

flavescens EBee EPfP MAvo WPGP

flavicans CBod CSpe EBee EPfP GBin

pallens GKev

rigida GBin MAvo

§ ***rubra*** ♀H7 CElw CSpe EBee ELan EPfP EWes GBin GQue MRav SMHy WBor WCot WPGP
- PAB 67 EHyd LEdu
- subsp. ***cuprea*** SBls

Chionodoxa see *Scilla*

gigantea see *Scilla luciliae* Gigantea Group

Chionographis (*Melanthiaceae*)

japonica GEdr

Chionohebe (*Plantaginaceae*)

§ ***densifolia*** GArf

pulvinaris WAbe

'Vera Cox' EPot WAbe

Chionophila (*Plantaginaceae*)

jamesii GEdr

× *Chionoscilla* see *Scilla*

Chiranthodendron (*Malvaceae*)

pentadactylon SPlb

Chirita see *Primulina*

sinensis see *Primulina dryas*

speciosa *Henckelia speciosa*

tamiana *Deinostigma tamiana*

Chironia (*Gentianaceae*)

baccifera SPlb

× *Chitalpa* (*Bignoniaceae*)

tashkentensis CBcs CEnd EPfP ESwi SBrt
- 'Morning Cloud' MBlu
- 'Pink Dawn' CBcs ESwi IPap MBlu SMad
- SUMMER BELLS ('Minsum') CCCN CSpe EBee EHed ELan ELon LPar WCot WLov

chives see *Allium schoenoprasum*

Chlidanthus (*Amaryllidaceae*)

fragrans CBor CCCN SDeJ

Chloranthus (*Chloranthaceae*)

fortunei CMiW ESwi WCot

glaber GPoy
- B&SWJ 11102 WCru

henryi GEdr SIvy WCot

japonicus GEdr GGro WCru

oldhamii EWld WPGP
- B&SWJ 2019 GEdr LEdu WCru

serratus GEdr GGro WCru

sessilifolius 'Domino' ESwi WCot

Chloris (*Poaceae*)

distichophylla see *Eustachys distichophylla*

Chlorogalum (*Asparagaceae*)

pomeridianum 'Berkeley Hills' SBrt
- tall, from Siskiyou Mountains, Oregon SBrt

Chlorophytum (*Asparagaceae*)

chinense SBrt

comosum EShb SEND SSal SVic
- 'Aureomarginata' (v) SEND
- 'Bonnie'PBR (v) EShb
- 'Variegatum' (v) ♀H2 EShb LCro LOPS NGBl SEND SPre SSal WSFF
- 'Vittatum' (v) ♀H2 CDoC EShb NGBl

graminifolium EBee

krookianum CPbh WCot

macrophyllum EShb

nepalense WPGP
- B&SWJ 2528 WCru
- PAB 13.034 LEdu

orchidastrum EShb

saundersiae CExl CPbh EPPr
- 'Starlight' (v) LCro LOPS SMad

Choisya (*Rutaceae*)

× ***dewitteana*** APPLE BLOSSOM ('Pmoore09'PBR) CBcs CBod CEnd CRos CSBt EGrI LCro LOPS LRHS MAsh SLon SPoG XSte
- 'Aztec Gold'PBR CBcs CDoC CRos EBee EGrI EHyd EPfP LPar LRHS MAsh MGos NLar NRHS SCob SCoo XSte
- 'Aztec Pearl' ♀H4 Widely available
- GOLDFINGERS ('Limo'PBR) CBar CBcs CMac CRos CWGN EBee EHyd ELan EPfP EShb LRHS LSRN MGos MPri MRav NHol NLar NRHS SCob SGBe SGbt SGsty SLon SPer SPoG SRms SWvt
- SNOW FLURRIES ('Lisflurry'PBR) CRos EHyd ELan EPfP LRHS MAsh MRav NRHS SPoG XSte

- WHITE DAZZLER ('Londaz'PBR) ♀H4	Widely available
dumosa var. ***arizonica*** 'Whetstone'	WPGP
ROYAL LACE ('Pmoore06'PBR)	LBuc LRHS SGBe SLon
ternata ♀H4	Widely available
- MOONSHINE ('Walcho'PBR)	CBcs NLar
- MOONSLEEPER	see *C. ternata* SUNDANCE
§ - SUNDANCE ('Lich') ♀H4	Widely available

Chondrosum (*Poaceae*)

gracile	see *Bouteloua gracilis*

Chordospartium see *Carmichaelia*

Chorisia (*Malvaceae*)

speciosa	CCCN SPlb

Chorizema (*Fabaceae*)

cordatum ♀H2	SVen
dicksonii	SPlb
ilicifolium	LRHS

Chromolaena (*Asteraceae*)

arnottiana RCB RA 2 **new**	EBee

Chronanthus see *Cytisus*

Chrysalidocarpus see *Dypsis*

Chrysanthemopsis see *Rhodanthemum*

Chrysanthemum ✿ (*Asteraceae*)

E.H. Wilson s.n.	ECre EShb EWes EWoo MHCG MNrw NWad WCot WMal
'Action Bronze' (22)	NWsh
'Action Yellow' (22) ♀H3	WFar
'Agnes Ann' (21d)	MNrw NWad
'Ahlemer Rote' (21)	MHCG MNrw NWad
'Alan Brown' (25a)	MCms
'Alan Foxall Yellow' (3b)	MCms
'Alec Bedser' (25a)	NHal
'Alex Young' (25b)	MCms
'Alfredo Mauve' (12)	MCms
'Alfredo Orange' (12)	MCms
'Alice Jones' (24b)	MCms
'Aline' (21)	MHCG
'Alison' (29c)	ECtt ELon EWoo MNrw WFar
'Alison's Dad'	MNrw NWad
'Allouise' (25b) ♀H3	NHal
'Allouise Orange' (25b)	MCms NHal
'Allouise Pink' (25b)	MCms
'Allyson Peace' (14a)	MCms NHal
alpinum	see *Leucanthemopsis alpina*
'Alyece Shaw' (29d)	NHal
'Amber Matlock' (24b)	MCms
'American Beauty Lemon' (5b)	MCms
'American Beauty Snowball' (5b)	MCms
'American Beauty White' (5b)	MCms
'Anastasia' ambig.	SAko WBor
'Anastasia' (21c)	CRos EBee EHyd ELon EWoo LRHS MNrw MRav NRHS SRms
'Anderton' (6b)	MCms
'Angela Blundell' (19b)	ECtt MACG MHCG MNrw WCot WFar
'Angelic' (21b) ♀H4	EBee EWoo
'Ann Dickson' (25a)	MCms
'Anne Jones' (24a) **new**	NHal
'Anne Ratsey' (21)	MNrw NWsh WBrk WFar
'Anne, Lady Brocket' (21d)	ECtt MNrw
'Anthony Peace' (25b)	MCms
'Antigua'PBR	MCms
'Apollo' H. Shoesmith	MNrw
'Apollo' (21)	ECtt MHCG SPhx WFar WHoo
'Apricot'	see *C.* 'Cottage Apricot'
'Apricot Chessington' (25a)	MCms
'Apricot Courtier' (24a)	MCms NHal
'Apricot Enbee Wedding'	see *C.* 'Bronze Enbee Wedding'
'Apricot Mundial' (6b)	MCms
'Arctic Beauty' (4b)	MCms
'Arctic Cream' (29b)	MCms
'Arctic Queen'PBR (23a)	MCms
'Arctic Queen Yellow' (23a)	MCms
'Arctic White' (9c)	MCms
'Arctic Yellow' (9c)	MCms
arcticum L.	see *Arctanthemum arcticum*
'Arthur Ellis' (25b)	MCms
'Astro' (25b)	MCms NHal
'Aunt Millicent' (21d) ♀H4	ECre MHCG NHal WCot
'Balcombe Perfection' (5a)	MCms NHal
balsamita	see *Tanacetum balsamita*
'Barbara Dakin' (25b)	MCms NHal
'Barbara Lambert' (21) **new**	EShb
BARBARA ('Yobarbara') (22)	NHal
'Barca'	MCms
'Beacon' (5a) ♀H2	MCms NHal
'Beechcroft' (29Rub)	MHCG MNrw WFar
'Belle' (21d)	MHCG MNrw WMal
'Beppie Bronze' (29e)	MCms
'Beppie Purple' (29e)	MCms
'Beppie Red' (29e)	MCms
'Beppie Rose' (29e)	MCms
'Beppie Yellow' (29e)	MCms
'Best Man' (29d)	MCms
'Betty Wiggins' (25b)	MCms
'Bienchen'	SAko WFar
'Bill Holden' (14a)	MCms NHal
'Bill Wade' (25a)	MCms NHal
'Billy Bell' (15a)	MCms NHal
'Blanche Poitevene' (5b)	EMal MCms
'Bob Green' (13b)	MCms
'Boulou Pink' (12)	MCms
'Boulou White' (12)	MCms
'Boulou Yellow' (12)	MCms
BRAVO ('Yobra') (22c)	NHal
* 'Breitner's Supreme'	ECtt MHCG MNrw WFar
'Brennpunkt'	MNrw NWad
'Bretforton Road'	ECtt MHCG MNrw WBrk WCot WFar WMal
'Brightness' (21)	MNrw
'Bronze Cassandra' (5b) ♀H2	MCms NHal
'Bronze Dee Gem' (29c)	MCms NHal
§ 'Bronze Elegance' (21b) ♀H4	CDor CRos CTri ECtt EHyd EPPr EShb LRHS MNrw NBir NGdn NRHS NWsh SHar SRms WBor
§ 'Bronze Enbee Wedding' (29d) ♀H3	MCms NHal
'Bronze Matlock' (24b)	MCms NHal
'Bronze Max Riley' (23b) ♀H3	MCms NHal
'Bronze Mayford Perfection' (5a) ♀H2	MCms
'Bronze Mei-kyō'	see *C.* 'Bronze Elegance'
'Bronze Talbot Parade' (29c) ♀H3	MCms
'Bronze William Florentine' (15a)	MCms

'Brooke Farm Red'	NWsh
'Brown Eyes' (21b) 🏆H4	MNrw
'Bryony Wade' (13b)	MCms NHal
'Bryony Wade White' (13b)	MCms
'Buff William Florentine' (15a)	MCms
'Bunty' (28)	SMad
burnt orange-flowered	CDor CFis MNrw WFar
'Burntwood Belle' (3b)	MCms
'Buxton Ruby'	EWoo MNrw NWad
'Candy John Wingfield' (14b)	MCms
'Capel Manor'	EBee MHCG MNrw WCot
'Capella' (10a)	MCms
'Cardinal Red'	EHyd
'Carlene Welby' (25b)	MCms
'Carmine Blush' (21d) 🏆H4	CDor GAbr LShi MHCG MNrw WBrk WCot WFar
'Casablanca' (25a)	MCms NHal
'Cassandra' (5b) 🏆H2	MCms NHal
'Cawthorne' (29d)	WFar
'Cerisa' (29d)	MCms NHal
'Charles Tandy' (5a)	MCms
'Charles Tandy Primrose' (15a)	MCms
'Charles Tandy Yellow' (15b)	MCms
'Charlie' (24b)	MCms
'Chatsworth' (29c)	NHal
'Chelsea Physic Garden'	EBee ELon EPfP EWoo GAbr MACG MHCG MNrw MPie SPhx WCot WFar WMal
'Chempak Rose' (14b)	MCms
'Cherry Chessington' (25a)	MCms
'Cherry Tracey Waller' (24b)	MCms
'Chesapeake Primrose' (10a)	MCms
CHESAPEAKE ('Yochesapeake'[PBR]) (10a)	MCms NHal
'Chessington' (25a)	MCms
'Chessington Oyster' (25a)	MCms
'Chestnut Talbot Maid' (29c)	MCms
'Chestnut Talbot Parade' (29c) 🏆H3	MCms WFar
'Chloe Ball' (13b)	MCms
'Christmas'	MNrw NWad WFar
'Christopher Lawson' (24b)	MCms NHal
cinerariifolium	see *Tanacetum cinerariifolium*
'Citronella'	MNrw
'Clapham Delight' (23a)	MCms NHal
'Clara Curtis' (21d)	CBod CDor CMac CRos ECha ECtt EHyd ELan EPfP EShb LRHS LShi MHol MNrw MPie MRav NPer NRHS SGbt SMrm SPoG SRms SSal WBrk WCAu WFar WSHC
'Clare Louise' (24b)	MCms
'Clarksdale' (15b)	MCms NHal
coccineum	see *Tanacetum coccineum*
'Colsterworth'	MHCG MNrw NWad WFar
'Coral Reef' (10b)	MCms NHal
'Corinna' (21d)	GBin MNrw NWad
'Cornetto' (25b)	MCms NHal
'Corsair' (9d)	MCms
corymbosum	see *Tanacetum corymbosum*
§ 'Cottage Apricot' (21)	CDor CRos EBee ECtt EHyd EPfP LRHS MBNS MRav NRHS SMHy SRms WFar
'Cottage Bronze'	MNrw NWad
'Cottage Lemon'	EShb MHCG MNrw NWad WFar
'Cottage Pink'	see *C.* 'Emperor of China'
'Courtier' (24a)	MCms NHal
'Cousin Joan' (21d) 🏆H4	CDor ECtt ELon MHCG MNrw SPhx WBor WCot WFar WMal
'Cream Dorridge Crystal' (24a)	MCms
'Cream John Hughes' (3b)	MCms
'Cream Patricia Millar' (14b)	NHal
'Cream Talbot Maid' (29c)	MCms
'Cream Talbot Parade' (29c) 🏆H3	MCms
'Cream West Bromwich' (14a)	MCms
'Cricket' (25b)	MCms
'Crimson Purple Glow' (5a)	MCms
DANA ('Yodana') (25b)	NHal
DANCE ('Fidance'[PBR]) (9f)	MCms
'Dance Red' (9f)	MCms
DANCE SALMON ('Fidancesal') (9f)	MCms
'Dance Sunny' (9f)	MCms
'Dance White' (9f)	MCms
'Daniel Cooper' (21d) 🏆H4	EBee ECtt MNrw SGro WFar
'Daphne Davis' (29d)	NHal
'Darren Pugh' (3b)	MCms NHal
'Darren Pugh Primrose' (3b)	MCms
'David Shoesmith' (25a)	MCms
'Dawn Charlton' (14a)	MCms
'Dee Gem' (29c) 🏆H3	MCms NHal WFar
'Denise Oatridge' (5a)	MCms
'Dernier Soleil'	EBee MNrw XLum
'Disco Club'	MCms
'Dixter Orange'	EBee EPPr EWTr EWes MHCG MNrw SMad SPhx WMal
'Dixter Pink'	WMal
§ 'Doctor Tom Parr' (21c)	CExl ELan EWoo MNrw
'Domingo' (14b)	MCms
'Doreen Hall' (15a)	NHal
'Doreen Statham' (4b)	MCms NHal
'Doris Ozols' (25a)	MCms NHal
'Dorothy Stone' (25b)	NHal
'Dorridge Crystal' (24a)	MCms NHal
'Dorridge King' (4b)	MCms
'Downpour' (10a)	MCms
'Dublin' (9f)	MCms
'Duchess of Edinburgh' (21d)	EBee ECtt EHyd ELan ELon EPfP EWoo LRHS LShi MHer MNrw NLar NRHS SPhx WCAu WFar WMal XLum
'Dulwich Pink' (21d) 🏆H4	MHCG MNrw NWad WCot WFar
'Early Yellow'	EBee ELon EWoo MNrw WCot WFar
'Edelweiss' (21)	EShb MNrw NWad
'Edina' (29d)	NHal
'Edmund Brown'	MNrw WCot WFar WMal
'Egret' (23b)	MCms NHal
'Elaine's Hardy White'	MHCG MNrw WCot WFar WMal
'Eliška'	MNrw
'Elizabeth Lawson' (5b)	NHal
§ 'Emperor of China' (21)	CDor ECha ECtt EWoo MHer MNrw MRav NHal SMad SRms WBor WFar XLum
'Enbee Wedding' (29d) 🏆H3	MCms NHal
'Energy'[PBR] (9)	MCms
'Erntekranz'	MNrw WMal
'Esther' (21d)	EBee EShb EWTr LEdu MHCG MHer MNrw SMad WFar
'Etta Dakin' (25b)	MCms NHal

'Fairweather' (3b)	MCms
'Fairweather Cream' (3b)	MCms
'Fairweather Peach' (3b)	MCms
'Fanfare Cherry'	EHyd
'Fanfare Claret'	EHyd ELan
'Fanfare Flame'	EHyd ELan
'Fanfare Glowing Embers'	EHyd
'Fanfare Orange'	EHyd
'Fanfare Pink Blush'	EHyd
'Fanfare Pink Pastel'	EHyd
'Fanfare Rosetta'	EHyd
'Fanfare Ruby'	EHyd
'Fanfare Sunset'	EHyd
'Feeling Green Dark'PBR	MCms
'Feeling Sunny'PBR	MCms
'Fellbacher Wein' (21)	XLum
'Finn Lyttle' (29d) **new**	NHal
'Fleur de Lis' (10a)	MCms
foeniculaceum (Willd.) Desf.	see *Argyranthemum foeniculaceum* (Willd.) Webb & Sch. Bip.
'Folk Song' (4b)	MNrw
'French Rose'	WFar
'Frizbee' (29d)	NHal
'Froggy'PBR (9)	MCms
frutescens	see *Argyranthemum frutescens*
'Gambit' (24a)	MCms NHal
'Geoff Amos' (3b)	MCms
'Geoff Brady' (5a)	MCms NHal
'George Griffiths' (24b)	MCms NHal
'George Simmonds' **new**	WHoo
'Gillette' (23b)	MCms
'Ginger Nut' (25b)	MCms
'Ginger Nut Yellow' (25b)	MCms
I 'Gladys' (12a)	NHal
'Gladys Emerson' (3b)	MCms NHal
'Gold Enbee Wedding' (29d) ♀H3	MCms
'Gold Hoagy' (29d) **new**	NHal
'Gold Mundial' (6b) ♀H2	MCms
'Golden Cassandra' (5b) ♀H2	MCms NHal
'Golden Chalice' (12a)	MCms NHal
'Golden Courtier' (24a)	MCms NHal
'Golden Masons' (7b)	MCms
'Golden Mayford Perfection' (5a) ♀H2	MCms
'Golden Rain' (10a) ♀H2	MCms NHal
'Golden Roy Coopland' (5b)	MCms
'Golden Shoesmith Salmon' (4a)	MCms
'Golden Splendour' (10a)	MCms NHal
'Golden William Florentine' (15a)	MCms
'Goldengreenheart' (21d) ♀H4	ECtt ELon EShb MHCG MNrw SPhx SRms WBrk WFar WHoo
'Goldmarianne' (21)	GBin WFar XLum
'Goodlife Sombrero' (29a) ♀H3	MCms
'Goshu Penta' (10a)	MCms
'Grace Riley' (24a)	MCms
'Grand Cherry'	MCms
'Grand Pink'	MCms
'Grand Salmon'	MCms
'Grandchild' (21c) ♀H4	MNrw NHal WMal
'Green Goddess' (2)	MCms
'Hanenburg' (25b)	MCms NHal
haradjanii	see *Tanacetum haradjanii*
'Hardwick Lemon' (29c)	MHCG
'Harold Lawson' (5a)	NHal
* 'Harry Lawson'	MCms
'Harry Woolman' (13b)	MCms
'Heather James' (3b)	MCms NHal
'Hebe' (21d)	EBee MNrw
'Heda'	MNrw
'Heide' (29c) ♀H3	NHal
'Helen Harrison'	MAvo MHCG
'Helen Louise' (25b)	MCms NHal
'Helen Ward'	MNrw
'Herbie McCauley' (24b)	NHal
'Herbstbrokat'	GBin WFar XLum
'Herbstfeuer' (21)	MNrw NWad
'Hillfield Apricot'	EShb
'Hillside Apricot'	ECtt
'Hoagy' (29d)	MCms NHal
'Holly Elizabeth' (14a)	MCms
HOLLY ('Yoholly') (22b) ♀H3	NHal
'Honey Enbee Wedding' (29d)	MCms NHal
hosmariense	see *Rhodanthemum hosmariense*
indicum	SVic
'Innocence' (21d) ♀H4	CDor CFis ECtt ELan ELon LShi MBNS MNrw MRav NGdn SHar WFar WHoo
'Jan Wardle' (5a)	MCms
'Janet South'	MNrw
'Jante Wells' (21b) ♀H4	EWoo MNrw
'Jasoda Dark Orange'PBR	LCro LOPS
'Jasoda Mauve'PBR	LCro LOPS
'Jasoda Pink'PBR	LCro LOPS
'Jasoda White'PBR	LCro LOPS
'Jasoda Yellow'PBR	LCro LOPS
'Jenny Wren' (12a)	NHal
'Jessie Cooper' misapplied	see *C.* 'Mrs Jessie Cooper' (21d)
'Jimmy Tranter' (14b)	NHal
'John Harrison' (25b)	MCms NHal
'John Hughes' (3b)	MCms NHal
'John Riley' (14a)	NHal
'John Wingfield' (14b)	MCms NHal
'John Wingfield Honey' (14b)	MCms
'John Wingfield Pearl' (14b)	MCms
'Jolie Rose'	WCot WFar
'Joyce Fountain' (24a)	MCms NHal
'Joyce Frieda' (13b)	MCms NHal
'Judy Dakin' (25b) **new**	NHal
'Julia' (28)	MNrw
'Julia Arnold'	WHoo
'Julia Peterson'	MHCG MHer MNrw SRms WCot WFar
JULIA ('Yojulia')	NLar
'Julie Lagravère' (28)	ECtt MHCG MNrw WFar
'Karen Taylor' (29c) ♀H3	NHal
'Kath Stephenson' (7b)	MCms
'Kath Stephenson Honey' (7b)	MCms
'Kath Stephenson Peach' (7b)	MCms
'Kath Stephenson Primrose' (7b)	MCms
'Kath Stephenson Rose' (7b)	MCms
'Kath Stephenson Salmon' (7b)	MCms
'Kay Woolman' (13b)	MCms NHal
'Kay Woolman Cream' (13b)	MCms
'Kay Woolman Primrose' (13b)	MCms
'Kay Woolman Yellow' (13b)	MCms

	'Killerton Tangerine'	MHCG MNrw WFar WMal
	'Kimberley Marie' (15b)	MCms NHal
	'Kiyomi-no-meisui'	MCms NHal
	'Kleiner Bernstein'	MNrw
	'Kurume' (12b) **new**	MCms
	'La Damoiselle'	WCot
§	'Lady in Pink' (21)	MNrw MPie NWad
	'Lakelanders' (3b)	MCms NHal
	'Laura Jayne' (25a)	MCms
	'Lava' (10a)	MCms
	'Leo' (21b) ♀H4	EWoo
	leucanthemum	see *Leucanthemum vulgare*
	'Lexy'PBR (9)	MCms
	'Lexy Red'PBR (9)	GBin MCms
	'Lighthouse'	NHal
	'Lilac Chessington' (25a)	MCms
	'Lilly Emily' (25b) **new**	NHal
	LINDA ('Lindayo') (22c) ♀H3	NHal
	'Liverpool Festival' (23b)	MCms
	'Lollipop'PBR (9e)	MCms
	LOLLIPOP PURPLE ('Filollipop Purple'PBR) (9e)	MCms
	'Lorna Wood' (13b)	MCms NHal
	'Lucy' (29a)	MCms NHal
	'Lucy Simpson' (21d)	EWoo
	'Lynn Johnson' (15a)	MCms
	LYNN ('Yolynn') (22c) ♀H3	NHal
	macrophyllum	see *Tanacetum macrophyllum* (Waldst. & Kit.) Sch.Bip.
	'Malcolm Perkins' (25a)	NHal
	'Mancetta Symbol' (5a)	MCms
	'Mandarin' (5b)	SAko
I	'Mandarin'	MNrw
	'Manito'	MNrw
	maresii	see *Rhodanthemum hosmariense*
	'Margaret Dear' (25a)	MCms
	'Margery Fish'	MNrw WFar
	'Marion' (25a)	MNrw WCot WFar
	'Marion Couchman' (25b) **new**	NHal
	'Martin Bell' (29d)	WFar
	'Martina' (24b)	MCms
	'Mary' (21f)	MHCG NHal
	'Mary Aldred' (29d) **new**	MCms
	'Mary Stoker' (21d)	CDor CTri EBee ECtt EHyd ELan EWoo LRHS MNrw MPie MRav NHal NLar NRHS NWsh WCAu
	'Mason's Bronze' (7b)	MCms
	'Matlock' (24b)	NHal
	'Mauve Gem' (21f) ♀H3	NHal
	'Mavis' (21)	MHCG MNrw
	'Mavis Smith'	EWoo MNrw
	'Max Riley' (23b) ♀H3	MCms NHal
	maximum misapplied	see *Leucanthemum* × *superbum*
	maximum Ramond	see *Leucanthemum maximum* (Ramond) DC.
	'Maxine Charlton' (24b)	NHal
	'Maxine Johnson' (25b)	MCms
	'May Shoesmith' (5a) ♀H2	MCms
	'Mayford Perfection' (5a) ♀H2	MCms
	'Megumi' (12b) **new**	MCms
	'Mei-Kyō' (28b) ♀H4	CDor CFis CMea CTri EBee ECre ECtt EHyd EPPr EPfP EShb EWoo LRHS MHCG MNrw MPie NRHS SRms WBrk WCAu WFar XLum
	'Membury' (24b)	NHal
	'Mezzo Bronze Red' (Poppins Series)	MCms
	'Mezzo Gold' (Poppins Series)	MCms
	'Mezzo Magenta' (Poppins Series)	MCms
	'Mezzo Pink' (Poppins Series)	MCms
	'Migdale' (24b)	MCms NHal
	'Milkshake' **new**	MNrw
	'Millennium' (25b) ♀H3	MCms NHal
	'Misty Cream' (25b)	MCms
	'Misty Golden' (25b)	MCms
	'Misty Lemon' (25b)	MCms
	'Moonlight' (29d/K)	MNrw MRav NWad
	'Morning Star' (12a)	NHal
	'Mount Fuji' (10b)	MCms
	'Mr Mappie' (21c) **new**	WCot
§	'Mrs Jessie Cooper' (21d) ♀H4	EBee ECtt ELon EWoo GBee GQue MACG MNrw NLar NWad NWsh SDys SMrm SRms WCot WFar WHoo
	'Mrs Jessie Cooper No 2'	MNrw
	'Mundial' (6)	MCms
	'Mundial Peach' (6b/9a)	MCms
	'Mundial Rose' (6b)	MCms
	'Mundial Ruby' (6b)	MCms
	'Muriel Odell' (7b)	MCms
	'Music' (23b)	MCms NHal
	'Muxton Sable' (10a)	MCms
	'Myss Debbie' (29e)	NHal
	'Myss Dorothy' (29c)	MCms NHal
	'Myss Eliza' (29c)	MCms
	'Myss Goldie' (29c)	MCms
	'Myss Rihanna' (29c)	MCms NHal
	'Myss Saffron' (29c) ♀H3	MCms NHal
	'Nancy Perry' (21d)	MRav XLum
	'Nantyderry Sunshine' (28b) ♀H4	CDor CRos EBee ECre EHyd ELon EWoo GAbr LRHS MHCG MNrw MPie NRHS NWsh SPhx SRms WCot WFar
	'Natalie Sarah' (29d) ♀H3	NHal
	'Nell Gwynn' (21d)	MNrw NHal
	'New Stylist' (24b)	MCms
	NICOLE ('Yonicole') (22c) ♀H3	NHal
	nipponicum	see *Nipponanthemum nipponicum*
	'Nutcracker' (23b)	MCms
	'Old Norwell'	WMal
	'Orange Enbee Wedding' (29d)	NHal
	'Orchid Helen'	MNrw
	'Pacific Lady' (29d)	NHal
§	***pacificum***	CBor WFar
	'Paloma Redeye' (29d)	NHal
	'Paloma Regent' (29d)	NHal
	parthenium	see *Tanacetum parthenium*
	'Pat Bahn' (29c)	NHal
	'Patricia Millar' (14b)	MCms
	'Patricia Millar Cerise' (14b)	MCms
	'Patricia Millar Coral' (14b)	MCms
	'Patricia Millar Orange' (14b)	MCms
	'Patricia Millar Yellow' (14b)	MCms
	'Paul Boissier' (30)	CDor CFis ECtt EWoo MNrw SPhx WFar XLum
	'Pauline White' (15a)	MCms
	'Peach Courtier' (24a)	NHal
	'Peach Enbee Wedding' (29d) ♀H3	MCms NHal
	'Peach John Wingfield' (14b)	MCms NHal
	'Peach Patricia Millar' (14b)	MCms

'Peach Southway Sheeba' (29d) NHal
'Pearl Celebration' (24a) MCms
'Pearl Dorridge Crystal' (24a) **new** MCms NHal
'Pearl Enbee Wedding' (29d) MCms
'Peggy' (28a) MHCG
'Pennine Bullion' NHal
'Pennine Gambol' (29a) MCms
'Pennine Jude' (29a) MCms
'Pennine Marie' (29a) ♀H3 MCms
'Pennine Oriel' (29a) ♀H3 MCms NHal
'Pennine Point' (19c) NHal
'Pennine Polo' (29d) NHal
'Pennine Swan' (29c) MCms NHal
'Penny's Yellow' WBrk
'Percy Salter' (24b) NHal
'Perry's Peach' (21d) ♀H4 ELon MHCG MNrw NHal NPer SPhx
'Peter Jolley' (25b) MCms
'Peter Rowe' (23b) MCms NHal
'Peterkin' CMac EBee ECtt EHyd ELon XLum
'Picasso' EShb GAbr MHCG MNrw WCot WFar
'Pink John Wingfield' (14b) NHal
'Pink Progression' see *C.* 'Lady in Pink'
'Pocahontas' (10a) MCms
'Poesie' ECtt MHer MNrw NWsh SAko WCot WFar WMal
'Polar Gem' (3a) MCms NHal
'Pomander' (25b) MCms
'Pot Black' (14b) MCms
'Prelude Apricot' (Poppins Series) MCms
'Prelude Autumn Bronze' (Poppins Series) MCms
'Prelude Popcorn' (Poppins Series) MCms
'Prelude Rose Pink' (Poppins Series) MCms
'Prelude White' (Poppins Series) MCms
'President Osaka' MNrw
'Primrose Allouise' (24b) ♀H3 MCms NHal
'Primrose Chessington' (25a) MCms
'Primrose Courtier' see *C.* 'Yellow Courtier'
'Primrose Cricket' (25b) MCms
'Primrose Dorridge Crystal' (24a) MCms
'Primrose Egret' (23b) MCms
'Primrose Enbee Wedding' (29d) ♀H3 MCms NHal
'Primrose Fairweather' (3b) MCms
'Primrose John Hughes' (3b) MCms
'Primrose Mayford Perfection' (5a) ♀H2 MCms
'Primrose Pauline White' (15a) MCms
'Primrose Pennine Oriel' (29a) MCms
'Primrose West Bromwich' (14a) MCms
'Princess' (21d) MNrw
'Princess Anne' (4b) MCms
'Promise' (25a) MCms NHal
'Purleigh White' (28b) ELon EPPr MNrw NWsh WFar
'Purple Chempak Rose' (14b) MCms
'Purple Dee Gem' (29c) NHal
'Purple Glow' (5a) MCms
'Purple Haze' (7b) MCms
'Raquel' (21) MNrw
'Ray's Red' MHCG MNrw
'Red Balcombe Perfection' (5a) MCms NHal
'Red Chempak Rose' (14b) MCms
'Red Goodlife Sombrero' (29a) MCms
'Red Mayford Perfection' (5a) MCms
'Red Regal Mist' (25b) MCms NHal
'Red Shirley Model' (3a) MCms NHal
'Redbreast' (12a) NHal
'Regal Mist' (25b) NHal
'Regal Mist Purple' (25b) MCms
'Regent' (5b) MCms
'Rejoyce' GBin
'Rejoyce Pink' **new** MCms
I 'Rhumba' MNrw WCot
'Rihanna' MCms
'Riley's Dynasty' (14a) MCms
'Ringdove' (12a) NHal
'Rita Fox' (25b) MCms NHal
'Rita McMahon' (29d) ♀H3 NHal
ROBIN ('Yorobi') (22c) NHal
'Roen Sarah' (29c) NHal
'Romantica' MNrw NWad
'Rose Enbee Wedding' (29d) MCms NHal
'Rose Madder' EWoo GAbr MNrw WCot WFar
'Rose Mayford Perfection' (5a) ♀H2 MCms
'Rose Patricia Millar' (14b) MCms NHal
'Rose Talbot Parade' (29c) MCms
'Rosedew' (25a) MCms
'Rosetta' MHCG MNrw
roseum see *Tanacetum coccineum*
'Rosie Lyttle' (29c) NHal
'Roter Spray' MNrw NWad
'Roy Bevan' (29d) MCms
'Roy Coopland' (5b) ♀H2 MCms
'Royal Command' (21a) MHCG MNrw WCot WHoo
'Royal Sport' MNrw
rubellum see *C. zawadzkii*
'Ruby Enbee Wedding' (29d) ♀H3 MCms WFar
'Ruby Glow' (7b) MCms
'Ruby Mound' (21c) ♀H3 CDor EWoo GAbr LShi MHCG MNrw NHal SDys SHar SPhx WCot WFar WMal
'Ruby Raynor' (21c) ♀H4 MNrw NHal WFar
'Rumpelstilzchen' (21d) CFis CMea ECtt ELon MHer MNrw WMal
'Rusty Margaret' (29c) **new** MNrw
'Salhouse Dream' (10a) MCms
'Salhouse Joy' (10a) MCms NHal
'Salmon Allouise' (25b) MCms NHal
'Salmon Enbee Wedding' (29d) ♀H3 NHal
'Salmon Fairweather' (3b) MCms
'Salmon John Wingfield' (24b) MCms
'Salmon Patricia Millar' (14b) MCms
'Salmon Pauline White' (15a) MCms
'Salmon Talbot Maid' (29c) MCms
'Salmon Talbot Parade' (29c) ♀H3 MCms WFar
'Salmon Tracey Waller' (24b) MCms

'Salmon Venice' (24b)	MCms
'Sam Vinter' (5a)	NHal
'Samba'	WCot WFar
'Samson'	MCms
'Samson Bronze'	MCms
'Samson Orange'	MCms
'Samson Purple'	MCms
'Sarah Louise' (25b)	NHal
'Savanna Charlton' (25a)	MCms NHal
'Schaffhausen'	WFar
'Schweizerland'	WFar
'Sea Urchin' (21f) 🏆H3	NHal
'Seaton's Galaxy' (10a)	MCms
'Senkyo Karyu' (10a)	MCms
'Senkyo Kenshin' (10a)	MCms NHal
'Shamrock' (10b)	MCms
'Sheffield'	XLum
'Sheila Harris' (3b)	MCms
'Shining Light' (21f)	WCot WFar
'Shoesmith Salmon' (4a)	MCms
'Shoesmith Salmon Bright Bronze' (4a)	MCms
'Shoesmith Salmon Crimson' (4b)	MCms
'Shoesmith Salmon Purple' (4a)	MCms
'Skomer' (9f)	MCms
'Skomer Pink' (9f)	MCms
'Skomer Yellow' (9f)	MCms
'Soir d'Orient'	WFar
'Sonya' (21)	MNrw
'Sound' (9d)	MCms
'Southway Semtex' (29d)	MCms
'Southway Sheba' (29d) 🏆H3	MCms NHal
'Southway Sheba Apricot' (29d) **new**	MCms
'Southway Sheba Bronze' (29d)	MCms
'Southway Sheba Chestnut' (29d) **new**	MCms
'Southway Sheba Salmon' (29d) **new**	MCms
'Southway Shimmer' (29d)	MCms NHal WFar
'Southway Shiraz' (29d)	MCms WFar
'Southway Sloe' (29d)	MCms NHal
'Southway Spectacular' (29d)	MCms
'Southway Spritzer' (29d)	MCms
'Southway Strontium' (29d)	MCms NHal
'Southway Sunbeam' (29d)	MCms
'Spartan Canary' (21d) 🏆H4	EWoo
'Spartan Display'	ECre EWes MNrw
'Spartan Seagull' (21d)	MNrw
'Spencer's Cottage' (13b)	MCms
'Stallion' (9)	GBin MCms
'Stallion Yellow'	MCms
'Starlet' (21f) 🏆H4	EWoo MHCG NHal
'Steve Packham' (23b)	NHal
'Stockton' (3b)	MCms
'Stratford Pink' (21d)	MNrw NWad
'Suffolk Pink'	ECtt EShb EWoo MNrw NWsh
'Sunny John Wingfield' (14b)	MCms NHal
'Super-Bronze Shoesmith Salmon' (4a)	MCms
'Susan Kate' (25b)	MCms
'Swan Cream'	MCms
SWAN ('Fiswan'PBR) (9)	MCms
'Swan Sunny'	MCms
'Sweetheart Pink'	MHCG MNrw WMal
'Syllabub' (21f) 🏆H3	ECtt MHer MNrw
'Symphony' (10a)	MCms NHal
'Talbot Maid' (29c)	MCms
'Talbot Parade' (29c) 🏆H3	MCms
'Talbot Parade Pink' (29c)	MCms
'Tapestry Rose' (21d)	CMea MNrw NWsh SPhx SRms WBrk WFar WHoo
'Thoroughbred' (24a)	NHal
'Tickle Pink' (29f/K)	MNrw NWad
'Tom Parr'	see *C.* 'Doctor Tom Parr'
'Tom Snowball' (3b)	MCms
'Tonto' (29d) **new**	NHal
'Topsy' (21d) 🏆H4	EWoo MHCG
'Tracey Waller' (24b)	MCms
§ ***trilobatum***	GKev
TRIUMPH ('Yotri') (22)	NHal
uliginosum	see *Leucanthemella serotina*
'Uri'	CFis EBee ELon MHCG MNrw SPhx WFar
'Vagabond Prince'	ECtt ELon EWoo MHCG MNrw SRms WFar WHoo
'Venice' (24b)	MCms NHal
'Venice Peach' (24b)	MCms
'Venice Rose' (24b)	MCms
'Venus' (21)	WCot WMal
'Venus One'	ECtt MNrw NHal
'Viking' (9)	MCms
'Vysočina'	MNrw
'Wedding Day' (29k)	MNrw NWad
'Wedding Sunshine' (21)	MNrw NWad WFar
welwitschii	see *Glebionis segetum*
'Wembley' (24b)	MCms
'Wendy Tench' (21d)	EBee MNrw NWsh
'West Bromwich' (14a)	MCms
weyrichii	CBor CTri CTsd EBou EHyd GGro GPSL LEdu MHol MNrw NFav NHpl SGro SRms WFar WIce
'White Allouise' (25b) 🏆H3	MCms NHal
'White Beppie' (29e)	MCms WFar
'White Bouquet' (28)	WFar
'White Cassandra' (5b)	MCms NHal
'White Enbee Wedding' (29d)	MCms NHal
'White Fairweather' (3b)	MCms
'White Gem' (21f)	MHCG NHal
'White Gloss' (21e)	MNrw
'White Pearl Celebration' (24a)	MCms
'White Tower' (27)	MNrw MPie NWad
'Wilder Charms'	MNrw NWad
'William Florentine' (15a)	MCms NHal
'Wills Wonderful' (21d) 🏆H4	MHCG MNrw WMal
'Wind Dancer' (10a)	MCms
'Winning's Red' (21)	ECtt MHCG SMad WCot WFar
'Winter Queen' (5b)	MCms
'Winter Queen Yellow' (5b)	MCms
'Woolley Globe' (15b)	MCms
'Woolman's Glory' (7a)	MCms
'Woolman's Glory Red' (7a)	MCms
'Woolman's Star' (3a)	MCms NHal
'Woolman's Venture' (14b)	NHal
'Woolman's Venture Red' (14b)	MCms
'Xiang'	NWad
'Yellow Allouise' (25b)	MCms
'Yellow American Beauty' (5b) 🏆H2	MCms
'Yellow Billy Bell' (15a)	NHal
'Yellow Chessington' (25a)	MCms
'Yellow Clapham Delight' (23a)	MCms NHal

§ 'Yellow Courtier' (24a) MCms NHal
'Yellow Egret' (23b) MCms
'Yellow Enbee Wedding' (29d) MCms NHal
'Yellow Goodlife Sombrero' (29a) MCms
'Yellow Heide' (29c) ♀H3 NHal
'Yellow Jewel' (Poppins Series) MCms
'Yellow John Hughes' (3b) ♀H2 MCms NHal
'Yellow John Wingfield' (14b) MCms
'Yellow Mayford Perfection' (5a) ♀H2 MCms
'Yellow Pennine Oriel' (29a) ♀H4 MCms NHal
'Yellow Spider' (10a) MCms
'Yellow Spray' (12b) SCob
'Yellow Talbot Parade' (29c) MCms
'Yellow Woolman's Glory' (7a) MCms
yezoense CDor MNrw SRms
- B&SWJ 10872 WCru
- 'Roseum' ECtt
aff. ***yezoense*** MHol
'Yvonne Arnaud' (24b) MCms
'Yvonne's Rot-Goldene' SAko
§ ***zawadzkii*** CMac SRms WFar

Chrysogonum (*Asteraceae*)

virginianum CMea EBee EWes SPer WFar
- var. ***australe*** EHyd SBrt
- - 'Andre Viette' CBod
- 'Golden Acres' ECtt

Chrysopogon (*Poaceae*)

gryllus EBee NDov WPGP

Chrysosplenium (*Saxifragaceae*)

alternifolium EBee GEdr
davidianum EBee EPot EWld GJos GKev NBid NHpl WBor WCru WSHC
- SBEC 233 CExl
aff. ***hebetatum*** B&SWJ 9835 NWad
lanuginosum var. ***formosanum*** GEdr
- - B&SWJ 6979 ESwi WCru
macrophyllum CExl EBee ECha EPPr EPfP EWld GBin GKev GMaP LEdu MNrw MPie NBid SDix SHar WBor WCot WCru WSHC
- green-flowered **new** GGro
oppositifolium CTtf ECha WSFF WShi

Chusquea (*Poaceae*)

culeou ♀H4 CBcs EPfP LEdu LPar MAvo MGos MWht SPlb SSta
- 'Purple Splendour' CDTJ
- weeping CDTJ
delicatula from Machu Picchu, Peru CExl
gigantea ♀H3 CBcs CDTJ CExl EPfP ESwi MAvo MWht WPGP
montana CDTJ
mulleri F&M 104A from Mexico CExl
nigricans MAvo

Cicer (*Fabaceae*)

arietinum **new** SPhx

Cicerbita (*Asteraceae*)

BO 16-085 **new** GGro
BWJ 7891 from China **new** GGro
§ ***alpina*** GAbr GBee NBid SPlb
bourgaei CFis MHol
macrophylla (Willd.) Wallr. MBow
- subsp. ***macrophylla*** CTtf
plumieri GAbr WCot WSHC
- 'Blott' (v) WCot

Cichorium (*Asteraceae*)

endivia 'Pancalieri' ♀H3 CHby EKin MCtn
intybus CHby CLau CSpe CTtf ELan ENfk EWTr EWoo GAbr GPoy GQue LShi LSun MHer MNHC NBir NGBl NMir SBut SPer SPlb SPoG SRms WFar WHrl WSHC WWild
- f. ***album*** CBod CTtf ECha ECtt EHyd EPPr LRHS MBel NGBl NRHS SBut SPer
- 'Brussels Witloof' SVic
- 'Indigo' LRHS NRHS
- 'Palla Rossa' ♀H5 CHby MCtn SRms
- 'Pan di Zucchero' ♀H5 CHby
- 'Red Rib' SRms
- 'Roseum' CBod CTtf ECha ECtt EHyd ELan EPPr LRHS MBel NRHS SBut SPer SPoG WHrl

Cimicifuga see *Actaea*

acerina see *Actaea japonica*
americana see *Actaea podocarpa*
cordifolia (DC.) Torrey & A.Gray see *Actaea cordifolia*
cordifolia Pursh see *Actaea podocarpa*
foetida see *Actaea cimicifuga*
racemosa var. ***cordifolia*** see *Actaea cordifolia*
- 'Purpurea' see *Actaea simplex* Atropurpurea Group
ramosa see *Actaea simplex* 'Prichard's Giant'
rubifolia see *Actaea cordifolia*
simplex var. ***matsumurae*** see *Actaea matsumurae*

Cineraria (*Asteraceae*)

× ***hybrida*** see *Pericallis* × *hybrida*

Cinnamomum (*Lauraceae*)

camphora CBcs CExl CKel
japonicum B&SWJ 14627 WCru

Circaea (*Onagraceae*)

lutetiana WHer
- 'Caveat Emptor' (v) NBid WCot

Cirsium (*Asteraceae*)

altissimum **new** SPhx
arvense WSFF
canum CSpe GQue MHol
diacantha see *Ptilostemon diacantha*
eriophoroides GEdr
eriophorum GGro
helenioides see *C. heterophyllum*
§ ***heterophyllum*** CDor GGro MHol NAts NChi NLar SHar
- PAB 067 LEdu WMal WPGP
- 'Pink Blush' CBcs CTtf EMor GBin LCro LOPS MHol NSti WNPC
japonicum 'Pink Beauty' EMor LRHS SBls SBut
- 'Rose Beauty' WSpi
'Mount Etna' CBod CSpe EBee EHyd ELan EPfP GDam GKin LRHS MBNS MBriF

	MMuc MSpe NDov NFav NGdn NRHS SEND SGbt WCAu
oleraceum	EBee GGro LEdu NBid NLar SBrt WKor
rivulare	Widely available
'Atropurpureum' ♀H7	
- FROSTED MAGIC ('Lowcir'PBR)	CBcs CBod CDor CSpe CTtf GMaP LBuc LCro LOPS LRHS MBNS MBel MHol MidI NDov NSti SEdd SGBe SMrm WCAu WFar WNPC WTor
- 'Trevor's Blue Wonder'	see *C. rivulare* 'Trevor's Felley Find'
§ - 'Trevor's Felley Find'PBR	Widely available
tuberosum	ECha LEdu LRHS SDix SPhx SSal WCot
vulgare	WSFF

Cissus (*Vitaceae*)

antarctica ♀H1c	CCCN EShb SEND
discolor	EShb
nodosa new	EShb
rhombifolia ♀H1c	EOHP EShb
- 'Ellen Danica' ♀H1c	EShb
rotundifolia new	EShb
§ ***striata***	CBcs CDoC CKel CMac EBee EHyd EPfP EShb LRHS MGil MRav NChi SBrt SEND SWvt

Cistanthe (*Portulacaceae*)

monosperma new	GAbr

Cistus ✿ (*Cistaceae*)

acutifolius misapplied	see *C.* × *pulverulentus*
× ***aguilarii***	CTri MRav WMal
- 'Maculatus' ♀H4	CBcs CBod CDoC CExl CKel CRos CSBt EGrI ELan EPfP LRHS LSRN NLar SEle SPer SPoG SWvt WKif WMal WPGP WSpi
albidus	WSpi XSen
algarvensis	see *Halimium ocymoides*
'Anne Palmer'	see *C.* × *fernandesiae* 'Anne Palmer'
× ***argenteus*** 'Blushing Peggy Sammons'	EHyd ELan EPfP LRHS NLar NRHS SEdd SWvt
- 'Paper Moon'	EWTr LSRN NLar SEdd
§ - 'Peggy Sammons'	CBrac ECha ELan EPfP LRHS LSRN MAsh MGos NLar SAko SCob SGbt SPer SWvt XSen
- 'Silver Ghost'	CDoC CKel LRHS SWvt
- 'Silver Pink' ambig.	Widely available
'Blanche'	see *C. ladanifer* 'Blanche'
× ***bornetianus*** 'Jester' ♀H4	CBod CBrac CKel CSBt EHyd ELan EPfP EWTr LRHS MAsh NLar NRHS SWvt WLov
× ***canescens*** f. ***albus***	XSen
'Christopher Gable' new	WMal
clusii subsp. ***multiflorus***	XSen
× ***corbariensis***	see *C.* × *hybridus*
creticus	CBcs CDoC CExl CRos EHyd GPoy LRHS MAsh MGos MPri SLon SNig SPoG SRms SWvt WSpi
- subsp. ***corsicus***	XSen
§ - subsp. ***creticus***	EBee ELan EPfP MRav SCoo SPer
- subsp. ***eriocephalus***	CBod
§ - subsp. ***incanus***	SGBe WCot
§ × ***crispatus*** 'Warley Rose'	GMaP WKif
crispus misapplied	see *C.* × *pulverulentus*, *C.* × *purpureus*
§ ***crispus*** L.	ELan XSen
- 'Prostratus'	see *C. crispus* L.
- 'Sunset'	see *C.* × *pulverulentus* 'Sunset'
§ × ***cyprius*** ♀H4	CBrac EBee EHyd ELan EPfP LRHS MNHC NRHS SDix SRms SWvt WKif WSpi
§ - var. ***ellipticus*** 'Elma' ♀H4	CRos EHyd ELan EPfP LRHS MAsh MHtn NLar NRHS SPer WAvo WCot
§ × ***dansereaui***	CKel CMac CSBt LRHS SWvt WSpi
- 'Decumbens' ♀H4	Widely available
- 'Jenkyn Place' ♀H4	CBod CDoC EBee ELan GMaP LRHS LSRN MBNS NLar SEdd SPer SPoG WKif
'Elma'	see *C.* × *cyprius* var. *ellipticus* 'Elma'
§ × ***fernandesiae*** 'Anne Palmer'	CBod CDoC CKel EBee EHyd MAsh NLar SEdd SGBe WMal WSpi
× ***florentinus*** misapplied	see × *Halimiocistus* 'Ingwersenii'
florentinus ambig.	WSpi XLum
§ ***florentinus*** Lam.	GMaP XSen
* - 'Tramontane'	XSen
'Gordon Cooper' ♀H4	ELan LSRN MMrt NLar SPoG WMal WSpi
halimifolius	see *Halimium halimifolium* Willk.
× ***heterocalyx*** 'Chelsea Bonnet'	EWTr GMaP MBNS NLar SCoo SEdd SPoG
'Highlights'	MAsh
§ × ***hybridus***	Widely available
- 'Coral Tears'	CKel LRHS
- 'Gold Prize' (v)	CWGN NLar SCob SWvt WGrn
- LITTLE MISS SUNSHINE ('Dunnecis'PBR) (v)	MAsh MGos NHol NLar SRms SWvt
- ROSPICO ('Rencis'PBR) (v)	EPfP NLar
incanus	see *C. creticus* subsp. *incanus*
ingwerseniana	see × *Halimiocistus* 'Ingwersenii'
'Jessamy Beauty'	WAvo
'Jessamy Charm'	SPhx
ladanifer misapplied	see *C.* × *cyprius*
ladanifer ambig.	CMac ECha SPer WKif
ladanifer L.	CBcs CSBt CSde CTri ELan EPfP GPoy LRHS MRav MSwo SCob SWvt WSpi XSen
- B&SWJ 15064 new	WCru
§ - 'Blanche'	EPfP LSRN NLar SPer SWvt WKif WSpi
§ - 'Paladin'	SArc
- Palhinhae Group	see *C. ladanifer* var. *sulcatus*
- 'Pat'	CDoC CRos EHyd ELan EPfP LRHS LSRN MAsh NLar NRHS SPoG SWvt
- var. ***petiolatus*** 'Bennett's White'	WAvo
§ - var. ***sulcatus***	ELan
lasianthus	see *Halimium lasianthum*
laurifolius	EPfP LRHS MGos SWvt WSpi XSen
- subsp. ***atlanticus***	XSen
× ***laxus*** 'Snow White' ♀H4	CBrac CWGN EBee EPfP NLar NPer SAko SLon
§ × ***lenis*** 'Grayswood Pink' ♀H4	CBrac CDoC CExl CKel CRos CTri EBee ELan EPfP EWTr LRHS LSRN MAsh MGos MSwo NLar SAko SCob SEND SEdd SGBe SPer SPhx SPlb SPoG SWvt XSen
× ***loretii*** misapplied	see *C.* × *dansereaui*
× ***loretii*** Rouy & Foucaud	see *C.* × *stenophyllus*
× ***lusitanicus*** Maund	see *C.* × *dansereaui*
'Merrist Wood Cream'	see × *Halimiocistus wintonensis* 'Merrist Wood Cream'
monspeliensis	CMac CRos EPfP LRHS MAsh MBNS MPri SLon SPer SPoG WLov XLum XSen
- 'Vicar's Mead'	CCCN EHyd LRHS WMal
monspeliensis × ***salviifolius***	see *C.* × *florentinus* Lam.
× ***oblongifolius***	SWvt XSen
× ***obtusifolius*** ambig.	CKel EBou ELan EPfP LRHS WSpi
× ***obtusifolius*** Sweet	WPGP
§ - 'Thrive' ♀H4	CRos EHyd EPfP LRHS MGos NRHS SCoo

	ocymoides	see *Halimium ocymoides*
	'Paladin'	see *C. ladanifer* 'Paladin'
	palhinhae	see *C. ladanifer* var. *sulcatus*
	parviflorus misapplied	see *C.* × *lenis* 'Grayswood Pink'
	'Peggy Sammons'	see *C.* × *argenteus* 'Peggy Sammons'
	× ***platysepalus***	SDix SPhx
	populifolius	CEme CMac ECha EHyd EPfP NLar SPer SWvt
	- var. ***lasiocalyx***	see *C. populifolius* subsp. *major*
§	- subsp. ***major***	LRHS LSRN WPGP WSpi
§	× ***pulverulentus***	CExl CTri ECha XLum XSen
	- (Delilei Group) 'Fiona'	WMal
§	- 'Sunset' ♀H4	Widely available
	- 'Warley Rose'	see *C.* × *crispatus* 'Warley Rose'
§	× ***purpureus*** ♀H4	Widely available
	- 'Alan Fradd'	CBcs CBod CDoC CMac CRos EHyd ELan EPfP LCro LOPS LRHS LSRN MAsh MGos MSwo NLar NRHS SCob SCoo SEND SGBe SGbt SPoG SWvt WFar WMal XLum XSen
	- 'Betty Taudevin'	see *C.* × *purpureus*
	- f. ***stictus***	WAvo
	× ***rodiaei*** 'Jessabel'	EPfP MAsh MRav NLar SWvt WPGP
	'Ruby Cluster'	CCCN CDoC
	sahucii	see × *Halimiocistus sahucii*
	salviifolius	CCCN XLum XSen
	- B&SWJ 15066 new	WCru
	- 'Avalanche'	WAbe
	- 'Gold Star'	CDoC NLar
	- 'May Snow'	MAsh SGBe
	- 'Prostratus'	CDoC CKel CSde ELan EPfP LRHS SWvt WSpi
	× ***argenteus*** 'Silver Pink' misapplied	see *C.* × *lenis* 'Grayswood Pink'
	× ***skanbergii***	CBod CDoC CEme CEnd CMac CTri ELan EPfP MGos MRav NBir NLar SCob SDix SEND WCFE WSpi XLum XSen
	'Snow Fire' ♀H4	CCCN CRos EBee ELan EPfP LRHS LSRN MAsh MMuc MNHC NLar SAko SCoo SWvt WAvo WGrn
§	× ***stenophyllus***	CMac
	'Thrive'	see *C.* × *obtusifolius* 'Thrive'
	× ***verguinii***	XSen
	villosus	see *C. creticus* subsp. *creticus*
	wintonensis	see × *Halimiocistus wintonensis*

Cistus × *Halimium* see × *Halimiocistus*

Citharexylum (*Verbenaceae*)

	quadrangulare Jacq.	see *C. spinosum*
	spicatum	CCCN CExl
§	***spinosum***	CBcs EBee

citrandarin see *Citrus reticulata* × *C. trifoliata*

citrange see *Citrus* × *insitorum*

citrangequat see *Citrus* × *georgiana*

citremon see *Citrus* × *limon* × *C. trifoliata*

× *Citrofortunella* see *Citrus*

mitis	see *Citrus* × *microcarpa*

citron see *Citrus medica*

Citronella (*Icacinaceae*)

§	***gongonha***	SVen
	mucronata	see *C. gongonha*

Citrullus (*Cucurbitaceae*)

lanatus 'Charleston Gray'	SVic

Citrus (*Rutaceae*)

§	× ***aurantiifolia*** (F)	CCCN EPfP SCit SPre
	- key lime	see *C.* × *aurantiifolia*
§	× ***aurantium*** (F)	SCit
	- 'Aber's Narrowleaf' (F)	SCit
	- subsp. ***bergamia***	see *C.* × *limon*
	- 'Bergamot de Versailles' (F)	EPfP
	- 'Bouquet de Fleurs'	see *C.* × *aurantium* (Sour Orange Group) 'Bouquet'
	- 'Gou-tou Cheng' (F)	SCit
§	- Grapefruit Group (F)	CCCN SPre SWeb
	- - 'Foster' (F)	SCit
	- - 'Golden Special' (F)	SCit
	- - 'Marsh' (F)	SCit
	- - 'Oroblanco' (F)	SCit
	- - 'Red Blush' (F/S)	SCit
	- - 'Star Ruby' (F/S)	CCCN SCit SPre SVic
	- - 'Wheeny'	see *C. maxima* 'Wheeny'
	- var. ***myrtifolia***	see *C.* × *aurantium*
	- 'Pursha' (F)	SPre
	- 'Robinson' (F)	SCit
§	- (Sour Orange Group) 'Bouquet' (F)	SCit
	- - 'Bouquetier de Nice' (F)	SCit
	- - 'Chinotto' (F)	SCit SPre SWeb
	- - 'Seville' (F)	LSRN SCit SPre
	- - 'Smooth Flat Seville' (F)	SCit
§	- Sweet Orange Group (F)	CCCN CDoC SCit SGsty SPre SVic SWeb
§	- - 'Baia' (F/S)	SCit SPre
	- - 'Embiguo' (F)	SCit
	- - 'Fukumoto' (F)	CCCN
	- - 'Jaffa'	see *C.* × *aurantium* (Sweet Orange Group) 'Shamouti'
	- - 'Lane Late' (F)	CCCN SCit SPre
§	- - 'Malta Blood' (F)	SCit
	- - 'Maltaise Sanguine'	see *C.* × *aurantium* (Sweet Orange Group) 'Malta Blood'
	- - 'Navelate' (F)	SCit
	- - 'Navelina' (F/S)	CCCN SCit SPre
	- - 'Newhall' (F/S)	NLar SCit
	- - 'Salustiana' (F/S)	SCit
§	- - 'Sanguinelli' (F)	CCCN SCit SPre SVic
§	- - 'Shamouti' (F)	SCit
	- - 'Spanish Sanguinelli'	see *C.* × *aurantium* (Sweet Orange Group) 'Sanguinelli'
	- - 'Succari' (F)	SCit
	- - 'Tarocco' (F)	SCit
	- - 'Valencia' (F)	CCCN SCit SPre
	- - 'Washington'	see *C.* × *aurantium* (Sweet Orange Group) 'Baia'
	- - 'Washington Navel'	see *C.* × *aurantium* (Sweet Orange Group) 'Baia'
§	- (Tangelo Group) 'Minneola' (F)	SCit
§	- - 'Nova' (F/S)	CCCN SCit SVic
	- - 'Orlando' (F)	SCit
	- - 'Seminole' (F)	SCit
	- - 'Ugli' misapplied	see *C.* × *aurantium* 'Minneola'
	- - 'Ugli' (F)	SCit
	- (Tangor Group) 'Dweet' (F)	SCit
	- - 'Ellendale' (F)	SCit
	- - 'Murcott' (F)	SCit
	australasica (F)	SCit SPre SVic
	australasica × (× ***floridana***) 'Eustis' (F)	SPre

	bergamia	see *C.* × *limon*
	- bergamot	see *C.* × *limon* Bergamot Group
	'Buddha's Hand'	see *C. medica* 'Fingered'
	calamondin	see *C.* × *microcarpa*
§	***cavaleriei*** (F)	WPGP
	citrandarin	see *C. reticulata* × *trifoliata*
	deliciosa	see *C. reticulata* 'Willowleaf'
§	× ***floridana***	SWeb
	- 'Eustis' (F)	SCit SPre
	- 'Lakeland' (F)	SCit SPre
	× ***georgiana*** 'Thomasville' (F)	SCit
§	***hystrix***	CCCN CDoC ELan LSRN NLar SCit SPre SWeb
	× ***insitorum*** 'C-35' (F)	SCit
	- 'Carrizo' (F)	SCit
	- 'Citromon' (F)	SCit
	- 'Curafora' (F)	SCit
	- 'Swingle' (F)	SCit
	- 'Us119' (F)	SCit
	- 'Venasca' (F)	SCit
	jambhiri	see *C.* × *taitensis*
§	***japonica*** (F) ♀H1c	CBcs ELan EPfP LCro LOPS SCit SPre SVic
	- Hong Kong kumquat (F)	SCit
	- 'Nagami' (F)	SPre SWeb
	- 'Reale'[PBR] (F)	SPre
§	× ***junos***	SCit SPre SVic
	kinokuni	see *C. japonica*
	kotokan	see *C.* × *aurantium*
	'Kucle' (F)	SCit SPre
	'Kulci' (F)	CCCN
	kumquat	see *C. japonica*
	'La Valette' (F)	CCCN SPre
	× ***latifolia*** (F/S)	CCCN CDoC EPfP SCit SPre SWeb
	- 'Bearss' (F)	SCit SVic
	- variegated (F/v)	SPre
	latipes Hook. f. & Thomson ex Hook. f.	see *C. hystrix*
	limetta (F)	CCCN SPre SVic SWeb
	limettioides (F)	SCit SPre
§	× ***limon*** (F)	LSRN SCit SPre SVic WKor
§	- Bergamot Group (F)	SPre
	- - 'Fantastico' (F)	SCit
	- 'Eureka'	see *C.* × *limon* 'Garey's Eureka'
	- 'Eureka Variegated' (F/v)	SCit
	- 'Fino' (F)	CCCN SCit
	- 'Four Seasons'	see *C.* × *limon* 'Garey's Eureka'
§	- 'Garey's Eureka' (F)	CCCN ELan EPfP ETod LCro LOPS NLar SCit SPre
	- 'Imperial' (F)	SCit SPre
	- 'Improved Meyer'	see *C.* × *limon* 'Meyer'
	- 'Lemonade' (F)	SCit
	- 'Lisbon' (F)	SCit
	- 'Lunario' (F)	SCit SPre
§	- 'Meyer' (F) ♀H2	CBcs CCCN CDoC CEme ELan EPfP LSRN NLar SCit SCoo SPer SPre SWeb
	- 'Ponderosa' (F)	SCit
	- 'Quatre Saisons'	see *C.* × *limon* 'Garey's Eureka'
	- 'Rangpur' (F)	SCit SPre
	- 'Romana' (F)	SCit
	- 'Sfusato d'Amalfi' (F)	SCit
	- 'Siracusano' (F)	SCit
	- 'Variegata' (F/v) ♀H2	CCCN ELan SCit SPre
	- 'Verna' (F)	CCCN SCit
	- 'Villa Franca' (F)	SCit
	- 'Yen Ben' (F)	SCit
	- 'Zagara Bianco' (F)	SCit
	× ***limonia***	see *C.* × *limon*
	'Lipo' (F)	CCCN SCit SPre
	macrophylla (F)	SCit
	madurensis	see *C. japonica*
	maxima (F)	SWeb
§	- 'Wheeny' (F)	SCit
§	***medica*** (F)	SWeb
	- 'Cedra' (F)	SPre
	- 'Cidro Digitado'	see *C. medica* 'Fingered'
	- var. ***digitata***	see *C. medica* 'Fingered'
	- 'Ethrog' (F)	SCit SPre
§	- 'Fingered' (F)	SCit SPre SWeb
*	- 'Rubra'	SPre
	- var. ***sarcodactylis***	see *C. medica* 'Fingered'
	× ***meyeri***	see *C.* × *limon*
§	× ***microcarpa*** (F) ♀H3	CCCN CDoC NLar SCit SPre SWeb
	- Philippine lime	see *C.* × *microcarpa*
§	- 'Tiger' (F/v)	SCit SPre SVic
	- 'Variegata'	see *C.* × *microcarpa* 'Tiger'
	× ***mitis***	see *C.* × *microcarpa*
	natsudaidai	see *C.* × *aurantium*
	'Nippon'	SCit
	× ***nobilis*** Lour.	see *C. reticulata* 'Willowleaf'
	- var. ***inermis***	see *C. japonica*
	- Ortanique Group	see *C.* × *aurantium* Sweet Orange Group
	× ***obovata*** (F)	SPre
	- 'Fukushu' (F)	CCCN SCit
	× ***paradisi***	see *C.* × *aurantium* Grapefruit Group
	- 'Wheeny'	see *C. maxima* 'Wheeny'
	'Pursta' (F)	CCCN
	reshni	see *C.* × *aurantium*
§	***reticulata*** (F)	CCCN SCit SPre SWeb
	- 'Clausellina' (F/S)	SCit
	- var. ***deliciosa***	see *C. reticulata* 'Willowleaf'
	- 'Fina' (F/S)	SCit
	- 'Hashimoto' (F/S)	SCit
	- 'Hernandina' (F)	CCCN
	- Mandarin Group (F)	EPfP SPre SWeb
	- - 'Clementine' (F)	EPfP SPre SWeb
	- - 'Encore' (F)	SCit
	- - 'Esbal' (F)	CCCN
	- - 'Fortune' (F)	SCit
	- - 'Fremont' (F)	SCit
	- - 'Nules' (F/S)	CCCN SCit SPre
	- 'Marisol' (F/S)	SCit
	- 'Miyagawa' (F)	CCCN SCit
	- 'Nour' (F)	SCit
	- 'Nova'	see *C.* × *aurantium* (Tangelo Group) 'Nova'
	- 'Okitsu' (F/S)	CCCN SCit
	- 'Owari' (F/S)	SCit
	- Satsuma Group	see *C. reticulata*
	- (Tangerine Group) 'Dancy' (F)	SCit
§	- 'Willowleaf' (F)	SCit
§	***reticulata*** × ***trifoliata***	SCit
	sinensis	see *C.* × *aurantium* Sweet Orange Group
	- 'Jaffa'	see *C.* × *aurantium* (Sweet Orange Group) 'Shamouti'
	- 'Washington'	see *C.* × *aurantium* (Sweet Orange Group) 'Baia'
§	× ***taitensis*** (F)	SCit SPre
	- 'Otaheite' (F)	CCCN SCit SPre
§	- rough lemon (F)	SCit
	- Schaub rough lemon	see *C.* × *taitensis* rough lemon
§	***trifoliata***	CAgr CBcs CBod CCCN CDoC CMCN EBee EHyd ELan ELon EPfP IDee MBlu MGil MMuc MRav SCit SMad SPer SPlb WFar WKor WSHC
	- 'Flying Dragon'	SCit
	unshiu	see *C. reticulata*

volkameriana	see *C.* × *limon*
wilsonii	see *C.* × *junos*

Cladrastis (*Fabaceae*)

§ ***kentukea***	CBcs CEme CLnd CMCN EBee ELan EPfP ESwi EWTr IPap LMaj MBlu MTrO MVil NLar SMad WMat WPGP
§ - 'Perkins Pink'	MBlu
- 'Rosea'	see *C. kentukea* 'Perkins Pink'
lutea	see *C. kentukea*
sinensis	CExl EBee EPfP MBlu WPGP
wilsonii	WPGP

Clarkia (*Onagraceae*)

CROWN DOUBLE MIXED (d)	SVic

Claytonia (*Portulacaceae*)

alsinoides	see *C. sibirica*
§ ***perfoliata***	GPoy MNHC WHer
§ ***sibirica***	CAgr CTtf LPot WKor XLum
- f. ***albiflora***	EWld MPie WCot
virginica	CBor EBee GKev WFar

Clematis ✿ (*Ranunculaceae*)

BWJ 7630 from China	WCru
CC 711	CExl
CC 4710	CExl
'Abigail' (Vt)	NHaw
ABILENE ('Evipo027'PBR) (EL)	CRos CWCL EHyd ELan EPfP LRHS MAsh NRHS NTay SCoo SNig SPoG
'Abundance' (Vt) ♀H6	CArg CBcs CRHN CWCL ELan EPfP ETho LCro LRHS LSRN MAsh NHol NTay SNig SPer WFar WSpi
ACROPOLIS ('Evipo078'PBR) (Boulevard Series)	CBod CWGN ELan ETho LRHS LSou NTay SCoo SNig
addisonii	NHaw
'Advent Bells' (C)	CWGN ETho LCro LOPS NTay WSpi
'Akaishi' (EL)	ETho SNig
akebioides	GKev
ALABAST ('Poulala'PBR) (EL) ♀H6	ETho LRHS SCoo WSpi
ALAINA ('Evipo056'PBR) (EL)	CRos EHyd LRHS NRHS NTay SCoo SLon SNig SPoG
'Alba Luxurians' (Vt)	CBcs CDoC CRHN CTri CWCL EHyd ELan EPfP EShb ETho LCro LOPS LRHS LSRN MGos NHol NRHS NTay SCob SPer SPoG
'Albiflora' (A)	NTay
'Albina Plena' (A/d)	ETho
'Alice Fisk' (EL)	EBee ETho LSRN MSwo
'Alionushka' (I) ♀H6	CRHN CWCL EHyd ELan EPfP ETho LRHS LSRN NTay
ALITA ('Evipo070'PBR) (Vt)	CRos CWCL EBee EHyd EPfP LRHS NTay SCoo SLon SNig
'Allanah' (LL)	CWCL ETho IPot LRHS LSRN NTay SCoo WSpi
alpina	GDam GKev GLog LCro LOPS LRHS LSRN MAsh MCot MRav NPer NTay SEWo SPlb SPre SWvt WFar
- 'Albiflora'	see *C. sibirica*
- 'Columbine White'	see *C.* 'White Columbine'
§ - 'Pamela Jackman' (A) ♀H6	CMac CRos CWCL EHyd ELan ETho LRHS LSRN MAsh NRHS SCob SCoo SPer SPoG SRkn SWvt WFar
- pink-flowered (A)	GKev
- 'Stolwijk Gold' (A)	CWGN EBee MBlu NTay SRms
alternata	CWGN EBee NHaw
'Amethyst Beauty' (A)	EHyd EPfP LRHS SCoo
AMETHYST BEAUTY ('Evipo043'PBR) (LL)	CRos ETho MAsh NLar NTay SLon SNig SPoG
'Andante' (I)	CWGN ETho WSpi
'Andromeda' (EL)	CDoC CRos EHyd EPfP ETho IPot LRHS NHaw NLar NRHS NTay SCoo SNig
ANETA ('Evipo055'PBR) (Vt)	CWGN NTay SLon
ANGELA ('Zoang'PBR) (EL)	LSRN NTay
ANGELIQUE ('Evipo017') (EL)	CRos CWGN EHyd ELan EPfP ETho LRHS MAsh MGos NRHS NTay SCoo SLon SNig SPer
'Anissa' (V)	NHaw
'Anita' (Ta)	EPfP ETho LSRN MAsh NHaw NTay
ANNA LOUISE ('Evithree'PBR) (EL) ♀H6	CRos CWCL EHyd EPfP ETho LRHS LSRN MGos NTay SCoo SLon SNig
'Annabel' (EL)	LSRN MAsh
ANNABELLA ('Zo08169') (V)	ETho
'Anniseed' (M) <u>**new**</u>	NHaw
ANNIVERSARY ('Pynot') (EL)	LSRN SCoo
'Aotearoa' (LL)	ETho NHaw
'Aphrodite' (I)	MAsh
'Aphrodite Elegafumina' (I)	CRHN CWGN EHyd
apiifolia	NHaw WSpi
'Apollonia'	CWGN
'Apple Blossom' (Ar) ♀H4	CBcs CBod CDoC CTri CWCL ELan EPfP ETho LBuc LCro LOPS LRHS LSRN MAsh MGos MRav NLar NRHS NTay SCob SCoo SPer SPoG SRkn SRms SWvt
'Arabella' (I) ♀H6	CRHN CRos CWCL CWGN EHyd ELan ELon EPfP EShb ETho LRHS LSRN MAsh MGos NLar NRHS NTay SCoo SNig SPer SRkn SWvt WFar WSpi
§ ARCTIC QUEEN ('Evitwo'PBR) (EL) ♀H6	CRos EHyd EPfP ETho LBuc LRHS LSRN MAsh NRHS SCoo SLon SPoG
armandi	Widely available
- 'Enham Star' (Ar)	CRos EHyd EPfP LRHS MGos NRHS
§ - 'Little White Charm' (Ar)	CRos EBee EHyd ELan EPfP LRHS NLar NRHS SCoo
- 'Meyeniana'	see *C. armandi* 'Little White Charm'
§ - 'Snowdrift' (Ar)	CBcs CBod CEme CRos EBee EHyd ELan EPfP ETho GDam LCro LOPS LRHS LSRN MAsh MGos MSwo NLar NRHS NTay SCoo SPer SPoG SRms WFar
× ***aromatica***	CWGN EBee EHyd ELan EPfP EShb ETho IPot LRHS MMrt NTay SCoo WCot WSpi
'Asao' (EL)	CArg CRos EHyd EPfP ETho LRHS NTay SCoo SNig SPoG
'Ascotiensis' (LL) ♀H6	CRHN EBee EHyd EPfP ETho LRHS NTay SCoo SLon
'Ashva' (LL)	CWGN NTay SNig
ASTRA NOVA ('Zo09085'PBR) (Vt)	CWGN IPot NTay WSpi
'Aureolin' (Ta)	NLar
AVANT-GARDE ('Evipo033'PBR) (Vt)	CDoC CRos CWCL CWGN EHyd ELan EPfP ETho LRHS NTay SLon
AZTEK	see *C.* 'Helios'
BABY DOLL ('Zobadol'PBR) (EL)	EBee ETho NLar NTay WSpi
'Baby Pink' (I)	NHaw
BABY STAR ('Zobast'PBR) (EL)	ETho NTay
§ 'Bagatelle' (LL)	EHyd ETho NHaw
'Bal Maiden' (Vt)	CRHN NHaw
'Barbara' (LL)	LSRN NTay
'Barbara Dibley' (EL)	CTri CWCL EHyd ETho MAsh NHaw SCoo SNig
'Barbara Harrington'PBR (LL)	EHyd LRHS LSRN
'Barbara Jackman' (EL)	CArg CWCL EHyd ETho LRHS LSRN MAsh MGos NTay SCob SCoo SLon SNig SPer

'Beata' (LL)	CWCL NHaw SNig
'Beautiful Bride'^{PBR} (EL)	ETho LCro LOPS NTay
'Beauty of Worcester' (EL)	CDoC CWCL ELan ELon EPfP ETho LRHS LSRN MAsh NTay SCoo SPer
'Bees' Jubilee' (EL)	CArg CBcs CMac CRos CWCL EBee EHyd ELan EPfP ETho LCro LOPS LRHS LSRN MAsh MGos MSwo NLar NTay SCoo SNig SPer SPoG SWvt
'Bella' (EL)	LSRN
'Belle Nantaise' (EL)	EHyd LRHS NRHS SRms
'Belle of Woking' (EL)	EHyd ELan ELon LRHS LSRN NTay SCoo SNig SWvt
'Benikomachi' **new**	SNig
BERNADINE ('Evipo 061'^{PBR}) (EL)	CBod CPla CRos CWGN EHyd ETho LRHS NRHS NTay SCoo SNig
'Best Wishes'	CRos EHyd ETho LRHS LSRN NRHS NTay WSpi
§ 'Beth Currie' (EL)	EHyd EPfP LRHS SCoo SNig
'Betty Corning' (Vt)	CRHN CRos CWCL CWGN EBee EHyd ELan EPfP ETho LRHS LSRN MGos NRHS NTay SCoo SLon SPoG SRms SWvt
bigelovii **new**	SBrt
BIJOU	see *C.* THUMBELINA
'Bill MacKenzie' (Ta) ♀H6	CArg CBcs CDoC CMac CRos CTri EHyd ELan EPfP ETho LRHS LSRN MAsh MGos MRav NFav NHol NRHS NTay SCoo SPer SPoG SRms SWvt WSHC
'Black Prince' (Vt)	CRHN CRos CWGN EHyd ELan EPfP ETho IPot LCro LRHS LSRN NLar NRHS NTay SLon SNig SPer SPoG SRms
'Black Tea' (LL)	CRos EHyd EPfP IPot LRHS LSRN NRHS NTay SLon
§ 'Błękitny Anioł' (LL) ♀H6	CRHN CWCL CWGN EBee EHyd ELan ELon EPfP ETho LCro LOPS LRHS MAsh NLar NRHS NTay SCoo SLon SNig SPoG WBor
BLUE ANGEL	see *C.* 'Błękitny Anioł'
'Blue Belle' (Vt)	CRHN ELan IPot LRHS NLar SLon WFar
'Blue Bird' (A/d)	CArg CBcs CWCL EBee ELan GDam LRHS MAsh NTay SRms
BLUE BLOOD	see *C.* 'Königskind'
'Blue Boy' (EL)	see *C.* 'Elsa Späth'
'Blue Boy' (I)	see *C.* × *diversifolia* 'Blue Boy' (I)
'Blue Dancer' (A)	CBcs CDoC CRos EHyd EPfP ETho LRHS MGos NLar NTay SCoo SNig SPer
'Blue Eclipse' (A)	CWGN EHyd ETho NHol NLar NRHS NTay SPoG
'Blue Explosion' (EL) **new**	SNig
'Blue Eyes' (EL)	ETho LSRN NLar
§ 'Blue Light'^{PBR} (EL/d)	CWGN ELan ETho NLar NTay
BLUE MOON ('Evirin'^{PBR}) (EL)	CRos CWCL EHyd EPfP ETho LRHS LSRN NTay SCoo SLon SNig
BLUE OCEAN ('Zo09045'^{PBR}) (I)	EBee IPot
BLUE PIROUETTE ('Zobluepi'^{PBR}) (I)	CWCL ELan ETho NTay
BLUE RAIN	see *C.* 'Sinii Dozhd'
'Blue Ravine' (EL)	EPfP SCoo
'Blue Ribbon' **new**	SGBe
BLUE RIVER ('Zoblueriver'^{PBR}) (I)	CWCL CWGN ELan ETho NTay
'Bolam Belle' (Vt)	NHaw
BONANZA ('Evipo031'^{PBR}) (Vt)	CRos EHyd EPfP LRHS NLar NTay SCoo SLon SNig SPoG
× ***bonstedtii*** 'Crépuscule' (H)	ECtt MCot WSpi
BOURBON ('Evipo018'^{PBR}) (EL)	CRos CWCL EHyd ELan EPfP ETho LRHS NTay SCoo SLon SNig
'Brianna' (Vt)	NHaw
'Brocade' (Vt)	CRHN NHaw
'Broughton Bride' (A)	CDoC CWCL CWGN EHyd EPfP ETho LRHS NHol NRHS NTay SRms
'Broughton Star' (M/d) ♀H5	Widely available
'Brunette' (A)	EHyd ELan EPfP ETho MAsh NTay SLon
buchananiana Finet & Gagnep.	see *C. rehderiana*
'Buckland Beauty' (V)	CWGN NHaw
'Buckland Pixie' (Vt)	NHaw
'Burford Bell' (V)	NHaw WSHC
'Burford Princess' (Vt)	CRHN NHaw
'Burford White' (A)	ETho
'Burma Star' (EL)	CWCL CWGN EPfP ETho NTay
BURNING LOVE ('Vitiwester'^{PBR}) (Vt)	ETho NTay
CADDICK'S CASCADE	see *C.* 'Semu'
calycina	see *C. cirrhosa* var. *balearica*
§ ***campaniflora***	CMea ETho NHaw NTay
- dark-flowered	CMea
'Candy Stripe'	EHyd LRHS NTay SCoo SNig SPoG
'Capitaine Thuilleaux'	see *C.* 'Souvenir du Capitaine Thuilleaux'
'Cardinal Wyszynski'	see *C.* 'Kardynał Wyszyński'
'Carlien' (Vt)	CRHN
'Carlotta' (Vt)	NHaw
'Carmencita' (Vt)	CRHN EBee LRHS LSRN NHaw NTay SCoo SLon
'Carnaby' (EL)	CArg CWCL EHyd ELan EPfP ETho LRHS LSRN MAsh NTay SCoo SNig SWvt WSpi
'Carol Klein' (I)	NHaw NTay
'Carol Leeds' (Vt)	NHaw
'Caroline' (LL)	CWGN LSRN NTay SNig
× ***cartmanii*** 'Avalanche'^{PBR} (Fo/m)	CRos EHyd ELan EPfP ETho LPar LRHS MGos NLar NRHS SCob SCoo SLon SNig SPoG SWvt
- 'Joe' (Fo/m) ♀H4	CBcs CDoC CRos CWCL EHyd ELan EPfP ETho EWes GKev ITim LCro LOPS LRHS LSRN NRHS NTay SCob SCoo SPoG SWvt WIce
- 'Joe' × ***cirrhosa***	CWCL
- 'Joe' × 'Sharon' (Fo)	LSRN
- MICHIKO ('Evipo044'^{PBR}) (Fo)	CRos EHyd EPfP ETho LRHS NRHS NTay SNig SPoG
- 'White Abundance'^{PBR} (Fo/f)	EHyd LRHS NLar
CASSIS ('Evipo020'^{PBR})	EHyd ETho LSRN NTay SCoo SLon SNig SPer
'Catherine Clanwilliam' (T)	CWGN NHaw
'Catherine Penny' (VT)	NHaw
'Celebration'^{PBR} Godfrey (EL)	ETho
CÉZANNE ('Evipo023'^{PBR}) (EL)	CRos CWCL EHyd ELan EPfP ETho LRHS MAsh MGos NLar NRHS NTay SCoo SLon SNig
'Chacewater' (Vt)	CRHN
'Chalcedony' (EL)	NTay
'Change of Heart' (EL) **new**	SNig
CHANTILLY ('Evipo021'^{PBR}) (EL)	CRos EHyd ELan EPfP ETho LRHS LSRN NRHS NTay SCoo SLon
'Charissima' (EL)	CWGN EHyd NTay SCoo
'Charlie Brown' (LL)	CRHN NHaw
CHARMAINE ('Evipo022'^{PBR}) (EL)	CRos CWGN EHyd EPfP ETho LRHS NLar NRHS NTay SCoo SNig SPoG
'Chatsworth' (Vt)	CRHN CWGN NHaw NTay SLon
CHELSEA ('Evipo100'^{PBR})	CRos EHyd EPfP ETho LRHS NRHS NTay SCoo SLon SNig

	CHEROKEE	see *C.* OOH LA LA
	CHEVALIER ('Evipo040'PBR) (EL)	CRos EHyd ELan EPfP ETho LRHS MAsh NLar NRHS NTay SCoo SLon SNig SPoG
	chinensis misapplied	see *C. terniflora*
	CHINOOK ('Evipo013'PBR)	EHyd SRms
	chrysantha	see *C. tangutica*
	chrysocoma misapplied	see *C. spooneri*
	chrysocoma Franch.	WSpi
	'Cicciolina' (Vt)	CRHN NHaw
	cirrhosa	CTri EHyd LRHS MAsh SNig
§	- var. ***balearica***	CBcs CDoC CMac CRos CTri CWCL EHyd ELan EPfP ETho LCro LOPS LRHS LSRN MAsh MGos MRav MSwo NTay SCob SCoo SEND SPoG SWvt
	- 'Jingle Bells' (C)	CDoC CMac CRos CWCL EBee EHyd ELan EPfP ETho LCro LOPS LRHS LSRN MAsh MGos NLar NRHS NTay SCoo SLon SNig SRms
	- 'Ourika Valley' (C)	CWGN EBee ELon ETho LRHS MAsh NLar NTay
	- var. ***purpurascens*** 'Freckles' (C) ♀H4	Widely available
	- - 'Lansdowne Gem' (C)	CMac CWCL CWGN EHyd ETho LRHS NLar NTay SCoo SPoG SWvt WSpi
	- 'Winter Parasol' (C)	EBee
	- 'Wisley Cream' (C) ♀H4	CBcs CDoC CMac CRos CWCL EBee EHyd ELan EPfP ETho LCro LOPS LRHS LSRN MAsh MSwo NLar NRHS NTay SCoo SNig SPer SPoG SRms SWvt
	cirrhosa × 'Early Sensation'	CWCL
	clarkeana misapplied	see *C. urophylla* 'Winter Beauty'
	'Cloudburst' (LL)	ETho
	coactilis	NHaw SBrt
	columbiana	GKev
	- var. ***tenuiloba*** 'Ylva' (A)	WAbe
	'Columbine' (A)	EBee EHyd EPfP NTay SCoo
	'Columella' (A)	CWGN EBee
	'Comtesse de Bouchaud' (LL) ♀H6	CArg CRos CTri CWCL EBee EHyd ELan EPfP EShb ETho LCro LOPS LRHS LSRN MAsh MGos MRav NRHS NTay SCob SCoo SNig SPer SPoG
	CONFETTI ('Evipo036'PBR) (Vt)	EHyd EPfP LSRN NTay
	'Congratulations' (EL)	EHyd LRHS LSRN NRHS NTay SPoG
	connata W/O 7066 **new**	GGro
	aff. ***connata*** HWJK 2176 from Nepal	WCru
	'Consort' (LL)	CWGN
	'Constance' (A) ♀H6	CArg CWCL EBee EHyd EPfP ETho LRHS LSRN NLar NRHS NTay SCoo SNig SPre SRms WFar
	'Continuity' (M)	CWGN NTay
	'Cora' (I)	CWGN
	'Coralie' (T)	NHaw
	CORINNE ('Evipo063'PBR) (EL)	CRos EHyd ETho LRHS MAsh NLar NRHS NTay SCoo SNig SPoG
	'Cornish Spirit' (Vt)	CRHN
	'Corona' (EL)	EPfP LRHS SCoo
	'Côte d'Azur' (H)	CExl ELan LRHS MNrw NTay WSFF
	'Countess of Lovelace' (EL)	CBcs ELan EPfP ETho LRHS LSRN NTay SCoo SNig
	COUNTRY ROSE ('Zocoro'PBR) (A)	NTay WSpi
	'Cragside' (A)	EHyd NRHS SCoo
§	'Crimson King' (LL)	ETho
	'Crinkle'PBR (M)	CCCN

§	***crispa***	CWGN NHaw SBrt
§	CRYSTAL FOUNTAIN ('Evipo038'PBR) (EL)	CDoC CRos CWCL CWGN EHyd ELan EPfP ETho LBuc LCro LOPS LRHS LSRN MGos NTay SCoo SLon SNig SPer SPoG SRms
	'Danae' (Vt)	NHaw
	DANCING KING ('Zodaki'PBR) (EL)	NTay
	DANCING QUEEN ('Zodaque'PBR) (EL)	NTay WSpi
	DANCING SMILE ('Zodasmi'PBR) (EL)	NTay
	'Daniel Deronda' (EL) ♀H6	CArg CDoC CRos CWCL CWGN EBee ELan EPfP ETho IPot LRHS LSRN MAsh NRHS NTay SCob SCoo SNig SPer SPoG
	'Darius' (EL)	SNig
	'Dark Eyes' (Vt)	CWGN ETho IPot LCro LOPS LRHS NTay SCoo SNig
	'Dark Secret' (A)	LBuc NHol NLar NTay
	dasyandra NJM 11.075	WPGP
	'Dawn' (EL)	CCCN CWCL EHyd ETho LRHS LSRN NTay SCoo SNig WSpi
	'Dazzle' (EL)	ETho NTay
	'De Vijfhoeven' (Vt)	NHaw
	'Débutante' (EL)	NHaw SNig
	'Dedication' (V) **new**	NHaw
	DELPHINE ('Bfccdel'PBR) (LL) **new**	NTay
	'Denny's Double' (EL/d)	CWCL CWGN NTay
	'Destiny' (EL)	SNig
	DIAMANTINA ('Evipo039'PBR) (EL)	CRos CWCL EHyd EPfP ETho LRHS NLar NRHS NTay SCoo SLon SNig
	'Diamond Anniversary' (A)	CWCL EPfP ETho LCro LOPS NTay
	'Diana' (LL)	LSRN NHaw NTay
	DIANA'S DELIGHT ('Evipo026'PBR) (EL)	CRos CWCL EHyd EPfP ETho LRHS LSRN MAsh NRHS NTay SLon SPoG
	dioscoreifolia	see *C. terniflora*
§	× ***diversifolia***	CRHN LRHS NHaw SWvt WCot
	- 'Benedikt' (I)	CWGN WSpi
§	- 'Blue Boy' (I)	CRHN NHaw WSpi
	- 'Heather Herschell' (I)	CRHN CTsd
§	- 'Hendersonii' (I)	CBod CWCL EGrI EHyd LRHS LSRN MRav NTay SPer SWvt WCot
§	- 'Olgae' (I)	CExl NHaw
	'Doctor Mary' (V)	NHaw NTay
	'Doctor Ruppel' (EL)	CArg CDoC CMac CRos CWCL EHyd ELon EPfP ETho GDam LCro LOPS LRHS LSRN MAsh MSwo NRHS NTay SCob SCoo SNig SPer
	'Dominika' (LL)	NHaw
	'Dorath'	CWGN EHyd EPfP LRHS
	'Dorothy Tolver' (EL)	ETho IPot
	'Dorothy Walton'	see *C.* 'Bagatelle'
	DOUBLE DELIGHT ('Doudeli'PBR) (M)	CWGN
	'Duchess of Albany' (1897) (T)	CArg CDoC CTri CWCL EHyd ELan EPfP ETho LRHS LSRN MGos NHol SPer SRkn
	'Duchess of Edinburgh' (EL)	CBcs CDoC CMac CWCL EHyd ELan EPfP ETho LRHS LSRN MAsh MGos MSwo NHol NRHS NTay SCob SCoo SNig SPer SPoG SWvt
	× ***durandii*** ♀H6	CBcs CRHN CRos CWCL EHyd ELan EPfP ETho IPot LRHS LSRN MAsh MGos MRav NRHS NTay SCob SCoo SNig SPoG SWvt WSpi
	'Dutch Sky' (LL)	CWGN ETho
	'Dzieci Warszawy' (EL) **new**	SNig
	'Early Sensation' (Fo/f)	CBcs CDoC CRos CTri CWCL EHyd ELan EPfP ETho LCro LOPS LPar

	LRHS LSRN MAsh NRHS NTay SCoo SGsty SPer SPoG SPre SWvt
EAST RIVER ('Zoeastri'PBR) (I)	NTay
EDDA ('Evipo074'PBR) (Boulevard Series) (EL)	CRos EHyd EPfP ETho LRHS MAsh NRHS NTay SCoo SNig
'Edith' (EL) ♀H6	CWCL ETho LSRN NHaw NTay
'Édouard Desfossé' (EL)	ETho LRHS
'Edward Prichard'	EPfP NTay
'Eetika' (LL)	CRHN NHaw
'Ekstra' (LL)	NHaw
'Eleanor' (Fo/f)	GEdr NFav
'Elf' (Vt)	CWGN NHaw
'Elizabeth' (M) ♀H5	Widely available
'Elly Elisabeth' (I) **new**	NHaw
§ 'Elsa Späth' (EL)	CArg CExl CMac CRos CTri EHyd ELan EPfP ETho LRHS LSRN MAsh NLar NRHS NTay SCoo SNig SPer SPoG SWvt
'Elvan' (Vt)	CRHN NHaw SNig
'Ember' (I)	CWGN NHaw
'Emerald Dream'PBR (Fo)	ELan EPfP LRHS NTay
'Emilia Plater' (Vt)	CRHN CWGN EPfP ETho NHaw NTay SLon
EMPRESS ('Evipo011'PBR) (EL)	EHyd ELan EPfP LRHS NLar NTay SLon SNig
'Empress Amy Lai'	CWCL
ENDELLION ('Evipo076'PBR) (EL)	CRos EHyd ETho LRHS NRHS NTay SNig
'Entel' (Vt)	CRHN EBee NHaw
× ***eriostemon***	see *C.* × *diversifolia*
'Ernest Markham' (LL) ♀H6	CDoC CMac CRos CWCL EHyd ELan EPfP ETho LRHS LSRN MAsh MGos MSwo NLar NRHS NTay NWea SCoo SNig SPer SPoG SWvt WSpi
ESME ('Evipo048'PBR)	CRos CWGN EPfP ETho LRHS NLar NTay SLon SNig
ESTHER ('Zo09143'PBR) (EL)	IPot NTay SNig
'Étoile Rose' (Vt)	CMac CRHN CTri EBee EHyd ELan EPfP ETho LRHS LSRN NHaw NHol NTay SCoo SLon SPer
'Étoile Violette' (Vt) ♀H6	Widely available
'Everett' (V)	WSHC
EXCITING ('Zoexci'PBR) (EL)	NTay SNig
'Fair Rosamond' (EL)	ETho NTay
FAIRY BLUE	see *C.* CRYSTAL FOUNTAIN
'Fairydust' (Vt)	NHaw
× ***fargesioides***	see *C.* 'Paul Farges'
fasciculiflora L 657	WCru WPGP
'Fascination'PBR (I)	CWCL CWGN LRHS NTay WCot WSpi
fauriei	WSHC
'Fay' (Vt)	NHaw
'Fenna' (EL)	CWGN
FILIGREE ('Evipo029'PBR) (EL)	CRos EHyd ETho LBuc LRHS MAsh MGos NLar NRHS NTay SCoo SNig
'Filomae' (Vt)	NHaw
finetiana misapplied	see *C. paniculata* J.G. Gmel.
'Fireworks' (EL)	CArg CWCL CWGN EHyd EPfP ETho LRHS LSRN MAsh MRav NLar NTay SNig SPer SPoG
'First Love' (EL) **new**	SNig
FLAMENCO DANCER ('Bfccfla'PBR)	ETho LCro LOPS
flammula	CArg CDoC EHyd ELan EPfP ETho LCro LOPS LRHS LSRN MAsh MBlu MRav NBid NLar NRHS NTay SPer SPoG SRms SWvt WSpi XSen
- B&SWJ 15041 **new**	WCru
- 'Rubra Marginata'	see *C.* × *triternata* 'Rubromarginata'
FLEURI ('Evipo042'PBR) (Boulevard Series) (EL)	CRos CWCL EHyd EPfP ETho LRHS LSRN NRHS NTay SCoo SLon SNig SPoG WSpi
florida	CWGN SWvt
- 'Bicolor'	see *C. florida* var. *florida* 'Sieboldiana'
- var. ***flore-pleno*** 'Plena' (d)	CCCN CRos CWCL EHyd ELan EPfP ETho IPot LRHS LSRN MAsh NRHS NTay SCoo SNig SPoG
§ - var. ***florida*** 'Sieboldiana' (d)	CBcs CRos CWCL CWGN EHyd ELan EPfP ETho LCro LOPS LRHS LSRN MAsh NRHS NTay SCob SCoo SNig SPoG SWvt
- var. ***normalis*** PISTACHIO ('Evirida'PBR) (LL)	CCCN CWCL CWGN EHyd ELan EPfP LRHS MAsh MGos NTay SLon SNig SPoG
'Floris V' (I)	CWCL EGrI MCot NHaw NLar
'Fluffy Duck' (Vt/d)	NHaw
'Fond Memories' (EL)	CWCL CWGN EHyd EPfP ETho LCro LOPS LSRN MAsh NHaw NLar NRHS NTay SLon
'Forever' (EL)	ETho
FOREVER FRIENDS ('Zofofri'PBR) (LL)	CWGN EHyd EPfP ETho LRHS NRHS NTay SLon
'Forget-me-not NLP1'	ETho LSRN NLar
forrestii	see *C. napaulensis*
§ ***forsteri***	WSHC
'Foxtrot' (Vt)	CRHN
'Foxy' (A) ♀H6	ETho LRHS NTay
FRAGRANT OBERON ('Hutbron'PBR) (Fo)	ETho LCro LOPS NTay SWvt
'Fragrant Spring' (M)	CBod CDoC CSBt CWGN EBee EHyd EPfP ETho NLar NTay SCoo WFar
'Frances Rivis' (A) ♀H6	CArg CBcs CDoC CRos CWCL EHyd ELan EPfP ETho GBin LCro LOPS LRHS LSRN MAsh MBlu MRav MSwo NLar NTay NWea SCob SPer SPoG SRms
'Francesca' (A)	LSRN
'Frankie' (A) ♀H6	EHyd ELan EPfP ETho LCro LOPS LRHS LSRN MAsh MGos MHer NTay SCoo
FRANZISKA MARIA ('Evipo008') (EL)	CRos EHyd EPfP LRHS MAsh MGos NTay SCoo SLon
'Freda' (M) ♀H6	CRHN CRos CTri CWGN ELan EPfP ETho LCro LOPS LRHS LSRN MAsh MBlu MRav NHol NTay SPer SRms
FREEDOM ('Zo06128'PBR) (EL)	NTay
fremontii	NHaw
'Fudō' (V)	NHaw
'Fujimusume' (EL) ♀H6	CRos CWGN EHyd EPfP ETho IPot LRHS MAsh NHaw NRHS NTay SNig SPoG
'Fukuzono' (I)	EHyd LRHS LSRN NHaw NRHS NTay
fusca misapplied	see *C. japonica*
fusca Turcz.	EWld
- B&SWJ 8431 large-flowered	WCru
- dwarf	CWGN
'Gabrielle' ambig.	LSRN
GALORE	see *C.* VESUVIUS
GAZELLE ('Evipo014'PBR) (I)	EHyd MAsh SRms
'Generał Sikorski' (EL)	CBcs CDoC CRos CWCL EHyd ELan EPfP ETho LRHS LSRN MAsh MGos NRHS NTay SCoo SNig SPer SWvt WSpi
gentianoides	SBrt
'Geoffrey Tolver' (LL)	CWGN
GIANT STAR ('Gistar'PBR) (M)	EHyd EPfP GDam LRHS NLar NPer NRHS SNig SPoG

	'Gillian Blades' (EL) Υ^{H6}	CRos EBee EHyd ELan EPfP ETho LBuc LRHS LSRN MAsh MGos NHaw NRHS NTay SCoo SNig SPoG SWvt
	GINA ('Evipo092') (Garland Series) (LL)	CWGN
	'Ginny' (V)	NHaw
§	'Gipsy Queen' (LL) Υ^{H6}	CArg CBcs CRos CWCL EHyd ELan ELon EPfP ETho LRHS LSRN MAsh MGos NTay SCoo SNig SPer SPoG SWvt
	GISELLE ('Evipo051'^{PBR})	CRos EHyd EPfP ETho LRHS NLar NRHS NTay SCoo SLon SNig SPoG
	'Gladys Picard' (EL)	NHaw
	glauca ambig.	SBrt
	glaucophylla	NHaw SBrt WSHC
	'Gojōgawa' (EL)	ETho
	'Golden Harvest' (Ta)	EPfP ETho LSRN NLar
	GOLDEN TIARA ('Kugotia'^{PBR}) (Ta) Υ^{H6}	CWGN ETho LSRN NTay SRms WCot
	'Grace' (Ta)	EPfP NHaw
	gracilifolia BWJ 8002	WCru
I	'Grandiflora' (F)	CDoC ETho WFar
	'Grandiflora Sanguinea' (Vt)	NHaw
	grata misapplied	see *C.* × *jouiniana*
	'Gravetye Beauty' (T)	CDoC CRHN CWCL EBee EHyd ELan EPfP ETho LRHS LSRN MGos NHol NTay SCoo SLon SNig SPoG SRms SWvt
§	'Grażyna' (LL)	ETho NTay
	GREEN PASSION ('Zo11050') (EL/d)	CWGN ETho LCro LOPS LRHS NTay
	GREFVE ERIK RUUTH ('Kbk02'^{PBR}) (EL)	CWGN
	'Guernsey Cream' (EL)	CDoC CRos CWCL EHyd EPfP ETho LCro LOPS LRHS LSRN MAsh MGos NLar NTay SCoo SRkn
	GUIDING PROMISE ('Evipo053'^{PBR})	NTay SCoo SLon SNig
	'Guiding Star' (EL)	IPot
	'H.F.Young' (EL)	CRos EHyd ELan EPfP ETho LRHS LSRN MGos NLar NTay SCob SCoo SNig SPer SWvt
	'Hågelby Blue' (Vt)	NHaw
	'Hågelby Pink' (Vt) Υ^{H6}	CRHN CWGN ELan NHaw
	'Hågelby White' (Vt)	CRHN CWGN ELan NHaw
	'Hagley Hybrid' (LL)	CArg CBcs CMac CRos CWCL EBee EHyd ELan EPfP ETho LRHS LSRN MAsh MGos MRav NLar NRHS NWea SCob SCoo SGsty SNig SPer SPoG SRms SWvt
	'Hakuōkan' (EL)	EPfP ETho IPot LSRN SCoo WSpi
	'Hanaguruma' (EL)	ETho LSRN SNig
	'Happy Anniversary' (EL)	ETho LBuc LCro LOPS LSRN NLar NTay
§	HAPPY BIRTHDAY ('Zohapbi'^{PBR}) (LL) Υ^{H6}	ETho LCro LOPS LSRN NTay SNig WSpi
	'Happy Diana' (T) **new**	NHaw
	HARLOW CARR ('Evipo004'^{PBR})	CRos EHyd EPfP LRHS NRHS NTay SCoo SRms
	'Haru Ichiban' (EL)	ETho
	'Hayate'	CWGN
§	'Helios' (Ta)	CRos ETho NTay
	'Helsingborg' (A) Υ^{H6}	CRos EHyd ELan EPfP ETho LRHS MAsh NLar NTay SCoo SNig SPoG SRms
	aff. 'Helsingborg' (A) **new**	NTay
I	'Hendersonii' (I)	LRHS LSRN MCot
	hendersonii Koch	see *C.* × *diversifolia* 'Hendersonii'
	hendersonii Stand.	see *C.* × *diversifolia*
I	'Hendersonii Rubra' (Ar)	LRHS SCoo
	'Hendryetta'^{PBR} (I)	CWGN EHyd NTay SWvt
	henryi	EHyd EShb LSRN MAsh NTay SNig
	- B&SWJ 3402	WCru
	- var. ***morii*** B&SWJ 1668	WCru
	'Henryi' (EL)	CDoC CMac CRos CTri CWCL EBee ELan EPfP LCro LOPS LRHS LSRN MRav MSwo NRHS SPer SPoG
	heracleifolia	CBod CMac CSBt ECtt ELan GLog MCot
	- 'Blue Dwarf' (H)	CWGN ETho
	- 'Cassandra' (H) Υ^{H6}	CRos CSpe CWCL CWGN ECtt EHyd ELan ELon EPfP ETho GLog LRHS LSRN MCot MHer MHol NRHS NTay SMrm WTre
	- 'China Purple' (H)	CExl ECtt GBin ILea LRHS MCot MHol
	- 'Pink Dwarf' (H)	CWGN NTay
	'Herbert Johnson' (EL)	NHaw
	hexapetala Forster	see *C. forsteri*
	hexasepala	see *C. forsteri*
	hirsutissima	SBrt
	- var. ***scottii***	EBee SBrt
	'Honora' (LL)	CRos CWGN EHyd LRHS MAsh NRHS NTay SCoo
	'Hope' (A) **new**	LRHS
	'Horn of Plenty' (EL)	EHyd LRHS NHaw
	'Hoshi-no-flamenco' (T)	CWGN IPot
	huchouensis	NHaw
	HUDSON RIVER ('Zo06137'^{PBR}) (I)	IPot NTay
	'Huldine' (LL) Υ^{H6}	CBcs CRHN CWCL ELan EPfP ETho LRHS LSRN MRav NTay SCoo SLon SNig SPer SWvt
	'Huvi' (LL)	CWGN NHaw
	'Hybrida Sieboldii' (EL)	SCoo
	HYDE HALL ('Evipo009'^{PBR}) (EL)	CMac CRos CWCL CWGN EHyd ELan EPfP LRHS MAsh MGos NRHS NTay SCoo SLon SNig SRms
	'Hythe Egret' (Fo)	WIce
	I AM A LITTLE BEAUTY ('Zolibe') (Vt)	CRHN EBee NHaw NTay SNig
	I AM HAPPY ('Zoiamha') (Vt)	CWGN ELan NTay
	I AM LADY J ('Zoiamlj') (Vt)	ELan IPot NHaw
	I AM LADY Q ('Zoiamladyq'^{PBR}) (Vt)	CWGN EBee ETho NHaw NTay SNig
	I AM RED ROBIN ('Zorero'^{PBR}) (A)	CWGN NTay
	ianthina var. ***kuripoensis***	SBrt
	- - B&SWJ 700	WCru
	'Ibi' (EL)	CWGN WSpi
	ICE BLUE ('Evipo003'^{PBR}) (Prairie Series) (EL)	CRos CWCL EHyd ELan EPfP ETho LRHS MAsh NLar NTay SCoo SLon SNig
	'Ice Queen' (EL)	MAsh
	indivisa Willd.	see *C. paniculata* J.G. Gmel.
	INES ('Evipo059'^{PBR}) (Boulevard Series)	CRos EHyd ETho LRHS NRHS NTay SNig
	'Ingrid Biedenkopf' (Vt)	NHaw
	'Innocent Blush'^{PBR} (EL)	EPfP ETho SNig
	'Innocent Glance'^{PBR} (EL)	ETho SNig
	INSPIRATION ('Zoin'^{PBR}) (I)	ELan NTay SCoo
	integrifolia	CBod CCBP CExl ELan EPfP GArf GKev GQue IPot LRHS MBriF MCot NChi NLar NPer NTay SRms WHil WHoo WMal
I	- 'Alba' (I)	CRos CWCL ECtt EPfP ETho GKev LRHS LSRN NHaw NLar NTay SCoo SRms
	- 'Baby Blue' (I)	NHaw
	- 'Blue Ribbons' (I)	CSpe MMrt NLar SBls SPhx
	- dark blue-flowered (I)	GKev

	- 'Gletschereis' (I)	CWCL
	- 'Hendersonii' Koch	see *C.* × *diversifolia* 'Hendersonii'
	- MONGOLIAN BELLS ('Psharlan') (I)	CSpe CWCL NHaw
	- 'Olgae'	see *C.* × *diversifolia* 'Olgae'
	- 'Ozawa's Blue' (I)	CWGN ETho MBNS NTay WAvo
	- violet-flowered (I)	GKev
	- white-flowered	see *C. integrifolia* 'Alba'
§	***intricata***	CExl
	- 'Harry Smith' (Ta)	NHaw WSpi
	ISABELLA ('Zo12220') (EL)	IPot LRHS NTay
	ispahanica	NHaw SBrt
	'Iubileinyi-70' (LL)	NHaw
	'Ivan Olsson' (EL)	CWCL ETho SNig
	'Jackmanii' (LL) 🏆H6	CArg CBcs CMac CRos CTri EBee EHyd EPfP ETho LCro LOPS LRHS LSRN MAsh MGos NTay NWea SCob SCoo SNig SPoG SWvt
	'Jackmanii Alba' (EL)	CRos CWCL EHyd ELan ELon EPfP ETho LRHS LSRN MAsh NTay SCoo SPoG
	JACKMANII PURPUREA ('Zojapur'PBR) (LL)	ETho NTay
	'Jackmanii Rubra' (EL)	NTay
	'Jackmanii Superba' misapplied	see *C.* 'Gipsy Queen'
	'Jackmanii Superba' ambig. (LL)	CDoC CRos CWCL EHyd ELan EPfP ETho LCro LOPS LRHS MAsh MGos MRav MSwo NPer NTay NWea SCob SNig SPer SPoG
	'Jacqueline du Pré' (A) 🏆H6	CBcs CDoC EBee ELan EPfP ETho LRHS NTay
	'James Mason' (EL)	ETho SNig
	'Jan Fopma'PBR (I)	CWGN NTay
	'Jan Lindmark' (A/d)	CDoC CRos EHyd EPfP LRHS MAsh NLar NRHS NTay SCoo SPoG SPre
§	'Jan Paweł II' (EL)	EHyd ELan ETho LRHS SCoo SPer
	'Jane Ashdown' (M)	NHaw
§	***japonica***	NHaw WFar
	'Jasper' (V)	ETho
	'Jean Caldwell' (Vt)	NHaw
	'Jean Cumpston' (C)	NHaw
	'Jeanne's Pink' (EL)	CWCL ETho NTay
I	'Jenny' (Cedergren) (LL)	ETho NHaw
	'Jenny' (M/d)	EHyd LRHS LSRN SPoG WSpi
	'Jenny Caddick' (Vt)	NHaw
	JESSICA ('Evipo012'PBR) (I)	EHyd
	JEWEL OF MERK	see *C.* HAPPY BIRTHDAY
	JOHN HOWELLS ('Zojohnhowells'PBR) (Vt)	CWCL CWGN ETho LSRN NTay SLon WSpi
	'John Huxtable' (LL)	EHyd ETho LRHS NTay SNig WSpi
	JOHN PAUL II	see *C.* 'Jan Paweł II'
	'John Treasure' (Vt)	CRHN NHaw
	'John Warren' (EL)	EHyd LRHS MAsh NRHS SCoo
	JOSEPHINE ('Evijohill'PBR) (EL)	CDoC CRos CWCL CWGN EHyd EPfP ETho LCro LOPS LRHS LSRN MAsh MGos NLar NRHS NTay SCoo SNig SPer SPoG SWvt WSpi
	'Josie's Midnight Blue' (V)	NHaw
§	× ***jouiniana***	MRav NHaw SEND SHar SWvt WSHC
	- 'Chance' (H)	NTay
	JULIANE ('Evipo049'PBR) <u>**new**</u>	ETho NTay SNig
	'Julka' (EL)	CDoC CWCL ETho NHaw WSpi
	'Justa' (Vt)	NHaw NLar
	'Juuli' (I)	LSRN NHaw
	'Kaaru' (LL)	CRHN NHaw
	'Kacper' (EL)	NHaw
	'Kaiser'PBR	ETho SNig
	'Kaiu' (V)	CWGN EHyd ETho NHaw NTay
§	'Kakio' (EL)	CWCL EHyd EPfP ETho LRHS LSRN MAsh MGos NTay SCoo SPer
I	'Kamilla' (EL)	CWGN
§	'Kardynał Wyszyński' (EL)	ETho SNig
§	'Kasmu' (Vt)	NHaw
	'Kathleen Dunford' (EL)	LSRN NTay SCoo
	'Kathryn Chapman' (Vt)	CRHN CWGN NHaw NTay
	'Kaunitar' (LL)	NHaw
	'Ken Donson' (EL) 🏆H6	LRHS SCoo
	'Kermesina' (Vt) 🏆H6	CDoC CRHN EBee EHyd ELan EPfP ETho LCro LOPS LRHS MAsh NTay SCoo SNig SPer SPoG SRms WBor
	'Kiev' (Vt)	NHaw
	'Killifreth' (Vt)	CRHN NHaw
	KIMIKO ('Evipo066'PBR) (Boulevard Series) (Fo)	CRos EHyd LRHS NRHS NTay SNig SPoG
	'King Edward VII' (EL)	LRHS
	KINGFISHER ('Evipo037'PBR) (EL)	CRos CWCL EHyd ELan EPfP LRHS NTay SCoo SLon SPoG
	'Kinju Atarashi' (LL)	CWCL ETho NTay
	'Kiri Te Kanawa' (EL)	CWCL ELon EPfP LRHS LSRN NLar NTay WSpi
	kirilowii	NHaw
	KITTY ('Evipo097') (EL)	CRos EHyd ETho LRHS NRHS NTay SCoo SPoG WSpi
	'Kommerei' (LL)	NHaw
	KÖNIGIN MAXIMA ('Wellmax'PBR) (T)	CWGN IPot NHaw
§	'Königskind' (EL)	ETho NLar
	koreana	MAsh WCru
	- AMBER ('Wit141205'PBR) (A)	EHyd ELan ETho IPot LCro LOPS LRHS NRHS NTay
	- var. ***carunculosa***	WSHC
	- - B&SWJ 12725	WCru
	- - 'Lemon Bells' (A)	CRos EHyd EPfP LRHS SCoo SLon SPoG
	- 'Love Child' (A)	NTay
	'Krakowiak'PBR (Vt)	NHaw SNig
	ladakhiana	EWld NHaw
	'Lady Betty Balfour' (LL)	CMac EHyd ETho LRHS NTay SCoo SWvt
	'Lady Bird Johnson' (T)	CWCL EHyd LRHS LSRN SCoo
	'Lady Caroline Nevill' (EL)	EHyd LRHS NRHS
	'Lady Kyoko' (d)	LCro LOPS
	'Lady Londesborough' (EL)	NHaw
	'Lady Northcliffe' (EL)	CTri CWCL EHyd EPfP ETho MAsh NTay
	'Lambton Park' (Ta) 🏆H6	CRHN ETho NHaw NLar NTay
	lasiandra	NHaw
	'Last Dance' (Ta)	CRHN EBee IPot
	LASTING LOVE	see *C.* 'Grażyna'
	'Lasurstern' (EL) 🏆H6	CArg CBcs CExl CMac CRos CTri EBee EHyd ELan EPfP ETho LCro LOPS LRHS LSRN MAsh NTay SCob SPer SPoG SWvt WFar
	'Laura Denny' (EL)	ETho
	'Lavender Twirl' (Vt)	CRHN
	'Lawsoniana' (EL)	LRHS SNig
	'Lech Wałęsa' (EL)	ETho
	'Lemon Beauty' (A)	ETho
	'Lemon Chiffon' (EL)	EHyd LRHS
	'Lemon Dream'PBR (A)	ETho LRHS
	LIBERATION ('Evifive'PBR) (EL)	EHyd NLar NTay SCoo SLon SNig WSpi
	LIBERTY ('Zo08095'PBR) (EL)	ETho IPot NTay SNig
	ligusticifolia	NHaw
	'Lilac Wine' (I)	NHaw
	'Lily the Pink' (Vt)	NHaw
	'Lincoln Star' (EL)	CArg CMac EHyd ELon LRHS MAsh SPer SWvt
	'Lisboa' (Vt)	NHaw
	'Little Bas' (Vt)	CDoC CRHN CWGN ELan ETho NHaw NTay SLon SNig

'Little Butterfly' (Vt)	CRHN NHaw
'Little Mermaid' (EL)	EPfP LCro LOPS NTay
'Little Nell' (Vt)	CCCN CRHN EBee ELan EPfP ETho LRHS LSRN MAsh NTay SCoo SLon
'Liviana' (V) **new**	NHaw
'Lord Herschell'	CWCL CWGN ETho
'Lord Nevill' (EL)	EPfP LRHS
'Louise Rowe' (EL)	CWCL EHyd ELan ETho LRHS LSRN NTay
'Love Jewelry' (EL)	SNig
LUCKY CHARM ('Zo09067'PBR) (LL)	CWGN IPot NTay SNig
LULA ('Evipo057'PBR) (Boulevard Series)	CWGN NTay SNig
'Lunar Lass' (Fo/f)	GArf NRHS NTay
'Luxuriant Blue' (Vt)	CRHN ELan MAsh NHaw NTay
'M. Koster' (Vt)	CDoC CRHN ETho LRHS NHaw NTay SLon SRms
macropetala (d)	CDoC CEme CRos EHyd ELan EPfP ETho LRHS MAsh MGos MRav NRHS SCoo SNig SPer
- 'Blue Lagoon'	see *C. macropetala* 'Lagoon' Jackman 1959
§ - 'Chili' (A/d)	IPot
- 'Harry Smith'	see *C. macropetala* 'Chili'
- 'Lagoon' Jackman 1956	see *C. macropetala* 'Maidwell Hall' Jackman
- 'Lagoon' ambig.	LSRN
§ - 'Lagoon' Jackman 1959 (A/d) ♀H6	EHyd ETho LCro LOPS LRHS LSRN MAsh MSwo NHol NRHS NTay SCoo
- 'Maidwell Hall' ambig.	LBuc
§ - 'Maidwell Hall' Jackman (A/d)	CTri EPfP LSRN MAsh NTay
- 'Maidwell Hall' O.E.P. Wyatt (A)	CBcs SCob
- 'Wesselton' (A/d) ♀H6	CDoC CRos CTri CWCL EHyd EPfP ETho LCro LOPS LRHS MAsh NLar NRHS NTay SPoG SPre SRms
- 'White Moth'	see *C.* 'White Moth'
'Madame Baron-Veillard' (LL)	EHyd LRHS SCoo
'Madame Édouard André' (LL)	CRos CWCL EHyd EPfP ETho LRHS MAsh NRHS NTay SCoo
'Madame Grangé' (LL)	EHyd LRHS NHaw SCoo
'Madame Julia Correvon' (Vt) ♀H6	CDoC CRHN CTri CWCL EBee EHyd ELan EPfP ETho LCro LOPS LRHS LSRN MAsh MGos MPri NLar NRHS NTay SCob SCoo SLon SNig SPer SPoG SSta SWvt
'Madame le Coultre'	see *C.* 'Mevrouw Le Coultre'
'Majojo' (Fo)	GEdr
MANON ('Evipo054'PBR) (Boulevard Series) (EL)	CRos EHyd LRHS NRHS NTay SNig
marata	WThu
'Margaret Hunt' (LL)	ETho LSRN NHaw NTay SNig
'Mari' (LL)	NHaw
'Maria' Kivistik (LL)	NHaw
'Maria Băsescu'	NTay
'Maria Cornelia'PBR (Vt)	CWGN ETho IPot LCro LOPS NTay SLon
'Maria Louise Jensen' (EL)	IPot
'Maria Skłodowska-Curie'PBR (EL)	ETho
'Marie Boisselot' (EL) ♀H6	CArg CBcs CMac CTri CWCL EHyd ELan EPfP ETho LRHS LSRN MAsh MGos MPri MSwo NLar NTay SCob SCoo SNig SPoG SWvt
'Marinka'	CWGN
'Marjorie' (M/d)	CArg CBcs CBod CBrac CDoC CTri CWCL EHyd ELan EPfP ETho GKin LRHS LSRN MAsh MGos MRav NRHS NTay SCob SCoo SNig SPer SPoG SRms WFar
'Markham's Pink' (A/d) ♀H6	CArg CBcs CDoC CTri CWCL EHyd ELan EPfP LCro LOPS LRHS LSRN MAsh MGos MRav MSwo NHol NLar NRHS NTay SCob SPer SPoG SRms SWvt WFar
marmoraria	CRos EHyd EPot LRHS NRHS SPlb SRms WAbe
'Marmori' (LL)	CWGN NHaw
MARTA ('Evipo071'PBR) (Garland Series)	SNig
'Mary Habberley' (Vt)	NHaw
'Mary Rose'	see *C. viticella* 'Flore Pleno'
MASA ('Evipo089'PBR) (Garland Series)	CWGN ETho
maximowicziana	see *C. terniflora*
'Mayleen' (M) ♀H4	CTri EPfP ETho LRHS MAsh MRav NRHS NTay SCoo SNig SPer SPoG SRms SWvt WFar
I 'Melodie' (Vt)	NHaw
§ 'Mevrouw Le Coultre' (EL)	NTay
'Mia' (EL/d)	CWGN
MIENIE BELLE ('Zomibel'PBR) (T)	CWGN NHaw
'Mikelite' (Vt)	LRHS NHaw
'Miniseelik' (LL)	NHaw
'Minuet' (Vt) ♀H6	CDoC CRHN EBee EHyd EPfP ETho LCro LOPS LRHS MAsh MGos NTay SCoo SLon SPer SPoG SWvt
MIRABELLE ('Evipo072'PBR) (Boulevard Series)	EHyd NTay SNig
MIRANDA ('Floclemi'PBR) (I)	CWGN
'Miss Bateman' (EL)	CDoC CMac CRos CTri CWCL EBee EHyd ELan EPfP ETho LCro LOPS LRHS LSRN MAsh MGos NRHS NTay SCob SCoo SNig SPer SPoG WBor
'Miss Christine' (M)	CDoC ELan ETho LCro LOPS LSRN NTay SPoG SWvt
MISSISSIPPI RIVER ('Zomisri') (I)	IPot LRHS
'Mister Hans Horn' (Vt)	NHaw
MON AMOUR ('Zomoa'PBR) (EL)	CWGN NTay
MON CHERRY ('Zomonch') (EL)	CWGN IPot NTay
montana	CExl CPla GDam MAsh SCob SEWo SGbt
- WJC 13713 from the Himalaya	WCru
- W/O 7064 **new**	GGro
- W/O 7065 **new**	GGro
- var. ***alba***	see *C. montana* var. *montana*
- 'Alexander' (M)	CRos EHyd EPfP LRHS NRHS SPoG
- 'Da Yun' (M)	CWGN EBee
- var. ***grandiflora*** (M) ♀H5	Widely available
§ - var. ***montana***	CBar CBcs CBod CSBt GDam LCro LOPS LRHS NWea SNig SPer SPoG WFar
- var. ***rubens*** misapplied	see *C. montana* var. *montana*
- var. ***rubens*** Buch.-Ham. ex DC.	CDoC CRos CSBt CTri EHyd ELan LRHS NHol NRHS SPlb
I - - 'Odorata' (M)	EPfP ETho GKin MRav NTay SCoo
- - 'Pink Perfection' (M)	CDoC CMac CRHN CRos EHyd ELan EPfP ETho GKin LCro LOPS LRHS LSRN MAsh NRHS NTay SCoo SNig SPer SPoG SWvt WFar
- - 'Tetrarose' (M) ♀H5	Widely available
I - - 'Rubens Superba' (M)	CTri ECtt GKin LPar NTay SRms WFar
- var. ***sericea***	see *C. spooneri*

	– var. ***wilsonii***	CBod CWCL ECtt EHyd ELan EPfP ETho GKin GLog LRHS LSRN MRav MSwo NTay SPer SPoG SRms SWvt
	'Monte Cassino' (EL)	CWGN SNig
	'Moonbeam' (Fo)	EPot GEdr ITim WIce
	'Moonglow' (EL) **new**	NTay SNig
§	'Moonlight' (EL)	LRHS MAsh
	MORNING CLOUD	see *C.* 'Yukikomachi'
	'Morning Heaven' (Vt)	CRHN NHaw NTay
	MORNING STAR ('Zoklako'[PBR]) (EL)	CWGN
	MORNING YELLOW ('Cadmy'[PBR]) (M)	CCCN LRHS SCoo
	'Mrs Cholmondeley' (EL) ♀H6	CWCL EHyd ELan EPfP ETho LRHS LSRN MAsh MGos MPri MSwo NTay SCob SCoo SNig SPer SPoG
	'Mrs George Jackman' (EL) ♀H6	CWCL EBee EHyd ETho LRHS NLar NTay SCoo SNig WSpi
	'Mrs James Mason' (EL)	EBee
	'Mrs N.Thompson' (EL)	CArg CDoC CMac CTri CWCL EBee EHyd ELan ELon ETho LCro LOPS LRHS LSRN MAsh MGos NHol NPer NTay SNig SPer
	'Mrs P.B.Truax' (EL)	EHyd EPfP ETho
	'Mrs Robert Brydon' (H)	CWCL ECtt NTay SRms
	'Mrs T. Lundell' (Vt)	CRHN EPfP LRHS NHaw
	'Multi Blue' (EL)	CArg CBcs CRos CWCL EHyd ELan ELon EPfP LRHS LSRN MAsh MGos NTay SCoo SNig SPer SPoG SRkn SRms WSpi
	'My Angel'[PBR] (Ta)	ELan IPot LCro LOPS LRHS NHaw NTay WSpi
	'My Darling' (EL) **new**	SNig
	'Myōjō' (EL)	LRHS
	MYOSOTIS ('Zo08159') (EL)	IPot LRHS
§	***napaulensis***	CWCL ELan EPfP ETho LCro LOPS MNrw NHaw WCru WSpi
I	'Natacha' (EL)	EBee NHaw NLar NTay SCoo
	'Natascha' (EL)	CWCL EHyd ETho LSRN SWvt
	'Negritianka' (LL)	NHaw
	'Negus' (LL)	NHaw
	'Nelly Moser' (EL) ♀H6	Widely available
	NEVA ('Evipo050'[PBR]) (Boulevard Series) (EL)	EHyd LRHS NLar NRHS NTay SNig
	'New Love'[PBR] (H)	CWGN ETho LCro LOPS LSRN NTay SPoG
	'Night Veil' (Vt)	CDoC NHaw SLon
	NINON ('Evipo052'[PBR]) (Boulevard Series)	CBod CWGN EPfP LRHS NTay SCoo SNig
	'Niobe' (EL) ♀H6	CArg CBcs CDoC CMac CRos CWCL EBee EHyd ELan EPfP EShb ETho LCro LOPS LRHS LSRN MAsh MGos MSwo NHol NLar NRHS NTay SCob SCoo SNig SPer SPoG SRms WSpi
	NUBIA ('Evipo079'[PBR]) (Boulevard Series) (LL)	CBod CRos CWCL CWGN EPfP ETho LRHS LSou NLar NTay
	'Nunn's Gift' (Fo)	NTay
	nutans var. ***thyrsoidea***	see *C. rehderiana*, *C. veitchiana*
	'Oberek' (Vt)	CRHN NHaw
	'Ocean Pearl' (A)	LSRN NTay
	ochroleuca	NHaw
	OCTOPUS ('Zooct'[PBR]) (A)	CWGN NTay
	'Odoriba' (V)	CRHN CWGN NHaw
	OLYMPIA ('Evipo099') (Boulevard Series) **new**	CBod LRHS
	'Omoshiro' (EL)	CWCL CWGN ETho IPot LRHS NHaw NTay
§	OOH LA LA ('Evipo041'[PBR]) (Boulevard Series) (EL)	CRos CWCL EHyd EPfP ETho LRHS MAsh NRHS NTay SCoo SNig SPer SPoG WSpi
	orientalis ambig.	SRms

	orientalis L.	EBee EPfP SCoo SWvt
	– PAB 13.731	LEdu
	– from Kyrgyzstan	WPGP
	orientalis × ***tangutica***	SWvt
	'Oshikiri' (V)	NHaw
	otophora	NHaw
	'Ovation'[PBR] (Fo)	LCro LOPS NTay
	'Pagoda' (Vt)	CRHN EBee EPfP IPot LRHS NTay SCoo SLon SRms
	PALETTE ('Zo08111') (EL)	IPot
	'Pamela' (F)	NHaw NTay
	'Pamela Jackman' (A)	see *C. alpina* 'Pamela Jackman'
	'Pamiat Serdtsa' (I)	ELon NHaw
	'Pamina' (EL)	ETho NLar
	'Pangbourne Pink' (I) ♀H6	CWCL EHyd EPfP ETho LRHS NHaw NRHS NTay SCoo
	paniculata Thunb.	see *C. terniflora*
§	***paniculata*** J.G. Gmel.	MNrw
	– var. ***lobata***	WSpi
	'Paola' (EL/d)	IPot
	'Paradise Queen' (EL)	NTay
	PARADISO ('Zo11154') (EL)	IPot LCro LOPS LRHS NTay
	'Parasol' (EL)	NTay
	PARISIENNE ('Evipo019'[PBR]) (Boulevard Series) (EL)	CRos CWCL CWGN EHyd ELon EPfP ETho LRHS MAsh NRHS NTay SCoo SLon SNig SPoG
	parviflora DC.	see *C. campaniflora*
	parviloba var. ***bartlettii*** B&SWJ 6788	WCru
	'Pastel Princess' (EL)	ETho
	'Pat Coleman' (EL)	CWCL ETho
	patens 'Korean Moon' (EL)	WCru
§	– 'Manshuu Ki' (EL)	CWCL EHyd ETho LRHS NTay
	– 'Yukiokoshi' (EL)	EBee ETho
	PATRICIA ANN FRETWELL ('Pafar') (EL)	NTay SNig
§	'Paul Farges' (Vb) ♀H6	CArg CDoC CWGN EPfP EShb ETho GLog IPot MNrw NHaw NLar NTay
	'Pauline' (A/d) ♀H6	CBcs EHyd LRHS LSRN NTay SCoo
	'Peggy West' (LL)	NHaw
	'Pendragon' (Vt)	CRHN NHaw
	'Pennell's Purity' (LL)	NTay
	PEPPERMINT ('Evipo005'[PBR]) (d)	EHyd ELan EPfP NTay SCoo SLon
	'Perida' (LL)	CWGN
	'Perle d'Azur' (LL) ♀H6	CBcs CDoC CRHN CRos CTri CWCL EBee EHyd ELan EPfP ETho LCro LOPS LRHS LSRN MAsh MGos MSwo NTay SCob SCoo SPer SPoG SRms WFar WSpi
	PERNILLE ('Zo09113'[PBR]) (Vt)	CWGN ETho IPot LCro LOPS LRHS NTay SGsty
	'Perrin's Pride' (Vt)	CRos EBee EHyd LRHS MGos NHaw NTay SCoo
	PETIT FAUCON ('Evisix'[PBR]) (I) ♀H6	CWCL EHyd EPfP ETho LRHS LSRN MGos MMrt NLar NTay SCoo SNig SPer SRms SWvt
	petriei	WThu
	'Peveril Pristine' (Vt)	CWGN NHaw
	'Peveril Profusion' (T)	NHaw
	PICARDY ('Evipo024'[PBR]) (EL)	CRos CWCL EHyd EPfP ETho LRHS MAsh NRHS NTay SCoo SNig SPoG WSpi
	PICOTEE ('Zo09124'[PBR]) (EL)	CWGN ETho IPot LRHS NTay SNig WSpi
I	'Picton's Variety' (M)	ETho
	'Piilu' (EL)	CArg CDoC CRos CWCL CWGN EBee EHyd ELan EPfP ETho LRHS LSRN MAsh MBNS NLar NTay SCoo SGsty SNig SRkn

PINK CHAMPAGNE	see *C.* 'Kakio'
'Pink Fantasy' (LL)	CRHN CTri EHyd ETho MAsh NLar NTay SCoo SNig SRkn
'Pink Flamingo' (A) ♀H6	CRos CWCL EHyd ELan EPfP ETho LRHS MGos NRHS NTay SCoo SNig SPoG
'Pink Ice' (I)	CWCL
'Pink Swing' (A)	ETho
'Pirko' (Vt)	NHaw
§ ***pitcheri***	CWGN NHaw SBrt
- from Illinois **new**	SBrt
'Pixie' (Fo/m)	CDoC ELan ELon EPfP ETho LCro LOPS LRHS MGos NLar NTay SCoo SPoG
I 'Pleniflora' (M/d)	NTay
pogonandra	NHaw
POLAR BEAR	see *C.* ARCTIC QUEEN
'Poldice' (Vt) ♀H6	CRHN
'Polish Spirit' (LL) ♀H6	Widely available
'Polonez' (Vt)	NHaw
potaninii 'Summer Snow'	see *C.* 'Paul Farges'
'Praecox' (H) ♀H6	CDoC CRHN CWCL EBee EHyd ELan EPfP ETho LRHS MCot NQui NTay SAdn SPer WCot
'Prairie River' (A)	WSpi
PRETTY IN BLUE ('Zopre'PBR) (F)	EBee ETho SWvt
'Primrose Star'	see *C.* 'Star'
'Prince Charles' (LL) ♀H6	CDoC CRHN CTri CWCL ELan EPfP EShb ETho LCro LOPS LRHS LSRN MAsh NHaw NLar NTay SCoo SNig SPer SWvt
'Prince George' (LL)	CDoC CWCL EPfP ETho LCro LOPS LSRN MGos NLar NTay
'Prince Philip' (EL)	ETho LCro LOPS
PRINCE WILLIAM ('Zo08171') (EL)	CWGN IPot LCro LOPS NTay
'Princess Charlotte' (EL)	ETho LCro LOPS NTay
§ 'Princess Diana' (T) ♀H5	CBcs CRHN CTri CWGN EBee EGrI EHyd ELan EPfP ETho IPot LBuc LCro LOPS LRHS LSRN MAsh MBlu MSwo NHol NTay SCoo SNig SPer SPoG SRms SWvt
PRINCESS KATE ('Zoprika'PBR) (T)	CWGN EBee EHyd EPfP ETho EWTr IPot LCro LOPS LPar LRHS MBlu MGos NRHS NTay SCoo SPer SPoG WBor WCot WSpi
§ 'Princess of Wales' (1875) (EL)	CDoC CWCL LSRN NLar SLon SWvt
'Propertius' (A)	CArg CWCL CWGN EHyd EPfP ETho LRHS MGos NTay SPoG WSpi
'Prosperity' (M)	CRHN ETho
'Proteus' (EL)	EHyd ELan EPfP ETho LRHS MAsh MGos NTay SCoo SNig
psilandra CWJ 12377	WCru
'Purple Dream'PBR (A)	ETho
'Purple Haze' (Vt)	CRHN NHaw
'Purple Princess' (H)	CDoC LRHS SCoo SPoG
'Purple Rain' (A)	CDoC LBuc NLar
'Purple Spider' (A/d)	EPfP ETho LRHS MAsh MBlu NTay SCoo
'Purpurea Plena Elegans' (Vt/d) ♀H6	CBcs CDoC CMac CRHN CRos CTri CWCL EBee EHyd ELan EPfP ETho IPot LCro LOPS LRHS LSRN MAsh MSwo NHol NRHS NTay SCob SCoo SNig SPer SPoG SWvt WBor
QUEEN MOTHER ('Zoqum') (Vt)	CWGN EBee EPfP ETho LRHS NTay SCoo
'Radiance'	CWGN NHaw
'Rahvarinne' (LL)	SNig
'Ramona' (LL)	EHyd LRHS LSRN NHaw
ranunculoides	NHaw
- W/O 7069 **new**	GGro
'Rapture' (T)	NHaw
'Raspberry Ripple' (V)	NHaw
'Rasputin' (LL)	CWGN ETho
REBECCA ('Evipo016'PBR) (EL)	CRos CWCL CWGN EHyd ELan EPfP ETho LCro LOPS LRHS LSRN MAsh NRHS NTay SCoo SLon SPer SPoG WSpi
recta	ECtt GAbr MNrw NHaw NLar SSal
- PAB 9005	LEdu
- 'Lime Close' seedlings	IPot
- 'Purpurea' (F)	CDor EHyd ELan EMor EPfP ETho GKev GWyn IPot LRHS MAvo MBriF MCot MHol MMrt MNrw NChi NTay SBls SEND SPtp
- 'Velvet Night' (F)	CBod ECtt IPot LRHS MBNS NLar NSti WCot
'Red 5' (T)	NHaw
'Red Pearl' (EL)	CWCL EHyd LSRN
I 'Red Star' (d)	EBee
REFLECTIONS ('Evipo035') (LL)	CRos EHyd EPfP LRHS MAsh NTay SLon SNig
§ ***rehderiana*** ♀H5	CDoC CRHN EBee ELan EPfP ETho LRHS MBlu NLar NTay SWvt WCot WFar WPGP WSHC
aff. ***rehderiana*** BO 16-026 **new**	GGro
REIKO ('Evipo088'PBR) (Garland Series)	CWGN ETho
'Reiman' (LL)	NHaw
'Remembrance' (LL) ♀H6	CWCL EPfP ETho LSRN NHaw
reticulata	NHaw
'Retrousse' (V) **new**	NHaw
'Reverie' (T)	NHaw
'Rhapsody' ambig.	CDoC EPfP IPot LBuc MAsh MGos SCoo SNig
'Rhapsody' B. Fretwell (EL)	CRos EHyd ETho LRHS LSRN NHaw NTay
'Ribble Red' (V)	NHaw
'Richard Pennell' (EL) ♀H6	CDoC EHyd LRHS
'Richard's Picotee' (Vt)	NHaw
'Rising Star'	NHaw SNig
'Ristimägi' (LL)	NHaw
'Rituaal' (LL)	NHaw
'Roelie' (Vt)	NHaw
'Roko' (LL)	CWGN
'Roko-Kolla' (LL) ♀H6	ETho NHaw SNig
'Romance' (Vt)	NTay
'Romantika' (LL)	CRos EHyd ELan ELon ETho LCro LRHS LSRN MAsh NHaw NRHS NTay SCoo SGsty
'Rooguchi' (I)	CDoC CWCL CWGN ETho NHaw NTay SCoo
'Rooran' (EL)	CWCL
'Rosa Königskind' (EL)	ETho NLar
ROSALYN ('Zo09087'PBR) (Vt)	CWGN ETho IPot NTay
I 'Rosea' (A/d)	EHyd
I 'Rosea' (I)	CWCL EPfP ETho LSRN NTay WHoo
I 'Rosea' Westphal. (Vt)	NHaw
ROSEBUD ('Robud'PBR) (M/d)	NPer
ROSEMOOR ('Evipo002'PBR) (EL)	CRos CWCL CWGN EHyd EPfP LRHS MAsh NRHS NTay SCoo SLon SNig SWvt
'Rosy O'Grady' (A) ♀H6	MAsh NLar SRms
'Rosy Pagoda' (A)	EHyd ELan ETho NLar NTay
'Rouge Cardinal' (LL)	CArg CBcs CDoC CRos EBee EHyd ELan ELon EPfP ETho LRHS LSRN

		MAsh MGos NRHS NTay SCob SCoo SNig SPer SPoG SRms
	'Royal Velours' (Vt)	CRHN CRos CTri CWCL ELan EPfP ETho IPot LCro LOPS LRHS LSRN MAsh MGos NHol NLar NRHS NTay SCob SCoo SNig SPer SPoG WSpi
	ROYAL VELVET ('Evifour'PBR) (EL)	EHyd LRHS LSRN SCoo
	'Royalty' (EL)	CDoC CWCL EHyd ELan EPfP ETho LRHS LSRN MAsh NTay SCoo WSpi
	'Rubens Superba'	see *C. montana* var. *rubens* 'Rubens Superba'
	'Rubra' (Vt)	IPot NTay
	'Ruby' (A)	CWCL ELan EPfP ETho LRHS LSRN MAsh NTay SCoo SPer SRms
	'Ruby Celebration' (A)	CDoC
	'Ruby Glow' (EL)	EHyd EPfP LRHS LSRN SCoo
	'Ruby Tuesday' (V)	NHaw
	'Ruby Wedding' Fretwell (T)	CWGN NHaw SWvt WSpi
	'Ruby Wedding NLP2' (EL)	CWCL EPfP ETho LBuc LCro LOPS LSRN NTay
	'Rüütel' (EL)	CWCL ELon ETho MAsh NHaw NTay SCoo
	'Saalomon' (LL)	NHaw
	SABINE ('Bfccsab'PBR) (LL)	CWGN
	SACHA ('Evipo060') (EL)	CRos EHyd EPfP ETho LRHS NLar NRHS NTay SCoo SNig SPoG
	'Sakala' (EL)	WSpi
	SALLY ('Evipo077'PBR) (EL)	CRos EHyd ELan EPfP ETho LRHS MAsh NLar NRHS NTay SCoo SNig SPoG
	SAMARITAN JO ('Evipo075')	CRos CWGN EHyd EPfP ETho LRHS MAsh NLar NRHS NTay SCoo SNig SPoG
	SARAH ELIZABETH ('Evipo098')	CRos ELan LRHS NLar NTay SCoo
	SAVANNAH ('Evipo015'PBR) (Vt)	MAsh
	'Scartho Gem' (EL)	EHyd LRHS SCoo SNig
	'Scented Clem'PBR (Vt) **new**	ETho
	SEA BREEZE ('Zo09063') (Vt)	CWGN ETho IPot LCro LOPS NTay SNig WSpi
§	'Semu' (LL)	CWGN ETho NHaw
	serratifolia	CBcs CTsd ECtt GLog SBrt SPlb
	- B&SWJ 8458 from Korea	WCru
I	'Sherriffii' (Ta)	SWvt
	'Shikoo' (EL)	CWCL ETho LSRN NTay
	SHIMMER ('Evipo028'PBR) (LL)	CRos EHyd EPfP LRHS MAsh NRHS NTay SLon SNig
§	***sibirica***	EHyd EPfP NRHS NTay
	- from Kazakhstan **new**	GGro
	- var. ***tianschanica***	NHaw
	'Signe' (Vt)	see *C.* 'Kasmu'
	'Siirus' (EL)	NHaw
	'Silver Moon' (EL)	CWCL EPfP ETho LRHS NLar SCoo WSpi
	simsii Small	see *C. pitcheri*
	simsii Sweet	see *C. crispa*
§	'Sinii Dozhd' (I)	CWCL
§	'Sir Edward Elgar' (A)	LRHS NRHS
	'Sir Eric Savill' (M)	ETho
	'Sir Trevor Lawrence' (T)	EHyd NHaw
	'Skyfall' (LL)	ETho
	'Snow Queen' (EL)	CDoC CWCL EHyd ELon EPfP ETho LRHS NTay SNig SRms
	'Snowbird' (A/d)	EHyd LRHS NTay SPoG
	'Snowdrift'	see *C. armandi* 'Snowdrift'
	SO MANY RED FLOWERS ('Zo06178'PBR) (EL)	NTay
	socialis	NHaw
	'Södertälje' (Vt)	CRHN ETho NHaw SCoo
	'Sokojiro' (EL)	EHyd ETho LRHS
	'Solidarność' (EL)	ETho SNig
	'Solina' (Vt)	NHaw
	songarica	GKev NHaw SBrt
	'Sonnette' (V)	CRHN CWGN NHaw
	'Sophie' (V)	NHaw
	SORBET ('Zosor'PBR) (A)	NTay
§	'Souvenir du Capitaine Thuilleaux' (EL)	ELon NTay SNig
	'Special Occasion' (EL)	CWGN EHyd EPfP ETho LRHS LSRN NLar NTay SCoo
	SPIKY ('Zospi'PBR) (A/d)	NTay
§	***spooneri***	CTsd EPfP LRHS NTay SCoo SGsty SWvt WSpi
	SPRING JOY ('Zo12053'PBR) (M)	NTay
	'Sputnik' (I)	NHaw
	stans	CDoC CExl EHyd ETho
	- B&SWJ 5073	WCru
	- B&SWJ 6345	WCru
§	'Star'PBR (M/d)	CDoC EHyd EPfP MGos NLar NTay
	'Star of India' (LL)	EHyd ELan EPfP ETho LRHS MGos NTay SCoo
	STAR OF PAKISTAN ('Zostapa') (LL)	CWGN
	STAR RIVER ('Zostarri'PBR) (I)	ELan IPot NTay
I	'Starfish' (EL)	NHaw
	'Starlight' (M)	CWCL ELon NTay
	'Stasik' (LL)	NHaw
	'Stefan Franczak' (EL)	ETho
	STILL WATERS ('Zostiwa'PBR) (EL)	ETho
	'Strawberry Kiss' (V)	NHaw
	'Strawberry Splash' (V) **new**	NHaw
	'Sue Reade' (V)	NHaw
	SUGAR CANDY ('Evione'PBR) (EL)	LRHS MAsh NTay SCoo SNig
	SUMMER SNOW	see *C.* 'Paul Farges'
	SUMMERDREAM ('Zosumdre') (EL)	NTay
	'Sundance' (Ta)	NHaw
	SUNNY SKY ('Zosusk'PBR) (Vt)	ELan NHaw NTay SGsty SNig
	'Sunrise' (M/d)	CDoC EBee EPfP ETho MSwo NLar NTay
	'Sunset' (EL) ♀H6	CArg CWCL EHyd ELon LRHS LSRN MGos NLar NTay SCoo SNig
	SUPER CUTE ('Zo09122') (Vt) **new**	CWGN
	SUPER NIGHT ('Zo11112') (Vt) **new**	CWGN
	SUPER NOVA ('Zo09088'PBR) (Vt)	ELan ETho IPot NTay
	'Suzy Mac' (EL) **new**	NTay
	'Swedish Bells' (I)	CWGN ETho
	'Sweet Scentsation' (F)	CDoC EPfP ETho MGos NHaw NTay WSpi
	'Sweet Summer Love'PBR (F)	CDoC CWGN ETho IPot LCro LOPS NHaw NTay SNig
	SWEETHEART ('Witswe'PBR) (I)	ELan ETho NTay
	'Sylvia Denny' (EL)	CArg EPfP ETho LRHS MAsh WSpi
	'Sylviorna' (v)	NHaw
	szuyuanensis CWJ 12455	WCru
	'Tae'	see *C.* 'Toltae'
	'Taiga'PBR (d)	CBcs CRos CWGN ELan ETho LCro LOPS LRHS NTay SCoo
	TAI YANG ('Evipo045'PBR) (Fo)	NTay
	'Tamakazura' (V)	CWGN NHaw

	'Tango' (Vt)	CRHN NHaw
§	***tangutica***	Widely available
	'Tapestry' (I)	NHaw
	'Tartu' (EL)	NHaw
	tashiroi 'Yellow Peril'	WCru
	TEKLA ('Evipo069'[PBR]) (LL)	CRos CWCL EHyd ETho LRHS NRHS NTay SCoo SNig SPoG WSpi
	'Teksa' (LL)	NHaw
	TEMPTATION ('Zotemp'[PBR]) (EL)	ETho MGos
	'Tentel' (LL)	NHaw
§	***terniflora***	EPfP ETho LRHS NHaw NTay SPtp
	- B&SWJ 5751	WCru
	- var. ***mandshurica***	ETho GBin NHaw WSpi
	- - dwarf	CWGN
	texensis	NHaw WSHC
	- 'The Princess of Wales'	see *C.* 'Princess Diana'
	'The Bride' (EL)	CWCL CWGN ETho LSRN NTay
	THE COUNTESS OF WESSEX ('Evipo073') (EL)	CRos CWCL EHyd EPfP ETho LRHS NRHS NTay SCoo SNig SPoG
	'The First Lady' (EL)	CWCL ETho
	'The President' (EL) Υ^{H6}	CArg CDoC CMac CTri CWCL EHyd ELan EPfP ETho GDam LCro LOPS LRHS LSRN MGos MSwo NLar NRHS NTay SCob SCoo SNig SPer SPoG SRms WFar WSpi
	'The Princess of Wales' (EL)	see *C.* 'Princess of Wales' (1875) (EL)
	'The Princess of Wales' (T)	see *C.* 'Princess Diana' (T)
	'The Vagabond' (EL)	CWCL CWGN ELan EPfP ETho LSRN MAsh NHaw NLar NTay SCoo SNig WSpi
§	THUMBELINA ('Evipo030'[PBR]) (EL)	CRos CWCL EHyd EPfP ETho LRHS NRHS NTay SCoo SNig SPoG
	thunbergii misapplied	see *C. terniflora*
	'Thyrislund' (EL)	SNig
	'Tibetan Mix' (Ta)	NHaw
	tibetana	NHaw
	- CC 7447	GKev
	- 'Black Tibet' (Ta)	CWGN NHaw
§	- subsp. ***vernayi***	SCob
	- - 'Glasnevin Dusk' (Ta)	WSHC
§	- - var. ***vernayi*** 'Orange Peel' (Ta)	ETho LRHS
	'Tie Dye' (LL)	CDoC CWGN EBee ELan EPfP ETho LRHS NTay SCoo SPoG SRms
	'Tim's Passion' (Vt)	CRHN
	'Titipu' (V)	NHaw
	'Toki' (EL)	CWGN ETho SCoo
§	'Toltae'[PBR] (EL)	CDoC CWGN EHyd ETho LRHS NRHS
	tongluensis	WPGP
	TRANQUILITÉ ('Evipo103')	CRos LRHS NTay SCoo
	'Tranquility'	CWGN
	'Triinu' (Vt)	NHaw
	'Trikatrei' (LL)	LRHS
§	× ***triternata*** 'Rubromarginata'	CDoC CMac CRHN CRos CWCL CWGN EHyd ELan EPfP ETho GArf LCro LOPS LRHS LSRN MAsh MGos MRav NLar NRHS NTay SCob SCoo SLon SPer SPoG SRms
	TRY ME ('Zotrym'[PBR]) (A/d) **new**	NTay
	TSUKIKO ('Evipo110') (Garland Series)	CWGN ETho
§	***tubulosa*** ALAN BLOOM ('Alblo'[PBR]) (H)	EHyd
	- 'Wyevale' (H)	CMac CRos EBee EHyd ELan EPfP ETho LRHS MCot MRav NRHS NTay SCoo SPer
	'Tuchka' (EL)	CWGN
	'Tudor' (EL)	SNig
	'Twilight' (EL)	CRos EHyd EPfP LRHS MAsh
	TWINKLE ('Zotwi') (I)	CWGN ETho LRHS NTay
	TWINKLE BELL ('Wer01')	NTay
	uncinata	CBcs
	'Uno Kivistik'[PBR] (LL)	NHaw
§	***urophylla*** 'Winter Beauty'	CDoC CWCL EBee ELan EPfP ETho LCro LOPS LRHS LSRN MAsh NTay SBrt SCoo SPoG WSpi
	urticifolia	GGro
	- B&SWJ 8651	WCru
	- B&SWJ 8852	WCru
	'Utopia' (EL)	CWGN
	'Valge Daam' (LL)	CWGN NHaw SNig
	'Valour' (Vt)	ETho NHaw
	'Van Gogh' (M)	CWGN ETho
	'Vanessa' (LL)	CRHN NHaw
	'Vanso'	see *C.* 'Blue Light'
	'Varenne' (EL)	EBee
§	× ***vedrariensis***	WSpi
§	***veitchiana***	EWld NHaw
	'Venosa Violacea' (Vt) Υ^{H6}	CDoC CRHN CRos EHyd ELan EPfP ETho LRHS LSRN MAsh NHaw NHol NTay SCob SCoo SNig SPer SPoG SRms
	'Vera' (M)	EPfP LRHS LSRN NTay SCoo
	'Veronica's Choice' (EL)	CWCL ELan ETho NTay SNig
	VERSAILLES ('Evipo025'[PBR]) (EL)	EHyd EPfP NTay
§	VESUVIUS ('Evipo032'[PBR]) (Vt)	EHyd SCoo SLon
	'Vicky' (A/d)	CRos LRHS
	VICTOR HUGO ('Evipo007'[PBR]) (LL)	CRos EHyd LRHS NLar SCoo
	'Victoria' (LL)	EHyd ETho LRHS LSRN NHaw NTay
	VIENNETTA ('Evipo006'[PBR]) (d)	CRos CWCL CWGN EHyd EPfP ETho LRHS MGos NTay SCoo SLon SNig SRms
	'Ville de Lyon' (LL)	CBcs CDoC CRHN CWCL EHyd ELan EPfP ETho LPar LRHS LSRN MAsh MGos NRHS NTay SCob SCoo SNig SPer SPoG
	vinacea	NHaw
	'Vince Denny' (Ta)	EBee NHaw
	VINO ('Poulvo'[PBR]) (EL)	EHyd NTay SCoo SNig
	'Viola' (LL)	ELon LRHS LSRN NHaw NTay
	viorna	CWGN EWld GKev NHaw
	virginiana misapplied	see *C. vitalba*
§	***vitalba***	NHaw NTay NWea SCob WHer WSFF WSpi
	viticella	CRHN NHaw NTay SCob SNig WSHC
	- subsp. ***campaniflora***	see *C. campaniflora*
§	- 'Flore Pleno' (Vt/d)	CRHN CRos EHyd ELan EPfP ETho IPot LCro LOPS LRHS LSRN NHaw NLar NRHS NTay SLon SPoG
	- 'Hanna' (Vt)	CRHN IPot LSRN NHaw SNig
	- 'Mary Rose'	see *C. viticella* 'Flore Pleno'
	'Vivienne'	see *C.* 'Beth Currie'
	VOLCANO ('Mazowsze') (LL)	SNig
	'Voluceau' (Vt)	CWCL EHyd ELan EPfP LRHS LSRN SCoo SNig SRms
	VOLUNTEER ('Evipo080') (EL)	CRos EHyd ETho LRHS NRHS NTay SNig
	'Vostok' (LL)	NHaw
	'Vyvyan Pennell' (EL)	CArg CBcs CDoC CMac CRos CTri CWCL EHyd ELan EPfP ETho LRHS LSRN MAsh NLar NTay SCob SCoo SNig SPer SPoG SWvt WFar WSpi
	'W.E. Gladstone' (EL)	EHyd LRHS
	WADA'S PRIMROSE	see *C. patens* 'Manshuu Ki'

'Walenburg' (Vt) ♀H6	CRHN CWGN ETho LRHS NHaw NTay SLon
'Walter Pennell' (EL)	EHyd SCoo
'Warsaw' (Ta)	NLar
'Warszawska Nike' (EL) ♀H6	CRHN CWCL EHyd ELan EPfP ETho LCro LOPS LPar LRHS MAsh MGos NTay SCob SCoo SNig SPoG
'Warwickshire Rose' (M)	CDoC CMac CRHN CTri CWGN EBee EHyd ELan EPfP ETho LRHS LSRN MAsh NTay SCoo SPoG
'Wedding Day' (EL)	EPfP ETho LCro LOPS LSRN NLar NTay
'Wee Willie Winkie' (M)	SRms
'Westerplatte' (EL)	CWCL CWGN EHyd EPfP ETho LRHS MGos NHaw NTay SCoo SNig SPoG WSpi
§ 'White Columbine' (A) ♀H6	ELan LRHS NTay SCoo SPer
'White Heart' (Vt)	CRHN NHaw
'White Magic'PBR (Vt)	NTay
§ 'White Moth' (A/d)	LSRN MAsh NHol NTay
WHITE PEARL ('Zo08080') (EL) **new**	NTay
'White Prince Charles' (LL)	CWGN NHaw
'White Satin' (A)	EHyd EPfP LRHS NTay SRms
'White Swan' (A/d)	ETho MAsh NHol NTay SCoo
'White Wings' (A/d)	LSRN
'Will Goodwin' (EL) ♀H6	CWCL EHyd ELan EPfP LRHS SNig SRms
'William Kennett' (EL)	CWCL ELan ETho LRHS
'Willy' (A)	CArg CRos EHyd ELan EPfP ETho LRHS MAsh MGos NLar NRHS NTay SCoo SRms
WISLEY ('Evipo001'PBR) (Vt) ♀H6	EPfP MGos NLar SLon
WONDERFUL ('Zo09073') (Vt)	CWGN LCro LOPS NTay SNig
'Xerxes' misapplied	see *C.* 'Elsa Späth'
XIU ('Evipo065') (Boulevard Series) (Fo)	LRHS NTay SNig
'Yellow Queen' Holland	see *C. patens* 'Manshuu Ki'
'Yellow Queen' Lundell/ Treasures	see *C.* 'Moonlight'
YUAN ('Evipo082'PBR) (Boulevard Series) **new**	LSou
§ 'Yukikomachi' (EL)	NHaw SNig WSpi
yunnanensis	WPGP
'Yvette Houry' (EL)	EBee
ZARA ('Evipo062'PBR) (EL)	ETho NTay SLon
'Zephyr' (Vt)	NHaw

Clematopsis see *Clematis*

Clementsia see *Rhodiola*

Cleome (*Cleomaceae*)

hassleriana 'Helen Campbell' ♀H2	CSpe LCro LOPS WHer
- 'Violet Queen'	LCro LOPS
SEÑORITA ROSALITA ('Inncleosr'PBR)	CSpe MHol

Clerodendrum (*Lamiaceae*)

CW&T 6506	CMCN
bungei	Widely available
- 'Pink Diamond' (v)	CCCN CKel CMac CWGN ELan EPfP EWes LRHS LSRN MGos NLar SGbt SPer SPoG SWvt
§ ***chinense*** var. ***chinense*** (d) ♀H1b	CCCN
colebrookianum B&SWJ 6651	WCru
- PAB 7794	LEdu
myricoides 'Ugandense'	see *Rotheca myricoides* 'Ugandense'
paniculatum 'Starshine'	CCCN
aff. ***subscaposum*** WWJ 11735	WCru
thomsoniae ♀H1b	EShb WSFF
trichotomum	CBcs CExl CMCN CTri EGrl EPfP IArd LRHS MTrO NLar SCob SLon SPer WBor WMat
- var. ***fargesii*** ♀H5	Widely available
- - 'Carnival' (v) ♀H5	CCCN CDoC CExl CKel CMac EBee EHed EHyd ELan EPfP EWes LRHS NLar SEle SMad SNig SPer SPoG SWvt WAvo WCot
- 'Purple Blaze'	CJun EBee LPar
- 'Purple Haze'	NLar
- 'Shiro'	WCru
wallichii	EShb
- 'Prospero'	CDoC

Clethra (*Clethraceae*)

CW&T 6497	CMCN
acuminata	NLar
alnifolia	CBcs CExl EBee SRms WFar
- 'Anne Bidwell'	MBlu NLar
- 'Creel's Calico' (v)	NLar
- 'Fern Valley Pink'	CCCN CDoC CKel CMac ELon EPfP LRHS NLar SRms WFar
- 'Hokie Pink'	ELon NLar
- 'Hummingbird' ♀H5	CCCN CDoC CEme CEnd CExl CKel CMac CRos ELan ELon EPfP LRHS MAsh MBlu NLar SCoo SEle SPad SPoG SWvt WFar XSte
- 'Paniculata'	CBod CKel EHed ELon LRHS MGil WPnP
- 'Pink Spice'	CRos
- 'Pink Spires'	CBcs CExl EGrl GKin LEdu MMuc MRav NLar SCoo SEle SIvy SNig SPer WBor WLov WPnP
- 'Rosea'	CTri GKin
- 'Ruby Spice' ♀H5	Widely available
- 'September Beauty'	CJun NLar
- 'Sixteen Candles'	GGGa IDee LRHS MPkF NLar XSte
- VANILLA SPICE ('Caleb')	CBcs
arborea	ECre IKel MGil
barbinervis ♀H5	CBcs CExl CKel EPfP GGGa LRHS MBlu MGil NLar WPGP WPnP
- B&SWJ 11562	WCru
- GREAT STAR ('Minbarb')	EHed EPfP LRHS WPGP XSte
- 'White Star'	CJun CKel CMac EBee EPfP LRHS
delavayi Franch.	CBcs CCCN CDoC CMCN EBee EGrl EPfP GGGa IArd IDee IKel MGil MMrt NLar WPGP
- SBEC 1513	CExl
fabri B&SWJ 11702	WCru
- FMWJ 13037	WCru
fargesii	CExl EBee EPfP IDee MBlu NLar SPtp WPGP
kaipoensis NJM 11.020	WPGP
- NJM 11.058	WPGP
- PAB 8571	LEdu
monostachya	CExl EBee MGil WPGP
pachyphylla	WPGP
petelotii FMWJ 13401	WCru
pringlei	CBcs EBee IArd IDee NLar WPGP
tomentosa 'Cottondale'	CJun IDee NLar

Cleyera (*Pentaphylacaceae*)

fortunei	see *C. japonica* 'Fortunei'
- 'Variegata'	see *C. japonica* 'Fortunei'
§ ***japonica*** 'Fortunei' (v)	CCCN CMac CWit EBee SSta
- var. ***japonica***	EBee WPGP

- 'Tricolor' (v) IDee SAko
- var. ***wallichii*** WPGP

Clianthus ✿ (*Fabaceae*)

maximus CTsd
- 'Kaka King' EWes LRHS MPkF XSte

* ***pauciflorus*** CCCN

§ ***puniceus*** 🏆H3 CAbb CBcs CCht CExl CSpe CTsd EBee EHyd EPfP EWld MGil MHtn SChF SEdd SEle SGbt SPer SPlb SPoG SWvt

§ - 'Albus' 🏆H3 CBcs CCCN CExl CSpe CTsd EBee EHyd EPfP EWld LRHS SChF SPer SPoG SWvt XSte
- 'Flamingo' see *C. puniceus* 'Roseus'
- 'Red Admiral' see *C. puniceus*
- 'Red Cardinal' see *C. puniceus*

§ - 'Roseus' 🏆H3 CBcs CCCN CExl CPla CWit EHyd EPfP LRHS NRHS SMad SPer SPoG XSte
- 'White Heron' see *C. puniceus* 'Albus'

Clinanthus (*Amaryllidaceae*)

incarnatus apricot-flowered WMal

Clinopodium (*Lamiaceae*)

acinos SPhx
alpinum EBou EDAr GJos SRms WJek
calamintha see *Calamintha nepeta*
corsicum WHoo WKif WSHC
grandiflorum see *Calamintha grandiflora*

§ ***menthifolium*** NLar

§ ***vulgare*** CHab EBee EHyd GPSL LShi MBow MHer MHol MNHC NAts NMir SBut SRms WWild
- PAB 7562 LEdu

Clintonia (*Liliaceae*)

andrewsiana GBin
borealis GAbr

Clivia ✿ (*Amaryllidaceae*)

caulescens NHoy WCot
- pink-flowered NHoy WCot

× ***cyrtanthiflora*** NHoy
gardenii NHoy WCot
miniata 🏆H1c CAbb CBcs CCCN CDoC CTsd LCro LOPS NHoy SAdn SEND SPlb WCot
- 'Anshan Variegated' (v) WCot
- 'Arturo's Yellow' NHoy WCot
- 'Aurea' CSpe
- Belgian hybrids NHoy WCot
- Belgian hybrids (improved strain) NHoy
- 'Beverley's Delight' NHoy WCot
- broad-leaved, variegated (v) NHoy WCot
- 'Chubb's Peach' × 'Vico Yellow' NHoy
- var. ***citrina*** 🏆H1c NHoy SDir
- - variegated (v) NHoy WCot
- 'Connemara Flame' NHoy
- 'Dancing Sisters' × 'Terracotta Green Throat' NHoy WCot
- Daruma Group WCot
- 'Florid White Lips' NHoy
- fragrant yellow-flowered NHoy
- green-centred NHoy WCot
- - orange-flowered NHoy
- historical clone NHoy
- 'Hot Number One' NHoy
- large strawberry orange-flowered NHoy
- 'Light of Buddha' (v) NHoy WCot
- 'Mitsuhashi Multipetal' WCot
- 'Mrs P. Lofus' NHoy
- Nakamura yellow-flowered NHoy
- 'Pale Majesty' NHoy
- pale yellow-flowered NHoy
- pastel shades NHoy WCot
- 'Pink Perfection' NHoy WCot
- 'Queen of the Strawberries' NHoy
- 'Strawberry Giant' NHoy
- 'Striata' (v) NHoy WCot
- 'Terracotta Treasure' (v) NHoy WCot
- 'Vico Shima' WCot
- 'Wide Leaf Monk' WCot

nobilis 🏆H1c NHoy SPlb WCot
robusta NHoy WCot
'San Marcos Yellow' × 'Solomone Yellow' WCot
'Sweet Undress' NHoy WCot

Clusia (*Clusiaceae*)

rosea CCCN

Clytostoma (*Bignoniaceae*)

§ ***calystegioides*** CCCN CRHN

Cnidium (*Apiaceae*)

officinale GPoy LEdu
silaifolium LEdu SPhx

Cobaea (*Polemoniaceae*)

pringlei CRHN WPGP
- CD&R 1323 SBrt WCot

scandens 🏆H2 CCCN CDTJ CSpe EShb SPhx
- f. ***alba*** CSpe EShb LCro LOPS

cobnut see *Corylus avellana*; see also AGM Fruit Section

Cocculus (*Menispermaceae*)

laurifolius IArd

§ ***orbiculatus*** CExl
- B&SWJ 535 WCru

trilobus see *C. orbiculatus*

Cochlearia (*Brassicaceae*)

armoracia see *Armoracia rusticana*
danica new CAgr
glastifolia CAgr
officinalis CAgr WHer

Cochliasanthus (*Fabaceae*)

§ ***caracalla*** CCCN EShb

Cocos (*Arecaceae*)

plumosa see *Syagrus romanzoffiana*

Codiaeum ✿ (*Euphorbiaceae*)

variegatum var. ***pictum*** 'Excellent' (v) LCro LOPS

Codonanthe (*Gesneriaceae*)

gracilis WDib
'Paula' WDib

Codonanthe × *Nematanthus* see × *Codonatanthus*

× *Codonatanthus* (*Gesneriaceae*)

	'Golden Tambourine'	WDib
	'Sunset'	WDib
	'Tambourine'	WDib

Codonopsis ✿ (*Campanulaceae*)

	HWJK 2105 from Nepal	WCru
	affinis	EBee
	- HWJCM 70	WCru
	- HWJK 2151	WCru
	benthamii GWJ 9352	WCru
	cardiophylla	EBee EWld GArf GKev WSHC
	aff. ***celebica***	WCru
	BWJ 15623 new	
	clematidea	CDor CSpe EBee EBou ECha EPfP EPot EWld GAbr GKev MNrw NLar SPlb SWvt
	convolvulacea misapplied	see *C. grey-wilsonii*
	convolvulacea ambig.	CWCL GKev
	- 'Alba'	see *C. grey-wilsonii* 'Himal Snow'
	- Forrest's form	see *C. forrestii* Diels
	convulvulacea subsp. ***vinciflora*** new	GKev
	'Dangshen'	see *C. pilosula*
	aff. ***deltoidea*** SSSE 86	EBee EWld
	dicentrifolia	NLar
	forrestii misapplied	see *C. grey-wilsonii*
§	***forrestii*** Diels	EWld GKev
	- BWJ 7847	WCru
§	***grey-wilsonii*** 🏆H5	CBro EWld GEdr GKev
	- B&SWJ 7532	WCru
§	- 'Himal Snow'	EWld GEdr GKev WCru WHil
	inflata GWJ 9442	WCru
	kawakamii	EBee EWld
	- B&SWJ 1592	WCru
	- RWJ 10007	WCru
§	***lanceolata***	CPla EPPr EWld SBrt
	- B&SWJ 562	WCru
	nepalensis Grey-Wilson	see *C. grey-wilsonii*
	obtusa	EBee EWld
	ovata	GKev NBro
§	***pilosula***	CDor EBee EWld GKev GPoy SBrt
	- var. ***modesta***	EBee GArf
	pinifolia	GKev
§	***rotundifolia*** var. ***angustifolia***	GKev WCru
	- var. ***grandiflora***	EBee GKev SBrt WSHC
	silvestris	see *C. pilosula*
	subscaposa	GArf MVil SBrt
	tangshen misapplied	see *C. rotundifolia* var. *angustifolia*
	tangshen Oliv.	WSHC
	ussuriensis	see *C. lanceolata*
	vinciflora	EWld
	viridis CC 7454 new	SBrt
	- HWJK 2435	WCru

Coffea (*Rubiaceae*)

	arabica	CCCN CWit SPre

coffee see *Coffea*

Colchicum ✿ (*Colchicaceae*)

	agrippinum 🏆H4	CWCL ECha EPot GKev MRav NBir NRog WAbe WCot WHoo WThu
	alpinum	GKev
	'Antares'	ECha NRog
	asteranthum	NRog
	atropurpureum	GKev
	'Autumn Herald'	NRog
	'Autumn Queen' 🏆H5	NRog
§	***autumnale***	CAvo CHab EPot GKev GPoy NRya SDeJ WShi
	- 'Alboplenum'	ERCP GKev NBir NRog SDeJ
	- 'Album' 🏆H5	CAvo ELan EPfP EPot GKev LCro LOPS NBir NRog SPeP WShi
	- 'Atropurpureum'	NRog
	- 'Karin Persson'	GKev
	- var. ***major*** hort.	see *C. byzantinum* Ker Gawl.
	- var. ***minor*** hort.	see *C. autumnale*
§	- 'Nancy Lindsay' 🏆H5	EPot GKev NRog WShi
	- 'Pannonicum'	see *C. autumnale* 'Nancy Lindsay'
§	- 'Pleniflorum' (d)	EGrI GKev NBir
	- 'Roseum Plenum'	see *C. autumnale* 'Pleniflorum'
	baytopiorum	GKev NRog WThu
	'Beaconsfield'	NRog
§	***bivonae***	EPot
	- 'Apollo'	NRog
	- 'Mount Giona'	GKev
	- 'Vesta'	GKev
§	***boissieri***	EPot GKev NRog
	bornmuelleri misapplied	see *C. speciosum* var. *bornmuelleri* hort.
	bornmuelleri Freyn	EGrI NBir NRog
	- 'Artur Klark' new	NRog
	bowlesianum	see *C. bivonae*
	byzantinum ambig.	GKev
§	***byzantinum*** Ker Gawl.	ELan NRog SDeJ WShi
	- ***album***	see *C. byzantinum* 'Innocence'
§	- 'Innocence' 🏆H5	GKev NRog WCot
	cilicicum	EGrI NBir NRog
	- 'Purpureum' 🏆H5	EPot GKev NRog
	'Conquest'	see *C.* 'Glory of Heemstede'
	corsicum	GKev WThu
	cupanii AH 9707	GKev
	'Daendels'	NRog
	davisii	GKev NRog
	'Dick Trotter'	EPfP EPot SDeJ WFar
	'Disraeli'	EPot GKev NRog
	'Faberge's Silver' new	NRog
	falcifolium	NRog
	'Flamenco Dance' new	NRog
§	***giganteum***	NRog
§	'Glory of Heemstede'	GKev NRog
	'Gothic Style' new	NRog
	'Gracia'	NRog
	graecum	GKev NRog
	'Hannibal'	GKev
	'Harlekijn'	EPot ERCP GKev NRog
	hungaricum	EPot GKev
	- 'Valentine'	GKev NRog
	- 'Velebit Star'	EPot GKev NRog
	illyricum	see *C. giganteum*
	'Jarka'	NRog
	'Jaroslavna'	NRog
	'Jochem Hof'	NRog
	kesselringii	NRog
	- 'My Choice' new	NRog
	- 'Purple Star' new	NRog
	kotschyi	NRog
	laetum misapplied	see *C. parnassicum*
	laetum Stev.	NRog
	'Larisa' new	NRog
	'Lilac Bedder'	GKev NRog
	'Lilac Wonder'	EGrI ELan LCro LOPS MRav NBir NRog SDeJ WCot WHoo
	longifolium	see *C. neapolitanum*
	luteum	NRog
	- from Chimgan, Uzbekistan new	NRog
	- 'Golden Baby' new	NRog
	- 'Vahsh' new	NRog

	'Lysimachus'	GKev
	macrophyllum	GKev NRog WCot
	minutum	NRog
	monatum 'Norman Barrett' **new**	NRog
	munzurense	NRog
§	***neapolitanum***	GKev NRog
	'Neptun'	NRog
	'Oktoberfest'	EPot
	parlatoris	GKev NRog
§	***parnassicum***	ECha GKev NRog
	'Poseidon'	GKev NRog
	'Prinses Astrid'	NRog
	procurrens	see *C. boissieri*
	pusillum	GKev
	robustum **new**	NRog
	'Rosy Dawn' ♀H5	ECha NRog
	sanguicolle	NRog
	sibthorpii	see *C. bivonae*
	'Snow of Highland' **new**	NRog
	'Spartacus'	GKev
	speciosum	CAvo ELan EPot GBin GKev NBir NRog WShi
	- 'Album' ♀H5	CAvo CWCL ECha EPot ERCP GAbr GKev LEdu NBir NRog SDeJ
	- 'Atrorubens' ♀H5	ECha EPot GKev
I	- var. ***bornmuelleri*** hort.	NRog WHoo
	- 'Dombai'	NRog
	- var. ***illyricum*** hort.	see *C. giganteum*
	- 'Ordu'	NRog
	szovitsii Fisch. & B. Mey.	GKev NRog
	- white-flowered	NRog
	tenorei ♀H4	EPot GKev NBir NRog
	'The Giant'	EPfP EPot LCro LOPS NRog SDeJ WFar
	trigynum **new**	GKev NRog
	triphyllum	GKev NRog
	variegatum	NRog
	'Violet Queen'	ERCP GAbr GKev NRog SDeJ
	'Waterlily' (d) ♀H5	CAvo CBod EGrI ELan EPot ERCP GKev LCro LOPS MBow NBir NPoe NRog SDeJ SPeP WCot WFar WHoo
	'William Dykes'	NRog
	'World Champion's Cup' **new**	NRog
	'Yeti' **new**	NRog
	zahnii from southern Greece **new**	NRog
	'Zephyr'	NRog

Coleonema (*Rutaceae*)

§	***pulchellum***	CCCN SVen
	- 'Aureum'	CSde
	- 'Breath of Gold'	CCCN
§	- 'Pink Fountain'	CAbb CCCN CTsd ECre EHyd ELan EPfP LRHS MPkF NRHS SEle SPoG WCot XSte
	pulchrum misapplied	see *C. pulchellum*
§	'Sunset Gold'	CAbb CBod CCCN CDoC CKel CPbh CSBt CSpe EBee EHyd ELan EPfP LRHS MPkF NRHS SCoo SEle SPlb SPoG XSte

Coleus see *Solenostemon*

Colignonia (*Nyctaginaceae*)

	ovalifolia B&SWJ 10644	WCru

Colletia (*Rhamnaceae*)

	armata	see *C. hystrix*
	cruciata	see *C. paradoxa*
§	***hystrix***	CBcs CMCN CMac CTri CTsd ELon EPfP MGil WPav
	- RCB RA S3	WCot
	- 'Rosea'	CMac MBlu SArc WPav
§	***paradoxa***	CBcs CCCN CWit ELan EPfP SArc SPlb SPoG WFar WPav
	spinosissima	WPav
	ulicina	SVen

Collinsonia (*Lamiaceae*)

	canadensis	LEdu WPGP

Collomia ✿ (*Polemoniaceae*)

	grandiflora	WCot

Colocasia (*Araceae*)

	antiquorum	see *C. esculenta*
§	***esculenta*** ♀H1b	CDTJ LCro LOPS SDir SPalm SPlb
	- B&SWJ 6909	ESwi WCru
	- 'Black Coral'	CAbb CBod LRHS SPad
	- 'Black Magic'	CDTJ EHyd SDir
	- 'Black Sapphire Gecko' **new**	MPkF
	- 'Blue Hawaii'	CAbb CCht CDTJ CPla SPad
	- burgundy-stemmed	CDTJ CTsd SPalm
	- 'Emerald'	CBct SDir
	- 'Fontanesii'	CBct CDTJ
	- 'Hawaiian Punch'	CAbb CDTJ
	- 'Illustris'	CAbb CDTJ
	- 'Jack's Giant'	CDTJ
	- 'Mammoth'	CDTJ
	- 'Maui Gold' **new**	CBct CBod
	- 'Mojito' (v)	CDTJ
	- 'Pink China'	CBct CBod SSal XSte
	- 'Sangria'	XSte
	gaoligongensis	CBct CDTJ CPHo SPlb
	'Madeira'	XSte

Colquhounia (*Lamiaceae*)

	coccinea	CCCN CSde EShb ESwi MBlu MGil MRav NLar NQui SBrt SEdd SIvy SLon SPoG WLov
	- Sch 2458	EPfP WPGP
§	- var. ***mollis*** B&SWJ 7222	WCru
	- var. ***vestita*** misapplied	see *C. coccinea* var. *mollis*
	- var. ***vestita*** ambig.	CBcs CKel CTsd CWit EBee EPfP LRHS MBNS SEND

Columnea (*Gesneriaceae*)

	'Aladdin's Lamp'	WDib
	× ***banksii*** ♀H1c	WDib
§	'Broget Stavanger' (v) ♀H1c	WDib
	'Chanticleer' ♀H1a	WDib
I	'Firedragon'	WDib
	'Gavin Brown'	WDib
	gloriosa	see *C. microcalyx*
	'Inferno'	WDib
	'Katsura'	WDib
	'Merkur'	WDib
§	***microcalyx***	EBak
I	'Midnight Lantern'	WDib
	'Rising Sun'	WDib
	schiedeana	WDib
	'Sherbert'	WDib
	'Stavanger' ♀H1a	WDib
	'Stavanger Variegated'	see *C.* 'Broget Stavanger'

Colutea (*Fabaceae*)

	arborescens	CAgr CBcs CExl EHyd ELan ESwi EWTr MBlu MGil MGos NWea SPlb

× ***media*** 'Copper Beauty'	CBcs ELan MMrt MPie NLar
orientalis	CCCN EBee

Colvillea (*Fabaceae*)

racemosa	SPlb

Colysis (*Polypodiaceae*)

elliptica new	WCot

Comarum see *Potentilla*

Combretum (*Combretaceae*)

fruticosum	CCCN
indicum	CCCN

Commelina (*Commelinaceae*)

coelestis	see *C. tuberosa* Coelestis Group
dianthifolia	EBee EHyd EPPr GEdr GKev LEdu LShi NHpl SBrt SBut
- 'Electric Blue'	ELan SVic
robusta	WCot WFar
tuberosa	GKev MAvo MGil NWad
- B&SWJ 10353	SBrt WCru
- blue-flowered	SDeJ
§ - Coelestis Group	CCBP CSpe CTtf ECha EGrI EWld LShi SDys SPtp WKif WSHC
- - 'Hopleys Variegated' (v)	WFar
- - 'Rhapsody'	WFar

Comptonia (*Myricaceae*)

peregrina	EBee WPGP

Conandron (*Gesneriaceae*)

ramondoides B&SWJ 8929	WCru

Conicosia (*Aizoaceae*)

pugioniformis	SVen

Coniogramme (*Pteridaceae*)

emeiensis	CBdn CBrP CTsd LEdu LLWG WCot
intermedia	LEdu WPGP
japonica	LEdu MAvo WCot WFib WPGP
- 'Flavomaculata'	EBee GGro LEdu MSCN WCot WFar WPGP

Conoclinium (*Asteraceae*)

§ ***coelestinum***	CBod CFoA EBee EHyd EShb LRHS NRHS SBrt

Conopodium (*Apiaceae*)

majus	CEls WShi

Consolida (*Ranunculaceae*)

§ ***ajacis***	CSpe SPhx
- Giant Imperial Series	SVic

Convallaria ✿ (*Asparagaceae*)

japonica	see *Ophiopogon jaburan*
keiskei	EPPr EPot MAvo WFar
I - 'Marginata' (v)	WCot
- 'Shiro-shima-fu' (v)	GEdr GGro WFar
majalis 🏆^{H7}	Widely available
- from Tatra Mountains new	EPPr
- 'Albostriata' (v)	CBct CTtf EBee EHyd EPPr EPri GKev GMaP LEdu LRHS MAvo MHer MHol MNrw MRav NBir NRHS WCot WFar WHer WHoo WPnP WTyc
- 'Aurea'	WFar
- 'Berlin Giant'	EPPr EPri MAvo NRya SDeJ WFar
- 'Blush'	CAvo WFar
- 'Bordeaux'	CBro CDor CExl CWCL ELan EMor EPPr EPri GPSL MAvo MBel NLar SEdd WCot WPnP WTyc
- 'Bridal Choice'	EBee EPot GBin GKev MAvo NLar WFar
- 'Cream da Mint' (v)	WFar
- 'Dorien'	CBct EMor EPPr MAvo WFar
- 'Fernwood's Golden Slippers'	CAvo GEdr WCot WFar
- 'Flore Pleno' (d)	EWld GEdr MBel MMrt WFar
- 'Géant de Fortin' 🏆^{H7}	CAvo CBct CBro CEme CExl EPot GEdr MRav NBir NLar WCot WFar
- 'Gérard Debureaux'	see *C. majalis* 'Green Tapestry'
- 'Golden Jubilee'	CBct EPri LEdu MAvo MNrw WCot WFar
- 'Grandiflora'	WFar
§ - 'Green Tapestry' (v)	CBct MAvo WCot WFar
- 'Haldon Grange' (v)	EPPr MAvo WFar
- 'Hardwick Hall' (v)	CAvo CBct CDor CExl CTtf CWCL EBee ECha EPri GEdr GKev LEdu MAvo MBel NSti SPeP WCot WFar
- 'Heitmann'	WFar
- 'Hitscherberger Riesenperle'	WFar XLum
- 'Hofheim' (v)	CAvo CBct ELon GEdr GKev LEdu MAvo WCot WFar WHal
- 'Landgraaf' (v)	MAvo WFar
- 'Lineata' (v)	WFar
- 'Marcel' (v)	WFar
- 'Mary Brooks'	WFar
§ - 'Polska Piękność' (v)	WFar
- 'Prolificans'	CBct CBod CDor EBee ECtt EPPr EPfP EWTr GEdr GKev ILea LCro LOPS MAvo MRav NBir NLar NSti WCot WFar WPnP
- var. ***rosea***	Widely available
- 'Rosea Plena' (d)	EGrI SPeP
- 'Silberconfolis' (v)	EPri WCot WFar
- 'Variegata' (v)	CPla EMor WFar WThu
- 'Vic Pawlowski's Gold' (v)	CBct CBro CDor CExl CMac EPPr GEdr LEdu MAvo WFar WPGP WSHC
- 'Vierländer Glockenspiel'	WFar
- 'Viktor'	WFar
* - 'Viridistriatus'	WFar
transcaucasica	GKev MAvo

Convolvulus (*Convolvulaceae*)

althaeoides	CFis ELan SBut
§ - subsp. ***tenuissimus***	EWes WCot
§ ***boissieri***	WAbe
cantabrica	EHyd SBut SPhx WSHC
chilensis	CCCN
cneorum 🏆^{H4}	Widely available
- 'Snow Angel'	LRHS SWvt
elegantissimus	see *C. althaeoides* subsp. *tenuissimus*
holosericeus new	GKev
lineatus	EWes
mauritanicus	see *C. sabatius*
nitidus	see *C. boissieri*
§ ***sabatius*** 🏆^{H3}	CCCN CCht CKel CTri EBee EBou ECtt ELan EPfP EPot EShb EWoo LRHS MCot SEND SGBe SMrm SPer SPlb SPoG SVen SWvt WCFE XLum
- dark-flowered	CCCN LSou
- 'Moroccan Beauty'^{PBR}	ECtt
- white-flowered	CCCN
tricolor 'Blue Ensign' 🏆^{H3}	CSpe LCro LOPS

× *Cooperanthes* see *Zephyranthes*

Cooperia see *Zephyranthes*

Coprosma (*Rubiaceae*)

acerosa 'Hawera'	CTrC
- 'Red Rocks'	CTrC
baueri misapplied	see *C. repens*
'Beatson's Gold' (f/v)	CBcs CDTJ CExl CTrC ELan EShb LRHS SEND SWvt
'Black Cloud'	CTrC ELon SEND
brunnea (f)	WThu
- (m)	WThu
'Cappuccino'	EShb SEle
'Clearwater Gold'	SIvy
'Coppershine'	CExl
× ***cunninghamii*** × ***macrocarpa*** (m)	CCoa
× ***cunninghamii*** × ***macrocarpa*** (f)	CTrC
depressa	WThu
'Evening Glow'PBR (f/v)	CBod CCCN CCht CDTJ CEnd CRos CSBt EHyd LRHS MGos NRHS SEle SIvy SRms WNPC
'Fire Burst'PBR (f/v)	CAbb CBcs CBct CCCN EHyd SEle SRms WNPC
'Inferno'PBR	CAbb CBcs CCht CDoC CKel SEle SPad
'Karo Red'PBR (v)	SRms
× ***kirkii*** 'Variegata' (f/v)	CKel CTsd ELan EPfP EShb GBin LRHS
'Lemon and Lime'PBR (v)	CBod CKel CRos EHyd LRHS NRHS SCoo SEle SGBe SGbt SIvy SPoG SRms
macrocarpa	CTrC
petriei	GAbr GArf WThu
- 'White Pearls'	WThu
propinqua	GKev
'Rainbow Surprise'PBR (v)	CCCN CDoC CExl CSBt EHyd MGos SRms WFar WNPC
§ ***repens***	CExl EShb SPlb SVen
- 'County Park Plum' (v)	SVen
- 'Inferno' (v)	CEnd CMCN
- 'Marble Queen' (m/v) ♀H3	EShb
- 'Midnight Martini' (v)	CRos EHyd LRHS NRHS SCoo WNPC
- 'Pacific Dawn'	CCht CEnd CSBt SEle WNPC
- PACIFIC NIGHT ('Hutpac'PBR) (m)	CBod CDoC CKel CSBt EBee EHyd LRHS MGos SCoo SGBe SGbt SLon WNPC
- PACIFIC SUNSET ('Jwncopps') (m/v)	CDoC LCro LOPS LSRN SEle SGbt
- 'Painter's Palette' (m)	SVen
- 'Picturata' (m/v) ♀H3	EShb
- 'Pina Colada'PBR (v)	CAbb CCht CDoC CRos CSBt EHyd LRHS NRHS SCoo SEle SGBe SGbt SPoG
- 'Tequila Sunrise'	CAbb CBcs CBod CCht CDoC CRos CSBt EHyd LRHS LSRN NRHS SEdd SEle
robusta	CTrC
'Roy's Red' (m)	CBod EShb LSRN
rugosa (f)	CExl
'Scarlet O'Hara'	CCht SEle SPoG
'Walter Brockie'	CSde CTrC

Coptis (*Ranunculaceae*)

chinensis B&SWJ 12865	WCru
japonica	GPoy WCru
- var. ***dissecta***	GEdr WCru
- var. ***major***	GEdr WCru WSHC
laciniata B&SWJ 12863	WCru
omeiensis	WCru
quinquefolia	GEdr
- B&SWJ 1677	WCru
ramosa B&SWJ 6000	WCru
- B&SWJ 6030	WCru
trifolia	WCru

Corallospartium see *Carmichaelia*

Cordyline ✿ (*Asparagaceae*)

australis ♀H3	Widely available
- 'Albertii' (v) ♀H3	CCCN SArc
- 'Atlantic Green'	CBrac EHyd SavN XSte
- 'Atropurpurea'	CBrac CCCN
- 'Black Night'	CCCN LRHS XSte
- CHARLIE BOY ('Ric01'PBR) (v)	CTsd ELon SPad XSte
- 'Claret'	CBcs
- 'Karo Kiri'	CCCN CCht
- 'Olive Fountain'	CCCN
- 'Peko'PBR	CCCN CDoC
- 'Purple Heart'	CCCN MSwo
- Purpurea Group	CBcs CDTJ CDoC ELan MGos SCob SEND SPlb SWeb WFar
- 'Red Comet'	XSte
- 'Red Sensation'	CCCN SWvt
- 'Salsa'	EHyd NRHS
- 'Sparkler' (v)	CCCN EHyd EPfP SEND
- 'Torbay Dazzler' (v) ♀H3	Widely available
- 'Torbay Sunset'	CCCN
- 'Variegata' (v)	CDoC LPar XSte
'Autumn'	CCCN
banksii	CCCN CCht
- ELECTRIC FLASH ('Sprilecflash'PBR) <u>**new**</u>	XSte
'Can Can'PBR (v)	SCob
'Cardinal'PBR	CBcs
'Cha Cha'PBR (v)	CCCN CEnd EBee SEND WAvo WCot
'Cherry Sensation' (v)	EHyd EPfP LRHS NRHS WFar XSte
'Coffee Cream'	CCCN
§ ***congesta***	SPlb
'Dark Star'	CCCN CDTJ
ELECTRIC PINK ('Sprilecpink')	ELan
'Eurostar' (v)	CCCN
'Firecracker'	CCCN
§ ***fruticosa*** 'Kiwi'	EHyd
§ ***indivisa***	CCCN CDTJ CPbh CTsd SArc SWeb
'Jive'PBR (v)	CBod EBee LCro LOPS SEND
kaspar	CCCN
mauritiana	WCot
obtecta	CCCN
'Pink Champagne' (v)	CCCN EHyd MSwo XSte
PINK PASSION ('Seipin'PBR)	CCCN CPla CRos ELan EPfP LBuc LRHS SCoo SGBe SGsty SPalm SPoG
'Pink Stripe' (v)	CCCN LSRN SWvt
'Purple Sensation'	CCCN
'Purple Tower' ♀H3	LRHS
'Red Heart'	CCCN
'Red Star'	CAbb CBcs CBod CCCN CChe CDoC CEme CEnd CRos CSBt EHyd EPfP LCro LOPS LRHS MSwo NPer NRHS SCob SCoo SEND SGbt SPoG SWeb SWvt WFar
'Salsa'PBR	XSte
'Southern Splendour' (v)	CBcs CCCN CDoC CEme CPla EHyd ELan EPfP LRHS MBros NRHS SCoo SGBe SPoG
'Sundance' ♀H3	CBcs EPfP MGos MSwo NPer SPoG SRms SWvt WFar
'Sunrise' (v)	CPla EHyd LRHS XSte
terminalis	see *C. fruticosa*

'Torbay Red' ♀H3	CBrac CCCN CEme CMac CPla EHyd EPfP LRHS LSRN MAsh MPri SCob SGBe SPalm SPeP SPer SPoG SWvt

Coreopsis (Asteraceae)

'Astolat'	CBod LRHS MRav SGbt SMrm
auriculata CUTTING GOLD	see *C.* 'Schnittgold'
- 'Elfin Gold'	EBou EHyd ELan EPfP XLum
- 'Nana'	MNrw
- 'Zamphir'	CDor EPfP WCot
'Baby Gold'	see *C. lanceolata* 'Sonnenkind' (unblotched)
'Calypso' (v)	SPoG
'Center Stage'	ELan LSou MACG
'Citrine'PBR (Hardy Jewel Series)	CWGN
'Cosmic Evolution' (Big Bang Series)	EBee EHyd ELan LRHS SPoG
'Cosmic Eye' (Big Bang Series)	EBee EHyd ELan LRHS NRHS SPoG WFar
'Cranberry Ice'	LRHS NRHS
'Daybreak' (Li'l Bang Series)	EHyd LRHS NRHS
'Enchanted Eve'PBR (Li'l Bang Series)	EHyd EPfP LRHS NRHS WFar
'Fool's Gold'	EBee
'Fruit Punch'PBR (Punch Series)	EHyd
'Full Moon'PBR (Big Bang Series)	EBee EHyd ELan LRHS NLar NRHS SPoG WFar XLum
'Galaxy' (Big Bang Series)	EBee EHyd ELan LRHS NRHS WFar
'Garnet'PBR (Hardy Jewel Series)	LRHS
gigantea	SPlb
grandiflora	GQue LRHS SBls
- 'Badengold'	CPla
- 'Bernwode' (v)	CMac SWvt
- COREY SINGLE GOLD ('Csgz0002'PBR) **new**	NBir
- 'Domino'	EBee EHyd
- 'Double the Sun' **new**	MHol
- 'Early Sunrise' ♀H5	CBod CRos CSBt EAJP EBee EHyd EPfP LCro LOPS LRHS MBow MNHC NBir NGBl NPer NRHS SCoo SGbt SPoG SWvt WFar XLum
- FLYING SAUCERS ('Walcoreop'PBR)	CRos EHyd EPfP LRHS NRHS SCoo SPoG
- 'Heliot'	MPie
- 'Illico'	EShb
- 'Mayfield Giant'	CBod EBee ELan EPfP EShb LPot LRHS MAsh SGbt SRms SWvt
- 'Presto' (d)	ELan MBros NGBl WFar WHil
- 'Rising Sun'	EHyd ELan EPfP
- Solena Series	LRHS
- 'Sunburst'	ELan EPfP XLum
- 'Sunfire'	CRos EHyd LRHS MBros NRHS SBls SCob WFar
- SUNKISS ('M8867p'PBR)	CBod LRHS MSCN
- 'Sunray'	CBcs CBod CChe CRos CSBt ECtt EHyd EPfP GDam LRHS NGdn NRHS SGbt SHar SPlb SPoG SRms SWvt XLum
'Highland Blast'	CRos LRHS
'Imperial Sun'PBR	ECtt ELan LSou
lanceolata 'Goldfink'	MRav SRms
- 'Goldteppich'	CRos EHyd EPfP LRHS NRHS
§ - 'Sonnenkind' (unblotched)	EPfP GMaP XLum
- 'Walter'	CBod EBee LRHS LSou SPoG WFar XLum XSen
'Limbo' (Coloropsis Series)	EAJP
'Limerock Passion'PBR	EHyd LRHS NRHS SCob SRkn
'Limerock Ruby'PBR	EHyd EWoo GMaP LRHS MHol NRHS SCob SPoG SRkn SWvt WFar XLum
major	EBee WFar
MANGO PUNCH ('Rp5') (Punch Series)	EBee MCot SGBe WCav
maximiliani	see *Helianthus maximiliani*
'Mercury Rising'PBR (Big Bang Series)	EBee EHyd EPfP LEdu LRHS LSou NRHS SHar
'Moonlight'PBR	LRHS
palmata	SPhx
'Pink Lady'PBR	SGBe WCav
pubescens 'Sunshine Superman'	EHyd ELan
'Red Elf'PBR (Li'l Bang Series)	EHyd LRHS NRHS
'Red Satin' (Permathread Series)	LRHS WTor
'Redshift'	EBee EHyd EMor ILea LRHS NRHS SCoo SPoG
rosea	NGBl
- 'American Dream'	CBod CFis CRos EHyd ELan EPfP GMaP LRHS MACG MAsh MHol NBir NBro NGdn NLar NRHS SBut SGbt SMrm SPer SPlb SRms SWvt WCav WFar WGwG
- 'Heaven's Gate'PBR	CSBt EGrl EHyd MHol WFar
- 'Nana'	XLum
'Route 66'PBR	WCAu WFar
'Ruby Frost' (Hardy Jewel Series)	CBcs EBee LRHS SEdd SGBe SMad SPoG
§ 'Schnittgold'	EHyd LRHS NRHS SHar
'Show Stopper'PBR	ELan LSou
'Sienna Sunset'	EHyd ELan LRHS NRHS
'Snowberry'	ELan LRHS MBNS NRHS
SOLANNA GOLDEN SPHERE	EPfP SPoG
'Solar Dance'	CWGN EWTr NLar SMad
I 'Sonnenkind' (red-blotched)	EHyd LRHS NRHS
'Star Cluster' (Big Bang Series)	CWGN EHyd ELan EMor EPfP LRHS LSou NRHS SMad SPoG WFar
'Starbright' (Li'l Bang Series) **new**	LRHS
'Starlight' (Li'l Bang Series)	EHyd LRHS NRHS WFar
'Starstruck' (Li'l Bang Series) **new**	LRHS
'Sterntaler'	CFoA EBee EBlo EHyd ELon EPfP EWoo GBee GWyn LPot LRHS LSou NCou NRHS SGBe SWvt XLum
'Sun Splash' (Big Bang Series) **new**	LRHS
SUNNY DAY ('Balcorsunay')	WFar
'Sweet Marmalade'PBR	EPfP LRHS NLar
tinctoria	MNHC SRms XAbr
- 'Amulet' **new**	CSpe
tripteris	ELan EPPr EPfP MHol SPhx XLum
- 'Mostenveld'	EBee
- 'Red November'	MNrw
(UpTick Series) UPTICK CREAM & RED ('Balupteamed'PBR)	LRHS LSou MACG
- UPTICK CREAM ('Balupteam'PBR)	CBod MSCN
- UPTICK GOLD AND BRONZE ('Baluptgonz'PBR)	LRHS LSou
- UPTICK YELLOW AND RED ('Baluptowed'PBR) ♀H3	CBod
verticillata	CMac CTri ECha EGrl MBel MBrN MHer NLar NPer SCob SRms WCAu
- 'Bengal Tiger'PBR	CMea ELan LSou MACG
- 'Crazy Cayenne' (Sizzle and Spice Series) **new**	LRHS
- CRÈME BRÛLÉE ('Crembru'PBR)	EHyd NLar SCoo SWvt

- 'Curry Up' (Sizzle and Spice Series) **new** — LRHS
I - 'Golden Gain' — ECtt EPfP MAsh NGdn WFar
- 'Golden Shower' — see *C. verticillata* 'Grandiflora'
§ - 'Grandiflora' ♀H5 — CBcs EHyd ELan ELon EMor EPfP GMaP LRHS MArl MRav NGdn NHol NRHS NWad SHar SPer WFar XLum
- 'Hot Paprika' (Sizzle and Spice Series) **new** — LRHS SEdd
- 'Limerock Dream' PBR — EBee EHyd LRHS NRHS
- 'Moonbeam' — Widely available
- 'Ruby Red' — CRos EHyd LRHS NRHS
- 'Sunbeam' — ELon
- 'Tweety' PBR — WFar
- 'Zagreb' ♀H5 — Widely available

coriander see *Coriandrum sativum*; also AGM Vegetables Section

Coriandrum (*Apiaceae*)

sativum — CArg CLau ENfk EWhm GPoy LCro LOPS LRHS MBros MHer MNHC MPri SPoG SRms XAbr
- 'Calypso' PBR ♀H2 — EKin MCtn
- 'Confetti' ♀H2 — EKin LCro LOPS MCtn
- 'Cruiser' PBR ♀H2 **new** — EDel
- 'Leisure' — LCro LOPS SVic
- 'Slobolt' — SPhx

Coriaria ✿ (*Coriariaceae*)

arborea — ESwi
intermedia B&SWJ 019 — WCru
japonica — CTsd ESwi MMrt NLar SVen WCru
- B&SWJ 2833 — WCru
- subsp. ***intermedia*** B&SWJ 3877 — WCru
kingiana — WCru
§ ***microphylla*** — WCru
- B&SWJ 8999 — WCru
- B&SWJ 14702 — WCru
myrtifolia — WCru
- B&SWJ 14003 — WCru
nepalensis — NLar
pteridoides — WCru
ruscifolia — WCru
- HCM 98178 — WCru
terminalis f. ***fructu-rubro*** — WCru
- var. ***xanthocarpa*** — WCru
- - GWJ 9204 — WCru
- - HWJK 2112c — WCru
thymifolia — see *C. microphylla*

Cornus ✿ (*Cornaceae*)

NJM 12.048 — WPGP
alba L. — CArg CCVT CLnd GArf MNic MRav NWea SEWo SRms WMou WTSh
- 'Alleman's Compact' — LRHS
- 'Aurea' ♀H7 — Widely available
- BATON ROUGE ('Minbat' PBR) — CBod CDoC CRos EBee EHyd ELan ELon EPfP LRHS LSRN MAsh MRav NRHS SGsty SPoG SWvt WFar
- 'Cream Cracker' PBR (v) — MRav
- 'Elegantissima' (v) ♀H7 — Widely available
- 'Gouchaultii' (v) — CEnd CMac EPfP GKin LPar LRHS MGos MRav NLar NRHS SCob SCoo SGol SGsty SPer SRms SWeb WFar
- 'Hessei' misapplied — see *C. sanguinea* 'Compressa'
- IVORY HALO ('Bailhalo' PBR) — CKel EMil EPfP LRHS LSRN MAsh MRav NLar NWea SPer
- 'Kesselringii' — Widely available
- RED GNOME ('Regnzam') — ELon EPfP MAsh
- 'Siberian Pearls' — CBcs CRos EHyd ELan GKin LRHS MBlu NLar NRHS SPoG
§ - 'Sibirica' ♀H7 — Widely available
- 'Sibirica Ruby' — SavN
- 'Sibirica Variegata' (v) ♀H7 — CEme CKel CMac CRos EBee EHyd ELon EPfP GKin LRHS LSRN MAsh MBlu MGos NRHS SCob SPer SWvt
- 'Spaethii' (v) ♀H7 — Widely available
§ - 'Variegata' (v) — WFar
- 'Westonbirt' — see *C. alba* 'Sibirica'
alternifolia — CCVT GArf LMaj SSta WMou
§ - 'Argentea' (v) ♀H6 — Widely available
- 'Brunette' — CJun MBlu
- GOLDEN SHADOWS ('Wstackman' PBR) (v) — CWGN LRHS SGsty
- 'Golden Surprise' — CJun
- 'Goldfinch' (v) — CJun MBlu
- 'Illusion' (v) — CJun
- 'Moonlight' (v) — CJun
- PINKY SPOT ('Minpinky') — LSRN NLar XSte
- 'Silver Giant' (v) — CJun NLar WSpi
- 'Variegata' — see *C. alternifolia* 'Argentea'
amomum — EBtc NLar
- 'Blue Cloud' — CBcs CBod CRos EHed LRHS MBlu MMuc
- 'Lady Jane' — NLar
'Ascona' — CBcs CEnd CJun CLnd EWTr NLar SGol SSta WGob
canadensis — Widely available
candidissima Marshall — see *C. foemina* Mill.
capitata — CBcs CBod CEme CJun CLnd CMac CPla CRos CTsd EBee EGrI EHed EHyd EPfP ESwi EWTr GKev IArd IDee MGil MGos NRHS SAko SEND SPoG WCru WFar WKor WPGP
- subsp. ***emeiensis*** — CJun
- 'Foreness Fog' (v) — SEND
- 'Kilmacurragh Rose' — IArd IDee
aff. ***capitata*** NJM 13.046 — WPGP
'Celestial Shadow' — see *C. × rutgersensis* 'Michael Steinhardt'
chinensis — SSta SWvt
controversa — CAco CBcs CCVT CMCN ELan EPfP EWTr IPap LCro LMaj LOPS MBlu MGil NLar NWea SEND SEWo SGol SSta SWvt WMou
I - 'Aurea' — MAsh
- 'Candlelight' — MBlu NLar SSta
§ - 'Frans Type' (v) — CJun
- 'Gosia' PBR (v) — CBcs
- 'Green Carpet' — LMaj NLar SSta
- 'Laska' — CJun LMaj MBlu NLar
- 'Lucia' — CJun LMaj NLar
I - 'Marginata Nord' — NLar
- 'Pagoda' — CJun LPar MBlu NLar
- 'Troya Dwarf' — CJun
- 'Variegata' (v) ♀H5 — Widely available
- 'Variegata' Frans type — see *C. controversa* 'Frans Type'
'Dorothy' — CJun
'Eddie's White Wonder' ♀H5 — Widely available
elliptica — WPGP
- EMPRESS OF CHINA ('Elsbry') **new** — EHed
- 'First Choice' — CJun
- 'Full Moon' — CJun
× ***elwinortonii*** SCARLET FIRE ('Rutpink') **new** — LRHS SMad
- VENUS ('Kn30 8' PBR) (Jersey Star Series) — CWGN EPfP LCro LOPS LPar LRHS MAsh MBlu SEWo SGsty SLon SMad SSta WPGP

excelsa F&M 57	WPGP
florida	CBcs CMCN EGrI ESwi IPap LCro LMaj MMuc MTrO NOra NOrn NWea SCob SGsty SPer SSta WMat WMou WTSh
- 'Appalachian Spring'	CJun
- 'Autumn Gold'	SSta
- CHEROKEE BRAVE ('Comco No 1')	CBcs EHyd LMil LRHS MAsh NRHS SPoG SSta WGob
- 'Cherokee Chief'	CBcs CEnd CJun CLnd CTri EGrI EHyd EWTr LMaj LPar LRHS LSRN NLar NRHS SGol SPer WHwl WSpi XSte
- 'Cherokee Daybreak'	see *C. florida* 'Daybreak'
- 'Cherokee Princess'	CJun EHyd EWTr LRHS MAsh MTrO NOra NOrn SGol SSta WMat
- 'Cherokee Sunset'	see *C. florida* 'Sunset'
- 'Clear Moon'	LPar
- 'Cloud Nine'	CBcs CEme EGrI EHed EWTr GKin LPar MTrO NLar NOrn SGsty WGob
- 'Comanche Chief'	LRHS
§ - 'Daybreak' (v) ♀H5	CBcs CEme EHyd LMaj LRHS LSRN MAsh MMrt MTrO NOra NOrn NRHS SGol SPer SPoG WMat
- 'First Lady' (v)	CWit WGob
- 'Fragrant Cloud'	SWvt
- 'Granary Gold'	SSta
- 'Junior Miss'	CEnd
- 'Pink Flame' (v)	SSta
- f. ***pluribracteata*** (d)	WHwl
- 'Rainbow' (v) ♀H5	CBcs EHed EHyd LPar LRHS MAsh MTrO NOra NOrn NRHS NWea SGol SPer SPoG WMat
- f. ***rubra***	CBcs CWit EGrI ELan GKin LCro LMaj LOPS LPar MGil MRav NOrn SGsty SPer SPoG WGob WHwl WMat
- - 'Red Giant'	CBcs EWTr
- - 'Spring Song'	CMac EGrI WGob
- 'Spring Day'	CMac WGob WHwl
- 'Stoke's Pink'	CEnd WGob
§ - 'Sunset' (v)	CEme CEnd EHyd ELan LCro LMaj LOPS LPar LRHS MAsh MMrt MTrO NLar NOrn NRHS SSta SWvt WGob WMat
- 'Sweetwater'	CJun SAko WGob
- subsp. ***urbiniana***	ELan LRHS WPGP
- 'Variegata' (v)	GKin
- 'White Cloud'	CJun LPar NOra WMat
§ ***foemina*** Mill.	SBrt
'Gloria Birkett'	CJun EHyd LMil LRHS MAsh WGob
hessei misapplied	see *C. sanguinea* 'Compressa'
hongkongensis	LMaj LRHS NLar WPGP XSte
- HWJ 1033	EPfP WPGP
- subsp. ***gigantea*** KWJ 12225	WCru
- subsp. ***melanotricha***	EBee
- subsp. ***tonkinensis*** B&SWJ 11791	WCru
'Jerry Mundy'	CMac
'Kelsey Dwarf'	see *C. sericea* 'Kelseyi'
'Kenwyn Clapp'	CJun
kousa	CBcs CCVT CDoC CMCN CMac EGrI ELan EPfP GArf GKev GKin LMaj LPar NLar SCob SGol SGsty SPer SPlb WKor WLov
- B&SWJ 12610 from Korea	WCru
- B&SWJ 14620 from Japan	WCru
- 'Akabana'	CJun
- 'Akatsuki' (v)	CJun NLar SSta
- 'All Summer'	CJun
- 'Autumn Rose'	CJun NLar SMad
- 'Beni-fuji'	CLnd EHed EHyd EWTr LRHS MBlu MPkF NLar NRHS
- 'Big Apple'	CJun CRos EHyd EPfP LMil LRHS MAsh NLar WGob
- 'Blue Shadow'	CBcs CJun EHed EPfP EWTr MBlu NLar SSta
- 'Bonfire' (v)	NLar
- 'Bultinck's Beauty'	EHed MPkF NLar
- 'Bultinck's Giant'	CLnd EWTr LRHS MBlu MPkF NLar WGob
- 'Cappuccino'	CDoC CJun EHed EWTr LPar LRHS MPkF NLar NRHS SMad WTSh
- 'Cherokee'	CJun NLar
- 'China Dawn' (v)	CJun SSta
- var. ***chinensis***	Widely available
- - 'Barmstedt'	SAko
- - 'Bodnant Form'	CEnd CJun EGrI EPfP LRHS NLar SSta WBor WGob WHwl
- - 'China Girl' ♀H5	Widely available
- - 'Claudia'	EPfP IArd LMaj SSta
- - 'Great Star'	EHed EPfP LSRN MAsh SGsty
- - 'Greta's Gold' (v)	CJun SSta
- - 'Ikone'	SAko
- - 'PVG'	CJun
- - 'Snowflake'	CJun
- - 'Spinners'	CJun
- - 'Summer Stars'	CJun
- - 'Tri-Splendor'	NLar
- - 'White Dusted' (v)	CJun MBlu NLar SMad
- - 'White Fountain'	EPfP LSRN MGos MPkF MPnt NLar NOra NOrn WMat
- - 'Wieting's Select'	CJun EHed EWTr MBlu MPkF NLar SAko
- - 'Wisley Queen' ♀H5	CJun CRos EHyd EPfP LMil LRHS MAsh SChF SPoG SSta WPGP
- - 'Xanthocarpa'	CBcs
- 'Claudine'	CJun
- 'Copacabana'	EHed LRHS MBlu MPkF
- 'Daybreak'	SGol
- 'Doctor Bump'	NLar
- 'Doubloon'	CJun
- 'Dwarf Pink'	CJun NLar
- 'Ed Mezitt'	CJun LRHS NLar
- 'Elizabeth Lustgarten'	CJun MBlu SSta
- 'Eurostar'	ELan MBlu
- 'Fanfare'	CJun
- 'Fernie's Favourite'	CJun
- GALILEAN ('Galzam')	EHed MThu WGob
- 'Gay Head'	CJun
- giant-flowered	MPkF
I - 'Girard's Nana'	CJun MPkF
- 'Gold Cup' (v)	CJun SSta
- 'Gold Star' (v)	CBcs CEnd CJun CMCN ELan EPfP LMil MAsh MBlu NLar SChF SPoG SSta WGob WHwl
- 'Greensleeves'	CJun EHyd EPfP GKev LMil LRHS MAsh SSta WGob
- 'Heart of Trobe' **new**	NLar
- HEART THROB ('Schmred')	CJun NLar SCoo SGol WGob
- 'Highland'	CJun NLar
- 'John Slocock' ♀H5	CJun IArd NLar WGob
- 'Koree'	NLar
- 'Kreutzdame'	CJun MBlu
- 'Laura'	CWGN ELon MBlu NLar SMad
- 'Little Beauty'	CJun
- 'Lizzie P'	NLar
- 'Lustgarten Weeping'	CJun
- 'Madame Butterfly'	CJun CRos LRHS MBlu NLar SPoG
- 'Marwood Dawn'	WPGP
- 'Marwood Twilight'	SChF

- 'Milky Way'	CBod CDoC CJun CLnd CMCN EPfP IPap LPar LRHS LSRN MAsh MBlu MGos MPkF MRav MTrO NLar SGol SGsty WGob WHwl WMat WSpi
- 'Milky Way Select'	CBcs CJun EHyd LRHS NRHS
- 'Miss Petty'	CJun NLar
- 'Miss Satomi' ♀H5	Widely available
- 'Moonbeam'	CDoC CJun EHed EWTr NLar SMad
- 'Mount Fuji'	CJun MBlu NLar SSta
- 'National'	CDoC CJun EGrl EHed ILea LMil LRHS MAsh NLar SSta WGob
- 'Nicole'	EHed MPkF WGob
- 'Ohkan'	CJun MPkF
- 'Pévé Foggy'	MThu
- 'Pévé Limbo' (v)	CJun
- 'Pévé Satomi Compact'	CJun NLar
- 'Pink Lips'	NLar
- 'Polywood'	CJun NLar
- RADIANT ROSE ('Hanros')	EPfP NLar SSta WGob WPGP
- 'Rasen'	CJun NLar
- 'Rel Whirlwind'	CJun NLar
* - 'Robert'	NLar
- 'Rosea'	CJun
- 'Rosemoor Pink'	CJun
- 'Rosy Teacups'PBR **new**	MTrO WMat
- SAMARITAN ('Samzam') (v)	CBcs CDoC CEnd EWTr LPar LSRN SSta
- 'Schmetterling'	CJun EPfP EWTr LPar MBlu MPkF NLar WHwl
- 'Sluis Slim'	EHed MBlu
- 'Snowbird'	CJun LRHS
- 'Snowboy' (v)	CEnd CLnd MBlu
- 'Snowflurries'	CJun
- 'Southern Cross'	CJun WGob
- 'Square Dance'	CJun NLar
- 'Steeple'	CJun
- 'Summer Fun' ♀H5	CJun CRos EHyd EWTr LMil LRHS SPoG SSta
- 'Summer Majesty'	CJun
- 'Sunsplash' (v)	CJun LRHS SPoG SSta
- 'Temple Jewel' (v)	CJun
- 'Teresa' (v)	NLar
- 'Teutonia' ♀H5	CJun EHed ELan EWTr IArd MGos MTrO NLar SAko SSta WGob WHwl WMat
- 'Trinity Star'	CJun
- 'Triple Crown'	CJun
- 'Tsukubanomine'	CJun CLnd
- 'Weaver's Weeping'	CJun EHed MPkF
- 'Weisse Fontäne'	CJun EHed MBlu MPkF NLar
- 'White Dream'	CJun EHed MPkF NLar
- 'White Giant'	CJun
- 'Wolf Eyes' (v) ♀H5	CJun EHed ELan EPfP LMil LRHS MAsh MBlu NLar SPoG SSta
macrophylla Wall.	EGrl IDee SPtp WCru WPGP
- MSF 821	WPGP
- var. ***macrophylla***	SSta
mas	Widely available
- 'Aurea' (v) ♀H6	CBcs CJun EPfP LMil LPar LRHS MAsh MBlu MRav NLar SSta WCot WLov
§ - 'Aureoelegantissima' (v)	CMac EHyd NLar WCot WLov
- 'Elegant' (F)	CAgr
- 'Elegantissima'	see *C. mas* 'Aureoelegantissima'
- 'Elena'	NLar
- 'Golden Glory' ♀H6	CJun CLnd EPfP LRHS NLar
- 'Gourmet' (F)	CAgr
- 'Happy Face'	NLar
- 'Hillier's Upright'	CJun
- 'Jolico' (F) ♀H6	CAgr CJun LEdu MBlu MTrO NLar WMat
- 'Kasanlaker' (F)	CAgr NLar
- 'Nikolka' (F)	NLar
- 'Pancharevo' (F)	CAgr
- 'Pioneer' (F)	CJun
- 'Redstone' (F)	CJun
- 'Shan' (F)	CAgr
- 'Shumen' (F)	CAgr NLar
- 'Spring Glow'	CJun NLar
- 'Variegata' (v) ♀H6	CAco CBcs CJun CMCN EHyd EPfP MAsh MBlu MGos NLar
- 'Vraća Kaštel' (F)	CAgr
- 'Xanthocarpa' (F)	CAgr CJun
mas × officinalis	CJun
'Norman Hadden' ♀H5	Widely available
nuttallii	CLnd ELan EPfP EWTr LPar SPer SWeb SWvt
- 'Colrigo Giant'	CJun
- 'Gold Spot' (v)	CJun
- 'Monarch'	CJun EHed EWTr LPar SPer
- 'North Star'	CJun NLar
- 'Osmunda'	CEnd
- 'Portlemouth'	CEnd CJun
- 'Zurico'	CJun
oblonga	CExl EBee WPGP
officinalis	CAgr CJun CMCN CMac EBee EHed EPfP LRHS MBlu NLar NOra SWvt WSpi
- 'Kintoki' ♀H6	NLar WLov
- 'Robin's Pride' **new**	LMaj
'Ormonde' ♀H5	CJun EGrl EPfP NLar SSta WGob WPGP
'Pink Blush'	CJun
'Porlock' ♀H5	CJun CMCN EHyd EPfP LRHS NLar NRHS SWvt WGob
pumila	NLar
racemosa	EBtc NLar
rugosa	EBtc
× ***rutgersensis***	LRHS
§ - 'Michael Steinhardt' (v)	MPkF SGol
- (Stellar Series) AURORA ('Rutban')	CJun MBlu MPkF SGol
§ - - CELESTIAL ('Rutdan')	CJun EHed EHyd LMil LRHS NRHS SGol WGob
- - CONSTELLATION ('Rutcan')	CJun LMil SGol
- - GALAXY	see *C.* × *rutgersensis* (Stellar Series) CELESTIAL
- - RUTH ELLEN ('Rutlan')	CJun EHed EWTr LMaj LRHS
- - STARDUST ('Rutfan')	SGol
- - STELLAR PINK ('Rutgan')	CBcs CJun CLnd EHed EHyd EWTr LRHS MGos MPkF NLar NRHS SAko SChF SCob SGol WGob WPGP
sanguinea	CBcs CCVT CHab CLnd CMac CTri EPfP LBuc MNic MRav MSwo NWea SCob SEWo SGol SPer SVic WMat WMou WTSh
§ - 'Anny'	CJun MBlu
- 'Anny's Winter Orange' ♀H6	CJun CMac CRos EHyd ELan ELon EPfP EShb LPar LRHS LSRN LSvl MAsh NRHS SGol SPoG WAvo WBrk WCot
§ - 'Compressa'	GKev MBlu MGil MRav NLar
- 'Magic Flame' ♀H6	CBod CDoC CJun CRos EHyd ELon EPfP LRHS MAsh MPri NLar NRHS SPoG SWvt WCot
- 'Midwinter Fire'	Widely available
- 'Winter Beauty'	CJun CSBt EBee EPfP MBlu NLar NWea SCob SLon SWvt WAvo
- WINTER FLAME	see *C. sanguinea* 'Anny'
sericea 'Bud's Yellow'	CRos EHyd ELon EPfP LRHS MBlu NLar NRHS

- 'Cardinal'	CRos EBee EHyd ELon EPfP LRHS MAsh MGos NLar NRHS
- 'Flaviramea' ♀H7	Widely available
- 'Hedgerows Gold' (v) ♀H7	CKel CRos EBee EHyd ELan ELon EMil EPfP LRHS MAsh MGos NEoE NRHS SCoo SPoG WFar WLov
§ - 'Kelseyi'	CMac EBee ELan EPfP ILea MRav NLar SBrt SCob SPoG
- KELSEY'S GOLD ('Rosco')	CRos LMil LRHS MAsh NRHS SPoG WLov
- subsp. ***occidentalis*** 'Sunshine'	EPfP NEoE NLar
§ - 'White Gold' (v)	CBod CKel EBee ELon EPfP LSRN MRav NLar SPer SPoG SRms WFar
- 'White Spot'	see *C. sericea* 'White Gold'
stricta	see *C. foemina* Mill.
suecica	NHar
× ***unalaschkensis***	GKev NHar
walteri	EBtc
wilsoniana	MBlu WPGP
'Winter Orange'	CDoC CJun NLar

Corokia ✿ (*Argophyllaceae*)

buddlejoides	CBcs CBod CCoa CSde CTrC CTsd CWit GBin NLar SEND WFar
cotoneaster	Widely available
'Geenty's Ghost'	CTrC
* ***parviflora***	CTrC
× ***virgata***	CChe CEnd CTrC CTri ELan EPfP NLar SArc SEdd SPlb SWvt WKif WSHC
- 'Banana Royal'	CBct CDoC LRHS
- 'Bronze King'	CBrac CTrC SPer SPlb SVen
- 'Coppershine'	CCoa
- 'Frosted Chocolate'	CBod CCoa CDoC CKel CSde CTrC CTsd ELan EPfP LRHS SEND SIvy SPoG SSta SVen SWvt WFar WGrn WLov
- 'Geenty's Green'	CCoa CRos CTrC
- 'Limey'	CBod LRHS
- 'Mangatangi'	CTrC
- 'Pink Delight'	CBod EPfP MRav SEdd
- 'Red Wonder'	CBod CEnd CKel CMac CTrC EHyd ELan EPfP LRHS SEND SPoG SVen WAvo WGrn WLov
- 'Sunsplash' (v)	CBod CBrac CCoa CDoC CEme CKel CMac CTrC CTsd ELan EPfP LRHS NLar SEND SEle SPoG SSta SWvt WFar WGrn
- 'Welsh Whiskey'	CBod CDoC LRHS SEle
- 'Yellow Wonder'	CBcs CKel CTrC ELan LRHS NLar SPlb SWvt

Coronilla (*Fabaceae*)

cappadocica	see *C. orientalis*
comosa	see *Hippocrepis comosa*
coronata	EHyd
emerus	see *Hippocrepis emerus*
glauca	see *C. valentina* subsp. *glauca*
minima	WAbe
§ ***orientalis***	EPPr
valentina	CRHN MGil
- 'Cotswold Cream' (v)	CSpe MPie SEdd SPoG WCot WMal
§ - subsp. ***glauca*** ♀H4	CDoC CKel CMac CSBt CSde CTri EBee ELan EPfP LEdu LRHS LSRN MNHC SEND SIvy SPer SRms SVen SWvt XLum XSen
- - 'Brockhill Blue'	CKel EPfP LRHS SAko WCot
- - 'Citrina' ♀H4	Widely available
- - 'Lauren Stevenson'	MHol WCot
* - - 'Pygmaea'	LRHS SEle SRms WAbe WCot WHwl
- - 'Variegata' (v)	CBcs CDoC CMac CRos CTri EBee EHed ELan EPfP IDee LRHS MAsh MGil MRav NQui SCoo SEle SLon SPer SPoG SRms SVen WCot
- - 'XXS'	WCot
varia	see *Securigera varia*

Correa ✿ (*Rutaceae*)

alba	CBod CCCN CExl CTrC EPfP
- 'Pinkie' ♀H3	CCCN CExl CSde CTrC CTsd WAbe
alba × ***backhouseana***	SEle
backhouseana ♀H3	CAbb CBcs CBod CCCN CExl CKel CSde CTri CTsd EBee EHed EHyd ELan EPfP IDee LRHS NLar SBrt SEle SRkn SVen WAbe WSHC
- 'Peaches and Cream'	CCCN SEle SRkn
decumbens	CTrC
'Dusky Bells' ♀H3	CAbb CBcs CBod CCCN CKel CSde CTrC CTri CTsd EBee EHed EHyd ELan EPfP LRHS MAsh MGil SEle SPlb SPoG SRkn SVen
'Dusky Maid'	CCCN CExl
'Federation Belle'	CCCN SVen
glabra	CTrC SEle
- var. ***glabra***	SPlb
'Harrisii'	see *C.* 'Mannii'
lawrenceana	CExl CTsd SEND SEle WPGP
- var. ***grampiana***	SVen
§ 'Mannii' ♀H3	CBcs CCCN CExl ELan EPfP MGil
'Marian's Marvel' ♀H3	CBcs CBod CCCN CExl CSde CTrC CTsd EBee ELan EPfP EWld IArd IDee MAsh SEND SEle SMad SRkn SVen WAbe
'Peachy Cream'	CAbb CCCN CSBt
'Poorinda Mary'	CCCN CKel CTrC LRHS MHtn SEle
pulchella ♀H3	CExl CMac CTri IDee SEle
- orange-flowered	WAbe
- 'Pink Mist'	CTrC WAbe WCot
reflexa ♀H3	CExl
- var. ***nummulariifolia***	CTsd MAsh MGil WAbe WCot WPGP
- var. ***reflexa***	CExl WCot
* - ***virens***	CExl
schlechtendalii	CCCN MGil SEle SVen

Cortaderia ✿ (*Poaceae*)

araucana	ELan
argentea	see *C. selloana*
fulvida misapplied	see *C. richardii* (Endl.) Zotov
§ ***fulvida*** (Buchanan) Zotov ♀H5	IArd IDee WCot
richardii misapplied	see *C. fulvida* (Buchanan) Zotov
richardii ambig.	CBod CChe CExl MMuc NBir NLar SGBe SPtp SWvt WSpi
§ ***richardii*** (Endl.) Zotov ♀H5	CBcs CDoC CKno EHyd ESwi EWes LRHS MAvo SArc SDix SRms WPGP
- Brown's strain	WCot
rudiuscula	EBee
§ ***selloana***	CBcs CBod CEme CTsd EBee MGos NBir NGrd SGsty SPlb
§ - 'Albolineata' (v)	CBcs ELon MWht SWvt
§ - 'Aureolineata' (v) ♀H6	CBcs CEme CKel CMac CSde EHyd ELan EPfP GMaP LRHS MWht NRHS SEND SPer SPoG SWvt
- 'Evita'PBR ♀H6	CChe ECtt ELan LPar NLar SPoG SWvt WCot
- 'Gold Band'	see *C. selloana* 'Aureolineata'
- 'Golden Goblin'PBR	CBod
- 'Icalma'	CSde EPPr
- 'Monstrosa' ♀H6	SEND SMad

- 'Patagonia' ♀H6 EPPr
- 'Pink Feather' EHyd ELan EPfP MSCN SCoo SEND SPer WFar
- 'Pink Phantom' EHyd
- 'Pointe du Raz' EBee ELan SWvt
- 'Pumila' ♀H6 Widely available
- 'Rendatleri' CBcs ELan SCoo SWvt
- 'Rosea' CBod EPfP LPar NLar SBls SCob WFar
- 'Senior' NLar
- 'Silver Comet' ECtt
- SILVER FEATHER ('Notcort') (v) ♀H6 SCob
- 'Silver Fountain' (v) EHyd ELan EPfP LRHS MAsh NRHS SPer SPoG
- 'Silver Stripe' see *C. selloana* 'Albolineata'
- 'Splendid Star'PBR (v) CRos EHyd LBuc LRHS MAsh MGos NRHS SCob SPoG SWvt
- 'Sunningdale Silver' ♀H6 CBcs CKel CMac ECha EHyd ELan ELon EPfP LSRN MGos SCob SCoo SEND SMad SPer SPoG SWvt

* - 'White Feather' CBod EHyd NLar SCoo SPer WFar

Toe Toe see *C. richardii* (Endl.) Zotov

Cortia (*Apiaceae*)

depressa GKev

Cortusa (*Primulaceae*)

altaica CBor
brotheri GKev
* ***caucasica*** GKev
* - 'Alba' EBee
§ ***matthioli*** CKel CPla EWld GGro GKev GPSL NHpl WFar XBar
- 'Alba' GKev
- var. ***congesta*** EBee GRum
- subsp. ***matthioli*** GKev
- subsp. ***pekinensis*** EBee GKev NBid WSHC WTyc
- - var. ***sachalinensis*** EBee GKev
turkestanica NWad

Corydalis ✿ (*Papaveraceae*)

'Ambigua' GKev
angustifolia WCot
anthriscifolia EWes EWld LEdu MMrt
'Blackberry Wine' CExl EBee ECtt LCro LOPS NSti SPoG
BLUE LINE ('Couriblue') CWGN GBin LRHS LSou NHar SCob SPoG XLum
'Blue Panda' see *C. flexuosa* 'Blue Panda'
brunneovaginata WCot
bulbosa misapplied see *C. cava*
bulbosa (L.) DC. see *C. solida*
buschii CWCL EBee GEdr GKev NRya
calycosa GBin IPot MAvo
'Canary Feathers'PBR CRos EHed EHyd LRHS NHpl NRHS
caseana CSpe
subsp. ***brandegeei*** new
cashmeriana EHyd GArf GKev LRHS NBid NRHS WAbe
- 'Kailash' EBee EHyd
cashmeriana × ***flexuosa*** WAbe
caucasica GKev
- var. ***alba*** misapplied see *C. malkensis*
§ ***cava*** EBee EMor GKev NHpl NRog WShi
- 'Albiflora' NRog
chaerophylla EWld
cheilanthifolia CElw CExl EGrI EWld GGro LEdu SRms
'Craigton Blue' CDor EPPr EWld GBin GEdr GKev GMaP GQue MNrw NHar NSti WAbe WFar WMal
'Craigton Purple' NHar
curviflora GKev WAbe
- subsp. ***rosthornii*** CExl
- - 'Blue Heron' CBct CBod CWCL CWGN ECtt EHyd EMor GEdr LRHS MBNS MPnt NHar NLar NRHS SPad SRkn WFar WSHC
davidii CExl
decipiens Schott, Nyman & Kotschy see *C. solida* subsp. *incisa*
decipiens misapplied EPot
densiflora GKev
'Dzukou Mousse' WPGP
elata CMea CSpe CTtf CWCL EHyd EWes GAbr GArf GWyn LRHS MArl MBel MBriF MCot MNrw NBid NBir NChi NRHS SPoG SPtp WCru WHal WSHC
- 'Blue Summit' EHyd EPPr MBel MPnt WFar
elata × ***flexuosa*** clone 1 CExl GEdr
erdelii NRog
flexuosa CSpe EPfP GKev GWyn MNrw WBor WSHC
- 'Balang Mist' CExl
- 'Blue Dragon' see *C. flexuosa* 'Purple Leaf'
§ - 'Blue Panda' ♀H5 CExl EPPr GKev GMaP MPnt NLar
- 'Blue Panther' LEdu
- 'Blue Summit' LEdu
- 'China Blue' Widely available
- 'Golden Panda' (v) NHpl
- 'Hale Cat' EPPr
- 'Nightshade' CExl EWld WCot
I - 'Norman's Seedling' EPPr
- 'Père David' CDor CMac CSBt CSpe EBee ECha EHyd ELan EMor EPPr EPfP GKev GWyn LEdu MHer NBir SPlb SPoG SRms SWvt WIce WPnP XLum
§ - 'Purple Leaf' ♀H5 Widely available
fumariifolia GKev
var. ***azurea*** new
glauca see *C. sempervirens*
glaucescens 'Early Beauty' NRog
'Heavenly Blue' GKev
henrikii GEdr
heterocarpa GGro
- var. ***japonica*** new EBee
integra GKev
'Kingfisher' CBor CDor CSma GKev NBir NLar NSla WAbe WSHC
'Korn's Purple' new ECha EPPr IPot NHar
ledebouriana CTtf NRog
leucanthema DJHC 752 CExl
- 'Silver Spectre' (v) CExl ECha
linstowiana GKev
- CD&R 605 CExl
§ ***lutea*** EPfP MMuc NBir NPer NWad SEND SRms WCot XLum
magadanica GKev
§ ***malkensis*** ♀H5 CBor EBee EMor EPot GKev NRya WThu
microflora new GKev
moorcroftiana CExl
mucronipetala GKev
nobilis GKev SPhx
ochotensis EHyd
§ ***ochroleuca*** CElw CSpe CWCL EPot XLum
omeiana ♀H5 EPPr NLar SPtp WCot WFar XLum
ophiocarpa ELan GGro
pachycentra CExl WAbe
paczoskii EHyd GKev NRHS NRog
petrophila new GGro

	'Porcelain Blue' new	GEdr LRHS NHar NLar
	pseudofumaria alba	see *C. ochroleuca*
	'Rainier Blue'	WFar
	'Rukšāns Red'	CWCL
	scandens	see *Dactylicapnos scandens*
	scouleri	NBir
§	***sempervirens***	GWyn
	shimienensis 'Berry Exciting'PBR	CBod CPla EMor MBNS MPnt NPer SPoG
	siamensis B&SWJ 7200	WCru
§	***solida***	CAvo CElw ECtt EHyd EMor EPot GKev LEdu LRHS MRav NLar NRHS NRog NRya SDeJ SPhx WBrk WCot WShi
	- 'Advocet'	GEdr
	- 'Bird of Paradise' new	GKev
	- 'Coscoroba'	CBor GKev NRog
	- 'Evening Shade'	GEdr
	- 'Fire Bird'	GEdr GKev
	- 'Firecracker'	CBor EHyd GKev LRHS NRHS SPhx
	- 'Gaviota'	GEdr
§	- subsp. ***incisa*** 🏆H5	EPot NRog SDeJ SPhx
	- - 'Giona'	GKev
	- 'Lucky Bird'	GKev
	- 'Paloma' new	NRog
	- 'Purple Beauty'	CBor CWCL GKev SPhx
	- 'Purple Bird'	CBor CWCL EPot ERCP GKev SDeJ WFar
	- 'Pussy'	CWCL EMor
	- RAINBOW (mixed)	GKev
	- 'Red Giant'	GKev
	- 'Robin'	GKev
	- 'Snowy Owl'	EPot GKev
§	- subsp. ***solida***	EPot GKev NBir NRya SPhx WCot
	- - 'Alba'	NSla
	- - 'Beth Evans'	CAvo CBcs CBro CWCL ECha EHed EMor EPot ERCP GEdr LEdu LRHS MNrw NBir NHpl NLar NRog SDeJ SPhx WBrk WCot WFar WShi
	- - 'Blushing Girl'	GEdr WFar
	- - 'Dieter Schacht'	GEdr
	- - 'Evening Shade'	GEdr
	- - 'George Baker'	Widely available
	- - 'Nettleton Pink'	GKev
	- - Prasil Group	CBor GEdr GKev NHpl SPhx
	- - 'White Knight'	GKev NHpl WCot
	- f. ***transsylvanica***	see *C. solida* subsp. *solida*
	- 'Turaco'	GKev NRog
	- 'White King'	WCot
	- 'White Swallow'	CBor CWCL EPot GEdr GKev SDeJ
	- 'Zwanenberg'	GKev
	'Spinners'	CDor CElw CFis CWCL EBee ECtt EHed ELon EPPr GKev GLog GPSL LEdu NQui WFar WPnP WSHC WTyc XLum
	stipulata B&SWJ 2951	WCru
	'Sylvia's Castle Haven'	MPie
	taliensis	CExl GJos GKev GLog
	tauricola	GEdr
	temulifolia 'Chocolate Stars'	CBcs CMiW CSpe CWCL CWGN EBee ECtt EHed EMor EWld ILea MBNS MHol MPie SPoG WCot WSHC WTre
	tomentella	GKev
	'Tory MP'	CDor CExl CMiW CRos EBee EHyd EPPr EPfP GEdr LEdu LRHS MNrw MPie NChi NRHS WFar WPGP WSHC
	transsylvanica hort.	see *C. solida* subsp. *solida*
	vittae	GKev
	vivipara	EPPr
	'Wildside Blue'	CDor CMil EPPr EWld NHar WSHC
	wilsonii	CExl GKev

Corylopsis (*Hamamelidaceae*)

	glabrescens	CBcs CJun EGrI EHyd EPfP LMil LRHS NLar WCFE
	- B&SWJ 14636	WCru
	- var. ***gotoana***	CJun EHyd EPfP LRHS MAsh NLar
	- - 'Chollipo'	CJun EHyd NLar SSta
	- 'Lemon Drop'	CJun NLar WPGP
	glandulifera	CJun
	pauciflora 🏆H5	CBcs CBod CDoC CEnd CJun CRos CTri EBee EHed ELan EPfP IDee LCro LOPS LPar LRHS LSRN MAsh MGil MPri MRav NLar SCob SGol SPer SPoG WCFE WPGP WSpi
	platypetala	see *C. sinensis* var. *calvescens*
	- var. ***laevis***	see *C. sinensis* var. *calvescens*
	sinensis	CBcs EBee EPfP GKev
§	- var. ***calvescens***	CBcs CJun EPfP NLar WCFE
§	- - f. ***veitchiana*** 🏆H5	CJun EHyd EPfP LRHS MAsh WCFE
§	- var. ***sinensis*** 🏆H5	CCCN CDoC CJun CMCN EBee ELan EPfP LRHS MAsh NLar SGol SLon WCFE WSpi
	- - 'Spring Purple'	CBcs CEnd CJun CMac EBee EHed EPfP EWes IDee LRHS MGos MPkF NLar NRHS SPoG WPGP WSpi XSte
	- 'Veitch's Purple'	CJun NLar
	spicata	CBcs CJun CMCN EGrI EHed IDee LRHS MBlu MGil MMuc MRav NLar SGbt SGol
	- 'Golden Spring'	CBcs
	- 'Red Eye'	CJun NLar
	veitchiana	see *C. sinensis* var. *calvescens* f. *veitchiana*
	willmottiae	see *C. sinensis* var. *sinensis*

Corylus ✿ (*Betulaceae*)

	avellana (F)	CArg CBcs CCVT CHab CLnd CMac CTri EPfP EPom GAbr GDam LBuc LCro LMaj LOPS MGos MNic MTrO NGrd NLar NWea SCob SEWo SGsty SPer SRms SVic WMat WMou WTSh
	- 'Anaconda'	MBlu
	- 'Anny's Compact Red'	WHwl
	- 'Anny's Purple Dream'PBR	IDee MBlu
	- 'Anny's Red Dwarf'	NLar
	- 'Aurea'	CBcs CEnd CTri EBee ELan EPfP LMaj MAsh MBlu MGos NLar NWea SLim SPer SPoG SSta SWvt WBor WFar
	- 'Bollwylle'	see *C. maxima* 'Halle'sche Riesennuss'
§	- 'Butler' (F)	CAgr CBod CEnd CMac CTri MTrO NRog SRms
	- 'Casina' (F)	CAgr
	- 'Clark' (F)	MCoo
	- 'Contorta' 🏆H6	Widely available
	- 'Corabel' (F)	CAgr NOra SKee SRms WMat
	- 'Cosford' (F)	CAgr CCVT CEnd CMac CSBt CTri EPom IArd LBuc MBlu MTrO NLar NOra NOrn NRog NWea SBdl SEWo SGol SKee SPer SRms SWvt WMat
	- Emoa Series	WMat
§	- 'Ennis' (F)	CAgr MTrO NLar NOra NRog
	- 'Feriale' (F)	CAgr
	- 'Gustav's Zeller' (F)	MTrO NOra WMat
§	- 'Heterophylla'	CEnd EBee NLar SSta WLov
	- 'Laciniata'	see *C. avellana* 'Heterophylla'
§	- 'Lang Tidlig Zeller' (F)	CAgr MCoo MNic MTrO NLar NOra NWea WMat
	- 'Lewis' (F)	CAgr

- 'Merveille de Bollwyller'	see *C. maxima* 'Halle'sche Riesennuss'
- 'Nottingham Prolific'	see *C. avellana* 'Pearson's Prolific'
- 'Pauetet' (F)	CAgr
§ - 'Pearson's Prolific' (F)	CAgr CSBt LBuc SBdl SGol SSFr
- 'Pendula'	LMaj MBlu NOra SCoo SRms WCot WHwl
- 'Princess' (F)	SVic
- 'Red Majestic'PBR ♡H6	Widely available
§ - 'Rotblättrige Zellernuss' (F) ♡H6	CEnd CHab EPom EShb IArd LMaj LPar MBlu MRav NLar NOrn SGol SPoG SSFT SWvt
- 'Rouge de Zeller'	see *C. avellana* 'Rotblättrige Zellernuss'
- 'Scooter'	IArd MPkF NLar SGsty XSte
- 'Tonda di Giffoni' (F)	NOra SKee WMat
- 'Twister' **new**	LRHS
- 'Webb's Prize Cob' (F)	CAco CAgr CBod CDoC CTri ELan GDam IArd LPar MBlu MCoo NLar NRog NWea SGol SKee SSFr SVic
chinensis	MBlu WPGP
colurna ♡H6	CAgr CCVT CDoC CLnd CMCN EBee ELan EPfP EWTr IArd IPap LMaj LPar MBlu MGos MNic MTrO MVil NOra NOrn NRog NWea SCob SCoo SGol SGsty SRms WMat WMou
× ***colurnoides*** 'Chinoka' (F)	CAgr NRog
- 'Freeoka' (F)	CAgr NRog
- 'Laroka' (F)	NRog
cornuta	WMou
EARLY LONG ZELLER	see *C. avellana* 'Lang Tidlig Zeller'
fargesii	WPGP
ferox	CJun
maxima (F)	CLnd CTri EPom MSwo NWea
- 'Butler'	see *C. avellana* 'Butler'
- 'Ennis'	see *C. avellana* 'Ennis'
- 'Fertile de Coutard'	see *C. maxima* 'White Filbert'
- 'Frizzled Filbert' (F)	SBdl
- 'Frühe van Frauendorf'	see *C. maxima* 'Red Filbert'
- 'Garibaldi' (F)	SBdl
- 'Grote Lambertsnoot'	see *C. maxima* 'Kentish Cob'
- 'Gunslebert' (F) ♡H6	CCVT CMac CTri MTrO NOra SBdl SPoG SRms SSFr WMat
- HALLE GIANT	see *C. maxima* 'Halle'sche Riesennuss'
§ - 'Halle'sche Riesennuss' (F)	CAgr CLnd CMac ELan LMaj NLar NOra SKee SSFr WMat
§ - 'Kentish Cob' (F) ♡H6	Widely available
- 'Lambert's Filbert'	see *C. maxima* 'Kentish Cob'
- 'Longue d'Espagne'	see *C. maxima* 'Kentish Cob'
- 'Monsieur de Bouweller'	see *C. maxima* 'Halle'sche Riesennuss'
- 'Nottingham Cobnut' (F)	CDoC CLnd MCoo SVic
- 'Purple Filbert'	see *C. maxima* 'Purpurea'
§ - 'Purpurea' (F)	Widely available
§ - 'Red Filbert' (F)	CEnd EPfP EPom MTrO NLar NOra NRog SCoo SGol SGsty SKee SLim SRms SSta WCot WHwl WLov
- 'Red Zellernut'	see *C. avellana* 'Rotblättrige Zellernuss'
- 'Spanish White'	see *C. maxima* 'White Filbert'
§ - 'White Filbert' (F)	CHab MCoo NRog SBdl
- 'White Spanish Filbert'	see *C. maxima* 'White Filbert'
- 'Witpit Lambertsnoot'	see *C. maxima* 'White Filbert'
'Nottingham Early' (F)	NLar
sieboldiana B&SWJ 11056	WCru
- var. ***mandshurica***	MBlu
'Te Terra Red'	CMCN EBee EHed ELan EPfP MAsh MBlu SLon SRms WMat WMou
tibetica	LEdu WPGP
× ***vilmorinii***	WPGP

Corymbia (*Myrtaceae*)

§ ***citriodora***	CWCL MHer SKin SPlb WGrf
§ ***eximia***	SPlb
- 'Nana'	SPlb
§ ***ficifolia***	CDTJ IDee WGrf

Corynabutilon see *Abutilon*

Corynephorus (*Poaceae*)

canescens	NBir
- 'Spiky Blue'	CBod

Cosmos (*Asteraceae*)

§ ***atrosanguineus***	CBcs CSpe CWGN ECtt ELan EPfP EWoo LCro LOPS LRHS LSRN MBow MRav NLar SCob SDeJ SDir SPoG SWvt WHoo
- 'Black Magic' **new**	SBls
- CHOCAMOCHA ('Thomocha'PBR)	CBcs CBod CCCN CDor CPla CRos CSpe CWGN EBee ECtt EHyd EPfP GMaP LCro LOPS LRHS LSou MBow MBros MGos NLar NRHS SGbt SMrm SPeP SPer SPoG
- DARK SECRET ('3013/01')	LRHS
- ECLIPSE ('Hamcoec'PBR)	CRos LRHS
- SPELLBOUND ('Hamcosp')	ECtt
bipinnatus	SVic
- 'Antiquity'	MBros SBut SPhx
- (Apollo Series) 'Apollo Carmine' ♡H3 **new**	LSou
- - 'Apollo Pink' ♡H3 **new**	LSou
- - 'Apollo White' ♡H3 **new**	LSou
- (Casanova Series) 'Casanova Pink'	SCob SPoG
- - 'Casanova Red'	SCob SPoG
- - 'Casanova Violet'	SCob SPoG
- - 'Casanova White'	SCob SPoG
- 'Cupcakes White' (Cupcakes Series)	CSpe
- 'Daydream' **new**	CArg
- 'Dazzler'	CArg LCro LOPS SPhx
- (Double Click Series) 'Double Click Cranberries' (d)	CArg CSpe SPhx
- - 'Double Click Rose Bonbon' (d) **new**	CArg
- - 'Double Click Snow Puff' (d)	CArg SPhx
- 'Fizzy Rose Picotee' (Fizzy Series) **new**	CArg
- 'Lemonade' **new**	SSal
- 'Purity'	CArg CSpe LCro LOPS SBut SMrm SPhx
- Razzmatazz Series	LCro LOPS MBros
- 'Rubenza' ♡H3	CSpe LCro LOPS SPhx
- SEA SHELLS (mixed)	SMrm
- Sensation Series	SBut
- - 'Sensation Picotee'	LCro LOPS
- - 'Sensation Pinkie' ♡H3	CArg LCro LOPS
- Sonata Series	MBros SCob SEle
- - SONATA CARMINE	CArg MPri
- - SONATA PINK	CArg MPri SCob
- - SONATA PURPLE SHADES ('Pas1248700') **new**	LSou
- - SONATA WHITE	CArg CSpe MBros MPri SCob
- 'Sweet Sixteen'	SPhx
- 'Xanthos'	CRos CSpe LCro LOPS MBros
peucedanifolius	CSpe

	- 'Flamingo'	SDeJ
	sulphureus	SSal
	- BUNTE LICHTER (mixed)	CSpe
	- LADYBIRD (mixed)	SVic
	'Yellow Garden'	SPhx

Cosmos × Dahlia (*Asteraceae*)

	'Mexican Black'	see *Dahlia* 'Mexican Black'

costmary see *Tanacetum balsamita*

Costus (*Costaceae*)

	barbatus	NGKo

Cotinus ✿ (*Anacardiaceae*)

	americanus	see *C. obovatus*
	'Candy Floss'	CRos EHyd EPfP LRHS MBNS NRHS
§	***coggygria***	CBcs CBrac CEme CMCN CMac EGrI ELan EPfP GDam MRav MSwo NLar NWea SCob SEND SGbt SGsty SPer SRms SWvt SavN WFar WHwl XSen
	- GOLDEN LADY ('Mincojau3'PBR)	EPfP LRHS SGsty
	- GOLDEN SPIRIT ('Ancot'PBR) 🏆H5	Widely available
	- GREEN FOUNTAIN ('Kolcot'PBR)	EBee LRHS
	- 'Kanari'	NLar
	- 'Lilla'PBR	EPfP LRHS MAsh MBlu MPkF NLar NRHS SCoo SGsty XSte
	- 'Notcutt's Variety'	EGrI MRav
	- 'Old Fashioned'PBR	CBod EPfP MPkF NEoE NLar WMou XSte
	- 'Pink Champagne'	NLar SSta
	- Purpureus Group	EPfP SRms
	- 'Red Beauty'	NLar
	- RED SPIRIT ('Firstpur')	NLar
	- 'Royal Purple' 🏆H5	Widely available
	- Rubrifolius Group	CBcs EPfP SEND SWvt
	- SMOKEY JOE ('Lisjo'PBR)	CBcs CBod CRos EHyd EPfP LRHS MAsh MPkF SLon SPoG SSta SWvt XSte
	- 'Velvet Cloak'	EPfP MGos NLar SLon SWvt
	- 'Well Spotted'	EMil
	- 'Westonbirt Orange'	NLar
	- 'Young Lady'PBR 🏆H5	CBcs CBod CDoC CMac ELan ELon EPfP EWes GBin LPar MAsh MBlu MPkF MRav MTin NLar SCob SCoo SPer SRms SWvt SavN WFar WMat XSte
	DUSKY MAIDEN ('Londus'PBR)	CBod CEme CSBt CTsd EHyd ELan ELon EPfP IArd IDee LRHS MAsh MGos NEoE NLar NRHS SLon WFar
	'Flame' 🏆H5	CBcs CDoC CKel CRos EBee EGrI EHyd ELan ELon EPfP EWTr LRHS MAsh MGos MRav NRHS SEdd SGbt SGsty SPer SPoG SWvt WAvo WFar XSte
	'Grace'	Widely available
§	***obovatus***	CMCN EGrI EPfP IArd LRHS MBlu MPkF MRav SSta WPGP
	'Ruby Glow'	CRos EHyd EPfP LCro LOPS LRHS MBNS MGos NRHS

Cotoneaster ✿ (*Rosaceae*)

	acuminatus	SRms
	acutifolius var. ***laetevirens***	see *C. laetevirens*
§	***adpressus*** 'Little Gem'	NHar NLar
	- 'Tom Thumb'	see *C. adpressus* 'Little Gem'
	affinis	SPtp SRms
	albokermesinus	SPtp SRms
	ambiguus Rehder & E.H.Wilson	NLar
	amoenus	NLar SRms
	- ACE 1028	SPtp
§	***apiculatus***	NLar SRms
§	***ascendens***	SRms
	assamensis	SRms
§	***astrophoros***	CMac GRum MBlu NLar
	atropurpureus	NLar SRms
§	- 'Variegatus' (v) 🏆H6	CBcs CBod CDoC CEme CMac CRos EHyd ELan ELon EPfP LRHS MAsh MGos NLar NPer NRHS SCob SCoo SDix SPer SPoG SRms SWvt WAvo WFar
	atuntzensis	SPtp
	aurantiacus	NLar SPtp
	beimashanensis	ELan SPtp
	boisianus	NLar SPtp SRms
	bradyi	EBee GBin GKev SRms
	brickellii	NLar SPtp
§	***bullatus***	CTri EPfP NLar SPtp SRms
	- 'Firebird'	see *C. ignescens*
	- f. ***floribundus***	see *C. bullatus*
	- var. ***macrophyllus***	see *C. rehderi*
	bumthangensis	NLar SRms
	buxifolius blue-leaved	see *C. lidjiangensis*
	- f. ***vellaeus***	see *C. astrophoros*
	camilli-schneideri	SRms
	canescens	NLar SRms
	chadwelli	NLar
	chuanus	NLar
	- L 624	SPtp
	chungtiensis	NLar
	cinerascens	SPtp
	- CLD 1440 **new**	SPtp
	cinnabarinus	SRms
§	***cochleatus***	NHar SPtp SRms
§	***congestus***	CSBt ELan MSwo NFav NLar SPer SPlb SRms XLum
	- 'Nanus'	CBor GEdr
	conspicuus	CBcs EWTr SPtp SRms
	- 'Decorus' 🏆H6	CBod CBrac CDoC CEme CSBt EHyd EPfP LRHS MGos MMuc MSwo NWea SCob SPer SPlb SPoG SWvt
	- 'Leicester Gem'	SRms
	- 'Red Glory'	CMac
	cooperi	SRms
	- 'Nicolette'	NLar
	cordifolius	MBlu NLar SRms
	- KW 13363	SPtp
	cornifolius	SRms
	- Og 93330	SPtp
§	'Cornubia' 🏆H6	Widely available
	crispii	NLar SPtp
	cuspidatus	MBlu NLar SPtp
	dammeri	CBcs CDoC CEnd CMac CRos CSBt CTri EBee EHyd ELan EPfP GDam LRHS MAsh MGos MRav MSwo NHol NLar NRHS NWea SCob SGol SNig SPer SPoG SRms SWvt WCFE WFar
§	- 'Major'	LBuc SCob
§	- 'Mooncreeper'	CDoC
	- 'Oakwood'	see *C. radicans*
	- var. ***radicans*** misapplied	see *C. dammeri* 'Major'
	- var. ***radicans*** (Dammer ex C.K.Schneid.) C.K.Schneid.	see *C. radicans*

	dammeri* × *microphyllus	CBrac
	dielsianus	NLar NWea SRms
	divaricatus	NLar SPer SRms
	duthieanus	NLar SPtp
	- 'Boer'	see *C. apiculatus*
	elatus	SRms
	elegans	SPtp SRms
	emeiensis	SRms
	encavei	NLar
	- KEKE 1239	SPtp
	'Erlinda'	see *C.* × *suecicus* 'Erlinda'
	'Exburiensis'	CBcs CBod CBrac CCVT CEme EBee EPfP MGos MMuc MNic MRav MTrO NLar NOrn SCob SEND SPer WFar WMat
	falconeri	SRms
	fastigiatus	SPtp SRms
	flinckii	NLar SRms
	floccosus	IArd SEND SPtp
	floridus	SRms
	forrestii	GKev MVil NLar SRms
	franchetii	Widely available
	frigidus	CBee CMCN SPtp SRms
§	- 'Pershore Coral'	WAvo
	froebelii	SPtp
	fulvidus	NLar
	gamblei	SRms
	- KR 1576	SPtp
	ganghobaensis	CMCN GKev NLar SPtp SRms
	- B&L 12234	WCru
	glabratus	SRms
	- KR 232	SPtp
	glacialis	LShi SRms
	glaucophyllus	IArd SRms
§	***glomerulatus***	NLar SRms
	gonggashanensis	SPtp
	gracilis	SRms
	granatensis	SRms
	'Green Fan'	SPtp
	harrovianus	SPtp SRms
	harrysmithii	NLar
	hebephyllus	NLar
	hedegaardii	SPtp
I	- 'Fructu Luteo'	SPtp SRms
	- 'Halliwell's Yellow' **new**	SPtp
	- yellow-fruited	SPtp
	henryanus	SRms
	- 'Corina'	SRms
	'Highlight'	see *C. pluriflorus*
	hillieri	NLar SPtp
§	***hjelmqvistii***	LBuc NLar SPtp SRms
	- 'Robustus'	see *C. hjelmqvistii*
	- 'Rotundifolius'	see *C. hjelmqvistii*
	hodjingensis	SRms
	horizontalis	Widely available
	- 'Variegatus'	see *C. atropurpureus* 'Variegatus'
	huahongdongensis	ELan
	hualiensis	NLar SRms
	- B&SWJ 3143	WCru
	humifusus	see *C. dammeri*
	hummelii	SRms
	hupehensis	NLar
§	'Hybridus Pendulus'	CBcs CBod CBrac CCVT CDoC CMac CTri EBee GArf IPap LCro LRHS LSRN MGos MPri MRav MTrO NLar NOrn NWea SCob SGbt SPer SPoG SRms SWvt WMat
§	***hylmoei***	ELan NLar SPtp SRms
	hypocarpus	SPtp SRms
	ignavus	SRms
§	***ignescens***	NLar SPtp SRms
	- CLD 612 **new**	SPtp
	ignotus	SRms
	incanus	NLar
	induratus	SRms
	insculptus	SPtp SRms
	insolitus	NLar SPtp
	integerrimus	SRms
§	***integrifolius***	ELan SPtp SRms
	kangdingensis	SRms
	kingdonii	NLar
	kitaibelii	NLar SPtp
	kongboensis	SPtp
	konishii	NLar
	kuanensis SICH 56A	SPtp
	kweitschoviensis	NLar
	lacteus ♀H6	Widely available
	- F 10419	ELan SPtp
	- 'Milkmaid' (v)	NLar
§	***laetevirens***	NLar
	lancasteri	NLar SRms
	- Og 94303 **new**	SPtp
	langei	SRms
	laxiflorus	SRms
§	***lidjiangensis***	NLar SPtp SRms
	lucidus	LPar SRms
	ludlowii	SPtp SRms
	magnificus	SRms
§	***mairei***	NLar SPtp SRms
	marginatus Lindl. ex Loudon	SRms
§	- 'Blazovice'	NLar SRms
§	- 'Brno'	SRms
	marquandii	NLar SRms
§	***meiophyllus***	MBlu NLar SPtp
	melanocarpus	NLar
	melanotrichus misapplied	see *C. cochleatus*
	melanotrichus (Franch.) G. Klotz	SPtp
	meuselii	NLar SRms
	- TSS 13864	SPtp
	microphyllus misapplied	see *C. purpurascens*
	microphyllus ambig.	CBcs CBod CKel EBee GBin NWea SCob
	microphyllus Wall. ex Lindl.	CTri LRHS SPer
	- NICE 004	WCFE
	- var. ***cochleatus*** (Franch.) Rehder & E.H.Wilson	see *C. cochleatus*
	- var. ***cochleatus*** ambig.	EPot NSla
	- 'Donard Gem'	see *C. astrophoros*
	- 'Teulon Porter'	see *C. astrophoros*
	- var. ***thymifolius*** (Lindl.) Koehne	see *C. integrifolius*
	- var. ***thymifolius*** ambig.	EHyd LRHS NLar
	milkedandaensis	SPtp SRms
	miniatus	SPtp SRms
	mirabilis	NLar SRms
	monopyrenus	SPtp SRms
	- F 11422	GKev
	'Mooncreeper'	see *C. dammeri* 'Mooncreeper'
	morrisonensis	SRms
	moupinensis	SRms
	- BWJ 8167	WCru
	mucronatus	NLar SPtp SRms
	'My Pet'	GAbr
§	***nanshan***	NWea SRms WAvo
	- 'Boer'	see *C. apiculatus*
	naoujanensis	EPfP NLar SPtp
	- 'Berried Treasure'	CRos EHyd EPfP LRHS MGos NRHS SPtp
	nepalensis	NLar
	newryensis	SRms

nitens	NLar SRms
nitidifolius	see *C. glomerulatus*
nohelii	NLar SRms
notabilis	SRms
nummularioides	SRms
nummularius Fisch. & C.A. Mey.	SRms
* ***obrienii*** new	GKev
obscurus	SPtp SRms
obtusus Wall. ex Lindl.	NLar SRms
ogisui	GBin LEdu SPtp
- Og 95101 new	SPtp
- Og 95105	EBee GKev WPGP
omissus	NLar SPtp
pangiensis	SRms
pannosus	SRms
paradoxus	SRms
parkeri	NLar SRms
parneyi new	SPtp
pekinensis	SRms
permutatus	see *C. pluriflorus*
perpusillus	SRms
§ ***pluriflorus***	GKev SRms
- LS&E 13310 new	SPtp
poluninii	NLar SPtp SRms
polycarpus	SRms
praecox 'Boer'	see *C. apiculatus*
procumbens	SRms
- 'Needham'	NLar
- 'Queen of Carpets' ♀H6	CBod CBrac CDoC CEme CKel CRos EHyd ELan EPfP LRHS LSRN MAsh MGos MRav NLar NRHS SCoo SLim SPoG SRms SWvt
- 'Streib's Findling'	see *C.* 'Streib's Findling'
prostratus	SRms
- 'Arnold-Forster'	ELan SPtp
przewalskii	SRms
pseudo-obscurus	SRms
* ***psikangensis***	NLar
§ ***purpurascens***	CSBt EHyd LRHS NLar NRHS
pyrenaicus misapplied	see *C. congestus*
qungbixiensis	NLar SRms
raboutensis	NLar
racemiflorus	SRms
§ ***radicans***	CMCN
§ ***rehderi***	NLar SPtp SRms
reticulatus	NLar SPtp
rhytidophyllus	ELan GKev SPtp
- Og 95102	SPtp
rokujodaisanensis	NLar
roseus	NLar SRms
'Rothschildianus' ♀H6	CBcs CBod CCVT CMac CRos CSBt CTri EBee EHyd ELan EPfP EWTr LRHS MBlu MGos MRav MSwo NLar NRHS NWea SCoo SEdd SGbt SPer SRms SSta SWvt
§ ***rotundifolius*** Wall. ex Lindl.	SPtp
rubens W.W. Sm.	NLar
rugosus E. Pritz. ex Diels	NLar SPtp SRms
'Saint Andrews Blaze'	ELan SPtp
'Saint Monica'	EPfP MBlu
salicifolius	CTri MSwo NLar NWea SCob SPtp SRms WFar
§ - 'Avonbank'	CEnd NLar WAvo
- 'Brno Orangeade'	SRms
- 'Fructuluteo'	SPtp
- 'Gnom' ♀H6	CChe CDoC CEme CKel CMac CRos EHyd ELan EPfP LRHS MAsh MGos NBir SCob SPer SPoG SPtp SRms WAvo
§ - 'Herbstfeuer'	MRav MSwo SPtp SRms
- 'Pendulus'	see *C.* 'Hybridus Pendulus'
- 'Pink Champagne' ♀H6	CMac EPfP
- 'Repens'	CBod CBrac EPfP MTrO NWea SCob SGol SPer SPoG SRms WMat
- var. ***rugosus***	see *C. hylmoei*
salwinensis	NLar SPtp SRms
sandakphuensis	SRms
scandinavicus	SRms
schantungensis	NLar SRms
schlechtendalii 'Blazovice'	see *C. marginatus* 'Blazovice'
schubertii	SRms
* ***sengorensis***	NLar
serotinus misapplied	see *C. meiophyllus*
serotinus Hutch.	SRms
shannanensis	ELan SPtp SRms
shansiensis	NLar SPtp SRms
sherriffii	NLar SRms
sikangensis	GBin SPtp SRms
simonsii	CCVT CEnd CLnd CMac EBee ELan GKev LBuc LRHS MGos MMuc NHol NWea SCob SPer SPtp SRms WFar
- MF 904	SPtp
soczavianus	NLar
§ ***splendens***	ELan GKev SPtp SRms
- 'Sabrina'	see *C. splendens*
spongbergii	SRms
staintonii	SRms
sternianus ♀H6	SPtp SRms
- ACE 2200	MSwo
aff. ***sternianus***	SPtp
- SICH 770	SPtp
- Yu 15716	SPtp
§ 'Streib's Findling'	EHyd GKev LPar LRHS MAsh NLar SGol SPtp
suavis	SRms
subacutus	SRms
subadpressus	SRms
submultiflorus	NLar
× ***suecicus*** 'Coral Beauty' ♀H6	Widely available
§ - 'Erlinda' (v)	CEnd SPoG SRms
- 'Ifor'	SRms
- 'Juliette' (v) ♀H6	CMac CRos EHyd LRHS LSRN MAsh MMrt MRav MTrO NLar NOrn NRHS SCoo SPer SPoG WMat
- 'Skogholm'	CBcs CRos ELan EPfP LRHS MGos SCob SPer SRms
svenhedinii	NLar
taoensis	SPtp SRms
taofuensis	SPtp
- Sich 1878	SPtp
tardiflorus	NLar SPtp SRms
tauricus	SRms
teijiashanensis	SPtp SRms
tengyuehensis	SPtp SRms
thimphuensis	NLar SRms
tomentellus	WCFE
tomentosus	SRms
transcaucasicus	NLar
turbinatus	NLar SPtp SRms
'Valkenburg'	SRms
vandelaarii	ELan NLar SPtp SRms
veitchii	NLar SRms
verruculosus	SRms
vestitus	NLar
villosulus	SRms
vilmorinianus	SPtp SRms
- F 5543 new	SPtp
wardii misapplied	see *C. mairei*
wardii W.W. Sm.	SRms

× ***watereri***	CBod CCVT ELon EPfP LRHS MSwo NWea
- 'Avonbank'	see *C. salicifolius* 'Avonbank'
- 'Cornubia'	see *C.* 'Cornubia'
- 'John Waterer'	EPfP SPer SPoG
- 'Pendulus'	see *C.* 'Hybridus Pendulus'
wilsonii	SRms
yalungensis	SRms
yinchangensis	SRms
zabelii	SPtp SRms

Cotula (*Asteraceae*)

coronopifolia	CBen CWat NPer
§ ***fallax***	CKel
hispida ambig.	CMea CPla EBou ECha ECtt EPfP GKev MACG SLee SRot
§ ***hispida*** (DC.) Harv.	CTri CWCL EDAr GMaP MAsh MHer NPer NRya SPoG SRms XLum
lineariloba misapplied	see *C. fallax*
lineariloba (DC.) Hilliard	EWes
pectinata	see *Leptinella pectinata*
perpusilla	see *Leptinella pusilla*
'Platt's Black'	see *Leptinella squalida* 'Platt's Black'
potentilloides	see *Leptinella potentillina*
pyrethrifolia	see *Leptinella pyrethrifolia*
reptans	see *Leptinella scariosa*
scariosa	see *Leptinella scariosa*
squalida	see *Leptinella squalida*

Cotyledon (*Crassulaceae*)

chrysantha	see *Rosularia chrysantha*
oppositifolia	see *Umbilicus oppositifolius*
orbiculata	CPbh EShb ETod SPlb WCot
- 'Cedric Morris'	EMal SChr
- var. ***oblonga***	CDoC EShb WCot
- 'Silver Waves'	MCot
- 'Snowline' **new**	WThu
pendens	EShb
simplicifolia	see *Umbilicus oppositifolius*
tomentosa subsp. ***ladismithensis*** ♀H1c	EShb

courgette see AGM Vegetables Section

Crambe (*Brassicaceae*)

sp. **new**	MAsh
abyssinica	SPhx
cordifolia ♀H5	Widely available
- 'Morning's Snow'	NLar
hispanica **new**	LRHS
maritima	Widely available
- 'Lilywhite'	CAgr LEdu SVic
orientalis	NLar WHil

cranberry see *Vaccinium macrocarpon*, *V. oxycoccos*

Craspedia (*Asteraceae*)

* ***hispidula*** **new**	GArf

Crassula ✿ (*Crassulaceae*)

arborescens	EShb SChr SSim XAbr
- subsp. ***undulatifolia***	CDoC
argentea	see *C. ovata*
arta	SChr
§ ***atropurpurea*** var. ***anomala***	SChr
- subsp. ***arborescens*** 'Blue Mist'	SEND
'Blue Waves' **new**	SIvy
'Buddha's Temple'	SSim
coccinea	CPbh EShb GBin SPlb WCot
columnaris	SSim
* ***coralloides***	SPlb
cordata	EShb
'Estagnol' **new**	SSim
I ***hystrix*** 'Variegata' (v)	SAll
muscosa	CBen EShb NCft SChr SIvy SPlb
§ - 'Variegata' (v)	SSim
§ ***ovata*** ♀H2	CBen EBak LCro LOPS NCft NGBl NPer SChr SEND SIvy SPlb SPre SSim SVen WThu
- 'Gollum' ♀H2	EShb NCft SEND SIvy
- 'Hummel's Sunset' (v) ♀H2	EShb NCft SSim
- 'Minima'	NCft SIvy SSim
- 'Undulata'	WCot
- 'Variegata' (v)	EBak EShb SIvy WCot
pellucida subsp. ***marginalis***	CDoC
- - f. ***rubra***	CDoC EShb
§ - - 'Variegata' (v)	SSim WFar
perfoliata var. ***falcata*** ♀H2	EShb WCot
perforata ♀H2	CDoC NCft SIvy
- 'Variegata' (v)	CDoC EShb LLWG NCft NWad SEdd SSim
portulacea	see *C. ovata*
rupestris ♀H2	CDoC SSim
- subsp. ***marnieriana***	CDoC SIvy
§ ***sarcocaulis*** ♀H3	CBcs CPla CTri CTtf EBou ELan GBin LLWG LRHS MAsh MCot NFav NHpl SBrt SIvy SLee SPlb SPoG SRms SRot SVen WAbe WCav WHoo WIce WMal WSHC XLum XSen
I - 'Alba'	NHpl
schmidtii	SSim
- dark-flowered	SSim
- white-flowered	SSim
sedifolia	see *C. setulosa* 'Milfordiae'
sediformis	see *C. setulosa* 'Milfordiae'
setulosa	SPlb
§ - 'Milfordiae'	CTri EPot NBir NHpl NRya SLee WAbe
socialis	ELan
tetragona	SEND
* ***tomentosa*** 'Variegata' (v)	EShb

+ *Crataegomespilus* (*Rosaceae*)

'Jules d'Asnières'	NLar

× *Crataegosorbus* (*Rosaceae*)

§ 'Granatnaja'	CAgr

Crataegus (*Rosaceae*)

sp.	SWvt
anomala 'Zbigniew' **new**	CAgr
arnoldiana	CAgr CLnd CTri EBee MAsh MCoo MTrO NLar NWea SPoG WMat
'Autumn Glory'	CEnd CLnd
azarolus	LEdu SGsty
- 'Geraki' (F) **new**	IArd
§ ***coccinea*** L.	CAgr CLnd LMaj NWea WMat
cordata	see *C. phaenopyrum*
crus-galli misapplied	see *C. persimilis* 'Prunifolia'
galli L.	CCVT CLnd EPfP MAsh NLar NRog NWea
douglasii	EBtc
× ***durobrivensis***	CAgr CLnd EBee MBlu
ellwangeriana	CAgr WCot
- 'Fire Ball'	EWTr MBlu
eriocarpa	CLnd
gemmosa	CAgr
× ***grignonensis*** ♀H7	CBcs CLnd ELan LPar MBlu MMuc NLar

harbisonii	IArd
jonesiae	EPfP
laciniata misapplied	see *C. orientalis*
§ ***laevigata***	GDam NWea SCob
- 'Coccinea Plena'	see *C. laevigata* 'Paul's Scarlet'
- 'Crimson Cloud'	see *C. laevigata* 'Punicea'
- 'Gireoudii'	CBod NLar
- 'Mutabilis'	CTri SGol
§ - 'Paul's Scarlet' (d) ♀H7	Widely available
- 'Pink Corkscrew'	EPfP MBlu WLov
- 'Plena' (d)	CBod CLnd CMac CSBt CTri EBee ELan EPfP GDam LPar LRHS MGos MRav MSwo MTrO NOra NOrn NRog NWea SCob SEWo SGol SLim SPer SWvt WMat
§ - 'Punicea' ♀H7	Widely available
- 'Rosea'	GKin
- 'Rosea Flore Pleno' (d) ♀H7	Widely available
× ***lavalleei***	CBod CCVT CLnd CMCN CTri ELan MRav MSwo NOrn NWea SCoo SLon WTSh
- 'Aurora'	NLar
- 'Carrierei' ♀H7	CMac EPfP EWTr LMaj LSRN MMuc MTrO NLar NRog NWea SCob SCoo SEND SEWo SGsty SPoG WMat WMou
§ ***mexicana***	EPfP IArd
mollis	CAgr EPfP WSpi
monogyna	Widely available
§ - 'Biflora'	CEnd CLnd CTri EBee MAsh MCoo MGos NWea SLim WMat WSpi
- 'Compacta'	LPar MBlu WCot WLov
- 'Praecox'	see *C. monogyna* 'Biflora'
- 'Stricta'	CCVT CLnd CSBt EPfP IDee LPar SCob SPer
- 'Variegata' (v)	SWeb
× ***mordenensis*** 'Toba' (d)	CLnd EWTr LRHS SGsty
§ ***orientalis*** ♀H6	CBod CCVT CDoC CEnd CMCN CTri ELan EPfP EWTr IArd MAsh MGos NLar NOrn NWea SCoo SLim WJas WMat WMou WSpi
oxyacantha misapplied	see *C. laevigata*
pedicellata	see *C. coccinea* L.
persimilis	LPar
§ - 'Prunifolia' ♀H7	Widely available
- 'Prunifolia Splendens'	CAgr CCVT EBar EBee EWTr LBuc LMaj LPar MTrO NOra NOrn WMat
§ ***phaenopyrum***	CLnd CMCN EBee EPfP SPtp
pinnatifida var. ***major***	CEnd EPfP NOrn NWea
- - 'Big Golden Star'	CAgr EBee EPfP MBlu MCoo MTrO NLar NOra NWea WMat WMou
pojarkovae new	CAgr
pontica 'Poltzi' new	CAgr
'Praecox'	see *C. monogyna* 'Biflora'
prunifolia	see *C. persimilis* 'Prunifolia'
pubescens f. ***stipulacea***	see *C. mexicana*
punctata f. ***aurea***	EPfP MBlu
pycnoloba	GKev
schraderiana	CAgr CLnd EBee EPfP EWTr MBlu NLar WMat
submollis	CLnd
succulenta	CAgr
- 'Jubilee' PBR	EBee EWTr MTrO NLar NOra WMat
- 'Long Thorn' new	MBlu
- var. ***macracantha***	CMCN
tanacetifolia	CAgr EPfP MBlu
viridis 'Winter King'	CAgr EPfP EWTr
wattiana	CLnd EBee ELan

Crataegus + *Mespilus* see + *Crataegomespilus*

Crataegus × *Mespilus* see × *Crataemespilus*

Crataegus × *Sorbus* see × *Crataegosorbus*

× *Crataemespilus* (*Rosaceae*)

gillotii new	NLar
grandiflora	CLnd

Cremanthodium (*Asteraceae*)

delavayi	GBin
lineare	GKev

Cremastra (*Orchidaceae*)

variabilis	WCot

Cremnophila (*Crassulaceae*)

Cremnophila × *Sedum* see × *Cremnosedum*

× *Cremnosedum* (*Crassulaceae*)

§ 'Little Gem'	SSim

Crenularia see *Aethionema*

Crepis (*Asteraceae*)

incana ♀H5	CBor ECtt EWld GBin MNrw NChi NSla SPhx SRms WAbe WMal
rubra	CSpe

Crinitaria see *Aster*

Crinodendron (*Elaeocarpaceae*)

hookerianum ♀H4	Widely available
- 'Ada Hoffmann'	CBcs CBod CBrac CCCN CEnd CExl CMac CPla CSde EHyd EPfP GDam GEdr GKin LRHS MBlu MGil MGos NLar SEle SGBe SGol SWvt WHwl WPav
- 'Ashmount' new	IArd
patagua	CBcs CCCN CExl CMac EBee EHed EHyd ELan ELon EPfP ESwi GBin MGil MVil NLar SEND SEle SPlb SVen WHwl WPav

Crinum (*Amaryllidaceae*)

amoenum	CCCN EShb GKev
§ ***bulbispermum***	CPrp
capense	see *C. bulbispermum*
'Carolina Beauty'	WCot
'Cintho Alpha'	GKev SDeJ SPer
'Elizabeth Traub'	WCot
'Ellen Bosanquet'	CCCN EHyd ELan GBin GKev SDir WCot
'Emma Jones'	WCot
'Hanibal's Dwarf'	WPGP
moorei	CBro SChr
- f. ***album***	CCCN EBee EPri GKev
- hybrid	WCot WMal
'Ollene'	WCot
§ × ***powellii***	CBcs CBro CExl CPrp CTsd EBak ECha EHyd ELan ELon EPfP EShb GKev LEdu LRHS MNrw MRav NRHS NWad SDeJ SDir SEND SPer SRms SSal WCot
- 'Album'	CAvo CBro CPrp CTri EBee ECha EHyd ELan EPfP EShb EWes GKev LEdu LRHS MRav NRHS SDeJ SDir SEND SMad SPer SRms SSal WAvo WCot WFar WPGP WSHC
- 'Bak-madder'	EBee
- 'Harlemense'	EBee
- 'Krelagei'	EBee

- 'Longifolium'	see *C. bulbispermum*
- 'Roseum'	see *C.* × *powellii*
'Sangria'	WCot
'Summer Nocturne'	WCot
'White Queen'	WCot
yemense misapplied	GKev

Criogenes see *Cypripedium*

Crithmum (*Apiaceae*)

maritimum	CCBP CEls GPoy MNHC NFav SBrt SPhx SPlb SRms WABo WJek

Crocosmia (*Iridaceae*)

'Abundant Joy'	EBee IBal
'African Beauty'	ECtt IBal
'Anna Marie'	CBro EBee ECtt ELan GAbr GKev LRHS SDir WCot WFar
'Apricot'	IBal
'Apricot Surprise'	ECtt IBal
aurea misapplied	see *C.* × *crocosmiiflora* 'George Davison' Davison
aurea ambig.	CPrp EHyd EShb
aurea (Pappe ex Hook.f.) Planch.	IBal IBlr LEdu
- from Swaziland	IBal
- subsp. ***aurea***	IBlr
- 'Golden Ballerina'[PBR]	EBee ECtt EWes IBal LRHS MAvo MBNS SGBe SPoG
'Auricorn'	IBal IBlr LEdu WPGP
'Aurora'	NGdn
'Ballyrogan Sundown'	IBlr
'Baywalker'	MAvo
'Beth Chatto'	IBal
'Big Top'	IBal
'Blaze'	IBal
'Bowland Blaze'	IBal MAvo
BRESSINGHAM BEACON ('Blos')	EHyd MSpe
'Bressingham Blaze'	CPrp CRos EBee EBlo EHyd IBal LRHS NGdn NHol NRHS
BRIGHT EYES ('Walbreyes'[PBR])	EHyd EPfP LRHS NRHS
'Buttercups'	CMea ECul ELan MACG SWvt WCAu
'Cadenza'	IBal IBlr NWad
'Caistor Sunset'	IBal
'Cascade'	IBal
'Chinatown'	IBal IBlr
'Chrome Spray'	IBlr
'Citronella' misapplied	see *C.* × *crocosmiiflora* 'Honey Angels'
'Comet' Knutty	CPrp EHyd EPPr IBal IBlr LRHS MAvo NRHS
'Cornish Copper'	CPrp
× ***crocosmiiflora***	CTri IBlr LCro LOPS SPlb SRms WBrk WShi XLum
- 'A.J. Hogan'	CPrp IBal NHol
- 'African Glow'	EBee IBal
- 'Amberglow'	CExl GWyn IBal NHol NPer WFar
- 'Apricot Queen'	NHol
- 'Baby Barnaby'	WFar
- 'Babylon' ♀H4	CBod CBor CDor CElw ECtt ELan ELon EPfP EPri GKev GWyn LEdu LRHS MACG MNrw MSCN NBid NBir NChi NLar NRHS SCob SDir SPad SPer SRms WBrk WFar WWtn
- 'Best of British'	ECtt
- 'Burford Bronze'	IBal NHol
- 'Burnt Umber'	IBal
- 'Buttercup'	CDor CRos ECtt EHyd EPfP GKev IBal LRHS NHol NRHS SGBe SRkn WFar WSpi
- 'Canary Bird'	CBro ECtt GAbr IBal NGdn NHol WBrk WSpi
§ - 'Carmin Brillant'	Widely available
- 'Challa'	ECtt IBal
- 'Citrina'	MNrw WSpi
- 'Citronella' J.E. Fitt	CBro CExl EBee EHyd EPfP EWoo GMaP LRHS MBel NGdn NHol NRHS SDix
§ - 'Coleton Fishacre'	CExl CNor CPrp CWCL ECha ECtt ELan ELon EPfP EPri GMaP IBal IBlr LRHS MMuc MNrw NBid NChi NHol SEND SEdd WCot WFar WHoo WSpi
§ - 'Columbus'	CAvo CBro CPrp EHyd EPfP EPri EWhm GKev IBal ILea LRHS MAvo NHol NRHS SDir SPer SRms WFar XLum
- 'Colwall'	IBal NWad WSHC
- 'Comet'	EBee IBal
- 'Constance'	CBro CDor ECtt EHyd EPri GAbr IBal LRHS MAvo NBid NGdn NHol NRHS WBrk WFar
- 'Corona'	CPrp IBal MAvo NHol
§ - 'Croesus'	IBal
- 'Custard Cream'	CPrp EHyd NHol
- 'Daisy Hill'	IBlr
- 'David Fitt'	IBal MAvo WFar
- 'Debutante'	CPrp EBee EPri IBal NHol SHar WHoo WSHC
§ - 'Diadème'	CWCL IBal
- 'Dusky Maiden'	CMac ECtt ELon GKin GMaP IBal MSwo NHol SRms SWvt
- 'Dwarf Gold'	IBal
- 'Eastern Promise'	IBal MAvo
- 'Elegans'	IBal
§ - 'Emily McKenzie'	Widely available
- 'Fantasie'	IBal
- 'Fire Jumper'	EBee EPfP GWyn IBal MAvo MSpe
- 'Fireglow'[PBR]	CRos ECtt EHyd IBal LRHS NRHS
- 'George Davison' misapplied	see *C.* × *crocosmiiflora* 'Golden Glory' ambig., *C.* 'Sulphurea'
§ - 'George Davison' Davison	Widely available
- 'Gillian'	IBal
- 'Gloria'	IBal MAvo
- 'Golden Glory' misapplied	see *C.* × *crocosmiiflora* 'Diadème'
§ - 'Golden Glory' ambig.	CBod CDor CExl CWCL ECul ELan ELon EShb GAbr GKev GWyn IBal MSwo NBir SGbt SRms
- 'Goldfinch'	CPrp EBee ELon
- 'Goldie'	WFar
- 'Hades'	IBal IBlr
- 'Harlequin'	CBcs CElw CKel CPrp EBee IBal ILea LRHS MAsh MAvo MBriF MHol MSCN SCoo SPoG SWvt WFar WSpi WTor
- 'His Majesty'	CBro CPrp IBal IBlr NHol WFar
§ - 'Honey Angels'	Widely available
- 'Honey Bells'	WBrk
- 'Irish Dawn'	IBal IBlr NHol NWad
§ - 'Jackanapes'	CBor CMea CRos ECtt ELon IBal IBlr LRHS MNrw SCob SCoo SRms WSpi
- 'Jackanapes VI'	IBal
- 'James Coey' misapplied	see *C.* × *crocosmiiflora* 'Carmin Brillant'
- 'James Coey' J.E. Fitt	CPrp ECha EPfP EShb EWoo GKin IBal LRHS MHer NLar SPoG
§ - 'Jessie'	CElw

- 'Judith'	IBal
- 'Kiautschou'	CPrp CWCL IBal NHol
- 'Lady Hamilton'	CDor CExl ECtt EHyd EPPr IBal LRHS NHol
- 'Lady McKenzie'	see *C.* × *crocosmiiflora* 'Emily McKenzie'
- 'Lady Oxford'	IBal NHol
- 'Lady Wilson'	CRos EHyd GBin LRHS NRHS
- 'Lambrook Gold'	CAvo IBal
- 'Lord Nelson'	CExl IBal NHol
- 'Loweswater'	IBal
- 'Lutea'	IBal LRHS
- 'Marjorie'	IBal
- 'Mars'	EWes IBal MAvo NGdn
- 'Mephistopheles'	CBor CPrp IBlr MSpe NHol WFar
- 'Merryman'	IBal
- 'Météore'	ECtt EHyd EPfP LRHS MPri NRHS WFar
- 'Morgenlicht'	IBal NHol WFar
- 'Mount Usher'	CPrp EPPr IBal MNrw NHol
§ - 'Mrs Geoffrey Howard'	EHyd GBin IBal NHol SHar SRms WCru
- 'Mrs Morrison'	see *C.* × *crocosmiiflora* 'Mrs Geoffrey Howard'
- 'Newry Seedling'	see *C.* × *crocosmiiflora* 'Prometheus'
- 'Nimbus'	CPrp IBal
§ - 'Norwich Canary'	ECha ECtt EGrI EHyd EPfP EPri GKev IBal LRHS MPie MRav NBir NGdn NHol NRHS SPer WSpi
- 'Olympic Fire'	NHol
- 'Pepper'	IBlr
- 'Plaisir'	IBal NBid NHol
- 'Polo'	CPrp CWCL ECtt EHyd IBal
- 'Princess'	see *C. pottsii* 'Princess'
- 'Prolificans'	IBal
§ - 'Prometheus'	EHyd IBal IBlr NHol
§ - 'Queen Alexandra' J.E. Fitt	CPrp ECha EWes WHal
- 'Queen Charlotte'	IBal
- 'Queen Mary II'	see *C.* × *crocosmiiflora* 'Columbus'
- 'Queen of Spain'	ELon IBal
- 'Rayon d'Or'	IBal
- 'Red David'	WFar
- 'Red King'	CBro CDor CEme EBee EHyd EPfP GKev IBal LRHS NLar NRHS SGBe WBrk WFar XLum
- 'Red Knight'	IBal
- 'Rheingold' misapplied	see *C.* × *crocosmiiflora* 'Diadème'
- 'Saint Clements'	IBal IBlr NHol
- 'Saracen' ♀H4	CBro CMac CWCL EBee ECtt EShb GKin IBal LEdu LRHS MAvo MHol MNrw NLar NSti SEdd SPoG SPtp WCot WFar
- 'Sir Mathew Wilson'	IBal
- 'Solfatare'	CBcs CEme CMac CPrp CWCL ECha ECtt EGrI EHyd ELan EPfP GKin IBal ILea LRHS MAvo MBel MHer NBid NGrd NHol SRms SWvt WCAu WFar WGwG WSHC WSpi
- 'Solfatare Coleton Fishacre'	see *C.* × *crocosmiiflora* 'Coleton Fishacre'
- 'Star of the East' ♀H4	Widely available
- 'Sultan'	CExl WFar
- 'Sunglow'	CBod CPla EBee ECtt EPfP GKev IBal MNrw NWsh SBls WHil WSpi
- 'Twilight Fairy Gold'	CBod CPrp EBee ECha ECtt IBal MACG MBNS MNrw NHpl SMad SMrm WCot WFar WMal WSpi
- 'Venus'	CDor ECtt IBal MHer MSpe NHol WSpi
- 'Vesuvius'	IBal WSHC
- 'Vic's Yellow'	IBal
- 'Voyager'	CPrp ECtt EHyd IBal NBir NHol NLar SDeJ SDir
- Wasdale strain	IBal
- 'Zeal Tan'	CBro CExl CPrp EBee ECtt ELan ELon EPfP EPri EWhm IBal LEdu LRHS MNrw MPie NLar NRHS NSti SDix SEdd SGbt SPoG WCAu WCot WFar WGwG WHoo
× ***crocosmioides*** 'Castle Ward Late'	CBro CPrp ECha ECtt EHyd EPfP IBal IBlr LEdu LRHS NHol NLar NRHS SRms WCot WFar WSpi
§ - 'Vulcan' Leichtlin	IBlr
'Darkleaf Apricot'	see *C.* × *crocosmiiflora* 'Coleton Fishacre'
'Doctor Marion Wood'	IBal
'Ellenbank Canary'	GBin IBal MAvo
'Ellenbank Firecrest' ♀H4	CPrp EBee IBal IPot MHCG
'Ellenbank Goldcrest'	IBal WSHC
'Ellenbank Skylark'	IBal
'Emberglow'	Widely available
'Fandango'	IBal NHol
'Fernhill'	IBal
'Fire King' misapplied	see *C.* × *crocosmiiflora* 'Jackanapes'
'Fire King' ambig.	EHyd IBal LRHS MPri NLar NRHS NSti SWvt
'Firebird'	CRos ECtt EHyd ELon IBal LRHS MHol NHol NRHS SRms WCot
'Firefly'	CPrp CRos EBee ECtt ECul EHyd EPfP GJos LRHS NRHS
'Firestarter' (Firestars Series) **new**	SHar
'Flaire'	IBlr
'Fleuve Jaune'	IBal
'Forest Fire'	IBal
fucata 'Jupiter'	see *C.* 'Jupiter'
fucata × ***paniculata***	IBal
'Fugue'	IBal IBlr SMad
'Golden Dew'	ECtt IBal MBNS WCot WFar
GOLDEN FLEECE *sensu* Lemoine	see *C.* × *crocosmiiflora* 'Coleton Fishacre'
'Harmonia'	EPri
'Hellfire' ♀H5	Widely available
'Highlight'	IBal MAvo NHol NWad
'Hot Spot' (Firestars Series) **new**	SHar
'Jennine'	IBal
JENNY BLOOM ('Blacro'PBR)	EBee EBlo EHyd IBal
'John Boots'	ECtt ELon IBal LRHS MCot NBid NLar SGBe SRms
§ 'Jupiter'	CWCL IBal LRHS NBir NChi NHol NLar
'Karin'	EBee EHyd GKev LRHS MACG NRHS SDir WFar WHil
'Kathleen'	CPrp
'Krakatoa'	CPrp EBee IBal MHer SWvt WFar
'Lady Ann'	CBro CPrp EBee MAsh
'Lady Jane'	CRos EBee EHyd EPfP GKev LRHS MAsh NRHS
'Lady Wilson' misapplied	see *C.* × *crocosmiiflora* 'Norwich Canary'
'Lana de Savary'	CPrp ECtt EPPr EWes IBal MNrw NBid NHol NWad WCot
'Late Cornish'	see *C.* × *crocosmiiflora* 'Queen Alexandra' J.E. Fitt
'Late Lucifer'	CTri IBal IBlr MNrw
'Late Yellow'	IBal WSMil
'Lemon Spray'	IBal IBlr
'Limpopo' ♀H5	Widely available
'Lucifer' ♀H5	Widely available
LUCIFER'S CHILDREN	ELan

'Marcotijn'	IBal
masoniorum 🏆H4	Widely available
- from Satan's Nek, South Africa	IBal
- 'African Dawn'	EBee ECtt
- 'Amber'	IBlr
- 'Dixter Flame'	SDix SMHy
- 'Golden Swan'	SRms
- 'Moira Reid'	IBal
- 'Rowallane Apricot'	IBlr
- 'Rowallane Orange'	GBin IBal IBlr
- 'Rowallane Yellow'	EBee EHyd EPPr EPri GBin IBal IBlr MNrw NHol WBor WMal WPGP WSHC
- 'Sherbert Orange'	IBal MAvo
- Slieve Donard selection	IBal
- 'Sunflare'	IBlr
- 'Tropicana'	IBlr
aff. ***mathewsiana***	IBal
'Mex'	IBal LEdu SMad WPGP
'Ministar'	CBod CBro CPrp CRos EBee EHyd LLWG LRHS NRHS WFar
'Minotaur'	IBal
'Miss Scarlet'	EHyd EPfP LRHS NRHS SAko
'Mistral'	CCCN CRos ECtt EHyd EPfP GAbr GKev IBal LRHS NHol NLar NRHS SCob SEdd WFar
'Moorland Sunset'	IBal
'Mr Bedford'	see *C.* × *crocosmiiflora* 'Croesus'
'Okavango'	CBcs CBor CBro CMac CPrp ECtt ELon EPfP EPri EShb IBal IPot LPla LRHS MAvo MBNS MCot MHol MNrw MSCN NLar NSti SDix WBor WCAu WCot WFar WSpi
OLD HAT	see *C.*'Walberton Red'
'Orange Devil'	ECtt EHyd EPfP EWes GKin IBal LRHS MBNS NRHS SGbt WGoo
ORANGE PEKOE ('Pek Or'PBR)	GBin IBal LCro LOPS MAvo NSti SMad
'Orange River'	WCot WFar
'Orangeade'	IBal NHol SRms
'Pageant'	IBal
§ ***paniculata***	CDor CMac GAbr LEdu NBid WBrk WPGP
- brown/orange-flowered	IBlr
- 'Cally Greyleaf'	EBee EPPr GBin IBal MAvo MNrw WCot WMal
- 'Cally Sword'	CSpe EPPr IBal MAvo
- 'Major'	CTri IBlr
- 'Natal'	CPrp IBal NHol
- red-flowered	IBal IBlr SWvt
- triploid	IBlr
'Paul's Best Yellow' 🏆H4	Widely available
'Peach Sunrise'	IBal
'Phillipa Browne'	CSde ECtt IBal IPot MNrw NLar WCot
'Plancheon'	IBal
pottsii	CRos EHyd GWyn LEdu LRHS NRHS
- 'Culzean Pink'	CElw CExl CPrp EBee EPPr EWhm GBin IBal IBlr LPla MNrw MSpe NBid NBir NHol NHpl WFar
- 'Grandiflora'	IBal
§ - 'Princess'	EBee ECtt EHyd GKev IBal LRHS NRHS
- tall	IBal
'Pride of Plantion'	CBro CPrp ILea
'Prince of Orange'	CBod CBro CPrp CRos EBee ECul EHyd EPfP ERCP GKev LRHS MSCN NRHS SDeJ WFar WWtn
'Queen Alexandria'	CRos EHyd LRHS NRHS WFar
'R.W.Wallace'	IBal
'Raspberry Spray'	IBlr
'Red Star'	IBal
rosea	see *Tritonia disticha* subsp. *rubrolucens*
'Rowden Bronze'	see *C.* × *crocosmiiflora* 'Coleton Fishacre'
'Rowden Chrome'	see *C.* × *crocosmiiflora* 'George Davison' Davison
'Ruby Velvet'	IBlr
'Sampford Yellow'	IBal
'Saturn'	see *C.*'Jupiter'
'Scarlatti'	EBee ECtt IBal NHol NWad
'Scorchio' (Firestars Series) **new**	SHar
'Severn Sunrise' 🏆H5	CBor CElw CExl CMac CPrp CRos ECha ECtt EGrI EHyd EPfP EWhm GKin GMaP IBal IBlr LRHS MHer NBir NGdn NHol NRHS SRms SWvt WBrk WCAu WFar WSHC WSpi
'Shocking'	IBal
'Spitfire'	CExl CPrp EBlo ECtt ELan IBal LRHS MArl MAvo MRav NHol SWvt WFar
§ 'Sulphurea'	CExl ECtt EPfP IBal LRHS MSpe NHol
'Sunzest'	ECtt MAvo WHoo
'Suzanna'	CPrp ECtt MAvo SDir
'Tai Pan'	IBal
'Tangerine Dream'	IBlr
'Tangerine Queen'	GAbr IBal IBlr NHol NWad
'Tangerine Spray'	IBlr
'Tanllyd' **new**	WCot
'Tiger'	CElw
'Toccata'	IBlr
'Twilight Fairy Crimson'	CWGN EBee ECtt EPri GBin LEdu LLWG NHpl NLar WFar WSpi
I 'Vulcan' A. Bloom	EBlo IBal IBlr LRHS MAvo
'Vulcan' Leichtlin	see *C.* × *crocosmioides* 'Vulcan' Leichtlin
§ 'Walberton Red'	EBee IBal LRHS MAvo NWad SMad
WALBERTON YELLOW ('Walcroy'PBR)	EHyd EPfP LRHS NRHS SMad
'Zambesi'	CBro CMac CPrp ECtt ELon GBin IBal IPot MAvo MBNS MNrw SMad WCot XLum
'Zeal Giant' 🏆H4	ECtt EPfP IBal IBlr LRHS NHol WMal
'Zeal Unnamed'	CBro CPrp IBal NHol

Crocus ✿ (*Iridaceae*)

'Advance'	GKev LCro LOPS NRog SDeJ SDir
ancyrensis	EPot GKev NRog SDeJ
- 'Golden Bunch'	EHyd LRHS NRHS SDeJ SDir WShi
§ ***angustifolius*** 🏆H6	EPot GKev SDeJ WShi
- 'Berlin Gold'	GKev
- 'Minor'	EPot
antalyensis	GKev
- yellow-flowered	GKev
'Ard Schenk'	CRos EHyd EPfP GKev LRHS NRHS NRog
asturicus	see *C. serotinus* subsp. *salzmannii*
asumaniae	EPot NRog
'Aubade'	EPot NRog
aureus	see *C. flavus* subsp. *flavus*
autranii	NRog
banaticus 🏆H6	EPot GArf GKev NDry NHar NHpl NRog
- 'First Snow' **new**	NRog
- 'Snowdrift'	NHar NRog

biflorus subsp. ***biflorus***	GKev
§ - - 'Parkinsonii'	GKev
- 'Blue Pearl' ♀H6	CAvo EPfP EPot ERCP GKev LCro LOPS LRHS NBir NRog SDeJ SDir SPer SPhx WCot WShi
- subsp. ***isauricus***	NRog
- subsp. ***melantherus***	GKev NDry NRog
- 'Miss Vain'	EPot ERCP GKev NRog SPer
- subsp. ***nubigena***	NDry
- var. ***parkinsonii***	see *C. biflorus* subsp. *biflorus* 'Parkinsonii'
- subsp. ***pulchricolor***	GKev
- subsp. ***stridii***	EPot GKev
- subsp. ***tauri***	EPot NRog
- subsp. ***weldenii*** 'Albus'	EPot GKev NRog
- - 'Fairy'	GKev NRog
'Blue Bird'	EPot
blue-flowered	EHyd LRHS NRHS
boryi	CAvo EHyd NRHS NRog
cancellatus	NRog SDeJ
§ - subsp. ***cancellatus***	EPot GKev
- var. ***cilicicus***	see *C. cancellatus* subsp. *cancellatus*
- subsp. ***damascenus***	NRog
- subsp. ***lycius***	EPot NRog
- subsp. ***mazziaricus***	NRog
- subsp. ***pamphylicus***	NRog
candidus 'Lune'	GKev
- var. ***subflavus***	see *C. olivieri* subsp. *olivieri*
cartwrightianus ♀H6	EHyd GKev NRHS NRog WShi
- from Crete **new**	NRog
- 'Albus' misapplied	see *C. hadriaticus*
- 'Albus' Tubergen	EPot GKev SDeJ
- 'Marcel'	GKev NRog
- 'Michel'	GKev NRog
'Celia' **new**	GKev
chrysanthus	CHab
- 'Blue Peter'	EPot
- 'Constellation'	EPot
- 'Cream Beauty' ♀H6	CAvo EHyd EPfP EPot ERCP LCro LOPS LRHS MBros NBir NRHS NRog SDeJ SDir WShi
- var. ***fuscotinctus***	EPot GKev LCro LOPS NRog SDeJ
- 'Goldene Sonne'	EPot
- 'Milea'	NRog
- 'Sunspot'	EPot
- 'White Beauty'	CWCL
- 'Zwanenburg Bronze' ♀H6	SDeJ
'Cloth of Gold'	see *C. angustifolius*
corsicus ♀H6	EPot GKev NRog
dalmaticus	EPot
- 'Petrovac'	GKev NRog
'Dorothy'	CAvo EPot NRog SDir WShi
'Dutch Yellow'	see *C.* × *luteus* 'Golden Yellow'
etruscus	GKev NRog
- 'Rosalind'	GKev NRog
- 'Zwanenburg'	EHyd EPot GKev LRHS NRHS NRog SDeJ SDir
'Fantasy'	WShi
§ ***flavus*** subsp. ***flavus*** ♀H6	EPot GKev WShi
fleischeri	EPot GKev NRog
'Florane' **new**	GKev
'Flower Record'	CArg CAvo GKev LRHS NBir NRog SDeJ
gargaricus	GKev
gilanicus	GKev
'Gipsy Girl'	EPot ERCP GKev LCro LOPS NRog SDir SPer
'Golden Mammoth'	see *C.* × *luteus* 'Golden Yellow'
'Goldilocks' ♀H6	EShb GKev NRog SDeJ
goulimyi ♀H6	CAvo EHyd EPot GKev LRHS NRHS NRog SDeJ WCot
- 'Albus'	see *C. goulimyi* subsp. *goulimyi* 'Mani White'
§ - subsp. ***goulimyi*** 'Mani White' ♀H4	EPot
- subsp. ***leucanthus***	GKev NRog
'Grand Maître'	GKev NRog SDeJ SDir
§ ***hadriaticus***	EHyd GKev NDry NRHS NRog WShi
- 'Annabelle'	GKev
- var. ***chrysobelonicus***	see *C. hadriaticus*
- subsp. ***hadriaticus*** f. ***lilacinus***	GKev
- 'Jumbo'	NRog
'Herald'	GKev NRog SDeJ
heuffelianus	GKev WShi
- 'Drina Marvel'	GKev NRog
- 'Krasno Polje'	NRog
- 'Michael's Purple'	GKev
- 'Shock Wave'	CWCL
- Uklin strain	GKev NRog
imperati	CWCL EPot
subsp. ***suaveolens***	
- - 'De Jager'	CAvo ERCP GKev NRog SDeJ
'Jeanne d'Arc'	CArg CAvo EPot GKev LCro LOPS LRHS NBir NRog SDeJ WShi
'Jeannine'	NRog SDeJ
× ***jessoppiae***	GKev
karduchorum	EPot GKev
'King of the Striped'	GKev NRog SDeJ SPer
korolkowii	GKev LHWs NRog
- 'Golden Nugget'	GKev
- 'January Gold'	CAvo
- 'Kiss of Spring'	EPot GKev NRog
- 'Mountain Glory'	NDry
kosaninii	GKev
kotschyanus ♀H6	EGrI GKev MBros NBir SDeJ
- 'Albus'	GKev NRog SDeJ
- subsp. ***cappadocicus***	NRog
§ - subsp. ***kotschyanus***	EPot GKev NRog SDeJ
- - var. ***leucopharynx***	NRog
- 'Reliance'	GKev NRog
'Ladykiller'	EPot GKev NRog WShi
laevigatus ♀H4	GKev NDry NRog WIce
- CE&H 612	EPot
- 'Fontenayi'	EPot ERCP GKev NRog
'Large Yellow'	see *C.* × *luteus* 'Golden Yellow'
large-flowered blue	SDir
× ***leonidii*** 'Early Gold'	GKev SDir
§ ***ligusticus*** ♀H6	EPot GKev NRog
'Little Amber'	GKev
longiflorus ♀H6	EHyd EPot GKev NRHS NRog
§ × ***luteus*** 'Golden Yellow' ♀H6	CArg CAvo EPot GKev LCro LOPS LRHS NRog SDeJ SDir WShi
§ - 'Stellaris'	EPot
malyi ♀H6	CWCL GKev NRog
- 'Ballerina'	GKev
- 'Sveti Roc'	GKev
mathewii	EPot GKev NDry NHpl NRog
- 'Dream Dancer'	EPot GKev NDry
medius	see *C. ligusticus*
minimus	EPot ERCP GKev NRog
- 'Spring Beauty'	CAvo ERCP GKev LCro LOPS SDeJ
'Negro Boy'	EPot
nevadensis	GKev
niveus	EHyd EPot GKev NRHS NRog
nudiflorus	EPot GKev NRog
ochroleucus	EPot GKev SDeJ
olivieri AH 0156	GKev
- subsp. ***balansae***	NRog

§ - - 'Orange Monarch'	ERCP GKev LHWs
- - 'Zwanenburg'	EPot
§ - subsp. ***olivieri***	GKev NRog
- - 'Little Tiger'	GKev
'Orange Monarch'	see *C. olivieri* subsp. *balansae* 'Orange Monarch'
oreocreticus	NRog
pallasii VV KR.75	GKev
- subsp. ***dispathaceus***	NRog
- subsp. ***pallasii***	NRog
- subsp. ***turcicus***	GKev
paschei	GKev
pelistericus	GKev
pestalozzae	GKev NRog
- subsp. ***violaceus***	GKev
'Pickwick'	CArg CAvo GKev LCro LOPS LRHS NBir NRog SDeJ WShi
'Prins Claus'	CAvo CRos EHyd EPot ERCP GKev LCro LOPS LRHS MBros NBir NRHS NRog SDeJ
pulchellus ♀H6	NRog SDeJ WCot
- 'Albus'	EPot NRog
- 'Inspiration'	GKev NRog
- 'Michael Hoog'	GKev NRog
puringii new	GKev
'Purple Heart'	NDry NRog
'Purpureus'	see *C.* 'Purpureus Grandiflorus'
§ 'Purpureus Grandiflorus'	SDeJ
'Queen of the Blues'	CAvo EPot NRog SDeJ
'Remembrance'	CArg CAvo EPot GKev LCro LOPS LRHS NBir NRog SDeJ WShi
robertianus	NRog
'Romance'	EHyd EPot GKev LCro LOPS LRHS NBir NRHS NRog SDeJ
'Ruby Giant'	CAvo CRos EHyd EMor EPfP EPot ERCP GKev LCro LOPS LRHS NBir NRHS NRog SDeJ SPer SPhx WShi
rujanensis	EPot GKev
salzmannii	see *C. serotinus* subsp. *salzmannii*
sativus	CAvo CBod CBor ELan EPot ERCP GKev GPoy ILea LCro LOPS MBow MHtn NBir NRog SDeJ SDir SVic XAbr
'Saturnus'	EPot
serotinus subsp. ***clusii*** 'Poseidon'	GKev NRog
§ - subsp. ***salzmannii***	GKev NRog
- - 'Atropurpureus'	WCot
- - 'Erectophyllus'	GKev NRog
sibiricus	see *C. sieberi*
§ ***sieberi***	EPot WShi
- 'Albus'	see *C. sieberi* 'Bowles's White'
- subsp. ***atticus***	NRog
- - 'Amfiklia'	GKev NRog
- - 'Firefly'	EHyd EPot ERCP GKev LRHS NRHS NRog SDeJ
§ - 'Bowles's White' ♀H6	EPot GKev NRog SDeJ
- 'Hubert Edelsten' ♀H6	EPot GKev NRog
- 'Ronald Ginns'	EPot
- subsp. ***sublimis***	GKev
- - 'Tricolor' ♀H6	CArg EHyd EPfP EPot GKev LCro LOPS LRHS NBir NRHS NRog SDeJ
'Snow Bunting' ♀H6	CAvo ELan EPot GKev LCro LOPS NBir NRog SDeJ SDir SPer WShi
speciosus ♀H6	CAvo LCro LOPS NBir SDeJ WShi
- 'Aino'	GKev
- 'Aitchisonii'	EHyd GKev NRHS
- 'Albus' ♀H6	CAvo EGrI EPot ERCP GKev LCro LOPS NRog SDeJ WShi
- 'Artabir'	EHyd GKev LRHS NRHS NRog SDeJ
- 'Cassiope'	EHyd GKev NRHS SDeJ
- 'Conqueror'	EHyd ELan ERCP GKev LCro LOPS LRHS NBir NRHS NRog SDeJ
- 'Oxonian'	EHyd ELan EPot GKev LRHS MCot NRHS NRog
- subsp. ***speciosus***	EPot GKev NBir NRog SDeJ
- subsp. ***xantholaimos***	NRog
aff. ***speciosus***	SDir
× ***stellaris***	see *C.* × *luteus* 'Stellaris'
striped	SDir
susianus	see *C. angustifolius*
suterianus	see *C. olivieri* subsp. *olivieri*
thomasii	GKev NRog
tommasinianus ♀H6	CArg CHab ELan EPot GKev LCro LOPS MRav NBir NRog SDeJ SDir SPhx SRms WShi
- 'Albus'	EPot GKev NRog WShi
- 'Barr's Purple'	EHyd EPot GKev LCro LOPS LRHS NBir NRHS NRog SDeJ
- 'Bobbo'	EHyd NDry
- 'Claret'	NDry
- 'Eric Smith'	EPot NDry
- 'Lilac Beauty'	EPot GKev NRog
- 'Pictus'	EPot GKev NDry NRog WShi
- 'Roseus'	EPot ERCP GKev NRog SDeJ SPhx WCot WShi
- 'Rubinetta'	GKev
- 'Whitewell Purple'	CAvo EHyd EPot ERCP GKev LCro LOPS LRHS NBir NRHS NRog SDeJ WCot WShi
tournefortii ♀H4	CAvo EHyd EPot GKev NRHS NRog
'Twinborn'	EPot
vallicola	EPot
'Vanguard' ♀H6	EPot GKev LCro LOPS NRog SDeJ WCot
veluchensis	NRog
vernus	GKev NRog WShi
- subsp. ***albiflorus***	see *C. vernus*
- blue-flowered	GKev
- 'Lavender Symphony'	GKev
- 'Purple Apex'	GKev
- 'Purple Desire'	GKev
- subsp. ***vernus*** 'Grandiflorus'	see *C.* 'Purpureus Grandiflorus'
versicolor JMH 8215	GKev
- 'Picturatus'	EPot GKev NRog SDeJ WShi
vitellinus	EPot GKev NRog
'Willem van Eeden' new	GKev
'Yalta'	CAvo GKev SPhx WCot
'Yellow Mammoth'	see *C.* × *luteus* 'Golden Yellow'
'Zenith'	EPot
'Zephyr' ♀H6	SDeJ SPhx
zonatus	see *C. kotschyanus* subsp. *kotschyanus*

Croomia (*Stemonaceae*)

heterosepala	WCru

Crossandra (*Acanthaceae*)

infundibuliformis ♀H1a	EShb

Crossyne (*Amaryllidaceae*)

flava	WCot

Crotalaria (*Fabaceae*)

laburnifolia ♀H2	CCCN

Crowea (*Rutaceae*)

exalata × ***saligna***	CExl

Crucianella (*Rubiaceae*)

stylosa	see *Phuopsis stylosa*

Cruciata (*Rubiaceae*)
§ ***laevipes*** NAts

Crusea (*Rubiaceae*)
coccinea GEdr SBrt WCot
- 'Crûg Crimson' WSHC

Cryptanthus (*Bromeliaceae*)
bivittatus ♀H1a NCft
- 'Pink Starlite' (v) ♀H1a NCft
- 'Red Star' **new** NCft
lacerdae 'Menescal' **new** NCft
'Strawberries Flambé' **new** NCft

Cryptanthus × *Billbergia* see × *Cryptbergia*

× *Cryptbergia* (*Bromeliaceae*)
'Rubra' SChr

Cryptocarya (*Lauraceae*)
alba GBin SVen

Cryptogramma (*Pteridaceae*)
crispa WHer

Cryptomeria ✿ (*Cupressaceae*)
fortunei see *C. japonica*
§ ***japonica*** CAco CBod CJun CMen EPfP IPap LPar MBlu MMuc NWea SCob SEND SWvt SavN WMou WTSh
- Araucarioides Group CAco SLim
- 'Atawai' NLar
- 'Bandai-sugi' ♀H6 CAco CKen CMac CMen IArd MGos NHol NLar SRms
- 'Barabits Gold' CAco LRHS SavN
- 'Bicton Broom' SLim
- 'Birodo' CKen
- 'Black Dragon' SLim
- 'Carmel' MBlu
- 'Compressa' CAco CKen EPfP LBee MAsh NLar SLim SRms
§ - 'Cristata' CAco CMac ELan LRHS MGos MPkF SLim SRms SavN
- 'Dacrydioides' CAco MGil NLar
- 'Dinger' CAco CKen LRHS NLar
- Elegans Group CBcs CEme CMac CSBt ELan EPfP LRHS MGos NLar NWea SCoo SEND SPer SPoG SRms WFar WMat
- - 'Elegans' ♀H6 CBrac MGil NOrn SGsty SLim
- 'Elegans Aurea' CBod CCVT CEme ELan LRHS SPoG SWvt WFar
- 'Elegans Compacta' ♀H6 CBod CEme CMac CSBt ELan GBin LBee LRHS MAsh MGil MMuc NLar NWea SCob SCoo SEND SLim SPad SRms SWvt WHwl
- 'Elegans Nana' MGil SRms WHwl
- 'Elegans Viridis' ♀H6 LPar MGil SGsty SLim WMat
I - 'Elegantissima' CCVT
- 'Globosa Nana' ♀H6 CAco EPfP LBee MGos NHol NPoe SArc SCob SCoo SGsty SPoG SWeb
- 'Golden Promise' ♀H6 CAco CBcs CBod MAsh NHol NWad SLim SWvt
- Gracilis Group CAco
- 'HB Bandai' MBlu
- 'Jindai-sugi' LRHS NLar WLea
- 'Kilmacurragh' CKen NWea
- 'Kohui-yatsubusa' CKen
- 'Koshyi' CKen
- 'Little Champion' CAco LRHS NLar SGsty SLim
- 'Little Diamond' CKen
- 'Little Sonja' CAco CKen SLim
- 'Little Yoko' CKen NLar
- 'Lobbii' LRHS
§ - 'Mankichi-sugi' CAco
- 'Midare' CAco NLar
- 'Monstrosa' LRHS NLar
- 'Monstrosa Nana' see *C. japonica* 'Mankichi-sugi'
- 'Mushroom' NLar SLim
§ - 'Nana' SRms
- 'Osaka-tama' CKen
- 'Pipo' CKen MBlu
- 'Pygmaea' CAco LRHS MGil NHol NLar SRms
- 'Rasen-sugi' IDee LRHS MGil NFav NLar
- 'Rein's Dense Jade' SLim
- 'Sekkan-sugi' ♀H6 CAco CBcs CBrac CCVT CEme CMac ELan EPfP ESwi GBin GKin IArd LBee LRHS MAsh MGos MTrO NLar NOrn NPoe SCoo SLim SPoG SWvt WBor WMat
- 'Sekka-sugi' see *C. japonica* 'Cristata'
§ - 'Spiralis' ♀H6 CAco CKen ELan EPfP LBee LRHS MAsh MGil MGos NHol NLar NWea SAko SCoo SLim SPoG SRms SWvt
§ - 'Spiraliter Falcata' NLar
§ - 'Tansu' CAco CKen MGil
- 'Tenzan-sugi' ♀H6 CKen NHol NLar
- 'Tenzan-yatsubusa' CMen
- 'Tilford Gold' LRHS LSRN NHol SCoo SLim
- 'Toda' CKen
- 'Tsukomo' **new** NLar
- 'Twinkle Toes' CKen
- 'Vilmorin Gold' CAco LRHS NHol
- 'Vilmoriniana' ♀H6 CEme CKen ELan EPfP GKin LSRN MAsh MGil MGos NHol NLar SCoo SLim SPer SPoG SWvt
- 'Winter Bronze' CKen
- 'Yatsubusa' see *C. japonica* 'Tansu'
- 'Yellow Twig' NLar
- 'Yokohama' **new** NFav
- 'Yore-sugi' see *C. japonica* 'Spiralis', 'Spiraliter Falcata'
- 'Yoshino' CKen SLim
sinensis see *C. japonica*

Cryptostegia (*Apocynaceae*)
grandiflora CCCN

Cryptotaenia (*Apiaceae*)
canadensis GGro
japonica CAgr CHby CLau GPoy MNHC SRms WHer WJek
- f. ***atropurpurea*** CDor CSpe EBee EWhm GGro LEdu MNrw WBor XLum

Ctenanthe (*Marantaceae*)
§ ***burle-marxii*** CDoC
§ ***oppenheimiana*** NGBl

Cucubalus (*Caryophyllaceae*)
baccifer GGro NLar

cucumber see AGM Vegetables Section

Cucumis (*Cucurbitaceae*)
melo 'Alvaro' ♀H1c **new** EDel
- 'Charentais' SVic
- 'Emir' ♀H1c EKin LCro LOPS MCtn
- 'Mini Yellow' LRHS NRHS
- 'Pepito' EHyd LRHS NRHS

Cudrania see *Maclura*

cumin see *Cuminum cyminum*

Cuminum (*Apiaceae*)

cyminum SRms SVic

Cunninghamia (*Cupressaceae*)

konishii CExl SMad
§ ***lanceolata*** CAco CMCN CMac EPfP IDee LRHS MGil SSta WPGP
- 'Glauca' CAco CExl CJun IDee
- 'Samurai' **new** CAco
sinensis see *C. lanceolata*
unicaniculata see *C. lanceolata*

Cunonia (*Cunoniaceae*)

capensis CExl

Cuphea (*Lythraceae*)

blepharophylla EWld
caeciliae WMal
cyanea CSpe LSvl SDix SEdd
hyssopifolia ♀H2 CTsd EShb SWvt WHil
- 'Alba' CCCN EShb SWvt
- pink-flowered CCCN
- red-flowered CCCN
- 'Rosea' SWvt
§ ***ignea*** ♀H2 CTsd ELan EWld
- 'Matchless' SVic
- 'Roxy' EPPr
'Lilac Belle' CSpe
§ ***llavea*** 'Georgia Scarlet' CCCN
maculata CCCN
platycentra see *C. ignea*
'Torpedo' MBros WHil
viscosissima CSpe ELan EWld MCot

× *Cupressocyparis* see × *Cuprocyparis*

Cupressus (*Cupressaceae*)

arizonica CAco CBod LPar SArc SWeb
I - 'Fastigiata Aurea' LPar SGsty SWeb
§ - var. ***glabra*** CAco
- - 'Angaston' SLim
- - 'Aurea' CAco CEme SGol SLim
- - 'Blue Ice' CAco CMac MAsh SLim SWvt
- - 'Compacta' CKen
I - - 'Fastigiata' CCVT SCob SGsty
- - 'Glauca' CAco
- var. ***nevadensis*** CAco
- 'Pyramidalis' ♀H5 SEND SGol
- 'Réka' **new** CAco
- var. ***stephensonii*** **new** CAco
I - 'Sulfurea' CAco
bakeri CAco
cashmeriana ♀H3 CAco SPtp
- KR 8688A WPGP
- 'Blue Wave' **new** SMad
chengiana CAco
duclouxiana CAco
dupreziana CAco SLim WPav
var. ***atlantica***
§ ***funebris*** CAco SMad
gigantea CAco
glabra see *C. arizonica* var. *glabra*
goveniana CAco
- var. ***abramsiana*** CAco
guadalupensis CAco
- var. ***forbesii*** CAco
- var. ***guadalupensis*** **new** CAco
× ***leylandii*** see × *Cuprocyparis leylandii*
lusitanica CAco
- var. ***benthamii*** **new** CAco
- 'Brice's Weeping' CKen SLim
- 'Pygmy' CKen
macnabiana CAco
macrocarpa CBcs CBod CCVT IPap SEND
- 'Compacta' CKen
- 'Gold Spread' SLim
- 'Goldcrest' ♀H4 CAco CBcs CBod CCVT CEme CMac ELan LPar LRHS MGos MPri NBir SCob SEWo SGol SGsty SLim SWeb SWvt
- 'Golden Pillar' SWvt
- 'Lohbrunner' CKen
I - 'Pendula' SLim
- 'Pygmaea' CKen
- 'Sulphur Cushion' CKen
- 'Wilma' ♀H4 CEme CSBt ELan EShb LBee MAsh MGos SCoo SGol SLim SPer SPoG SWeb SWvt
- 'Woking' CKen
nootkatensis see *Xanthocyparis nootkatensis*
sargentii CAco
sempervirens CEme LPar MGil SPlb SWeb
- 'Agrimed' CCVT LPar
- 'Bolgheri' LSRN
- 'Green Pencil' CKen
- 'Karaca Fastigiata Aurea' **new** CAco
- 'Pyramidalis' see *C. sempervirens* Stricta Group
- var. ***sempervirens*** see *C. sempervirens* Stricta Group
§ - Stricta Group CBcs CBrac CCVT EPfP LMaj LRHS NLar NOrn SArc SCob SEND SEWo SGol SGsty WSpi
- 'Stricta Blue' **new** CAco LRHS
- 'Swane's Gold' CKen MAsh
- 'Totem Pole' CAco CBod CCVT CKen CSBt CTri ELan EPfP IPap LBee LRHS MAsh MGos SCoo SGsty SLim SPad SPoG SWeb SWvt
torulosa CAco

Cupressus × *Xanthocyparis* see × *Cuprocyparis*

× *Cuprocyparis* ✿ (*Cupressaceae*)

§ ***leylandii*** CAco CArg CBcs CBrac CCVT CEme CMac CTri EPfP LBuc LPar LSRN MAsh MGos MHed MPri NWea SCob SGol SGsty SLim SPer SPoG SWeb SWvt WAvo WFar WMou
I - '2001' CBod CCVT SGol
- 'Blue Jeans'PBR LPar SEND
§ - 'Castlewellan' CBcs CBod CCVT CEme CMac CTri EPfP LBuc LMaj LPar LSRN MAsh MGos MPri NWea SCob SEND SGol SGsty SLim SPer SPoG SWeb SWvt WAvo WFar WTSh
- EXCALIBUR GOLD ('Drabb'PBR) SCob
- 'Ferngold' MAsh
- 'Galway Gold' see × *C. leylandii* 'Castlewellan'
- 'Gold Rider' ♀H6 CBod CCVT CMac ELan MAsh NWea SCoo SEND SGol SGsty SLim SMad SPer SPoG SWeb SWvt
- 'Green Ornament' **new** SMad
- 'Haggerston Grey' SEND
§ - 'Harlequin' (v) CMac SEND SGsty SWvt
- 'Leighton Green' WTSh
- 'Naylor's Blue' CMac SEND
- 'Olive's Green' SWvt

- 'Robinson's Gold' CMac SGol
- 'Silver Dust' (v) WAvo
- 'Variegata' see × *C. leylandii* 'Harlequin'

Curculigo (*Hypoxidaceae*)

crassifolia B&SWJ 2318 WCru
- NJM 10.123 WPGP

Curcuma ✿ (*Zingiberaceae*)

alismatifolia SDeJ
longa GPoy SPlb SPre
roscoeana SDeJ
zedoaria 'Bicolor Wonder' CCCN
- 'Pink Wonder' CCCN
- 'White Wonder' CCCN GBin SDeJ

Curio (*Asteraceae*)

§ ***articulata*** EShb
§ ***ficoides*** EShb NGBl
- 'Mount Everest'PBR EShb
radicans new SIvy
§ ***repens*** CDoC CKel EShb SEdd SIvy SSim
§ ***rowleyanus*** EBak EShb LCro LOPS NCft SIvy SSim WSMil
talinoides 'Himalayan Blue' new WCot
§ - subsp. ***mandraliscae*** WSMil
- - 'Blue Finger' WCot

Curtonus see *Crocosmia*

Cussonia (*Araliaceae*)

gamtoosensis WCot
natalensis WCot
paniculata CDTJ CWGN SPlb
sphaerocephala SPlb WCot
spicata CDTJ SPlb
transvaalensis CDTJ
zuluensis WCot

custard apple see *Annona cherimola*

Cyananthus (*Campanulaceae*)

incanus GEdr GKev
integer misapplied see *C. microphyllus*
lobatus ♀H5 WAbe
- 'Albus' NHar WAbe
- giant GEdr NHar
lobatus* × *microphyllus GEdr WAbe
longiflorus GKev
macrocalyx NHar
§ ***microphyllus*** ♀H5 GEdr GKev NHar NSla WAbe
microphyllus × 'Sherriff's Variety' NHar
sherriffii WAbe

Cyanastrum (*Tecophilaeaceae*)

cordifolium GKev

Cyanella (*Tecophilaeaceae*)

lutea NRog

Cyanotis (*Commelinaceae*)

sp. new WHil
beddomei ♀H1b EShb
somaliensis ♀H1b EShb

Cyathea (*Cyatheaceae*)

atrox CKel
australis CBdn CDTJ CKel CTrC CTsd EHed ESwi ETod IKel SPlb
brownii CKel ETod
cooperi ♀H2 CAbb CBct CBdn CBrP CCht CDTJ CKel CTrC CTsd ESwi ETod IKel LRHS MHtn NBro WFib XSte
- 'Brentwood' EBee EHed ESwi
cunninghamii CKel
dealbata CBdn CDTJ CKel ETod IKel
dregei SPlb
medullaris CBdn CKel ETod IKel
robusta CKel
smithii CDTJ CKel ETod IKel
tomentosissima CDTJ CKel IKel

Cyathodes (*Ericaceae*)

colensoi see *Leucopogon colensoi*
fraseri see *Leucopogon fraseri*

Cycas (*Cycadaceae*)

panzhihuaensis CBrP SPlb
revoluta ♀H2 CAbb CBcs CBrP CCCN CDoC CTsd EOli EPfP EShb LCro LOPS LPar SArc SChr SEND SGsty SPalm SPlb SWeb WSMil
revoluta* × *taitungensis CBrP
§ ***rumphii*** CBrP
taitungensis CBrP
thouarsii see *C. rumphii*

Cyclamen ✿ (*Primulaceae*)

abchasicum see *C. coum* subsp. *caucasicum*
africanum CBro EHyd GKev LRHS MAsh NRHS
§ ***alpinum*** CRos EHyd EPot GKev LRHS MAsh NRHS NRog SDeJ
- 'Nettleton White' MAsh
balearicum EHyd EPot GKev NRHS NRog
cilicium ♀H3 CBro EGrI EHyd EPot ERCP GKev GRum LCro LOPS LRHS MAsh NHpl NRHS NRog NSla WHoo WShi
- f. ***album*** EGrI EHyd EPot GKev LRHS MAsh NRHS
colchicum MAsh
confusum GKev
§ ***coum*** ♀H5 Widely available
- var. ***abchasicum*** see *C. coum* subsp. *caucasicum*
- 'Ashwood Snowflake' MAsh
§ - subsp. ***caucasicum*** GKev MAsh
- subsp. ***coum*** CBro
- - f. ***albissimum*** GKev
- - - 'George Bisson' MAsh
- - - 'Golan Heights' MAsh
- - - 'Lake Effect' MAsh
- - f. ***coum*** Nymans Group GRum
- - - Pewter Group ♀H5 GEdr GKev NRog WCot
- - - - 'Maurice Dryden' CBro CRos EHyd EPot GKev LEdu LRHS MAsh NRHS NRog WHoo
- - - - 'Tilebarn Elizabeth' GRum MAsh NBir WHoo
- - - 'Roseum' CAvo
- - - Silver Group CBro CRos EHyd EPot LRHS NRHS NRya WHoo
- - - - red-flowered WHoo
- - magenta-flowered WHoo
- - f. ***pallidum*** 'Album' CAvo CWCL EGrI EMor EWhm EWoo GEdr GKev GMaP GWyn LCro LOPS NRog SDeJ SEdd SPeP SPer WHoo WPnP WShi
- dark pink-flowered CAvo WHoo
- hybrid ERCP
- marble-leaved SBea WHoo
- 'Marianne' SAko
- 'Meaden's Crimson' GRum

	- red-flowered	EGrI
I	- 'Rubrum'	EWoo GKev GWyn LCro LOPS
	- silver speckled leaf	CAvo
	creticum* × *repandum	see *C.* × *meiklei*
	cyprium	EHyd EPot GKev GRum LRHS MAsh NRHS
	- 'E.S.'	WThu
	- 'Galaxy'	MAsh
	elegans	GKev MAsh
	europaeum	see *C. purpurascens*
	fatrense	see *C. purpurascens* from Fatra, Slovakia
	graecum	CBro EHyd EPot GKev LRHS MHer NRHS WAbe WHoo WThu
	- subsp. ***candicum***	WThu
	- subsp. ***graecum*** f. ***album***	EHyd GKev MAsh NRHS
	- - f. ***graecum*** 'Glyfada'	GKev
§	***hederifolium*** ♀H5	Widely available
	- S&L 175/1	WCot XLum
	- 'Amazeme'	WBrk WCot
	- 'Amazeme Pink' **new**	LRHS
	- subsp. ***crassifolium***	MAsh
	- var. ***hederifolium*** f. ***albiflorum*** ♀H5	CAvo CBro CTsd EBee EGrI EMor EWoo GKev LCro LEdu LOPS NRog NWad SBea SDeJ SEND SEdd SPeP WHoo WPnP XLum
	- - - 'Album'	CWCL EWTr SDeJ WShi
	- - - Bowles's Apollo Group	NWad
	- - - 'Discovery'	WCot
	- - - 'Nettleton Silver'	see *C. hederifolium* var. *hederifolium* f. *albiflorum* 'White Cloud'
	- - - 'Perlenteppich'	GMaP
	- - - silver-leaved	SDys
§	- - - 'White Cloud' ♀H5	GRum MAsh NHpl WHoo
	- - f. ***hederifolium*** 'Fairy Rings'	MAsh
	- - - 'Rosenteppich'	CMiW CTsd
	- - - 'Ruby Glow'	EHyd LRHS MAsh NBir NRHS WThu
	- - - Silver Cloud Group ♀H5	CBro GRum MAsh NBir WHoo
	- - - 'Silver Shield'	MAsh
	- - - 'Stargazer'	MAsh
	- island scented strain	WCot
	- 'Lysander'	GKev MAsh
	- 'Pewter Mist'	SPeP
	- 'Red Sky'	CAvo CBro GRum MAsh
	- 'Rosy Pink' **new**	EGrI
	- 'Silver Leaf'	see *C. hederifolium* Silver-leaved Group
§	- Silver-leaved Group	CAvo CRos EHyd EPot GAbr GEdr GKev LRHS NRHS NSla
	- - 'Silver Leaf Pink'	GMaP
	- - 'Silver Leaf White'	GMaP NWad
	- 'Silverme Pink' **new**	EPPr
	- 'Silverme White' **new**	WBrk
	× ***hildebrandii***	GKev
	ibericum	see *C. coum* subsp. *caucasicum*
	'Indiaka Violet' **new**	CRos
	intaminatum	EHyd EPot GKev GRum LRHS MAsh NRHS WHoo
	- plain-leaved	WThu
	latifolium	see *C. persicum*
	libanoticum	CBro EHyd EPot GKev LRHS MAsh NRHS WThu
§	× ***meiklei***	GKev
	mirabile ♀H4	EGrI EHyd EPot GKev GRum LRHS MAsh NHpl NRHS NSla SDeJ
	- 'Alba'	EGrI GKev SDeJ
	- f. ***mirabile*** 'Tilebarn Anne'	MAsh
	- - 'Tilebarn Nicholas'	MAsh
	- f. ***niveum***	SDeJ
	- - 'Tilebarn Jan'	MAsh
	neapolitanum	see *C. hederifolium*
	orbiculatum	see *C. coum*
	parviflorum	GKev
§	***persicum***	CWCL EHyd GKev LRHS MAsh NRHS NRog WCot
	- Ashwood silver-leaved	MAsh
	- Metis Series	SCob
	- (Super Verano Series) VERANO NEON PINK	LCro LOPS
	- - VERANO RED	LCro LOPS
	- WINFALL WHITE ('Synwinfwhi') (Winfall Series)	LCro LOPS
	pseudibericum ♀H4	CBro CRos EHyd EPot GKev GRum LRHS MAsh NRHS SDeJ WCot
	- AC&W 664	NWad
	- f. ***roseum***	GKev ITim MAsh
§	***purpurascens***	CBro GKev GRum MAsh NHpl NRog NSla WHoo WThu
§	- from Fatra, Slovakia	GKev
	- var. ***fatrense***	see *C. purpurascens* from Fatra, Slovakia
	- 'Lake Garda'	MAsh
	repandum	CAvo CBro CRos CTtf EHyd EPot GKev LRHS MAsh NRHS NRog WHer
	- 'Pelops' misapplied	see *C. rhodium* subsp. *peloponnesiacum*
	- subsp. ***repandum*** f. ***album***	GKev
	rhodium	GKev
§	- subsp. ***peloponnesiacum***	GKev
	rohlfsianum	EHyd GKev MAsh NRHS
	× ***schwarzii***	MAsh
	'Trena'	SDeJ
	trochopteranthum	see *C. alpinum*

Cyclosorus (*Thelypteridaceae*)

	tottoides	LEdu WPGP

Cydonia ✿ (*Rosaceae*)

	japonica	see *Chaenomeles japonica*
	oblonga (F)	GKev SGsty SPre
	- 'Agvambari' (F)	SKee
	- 'Aromatnaya' (F)	MCoo MTrO NOra SKee WMat
	- 'Bereczki'	see *C. oblonga* 'Bereczki'
§	- 'Bereczki' (F)	MTrO
	- 'Champion' (F)	CAgr CHab EBee EPom LBuc LPar MCoo MTrO NOra NRog SEdi SGsty SKee SVic WMat
	- 'Cydora Robusta'^{PBR} (F) **new**	LPar
	- 'Early Prolific' (F)	SEND SEdi
	- 'Ekmek' (F)	SKee
	- 'Gamboa' (F)	SKee
	- 'Iranian' (F)	CAgr
	- 'Isfahan' (F)	MTrO SKee WMat
	- 'Krymsk' (F)	CAgr WWct
	- 'Leskovac' (F)	CAgr EPom LMaj LPar NOra WWct
	- 'Ludovic' (F)	LPar NRog
§	- 'Lusitanica' (F)	CAgr CHab ELan EPom LPar LRHS MTrO NRog SKee SPer SSFr WMat
	- 'Meech's Prolific' (F)	CAgr CHab CLnd CTri EBee ELan EPom LCro LOPS LRHS MGos MMuc MRav MTrO NLar NOra NRog NWea SEdi SKee SPer SSFT SSFr WMat WWct
	- pear-shaped (F)	CHab NRog SPer
	- PORTUGAL	see *C. oblonga* 'Lusitanica'

	- 'Rea's Mammoth' (F)	CHab LPar NLar NRog
	- 'Serbian Gold' (F) ♀H5	CMac EBee EPom GQue LRHS MTrO NLar NOra NRog SKee SSFT WMat
	- 'Shams' (F)	NRog
	- 'Smyrna' (F)	NLar NOra NRog WMat
	- 'Sobu' (F)	SKee
	- 'Vranja' misapplied	see *C. oblonga* 'Bereczki'
	- 'Vranja' ambig. (F)	CBcs CBod CDoC IPap LMaj LPar MAsh MTrO NRog SBdl SCoo SEdi SPoG WHwl
	- 'Vranja' Nenadovic (F)	Widely available

Cylindropuntia (*Cactaceae*)

	imbricata	SPlb XSen
	leptocaulis	XSen
§	***spinosior***	XLum
	versicolor	XSen

Cymbalaria (*Plantaginaceae*)

	aequitriloba 'Alba'	GAbr NRya
§	***hepaticifolia***	CSma SBrt SPlb
§	***muralis***	CBod ECtt GAbr GJos LLWG MHer NRya WHer WIce WTor
	- 'Kenilworth White'	GJos WCot
	- 'Nana Alba'	ECtt EPfP
§	- 'Pallidior'	SPhx
	- 'Snow Wave'	WCot WFar
§	***pallida***	CSma EPfP MAsh MMuc SEND SGro SLee SPlb WCav WFar
	- 'Alba'	EPfP WFar
§	***pilosa***	ECtt NLar

Cymbopogon (*Poaceae*)

	citratus	CBod CCCN ENfk GPoy LCro LOPS MNHC SEdi SPlb SPre SRms SVic XAbr
	flexuosus	CCCN MHer SRms WJek
	nardus	GPoy

Cynanchum (*Apocynaceae*)

	ascyrifolium	EBee LEdu SBrt
	atratum	GEdr

Cynara (*Asteraceae*)

	cardunculus ♀H5	Widely available
	- 'Bianco Avorio'	SVic
I	- 'Cardy'	EWoo
	- dwarf	SDix SSal
	- subsp. ***flavescens***	SBrt
I	- 'Florist Cardy'	NLar
	- 'Gobbo di Nizza'	SRms
	- 'Porto Spineless'	CAgr
§	- Scolymus Group	CBcs CMea EGrl EHyd EPfP EWes GPoy LCro LOPS LRHS LSRN MNHC MRav NRHS SCob SGBe SPhx SPoG WHer
	- - 'Bere'	LEdu
	- - 'Gros Camus de Bretagne'	MAvo WCot
	- - 'Gros Vert de Lâon' ♀H5	CBcs CLau ELan LRHS WCot
	- - 'Monica Lynden-Bell'	WCot
	- - 'Purple Globe'	LEdu SRms
	- - 'Romanesco'	CLau LCro LOPS SRms SVic
	- - 'Rouge d'Alger'	CAgr WLov
	- - 'Tavor'	CLau SVic
	- - 'Vert Globe'	CLau CTsd ENfk LCro LEdu LOPS NLar NPer SRms SVic SWvt
	- - 'Violet de Provence'	CSBt MHer SRms
	- - 'Violetto di Chioggia' ♀H4	CLau
	cornigera	SPhx
*	***gomerensis***	WCot
	humilis white-flowered	SBrt
	scolymus	see *C. cardunculus* Scolymus Group
	syriaca	SPhx

Cynodon (*Poaceae*)

	aethiopicus	EBee EPPr NWsh

Cynoglossum (*Boraginaceae*)

	amabile ♀H5	CSpe LCro LOPS
	grande	SBrt
	nervosum	EBee EPPr MBel MHol MMuc SEND SPer WCAu WCot WTyc
	officinale	GGro

Cynosurus (*Poaceae*)

	cristatus	CHab NMir SVic WWild

Cypella (*Iridaceae*)

	aquatilis	EWat

Cyperus (*Cyperaceae*)

§	***albostriatus***	CCCN EShb
	alternifolius misapplied	see *C. involucratus*
	alternifolius L.	CBen CCCN EPfP SArc WMAq
	'Chira'	NWsh
§	***eragrostis***	EPPr LPot MWts NSti SDix SPlb SSal WMAq
	esculentus	CAgr EShb
	glaber	EHyd
	haspan L.	WCot
§	***involucratus*** ♀H1c	EShb EWat MWts SEND WSMil XLum
§	- 'Nanus'	EShb
	longus	CAgr CBen CPud CWat EWat MMuc MWts NPer SEND SMad SPlb SSal WMAq WWtn
	papyrus ♀H1c	CCCN CDTJ CDow CTsd EShb LCro LOPS LSun MHer SIvy SPlb WSMil
	- 'Perkamentus' PBR	CCCN EShb
	prolifer	EShb
	vegetus	see *C. eragrostis*
	'Zumila'	EShb

Cyphomandra see *Solanum*

Cyphostemma (*Vitaceae*)

	mappia	SPlb

Cypripedium (*Orchidaceae*)

	Achim gx	XFro
	Aki gx	NLAp XFro
	- 'Pastel'	XFro
	Ann Elizabeth gx new	NLAp
	Anna gx	NLAp XFro
	× ***barbeyi***	see *C.* × *ventricosum*
	Barry Phillips gx	GKev NLAp
	Bernd gx	NLAp
	- white-flowered	NLAp
	Birgit gx pastel-flowered	XFro
	calceolus	GBin GKev SDir
	Chauncey gx	XFro
	Christian gx new	XFro
	Cleo Pinkepank gx	NLAp XFro
	corrugatum	see *C. tibeticum*
	Dietrich gx ♀H5	XFro
	Emil gx	NLAp XFro
	Eurasia gx	NLAp XFro
	flavum	NLAp
	formosanum ♀H3	EPot EWld GKev NLAp SDir
	Francis gx new	NLAp

Gabriela gx 🏆^{H5}	NLAp
- 'Kentucky Maxi'	GKev NHpl
Gisela gx	CAvo XFro
GPH Quiet Waters gx new	NLAp
guttatum	NLAp
Hank Small gx 🏆^{H5}	XFro
Hans Erni gx	XFro
Henric gx new	NLAp
henryi	NLAp
Inge gx	NLAp XFro
Ingrid gx	XFro
Ivory gx	NLAp
Jimmy gx new	NLAp
Karl Heinz gx	XFro
kentuckiense 🏆^{H5}	CCCN GBin GKev NHpl NLAp SDir
'Kentucky Pink'	see *C.* Philipp gx 'Kentucky Pink'
Kristi Lyn gx	NLAp XFro
Lady Dorine gx	NLAp
Lucy Pinkepank gx	NLAp XFro
- 'Kentucky Pink Blush'	NHpl
macranthos	GKev
- 'Album'	GKev
- John Hagger Group	XFro
- var. ***speciosum*** × ***tibeticum*** new	NLAp
Maria gx	XFro
Memoriam Shawna Austin gx	NLAp
§ **Michael gx** 🏆^{H5}	NLAp XFro
Monto gx	XFro
Mops gx	XFro
Otto gx	NLAp
parviflorum	GKev SDir
§ - var. ***pubescens***	GBin GKev NHpl NLAp
'Parville'	NHpl SDir
Paul gx	XFro
Peter gx	XFro
Philipp gx 🏆^{H5}	NLAp XFro
§ - 'Kentucky Pink'	GBin GKev NHpl SDir
Pluto gx	NLAp XFro
pubescens	see *C. parviflorum* var. *pubescens*
Rascal gx	XFro
reginae 🏆^{H5}	CCCN GKev NHpl NLAp SDir
- f. ***albolabium***	GBin NHpl
- f. ***album***	GKev LRHS NLAp SDir
Renate gx pastel-flowered	XFro
Sabine gx 🏆^{H5}	GBin NLAp XFro
- pastel-flowered	NLAp XFro
Schoko gx	GBin
Sebastian gx	XFro
- 'Frosch's Mountain King'	XFro
- 'Multiflower White'	NHpl
Sunny gx	GBin XFro
§ ***tibeticum***	NLAp
Tilman gx	NLAp XFro
Ulla Silkens gx 🏆^{H5}	NLAp XFro
Ursel gx	NLAp XFro
§ × ***ventricosum***	GKev NLAp XFro
- 'Frosch's Queen of the Mist'	XFro
- 'Pastel'	NLAp XFro
- white-flowered	GKev
Victoria gx	NLAp XFro
Wim gx new	NLAp

Cyrilla (*Cyrillaceae*)

racemiflora	CMac

Cyrtanthus (*Amaryllidaceae*)

§ ***brachyscyphus***	EGrI EShb
breviflorus	CPbh WCot WPGP
'Edwina'	CCCN
§ ***elatus*** 🏆^{H2}	CTsd EShb GKev NSti SPtp WCot
'Elizabeth'	CCCN
epiphyticus	WCot
falcatus 🏆^{H2}	WCot
mackenii	EShb WPGP
- cream-white-flowered	CCCN EShb GKev
- 'Himalayan Pink'	CCCN EShb GKev
- red-flowered	CCCN EShb GKev
montanus	WCot
parviflorus	see *C. brachyscyphus*
purpureus	see *C. elatus*
sanguineus	WCot
speciosus	see *C. elatus*

Cyrtomium (*Dryopteridaceae*)

§ ***caryotideum***	CLAP
devexiscapulae	CLAP CTsd LEdu LLWG WPGP
§ ***falcatum*** 🏆^{H3}	CBod CDoC CKel CLAP CRos EFer EHyd EMor EPfP GMaP LEdu LPar LRHS MACG MAsh NLar NRHS SCob SCoo SDix SEND SEdd SPlb SPoG SRms SRot WCot XLum XSte
- 'Maritimum'	CBdn
- 'Rochfordianum'	CCCN CRos EHyd GBin LEdu LRHS MRav NRHS WFib
§ ***fortunei*** 🏆^{H3}	CBct CBdn CBod CKel CLAP CRos EAJP EFer EHyd EPfP GKev LCro LOPS LRHS MGos MRav NBid NBro NLar NRHS SCob SPer SPoG SRms SRot WCFE WFib WPnP XLum
- var. ***clivicola***	CBdn EBee EHed EHyd EPfP EShb LEdu LRHS MGos MRav NBro NGrd NLar NRHS SBea SCoo WBrk WCot XLum
macrophyllum	CLAP CRos EBee EHyd LEdu LRHS NRHS WPGP
tukusicola	EBee

Cystopteris ✿ (*Woodsiaceae*)

bulbifera	WCot
dickieana	WFib
fragilis	EFer GKev LEdu WFib
moupinensis B&SWJ 6767	WCot WCru

Cytisus (*Fabaceae*)

'Andreanus'	see *C. scoparius* f. *andreanus*
battandieri	see *Argyrocytisus battandieri*
× ***beanii*** 🏆^{H5}	CRos EHyd ELan EPfP LRHS MAsh NLar SLon
'Boskoop Glory'	NLar
× ***boskoopii*** 'Apricot Gem'	CBod CSBt ELan ELon NLar
- 'Boskoop Ruby' 🏆^{H5}	CBod CBrac CDoC CEme CMac CRos CSBt EHyd ELan EPfP GKin LCro LOPS LRHS LSRN MAsh NHol NRHS SCob SGbt SNig SPer SWvt
- 'Dukaat'	NLar
- 'Hollandia' 🏆^{H5}	CBcs CSBt ELan EPfP GKin MRav NLar SPer
- 'La Coquette'	CBod CDoC EPfP SPlb
- 'Windlesham Ruby'	CExl EHyd ELan EPfP LSRN NLar WFar
- 'Zeelandia' 🏆^{H5}	CMac EBee EHyd ELan EPfP NHol NLar SCob SGsty SPer
'Burkwoodii' 🏆^{H5}	CBcs CBod EHyd ELan ELon EPfP LSRN MSwo SCob SNig SPoG WFar
§ ***decumbens***	GArf GKev MAsh
demissus 🏆^{H5}	WAbe
'Dorothy Walpole'	ELon
'Eastern Queen'	ELon
'Golden Cascade'	CBcs CBod EHyd ELan LRHS MAsh NRHS

'Goldfinch'	CBrac CRos EHyd ELan LRHS MSwo NHol NLar NRHS SNig WFar
§ ***hirsutus***	CExl SBrt
× ***kewensis*** ♀H5	EHyd ELan EPfP LRHS MAsh MGos MRav NLar NRHS SRms
- 'Niki'	CEme EPfP MAsh NLar SPer
'Killiney Red'	ELan
'Killiney Salmon'	CKel EMil GKin LSRN MMrt MRav
'Lena' ♀H5	CEme CKel CMac CRos CSBt EHyd ELan EPfP GDam GKin LRHS LSRN MGos NBir NHol NLar NRHS SCob SGbt SPoG WFar
'Luna'	ELon EPfP LRHS SCob
'Minstead'	SPer
'Moyclare Pink'	LCro LOPS
'Newry Seedling'	CMac
nigricans 'Cyni' ♀H5	CRos EHed EHyd ELan LRHS MAsh SPer SPoG
'Palette'	SCob
'Porlock'	see *Genista* 'Porlock'
× ***praecox***	CMac CRos EHyd ELon EPfP LRHS MAsh NRHS NWea SCob SPlb SPoG WFar
- 'Albus'	CBcs CBod CBrac CDoC CMac CRos EHyd ELan EPfP LPar LRHS LSRN MAsh MGos MMuc MRav NHol NRHS SCob SPer WFar
- 'Allgold' ♀H5	Widely available
- 'Frisia'	WFar
- 'Lilac Lady'	CRos EHyd LRHS
- 'Warminster' ♀H5	CBrac EPfP GKin MMuc MRav SPer SRms
proliferus	CExl
purpureus	EBee EPfP MMrt MRav WSHC
- 'Atropurpureus'	EPfP
racemosus	see *Genista* × *spachiana*
'Red Wings'	CBrac
scoparius	NWea SCob WTSh
§ - f. ***andreanus***	CTri EPfP
- - 'Splendens'	SPer
- 'Cornish Cream'	CSBt ELan EPfP NWea
- 'Firefly'	CBcs CMac
- 'Fulgens'	EPfP
- 'Golden Sunlight'	CSBt MSwo SNig
§ - subsp. ***maritimus***	CMac
- var. ***prostratus***	see *C. scoparius* subsp. *maritimus*
- 'Tiltstone Moonglow'	GBin
× ***spachianus***	see *Genista* × *spachiana*
supinus	see *C. hirsutus*
'White Lion'	CMac

D

Daboecia ✿ (*Ericaceae*)

§ ***cantabrica*** f. ***alba***	MAsh NWad
- - 'Alba Globosa'	GPer
- - 'Alberta White'	CFst
- 'Andrea'	CFst
- 'Angelina'^{PBR}	CFst
- f. ***blumii*** 'Pinky Perky'	CFst
- - 'Purple Blum'	CFst
- - 'White Blum'	CFst
§ - 'Donard Pink'	GJos GPer
- 'Glamour'	CFst
I - 'Globosa Pink'	NWad
- 'Heather Yates'	CFst
- 'Lilac Osmond'	CFst
- 'Pink'	see *D. cantabrica* 'Donard Pink'
- 'Romantic Muxoll' (d)	CFst
- 'Rosella'^{PBR}	CFst
- subsp. ***scotica***	see *D.* × *scotica*
- 'Stardust Muxoll'	CFst
- 'Sun Seeker'	CFst
- 'Vanessa'^{PBR}	CFst
× ***scotica*** 'Ben'	CFst
- - 'Cora'	CFst
- - 'Goscote'	MGos
- - 'Jack Drake'	CFst
- - 'Katherine's Choice'	CBcs CFst
- - 'Silverwells' ♀H5	CBcs MAsh
- - 'Thumbelina'	CFst
- - 'William Buchanan' ♀H5	GAbr GJos GPer MAsh NWad SCoo

Dacrycarpus (*Podocarpaceae*)

§ ***dacrydioides***	CBrP CTsd

Dacrydium (*Podocarpaceae*)

cupressinum	SPlb WThu
franklinii	see *Lagarostrobos franklinii*

Dactylicapnos (*Papaveraceae*)

macrocapnos	CSpe LRHS MGil WBor WCru
platycarpa	WPGP
§ ***scandens***	CRHN CSpe GEdr IRos SBrt WAvo WHil XLum
- GWJ 9438	WCru
- WJC 13793	WCru
- 'Shirley Clemo'	CExl
§ ***ventii*** GWJ 9376	WCru
- WJC 13786	WCru

Dactylis (*Poaceae*)

glomerata	CHab SVic WSFF
- 'Variegata' (v)	MMuc NBid

Dactylorhiza (*Orchidaceae*)

§ ***elata*** ♀H5	GKev
Foliorella gx	GBin NLAp
§ ***foliosa*** ♀H4	CCCN ECha GKev MAvo NChi NLAp WSHC
§ ***fuchsii***	CCCN CHab CMil EPot EWat GKev LEdu MNrw NBir NLAp NRya WHer WSFF
- 'Bressingham Bonus'	GKev
- 'Eleanor'	MPhe
× ***grandis***	IBlr NLAp
- Blackthorn hybrid	CBor CJun IBlr
'Harold Esslemont'	GKev IBlr
hybrid	LEdu NRya
iberica **new**	NLAp
incarnata	NBid
§ ***maculata***	EHyd GKev NLAp
- subsp. ***ericetorum***	NLAp
maderensis	see *D. foliosa*
§ ***majalis***	NLAp WSFF
mascula	see *Orchis mascula*
praetermissa	CCCN CHab NLAp
purpurella	CHab CMiW GAbr GJos NFav NLAp NRya

Dahlia ✿ (*Asteraceae*)

'A la Mode' (D)	CWGr
'Abbie' (D)	NHal
I 'Abigail' (Fim) **new**	LHWs
'Abingdon Ace' (D)	CWGr SGbt
'Abridge Alex' (D)	CWGr
'Abridge Ben' (D)	CWGr
'Abridge Primrose' (WL)	CWGr

	'AC Abby' (C)	WPhe
I	'Acapulco' (S-c)	ERCP
	'Ace Summer Emotions'PBR (D)	SDeJ
	'Ace Summer Sunset'PBR (D)	CBod
	'Addison June' (Ba)	ERCP
	'Adelaide Fontane' (D)	CWGr
	'Admiral Rawlings' (D)	CWGr
	'After Dusk' (D)	SSal WPhe
	'Aggie White' (D)	NHal
	'Aimie' (D)	CWGr
	'Aitara Caress' (C)	SGbt
	'Aitara Diadem' (D)	LSou
	'Akita' (Misc)	CWGr ELan LCro LOPS MBros SGbt
	'Aladdin's Lamp' (WL)	NJRG
	'Alamos Luz'PBR **new**	MBros
	'Alauna Clair-Obscur' (Fim)	ERCP LCro LHWs LOPS SDir
	'Albert Schweitzer' (S-c)	CWGr SGbt
	'Alden Regal' (C)	CWGr
	'Alfred Grille' (S-c)	CWGr LCro LOPS SDeJ SGbt
	'Alf's Mascot' (D)	NJRG WPhe
	'All Triumph' (S-c)	CWGr
	'Allan Sparkes' (WL) ♀H3	CWGr MCot
	'Alloway Candy' (Misc)	ERCP
	'Alloway Cottage' (D)	CWGr NHal SGbt WPhe
	'Alltami Apollo' (S-c)	CWGr
	'Alltami Ruby' (S-c)	CWGr
	'Almand's Climax' (D) ♀H3	CWGr SGbt
	'Alpen Fern' (Fim)	CWGr
	'Alpen Pauline' (D) **new**	LHWs
	'Alpen Sun' (S-c)	CWGr
	'Alstergruss' (Col)	CWGr SDeJ
	'Alva's Doris' (S-c) ♀H3	CWGr LAyl
	'Alva's Lilac' (D)	CWGr
	'Alva's Supreme' (D) ♀H3	CWGr LAyl NHal WPhe
	'Amanda Jarvis' (C)	CWGr
	'Amante' (D)	LCro LOPS
	'Amaran Guard' (D)	CWGr
	'Amaran Relish' (D)	CWGr SGbt
	'Amaran Royale' (D)	CWGr
	'Amaran Troy' (WL)	CWGr
I	'Amazone' (Sin/DwB)	CRos SPoG
	'Amber Banker' (C)	CWGr SGbt
	'Amber Quartz' (Misc)	SSal
	'Amberglow' (Ba)	CWGr
	'Ambition' (S-c)	CWGr ERCP LCro LOPS
	'Amelia's Surprise' (D)	CWGr
	'American Copper' (D)	CWGr
	'American Dawn' (D)	ERCP LCro LHWs LOPS SPer SSal WPhe
	'American Moon' (D)	LOPS
	AMERICAN PIE ('Vdtg26'PBR) (Dark Angel Series) (Sin)	CWGr SDeJ
	'American Sun' (D)	ERCP
	'Amgard Coronet' (D)	CWGr
	'Amgard Delicate' (D)	CWGr SGbt
	'Amy Cave' (Ba)	NHal WPhe
	'Amy Madison' (S-c)	CWGr
	'Andrea Clark' (D)	NHal WPhe
	'Andrea Lawson' (Ba)	WPhe
	'Andrew Mitchell' (S-c)	CWGr NHal
	'Andries' Amber' (S-c)	CWGr
	'Andries' Orange' (C)	LRHS
	'Andries' Orange As' (S-c)	CWGr
	'Andy Murray' (Sin)	CWGr
	'Angora' (Fim)	SGbt
	'Ann Breckenfelder' (Col) ♀H3	CWGr ECtt ERCP NHal NJRG SMrm WPhe
I	'Anna' (Sin)	WPhe
	'Anne Cornelia' (D)	LHWs WPhe
	'Annika' (Sin)	SDeJ
	'Another Pet'	see *D.* 'Mystic Enchantment'
	'Antique'PBR (Sin)	EHyd LRHS
	'Apache' (Fim)	CWGr ERCP SDeJ SGbt SPer
	'Apache Blauw' (Fim)	ERCP
	'Apopa Sky' (Sin)	NJRG
	'Apple Blossom' (C)	SGbt
I	'Appleblossom' (Col)	CWGr
	'Apricot Desire' (WL)	ERCP
I	'Apricot Parfait' (Fim)	CWGr
	'April Dawn' (D)	CWGr
	'April Heather' (Col) ♀H3	NHal WPhe
	'Arabian Night' (D)	CAvo CBcs CWCL CWGr EBee ECtt ELan EPfP ERCP EWoo LAyl LCro LOPS LRHS LSRN LSun NLar SDeJ SDir SEND SGbt WCot WPhe WSpi
	'Arbatax' (D)	ERCP SDir
	'Arc de Triomphe' (D)	CWGr
	'Ariko Zsaza' (D) **new**	LHWs
	'Arlequin' (D)	SGbt
	'Arnhem' (D)	CWGr
	'Arthur Godfrey' (D)	CWGr
	'Asahi Chohje' (Anem) ♀H3	CWGr
	'Ashpire Girl' (Col) **new**	NJRG
	'Ashpire Julie' (Col) **new**	NJRG
	'Ashpire Lady' (Col) **new**	NJRG
	'Askwith Edna' (D)	WPhe
	'Askwith Josephine' (D)	WPhe
	'Askwith Minnie' (D)	LHWs NHal WPhe
	'Askwith Rodger' (D)	WPhe
	'Aspen' (S-c)	CWGr
	'Athalie' (C)	CWGr
	'Athelstan John' (C)	CWGr
	'Atilla' (D)	CWGr
I	'Atlanta' (D)	CWGr SGbt
	'Audacity' (D)	CWGr LAyl SGbt
	'Aurora's Kiss' (Ba)	ERCP NHal SGbt
	'Aurwen's Violet' (Pom)	CWGr NHal WPhe
	australis	CSpe EBee
	– B&SWJ 10389	WCru
I	'Autumn Fairy' (S-c)	SCob SDeJ
	'Avignon' (D)	SDeJ
	'Avoca Amanda' (D)	NHal WPhe
	'Avoca Comanche' (S-c)	NHal
	'Avoca Cree' (S-c)	CWGr
	'B.J. Beauty' (D)	CWGr NHal NJRG WPhe
	'Babette' (S-c)	CWGr
	'Baby Royal' (D)	CWGr
	'Babylon' (D)	LRHS SGbt
§	'Babylon Brons' (D)	ERCP LHWs SGbt
	'Babylon Bronze'	see *D.* 'Babylon Brons'
	'Babylon Lila' (D)	LHWs SGbt
§	'Babylon Paars' (D)	ECtt LHWs LRHS SDeJ SGbt
	'Babylon Purple'	see *D.* 'Babylon Paars'
	'Babylon Rose' (D)	LRHS SGbt
	'Bacardi' (D)	ERCP LHWs
	'Badger Twinkle' (S-c)	WPhe
	'Bahama Lemon'	see *D.* 'Lemon Cane'
	'Balham' (Sin)	WCot
	'Ballego's Glory' (D)	CWGr SGbt
	'Balthasar' (D)	ERCP
	'Bambino' (Lil)	CWGr
	'Bantling' (Pom)	CWGr ERCP SDir SGbt
	'Barbara Heritage' (D) **new**	CWGr
	'Barbara's Pastelle' (S-c)	CWGr NJRG SGbt
	'Barbara's Yellow' (S-c)	NJRG
	'Barbarry Aleks' (D)	WPhe
	'Barbarry Ball' (Ba)	CWGr
	'Barbarry Banker' (D)	LAyl
	'Barbarry Bluebird' (D)	SGbt
	'Barbarry Carousel' (Ba)	CWGr
	'Barbarry Chevron' (D)	CWGr

	'Barbarry d'Amour' (D)	NHal
	'Barbarry Delegate' (D)	NHal
	'Barbarry Drum' (D)	NHal
	'Barbarry Gem' (Ba)	CWGr
	'Barbarry Maverick' (D)	LHWs WPhe
	'Barbarry Monitor' (Ba)	SGbt
	'Barbarry Olympic' (Ba)	CWGr
	'Barbarry Oracle' (D)	CWGr
	'Barbarry Patriot' (Ba)	NHal
	'Barbarry Pip' (D)	NHal WPhe
	'Barbarry Primrose Hall' (D)	NHal WPhe
	'Barbarry Rover' (D)	WPhe
	'Barbarry Sultan' (D)	NHal
	'Barbarry Triumph' (D)	CWGr
	'Barbarry Vulcan' (D)	NHal WPhe
	'Barbette' (D)	CWGr
	'Bareham's Beauty' (D)	CWGr
	'Baret Joy' (S-c)	CWGr WPhe
	'Bargaly Blush' (D)	NHal
	'Baron Ray' (D)	CWGr
	'Barry Williams' (D)	SGbt
	'Bart' (D)	CWGr
	'Bayamo' (D) **new**	LHWs
	'Bayou'[PBR] (Anem)	ERCP LAyl LCro LOPS LSou NHal NJRG SGbt WPhe
	'Beatrice' (D) **new**	CWGr
	'Bedford Sally' (D)	CWGr
	'Bednall Beauty' (Misc/DwB) $\mathbb{Y}^{H3}$	ECtt ELan LRHS NJRG WSpi
	'Belinda Appleyard' (Ba)	CWGr
	'Bell Boy' (Ba)	SGbt
	'Belle Moore' (D)	CWGr
	'Belle of Barmera' (D)	CWGr ERCP
	'Bell's Delight' (S-c)	CWGr
	'Bengale' (D)	CWGr
	'Berger's Rekord' (S-c)	CWGr
	'Berwick Wood' (D)	CWGr NHal SGbt WPhe
	'Best Bett'	see *D.* MYSTIC SPIRIT
	'Best Girl' (S-c) **new**	CWGr
	'Beth's Chaplet' (Sin)	WCot
	'Betty Ann' (Pom)	CWGr
	'Beyond the Fringe' (D) **new**	CWGr
	'Biddenham Strawberry' (D)	CWGr SGbt
	'Bilbao'[PBR] (D)	SDeJ
	'Bill Holmberg' (D)	CWGr SGbt WPhe
	'Bingo' (D)	SGbt
	'Birkenshaw Garden Friends' (Col)	NJRG
	'Bishop of Auckland'[PBR] (Misc)	CBod CCBP CRos CWCL CWGN CWGr ECtt EHyd EPfP ERCP LCro LOPS LRHS MGos NJRG NRHS SDeJ SDir SGbt SSal WCot WHil
	'Bishop of Cambridge' (Sin)	SDir
	'Bishop of Canterbury'[PBR] (P)	CBod CRos CWGr ECtt EHyd ELan EPfP LCro LOPS LRHS LSou MBros MGos NHal NRHS SDeJ SDir SGbt SPoG SSal WPhe
	'Bishop of Dover' (Sin)	CWGr EPfP LCro LOPS LRHS SDeJ SDir SGbt SSal WPhe
	'Bishop of Lancaster' (Misc)	NLar SDir
	'Bishop of Leicester' (Misc)	CWGr EHyd ELan EPfP EWoo LCro LOPS LRHS NLar NRHS SDeJ SDir SGbt SHar WHil WPhe
	'Bishop of Llandaff' (P) $\mathbb{Y}^{H3}$	Widely available
	'Bishop of Oxford' (Misc)	CBod CCht CRos CWGr ELan EPfP ERCP EWoo LCro LOPS LRHS MBros MGos NJRG NRHS SCoo SDeJ SDir SGbt SPoG WHoo WPhe
	'Bishop of Salisbury' (D) **new**	CWGr
	'Bishop of York' (Misc)	CBod CRos CWGr ECtt EHyd ELan EPfP EWoo LAyl LCro LOPS LRHS LSou MBow MBros MGos MSCN NGdn NLar NRHS SDeJ SGbt SPoG SSal WHil WPhe XSte
	'Bishop Peter Price' (Sin)	CWGr
	'Black Fire' (D)	CWGr ECtt
	'Black Jack' (D)	CWGr ERCP NHal NJRG WPhe
	'Black Monarch' (D)	CWGr NHal SGbt
	'Black Narcissus' (C)	CWGr ERCP SGbt
I	'Black R. Jack' (Misc)	NJRG
	'Black Spider' (S-c)	CWGr
	'Black Touch' (Fim)	CWGr ERCP
	'Blackberry Ripple' (S-c)	CWGr SDir
	'Blaze' (D)	CWGr
	'Blithe Spirit' (D)	CWGr
	'Bloemfontein' (D)	CWGr
	'Bloodstone' (D)	CWGr SGbt
	'Bloody Mary' (D)	ERCP
	'Bloom's Graham' (S-c)	CWGr
	'Bloom's Kenn' (D)	CWGr SGbt
	'Blue Beard' (S-c)	CWGr
	'Blue Bell' (D)	CBod
	'Blue Boy' (D)	ERCP LCro LOPS LSou SSal
	'Blue Diamond' (C)	CWGr
	'Blue Wish' (WL)	ERCP LCro LOPS NJRG
	'Blueberry Hill' (Col)	LAyl
	'Blues Bird' (D) **new**	ERCP
	'Bluesette' (D)	CWGr WPhe
	'Bluetiful' (D) **new**	ERCP
	'Blyton Everest' (D)	NHal
	'Blyton Golden Girl' (D)	LHWs NHal WPhe
	'Blyton Lady in Red' (D)	LAyl NHal WPhe
	'Blyton Romance' (D)	NHal
	'Blyton Shiraz' (D)	WPhe
	'Blyton Softer Gleam' (D) $\mathbb{Y}^{H3}$	CWGr LAyl NHal NJRG SGbt WPhe
	'Blyton Stella' (D) **new**	NHal
	'Bob Fitzjohn' (S-c)	CWGr
	'Bobby' (D) **new**	CWGr
	'Bob's Bonaventure' (D)	CWGr NHal WPhe
	'Bodacious' (D)	CWGr
	'Bohemian Spartacus' (D) **new**	LHWs
	'Bonesta' (D)	CWGr SSal
	'Bonny Blue' (Ba)	CWGr
	'Boogie Woogie' (Anem)	CWGr SDeJ WPhe
	'Boom Boom Red' (Ba)	LHWs
	'Boom Boom White' (Ba)	CWGr ERCP
	'Boom Boom Yellow' (Ba)	ERCP SDeJ
	'Bora Bora' (S-c)	CWGr
	'Border Princess' (C/DwB)	SGbt
	'Boy Scout' (Ba)	CWGr
	'Bracken Lorelei' (WL)	NJRG
	'Brackenridge Ballerina' (WL)	CWGr NHal NJRG SGbt SSal WPhe
	'Brandaris' (S-c)	CWGr SGbt
	'Brandon James' (D)	SDeJ
	'Brandysnap' (D)	SGbt
	'Brasilia' (Dalina Series) (D)	CWGr
	BRAVEHEART ('Vdtg67'[PBR]) (Dark Angel Series) (Sin)	LCro LOPS SDeJ SPer
	'Brian's Dream' (D)	LAyl NHal
	'Bride's Bouquet' (Col)	CWGr ERCP LRHS
	'Bridge View Aloha' (S-c) $\mathbb{Y}^{H3}$	MBros SGbt
	'Bright Diamond' (D)	SDeJ
	'Bright Eyes' (Sin)	ERCP SSal
	'Brindisii' (Anem)	SDeJ
	'Bristol Stripe' (D)	CWGr
I	'Bronze Queen' (Ba) **new**	LHWs
	'Brookfield Rachel' (Ba)	CWGr
	'Brookfield Snowball' (Ba)	CWGr

	'Brookside Cheri' (C)	CWGr
	'Brookside Snowball' (Ba)	CWGr
	'Brown Sugar' (Ba)	LHWs WPhe
	'Bryce B. Morrison' (D)	CWGr
	'Bryn Terfel' (D)	CWGr GWyn NHal SGbt WPhe
	'Bull's Pride' (D)	CWGr
	'Buran' (D) **new**	LHWs
	'Burlesca' (Ba)	ERCP LHWs
	'Butch' (D)	CWGr
	'Butterball' (D/DwB)	SDeJ
	'By George' (D)	CWGr
	'Caballero' (WL)	CWGr
	'Café au Lait' (D)	CWCL CWGr ELan ERCP EShb IPot LAyl LCro LHWs LOPS LRHS MBros MSCN NHal NJRG SDeJ SDir SGbt WPhe WSpi
	'Café au Lait Rose' (D) **new**	LHWs
	'Caitlin's Joy' (Ba)	WPhe
	'Calgary' (D)	CWGr
	'Calima' (D) **new**	LHWs
	'Calin' (WL)	CWGr
	'Camano Ariel' (C)	CWGr
	'Camano Passion' (S-c)	CWGr
	'Camano Poppet' (Ba)	CWGr
	'Camano Regal' (S-c)	CWGr
	'Cambridge' (D)	LHWs
I	'Cameo' (WL)	CWGr ELan LAyl NHal NJRG SGbt WPhe
	campanulata	CWGr EShb
	'Campos Billy M' (S-c)	CWGr
	'Canary Fubuki' (Fim)	CWGr ERCP SDeJ SGbt SPer
	'Cancun' (D)	LRHS
	'Candy Cane CZ' (D)	CWGr
	CANDY EYES	see *D.* 'Zone Ten'
	'Candy Hamilton Lillian' (D)	CWGr
	'Candy Keene' (S-c)	NHal
	'Caprice' (D)	CWGr
	'Caproz Pizzazz' (D) **new**	LHWs
	'Captain Bruce Bairnsfather' (C)	CWGr
	'Caribbean Fantasy' (D)	CBod CWGr LHWs
	'Caribbean Sunset' (Misc)	SSal
	'Carlien' (WL)	WPhe
	'Carol Klein' (Sin/DwB)	CWGr
	'Carola' (S-c)	CWGr
	'Carole Chamberlain' (Col)	NJRG
	'Carolina Moon' (D)	CWGr NHal SGbt SSal
	'Carol's Spanish Dancer' (C)	LAyl NJRG WPhe
	'Carstone Firebox' (Col)	LAyl WPhe
	'Carstone Ruby' (D)	NHal
	'Carstone Suntan' (C)	CWGr
	'Carstone Valiant' (Ba)	NHal WPhe
	'Cartouche' (D)	CWGr ERCP
	'Catherine Deneuve' (Misc)	CWGN CWGr NJRG SGbt SSal
	'Cerise Prefect' (S-c)	CWGr
	'Cha Cha' (S-c)	CWGr MBros SGbt
	'Charles de Coster' (D)	CWGr
	'Charles Dickens' (Ba)	CWGr
	'Charlie Dimmock' (WL) 𝕐H3	CWGr NJRG SGbt WPhe
	'Charlie Kenwood' (D)	CWGr
	'Charlie Two' (D)	CWGr NHal WPhe
I	'Charlotte' (Sin)	CWGr
	'Charlotte Bateson' (Ba)	CWGr
	'Chat Noir' (S-c) 𝕐H3	CWGr ERCP EShb LAyl LCro LOPS LRHS SDir SGbt WPhe WTre
	'Chatsworth Splendour' (Sin/DwB)	CWGr
	'Checkers' (D)	CWGr WPhe
	'Chee' (WL)	CWGr
	'Cheerio' (S-c)	ECtt EHyd LRHS NRHS
	'Cherish' (D) **new**	LHWs
	'Cherokee Beauty' (D)	CWGr
	'Cherwell Goldcrest' (S-c)	CWGr NHal SGbt WPhe
	'Cherwell Linnet' (Ba)	NHal WPhe
	'Chilson's Pride' (D)	CWGr SGbt
	'Chiltern Amber' (D)	CWGr
	'Chiltern Fantastic' (C)	CWGr
	'Chiltern Herald' (S-c)	CWGr
	'Chiltern Sylvia' (S-c)	CWGr
	'Chimacum Davi' (Ba) **new**	LHWs
	'Chimacum Topaz' (S-c)	CWGr
	'Chimborazo' (Col)	CWGr EWes LAyl SGbt SSal
	'Chinese Lantern' (D)	CWGr
	'Chloe's Keene' (S-c)	CWGr
	'Christine' (D)	CWGr
I	'Christine' (WL)	SGbt
	'Christmas Carol' (Col)	CWGr ECtt NHal NJRG WPhe
	'Christmas Star' (Col)	CWGr
	'Christopher Nickerson' (S-c)	CWGr SGbt
	'Christopher Taylor' (WL)	NHal SGbt SHar WPhe
	'City of Alkmaar' (C)	LRHS SSal
	'City of Leiden' (S-c)	LCro LOPS
	'Clair de Lune' (Col) 𝕐H3	CWGr ECtt LRHS NHal NJRG SGbt WCot WPhe WSpi
	'Claire Louise Downting' (D)	WPhe
	'Clara May' (Fim)	CWGr
	'Clarion' (S-c)	NRHS
I	'Clarion' (Sin)	CWGr WPhe
	'Classic A.1' (C)	CWGr
	'Classic Rosamunde'^{PBR} (Misc) 𝕐H3	NHal
	'Classic Summertime' (Misc)	CWGr
§	'Classic Swanlake'^{PBR} (Misc)	CWGr ERCP LCro NJRG SSal
	'Clayt's Candy' (S-c)	NHal WPhe
	'Clearview Audrey' (S-c)	NHal WPhe
	'Clearview Daniel' (Ba) 𝕐H3	NHal
	'Clearview Debby' (D)	WPhe
	'Clearview Dorothy' (S-c)	WPhe
	'Clearview Edie' (DblO)	NHal WPhe
	'Clearview Irene' (S-c)	NHal
	'Clearview Louise' (S-c)	NHal WPhe
	'Clearview Sundance' (C)	NHal WPhe
	'Clearview Tammy' (S-c)	NHal WPhe
	'Cleo Laine' (S-c)	CWGr NHal
	coccinea	CExl CSpe CWGr EShb MCot SGbt SMHy WPGP
	– NJM 05.072	WPGP
	– orange-flowered	CWGr
	– var. ***palmeri***	CAvo CSpe WPGP
	– yellow-flowered	CWGr
	'Cocktail' (S-c)	CWGr
	'Color Spectacle' (S-c)	CWGr
	'Coltness Gem' (Sin/DwB)	CWGr
	'Como Polly' (D)	CWGr
	'Contessa' (D)	SDeJ
	'Coral Jupiter' (S-c)	CWGr NHal WPhe
	'Coral Strand' (D)	CWGr
	'Cornel' (Ba)	CWGr ERCP NHal NJRG SGbt WPhe
	'Cornel Brons' (Ba)	ERCP WPhe
	'Cornish Ruby' (Sin)	CBod EBee EPfP
I	'Corona' (S-c/DwB)	SDeJ
	'Coronella' (D)	SGbt
	'Corson George' (S-c)	NHal
	'Corson Gold' (S-c)	NHal
	'Cortez Silver' (D)	CWGr
	'Corton Olympic' (D)	CWGr
	'Country Boy' (S-c)	CWGr

	'Coupe de Soleil' (D)	CWGr
	'Craigowan' (S-c)	WPhe
	'Crazy Legs' (DblO)	SGbt
	'Crazy Love' (D)	CWGr LCro LOPS MBros
	'Cream Alva's' (D) 𝕐H3	CWGr
	'Cream Diane' (D)	NHal
	'Cream Elegans' (S-c)	CWGr
	'Cream Klankstad' (C)	CWGr
	'Cream Linda' (D)	CWGr
	'Cream Moonlight' (S-c)	CWGr NHal NJRG SGbt
	'Cream Reliance' (D)	CWGr
	'Cream Ruskin Diane' (D)	WPhe
	'Crème de Cassis' (D)	CWGr ERCP EWoo LCro LHWs LOPS NHal WPhe
	'Crème de Cognac' (D)	ERCP LHWs
	'Crève Coeur' (D)	CWGr
	'Crichton Cherry' (D)	CWGr
	'Crossfield Anne' (D)	CWGr
	'Croydon Ace' (D)	CWGr
	'Croydon Snotop' (D)	CWGr
	'Croydon Superior' (D)	SGbt
	'Cryfield Harmony' (Ba)	CWGr WPhe
	'Cryfield Jane' (Ba)	CWGr
	'Cryfield Keene' (S-c)	CWGr
	'Crystal Ann' (S-c)	CWGr
	'Culdrose' (D)	SGbt
	'Curate' (Misc)	CWGr
	'Curiosity' (Col)	NJRG
	'Currant Cream' (Ba)	CWGr SGbt
	cuspidata	EBee
	'Cycloop' (S-c)	CWGr
	'Cynthia Louise' (D)	CWGr
	'Czar Willo' (Pom)	CWGr
	DAHLEGRIA WHITE ('Dahlgr95'^{PBR}) (Dahlegria Series) (Sin) **new**	ERCP
	DAHLIETTA ISABELLE	see *D.* 'Isabella'
	'Daily Mail' (D)	CWGr
	'Daisy Duke' (D)	ERCP LHWs
	'Daleko Gold' (D)	CWGr
	'Daleko Jupiter' (S-c)	CWGr NHal WPhe
	'Daleko National' (D)	CWGr
	'Daleko Tangerine' (D)	CWGr
	DALINA COZUMEL (Dalina Maxi Series) (D/DwB)	LRHS
	'Dame Deidre' (S-c)	CWGr
	'Dana Audrey' (C)	CWGr
	'Dana Dream' (S-c)	CWGr
	'Dana Iris' (S-c)	CWGr
	'Dana Sunset' (C)	CWGr
I	'Dandy' (Col)	SVic
	'Danjo Doc' (D)	SGbt
	'Dannevirke' (Sin)	CWGr
	'Danum Gail' (D)	CWGr
	'Danum Hero' (D)	CWGr
	'Danum Meteor' (S-c)	CWGr
	'Danum Rebel' (S-c)	CWGr
	'Danum Rhoda' (D)	CWGr
	'Danum Salmon' (S-c)	CWGr
	'Danum Torch' (Col)	CWGr ECtt SGbt
	'Dao Stan' (Sin) **new**	CWGr
	'Dark Butterfly' (D)	CWCL CWGr ERCP LCro LOPS SSal
	'Dark Desire' (Sin/DwB)	CBod ERCP MCot
	'Dark Fubuki' (Fim)	ERCP LHWs
§	'Dark Side of the Sun'^{PBR} (Sin)	CRos EHyd LRHS LSou NRHS SCoo SPoG WPhe
	'Dark Spirit' (D)	ECtt LRHS SDeJ SGbt SSal WPhe
	'Darkarin' (Misc)	ERCP
	'Darlington Jubilation' (S-c)	CWGr
	'Davenport Lesley' (D)	CWGr
	'Davenport Sunlight' (S-c)	CWGr
	'Dave's Choice' (Ba)	WPhe
	'Dave's Snip' (D)	CWGr
	'David Digweed' (D)	SGbt
	'David Howard' (D) 𝕐H3	CBod CWGr ECtt EHyd ELan EPfP ERCP EWoo LAyl LCro LOPS LRHS LSou LSun NHal NJRG NRHS SCob SGbt SMrm SPer SSal SWvt WCot WFar WHoo WPhe WSpi
	'David Wright' (S-c)	CWGr
	'David's Choice' (D)	CWGr
	'Dawn Sky' (D)	LAyl
	'Dazzling Sun' (D) **new**	CBod LRHS
	'Debora Renae' (WL)	ERCP
	'Deborah's Kiwi' (C)	NHal SGbt
	'Debra Anne Craven' (S-c)	NHal WPhe
	'Decorette' (D/DwB)	SGbt
	'Deepest Yellow' (Ba)	CWGr SDeJ SGbt
	'Défilé' (D)	CWGr
	'De-la-Haye' (S-c)	NHal
	'Demi Schneider' (Col)	CWGr
	'Dentelle de Venise' (C)	CWGr
	'Deuil du Roi Albert' (D)	CWGr
	'Devon Elegance' (S-c)	CWGr
	'Devon Liam' (S-c)	CWGr
	DIABLO MIXED (Misc/DwB)	MBros
	'Diamond Wedding' (D)	SGbt
	'Diamond Years' (D)	SGbt
	'Diana Gregory' (Pom)	CWGr SGbt
	'Diana's Memory' (D)	LCro LHWs LOPS
	'Dikara Jodie' (D)	NHal WPhe
	'Dikara Superb' (D)	LAyl NHal NJRG
	'Dilys Ayling' (Col)	NHal NJRG WPhe
	'Dionne' (Misc)	WPhe
I	'Disneyland' (Col)	SGbt
	dissecta	CExl EBee
	'Diva US' (D)	ERCP SDeJ
	'Dixieland' (D)	CBod
	'Doctor Arnett' (S-c)	CWGr
	'Doctor John Grainger' (D)	LRHS
	'Doctor P.H. Riedl' (D) **new**	LHWs
	'Don Hill' (Col) 𝕐H3	NJRG WPhe
	'Doris Bacon' (Ba)	CWGr
	'Doris Day' (C)	CWGr NHal SGbt
	'Doris Muldoon' (WL)	CWGr
	'Doris Rollins' (C)	CWGr
	'Dorothy Rose' (D)	WPhe
	'Dottie D.' (Ba)	CWGr
	'Double Dream Fantasy' (Dreamy Series) (Misc)	EHyd EPfP LRHS NRHS
	'Double Shine' (D) **new**	LHWs
	'Dovegrove' (Sin) 𝕐H3	CWGr
	'Downham Royal' (Ba)	CWGr ERCP LCro LOPS
	'Dr Caroline Rabbit' (D)	SGbt
	DRAGON BALL ('Vdtg31'^{PBR}) (Dark Angel Series) (Sin)	SDeJ
	'Dream Seeker' (Col)	WPhe
	(Dreamy Series) DREAMY BLUSH WHITE (Misc)	EHyd
	- DREAMY EYES (Misc)	CWGr LRHS NLar
	- DREAMY FANTASY (Misc)	CWGr ELan LRHS MCot
	- DREAMY INSPIRE (Misc)	EHyd NLar
	- DREAMY KISS (P)	EHyd LRHS NLar NRHS
	- DREAMY LIPS (P)	LRHS NLar
	- DREAMY MOONLIGHT (Sin)	EHyd LRHS
	- DREAMY NIGHTS (Misc)	EHyd LRHS NRHS
	- DREAMY PASSION (Sin)	EHyd
	'Duddon Grace' (WL)	SSal
	'Duet' (D)	CWGr ELan SGbt
	'Dusky Harmony' (WL)	SGbt
	'Dutch Carnaval' (D) **new**	CWGr

	'Dutch Explosion' (S-c)	ELan
	'Dynamite' (D) **new**	LHWs
	'Earl Marc' (C)	CWGr
	'Early Harvest' (D)	SGbt
	'East Anglian' (D)	CWGr
	'Eastwood Moonlight' (S-c)	CWGr NHal SGbt WPhe
	'Eastwood Star' (S-c)	CWGr
	'Ebbw Vale Festival' (D)	CWGr
	'Edge of Joy' (D)	LCro LOPS SRms
	'Edinburgh' (D)	CDoC CWGr ERCP NHal SDeJ SDir SGbt WPhe
	'Edith Jones' (Col)	CWGr NHal NJRG SSal
	'Edith Mueller' (Pom)	CWGr
	'Edmund' (Sin)	WCot
	'Edna C' (D)	CWGr
	'Edwin's Sunset' (WL) ♀H3	NHal WPhe
	'Eileen Denny' (S-c)	CWGr
	'El Cid' (D)	CWGr
	'El Paso' (D)	CWGr LHWs MBros SDeJ
	'Elaine Beedle' (D)	CWGr
	'Elga-Bergerhoff' (C)	ERCP
	'Elgico Leanne' (C)	CWGr SGbt
	'Elizabeth Macnamara' (D) **new**	CWGr
	'Elizabeth Reeves' (Sin) **new**	CWGr
	'Elizabeth Sawyer' (C)	CWGr
	'Ella Britton' (D)	EHyd LRHS NRHS
	'Ellen Huston' (Misc/DwB) ♀H3	ECtt ERCP SGbt
	'Ellie Taylor' (Col) **new**	NJRG
I	'Elly' (WL)	WPhe
	'Elma E' (D)	CWGr LHWs NHal WPhe
	'Elmbrook Rebel' (S-c)	CWGr
I	'Elsi' (D) **new**	LHWs
	'Elsie Merina' (D)	CWGr
I	'Embrace' (C)	WPhe
	'Emma's Coronet' (D)	CWGr WPhe
	'Emmaus' (Fim)	CWGr
	'Emmie Lou' (D)	CWGr
	'Emory Paul' (D)	CWGr ERCP
	'Emperor' (D)	CWGr
I	'Encore' (Fim)	CWGr ERCP
	'Engelhardts Matador' (D)	CBod ECtt ERCP LHWs LRHS NJRG SGbt SSal WCot
	'Enid Adams' (D)	CWGr
	'Epping Forest' (D)	CWGr
	'Esau' (D)	CWGr
	'Esther' (Col)	SDeJ
	'Esther Chamberlain' (Col)	NJRG
	'Etheral' (Sin)	CWGr
	'Eunice Arrigo' (S-c)	CWGr
I	'Eurydice' (Fim)	CWGr
	'Evanah' (D) **new**	ERCP
	'Eveline' (D)	CWGr ERCP EShb LCro LOPS SDeJ SGbt
	'Evelyn Rumbold' (D)	CWGr SGbt
	'Evelyn Taylor' (S-c)	NJRG
	'Evening Breeze' (D)	ERCP SSal
I	'Evita' (Anem)	NJRG
	excelsa (B)	NJRG
	– B&SWJ 10238	ESwi
	– 'Penelope Sky' (Sin)	ESwi WCru
	'Excentrique' (Misc)	CWGr ERCP NJRG
	'Exotic Dwarf' (Sin/Lil) ♀H3	NJRG
	'Explosion' (S-c)	CWGr LRHS
	'Extase' (S-c)	CWGr
	'Eye Candy' (Sin)	LRHS NJRG NRHS
	'Fabula' (Col)	CWGr
	'Fairway Pilot' (D)	CWGr NHal WPhe
	'Fairway Spur' (D)	CWGr NHal WPhe
	'Fairy Queen' (C)	CWGr SGbt
	'Falcon's Future' (S-c)	CWGr
§	'Famoso' (Col)	ERCP
	'Fantasie du Cap' (Fim)	ERCP
	'Fascination' (P) ♀H3	CBod CCht CWGr ECtt EHyd ERCP LAyl LRHS LSRN MCot MSCN NLar NRHS SCob SCoo SDeJ SGbt WHoo WSpi
	'Fashion Monger' (Col)	ECtt ERCP NHal NJRG SGbt WPhe
	'Fata Morgana' (Anem)	NJRG SGbt
	'Fatima' (Pom)	LHWs
	'Ferncliff Illusion' (D)	CWGr ERCP SGbt
	'Ferncliff Inspiration' (D)	LHWs
	'Fernhill Champion' (D)	CWGr
	'Festivo' (Col)	CWGr
	'Feu Céleste' (Col)	CWGr
	'Fidalgo Blacky' (D)	CWGr
	'Fidalgo Climax' (Fim)	CWGr
	'Fidalgo Supreme' (D)	LAyl
I	'Fiesta' (Pom)	SDeJ
	Figaro Series (Misc/DwB)	MBros MPri SCob
	'Figurine' (WL) ♀H3	NJRG SHar
	'Fille du Diable' (S-c)	CWGr SGbt
	'Finchcocks' (WL) ♀H3	CWGr LAyl
	'Fiona Stewart' (Ba)	CWGr
	'Fire and Ice' (Misc)	CWGr SDeJ
	'Fire Mountain' (D)	LAyl NHal NJRG SSal WPhe
	'Firebird' (S-c)	see *D.* 'Vuurvogel'
	'Firebird NL' (Sin)	CAvo CWGr
	'Firebrand' ambig. (S-c)	SGbt
	'Firepot' (D)	ERCP LRHS SGbt SSal
	'First Lady' (D)	CWGr
	'Fleur'	see *D.* 'Fleurel'
§	'Fleurel' PBR (Fim)	ERCP LRHS MSCN SDeJ
	'Floorinoor' (Anem)	ERCP GWyn LCro LOPS SGbt WPhe
	'Florence Vernon' (Ba)	CWGr
	'Fontmell Kaz' (Col)	NJRG SGbt
	'Formby Art' (D)	LAyl WPhe
	'Formby Supreme' (D)	SGbt
	'Forrestal' (S-c)	CWGr
	'Fortuna' (Col/DwB)	CWGr
I	'Forty Niner' (WL)	WPhe
	'Frank Heritage' (S-c) **new**	CWGr
	'Frank Hornsey' (D)	CWGr
	'Frank Lovell' (S-c)	CWGr
	'Franz Kafka' (Pom)	CAvo CWGr ERCP MBros NHal NJRG SDeJ SDir WPhe
	'Frau Louise Mayer' (S-c)	CWGr
	'Fred Wallace' (C)	CWGr
	'Freelancer' (C)	CWGr SGbt
	'Freestyle' (C)	NJRG
§	'Freya's Paso Doble' (Anem) ♀H3	CWGr LAyl SGbt WPhe
	'Freya's Thalia' (Sin/Lil)	CWGr
	'Friendship' (C)	CWGr
	'Frigoulet' (C)	CWGr SGbt
	'Fringed Star' (S-c)	CWGr
	'Frost Nip' (D)	CWGr
	'Funfair' (D)	CWGr
	'Fusion' (D) ♀H3	SGbt SHar WCot
	'G.F. Hemerik' (Sin)	CWGr
	'G.I. Joe' (D)	SGbt
	(Gallery Series) 'Gallery Art Deco' PBR (D) ♀H3	CAvo CRos CWGr ERCP LRHS NHal NRHS SGbt WPhe
	– 'Gallery Art Fair' PBR (D) ♀H3	ERCP LCro LOPS NLar SDeJ
	– 'Gallery Art Nouveau' PBR (D) ♀H3	CAvo CWGr ERCP LRHS MBNS NHal NRHS SDeJ WFar WPhe
	– 'Gallery Bellini' PBR (D)	CRos EHyd LRHS NRHS SDeJ
	– 'Gallery Cézanne' PBR (D)	CWGr SDeJ SGbt
	– 'Gallery La Tour' PBR (D) ♀H3	SDeJ

	– 'Gallery Leonardo'PBR (D) ♀H3	CWGr LCro LOPS SDeJ
	– 'Gallery Matisse'PBR (D)	NLar
	– 'Gallery Monet'PBR (D)	CAvo
	– 'Gallery Pablo'PBR (D) ♀H3	CAvo CWGr LSou SGbt
	– 'Gallery Pinto'PBR (D)	CRos CWGr EHyd LRHS MBNS NRHS
	– 'Gallery Rembrandt'PBR (D) ♀H3	CWGr LCro LOPS
	– 'Gallery Renoir'PBR (D) ♀H3	CWGr
	– 'Gallery Rivera'PBR (D)	LRHS MBNS NLar NRHS SDeJ
	– 'Gallery Salvador'PBR (D)	CAvo SGbt
	– 'Gallery Serenade'PBR (D)	CAvo
	– 'Gallery Singer'PBR (D)	CWGr SDeJ
	– 'Gallery Valentin'PBR (D)	CRos EHyd LRHS MBNS NRHS WFar
	– 'Gallery Vermeer'PBR (D)	SGbt
	– 'Gallery Vincent'PBR (D) ♀H3	CAvo CWGr EShb
	'Gardaia' (Anem)	CWGr
	'Garden Festival' (WL)	CWGr
	'Garden Miracle' (D)	NJRG SSal
	'Garden Princess' (C/DwB)	SGbt
	'Garden Wonder' (D)	CBod SDeJ
	'Gargantuan' (S-c)	CWGr
	GATESHEAD FESTIVAL	see *D.* 'Peach Melba'
	'Gay Triumph' (S-c)	CWGr
	'Geerlings Babette' (Ba)	ERCP
	'Geerlings Camelea' (Pom)	WPhe
	'Geerlings Cupido' (WL)	SGbt
	'Geerlings Daydream' (D)	NJRG WPhe
	'Geerlings Indian Summer' (S-c)	CWGr NHal
§	'Geerlings Sorbet' (S-c)	LAyl MBros NHal SGbt WPhe
	'Gelber Vulkan' (S-c)	SGbt
	'Gemma Darling' (D)	CWGr
	'Genova' (Ba)	CAvo ERCP LHWs LRHS SDeJ SGbt SSal WPhe
	'Gerald Grace' (S-c)	CWGr
	'Geri Scott' (S-c)	LHWs WPhe
	'Gerlos' (D)	CWGr
I	'Geronimo' (S-c)	CWGr
	'Gerrie Hoek' (WL)	CWGr EHyd ERCP LRHS NJRG NRHS SDeJ SGbt WPhe WSpi
	'Gilwood Terry G' (C)	WPhe
	'Gina Lombaert' (S-c)	CWGr
	'Ginger Snap' (WL) **new**	LHWs
	'Gipsy Boy' (D)	LAyl
	'Gipsy Night' (Ba)	ERCP SDeJ
	'Giraffe' (DblO)	CWGr SGbt
	'Gitts Attention' (Fim) **new**	LHWs
	'Gitty' (Ba)	CWGr
	'Gitty Up' (Anem)	WPhe
	'Glen Afton' (Pom)	CWGr
	'Glen Gharry' (Col)	CWGr
	'Glenbank Twinkle' (C)	CWGr
	'Globular' (Ba)	CWGr
	'Glorie van Heemstede' (WL) ♀H3	CWGr ERCP EShb EWoo LCro LOPS NHal NJRG SDeJ SGbt WPhe
	'Glorie van Naardwijk' (D)	CWGr
	'Glorie van Noordwijk' (S-c)	ERCP SDeJ SGbt
	'Glory' (D)	CWGr
I	'Glow'	SPer
	'Glow Orange' (Ba)	CWGr
	'Go American' (D)	CWGr NHal WPhe
	'Gold Crown' (S-c)	SDeJ
	GOLDALIA ROSE ('Goalia Rossa'PBR) (Col) **new**	CRos
	GOLDALIA SCARLET ('Goalia Scarl'PBR) (Col) **new**	CRos
	'Golden Charmer' (C)	CWGr
I	'Golden Emblem' (D)	CWGr ECtt SDeJ
	'Golden Fizz' (Ba)	CWGr
	'Golden Leader' (D)	CWGr
	'Golden Scepter' (D)	CWGr ERCP MBros SDeJ SGbt SPer SSal
	'Golden Symbol' (S-c)	CWGr
	'Golden Vulcan' (S-c)	WPhe
	'Goldie Gull' (Anem)	NJRG
	'Goldorange' (S-c)	CWGr
	'Good Earth' (C)	CWGr SDeJ SSal
	'Gor Blimey' (Col) **new**	CWGr
	'Goya's Venus' (S-c)	CWGr
	'Gracie S' (C)	NJRG
	'Gramma's Lemon Pie' (D)	CWGr
	'Grand Finale' (S-c)	SDeJ
	'Grand Prix' (D)	CWGr SDeJ SGbt
	'Great Hercules' (D) **new**	ERCP LHWs
	'Great Silence' (D) **new**	LHWs
	'Greenway Zoe' (S-c)	NHal
	'Grenadier' (D) ♀H3	CWGr ECtt ERCP LRHS NJRG NLar SGbt SSal WCot
	'Grenidor Pastelle' (S-c)	CWGr NHal NJRG WPhe
	'Gretchen Heine' (D)	CWGr
	'Groovy' (D)	SSal WPhe
	'Gryson's Yellow Spider' (C) ♀H3	SSal WPhe
	'Gun Yuu' (D)	CWGr
	'Gurtla Twilight' (Pom)	NHal NJRG WPhe
	'Gwyneth' (WL)	NHal NJRG WPhe
	'Gypsy Girl' (D)	SGbt
	'Hadrian's Midnight' (Sin)	LAyl NHal WPhe
	'Hadrian's Sunlight' (Sin) ♀H3	NHal
	'Hadrian's Sunset' (Sin)	NHal
	'Hale Bopp' (Fim) **new**	ERCP
	'Hallmark' (Pom)	NJRG
	'Hamari Accord' (S-c) ♀H3	LAyl
	'Hamari Bride' (S-c) ♀H3	CWGr
	'Hamari Girl' (D)	CWGr SGbt
	'Hamari Gold' (D) ♀H3	CWGr NHal SGbt WPhe
	'Hamari Rosé' (Ba) ♀H3	CWGr NHal SGbt SHar
	'Hamari Sunshine' (D)	SGbt
	'Hamilton Lillian' (D) ♀H3	CWGr
	'Hanny' (WL)	WPhe
	'Hans Ricken' (D)	CWGr
	'Hapet Blue Eyes' (D)	LHWs WPhe
	'Hapet Charmant' (WL)	NJRG
	'Hapet Duo' (D)	WPhe
	'Hapet Pearl' (Ba)	WPhe
	'Hapet Perfekt' (Fim)	WPhe
	'Hapet Skyline' (S-c)	WPhe
	'Hapet Vinete' (Pom)	WPhe
	'Happy Butterfly' (D)	LHWs
	HAPPY DAYS CREAM ('Hdw79'PBR) (Sin)	LRHS
	HAPPY DAYS NEON ('Hdne33'PBR) (Sin)	ERCP LRHS
	HAPPY DAYS PINK ('Hdpi117'PBR) (Sin) ♀H3	ERCP LRHS MPri WFar
	HAPPY DAYS PURPLE ('Hdpu165'PBR) (Sin) ♀H3	ERCP LRHS
	HAPPY DAYS RED FLAME ('Hdrf155'PBR) (Sin)	EPfP
	'Happy Go Lucky' (D)	SDeJ
	'Happy Halloween' (D)	CWGr
	'Happy Hour'PBR (Ba)	ERCP
	(Happy Single Series) HAPPY SINGLE DATE ('HS Date'PBR) (Sin)	CWGr ERCP SDeJ WHil

- HAPPY SINGLE FIRST LOVE ('HS First Love'PBR) (Sin)	ERCP SDeJ
- HAPPY SINGLE FLAME ('HS Flame'PBR) (Sin) ♀H3	CAvo CWGr ERCP LRHS NJRG SDir SSal WHil
- HAPPY SINGLE JULIET ('HS Juliet'PBR) (Sin)	CBod CWGr ERCP SDeJ SSal
- HAPPY SINGLE KISS ('HS Kiss'PBR) (Sin)	CAvo CWGr
- HAPPY SINGLE PARTY ('HS Party'PBR) (Sin)	CWGr SDeJ
- HAPPY SINGLE PRINCESS ('HS Princess'PBR) (Sin) ♀H3	CAvo CWGr ERCP LRHS SDeJ
- HAPPY SINGLE ROMEO ('HS Romeo'PBR) (Sin)	CWGr LRHS SDeJ WFar WPhe
- HAPPY SINGLE WHITE ('HS White') (Sin)	WHil
- HAPPY SINGLE WINK ('HS Wink'PBR) (Sin) ♀H3	CWGr ERCP LCro LOPS SDeJ SDir WPhe
'Haresbrook' (Sin)	SHar WSpi
'Harriet G' (WL)	NJRG
'Hartenaas' (Col/DwB)	SDeJ
'Harvest' (Fim)	CWGr
'Harvest Brownie' (Sin/Lil)	CWGr
§ 'Harvest Imp' (Sin/Lil)	CWGr
§ 'Harvest Samantha' (Sin/Lil) ♀H3	CWGr NHal
'Hawai'PBR (Dalina Series) (D)	CWGr
'Hawaiian Dreams'PBR (Sin)	CWGr EHyd LRHS WPhe
'Hayley Jayne' (C)	CWGr LSou NJRG SGbt
'Heather Huston' (D)	CWGr
'Heather Linford' (Fim)	CWGr NHal
'Helma Rost' (S-c)	CWGr
'Hemera' (Sin)	CWGr
'Henriette' (C)	CWGr WPhe
'Herbert Smith' (S-c)	CWGr
'Hexton Copper' (Ba)	CWGr SGbt
'Higherfield Champion' (S-c)	CWGr
'Highness' (S-c)	CWGr
'Hildepuppe' (Pom)	CWGr
'Hillcrest Amour' (D)	CWGr SGbt
'Hillcrest Aura' (D)	WPhe
'Hillcrest Camelot' (S-c)	CWGr
'Hillcrest Candy' (S-c) ♀H3	CWGr NHal NJRG SGbt WPhe
'Hillcrest Contessa' (Ba)	CWGr
'Hillcrest Delight' (D)	NHal SGbt
'Hillcrest Duncan Edwards' (S-c)	NHal WPhe
'Hillcrest Fiesta' (S-c)	CWGr
'Hillcrest Firecrest' (D)	LAyl NHal
'Hillcrest Heights' (S-c)	CWGr
'Hillcrest Jake' (S-c)	WPhe
'Hillcrest Jersie' (S-c)	NHal NJRG WPhe
'Hillcrest Jessica J' (C)	WPhe
'Hillcrest Jonathan' (D) **new**	NHal
'Hillcrest Kismet' (D)	NHal NJRG
'Hillcrest Matt' (D)	WPhe
'Hillcrest Regal' (Col) ♀H3	CWGr SGbt
'Hillcrest Royal' (C) ♀H3	CWGr ELan LAyl NHal SGbt WPhe
'Hillcrest Suffusion' (D)	CWGr NJRG WPhe
'Hill's Delight' (S-c)	CWGr
'Hindu Star' (Ba)	CWGr
'Holland Festival' (D)	CWGr LHWs SDir SGbt
'Hollyhill Big Pink' (S-c)	SGbt
'Hollyhill Calico' (Ba) **new**	LHWs
'Hollyhill Lemon Ice' (P) **new**	LHWs
'Hollyhill Spiderwoman' (Misc)	CWGr EPfP ERCP
'Home Run' (Sin)	CWGr
'Honey' (Anem/DwB)	CWGr SDeJ
'Honeypot' (Ba)	SGbt
'Honka' (SinO) ♀H3	CWGr ECtt ERCP LAyl LCro LOPS LRHS NHal NJRG SDeJ WCot WHil WPhe
'Honka Black' (SinO)	ERCP
'Honka Fragile' (SinO)	CSpe ERCP EWoo LCro LOPS SDeJ
'Honka Orange' (SinO)	ERCP NJRG
'Honka Pink' (SinO)	EWoo WPhe
'Honka Pink Edge' (SinO)	NJRG
'Honka Red' (SinO)	EWoo LCro LOPS NHal SDeJ SSal WHil
'Honka Rose' (SinO)	ERCP NJRG SDeJ SSal WPhe
'Honka Surprise' (SinO)	EBee ECtt ERCP LCro LOPS NJRG SDeJ WCot WHil
'Honor Francis' (Misc)	WCot
'Hootenanny - Swan Island' (Col) ♀H3	SSal WPhe
'Hot Chocolate' (D)	SGbt
'Hugh Mather' (WL)	CWGr
'Hy Clown' (D)	CWGr
'Ian Hislop' (Sin)	CWGr
'Ice Crystal' (Fim)	LSou
'Ice Cube' (D)	SDeJ
'Ice Queen' (WL)	CWGr
'Icoon'PBR (D) **new**	LRHS
'Ida Gayer' (D)	CWGr
I 'Idylle' (S-c)	CWGr
'Ieda' (Sin)	NJRG
'Ike' (Fim)	CWGr
'I-lyke-it' (S-c)	CWGr
'Imp'	see *D.* 'Harvest Imp'
imperialis (B)	CDTJ CWGr ERCP ESwi EWes ILea LEdu LRHS NJRG SChr SDir SGbt
- B&SWJ 8997	WCru
- B&SWJ 14341	WCru
- 'Alba' (B)	CWGr SDir
- pink double-flowered (B/d)	CExl
- white-flowered (B) **new**	ERCP
aff. ***imperialis***	CWGr LHWs XLum
'Inca' (Anem)	SDeJ
'Inca Dambuster' (S-c)	SGbt WPhe
'Inca Royale' (D)	CWGr
'Inca Vanguard' (D)	CWGr
'Independence' (D)	SGbt
'Inglebrook Jill' (Col)	CWGr
'Inland Dynasty' (S-c)	CWGr
'Inn's Gerrie Hoek' (D)	CWGr
'Irene van der Zwet' (Sin)	CWGr
'Irish Glow' (Pom)	LAyl NHal WPhe
'Irish Pinwheel' (Misc)	LHWs
§ 'Isabella' (Dahlietta Surprise Series) (DwB) **new**	LHWs
'Isadora' (D)	WPhe
'Islander' (D)	CWGr ERCP LHWs
'Ivanetti' (Ba)	CWGr ERCP NHal SGbt WPhe
'Ivor's Rhonda' (Pom)	NHal
'Ivy Della' (D)	CWGr
'J.R.G.' (Misc) ♀H3	NJRG SSal
'Jack Hood' (D)	CWGr SGbt
'Jackie Magson' (S-c)	CWGr
'Jaldec Jerry' (S-c)	CWGr
'Jamaica' (Dalina Series) (D)	CWGr SGbt
'Jan van Schaffelaar' (Pom)	ERCP SDeJ
'Janal Amy' (S-c)	CWGr NHal SGbt WPhe
'Jane Horton' (Col)	CWGr SGbt
'Javier G' (WL) **new**	ERCP LHWs
'Jazzy' (Col)	CWGr
'Je Maintiendrai' (D)	CWGr
'Jean Ellen' (Fim)	WPhe
'Jean Fairs' (WL) ♀H3	CWGr SGbt

	'Jean Marie'PBR (D)	CWGr
	'Jean Melville' (D)	CWGr
	'Jean Shaw' (D)	NHal
	'Jean's Carol' (Pom)	CWGr
I	'Jennie' (Fim)	CWGr
§	'Jenny' (Dahlietta Select Series) (Misc)	SGbt
	'Jersey Beauty' (D)	CWGr
	'Jescot Jess' (D)	CWGr
	'Jescot Jim' (D)	CWGr
	'Jescot Julie' (DblO)	ERCP LAyl LCro LOPS NJRG
	'Jescot Lingold' (D)	SGbt
	'Jescot Redun' (D)	CWGr
	'Jessica' (S-c)	WPhe
	'Jessie G' (Ba)	CWGr ERCP
	'Jessie Ross' (D/DwB)	CWGr
	'Jet' (S-c)	CWGr
	'Jet VI' (Sin) **new**	CWGr
	'Jewel Red' (D) **new**	CWGr
	'Jill Doc' (D)	CWGr
	'Jim Branigan' (S-c)	NHal
	'Jive' (Anem)	ELan ERCP SDeJ
	'Joan Walker' (D)	WPhe
	'Jocondo' (D)	CWGr NHal SGbt WPhe
	'Jodie Wilkinson' (Ba) ♀H3	NHal WPhe
	'Joe Swift' (Sin)	CWGr
	'Johann' (Pom)	CWGr NHal
	'John Friend' (D) **new**	CWGr
	'John Hill' (D)	NHal
	'John Prior' (D)	CWGr
	'John Street' (WL)	CWGr WSpi
	'Johnnie Ellis' (S-c) **new**	CWGr
	'John's Champion' (D)	CWGr
	'Jolly Good' (Sin)	WPhe
	'Jomanda' (Ba) ♀H3	CWGr ERCP NHal NJRG SGbt WPhe
	'Jo's Choice' (D)	CWGr
	'José Maria'	WPhe
	'Josie Gott' (Ba) ♀H3	NJRG SGbt WPhe
	'Josudi Andromeda' (C) **new**	NHal
	'Josudi Aurora' (C)	NHal
	'Josudi Hercules' (S-c)	NHal WPhe
	'Josudi Neptune' (S-c)	NHal
	'Josudi Polaris' (C) **new**	NHal
	'Josudi Telstar' (C)	NHal
	'Jowey Arenda' (Ba) **new**	LHWs
	'Jowey Chantal' (D) **new**	LHWs
	'Jowey Frambo' (Ba)	LHWs
	'Jowey Joshua' (Ba) **new**	LHWs
	'Jowey Linda' (Ba)	ERCP
	'Jowey Marilyn' (Misc) **new**	LHWs
	'Jowey Mirella' (Ba)	ERCP LHWs
	'Jowey Winnie' (Ba)	ERCP SSal
	'Joy Donaldson' (C)	CWGr
	'Joyce Green' (S-c)	CWGr SGbt
	'Joyful Investment' (Col)	WPhe
	'JS Dorothy Rose' (D)	NHal
	'Jules Dyson' (Misc)	SDys
	'Julie One' (DblO)	CWGr ECtt SGbt
	'Julie's Delight' (S-c)	CWGr
	'Jura' (S-c)	CWGr
	'Kaga-komachi' (D)	LRHS NRHS
	'Karen G' (Col)	NJRG
	'Karenglen' (D) ♀H3	CWGr NHal SGbt
	'Kari Quill' (C)	CWGr
	'Karma Amanda'PBR (D)	CWGr
	'Karma Amora'PBR (D) **new**	LHWs LRHS
	'Karma Bon Bini'PBR (C)	LRHS LSou SGbt
	'Karma Choc'PBR (D) ♀H3	CBod CSpe CWGr EBee EHyd ERCP EWes LCro LHWs LOPS LRHS NRHS SDir SEND SGbt SPer SSal WBor WCot WFar WHoo WPhe

	'Karma Corona'PBR (C)	CWGr LHWs SGbt
	'Karma Fiesta'PBR (D)	ERCP
	'Karma Fuchsiana' (D)	CWGr ERCP LCro LOPS SGbt WPhe
	'Karma Gold'PBR (D) **new**	LHWs
	'Karma Irene'PBR (D)	CWGr LHWs
	'Karma Lagoon'PBR (D)	CWGr ERCP LHWs LRHS SGbt WPhe
	'Karma Maarten Zwaan'PBR (WL)	CWGr ERCP
	'Karma Naomi'PBR (D)	ERCP LHWs SGbt
	'Karma Pink Corona'PBR (C)	LCro LOPS
	'Karma Prospero'PBR (D)	ERCP LCro LOPS
	'Karma Red Corona'PBR (C)	LRHS SDeJ SGbt
	'Karma Sangria'PBR (C)	CWGr LCro LHWs LOPS SDeJ SGbt
	'Karma Serena'PBR (D)	LHWs LRHS SDeJ
	'Karma Yin Yang' (D)	CWGr LRHS SGbt
	'Karras 150' (S-c)	CWGr
	'Kate Mountjoy' (Col)	SGbt
	'Kate's Dream' (D)	WPhe
	'Katie's Velvet' (Col)	NHal
	'Kayleigh Spiller' (Col)	SGbt
	'Keith's Choice' (D)	NHal SGbt WPhe
	'Kelsea Carla' (S-c) ♀H3	CWGr
	'Kelsey Annie Joy' (Col)	NJRG WPhe
	'Kelsey Sunshine' (Col) **new**	ERCP
	'Kelvin Floodlight' (D)	CBod CWGr SDeJ SGbt
	'Kennemerland' (S-c)	CWGr LCro LOPS SDeJ SGbt
	'Kenora Challenger' (S-c)	CWGr NHal NJRG SGbt WPhe
	'Kenora Clyde' (S-c)	CWGr
	'Kenora Fireball' (Ba)	CWGr
	'Kenora Frills' (Fim)	NHal
	'Kenora Jubilee' (S-c)	SGbt WPhe
	'Kenora Lisa' (D)	CWGr
	'Kenora Macop-B' (Fim)	CWGr ECtt ERCP LAyl NHal SSal WPhe
	'Kenora Moonbeam' (D)	CWGr
	'Kenora Ontario' (S-c)	CWGr
	'Kenora Sunburst' (D)	CWGr
	'Kenora Sunset' (S-c) ♀H3	CWGr NHal SGbt
	'Kenora Superb' (S-c)	SGbt
	'Kenora Valentine' (D) ♀H3	CWGr LAyl NHal SGbt WPhe
	'Kenora Wow' (S-c)	NHal WPhe
	'Ken's Flame' (WL)	CWGr SGbt
	'Ken's Rarity' (WL)	NHal NJRG SGbt
	'Kerry Mitchell' (Col) **new**	NJRG
	'Kick Off' (D) **new**	LHWs
§	'Kidd's Climax' (D) ♀H3	CWGr ERCP WPhe
	'Kiev' (D)	LCro LOPS SPer
	'Kikoski' (C)	SGbt
	'Kilburn Fiesta' (S-c)	NHal WPhe
	'Kilburn Glow' (WL)	LHWs NHal NJRG WPhe
	'Kilburn Rose' (WL) ♀H3	NJRG WPhe
	'Kilmorie' (S-c)	NHal WPhe
	'Kingston' (D)	CWGr SGbt
	'Kirsty G' (Col)	NJRG WPhe
	'Kismet' (Ba)	CWGr
	'Kit Kat' (C)	CWGr
	'Kiwi Brother' (S-c)	CWGr
	'Kiwi Gloria' (C)	CWGr NHal NJRG WPhe
	'Kiwi Sister' (S-c)	CWGr
	'Klondike' (S-c)	WPhe
	'Knockout' (S-c)	CRos EHyd LSou
I	'Knockout'PBR (Sin) ♀H3	CBcs CWGr ERCP LRHS LSRN NRHS SDys SPoG SSal
	'Kochelsee' (Ba)	CWGr
	'Kordessa' (D)	SDir
	'Kym Willo' (Pom)	CWGr
I	'Kyoto' (WL)	CWGr SGbt
	'L.A.T.E.' (Ba)	CWGr LAyl NHal SGbt
	'La Gioconda' (Col)	CWGr

'La Recoleta' (D) CWGr ERCP
'Labyrinth' (D) ERCP WPhe
'Lady Darlene' (D) CWGr LSou
'Lady Kate' (D) LCro LHWs LOPS
'Lady Liberty' (D) ERCP
'Lady Linda' (D) CWGr SGbt
'Lady Orpah' (D) CWGr
'Laguna Beach' (Ba) CWGr
'Lake Carey' (D) LCro LOPS LRHS
'Lake Ontario' (D) CWGr
'Lakeland Polly' (Pom) CWGr NHal NJRG WPhe
'Lambada' (Anem) ELan
'L'Ancresse' (Ba) CWGr LAyl LHWs NHal NJRG
'Last Dance' (D) CWGr
'Laura's Choice' (D) CWGr
'Lavender Freestyle' (C) CWGr
'Lavender Leycett' (D) CWGr
'Lavender Line' (S-c) NHal
'Lavender Perfection' (D) CWGr SDeJ
'Lavender Ruffles' (D) CWGr
'Le Baron' (D) CWGr ERCP MCot
'Le Castel' (WL) $\mathbb{Y}^{H3}$ CWGr SDeJ
'Le Feu du Soleil' (Fim) NHal
'Le Patineur' (D) CWGr
'Le Vonné Splinter' (S-c) CWGr
'Lee Marshall' (C) CWGr
'Leila Savanna Rose' (D) CWGr
§ 'Lemon Cane' (D) CWGr
'Lemon Crest' (S-c) WPhe
'Lemon Elegans' (S-c) $\mathbb{Y}^{H3}$ CWGr NHal
'Lemon Meringue' (D) CWGr ECtt SGbt
'Lemon Puff' (Anem) CWGr
'Lemon Symbol' (S-c) CWGr
'Lemon Zing' (Ba) LAyl NHal SGbt
'Leopold Chloe' (D) WPhe
'Leopold Sophie' (D) WPhe
'Leslie Skinner' (Col) CWGr
'Leycett' (D) CWGr
'Libretto' (Col) CWGr
'Life Force' (D) CWGr SGbt
'Lilac Athalie' (C) CWGr
'Lilac Bull' (D) ERCP EShb LHWs LRHS
'Lilac Marston' (D) $\mathbb{Y}^{H3}$ NHal
'Lilac Pathfinder' (Sin) NJRG
I 'Lilac Time' (D) CWGr ERCP SDeJ SGbt
'Lilac Willo' (Pom) CWGr
lilac-flowered B&SWJ 14942 from Colombia WCru
'Lilian Alice' (Col) SSal
'Lilianna W' (Sin/DwB) NJRG
'Lillian' (Ba) **new** CWGr
'Lillianne Ballego' (D) CWGr
'Linda's Baby' (Ba) ERCP SPer
'Linda's Chester' (C) CWGr
'Linda's Diane' (D) CWGr
'Linda's Polly' (Pom) NJRG
'Linz' (D) WPhe
'Lisa' (WL) CWGr
'Lismore Carol' (Pom) NHal WPhe
'Lismore Moonlight' (Pom) CWGr NHal WPhe
'Lismore Robin' (D) NHal
'Lismore Sunset' (Pom) CWGr SGbt
'Lisonette' (C) WPhe
I 'Little Darling' (S-c) WPhe
'Little Dorrit' (Sin/Lil) CWGr NJRG
'Little Fawn' (S-c) CWGr
'Little Glenfern' (C) CWGr
'Little Matthew' (Pom) CWGr SGbt
'Little Robert' (D) ERCP SDir SGbt
'Little Sally' (Pom) CWGr SGbt
'Little Scottie' (Pom) CWGr
'Little Snowdrop' (Pom) CWGr SGbt
'Little Sun' (WL) WPhe
'Little Willem' (Pom) SDeJ SGbt
'Liz' (S-c) CWGr
'Lloyd Huston' (S-c) CWGr
'Lois Walcher' (D) CWGr
'Lololove' (Sin) SSal
'Long Island Lil' (D) CWGr
'Loraine Mitchell' (WL) NJRG
'Lorona Dawn' (SinO) WPhe
'Loud Applause' (C) CWGr
'Louie Meggos' (D) NHal
'Louis V' (Fim) SGbt
'Louisa Mekarni' (D) **new** CWGr
'Louise Bailey' (D) CWGr
LUBEGA BURGUNDY (D) **new** LRHS
LUBEGA POWER BRONZE BICOLOR (D) **new** LRHS
LUBEGA POWER BURGUNDY (D/DwB) CRos LRHS
LUBEGA POWER SCARLET-WHITE (D) **new** LRHS
LUBEGA POWER TRICOLOR ('Voldah5612') **new** LRHS
LUBEGA SCARLET (D) **new** LRHS
LUBEGA WHITE (D) **new** LRHS
LUBEGA YELLOW (D) **new** LRHS
LUBEGA YELLOW ORANGE (D) **new** LRHS
'Lucky Number' (D) CWGr ERCP
'Luka Johanna' (WL) LHWs
'Lula Pattie' (D) NHal
'Lupin Dixie' (C) CWGr
'Mabel Ann' (D) CWGr LAyl WPhe
'Madame Simone Stappers' (WL) ECtt EHyd LAyl LRHS NRHS WSpi
'Madame Vera' (D) CWGr
'Maddie Grace' (D) CWGr
'Magenta Magenta' (D) LAyl SGbt
'Magenta Magic' (Sin/DwB) NHal
'Magenta Star' (Sin) $\mathbb{Y}^{H3}$ CWGr ERCP SGbt WHoo WPhe
'Maggie Pickering' (Sin) **new** CWGr
'Maiko Girl' (DblO) $\mathbb{Y}^{H3}$ LAyl
'Maisha' (D) CWGr
'Maisie' (D) CWGr
'Maisie Mooney' (D) CWGr
'Malvern Spring' (Sin) CWGr
'Mambo NL' (Anem) CWGr ERCP SDeJ
'Mandy' (D) CWGr
'Manhattan Island' (D) CBod CWGr MSCN SDeJ
'Manuel' (D) CWGr
'Marble Ball' (D) EPfP SDeJ SGbt
'Margaret Anne' (D) CWGr
'Marie' (D) CWGr
'Marie Schnugg' (SinO) $\mathbb{Y}^{H3}$ CWGr NJRG SGbt
'Mark Damp' (S-c) CWGr
'Mark Hardwick' (D) WPhe
'Market Joy' (S-c) CWGr
'Marla Lu' (C) CWGr
'Marlene Joy' (Fim) CWGr SGbt
'Maroon Fox'^{PBR} (Ba) **new** ERCP
'Marrakech' (WL) CWGr
I 'Mars' (Col) SGbt SSal
'Marston George' (Ba) NHal NJRG WPhe
'Marston Karen' (D) WPhe
'Marston Suzanne' (D) NHal WPhe
'Martina' (D) WPhe
'Martin's Border Triumph' (D) **new** CWGr
'Martin's Yellow' (Pom) NHal
I 'Mary Eveline' (Col) ECtt NHal

	'Mary Evelyn' (C)	SDir SGbt
	'Mary Hammett' (D)	WSpi
	'Mary Margaret Row' (D) **new**	NHal
	'Mary Pitt' (D)	SGbt
	'Mary Richards' (D)	CWGr
	'Mary's Jomanda' (Ba) ♀H3	CWGr NHal NJRG SGbt SSal WPhe
	'Mas Michael' (Fim) **new**	CWGr
	'Mas Sixty' (D)	CWGr
	'Mascot Maya' (D)	NJRG
	'Matador' (D)	WPhe
	'Match' (S-c)	CWGr WPhe
	'Matchless' (C)	CWGr
	'Matilda Huston' (S-c)	CWGr NHal
	'Matt Armour' (Sin)	CWGr
	'Maureen Hardwick' (D)	CWGr SGbt
	'Maureen Jones' (Col)	NJRG
	'Maxi Romero' (Maxi Series) (D)	LRHS
	'Maxime' (D)	ERCP LHWs SDir SSal WPhe
	'Maxine Bailey' (D)	CWGr
	'Mayan Pearl' (DblO) ♀H3	CWGr LAyl NHal SGbt SSal WPhe
	'Mayan Swan' (S-c)	SGbt
	'Mayan Warrior' (S-c)	NJRG
	'Megan Dean' (Ba)	NHal WPhe
	'Meiro' (D)	CWGr
	'Melanie Jane' (S-c)	CWGr
	'Melody Allegro'PBR (D)	CAvo ERCP LHWs LRHS NRHS WFar
	'Melody Bolero'PBR (D)	CWGr LRHS SDeJ WFar WHil
	'Melody Dixie'PBR (D)	WFar
	'Melody Dora'PBR (D)	CWGr LCro LOPS LRHS
	'Melody Fanfare'PBR (D)	LHWs SDeJ
	'Melody Gipsy'PBR (S-c)	CWGr LHWs LRHS
	'Melody Harmony'PBR (D) ♀H3	CAvo CWGr LRHS
	'Melody Latin'PBR (D)	CAvo CWGr LRHS
	'Melody Lizza'PBR (D)	NRHS WPhe
	'Melody Mambo'PBR (D)	CAvo LHWs LRHS
	'Melody Pink Allegro' (D)	ERCP
	'Melody Swing'PBR (D)	CAvo CWGr ERCP LRHS
	'Mel's Orange Marmalade' (Fim)	ERCP LCro LOPS WPhe
	'Menorca' (D)	ERCP LRHS
	'Mercator' (S-c) **new**	SPer
	merckii	CExl CSpe CTtf ECha EHyd EPPr EShb EWes LRHS MCot MMrt MNrw MRav NRHS SBut SHar SIvy SMHy SMrm WSHC
	- 'Alba' (B)	CExl CSpe WFar
	- compact	WPGP
	- dark-flowered	WPGP
§	'Mexican Black' (Misc)	CWGr EBee ECtt ERCP EWoo NJRG SIvy SSal WPGP
	'Mexican Star' (Sin)	ERCP LRHS
	'Mexico Mogul' (D)	SGbt
	'Miami' (D)	CWGr
	'Michael Haynes' (D)	CWGr
	'Michigan' (D)	CWGr
	'Mick's American Dream' (S-c)	WPhe
	'Mick's Peppermint' (S-c)	CWGr SGbt WPhe
	'Midas' (S-c)	CWGr
	'Midnight' (Pom)	SGbt
	'Midnight Star' (SinO)	NHal NJRG
	'Mies' (Sin)	CWGr
	'Milk Shake' (D)	CWGr NRHS
	'Mingus Alex' (S-c)	CWGr SSal
	'Mingus Gregory' (S-c)	CWGr SDeJ
*	'Mingus Max'	ERCP
	'Mingus Nichole' (D)	CWGr
	'Mingus Randy' (S-c)	CWGr LRHS
	'Mingus Toni' (D)	ERCP
	'Mingus Tracy Lynn' (S-c)	CWGr
	'Minley Carol' (Pom)	CWGr NHal NJRG WPhe
	'Minnesota Migrant' (S-c)	CWGr
	'Minouche' (S-c) **new**	CWGr
	'Miss Ellen' (Misc)	CWGr
	'Miss Rose Fletcher' (S-c)	CWGr
	'Miss Sophie' (S-c)	ERCP
	'Mister Frans' (D)	ERCP LRHS
	'Misterton' (D)	CWGr SGbt
	'Mistill Delight' (D)	CWGr
	'Mom's Special' (D)	CBod CWGr
I	'Mon Trésor' (S-c)	CWGr
	'Monet Mystique' (WL)	SGbt
	'Monet Sunlight' (WL)	SGbt
	'Monkstown Diane' (C)	CWGr
	'Monrovia' (Ba)	CWGr
	'Moonfire' (Sin) ♀H3	CBcs CBod CCht CRos CWGN CWGr ECtt EHyd ELan EPfP LAyl LRHS NHal NJRG NLar NRHS SCoo SGbt WCot WHoo WPhe WSpi
	'Moonlady' (D)	ERCP
	'Moor Place' (Pom)	CWGr NHal NJRG SGbt SSal WPhe
	'Moret' (S-c)	CWGr
	'Motto' (D)	CWGr
	'Mr Sandman' (Fim)	MSCN
	'Mrs Black' (Pom)	CWGr
	'Mrs Eileen' (D)	SDeJ SGbt
	'Mrs H. Brown' (Col)	SGbt
	'Mrs McDonald Quill' (D)	CWGr SGbt
	'Mrs Silverston' (D)	CWGr
	'Ms Kennedy' (Ba)	LAyl NHal WPhe
	'München' (D)	SDeJ SGbt
	'Murdoch' ambig. (D)	ECtt LRHS WCot WSpi
	'Murillo' (Sin)	LAyl
	'Murray May' (WL)	CWGr
	'Murray Petite' (S-c)	CWGr
	'Musette' (D)	CWGr SGbt
	'Musson's Silverback' (Fim)	CWGr
	'My Irene' (WL)	NJRG
	'My Love' (S-c)	CWGr ECtt ERCP LCro LOPS SEND SGbt SPer
	'My Neddy' (D)	SGbt
I	'My Pride' (D)	ERCP
	'Myama Fubuki' (Fim)	ELan ERCP
	'Myrtle's Folly' (Fim)	SDeJ WPhe
	'Mystère' (Anem)	CWGr
	'Mystery Day' (D)	CWGr SDir
	MYSTIC DESIRE	see *D.* 'Scarlet Fern'
	MYSTIC DREAMER	see *D.* 'Zone Ten'
§	'Mystic Enchantment'PBR (Sin)	CRos EHyd ELan EPfP LRHS LSou NRHS SDys SGBe SPoG
	'Mystic Haze'	see *D.* 'Dark Side of the Sun'
	MYSTIC ILLUSION	see *D.* 'Knockout' (Sin)
	MYSTIC MARS	see *D.* 'Scarlet Fern'
§	MYSTIC SPIRIT ('Hamspirit'PBR) (Sin)	CRos EHyd ELan LRHS LSou NRHS SSal WPhe
	'Mystic Wonder' (Sin)	EHyd ELan LRHS NRHS WPhe
	'Nadia Ruth' (Fim)	ERCP LRHS
	'Nagano' (D)	SDeJ
	'Nancy H' (Ba)	CWGr
	'Nargold' (Fim)	CWGr LAyl
	'Narrow's Tricia' (S-c)	NJRG WPhe
	'Natal' (Ba)	CAvo ECtt LRHS MBros SDeJ
	'Natalie G' (D)	ERCP NJRG SSal
	'Nathalie's Wedding' (WL)	ERCP
	'Neal Gillson' (D)	CWGr
	'Nenekazi' (Fim)	LAyl LHWs NJRG WPhe
	'Néo' (D)	CWGr LHWs
	'Nepos' (WL)	CWGr GWyn NJRG SGbt WPhe

	'Nescio' (Pom)	CWGr ERCP LSou MBros SDeJ
I	'New Baby' (Ba)	CWGr ERCP LCro LOPS MBros SGbt
	'New Dimension' (S-c)	CWGr
	'Newby' (D)	CWGr
	'Newquay' (Sin)	CWGr
	'Nicholas' (D)	CWCL ERCP LHWs
	'Nick Sr' (D)	WPhe
	'Nienke' (D)	NJRG
	'Night Butterfly' (Col)	WBor
I	'Night Queen' (Ba)	MBros
I	'Nina' (D)	WPhe
	'Nippon' (Sin)	EHyd LRHS
	'Nonette' (WL)	CWGr EBee ECtt SGbt WCot
	'Nora Lilian Grant' (WL) **new**	CWGr
	'Norbeck Dusky' (S-c)	CWGr
	'Noreen' (Pom)	NHal WPhe
	'Norman Lockwood' (Pom)	CWGr
	'Normandie Frills' (Fim)	NHal
	'Normandie Wedding Day' (Fim)	NHal WPhe
§	'Nuit d'Eté' (S-c)	CWGr ELan ERCP EWoo LCro LOPS LRHS SDeJ SGbt SSal WPhe
	'Nuland's Josephine' (Ba)	NHal NJRG WPhe
	'Nunton Harvest' (D)	CWGr
	'Oakwood Belle' (C)	CWGr
	'Oakwood Christina' (Ba)	CWGr
	'Oakwood Dazzle' (D)	CWGr
	'Oakwood Diamond' (Ba)	CWGr
	'Oakwood Duchess' (D)	CWGr
	'Oakwood Fire' (S-c)	CWGr WPhe
	'Oakwood Firelight' (S-c)	CWGr
	'Oakwood Goldcrest' (S-c)	CWGr NHal WPhe
	'Oakwood Heather' (Ba)	CWGr
	'Oakwood Katie' (S-c)	CWGr
	'Oakwood Kim' (D)	CWGr
	'Oakwood Lyndon S' (S-c)	CWGr
	'Oakwood Naranga' (D) 🏆^{H3}	CWGr
	'Oakwood Natasha' (Pom)	CWGr
	'Oakwood Royale' (D)	CWGr
	'Oakwood Vivian S' (S-c)	CWGr
	'Ocean Bird'^{PBR} (D) 🏆^{H3}	ERCP
	'Okapi's Sunset' (S-c) **new**	LHWs
I	'Old Gold' (D)	CWGr SGbt
I	'Olivia' (Col)	CWGr NJRG WPhe
	'Olivia Mari' (WL)	NHal WPhe
	'Omega' (Fim) **new**	LHWs
	'Omo' (Sin/Lil) 🏆^{H3}	NJRG
	'Onesta' (D)	CWGr ERCP SDeJ
	'Onslow Renown' (S-c)	CWGr
	'Optic Illusion' (D)	CWGr
	'Opus' (D)	SGbt
	'Orange Chum' (D)	CWGr
	'Orange Cushion' (D)	CWGr
	'Orange Explosion' (Misc)	SGbt
	'Orange Fire' (S-c)	CWGr
	'Orange Fubuki' (D)	ERCP LHWs
	'Orange Keith's Choice' (D)	CWGr WPhe
	'Orange Kiss' (Col)	NJRG WPhe
	'Orange Mullett' (D/DwB)	CWGr
	'Orange Nugget' (Ba)	CWGr SDeJ
	'Orange Pathfinder' (Misc)	NJRG
	'Orange Pekoe' (D)	ERCP LHWs
	'Orange Pygmy' (S-c) **new**	LRHS
I	'Orange Queen' (C)	CWGr SGbt
	'Orange Sun' (D)	CWGr
	'Orchid Lace' (C)	CWGr
	'Orel' (Col)	SGbt
	'Oreti Bliss' (C)	LAyl NHal
	'Oreti Classic' (D)	NHal
	'Orfeo' (C)	LCro LOPS LRHS MNrw SDeJ SGbt
	'Ornamental Rays' (C)	CWGr
	'Ossie Latham' (Sin)	CWGr SGbt
	'Othello' (S-c)	CWGr
	'Otto's Thrill' (D) 🏆^{H3}	ERCP LRHS MSCN
	'Pacific Ocean' (WL)	ERCP
	'Paint It Black' (D) **new**	LHWs
	'Painted Girl' (D)	ERCP LSou
	'Palmares' (D)	LSou
	'Pam Howden' (WL)	NHal NJRG SGbt
	'Paradise City' (D)	SSal
	'Pari Taha Sunrise' (S-c)	CWGr
	'Park Princess' (C/DwB)	CWGr LAyl NHal NRHS SDeJ SGbt SSal
	'Park Record' (S-c)	LCro LOPS
	'Parkflamme' (D)	CWGr
	'Parkland Glory' (D)	LSou
	'Parkland Rave' (S-c)	CWGr NHal
	'Paso Doble' misapplied	see *D.* 'Freya's Paso Doble'
	'Passion' (D)	CWGr
	'Pat Knight' (Col)	CWGr NJRG WPhe
	'Pat Mark' (S-c)	CWGr
	'Pat 'n' Dee' (D)	CWGr
	'Pat 'n' Perc' (Col)	NHal NJRG SGbt WPhe
	'Pat Seed' (D)	CWGr
	'Paul Chester' (C)	CWGr
	'Paul Critchley' (C)	CWGr
	'Paul Smith' (Ba)	CWGr
	'Peach Athalie' (C)	CWGr
	'Peach Brandy' (WL)	SSal
	'Peach Delight' (S-c)	SGbt
§	'Peach Melba' (D)	NHal WPhe
	'Peaches and Cream'^{PBR} (D)	CWGr ECtt LHWs MBros
	'Peachette' (Misc/Lil)	CWGr
	'Pearl of Heemstede' (D) 🏆^{H3}	CWGr LAyl NHal NJRG
	'Pearl Sharowean' (S-c)	CWGr
	'Pearson's Ben' (S-c)	CWGr NJRG
	'Pearson's Melanie' (C)	CWGr
	'Pearson's Patrick' (S-c)	CWGr
	'Penhill Autumn Shade' (S-c)	NJRG SGbt
	'Penhill Dark Monarch' (D)	ERCP
	'Penhill Watermelon' (D)	ERCP SDeJ
	'Penny Lane' (D)	MBros SDir SPer
	'Peppermint Splash' (D)	WPhe
I	'Perfect' (D)	CWGr
	'Peter' (D)	CWGr SGbt
	'Petite Harvest' (Misc/DwB)	NJRG
	'Petite Lilliput' (Sin/Lil)	WPhe
	'Petite Sunrise' (Sin)	NJRG
	'Petite Sunset' (Misc/Lil)	NJRG
	'Petra's Wedding' (D)	CWGr ERCP
	'Philadelphia' (D)	CWGr
	'Phyllis Farmer' (WL)	CWGr
	'Pianella' (S-c)	CWGr SGbt
	'Pineapple Lollipop' (Ba)	CWGr
	'Pinelands Pam' (Fim)	CWGr
	'Pinelands Princess' (Fim)	ERCP SGbt
	'Pink Attraction' (D)	CWGr
	'Pink Carol' (Pom)	CWGr NJRG
	'Pink Giraffe' (DblO) 🏆^{H3}	CWGr ERCP LRHS SGbt
	'Pink Isa'^{PBR} (D)	CWGr ERCP
	'Pink Jean Fairs' (WL)	CWGr
	'Pink Jupiter' (S-c)	CWGr NHal SGbt SSal WPhe
	'Pink Katisha' (D)	CWGr
	'Pink Leycett' (D)	CWGr
	'Pink Magic'^{PBR} (D) **new**	LRHS
	'Pink Pastelle' (S-c) 🏆^{H3}	SGbt
	'Pink Pat and Perc' (Col)	NHal NJRG SSal WPhe
	'Pink Perception' (WL)	ERCP
	'Pink Preference' (S-c)	CWGr

	'Pink Runner' (D)	ERCP
	'Pink Sensation' (C)	CWGr
	'Pink Silk' (D)	ERCP SPer
	'Pink Skin' (D)	ECtt LRHS SDeJ
	'Pink Spur' (D)	NHal
	'Pink Suffusion' (D)	WPhe
	'Pinkie Swear' (D)	ERCP
	pinnata B&SWJ 10240	WCru
	– B&SWJ 14901 from Colombia	WCru
	'Piperoo' (C)	CWGr SGbt
	'Piper's Pink' (S-c/DwB)	ECtt EHyd LRHS NRHS SGbt
I	'Pippa' (WL)	CWGr
I	'Pippi' (D)	CWGr
	'Pitchoun' (Sin)	CWGr
	'Platinum Blonde' (Anem)	ERCP WPhe
	'Playa Blanca' (C/DwB)	SGbt
	'Playboy' (D)	CWGr
	'Polar Ice' (D)	CWGr
	'Polka NL' (Anem)	LHWs NJRG SDeJ SGbt WPhe
	'Polventon Kristobel' (D)	NHal WPhe
	'Polventon Supreme' (Ba)	WPhe
	'Pontiac' (C)	CWGr SGbt SSal
	'Pooh' (Col)	see *D.* 'Pooh - Swan Island'
§	'Pooh - Swan Island' (Col) ♀H3	CBod CWGr EBee ECtt ERCP ESwi LAyl NHal NJRG SSal WCot WPhe
	'Pop Harris' (D)	CWGr
	'Pop Willo' (Pom)	NJRG
I	'Poppet' (Pom)	CWGr
	'Poppyscotland' (Sin)	CWGr
	'Porcelain' (WL)	WPhe WSpi
	'Pot Black' (Ba)	CWGr
	'Potgeiter' (Ba)	CWGr
	'Preference' (C)	CWGr ERCP SDeJ SGbt
	'Preston Park' (Sin/DwB) ♀H3	LAyl NHal
	PRETTY WOMAN ('Vdtg43'PBR) (Dark Angel Series) (Sin) ♀H3	LCro LOPS
	'Priceless Pink' (Misc)	ERCP
	PRIDE OF BERLIN	see *D.* 'Stolz von Berlin'
	'Primrose Diane' (D)	WPhe
	'Prince Valiant' (D)	CWGr
I	'Princess' (Col)	SDeJ
	'Princess Amalia' (D)	WPhe
	'Princess Marie José' (Sin)	CWGr
	'Prinzessin Irene von Preussen' (D)	CWGr
	'Procyon' (D)	CBod CWGr SGbt
	'Profundo' (D)	ERCP LHWs
	'Promise' (Fim)	CWGr ECtt SDeJ
	aff. ***pteropoda*** F&M 312	WPGP
	PULP FICTION ('Vdtg61'PBR) (Dark Angel Series) (Sin)	CWGr SSal
	'Purbeck Lydia' (S-c)	CWGr
	'Purpinca' (Anem)	CWGr
	'Purple City' (S-c) **new**	SPer
	'Purple Duncan Edwards' (S-c)	NHal
	'Purple Flame'PBR (D)	ERCP SSal
	'Purple Fox'PBR (Ba)	ERCP
	'Purple Gem' (S-c)	CWGr ERCP LCro LOPS MSCN SDeJ SGbt
	'Purple Haze' (Misc)	ERCP LCro LOPS LSRN
	'Purple Pearl' (D)	NHal SSal WPhe
	'Purple Petite' (Sin)	NJRG
	'Purple Planet' (D) **new**	LHWs
	'Purple Puff' (Anem)	LAyl NHal NJRG WPhe
	'Purple Sensation' (S-c)	CWGr
	'Purple Splash' (WL)	CWGr

	'Purple Taiheyō' (D)	CWGr ERCP
	aff. ***purpusii*** B&SWJ 10321	WCru
	'Pussycat' (D)	CWGr
	'Quel Diable' (S-c)	CWGr
	'Quinty' (D)	WPhe
	'R. Mona' (WL)	WPhe
	'Rachel de Thame' (Sin)	CWGr
	'Rachel's Place' (Pom)	CWGr
	'Radiance' (C)	CWGr
I	'Radjah' (Pom)	NRHS
	'Ragged Robin' (Misc)	CSpe ECtt ERCP LRHS SSal
	'Rainbow Silence' (S-c) **new**	LHWs
	'Raisa' (D)	WPhe
	'Raiser's Pride' (C)	WPhe
	'Rancho' (WL)	WPhe
	'Raspberry Valiant' (B)	NHal
*	'Raymond Guernsey'	ECtt
	'Razzle Dazzle' (D)	ERCP SSal
	'Rebecca Lynn' (D)	CWGr
	'Rebecca's World' (D)	CWGr ECtt ERCP LCro LOPS SSal
	'Red and White' (D)	CWGr SGbt
	'Red Arrows' (D)	CWGr
	'Red Cap' (D)	CWGr
	'Red Carol' (Pom)	CWGr
	'Red Diamond' (D)	NHal
	'Red Fox'PBR (Ba)	CWGr LCro LOPS
	'Red Fubuki' (D)	SDeJ
	'Red Majorette' (S-c)	SDeJ
	'Red Pathfinder' (Sin)	NJRG
	'Red Pimpernel' (D)	WPhe
	'Red Pygmy' (S-c)	CWGr SDeJ
	'Red Riding Hood' (Sin)	CWGr
	'Red Squirrel' (P/DwB) **new**	CWGr
	'Red Sun' (D)	CWGr
	'Red Symphony' (Ba) **new**	LHWs
	'Red Velvet' (WL)	CWGr
	'Rees' Dream' (D)	CWGr
	'Reginald Keene' (S-c)	CWGr NHal WPhe
	'Renato Tosio' (D)	WPhe
	'Reputation' (C)	CWGr SGbt
	'Requiem' (D)	ECtt ERCP NHal NJRG SSal
	'Reverend P. Holian' (S-c)	SGbt
	'Revive' (Misc)	CWGr
	'Rhonda' (Pom)	NHal WPhe
	'Rhubarb and Custard' (Sweet Candy Series) (Col)	WPhe
	'Richstone' (D)	CWGr
	'Riisa' (Ba)	CWGr
	'Rip City' (S-c)	CWGr ERCP LCro LOPS LRHS MCot
	'Rising Sun' (S-c)	CWGr WPhe
	'Rita Easterbrook' (D)	CWGr
	'Rita Rosina' (D)	CWGr
	'Rita Shrimpton' (Misc)	CWGr
	'Robann Regal' (D)	CWGr
	'Robann Royal' (Ba)	CWGr
	'Robert Too' (D)	CWGr
	'Rocco' (Ba)	ERCP LCro LOPS LSou SGbt WBor
	'Rockcliffe Billy' (S-c)	NJRG
	'Roger Turrell' (D)	NHal
	'Rokewood Opal' (C)	CWGr
	'Romance' (C)	CWGr
	'Rosalinde' (S-c)	CWGr
	'Rose Jupiter' (S-c)	CWGr NHal WPhe
	'Rose Tendre' (S-c)	CWGr
	'Rosella' (D)	CWGr SDeJ SGbt SSal
	'Rosemary Dawn' (Ba) **new**	NHal
	'Rosemary Webb' (D)	SGbt
	'Rossendale Flamenco' (D)	NHal
	'Rossendale Heide' (D)	WPhe

	'Rossendale Hero' (Ba)	NHal
	'Rossendale Jojo' (D) **new**	NHal
	'Rossendale Mollie' (D)	WPhe
	'Rossendale Natasha' (Ba)	NHal SGbt
	'Rossendale Parky' (D)	NHal
	'Rossendale Roxy' (D)	NHal WPhe
	'Rosy Cloud' (D)	CWGr
	'Rothesay Castle' (D/DwB)	CWGr
	'Rothesay Reveller' (D)	CWGr
	'Rothesay Rose' (WL)	CWGr
I	'Roxy' (Sin/DwB)	CBcs CBod CRos CWGr EBee ECtt EHyd ELan EPfP ERCP LAyl LRHS LSRN NJRG NRHS SGbt SSal WCot WPhe WSpi
	'Royal Blood' (Misc)	LAyl
	'Royal Mail' (D)	SGbt
	'Royal Visit' (D)	CWGr SGbt
	'Royal Wedding' (S-c)	CWGr
	'Ruby Red' (Ba)	CWGr
	'Ruby Wedding' (D)	CWGr SGbt
	rudis	CExl EBee WPGP
	'Ruskin Andrea' (S-c)	NHal WPhe
	'Ruskin Avenger' (S-c)	NJRG WPhe
	'Ruskin Belle' (S-c)	CWGr
	'Ruskin Buttercup' (D)	SGbt
	'Ruskin Charlotte' (S-c)	CWGr
	'Ruskin Diane' (D)	CWGr NHal NJRG WPhe
	'Ruskin Dynasty' (D)	CWGr
I	'Ruskin Harmony' (S-c)	CWGr
	'Ruskin Harmony' (Ba)	WPhe
	'Ruskin Limelight' (C)	NHal
	'Ruskin Marigold' (S-c)	CWGr NHal
	'Ruskin Michelle' (S-c)	NHal SSal WPhe
	'Ruskin Myra' (S-c)	NHal WPhe
	'Ruskin Respectable' (S-c)	NJRG
	'Ruskin Tangerine' (Ba)	NHal SGbt WPhe
	'Rustig' (D)	CWGr
I	'Rusty' (Sin)	CWGr
I	'Ruth Ann' (Ba)	NHal
	'Ruth Parker' (Col)	CWGr
	'Ryecroft Bella' (Ba)	NHal
	'Ryecroft Blackberry' (Pom)	NHal
	'Ryecroft Brenda T' (D)	NHal NJRG
	'Ryecroft Helen' (S-c)	NHal
	'Ryecroft Huntsman' (D)	NHal
	'Ryecroft Ice' (D)	SGbt
	'Ryecroft Jan' (Ba) ♀H3	NHal WPhe
	'Ryecroft Jim' (Anem)	LAyl NHal WPhe
	'Ryecroft Laura' (Ba)	LAyl NHal
	'Ryecroft Misty' (D)	NHal
	'Ryecroft Pixie' (C)	NHal
	'Ryecroft Rebel' (D)	WPhe
	'Ryecroft Sparkler' (C)	SGbt
	'Ryecroft Zoe' (S-c)	NHal
	'Ryedale Pinky' (D)	CWGr
	'Ryedale Prince' (D)	CWGr
	'Ryedale Rebecca' (S-c)	CWGr
	'Sabrina' (D)	WPhe
	'Saint Croix' (S-c)	CWGr
	'Saint Martin' (D)	ERCP
	'Saint-Saëns' (S-c)	SDeJ
	'Sakura Fubuki' (Fim)	ERCP
	'Salmon Runner' (D) **new**	ERCP
	'Salvation' (Ba) **new**	LHWs
	'Sam Hopkins' (D)	ERCP LAyl NHal WPhe
	'Sam Huston' (D)	CWGr SGbt
	'Samantha'	see *D.* 'Harvest Samantha'
	'Sandia Serenity' (WL)	NJRG
	'Sandra' (D)	ERCP LCro LOPS
	'Sans Souci' (C)	CWGr
	'Santa Claus US' (D)	LHWs SGbt WPhe
	'Sarabande' (S-c)	CWGr
	'Sarah' (S-c)	CWGr ECtt EHyd LRHS NRHS SSal
	'Sarah Bryant' (D)	NHal
I	'Sarah Elisabeth' (WC)	WPhe
	'Sarah G' (S-c)	CWGr
	'Sascha' (WL) ♀H3	NHal
	'Sassy' (D)	SGbt
	'Scarborough Ace' (D)	CWGr
	'Scarlet Comet' (Anem)	CWGr
§	'Scarlet Fern' (Sin)	CWGr EHyd
	'Scarlet O'Hara' (D)	NJRG
	'Scarlet Rotterdam' (S-c)	CWGr
	'Scarlet Star' (S-c)	CWGr
	'Scaur Sunrise' (D)	NJRG
	'Scaur Swinton' (D)	NHal SGbt
	'Scaur Topper' (Ba)	WPhe
	'Schneeflocke' (Ba)	CWGr
	'Schweitzer's Kokarde' (D)	CWGr
	'Scottish Impact' (S-c)	CWGr
	'Seattle' (D)	CBod CWGr
	'Seduction' (D)	ERCP LHWs
	'Sefton Silvertop' (D)	NHal
	'Seirō' (S-c)	SGbt
	'Seniors Art' (Misc) **new**	EShb
	'Seniors Hope' (Misc) **new**	ERCP
	'Seniors Love' (Misc) **new**	LHWs
	'Seniors White' (D) **new**	SPer
	'Shandy' (S-c)	CWGr LAyl SHar
I	'Sheila' (Ba)	WPhe
	'Shep's Memory' (WL) ♀H3	NJRG
	sherffii	NJRG
	'Sherwood Titan' (D)	CWGr
	'Sherwood's Peach' (D)	CWGr
	'Sheval Megan' (D)	NHal WPhe
	'Shiloh Noelle' (D)	ERCP
	'Shining Star' (C)	CWGr
	'Shirley Pillman' (Misc)	CWGr
	'Shirley Westwell' (D)	CWGr
	'Shirwell Greta' (D)	NHal WPhe
	'Shooting Star' (S-c)	CWGr
	'Show 'n' Tell' (Fim)	CWGr ERCP SGbt SSal WPhe
	'Shy Princess' (C)	CWGr
	'Silver City' (D)	CWGr NHal SGbt WPhe
	'Silver Slipper' (S-c)	CWGr
	'Silver Years' (D)	CWGr LHWs
	'Silvie's Queen' (D)	SDeJ
*	'Simon' (D)	CWGr
	SINCERITY ('Dahsc266'PBR) (D) **new**	LRHS
	'Sir Alf Ramsey' (D)	CWGr LAyl NHal SDir SGbt WPhe
	'Skipper Rock' (D)	CWGr
	'Small World' (Pom) ♀H3	CWGr LAyl NHal WPhe
	'Smiling Don' (D) **new**	LHWs
	'Smokey' (D)	CWGr
	'Sneezy' (Sin/DwB)	CWGr
	'Snoho Sonia' (Ba)	WPhe
	'Snow Cap' (S-c)	SDeJ
	'Snowbound' (D)	SGbt
I	'Snowflake' (Pom)	ERCP SDeJ
I	'Snowstorm' (D)	CWGr LRHS SGbt
	'Snowy' (Ba)	CWGr
	'So Dainty' (S-c) ♀H3	CWGr
I	'Sofia' (WL)	CWGr
	'Sonia Henie' (Ba)	CWGr
	'Sophie Taylor' (SinO)	NJRG
	'Sorbet' (S-c)	see *D.* 'Geerlings Sorbet' (S-c)
	sorensenii	CWGr
	'Soulman' (Anem)	CWGr ERCP SGbt SSal WPhe
	'Sourire de Crozon' (D)	CWGr
	'Souvenir d'Eté' (Pom)	LRHS SDeJ
	'Spanish Conquest' (D)	CWGr NHal SGbt SSal

	'Spartacus' (D)	CWGr ERCP NHal
	'Spassmacher' (S-c)	CWGr
	'Spectacular' (D)	CWGr SGbt
	'Spencer' (D)	CWGr
I	'Spike' (S-c)	SGbt
	'Spikey Symbol' (S-c)	CWGr
	'Staleen Condesa' (S-c)	SGbt WPhe
	'Stan's Nirvana' (WL)	CWGr
	'Star Elite' (C)	CWGr
	'Star Surprise' (C)	SDeJ
	STAR WARS ('Vdtg14'^{PBR}) (Dark Angel Series) (Sin)	LCro LOPS SDeJ SPer
	'Starlight Keene' (S-c)	CWGr
	'Starry Night' (S-c)	CWGr
	'Star's Favourite' (C)	SDeJ
	'Star's Lady' (C)	CWGr
	'Stefan Bergerhoff' (D)	CWGr
	'Stella J' (WL)	CWGr
	'Stephanie' (S-c)	CWGr
	'Steve Bradley' (Sin) **new**	CWGr
	'Steve Meggos' (D)	WPhe
	'Stevie D' (D) ♀H3	CWGr SGbt
§	'Stolz von Berlin' (Ba)	CWGr ERCP LRHS MBros SDeJ SGbt
	'Storm Warning' (D)	CWGr
	'Storrs Julie' (Pom)	NJRG WPhe
	STRAWBERRY ICE	see *D.* 'Kidd's Climax'
	'Strike a Light' (C)	CWGr
	'Striped Ambition' (Fim)	CWGr
	'Striped Vulcan' (S-c)	WPhe
	'Sue Mountjoy' (Col)	CWGr
	'Sue's Kilmorie' (S-c)	NHal
	'Suffolk Punch' (D)	CWGr ELan LAyl
	'Suitzus Julie' (Misc)	CWGr NJRG WPhe
	'Summer Festival' (D)	CWGr SGbt
	'Summer Night' (S-c)	see *D.* 'Nuit d'Eté'
	'Summer Nights' (Misc)	CWGr NJRG SSal
	'Sungold' (Ba)	CWGr
	'Sunlady' (D)	LSou
	'Sunny Boy' (Ba)	CWGr MBros SDeJ
	'Sunray Silk' (S-c)	CWGr
	'Sunset' (D)	MBros
	'Sunshine Girl' (Col)	NHal NJRG
	'Super Rays' (C)	CWGr
	'Superfine' (C)	CWGr
	'Susan Gilbert' (Col) ♀H3	NHal NJRG SSal WPhe
	'Susan Gilliott' (S-c)	NHal
	'Susan Willo' (Pom)	CWGr
I	'Suzanne' (Col)	NJRG
	'Suzette' (D/DwB)	SGbt
	'Swan Lake'	see *D.* 'Classic Swanlake'
	'Swanvale' (D)	CWGr SGbt
	'Sweet Content' (D)	CWGr SGbt
	'Sweet Love' (D)	ERCP
I	'Sweet Sixteen' (WL)	CWGr
	'Sweet Surprise' (D)	ERCP
	'Sweet Tiamo' (D) **new**	ERCP
	'Sweetheart' (D)	CWGr NJRG SDeJ
I	'Sylvia' (Ba)	CWGr ERCP LCro LOPS SSal
	'Sylvia's Desire' (C)	CWGr
	'Sympathy' (WL)	CWGr
	'Table Dancer' (Fim)	MBros SDir
	'Tahiti Sunrise' (S-c)	LRHS LSou MBros
	'Take Off' (Anem)	ERCP SDeJ WBor
	'Tally Ho' (Sin) ♀H3	CWGr ECtt EHyd EPfP LRHS NJRG NRHS SDys WCot
	'Tam Tam' (Ba)	CWGr SPer
	'Tamburo' (S-c)	ERCP SPer SSal
	'Tanjoh' (S-c)	SPer
I	'Tapestry' (Sin)	CWGr SGbt
	'Taratahi Ruby' (WL) ♀H3	CWGr ERCP NHal NJRG WPhe
	'Tartan' (D)	CWGr ERCP EWTr LSou WPhe
	'Tartarus' (P)	CWGr
	'Teesbrooke Audrey' (Col)	CWGr ECtt LCro LOPS NHal NJRG WPhe
	'Teesbrooke Red Eye' (Col)	CWGr NJRG SGbt SSal WPhe
	tenuicaulis	CDTJ CExl
	'Terracotta' (Misc/DwB)	NJRG
	'Terrie Bandey' (Fim)	LAyl WPhe
	'Thais' (Col)	NJRG
	'The Baron' (D)	CWGr
	'The Big Wow' (D)	CWGr
	'The Phantom' (Anem)	NJRG SDeJ
I	'The Queen' (S-c)	CWGr
	'Theo Sprengers' (D)	CWGr
	'Thomas A. Edison' (D)	CBod CWGr ERCP LCro LOPS MBros MSCN SDeJ SGbt
	'Tiffany Lynn' (SinO)	CWGr
I	'Tiger' (Sin/DwB)	CWGr
	'Tiger Eye' (D)	SGbt
	'Tiger Tiv' (D)	CWGr
	'Tinker's White' (D)	CWGr
	'Tioga Spice' (Fim)	CWGr SSal
	'Tohsuikyoh' (Misc)	CWGr SGbt
	'Tommy Doc' (S-c)	CWGr
	'Tomo' (D)	ELan LAyl NHal
	'Tom's August Bride' (S-c)	CWGr
	'Top Choice' (S-c)	CWGr
I	'Topaz Puff' (Anem)	CWGr
	'Topmix' (Sin/DwB)	SDeJ
	'Topmix Apricot' (Sin) **new**	ERCP
	'Topmix Mama' (Sin)	NJRG
	'Topmix Orange' (Sin)	NJRG SDeJ
	'Topmix Pink' (Sin/DwB)	CWGr SDeJ
	'Topmix Purple' (Sin)	NJRG
	'Topmix Red' (Sin/DwB)	NJRG SDeJ
	'Topmix Reddy' (Sin)	NJRG
I	'Topmix Rose' (Sin)	NJRG
	'Topmix Salmon' (Sin)	ERCP
	'Topmix White' (Sin/DwB)	ERCP SDeJ
	'Topmix Yellow' (Sin/DwB)	SDeJ
	'Totally Tangerine' (Anem)	CWGr ERCP SSal WPhe
	'Toto' (Anem)	ERCP SDeJ
	'Tour du Monde' (WL)	CWGr
	'Trebbiano' (S-c)	ERCP MBros
	'Trelissick Purple'	CWGr
	'Trelyn Amber' (Col)	WPhe
	'Trelyn Crimson' (Col) ♀H3	WPhe
	'Trelyn Daisy' (Col) ♀H3	CWGr
	'Trelyn Kiwi' (S-c) ♀H3	NHal NJRG SGbt WPhe
	'Trelyn Kristia' (Col)	WPhe
	'Trelyn Rebecca' (Col)	WPhe
	'Trelyn Red Dragon' (SinO)	NJRG WPhe
	'Trelyn Rhiannon' (C) ♀H3	WPhe
	'Trelyn Seren' (SinO)	LAyl WPhe
	'Trengrove Autumn' (D)	CWGr SGbt
	'Trengrove Millennium' (D)	CWGr NHal NJRG SGbt WPhe
I	'Trevor' (Col)	CWGr ECtt SGbt
	'Tricolor' ambig.	LSou MSCN
	'Trooper Dan' (S-c)	WPhe
	'Troy Dyson' (Misc)	SDys
	'Truly Scrumptious' (S-c)	SGbt
	'Tsuki-yori-no-shisha' (Fim)	LCro LOPS
	tubulata	EBee
	'Tui Avis' (C)	NJRG
	'Tui Orange' (S-c)	CWGr
	'Tula Rosa' (Pom)	CWGr
	'Tu-tu' (S-c)	CWGr SGbt
	'Twiggy' (WL)	SGbt
	'Twilight Time' (D)	CWGr SDeJ WPhe
	'Twilite' (Anem)	CWGr
*	'Twinkle Stars'	SDeJ

	'Twyning's After Eight' (Sin) ♀H3	CExl CRos CSpe CWGN CWGr ECtt EHyd ELan EPfP ERCP EShb EWoo LAyl LCro LOPS LRHS LSun NHal NJRG NRHS SDys SGbt SSal WBor WCot WHoo WPhe
	'Twyning's Aniseed' (Sin)	CWGr
	'Twyning's Black Cherry' (D)	CWGr ECtt
	'Twyning's Candy' (Sin)	CWGr
	'Twyning's Chocolate' (Sin)	CWGr
	'Twyning's Peppermint' (Sin)	CWGr
	'Twyning's Pink Fish' (Col)	CWGr
	'Twyning's Revel' (Sin) ♀H3	CWGr WMal
	'Twyning's Smartie' (Sin)	CBod CWGr EBee ECtt LCro LOPS LRHS SPer SSal WPhe
	'Twyning's Velvet' (Sin)	CWGr
	'Twyning's White Chocolate' (Sin)	CWGr ERCP
	'Uchuu' (D)	CWGr
	'Union Jack' (Sin)	CWGr
	'Uniquity' (Sin)	WCot
	'United' (D)	CWGr
	'Urchin' (C)	CWGr SSal
	'Val Saint Lambert' (Fim)	CWGr
I	'Valentino' (WL/DwB)	CWGr
	'Valerie Moody' (D)	CWGr
	'Val's Candy' (S-c)	NHal NJRG WPhe
	'Vancouver' (Misc)	CBod CWGr ECtt LCro LOPS SDeJ WFar
	'Variace' (Ba)	CWGr
	'Vassio Meggos' (D)	CWGr ERCP LHWs NHal WPhe
	'Veritable' (S-c)	LCro LOPS
	'Verrone's Obsidian' (SinO)	CSpe CWGr EPfP ERCP EWoo LCro LOPS LRHS SSal WPhe
	'Verwer's Heatwave' (D)	ERCP
	'Viking' (Pom)	CWGr
	'Vino' (Pom)	WPhe
	'Violet Davies' (S-c)	CWGr
	'Vivex' (Pom)	CWGr
	'Vivian Russell' (WL)	NHal NJRG WPhe
	'Vossens Discovery' (Sin) **new**	CWGr
	'Vulcan' (S-c)	CWGr ERCP SGbt WPhe
§	'Vuurvogel' (S-c)	SDeJ
	'Walter Hardisty' (D)	CWGr
	'Walter James' (D)	CWGr
	'Waltzing Mathilda' (Misc) ♀H3	CWGr ERCP LCro LOPS WPhe
	'Wanborough Gem' (Ba)	CWGr
	'Wanda's Capella' (D)	CWGr
	'Wandy' (Pom)	CWGr
	'War of the Roses' (D)	EWes SIvy WHer
	'Warkton Willo' (Pom)	CWGr
	'Warmunda' (Ba)	CWGr
I	'Waterlily' (Sin)	EHyd NRHS
	'Weddington Pink' (C) **new**	SSal
I	'Welcome Guest' (S-c)	CWGr
	'Westerton Ella Grace' (D)	NHal NJRG
	'Westerton Folly' (Ba) ♀H3	NHal WPhe
	'Westerton Harry' (D)	NHal
	'Westerton J.W.H.' (D)	NHal WPhe
	'Westerton Lilian' (D)	NHal WPhe
	'Westerton Southside' (D)	NHal
	'Weston Buccaneer' (C)	NHal
	'Weston Corsair' (C)	NJRG WPhe
	'Weston Forge' (C)	CWGr
	'Weston Miss' (S-c)	NJRG WPhe
	'Weston Nugget' (C)	CWGr
	'Weston Pirate' (C) ♀H3	CWGr LAyl NHal NJRG WPhe
	'Weston Spanish Dancer' (C) ♀H3	CWGr ERCP NHal NJRG SGbt WPhe
	'Weston Stardust' (C) ♀H3	NJRG WPhe
	'Weston Tea-time' (C)	CWGr
	'Weston Torero' (C)	CWGr
	'Whale's Rhonda' (Pom)	NHal
	'Wheels' (Col)	CWGr NJRG
	'White Alva's' (D) ♀H3	CWGr LAyl NHal SGbt WPhe
	'White Apollo' (Col) **new**	CWGr
	'White Aster' (Pom)	CWGr ERCP SPer
	'White Ballerina' (WL)	NHal SGbt
	'White Ballet' (D) ♀H3	CWGr LAyl SGbt
	'White Cameo' (WL)	CWGr
	'White Charlie Two' (D)	NHal
	'White Hallelujah' (Sin)	CWGr
	'White Hamari Katrina' (S-c)	WPhe
	'White Klankstad' (C)	CWGr
	'White Knight' (D)	NHal
	'White Lace' (Fim)	WPhe
	'White Moonlight' (S-c)	CWGr NHal WPhe
	'White Nettie' (Ba)	SGbt
	'White Onesta' (D)	ERCP EWoo SDeJ
	'White Pastelle' (S-c)	CWGr WPhe
	'White Perfection' (D)	CWGr ECtt SDeJ SDir WSpi
	'White Rustig' (D)	CWGr
	'White Seedling' (Sin)	CWGr
	'White Star' (S-c)	CWGr LCro LOPS LRHS SDeJ
	'White Swallow' (S-c)	NHal
	white-flowered B&SWJ 14340 from Colombia	WCru
	'Who Dun It' (D)	CWGr
	'Wicky Woo' (D)	CWGr
	'Wildwood Marie' (WL)	CWGr NJRG
	'William John' (Pom)	CWGr
	'Williamsburg' (S-c)	CWGr
	'Willo's Borealis' (Pom)	NHal
	'Willo's Night' (Pom)	CWGr
	'Willo's Surprise' (Pom)	SGbt
	'Willo's Violet' (Pom)	NHal NJRG SGbt WPhe
	'Will's Ringwood Rosie' (Pom)	CWGr
	'Windmill' (C)	WHil
	'Wine & Roses' (WL)	SGbt
	'Wine-eyed Jill' (Ba)	ERCP
	'Winholme Diane' (D)	CWGr NHal WPhe
	'Winkie Colonel' (D)	CWGr
	'Winkie Lambrusco' (Pom)	NHal NJRG WPhe
	'Winston Churchill' (WL)	WSpi
	'Wishes n Dreams' (Sin)	NJRG
	'Wisk' (Pom)	CWGr
	'Wittem' (D)	CWGr SDir
	'Witteman's Best' (S-c)	CWGr ERCP MCot SGbt
	'Witteman's Superba' (S-c) ♀H3	NHal
	'Wizard of Oz' (Ba)	CWGr ERCP LCro LHWs LOPS
	'Woodbridge' (Sin)	CWGr SGbt SSal
	'Woodside Finale' (D)	NHal
	'Wootton Cupid' (Ba) ♀H3	CWGr
	'Wootton Impact' (S-c) ♀H3	WPhe
	'Wootton Tempest' (S-c)	CWGr
	'Wootton Windmill' (Col)	CWGr
	'Worton Blue Streak' (S-c)	CWGr SGbt
	'Worton Superb' (D)	CWGr
	'X Factor' (D)	CWGr LHWs SDir
	'Yamabiraki' (D)	CWGr
	'Yellow Bulldog' (Sin)	CWGr
	'Yellow Galator' (C)	SGbt
	'Yellow Hammer' (Sin/DwB) ♀H3	NHal NJRG SGbt
	'Yellow Linda's Chester' (C)	CWGr
	'Yellow Passions' (D)	ERCP
	'Yellow Perception' (WL)	ERCP SDeJ
	'Yellow Pet' (D)	CWGr

	'Yellow Sneezy' (Sin/Lil)	SDeJ WHil
	'Yellow Star' (S-c)	CWGr ERCP SDeJ
	'Yellow Vulcan' (S-c)	CWGr
	'Yelno Enchantment' (WL)	CWGr
	'Yelno Petite Glory' (D)	CWGr
	'Yiayia Chariklia' (D) **new**	CWGr
	'Yolande Ruth' (D) **new**	CWGr
	'York and Lancaster' (D)	CWGr EBee SGbt WAvo
	'Young Bees' (D)	CWGr
I	'Yvonne' (WL)	WPhe
	'Zest' (D)	CWGr
	'Zingaro' (D)	LCro LOPS
	'Zippity Do Da' (Pom)	ERCP
	'Zirconia' (D)	ERCP LHWs
	'Zoey Rey' (D)	WPhe
§	'Zone Ten'^{PBR} (Sin/DwB)	CRos CWGr EHyd EPfP LRHS LSou NRHS SCoo SDys SPoG SSal WBor WPhe
	'Zorro' (D) $\mathbb{Y}^{H3}$	CWGr ERCP NHal SGbt
	'Zundert Mystery Fox'^{PBR} (Ba)	ERCP
	'Zurich' (S-c)	CWGr

Dais (*Thymelaeaceae*)

	cotinifolia	EShb

Daiswa see *Paris*

Dalea (*Fabaceae*)

	candida	EBee
	purpurea	EBee SBut
	- 'Stephanie'	CSpe LRHS

damson see *Prunus insititia*

Danae (*Asparagaceae*)

§	***racemosa*** $\mathbb{Y}^{H5}$	CBcs CEme CMac CTri EBee EPfP EWes LEdu LPar LRHS MGil MGos MRav NFav SEND SRms SWvt WCot WCru WPGP WSpi

Daphne (*Thymelaeaceae*)

	acutiloba	GKev WSpi
	- 'Fragrant Cloud'	CExl CJun CTrC EWes SChF WPGP
	albowiana	CBcs CCCN CJun EPfP GKev LRHS NLar SChF WSpi
	alpina	GKev WThu
	altaica	CJun
	arbuscula $\mathbb{Y}^{H5}$	EPot
	aurantiaca	IDee
	- 'Gang-ho-ba'	CJun
	bholua	CBct CCCN CJun EPfP ESwi GKev LRHS NLar SChF SavN WSpi
	- B&SWJ 8275 from Fansipan, Vietnam	WCru
	- GWJ 9436 from India	WCru
	- NJM 13.115	WPGP
I	- 'Alba'	GKev SSta WPGP WSpi
	- 'Cobhay Coral'	CJun
	- 'Cobhay Debut'	CJun
	- 'Cobhay Pink Delight'	CJun
	- 'Cobhay Snow'	CJun
	- 'Darjeeling'	CBod CCCN CExl CJun EBee ELan LRHS WPGP WSpi
	- 'Garden House Enchantress'	WPGP
	- 'Garden House Ghost'	SChF WPGP
	- 'Garden House Red Stem'	WPGP
	- 'Garden House Sentinel'	WPGP
	- var. ***glacialis*** 'Gurkha' $\mathbb{Y}^{H4}$	CExl CJun SChF WPGP
	- - 'Gurkha' × ***mezereum***	WSpi
	- 'Jacqueline Postill' $\mathbb{Y}^{H4}$	Widely available
	- 'Limpsfield'	CJun EBee LRHS SChF SSta WPGP
	- 'Penwood'	CJun
	- 'Peter Smithers'	CExl CJun SSta WPGP
	blagayana	GKev SRms
	- 'Brenda Anderson'	CJun EPot WAbe
	'Bramdean'	see *D.* × *napolitana* 'Bramdean'
	× ***burkwoodii*** 'Albert Burkwood'	CJun
	- 'Astrid' (v)	ELon LPar LRHS MGil SGol
§	- 'Carol Mackie' (v)	CJun
	- 'G.K.Argles' (v)	CJun
I	- 'Gold Sport'	CJun
	- 'Golden Treasure'	CCCN CJun LRHS NLar
	- 'Lavenirii'	CJun
	- 'Marjolein'^{PBR}	LRHS NLar
	- 'Moonlight Sonata' **new**	NLar
	- 'Somerset' $\mathbb{Y}^{H4}$	CBcs CCCN CJun ELan LCro LOPS LRHS MGil MSwo WSpi
§	- 'Somerset Gold Edge' (v)	CJun
§	- 'Somerset Variegated' (v)	EPot
	- 'Variegata' broad cream edge	see *D.* × *burkwoodii* 'Somerset Variegated'
	- 'Variegata' broad gold edge	see *D.* × *burkwoodii* 'Somerset Gold Edge'
	- 'Variegata' narrow gold edge	see *D.* × *burkwoodii* 'Carol Mackie'
	caucasica	CJun GKev
	cneorum	CBcs EWes GKev NLar
	- 'Benaco'	EPot
	- 'Eximia' $\mathbb{Y}^{H5}$	GKev
	- 'Grandiflora'	see *D.* × *napolitana* 'Maxima'
	- 'Major'	EPot
	- var. ***pygmaea***	EPot
	- 'Variegata' (v)	EWes GEdr
	- var. ***verlotii***	EPot SChF
	collina	see *D. sericea* Collina Group
	domini	GKev
§	***gemmata***	CBcs NLar
	- 'Royal Crown'	CCCN LRHS WSpi XSte
	genkwa	CJun LRHS
	giraldii	GKev
	aff. ***giraldii***	WSpi
	glomerata	GKev
	gnidium PAB 8371	LEdu
	× ***hendersonii*** 'Apple Blossom'	EPot
	- 'Aymon Correvon'	WThu
	- 'Bonnie Glen'	EPot
	- 'Ernst Hauser'	CJun WIce WThu
	- 'Fritz Kummert'	WAbe WThu
	- 'Jeanette Brickell'	WThu
	- 'Kath Dryden'	EPot GEdr
	- 'Marion White'	EPot
	- 'Rosebud'	EPot WThu
	'Hinton'	CJun
	× ***houtteana***	CJun
	japonica 'Striata'	see *D. odora* 'Aureomarginata'
	jasminea upright	EPot
	jezoensis	SSta
	kamtschatica	GKev
	'Kilmeston Beauty'	CJun
	kosaninii	GKev
	kurdica	GKev
	× ***latymeri*** 'Spring Sonnet'	SChF
	laureola	CJun EBee EPfP GKev GPoy MMrt NBid NBir NLar NPer WSpi
	- 'Margaret Mathew'	EPot NLar SChF WSpi
	- subsp. ***philippi***	CBcs CCCN CJun CMac EBee EGrI EPfP EWes IDee LCro LOPS MAsh MBlu MGil NLar WCot WPGP WSpi
	limprichtii	GKev

	longilobata	EBee GEdr GKev
	malyana **new**	GKev
	× ***mantensiana*** 'Audrey Vockins'	CJun
	- 'Manten'	CJun
	× ***mauerbachii*** 'Perfume of Spring'	CJun
	'Meon'	see *D.* × *napolitana* 'Meon'
	mezereum	CMea GKev GPoy LPar LRHS MAsh NWea SChF SCob SWvt WCot WFar WHwl WPGP
	- f. ***alba***	CMea GAbr GBin GKev GLog MAsh SRms SWvt WSpi
	- - 'Bowles's Variety'	EPot
I	- var. ***alpina*** hort.	GKev
	- 'Rosea'	MAsh SRms
	- var. ***rubra***	CBcs CCCN CDoC ELan GKin LRHS MGil MRav MSwo SPer WFar WSpi
	modesta	WAbe
	× ***napolitana*** ♀^{H4}	CJun
§	- 'Bramdean'	CJun SChF
§	- 'Maxima'	MAsh
§	- 'Meon'	CJun ELan EPot SChF WThu
	odora	CBcs CCCN CJun CSBt EPfP GKev LCro LOPS LPar LRHS MSwo NRHS SCob SEle SGbt SGol SavN WPGP WSpi
§	- f. ***alba***	CCCN LRHS NLar
	- - 'Sakiwaka'	CCCN CExl WLov
§	- 'Aureomarginata' (v)	Widely available
I	- 'Aureomarginata Alba' (v)	WSpi
	- 'Cameo'	CCCN CRos CSBt LRHS NLar
	- 'Double Cream' (v)	CJun
	- 'Geisha Girl' (v)	CCCN LRHS
	- var. ***leucantha***	see *D. odora* f. *alba*
	- 'Mae-jima' (v)	CBcs CExl LRHS MAsh SLon WSpi
	- 'Marginata'	see *D. odora* 'Aureomarginata'
	- MARIANNI ('Rogbret') (v)	CBcs CCCN CEnd CTrC EBee LRHS MMrt MRav NLar SEdd SGol SWvt
	- REBECCA ('Hewreb') (v)	CBct CMea CRos EBee ECre EHyd ELan ELon EPfP LBuc LCro LOPS LRHS MAsh MBNS MGos NRHS SEdd SLon SPoG WSpi
	- var. ***rubra***	CCCN CMac LRHS SGol
	- 'Sweet Amethyst'	CCCN LCro LOPS
	- 'Walberton' (v)	EHyd EPfP LRHS NRHS
	oleoides	EPot GKev
	papyracea	CExl WPGP
	PERFUME PRINCESS ('Dapjur01')	CBcs CBod CCCN CDoC CPla CWGN EBee ECul ELan ELon ESwi GBin ILea LRHS LSRN MBNS MGos MHtn MMrt MThu NLar NRHS SEdd SHor SPer WLea WSpi XSte
	petraea	WAbe
	pontica	CBcs CCCN CJun CMac EPfP GBin LRHS NLar NRHS SChF SHor SPer SPoG SavN WPGP WSpi
	retusa	see *D. tangutica* Retusa Group
	'Richard's Choice'	CJun
	× ***rollsdorfii*** 'Arnold Cihlarz'	CJun SChF WAbe
	- 'Wilhelm Schacht' ♀^{H5}	CJun EPot MAsh SChF WThu
	'Rosy Wave'	CJun SChF
	× ***schlyteri*** 'July Glow'	EPot GEdr SChF
	- 'Lovisa Maria'	EPot GEdr GKev
	× ***seibertii*** **new**	GKev
	sericea	CJun GKev
§	- Collina Group	SChF WIce
	'Spring Beauty'	CBct CCCN CEnd CJun CRos EPfP GBin IDee LRHS LSRN MAsh NLar SChF SHor WPGP WSpi XSte
	'Spring Herald'	CCCN CJun EPfP LRHS MMrt NLar SChF SHor SPer WPGP WSpi
	'Stasek' (v)	CJun
	× ***suendermannii*** 'Franz Suendermann'	EPot MMrt
	× ***susannae*** 'Anton Fahndrich'	GKev NLar WSpi WThu
	- 'Cheriton' ♀^{H5}	CJun ELan EPot LRHS SChF WThu
	- 'Tichborne'	EPot GEdr MMrt SChF WIce WThu
	tangutica ♀^{H5}	CBcs CBor CExl CJun CRos CSpe CTri EPfP GArf GKev LCro LOPS LRHS LSRN MAsh MGos NHol NLar SEdd SHor SRkn SRms WKif WPGP WSpi
	- 'Golden Thread' (v)	LRHS
§	- Retusa Group ♀^{H5}	CExl CJun EPot EWes EWld GBin GEdr GKev LRHS SRms WSpi
	× ***thauma***	EPot
	× ***transatlantica*** 'Beulah Cross' (v)	CJun
	- ETERNAL FRAGRANCE ('Blafra'PBR) ♀^{H5}	Widely available
§	- PINK FRAGRANCE ('Blapink'PBR)	CBcs CDoC CRos EBee ECul EHyd ELan EPfP GBin GKev ILea LCro LOPS LRHS MAsh MGos MMrt MRav NRHS SCoo SEdd SGol SHor SPer SPoG WSpi XSte
	- SPRING PINK ETERNAL FRAGRANCE	see *D.* × *transatlantica* PINK FRAGRANCE
	'Valerie Hillier'	CJun GBin GKev WSpi
	velenovskyi	GKev
	- 'Weber's Findling'	SChF
	'White Queen'	CCCN LCro LOPS LRHS NLar SHor SavN WSpi
	× ***whiteorum*** 'Beauworth'	EPot LRHS WAbe
	wolongensis	GKev
	- ex 'Guardsman'	GKev
	- 'Guardsman'	CCCN CJun ELan GBin LRHS SHor
	- 'Kevock Star'	CExl GKev

Daphniphyllum (*Daphniphyllaceae*)

aff. ***angustifolium*** B&SWJ 8225	WCru
- B&SWJ 11804	WCru
- WWJ 12020	WCru
chartaceum KWJ 12244	WCru
- KWJ 12313	WCru
glaucescens	WCru
subsp. ***oldhamii*** var. ***kengii*** B&SWJ 7119	
- - var. ***oldhamii*** CWJ 12351	WCru
himalaense	IDee
humile	see *D. macropodum* var. *humile*
aff. ***longeracemosum*** B&SWJ 11788	WCru
macropodum	CBcs CBct CCCN CEme CSpe EBee ELan EPfP LEdu LRHS MPkF NLar SArc SMad SPer SVen WCru WPGP XSte
- B&SWJ 581	WCru
- B&SWJ 2898	WCru
- B&SWJ 6809 from Taiwan	WCru
- B&SWJ 8507 from Ulleungdo, South Korea	WCru
- B&SWJ 8763 from Jejudo, South Korea	WCru
- B&SWJ 11489 from Yakushima, Japan	WCru
- B&SWJ 12691	WCru

- dwarf WCru
§ - var. ***humile*** B&SWJ 11232 WCru
majus B&SWJ 11744 WCru
paxianum B&SWJ 9755 WCru
pentandrum B&SWJ 6888 WCru
- B&SWJ 7056 WCru
- CWJ 12393 WCru
- RWJ 9836 WCru
teysmannii B&SWJ 11112 WCru
- B&SWJ 14626 from Japan WCru
aff. ***teysmannii*** CWJ 12350 from Taiwan WCru

Darlingtonia (*Sarraceniaceae*)

californica ♀H3 CHew SHmp SPlb WSSs WTyc

Darmera (*Saxifragaceae*)

peltata ♀H6 Widely available
- 'Nana' EBee ECha ELan EPfP MBel NBid NHol NLar WFar

Dasylirion (*Asparagaceae*)

§ ***acrotrichum*** CDTJ CExl EShb SArc
berlandieri CExl
cedrosanum CDTJ CJun SPlb
glaucophyllum CCht CJun
gracile Planchon see *D. acrotrichum*
leiophyllum LRHS SPlb
longissimum CCCN EOli EShb XSen
miquihuanense CCht CTsd
- F&M 321 EBee
quadrangulatum SPlb
serratifolium EOli LPar
wheeleri ♀H2 CBrP EOli SPlb XSen

Dasyphyllum (*Asteraceae*)

diacanthoides WPGP

date see *Phoenix dactylifera*

Datisca (*Datiscaceae*)

cannabina CDTJ CSpe ECha LEdu LRHS LShi SBls SMad WHer

Datura (*Solanaceae*)

arborea see *Brugmansia arborea*
cornigera see *Brugmansia arborea*
metel SAdn
- 'Double Purple' (d) **new** LSou
rosei see *Brugmansia sanguinea*
sanguinea see *Brugmansia sanguinea*
stramonium EBtc
suaveolens see *Brugmansia suaveolens*
versicolor 'Grand Marnier' see *Brugmansia* × *candida* 'Grand Marnier'

Daucus (*Apiaceae*)

carota CHab LShi SPhx SRms SVic WHer WSFF WWild

Davallia (*Davalliaceae*)

canariensis ♀H1c LEdu
trichomanoides CLAP
- f. ***barbata*** CMen

Davidia (*Nyssaceae*)

involucrata ♀H5 Widely available
- 'Crimson Spring' NLar
- 'Lady Dahlia' (v) NLar
- 'Sonoma' CAco CLnd LRHS MBlu MPkF NLar SWeb
- var. ***vilmoriniana*** ♀H5 CBcs CRos EHyd ELan EPfP LRHS MAsh MBlu NOrn SLim SPtp WHwl

Daviesia (*Fabaceae*)

cordata SPlb
* ***ovalifolia*** SPlb
pectinata SPlb

Debregeasia (*Urticaceae*)

longifolia SVen
- WWJ 11686 ESwi WCru

Decaisnea (*Lardizabalaceae*)

fargesii Widely available
insignis WJC 13740 WCru

Decumaria (*Hydrangeaceae*)

barbara CMac NLar WCru
- 'Vicki' NBro NLar
sinensis CKel CRos EBee EHyd EPfP LRHS NRHS SLon SPoG WCru

Degenia (*Brassicaceae*)

velebitica GKev WAbe

Deinanthe (*Hydrangeaceae*)

bifida CBct CExl CMil EBee EHyd EPfP EWes EWld GEdr GKev MMrt WCru WPGP
- B&SWJ 5436 WCru
- B&SWJ 5551 WCru
- B&SWJ 5655 LEdu NLar
- 'Pink-Kii' WCru
- 'Pink-Shi' CMil EWld IPot WCru WSHC
bifida × ***caerulea*** WCru
'Blue Blush' WCru
caerulea CMil EWes GEdr GKev LEdu LRHS NLar WCru WSHC
- 'Blue Wonder' CExl CTtf

Deinostigma (*Gesneriaceae*)

§ ***tamiana*** WDib

Delairea (*Asteraceae*)

§ ***odorata*** CCCN CExl WPGP

Delonix (*Fabaceae*)

decaryi SPlb
* ***grandiflora*** SPlb
regia SPlb

Delosperma (*Aizoaceae*)

from Graaf Reinet, South Africa EPot NSla XLum XSen
§ ***aberdeenense*** ♀H3 EWes SAko SLee SSim XLum XSen
alpinum see *Ectotropis alpina*
ashtonii CCCN EWes NSla SLee WThu XLum
basuticum MAsh NHpl NSla
'Beaufort West' EDAr EHyd EWes NRHS NSla
congestum misapplied see *Malotigena frantiskae-niederlovae*
congestum ambig. CTsd EPot SLee SMad WIce XLum
cooperi CCCN CRos CTri ECtt EHyd ELan EPfP EPot EWTr GArf GBin GKev ITim LRHS MHer NFav NHpl NRHS SChr SEdd SIvy SPlb SSim SVen WIce XLum XSen
- (Jewel of Desert Series) GRENADE ('Dsaa13-1') CPla EWTr SEdd SPad
- - 'Jewel of Desert Garnet'PBR CCCN ECtt EHyd LCro LOPS LRHS NHpl NRHS SEdd SPad SPoG

	- - 'Jewel of Desert Moon Stone'PBR	CBod CCCN ECtt EHyd LRHS NHpl NRHS WIce
	- - 'Jewel of Desert Peridott'PBR	CCCN CWGN ECtt EHyd LRHS NHpl NRHS SPad SPoG WIce
	- - JEWEL OF DESERT ROSEQUARTZ ('12Rosk1'PBR)	CCCN EHyd LRHS NRHS SPoG
	- - 'Jewel of Desert Ruby'PBR	CCCN CWGN NHpl SEdd WIce
	- - 'Jewel of Desert Topaz'PBR	CCCN CWGN ECtt EHyd LRHS NHpl NRHS SPad SPoG WIce
	- (Wheels of Wonder Series) FIRE WONDER ('Wowdry2'PBR) **new**	CPla
	- - GOLDEN WONDER ('Wowd20111'PBR)	CCCN LCro LOPS SPoG
	- - HOT PINK WONDER ('Wowdry1'PBR)	CPla LCro LOPS
	- - ORANGE WONDER ('Wowdoy3'PBR)	CBod CCCN SPoG
	- - VIOLET WONDER ('Wowdrw5'PBR)	CCCN MPri SPoG
	- - WHITE WONDER ('Wowdw7'PBR)	CCCN MPri SPoG
	dyeri RED MOUNTAIN ('Psdold')	CRos EHyd LRHS NRHS SAko WIce XLum
	ecklonis	GKev
	'Emotion de Feu' **new**	LRHS SPer
	FIRE SPINNER ('P001s')	EDAr WIce XLum
	floribundum 'Starburst'	SSim
	- 'Stardust'	EWes
§	'John Proffitt'	CCCN EDAr GKev SAko SPer SPlb SRot WMal
	lavisiae ♀H6	ELon EWes NSla SPlb
	- 'Letseng' **new**	LRHS
	'Lesotho Pink'	EWes
	'Lilac Queen' **new**	SRot
	lineare	XLum
	MESA VERDE ('Kelaidis')	ECtt SAko SPer XLum
	nubigenum	CSma CTri EBou ECtt ELan EPot GAbr GArf GKev NHpl SLee SPlb SSim XLum XSen
	'Ruby Coral'	CRos ECtt EHyd LRHS NRHS
	sphalmanthoides	GEdr NHpl NSla SPlb SSim
	SUNDELLA RED **new**	CBod
	sutherlandii ♀H3	CCCN CSma EDAr GBin NHpl SEdd SIvy
	- 'Peach Star'	CCCN EDAr NHpl SSim WIce
	TABLE MOUNTAIN	see *D.* 'John Proffitt'

Delphinium ✿ (*Ranunculaceae*)

	'After Midnight'	LHom
	'Alice Artindale' (d)	CMea EWes LHom WCot
	'Ann Woodfield'	CNMi LHom
	'Ariel' ambig.	LRHS
	Astolat Group	CBcs CBod CTri EHyd ELan EPfP EWTr EWoo GMaP LCro LOPS LRHS MGos NHol NLar NRHS SCob SGbt SPer SPoG SWvt WCAu
	'Atholl' ♀H5	CNMi
	(Aurora Series) 'Aurora Deep Purple'	LCro LOPS
	- 'Aurora Lavender'	LCro LOPS
	'Austin's Dawn Chorus' **new**	LHom
	'Bambi'	CNMi
	beesianum	GKev
	Belladonna Group	ELan
	- 'Atlantis'	ECha EHyd NLar NRHS WCot WSpi
	- 'Bellamosum'	EPfP GMaP LRHS MNrw WSpi
	- 'Casa Blanca'	EPfP GMaP LRHS NLar SEdd WSpi
	- 'Cliveden Beauty'	EPfP EWTr LRHS NLar SBls WSpi
	- 'Gute Nacht'	LRHS
§	- 'Janny Arrow'	LRHS
	- 'Moerheimii'	WSpi
	- 'Piccolo'	ECha NLar
	- 'Pink Sensation'	see *D.* × *ruysii* 'Pink Sensation'
	- 'Völkerfrieden'	LRHS MCot MNrw NLar WCot WSpi
	'Berghimmel'	LRHS
	'Beryl Burton'	CNMi
	Black Knight Group	CBcs CBod CKel CTri ECtt EHyd ELan EPfP EWoo GMaP GWyn LCro LRHS LSRN MGos NGdn NHol NLar NMir NRHS SCob SGbt SPer SPlb SPoG SWvt WCAu WFar WHil
	'Black-eyed Angels' (New Millennium Series)	EHyd ELan IPot LRHS NRHS SBls SGbt
	'Blauwal'	WSpi
	'Blue Arrow'	see *D.* (Belladonna Group) 'Janny Arrow', *D.* 'Blue Max Arrow'
	Blue Bird Group	CBcs CTri EHyd ELan EPfP EWTr GMaP LRHS MGos NRHS SCob SEdd SGbt SPer SPoG WCAu
	'Blue Butterfly'	see *D. grandiflorum* 'Blue Butterfly'
	'Blue Dawn' ♀H5	CNMi LHom
	Blue Fountains Group	EPfP LSRN SPoG SRms
	Blue Jade Group	LHom
	'Blue Jay'	EPfP LSRN WSpi
	'Blue Lace'	CDor CPla CWCL EHyd IPot SEdd SGbt
I	'Blue Lace' (New Millennium Series)	ECtt EPfP LCro LOPS NLar SCoo SHar WSpi
§	'Blue Max Arrow'	LRHS
	'Blue Nile' ♀H5	CNMi LHom LRHS NRHS SPoG
	'Blue Oasis'	CNMi
	Blue Springs Group	NGdn
	'Blue Tit'	CNMi LHom
	'Blueberry Pie' (Highlander Series) (d)	LRHS SCob SPoG WCot WSpi
	'Bolero'	EHyd EPfP LRHS MPri NRHS SCoo SPoG WCot
	'Boudicca'	CNMi
	'Bruce' ♀H5	CNMi LHom LRHS
	brunonianum	GKev GRum
	'Butterball'	CNMi LHom WSpi
	Cameliard Group	CBcs ELan EPfP LCro LOPS NLar NRHS SPer SPoG
	cashmerianum	CSpe EBee GKev GRum
	'Cassius'	LHom
	(Centurion Series) 'Centurion Sky Blue' ♀H5	LCro
	- 'Centurion White'	LCro LOPS
	'Cha Cha'	CBcs EBee EHyd EPfP LRHS MPri NLar NRHS SPad WCot WTor
	'Chelsea Star'	LHom LRHS
	'Cherry Blossom'	EHyd EPfP NLar
	'Cherub' ♀H5	CRos EHyd LRHS NRHS
	'Christel'	LRHS LSRN MCot NLar
	'Claire'	CNMi
	'Clifford Sky' ♀H5	CRos EHyd LRHS NRHS
	'Cobalt Dreams' (New Millennium Series) **new**	CDor LSun SGBe
	confusum	EBee
	Connecticut Yankees Group	SBls
	'Conspicuous' ♀H5	LHom
	'Constance Rivett'	LHom
	'Cranberry Delight'	CNMi
	'Crown Jewel'	LRHS
	'Crystal Delight' (Highlander Series) (d)	EHyd LRHS MBriF MPri NRHS SCob SPad SPoG WCot
	'Cupid'	LHom
	'Dark Blue Black Bee' (Excalibur Series)	SPoG

'Dark Blue Black' (Excalibur Series)	EPfP
'Dark Blue White Bee' (Excalibur Series)	EPfP LRHS SPoG
'Darling Sue'	CNMi LHom
dasyanthum **new**	GKev
'Diamant'PBR	LRHS
'Dreaming Spires'	SRms
'Dunsden Green'	CNMi LHom
Dusky Maidens Group	CDor EHyd ELan EPfP LCro LOPS LRHS NLar SCoo SGbt SPoG
elatum (Aurora Series) 'Aurora Blue'	LCro LOPS
- - 'Aurora Light Blue'	LCro LOPS
- - 'Aurora White'	LCro LOPS
- 'Blushing Brides' (New Millennium Series)	EBee EHyd EPfP LRHS SPoG
- 'Dasante Blue'	LRHS
- 'Double Innocence' (New Millennium Series) (d)	CDor EHyd ELan EPfP IPot LRHS NLar NRHS SCoo
- 'Morning Lights' (New Millennium Series)	CDor EHyd EPfP IPot LRHS NLar NRHS SPoG
- 'Sweethearts' (New Millennium Series) 🏆H5	EBee ECtt EPfP LCro LOPS SBls SCoo SGBe
'Elizabeth Cook' 🏆H5	CNMi LHom
'Elmfreude'	LRHS WSpi
'Emily Hawkins' 🏆H5	CNMi LHom
exaltatum	CSpe
'Fanfare'	LHom
'Faust' 🏆H5	CNMi CRos EHyd IPot LHom LRHS MCot NRHS SCoo SPoG WSpi
'Fenella' 🏆H5	CNMi CRos EHyd LHom LRHS NRHS
'Finsteraarhorn'	LRHS MCot WSpi
'Flamenco'	CBcs CMiW EHyd EPfP LRHS MBriF MPri NLar NRHS SCob SPad SPoG WCAu WCot WTor
flexuosum	CSpe
'Foxhill Nina' 🏆H5	LHom
Galahad Group	CBcs ECtt EHyd ELan EPfP EWoo GMaP LRHS NGdn NHol NRHS SCob SGbt SPer SPlb SPoG WCAu
'Galahad' (Pacific Hybrid Series)	LCro LOPS MGos NLar
'Gemini'	CNMi LHom
'Gemma'	CNMi LHom
'Gillian Dallas'	IPot LHom
glaciale HWJK 2299	WCru
'Gordon Forsyth'	LHom
'Gossamer'	CNMi ECtt IPot NLar
§ ***grandiflorum***	EBee
§ - 'Blue Butterfly'	CMea CSpe EPfP LRHS NRHS SPlb SPoG
- 'Delfix Rose' (Delfix Series)	EPfP
- Delfix Series	CRos LRHS
- 'Summer Nights' (Summer Series)	CRos EHyd EPfP LRHS NRHS SCoo SPoG
- 'White Butterfly'	EHyd LRHS NRHS
'Green Twist' (New Millennium Series)	CDor EHyd EPfP LRHS NRHS SCob
Guardian Series	WFar
- 'Guardian Blue'	LRHS NRHS SPoG
- 'Guardian Lavender'	LRHS NRHS SPoG
- 'Guardian White'	LRHS NRHS SPoG
Guinevere Group	CBcs ECtt EPfP SPer SPoG
'Guy Langdon'	CNMi
himalayae	GKev
hotulae	EBee
iliense from Kyrgyzstan **new**	GGro
I 'Independence'	LRHS

'Innocence'	LRHS LSun SCob SGBe WSpi
ithaburense	SPhx
'Jill Curley' 🏆H5	CRos EHyd LRHS NRHS
kamaonense **new**	GGro
'Kennington Classic' 🏆H5	LHom
'Kestrel' 🏆H5	CNMi LHom
King Arthur Group	CBcs CBod CTsd ELan EPfP LCro LOPS LSRN MGos SCob SCoo SHar SPer SPoG
'La Bohème'	WSpi
'Langdon's Orpheus'	LHom
§ 'Langdon's Royal Flush'	CRos EHyd LRHS NRHS
'Lanzenträger'	LRHS
'Leonora'	CNMi
'Light Blue' (Excalibur Series)	EPfP
'Light Blue White Bee' (Excalibur Series)	SPoG
'Lillian Basset'	LHom
'Loch Leven'	CNMi
'Loch Nevis'	LHom
'Lord Butler' 🏆H5	CNMi EBee LHom LRHS
'Lucia Sahin' 🏆H5	CNMi LHom
maackianum	GGro WCot
Magic Fountains Series	LRHS MBros SPlb SPoG SVic
- 'Magic Fountains Blue/White Bee'	CBod EPfP MBros
- 'Magic Fountains Cherry Blossom'	CBod EPfP SPoG
- 'Magic Fountains Dark Blue'	CBod EPfP GMaP LSRN NLar SPoG WFar
- 'Magic Fountains Deep Rose/White Bee'	MBros
- 'Magic Fountains Lavender'	EPfP NLar NRHS
- 'Magic Fountains Lilac Pink'	EPfP SPoG WFar
- 'Magic Fountains Lilac Rose'	NRHS
- 'Magic Fountains Pure White'	EPfP MBros NRHS WFar
- 'Magic Fountains Sky Blue'	EPfP SPoG WFar
'Margaret' 🏆H5	LHom
'Marilyn Clarrissa'	CNMi
'Melanie Avery'	LHom
'Merlin' ambig.	LRHS
'Michael Ayres' 🏆H5	CNMi LHom
'Mighty Atom'	CNMi LHom
'Min' 🏆H5	CNMi LHom
'Misty Mauves' (New Millennium Series) (d)	EHyd EPfP LRHS NRHS SCoo WSpi
'Molly Buchanan'	CNMi NLar
'Moon Light'PBR (Highlander Series) (d)	ECtt EPfP LBuc LRHS LSun MPri SCob SPoG WCot WSpi XLum
'Moonbeam'	LRHS SPoG
'Moonlight Blues' (New Millennium Series)	EHyd LPla LSun SGbt
'Morgentau'	LRHS NLar
'Morning Sunrise'PBR (Highlander Series) (d)	LPla LRHS LSun SCob SPoG WCot
'Mrs Newton Lees'	LRHS
'Mydark'	LHom
New Zealand hybrids	WFar
nudicaule	SPlb
- 'Redcap'	CRos LRHS
'Olive Poppleton' 🏆H5	LHom
'Oliver' 🏆H5	LHom
'Our Deb' 🏆H5	LHom
'Ouvertüre'	LRHS
oxysepalum	GKev
Pacific hybrids	EPfP LCro LOPS LSRN MHer SRms SWvt WBor WCav

'Pagan Purples' (New Millennium Series) (d)	EHyd EPfP LCro LOPS LRHS MBros NLar NRHS SCoo WSpi
'Patricia Johnson'	CNMi
Percival Group	EPfP
'Pericles'	LHom
'Pink' (Excalibur Series)	EPfP SPoG
'Pink Punch' (New Millennium Series)	ELan EPfP LRHS LSun
'Pink Ruffles'	LHom
'Plagu Blue'PBR	WSpi
PRINCESS CAROLINE ('Odabar')	LRHS
'Pure White'	CBod
'Pure White' (Excalibur Series)	EPfP SPoG
'Purple Passion' (New Millennium Series)	CDor EHyd ELan EPfP LRHS SBls SPoG
'Purple Surprise' (Highlander Series) (d) **new**	LRHS
'Red Caroline'	SPeP
requienii	CBgR CCBP CSpe SPhx SSal WKif
'Rose Butterfly' (d)	EHyd LRHS NRHS
'Rosemary Brock' ♀H5	LHom
'Royal Aspirations' (New Millennium Series)	EHyd ELan EPfP LRHS SGbt SPoG
'Ruby'	CNMi
'Ruby Tuesday'	CNMi
'Ruby Wedding'	CNMi LHom
§ × ***ruysii*** 'Pink Sensation'	LRHS SGbt WSpi
'Sandpiper'	CNMi LHom
'Schildknappe'	LRHS
'Schönbuch'	LRHS
'Secret'PBR	LRHS WCot
'Sherbet Lemon' **new**	WTor
'Shieldbearer'	LRHS
'Sky Sensation'	IPot LRHS
'Snow Queen Arrow'	LRHS
'Sommerabend'	LRHS
'Sooty'	CNMi
'Spindrift' ♀H5	CNMi CRos EHyd LHom LRHS NRHS
staphisagria	XAbr
'Starlight'PBR	LRHS WSpi
'Strawberry Fair'	LRHS NLar NRHS SPoG
Summer Skies Group	CBcs CTsd ELan EMor EPfP EWTr EWoo LCro LOPS LRHS MGos SCob SEdd SPer SPoG WCAu
'Summerfield Diana'	CNMi
'Summerfield Oberon'	LHom WCot
'Sungleam' ♀H5	CKel ECtt EWTr EWes IPot LHom NRHS WSpi
'Sunkissed' ♀H5	CNMi LHom
'Sunny Skies' (New Millennium Series)	EHyd ELan LRHS
sutchuenense	EWld
'Sweet Sensation'PBR (Highlander Series) (d)	EHyd EPfP LPla LRHS LSun NLar NRHS SCob SPoG WCot WSpi WTor WTyc
'Sweetheart'	EHyd LRHS NRHS
'Tiger Eye'	LHom
'Titania'	LHom
trolliifolium **new**	CSpe
'Trudy'	CNMi
'Turkish Delight'	LHom
uliginosum	SPlb
'Vanessa Mae'	CNMi LHom
variegatum	SBrt
vestitum	GGro
'Walton Benjamin'	LHom
'Walton Gemstone' ♀H5	LHom
'White Swan'	EPfP
'Wishful Thinking'PBR	CBcs
'Yvonne'	LRHS
'Zauberflöte'	LRHS

Dendranthema see *Chrysanthemum*

Dendriopoterium see *Sanguisorba*

Dendrobenthamia see *Cornus*

Dendromecon (*Papaveraceae*)

rigida	WPGP

Dendropanax (*Araliaceae*)

cf. ***kwangsiensis*** FMWJ 13274	WCru
trifidus	WPGP
- B&SWJ 11230	WCru

Dendroseris (*Asteraceae*)

litoralis	CCCN

Dennstaedtia (*Dennstaedtiaceae*)

punctilobula	EHyd LRHS NRHS

Dentaria see *Cardamine*

pinnata	see *Cardamine heptaphylla*
polyphylla	see *Cardamine kitaibelii*

Deparia (*Woodsiaceae*)

japonica **new**	WCot

Dermatobotrys (*Scrophulariaceae*)

saundersii	ECre WCot

Derwentia see *Parahebe*

Deschampsia ✿ (*Poaceae*)

cespitosa	CBod CEme CKel CKno CNat EPPr EPfP GKev LCro LOPS LRHS MBel SCoo SEdd SPhx SPlb WCot WHwl XLum
- BRONZE VEIL	see *D. cespitosa* 'Bronzeschleier'
§ - 'Bronzeschleier'	CBod CDor CWCL EBee EGrI EHyd ELan ELon EMor EPPr EPfP GMaP GWyn LRHS MAsh MHol NGdn NRHS NWsh SCob SPer SPhx SRms SWvt WFar WHwl XLum
- 'Cabana Buta'	LEdu SPhx WPGP
- 'Coral Cloud'	GQue
- 'Fairy's Joke'	see *D. cespitosa* var. *vivipara*
- 'Garnet Schist'	EPPr GQue LEdu LRHS SPhx WPGP
- GOLD DUST	see *D. cespitosa* 'Goldstaub'
- GOLDEN DEW	see *D. cespitosa* 'Goldtau'
- GOLDEN PENDANT	see *D. cespitosa* 'Goldgehänge'
- GOLDEN SHOWER	see *D. cespitosa* 'Goldgehänge'
- GOLDEN VEIL	see *D. cespitosa* 'Goldschleier'
§ - 'Goldgehänge'	EPPr NBir XLum
§ - 'Goldschleier' ♀H6	CBar CBod CRos CWCL EBee ECha EHyd ELon EMor EPPr EPfP GBin GMaP LRHS MAsh NGdn NRHS NWsh SCob SPer SPhx SWvt WFar WHwl WSpi XLum XSen
§ - 'Goldstaub'	EPPr
§ - 'Goldtau' ♀H6	Widely available
- 'Mill End'	CKno LEdu WPGP
- 'Morning Dew'	WFar
- 'Northern Lights' (v)	CSBt ELan EPfP LRHS SPoG SRms SWvt WPnP XLum
- 'Palava' **new**	EPPr
- 'Pixie Fountain'	CBod EHyd GQue LRHS MNrw NDov NWsh SBls

- 'Schottland'	CKno EBee ECha ELon EPPr GBin LEdu
- 'Tardiflora'	EBee EPPr XSen
- 'Tauträger'	EBee ELon EPPr GQue SMHy
§ - var. ***vivipara***	EPPr GBin NBro
- 'Waldschatt'	EBee ECha EPPr
- 'Willow Green'	SCoo
- 'Yunnan'	EPPr
flexuosa	CKno EHyd LRHS NBir NRHS NWsh SPhx
- 'Tatra Gold' 𝕐H6	CBod CWCL ECha ECtt EHyd ELan GMaP LRHS MACG MBel MRav NBir NBro NLar NRHS NSti SCob SCoo SPer SPoG SRot SWvt

Desfontainia (*Columelliaceae*)

§ ***spinosa*** 𝕐H4	CAbb CBcs CDoC CKel CMac CPla CTri EBee EHyd ELan ELon EPfP GAbr GArf GKev GKin IArd LRHS MAsh MBlu MGil NFav NLar SPer SPoG SRms WFar WPav WSHC
- 'Harold Comber'	CMac
- f. ***hookeri***	see *D. spinosa*

Desmodium (*Fabaceae*)

callianthum	CMac EHyd SMad WSHC
canadense	EBee MNrw NLar SBrt SPhx XAbr
§ ***elegans***	CBcs CExl EBee ELan EPfP LPar NLar NSti SBrt SMad SVen WSHC
- dark-flowered	SMad WPGP
glutinosum	EBee
praestans	see *D. yunnanense*
tiliifolium	see *D. elegans*
§ ***yunnanense***	CExl WSHC

Deuterocohnia (*Bromeliaceae*)

sp.	WCot
brevifolia 𝕐H2	NCft WCot WPGP
lotteae	WCot

Deutzia ✿ (*Hydrangeaceae*)

CC 4548	CExl
CC 4550	CExl
bhutanensis HWJK 2180	WCru
'Bright Eyes'	WPGP
calycosa	MBlu
- BWJ 8007	WCru
- 'Dali'	CBcs CExl EHed EPfP IArd IDee NLar SDys SMad
chunii	see *D. ningpoensis*
compacta	CBcs CMCN SLon WPGP
- 'Lavender Time'	CDoC CExl CKel CMac EBee ELan EPfP LRHS MAsh NLar SWvt WGob
cordatula B&SWJ 3720	WCru
- B&SWJ 6917	WCru
corymbosa	MRav
- GWJ 9202	WCru
- GWJ 9203	WCru
- GWJ 9339	WCru
- var. ***corymbosa***	WSpi
crenata B&SWJ 8886	WCru
- B&SWJ 8896	WCru
- B&SWJ 8924	WCru
- 'Flore Pleno'	see *D. scabra* 'Plena'
- var. ***heterotricha*** B&SWJ 5805	WCru
- - B&SWJ 8879	WCru
- var. ***nakaiana*** B&SWJ 11184	WCru
- - 'Nikko'	see *D. gracilis* 'Nikko'
§ - 'Pride of Rochester' (d) 𝕐H5	CBcs CDoC CMCN CTsd ELan EPfP GKin MBlu MGil MMuc MRav NLar SCob SEle SPoG SWvt WLov WPnP
'Dark Eyes'	CExl GBin SMad
discolor 'Major'	CExl WCru WGob
× ***elegantissima***	SRms
- 'Fasciculata'	CBod CKel EHyd ELan EPfP EWTr LRHS MGil NLar SPer SWvt WBor WSpi
- 'Rosealind' 𝕐H5	CBcs CCCN CDoC CExl CKel CMac CRos CTri EBee ELan EPfP GKin IArd LRHS LSRN MGil MRav SPer SRms SWvt WCFE WGob WKif WSpi
glabrata B&SWJ 617	WCru
- B&SWJ 8427	WCru
glomeruliflora	CMCN
- BWJ 7742	WCru
gracilis	CSBt ELan EPfP GArf GKin LPar MAsh MGil MGos MRav MSwo NLar SNig SPer WFar WGob WSpi
- B&SWJ 8927	WCru
- 'Aurea'	CMac EPfP
- 'Carminea'	see *D.* × *rosea* 'Carminea'
§ - 'Marmorata' (v)	WAvo
§ - 'Nikko' 𝕐H5	Widely available
- var. ***ogatae*** B&SWJ 8911	WCru
- 'Rosea'	see *D.* × *rosea*
hookeriana	CKel EHyd EPfP LRHS NRHS SWvt WGob
× ***hybrida*** 'Contraste' 𝕐H5	CMac WLov
- 'Iris Alford'	CExl CKel CRos EHyd EPfP LRHS MGos NRHS SLon WPGP
- 'Joconde' 𝕐H5	CExl WFar
- 'Magicien' misapplied	see *D.* × *hybrida* 'Strawberry Fields'
- 'Magicien' ambig.	CBod CKel EGrI SGBe WAvo WSpi
- 'Magicien' Lemoine	CExl CMac CRos CSBt EBee EHyd ELan EPfP LRHS MAsh MRav MSwo NBir SLon SPer SRms SWvt WFar WKif WLov WSpi
- 'Mont Rose' 𝕐H5	Widely available
- 'Perle Rose'	NLar
§ - 'Strawberry Fields' 𝕐H5	Widely available
× ***kalmiiflora***	CBod CBrac CExl CMac CSBt CTri EBee ELan GKin MAsh MGil MMrt MRav NLar SPer SRms WFar WLov
× ***lemoinei***	EPfP
longifolia	CMCN WPGP
- 'Veitchii'	CSBt EPfP MGil MRav WSpi
- 'Vilmoriniae'	MRav
× ***magnifica***	MMrt NLar SCob SGbt SGsty SRms
- 'Rubra'	see *D.* × *hybrida* 'Strawberry Fields'
maximowicziana B&SWJ 11567	WCru
monbeigii 𝕐H5	CExl CKel ELan EPfP LRHS MRav SWvt WGob WKif WSpi
- BWJ 7728	WCru
multiradiata	CExl EBee GBin LRHS MBlu WPGP
§ ***ningpoensis***	CExl EBee EHed ELan EPfP MGil SPer WCFE WPGP WSpi
paniculata B&SWJ 8592	WCru
- B&SWJ 8952	ESwi
parviflora var. ***barbinervis*** B&SWJ 8478	WCru
'Pink Pompon'	see *D.* 'Rosea Plena'
prunifolia B&SWJ 8588	WCru
pulchra	CBcs CDoC CEnd CKel CMCN EBee EHyd ELan EPfP EWTr LRHS MGil MMuc MRav SBrt SGBe SLon SPer SPoG WGob WLov WPGP WSpi
- B&SWJ 1738	WCru
- B&SWJ 3870	WCru

	- B&SWJ 3948 from the Philippines	WCru
	- B&SWJ 6908	WCru
	- pink-tinged	WPGP
	purpurascens	GKev
	- BWJ 7859	WCru
	- 'Alpine Magician'	WKif
	RASPBERRY SUNDAE ('Low18') **new**	LRHS SGBe
§	× ***rosea***	CEnd CRos EHyd EPfP LRHS MAsh NRHS SNig SRms WGob WKif
	- 'Campanulata'	CExl MSwo
§	- 'Carminea'	ILea MGil SDix SPlb SRms WFar WLov
§	'Rosea Plena' (d)	CBod CEme CEnd CExl CMac CSBt EHyd ELan EPfP GKin LBuc LRHS MAsh MGos NLar NRHS SEle SPoG SRms SWvt WFar WGob
	× ***rosea*** YUKI CHERRY BLOSSOM ('Ncdx2')	CBcs EHed LBuc LRHS NLar SGol
	- YUKI SNOWFLAKE ('Ncdx1')	EHed LRHS NLar
	scabra	CBrac CTri
	- B&SWJ 11127	WCru
	- B&SWJ 11168	WCru
§	- 'Candidissima' (d) ♕H5	EWTr MGil MMuc MRav SEND SPer WGob WLov
	- 'Codsall Pink' ♕H5	MRav
§	- 'Plena' (d)	CBrac CExl EPfP GKin NLar SGsty SPer SPoG WCFE
	- 'Pride of Rochester'	see *D. crenata* 'Pride of Rochester'
	- 'Punctata' (v)	MAsh SRms
	- 'Robert Fortune'	SPlb
	- 'Variegata' (v)	CMac
	setchuenensis	CMac MRav
	- PAB 7449	LEdu
	- var. ***corymbiflora*** ♕H5	CBcs CExl CKel CMCN CTri EBee ECre EHyd ELan EPfP GKev LRHS MMuc MSwo NLar SAko SChF SEle SPoG SWvt WFar WGob WKif WLov WPGP WSpi
	- - NJM 11.096	WPGP
	- - 'Kiftsgate'	CExl WPGP
	taiwanensis	CMCN EBee EPfP SChF WPGP
	- B&SWJ 6858	WCru
	- CWJ 12443	WCru
	- CWJ 12459	WCru
	× ***wellsii***	see *D. scabra* 'Candidissima'
	× ***wilsonii***	SRms

Dianella ✿ (*Hemerocallidaceae*)

	caerulea	CMac EBee EPri MMrt NBir NLar
	- CASSA BLUE ('Dbb03'PBR)	CCht CEme EHyd LRHS MHol NRHS
	- LITTLE JESS ('Dcmp01'PBR)	CExl EBee
	- 'Variegata'	see *D. tasmanica* 'Variegata'
	longifolia **new**	GKev
	nigra	CExl LEdu
	- 'Margaret Pringle' (v)	CExl
	revoluta	CBor
§	- 'Allyn Citation'PBR	EBee
	- 'Blue Stream'	EBee
	- LITTLE REV ('Dr5000'PBR)	EBee EPfP SEle WSHC XSte
	'Silver Streak' (v)	EHyd
	'Streetscape'	EBee
	tasmanica	CAbb CBor CElw CExl CKno CMac CTri CTsd ECre ELan EPfP EShb GBin LEdu SEle SMad SRms SVen WAvo WSHC WSMil
	- DESTINY ('Tas100')	CCht CPla ELan LRHS MCot
	- 'Emerald Arch'	LEdu
	- 'Splice'	CDTJ
	- TASRED ('Tr20'PBR)	CBod CCht CExl ELan EPfP MBNS SCob SIvy
§	- 'Variegata' (v)	CCCN CDTJ CExl WSMil

Dianthus ✿ (*Caryophyllaceae*)

	'Alan Titchmarsh' (p)	ECtt EHyd EPfP MGos SPoG SWvt
	'Alice Lever' (p)	WAbe
	'Allspice' (p)	CFis MRav WHoo
	Allwoodii Alpinus Group (p)	NGdn SRms XLum
	(Allwoodii Group) 'Alice' (p)	CCal
	- CHERRY DAIQUIRI ('Wp15 Pie42') (Cocktails Series) (p)	CCal EHyd EPfP LRHS NRHS SRGP WCot
	- 'Doris' pre-1932 (p)	LShi
	- 'Doris' pre-1954 (p) ♕H6	CBcs CBod CCal ECtt EGrI EHyd EPfP GJos GMaP GQue LCro LOPS LRHS LSRN LShi MGos MHer MRav NGdn NRHS SCob SEND SPer SPlb SPoG SRGP SWvt WCAu WCFE WGwG
	- 'Hope' Allwood, 1946 (p)	CCal LShi
	- SHIRLEY TEMPLE ('Wp15 Pie44') (Cocktails Series) (p)	CCal EHyd EPfP LRHS NRHS
	- 'Susan' (p)	CCal
	- TEQUILA SUNRISE ('Wp15 Pie45') (Cocktails Series) (p)	CCal EHyd LRHS NRHS SRGP
	alpinus ♕H6	GJos MMuc NSla
	- 'Albus' (p)	GArf NWad
	- 'Darcie's Love' (p)	EDAr
	- 'Joan's Blood' (p) ♕H6	NHpl
	- 'Millstream Salmon' (p)	WFar
	- red-flowered	NSla
	amurensis	EPPr SPhx XLum
	- 'Siberian Blue' (p)	EPPr
	anatolicus	CCal CRos EBou EDAr EHyd GJos GQue LRHS MBel MHer NGdn NRHS XLum
	'Anders Irene Ann' (pf)	CNMi
	'Anders Patricia Griffiths' (p)	CNMi
	'Anders Supernova' (p)	CTri
	'Angela Carol' (pf)	CNMi
	'Ann Franklin' (pf) ♕H2	CNMi
	'Annette' (p)	CCal CMea CRos EDAr EHyd LRHS LSRN NGdn NHol NRHS SLee SRGP SRot SWvt
	'Annie Claybourne' (pf)	CNMi
	ARCTIC STAR	see *D.* 'Devon Arctic Star'
	arenarius	GKev NGdn SBls SPlb
	- 'Little Maiden' (p)	CCal CSpe EDAr GWyn MACG NGdn SBls SLee
	- 'Snow Flurries' (p)	ITim
	'Argus' (p)	LShi
	armeria	CBgR CCBP CFis CSpe NAts WHer
	arpadianus var. ***pumilus***	EPot
	'Arthur Holmes' (pf)	CNMi
§	× ***arvernensis*** (p) ♕H6	ECha SGro
	'Ashley Reay' (p)	CNMi
	'Audrey Robinson' (pf)	CNMi
	'Auvergne'	see *D.* × *arvernensis*
	'Averiensis'	see *D.* 'Berlin Snow'
	'Bailey's Celebration' (p)	CCal
	barbatus	MPri
	- 'Black Adder' (p,a)	CSpe

- Dash Series (p,a) MHol
- - 'Dash Crimson' (p,a) MHol SPhx
- - 'Dash Magician' (p,a) CBod MHol SCob WHil
- (Diabunda Series) 'Diabunda Purple Picotee' (p,a) SCob
- - 'Diabunda Red' (p,a) SCob
- - 'Diabunda Rose' (p,a) SCob
- Festival Series (p,a) MBros
- - 'Festival Raspberry' (p,a) SCob
- - 'Festival Red' (p,a) SCob
- - 'Festival White Flame' (p,a) SCob
- GREEN TRICK ('Temarisou'PBR) (p,a) CBod LCro LOPS WNPC
- 'Heart Attack' (p,a) WCot WMal
- Indian Carpet Group (p,a) LCro LOPS MBros
- Messenger Group (p,a) SVic
- 'Monksilver Black' (p,a) CBod CSpe EBee ECtt LShi LSun MBNS MPie NCou NSti SIvy SMad SPad WBrk WCot WMal WSHC WTyc
- Nigrescens Group (p,a) ♀H7 CSpe SPhx
- - 'Sooty' (p,a) GJos MACG SAng SBls WCFE WFar WHer
- 'Oeschberg' (p,a) MACG SAko

* - 'Roseus' (p,a) GWyn

§ 'Bat's Double Red' (p) LShi

'Becky Robinson' (p) ♀H6 CNMi LShi

§ 'Berlin Snow' (p) CRos EHyd EPot GArf ITim LRHS LShi NRHS

'Betty Morton' (p) ♀H6 EHyd LRHS NRHS

'Betty's Choice' (pf) CNMi

'Bill Smith' (pf) CNMi

'Binsey Red' (p) SBut SGro

'Black and White Minstrels' (p,a) CCal

'Blue Hills' (p) GKev

'Blush' see *D.* 'Souvenir de la Malmaison'

'Bob's Highlight' (pf) CNMi

'Bombardier' (p) ECtt GMaP

'Bouquet Purple' (p) CSpe WMal

'Bramdean' (pf) CNMi

brevicaulis CCal GJos

'Bridal Veil' (p) CCal LShi SBut SGro SRGP WHer

'Brilliant' see *D. deltoides* 'Brilliant'

'Brilliant Star' (p) ♀H6 ECtt EHyd LRHS NRHS SBut SWvt WIce

'Brockenhurst' (pf) CNMi

'Brympton Red' (p) CCal CFis ECha

BUBBLEGUM ('Wp15val12') (p) CCal

§ 'Caesar's Mantle' (p) EPPr

caesius see *D. gratianopolitanus*

'Calypso Star' (p) ECtt SPoG

'Can-can' (pf) ECtt

CANDY FLOSS see *D.* 'Devon Flavia'

'Candy Spice' (p) MRav

§ 'Carmine Letitia Wyatt'PBR (p) ♀H6 CCal CRos ECtt EHyd NRHS SPoG

carthusianorum Widely available

- W&B BGL-1 WCot

I - 'Rupert's Pink' (p) CCal EBee NGdn SHar SWvt

- tan-flowered (p) SMHy

caryophyllus CLau ENfk SVic

'Casser's Pink' (p) NWad

'Charles' (p) LShi

'Charles Musgrave' see *D.* 'Musgrave's Pink'

'Chastity' (p) CCal ECtt WHoo

Cheddar pink see *D. gratianopolitanus*

'Cheryl' see *D.* 'Houndspool Cheryl'

'Chetwyn Ruth Gillies' (pf) CNMi

chinensis 'Black and White' (p,a) CCal CSpe

I - 'Valentine' (p,a) LRHS

'Chomley Farran' (b) CSpe

cintranus subsp. ***cintranus*** WCot

'Claret Joy' (p) ♀H6 ECtt MMuc SEND

'Cleopatra' (pf) EMal

'Clifford Pipperoo' (pf) WCot

§ 'Cockenzie Pink' (p) CCal LShi SGro WHer

COCONUT SUNDAE ('Wp 05 Yves'PBR) (Scent First Series) (p) ♀H6 CCal ECtt EHyd ELan ELon EPfP LRHS LSRN MCot NRHS SCob SCoo SGBe

'Constance Finnis' see *D.* 'Fair Folly'

'Conwy Silver' (p) WAbe

'Conwy Star' (p) EPot WAbe

'Coral Reef'PBR (Scent First Series) (p) CCal ECtt EHyd ELan LRHS NRHS SGBe SPoG

'Corona Blueberry Magic' (p,a) **new** LRHS

'Corona Iceberry Magic' (p,a) EHyd LRHS NRHS

'Corona Lavender Magic' (p,a) **new** LRHS

'Corona Raspberry Magic' (p,a) **new** LRHS

'Corona Strawberry Magic' (p,a) LRHS

'Coronation Ruby' (p) ♀H6 LShi

corsicus XSen

COSMOPOLITAN ('Wp15 Pie43') (p) CCal CRos EHyd EPfP LRHS NRHS

'Coste Budde' (p) WSHC

§ CRACKER ('Wp10 Sab06'PBR) (Early Bird Series) (p) CCal EHyd LRHS NRHS

'Cranberry Crush' (pf) CNMi

'Cranmere Pool' (p) ♀H6 CBcs CCal ECtt EHyd ELan EPfP GQue LCro LOPS LRHS LShi NFav NRHS SEND SPoG SWvt WCAu WFar

'Crimson Warrior' (pf) CNMi

'Crompton Classic' (pf) CNMi

'Crompton Princess' (pf) CNMi

cruentus Widely available

'Cumbria' (pf) CNMi

'D.D.R.' see *D.* 'Berlin Snow'

'Dad's Favourite' (p) LShi

'Dainty Dame' (p) ♀H4 CRos CSpe CTri ECtt EHyd EPfP LRHS MNHC NRHS SGro

'Dancing Geisha' EDAr MACG SBls WHil

'Dante' (Sprint Series) (pt) **new** LRHS

'David' (p) SCob

'Dawn's Delight' (pf) CNMi

'Dedham Beauty' (p) MPie SEND WCot

deltoides ♀H6 EGrl ENfk EPfP EWld GQue LCro LEdu LOPS MBow MNHC NAts SCob SDix SPlb SRms WFar WWild

- 'Albus' (p) ECha EPfP GWyn LShi NGdn
- 'Arctic Fire' (p) CCal EPfP GWyn NFav NGdn NHol NSla SBls WFar
- 'Bright Eyes' (p) CCal

§ - 'Brilliant' (p) CCal GJos GWyn LShi NGdn NHol SRms SVic

- FLASHING LIGHT see *D. deltoides* 'Leuchtfunk'

§ - 'Leuchtfunk' (p) CCal ECha EHyd LShi NRHS NSla SPoG WFar

I	- 'Luneburg Heath Maiden Pink' (p)	NGdn
	- 'Nelli' (p)	NGdn
	- 'Roseus' (p)	GJos
	- 'Shrimp' (p)	ECtt NGdn
	'Desmond'	ELon
§	'Devon Arctic Star' (Early Bird Series) (p)	CCal CMea CRos CTri EHyd ELan GMaP LRHS NRHS SEdd SPoG SWvt WIce
	'Devon Cream' (p)	CCal ELan LRHS
	'Devon Dove'^{PBR} (p) $\mathbb{Y}^{H6}$	CCal CTri ECtt EHyd ELan EPfP LRHS MBel MRav MSpe NDov NRHS SGbt
	'Devon Fatima'	see *D.* ICED GEM
§	'Devon Flavia'^{PBR} (Scent First Series) (p) $\mathbb{Y}^{H6}$	CCal CRos EHyd GDam LRHS NRHS SCob SCoo SEdd SPad SPoG
	'Devon Flores'	see *D.* SHOOTING STAR
	'Devon General'^{PBR} (p)	CCal
§	'Devon Louise'^{PBR} (p)	WFar
	'Devon Magic'^{PBR} (p) $\mathbb{Y}^{H6}$	CCal ECtt LRHS
	'Devon Sapphire'	see *D.* MYSTIC STAR
§	'Devon Winnie'^{PBR} (p)	CCal
	'Devon Wizard' (p) $\mathbb{Y}^{H6}$	CBod CCal ECtt EHyd EPfP LCro LOPS LRHS MBel MRav MSpe NDov NRHS SGbt WCAu
§	'Devon Xera' (p) $\mathbb{Y}^{H6}$	CCal GDam SEND
§	'Devon Yolande'^{PBR} (Scent First Series) (p)	CCal EHyd EPfP LRHS LSRN NRHS SCoo SPoG
	'Dewdrop' (p)	CCal CMea EHyd EWTr LShi MAsh MMuc NBir SEND
	'Diana'	see *D.* DONA
	'Diana Lavender Picotee' (p,a)	EHyd
	'Diane' (p) $\mathbb{Y}^{H6}$	ELon EPfP LShi SPoG SRGP SWvt WFar
	DIANTICA DARK RED PINK EYE (pt)	EHyd
	DIANTICA EARLY LOVE ('Kledg18267') (pt) **new**	CRos
	DIANTICA PEACH PARTY ('Kledg12163') (pt) **new**	CRos LRHS
	DIANTICA PURPLE WEDDING ('Kledg18274') (pt) **new**	CRos LRHS
	DIANTICA STRAWBERRY CREAM ('Kledg15176') (pt)	EPfP LRHS
	DIANTICA WHITE WITH EYE ('Kledg11116') (pt)	EHyd LRHS NRHS
§	DONA ('Brecas') (pf)	XLum
	'Dora' (p)	EHyd NRHS
	'Doreen Hodgson' (p)	ECtt
	'Doris Allwood' (pf)	CNMi EMal
	'Doris Ruby'	see *D.* 'Houndspool Ruby'
	'Double Lace' (b)	ECtt
	'Double North' (p)	CTri
	'Duchess of Roxburghe' (pf)	EMal
	'Duchess of Westminster' (M)	EMal LShi
	'Duke of Norfolk' (pf)	EMal
	'Dunkirk Spirit' (pf)	CNMi
	'Dusky Janelle' (pf)	CNMi
	'Earl Kelso' (pf)	EMal
	'Earl of Essex' (p)	LShi SBut
	'Eileen Lever' (p)	EPot GArf WAbe WHoo
	'Eira Wen' (p)	EPot
	'Eleanor Parker' (p)	WAbe
	'Eleanor's Old Irish' (p)	ECtt LRHS WCot WHer
	'Elizabethan' (p)	CFis CMea EWTr GBin MCot SGro SRms WTor
*	'Elizabethan Pink' (p)	CCal LShi
	'Elsie Ketchen' (pf)	CNMi
	'Emmeline Pankhurst' (pf)	CNMi
	'Emperor'	see *D.* 'Bat's Double Red'
	erinaceus	EPot GArf GJos LShi
	- var. ***alpinus***	EPot ITim
	- Duguid's	WAbe
	'Evelyn Berry' (p)	CNMi
	'Evening Star' (p) $\mathbb{Y}^{H6}$	CCal CRos CTri EHyd LRHS NRHS SPoG SWvt WIce
	'Eve's Holly' (pf)	CNMi
§	'Fair Folly' (p)	CCal LShi WHer
	'Farnham Rose' (p)	LShi
	ferrugineus	EPPr LRHS SBrt SPhx
	'Fettes Mount' (p)	WAvo WBrk WCot WMal
	'Feuerhexe' (p)	XLum
	'Fimbriatus' (p)	WHoo
	FIRE STAR	see *D.* 'Devon Xera'
	'Firestar' (p)	CCal CTri EHyd ELan GMaP MAsh NRHS SWvt
	FIZZY ('Wp08 Ver03'^{PBR}) (Early Bird Series) (p)	CRos EHyd ELan LRHS NRHS
	'Flashdance' (pf)	CNMi
	'Fleur' (p)	CCal
	'Florence Franklin' (pf)	CNMi
	'Flutterby' (p) **new**	WIce WTor
	'Fragrant Ann' (pf) $\mathbb{Y}^{H6}$	EMal
	'Frances Isabel' (p)	LShi
	'Frank Bruno' (pf)	CNMi
	'Freda Woodliffe' (p)	WAbe WHoo
	FRENCH RED (pf)	EMal
	freynii	EPot GKev WAbe
	FRILLY ('Wp08 Ulr03'^{PBR}) (Early Bird Series) (p)	CCal CRos EHyd LRHS
	fringed pink	see *D. superbus*
	'Fusilier' (p)	CCal CRos CTri EBou ECtt EHyd EPfP EWoo GDam GMaP LRHS LShi MAsh MTin NRHS SHar SWvt
	'Garland' (p)	CMea
	giganteus	LRHS SPhx
	'Gingham Gown' (p)	CCal ECtt EPot LShi NBir
	glacialis	CCal
	'Gold Dust' (p)	ECtt EPot EWTr GArf SGro
	'Gold Embrace' (pf)	CNMi
	'Grandma Calvert' (p)	LShi
	'Gran's Favourite' (p) $\mathbb{Y}^{H6}$	CBcs CBod CCal ECtt EGrI EHyd ELan EPfP LCro LOPS LPot LRHS LSRN LShi MCot MGos MHol MMuc NGdn NRHS SEND SPlb SPoG SRGP SWvt WHer
§	***gratianopolitanus*** $\mathbb{Y}^{H6}$	CBod CCal CTri EDAr ENfk EPfP GJos GKev GQue MBow MHer MRav NBid
	- from Cheddar	WWild
	- 'Albus' (p)	MHer
	- dwarf	WAbe
*	- 'Karlik' (p)	GQue
	- 'Rosenfeder' (p)	XLum
§	- 'Tiny Rubies' (p)	EDAr
	'Greensides' (p)	LShi
	Grenadin Group	CCal
	'Gypsy Star' (p)	SPoG
	haematocalyx	GArf GJos
	- 'Alpinus'	see *D. haematocalyx* subsp. *pindicola*
§	- subsp. ***pindicola***	GKev NSla WAbe
	'Hamish Berry' (p)	CNMi
	'Hampshire' (pf)	CNMi
	'Hayden' (pf)	CNMi
	HAYTOR	see *D.* 'Haytor White'
	'Haytor Rock' (p) $\mathbb{Y}^{H6}$	CCal EPfP LRHS LShi
§	'Haytor White' (p) $\mathbb{Y}^{H6}$	CBcs CBod CCal CTri EGrI EPfP LCro LOPS LRHS LShi SCob WFar

'Heath' (p)	LShi
'Helen' (p)	LShi
'Helena Allwood' (pf)	EMal
'Herbert's Pink' (p)	SPhx
'Hercules' (pf)	CNMi
'Hereford Butter Market' (p)	EBee SBut
'Hidcote' (p)	CTri EHyd LRHS NRHS
'Highland Fraser' (p)	WKif
'Hot Spice' (p)	SPoG
§ 'Houndspool Cheryl' (p) ♀H6	CBcs CCal ECtt EHyd EPfP GJos LRHS NRHS SRGP WCAu WFar
§ 'Houndspool Ruby' (p) ♀H6	CCal EPfP GQue LSRN SRGP
hyssopifolius	CCal EDAr GQue LShi
§ ICED GEM ('Wp06 Fatima'[PBR]) (Scent First Series) (p)	EHyd ELan LSRN SPoG
'Icomb' (p)	WHoo
'Ike' (Sprint Series) (pt) **new**	LRHS
'Inchmery' (p)	CCal LRHS LShi WHer WHoo
'India Star'[PBR] (p) ♀H6	CCal CTri EHyd EPfP LRHS NRHS
'Ine' (p)	MBel
'Inshriach Dazzler' (p) ♀H6	CCal ECtt EPot GArf GEdr GMaP LRHS MAsh MHer NHol NSla SLee SRot WCav WTor
'Inshriach Startler' (p)	CMea
× ***isensis***	GEdr SBut
'James Muir' (M)	EMal
'Janelle Welch' (pf)	CNMi
'Janet Walker' (p)	GMaP
japonicus	CSpe GKev
'Jess Hewins' (pf)	CNMi
'Joanne' (pf)	CNMi
'Joanne's Highlight' (pf)	CNMi
'John Ball' (p)	SBut
'Josephine' (pf)	CNMi
'Joy' (p) ♀H6	CCal EPfP SPoG
'Julie Martin' (pf)	CNMi
'Just Jodie' (pf)	CNMi
'Kahori' (p)	MACG
'Kelly's Kiss' (p)	CNMi
'Kent' (pf)	CNMi
'Kessock Rose Blush' (p)	CCal
'Kesteven Kirkstead' (p) ♀H6	GAbr MNrw
knappii	EDAr GWyn LRHS MACG SBut SDix SHar SPhx WSHC XLum
- 'Yellow Harmony' (p,a)	CCBP CCal GQue
'Kristina' (pf) ♀H2	CNMi
'La Bourboule' (p) ♀H6	CCal CMea ECtt EHyd GMaP LShi NRHS SEdd
'La Bourboule Alba' (p) ♀H6	CTri ECtt MAsh
'Laced Joy' (p)	LShi
'Laced Monarch' (p)	CBcs CCal ECtt EGrI EHyd ELan EPfP LRHS LShi NRHS SMrm SPlb SPoG WHer
'Laced Mrs Sinkins' (p)	CCal LShi WHer
'Laced Prudence'	see *D.* 'Prudence'
'Laced Romeo' (p)	LShi
'Laced Treasure' (p)	CCal LShi
'Lady Granville' (p)	CCal LShi SBut
LADY IN RED ('Wp04 Xanthe'[PBR]) (p)	CBod CCal ECtt EHyd ELan EPfP LRHS NBir NRHS
'Lady Windermere' (M)	EMal
'Lancing Supreme' (p)	WHer
'Langford Manor' (pf)	CNMi
'Langport Lady' (pt)	CNMi
'Layla Jane' (p)	CNMi
'Leatham Pastel' (pf)	CNMi
'Lemsii' (p) ♀H6	NGdn
'Letitia Wyatt' (p) ♀H6	CBod CCal CRos EGrI EHyd ELan EPfP LRHS NRHS SPoG SRGP
'Leuchtkugel' (p)	EPot WAbe
LILY THE PINK ('Wp05 Idare'[PBR]) (p) ♀H6	CBod CCal EHyd LRHS NRHS SRGP
'Lime Crush' (pf)	CNMi
LIMONI ('Kolim') (pt)	LRHS
'Linfield Annie's Fancy' (pf)	CNMi
'Linfield Pink Margaret' (p)	CNMi
'Little Ben' (p)	LShi
'Little Jock' (p)	CCal ECtt EHyd EPot GEdr GQue LRHS LShi MAsh NRHS SPlb SRms
'London Brocade' (p)	LShi
'London Glow' (p)	LShi
'London Lovely' (p)	LShi SBut
'London Poppet' (p)	ECtt LShi
'Loveliness' (p,a)	CTtf
lumnitzeri	XLum
'Maggie' (p)	MBel
'Manon des Sources' (pf)	CNMi
'Marian Allwood' (pf)	EMal
'Marilyn's Highlight' (pf)	CNMi
'Marmion' (pf)	EMal LShi
'Matthew' (p)	WHoo
'Maxine' (pf)	CNMi
'Maybush' (pf)	CNMi
MEMORIES ('WP11 Gwe04'[PBR]) (Scent First Series) (p)	CCal CRos EBee EHyd ELan EPfP LBuc LPot LRHS NRHS SCob SCoo SGBe SPoG WCot WFar WTor
MENDLESHAM MINX ('Russmin'[PBR]) (p)	CCal EHyd ELan EPfP LRHS NRHS SWvt
'Messines Pink' (p)	LShi WHer
microlepis	EDAr EPot LShi NGdn NSla
- f. ***albus***	NSla
- ED 791562	NGdn
- 'Rivendell' (p)	WAbe
'Miss Farrow' (p)	EHyd EWes SPhx
'Miss Sinkins' (p)	CTri
MOJITO ('Wp15 Pie41') (p)	CCal EHyd LRHS MPri NRHS WCot
'Monica Wyatt' (p) ♀H6	CCal ECtt EHyd ELan EPfP LRHS NRHS SPoG
'Montrose Pink'	see *D.* 'Cockenzie Pink'
'Monty's Pink' (pf)	EMal
'Moor Editha' (p)	CNMi
'Morrissey' (pf)	CNMi
'Mottisfont Pink'	NWad
'Moulin Rouge' (p) ♀H6	CBod CCal CTri ECtt EHyd ELan EPfP LCro LOPS LRHS NRHS SPoG
'Mrs Sinkins' (p)	Widely available
'Murray Douglas' (p)	LShi SBut
'Murray's Laced Pink' (p)	SBut
'Musgrave's Pink' (p)	ECha LShi MRav WHer
'Musgrave's White'	see *D.* 'Musgrave's Pink'
myrtinervius	CCal EDAr ETod GPSL NGdn WAvo
§ MYSTIC STAR ('WP 05 Saphire') (p) ♀H6	CCal ELan WIce
'Napoleon III' (p)	LShi WMal
nardiformis	XLum
neglectus misapplied	see *D. pavonius*
'Neon Star'[PBR] (p) ♀H6	CCal CRos CTri EHyd ELan GKev LRHS NRHS SEdd SPoG
'Night Star' (p) ♀H6	CCal CPla CRos EHyd ELan EPfP GMaP GWyn LPot LRHS NRHS NSla SEND
nitidus	EPot GKev LShi
noeanus	see *D. petraeus* subsp. *noeanus*
'Nomie' (pf)	CNMi
'Northland' (pf)	CNMi EMal
'Nyewoods Cream' (p)	CMea EPot GArf GMaP LShi MHer NGdn NWad SGro SLee
'Oakwood Erin Mitchell' (p)	CNMi

'Oakwood Sweetheart' (p) LShi
'Odessa Red' (Odessa Series) (pt) SRms
'Old Blush' see *D.* 'Souvenir de la Malmaison'
'Old Dutch Pink' (p) NWad
'Old Fringed White' (p) EWTr
'Old Mother Hubbard' (p) SGro
'Old Red Clove' (p) ECtt GBee NFav WCot
'Old Rose' (pf) EMal
§ 'Old Square Eyes' (p) CCal EPPr MNrw SHar WHer WMal
'Old Velvet' (p) CCal LShi
'Oscar' (b) SCob
'Oxford Magic' (p) LShi
'Painted Lady' (p) LShi
'Paisley Gem' (p) LShi SBut
PASSION ('Wp Passion'^{PBR}) (Scent First Series) (p) CCal CRos EBee ECtt EHyd ELan EPfP LRHS MHer NRHS SCob SCoo SEND SGBe SPoG WCot
§ ***pavonius*** CCal EDAr EHyd EWes LRHS NGdn NRHS
'Peach' (p) SEND
'Peppermint Magic' **new** LRHS
§ ***petraeus*** EWes NGdn XLum
§ - subsp. ***noeanus*** WHal
'Petticoat Lace' (p) LShi
'Pheasant's Eye' (p) LShi WHer
* 'Picton's Propeller' (p) EPPr NWad
PIERROT ('Kobusa') (pf) CNMi
'Pike's Pink' (p) ♀H6 CRos CSpe CTri EHyd ELan EPfP EWTr LRHS MAsh MMuc NBir NGdn NRHS SEND
PINBALL WIZARD ('Wp15mow08') (p) CCal EHyd LRHS NRHS
pindicola see *D. haematocalyx* subsp. *pindicola*
pinifolius EDAr LShi SBrt
'Pink Doris' (pf) CNMi
'Pink Jewel' (p) CMea ECha EPot GKev MAsh MNHC SLee XLum
PINK KISSES ('Kledg12163') (pt) CRos EHyd LCro LOPS LRHS NRHS SPoG
'Pink Mrs Sinkins' (p) CCal LShi
'Pixie' (b) EPot
'Pixie Star'^{PBR} (p) ♀H6 CCal EPfP EWoo SPoG
plumarius LShi SBls SBut XLum
- 'Albiflorus' (p) XLum
- Ipswich Pinks Group (p) CCal
- 'Maischnee' (p) **new** ECha
§ POP STAR ('Wp04 Esther'^{PBR}) (p) CCal LRHS SGbt WIce
'Pretty' (p) ECtt
PRETTY FLAMINGO see *D.* 'Carmine Letitia Wyatt'
'Prince Charming' (p) MAsh
'Princess of Wales' (M) EMal LShi
§ 'Prudence' (p) LShi
'Pudsey Prize' (p) EPot
'Purple Frosted' (pf) EMal
pygmaeus NMWJ 14561 WCru
§ 'Queen of Henri' (p) CRos EHyd LRHS NRHS
'Queen of Sheba' (p) LShi WHer WKif
'Rachel' (p) ELon LShi
'Rainbow Loveliness' (p,a) CCal
RAINBOW LOVELINESS IMPROVED MIXED (p,a) **new** WHil
RASPBERRY SUNDAE see *D.* 'Devon Yolande'
'Ray' (Sprint Series) (pt) **new** LRHS
REBEKAH ('Wp09 Mar05'^{PBR}) (Early Bird Series) (p) ♀H6 CCal CMea CRos EHyd ELan LRHS NRHS
'Red Dwarf' see *D.* 'Red Star'
§ 'Red Star'^{PBR} (p) ♀H6 CCal EHyd GAbr GJos LRHS MAsh NRHS WIce
'Ringwood Belle' (pf) CNMi
'Rizalene' (p) CNMi
'Robert Allwood' (pf) EMal
'Robin Ritchie' (p) WHoo
'Robina's Daughter' (p) GAbr
ROCKIN' PURPLE (p,a) **new** CBod
ROMANCE ('Wp09 Wen04'^{PBR}) (Scent First Series) (p) ♀H6 CCal CRos EHyd EPfP LRHS NRHS SCob
'Romsey' (pf) CNMi
'Roodkapje' (p) XLum
'Rose de Mai' (p) CFis CNMi LShi SBut WHer WHoo
'Rose Joy' (p) ♀H6 SRGP
ROSEBUD ('Wp08 Ros03'^{PBR}) (Early Bird Series) (p) CCal EHyd NRHS
'Royal Crimson' (pf) EMal
'Royal Salmon' (pf) EMal
'Ruby' see *D.* 'Houndspool Ruby'
'Ruby Doris' see *D.* 'Houndspool Ruby'
rupicola CSpe WCot WSHC
'Saint Nicholas' (p) WThu
'Sam Barlow' (p) LShi
'Seraphina' (pf) CNMi
serotinus EPot LShi WCot
SHERBET ('Wp08 Nik03'^{PBR}) (Early Bird Series) (p) WIce
§ SHOOTING STAR ('Wp04 Flores'^{PBR}) (p) CCal ELan LRHS SRms WIce
'Shot Silk' (pf) EMal
'Show Aristocrat' (p) CCal
SHOW GIRL ('Hilshow') (pt) EHyd
SILVER STAR ('Wp10 Hel01'^{PBR}) (p) CCal CTri EHyd EPfP LRHS NRHS
simulans SRot
'Singapore Girl' (Kiwi Series) (p) EWTr
'Sir David Scott' (p) SBut
* 'Six Hills' (p) NWad
SLAP 'N' TICKLE ('Wp 05 Pp 22'^{PBR}) (Scent First Series) (p) ♀H6 CRos ECtt EHyd EPfP LRHS LSRN NRHS SCoo SPoG
'Solomon' (p) CCal LShi
'Somerset' (pf) CNMi
'Sops-in-wine' (p) CCal CFis ECha ECtt LShi MSCN
§ 'Souvenir de la Malmaison' (M) EMal LShi
spiculifolius EPot LShi MMuc
Spooky Group (p) CCal
'Square Eyes' see *D.* 'Old Square Eyes'
squarrosus EPot LShi SRot
- 'Nanus' see *D.* 'Berlin Snow'
'Starburst'^{PBR} (p) CCal CPla
STARGAZER ('Wp13 Gil05'^{PBR}) (Whetman Stars Series) (p) CCal EWoo
'Starlette'^{PBR} (Star Double Series) (p) CCal EHyd LRHS NRHS SCoo SGBe WIce
STARLIGHT ('Hilstar') (pf) CCal SRms
STARLIGHT ('Wp 06 Parnia'^{PBR}) (p) CCal EWoo
'Starry Eyes' (p) ♀H6 CCal CRos EHyd ELan EWoo GMaP LRHS NRHS SRms SWvt WIce
'Storm' (pf) EMal
'Strawberries and Cream' (p) ECtt SPoG
strictus EPot SLee WCot

* - subsp. ***pulchellus***	GEdr NSla WFar
subacaulis	EDAr EWTr SBut XLum
- subsp. ***brachyanthus***	GJos
- - 'Murray Lyon' (p)	WThu
suendermannii	see *D. petraeus*
SUGAR PLUM ('Wp08 Ian04'[PBR]) (Scent First Series) (p)	CCal EBee ECtt EHyd ELan LRHS NRHS SCob SCoo SGBe
SUNFLOR CHARMY ('Hilcharm') (Sunflor Series) (pt)	LRHS
§ ***superbus***	CCal EPPr EWld LRHS SBrt SPhx SPtp WHer
- BO 15-070 **new**	GGro
- from Japan **new**	GGro
- var. ***longicalycinus*** dark-flowered **new**	GGro
- - white-flowered **new**	GGro
I - 'Primadonna' (p)	SHar
SUPERNOVA ('Wp11 Tyr04'[PBR]) (pf) ♀H6	CCal CMea
SUPERTROUPER AMY ('Kledp15187') (pt) **new**	LRHS
SUPERTROUPER CARMEN ('Kledp11106') (pt)	LRHS
SUPERTROUPER CARMEN PURPLE (pt) **new**	LRHS
SUPERTROUPER CARMEN RED ('Kledp16214') (pt) **new**	LRHS
SUPERTROUPER DIWALI ('Kledcp05070') (pt) **new**	LRHS
SUPERTROUPER ELISE ('Kledp07093') (pt) **new**	LRHS
SUPERTROUPER GRACE ('Kledp16188') (pt) **new**	LRHS
SUPERTROUPER MARIE (pt) **new**	LRHS
SUPERTROUPER SISSY ('Kledp07088'[PBR]) (pt) **new**	LRHS
'Sweet Cecille' (pf)	CNMi
SWEETNESS (mixed) (p)	CCal
sylvestris	GArf GJos
'Tatra' (pf)	NQui WMal
'Tatra Blush' (p)	EPPr EWTr
'Tatra Fragrance' (p)	EPPr LShi
'Tayside Red' (M)	EMal
the Bloodie pink	see *D.* 'Caesar's Mantle'
THE WESSEX PINK ('Wp15val11') (p)	CCal ECtt EHyd EPfP
'Thora' (M)	EMal
'Thunderstorm' (pf)	CNMi
tianschanicus	GKev LRHS SPhx
TICKLED PINK ('Devon Pp 11'[PBR]) (Scent First Series) (p) ♀H6	CCal CTri ECtt EHyd ELan EPfP LRHS LSRN NRHS SCoo SGBe SPoG
'Tiny Rubies'	see *D. gratianopolitanus* 'Tiny Rubies'
'Tony's Choice' (pf)	CNMi
tristis	XLum
'Tropic Butterfly' (p)	LPot
'Tudor'	MNrw
'Tudor Rose' (b)	MNrw
turkestanicus	WMal
'Unique' (p)	CCal LShi
'Valda Wyatt' (p) ♀H6	CBcs CCal ELan EPfP SEND SPoG SWvt WFar
'Velvet Pelargonium' (pf)	EMal
'Vic Masters' (p)	SGro
'Violet Yates' (pf)	CNMi
'W.A. Musgrave'	see *D.* 'Musgrave's Pink'
'Waikiki Pink' (pt) **new**	SEdd
'Waithman Beauty' (p)	CCal LShi WHoo
'Waithman's Jubilee' (p)	CCal SGro
'Warden Hybrid' (p)	CCal CRos CTri ECtt EHyd EPfP LRHS MNHC NRHS NWad SHar SPoG SWvt
'Waterloo Sunset'[PBR] (p)	CCal
'Weetwood Double' (p)	SGro
'Wessex' (pf)	CNMi EHyd LRHS NRHS
weyrichii	EPot
'Whatfield Anona' (p)	CCal
'Whatfield Beauty' (p)	ECtt
'Whatfield Cancan' (p) ♀H6	CCal CMea CRos ECtt EHyd ELan EPfP EPot GMaP LRHS MNHC NFav NGdn NHol NRHS NRya NSla SGro SPoG SWvt WCAu
'Whatfield Cyclops' (p)	CCal
'Whatfield Dorothy Mann' (p)	CCal WIce
'Whatfield Gem' (p)	CCal CPla ECtt ELan EPfP LShi MNHC NGdn SLee SWvt WCav WIce
'Whatfield Joy' (p)	CCal CRos ECtt EHyd ELan EPfP LRHS NGdn NRHS SLee
'Whatfield Magenta' (p) ♀H6	CRos ECtt EHyd ELan EPot LRHS LShi NRHS SLee SPoG SRms
'Whatfield Mini' (p)	SRot
'Whatfield Misty Morn' (p)	ECtt
'Whatfield Peach' (p)	CCal
'Whatfield Ruby' (p)	ECtt LShi
'Whatfield White' (p)	CCal ECtt LShi
'Whatfield Wisp' (p)	EPfP EPot GArf LShi MRav NBir
'White Joy'[PBR] (p) ♀H6	MRav
'White Ladies' (p)	LShi MRav
'Widecombe Fair' (p) ♀H6	CBod CCal LShi SPoG

Diapensia (*Diapensiaceae*)

lapponica var. ***obovata***	GArf

Diarrhena (*Poaceae*)

japonica	MAvo
obovata	EPPr

Diascia (*Scrophulariaceae*)

'Andrew'	SGro
'Appleby Appleblossom'	CPla
'Aurora Apricot' (Aurora Series)	EHyd EPfP LRHS NRHS
barberae 'Belmore Beauty' (v)	EWes
- 'Blackthorn Apricot' ♀H4	EBee ECha EHyd ELan EPfP GWyn LSRN MBow NDov NRHS SPer SPlb SPoG SRms SWvt
§ - 'Fisher's Flora' ♀H4	WFar
- JULIET RED ('Baljuled') **new**	WHil
§ - 'Ruby Field' ♀H4	EBee ECha EHyd EPfP LRHS LSRN NFav NRHS SPer SPoG SRms SWvt
BLUE BONNET ('Hecbon')	SWvt
'Bluebelle' (Maritana Series)	ECha NDov
'Blush'	see *D. integerrima* 'Blush'
(Breezee Series) BREEZEE APPLE BLOSSOM	LSou NLar SMrm
- BREEZEE APRICOT ('Diaspritwo'[PBR])	NLar SMrm
- BREEZEE RED (Breezee Series)	NLar

- Breezee Snow ('Inndiabzsno'PBR)	ELan NLar SMrm
'Coldham'	WGoo WMal WSHC
Coral Belle ('Hecbel'PBR) ♀H3	CRos EHyd LRHS NRHS
'Coral Spires' **new**	CSpe
cordata ambig.	WFar
'Denim Blue'	ECtt EDAr WFar
'Diamond Fuchsia'	LSou
'Divara Orange' (Divara Series) **new**	LSou
elegans misapplied	see *D. fetcaniensis*, *D. vigilis*
'Emma'	NDov SMHy SWvt WGoo
felthamii	see *D. fetcaniensis*
§ ***fetcaniensis***	CKel CMea EBee EPfP LEdu LRHS MCot NDov NLar SIvy SWvt WHal WSHC
- 'Daydream'	LBuc LShi MNrw MPie SGro WCFE WFar
flanaganii misapplied	see *D. vigilis*
(Flying Colours Series) Flying Colours Antique Rose ('Diastu'PBR)	SPoG
- Flying Colours Appleblossom ('Diastara')	SPoG
- Flying Colours Apricot ('Diastina')	SPoG
- Flying Colours Deep Salmon Improved ('Dala Depsam'PBR)	SPoG
- Flying Colours Red ('Diastonia')	SPoG
'Hector Harrison'	see *D.* 'Salmon Supreme'
'Hector's Hardy' ♀H3	XLum
§ 'Hopleys'	ECha EHyd EWes MHCG MPie MSCN NLar NRHS SMHy SWvt WAvo WFar WWtn
Ice Cracker ('Hecrack')	CMea CRos EHyd ELan LRHS NRHS SRms
Iceberg ('Hecice')	NDov SWvt
§ ***integerrima*** ♀H4	ECha MCot
- 'Alba'	see *D. integerrima* 'Blush'
§ - 'Blush'	CSpe EBee NDov WGoo
- 'Ivory Angel'	see *D. integerrima* 'Blush'
integrifolia	see *D. integerrima*
'Jacqueline's Joy'	CMea NPer
'Joyce's Choice' ♀H3	CRos EHyd LRHS NRHS SRms
'Katherine Sharman' (v)	EWes
'Lilac Belle' ♀H3	EDAr EHyd ELan EPfP LRHS NBir NRHS SPlb SPoG SRms
'Lilac Mist' ♀H3	NPer
Little Dancer ('Pendan'PBR)	ELan NLar
Little Dreamer ('Pender'PBR)	NLar
Little Drifter ('Pendrif'PBR)	NLar
Little Maiden ('Penmaid'PBR)	NLar
Little Tango ('Pentang'PBR)	NLar SRms
'Monhop White' **new**	EWld
personata	Widely available
- 'Hopleys'	see *D.* 'Hopleys'
- orange-flowered	CDor CTtf WMal
'Peter'	NDov
Pink Panther ('Penther')	SWvt
Red Ace ('Hecrace')	MBow NPer SWvt
Redstart ('Hecstart')	SWvt
rigescens ♀H3	CCBP CEme CWCL ECtt ELan EPfP GWyn MBow NLar NPer SChF SIvy SPer SPlb SPoG SWvt WAbe WAvo WCFE WSHC WSpi
§ - 'Anne Rennie'	LRHS SWvt
'Ruby Field'	see *D. barberae* 'Ruby Field'
'Rupert Lambert' ♀H3	NDov
§ 'Salmon Supreme'	EHyd EPfP LRHS NPer NRHS SPoG SRms
Sundiascia Upright Bright Pink ('Sunjodiblupi'PBR) (Sundiascia Series)	CWCL
tetcaniensis 'African Queen'	SIvy
Towers of Flowers Aurora Cherry Blossom	ELan LRHS
Towers of Flowers Aurora Dark Pink	ELan LRHS
Towers of Flowers Aurora Light Pink	ELan LRHS
'Twinkle' ♀H3	CRos EHyd LRHS NBir NPer NRHS SRms
§ ***vigilis*** ♀H3	CExl CMea EBee EHyd EMor EPot NBro NRHS SRms WHal

Dicentra ✿ (*Papaveraceae*)

CC 4452	CExl
'Adrian Bloom'	CExl EPfP GLet SWvt WFar
(Amore Series) 'Amore Pink'	CMiW CWGN EMor NLar
- 'Amore Rose'PBR	CWGN GBin NHpl
'Aurora'	CBcs CMac CMiW ECha ECtt EHed EHyd ELon EMor EPfP GKev GMaP GWyn ILea LCro LOPS LRHS MRav NGdn NLar NRHS SCob SPer SPoG SWvt WCAu
'Boothman's Variety'	see *D.* 'Stuart Boothman'
'Bountiful'	CMac ECtt EHyd GLet LRHS MRav NGdn NRHS SWvt
'Burning Hearts'PBR	CMiW CWCL CWGN ECtt EGrl EMor EPot GEdr LRHS MHol MPnt NSti SPer SPoG WCAu WHil
canadensis	CMiW EBee LEdu MAvo MNrw WAbe WFar WHal WPGP
'Candy Hearts'PBR	EBee ECtt ELan EMor SCob
cucullaria	CElw CMea CMiW CWCL EBee EHyd EMor EPPr EPot GAbr GArf GEdr GKev GLet LEdu LRHS MNrw MRav NHpl NLar NRHS WAbe WFar
- 'Little Angels' (d)	WFar
- 'Pink Punk'	EBee EMor EPPr LEdu NLar WFar WMal
- 'Pittsburg'	EBee EPPr LEdu MNrw WSpi
eximia misapplied	see *D. formosa*
eximia ambig.	CMac EPfP GPSL WFar
eximia (Ker Gawl.) Torr.	GJos
- 'Alba'	see *D. eximia* (Ker Gawl.) Torr. 'Snowdrift'
§ - 'Snowdrift'	CDor SRms WFar
'Filigree'	CSpe ECha LEdu SPVi
'Firecracker'	MPnt
§ ***formosa***	CBcs CEme CTri ECha EGrl EHyd ELan EPfP GGro GKev LRHS NBro NGdn NRHS SPlb SRms WCAu
- f. ***alba***	CTri ECha GAbr GLet GLog NBir SRms WCru WFar WKif
- 'Bacchanal' ♀H5	Widely available
- 'Cox's Dark Red'	CExl EWes GAbr GBin GKev GLet NHpl

- 'Langtrees' ♀H5 CMac CRos ECha EHyd EMor EPfP LEdu LRHS MRav NBro NLar NRHS SRms SSut SWvt WCru WFar WSpi
- 'Moorland Mist' WFar
- 'Moorland Pearl' WFar
- subsp. ***oregana*** EGrI EPPr WHal
- SNOWFLAKES ('Fusd') MRav
- 'Spring Gold' CBod ECha EGrI EHyd ELon EMor EPPr LSou NLar WFar
- 'Spring Magic' CRos ECtt EHyd EMor EPPr EPfP GWyn LRHS LSou MRav NLar NRHS WSpi

'Ivory Hearts'[PBR] CWGN EBee ELan EMor MAvo NLar NSti SCob SPer
§ 'Katie' EPPr
'Katy' see *D.* 'Katie'
'King of Hearts' Widely available
'Love Hearts'[PBR] MHol
'Luxuriant' ♀H5 CBcs CBod CRos EBee ECtt EHyd ELan EMor EPfP EShb LRHS LSRN MCot MGos MRav NRHS SPer SPoG SRms SWvt WCAu WFar
macrantha see *Ichthyoselmis macrantha*
'Pearl Drops' EHyd GLog GMaP GWyn LRHS MCot MHCG MMrt NBid NLar NRHS SRms WFar
peregrina WAbe
- ***alba*** GEdr
'Red Fountain'[PBR] CWCL EMor MPnt NSti
scandens see *Dactylicapnos scandens*
'Silver Beads' ELon
spectabilis see *Lamprocapnos spectabilis*
'Spring Morning' CDor CElw EMor EPPr GLet LEdu NGdn WSpi
§ 'Stuart Boothman' ♀H5 CMac CWCL ECtt EPfP GBin GLet GMaP ILea LEdu LRHS MCot MRav NBro NGdn NLar NQui SPer SPoG SRms SWvt WCAu WFar WKif
thalictrifolia see *Dactylicapnos scandens*
ventii see *Dactylicapnos ventii*

Dichelostemma (*Asparagaceae*)

capitatum 'Ginny's Giant' **new** CSpe
congestum CAvo CBor GKev SDeJ WCot
§ ***ida-maia*** CAvo CBor CWCL EPot GKev SDeJ
- 'Pink Diamond' CBor GKev SDeJ
multiflorum NRog
volubile GKev NRog
- 'Pink Giant' SDeJ

Dichondra (*Convolvulaceae*)

argentea 'Silver Falls' EShb MBros SCoo SPer SPoG WSMil
§ ***micrantha*** CKel EShb
repens misapplied see *D. micrantha*

Dichroa (*Hydrangeaceae*)

PAB 8488 LPla
from Guizhou, China EHed WCot WPGP
cyanea LRHS
- B&SWJ 2367 **new** WCru
- NJM 13.104 WPGP
febrifuga B&SWJ 9734 WCru
- B&SWJ 9753 WCru
- NJM 10.042 WPGP
- PAB 8639 LEdu
hirsuta LRHS
- NJM 10.051 WPGP
- B&SWJ 8207 from Vietnam WCru
aff. ***hirsuta*** B&SWJ 8371 from Laos WCru
'Long March' **new** LEdu WPGP
yunnanensis **new** WPGP
aff. ***yunnanensis*** B&SWJ 9734 WCru

Dichroa × *Hydrangea* see × *Didrangea*

Dichromena see *Rhynchospora*

Dichrostachys (*Fabaceae*)

cinerea SPlb

Dicksonia ✿ (*Dicksoniaceae*)

antarctica ♀H3 Widely available
berteriana IKel
fibrosa ♀H3 CDTJ CKel CTrC ETod IKel LRHS XSte
sellowiana CDTJ CKel ETod IKel
squarrosa ♀H3 CBdn CCCN CDTJ CKel ETod LRHS XSte
youngiae CDTJ CKel IKel

Dicliptera (*Acanthaceae*)

§ ***sericea*** CCCN ECtt EShb EWld SEND SGro SRkn WSHC XLum XSen
suberecta see *D. sericea*

Dictamnus (*Rutaceae*)

albus CBcs CKel CSpe EBee ECha EHyd ELan EMor EPfP LRHS MBel MCot MRav NRHS SMHy SMad SPer SPoG SWvt WCAu WSpi XAbr
- var. ***albus*** ♀H6 CDor EWoo SWvt
§ - var. ***purpureus*** ♀H6 CSpe EBee ECha EHyd ELan EMor EPfP GBin ILea LRHS LSun MBel MRav NGBl NRHS SPer SPoG SRms SWvt WCAu WKif WSpi
fraxinella see *D. albus* var. *purpureus*

× *Didrangea* (*Hydrangeaceae*)

versicolor CAbb CBcs CAbb CBcs CDoC CExl CKEl CMCN CWit EBee EHyd EMdy EPfP ESwi LRHS MGil SBrt SEdd SIvy SPoG SWvt WJek WPGP
ytiensis B&SWJ 11790 WCru

Didymochlaena (*Dryopteridaceae*)

lunulata see *D. truncatula*
§ ***truncatula*** CDoC EShb

Dierama ✿ (*Iridaceae*)

CD&R 192 CElw
adelphicum CElw GAbr GKev WHil WSHC
ambiguum CElw EBee GAbr XLum
argyreum CBcs CBct CBod CBor CCCN CElw CMiW CTsd EBee EPri EWoo GKev ITim NLar SEdd SPoG WGob XSte
atrum EBee
'Autumn Dazzler' CPla
Barr hybrids CBro WHil
'Black Knight' CExl
'Blackberry Bells' CBct CBod CBor CDor CPla CWCL CWGN EBee EHyd ELan EPfP EPri GKev GWyn LLWG LRHS MAvo NLar NWad SChF SMrm SPad SPoG WSpi
'Blood Drops' GAbr
BLUE BELLE ('Rowblu'[PBR]) CBor CWCL EBee ECtt GBin
'Candy Stripe' EBee IBal
'Carmine' CWCL

'Cinnamon Fairy'	EBee EHyd EPfP IBal
cooperi	CBor EBee EPfP NBir
'Coral Belle'	EBee IBal LRHS
'Coral Bells'	CCCN IBal MNrw WPGP
'Cosmos'	CBcs CExl EPri LRHS LShi NWad WFar
'Dark Angel'	GAbr
§ ***dracomontanum***	CBor CBro CCCN CElw CExl CRos CWCL EBee EHyd EPfP EPri EWTr GKev GMaP LRHS MBel NBir NLar NRHS SEdd SPeP WFar WGob WGwG WHoo XLum
- dwarf, pink-flowered	GArf
dracomontanum* × *pulcherrimum	GDam SMad
ensifolium	see *D. pendulum*
erectum	CBcs CBct CBor CCCN CWCL EPri NLar SEdd SPeP WGob WHil XSte
formosum	EBee
galpinii	CCCN CPla CWCL EPri SEdd
grandiflorum	WSHC
'Guinevere'	CBor CDor CExl CWCL CWGN EBee EPri EWTr GMaP GWyn IBal LEdu LRHS MMrt MRav NBir NChi NGdn NQui SCob SEdd SMrm SPoG SVen WFar WGwG WHil WHoo WSHC
igneum	Widely available
- CD&R 278	CExl
insigne	CCCN CPla CTsd CWCL EBee EHyd EPPr NLar NWad SChF WCot
jucundum	CWCL EMor EPri EWes LRHS SEdd WCot WSMil
'Kilmurry White'	IBal
'Lancelot'	CExl EBee ECtt IBal LRHS NBir SCob SWvt WCot WFar WKif WSHC
latifolium	WGob
luteoalbidum	GKev
'Milkmaid'	CExl
'Miranda'	CBcs EBee ECtt ELan IBal LRHS NLar SEdd
mossii	CBcs CBor CCBP CCCN CExl CTsd CWCL EPfP EPri LEdu LRHS MSCN NLar NQui NWad SEdd SPeP SPlb SPoG SVen WGob XLum
nixonianum	GAbr MHer
'Painted Lady'	EHyd IBal SLon
'Pale Pink'	CWCL
pallidum	CExl
'Pamina'	CExl
pauciflorum	CCCN CExl CRos CTsd CWCL EBee EPri LRHS NBir NLar NSla SEdd WCot WGob WSHC
§ ***pendulum***	CBro GKev LRHS MRav SWvt WCot WFar WGob
pendulum* × *pulcherrimum <u>new</u>	GKev
'Pink Dragon' <u>new</u>	LRHS
'Pink Rocket'	CBct CBor CMiW CPla LLWG LRHS MHer MHtn NHol SPad SPeP XSte
Plant World hybrids	ELon WFar
PLANT WORLD JEWELS	CBct CWCL NWad WFar
'Pretty Flamingo'	CExl
'Puck'	MRav
pulcherrimum	Widely available
- var. ***album***	CBod CBor CCCN CEme CWCL GKev MAvo MHer MNrw NQui SMrm WHil
- 'Blackbird'	CBcs CBod CBor CCCN CExl CPla CWCL EBou ELan EPri GKev LLWG LRHS LSRN MHer MSCN NHol NLar SChF SPeP SPoG SWvt WFar WGob WHoo WPGP
- dark cerise-flowered	GKev
- 'Flaring Tips'	GKev LRHS
- 'Merlin'	CDor CExl EBee ECtt IBal LRHS NBir SCob SVen SWvt WFar XSte
- pale-flowered	ECha
- purple-flowered	CSpe CWCL
- Slieve Donard hybrids	CWCL WFar
pumilum misapplied	see *D. dracomontanum*
'Queen of the Night'	EPri
reynoldsii	CBod CBor CCCN CExl CPla CTsd CWCL EPri EWoo GBin NWad SBrt SEdd SPlb SPoG SRkn SVen WFar WSpi
robustum	CAbb CBod CCCN CExl CPla CTsd CWCL EWes LRHS WCot WFar WPGP
'Sarastro'	CExl
'Senlisse' <u>new</u>	LRHS
'Spring Dancer'	CPla CWCL EBee MHer NHol SPlb
'Tiny Bells'	EBee EDAr IBal WSHC
'Titania'	GBin IBal
trichorhizum	CCCN CElw CExl CPla CWCL EPri GKev LPla LRHS NWad XLum
white-flowered	MBel
Wildside hybrids	WSHC

Diervilla (*Caprifoliaceae*)

middendorffiana	see *Weigela middendorffiana*
rivularis HONEYBEE ('Diwibru01'^{PBR})	CBod CSBt LCro LOPS MMrt NEoE NLar SGBe SGol SPoG WHil
- 'Troja Black'	EPPr EPfP MBlu NLar SGol
§ ***sessilifolia***	CBrac CMac EBee EPPr EWTr MBlu MRav SLon WCot
- 'Butterfly'	CMac EPPr LCro LOPS NLar WFar
- COOL SPLASH ('Lpdc Podaras'^{PBR}) (v)	CMac EBee NEoE SPoG SWvt
× ***splendens***	CBrac CExl EBee EHyd EPPr EPfP IDee LRHS MBNS MBlu MGil MSwo NLar SIvy SPer SPoG SWvt
- DIVA	see *D.* × *splendens* 'El Madrigal'
§ - 'El Madrigal'^{PBR}	CBod LRHS MMrt NLar NSti

Dietes (*Iridaceae*)

bicolor	CAbb CBor CExl CPbh CPrp CSpe EBee EPri ESwi LEdu SBrt SChr SPoG WCFE WSHC
grandiflora	CAbb CExl CPbh ESwi SBls SChr SVen WCFE WCot
§ ***iridioides***	CPrp EPri ESwi WGob XLum
robinsoniana	WCot

Digitalis ✿ (*Plantaginaceae*)

NJM 13.013	WPGP
'Albino'	CRos EHyd EPfP LRHS NRHS
ambigua	see *D. grandiflora*
apricot hybrids	see *D. purpurea* 'Sutton's Apricot'
canariensis	CAbb CBcs CCBP CCCN CDTJ CKel CSpe CTsd MEch MGil MMrt SEle SIvy SPad SPlb SVen WCFE
ciliata	GKev
davisiana	CExl CPla GLog MNHC
'Elsie Kelsey'	ECtt EPfP SWvt
eriostachya	see *D. lutea*
ferruginea 🏆^{H6}	CDor CSpe EBee ECha ECtt EHed ELan EPPr EPfP GArf GKev GQue LEdu LRHS MRav NBir NDov NGdn NRHS SCob SPer SRms SVen WCAu WKif
- B&SWJ 15395 <u>new</u>	WCru

- 'Gelber Herold' CDor CElw EMor ETod GKev GMaP SBls SCob SMrm WFar WSpi
- 'Gigantea' ♀H7 CFoA ECtt ELan EMor EPfP EWoo GAbr LBuc LEdu LRHS LShi MBNS NDov SPlb WPGP
× ***fucata*** 'Miranda' SWvt
- 'Pink Chapel' ECtt
- 'Red Skin' NWad
'Glory of Roundway' ♀H6 CBod CDor EBee ECtt EShb LCro LOPS MNrw NCou SCob WCAu WCot
§ GOLDCREST ('Waldigone'PBR) CBcs CRos CWGN ECtt EHyd EPfP LBuc LRHS LSou NRHS SHar SPad SPoG WHil WNPC
§ ***grandiflora*** ♀H6 Widely available
- 'Carillon' ♀H5 CBod EAJP EBee EHyd ELan EMor EPfP GDam GJos LRHS SPeP WCav WHoo
- 'Cream Bell' EPfP
Illumination Series see *D.* × *valinii* Illumination Series
isabelliana CBod CCCN WKif
'John Innes Tetra' CTtf MBriF MMrt MNrw SPtp
kishinskyi see *D. parviflora* Jacq.
laevigata CTtf EBee LEdu LShi NBro SEND
- white-flowered WCot
lamarckii misapplied see *D. lanata*
§ ***lanata*** CRos EBou ECtt EHyd ELan EPfP LRHS MBNS MHol MNHC MPie NGdn NRHS SGbt SPlb SRms
- 'Café Crème' CDor EMor
§ ***lutea*** ♀H6 Widely available
I - 'Aurea' LPla
× ***mertonensis*** ♀H5 Widely available
- 'Summer King' CBod CChe CDor ECtt ELan GJos LSRN MBow SBls SPtp WFar
minor EWes LShi
obscura CCCN EAJP SBls SBrt SPlb SVen
- 'Sunset' SBut
orientalis see *D. grandiflora*
§ ***parviflora*** Jacq. ♀H5 ECha ECtt EHed EPPr EPfP EWTr GKev LCro LRHS MBNS MMrt NBro NChi SEND
- 'Milk Chocolate' ♀H5 CAbb CBod CDor CElw CFoA CSpe CWCL ECtt ELan EMor EPfP ETod GKev LRHS LSRN MBros NFav NHpl NLar SBls SEdd SPtp
'Polkadot Polly' (Polkadot Series) MBriF
purpurea CBod CCBP CHab EBou EHyd ELan ENfk EPfP EWoo GDam GPoy LCro LOPS LRHS LSun MBow MHer MNHC MPri NMir SCob SPlb SPoG SVic WBrk WSFF WShi WWild
- 'Alba' see *D. purpurea* f. *albiflora*
§ - f. ***albiflora*** Widely available
- - 'Anne Redetzky'PBR LRHS
- 'Apricot Delight' EBee EHed SBut WCAu
- Camelot Series MBros SHar SVic
- - 'Camelot Cream' ♀H5 EHyd ELan EPfP SWvt
- - 'Camelot Lavender' ♀H5 EHyd ELan EPfP SWvt
- - 'Camelot Rose' ♀H5 EHyd ELan EPfP SWvt
- - 'Camelot White' ♀H5 EHyd ELan EPfP
- 'Campanulata' LShi
- 'Cream Carousel' (Carousel Series) EBee EHyd LRHS NRHS
- Dalmatian Series SCob
- - 'Dalmatian Crème' ♀H7 CRos EPfP LRHS MAsh MPri NRHS SCob SCoo WHil
- - 'Dalmatian Peach' ♀H5 CBod ELan EPfP LRHS MAsh MBros WHil
- - 'Dalmatian Purple' ♀H5 CBod ELan EPfP LCro LOPS LRHS MAsh MPri SCob SCoo
- - 'Dalmatian Rose' ♀H5 CBod CRos ELan EPfP LCro LOPS LRHS MAsh MPri NRHS SCob SCoo
- - 'Dalmatian White' ♀H5 CBod ELan EPfP LCro LOPS LRHS MBros MPri SCob SCoo
- Excelsior Group CBcs CDor CMac CRos CSBt CTri ECtt EHyd EPfP GJos GMaP LCro LOPS LRHS NHol NMir NRHS SCob SGbt SPer SPoG SRms SVic SWvt
- - (Suttons; Unwins) ECtt MRav
- - white-flowered CTri
- Foxy Group CBod EHyd EPfP LRHS MNHC SPoG
- Giant Spotted Group CRos ECtt EHyd EPfP LRHS NRHS SPoG
§ - subsp. ***heywoodii*** CSpe
- - 'Silver Fox' CBod NRHS SCob SPeP WHil
- 'Lavender Carousel' (Carousel Series) EHyd LRHS NRHS
- 'Monstrosa' CBod
- 'Orchid Carousel' (Carousel Series) EHyd LRHS NRHS
- 'Pam's Choice' ♀H7 CBod CChe CDor CExl CRos CSpe EAJP EBee EBlo ECtt EHed EHyd ELan EPfP GBin LCro LOPS LRHS LSRN LSun NHol NLar NRHS SCob SCoo SPer STPC WCAu
- 'Pam's Split' SCob
- 'Primrose Carousel' (Carousel Series) NLar SCob SCoo
- 'Purple Carousel' (Carousel Series) EHyd LRHS NRHS
- 'Serendipity' CRos EHyd EPfP LRHS NRHS
- 'Snow Thimble' CBod CDor EBlo EHyd ELan EPfP LRHS LSun MACG MBros NCou NLar NRHS SCoo STPC
§ - 'Sutton's Apricot' CBcs CBod CDor CKel CRos EBlo ECha ECtt EHyd ELan EPfP EWoo GMaP LCro LOPS LRHS MBriF MRav NGdn NLar NRHS SCob SCoo SGbt SPer SPoG SWvt WCot
- (Virtuoso Series) 'Virtuoso Cream' CRos LRHS
- - 'Virtuoso Lavender' CRos LRHS
- - 'Virtuoso Rose Compact' CRos LRHS
- - 'Virtuoso White' LRHS
- 'White Carousel' (Carousel Series) EHyd LRHS NRHS
sceptrum CCCN CExl CTsd SIvy SPlb SVen
'Spice Island' CBod EBee ECtt EPfP EShb EWes LCro LOPS LRHS LSou LSun MNrw NLar SEdd SPad SPer WCot WSpi
* ***stewartii*** EWes NWad
thapsi EAJP EPPr EPfP
- 'Spanish Peaks' GEdr
- white-flowered EPPr
trojana GKev LShi
- 'Helen of Troy' WSpi
× ***valinii*** 'Berry Canary' CCht EPfP LRHS SPad SPoG WHil
- 'Firebird' **new** CRos
- Foxlight Series **new** LBuc
- - FOXLIGHT PLUM GOLD ('Takfoplgo'PBR) CWGN ECtt LCro LOPS LRHS SCoo WHil
- - FOXLIGHT ROSE IVORY ('Takforoiv'PBR) **new** LRHS WHil
- - FOXLIGHT RUBY GLOW ('Takforugl'PBR) CBod LRHS LSou WHil
§ - 'Harkstead Apricot' (Illumination Series) CCCN EPfP LRHS NHpl SEle
§ - 'Harkstead Flame'PBR (Illumination Series) CCht CRos EHyd EPfP LRHS NHpl NRHS SCoo SEdd SPoG
- 'Harkstead Red' (Illumination Series) CCCN EPfP MHtn

§ - Illumination Series	CKel EHyd LRHS SCob
- - ILLUMINATION APRICOT	see *D.* × *valinii* 'Harkstead Apricot'
- - ILLUMINATION CHERRY BRANDY	see *D.* × *valinii* (Illumination Series) ILLUMINATION RUBY SLIPPERS
- - ILLUMINATION FLAME	see *D.* × *valinii* 'Harkstead Flame'
- - ILLUMINATION PINK ('Tmdgfp001'[PBR])	CAbb CDor CRos EBee EPfP LBuc LCro LOPS LRHS LSun MSCN NHpl SPoG WCot
§ - - ILLUMINATION RUBY SLIPPERS ('Tmdg1204'[PBR])	CRos EBee EHyd EPfP LRHS NHpl NRHS
Vesuvius Group	LShi
viridiflora	CExl CSpe GQue
'Walberton's Goldcrest'	see *D.* GOLDCREST

dill see *Anethum graveolens*

Dionaea ✿ (*Droseraceae*)

muscipula	CHew LCro LOPS SHmp SPlb WSSs WTyc
- 'Akai Ryu' 🏆H3	SHmp WSSs
- 'B52'	WSSs
- 'Bohemian Garnet'	WSSs
- 'Cross Teeth'	CHew
- 'Darwin'	WSSs
- (Dentate Traps Group) 'Dentate Traps'	CHew WSSs
- 'Mk1979'	WSSs
- 'Red Piranha'	CHew
- 'Royal Red'	CHew WSSs
- 'Sawtooth'	WSSs
- 'South West Giant' 🏆H3	WSSs
- 'Tiger Fangs'	WSSs

Dionysia (*Primulaceae*)

'Annielle'	WAbe
aretioides 🏆H4	WAbe
- 'Bevere'	EPot WAbe
bryoides	WAbe
'Charlson Emma'	WAbe
'Charlson Jake'	WAbe
'Charlson Petite'	WAbe
'Charlson Pip'	WAbe
'Corona'	WAbe
curviflora	WAbe
'Eric Watson'	WAbe
'Geist'	WAbe
'Inka Gold'	WAbe
janthina	WAbe
'Judith Bramley'	WAbe
'Mike Bramley'	WAbe
'Monika'	WAbe
'Pascal'	WAbe
sarvestanica	WAbe
tapetodes	EPot GKev WAbe
- 'Brimstone'	WAbe
'Tess'	WAbe
'Zdeněk Zvolánek'	WAbe

Dioon (*Zamiaceae*)

argenteum	CBrP
califanoi	CBrP
caputoi	CBrP
edule 🏆H1b	CBrP SPlb
- var. ***angustifolium***	CBrP
merolae	CBrP
rzedowskii	CBrP
spinulosum	CBrP CCCN

Dioscorea (*Dioscoreaceae*)

BO 15-072 **new**	GGro
bulbifera	SPlb
deltoidea	CExl
japonica	CAgr CLau GGro LEdu
opposita	GGro
polystachya	CAgr CRHN GPoy LEdu
villosa	GGro LEdu

Diosma (*Rutaceae*)

ericoides L.	GAbr SWvt
hirsuta 'Silver Flame'	CBod
'Pink Fountain'	see *Coleonema pulchellum* 'Pink Fountain'
'Sunset Gold'	see *Coleonema* 'Sunset Gold'

Diosphaera (*Campanulaceae*)

asperuloides	see *Trachelium asperuloides*

Diospyros (*Ebenaceae*)

austroafricana	SPlb
glabra	SVen
* ***hyrcanum***	NLar
kaki (F)	CBcs CMCN CWit EPfP IDee NLar WCot
- 'Fuyu' (F)	CAgr
- 'Kostata' (F)	CAgr
- 'Mazelii' (F)	CAgr WPGP
- 'Rojo Brillante' (F)	SVic
lotus	CAgr CBcs CMCN LEdu NLar SPlb WKor WMat
- FMWJ 13164	WCru
- PAB 10032	LEdu WPGP
- (f)	IDee LMaj
- 'Albert' (m)	CAgr
- 'Browny' (f/F)	CAgr
lycioides	CPbh SPlb
'Mount Goverla' (F)	CAgr
'Nikita's Gift' (F)	CAgr
'Nikita's Russian' (F)	CAgr
'Nikshoo' (F)	CAgr
ramulosa	SPlb
rhombifolia	NLar
'Russian Beauty' (F)	CAgr
'Russian Red' (F)	CAgr
virginiana (F)	CBcs CMCN EBee IDee NLar SPlb WKor
- 'Morris Burton' (F)	CAgr
- 'Nc-10' (F)	CAgr

Dipelta (*Caprifoliaceae*)

floribunda 🏆H5	CBcs CExl CMCN EHyd ELan EPfP IDee MBlu MGil SWvt WPGP
ventricosa	CBcs CExl EHyd EPfP IDee LRHS MBlu MGil NLar SBrt SPoG WPGP
yunnanensis	CBcs CCCN CExl CKel EBee EHyd EPfP IArd IDee MBNS NLar SMad SPoG SWvt WPGP WPav

Diphylleia (*Berberidaceae*)

cymosa	ECha GEdr GKev LEdu LPla MNrw MRav SPhx WCot WCru
grayi	GEdr LEdu WCru
sinensis	CExl GKev LEdu WCru

Diplacus see *Mimulus*

Dipladenia see *Mandevilla*

Diplarrena (*Iridaceae*)

§ ***latifolia***	CNor IBlr LRHS SGBe
moraea	CDor CElw CMac CSpe CTsd CWCL EBee EGrI IBlr ITim LEdu MBel WSHC

- ***minor*** IBlr
- 'Slieve Donard' IBlr
- West Coast form see *D. latifolia*

Diplopanax (*Cornaceae*)

stachyanthus B&SWJ 11803 WCru

Diplotaxis (*Brassicaceae*)

erucoides new CArg
muralis CLau
tenuifolia CAgr CLau ENfk EWhm LCro LOPS MNHC SRms

Dipsacus (*Caprifoliaceae*)

asper PAB 8884 LEdu
asperoides new GGro
dipsacoides LEdu WPGP
§ ***fullonum*** CBod CHab ENfk EPfP GQue LCro LOPS MNHC MPri NGrd NMir SDix SEdd SRms SSal WHer WSFF WWild
inermis ECha GGro NBid
japonicus HWJ 695 SPhx WCru
pilosus CBgR NDov
pinnatifidus PAB 2845 LEdu
strigosus SPhx
sylvestris see *D. fullonum*

Dipteracanthus see *Ruellia*

Dipteronia (*Sapindaceae*)

sinensis CBcs CMCN MBlu SMad WLov

Disa (*Orchidaceae*)

aurata NDav
Bride's Dream gx NDav
Child Safety Transvaal gx NDav
- 'Sonia' NDav
Colette Cywes gx 'Blush' NDav
Constantia gx NDav
Diores gx NDav
- 'Inca City' NDav
- 'Inca Gold' NDav
- 'Inca Princess' NDav
- 'Inca Warrior' NDav
Diorosa gx NDav
Foam gx NDav
- 'Zoe' NDav
Glasgow Orchid Conference gx NDav
Ivan Watson gx NDav
Kalahari Sands gx NDav
- 'Tina' NDav
Kewbett gx NDav
- 'Pink Gem' NDav
Kewdior gx NDav
Kewensis gx 'Alice' NDav
- 'Ann' NDav
- 'May' NDav
- 'Milkmaid' NDav
- 'Ruth' NDav
Reheat gx NDav
Riette gx NDav
Robert Parkinson gx NDav
Sealord gx NDav
Tracey Parkinson gx NDav
tripetaloides NDav
Unidiorosa gx 'Tracey' NDav
uniflora NDav SPlb
- carmine-flowered NDav
- pink-flowered NDav
- red-flowered NDav
Unifoam gx NDav
- 'Firebird' NDav
Unilangley gx NDav
Watsonii gx 'Bramley' NDav
- 'Candy' NDav
- 'Don' NDav
- 'Sandra' NDav

Disanthus (*Hamamelidaceae*)

cercidifolius ♀H5 CBcs CMCN CMac CRos EGrI EHyd EPfP GKin LRHS MBlu MPkF NLar SPoG WMat WPGP
- 'Ena-nishiki' (v) MBlu NLar WPGP
ovatifolius WPGP
- B&SWJ 11706 WCru
- FMWJ 13365 WCru
- WWJ 11933 WCru
- WWJ 11994 WCru

Discaria (*Rhamnaceae*)

chacaye WPav

Dischidia (*Apocynaceae*)

'Geri' new EShb
ruscifolia CDoC EShb

Diselma (*Cupressaceae*)

archeri 'Read Dwarf' CKen

Disepalum (*Annonaceae*)

petelotii FMWJ 13375 WCru

Disphyma (*Aizoaceae*)

australe new GKev

Disporopsis (*Asparagaceae*)

sp. WBor
B&SWJ 229 from Taiwan WCru
B&SWJ 1864 from Taiwan WCru
from Taiwan ESwi
aspersa CAvo CBro EPPr EPot ESwi EWld ITim LEdu MAvo MBriF MNrw NBir WCru WFar WPGP
- tall CBct CExl ESwi MACG WCru
bodinieri FMWJ 13457 WCru
- KWJ 12277 ESwi WCru
fuscopicta CBct EPPr LEdu MACG MAvo WCru
longifolia B&SWJ 5284 WCru
luzoniensis WPGP
- B&SWJ 3891 CBct CExl EPPr ESwi GEdr LEdu WCru
'Min Shan' CExl ELon
* ***nova*** EPPr ESwi MAvo
§ ***pernyi*** Widely available
- B&SWJ 1864 EPPr GEdr
- 'Bill Baker' CBct EBee EPPr ESwi LEdu MAvo WSHC
aff. ***pernyi*** MBriF
taiwanensis CAvo EBee LEdu
- B&SWJ 3388 CBct GEdr WCru
undulata CBct EBee EPPr EPot ESwi GGro ILea LEdu MAvo NBid SHar WCru WPGP

Disporum (*Colchicaceae*)

bodinieri CExl CTtf EMor EPfP GKev ILea SBea
- DJHC 765 WCru
cantoniense CBct LEdu SDir WCru WFar WHil WPnP
- B&L 12512 CExl

	- B&SWJ 1424	WCru
	- B&SWJ 9715	WCru
	- DJHC 98485	LEdu WPGP
	- PAB 8339	LEdu
I	- 'Aureovariegata'	CBct EPfP ESwi LEdu WCot
	- 'Blueberry Bere'	LEdu MAvo
	- var. ***cantoniense*** f. ***brunneum*** B&SWJ 5290	WCru
	- 'Leigong'	WPGP
	- 'Leigong Chocolate' new	LEdu
	- 'Moonlight'PBR (v)	CBct LEdu LRHS XSte
	- var. ***multiflorum*** B&SWJ 11252	WCru
	- - B&SWJ 11291	WCru
	- var. ***sikkimense*** B&SWJ 2337	WCru
	- - B&SWJ 2358	LEdu WCru
	- - PAB 13.1711	LEdu
	- var. ***y-tiense*** HWJ 1045	WCru
	hookeri	see *Prosartes hookeri*
	kawakamii B&SWJ 350	WCru
	- RWJ 10103	CBct WCru
	lanuginosum	see *Prosartes lanuginosa*
	leschenaultianum B&SWJ 9484	WCru
	- B&SWJ 9505	WCru
	leucanthum	EBee ECha WCru
	- B&SWJ 2389	WCru
	longistylum	EBee EHed EPfP LEdu LRHS
	- B&SWJ 2859	WCru
	- BWJ 8128	WCru
	- L 1564	CBct ESwi EWld WCru
	- 'Green Giant'	CBct CExl CMiW CSpe CTtf EBee EPfP GEdr GKev IDee ILea LEdu LPla LRHS NHar NLar SBea SHar SMad WFar WHil WSHC XSte
	- 'Night Heron' ♀H6	CDor CExl CTtf ECha EHyd GKev IPot LEdu LRHS NRHS SHar SMHy WCot WFar XSte
	aff. ***longistylum***	EHed
	- NJM 11.011	WPGP
	lutescens	EBee EPot LEdu WCru WPGP
	maculatum	see *Prosartes maculata*
	megalanthum	CBct CExl CMiW EBlo EMor GKev ILea LEdu NHar WCru WFar WPGP
	- CD&R 2412B	CExl EBee
	menziesii	see *Prosartes smithii*
	nantouense B&SWJ 359	LEdu WCru
	- B&SWJ 6812	WCru
	oreganum	see *Prosartes hookeri* var. *oregana*
	sessile	EBee LEdu NBir WCru
	- B&SWJ 2824	WCru
I	- 'Aureovariegatum' (v)	WCru
	- 'Awa-no-tsuki' (v)	GEdr
	- 'Kinga' (v)	GKev LEdu
	- f. ***macrophyllum*** B&SWJ 4316	WCru
	- 'Snow Stream' (v)	GEdr WFar
	- 'Variegatum' (v)	CDor CExl CTtf EBee EBlo ECha EHyd ELan ELon EMor EPPr EPfP ESwi LEdu LRHS MNrw NBir NHpl NLar NQui NRHS SPhx WCru WFar WHil WPGP WSHC
	- var. ***yakushimense***	LEdu
	- yellow-margined variegated (v)	GKev
	shimadae	GKev
	smilacinum	NLar WCru
	- B&SWJ 713	CBct WCru
*	- 'Aureovariegatum' (v)	EPot LEdu WCru
	- 'Dai-setsurei' (v)	WCot
	- 'Ki-naka-fu' (v)	WFar
	- 'Koutei' (v)	WFar
	- pink-flowered	CBct ESwi LEdu WCot WCru WSHC
	- 'Roseum'	GKev
	smithii	see *Prosartes smithii*
	taiwanense	LEdu
	- B&SWJ 1513	WCru
	- B&SWJ 2018	WCru
	tonkinense B&SWJ 11814	WCru
	trabeculatum	CBct CDor WCru
	- 'Nakafu' (v)	EBee WCru
	trachycarpum	see *Prosartes trachycarpa*
	uniflorum	CBct CBod CBor CMiW CRos EHyd EMor EPfP ESwi GKev LEdu LRHS MHid MMrt MNrw NBid NRHS WSHC
	- B&SWJ 651	CBct LEdu WCru
	- B&SWJ 872	WCru
	- B&SWJ 4100	WCru
	- MSF 800	LEdu
	viridescens	CBct EBee EBlo EMor EPPr LEdu WCru
	- B&SWJ 4598	EPot WCru
	- B&SWJ 4958	ESwi

Distyliopsis (*Hamamelidaceae*)

tutcheri	CJun

Distylium (*Hamamelidaceae*)

BLUE CASCADE ('Piidist-ii') new	CBcs LRHS MMrt NLar XSte
myricoides	NLar
racemosum	CBcs CCCN CMac EBee EPfP MBlu NLar SSta

Dittrichia (*Asteraceae*)

viscosa	WCot

Diuranthera see *Chlorophytum*

Dizygotheca see *Schefflera*

Docynia (*Rosaceae*)

delavayi	SPtp

Dodecatheon (*Primulaceae*)

	alpinum	GKev NHar
	amethystinum	GKev
	'Aphrodite'PBR	ECtt NLar
	austrofrigidum	GEdr LEdu SBrt WFar
	clevelandii	GEdr GKev
	- subsp. ***insulare***	GKev
	- subsp. ***patulum***	EHyd NRHS
	'Comet'	CBor WFar
	conjugens	GKev
	cusickii	see *D. pulchellum* subsp. *cusickii*
	dentatum	GEdr LEdu NHar NRya SBrt WAbe WFar
	- subsp. ***ellisiae***	GKev
	- subsp. ***utahense***	GEdr NHar NRya WFar
	frigidum	GEdr GKev
§	***hendersonii***	GKev
	integrifolium	see *D. hendersonii*
§	***jeffreyi***	ECtt EHyd EPPr EPfP GEdr GKev MBNS MHol MNrw NLar SRkn WFar XLum
	- subsp. ***pygmaeum***	EBee GKev
	- 'Rotlicht'	EHyd LRHS NRHS
§	***meadia*** ♀H5	Widely available
	- from Cedar County, USA	WAbe

- f. ***album*** ♀H5	CBro CRos CTtf EHyd ELan EMor EPot GKev LEdu LRHS MBel NHol NHpl NRHS SDir SPer SWvt WFar WPnP WSpi WTyc
- 'Aphrodite'	WFar
- 'Goliath'	GAbr GWyn
- membranaceous	WAbe
- 'Queen Victoria'	GKev LEdu NLar WFar
'Meteor'	CBor WFar
pauciflorum misapplied	see *D. pulchellum*
pauciflorum (Dur.) E. Greene	see *D. meadia*
poeticum	SPlb
§ ***pulchellum*** ♀H5	EBee EGrI EHyd GEdr GKev LEdu LLWG LRHS MNrw NRHS NRya WIce
- ***album***	GKev WCav
§ - subsp. ***cusickii***	LEdu
- subsp. ***pulchellum***	GKev
- - 'Red Wings'	CBor CTtf EBee EGrI ELan EPot EWoo GKev GWyn LEdu LRHS NHar NHpl NLar WCav WTyc
- Radicatum Group	CRos LRHS
- 'Sooke Variety'	NRya WAbe
tetrandrum	see *D. jeffreyi*

Dodonaea (*Sapindaceae*)

viscosa	EPfP SPlb
- 'Purpurea'	CBcs CBod CExl CTsd EBee LRHS MGil MHtn SEdd SGBe SGsty SIvy SPoG SVen XSte
- 'Red Wings' (f)	SRkn

Doellingeria (*Asteraceae*)

scabra	see *Aster scaber*
umbellata	CKno ECha EPPr LEdu LRHS MMuc NBir NDov NLar SSal WCot WSpi
- 'Weisser Schirm'	MNrw

Dolichandra (*Bignoniaceae*)

§ ***unguis-cati*** ♀H3	CCCN CRHN EShb

Dolichos (*Fabaceae*)

purpureus	see *Lablab purpureus*

Dombeya (*Malvaceae*)

wallichii	CCCN

Dondia see *Hacquetia*

Doodia (*Blechnaceae*)

aspera	CLAP IKel NBro
- 'Rough Ruby'	CBdn CMiW CTsd MAsh NBro SIvy SPad XSte
§ ***caudata***	NBro
media	CAbb CBct CBdn CBod CBrP CKel CLAP CMiW EBee EHyd EShb IKel LEdu LLWG LPar LRHS NBro NRHS SPalm SPlb WCot XSte
squarrosa	see *D. caudata*

Dorema (*Apiaceae*)

ammoniacum	SPhx

Doronicum (*Asteraceae*)

austriacum	MSCN NBid
caucasicum	see *D. orientale*
§ ***columnae***	CBcs
cordatum	see *D. columnae*
§ × ***excelsum*** 'Harpur Crewe'	EBee LEdu LShi MRav NPer SHar
'Finesse'	CRos EPfP GJos LRHS NRHS SRms
'Little Leo'	CBod ELan EPfP GJos GMaP LRHS LSRN MBow MTin NFav NLar SCob SPoG SRms WFar
§ ***orientale***	ELan EPfP GJos MBel MPri SPoG
- 'Leonardo'	CBod CRos EHyd EPfP LRHS NGrd NRHS
- 'Leonardo Compact'	GArf SCoo
- 'Magnificum'	CRos CSBt EHyd EPfP GMaP LRHS NGBl NRHS SCob SPoG SRms WCAu WFar
pardalianches	CMea GAbr GJos LPla NFav WBrk
- 'Goldstrauss'	EBee
plantagineum	MMuc
- 'Excelsum'	see *D.* × *excelsum* 'Harpur Crewe'

Doryanthes (*Doryanthaceae*)

palmeri	CBrP

Dorycnium see *Lotus*

Douglasia see *Androsace*

vitaliana	see *Vitaliana primuliflora*

Doxantha see *Macfadyena*

Draba (*Brassicaceae*)

acaulis	WAbe
aizoides	CRos EBou EHyd GJos LRHS NRHS SPlb SRms
aizoon	see *D. lasiocarpa*
alpina	GKev
§ ***aspera***	GJos
athoa	ITim
aurea var. ***leiocarpa***	CBor ITim
bertolonii Boiss.	see *D. loeseleurii*
bertolonii Nyman	see *D. aspera*
breweri	GJos
bruniifolia subsp. ***olympica***	GJos
'Buttermilk'	WAbe
compacta	see *D. lasiocarpa* Compacta Group
* ***condensata***	GJos
cretica	GJos ITim
cusickii	CPla GKev
cuspidata	GJos
dedeana	EPot GJos ITim WAbe
gilliesii	GJos
hispanica	CPla ITim
'John Saxton'	EPot WAbe
kotschyi	SPlb
§ ***lasiocarpa***	GJos SPhx
§ - Compacta Group	ITim
§ ***loeseleurii***	GJos
longisiliqua ♀H5	EPot WAbe
mollissima	EPot SPlb WAbe
- 'Göteborg'	EPot
nivalis	GJos SPlb
norvegica	GJos ITim
oligosperma	EDAr GJos WAbe
ossetica	WAbe
parnassica	GJos
paysonii	ITim
polytricha	NSla
rigida var. ***bryoides*** compact	EPot WAbe
* - var. ***imbricata***	NSla
rosularis	EDAr EPot GJos WAbe
scardica	see *D. lasiocarpa*
sphaeroides	GJos NSla SPlb
yunnanensis	WAbe

Dracaena ✿ (*Asparagaceae*)

	cochinchinensis	SPlb
	congesta	see *Cordyline congesta*
	draco 🏆H1c	CCCN CMCN EShb SPlb
	fragrans (Compacta Group) 'White Jewel'PBR	LCro LOPS
	- (Deremensis Group) 'Lemon Lime' (v) 🏆H1b	LCro LOPS
	- 'Janet Craig'	LCro LOPS
	- 'Janet Lind' (v)	LCro LOPS
	indivisa	see *Cordyline indivisa*
	marginata (v) 🏆H1b	LCro LOPS

Dracocephalum (*Lamiaceae*)

	sp.	XAbr
	argunense	GBin SPhx SRms
	- 'Fuji Blue'	CExl CPla EDAr EPfP EWes MHol SBut SPoG WMal
	- 'Fuji White'	CExl EDAr
	austriacum	SBrt
	bipinnatum new	GKev
	botryoides	EDAr SPhx
	calophyllum	GKev
	discolor new	GKev
	forrestii	CPla GKev
	grandiflorum	SPhx WCot
§	***imberbe***	SPhx
	moldavica	LRHS SPhx
	nutans	SPhx
	peregrinum 'Blue Dragon'	SPhx
	prattii	see *Nepeta prattii*
	rupestre	CSpe MHol SBls SPhx
	ruyschiana	CFis EBee MMrt
	- 'Blue Moon'	CWCL MHol
	sibiricum	see *Nepeta sibirica*
*	***tataricum***	EHyd
	virginicum	see *Physostegia virginiana*

Dracunculus (*Araceae*)

	canariensis	EBee ESwi WCot
	muscivorus	see *Helicodiceros muscivorus*
§	***vulgaris***	EBee EHyd EPfP EPot ESwi GKev LRHS NRHS NRog SEND SPlb WCot WHil
	- white-flowered	WCot

Drapetes (*Thymelaeaceae*)

	dieffenbachii	GArf

Dregea (*Apocynaceae*)

	sinensis	CBcs CBct CCCN CKel CRHN CRos EBee ECre EGrl ELan EPfP EShb EWes LRHS MRav SEND SPer SPoG SWvt WHil WPGP WSHC
	- 'Brockhill Silver'	CKel EPfP SPoG SWvt
	- 'Variegata' (v)	EShb EWes

Drepanostachyum (*Poaceae*)

	falconeri J.J.N. Campbell. ex D. McClintock	see *Himalayacalamus falconeri* 'Damarapa'
	hookerianum	see *Himalayacalamus hookerianus*
§	***khasianum***	CExl

Drimiopsis (*Asparagaceae*)

	maculata	CBor EShb

Drimys (*Winteraceae*)

	andina	CExl MGil MMuc
	aromatica	see *Tasmannia lanceolata*
	colorata	see *Pseudowintera colorata*
	granadensis	WCru
	var. ***grandiflora*** B&SWJ 10777	
	winteri 🏆H4	Widely available
§	- var. ***chilensis***	CBcs CExl EHyd EPfP LRHS WCru WPGP
	- Latifolia Group	see *D. winteri* var. *chilensis*
	- var. ***winteri***	SRms

Drosanthemum (*Aizoaceae*)

	eburneum	SSim
	flammeum	SSim
	floribundum	SSim
	hispidum	CRos EHyd ELan EPot ITim LRHS MAsh NRHS SPlb SPoG SRot SSim WIce
	micans	SSim
*	***sutherlandii***	SRot

Drosera ✿ (*Droseraceae*)

	adelae	CHew
	admirabilis	CHew
	aliciae 🏆H3	CHew SHmp
	'Andromeda'	CHew
	ascendens	CHew
	binata	CHew SHmp
§	- subsp. ***dichotoma*** 🏆H3	SHmp
	capensis	CHew LCro LOPS SHmp SPlb
	- 'Albino' 🏆H3	CHew SHmp
	cuneifolia	CHew
	dichotoma	see *D. binata* subsp. *dichotoma*
	filiformis var. ***filiformis***	CHew SHmp SPlb
	- var. ***floridana***	CHew
	hamiltonii	CHew
	latifolia	CHew
	madagascariensis	SHmp
	nidiformis	CHew
	regia	CHew
	rotundifolia	SHmp
	schizandra	CHew
	scorpioides	SHmp
	slackii 🏆H3	CHew
	spatulata	CHew SHmp

Drosophyllum (*Drosophyllaceae*)

	lusitanicum	CHew

Dryandra see *Banksia*

	quercifolia	see *Banksia heliantha*

Dryas (*Rosaceae*)

	octopetala 🏆H7	CMea CPla EHyd GArf GKev LRHS NFav NRHS SPoG SRms SWvt WAbe WHoo
§	- 'Minor' 🏆H7	EPot GArf WAbe
	× ***suendermannii*** 🏆H7	EPot GArf GBin NHar SGro WAbe
	tenella misapplied	see *D. octopetala* 'Minor'

Drynaria (*Polypodiaceae*)

	baronii	LEdu WCot
	propinqua new	LEdu

Dryopteris ✿ (*Dryopteridaceae*)

	aemula	EFer LEdu
§	***affinis*** 🏆H5	Widely available
	- 'Angustata Crispa'	EBee SRms
	- subsp. ***cambrensis*** 'Insubrica'	EFer
	- 'Congesta Cristata'	CWCL ECtt EFer GMaP SCob

	- Crispa Group	CBdn CBod CLAP EHyd EMor EPfP LRHS NRHS WBrk
	- 'Crispa Congesta Grandiceps' new	MAsh
§	- 'Crispa Gracilis' ♀H5	CBod CLAP CMiW CSta EHyd ELan LRHS NBir NHol NLar NRHS
*	- 'Crispa Gracilis Congesta'	EMor LLWG MRav NGdn WFib
§	- 'Cristata' ♀H5	Widely available
	- 'Cristata Angustata' ♀H5	CKel CLAP EFer ELan EMor EPfP LLWG NBid NBro NGdn NHol SCob WFib
	- 'Cristata The King'	see *D. affinis* 'Cristata'
	- 'Grandiceps Askew'	GBin WFib
	- 'Pinderi'	CBdn CLAP EBee EMor EPfP GBin LEdu LPar MPie MPnt NLar NRHS SCob WCot WSpi
	- Polydactyla Group	SPlb
	- - 'Polydactyla Dadds'	CBdn CLAP EBee EMor NLar
	- - 'Polydactyla Mapplebeck' ♀H5	CLAP NBid WFib
	- 'Revolvens'	EFer
	atrata misapplied	see *D. cycadina*
	atrata (Wall. ex Kunze) Ching	CDTJ CKel CPla CWCL EHyd ELan LLWG LRHS NLar NRHS SPoG
	× ***australis***	CLAP EBee EHed
	austriaca	see *D. dilatata*
	buschiana	EBee EMor MRav NLar
	carthusiana	EBee EFer EMor NLar WSpi XLum
	- 'Cristata'	EFer
	celsa	EBee
	championii	CBdn CCCN CLAP EBee EHyd ELan EMor NBro NLar NRHS SRot
	clintoniana	EBee ECtt EFer EHyd GQue ITim LPla MPie NRHS
	× ***complexa***	CBdn CLAP
	- 'Stablerae' ♀H7	CLAP EFer GBin WFib
	- 'Stablerae' crisped ♀H7	WFib
	coreanomontana	EMor NLar
	crassirhizoma ♀H6	CCCN CLAP CRos EBee ECtt EHyd ELan EMor EPfP GAbr LEdu LPla LRHS LSun NLar NRHS SCoo SPoG WCot WSpi
	cristata	CLAP CWCL EBee EPfP
§	***cycadina*** ♀H4	CBcs CBdn CLAP CRos EBee EFer EHyd ELan EMor EPPr EPfP EShb GBin GKev LEdu LPar LRHS MAsh MGos NBid NBir NRHS SCob SEdd SPlb WCot WFib WLov
§	***dilatata*** ♀H6	CLAP ECha EFer EHyd ELan EPfP LRHS MMuc MRav NRHS WFib WShi
	- 'Crispa Whiteside' ♀H6	CDor CLAP CMiW CRos CWCL EBee EFer EHyd ELan EMor EPfP EShb LRHS MHost MRav NBro NLar NRHS SCoo SPlb SPoG SRot WFib WLov
	- 'Cristata'	LSun
	- 'Grandiceps'	CMac EFer GBin WFib
	- 'Jimmy Dyce'	CLAP CRos EBee EHyd LEdu LRHS MAsh NBro NRHS
I	- 'Lepidota Crispa'	EHyd LRHS NRHS
	- 'Lepidota Crispa Cristata'	CLAP EBee
	- 'Lepidota Cristata' ♀H6	CBdn CMiW CWCL ELan EMor GBin GKev LEdu NBro SCoo WFib
*	- 'Recurvata'	CLAP NLar
	erythrosora ♀H4	Widely available
	- from Guizhou, China	WPGP
	- 'Brilliance' ♀H5	CBcs CBct CBdn CBod CCCN CDoC CLAP CRos EBee ECtt EHyd LEdu LLWG LRHS LSun MAsh MAvo NCou NRHS SCoo SEdd WCot
	- dwarf	CBod CMiW LEdu
	- var. ***koidzumiana***	CLAP EHyd LEdu LRHS NRHS WCot
	- var. ***prolifica***	CBod CKel CLAP CRos EHed EHyd ELan EMor EPPr EPfP GMaP LEdu LRHS LSun MACG MAsh MGos NBir NLar NRHS SCoo SPoG SRot WFar WFib WLov
	filix-mas ♀H7	Widely available
	- 'Barnesii'	CBdn CEme CKel CLAP CRos CWCL EFer EHyd ELan GBin LRHS MAsh NLar NRHS SEND SPlb WFar WLov
	- 'Crispa'	CRos EHyd EPfP LEdu LRHS MPnt NRHS WFib
	- 'Crispa Congesta'	see *D. affinis* 'Crispa Gracilis'
	- 'Crispa Cristata' ♀H7	CBod CChe CKel CLAP CRos CSta CWCL EBee ECtt EFer EHed EHyd ELan EPfP GMaP GWyn LLWG LRHS NBid NBir NBro NRHS SCob SPoG WFib
	- 'Crispatissima'	EBee
	- 'Cristata' ♀H7	CChe CLAP EBee ECtt EFer ELan EMor LCro LLWG LOPS NBro SEND XSte
	- Cristata Group	EFer
*	- - 'Cristata Grandiceps'	EFer
	- - 'Cristata Jackson'	SPlb
	- - 'Cristata Martindale'	CLAP EBee NBid WFib
	- - 'Fred Jackson'	WFib
	- 'Depauperata'	CLAP
	- 'Furcans'	CRos EBee ECtt EHyd ELan LRHS NRHS
	- 'Grandiceps Wills' ♀H7	NBid WFib
	- 'Linearis'	EFer EHyd ELan EWoo LRHS MCot MGos NRHS WFib
	- 'Linearis Polydactyla' ♀H7	CBdn CBod CDor CLAP CMac CRos CSta CWCL EFer EHyd ELan EPPr EPfP EShb LEdu LRHS MMuc MRav NHol NLar NRHS SCob SCoo SEND SPoG WPnP XLum
	- 'Parsley'	CLAP EBee NBro
*	- Polydactyla Group	MRav
I	- 'Revolvens'	WFib
	formosana	WPGP
	goldieana	CDTJ CLAP CRos EBee ECha ECtt EFer EHyd ELan EMor EWTr GMaP LLWG LRHS NBid NBir NLar NRHS WFar WFib WPnP WSpi XLum
	hirtipes misapplied	see *D. cycadina*
	intermedia	CBdn EBee
	kuratae	LEdu LLWG NBro NLar WPGP
	labordei	CLAP EBee EHyd
	lepidopoda	CBcs CDoC CDor CLAP CRos EBee ECtt EHyd EMor ITim LEdu LRHS MAsh MPie NBro NRHS SPoG WCot WPGP WSpi
	ludoviciana	CRos EBee EHyd LRHS NLar NRHS WSpi
	marginalis	CDTJ EHyd EMor NLar NRHS SCob
	namegatae	WCot
	oreades	WCot
	pseudomas	see *D. affinis*
	pulcherrima	CBdn CLAP CRos EHyd LRHS NRHS
	pycnopteroides	CLAP
	× ***remota***	CLAP EBee EFer LRHS
	sieboldii ♀H6	CBcs CLAP CRos CSta CTsd CWCL ECtt EFer EHyd ELon EMor EPfP EShb LEdu LLWG LRHS NBid NBir NBro NCou NLar NRHS SCob SPer SPlb SRot WCot WPGP XLum
	stewartii	CBod CLAP EMor NBro NLar

	submontana	CRos EHyd LRHS MAsh NRHS
	tokyoensis 🏆^{H6}	CDTJ CLAP EHyd NLar NRHS WSpi
	uniformis	CLAP EFer
	wallichiana 🏆^{H5}	Widely available
	- JURASSIC GOLD ('Hollasic') **new**	WPnP

Duchesnea (*Rosaceae*)

	chrysantha	see *D. indica*
§	***indica***	GJos MRav SEND WKor
§	- 'Harlequin' (v)	CExl

Dudleya (*Crassulaceae*)

	calcicola	SPlb
	cymosa	SPlb
	lanceolata	SPlb

Dugaldia (*Asteraceae*)

	hoopesii	see *Hymenoxys hoopesii*

Dulichium (*Cyperaceae*)

	arundinaceum	LLWG
	- 'Tigress'	LLWG

Dunalia (*Solanaceae*)

	australis	see *Eriolarynx australis* AGM

Duranta (*Verbenaceae*)

§	***erecta***	CCCN
§	- 'Geisha Girl'	CCCN EShb
	- 'Golden Edge' (v) **new**	EShb
	- 'Variegata' (v)	CCCN EShb
	- white-flowered	SVen
	serratifolia	CCCN

Duvernoia see *Justicia*

Dyckia (*Bromeliaceae*)

	brevifolia	WCot
	'Burgundy Ice'	WCot
	'Cherry Coke'	WCot
	floribunda	EShb
	frigida	WCot WGrn
	goehringii	WCot
	jonesiana	WCot
	leptostachya	SEND SPlb WCot WGrn
	'Morris Hobbs'	WCot
	remotiflora	SChr

Dypsis (*Arecaceae*)

§	***decaryi***	CCCN SPlb
	lutescens 🏆^{H1a}	LCro LOPS

Dysosma see *Podophyllum*

Dystaenia (*Apiaceae*)

	takesimana	CAgr CSpe EBee LEdu SPhx

E

Ecballium (*Cucurbitaceae*)

	elaterium	CDTJ LEdu WCot WPGP
	- 'Lahij'	WPGP

Eccremocarpus (*Bignoniaceae*)

	scaber	CBcs CWCL ELan EShb NPer SPlb SPoG
	- 'Carmineus'	EPfP
	- 'Coccineus'	CPla
	- red-flowered	EPPr
	- 'Tangerine'	CSpe
	- (Tresco Series) 'Tresco Cream'	EPPr
	- - 'Tresco Gold' **new**	CSpe

Echeveria ✿ (*Crassulaceae*)

	affinis	CBod CDTJ MHer SEdd
	agavoides 🏆^{H2}	CDTJ CDoC LCro LOPS MRav SIvy
	- 'Ebony'	WCot
	- 'Lipstick'	WCot
	- 'Red Edge'	SSim
	alpina	see *E. secunda*
	amoena	SEdd
	bicolor B&SWJ 14388	WCru
	- B&SWJ 14849	WCru
*	'Black Knight'	CBod EGrI LRHS MCot SEdd SIvy SSim
*	'Black Prince'	CDTJ CDoC ELan LCro LOPS NPer SPlb WCot
	'Blue Bird'	CDoC
	'Blue Waves'	WCot
	cante 🏆^{H2}	SPlb
	chihuahuaensis 🏆^{H2} **new**	CAbb CBod SEdd
	coccinea	ELan
	'Corymbosa'	WCot
	'Curly Locks'	CAbb SEdd SIvy WCot WGrn
	cuspidata × ***setosa*** var. ***ciliata***	SSim
	derenbergii 🏆^{H2}	MHCG
	× ***derosa***	CDTJ
§	***desmetiana***	MHer SMrm SPlb WCot
	'Duchess of Nuremberg'	CBod CPla SEdd SIvy SPlb SSim
	'Easter Bonnet'	SSim
	elegans 🏆^{H2}	CDTJ CDoC CPla EPfP EWes LSun NCft SEND SIvy SPlb SSim WSMil
	'Ghost Buster'	WPGP
	'Giant Blue'	CDoC
*	× ***gilva*** 'Red'	CAbb LSun SEdd WCot
	glauca Baker	see *E. secunda* f. *secunda*
	'Green Pearl'^{PBR}	LCro LOPS
	'Lepus' **new**	WOld
	lilacina 🏆^{H2}	CDoC CPla EShb LCro LOPS MHol NCft SEdd SPlb SSim
	'Mahogany'	WCot WGrn
	'Mauna Loa'	CAbb MHol SEdd WCot WGrn
	maxonii B&SWJ 10396	WCru
	minima 🏆^{H2}	SPlb
	montana B&SWJ 10277	WCru
	nodulosa	SEdd SIvy WCot
	- 'Nicolas Bravo'	SSim
	'Perle von Nürnberg' 🏆^{H2}	CAbb CCBP CDoC EShb LCro LOPS LRHS SMad
	prolifica	SPlb
	pulidonis 🏆^{H2}	MHer NFav SSim
	pulvinata 🏆^{H2}	MHCG SEdd
I	- 'Rubra'	SPlb
	purpusorum	CDoC SPlb
	quitensis B&SWJ 14393	WCru
	'Ramillette'	WMal
	'Red Prince'	CDoC
	rosea 🏆^{H2}	MHer SPlb SSim WCot WMal
	runyonii 🏆^{H2}	CDoC
	- 'Topsy Turvy' 🏆^{H2}	CDTJ MHer SEdd SIvy SSim WCot
§	***secunda***	CAbb SPlb
§	- f. ***secunda***	CDTJ CDoC ELan EShb GAbr NCft NFav SIvy WCav WPGP
	- - 'Compton Carousel' 🏆^{H2}	SSim WCot
*	- - 'Gigantea'	NPer

– var. ***glauca***	see *E. secunda* f. *secunda*
'Set-Oliver' × ***setosa***	SEdd
setosa 🏆H2	CDTJ NCft SIvy
– var. ***ciliata***	EShb
– var. ***deminuta***	SIvy
shaviana 🏆H2	CDTJ SSim WCot
– 'Pink Frills' **new**	SIvy
'Son of Pearl'	MHtn
subsessilis	see *E. desmetiana*
'Violet Queen'	EShb
xichuensis **new**	SSim
'Zonnestraal' **new**	EGrI

Echeveria × *Pachyphytum* see × *Pachyveria*

Echeveria × *Sedum* see × *Sedeveria*

Echinacea (*Asteraceae*)

§ 'Adam Saul'	EHyd
§ 'After Midnight'PBR (Big Sky Series)	EGrI
'Aloha'PBR	LRHS NLar NRHS SPad SPoG WCAu
'Amazing Dream'PBR	CAbb CWGN EBee LCro LOPS LRHS MAvo NRHS SEdd WSpi
angustifolia	CBod ENfk EPfP GPoy LRHS MHer SPhx XAbr
§ 'Art's Pride'PBR	EGrI
'Big Kahuna'PBR	CAbb CPar CWGN LRHS SCob SEdd SPad SPeP
'Buttercream' (Cone-fections Series) (d)	EBee
'Butterfly Kisses'PBR (Cone-fections Series) (d)	LCro LOPS LRHS SGBe
'Cantaloupe' (Supreme Series) (d)	CWGN SPad
'Caribbean Green'	EBee
CHERRY FLUFF ('Echcher298'PBR) (Cone-fections Series) (d)	CWGN LRHS
CHEYENNE SPIRIT (mixed)	CBod CDor EBlo ELan EPfP LEdu LRHS MACG MBros SPhx WFar WHil WSpi WTor
'Chiquita'PBR (Prairie Pixie Series)	EHyd LSou SPoG XSte
CHUNKY PURPLE ('Noecone')	MHtn
'Cinnamon Cupcake'PBR	EBee SPoG
'Cleopatra'PBR (Butterfly Series)	CWGN EBee EPfP LRHS NLar SCoo SEdd SGBe SPoG WCot
'Colorburst Orange' (Colorburst Series) (d)	CWGN
'Daydream'PBR	CWGN EBee WSpi
DELICIOUS CANDY ('Noortdeli'PBR) (d)	CBod CPar CWGN LPla MPri SEdd WCot WHil WTor WTyc
DELICIOUS NOUGAT ('Noecthree') (d) **new**	SPeP
(Dixie Series) 'Dixie Belle'	CAbb
– 'Dixie Scarlet'PBR	CAbb CBod
(Double Scoop Series) DOUBLE SCOOP BUBBLEGUM ('Balscblum'PBR) (d)	LRHS
– DOUBLE SCOOP CRANBERRY ('Balscanery'PBR) (d) **new**	LRHS MACG
– DOUBLE SCOOP MANDARIN ('Balscandin') (d)	LRHS
– DOUBLE SCOOP ORANGEBERRY ('Balscoberr'PBR) (d)	LRHS
– DOUBLE SCOOP RASPBERRY ('Balsceras'PBR) (d)	LRHS
'Eccentric'PBR (d)	CPar CWGN EWTr LRHS SMad WSpi WTor
ECCENTRIC YELLOW ('Noectwo') (d)	CBod CWGN
'Emily Saul'	see *E.* 'After Midnight'
'Evan Saul'	see *E.* 'Sundown'
EVENING GLOW ('Eglow'PBR)	CWGN EBee LRHS WSpi
'Ferris Wheel' (Carnival Series)	WSpi
'Fiery Meadow Mama' **new**	CBod
'Flame Thrower'PBR	LCro LOPS
'Flamingo'PBR (Supreme Series) (d) **new**	CPla SPad
'Fourth of July'PBR	EHyd LRHS NRHS
'Funky White'	CWGN WTor
'Funky Yellow'	CWGN WCot
'Gemini Pink'	EHyd
GOLDEN SKIPPER ('Echgol243'PBR) (Butterfly Series)	ECtt EHyd LRHS MAvo NRHS XSte
'Green Envy'PBR	CBcs CWGN EBee EHyd ELan EPfP EWoo GMaP LCro LOPS LRHS MBel MCot MNrw NLar NRHS SMad WCAu WTor
'Greenline'PBR	EBee
'Guava Ice'PBR (Cone-fections Series) (d)	CDor WSpi
§ 'Harvest Moon'PBR (Big Sky Series)	EBee EGrI EPfP LRHS MBNS SWvt
'Honeydew'PBR (Cone-fections Series) (d)	EBee
'Hot Lava'PBR	CWGN EBee EHyd LCro LRHS NRHS SCob
'Hot Papaya'PBR (Cone-fections Series) (d)	CPla CWCL CWGN ECtt ELan EPfP LCro LOPS LRHS MHol SCob SMad SMrm SPoG SWvt
'Hot Summer'PBR	CBcs CWGN EBee EGrI EHyd EWoo LEdu LRHS SGbt
'Indian Summer'	EBee
'Irresistible'PBR (d)	CWGN EBee EHyd LCro LOPS WTor
'Julia'PBR (Butterfly Series)	ECtt LRHS SGBe SPad
'Katie Saul'	see *E.* 'Summer Sky'
'Leilani'PBR	CAbb WCAu
'Light Purple' (Fountain Series) **new**	CBod SPad
'Mac 'n' Cheese'PBR	EBee LRHS SCob
'Mama Mia'PBR	CAbb CWGN LCro LOPS SGbt
MANGO MEADOWBRITE ('CBG Cone3')	EHyd
'Marmalade'PBR (Cone-fections Series) (d)	CDor CWCL CWGN EBee ECul EWTr LRHS SCob SGBe SPad SPoG WCAu
'Matthew Saul'	see *E.* 'Harvest Moon'
'Maui Sunshine'PBR	CAbb
'Meditation'PBR	WCot
'Mellow Yellow'	see *E. paradoxa* 'Yellow Mellow', *E. purpurea* 'Mellow Yellows'
(Meteor Series) 'Meteor Pink'PBR (d) **new**	LRHS
– 'Meteor Red'PBR (d)	CRos ECtt EHyd LRHS NRHS
(Mooodz Series) MOOODZ AWAKE ('Hilmoooawak')	LRHS NRHS
– MOOODZ COSY ('Hilmoocosy')	LRHS MPri
– MOOODZ COURAGE ('Hilmoocour') **new**	MPri

- MOOODZ FUNNY ('Hilmoofun') **new**	MPri
- MOOODZ PEACE ('Hilmoopea') **new**	MPri
- MOOODZ SHINY ('Hilmooshin')	LRHS NRHS
'Mozzarella' (d)	EBee
§ 'Noam Saul'	EHyd
'Now Cheesier'PBR	EHyd LCro LOPS SMad
ORANGE MEADOWBRITE	see *E.* 'Art's Pride'
ORANGE PASSION ('Orpass'PBR)	CWGN EGrI LRHS WCAu
ORANGE SKIPPER ('Echor273'PBR) (Butterfly Series)	CRos EHyd EPfP LRHS NRHS XSte
'Pacific Summer'	CWGN WSpi
pallida	CCBP CKno CRos CSpe EBee EBlo EHyd ELan EMor EPfP EShb EWoo LCro LOPS LRHS MBel MGos NDov NGdn NRHS SBut SIvy SPer SPhx SPtp SRms SWvt WCAu WSpi
- 'Hula Dancer'	CDor EAJP EWTr GWyn MACG NGdn SBut SPeP SPhx
(Papallo Series) 'Papallo Classic Rose' **new**	LRHS
- 'Papallo Compact Pink'	LRHS
- 'Papallo Compact White'	LRHS NLar
- 'Papallo Power Coral Red' **new**	LRHS
paradoxa	CBcs EHyd ELan EMor EPfP LRHS NDov NRHS SPer SPhx SPlb SWvt WCAu
- var. ***paradoxa***	CCBP MACG WSpi
- 'Yellow Mellow'	EWTr
'Parrot' (Fine Feathered Series) **new**	SPad
'Pineapple Sundae'PBR	CWGN EBee
'Pink Tip'	CBod LPla
PIXIE MEADOWBRITE ('CBG Cone 2')	CWGN
POSTMAN ('Post301'PBR) (Butterfly Series)	CPar NLar SPad SPoG WTor
'Purple Emperor'PBR (Butterfly Series)	ECtt SGBe
§ ***purpurea***	Widely available
I - 'Alba'	CBod CRos ECha EHyd EPfP LRHS NRHS WCot WFar XLum
- 'Amber Mist'PBR (Mistical Series)	EBee
- 'Augustkönigin'	EBee LRHS WCAu WCot
- 'Avalanche'PBR (Butterfly Series)	CBod CWGN LPla
- 'Baby Swan Pink'	CRos EBlo EHyd LRHS NLar NRHS
- 'Baby Swan White'	CRos EBee EHyd ELan EPfP LRHS NLar NRHS
- Bressingham hybrids	CBod CRos EHyd LRHS LSou MArl MPie MRav NDov NRHS SGbt SPer
- 'Catharina'PBR	CWGN ECtt
- 'Coconut Lime'PBR (Cone-fections Series) (d)	CWGN ECul EPfP LCro LOPS WCAu WTor
- DOPPELGANGER	see *E. purpurea* 'Doubledecker'
§ - 'Doubledecker'	EBee ELan EPfP GWyn NGdn SGbt SPeP
- ELTON KNIGHT ('Elbrook'PBR) 🏆H5	LRHS SWvt WCot
- 'Fatal Attraction'PBR	CBcs CBod CWGN EHyd ELan EPfP ETod EWTr GMaP LEdu LPla LRHS LSRN LSou MBNS MRav NLar NRHS SCob SEdd SPad SPoG SWvt WCot
- 'Firebird'PBR	SGbt SPoG
- 'Fragrant Angel'PBR	ECul LRHS MBNS MBel NLar SWvt

- 'Green Eyes'	EBee
- 'Green Jewel'PBR	CBcs CBod CDor CPar CWGN EBee ECul EHyd EPfP ETod EWoo LCro LOPS LPla LRHS MBel MCot MNrw NLar NRHS NSti SEdd SGbt SPad WCAu WCot WSpi
- 'Green Twister'	CBod CWGN EAJP EWTr LPla MBel SPad WHil
- 'Happy Star'	CDor CRos EAJP EBee EHyd EPfP LRHS LSou NRHS SGbt
- 'Hope'PBR	EHyd MBel NLar WCAu
- 'Jade'	EBee LSRN MBNS NLar
- 'JS Purple Prairie'	IPot
- 'Kim's Knee High'PBR	ELan EPfP EWoo GMaP LRHS MBel MTin NLar SPer SPoG SWvt
- 'Kim's Mop Head'	EPfP MRav NLar
§ - 'Leuchtstern'	CKno EHyd ELan EPfP LRHS NBir NGdn NRHS
- 'Lilliput'PBR	NLar
- 'Little Magnus'PBR	EHyd SCob SPoG
- 'Lucky Star'	EHyd ELan EPfP
- 'Magnus'	Widely available
- 'Magnus Superior'	CDor CKno CMea CRos CSpe EAJP EBee EHyd EPfP LRHS LSou LSun MHer MNrw NDov NRHS SBut SEdd SGbt SMrm SPhx SWvt
- 'Maxima'	LRHS
- 'Mellow Yellows' **new**	EAJP SBls
- 'Meringue'PBR (Cone-fections Series) (d)	SGBe
- 'Merlot'PBR	NLar
- 'Milkshake'PBR (d)	CWGN EBee ECul SMrm WSpi
- MISTRAL ('Echmis'PBR)	EHyd
- 'Pica Bella'	CBod CRos CWGN EHyd EPfP LRHS NRHS SPad
- 'Pink Double Delight'PBR (Cone-fections Series) (d)	LCro LOPS LRHS MRav NGdn
- 'Pink Glow'	NDov
- 'Pink Parasol' **new**	SBls
- 'Pink Sorbet'PBR (Cone-fections Series) (d)	SCob
- (PowWow Series) POWWOW WHITE ('Pas709018')	CBod CWGN SCob SPoG WTor
- - POWWOW WILD BERRY ('Pas702917'PBR)	CBod CRos CWGN EHyd EPfP LRHS MBros MHol NRHS SPoG WFar WTor
- PRAIRIE SPLENDOR	EPfP LPar SPhx
- (Primadonna Series) 'Primadonna Deep Pink' **new**	EPfP
- - 'Primadonna Deep Rose'	ELan LEdu LRHS NGBl SVic
- 'Primadonna White' (Primadonna Series)	CSpe EHyd EPfP LRHS SBls SRms
- 'Purity'PBR	SPoG
- RAINBOW MARCELLA ('Rainb299'PBR) (Butterfly Series)	LRHS
- 'Razzmatazz'PBR (d)	CMac EBee ELan MRav NSti SWvt WCot
- 'Red Knee High'PBR	NLar
- 'Robert Bloom'	NBir SWvt WSpi
- 'Rubinglow'	ECtt LCro LOPS LSou NBir NDov NLar SWvt
- 'Rubinstern'	Widely available
- 'Ruby Giant' 🏆H5	CDor CKno EHyd ELan EWoo GBin GMaP LRHS LSRN LSou LSun NLar NRHS SEdd SGbt WCot
- 'Sensation Pink'PBR	CBod CKno CPar CWGN EHyd LRHS LSou MMrt MPri NRHS XLum

- 'Southern Belle'PBR (Cone-fections Series) (d) — CDor CNor CWCL CWGN ELan MBNS MHol SCoo SMad WSpi
- 'Summer Salsa'PBR — CWGN WCot
- 'The King' — CRos EHyd ETod LRHS NGdn NLar NRHS WSpi
- 'Vanilla Cupcake'PBR (d) — EPfP LRHS
- 'Vintage Wine'PBR — CRos EGrI ELan EPfP LCro LOPS LRHS NLar NSti SPoG SWvt WCAu
- 'Virgin'PBR — LCro LOPS MAvo MBel NDov NLar SCob SPad WCAu
- 'White Double Delight'PBR (Cone-fections Series) (d) — LRHS
- 'White Lustre' — SRms
- 'White Swan' — Widely available

'Raspberry Truffle'PBR (Cone-fections Series) (d) — EBee ECul EPfP EWTr LRHS
'Red Pearl' **new** — WSpi
ROBIN HOOD ('JS Roho') — IPot
'Rosita'PBR **new** — LRHS
(Secret Series) 'Secret Affair' — EHyd LRHS
- 'Secret Passion'PBR (d) — CWGN SGbt
- 'Secret Romance'PBR — WCAu

simulata — EBee MACG
'Solar Flare'PBR (Big Sky Series) — EBee LRHS
(Sombrero Series) SOMBRERO ADOBE ORANGE ('Balsomador'PBR) — CBcs CBod MACG
- SOMBRERO BAJA BURGUNDY ('Balsombabur'PBR) — CBod LRHS
- SOMBRERO BLANCO ('Balsomblanc') — LRHS LSou
- SOMBRERO FLAMENCO ORANGE ('Balsomenco'PBR) — LRHS MAvo
- SOMBRERO HOT CORAL ('Balsomcor'PBR) — EWTr LRHS
- SOMBRERO LEMON YELLOW ('Balsomemy'PBR) — MACG
- SOMBRERO SALSA RED ('Balsomsed'PBR) — CBcs CBod LRHS

'Starlight' — see *E. purpurea* 'Leuchtstern'
'Strawberry Shortcake' — EBee
'Summer 3000' **new** — LRHS
'Summer Cloud' — CWGN EHyd LCro LOPS LRHS NRHS SMad WTor
'Summer Cocktail'PBR — CWGN EHyd ELan LCro LOPS LRHS SPoG WSpi WTor
'Summer Fire' **new** — LRHS
'Summer Passion' — CWGN
§ 'Summer Sky'PBR (Big Sky Series) — EHyd EPfP
'Summer Sun'PBR — SPoG
§ 'Sundown'PBR (Big Sky Series) — EBee EHyd EPfP LCro LOPS NLar SCob SGbt SWvt WCAu
'Sunrise'PBR (Big Sky Series) — EBee EHyd ELan EPfP GMaP LRHS MBNS NLar NSti SCob SGbt SPoG SWvt WCAu WSpi
SUNSEEKERS MAGENTA ('Apecssima'PBR) (SunSeekers Series) **new** — LRHS MPri
SUNSEEKERS ORANGE ('Apecssior'PBR) (SunSeekers Series) — LRHS MPri WTor
SUNSEEKERS PINK **new** ('Apecssipi') (SunSeekers Series) — MPri
SUNSEEKERS PURPLE ('Apecssipu') (SunSeekers Series) — CRos EPfP LRHS
SUNSEEKERS RED ('Apecssired') (SunSeekers Series) — CRos LRHS MHtn
SUNSEEKERS SALMON ('Ifecsssal') (SunSeekers Series) **new** — MPri WTor
SUNSEEKERS WHITE ('Apecssiwh') (SunSeekers Series) — LRHS
SUNSEEKERS YELLOW ('Apecssiye'PBR) (SunSeekers Series) — CRos LRHS MPri
'Sunset'PBR (Big Sky Series) — ELan LSRN SWvt WSpi
'Sweet Sixteen' (Cone-fections Series) (d) **new** — LRHS
'Tangerine Dream'PBR — EBee EHyd EPfP LRHS SCob WCAu WSpi
tennesseensis 'Rocky Top' — EBlo EHyd ETod GAbr GPSL LRHS MBNS MGos SBut
'Tiki Torch'PBR — CBcs EHyd LCro LOPS LRHS SCob SPoG SWvt WCot WTor
'Tomato Soup'PBR — CBcs CBod CRos CSpe CWGN EBee ECtt ELan EPfP LCro LOPS LPla LRHS LSRN MNrw NLar SCob SEdd SGbt SPeP SPoG SWvt WCAu WCot WHil
'Twilight'PBR (Big Sky Series) — EGrI
'White Meditation'PBR — CBcs CBod CKno EHyd EPfP LRHS MPri NRHS SPoG XSte

Echinocereus (*Cactaceae*)

viridiflorus **new** — SPlb

Echinops (*Asteraceae*)

§ ***bannaticus*** — CBcs CMac MAsh NBid WWtn
* - 'Albus' — WCAu
- 'Blue Globe' — CRos EGrI EHyd ELan EPfP LRHS LSRN MBriF MCot MGos NGdn NHol NRHS SCob SGbt SPoG WFar WHoo
- 'Blue Glow' — CBod NLar SBls SCoo SPhx
- 'Star Frost' — CBod CRos EBee EHyd ELan EPfP GJos LRHS NLar NRHS SBls SCob SPeP SPhx SRms WFar
- 'Taplow Blue' — Widely available
- 'The Giant' — CBod

maracandicus — LPla WCot
§ 'Nivalis' — EHyd
ritro misapplied — see *E. bannaticus*
§ ***ritro*** L. 🏆H7 — Widely available
- ***alba*** **new** — GJos
- 'Blue Cloud' — EBee
- subsp. ***ruthenicus*** 🏆H7 — GKev MRav WCot
- - 'Platinum Blue' — CRos EBee ECtt ELan LRHS NLar SCoo SPhx SRms
- 'Veitch's Blue' misapplied — see *E. ritro* L.
- 'Veitch's Blue' — Widely available

sphaerocephalus — GJos NBir SMrm SPlb SSal
- 'Arctic Glow' — CBod CRos EBee EBlo ECha ECtt EHyd ELan EPfP GMaP LRHS MAsh MBriF MCot MPri NDov NGdn NLar NRHS SCob SGbt SPeP SPer SPlb SPoG SWvt WFar

tjanschanicus — CPla CRos EBee EHyd GJos GPSL LRHS MMuc NLar NRHS SEND

Echium ✿ (*Boraginaceae*)

aculeatum — MEch
amoenum — CSpe EHyd LRHS MEch NRHS SPhx
angustifolium Mill. — MEch SPhx
asperrimum — MEch
bethencourtianum — MEch SVen

'Blue Steeple' CPla CWCL MEch SMad
boissieri CCCN MEch
brevirame MEch
callithyrsum MEch
candicans 🏆H1c CAbb CBcs CBod CCCN CKel CPbh CPla CTrC CTsd ECre ELan MEch SVen WSMil
- 'Dwarf Blue' CCCN
decaisnei MEch SVen
subsp. ***decaisnei***
fastuosum CCht CDoC CKel SArc SBls SEND SEdd WABo WSMil
gentianoides MEch SPlb SVen
giganteum MEch
hierrense MEch
italicum CCCN MEch
lusitanicum CCCN
nervosum MEch
onosmifolium MEch SVen
'Pearce's Grey' SVen
pininana 🏆H3 CAbb CBcs CBod CCht CPbh CPla CTrC CTsd ECre ELan LRHS MEch NLar SArc SChr SEND SPhx SVen WABo WSMil XSte
- 'Snow Tower' CCCN CDTJ CPla CTrC CWCL ELan LRHS MEch
pininana × 'Red Rocket' CPla
pininana × ***wildpretii*** CPla MEch
'Pink Fountain' CCCN CDTJ CKel CPla CTrC CWCL ELan GJos LRHS MEch SPhx
'Red Rocket' CBcs CCCN CDTJ
rosulatum CCCN
russicum CCCN CSpe CTsd EHyd ELan LPot MEch SBls SBut SPad SPhx SPlb XSen
sabulicola MEch
simplex 🏆H1c MEch
strictum CCCN MEch
sventenii MEch SPlb
tuberculatum EWld LRHS MEch SPhx
virescens MEch SVen
vulcanorum MEch
vulgare CCCN CHab CSpe CTtf ELan ENfk GQue LCro LOPS MEch MHer MNHC NGrd SBut SPhx WABo WSFF WTre WWild
- from Armenia WCot
- 'Blue Bedder' 🏆H7 CSpe MEch SPhx WSFF
- 'Pink Bedder' MEch
- 'White Bedder' MEch
webbii CKel MEch MMrt SVen
wildpretii 🏆H2 CCCN CDTJ CDoC CPla CTsd ECre MEch NLar SBls SPhx SPlb SVen WABo WSMil
- subsp. ***wildpretii*** MEch

Ectotropis (*Aizoaceae*)

§ ***alpina*** EHyd EWes GEdr
seanii-hoganii EPot EWes GEdr NSla SLee WAbe XLum

Edgeworthia (*Thymelaeaceae*)

§ ***chrysantha*** CBcs CCCN CExl CKel CRos EBee EHyd ELan EPfP GKev LCro LEdu LOPS LPar LRHS MGos MVil NLar NRHS SArc SCob SEWo SGsty SPer SPoG SWeb SavN WHwl
I - 'Grandiflora' CBcs CDoC EBee EHed ESwi GBin IDee LPar LRHS MGos NLar WHwl WPGP XSte
- 'Nanjing Gold' LRHS
§ - 'Red Dragon' GKev LCro LOPS LRHS MVil SPer SavN WHwl XSte
- f. ***rubra*** hort. see *E. chrysantha* 'Red Dragon'
- 'Winter Liebe' EHed GKev LRHS NLar WHwl
papyrifera see *E. chrysantha*

Edraianthus (*Campanulaceae*)

croaticus see *E. graminifolius*
dalmaticus albus GKev
glisicii GKev
§ ***graminifolius*** GEdr GKev
- from Durmitor, Montenegro NSla
- subsp. ***graminifolius*** EPot GKev
niveus GKev NSla
pilosulus GKev
pulevicii new GKev
§ ***pumilio*** 🏆H5 GArf GEdr GJos GKev NSla SRms WAbe
- silver-leaved EPot
serbicus GKev
§ ***serpyllifolius*** GKev
- 'Major' GKev
sutjeskae GKev
tenuifolius CSpe GKev
wettsteinii GKev
zogovicii see *E. graminifolius*

Egeria (*Hydrocharitaceae*)

§ ***densa*** CBen

Ehretia (*Boraginaceae*)

anacua CBcs
rigida SPlb

Elaeagnus (*Elaeagnaceae*)

angustifolia CAgr CArg CBcs EPfP IDee LMaj LPar MCoo MGos NLar NWea SPer SRms WKor XSen
- Caspica Group see *E.* 'Quicksilver'
argentea Pursh see *E. commutata*
§ ***commutata*** CBcs CMac EPfP MBlu MCoo NLar SPer
I - 'Aurea' NLar
- 'Zempin' EPfP LPar LRHS NLar
× ***ebbingei*** see *E.* × *submacrophylla*
macrophylla EBee EPfP LRHS
multiflora MBlu NLar SPer WPGP
- 'Sweet Scarlet' CAgr
parvifolia CCCN ELan
pungens 'Argenteovariegata' see *E. pungens* 'Variegata'
- 'Aureovariegata' see *E. pungens* 'Maculata'
- 'Dicksonii' (v) EHyd LRHS NLar SLon SPer SRms WFar
- 'Forest Gold' (v) EHyd EPfP LRHS
- 'Frederici' (v) CCCN CDoC CEnd CMac EBee EHyd ELan LRHS MAsh MRav NLar SCob SPer SWvt WAvo
- 'Hosoba-fukurin' (v) CKel EBee ELan EPfP NLar SLon
§ - 'Maculata' (v) Widely available
§ - 'Variegata' (v) CBcs CMac SPer SavN
§ 'Quicksilver' Widely available
§ × ***submacrophylla*** 🏆H5 Widely available
- 'Coastal Gold' (v) CBcs CBod CCoa CDoC CEme CSde EBee EPfP LSRN MGos SGol SRms WAvo WFar
I - 'Compacta' CBod CCCN CCoa EBee ELan EPfP LRHS LSou MGos MNic SCob SGsty
- 'Gilt Edge' (v) 🏆H5 Widely available
- GOLD SPLASH ('Lannou') (v) CKel CMac EPfP SGol SWvt
- 'Limelight' (v) Widely available
- MARYLINE ('Abrela') new NLar

- 'Moonlight' EPfP MAsh
- 'Salcombe Seedling' CCCN
- 'Svelte Edge' NLar
- 'Viveleg'PBR (v) CCVT CDoC CRos EHyd ELan EPfP LPar LRHS MGos NLar NRHS SCob SEWo SGsty
umbellata CBcs CEnd CExl EBee EPfP IDec LEdu MBlu NLar SPer WKor WLov WSHC
- 'Amber' (F) CAgr NLar
- 'Big Red' (F) CAgr
- var. **borealis** 'Polar Lights' NLar
- 'Brilliant Rose' (F) CAgr
- 'Garnet' (F) CAgr
- 'Hidden Springs' (F) CAgr LEdu
- 'Jewel' (F) CAgr
- 'Late Scarlet' (F) CAgr
- 'Newgate' (F) CAgr
- POINTILLA SWEET'N'SOUR (Pointilla Series) (F) **new** EGrI
- 'Red Cascade' (F) CAgr LEdu MBlu NLar
- var. **rotundifolia** CWJ 12835 WCru
- 'Ruby' (F) CAgr NLar
- 'Sweet 'n' Tart' (F) CAgr LEdu WLov WPGP

Elaeocarpus (*Elaeocarpaceae*)
sylvestris var. **ellipticus** WPGP

Elatostema (*Urticaceae*)
CHB 14 from Yunnan **new** GGro
umbellatum 'Dents de Kyoto' **new** GGro
- 'Snow Patch' (v) **new** GGro

elderberry see *Sambucus nigra*

Elegia (*Restionaceae*)
capensis CCCN CDTJ CExl CPbh CTrC LRHS MPkF SPlb WPGP XSte
elephantina CPbh CTrC LRHS XSte
equisetacea CPbh
grandis SPlb
macrocarpa CCCN CPbh SPlb
tectorum ♀H2 CBod CEme CPbh CTrC CTsd LRHS SPlb SPoG WSMil XSte
- dwarf CPbh LRHS
- 'Fish Hoek' CPbh LRHS

Eleocharis (*Cyperaceae*)
acicularis CPud LLWG
palustris LLWG

Eleorchis (*Orchidaceae*)
japonica NLAp
* - f. **alba** NLAp

Elettaria (*Zingiberaceae*)
cardamomum EShb GPoy LEdu SPre WJek

Eleutherococcus (*Araliaceae*)
sp. CEme
from Manipur, India WPGP
divaricatus B&SWJ 5027 WCru
giraldii BWJ 8091 WCru
hypoleucus B&SWJ 5532 WCru
aff. **leucorrhizus** PAB 8119 WPGP
pictus see *Kalopanax septemlobus*
senticosus GPoy
- B&SWJ 4568 WCru
septemlobus see *Kalopanax septemlobus*
sessiliflorus ESwi
- B&SWJ 4528 WCru
- B&SWJ 8457 WCru
- B&SWJ 8618 WCru
sieboldianus MRav SEND
- 'Variegatus' (v) CCCN EBee EHed ELan ELon EPfP EShb ESwi LRHS MGil MRav NLar SPoG WCFE WPnP
trifoliatus RWJ 10108 WCru

Ellisiophyllum (*Plantaginaceae*)
pinnatum B&SWJ 197 WCru

Elmera (*Saxifragaceae*)
racemosa GAbr

Elodea (*Hydrocharitaceae*)
canadensis LLWG NBir WMAq
densa see *Egeria densa*

Elsholtzia (*Lamiaceae*)
flava PAB 13.012 WPGP
- 'Dzhouku Choc' **new** LPla
stauntonii CBcs CKel EBee ECha ELan EPPr LRHS MGil MHer NLar NQui SPhx SRms SWvt WBor WJek XLum XSen

Elymus (*Poaceae*)
arenarius see *Leymus arenarius*
canadensis EPPr
- 'Icy Blue' SMea
dahuricus from Olomouc **new** EPPr
glaucus misapplied see *E. hispidus*
§ **hispidus** ♀H6 CBod EPPr MBlu NDov SCob SPer WCot
hystrix **new** LRHS
§ **magellanicus** Widely available
- 'Blue Sword' EHyd ELan MGos NRHS SPtp SRkn SRms
riparius EPPr
villosus EPPr
- var. **arkansanus** EPPr
virginicus EPPr SPhx

Embothrium ✿ (*Proteaceae*)
coccineum CBcs CPla EHyd EPfP GBin GDam MGil SPlb WPGP WPav XSte
- Lanceolatum Group CBcs CEnd CTrC CTsd EHyd EPfP GAbr MBlu SArc SIvy SSta SWvt WLov XSte
- - 'Inca Flame' CBrac CCCN CJun CTrC EHyd EPfP LRHS SWvt
- Longifolium Group CCCN EPfP IBlr WPGP

Emilia (*Asteraceae*)
coccinea CSpe

Emmenopterys (*Rubiaceae*)
henryi CBcs CMCN EPfP MBlu

emperor's mint see *Micromeria*

Empetrum (*Ericaceae*)
nigrum GPoy WKor
- 'Bernstein' GArf
rubrum MGil

Empodium (*Hypoxidaceae*)
namaquensis NRog
plicatum CBor NRog

Encephalartos ✿ (*Zamiaceae*)

altensteinii	CBrP
ferox	CBrP
horridus	CBrP
lebomboensis	CBrP
lehmannii	CBrP
natalensis	CBrP

endive see AGM Vegetables Section

Endymion see *Hyacinthoides*

Engelmannia (*Asteraceae*)

peristenia	WKif

Enkianthus ✿ (*Ericaceae*)

campanulatus ♀H5	Widely available
- var. ***campanulatus*** f. ***albiflorus***	GKin NLar
- 'Miyama-beni'	NLar
I - 'Pagoda'	CBcs IArd IDee NLar SAko
- var. ***palibinii***	CBcs EHed EHyd EPfP GKin LRHS MAsh MMrt NLar
- 'Red Bells'	CBcs EGrI EPfP GKin MAsh NLar SGol SWvt WFar XSte
- 'Red Velvet'	CBcs GKin NLar
- 'Ruby Glow'	CBcs NLar SAko
- 'Showy Lantern'	NLar
- var. ***sikokianus***	NLar
- 'Sinsetu'	NLar
- 'Tokyo Masquerade' (v)	EHyd LRHS SPoG
- 'Venus'	CBcs EPfP GKin NLar
- 'Victoria'	CBcs IArd NLar
- 'Wallaby'	CBcs GKev IDee NLar WAbe
cernuus f. ***rubens*** ♀H5	NLar WAbe
chinensis	CBcs CRos EHyd EPfP LRHS MAsh SPoG
deflexus	CBcs EHyd IArd IDee LRHS WPGP
perulatus ♀H5	CBcs CBod CCCN CEnd CWit EBee EPfP LPar LRHS MGil SPer
serrulatus	GGGa

Ennealophus (*Iridaceae*)

fimbriatus	CBor GKev

Ensete (*Musaceae*)

glaucum	CDTJ
§ ***ventricosum*** ♀H2	CCCN CDTJ SArc
§ - 'Maurelii' ♀H2	CBod CCCN CCht CDTJ CDoC CSBt CTsd ELan ESwi ETod LCro LOPS SChr SDix SEND SPoG WSMil XSte
- 'Rubrum'	see *E. ventricosum* 'Maurelii'
- 'Tandarra Red'	CAbb

Entelea (*Malvaceae*)

arborescens	EShb SPlb

Eomecon (*Papaveraceae*)

chionantha	CBor CExl CMiW CPla CTtf EBee EWld GAbr GEdr GGro LEdu LRHS MAvo MPie MRav NBro NHpl NQui NSti SBrt WCru WFar WPGP WPnP XLum

Epacris (*Ericaceae*)

paludosa	GArf GKev
serpyllifolia	WThu

Ephedra (*Ephedraceae*)

sp.	MPie SArc
altissima new	XSen
distachya	GPoy WKor
equisetina RCB/TQ K-1	WCot
fedtschenkoi	GKev
fragilis	GKev XSen
gerardiana	LEdu LRHS
- CC 3925	WCot
- var. ***sikkimensis***	GGro XSen
§ ***major***	XSen
monosperma	WThu

Epilobium (*Onagraceae*)

angustifolium f. ***leucanthum***	see *Chamaenerion angustifolium* 'Album'
californicum misapplied	see *Zauschneria californica*
dodonaei	see *Chamaenerion dodonaei*
garrettii	see *Zauschneria californica* subsp. *garrettii*
glabellum misapplied	NSla
glabellum G. Forst.	WKif
rosmarinifolium	see *Chamaenerion dodonaei*
septentrionale	see *Zauschneria septentrionalis*
'White Wonder Bells'PBR	GWyn

Epimedium ✿ (*Berberidaceae*)

from Jian Xi, China	GEdr
from Yunnan, China	WPGP
acuminatum	CWCL ESMi GEdr GPSL LEdu MNrw NLar NSum WFar WPGP WSHC
- L 575	CElw CExl
- 'Galaxy'	CExl CJun LEdu
- 'Night Mistress' ♀H6	CSta CTtf ESMi GPSL LEdu SPVi WPGP
- yellow-flowered	SPVi WPGP
- - CC 01141	CSta
'Akebono'	Widely available
ALABASTER ('Conalba')	CBar EBee ELan GPSL SPer WFar
alpinum	CBod CMac CWCL EBee EHed EHyd EPfP EPot GBin GLog LEdu LRHS MHer NChi NRHS SHar SPer SRms WFar
- 'Samobor'	LEdu
'Amanogawa'	CJun CTtf GEdr LEdu WCot
'Amber Queen'PBR ♀H6	Widely available
'André Charlier'	CElw CMil CSta
'Anju'	GEdr
'Arctic Wings'PBR	CMil CSta CTtf CWCL EBee EPfP GEdr LPla NGdn SMHy SPVi SWvt
'Asiatic Hybrid'	CJun WFar WHal XSte
'Autumn Raspberry'	CJun
'Beni-goromo'	GEdr
'Beni-kujaku'	CJun EBee EMor GEdr GPSL SPad WCot WFar
'Beni-yushima'	GEdr
'Bieke'	SMHy
'Black Sea'	CDor CElw CJun CMil CSpe CWCL EBee EMor EPPr ESMi GBin GPSL LEdu LRHS MAvo MBriF MNrw MPnt NLar NSum SPVi WBor WFar WPnP WSpi
brachyrrhizum	CExl CJun CTtf GPSL NLar NSum
brevicornu	CDor GEdr WPGP
- Og 82.010	CExl CJun
- Og 88.010	CJun SPVi
'Buckland Buzz'	EBee
'Buckland Spider'	CBor CFis CSta EBee EHed EPPr GEdr MNrw WCot WFar WPGP
'Buff Beauty'	ESMi
'Buttered Popcorn'	EBee
campanulatum	CDor
- Og 93.087	CExl CJun EBee

× ***cantabrigiense***	CBro CDor CMac CWCL ECtt EGrI EHyd EPPr GKev GMaP GPSL ILea LPla MRav NHpl NLar SRms XLum
chlorandrum	CDor EBee EPPr LEdu WPGP
creeping yellow	EBee EMor EWTr MNrw WFar WHil
cremeum	see *E. grandiflorum* subsp. *koreanum*
'Dark Secret'	ESMi
'Darrell's Pink'	EBee
davidii	CBor CDor CTtf EBee EMor EPPr ESMi GEdr LEdu MNrw NLar NSum SPVi WHal WHoo WPGP WSHC
- CPC 960079	CExl
- EMR 4125	CElw CExl CJun
- dwarf	CExl
diphyllum	CExl EBee EPfP GEdr WHal WPGP
dolichostemon	CElw GPSL NChi
- Og 81.010	CJun WPGP
'Domino' ♀H6	CTtf ESMi GPSL LEdu SPVi WPGP
ecalcaratum	EBee LEdu WCot WPGP
- Og 93.082	CExl CJun
'Egret'	CElw CSta CTtf EBee LEdu SMHy WPGP
'Emperor'	see *E.* 'Phoenix'
'Enchantress'	CDor CElw CJun CMiW EMor ESMi EWld LPla MNrw NLar NSum SPVi WHal
epsteinii	CDor CMil EBee EHed EPPr ESMi EWld GEdr GGro LEdu MNrw SBrt WCot WPGP WSHC
- CPC 940347	CElw CExl CJun
fangii	CExl
fargesii	CDor CExl EBee GEdr LEdu MNrw NSum SPVi WCAu WPGP WSHC
- 'Pink Constellation' ♀H6	CDor CExl CJun CMil CSta CTtf EBee GEdr LEdu MNrw SGro SMHy SPVi WCot WPGP
'Fire Dragon'PBR	CBor ECtt EPfP MBNS MNrw SPoG WFar
flavum	EBee WKif WPGP
- Og 92.036	CExl CJun EBee
'Flowers of Sulphur'PBR	CSta EBee EHed EMor EPfP GEdr SPVi WFar WSpi XSte
franchetii	CElw CExl CTsd GEdr
- 'Brimstone Butterfly' ♀H6	CBor CDor CExl CFis CJun CTtf EHed EPPr EPot ESMi GEdr GPSL LEdu LPla NLar NSum SPVi WCot WHoo WPGP WSpi
'Fukujuji'	GEdr
'Golden Eagle'	CElw CExl CJun EBee EWes MNrw SPVi
§ ***grandiflorum***	CBcs CElw CRos CTri CTsd CWCL EGrI ELan ELon EMor EPfP EWTr GLog LRHS NBir NHpl NLar SEdd SPVi WCAu WFar WPnP
- 'Akagi-Zakura'	CSta SPVi
- 'Akakage'	CExl
- 'Beni-chidori'	CJun GEdr NSum
- 'Bronze Trim'	SMHy
- 'Circe'	SPVi
- 'Cranberry Sparkle'	EBee
- 'Crimson Beauty'	CJun CTtf ECha NLar WHal WHoo WSHC
- dwarf, pink-flowered	SMHy
- 'Elfenkönigin'	EBee NLar
- 'French Braid'	EBee
- 'Freya'	CExl EBee ECha NSum SMHy SPVi WSHC
- 'Freya Mk II'	SMHy
§ - var. ***higoense***	CJun GEdr WHal WPGP
- - 'Bandit'	GEdr GPSL SPVi
- 'Jennie Maillard'	ELon ESMi WCot
- 'Koji'	EBee NLar SEdd WHil WSHC
§ - subsp. ***koreanum***	ECha ESMi GEdr LPla NSum
- 'Kourin'	CSta GEdr
- 'La Rocaille'	CElw EWld SMHy SPVi
- lilac-flowered	WHal
- 'Lilafee'	Widely available
- 'Mount Kitadake'	SPVi WAbe
- 'Mugawa-gen-pan'	SPVi
- 'Nanum'	CJun EBee EMor ESMi GArf MCot MNrw NHar NSum NWad SMHy WAbe WPGP
- pink-flowered	MCot
- 'Purple Pixie'PBR	CBod CDTJ CWCL ECtt EMor GPSL LSou MBel NLar SCob SCoo SPer WCAu WFar
- 'Purple Prince'	CExl CMil EBee WPGP
- 'Queen Esta'	CExl CJun CMil EBee ECha ESMi LEdu MNrw MRav NSum SPVi WPGP WSHC
- 'Red Beauty'	Widely available
- 'Red Queen'	WCAu
- 'Rose Queen'	CWCL EBee EGrI ELan ELon EMor EPfP ESMi LEdu LRHS MNrw MRav NBir NSti NSum SEdd SPVi SWvt WFar WPGP
- 'Roseum'	CBod CMac CMil GMaP GPSL SWvt
- 'Rubinkrone'	CWCL EHed GMaP MNrw
- 'Sirius'	CJun
- 'Spring Wedding' **new**	CMil
- var. ***thunbergianum***	CSta
- f. ***violaceum***	CElw CJun EBee NSum WCFE
- 'Waterfall'	CSta SPVi
- 'White Beauty'	WSHC
- 'White Queen'	CJun EBee EPPr ESMi EWTr MBel SMHy WCot WHal
- 'White Winkie'	SMHy
- 'Wildside Red'	CJun WSHC
- 'Yellow Princess'	CElw CJun EBee
- 'Yubae'	CSta GEdr
'Hagoromo'	GEdr
'Hakubai'	GEdr
'Harugasumi'	GEdr
'Heavenly Purple'	CJun
higoense	see *E. grandiflorum* var. *higoense*
'Hina Matsuri'	GEdr
ilicifolium	CDor CJun CSta CTtf LEdu WCot WPGP
'Jean O'Neill'	CDor CSta ECha EPPr EPri LEdu WCot WPGP WSHC
'Jenny Pym'	EBee
'Jinto Shan' **new**	EHed
'Kaguyahime'	CElw CJun EPPr GPSL LEdu WSHC
'King Prawn'	CSta LEdu SMHy SPVi WPGP
'Knight Star'	CSta ESMi
'Kodai Murasaki'	SPVi
'Koki'	CBor GEdr
'Korin'	SPVi
'Kotobuki'	GEdr
latisepalum	EBee ESMi GEdr LEdu MNrw WCot WSHC
- Og 91.002	CJun
'Lemon Meringue Pie'	CJun
'Lemon Zest'	CMil EBee ESMi
leptorrhizum	CDor CElw CExl CJun CWCL EBee EHed ELon EPPr ESMi EWld GEdr LEdu MNrw NLar NSum SBrt WCot WHal
- Og Y44	CExl WSHC
- 'Mariko'	CExl CJun CMil CTtf LEdu MNrw SPVi

lishihchenii	CExl CJun CMiW GEdr WPGP
- CC 96024	SPVi
'Little Shrimp'	CJun CTri EBee EBlo EHed EHyd ELon GMaP GPSL MNrw NLar NSum WSHC
macranthum	see *E. grandiflorum*
macrosepalum	GEdr GPSL WPGP
'Mandarin Star'	CWCL EBee EHed EMor ESMi GEdr GPSL SPVi
'Marchant's Sulphur Queen'	SMHy
'Marchant's Twin Set'	SMHy
membranaceum	EBee EGrI ESMi GEdr LEdu WHal WPGP
- Og 93.047	CExl CJun EPPr GEdr LEdu
mikinorii	CExl GEdr GGro
- CC 990001	LEdu WPGP
'Milky Way'	MNrw
'Mine-no-fubuki'	GEdr
'Moonlight'	SPVi
'Myojo'	EBee GEdr
myrianthum	CDor CJun EBee GEdr GPSL LEdu WPGP
'Never the Red Rooster'	CSta
ogisui	CDor CElw CMil CTtf EHed ESMi LEdu MRav SPVi WPGP
- Og 91.001	CExl CJun EBee MNrw
- 'Diane'	LEdu SPVi
§ × ***omeiense*** 'Akame'	CExl CJun CMil EPPr GEdr LEdu MNrw SPVi
- 'Emei Shan'	see *E.* × *omeiense* 'Akame'
- 'Myriad Years'	SPVi
- 'Pale Fire Sibling'	CJun CMil GEdr
- 'Stormcloud'	CElw CExl CJun CMiW CMil CTtf EHed EPPr LEdu
'Pathfinder'	EBee ESMi GEdr
pauciflorum	EBee EPPr GEdr LEdu LPla WPGP
- Og 92.123	CExl CJun
× ***perralchicum***	CBro CJun CTri ECha GKev LRHS NLar WSHC
- 'Fröhnleiten'	Widely available
- 'Lichtenberg'	EBee EWes
- 'Nachfolger'	SPVi
- 'Wisley'	CDor CElw CJun EWes SPVi
perralderianum	CMac CSta CWCL EBee GMaP MBel MCot MNrw SRms WHal
- 'Weihenstephan'	CRos CWCL LRHS NLar WPnP
aff. ***perralderianum***	MPnt
'Perrine's Pink' (Magique Elfes Series)	WCot
§ 'Phoenix'	CDor CExl CSta CTtf ESMi WCot
'Pink Champagne'	CMil CSta CTtf EPfP ESMi GEdr LEdu SCob SPVi WCot WFar WPGP
'Pink Elf'^{PBR}	CDor CMil CSta CWCL CWGN EBee EHed EMor EPfP EWTr GBin GEdr GPSL MBNS MBriF MHol MNrw NGdn NLar NSti NSum SEdd SMad SPVi SRms WCAu WFar WPnP
pinnatum	CBod EBee GMaP WHal XLum
§ - subsp. ***colchicum*** 🏆H7	CJun CTtf CWCL ELan EMor EPfP EWTr GLog GQue LEdu LRHS MBel MCot MRav NGdn NLar SCob SDix SPVi SPer WCAu WCot WFar WPnP WSpi
- - L 321	WPGP
- - 'Thunderbolt'	EBee
- ***elegans***	see *E. pinnatum* subsp. *colchicum*
platypetalum	ESMi SBrt WCot
- Og 93.085	CExl CJun EBee
'Pretty in Pink' **new**	CSta EHed EPfP
'Prince Shrimp'	SMHy
pubescens Og 91.003	CExl CJun EBee WPGP

- from Shaanxi, China	SPVi
pubigerum	CDor CJun CRos CWCL EBee ECha EGrI EHed EMor ESMi GLog ILea LEdu LPla LRHS MAsh MMuc NHpl NLar NSum SEND SIvy SPVi SRms SWvt WCAu WFar WSpi
'Red Maximum'	CMil ESMi LEdu SPVi WCot WPGP
reticulatum	GEdr
rhizomatosum	CDor EPPr ESMi GEdr GMaP WPGP
- Og 92.114	CJun LEdu WCot WPGP
'Rhubarb and Custard'	ESMi
'Royal Purple' 🏆H6	LEdu
× ***rubrum*** 🏆H7	Widely available
- 'Galadriel'	CBor CDor EMor EPfP ESMi GBin SPad WCAu WFar WHil WHoo
- 'Sweetheart'	GEdr
sagittatum 'Warlord'	WPGP
'Sakura-maru'	CBor GEdr
'Sam Taylor'	SPVi
'Sasaki'	CBor CWCL EPot ESMi GBin GPSL NLar WHil
sempervirens	CJun WHal
- 'Candy Hearts'	WCot
- 'Creamsickle' (v)	GEdr
- 'Okuda's White'	EBee
× ***setosum***	CJun ESMi NLar NSum SPlb WHal
'Shiho'	CWCL EBee GPSL MAvo NLar
shuichengense	GEdr
'Simple Beauty'	CSta
'Sphinx Twinkler'	see *E.* 'Spine Tingler'
§ 'Spine Tingler' 🏆H6	Widely available
'Spinners'	EBee ESMi WCot
'Starcloud'	EBee
stellulatum	GEdr
- long-leaved	ESMi
- 'Wudang Star'	CDor CExl CJun CRos CSpe EBee EHed EPfP EPot EWTr EWes GEdr GPSL LEdu LRHS MCot NSum SEdd SPVi WFar WHil WSHC
sulphureum 'Plena'	see *E.* × *versicolor* double-flowered
'Sunny and Share' **new**	EMor GBin
'Sunshowers'	CSta
'Suzuka'	GEdr LEdu WPGP
'Tama-no-genpei'	CJun CSta GEdr LEdu WCot
'Tanima-no-yuki'	GEdr
'The Giant'	SPVi WCot WPGP
'Togen'	SPVi WCot
'Tokiwa-gozen'	GEdr
'Totnes Turbo'	CSta EBee ESMi
trifoliolatobinatum CC 950046	LEdu
'Valor'	WCot
× ***versicolor***	CExl EShb SSut
- 'Cherry Tart'	EBee ESMi
- 'Cupreum'	CFis CJun CWCL EGrI EHed EMor GPSL LEdu LRHS SPVi WCAu WFar WHil
§ - 'Discolor'	CElw CMiW CSta ECha EPPr NBir SMHy WCot
§ - double-flowered (d)	MHol
- 'Neosulphureum'	CBro CTtf CWCL EBee EPPr LRHS WFar WPGP WSHC WThu
- 'Sulphureum' 🏆H7	Widely available
- 'Versicolor'	see *E.* × *versicolor* 'Discolor'
× ***warleyense***	Widely available
- 'Orangekönigin'	Widely available
'Wildside Amber'	CSta
'Wildside Ruby'	CMil CSta CTtf ESMi
'William Stearn'	CExl CJun CSta GEdr SPVi WCot WPGP
'Windfire'	EBee

'Winter's End' 🏆H6 **new**	SPVi
wushanense	CDor EBee EPPr ESMi GEdr LEdu
- CC 14193	WPGP
- Og 93.019	CExl CJun WPGP
- 'Caramel'	CExl CJun CMil CSta EBee EHed GEdr GPSL LEdu NSum WCAu WCot WSHC
- 'Cardiff Star'	CSta WMal
- 'Sandy Claws'	CSta SPVi WCot
- spiny-leaved	CMil ESMi SPVi WCot WFar XLum
- - CC 014631	WPGP
'Yachimata-hime'	GEdr
'Yokihi'	CSta GEdr SPVi
× ***youngianum*** 'Beni-kujaku'	EWTr WFar
- 'Fairy Dust'	EBee
- 'Grape Fizz'	EBee
- 'Marchacos Sprite'	EBee
- 'Merlin'	CDor CElw CJun CWCL EBee EMor EPPr EPfP ESMi EWTr GEdr GPSL LSou MGos NLar NSti NSum WFar WHal WSHC
- 'Niveum'	Widely available
- 'Roseum'	CDor CRos CSta CWCL EMor EPfP EShb EWoo GKev GKin LRHS LSRN MAsh MBel MCot MRav NHpl NLar NRHS NSti NSum SCob SCoo SEdd SPer SPlb SRms SWvt WFar WPnP
- 'Ruby Tuesday'	EBee
- 'Shikinomai'	CExl CJun
- 'Tamabotan'	GEdr MNrw MRav
§ - 'Typicum'	CElw WSHC
- 'Yenomoto'	CJun
- 'Youngianum'	see *E.* × *youngianum* 'Typicum'
zhushanense	EBee ESMi GEdr LEdu SPVi WCot WPGP
- CC 022403 **new**	SPVi

Epipactis (*Orchidaceae*)

Catalina gx	CJun GEdr MNrw NLAp
gigantea	CBor CJun CPla EBee ECha ELan EWld GBin GEdr GKev MHer MNrw MRav NDav NLAp WPGP
- 'Serpentine Night'	CJun NLAp
helleborine	WHer
Lizzy Lou gx	CJun NLAp
Lowland Legacy gx	CJun
- 'Edelstein'	MNrw WFar
palustris	CBod CBor EHed ELan GBin IPot MBNS MNrw NLAp WHer WPnP
Passionata gx Light Royals Group	CJun
Renate gx	CJun NLAp
royleana	CJun GEdr
Sabine gx	CJun NLAp
- 'Frankfurt'	EWld MNrw WFar
gigantea 'Serpentine Night' × ***thunbergii***	NLAp
thunbergii × ***veratrifolia*** **new**	NLAp

Epipremnum (*Araceae*)

§ ***aureum*** 🏆H1b	LOPS

Episcia (*Gesneriaceae*)

dianthiflora	see *Alsobia dianthiflora*
'San Miguel'	see *Alsobia* 'San Miguel'

Equisetum ✿ (*Equisetaceae*)

'Bandit' (v)	CNat SMad WPGP
× ***bowmanii***	CNat
* ***camtschatcense***	CBod CEme EShb SArc SMad SPlb SSal WSMil XLum
fluviatile	CNat CPud
giganteum 'El Tabacal' **new**	GGro
hyemale	CBen CPud EWat GQue LLWG MAvo NBro NPer NSti SBls SPlb WCot WWtn XLum
§ - var. ***affine***	CBdn CNat EBee ELan LEdu WMAq WPGP
- var. ***robustum***	see *E. hyemale* var. *affine*
ramosissimum var. ***japonicum***	WPGP
scirpoides	EFer EWat LLWG MWts NPer NWad WMAq XLum
sylvaticum	CNat
telmateia	LEdu SMad WPGP
variegatum	EBee EFer GGro

Eragrostis (*Poaceae*)

curvula	CBod CElw CKno CMea CWCL ECha EHyd EPPr EPfP EWTr LRHS MAvo NBir NGdn NWsh SEND SPhx SSal XLum
- S&SH 10	CElw EPPr SMHy WPGP
- 'Totnes Burgundy'	CExl CKno CRos CSde EHyd ELan EMor EPPr EPfP EShb LRHS MAsh MAvo NRHS SPhx SRms WPGP
elliottii	CSpe ECha EPPr EShb LRHS MAvo SEND SMea
- 'Wind Dancer'	CSde EBee SRms XSen
spectabilis	CBod CKno CSde EAJP EBee EHyd ELan EPfP LRHS NGdn SBls SMea XLum XSen
trichodes	CBod CKno LEdu NWsh SEdd SMea XSen

Eranthemum (*Acanthaceae*)

pulchellum 🏆H1b	ECre

Eranthis (*Ranunculaceae*)

albiflora	GKev
cilicica	see *E. hyemalis* Cilicica Group
§ ***hyemalis*** 🏆H6	CArg CBro CMea CRos CWCL EHyd ELan EMor EPfP EWoo GKev LCro LOPS LRHS MBow MPri NHpl NRHS NRog SDeJ SDir SPhx SWvt WCot WHoo WShi
§ - Cilicica Group	EHyd EPot GEdr GKev GMaP LRHS NBir NLar NRHS NRog SDeJ SDir SPer SPhx SPlb WCot WShi
- 'Flore Pleno' (d)	GEdr GKev NRog WCot
- 'Grünling'	CAvo WCot
- 'Grünspecht'	GEdr
- 'Orange Glow'	EPot GEdr
- 'Schwefelglanz'	CAvo CBro EPot GEdr GKev WCot
§ - Tubergenii Group	EPot GKev
- - 'Guinea Gold' 🏆H6	GEdr NRog
- - 'Sachsengold' **new**	GKev
pinnatifida	GEdr GKev
× ***tubergenii***	see *E. hyemalis* Tubergenii Group

Ercilla (*Phytolaccaceae*)

volubilis	CBcs CBod CExl CRHN CWGN EGrl EPfP EShb EWld MGil SBrt WCru WSpi

Eremophila (*Scrophulariaceae*)

longifolia	SPlb

Eremostachys (*Lamiaceae*)

laciniata	SPhx

Eremurus (*Asphodelaceae*)

bungei — see *E. stenophyllus* subsp. *stenophyllus*
'Foxtrot' — GKev SDeJ
fuscus — GKev
'Helena' — LRHS SDir SPhx
himalaicus — ELan EPot ERCP GBin GKev GMaP ILea LRHS NLar NRog SDeJ SDir SPhx
'Image' — EHyd NRog
× ***isabellinus*** 'Cleopatra' — CBod CMea EGrI EHyd EPfP EPot ERCP EWhm GKev GMaP LCro LOPS LRHS MBNS MHer NLar NRog SDeJ SPad SPeP SPer SPhx SPoG WCot
- 'Emmy Ro' — GKev LRHS NLar NRog
- 'Obelisk' — EHyd NRog
- 'Pinokkio' — EHyd GKev LCro LOPS LRHS NLar NRog SDeJ
- Ruiter hybrids — CBod EHyd ELan EPfP GKev GMaP MGos NLar NRog SCob SDeJ SPer
- Shelford hybrids — CBcs EHyd GKev MBros NRog SDeJ SPer
- 'Tropical Dream' — GKev LRHS
'Jeanne-Claire' — SDir
'Joanna' ♀H6 — LCro LOPS NLar SDir SPhx
'Lemon Fizz' — NLar SDir SPhx
'Line Dance' — EHyd LRHS NRHS
'Moneymaker' — GKev NRog
'Oase' — EHyd GKev NRog SDeJ
'Pink Persuasion' — NLar
'Rexona' — GKev NRog SDeJ
robustus ♀H6 — CBcs EHyd ELan EPot ERCP GKev NLar NRog SDeJ SDir SPeP SPhx SPlb WCot
'Roford' — NRog
'Romance' — EHyd ERCP GKev IPot LRHS NRHS NRog SDeJ
'Rumba' — NLar SDir
'Sarah Cato' — GKev SPhx
stenophyllus ♀H6 — EHyd EPot ERCP GKev LCro LOPS NLar SCob SDeJ SDir SPhx SPoG
§ - subsp. ***stenophyllus*** — CBcs EPfP GMaP LRHS MHer MNrw NPer NRog SPer
'Tap Dance' — EHyd GKev NLar
'White Beauty Favourite'PBR — ERCP GKev LCro LOPS MHer SDeJ SPeP
'White Sensation' — LRHS NLar SDir
'Yellow Giant' — GKev
zenaidae JCA 0.444.409 — WCot

Erepsia (*Aizoaceae*)

lacera — SPlb

Erianthus see *Saccharum*

Erica ✿ (*Ericaceae*)

aestiva — SPlb
alopecurus — SPlb
andevalensis f. ***albiflora*** — CFst
arborea — CTsd SPlb
- var. ***alpina*** ♀H4 — CTri EPfP GAbr
§ - - f. ***aureifolia*** 'Albert's Gold' ♀H4 — CBcs CDoC CRos CSBt CTri ELan EPfP GAbr GArf LRHS MAsh MGos MMrt NHol NRHS SCoo SPer SPoG
- 'Arbora Gold' — see *E. arborea* var. *alpina* f. *aureifolia* 'Albert's Gold'
- 'Arnold's Gold' — see *E. arborea* var. *alpina* f. *aureifolia* 'Albert's Gold'
- f. ***aureifolia*** 'Golden Joy' — CFst
- 'Estrella Gold' ♀H4 — CBcs CDoC CRos CSBt CTri EHyd ELan EPfP LRHS MAsh NHol NRHS SCoo SPer SPoG
australis f. ***albiflora*** 'Polar Express' — CFst
- 'Holehird' — CDoC
- 'Riverslea' ♀H4 — CDoC CRos CTri EHyd LRHS NRHS SPoG
- 'Trisha' — CFst
bauera — CPbh
caffra — CPbh SPlb
canaliculata ♀H3 — CBcs
carnea 'Adrienne Duncan' ♀H6 — GPer SCoo SRms
- f. ***alba*** 'Golden Starlet' ♀H6 — CFst CSBt CTri MAsh NHol SCoo SRms
- - 'Ice Princess' ♀H6 — ELan MAsh SCoo SRms
- - 'Isabell' ♀H6 — CBcs CSBt MAsh SCoo SRms
- - MADAME SEEDLING — see *E. carnea* 'Weisse March Seedling'
- - 'Rosalinde Schorn' — SRms
- - 'Schneesturm' — SRms
- - 'Snow Queen' — SRms
- - 'Springwood White' ♀H6 — CFst CSBt CTri ELan MAsh MMuc NHol SPer SRms
- - 'Whitehall' — CFst LCro LOPS MAsh SCoo SRms
- - 'Winter Snow' ♀H6 — CFst CSBt ELan SCoo SPer SRms
- 'Ann Sparkes' ♀H6 — CBcs CFst CSBt CTri ELan GPer MAsh NHol SCoo SRms SVic
- f. ***aureifolia*** 'Aurea' — MAsh SCoo SRms
- - 'Barry Sellers' — SRms
§ - - 'Bell's Extra Special' — SRms
- - 'Dorset Sunshine' — CFst
- - 'Foxhollow' ♀H6 — CBcs CFst CTri IArd MAsh NHol SCoo SPer SRms SVic
- - 'Gelber Findling' — SRms
- - 'Hilletje' — SRms
- - 'January Sun' — SRms
- - 'Westwood Yellow' ♀H6 — CSBt MAsh NHol SRms
- 'Aztec Gold' — CFst SPer
- 'Beoley Pink' — SRms
- 'Branton Bamford' — CFst
- 'C.J. Backhouse' — SRms
- 'Challenger' ♀H6 — ELan GPer MAsh SCoo SRms SVic
- 'Clare Wilkinson' — SRms
- 'Claribelle' — CFst
- 'Corinna'PBR — CFst
- 'December Red' — CFst ELan MAsh MMuc SCoo SEND SRms SVic
- 'Diana Young' — SCoo
- 'Dømmesmoen' — SRms
- 'Early Red' — SRms
- 'Eileen Porter' — MMuc
- 'Eva' ♀H6 — CBcs CFst SRms
- 'Foxhollow Fairy' — SRms
- 'Gracilis' — SRms
- 'Heathwood' — SRms
- 'James Backhouse' — CFst CTri
- 'Jason Attwater' — SRms
- 'Jennifer Anne' — SRms
- 'John Kampa' — SRms
- 'John Pook' — SCoo SRms SVic
- 'King George' — CTri SRms
- 'Lohse's Rubin' — SRms
- 'Loughrigg' ♀H6 — CTri MAsh NHol SCoo SRms SVic
- 'March Seedling' ♀H6 — CFst MAsh NHol SCoo SRms
- 'Margery Frearson' — SRms
I - 'Martin' — SRms
- 'Myretoun Ruby' ♀H6 — CBcs CFst CSBt CTri GPer LCro LOPS MAsh NHol SCoo SRms
- 'Nathalie' ♀H6 — CFst CSBt MAsh SCoo SRms

- 'Pink Cloud'	CFst
- 'Pink Mist'	SRms
§ - 'Pink Pearl'	CFst
- 'Pink Spangles' 𝕐H6	CBcs CFst CSBt CTri MAsh SCoo SPer SRms
- 'Pirbright Rose'	SRms
- 'Polden Pride'	SRms
- 'Praecox Rubra'	NHol SCoo SRms
- 'Queen Mary'	SRms
- 'Queen of Spain'	CFst SRms
- 'R.B. Cooke'	MAsh SCoo SRms
- 'Robert Jan'	SRms
- 'Rosalie' 𝕐H6	CFst IArd MAsh SCoo SPer SRms
- 'Rosantha'	SRms
- 'Rosea'	SPlb
- 'Rosy Morn'	SRms
- 'Rotes Juwel'	SRms
- 'Rubinteppich'	SRms
- 'Ruby Glow'	NHol
- 'Sally'	CFst
- 'Saskia'	CFst
- 'Scatterley'	SRms
- 'Schatzalp'	SRms
- 'Sherwood Creeping'	SRms
- 'Smart's Heath'	SRms
- 'Springwood Pink'	CSBt CTri GPer MAsh NHol SRms
- 'Tanja'	CFst
- 'Viking'	MAsh
- 'Vivellii' 𝕐H6	CTri GPer MAsh NHol SCoo SRms
- 'Walter Reisert'	SRms
§ - 'Weisse March Seedling'	CFst
- 'Wentwood Red'	SRms
- 'Winter Beauty'	NHol
- 'Winter Rubin'	CFst SRms
- 'Wintersonne' 𝕐H6	MMuc SRms
cerinthoides 𝕐H2	CPbh
- 'Albertina' **new**	CPbh
ciliaris f. ***albiflora*** 'Stoborough'	CFst
- 'Corfe Castle'	CFst
- 'David McClintock'	CFst
- 'Wych'	CFst
cinerea f. ***alba*** 'Alba Minor'	CFst MAsh
- - 'Hookstone White'	CFst
- - 'White Dale'	CFst
- 'Atrosanguinea Smith's Variety'	CFst
- f. ***aureifolia*** 'Fiddler's Gold'	MAsh
- - 'Golden Drop'	CFst
- - 'Goldilocks'	CFst
- 'Bucklebury Red'	CFst
- 'C.D. Eason' 𝕐H7	CFst CTri GPer SCoo
- 'Cevennes'	GPer
- 'Champs Hill'	CFst
- 'Creepy Crawly'	CFst
- 'Discovery'	CFst
- 'Eden Valley'	CFst GPer SCoo
- 'Glencairn'	GPer
- 'John Ardron'	CFst
- 'Joseph Murphy'	CBcs CFst
- 'Joyce Burfitt'	CFst
- 'Katinka'	CBcs CFst GPer
- 'Lady Skelton'	CFst
- 'Lilac Time'	CFst GPer
- 'Mrs E.A. Mitchell'	GPer SPlb
- 'My Love'	CFst SPer
- 'Pentreath'	GPer
- 'Pink Ice' 𝕐H7	CFst CTri GPer MAsh NHol
- 'Providence'	CFst
- 'Purple Beauty'	GPer
- 'Romantic Scotland'	GPer
- 'Rosea'	GPer
- 'Rosita'	CFst
- 'Sandpit Hill'	CFst
- 'Sherry'	NHol
- 'Stephen Davis' 𝕐H7	CFst GPer NHol SCoo
- 'Velvet Night' 𝕐H7	GPer MAsh NHol
- 'Vivienne Patricia'	CFst
coccinea	CPbh
cooperi	SPlb
curviflora	SPlb
× ***darleyensis*** 'Alba'	see *E.* × *darleyensis* f. *albiflora* 'Silberschmelze'
- f. ***albiflora*** 'Ada S. Collings'	MAsh SRms
- - 'Bing'	SCoo
- - 'N.R. Webster'	SRms
§ - - 'Silberschmelze'	CSBt CTri GJos MAsh MMuc SCoo SRms
- - 'White Glow'	CTri MAsh SRms
- - 'White Perfection' 𝕐H5	CBcs CDoC CFst IArd MAsh MNHC NHol SCoo SPoG SRms
- 'Archie Graham'	SRms
- 'Arthur Johnson' 𝕐H5	CFst CTri MAsh SRms
§ - f. ***aureifolia*** 'Eva Gold'PBR	CFst
- - 'Golden Perfect'	CFst
- - 'Jack H. Brummage'	CSBt CTri MAsh SRms
- - 'Mary Helen'	CSBt MAsh NHol SCoo SRms
- - 'Moonshine'	CFst SRms
- - 'Tweety'	CBcs CFst CSBt SRms
- 'Aurélie Brégeon'	SRms
- 'Cherry Stevens'	see *E.* × *darleyensis* 'Furzey'
§ - 'Darley Dale'	CEme CSBt ELan GJos GPer MAsh MMuc MNHC SCoo SPoG SRms
- 'Epe'	CFst SRms
§ - 'Furzey' 𝕐H5	CSBt GPer LCro LOPS MAsh NHol SCoo SRms
- 'George Rendall'	CTri MAsh SCoo SRms
- 'Ghost Hills' 𝕐H5	CEme CSBt LCro LOPS MAsh SCoo SPoG SRms
- 'Irish Treasure'	CFst
- 'J.W. Porter' 𝕐H5	CEme MAsh MMuc SCoo SRms
- 'James Smith'	SRms
- 'Jenny Porter' 𝕐H5	ELan SCoo
- 'Katia'PBR (Winter Belles Series)	CFst SPer
- 'Kramer's Rote' 𝕐H5	CEme CFst CSBt CTri ELan NHol SCoo SPoG SRms
- 'Lucie'PBR (Winter Belles Series)	CFst GJos
- 'Margaret Porter'	CFst SCoo
- MOLTEN SILVER	see *E.* × *darleyensis* f. *albiflora* 'Silberschmelze'
- 'Phoebe'PBR (Winter Belles Series)	CBcs CFst
- 'Pink Perfection'	see *E.* × *darleyensis* 'Darley Dale'
- 'Spring Surprise'PBR 𝕐H5	CFst SCoo
- 'W.G. Pine'	SRms
- 'Winter Surprise'	CFst
- 'Winter Treasure'	CFst
discolor	CPbh
§ ***erigena***	XSte
- f. ***alba*** 'W.T. Rackliff' 𝕐H5	CBcs CSBt GPer MAsh NHol SCoo SRms
- f. ***aureifolia*** 'Golden Jubilee'	CFst
- - 'Golden Lady'	CSBt MAsh NHol SCoo SRms
- - 'Thing Nee'	CFst SRms
- 'Brightness'	CSBt NHol SCoo
- 'Irish Dusk' 𝕐H5	CBcs CSBt CTri GPer MAsh MMuc SCoo SRms
- 'Superba'	SRms

formosa	CPbh
glandulosa	CPbh
glauca var. ***glauca***	SPlb
gracilis	CDoC NBir
× ***griffithsii*** 'Ashlea Gold'	CFst
- 'Elegant Spike'	CFst
- 'Jacqueline'	CFst
- 'Valerie Griffiths'	CFst GPer NHol
hibernica	see *E. erigena*
lusitanica f. ***aureifolia*** 'George Hunt'	CFst EHyd ELan LRHS
§ - 'La Vasterival'	CFst XSte
- 'Sheffield Park'	EHyd LRHS NRHS SPoG
mackayana f. ***eburnea*** 'Shining Light'	CFst
- 'Errigal Dusk'	CFst
mammosa ♀H2	CPbh SPlb
- cream-flowered	CPbh
- pink-flowered	CPbh
- red-flowered	CPbh
- white-flowered	CPbh
manipuliflora 'Elegant Spike'	CFst
mediterranea misapplied	see *E. erigena*
multiflora	XSen
oatesii new	CPbh
× ***oldenburgensis*** 'Ammerland' ♀H5	SCoo SRms
'Pat Turpin'	CFst
patersonia	SPlb
perspicua	CPbh SPlb
platycodon	CFst
subsp. ***maderincola*** f. ***aureifolia*** 'Levada Gold'	
plukenetii	CPbh
scabriuscula	CPbh
§ ***scoparia*** 'Minima'	CCCN
sessiliflora	CPbh
straussiana	SPlb
× ***stuartii*** 'Irish Lemon' ♀H5	CFst GPer NHol
- 'Irish Orange'	GPer NHol
terminalis 'Thelma Woolner'	CFst
tetralix f. ***alba*** 'Alba Mollis' ♀H6	CFst GPer MAsh
- f. ***aureifolia*** 'Ruth's Gold'	NHol
- 'Con Underwood'	CFst GPer
- 'Hookstone Pink'	CFst
- 'Ken Underwood'	CFst
- 'Riko'	CFst
- 'Samtpfötchen'	CFst
- f. ***stellata*** 'Pink Star' ♀H6	CFst NHol
vagans f. ***alba*** 'Cornish Cream' ♀H5	GPer NHol
- - 'Diana's Gold'	SRms
- - 'Golden Triumph'	CFst
- - 'Kevernensis Alba' ♀H5	GPer
- - 'Lyonesse' ♀H5	MAsh MMuc NHol
- f. ***aureifolia*** 'Valerie Proudley' ♀H5	GPer MAsh NHol
- - 'Yellow John'	CFst CSma SRms
- 'Birch Glow' ♀H5	CFst CSma
- 'Keira'	CFst CSma SRms
- 'Mrs D.F. Maxwell' ♀H5	CBcs CFst GPer MMuc NHol
- 'Mrs Donaldson'	CFst
- 'Saint Keverne'	CFst IArd MAsh MMuc NHol
- 'Summertime'	CFst
× ***veitchii*** 'Exeter' ♀H4	CDoC CFst CRos CSBt EHyd ELan LRHS MAsh NRHS SPoG
- 'Gold Tips' ♀H4	CFst CSBt
versicolor ♀H2	CPbh SPlb
verticillata	CPbh
× ***watsonii*** 'Cherry Turpin'	CFst
- 'Claire Elise'	CFst
- 'Dorothy Metheny'	CFst
× ***williamsii*** 'Ken Wilson'	CFst GPer
'Winter Fire'	CDoC CPbh
woodii	SPlb

Erigeron (*Asteraceae*)

'Adria'	CRos EHyd ELon LRHS MHol NRHS
§ ***alpinus***	SLee
annuus	CKel CSpe ECha MHol MNrw NDov SDix SPhx WBrk WMal WSHC
aurantiacus	CBcs CBor CSpe ELan GKev LPot SMad
aureus 'Canary Bird' ♀H4	EPot NSla WAbe
- 'The Giant'	WAbe
AZURE FAIRY	see *E.* 'Azurfee'
§ 'Azurfee'	CSBt ELan EPfP GKev GMaP MACG NBir NLar SPer SPoG SWvt WFar
BLACK SEA	see *E.* 'Schwarzes Meer'
'Blue Beauty'	CMac CRos EHyd EPfP LRHS NRHS SRms
'Charity'	MHCG MRav
chrysopsidis	GKev
- 'Grand Ridge'	EHyd EPot NRHS WAbe
compositus	GKev SRms WCav
§ - var. ***discoideus***	CMea NSla SLee SPlb WHal
- 'Rocky'	NSla
DARKEST OF ALL	see *E.* 'Dunkelste Aller'
'Dignity'	CBod EBee EHyd ELan MBrN MPie MRav NHol SWvt
'Dimity'	ECha NBir WFar WHal
'Dominator'	CWGN MHol WCot WFar
I 'Dunkelste Aller'	CBcs CBod EHyd ELan EPfP GLog GMaP LRHS LSou MAsh MBel MHol MPie MRav NLar NRHS NSti SGbt SPoG SRms SWvt WFar
flettii	GKev
'Foersters Liebling' ♀H5	EBee MBel
'Four Winds'	ECtt ELan EWes GKev NGdn NHpl WIce
glaucus	CCCN CSBt GQue MRav NGdn SEND SMad WBrk
- 'Albus'	ELon NLar WFar
- 'Elstead Pink'	CTri ECtt ELan WFar WSHC
- large-flowered	ELon
- 'Roger Raiche'	CFis MHol MRav
- 'Roseus'	SEND
- 'Sea Breeze'	Widely available
- 'Sennen'	MHCG NFav
- 'Viewpoint Blue'	ELon
grandiflorus	MHol
howellii	MHol
'Karminstrahl'	ELon
§ ***karvinskianus*** ♀H5	Widely available
- 'Kew Profusion'	CKel CRos EHyd LRHS NRHS
- 'Lavender Lady'	CTtf GBin LPla MAvo MHol SPhx WCot WMal WNPC WTor
- 'Sea of Blossom'	CBod CCht LRHS LSou MBow MHol NCou
- 'Stallone'	LSun NLar SBls
leiomerus	GEdr GKev
linearis	CPla GEdr
'Mrs F.H. Beale'	GBin MACG WCot
mucronatus	see *E. karvinskianus*
'Nachthimmel'	NGdn
nanus	GEdr

philadelphicus	CElw MNrw NBir NBro WFar
PINK JEWEL	see *E.* 'Rosa Juwel'
pinnatisectus	GArf NFav
'Professor Korodi' (d)	EBee
'Profusion'	see *E. karvinskianus*
pulchellus	WBrk
pumilus	WGoo
§ ***pyrenaicus*** Rouy	see *Aster pyrenaeus*
'Quakeress'	CBod CMea CTtf ECtt ELon EPri GMaP GQue LSou MBel MHol MMuc MNrw MRav NGdn SDix SMrm SWvt WFar WGwG
§ 'Rosa Juwel'	CSBt ECtt EHyd ELan EPfP GBin GMaP LRHS MRav NBir NRHS SPer SPoG SRms SWvt WCAu WFar
§ 'Rosa Triumph'	EBee
'Rotes Meer'	CMac EBee MRav
rotundifolius 'Caerulescens'	see *Bellis caerulescens*
salsuginosus misapplied	see *Eurybia sibirica*
§ 'Schneewittchen' ♀H5	CBod CCBP CRos EBee ECha ELan ELon MACG MBNS MBel MHol MPie MRav NRHS SRms SWvt WGwG
§ 'Schwarzes Meer'	EBee ELon WCot
scopulinus	EPot GEdr ITim WAbe
simplex	EHyd LRHS NRHS
'Snow Queen'	SWvt
SNOW WHITE	see *E.* 'Schneewittchen'
'Sommerneuschnee'	EBee LPla NDov WCAu
'Synehurst'	SSal WCot WFar
trifidus	see *E. compositus* var. *discoideus*
uniflorus	SRms
'Violetta'	SPoG
'Wayne Roderick'	CBod CRos EHyd ELan EPfP LRHS MACG NRHS SCoo WFar
'White Quakeress'	CFis CMea MHCG MRav SMrm WCot WFar

Erinacea (*Fabaceae*)

§ ***anthyllis*** ♀H5	GArf WAbe WThu
pungens	see *E. anthyllis*

Erinus (*Plantaginaceae*)

alpinus ♀H6	ECtt EDAr GAbr GJos GKev MAsh NBir NGrd SLee SRms SRot
- var. ***albus***	GMaP SRms WHoo
- 'Doktor Hähnle'	EDAr GJos MBel SRms WHoo

Eriobotrya (*Rosaceae*)

'Coppertone'	see × *Rhaphiobotrya* 'Coppertone'
japonica (F) ♀H4	CBcs CCCN CDoC CTsd EHyd ELan EPfP LMaj LRHS MGos MMuc MNic NLar SArc SCoo SEND SGsty SPer SPlb SSta SVic SWeb WKor WLov WPGP
- 'Mrs Cookson' (F)	CAgr WMat
- 'Oliver' (F)	CAgr WMat
- 'Rose-Anne' (F)	WPGP

Eriobotrya × *Rhaphiolepis* see × *Rhaphiobotrya*

Eriocapitella see *Anemone*

Eriocephalus (*Asteraceae*)

africanus	CBod SPlb WJek

Eriogonum (*Polygonaceae*)

alleni 'Little Rascal'	ELan
cespitosum	WAbe
ovalifolium Wellington form	GEdr GKev
umbellatum	GKev
- var. ***humistratum***	SLee
- var. ***torreyanum***	CMea
wrightii var. ***subscaposum***	GKev

Eriolarynx (*Solanaceae*)

§ ***australis*** ♀H3	CBcs CCCN CDow CExl CSpe EBee ELan EMdy LSRN MGil NGKo NSti SEND SIvy SPlb SPoG SPtp SVen WCot WPGP
- 'Andean Snow'	CCCN CDow CSpe EShb MGil NGKo WHil WPGP

Eriophorum (*Cyperaceae*)

angustifolium	CBen CPud CTtf CWat EWat LLWG MWts SPlb WMAq WPnP WWtn
chamissonis	MWts
latifolium	LLWG MACG
rousseauianum	LLWG
vaginatum	EWat LLWG MACG

Eriophyllum (*Asteraceae*)

lanatum	ECha EPfP NBid NGBl SAko

Eriostemon (*Rutaceae*)

myoporoides	see *Philotheca myoporoides*

Eritrichium (*Boraginaceae*)

aretioides	SPlb
§ ***canum***	GKev
pectinatum new	GKev
rupestre	see *E. canum*
strictum	see *E. canum*

Erodium (*Geraniaceae*)

absinthoides	EHyd EPot NRHS XSen
- var. ***amanum***	see *E. amanum*
§ ***acaule***	EPPr GKev
'Almodovar'	WCot WFar
§ ***amanum***	CSpe EWes GMaP
'Ardwick Redeye'	EPot
balearicum	see *E.* × *variabile* 'Album'
'Caroline'	CMea WHoo
§ ***castellanum***	NLar
celtibericum	EPot
- 'Peñagolosa'	XSen
chamaedryoides	see *E. reichardii*
- 'Roseum'	see *E.* × *variabile* 'Roseum'
§ ***cheilanthifolium***	SLee SRot
- 'David Crocker'	EPot
chrysanthum	CTri EBou ECha ECtt EDAr EGrI ELan EPfP EPot EWTr EWoo LShi MMuc MPnt NChi NLar SEND SLee SPtp SWvt WKif WMal XLum XSen
- (f)	SRot WFar
- (m)	NRya
- 'Arcadia'	CMea SPhx
- pink-flowered	CSpe ECtt MMuc SLee XLum
'County Park'	ECha SBut SRms WFar XLum XSen
daucoides misapplied	see *E. castellanum*
'Eileen Emmett'	EPot
foetidum hybrids	SRot
'Fran's Delight'	CMea EPot SGro WFar WHoo
'Freedom'	CBor WFar WIce
'Fripetta'	WIce
'Gini's Choice'	WCot
glandulosum ♀H5	EBee ELan EPfP MAsh MMuc SEND SPtp SRms WFar WKif XLum XSen
gruinum	SPhx
guttatum misapplied	see *E.* 'Katherine Joy'
guttatum (Desf.) Willd.	CWGN EPot EWTr EWoo GMaP SRms

	hymenodes L'Hér.	see *E. trifolium*
	'Julie Ritchie'	WHoo
§	'Katherine Joy'	CBor EWes MHer NRya SRot WFar
	× ***kolbianum***	WCot WFar WHoo WMal
	- 'Natasha'	CBor ELan EPot EWes MHer MMuc SRot WIce WKif XLum
	'Las Meninas'	CMea WCot
	× ***lindavicum***	MHer NChi
	macradenum	see *E. glandulosum*
	manescavii ♀H5	Widely available
	'Marchants Mikado'	WKif
	'Maryla'	CBor CMea WFar WIce
	'Merstham Pink'	SRms
	'Mesquita'	CMea
	'Milly'	CMea
	paularense new	GKev
	pelargoniiflorum	CRos CSpe EBee EHyd EMor EPfP EWoo LRHS MCot MNHC NRHS SAko SMrm SRms SWvt WCAu WFar WHil WKif
	'Peter Vernon'	MHer
	petraeum subsp. ***petraeum***	EPot
	'Pippa Mills'	CMea
	'Purple Haze'	EHyd ELan EMor EPfP SLee SRms WFar
§	***reichardii***	CRos CTri ECtt EHyd LRHS MBrN NRHS SPoG SRms WCav
	- 'Album'	CRos EHyd EPfP MAsh NHpl NRHS SLee SPoG WFar WHoo XLum
	- 'Bianca'	ELan EPfP
	- 'Jenny'	NHpl
	- 'Rubrum'	MAsh
	rodiei	EWes
	romanum	see *E. acaule*
§	***rupestre***	SRms WIce
	'Sans-culottes'	EWes
	'Spanish Eyes'	CDor EBee LSun SMad SRot SWvt WCot WFar WKif XLum
	'Special Rose'	CSpe
	'Stephanie'	CBor ELan EWes MHer MMuc NLar WIce XSen
	'Tiny Kyni'	WFar
	trichomanifolium L'Hér.	EWes
§	***trifolium***	MHer SPhx WBrk
	× ***variabile***	LLWG WFar
§	- 'Album'	CMea CRos EHyd EPfP EPot GKev GMaP LRHS MHer NGrd NRHS NRya SRms SRot SWvt WFar WTor
	- 'Candy'	ECtt MHer NHpl SLee SRot
	- dwarf white	CBod
	- 'Flore Pleno' (d)	CRos CTri EHyd ELan EPfP EWes LLWG LRHS MHer NHpl NRHS SLee SPoG SRms SRot WFar
	- 'Red Rock'	CTri
§	- 'Roseum' ♀H5	ECtt ELan EWoo LLWG LRHS NCou SEND SLee SPlb SRms WBrk
	- 'William Bishop'	CBod CMea CRos ECha EHyd EPfP EPot GJos GMaP LLWG LRHS LShi MAsh MBow NQui NRHS NRya SPoG SRms SRot SWvt WBrk WFar WHoo WIce WLov

Erophila (*Brassicaceae*)

verna new	SPhx

Erpetion see *Viola*

Eruca (*Brassicaceae*)

vesicaria	ENfk
- subsp. ***sativa***	CSpe GPoy MHer MNHC SRms SVic

Eryngium (*Apiaceae*)

	from Mexico	SBrt
§	***agavifolium***	Widely available
	- giant	SMad WPGP
	alpinum	CPla CSpe ECha GKev GMaP LRHS MGos MSCN NBir SPer SPhx SRms WCAu WFar
	- 'Blue Star'	CExl EBee ECtt ELan EPri GJos MNHC NLar WFar WSpi
	- 'Slieve Donard'	see *E.* × *zabelii* 'Donard Variety'
	- 'Superbum'	ECtt EHyd MBriF SRms
	amethystinum	CBod CPla EPri EWes LRHS NFav SPhx SPtp XLum
	'Blue Jackpot'	CBod EBee ECtt EPfP EWes MBros MNrw
	bourgatii	Widely available
	- Graham Stuart Thomas's selection	CDor CEme CExl CRos CSpe ECtt EHyd ELan EPPr GAbr GMaP LRHS MBel NBir NLar NRHS SEdd SPad SPer SRms WCAu WCot WHoo WKif WSpi
	- 'Oxford Blue' ♀H5	GKev NLar NSla SPtp SWvt
	- 'Picos Amethyst'	CBcs CBct CBod CMac EBee ECtt EHyd EMor LCro LEdu LOPS LRHS MAsh MAvo MCot MHol NLar SCob SCoo SEdd SPtp SRkn SRms WABo WNPC WSHC XSte
	- 'Picos Blue' PBR ♀H5	Widely available
	bromeliifolium misapplied	see *E. agavifolium*, *E. eburneum*
	bromeliifolium F. Delaroche	EHyd
	campestre	SPhx SPtp
	'Cobalt Star'	GWyn MRav SMHy
	creticum	MNrw
	cymosum	ESwi SPtp
	- B&SWJ 10267	WCru
	decaisneanum misapplied	see *E. pandanifolium*
	deppeanum F&M 54	WPGP
	ebracteatum	CSpe LEdu WPGP
	- var. ***poterioides***	ELan ILea IPot LCro LOPS LPla LRHS MBel NDov SEdd SPhx SPtp
§	***eburneum***	CBod ECha EGrI ELan EPfP EWes GMaP ILea LRHS MSpe SMad SPtp
	- 'Fromefield Rapier' new	SPtp
	aff. ***eburneum***	CMac
§	***giganteum*** ♀H6	Widely available
	- 'Silver Ghost' ♀H6	CExl CPla CSpe CTtf ECtt GMaP LCro LOPS LRHS NDov NGdn NLar SPhx SWvt WAvo WCot WFar WSpi
	gracile B&SWJ 10441	WCru
	'Green Jade'	NRHS
	guatemalense B&SWJ 10397	ESwi WCru
	horridum misapplied	see *E. eburneum*
	horridum ambig.	ECha EWes NLar SArc
	horridum Malme	WCot
	humboldtii B&SWJ 14342	WCru
	aff. ***humboldtii*** B&SWJ 14367	WCru
	humile	MHol
	- B&SWJ 10464	WCru
	- var. ***brevibracteatum*** B&SWJ 14735	WCru
	leavenworthii	EHyd
	longifolium B&SWJ 14786	WCru
	maritimum	CEls CSpe GPoy MNHC NFav SEdd SPhx SPlb SRms
	Miss Willmott's ghost	see *E. giganteum*
	× ***oliverianum*** ♀H5	CDor CMea CTri ECtt ELan EPfP GAbr GKev LRHS MCot MRav NBir NLar SPoG SWvt WCot WKif

§	***pandanifolium*** 🏆H4	ELan EWes MNrw SArc SBls SEND SMHy SMad SPlb SPoG SWvt WPGP
	- 'Physic Purple'	CDor CSpe ECha ELan LRHS MAvo SDix SPtp WCot
	paniculatum B&SWJ 14367	WCru
	- B&SWJ 14826	WCru
	'Pen Blue'	CAvo CBod CCBP CDor CMea CSpe CTtf ECha ECtt ECul EPfP LRHS MGos MHol MNrw NDov SAko SPoG WCAu WCot WHoo WTor
	planum	Widely available
§	- 'Blauer Zwerg'	EWTr GMaP LRHS NLar WFar
	- 'Blaukappe'	CExl CMea CRos EBee EBlo ECha EHyd ELan ELon EPfP GJos LRHS LSun MMuc NLar NRHS SCoo SEND SMHy SPhx SRms WFar
	- BLUE DWARF	see *E. planum* 'Blauer Zwerg'
	- 'Blue Glitter'	CCBP CDor EBee GJos NLar SPhx SWvt
	- 'Blue Hobbit'	Widely available
	- 'Flüela'	ECtt EHyd EPfP EWes LRHS LSRN MAvo NRHS WGwG
	- 'Jade Frost'^{PBR} (v)	Widely available
	- 'Little Blue Wonder'^{PBR}	NHol
	- MAGICAL ANITA ('Kolmanita'^{PBR}) **new**	MHol
	- MAGICAL BLUE GLOBE **new**	MPri NLar
	- MAGICAL BLUE LAGOON ('Kolmblula'^{PBR}) **new**	ECul LRHS MHol XSte
	- MAGICAL PURPLE FALLS ('Kolmapufa'^{PBR})	IPot MHol NLar
	- MAGICAL SILVER ('Kolmagsil') **new**	ECul LRHS NLar
	- MAGICAL SYMPHONY ('Kolmasy') **new**	LRHS MHol NLar XSte
	- MAGICAL WHITE FALLS ('Kolmwhifal') **new**	MHol NLar
	- 'Naughty Jackpot' (v)	NLar
	- 'Paradise Jackpot'^{PBR}	SRms
	- 'Seven Seas'	ECtt EHyd LRHS MBNS NRHS
	- 'Silver Salentino'	CBod GPSL
	- 'Silver Stone'	SRms
	- 'Tetra Petra'	LRHS SRms
	- 'Tiny Jackpot'	GMaP NLar
	- 'White Glitter'	EBee ELan EPfP
	proteiflorum	CDor LRHS NDov SPlb WFar
	serbicum	SDix
	serra	EBlo EHyd EWes
	tricuspidatum	CDoC CRos EBee EBlo ECtt EHyd LRHS NRHS
	× ***tripartitum*** 🏆H5	CBcs CBod CTri EBee ECha ECtt EHyd EMor EPfP GJos GMaP LRHS LSRN MBel MNrw MRav NBro NLar NRHS SWvt
	variifolium	Widely available
	- 'Miss Marble'	EPfP LPot LSun NGrd SBls SIvy SRms WFar WSHC
	venustum	EHyd GGro NFav SMad SPhx SPtp WPGP
	vesiculosum **new**	SPlb
	yuccifolium	CBod CSpe EBee ECha EMor EPfP EWes LRHS MAvo SPeP SPhx SPlb SPtp SWvt XLum
	- 'Kershaw Blue'	WPGP
	× ***zabelii***	ECha
	- 'Big Blue' 🏆H5	Widely available
	- 'Blue Waves' **new**	LRHS MBNS SMad
§	- 'Donard Variety'	EHyd ILea LRHS MCot NLar
	- 'Forncett Ultra'	MNrw
	- 'Jos Eijking'	Widely available
	- 'Neptune's Gold'^{PBR}	Widely available
	- 'Violetta'	CBod CDor CSpe EBee ECha EHyd ELon EMor EPfP EPri IPot LRHS MAvo MCot MNrw NDov NLar NRHS WCAu WFar WTor

Erysimum ✿ (*Brassicaceae*)

	allionii misapplied	see *E.* × *marshallii*
	alpinum misapplied	see *E. hieraciifolium*
*	***altaicum*** var. ***humillinum***	GEdr
	'Apricot Delight'	see *E.* 'Apricot Twist'
§	'Apricot Twist'	CBcs CBod CMea CSpe CWCL CWGN ECtt EHyd ELan ELon EPfP GKev LRHS LShi MAsh MCot NLar NRHS SCoo SPer SPoG SRms SWvt WCav WFar WHoo WMal
	arkansanum	see *E. helveticum*
	'Audrey's Pink'	CCBP WMal
	bonanianum	WCot
	'Bowles's Mauve' 🏆H4	Widely available
	'Bowles's Purple'	SRms SWvt
	'Bowles's Yellow'	MHCG NFav WCot
	'Bredon'	NPer WKif WMal
	'Canaries Yellow'	CBod LRHS
	'Caribbean Island'	LShi SGBe
	cheiri	MHer MPri NGrd
	- 'Baden-Powell' (d)	EPPr WMal
	- 'Blood Red'	CArg CSpe LCro LOPS SPhx
	- 'Bloody Warrior' (d)	CElw
	- 'Cloth of Gold' **new**	CArg CKel
	- 'Fire King'	CArg CKel LCro LOPS
	- 'Giant Pink' **new**	CKel
	- 'Harpur Crewe' (d)	NPer SRms WHer WMal
	- 'Ivory White' **new**	CKel
	- 'Persian Carpet' (mixed) 🏆H5	CKel LCro
	- Sunset Series	MBros
	- 'Vulcan'	CArg
	Citrona Series **new**	MACG
	'Constant Cheer'	CElw CMea CSBt EHyd ELan EPfP LShi MBow MCot NLar NPer SRGP SRms SWvt WBor WHoo WSpi XLum
	'Cotswold Gem' (v)	ELon MHer NPer SWvt
	'Desert Island'	CKel ECtt SGBe
	'Dorothy Elmhirst'	see *E.* 'Mrs L.K. Elmhirst'
	'Gogh's Gold' (Artist Series)	LShi
	'Golden Jubilee'	ECtt EHyd SGBe SRms WCav WIce
§	***helveticum***	LShi SRms
§	***hieraciifolium***	LShi
	'Honeyberry' **new**	LRHS
	'Jacob's Jacket'	ECha EWld MHer NPer
	'Jenny Brook'^{PBR}	XLum
	'John Codrington'	GBin NPer WSpi
	'Joseph's Coat'	MHCG
	kotschyanum	CBor EBou EPot NSla SRms WHal
	'Lady Roborough'	NQui
	'Lemon Light'	WHoo
	linifolium	SRms
§	- 'Variegatum' (v)	CCCN CSBt ECtt ELan EPfP LShi MCot MPri NPer SHar SPer SPoG WCav WHer XLum
	- 'Variegatum' peach-flowered (v)	LRHS NQui
§	× ***marshallii***	LShi
	'Monet's Moment' (Artist Series) **new**	LShi SGBe
	'Moonlight'	GMaP MRav SRms WHoo
§	'Mrs L.K. Elmhirst'	NPer
	mutabile	ECha EHyd EPfP WHal
	'Orange Flame'	CBor CMea ECha GArf MHer NPer WHoo

'Orange Zwerg'	LRHS MMuc WIce
'Paint Box' (Artist Series)	CBod SCob SCoo SGBe WCav
'Parish's'	CCBP CElw CFis CSpe ECha WGoo WHoo WMal
'Parkwood Gold'	NHpl
'Pastel Patchwork'	CSpe ECtt EPfP LCro LOPS LRHS NRHS WCot WFar
Perry's hybrid	NPer
'Perry's Peculiar'	NPer
'Perry's Surprise'	NPer
'Perry's Variegated' (v)	NPer
'Plant World Lemon'	NLar
'Primrose Dame' **new**	CKel
§ ***pulchellum***	ECha EPot GKev
pumilum DC.	see *E. helveticum*
'Purple Jep'	LRHS
'Purple Shades' **new**	CKel
'Red Jep'	CDoC CSpe EHyd ELan EPfP LRHS NLar NRHS SAdn SAng SCoo SPer WCot WNPC WTor
rupestre	see *E. pulchellum*
'Ruston Royal'	CElw ECha WKif WMal
RYSI COPPER	CRos EHyd EPfP LRHS NRHS SPoG
RYSI MOON	CBod
scoparium	LShi
'Sissinghurst Variegated'	see *E. linifolium* 'Variegatum'
'Spice Island'	ECtt SCob SGBe
'Sprite'	CMea NPer
'Stars and Stripes' (v)	CBod ECtt SRkn
Sugar Rush Series	MBros
SUNBURST ('Listrace')	CBod CWCL ECtt MBNS WCot
'Sweet Sorbet'	EPfP GKev MBNS NLar SRkn SWvt
'Variegatum' ambig. (v)	SGBe SRot
WALBERTON'S FRAGRANT STAR ('Walfrastar'[PBR]) (v)	EHyd EPfP LRHS MAsh NRHS SCoo SPoG SRms
WALBERTON'S FRAGRANT SUNSHINE ('Walfrasun')	CRos EHyd EPfP LRHS NRHS SCoo SPoG
'Wenlock Beauty'	CFis SRms
'Winter Joy'	ELan EPfP LRHS MBNS SHar
'Winter Light'	LRHS
WINTER ORCHID	CBod CWGN GMaP LRHS SAng SGBe
'Winter Party'	LRHS
'Winter Passion'	CRos CWCL EHyd EPfP LRHS MBNS NLar SPoG
WINTER SORBET ('Inneryws'[PBR])	ECtt ELan LRHS NLar SGBe

Erythraea see *Centaurium*

Erythrina (*Fabaceae*)

abyssinica	SPlb
amazonica	SPlb
arborescens	SPlb
× ***bidwillii***	CCCN WPGP
crista-galli ♀H3	CBcs CCCN CDTJ CKel CSpe EHyd ELan EPfP LRHS MGil MVil SPlb WPGP
- 'Compacta'	LRHS MPkF XSte
flabelliformis	SPlb
guatemalensis	SPlb
herbacea	SPlb
§ ***humeana***	SPlb
latissima	SPlb
lysistemon	SPlb
princeps	see *E. humeana*
rubrinervia	SPlb
speciosa	SPlb
vespertilio	SPlb

Erythronium ✿ (*Liliaceae*)

albidum	GEdr GKev IBlr NRog
americanum	GKev IBlr MNrw NRog WAbe
- 'Cincinnati' **new**	NRog
'Apple Blossom' ♀H4	IBlr
'Ballyrogan's Blaze'	IBlr
'Beechpark'	IBlr
'Blush'	IBlr
'Bronze Beauty'	IBlr
'Bryn Meifod'	WAbe
'Californian Star'	IBlr
'Californian Sunshine'	IBlr
californicum	CWCL EBee EHyd GKev IBlr LEdu MAvo MNrw NRHS NRog WAbe
- 'Ballyrogan Bronze Bounty'	IBlr
- 'Brimstone'	IBlr
- 'Brocklamont Inheritance' ♀H5	IBlr
- 'Bronze Edge'	IBlr
- 'Dark Delight'	IBlr
- Plas Merdyn form	IBlr
- 'Sonoma' **new**	NRog
- 'Stellar'	IBlr
- 'White Beauty' ♀H5	Widely available
californicum × ***citrinum*** **new**	NRog
'Carol Scott'	IBlr
caucasicum	EPot GKev
- from Krasnodar **new**	NRog
'Citronella'	GKev IBlr NRog
cliftonii hort.	see *E. multiscapideum* Cliftonii Group
'Craigton Beauty'	IBlr
'Craigton Cover Girl'	IBlr
'Craigton Cream'	IBlr
'Delicacy'	IBlr
dens-canis	CAvo CBod CBro CTtf CWCL ECha ELan EMor EPot GAbr GEdr GKev GMaP IBlr ILea LCro LEdu LOPS MNrw NBir NHol NRog NRya SCob WAbe WPnP WShi
- from Montenegro **new**	NRog
- from NE Spain **new**	NRog
- 'Charmer'	GEdr MNrw NRog
- dark	CBor
- 'Frans Hals'	EPot GEdr GKev LEdu NRog WAbe
- 'Lilac Wonder' ♀H5	CBor EBee EPot GEdr GKev GMaP LEdu MNrw NRog SDeJ
* - 'Moerheimii' (d)	GEdr GKev IBlr NRog
- var. ***niveum***	GEdr NRog
- 'Old Aberdeen' ♀H5	CAvo CRos EHyd IBlr LRHS MAvo NLar NRHS NRog WAbe
- 'Pink Perfection'	CBor EBee GEdr GKev LEdu MNrw NRog SDeJ WAbe
- 'Purple King'	CBor EBee EPot GEdr GKev GMaP LEdu MNrw NHol NHpl NRog SDeJ WAbe
- 'Rose Queen'	CBor EGrI EPot GEdr GKev GMaP LEdu MAvo MNrw NLar NRog SDeJ
- 'Snowflake'	CAvo CBor CRos EHyd EPot GEdr GKev LEdu LRHS MNrw NBir NHol NHpl NLar NRHS NRog SDeJ WAbe
- 'White Splendour'	EPot GEdr IBlr LEdu MAvo MNrw NRog
'Eirene'	IBlr
elegans	NHpl NRog
'Flaire'	IBlr
'Flash'	IBlr NHar
§ ***grandiflorum***	EBee GKev NRog
- subsp. ***chrysandrum***	see *E. grandiflorum*

	'Harvington April Sunrise' **new**	LRHS
	'Harvington Snowgoose'	CRos EHyd LRHS MCor NHar NRHS
	'Harvington Sunshine'	LRHS NHar
	helenae	MNrw
	hendersonii ♀H5	EHyd GKev IBlr LRHS NRHS NRog SPlb WAbe
	- 'Pacific Skies'	IBlr
	- 'Pacific Sunshine'	IBlr
	hendersonii* × *klamathense **new**	NRog
	'Hidcote Beauty'	CRos EHyd LRHS MAvo NRHS
	howellii* × *revolutum **new**	LRHS
	'Janice' ♀H5	IBlr MCor WAbe
	japonicum	CMiW EPot GKev MNrw NRog
	'Jeanette Brickell'	IBlr MCor
	'Jeannine'	GKev IBlr NRog WAbe
	'Joanna' ♀H5	CTtf GEdr IBlr MAvo MCor MNrw NHar NRog WAbe
	'John Brookes'	IBlr MCor
	'Keith'	MCor
	'Kinfauns Pink'	CBor CWCL EBee ELon EMor GBin GEdr GKev GMaP IBlr NRog
	'Kondo'	CBcs CBor EHyd EPfP GMaP IBlr NBir NHol NLar NRog SCob SDeJ
	'Lavender Eye'	IBlr
	'Margaret Mathew'	IBlr LEdu WAbe
	'Minnehaha'	IBlr
	'Miss Jessopp'	NRog
	montanum	GKev
§	***multiscapideum***	EMor GKev MNrw NRog WSHC
	- from Pulga, California **new**	NRog
§	- Cliftonii Group ♀H4	MAvo WAbe
	'Oregon Encore'	IBlr
	oregonum	CRos EBee EHyd GBin GKev LRHS MNrw NHpl NRHS NRog WAbe
	'Pagoda' ♀H5	Widely available
	purdyi	see *E. multiscapideum*
	'Purple Heart'	IBlr
	revolutum	CAvo CBro CTtf CWCL EBee EHyd ELon GBin GEdr GKev GMaP IBlr LRHS MNrw NHar NHpl NLar NRHS NRog SChF
	- from God's Valley, Oregon	MNrw
I	- 'Album'	IBlr
	- 'Ballyrogan White Blusher'	IBlr
	- 'Dark Dapple'	IBlr
	- 'Galactic Star' **new**	IBlr
	- giant pink-flowered **new**	NRog
	- 'Guincho Splendour'	IBlr
	- 'Inferno'	IBlr
I	- 'Inshriach Form'	IBlr
	- Johnsonii Group	EPot WAbe
	- 'Knightshayes'	CRos EBee EHyd LRHS MAvo NRHS
	- 'Knightshayes Pink'	CAvo WShi
	- 'Pink Beauty'	GKev NRog
	- 'Rose Beauty'	GKev NRog
	- 'Wild Salmon'	EBee EHyd LRHS MAvo NHar NRHS
	'Rippling Waters'	IBlr
	'Rosalind'	IBlr NHar NRog WAbe
	sibiricum	GKev NHpl NRog
	- subsp. ***altaicum***	NRog
	- 'Gornaya Shoria' **new**	NRog
	- 'Kemerov' **new**	NRog
	- 'Lilac Cloud' **new**	NRog
	- subsp. ***sibiricum***	NRog
	- 'Tomsk' **new**	NRog
	- white-flowered	NRog
	'Spring Fresh'	IBlr
	'Sundisc' ♀H4	CBro ECha GKev IBlr NRog WAbe
	'Sunshine'	IBlr
	'Susannah'	EHyd IBlr MCor NRHS
	tuolumnense	CWCL EBee EMor GEdr GKev GMaP IBlr MCor MCot MNrw NHpl NRog SDeJ WAbe
	- EBA clone 2	IBlr MCor
	- EBA clone 3	IBlr
	- Plas Merdyn form	IBlr
	- 'Spindlestone'	CRos EHyd GEdr IBlr LRHS NHar NRHS WAbe
	umbilicatum	EPot GEdr GKev NHpl NRog
	'White Star'	IBlr
	'Winifred Loraine'	IBlr

Escallonia (*Escalloniaceae*)

	angustifolia var. ***coquimbensis***	WPav
	'Apple Blossom' ♀H4	Widely available
§	***bifida*** ♀H3	CRos EHyd ELan EPfP EWes LRHS MAsh NRHS WPGP
	'C.F. Ball'	CBrac CTri EHyd ELan EPfP IArd MAsh MSwo NWea SGol SRms
	'Donard Beauty'	CBrac NWea SRms
	'Donard Brilliance'	SGol SRms
	'Donard Radiance' ♀H4	CBrac CEnd CMac CSBt EPfP EShb NLar NWea SCob SGbt SGol SPer SPoG SRms SWvt WFar
	'Donard Seedling'	CBcs CBrac CCVT CRos EHyd ELan EPfP GArf GDam LPar LRHS MAsh MGos MMuc MSwo NPer NRHS NWea SCob SPer SRms SWvt WFar
	'Donard Star'	EPfP NLar NWea WCFE
	'Donard White'	EPfP NLar SPoG
	'Edinensis'	EPfP NLar SRms WSpi
	'Everest'	EHyd SLon
	× ***exoniensis***	SRms
	GLOWING EMBERS ('Low21')	LRHS MAsh SCoo SGBe
	GOLDEN CARPET ('Alcaura'PBR)	CBod CRos EHyd ELan GBin LPar LRHS MAsh MTin NRHS SCob SLon SNig SPoG WNPC
	'Hopleys Gold'	see *E. laevis* 'Gold Brian'
	illinita	NLar WPav
	'Iveyi' ♀H4	Widely available
§	***laevis*** 'Gold Brian'	CMac CRos EHyd EPfP LRHS MAsh MGos NRHS SPer
	- 'Gold Ellen' (v)	CBrac CDoC CEme CRos CSBt CTri EHyd ELan EPfP LRHS MAsh MGos MRav MSwo NHol NLar NRHS SCob SCoo SGBe SNig SPer SPoG SRms SWvt
	- PINK ELLE ('Lades'PBR)	CBod CDoC CRos CSBt EBee EHyd ELan EPfP LCro LOPS LRHS MAsh MGos NRHS SCob SCoo SGBe SPoG SWvt WFar WNPC
	'Langleyensis' ♀H4	CMac CTri SRms
	× ***mollis***	SPer
	montevidensis	see *E. bifida*
	myrtilloides B&SWJ 14329	WCru
	'Peach Blossom' ♀H4	CBar CBcs CDoC CEnd CRos EBee EHyd ELan EPfP LRHS MAsh MSwo NHol NRHS SCob SCoo SGbt SGol SPer SRms WFar
	'Pride of Donard' ♀H4	CSBt EPfP LRHS SCob SGsty SRms
	pulverulenta	WPav
	RED CARPET ('Loncar'PBR)	CBcs CBod GBin SCob SLon WNPC
	'Red Dream'	CSBt EHyd EPfP GBin LPar LRHS MAsh MGos MSwo SCob SCoo SGsty SPoG SRms SWvt WAvo WFar
	'Red Elf'	CMac CRos EHyd ELan EPfP GKin LPar LRHS MGos SPer SPlb SRms SWvt WFar

'Red Hedger'	CBod CSBt CTsd ELan LPar MRav SRms
'Red Knight'	CEnd EHyd LRHS MAsh NHol NRHS WNPC
resinosa	CExl CMCN SPlb SRms SVen WPav
revoluta	CTri MGil WPav
rubra 'Crimson Spire' ♀H4	CBar CBcs CBod CBrac CEnd CSBt CTri EPfP GKin LSRN MAsh MGos MMuc MRav NWea SCob SEND SGbt SNig SPer SPlb SRms
- 'Ingramii'	SEND
- var. ***macrantha***	CBar CBcs CBod CBrac CCVT CDoC CEme CEnd CMac CSBt CTri EHyd ELan EPfP GArf GKin IArd LPar LRHS MHed NRHS NWea SCob SCoo SNig SPer SPoG SRms WAvo
- 'Pygmaea'	see *E. rubra* 'Woodside'
§ - 'Woodside'	CMCN SRms
'Silver Anniversary'	MSwo
'Slieve Donard'	CBrac CMac MRav NWea SRms
'Tall Boy' **new**	LRHS
tucumanensis	SPlb
'Ventnor'	SPlb SVen
virgata	WPav

Eschscholzia (*Papaveraceae*)

caespitosa 'Sundew'	SPhx
californica	MBel
- 'Alba'	CSpe
- 'Apricot Chiffon' (Thai Silk Series) ♀H3	LCro LOPS
- 'Ivory Castle'	CKel SMrm SPhx
- var. ***maritima***	CSpe SPhx
- subsp. ***mexicana*** 'Sun Shades'	SPhx
- 'Mission Bells'	LCro
- 'Orange King'	LRHS SPhx
- 'Red Chief'	CSpe LRHS SMrm SPhx

Esterhuysenia (*Aizoaceae*)

alpina	SPlb

Eucalyptus ✿ (*Myrtaceae*)

aggregata	EBee SArc SKin WGrf
alpina	SPlb WPav
amygdalina	SPlb
apiculata	WGrf
approximans	SKin WGrf
archeri	CDTJ CDoC CTsd ELan EPfP MGos MHtn MMuc SEdd SKin WGrf
§ ***bridgesiana***	WGrf
caesia ♀H2	SPlb
- subsp. ***magna***	WGrf
camaldulensis	SPlb
camphora	CCCN SKin WGrf
cinerea	CTsd SKin SPlb SWeb WGrf
citriodora	see *Corymbia citriodora*
coccifera	CBod CDoC CSBt CTsd EBee EPfP MMuc NPer SEdd SKin SPlb WGrf
cordata	CDoC EBee EPfP IDee SKin WGrf WPGP
crenulata	EBee SEdd SKin WGrf
crucis subsp. ***crucis***	SPlb
cypellocarpa	SPlb
dalrympleana ♀H5	CDoC CMac CRos EPfP IPap LSRN MGos MMuc NPer SEND SKin SLim SPer SPlb WGrf WPGP
deanei	WGrf
debeuzevillei	see *E. pauciflora* subsp. *debeuzevillei*
deglupta	WGrf
delegatensis	NPer WGrf
denticulata **new**	WGrf
divaricata	see *E. gunnii* subsp. *divaricata*
elliptica	WGrf
erythrocorys	SPlb
eximia	see *Corymbia eximia*
ficifolia	see *Corymbia ficifolia*
fraxinoides	SPlb
gamophylla	SPlb
glaucescens	CAbb LPar SArc SKin WGrf
globulus	CWCL SPlb
- subsp. ***bicostata***	WGrf
- coastal **new**	WGrf
goniocalyx	WGrf
§ ***gregsoniana***	EBee EPfP SKin SMad SPlb WGrf
gunnii ♀H5	Widely available
- AZURA ('Cagire'PBR)	CDoC IBal LCro LOPS LPar LSRN MTrO NLar SCob SLim WGrf WMat XSte
§ - subsp. ***divaricata***	SKin WGrf
- FRANCE BLEU ('Rengun'PBR) **new**	WGrf
* - 'Silver Drop'	WFar
- SILVERANA ('Lon40') **new**	SGsty
johnstonii	ELan SEdd SKin SPer WGrf
kitsoniana	SKin WGrf
kruseana	SPlb
kybeanensis	SKin WGrf
§ ***lacrimans***	WGrf
leucoxylon subsp. ***megalocarpa***	SKin SPlb WGrf
ligustrina	SKin WGrf
macrocarpa	SPlb WGrf
mitchelliana	SEdd SKin WGrf
moorei var. ***moorei***	WGrf
- var. ***nana***	CDTJ
neglecta	SKin WGrf
nicholii	CBcs CDoC CSpe CTsd EBee EPfP MGos SCoo SKin SPoG WGrf WPGP
niphophila	see *E. pauciflora* subsp. *niphophila*
nitens	CDTJ SKin SPlb WGrf
§ ***nitida***	SKin WGrf
obliqua	WGrf
paliformis	WGrf
parviflora	CBod SKin
parvula ♀H5	CCCN CMac CTsd EPfP MMuc SEND WGrf
pauciflora	CCCN EBee SCob SEdd SPer
§ - subsp. ***debeuzevillei*** ♀H5	CAbb CBod EPfP NOrn SArc SKin WGrf WPGP
- var. ***nana***	see *E. gregsoniana*
§ - subsp. ***niphophila*** ♀H5	Widely available
- - from Mount Bogong, Australia **new**	WGrf
- - 'Pendula'	see *E. lacrimans*
- subsp. ***pauciflora***	WGrf
- - from Mount Buffalo, Australia	WGrf
perriniana	CEme CEnd ELan EPfP MGos MHtn MTrO NOrn SKin SPer SPlb SPoG SWvt WFar WGrf WMat
pulchella	WGrf
pulverulenta	CMac SPlb WFar WGrf
- 'Baby Blue'	CTsd SGBe SKin SWvt WFar WGrf XSte
regnans	IDee SKin WGrf
risdonii	WGrf
rodwayi	WGrf
rossii	SPlb
rubida	CCCN SKin WGrf
saxatilis	SKin

	'Shannon Blue' **new**	WGrf
	sideroxylon	SPlb
	- 'Rosea'	SPlb
	simmondsii	see *E. nitida*
	stellulata	SKin WGrf
	stricta	SKin WGrf
	stuartiana	see *E. bridgesiana*
	sturgissiana	WGrf
	subcrenulata	CDoC CTsd EPfP SKin WGrf
	tetraptera	SPlb
	torquata	SPlb
	urnigera	CTsd EPfP SEdd SMad WGrf
	vernicosa	SKin WGrf
	viminalis	IDee SKin

Eucharidium see *Clarkia*

Eucharis (*Amaryllidaceae*)

§	***amazonica*** ♀^{H1b}	CCCN EShb SDeJ SDir
	grandiflora misapplied	see *E. amazonica*

Eucomis ✿ (*Asparagaceae*)

	ALOHA	see *E.* 'Leia'
	autumnalis misapplied	see *E. zambesiaca*
§	***autumnalis*** (Mill.) Chitt. ♀^{H4}	CBro EPot ERCP GKev LRHS SDeJ SDir SPer SPlb WCot
	- subsp. ***amaryllidifolia***	CBro
	bicolor ♀^{H4}	Widely available
	- 'Alba'	CBro CExl GKev
§	***comosa***	CAvo CBro EBee EHyd EShb GKev MPtr NGKo SBls SDeJ SDir WCot
	- 'Can Can' **new**	LRHS XSte
	- 'Cornwood'	CAvo CBro GKev
	- 'Johannesburg'	CBro EBee GKev
	- 'Kilimanjaro'	EBee
	- 'Oakhurst'	CChe CPla ECtt ESwi LRHS WABo WCot
	- purple-leaved	CAvo EShb
	- 'Sparkling Burgundy' ♀^{H4}	Widely available
	- 'Sparkling Rosy'	GKev IPot MPtr NGKo SDir WFar
	- var. ***striata***	EBee
	'Dark Star'	ECtt IPot LRHS XSte
	'Freckles'	EPPr NGKo SPoG SRms
	'Glow Sticks'	CWGN ECtt
	humilis 'Twinkle Stars'	GKev MPtr SDeJ WFar WSMil
	'Joy's Purple'	CBro CPar EPri
§	'Leia'^{PBR} (Aloha Lily Series)	CAvo CBod CBro EShb GKev LSou SPad
	MAUI ('Gsalkele'^{PBR}) (Aloha Lily Series)	LSou
	montana	CBro CPla EBee EPot GKev SDeJ SDir WCot
	NANI ('Gsalipol'^{PBR}) (Aloha Lily Series)	LSou WHil
	pallidiflora ♀^{H3}	LEdu NGKo WPGP
§	- subsp. ***pallidiflora***	CBro CExl CPar EGrI EPPr EPri EShb LRHS MRav NGKo SDeJ SDir SMrm SPeP SPtp WAvo WSHC WSMil XSte
	- - dark	GKev
	- - pink-flowered	CPar
I	- - 'Purpurea'	CExl
	- subsp. ***pole-evansii*** misapplied	see *E. pallidiflora* subsp. *pallidiflora*
	'Pink Gin'	CAvo IPot
	'Playa Blanca'	EBee EPri EShb GKev LRHS XSte
	punctata	see *E. comosa*
	regia JCA 3.230.709	WCot
	schijffii **new**	WHil
	'Swazi Pride'	NGKo
	'Tugela Jade' **new**	LRHS XSte
	undulata	see *E. autumnalis* (Mill.) Chitt.
	vandermerwei ♀^{H3}	CBro EBee EGrI EPot LEdu NGKo NWad SDeJ SDir SPlb
	- 'Octopus'	CCCN CExl ELan EPfP GKev WFar WSMil XSte
§	***zambesiaca***	CAvo CBro CPla GKev NGKo SMHy WPGP
	- JCA 3.230.709	WCot
	- JCA 3.231.010	WCot
	- 'White Dwarf'	CBcs EPri SPer WFar WGwG
	'Zeal Bronze'	WAvo WCot
	'Zulu Flame'	IPot LRHS XSte

Eucommia (*Eucommiaceae*)

	ulmoides	CMCN NLar

Eucryphia ✿ (*Cunoniaceae*)

	cordifolia	CMac IDee LRHS MBlu MGil NLar WPav
§	***cordifolia*** × ***lucida***	CCCN
	glutinosa ♀^{H4}	CCCN EHyd EPfP GGGa GKev IDee LRHS MAsh MGil SAko SCob WPav
	× ***hillieri***	WSpi
	- 'Winton'	CBct EBee SChF WPGP
	× ***intermedia***	CCCN CDoC CExl CMac NLar SRms SSta
	- 'Miniature'	EPfP
	- 'Rostrevor' ♀^{H4}	CBcs CExl CJun CMac EHyd ELan EPfP GGGa IArd LRHS LSRN MAsh MBlu NLar SChF SMad SPer SSta WPGP XSte
	'Leatherwood Cream'	WSpi
	lucida	CCCN EHyd LRHS MMuc NLar NRHS WSpi XSte
	- 'Ballerina' ♀^{H4}	CBcs CJun CMac CRos EBee EHyd ELan EPfP GKin LRHS MAsh NLar NRHS SAko SChF SCoo SMad SPoG WPGP
	- 'Carousel' **new**	CRos
I	- 'Chaplin's Variety'	WPGP
	- 'Dumpling'	CExl WPGP
	- 'Gilt Edge' (v)	CBcs CRos EHyd LRHS NRHS SPoG XSte
	- 'Leatherwood Cream' (v)	ELon
	- 'Pink Cloud'	CBcs CCCN CDoC CExl CJun CMac CRos EGrI EHed EHyd ELan EPfP GKin LRHS LSRN MBlu MGil MGos NLar NRHS SPer SWvt WPGP
	- 'Spring Glow' (v)	CExl CRos EHyd LRHS MAsh NLar NRHS
	milliganii	CCCN CDoC CMac EHyd ELon EPfP LRHS MBlu MRav SPer SRms SSta WPGP WSpi
	moorei	CCCN CExl CMac IDee LRHS WPGP
	× ***nymansensis***	CHab SArc SRms WSpi
	- 'George Graham'	GGGa IArd WPGP
	- 'Nymans Silver' (v)	CBcs CDoC CJun CKel CLnd CMac EHyd ELan EPfP GGGa LRHS MAsh SPer SPoG SSta
	- 'Nymansay' ♀^{H4}	Widely available
	'Penwith' ambig.	IDee NLar

Eugenia (*Myrtaceae*)

	uniflora	CCCN

Eumorphia (*Asteraceae*)

	sericea	GBin

Eunomia see *Aethionema*

Euodia (*Rutaceae*)

daniellii	see *Tetradium daniellii*
hupehensis	see *Tetradium daniellii* Hupehense Group

Euonymus ✿ (*Celastraceae*)

	B&L 12543	EWes
	CC 4522	CExl
	NJM 09.109	CRHN
	NJM 10.106	WPGP
	from Kachin, Burma	WPGP
	alatus	Widely available
	- B&SWJ 8794	WCru
	- var. ***apterus***	EPfP SPtp WGrn
	- 'Blade Runner'	CDoC CRos EHed EHyd EPfP ESwi LRHS MBlu MGos NLar NRHS SGol
	- CHICAGO FIRE	see *E. alatus* 'Timber Creek'
	- 'Ciliodentatus'	see *E. alatus* f. *striatus*
	- 'Compactus' 🏆H6	Widely available
	- 'Fastigiata'	CJun
§	- 'Fire Ball'	CJun
*	- 'Macrophyllus'	CJun
	- 'Rudy Haag'	CJun EPfP
	- 'Select'	see *E. alatus* 'Fire Ball'
	- 'Silver Cloud'	NLar
§	- f. ***striatus***	CJun
	- - B&SWJ 11051	ESwi WCru
§	- 'Timber Creek'	CJun EPfP MBlu
	americanus	EPfP MBlu NLar SMad
	- var. ***angustifolius*** B&SWJ 12905	ESwi WCru
	bungeanus	EPfP WLov
	- B&SWJ 8782 from South Korea	WCru
	- 'Dart's Pride'	CJun EPfP NLar
	- 'Fireflame'	CJun NLar WCot
	- 'Pendulus'	MBlu
	- var. ***semipersistens***	CJun NLar WCru
§	***carnosus***	CJun CMCN
	- CWJ 12425	WCru
	- NMWJ 14515 **new**	WCru
	- 'Belmonte' **new**	NLar
	- 'Red Wine'	CJun EBee EPfP LEdu LRHS MBlu NLar WCot WLov
	- 'Trompenburg Lustre'	NLar
	chibae B&SWJ 11159	WCru
	clivicola	CJun SMad SPtp WCru
	aff. ***clivicola*** HIRD 103	SBrt
	cornutus	SPtp WPGP
	- var. ***quinquecornutus*** 🏆H6	CJun CMCN CSpe EBee ELan EPfP ESwi IArd MBlu MGil MMrt SPoG WPGP
	'Den Haag'	CJun EPfP LRHS
	echinatus	IDee
	europaeus	Widely available
	- from Slovakia	WCru
	- f. ***albus***	EPfP NLar SMad SPoG
	- 'Atropurpureus'	CMCN EPfP NLar
	- 'Atrorubens'	CJun
	- 'Aucubifolius' (v)	CMac
*	- 'Aureus'	CNat
	- 'Brilliant'	CJun EPfP LRHS NLar
	- 'Chrysophyllus'	EPfP MBlu
	- var. ***intermedius***	CJun EPfP MBlu NLar
	- 'Miss Pinkie'	CEnd NOrn
	- 'Red Cascade' 🏆H6	Widely available
	- 'Scarlet Wonder'	CJun EPfP LRHS MAsh NLar WMat
	- 'Thornhayes'	EPfP
	farreri	see *E. nanus*
	fimbriatus	CJun
	fortunei	SavN
	- BLONDY ('Interbolwi') (v)	CBcs CEme CRos CTri EHyd ELan EPfP LRHS MAsh MGos MMuc MSwo NLar NRHS SCob SCoo SGBe SGol SLim SPer SPoG SRms SavN
	- 'Canadale Gold' (v)	CMac EHyd EPfP LRHS MAsh NHol NRHS SGsty SLon SPer
	- 'Coloratus'	EPfP MBlu MSwo SEND WFar
	- 'Country Gold'	WFar
	- DAN'S DELIGHT ('Dandel'^{PBR}) (v)	LCro LOPS MThu SGol SPoG
	- 'Dart's Blanket'	EBee ELan EPfP MRav SCob SGol SavN
	- 'Emerald Gaiety' (v) 🏆H5	Widely available
*	- 'Emerald Green'	SavN
	- 'Emerald 'n' Gold' (v) 🏆H5	Widely available
	- 'Gold Spot'	see *E. fortunei* 'Sunspot'
	- 'Gold Tip'	see *E. fortunei* 'Golden Prince'
	- GOLDEN HARLEQUIN ('Hoogi'^{PBR}) (v)	CBcs CBod CEme EBee EPfP MAsh MThu NWad SGBe SPoG SWvt
§	- 'Golden Prince' (v)	CMac MRav MSwo NLar SRms
	- GOLDY ('Waldbolwi'^{PBR})	CBod EPfP NLar SGol SPoG
	- 'Harlequin' (v)	CBcs CBrac CKel CMac CSBt EHyd ELan EPfP LBuc LPar LRHS LSRN MAsh MBlu MGos MRav NRHS SCob SGBe SGol SNig SPer SPoG SRms SWvt SavN WFar
	- 'Heins Silver'^{PBR}	EBee
	- 'Hort's Blaze'	EBee
	- 'Kewensis' 🏆H5	CBod CMac EHyd ELan LRHS SArc SPoG WCFE WCru
	- 'Kewensis Variegatus' (v)	MRav
	- 'Minimus'	CSpe EPPr MSwo WPGP XLum
*	- 'Minimus Variegatus' (v)	EPPr SPlb
	- 'Perrolino'	SavN
	- 'Prince John'	CSBt
	- 'Sheridan Gold'	MRav
	- 'Silver Queen' (v)	Widely available
	- 'Silverstone'^{PBR} (v)	CKel EPfP SPoG
	- 'Sunshine' (v)	CKel CRos EHyd ELan EPfP LRHS MAsh SLon SPoG WAvo
§	- 'Sunspot' (v)	CBcs CBod CMac EBee ELan MMuc MSwo SGol SRms
§	- 'Variegatus' (v)	SRms
	- var. ***vegetus***	WFar
	- 'Wolong Ghost' 🏆H5	CBcs CBod CDoC CExl CKel CMCN CRos EHyd ELan EPPr GGro LPla LRHS MBlu MMuc NLar NRHS SBrt SWvt WCot WLov
	frigidus KWJ 12275	WCru
	- var. ***elongatus*** GWJ 9378	WCru
	grandiflorus misapplied	see *E. carnosus*
§	***grandiflorus*** Wall.	CJun EPfP IArd NLar SCoo WCot
	- f. ***salicifolius*** misapplied	see *E. grandiflorus* Wall.
	- 'Ruby Wine'	CBcs LRHS MGos MPkF MTrO WMat XSte
	hamiltonianus	CMCN ELan EPfP EWTr LRHS MMuc SMad WLov
	- 'Fiesta'	CJun NLar
	- subsp. ***hians***	see *E. hamiltonianus* subsp. *sieboldianus*
	- 'Indian Summer'	CJun EHyd EPfP LRHS MAsh MTrO NLar SPoG WMat
	- 'Koi Boy'	CJun EPfP LSRN MAsh MTrO SPoG WMat
	- 'Miss Pinkie'	CJun EPfP LRHS NLar WLov
	- 'Pink Delight'	CJun
	- 'Poort Bulten'	CJun
	- 'Popcorn'	CJun EPfP LRHS WLov
	- 'Rainbow'	CJun EPfP MMrt
	- 'Red Chief'	CJun

- 'Red Elf'	CJun NLar
- 'Rising Sun'	CJun EPfP NLar
§ - subsp. ***sieboldianus***	CExl EPfP MRav WLov
- - B&SWJ 10941	SAko WCru
- - PAB 5337	LEdu
- - 'Calocarpus'	CJun EPfP
- - 'Coral Charm'	CBcs CJun EBee EPfP NLar WLov
- 'Snow' (v)	WCot WLov
- 'Winter Glory'	CJun NLar
§ ***huangii***	CJun CMCN WLov
- B&SWJ 3700	WCru
japonicus	CBcs CBod CCoa CDoC CMac EPfP LRHS MNic SArc SCob SEND SEWo SGsty SPer SWeb SavN
- 'Albomarginatus' (v)	CTri EPfP MPri SCob SEND SRms
- 'Argenteovariegatus' (v)	SGsty
§ - 'Aureomarginatus' (v)	CAco CBrac CCVT GBin LRHS MPri SWeb
- 'Aureopictus'	see *E. japonicus* 'Aureus'
- 'Aureovariegatus'	see *E. japonicus* 'Ovatus Aureus'
§ - 'Aureus' (v)	CBcs CDoC CKel CSBt EPfP MPri NRHS SCob SCoo SEND SLon SPer
- 'Benkomasaki'	LRHS LSRN SGsty
- 'Bravo' (v)	CBar CBod CCVT CDoC CEme CKel CRos EHyd EPfP GDam LPar LRHS MAsh MGos MPri NRHS SArc SCob SCoo SEWo SGsty SPer SPoG SWeb SWvt WCot WFar
- 'Charles' PBR	SPoG
- 'Chollipo' (v) 🏆H5	CKel EBee ELan EPfP SEND SPoG WAvo
- 'Compactus'	SCoo
- 'Duc d'Anjou' Carrière (v)	CKel EBee ELan EPfP EWes MRav SEND SPoG
- 'Elegantissimus Aureus'	see *E. japonicus* 'Aureomarginatus'
- EXTASE ('Goldbolwi' PBR) (v)	WCot
- 'Francien' (v)	EHyd EPfP LRHS NLar NRHS
- 'Gold Queen'	NLar
- 'Golden Maiden' (v)	CKel EHyd ELan EPfP MAsh SCoo SLim SLon SPoG SRms SWvt
- GREEN MILLENIUM ('Minmil' PBR)	LRHS
- 'Green Rocket'	CBod CCVT CCoa CEme CEnd CKel CRos EBee EHyd EPfP GBin LRHS LSRN MGos MNic MRav NRHS SGol SPoG SSta SWvt WCot WFar
- 'Green Spider'	SPoG
- 'Green Spire'	CDoC CEnd MNic NLar SWvt
- 'Happiness' PBR	CBod MTin
- 'Kathy' PBR	CRos EHyd ELan ELon EPfP LPar LRHS LSRN MAsh NLar NRHS SPoG SavN
§ - 'Latifolius Albomarginatus' (v)	CKel ELan EPfP MRav MSwo SPer SWvt
- 'Luna'	see *E. japonicus* 'Aureus'
- 'Macrophyllus'	SavN
- 'Macrophyllus Albus'	see *E. japonicus* 'Latifolius Albomarginatus'
- 'Maiden's Gold'	CSBt
- 'Marieke'	see *E. japonicus* 'Ovatus Aureus'
- 'Mediopictus'	LPar
- 'Microphyllus'	CMac LPar MNic MRav SArc SGol SRms
§ - 'Microphyllus Albovariegatus' (v)	CBod CKel CMac CSBt CTri EHyd ELan EPfP LRHS MGos SCob SRms SWvt WAvo WFar
§ - 'Microphyllus Aureovariegatus' (v)	CMac CRos CSBt EHyd ELan ELon EPfP LRHS MAsh MMuc NLar NRHS SGsty
- 'Microphyllus Aureus'	see *E. japonicus* 'Microphyllus Pulchellus'
- 'Microphyllus Gold Dust'	CBod
§ - 'Microphyllus Pulchellus' (v)	CBcs CDoC CKel CMac CSBt EPfP LRHS MGos MMuc SPoG SWvt
- 'Microphyllus Variegatus'	see *E. japonicus* 'Microphyllus Albovariegatus'
§ - 'Ovatus Aureus' (v) 🏆H5	Widely available
- PALOMA BLANCA ('Lankveld03' PBR)	CRos EHyd EPfP LCro LOPS LPar LRHS NRHS SCoo SPoG SavN WFar
- 'Président Gauthier' (v)	CDoC EBee ELan GArf LPar LRHS SCob SCoo SGsty SPer SWeb SWvt
- 'Pulchellus Aureovariegatus'	see *E. japonicus* 'Microphyllus Aureovariegatus'
- 'Robustus'	CBod
- 'Rokujo'	GEdr
- 'Silver King'	CMac SGsty
- 'Silver Krista' (v)	NLar
- 'Susan' (v) 🏆H5	CMac MAsh SGsty
§ - 'Viridivariegatus' (v)	LRHS WAvo
- 'White Spire' PBR (v) **new**	LRHS MGos WLea
kachinensis B&SWJ 11668	WCru
kiautschovicus 'Berry Hill'	NLar
- 'Manhattan'	NLar
latifolius	CJun CMCN EPfP IDee LEdu WCru
aff. ***latifolius*** NJM 13.024	WPGP
§ ***laxiflorus*** GWJ 9351	WCru
- HWJ 890	WCru
lucidus	CBcs CExl IDee
macropterus	CJun CMCN IArd
- B&SWJ 12591	WCru
morrisonensis	see *E. huangii*
myrianthus	CJun EPfP EWTr IArd IDee LRHS MBlu MPkF NLar SPtp
aff. ***myrianthus*** slim-leaved NJM 11.016	WPGP
§ ***nanus***	NLar WLov
- var. ***turkestanicus***	EPfP NLar SBrt SMad SRms
obovatus	SBrt
'Ogisu'	GKev
oxyphyllus 🏆H6	CJun CMCN ELan EPfP LRHS MMuc NLar SPtp WCru WLov
- 'Waasland'	CJun NLar
phellomanus 🏆H6	CBcs CKel EBee ELan EPfP GKin IDee LPar LRHS MBlu MGil MGos MMuc MPkF MRav MSCN MTrO NLar NOrn SCoo SPer SPoG SWvt WMat WPGP
PIERROLINO ('Heespierrolino' PBR)	MRav NLar SCoo
§ ***planipes***	Widely available
- B&SWJ 8660	WCru
- 'Dart's August Flame'	CJun
- 'Sancho' 🏆H6	CJun EPfP LRHS NLar WMat
porphyreus B&SWJ 13914	WCru
- GWJ 9377	WCru
quelpaertensis	CJun
'Rokojō Variegated' (v)	WCot
rosmarinifolius	see *E. nanus*
rubescens	see *E. laxiflorus*
sachalinensis misapplied	see *E. planipes*
sachalinensis (F. Schmidt) Maxim. B&SWJ 10835	WCru
sacrosanctus	CJun MBlu
sanguineus	CJun NLar
semenovii	WPGP
sieboldianus	WCru
var. ***sanguineus*** B&SWJ 11140	

- - B&SWJ 11386 WCru
spraguei NFav SBrt
- CWJ 12446 WCru
tingens CJun CMCN SPtp WPGP
tonkinensis WCru
FMWJ 13350 new
trapococcus EPfP SPtp
vagans Wall. WCot
velutinus NLar SPtp
verrucosus CJun NLar
- NJM 13.024 new WPGP
wilsonii EWTr MBlu NLar
yedoensis see *E. hamiltonianus* subsp. *sieboldianus*

Eupatoriadelphus see *Eupatorium*

Eupatorium ✿ (*Asteraceae*)

B&SWJ 9052 from Guatemala WCru
FMWJ 13428 from Northern Vietnam WCru
album misapplied see *Ageratina altissima*
album L. NBid
altissimum SRms
amabile NMWJ 14456 WCru
cannabinum CBod CHab CPla CPud EBee EGrI GJos GPoy GQue LLWG LShi MBNS MHer MMuc MNHC MWts NAts NBir NMir NPer SEND SPhx SSal WHer WSFF
§ - f. ***albiflorum*** SPhx
- f. ***cannabinum*** 'Flore Pleno' (d) CMac ECtt ELan ELon MBel MHer MRav NBir NGdn NLar SDix WCot WFar WSFF WWtn
- - 'Spraypaint' (v) WSFF
capillifolium ♀H3 CTtf EBee ECtt ESwi EWes MBel MNrw MPie SDix SHar SMad SMrm SSal
- 'Elegant Plume' EBee
coelestinum see *Conoclinium coelestinum*
dubium 'Baby Joe'PBR CBod CKno CWGN EBee ECtt EHyd ELan EShb EWTr IPot LRHS MBNS MNrw MPie NLar NRHS SEdd SGBe SHar SPad SPeP WNPC WSFF
- 'Little Joe' CBod CTtf EBee GBin LEdu MNHC WCAu WSFF WWtn
fistulosum EBee
- f. ***albidum*** ECha EWhm
- - 'Bartered Bride' CKno EBee ECtt EPPr EWes LPla MBel NLar SPeP WCot WSFF
- - 'Ivory Towers' CBod CDor CRos EBee ECha EHyd GJos LRHS MACG NRHS SBls SPtp WCot WSFF
- - 'Massive White' ♀H7 ELon GBee MNrw NBir NSti
- 'Berggarten' WSFF
- 'Carin' WSFF
fortunei 'Capri' (v) WCot WHil
- 'Fine Line' (v) WSFF
- 'Pink Elegance' (v) CBod EBee ECtt EHyd EMor EShb LRHS LShi LSou MNrw NRHS SDix SGbt SPoG SRms WWtn
- 'Pink Frost' (v) GBee MWts NGdn SCob SPeP
japonicum GPoy
ligustrinum see *Ageratina ligustrina*
lindleyanum LEdu WSFF
- var. ***trisectifolium*** B&SWJ 12742 WCru
maculatum NGdn NLar
- Atropurpureum Group Widely available
- - 'Ankum's August' EBee LPla SMHy
- - 'Gateway' CBod CDor EBee ECtt EHyd ELon EPPr EPfP EWTr LEdu LRHS MBel NBid NLar SWvt WSFF WWtn
- - 'Glutball' CKno EHyd ELon LPla LRHS LSun MNrw NChi SMad SPeP
- - 'Little Red' WSFF
- - 'Orchard Dene' ♀H7 ECha LEdu SMHy
- - 'Phantom'PBR CRos EBee ECtt EHyd ELon EMor EWTr EWoo GBin LRHS MHol NLar NRHS SAko SMad SPoG WFar WSFF
- - 'Prairie Giant' MAvo NDov
- - 'Purple Bush' ♀H7 CDor CKno EBee ECtt EHyd ELon GBee GQue ILea LCro LOPS LRHS MHer NDov NGrd SDix SWvt WSFF
- - 'Red Dwarf' CBod CKno ECtt EHyd ELon EPfP EShb GQue LEdu LRHS MCot MPie NFav NRHS SPoG SWvt WHil WHoo
- - 'Riesenschirm' ♀H7 Widely available
- 'J.S. Humble' IPot LRHS MNrw
- 'Snowball'PBR CBod EPfP
makinoi var. ***oppositifolium*** B&SWJ 8449 WCru
'Mask' IPot MNrw NLar
micranthum see *Ageratina ligustrina*
perfoliatum EMor GPoy IPot MMuc NLar WSFF
purpureum CBcs CBod CHby ECha ECtt ELon GDam GMaP GPoy LLWG MHer MNHC NBro NChi NGdn SBut SCob SMrm SPer SPlb SRms WCAu WHer WSFF
- 'Album' CTri SWvt
rugosum see *Ageratina altissima*
* 'Snowball' LSou NDov SPoG
weinmannianum see *Ageratina ligustrina*
yakushimaense GEdr

Euphorbia ✿ (*Euphorbiaceae*)

'Abbey Dore' ♀H7 GBin MAvo SPhx WCot WSHC
amygdaloides ECtt SWvt XSen
- 'Bob's Choice' WSHC
- 'Craigieburn' CKel EHyd LRHS MRav NRHS
- 'Frosted Flame'PBR MHol
§ - 'Purpurea' Widely available
§ - var. ***robbiae*** ♀H6 Widely available
- - dwarf EWes
- - 'Redbud' EWes
- 'Rubra' see *E. amygdaloides* 'Purpurea'
- RUBY GLOW ('Waleuphglo') CSpe SPeP
* × ***arendsii*** new ECha SMHy
baselicis EWes
biglandulosa Desf. see *E. rigida*
BLACKBIRD ('Nothowlee'PBR) CBcs CExl CMac CWCL CWGN ECtt EPfP EWTr LCro LOPS LRHS MBel MGos MRav NLar SCob SEdd SMad SWvt WHil WSpi XSen
'Blue Haze' LPla WCot WFar WMal WSHC WSpi
cactus CDoC
capitulata SBrt
cashmeriana CC&McK 607 EWes
ceratocarpa ♀H4 CSpe ECha ECtt EWes GMaP SMad SPhx WAvo WCot WSHC WSpi WTor XSen
characias CBcs CMac EHyd EPfP EWoo MCot MRav NPer NRHS SPer SRms SWvt WBrk WCot WSMil XSen
- 'Ascot Moonbeam' LRHS SGBe SPoG
- 'Black Pearl' CBcs CEme CKel CRos ECtt EHyd ELan EPfP GKev LRHS MAvo MBel MHol MPri NLar NRHS SCob SGBe SGbt SPoG SRkn SWvt WSpi XSte

- 'Blue Wonder'	CExl CSpe ECtt EHyd ELan EPfP EWes GMaP LRHS NLar SCob WCot WNPC XSen
- 'BQ'	WCot
- subsp. ***characias***	CBod EPfP NLar SEND
- - 'Blue Hills' ♀H4	ECtt GKev
- - 'Burrow Silver' (v)	EPfP MRav SWvt WNPC
- - 'Humpty Dumpty'	CExl CRos EBee ECtt EHyd ELan EPfP EWoo GMaP GWyn LRHS LSRN MPri NLar NPer NRHS SCob SPer SRms SWvt WFar
- - 'Joshua'	WCot
- 'Eye-catcher'	WCot
- 'Forescate'	EBee EHyd EPfP NRHS
- 'Glacier Blue'PBR (v)	CBct CBod CRos CSpe CTsd CWGN EBee ECha EHyd ELan EPfP GKev LRHS LSRN MAsh MBel MHol NHpl NLar NRHS SCob SCoo SEdd SGBe SHeu SPeP SPoG SRms WCot WNPC
- 'Goldbrook'	EPfP LRHS MBriF MRav NRHS
- 'Kestrel' (v)	WCot
- 'Portuguese Velvet'	CBct CExl CRos ECtt EHyd ELan EPfP GWyn LRHS MCot MHol MRav NLar NRHS SArc SMrm SPtp WCot XLum XSen
- 'Silver Edge' (v)	LSou MHol NSti SCoo SGBe WNPC XSte
- SILVER SWAN ('Wilcott'PBR) (v)	Widely available
- 'Tasmanian Tiger'PBR (v) ♀H4	CRos CWGN EPfP EWTr EWes GMaP LRHS LSRN MGos MHol NHpl NLar NRHS SCob SGBe SHeu SPoG SRms SWvt WCot WNPC WSpi
- subsp. ***wulfenii***	Widely available
- - 'Bosahan'	CExl
- - 'Emmer Green' (v)	CExl ECtt EWes NSti WCot
- - 'Jayne's Golden Giant'	SMad
- - 'Jimmy Platt' ♀H4	SRms WCot
§ - - 'John Tomlinson'	EGrl EWes MRav SPtp WAvo WSpi
- - Kew form	see *E. characias* subsp. *wulfenii* 'John Tomlinson'
- - 'Lambrook Gold'	MRav NLar NPer SCob WSpi
- - 'Lambrook Gold' seed-raised	see *E. characias* subsp. *wulfenii* Margery Fish Group
§ - - Margery Fish Group	EHyd EPfP LRHS MCot NBir NRHS SPer
- - 'Perry's Tangerine'	EWes NPer
§ - - 'Purple and Gold'	MAvo NLar SGBe SWvt XLum XSen
- - 'Purpurea'	see *E. characias* subsp. *wulfenii* 'Purple and Gold'
- - 'Shorty'	EBee ECtt EHyd EPfP LRHS NLar NRHS SGBe SPoG XSen
- - 'Silver Shadow' (v)	EBee NGBl WCot
- - 'Thelma's Giant'	MAvo
- - 'Westacre Giant'	EWes
clavarioides	WAbe
- var. ***truncata***	WCot
'Copton Ash'	CBcs EBee ECha ECtt GBin IPot SPhx XSen
corallioides	CBod ECha EPfP GWyn LSun NLar NPer NSti WHer WNPC
§ ***cornigera*** ♀H5	CDor EBee ECha EGrl EHyd EPfP LRHS MMuc NBid NGdn NLar NRHS NSti SEND SPhx WCru WFar
- 'Goldener Turm'	ECtt EHyd EPfP LCro LOPS LRHS LSou SPer SPhx
corollata	CSpe IPot
cyparissias	ECha ELan EWoo GQue MRav NBir NGdn NLar SRms WBrk WFar XLum XSen
- 'Betten'	see *E.* × *gayeri* 'Betten'
- 'Clarice Howard'	see *E. cyparissias* 'Fens Ruby'
- clone 2	WCot
§ - 'Fens Ruby'	Widely available
- 'Orange Man'	CBcs CKel CRos ECtt EHyd ELan EPfP EWes LRHS LSou MCot NGdn NLar NRHS SPoG SVen SWvt WBrk WFar WSMil
- 'Purpurea'	see *E. cyparissias* 'Fens Ruby'
- 'Red Devil'	CDor
- 'Tall Boy'	EBee EWes
deflexa	ECha EWes MAvo NLar WMal
dendroides	CKel SPtp
'Despina'PBR	SGBe
§ ***donii***	ECha EWes MAvo NFav SPtp WSpi
- HWJK 2405	WCru
- 'Amjillasa'	ECha SDix
dulcis	NBro
- 'Chameleon'	CDor ECtt EGrl ELan ELon EPfP GQue GWyn MGos MRav NBid NBir NFav NLar NPer SCob SPlb SWvt WBrk WCAu WCot WFar WSpi
'Efanthia'PBR	CRos EWes GBin LRHS NRHS SGBe
§ ***epithymoides***	Widely available
- 'Bonfire'PBR	CBod ECha EGrl GBin LSun MAvo MBNS MBel MHol NGBl NLar SPer SPoG WCot WHil
§ - 'Candy'	CBod ECha LPla MACG MHol NLar SMrm WFar
- 'First Blush' (v)	NLar WCot WFar
- 'Golden Fusion'	EPfP
§ - 'Lacy' (v)	EWes WFar
§ - 'Major' ♀H6	CExl EBee SDix WKif
- 'Midas'	GBin MNrw SEdd SMHy SMrm WMal
- 'Senior'	CRos EHyd EPfP GBin LRHS MNrw NLar NRHS SEdd
EXCALIBUR ('Froeup'PBR)	CEme CExl CMac CWCL ELan ELon LSRN MBNS MMuc MRav NBir NLar NRHS NSti SEND SIvy SSal SWvt
fischeriana B&SWJ 8575	WCru
§ × ***gayeri*** 'Betten'	EBee EWes NLar
'Golden Foam'	see *E. stricta*
graminea 'Glitz' **new**	SPhx
'Grey Hedgehog'	CKel
griffithii	GQue LEdu NBro WFar WWtn
- 'Dixter'	Widely available
- 'Fern Cottage'	EWes
- 'Fireglow'	Widely available
- 'King's Caple'	EWes LRHS NLar SPoG WCru
- 'Wickstead'	EMor NLar
'Helena'PBR (v)	CExl LSRN NLar SWvt
henryi	see *E. sieboldiana*
heptagona	SEND
hierosolymitana	SBrt
horrida ♀H2	SPlb
hypericifolia DIAMOND FROST ('Inneuphe'PBR)	CSpe LCro LOPS LSou SRkn WCot
- 'Diamond Star'	LSou
- 'Silverfog'PBR	LSou MCot
- STARPLEASURE **new**	LSou
jacquemontii	MRav NLar WCot
'Jade Dragon'	LRHS SMHy SWvt
'Jessie'	NLar
jolkinii	CExl
KALIPSO ('Innkalff')	EPfP NLar
'Lambrook Silver'	SRkn
lathyris	NLar NPer SRms SVic WHer
longifolia misapplied	see *E. cornigera*
longifolia D. Don	see *E. donii*
longifolia Lam.	see *E. mellifera*
margalidiana ♀H4	ECha EWes GBin WCot

marginata **new**	CSpe
× ***martini***	Widely available
- 'Aperitif'	SPoG
- 'Ascot Rainbow'PBR (v) 🏆H5	Widely available
- 'Baby Charm'	CRos EPfP LRHS LSRN MBel MGos NLar NRHS SCob SGBe SMrm WNPC XSen
- 'Helen Robinson' 🏆H5	WCot
- 'Kolibri'	EHyd EPfP LRHS NRHS SCoo SWvt
- 'Rudolph'PBR	CBod ELan NLar SPoG
- TINY TIM ('Waleutiny')	CBod EBee ECtt EHyd EPfP LRHS MPri NChi NFav NRHS SWvt
- 'Walberton's Red Flush'	CRos EHyd LRHS NRHS
- WALBERTON'S RUBY GLOW ('Waleuphglo') **new**	EPfP LRHS
mauritanica	EShb
§ ***mellifera*** 🏆H3	Widely available
milii 🏆H1b	EBak
myrsinites 🏆H5	Widely available
- 'Washfield'	WSHC
nereidum 🏆H5	EWes WMal
nicaeensis	EBee LRHS SPhx WCot XSen
oblongata	CSpe LRHS NLar SEND SPhx WCot
palustris 🏆H7	Widely available
- 'Teichlaterne'	GBin SAko
- 'Walenburg's Glorie'	EBee ECha ELon EWTr EWoo GBin LCro LOPS LRHS MNrw MRav NLar NSti SMad WKif XLum
- 'Woodchippings'	WCot
- 'Zauberflöte'	SRms
paralias	WHer
§ × ***pasteurii***	CBcs CBct CDTJ CKel ELan EPfP EWes GMaP GWyn LShi MBNS MNrw MRav NBir NLar SIvy SPhx WCot WMal WPGP
- Brown's strain	CBod EWoo LPla LRHS MBNS SEdd WCot
- 'Honey Pot' 🏆H6 **new**	CDoC LRHS
- 'John Phillips' 🏆H4	CBct CExl EBee EGrI EPfP LRHS MAvo SChF SSal WPGP
- 'Phrampton Phatty' 🏆H4	LRHS MAvo WCot WPGP
- 'Roundway Titan' 🏆H6	CKel ELan EMil EPfP LRHS SWvt
- 'Skinny Bere'	LEdu
pentagona	SVen
pilosa 'Major'	see *E. epithymoides* 'Major'
pithyusa	CPla ECha EGrI ELan SEND SPlb WSHC XSen
- subsp. ***cupanii*** 'Ponte Leccia' **new**	NLar
polychroma	see *E. epithymoides*
- 'Purpurea'	see *E. epithymoides* 'Candy'
- 'Variegata'	see *E. epithymoides* 'Lacy'
portlandica	EGrI SVen WHer
REDWING ('Charam'PBR)	CBcs CMac ECul ELan GWyn LBuc LSou MHol MNrw MRav NLar SGBe SPoG SWvt WCot
reflexa	see *E. seguieriana* subsp. *niciciana*
§ ***rigida*** 🏆H6	CBro CKel ELan EWes SPhx WCot WSpi XSen
robbiae	see *E. amygdaloides* var. *robbiae*
sarawschanica	ECha GKev LPla SMad SPhx
schillingii 🏆H5	CDor CRos EBee ELan EPfP EWTr EWoo GBin GMaP GWyn IPot LRHS LSRN MMuc MRav NLar SMad SPhx SPlb SPoG SPtp SRms SWvt WCAu WCru WFar WSHC WSpi
schoenlandii	SPlb
seguieriana	ECha EGrI EWes SAng
§ - subsp. ***niciciana***	EWTr GBin LCro LOPS LRHS MAvo SMHy SPhx WCAu WHoo XSen
serrulata Thuill.	see *E. stricta*
§ ***sieboldiana*** **new**	MHol
sikkimensis 🏆H5	CExl CMea ECha EHyd EWes GLog GWyn LPla LRHS NLar NPer NRHS SRms SSal WCru WFar
- 'Crûg Contrast'	MAvo WCru WFar
spinosa	CKel SPlb XLum
§ ***stricta***	CBgR CSpe GWyn NWad WSpi
stygiana	CAbb CBcs CBod CDTJ CExl ECre EGrI ELan ELon EPfP EWes GBin LPla LRHS LShi MCot MHol MNrw SAko SMad SPlb SPtp WCot WCru WPGP WSHC
- subsp. ***santamariae***	CDTJ SPeP WMal WPGP WSHC
- subsp. ***stygiana***	EBee WPGP
- 'Torridge' 🏆H4	WCot
tirucalli	EShb
valdevillosocarpa	GJos GWyn LPla NLar SPhx WFar
'Velvet Ruby'	GWyn LSRN SWvt XSen
wallichii misapplied	see *E. donii*
wallichii Kohli	see *E. cornigera*
wallichii ambig.	EWoo LOPS LRHS MCot MRav NSti
wallichii Hook. f.	CExl EPfP LCro LOPS MNrw SPhx WCot
'Whistleberry Garnet' 🏆H7	CBar CKel CMac EBee ELan EPfP EWTr GBin LRHS MMuc SPhx SWvt WNPC

Euptelea (*Eupteleaceae*)

franchetii	see *E. pleiosperma*
§ ***pleiosperma***	CBcs EWTr NLar
polyandra	EBee EPfP NLar SBrt WPGP

Eurya (*Pentaphylacaceae*)

japonica	IDee
- 'Moutiers' (v)	CBcs LRHS MGil MPkF XSte
- 'Variegata' misapplied	see *Cleyera japonica* 'Fortunei'

Eurybia (*Asteraceae*)

§ ***divaricata***	Widely available
§ - 'Eastern Star'	LPla WCot WFar WSpi
- Raiche form	see *E. divaricata* 'Eastern Star'
- 'Snow Heron'	MNrw
- 'Tradescant'	MNrw NLar SMad
§ ***furcata***	XLum
§ × ***herveyi***	CBod EAJP ECha ECtt EHyd ELan ELon EPPr EWoo GLog LCro LEdu LOPS LRHS MACG MAvo MBel MSpe NDov NLar NSti NWsh SPer SPhx WCot WFar WSHC XLum
§ ***macrophylla***	EHyd ELan EWoo GQue LRHS MHol NLar NRHS SPhx WFar
- 'Albus'	EPPr WFar
- 'Twilight'	see *E.* × *herveyi*
§ ***radula***	EPPr EWes MACG MAvo MNrw NLar NWsh WSHC
- 'August Sky'	CKno EBee EPPr GBee LRHS NDov SHar SPhx WCot WFar WHoo
§ ***schreberi***	CDor ECha EPPr EWes LEdu LPla MACG MAvo MHol MNrw MPie MSpe NWsh WCot WFar WHoo WPGP
§ ***sibirica***	EBou NLar
§ ***spectabilis***	EBou EHyd WFar
- 'JS Macho Blue'	IPot MNrw WFar

Euryops (*Asteraceae*)

abrotanifolius	CCCN SVen
§ ***acraeus*** 🏆H4	CMea ECtt ELan EPot EWes WAbe
brachypodus	SVen
§ ***chrysanthemoides***	CBcs CCCN CSde EShb SEND SVen

- 'Sonnenschein'	ECre
evansii Schltr.	see *E. acraeus*
lateriflorus	SPlb
pectinatus 🏆H3	CBcs CBod CCCN CCht CDTJ CDoC CExl CKel CRos CSBt CSde CTri CTsd EHyd ELan EPfP EShb LRHS MGil MSCN NFav SEND SGBe SMrm SVen SWvt
- double-flowered (d)	CCCN
tenuissimus	SVen
tysonii	ELon EWes SPlb SVen
virgineus	CCCN CExl CKel SPlb SVen

Euscaphis (*Staphyleaceae*)

japonica	SPtp
- B&SWJ 11359	WCru
- B&SWJ 12739	WCru

Eustachys (*Poaceae*)

§ ***distichophylla***	EHyd NWsh XLum

Eustephia (*Amaryllidaceae*)

coccinea	WCot

Eutrema (*Brassicaceae*)

§ ***japonicum***	CExl GGro GPoy LEdu
- 'Monzen'	GPoy

Eutrochium see *Eupatorium*

Ewartia (*Asteraceae*)

planchonii	SPlb WAbe

Exbucklandia (*Hamamelidaceae*)

populnea	WPGP
tonkinensis KWJ 12209	WCru

Exochorda (*Rosaceae*)

alberti	see *E. korolkowii*
giraldii var. ***wilsonii***	CExl CKel CMac EBee EHed ELan EMil EPfP MBlu MMuc MRav NLar SWvt WCFE
§ ***korolkowii***	MAsh
× ***macrantha***	ILea
- 'Irish Pearl'	CExl
§ - 'Niagara'PBR	CAco CBcs CBod CDoC CMac CRos EBee EHyd EPfP EShb GKev LCro LOPS LRHS LSRN MGos NLar NRHS SCob SGol SPoG SavN
- SNOW DAY SURPRISE	see *E. × macrantha* 'Niagara'
- 'The Bride' 🏆H6	Widely available
MAGICAL SPRINGTIME ('Kolmaspirit')	LRHS MPkF NLar SCoo WFar
racemosa	EPfP NLar SPer
- MAGICAL SNOWDROPS ('Kolmagisno'PBR) **new**	LRHS
serratifolia	CBcs CKel EBee ELan EMil EPfP LRHS SPoG
- 'Snow White'	CEnd CJun EHed EWes GKin IArd IDee ILea LRHS MAsh MBlu MPri NLar SLon SWvt

F

Fabiana (*Solanaceae*)

imbricata	CBod CPbh EPfP MGil SLon SPlb WPav
- 'Prostrata'	CBod ELan SNig SVen WPav

- f. ***violacea*** 🏆H4	CExl CMac CSBt CTri ELan EPfP LRHS MMuc SGBe SNig SPad SWvt WAvo WKif WPav WSMil
- - dark-flowered	CBcs

Fagopyrum (*Polygonaceae*)

cymosum	see *F. dibotrys*
§ ***dibotrys***	CSpe EBee ECha EWld LEdu XLum
I - 'Cally Form'	ESwi

Fagraea (*Gentianaceae*)

ceilanica FMWJ 13099	WCru

Fagus ✿ (*Fagaceae*)

from Guangxi, China	WPGP
from Vietnam	WPGP
§ ***crenata***	CMCN CMen MBlu
- 'Mount Fuji'	CAco CMen
engleriana	CExl LRHS
grandifolia subsp. ***mexicana***	WPGP
longipetiolata	CBcs CExl CMCN EPfP WPGP
- NJM 11.036	WPGP
lucida	CExl CMCN MBlu
orientalis	CBcs CMCN
- 'Iskander'	EBee IArd IDee MBlu SGol SMad
sieboldii	see *F. crenata*
sylvatica 🏆H6	Widely available
- 'Albovariegata' (v)	CLnd
- 'Aniek'	SGol
- 'Asterix'	MBlu
- Atropurpurea Group	Widely available
- - 'Purpurea Pendula'	CAco CBcs CCVT CEnd CMCN CMac CSBt CTri EBee ELan EPfP GKin IPap LMaj LPar MGos MTrO NOrn NRog NWea SCoo SGol SLau SLim SPer SPoG WFar WMat WMou WTSh
- - 'Riversii' 🏆H6	CBcs CEnd CLnd CMCN CTri ELan EPfP GKin LMaj MGos MNic MTrO NOrn NRog NWea SGsty SPer WMat
- - 'Swat Magret'	EPfP LMaj
- 'Aurea Pendula'	CEnd MBlu SMad
- 'Bicolor Sartini' (v)	MBlu
- 'Birr Zebra'	CEnd
- 'Black Swan'	CLnd CMCN EBee ELan LPar LSRN MAsh MBlu MGos MTrO NHol NOra NOrn SLon SPoG WMat WMou
- 'Bornyensis'	MBlu
- 'Brathay Purple'	MBlu SMad
- 'Cochleata'	CMCN
- 'Cockleshell'	MBlu
- 'Cristata'	MBlu
§ - 'Dawyck' 🏆H6	CBcs CLnd CMac ELan EPfP LMaj LPar MGos NLar NRog NWea SCob SGol SLau SPer
- 'Dawyck Gold' 🏆H6	CAco CBcs CBod CEnd CLnd CMCN CMac CSBt CTri ELan GKin IPap LMaj LPar MAsh MBlu MGos MNic MTrO NLar NOra NOrn NRog NWea SCob SGol SLau SPer WMat
- 'Dawyck Purple' 🏆H6	Widely available
- 'Fastigiata' misapplied	see *F. sylvatica* 'Dawyck'
- 'Franken' (v)	CAco MBlu SMad
- 'Grandidentata'	LMaj
- 'Green Obelisk'	MBlu
- 'Greenwood'	MBlu
- var. ***heterophylla***	CLnd NRog NWea
- - 'Aspleniifolia' 🏆H6	CEnd CMCN CMac EBee EPfP EWTr GBin GKin LMaj LPar MBlu MGos MTrO SCoo SGol SLau SPer SPoG WMat

- - (Atropurpurea Group) 'Ansorgei' CEnd MBlu
- - 'Incisa' MBlu
- - f. ***laciniata*** MBlu
- - 'Mercedes' CAco CMCN MBlu WLov
- 'Horizontalis' MBlu
- 'Pendula' 🏆H6 CAco CBcs CCVT CEnd CLnd CMCN CMac CSBt ELan EWTr LPar MGos MSwo NOra NRog NWea SGol SLau SPer WMat WMou WTSh
- 'Purple Fountain' 🏆H6 CAco CEnd CMCN ELan LMaj LPar MAsh MBlu MGos MTrO NLar NOra NOrn NWea SLau SWeb WMat
- Purple-leaved Group see *F. sylvatica* Atropurpurea Group
§ - 'Purpurea Tricolor' (v) CAco CEnd CMCN CMac EBee LMaj MBlu MGos MTrO NOra NRog NWea SCoo WMat
- 'Red Obelisk' see *F. sylvatica* 'Rohan Obelisk'
- 'Rohan Gold' CEnd CMCN SGol
§ - 'Rohan Obelisk' CAco CEnd CMCN EBee ELan LMaj LPar MBlu
I - 'Rohan Pyramidalis' CEnd CMCN
- 'Rohan Trompenburg' CMCN MBlu
- 'Rohan Weeping' MBlu
- 'Rohanii' CBcs CEnd CMCN ELan EPfP GKin MGos NRog SLau
- 'Rolf Marquardt' (v) SMad
- 'Roseomarginata' see *F. sylvatica* 'Purpurea Tricolor'
- 'Rotundifolia' LMaj MBlu
- 'Silver Wood' SMad
- 'Spaethiana' GKin
- 'Striata' CAco
- f. ***tortuosa*** MBlu MPkF
- - 'Rot Süntel' CAco MTrO
- 'Tricolor' misapplied (v) see *F. sylvatica* 'Purpurea Tricolor' (v)
- 'Tricolor' ambig. (v) SLau
- 'Tricolor' (v) CBcs CLnd NHol NOra SGol
- 'Tur' SMad
- 'Zlatia' CLnd CMCN LPar MBlu MGil MGos NRog SGol SLau

Falcaria (*Apiaceae*)

vulgaris **new** WCot

Fallopia (*Polygonaceae*)

aubertii see *F. baldschuanica*
§ ***baldschuanica*** CBcs CBod CDoC CMac CRos CSBt CTri EBee EHyd ELan EPfP LBuc LCro LOPS LRHS MAsh MGos MMuc MPri MSwo NRHS SEND SGbt SLon SNig SPer SPlb SPoG SWvt WFar
§ ***multiflora*** LEdu
- var. ***hypoleuca*** CSde SCoo SPoG
- - B&SWJ 120 WCru

Farfugium (*Asteraceae*)

§ ***japonicum*** GGro SBrt WSMil
- B&SWJ 884 WCru
- B&SWJ 14699 WCru
- 'Argenteum' (v) EMil SMad WCot
§ - 'Aureomaculatum' (v) 🏆H3 XSte
- 'Bumpy Ride' WCot
- 'Crispatum' LEdu LPla XLum XSte
- double-flowered (d) WCru
- var. ***formosanum*** NMWJ 14574 WCru
- var. ***giganteum*** XSte
- 'Kaimon Dake' (v) WCot
- 'Kinkan' (v) WCot
- 'Shishi Botan' XSte
I - 'Tsuwa-buki' WCot
- 'Wavy Gravy' **new** XSte
'Last Dance'^{PBR} EBee ECtt
tussilagineum see *F. japonicum*

Fargesia (*Poaceae*)

from Jiuzhaigou, China CDTJ MAvo MMuc MWht NLar SCoo WPGP
adpressa MWht
apicirubens 'White Dragon' CDTJ CExl
confusa CDTJ
demissa 'Gerry' **new** CKel
denudata CBct CDTJ ESwi
- L 1575 CExl MWht
- Xian 1 CDTJ
dracocephala CBdn CExl GBin MAvo MBrN MMuc MWht NLar
'Jiuzaighou 9' GBin GDam
§ ***murielae*** 🏆H5 CAgr CBdn CDoC CEme EGrI ELan EPau EPfP GArf LCro LOPS LPar MACG MGos MMuc MWht NFav NWea SArc SCob SPlb WFar
- 'Bimbo' CBod CDoC EPfP LPar MAvo MWht NLar SWvt
- 'Dana Jumbo' EHyd LRHS NRHS
- 'Grüne Hecke' MWht
- 'Harewood' MWht SWvt
- 'Joy' CBct CBod GBin NLar
- 'Jumbo' CBcs CBod CDoC CSBt ELon EPfP GDam MAvo MGos MWht NGdn NLar NRHS SGsty SPer SRms SWvt
- 'Luca'^{PBR} **new** LRHS
- 'Mae' CDTJ MWht
- 'Panda'^{PBR} EHyd LRHS NRHS
- 'Simba' CBct CBod CExl EHyd EPfP GBin GDam GMaP LMaj LPar LRHS LSRN MBrN MGos MWht NGdn NLar NRHS SCob SGsty SPer SPlb SPoG SWeb SWvt WFar WPGP
murieliae BLUE DRAGONSCALE see *F. murieliae* BLUE LIZARD
§ - BLUE LIZARD ('Japo 72'^{PBR}) MWht SCoo
- RED ZEBRA ('Japo 51'^{PBR}) MWht
§ ***nitida*** CAbb CBcs CEme CEnd EHyd ELan EPfP GArf LRHS MAsh MGos MWht NRHS SCob SCoo SPoG SRms SWvt WPGP
- 'Black Pearl' GDam LPar MAvo WPGP
- 'Great Wall' CBod CDTJ CDoC CSBt ELan GBin MWht NLar
- Jiuzhaigou 1 see *F.* RED PANDA
- 'Jiuzhaigou 2' MWht
- 'Jiuzhaigou 4' CDTJ CExl WPGP
- 'Jiuzhaigou 8' CDTJ
- 'Jiuzhaigou Genf' CDTJ MWht NLar WPGP
- 'Volcano' SCoo
'Obelisk'^{PBR} LPar
§ RED PANDA ('Jiu') 🏆H4 CExl LCro LOPS SPoG SWvt
§ ***robusta*** 🏆H5 CAbb CBct CBod CDTJ CSBt ELan EPfP MAvo MBrN MMuc MWht NGdn NLar SCob SSut WPGP
- 'Asian Wonder' CBod CKel LCro LOPS LPar LRHS MHtn NFav NLar SEdd SGsty XSte
- 'Campbell' CBdn CDoC ELon LPar NLar SGsty
- 'Ming Yunnan' LEdu WPGP
- 'P. King' MWht

- 'Pingwu'	CBdn CBod CDTJ CDoC GDam LPar MGos MWht SGsty
- 'Red Sheath'	CDTJ CExl MWht WPGP
- 'Wenchuan'	CKel
- 'Wolong'	CBdn CExl LPar MWht NLar WPGP
rufa ♀H4	CAbb CBcs CBdn CBod CDoC CExl CSBt ELan ELon EPfP EShb LCro LOPS LSRN MAvo MBlu MBrN MGos MMuc MWht NFav NLar SCob SWeb WFar WPGP XSte
scabrida misapplied	see *F. robusta*
similaris KR 4175	MWht
spathacea misapplied	see *F. murielae*
utilis	MMuc MWht SEND
'Winter Joy'	SCoo
yulongshanensis	MWht

Fascicularia (*Bromeliaceae*)

andina	see *F. bicolor*
§ ***bicolor***	Widely available
- subsp. ***bicolor***	CDoC CMac SPtp
- subsp. ***canaliculata***	ELon LEdu MNrw SChr SIvy SPad WPGP
kirchhoffiana	see *F. bicolor*
litoralis	see *Ochagavia litoralis*
pitcairniifolia misapplied	see *F. bicolor*
pitcairniifolia (Verlot) Mez	see *Ochagavia litoralis*

× *Fatshedera* (*Araliaceae*)

lizei ♀H3	CBcs CMac CRos CSde CTri EBee ELon EPfP GBin LRHS MAsh MRav SArc SDix SEND SPer SPlb SPoG SRms SWvt WAvo
§ - 'Annemieke' (v) ♀H3	CBcs CBod CKel EHyd ELan ELon EPfP LRHS MMuc MRav SEND SEle SPer SPoG WAvo
§ - 'Aurea' (v)	CRos
- compact	CKel EPfP
- 'Lemon and Lime'	see × *F. lizei* 'Annemieke'
- 'Maculata'	see × *F. lizei* 'Annemieke'
- 'Variegata' (v) ♀H3	CSde EBee ELan ELon EPfP LRHS SDix SEND SPer SWvt WAvo
- 'Variegata' compact (v)	SPoG

Fatsia (*Araliaceae*)

§ ***japonica*** ♀H5	Widely available
- 'Annemie' (v)	WSMil
- 'Moseri'	CBod CExl ELan ELon ESwi LEdu MBNS SWvt WCot
- 'Spider's Web' (v)	Widely available
- 'Variegata' (v) ♀H5	CMac ELan EPfP LPar MAsh MGos MRav SCob SEND SLon SPoG WCot
I 'Megafatsia'	CDTJ
papyrifera	see *Tetrapanax papyrifer*
polycarpa	CDTJ CDoC CExl
- B&SWJ 1776	WCru
- B&SWJ 3467	WCru
- B&SWJ 7144	CExl WCru
- RWJ 10133	WCru
- from Tregye	IKel
- deeply cut leaf	GBin IKel MBNS SMad WCot WPGP
- GREEN FINGERS **new**	LRHS

Fatsia × *Hedera* see × *Fatshedera*

Faucaria (*Aizoaceae*)

tuberculosa ♀H2	CBod CPbh SEdd SSim

Fauria see *Nephrophyllidium*

Feijoa see *Acca*

Felicia (*Asteraceae*)

§ ***amelloides***	CCCN CPbh SPlb
- 'Santa Anita'	CTri SVen
§ - variegated (v)	CCCN ECtt NPer
§ ***amoena***	CTri
- 'Variegata' (v)	CCCN CTri
capensis	see *F. amelloides*
coelestis	see *F. amelloides*
echinata	CCCN
FELICITARA BLUE ('Wigetablue'PBR)	SPoG
filifolia blue-flowered	SVen
'Forever Blue'	CWCL
natalensis	see *F. rosulata*
pappei	see *F. amoena*
§ ***petiolata***	CFis CTri EBee EWes MMuc MNrw
§ ***rosulata***	CMea CSma GArf GEdr MAsh MHol NBro NLar SBrt WFar WIce
tenella	WSpi
uliginosa	EWes SBrt SPlb WIce
wrightii	GEdr

Fenestraria (*Aizoaceae*)

rhopalophylla subsp. ***aurantiaca*** ♀H2	SSim

fennel see *Foeniculum vulgare*

fenugreek see *Trigonella foenum-graecum*

Ferraria (*Iridaceae*)

§ ***crispa***	CBor GKev NRog WCot
- var. ***nortieri***	NRog WCot
divaricata	NRog WCot
- subsp. ***arenosa***	NRog
schaeferi	CBor NRog WCot
undulata	see *F. crispa*
variablis	WCot

Ferula (*Apiaceae*)

assa-foetida	WJek
chiliantha	see *F. communis* subsp. *glauca*
§ ***communis***	CCBP CElw CKel CMea CSpe ECha ELan EPri EWes GBin GPoy LEdu LRHS LShi SDix SEND SPad SPhx SPlb SPoG SPtp SSal WJek WSHC
- 'Cretan Giant'	WPGP
- 'Gigantea'	see *F. communis*
§ - subsp. ***glauca***	EBee ECha EWes LEdu SDix SMHy SPhx SSut WCot
- - B&SWJ 12999	WCru
- - NJM 13.001	WPGP
'Giant Bronze'	see *Foeniculum vulgare* 'Giant Bronze'
linkii	SPhx
tingitana B&SWJ 14005	WCru
- 'Cedric Morris'	ECha SDix SPhx WCot

Ferulago (*Apiaceae*)

cassia	WCot
nodosa **new**	SPhx
stellata	WCot
sylvatica	SPhx
- PAB 2875	LEdu WPGP

Festuca (*Poaceae*)

actae	XLum
amethystina	CBod CKel CKno EShb LCro LOPS LRHS MBel MMuc NGdn SCob SEND SMea SPhx

	- 'Aprilgrün'	XLum
	arundinacea	CHab MMuc SEND
	californica	XLum
	curvula	EShb
	subsp. ***crassifolia***	
	elegans	EPPr
	eskia	XLum
	filiformis	CHab
§	***gautieri***	CPla NWsh WSpi XLum
	- 'Pic Carlit'	NLar XLum
	gigantea	CHab MMuc SEND
	glacialis	XLum
	- 'Czakor'	XLum
	glauca Vill.	CBcs CBod EShb GMaP GWyn MBNS MGos MRav NGdn SPer SPlb SRms XSen
I	- 'Auslese'	CBod CExl EShb NGdn
	- 'Azurit'	CBod EWes NLar NWad SCob SPoG SRms
§	- 'Blaufuchs'	CEme CSBt EHyd ELan EPfP EWes GMaP LRHS MAsh MBlu MGos NLar NRHS NWad NWsh SCob SPer SPlb SWvt WFar WSpi XLum
§	- 'Blauglut'	EHyd MRav SCob SRms
	- BLUE FOX	see *F. glauca* 'Blaufuchs'
	- 'Blue Select'	LSun
	- 'Elijah Blue'	Widely available
	- 'Golden Toupee'	ECha EHyd ELan EPfP LRHS MBlu MGos NLar NRHS SPer SPlb SWvt XLum
	- 'Harz'	XLum
	- INTENSE BLUE ('Casblue'PBR) ♀H5	CBod CKno CPla CRos EBee EHyd ELan EPfP EWes LCro LOPS LRHS LSRN MAsh MGos NRHS NWsh SCoo SMad SPeP SPoG SRms
*	- ***minima***	CCCN NWsh
§	- 'Seeigel'	NRHS
	- SELECT	see *F. glauca* 'Auslese'
	- 'Solling'	XLum
	- 'Uchte'	ECha
	idahoensis	EShb
	- 'Tomales Bay'	CKno
	liviensis	XSen
	mairei	CBod ECha LPla NWsh SEdd XLum
	ovina	CHab SPhx WSFF
	- var. ***gallica***	NWsh
*	- 'Tetra Gold'	SWvt
	paniculata	CKno
	pratensis	CHab SVic
	punctoria	MMuc
	rubra	CHab CKno SVic WSFF
	scoparia	see *F. gautieri*
	tatrae	MMuc SEND
	valesiaca var. ***glaucantha***	CBod LRHS NGdn XLum
§	- 'Silbersee'	SRms
	vivipara	NBid XLum
*	'Willow Green'	SPlb

Fibigia (*Brassicaceae*)

	eriocarpa	LRHS SPhx

Ficaria (*Ranunculaceae*)

	fascicularis	MNrw NRog NRya WCot
	verna	GKev
	- Alba Group	LEdu NRya
	- anemone-centred	see *F. verna* 'Collarette'
§	- Aurantiaca Group	CDor ECha NLar NRya SPhx
	- var. ***aurantiacus***	see *F. verna* Aurantiaca Group
	- 'Bowles's Double'	see *Ficaria verna* 'Double Bronze'
	- 'Brambling'	EBee LEdu
	- 'Brazen Child'	SHar
	- 'Brazen Hussy'	Widely available
	- subsp. ***bulbilifer***	see *F. verna* subsp. *verna*
§	- subsp. ***chrysocephala***	EBee ECha MNrw WCot
	- 'Coffee Cream'	NSum
§	- 'Collarette' (d)	EBee ELan EMor LEdu LLWG MHer NBir NLar NRog NRya NSum WFar
	- 'Coppernob'	CDor CFis WCot
	- 'Cupreus'	see *F. verna* Aurantiaca Group
	- double, cream-flowered	see *F. verna* 'Double Mud'
	- - white-flowered (d) **new**	NRog
	- - yellow-flowered	see *F. verna* Flore Pleno Group
§	- 'Double Bronze' (d)	LEdu NBir NRya NSum WFar
§	- 'Double Mud' (d)	EPPr LEdu NLar NRya NSum SHar WFar WHal
	- 'Dusky Maiden'	NLar NRya NSum WFar
	- 'E.A. Bowles'	see *F. verna* 'Collarette'
§	- Flore Pleno Group (d)	CBod CDor CMac CTri ECha ELan EPPr EPfP LShi NRya NSum SRms WCot WFar
	- 'Fried Egg'	LShi NSum WFar
	- 'Green Petal' (d)	EPPr NBir NRya NSum WFar WHal WHer
	- 'Green Rim'	CNat
	- 'Hyde Hall'	NLar WCot
	- 'Ken Aslet Double' (d)	EPPr MHer NSum WHal
	- 'Kingscot'	CNat
	- 'Lemon Dazzler'	EBou
	- subsp. ***major***	see *F. verna* subsp. *chrysocephala*
	- 'Martin Gibbs' Progeny'	CNat
	- 'Montacute' (d)	CDor
	- 'Old Master'	WCot
	- 'Orange Sorbet' (d)	NSum WFar
	- 'Petrol Spillage'	CNat
	- 'Primrose'	NRya NSum
	- 'Randall's White'	CDor CFis ECha EPfP NSum SHar WFar
	- 'Richard and Val'	WCot
	- 'Rita Pirouet'	WCot
	- 'Salmon's White'	EPPr NBir NRog NRya NSum SHar WFar WHal
	- 'Silver Collar' (d)	LEdu
	- 'Suffusion'	CNat
	- 'Tortoiseshell'	EPPr
§	- subsp. ***verna***	CTri WHer WSFF WShi
	- - 'Chedglow'	WCot
	- 'Wisley Double'	see *Ficaria verna* 'Double Bronze'
	- 'Yaffle'	WBor

Ficinia (*Cyperaceae*)

§	***nodosa***	SPlb
	truncata	CBor WCot
	- 'Ice Crystal' (v)	EHyd ELan LEdu LRHS NRHS SPoG

Ficus (*Moraceae*)

	afghanistanica 'Silver Lyre'	EBee EPfP SMad SVen WPGP
	benjamina 'Danielle'PBR	LCro LOPS
I	***binnendijkii*** 'Alii'	CDoC
	carica (F)	CCCN ERom LPar SArc SEWo SLon SPad
	- 'Adam' (F)	CCCN LEdu NLar NRog SEND SVen WPGP
I	- 'Bauern Feige' (F)	SRms
	- 'Beall' (F)	CCCN
	- 'Black Ischia' (F)	CCCN SDix SMHy
	- 'Bornholm' (F)	CCCN SPre SWeb
	- 'Bourjassotte Grise' (F)	CAgr XSen
	- 'Brogiotto Nero' (F) **new**	NRog
	- 'Brown Turkey' (F) ♀H4	Widely available

- 'Brunswick' (F) CAgr CBod CCCN CEme CRHN CTri ELan EPfP EPom EShb LEdu MTrO NLar NRHS NRog SDix SEND SKee SRms SVen WCot WFar WMat WTyc
- 'Califfo Blue' (F) SRms
- 'Cambridge Builder' (F) SVen
- 'Castle Kennedy' (F) CCCN
- 'Celeste' (F) SRms
- 'Chicago Hardy' (F) **new** NRog
- 'Col de Dame Blanc' (F) NRog XSen
- 'Col de Dame Noir' (F) XSen
- 'Colummaro Black Apulia' (F) CCCN
- 'Colummaro White Apulia' (F) CCCN
- 'Dalmatie' (F) CAgr CCCN CDoC ELan EPfP LRHS MTrO NOra NRog SEND SRms WMat WPGP XSen

I - 'Digitata' (F) MBlu
- 'Dorée' (F) EPom NRog XSen
- 'Dorée de Porquerolles' (F) CCCN
- 'Filacciano' (F) CCCN
- 'Fiorone Verde' (F) SVen
- 'Flanders' (F) CCCN
- 'Gianchetta' SVen
- 'Goutte d'Or' (F) CAgr CCCN EPfP EPom
- 'Green Ischia' (F) CCCN
- 'Grise de Marseille' (F) CCCN
- 'Grise de Saint Jean' (F) CCCN NRog XSen
- 'Ice Crystal' (F) ♀H5 CBod CDoC CKel CRos EBee ELan EMil EPfP EShb LEdu LPar LRHS MBlu MTrO NLar NOra SCoo SMad SPoG SRms SVen WCot WMat
- 'Jordan' (F) LRHS MTrO NOra
- 'Kadota' (F) CCCN NRog SVen
- 'Longue d'Août' (F) NRog XSen
- 'Lupo' (F) SVen
- 'Madeleine des Deux Saisons' (F) EPom SEND SKee XSen XSte
- 'Marseillaise' (F) XSen
- 'Melanzana' (F) CCCN
- 'Morena' (F) SRms
- 'Negretta' (F) SVen
- 'Negrétte de Porquerolles' (F) CCCN
- 'Nero' (F) SGsty
- 'Newlyn Harbour' (F) ELon
- 'Noire de Barbentane' (F) XSen
- 'Noire de Caromb' (F) CAgr CCCN EPfP LRHS MTrO SKee SRms WMat XSen
- 'Osborn's Prolific' (F) EPfP SEND SGol SWvt WCot
- 'Panachée' (F) CBod CCCN EPom MTrO NLar NOra SMad SRms
- 'Pastilière' (F) XSen
- 'Perretta' (F) LRHS
- 'Peter's Honey' (F) NRog
- 'Précoce de Dalmatie' (F) CCCN EMil EPfP EShb LEdu NLar SRms WCot
- 'Quinta' (F) CCCN

§ - 'Reculver' (F) SEND
- 'Ronde de Bordeaux' (F) CCCN EPfP NRog SEND SWeb XSen
- 'Rouge de Bordeaux' (F) CAgr CBod CCCN CTsd EPom LRHS SKee SMad SPlb SRms SSta XSte
- 'Rubado' (F) SVen
- 'Safi' (F) CCCN
- 'San Piero' (F) SVen
- 'Sucre Vert' (F) **new** NRog
- 'Sultane' (F) CAgr EPom IDee SVen WPGP XSen
- 'Tayip 1' (F) CAgr
- 'Tayip 2' (F) CAgr
- 'Tena' (F) NRog
- 'Verte d'Argenteuil' (F) CCCN
- 'Violette Dauphine' (F) EPfP LEdu NLar NRog SEND SKee
- 'Violette de Sollies' (F) XSen
- 'Violette Normande' (F) SEND XSte
- 'White Adriatic' (F) CAgr NLar NRog SRms
- 'White Genoa' see *F. carica* 'White Marseilles'

§ - 'White Marseilles' (F) CAgr CCCN CMac CRHN EPfP MTrO NRog SEND SKee SRms WMat WPGP
- 'Zamoreica' (F) SEND
- 'Zidi' (F) CCCN

carica* × *pumila **new** WPGP
elastica XAbr
- 'Robusta' CDoC LCro LOPS
- 'Tineke' (v) CDoC LCro LOPS

lyrata ♀H1b CDoC
- 'Bambino'PBR LCro LOPS

microcarpa CDoC
aff. ***oligodon*** SVen
pubigera CExl
pumila ♀H2 CDoC CTsd EShb
- 'Nana' NWad
- 'Sonny' (v) NWad
- 'Variegata' (v) ♀H2 EShb

punctata EShb
retusa (F) NGKo
tikoua IArd
vaccinioides **new** WPGP

fig see *Ficus carica*; see also AGM Fruit Section

filbert see *Corylus maxima*

Filipendula (*Rosaceae*)

alnifolia 'Variegata' see *F. ulmaria* 'Variegata'
camtschatica EBee ECha ELan LPla LRHS MMuc NBid NFav NLar WPGP WWtn
- B&SWJ 10987 WCru
- RBS 0224 NLar
- 'Rosea' CTtf

digitata 'Nana' see *F. multijuga*
hexapetala see *F. vulgaris*
- 'Flore Pleno' see *F. vulgaris* 'Multiplex'

'Kahome' CRos CTtf EHyd ELon EShb EWhm GAbr GLog GMaP LRHS NBid NBir NGdn NLar NRHS NSti SCob SPer SPhx WFar WPnP
kamtschatica 'Moe Ki Fukurin Fu' **new** GGro
kiraishiensis EBee
- B&SWJ 1571 WCru

koreana CRos EBlo EHyd LRHS NRHS
§ ***multijuga*** EBee EGrI EWhm NHol NLar NWad
- B&SWJ 10950 WCru
- 'Hjördis' CBod CKel EBee ELon EMor MACG MAvo MBel MNrw MSCN SPad SPeP WHil WHoo
- var. ***yezoensis*** B&SWJ 10828 WCru

palmata ECha EGrI EHyd WFar
- 'Digitata Nana' see *F. multijuga*
- dwarf GRum
- 'Elegantissima' see *F. purpurea* 'Elegans'
- 'Göteborg' EBee NLar
- 'Nana' see *F. multijuga*
- 'Rosea' CMac NBir
- 'Rubra' CRos EBee EBlo EHyd LRHS MRav NGdn NRHS

	purpurea	EBee ECha GQue ILea LCro LLWG MMuc SCob SEND SRms WCru WFar WTyc
	- f. ***albiflora***	ILea
§	- 'Elegans'	EBee EGrI EHyd ELon ILea NBid NHol NWad SCob SPer SRms WFar WPnP WTyc
	- 'Pink Dreamland'	SPhx
*	- 'Plena' (d)	NLar
	- 'Rhapsody' **new**	LPla
§	***rubra*** 'Venusta' ♀H5	Widely available
	- 'Venusta Magnifica'	see *F. rubra* 'Venusta'
	rufinervis	LPla
	- B&SWJ 8469	WCru
	- B&SWJ 8611	WCru
§	***ulmaria***	CBen CCBP CHab CHby CWat ENfk EWoo GBin GJos GMaP GPoy GQue LCro LOPS MBow MCot MHer MNHC MWts NGrd NMir SPhx WHer WPnP WSFF WShi WWild XLum
	- 'Aurea'	CBod CDor CMac CTri CWCL EBee ECha ECtt EGrI EHyd ELan EMor EWhm GBin GMaP LEdu LRHS MHol MRav NBid NFav NLar SPer SRms WCot WFar WSHC
	- 'Corinne Tremaine'	WHer
	- 'Flore Pleno' (d)	MRav NBid SPer WCot WFar WHrl
	- 'Rosea'	EHyd LEdu LLWG LRHS
§	- 'Variegata' (v)	CWCL EBee ECtt EHyd ELan EWhm GQue LRHS MHol NBid NGdn NLar NRHS SPer SRms WFar WHer XLum
§	***vulgaris***	CDor CHab CKel GLog LEdu LRHS MBow MMuc MNHC NBro NGrd NMir NQui SPhx WHer
	- 'Devon Cream'	MAvo
	- 'Flore Pleno'	see *F. vulgaris* 'Multiplex'
	- 'Grandiflora'	EGrI
§	- 'Multiplex' (d)	CDor CMac CSpe CTtf ECha EHyd ELan GMaP LLWG LPot LRHS MHer MMrt MMuc MNHC MRav MSCN NBid NBir NLar NRHS NRya NSti SCob SEdd SRms WFar
	- 'Plena'	see *F. vulgaris* 'Multiplex'

Firmiana (*Malvaceae*)

	simplex	CBcs EBee EShb ESwi LEdu MBlu SBrt SMad WPGP

Fittonia (*Acanthaceae*)

	albivenis Argyroneura Group ♀H1a	EShb
§	- Verschaffeltii Group ♀H1a	EShb

Fitzroya (*Cupressaceae*)

	cupressoides	CAco CBcs IArd IDee LRHS SLim WPav
	- 'Borde Hill' (f)	CAco

Flueggea (*Phyllanthaceae*)

	suffruticosa	SBrt

Foeniculum (*Apiaceae*)

	vulgare	Widely available
	- 'Bronze'	see *F. vulgare* 'Purpureum'
	- var. ***dulce***	ENfk
§	- 'Fino' ♀H2	EKin MCtn NRob
§	- 'Giant Bronze'	CKel GWyn LCro LEdu LOPS LRHS SCob SPhx WGrn WSpi XSen
	- 'Orion' ♀H2	EKin
§	- 'Purpureum'	Widely available
	- 'Smoky'	ECha MRav
	- 'Sweet Florence'	LCro SVic
	- 'Zefa Fino'	see *F. vulgare* 'Fino'

Fontanesia (*Oleaceae*)

	fortunei	EBtc

Fontinalis (*Fontinalaceae*)

	sp.	CPud
	antipyretica	CPud

Forsythia (*Oleaceae*)

	'Arnold Dwarf'	SRms
	'Beatrix Farrand' ambig.	CTri EPfP NWea SEND SRms
	'Beatrix Farrand' K. Sax	LRHS MMuc NLar
	'Fiesta' (v)	CBod ELon EPfP LRHS MAsh MRav MSwo NLar SPer WCot WFar
	giraldiana	MSwo SRms
	GOLD TIDE	see *F.* MARÉE D'OR
	'Golden Nugget'	CBod CMac ELan EPfP MAsh SLon SNig SPoG WCFE WFar
	'Golden Times' (v)	CMac CRos EHyd LRHS MAsh MSwo NEoE NHol NRHS SPoG SWvt WAvo WCot WFar
	'Goldstream' (v)	NWad
	× ***intermedia***	EShb
	- 'Arnold Giant'	MBlu
	- 'Goldrausch'	CRos EHyd LCro LOPS LPar LRHS NLar NRHS SAko
	- 'Goldzauber'	CBrac
	- 'Lynwood Variety' ♀H5	Widely available
	- 'Lynwood Variety' variegated (v)	CMac MTrO
	- MINIGOLD ('Flojor')	CBrac CMac CSBt ELan MSwo NLar SRms
	- 'Nimbus'PBR	CBod EBee EPfP LRHS NLar WFar
	- SHOW OFF ('Mindor'PBR)	CRos LBuc LRHS
	- 'Spectabilis'	CBrac EPfP LBuc NWea SCoo SGol SLim WFar
	- 'Spectabilis Variegated' (v)	NEoE
	- 'Spring Glory'	MHer WAvo WLov WSpi
	- 'Susan Gruninger' (v)	WCot
	- 'Variegata' (v)	CBrac SRms
	- WEEK END ('Courtalyn') ♀H5	CBod CDoC CEme CEnd CRos EHyd ELan EPfP LBuc LCro LOPS LPar LRHS MAsh MMuc NHol NLar NRHS SCob SCoo SEND SGol SGsty SLon SPlb SavN WFar
	'Kanarek'	NLar
	× ***mandschurica***	CBcs SAko
§	MARÉE D'OR ('Courtasol') ♀H5	CRos EPfP LRHS MAsh MRav NLar NRHS SLon SPer SPoG WFar
	MÊLÉE D'OR ('Courtaneur')	SGol WBor
	'Northern Gold'	MBlu
	ovata 'Ottawa'	WLov
	'Paulina'	WCot
	suspensa	CMac CTri EPfP ESwi NWea SPlb SRms WSpi
	- f. ***atrocaulis***	NWea WSpi
	- 'Nymans'	EPfP EWTr MRav NLar NSti SBrt SEND SPer
§	- 'Taff's Arnold' (v)	CExl WSpi
	- 'Variegata'	see *F. suspensa* 'Taff's Arnold'
	viridissima	NWea
	- 'Bronxensis'	EPot MAsh NBir WAbe WCot
	- CITRUS SWIZZLE ('Mckcitrine'PBR)	NLar WCot
	- var. ***koreana*** 'Kumsom' (v)	EBee LRHS NLar SAko
	- 'Weber's Bronx'	GKev NLar NWea

Fortunella see *Citrus*

Fothergilla (*Hamamelidaceae*)

gardenii	CBcs CJun EHyd EPfP MBlu MRav NLar SPer SWvt
– 'Blue Mist'	CCCN CEnd CExl CJun CWit EBee EHyd ELan EPfP LRHS MAsh NLar SPer SPoG SSta WFar
– 'Brian Upchurch'	NLar
– 'Glaucophylla'	NLar
– 'Suzanne'	CJun NLar
– 'Zundert'	NLar
× ***intermedia*** BEAVER CREEK ('Klmtwo')	NLar
– 'Blue Shadow'	CBcs CBod CCCN CJun EHyd GKev LRHS MGos MPkF MRav NLar NRHS WFar
– 'Mount Airy' 🏆H5	CJun CMCN EPfP LRHS MPkF NLar SSta XSte
– 'Red Licorice'	CBcs CJun EPfP NLar
– 'Sea Spray'	CJun NLar
– 'Windy City'	CJun NLar
major 🏆H5	CBcs CBod CDoC CEme CJun EBee EGrI EHed EHyd ELan EPfP LCro LOPS LPar LRHS MAsh MBlu MGil MGos MPri MRav NLar SPer SWvt WFar WMat WTSh XSte
– 'Bulkyard'	CJun
– Monticola Group	CEnd CJun CRos EHyd EPfP LRHS MAsh MMuc SCob SGbt SSta
– – 'Huntsman'	CCCN CJun EPfP SPer SSta

Fouquieria (*Fouquieriaceae*)

columnaris	SPlb
splendens	SPlb

Fragaria ✿ (*Rosaceae*)

alpina 'Alba'	see *F. vesca* 'Semperflorens Alba'
× ***ananassa*** 'Albion'^{PBR} (F)	CArg CMac LCro LOPS LSRN NRog
– 'Alice'^{PBR} (F) 🏆H6	CAgr CMac EPom
§ – 'Anablanca' (F)	LRHS
– 'Anaïs' (F) **new**	LRHS
– 'Aromel' (F)	CTri
– bubbleberry (F)	LCro LOPS LRHS
– 'Buddy'^{PBR} (F)	CArg EPom
– 'Cambridge Favourite' (F) 🏆H6	CAgr CArg CMac CRos CSBt CTri EHyd EMil EPfP EPom GDam GQue LBuc LCro LOPS LRHS MGos MPri NRHS NRog SEdi SPlb
– 'Cambridge Vigour' (F)	NRHS
– 'Charlotte'^{PBR} (F)	LRHS
– 'Christine' (F)	CAgr CArg EPom
– 'Cupid'^{PBR} (F)	CArg EPom LCro LOPS NRog
– 'Darselect'^{PBR} (F)	EPom
– 'Delia' (F)	CRos EHyd LRHS NRHS
– 'Delician' (F) **new**	LRHS
– DELIZZ ('Liza'^{PBR}) (F)	EHyd LRHS NRHS
– 'Elan'^{PBR} (F)	NRHS SCoo
– 'Elegance'^{PBR} (F)	CArg EPom NRog
– 'Elsanta' (F)	CArg CRos CSBt CTri EHyd EPfP EPom GDam IArd LBuc LRHS MBros MPri NRHS NRog SEdi SPer WMat
– 'Everest'^{PBR} (F)	NRHS
– 'Fenella'^{PBR} (F)	CArg CMac EPom LCro LOPS
– 'Finesse' (F) 🏆H6	NRHS NRog
– 'Flamenco'^{PBR} (F)	CArg EPom LEdu NRog
– 'Florence'^{PBR} (F) 🏆H6	CAgr CArg CRos CSBt CTri EHyd EPom LBuc LRHS NRHS NRog SPer
– 'Florian' (F)	LEdu
– (Fragoo Series) FRAGOO DEEP ROSE ('Tarpan') (F)	CRos EHyd LRHS NRHS
– – FRAGOO PINK ('Pikan') (F)	CRos EHyd LRHS NRHS
– – FRAGOO WHITE ('Belton') (F)	CRos EHyd LRHS NRHS
– Fraise des Bois	see *F. vesca*
– 'Framberry' (F)	EPom LEdu LRHS
– 'Frau Mieze Schindler' (F)	LEdu
* – 'Fresca' (F)	EHyd LRHS NRHS
– 'Gariguette' (F)	EPom LRHS
– 'Gorella' (F)	LRHS
– 'Hapil' (F) 🏆H6	EPfP EPom GDam LBuc NRog
– 'Honeoye' (F) 🏆H6	CAgr CArg CMac CSBt EPfP EPom GDam LBuc LCro LEdu LOPS LRHS NRog SPer
– 'Judibell'^{PBR} (F)	NRog
– 'Korona'^{PBR} (F)	CMac EPom LRHS
– 'Leo Alba' (F)	CArg
– 'Loran' (F)	LRHS MBros SCoo
– 'Lucy'^{PBR} (F)	CMac
– 'Mae'^{PBR} (F)	CArg LEdu
– 'Magnum' (F) **new**	LRHS
– 'Malling Centenary'^{PBR} (F) 🏆H6	EPom LRHS NRog
– 'Malling Opal'^{PBR} (F)	EPom NRog
– 'Malwina'^{PBR} (F)	EPom NRog SVic
– 'Manille' (F)	EPom
– 'Marshmello' (F) **new**	EPom
– 'Mount Everest' (F)	LCro LRHS
– 'Ostara' (F)	MBros
– 'Pandora' (F)	LEdu
– 'Pegasus' (F) 🏆H6	CAgr CRos CSBt EHyd EPfP EPom LRHS NRHS
– pineberry (F)	EWhm LEdu
– PINK PANDA ('Frel') (F)	CBod CMac EBee EHyd ELan GDam LRHS MBel MHer MRav NGdn NLar NRHS SGbt SIvy SPer SPoG WBor WCAu WCav WSMil
– pink-flowered (F)	GAbr
– 'Red Dream' (F)	LCro LOPS
– 'Red Glory'^{PBR} (F)	NRHS
– 'Red Princess'^{PBR} (F)	NRHS
– RED RUBY	see *F.* × *ananassa* 'Samba'
– 'Redgauntlet' (F)	CRos EHyd EPfP LRHS NRHS NRog
– 'Rhapsody' (F) 🏆H6	CRos EHyd LRHS LSRN NRHS
– 'Roman' (F)	SCoo
– 'Royal Sovereign' (F)	CMac CTri EPfP EPom LRHS NBir SVic
– 'Ruby Ann' (F) **new**	SCoo
§ – 'Samba'^{PBR} (F)	CBod EHyd ELan GLog LRHS MBel NGdn NLar NRHS SGbt
– 'Senga Sengana' (F)	SVic
– SNOW WHITE ('Hansawhit'^{PBR}) (F)	EPom LEdu LRHS SVic
– 'Sonata'^{PBR} (F)	ELan EPom LRHS
– 'Sweet Ann'^{PBR} (F)	LRHS
– 'Sweet Eve'^{PBR} (F) **new**	LRHS
– 'Sweetheart' (F)	EPfP EPom LCro LOPS NRog
– 'Symphony'^{PBR} (F) 🏆H6	CAgr CRos EHyd EPfP EPom LBuc LRHS LSRN NRHS SCoo
– 'Temptation' (F)	CRos EHyd LRHS MBros NRHS SVic
– 'Toscana'^{PBR} (F)	SCoo
§ – 'Variegata' (v)	CMea LRHS MRav SGbt SPer SPoG
– 'Vibrant'^{PBR} (F) 🏆H6	EPom NRog
– 'White Dream' (F)	LCro LOPS
'Bowles's Double'	see *F. vesca* 'Multiplex'
chiloensis (F)	LEdu WKor
– 'Chaval' (F)	ECha MRav WMal
– 'Variegata' misapplied	see *F.* × *ananassa* 'Variegata'
indica	see *Duchesnea indica*
'Lipstick'	EBee NFav NLar SIvy WSpi
moschata	CAgr CLau WKor

nubicola	CAgr GPoy
'Variegata'	see *F.* × *ananassa* 'Variegata'
§ ***vesca*** (F)	CAgr CBcs CBee EHyd ELan EPfP GBin GPoy GQue LCro LEdu LOPS LRHS MBow MBros MHer MNHC MPri NMir NPol NRHS SPlb SRms SVic WGwG WKor WSFF WShi WWild
* - var. ***albescens***	CLau
- 'Alexandria' (F)	CLau ENfk NPol
- 'Alpina Scarletta' (F)	ENfk
- 'Baron Solemacher' (F)	NPol SPhx WHer
- 'Capron Royale' (F)	CAgr
- 'Flore Pleno'	see *F. vesca* 'Multiplex'
- 'Fructu Albo' (F)	CAgr
- 'Golden Alexandra' (F)	ECha EWes EWhm NPol NWad
- 'Mara des Bois' (F)	EPom EShb LRHS SPer SVic
- 'Mignonette'	CLau EWhm NPol
- 'Monophylla' (F)	LEdu NPol WHer
§ - 'Multiplex' (d)	EPPr NPol WHer
§ - 'Muricata'	LEdu
- 'Patchwork'	NPol
- 'Pineapple Crush' (F)	NPol WHer
- 'Plymouth Strawberry'	see *F. vesca* 'Muricata'
- 'Reine des Vallées' (F)	LRHS
- 'Rügen' (F)	NPol
- 'Scarlet Beauty' (F)	EPom MNHC NPol
§ - 'Semperflorens Alba' (F)	CAgr NWad
- 'Variegata' misapplied	see *F.* × *ananassa* 'Variegata'
- 'White Soul' (F)	NPol
- 'Yellow Wonder' (F)	LRHS NPol
virginiana	CAgr WKor
viridis	CAgr WKor

Francoa ✿ (*Francoaceae*)

appendiculata	ILea MGil NBir NFav NWad SGBe SHeu WHer WPav
Ballyrogan strain	IBlr
'Confetti'	CExl CMea
* dwarf purple	CElw
'Purple Spike'	see *F. sonchifolia* Rogerson's form
ramosa	CTri EBee GKev IBlr ILea NBir NBro SDix WKif
sonchifolia	Widely available
- 'Alba'	EBee
- 'Cally Dwarf Purple'	SHeu
- 'Culm View Lilac'	CKel EBee LRHS
- 'Molly Anderson'	MAvo
- 'Petite Bouquet'	CKno EWes GKev SRms WNPC XSte
- 'Pink Bouquet'	CAbb CKno CMac CWGN EBee LRHS LSRN MHol SHeu SRkn WFar XSte
- 'Pink Giant'	CBod CPla CSpe EHyd EPau EPfP EWhm EWoo GAbr GKev LPot LRHS MBel MPie NRHS NWad SHeu SMrm WFar
§ - Rogerson's form	CElw CMiW CRos CTri EHyd ELon EShb GBin GGro LRHS NBir NChi NRHS SDix SHeu SPeP WFar

Frangula (*Rhamnaceae*)

§ ***alnus***	CArg CCVT CHab CTri EPfP LBuc LPar MBlu MGos NWea SCob SEWo SavN WFar WMou WSFF WTSh
- 'Aspleniifolia'	EPfP IDee LMaj LRHS MBlu MGil MMuc MRav NLar WCFE WGrn WLov WPGP
- 'Fine Line'	CRos EHed EHyd ELan EPfP LRHS MPkF NLar NRHS SPoG SavN
- 'Minaret'	MBlu
- 'Ron Williams'	MBlu WMat
californica B&SWJ 14057	WCru

Frankenia (*Frankeniaceae*)

laevis	CKel SRms
thymifolia	CKel CTri EBou ECtt EPfP MAsh MHer SLee SPlb WHoo XLum

Franklinia (*Theaceae*)

alatamaha	CBcs IDee LRHS MBlu MGil WPGP XSte

Franklinia × *Gordonia* see × *Gordlinia*

Fraxinus ✿ (*Oleaceae*)

Movement of ash seeds, plants and trees is currently prohibited under a Plant Health Order. Please see p.29 for a fuller explanation.

Freesia (*Iridaceae*)

alba Foster	see *F. lactea*
alba (G.L. Mey.) Gumbl.	CPbh
'Algarve' (d) **new**	NRog
andersoniae	NRog
'Anouk' **new**	NRog
'Athene' **new**	NRog
'Ballerina'	NRog
'Bloemfontein' **new**	NRog
'Blue Bayou' (d) **new**	NRog
'Blue Moon'	LCro LOPS
'Blue Sky' **new**	NRog
'Calgary' **new**	NRog
'Chiron' **new**	NRog
'Clazina' **new**	NRog
'Corona' **new**	NRog
corymbosa	NRog
- cream-flowered **new**	NRog
- pink-flowered **new**	NRog
- white-flowered **new**	NRog
'Delta River'	EPfP SPoG
'Epona' **new**	NRog
'Fantasy' (d)	NRog
fergusoniae **new**	NRog
'Figaro' (d) **new**	NRog
'Fragrant Sunburst'	CRos EPfP SCoo SPoG
fucata	CPbh
'Gold River'	SPoG
'Golden Melody' **new**	NRog
grandiflora	CExl
'Jessica' **new**	NRog
§ ***lactea***	CBor
'Lady Brunet' (d) **new**	NRog
§ ***laxa*** ♀H3	CExl CPbh CSpe CTri CTtf EPri GKev LEdu LRHS NHpl WFar
- var. ***alba*** ♀H3	CBor CExl CPbh EPri GKev SChr WFar
- 'Joan Evans'	CBor CTtf WFar
- red-spotted	CExl
- ***viridiflora***	CTtf
leichtlinii	CLan
(Lovely Series) 'Lovely Blue'	CRos LRHS
- 'Lovely Creame'	CRos LRHS
- 'Lovely White'	CRos LRHS
'Oberon'	NRog
'Pink Fountain' **new**	NRog
'Purple Rain' (d) **new**	NRog
'Red Beauty' (d) **new**	NRog
'Red River'	SPoG
refracta	CPbh
'Romany' (d)	NRog
'Royal Blue'	NRog

'Santorini' **new**	NRog
'Sevilla' **new**	NRog
sparrmannii	NRog
'Striped Pearl' **new**	NRog
'Troubadour' (d) **new**	NRog
viridis	CBor CExl NRog
'White River'	EPfP SPoG
xanthospila	NRog

Fremontodendron (*Malvaceae*)

'California Glory' ♀H4	CBcs CBrac CDoC CMac CRos EHyd EPfP LRHS LSRN MAsh MBlu MGil MGos MHol NRHS SArc SCob SEle SGbt SGol SGsty SIvy SMad SPer SPoG SVen SWvt WSMil
californicum	CTri EBee ELan LPar NLar SEND SPlb WFar
- subsp. ***decumbens***	SBrt
'Pacific Sunset'	MGos MRav

Freylinia (*Scrophulariaceae*)

cestroides	see *F. lanceolata*
§ ***lanceolata***	CBcs CCCN CWit EBee SPlb SVen
tropica	MGil
visseri	SVen

Fritillaria ✿ (*Liliaceae*)

acmopetala ♀H4	CAvo CBor CMiW CWCL EMor EPot ERCP GArf GKev ITim MBow MNrw NRog SDeJ SDir SHar WCot WSHC
- 'Brunette'	NRog
- 'Paul Furse'	ITim
- subsp. ***wendelboi***	NRog
- - 'Zwanenburg'	GKev
affinis	CWCL GKev NHpl
- yellow-flowered	CWCL
alburyana	NRog
amana	CWCL EMor ERCP GKev ITim NRog WCot
- 'Cambridge'	WCot
arabica	see *F. persica*
assyriaca	EPot
aurea	NRog
- 'Golden Flag'	SDeJ
ayakoana	GKev
biflora 'Martha Roderick'	SDeJ
§ ***bithynica***	ITim NRog
bucharica	EPot GKev NRog
- 'Hodji-obi-Garm' **new**	NRog
camschatcensis	CWCL EHyd EMor EPot ERCP GArf GBin GEdr GKev GMaP NBir NHpl NLar NRog SDeJ WCot WTyc
- 'Alaska'	GArf NHar
- 'Aurea'	GRum NHar
- black-flowered	NHar
- double-flowered (d)	GKev
- dwarf	GRum
- f. ***flavescens***	GEdr GKev
carduchorum	see *F. minuta*
carica	CBor NRog
cirrhosa	NRog
citrina	see *F. bithynica*
crassifolia	GKev NRog
subsp. ***crassifolia***	
§ - subsp. ***kurdica***	ITim NRog
davidii	NDry
davisii	EPot GKev NRog SDeJ
eduardii	GKev NRog
- 'Castor'	EPot GKev IPot
- 'Pollux'	GKev
elwesii	CAvo EPot ERCP GKev ITim NLar NRog SDeJ SDir
* ***glauca*** 'Golden Flag'	NRog SDeJ
- 'Goldilocks'	SDeJ
graeca	ITim NRog SDeJ
grandiflora	NRog
hispanica	see *F. lusitanica*
imperialis ♀H7	CKel
- 'Argenteovariegata' (v)	NRog
- 'Aureomarginata' (v)	NRog SDir
- 'Aureovariegata' (v)	SDir
- 'Aurora'	CBcs CRos EHyd EPot ERCP GKev LRHS MPtr NLar NPer NRHS SCob SDeJ SPer SPhx WPhe
- 'Bach' (Rascal Series)	GKev
- 'Beethoven' (Rascal Series)	GKev NRog WCot
- 'Brahms' (Rascal Series)	GKev
- 'Chopin' (Rascal Series)	CAvo GKev NRog
- 'Early Fantasy'	GKev
- 'Early Magic'	GKev NRog
- 'Early Passion'	GKev SDir
- 'Garland Star'	CRos EHyd GKev LRHS LSun NLar NRHS NRog SDeJ SDir SPhx
- var. ***inodora***	GKev
- 'Lutea'	CAvo CRos EHyd ERCP GKev LRHS LSun MPtr NRHS SCob SPoG WPhe
- 'Mahler' (Rascal Series)	GKev
- 'Maxima'	see *F. imperialis* 'Rubra Maxima'
- 'Maxima Lutea' ♀H7	CRos EHyd ELan EPfP EPot ERCP GKev LRHS NLar NRHS SDeJ SPhx SPoG
- 'Orange Beauty'	CRos EHyd GKev LRHS NRHS NRog SDeJ WPhe
- 'Prolifera'	GKev NRog SDeJ SPeP
- 'Rubra'	CBod EHyd ERCP GKev LCro LOPS LRHS MPtr NLar NRHS SCob WFar WPhe
§ - 'Rubra Maxima'	CRos EHyd ELan EPot ERCP GKev LRHS NRHS SDeJ SPhx
- 'Satie' (Rascal Series)	GKev
- 'Slagzwaard'	NRog
- 'Striped Beauty'	EPot GKev SDeJ SDir WPhe
- 'Sulpherino'	NRog
- 'Sunset'	GKev
- 'The Premier'	GKev NRog SDeJ
- 'Vivaldi' (Rascal Series)	EPot GKev NRog
- 'William Rex'	CAvo CRos CWCL EHyd EPfP EPot ERCP GKev LBuc LRHS NLar NRHS NRog SDir SPhx SPoG
involucrata	WCot
karadaghensis	see *F. crassifolia* subsp. *kurdica*
koidzumiana	GKev
latakiensis	EPot GKev NRog
§ ***lusitanica***	ITim
meleagris ♀H5	Widely available
- var. ***unicolor*** subvar. ***alba*** ♀H5	ERCP GKev ILea LCro LOPS NHol NRog SDeJ SPer SPhx WPnP WShi
- - - 'Aphrodite'	EPot NBir WCot
§ ***messanensis***	ITim
- subsp. ***gracilis***	ITim
michailovskyi	CAvo CRos EHyd EPot ERCP EWhm GKev LRHS MNrw NHpl NRHS NRog SDeJ SRms WFar WPhe
- 'Multiflorum'	GKev
§ ***minuta***	ERCP NRog SDeJ
montana	NRog
nigra Mill.	see *F. pyrenaica*
olgae **new**	NRog
olivieri	GKev

pallidiflora ♀H5	CAvo CMiW CWCL EPot ERCP GKev NBir NHpl NRog SDeJ SPhx
- yellow-flowered	ITim
§ ***persica***	CBcs CKel CPla ECha EHyd EPfP EPot ERCP EWhm LCro LOPS LRHS MBow NChi NLar NRHS NRog SPeP SPhx WPhe
- 'Adiyaman' ♀H4	ELan SDeJ
- 'Alba'	GKev NRog SDeJ SPeP SPhx
- 'Green Dreams'	ELan GKev NLar SPhx
- 'Ivory Bells'	EPot ERCP GKev LCro LOPS NLar NRog SDeJ WPhe
- 'Midnight Bells'	NRog
- 'Pastel'	NRog
- 'Purple Favorite' **new**	GKev
* - 'Senkoy'	GKev NRog
- 'Twin Towers Tribute'	GKev NLar SPhx
pontica ♀H4	CAvo CWCL EPfP EPot ERCP GKev ITim NHpl NRog SDeJ SPhx WCot
pudica	ITim
- 'Giant'	NRog SDeJ
§ ***pyrenaica*** ♀H5	NRog
raddeana	CAvo EMor EPot ERCP GBin GKev NLar NRog SDeJ SPhx WCot
roylei	ITim
rubra major	see *F. imperialis* 'Rubra Maxima'
sewerzowii	EPot GKev NRog WCot
sphaciotica	see *F. messanensis*
stenanthera	EPot GKev NRog
- 'Cambridge' **new**	NRog
- 'Ihnatschai' **new**	NRog
- 'Ugam' **new**	NRog
stribrnyi	EPot GKev NRog
thunbergii	NRog WCot
uva-vulpis	CAvo CRos EAJP EHyd EPot ERCP EWoo GKev GWyn LRHS MBow MNrw NBir NRHS NRog SDeJ WFar WShi
verticillata	ECha
- 'Urdzhar' **new**	NRog
whittallii	NRog

Fuchsia ✿ (*Onagraceae*)

'A.M. Larwick'	EBak SLBF
'A.W. Taylor'	EBak
'Abbé Farges' (d)	CLoc CRos EBak EHyd EPts LRHS NRHS SLBF SVic WRou
'Abigail' (d) **new**	WRou
'Abigail' ambig.	WRou
'Abundance'	EHDe
'Achievement' ♀H4	CLoc MJac SVic
'Adinda' (T) ♀H1c	EPts MHer WRou
'Adrienne' (d)	EPts WRou
'Ailsa Garnett' (d)	EBak
'Aisen'	WRou
'Alan Titchmarsh' ♀H2	EPts SLBF
'Alaska' (d)	CLoc
'Alderford'	SLBF
'Alfonso' (d)	SLBF
'Alice Ashton' (d)	EBak
'Alice Hoffman' (d) ♀H4	CCCN CEnd CLoc CMac CRos CSBt EBak EBee EHDe EHyd ELan EPfP EPts LRHS MAsh MGos MJac NLar NRHS SCob SLBF SLim SPer SPoG SVic WFar WLov WRou
'Alicia Sellars'	SLBF WRou
'Alison Ewart'	CLoc SVic
'Alison Patricia' ♀H2	EBak MJac SLBF SVic WRou
'Alison Reynolds' (d)	WRou
'Alison Ruth Griffin' (d)	MJac
'Alison Ryle' (d)	EBak
'Alison Sweetman' ♀H2	MJac
'All Summer Beauty' (T)	SLBF WRou
'Allen Jackson'	SLBF WRou
alpestris	EBak
'Alyce Larson' (d)	EBak
'Alyssa May Garcia' (d)	EPts MJac SLBF WRou
'Amazing Maisie' (d)	SLBF
'Amelia Rose'	SLBF
'Amelie Aubin'	CLoc EBak WRou
'Amy'	MJac
'Amy Lye'	CLoc EHDe SVic
§ 'Andenken an Heinrich Henkel' (T)	CLoc EBak
'André Le Nostre' (d)	EBak
'Andrew Carnegie' (d)	CLoc
'Angela' (d)	WRou
'Angela Dawn'	WRou
'Angela King'	WRou
'Angela Leslie' (d)	EBak SVic
'Angel's Flight' (d)	EBak
'Angel's Kiss' (E)	SLBF
'Anita'	CLoc EPts MJac SLBF WRou
'Ann Howard Tripp'	CLoc EPts MJac SVic WRou
'Ann Reid'	SLBF
'Anna Sunshine' (T)	EPts WRou
'Annabel' (d) ♀H4	CLoc CTri EBak EPts MJac SLBF SVic WRou
'Annie Earle'	EHDe
'Annie M.G. Schmidt'	EPts WRou
'Anthea Day' (d)	CLoc
'Anthonie Sherwood' (T)	WRou
'Antigone'	SLBF
'Antoinette Peeters' (d) **new**	WRou
'Applause' (d)	CLoc EBak EPts SLBF
aprica misapplied	see *F.* × *bacillaris*
aprica Lundell	see *F. microphylla* subsp. *aprica*
'Apricot Ice'	CLoc SVic
'Arabella Improved'	EHDe
arborea	see *F. arborescens*
§ ***arborescens***	CBcs CBod CLoc CTsd CWCL EBak ECre EHDe EHed EWld IDee LSou MCot SDys SIvy SVic WRou
- B&SWJ 10475	WCru
'Arcady'	CLoc
'Ariel' (E)	LRHS SVic
'Arkie'	MJac
'Army Nurse' (d) ♀H4	CBod CEnd CLoc CRos EHyd ELan EPfP EPts LRHS MGos NBir NLar NRHS SGBe SGol SLBF SVic WLov WRou
'Ashtede'	SLBF
'Ashville'	SLBF WRou
'Atlantic Star'	MJac
'Aubergine'	see *F.* 'Gerharda's Aubergine'
'Auenland'	MJac
'Auntie Jinks' ♀H2	EBak MJac
'Aurora Superba'	CLoc EBak SLBF
'Autumnale' ♀H2	CLoc EBak EHDe EPts SLBF SPoG WRou
'Avalanche' ambig. (d)	EBak SLBF
'Avocet'	CLoc
'Avon Celebration' (d/v)	CLoc
'Avon Gem'	CLoc
'Avon Glow' (d)	CLoc
'Avon Gold'	CLoc
'Awake Sweet Love' (T)	EPts
'Aylisa Rowan' (E)	SLBF WRou
'Azure Sky' (d)	MJac
'Baby Blue Eyes' ♀H4	CBod CLoc CRos EHDe EHyd ELan LRHS LSRN MAsh NRHS SLBF SVic WRou

	'Baby Thumb' (v)	EPts
§	× ***bacillaris*** (E)	CAbb CChe EPPr EWes SEle SIvy SLBF SPoG WHer XLum
§	- 'Cottinghamii' (E)	EWld ILea WRou WSHC
§	- 'Reflexa' (E)	CCCN CTrC NQui
	'Bagworthy Water'	CLoc
	'Baker's Tri' (T)	EBak
	'Balkonkönigin'	CLoc
	'Ballerina Girl' (E)	SLBF WRou
	'Ballet Girl' (d) ♀H2	CLoc EBak SLBF
	'Bambini'	EPts
	'Banks Peninsula'	GBin
	'Barbara'	CLoc EBak EPts MJac SVic
	'Barbara Reynolds'	MJac WRou
	'Barbara Windsor'	MJac
	'Barry's Queen'	see *F.* 'Golden Border Queen'
	'Bart Comperen' (d)	WRou
	'Bashful' (d)	EPts SVic
	'Beacon'	CLoc CMac CRos EBak EHyd EPfP EPts LRHS MJac NRHS SGol SLBF SPoG SVic WRou
	'Beacon Rosa' ♀H4	CLoc EHyd EPfP EPts LRHS MJac NRHS SLBF SPoG SVic WRou
	'Beauty of Bath' (d)	CLoc
	'Beauty of Clyffe Hall' Lye	EBak EHDe
	'Beauty of Exeter' (d)	EBak
	'Beauty of Prussia' (d)	CLoc
	'Beauty of Swanley'	EHDe
	'Beauty of Trowbridge'	EHDe
	'Bella Rosella' (California Dreamers Series) (d) ♀H2	CLoc EPts MBros MJac SCoo WRou
	'Belvoir Beauty' (d)	CLoc
	'Ben de Jong'	SLBF WRou
	'Ben Jammin'	CDoC CLoc EPfP EPts SVic
	'Ben-Ben'	SLBF WRou
	'Berliner Kind' (d)	EBak
	'Bernice Elizabeth' (d)	SLBF WRou
	'Bernie's Big-un' (d)	SLBF
	'Bernisser Hardy' ♀H4	EPts LRHS NQui SLBF XLum
	'Betsy Huuskes'	SLBF
	'Beverley'	EBak EPts
	'Bicentennial' (d)	CLoc EBak EPts MBros MJac SLBF
	'Billy Green' (T) ♀H2	CLoc EBak EHDe EPts MHer MJac SVic
	'Blacky' (d)	CCCN CPla EBak GBin SDix SDys WRou
	'Bland's New Striped'	CLoc EBak EPts SLBF
§	'Blauer Engel' (d)	MJac WRou
	'Blaze Away' (d)	MJac WRou
	BLUE ANGEL	see *F.* 'Blauer Engel'
	'Blue Bush'	EPts MJac SVic XLum
I	'Blue Danube' Blackwell (d) **new**	CLoc
	'Blue Gown' (d)	CLoc EBak SVic
	'Blue Lace' (d)	SVic
	'Blue Mirage' (d)	CLoc SVic
	'Blue Pearl' (d)	EBak
	'Blue Pinwheel'	EBak
	'Blue Veil' (d)	CLoc MJac SCoo
	'Blue Waves' (d)	CLoc CSBt EBak SVic
	'Blush o' Dawn' (d)	CLoc EBak SVic
	'Bobby Shaftoe' (d)	EBak
	'Bobby Wingrove'	EBak
	'Bobby's Girl'	EPts
	'Bobolink' (d)	EBak
	'Bob's Best' (d)	EPts
	boliviana ambig.	CBcs IDee MHer
§	***boliviana*** Carrière	EGrI EPPr WRou
§	- var. ***alba*** ♀H2	CLoc EBak EPts WFar
	- var. ***boliviana***	CRHN
	- var. ***luxurians*** 'Alba'	see *F. boliviana* Carrière var. *alba*
	- f. ***puberulenta*** Munz	see *F. boliviana* Carrière
	- 'Pink Cornet'	WRou
	'Bon Accorde'	CLoc EBak EPts SLBF SVic
	'Bonnie Lass' (d)	EBak
I	'Boogie Woogie'	EPts MJac SLBF WRou
	'Borde Hill' (d)	EPts
	'Border Princess'	EBak
	'Border Queen' ♀H4	CLoc EBak EHDe EPts MJac SLBF SVic
	'Börnemann's Beste'	see *F.* 'Georg Börnemann'
	'Bouquet' (d)	SLBF
	'Bow Bells'	CLoc MJac
	'Boy Marc' (T) ♀H1c	SLBF
	'Brandt's 500 Club'	CLoc
	'Breckland'	EBak
	'Breeder's Dream' (d)	EBak
	'Breevis Minimus'	SLBF
	'Brenda White'	CLoc EBak
	'Brian G. Soanes'	EBak
	'Brian McFetridge' (d)	WRou
	'Bridesmaid' (d)	EBak
	'Brilliant' ambig.	EHDe
	'Brilliant' Bull, 1865	CLoc EBak
	'Brookwood Belle' (d) ♀H3	EPts MJac SLBF
	'Brutus' ♀H4	CLoc EBak EHDe EHyd EPfP EPts LRHS NRHS SCoo SLBF SVic WFar WRou
	'Bryan Breary' (E)	WRou
	'Bryn Derw' **new**	WRou
	'Bryn Seren' **new**	WRou
	'Bryn-y-Baal' **new**	WRou
	'Buddha' (d)	EBak
	'C.J. Howlett'	EBak
	'Caesar' (d)	EBak
	'Cambridge Louie'	EBak
	'Campo Thilco' **new**	WRou
	campos-portoi	EBee MGil WPGP
	'Candy Bells' (d)	CSBt
	'Canny Bob'	MJac
	'Cara Mia' (d)	CLoc
	'Caradela' (d)	CLoc MJac
	'Cardinal'	CLoc
	'Cardinal Farges' (d)	CLoc SLBF SVic WRou
	'Careless Whisper'	SLBF
	'Carla Johnston' ♀H2	CLoc EPts MJac SVic WRou
	'Carmel Blue'	CLoc SCob SVic WRou
	'Carnoustie' (d)	EBak
	'Carol Grace' (d)	CLoc
	'Caroline'	CLoc EBak EPts SVic
	'Caroline's Joy'	MJac SCoo
	'Cascade'	CLoc EPts MJac
	'Cecil Glass'	EHDe
	'Cecile' (d)	CCCN EPts MJac SLBF
	'Celebration' (d)	CLoc
	'Celia Smedley' ♀H3	CLoc CRos EBak EHDe EHyd EPts LRHS MJac NRHS SLBF SVic WRou
	'Centerpiece' (d)	EBak
	'Ceri'	CLoc WMal
	'Champagne Celebration'	CLoc
	'Chang' ♀H2	CLoc EBak SLBF SVic WRou
	'Chantelle Garcia' (d)	EPts MJac SLBF
	'Chapel Rossan' (E)	SLBF WRou
	'Charles Welch'	EPts
	CHARLIE DIMMOCK ('Foncha'PBR) (d)	CLoc
	'Charlie Gardiner'	EBak
	'Charming'	CLoc EHDe EHyd EPfP LRHS MAsh MJac NRHS SVic
	'Chatt's Delight'	SLBF
	'Checkerboard' ♀H3	CLoc EBak EHDe EPts MHer MJac SLBF SVic WRou

	'Chelsea Louise'	EPts
	'Cherry Lee'	SLBF WRou
	'Cherry Pop' (E)	WRou
	'Chessboard'	CLoc
	'Chillerton Beauty' $\mathbb{Y}^{H4}$	CLoc CTri EHDe EHyd ELan ELon EPts LRHS MJac NLar NRHS SLBF SVic WFar WRou
	'Chilli Red'	CBcs EHyd EPfP EPts LRHS MAsh MPri NRHS SIvy
	'China Lantern'	CLoc SVic
	'Chloe Christina' (E)	WRou
	'Chris Bright'	MJac WRou
	'Chris Tarrant' (d)	EPts
	'Cinnabarina' (E)	CLoc SVic
	'Citation'	EBak SVic
	'City of Adelaide' (d)	CLoc
	'Clair de Lune'	EBak SLBF
	'Claudia' (d)	EPts MBros MJac SLBF WRou
	'Cliff's Hardy'	SVic
	'Cliff's Own'	SVic
	'Cliff's Unique' (d)	EPts
	'Clifton Beauty' (d)	MJac
	'Clifton Charm'	EPts MJac SVic
	'Clifton Pride'	MJac WRou
	'Clipper'	EHDe
	'Cloth of Gold'	CLoc EBak EHDe MJac SLBF SVic
	'Cloverdale Pearl'	EBak MAsh SPoG
	'Coachman' $\mathbb{Y}^{H4}$	CLoc EBak EHDe EPts MBros SLBF WRou
	coccinea	CSde SVic
	'Colette Kelly'	SVic
	'Collingwood' (d)	CLoc
	'Colne Raider' **new**	WRou
	'Conchetta Garcia'	WRou
	'Connie' (d)	EBak SVic XLum
	'Connor's Cascade'	SLBF
	'Conspicua' $\mathbb{Y}^{H4}$	LRHS SIvy SLBF SVic WRou
	'Constance' (d)	CLoc MJac SLBF SVic
	'Constance Comer'	MJac SVic WRou
	'Constellation' Schnabel, 1957 (d)	EBak
	'Coquet Bell'	EBak
	'Coral Baby' (E)	SLBF
	'Coralle' (T) $\mathbb{Y}^{H1c}$	CCCN CLoc EBak EPts MBros MJac SLBF WRou
	'Corallina' $\mathbb{Y}^{H4}$	CLoc SVic
*	***cordata*** B&SWJ 10325	WCru
	- B&SWJ 9095	WCru
	cordifolia misapplied	see *F. splendens*
	'Core'ngrato' (d)	CLoc
	'Cornish Blue'	CLoc
	'Cornwall Calls' (d)	EBak EHDe
	'Corsair' (d)	EBak
	corymbiflora misapplied	see *F. boliviana* Carrière
	'Costa Brava'	CLoc
	'Cotta Christmas Tree' (E)	SLBF WRou
	'Cottinghamii'	see *F.* × *bacillaris* 'Cottinghamii'
	'Cotton Candy' (d)	CLoc SVic
	'Countdown Carol' (d)	EPts
	'Countess of Aberdeen'	EBak SLBF
	'Countess of Maritza' (d)	CLoc
	'Cover Girl' (d)	EPts
	'Coxeen'	EBak
	'Crackerjack'	CLoc
	'Crescendo' (d)	CLoc
	'Crinkley Bottom' (d)	EPts MJac SLBF
	'Crosby Serendipity'	CLoc
	'Crystal Blue'	EBak
	'Cuddles and Kisses' (d)	SLBF
	'Cupid'	EBak
	'Curly Q'	EBak

	'Curtain Call' (d)	EBak
	cylindracea misapplied	see *F.* × *bacillaris*
	'Dainty'	EBak
	'Dainty Lady' (d)	EBak
	'Daisy Bell'	CLoc EBak MJac
	'Dana Samantha'	EPts
	'Dancing Bloom'	EPts
	'Dancing Flame' (d) $\mathbb{Y}^{H3}$	CLoc EBak EPts MBros MJac SLBF WRou
	'Daniel Pfaller' (d)	MJac
	'Danny Boy' (d)	CLoc EBak
	'Dark Eyes' (d) $\mathbb{Y}^{H4}$	CLoc EBak MJac SLBF
	'Dark Secret' (d)	EBak
	'David' $\mathbb{Y}^{H4}$	CLoc EHDe ELon EPts LSRN MJac SLBF SPoG WAvo WCot WLov WRou
	'David Clifford'	EHDe
	'David Lockyer' (d)	CLoc
	'Dawn Fantasia' (v)	CLoc EPts
	'Dawn Star' (d)	CLoc
	'Debby' (d)	EBak
	'Deborah Street' (d)	CLoc
	'DebRon's Black Cherry'	SLBF
	'DebRon's White Linen' (d)	WRou
	'Dee Copley' (d)	EBak
	'Deep Purple' (d)	CLoc EPts MJac SCoo WRou
	'Delia Smith' (d)	EPts
	'Delicate Blue'	SLBF
	'Delicate Purple'	EPts SLBF WFar WMal WRou
	'Delphobe'	EPts
	'Delta's Bride'	SLBF
	'Delta's Groom'	SLBF
	'Delta's Sara'	CBcs CBod CRos EHyd ELon EPfP EPts GBin LBuc LCro LOPS LRHS MAsh MBow MBros MHer MJac MMrt MSCN NRHS SCob SGBe SLim SLon SPad SPoG SVic WFar WLov WRou
§	***denticulata*** $\mathbb{Y}^{H2}$	CLoc EBak EHDe EHyd EPts LRHS MHer NRHS SLBF SVic
	'Desperate Daniel'	EPts
	'Devonshire Dumpling' (d) $\mathbb{Y}^{H2}$	CLoc EBak EPts MJac SLBF WRou
	'Diablo' (d)	EBak
	'Diamond Wedding'	SVic
	'Diana Wright'	WAvo WLov
	'Diane Stephens'	WRou
	'Dipton Dainty' (d)	CLoc EBak SVic
	'Display' $\mathbb{Y}^{H4}$	CLoc CRos EBak EHDe EHyd EPfP EPts LRHS MGos MJac NPer NRHS SCob SGBe SGol SLBF SPoG SVic WRou
	'Diva'	WCot
	'Doc'	EPts SVic
	'Docteur Topinard'	CLoc
	'Doctor'	see *F.* 'The Doctor'
	'Doctor Foster' $\mathbb{Y}^{H4}$	CLoc CTri EBak EHDe SVic
	'Doctor Olson' (d)	CLoc
	'Doctor Robert'	EPts MJac
	'Doctor Sat Sandilands' (d)	WRou
	'Dodo'	SLBF
§	'Dollar Prinzessin' (d) $\mathbb{Y}^{H4}$	CLoc CMac CRos EBak EHyd EPfP EPts EShb LRHS MBros MGos MJac NPer NRHS SGol SLBF SLim SPlb SVic WFar WRou
	'Dominyana'	EBak EHDe
	'Dopy' (d)	EPts SVic
	'Doray'	EPts
	'Doreen Redfern'	CLoc MJac SVic
	'Doris Joan'	SLBF
	'Dorothea Flower'	CLoc EBak

	'Dorothy'	EPts SLBF
	'Dorothy Ann'	SLBF
	'Dorothy Day' (d)	CLoc
	'Dorothy Hanley' (d)	CCCN CLoc EPts MJac SCob SLBF SVic WRou
	'Drake 400' (d)	CLoc
	'Drame' (d)	EBak EHDe SVic
	'Duchess of Albany'	CLoc EHDe
	'Duchess of Cornwall' (d)	EPts
	'Duke of Wellington' Haag, 1956 (d)	CLoc
	'Dulcie Elizabeth' (d)	EBak MJac
	'Dunrobin Bedder'	SLBF
	'Dusky Rose' (d)	CLoc EBak MJac
	'Dutch Mill'	CLoc EBak
	'Dying Embers' ♀H4	CLoc EShb GBin MHer SDix SVen WRou
	'Earre Barré'	SLBF
	'East Anglian'	CLoc
	'Easter Belle'	EHyd LRHS NRHS
	'Ebb 'n' Flow'	EBak
	'Ebbtide' (d)	CLoc
	'Ed Largarde' (d)	EBak
	'Eden Lady'	CLoc
	'Eden Princess'	MJac
	'Eden Rock' (d)	CLoc
	'Edith' ambig.	EPts
	'Edith' Brown (d)	SLBF
	'El Cid'	CLoc EBak SVic
	'Ela' **new**	WRou
	'Elaine Ann'	EPts MJac
	'Elaine Cosgrove' **new**	WRou
	'Eleanor Leytham'	EBak
	ELECTRIC LIGHTS ('Nufu1'PBR)	LRHS
	'Elfin Glade'	CLoc EBak SVic
	'Elfriede Ott' (T) ♀H1c	CLoc EBak WRou
	'Ellie's Charm'	SLBF
	'Elma'	MJac WRou
	'Elsa' (d)	SVic
	'Elsie Lowis Kay' **new**	WRou
	'Emily Bright'	EHDe
	'Emily Eve' (d)	EPts MJac SLBF
	'Emma Payne'	SLBF
	'Empress of Prussia' ♀H4	CLoc EBak EPPr EPts SLBF SVic
	encliandra (E)	NWad
§	'Enfant Prodigue' (d)	CLoc SDix SLBF SVic XLum
	'Eppsii'	SLBF
	'Eric's Majestic' (d)	MJac
	'Ernie'PBR	EPts SLBF WRou
	'Eruption' (T)	CLoc CPla CWCL MJac
	'Esmay' **new**	WRou
	'Estelle Marie'	CLoc EBak WRou
	'Eternal Flame' (d)	EBak EPts
	'Eternity' (d) **new**	WRou
	'Ethel May' (d)	MJac
	'Eva Boerg' ♀H4	CCCN CLoc CTri EBak EPts MBros WKif WRou
	'Evensong'	CLoc EBak SVic
	'Evita'PBR (Bella Series)	LCro LOPS
	excorticata	CBcs CCCN CExl CTsd ESwi SIvy SPlb WBor
	'Fairy Lights' **new**	CBcs
	'Falklands' (d)	EPts SLBF
	'Falling Stars'	CLoc
	'Fancy Pants' (d)	CLoc SVic
	'Felicity Kendal' (d)	SCoo
	'Festival Lights' (E)	SLBF WRou
	'Ffion'	EPts WRou
	'Fiery Spider'	EBak
	'Finn'	EPts
	'Fiona'	CLoc EBak SVic
	'Fire Mountain' (d)	CLoc
	'Firecracker'	see *F.* 'John Ridding'
	'Firelite' (d)	EBak
	'Flair' (d)	CLoc
	'Flamingo Wings' (d)	EPts
	'Flanders Field'	SLBF WRou
	'Flash' ♀H4	CLoc CTri EHyd ELan EPts LRHS MJac MRav NRHS SLBF SPoG SVic WRou
	'Flashlight'	EWld MAsh MJac SCoo
	'Flat Jack o' Lancashire' (d)	SLBF
	'Fleur de Picardie'	SLBF
	'Flirtation Waltz' (d)	CLoc EBak MJac SVic
	'Flocon de Neige'	SLBF
	'Florence Turner'	EBak
	'Florentina' (d)	EBak SVic
	'Florrie's Gem' (d)	SLBF
	'Flying Cloud' (d)	CLoc EBak SVic
	'Flying Scotsman' (d)	CLoc EBak EPts SCoo SVic WRou
	'Foolke'	EBak
	'Forget-me-not'	CLoc SVic
	'Fort Bragg' (d)	EBak
	'Four Farthings' (d)	EPts WRou
	'Foxgrove Wood' ♀H4	EBak EPts LRHS SLBF SVic
	'Frances Haskins'	WRou
	'Frank Saunders'	SLBF WRou
	'Frank Unsworth' (d)	EPts MJac
	'Frankfurt 2006'	MJac
	'Frankie Boy'	SLBF
	'Frankie's Magnificent Seven' (d)	EPts
	'Frans Boers'	SLBF
	'Frau Hilde Rademacher' (d)	EBak EPts SLBF SVic WRou
	'Fred Hansford' (v)	SLBF
	'Fred's First' (d)	SVic
	'Friendly Fire' (d)	CLoc
	'Frosted Flame'	CLoc MJac SLBF
	'Frozen Tears'	EPts
	'Frühling' (d)	EBak
	'Fuchsiade '88'	CLoc
	'Fuji-san'	ELon EPts
	fulgens (T) ♀H2	EPPr WRou
*	- 'Variegata' (T/v)	EPts WRou
	'Fulpila'	SLBF
	'Gail Barber' **new**	WRou
	'Gala' (d)	EBak
	'Galadriel'	SLBF
	'Garden News' (d) ♀H4	CBod CEnd CLoc CRos EHyd EPfP EPts LRHS MAsh MBow MBros MJac NBir NGBl NPer NRHS SCob SGol SLBF SVic WFar WRou
	'Gartenmeister Bonstedt' (T) ♀H1c	CLoc EWld WRou
	'Gary Rhodes' (d)	EBak SCoo
	'Gay Fandango' (d)	CLoc
	'Gay Señorita'	EBak
	'Gay Spinner' (d)	CLoc
	'Gemma Fisher' (d)	EPts
	GENE ('Goetzgene'PBR) (Shadowdancer Series)	SCoo
	'Général Monk' (d)	EBak EPts SGol
	'Genii' ♀H4	Widely available
	'Geoff Oke'	WRou
	'Geoffrey Smith' (d)	EPts
§	'Georg Börnemann' (T) ♀H2	CLoc EBak MJac
	'George Barr'	EHyd LRHS NRHS
§	'Gerharda's Aubergine'	CLoc
	'Gesneriana'	EBak
	'Giant Pink Enchanted' (d)	CLoc

	'Gilda' (d)	MJac
	'Gilt Edge' (v)	CLoc
	'Gina Bowman' (E)	EPts SLBF WRou
	GINGER ('Goetzginger'PBR) (Shadowdancer Series)	SCoo
	'Gipsy Princess' (d)	CLoc
	'Gladiator' (d)	CMac EBak EHDe
	'Gladys Lorimer'	EHyd EPfP EPts LRHS NRHS
	glazioviana ♀H2	CSde EPPr EPts MHer SLBF SMHy SVen
	'Glitters'	EBak
§	'Globosa'	CAgr
	'Glowing Embers'	EBak WRou
	'Glowing Lilac' (d)	EPts
	'Golden Anniversary' (d)	CLoc EBak
§	'Golden Border Queen'	CLoc EBak EHDe
	'Golden Dawn'	CLoc SVic
	'Golden Girl'	SLBF
	'Golden Herald'	SLBF
	'Golden Marinka' (v) ♀H2	CLoc EBak EHDe
	'Golden Swingtime' (d)	MJac
	'Golden Treasure' (v)	CLoc
	'Good as Gold' **new**	WRou
	'Governor Pat Brown' (d)	EBak
	'Grace Darling'	EBak
	gracilis	see *F. magellanica* var. *gracilis*
	'Graf Witte'	EPPr SVic
	'Grandad Fred' (d)	SLBF
	'Grandma Sheila' **new**	WRou
	'Grandma Sinton' (d)	CLoc
	'Grandpa Jack' (d)	SLBF
	'Grayrigg'	ELon EPPr EPts EShb LSRN MHer SGBe SLBF SVic WRou
	'Great Ouse' (d)	EPts
	'Great Scott' (d)	CLoc
	'Green 'n' Gold'	EBak EHDe
	'Greenpeace'	SLBF
	'Grumpy'	EPts SVic
	'Gruss aus dem Bodethal'	CLoc EBak EPts
	'Gunton Park' (T)	EHDe
	'Gustave Doré' (d)	EBak
	'H.G. Brown'	EBak SLBF
	'Hannah Louise' (d)	EPts
	'Happy'	EPts MHer SVic
	'Happy Anniversary'	CLoc
	'Happy Fellow'	CLoc EBak WRou
	'Happy Wedding Day' (d)	CLoc EPts MJac SCoo SVic
	'Hapsburgh'	EBak EHDe
	'Harbour Lites'	SLBF
	'Harlow Car'	EPts
	'Harmony' Niederholzer, 1946	EBak
	'Harriet Lye'	EHDe
	'Harry Gray' (d) ♀H2	CLoc EBak EPts MJac WRou
	'Harry Taylor' (d)	EPts
	'Harry's Sunshine'	SLBF
	hartwegii	MHer
	'Harvey's Reward'	SLBF
	'Hastings'	SLBF
	'Hathersage' (d)	EBak
	hatschbachii ♀H2	EBee EHDe EHyd EPPr EPfP EShb EWes LRHS MCot SBrt SDix SGBe SIvy SLon SMHy SPlb SSal SVen WFar WPGP
	'Haute Cuisine' (d)	CLoc
	'Hawaiian Sunset' (d)	CLoc EPts SLBF
	'Hawkshead' ♀H4	Widely available
	'Hayley Jackson' **new**	MJac
	'Hayley Jay' (d)	SLBF
	'Hazel Elizabeth'	WRou
	'Heidi Ann' (d) ♀H4	CLoc CRos EBak EHyd EPts LRHS MAsh MBros MRav NRHS SLBF SVic

§	'Heidi Weiss' (d)	CLoc
	'Heinrich Henkel'	see *F.* 'Andenken an Heinrich Henkel'
	'Helen Clare' (d)	CLoc
	'Helen Storer'	MJac
	'Hemsleyana'	see *F. microphylla* subsp. *hemsleyana*
	'Henri Poincaré'	EBak
	'Her Majesty's Crown' (T)	SLBF
	'Herald' ♀H4	CRos EHyd LRHS MGos SLBF SVic
	'Herbé de Jacques'	see *F.* 'Mr West'
	'HeRi Trevally'	SLBF
	'Heritage' (d)	CLoc EBak
	'Herman de Graaff' (d)	SLBF
	'Hermiena'	CLoc EPts MHer SLBF SVic
	'Herps Pierement'	SLBF
	'Herps Serang'	SLBF
	'Hessett Festival' (d)	EBak
	'Hi Di'	SLBF WRou
	'Hidcote Beauty' ♀H2	CLoc SLBF
	'Hindu Belle'	EBak
	'Hobson's Choice' (d)	SLBF
	'Holly's Beauty' (d)	CLoc EPts WRou
	'Hot Coals'	EPts MJac SVic WRou
	'Howlett's Hardy' ♀H4	CLoc EBak SVic
	'Hula Girl' (d)	EBak MJac
	'Huntsman' (d)	CCCN
	'I Love You'	WRou
	'Ian Storey'	EHyd EPfP LRHS NRHS WRou
	'Iceberg'	EBak
	'Icecap'	SVic
	'Iced Champagne'	CLoc EBak MJac
	'Ichiban' (d)	CLoc
	'Icicles Chandelier'	SLBF
	'Icy Pink' (d)	WRou
	'Ida' (d)	EBak
	'Igloo Maid' (d)	CLoc EBak
	'I'm in Charge' **new**	WRou
	'Imogen Faye' (d)	SLBF WRou
	'Impudence'	CLoc EBak
	'Impulse' (d)	CLoc
	'Indian Maid' (d)	EBak
	'Insulinde' (T)	EPts MHer MJac SLBF
	'Iona'	WRou
	'Irene Sinton' (d)	MJac
	'Isn't She Lovely'	SLBF
	'Italiano' (d)	MJac
	'Ivana van Amsterdam'	WRou
	'Jac Damen'	SLBF
	'Jack Shahan' ♀H2	CCCN CLoc EBak EPts MBow MJac WRou
	'Jack Siverns'	WRou
	'Jackpot' (d)	EBak
	'James Lye' (d)	EBak EHDe
	'Jan Everett' (d)	SLBF
	'Janice Perry's Gold' (v)	MJac
	'Janie' (d)	EHyd EPfP LBuc LRHS MAsh NRHS SVic
	'Jasper's Formidable' (T)	SLBF
	'Jasper's Lightning' (T)	SLBF
	'Jasper's Unbelievable'	WRou
	'Jean Frisby'	CLoc
	'Jean Harper' **new**	WRou
	'Jean Taylor'	EPts WRou
	'Jean Webb' (v)	WCot
	'Jeanie J' **new**	WRou
	'Jef van der Kuylen' (d)	WRou
	'Jennifer'	MJac
	'Jennifer Ann'	MPri NRHS SLBF
	'Jenny Carr' **new**	WRou
	'Jenny May'	CLoc EPts

'Jess' SLBF
'Jessica Reynolds' WRou
'Jester' Holmes (d) CLoc
'Jet' MJac
'Jiddles' (E) SLBF
'Jill Holloway' (T) SLBF
'Jim Dodge' (d) EPts
'Jimmy Cricket' (E) WRou
'Joan Cooper' CLoc SLBF SVic
'Joan Knight' CLoc
'Joan Margaret' (d) MJac
'Joan Morris' SLBF
'Joanna Lumley' (d) EPts
'Jo-Anne Fisher' (d) EPts
'Joanne Jackson' MJac
'Joe Kusber' (d) EBak
'John Bartlett' CLoc
'John Boy' (d) WRou
'John Egan' **new** WRou
'John Galea' SLBF WRou
'John Grooms' (d) WRou
'John Hitchcock' (d) WRou
'John Lockyer' CLoc
'John Maynard Scales' (T) ♀H2 MJac WRou
'John Nicholass' SLBF
§ 'John Ridding'PBR (T/v) ♀H1c SPoG
'Johnny Boy' SLBF
JOLLIES FORCE BONDY **new** WRou
JOLLIES FORCE PARIS ('Brfu 09721'PBR) **new** WRou
JOLLIES MACON ('Brfu 12811') **new** WRou
JOLLIES MENTON ('Brfu 0543'PBR) **new** WRou
JOLLIES NANCY ('Brfu 07951'PBR) **new** WRou
JOLLIES REIMS **new** WRou
JOLLIES TARBES ('Brfu 0582') **new** WRou
JOLLIES TRAILING BELFORT ('Brfu 10681'PBR) **new** WRou
'Jon Oram' CLoc
I 'Joy' SLBF
'Joy Patmore' CLoc SLBF
'Joyce Sinton' CLoc
'Juella' WRou
'Jules Daloges' (d) EBak
I 'Julia' (Bella Series) (d) **new** WRou
'Julie Marie' (d) MJac
'June Marie Shaw' MJac
'Jungle' SLBF
'Just Pat' MJac
'Just Terry' (d) **new** SLBF
'Kaley Jackson' MJac WRou
'Karen Isles' (E) SLBF WRou
'Karen Louise' (d) CLoc
'Kate Taylor' (d) SLBF
'Kath van Hanegem' CLoc
'Katie Alice' **new** WRou
'Katie Coast' WRou
'Katie Rogers' EPts
'Katjan' EHDe GBin SLBF WFar WRou
'Katrina Thompsen' CLoc EPts SLBF
'Ken Tudor' MJac
'Kenny Walkling' ♀H2 MJac SLBF
'Kernan Robson' (d) EBak
'Keystone' EBak
'Kimberly' (d) MJac
'King's Ransom' (d) CLoc EBak
'Kit Oxtoby' (d) CLoc MJac
'Kiwi' (d) EBak
'Knight Errant' SLBF
'Kobold' MJac
'Kolding Perle' SLBF
'Kuniko Atarashi' (d) WRou
'Kwintet' EBak MJac
'La Bianca' EBak
'La Campanella' (d) ♀H2 CCCN CLoc EBak EPts MBros MJac
'La France' (d) EBak
'La Rosita' (d) EBak
I 'La Traviata' Blackwell (d) EBak
'Lace Petticoats' (d) EBak
'Lady Boothby' ♀H4 Widely available
'Lady Framlingham' (d) EPts
'Lady in Black' (d) CBcs ELan LSou MCot SIvy SPoG WLov
'Lady in Red' (d) WRou
'Lady Isobel Barnett' CLoc EBak MJac SLBF
'Lady Ramsey' EBak
'Lady Rebecca' (d) CLoc
'Lady Thumb' (d) ♀H3 Widely available
'Laing's Hybrid' EBak
'Lakeland Princess' EBak
'Lambada' CLoc WRou
'Lancashire Lad' (d) MJac
'Lancelot' EBak
'Land van Beveren' SLBF
'Lapshead White' CExl
'Lassie' (d) CLoc EBak
'Last Chance' (E) SLBF
'Laura' ambig. SVic
I 'Laura' (Dutch) CLoc EPts SLBF
'Laura Cross' (E) SLBF WRou
'Lauren' WRou
'Lavender Kate' (d) EBak
'Lechlade Gorgon' EHyd LRHS NRHS SLBF
'Lechlade Magician' EPts SEND SLBF WMal WRou
'Lena' (d) ♀H2 CLoc CMac CTri EBak EPts MJac SLBF SMrm SPlb SVic
'Lena Dalton' (d) CLoc EBak
'Leonora' CLoc SLBF SVic WRou
'Lesley's Wonder' MJac
'Leslie Bowman' ♀H2 EHDe SLBF WRou
'Lett's Delight' (d) EPts
'Letty Lye' EBak EHDe
'Leverhulme' see *F.* 'Leverkusen'
§ 'Leverkusen' (T) CLoc EBak MJac
'Liebriez' (d) ♀H4 EBak SVic WRou
'Lilac Lustre' (d) CLoc SVic
'Lilac Mist' SLBF
'Lilac Queen' (d) EBak
'Lilian' MJac
'Lillian Annetts' (d) ♀H2 MJac SLBF WRou
'Lillibet' (d) CLoc
'Lincoln Castle' WRou
'Linda Goulding' EBak
'Linda Grace' MJac
'Linda Hinchliffe' EPts MJac SLBF WFar WRou
'Lindisfarne' (d) CLoc EBak MJac
'Lionel' WRou
'Lisa' (d) EPts
'Little Beauty' SVic
'Little Boy Blue' EPts
'Little Brook Gem' SLBF
'Little Catbells' (E) SLBF
'Little Cracker' SPoG
'Little Gene' EBak
'Little Jessica' (E) MJac SLBF WRou
'Little Nan' SLBF
'Little Tony' SLBF WRou

	'Loeky'	CLoc SVic
	'Logan Garden'	see *F. magellanica* 'Logan Woods'
	'Lolita' (d)	EBak
	'London 2000'	CLoc EPts MJac SLBF WRou
	'London in Bloom'	SLBF
	'Lonely Ballerina' (d)	CLoc
	'Lord Byron'	CLoc
	'Lord Lonsdale'	EPts WRou
	'Lord Roberts'	CLoc SLBF
	'Lorna Swinbank'	SVic
	'Lottie Hobby' (E) ♀H3	CLoc CMac CMea EGrI EHyd EPts ITim NWad SVic WCot WRou
	'Louise Emershaw' (d)	EBak MJac
	'Louise Nicholls'	MJac
	'Loveliness'	CLoc EHDe SVic
	'Lovely Linda'	SLBF
	'Love's Reward' ♀H2	CLoc MJac SLBF SVic
	loxensis misapplied	see *F.* 'Speciosa'
	'Lucy Locket'	MJac
	'Lye's Elegance'	EHDe
	'Lye's Excelsior'	EHDe
	'Lye's Favourite'	EHDe
	'Lye's Own'	EHDe SLBF
	'Lye's Perfection'	EHDe
	'Lye's Unique' ♀H3	CLoc EBak EHDe EPts MJac SLBF SVic
	'Lyndon'	MJac
	'Lyndon Clements' new	MJac
	'Lynette' (d)	CLoc
	'Lynne Patricia' (d)	EPts SLBF
	'Machu Picchu'	CLoc EPts
	'Madame Cornélissen' (d) ♀H4	CLoc CMac CRos CSBt CTri EBak EHDe EHyd ELan EMor EPfP EPts LRHS MAsh NLar NRHS SCoo SEND SLBF SLim SPer SVic WFar WRou XLum
	magellanica ♀H4	CBcs EHyd GArf LRHS MGil NLar NPer NRHS NWea SPer SSal SVic WCAu WFar WGwG WSpi
	- 'Alba'	see *F. magellanica* var. *molinae* 'Alba'
	- 'Alba Variegata' (v)	SPer WFar
	- 'Angel's Teardrop'	WRou
	- 'Arauco'	SBrt
	- 'Floriade'	CCoa
	- 'Folius Aureus'	WFar
§	- var. ***gracilis*** ♀H4	CAgr CLoc CTri EHyd EPfP NBro
	- - 'Aurea' ♀H4	CBcs CMac CSde EHyd ELan ELon EPPr EPfP LRHS MHer MRav NRHS SCoo SDix SLBF SPer SRms SVic WAvo WRou XLum
	- - 'Purple Mountain'	CBod LPla
	- - 'Variegata' (v) ♀H4	EBak EHyd EPfP MGos MRav SVic
§	- - 'Versicolor' (v) ♀H4	Widely available
	- 'Lady Bacon'	CBcs CBod EBee EHyd ELon EPts EShb EWes LRHS MCot MHer NLar NRHS SBrt SDys SEND SLBF SPoG WBor WMal WPGP WRou WSHC
§	- 'Logan Woods'	EBee ELon EPfP GKin SLBF SMad SMrm WPGP
	- 'Lyonesse Lady'	WRou
	- var. ***molinae***	CTri EBak EBee ELan EPfP EShb GBin GWyn MBlu MNrw MSwo NBid NPer SCob SPer SPlb WFar
§	- - 'Alba' ♀H4	CBod CDoC EHDe EPts GArf MPie NLar SGol WFar WGwG WSpi
I	- - 'Alba Aureovariegata' (v)	CBcs CMac WFar
	- - 'Golden Sharpitor' (v)	CCCN WFar
	- - 'Mr Knight's Blush'	WSpi

§	- - 'Sharpitor' (v) ♀H4	CCoa CDoC CKel CSde EBak EBee ECha ELan ELon EPfP LRHS NChi NPer SGol SPer SPoG WFar WKif WRou WSHC WSMil
	- 'Mountain Gold'	CBod WFar
	- 'Pumila'	CMea EWes GArf MAsh MHer SMHy WAbe WFar WHal WPGP
	- 'Purpurea'	LRHS SGBe
§	- 'Thompsonii' ♀H4	EHDe SMHy
	- 'Variegata Aurea' (v)	SGBe SGol WFar
	'Magic Flute'	CLoc MJac
	'Major Heaphy'	EBak
	'Mama Bleuss' (d)	EBak
	'Mandarin Cream'	CLoc
	'Mantilla' (T)	MJac
	'Maori Maid' (d)	MJac
	'Marble Crepe' (T)	SLBF
	'Marcia' PBR (Shadowdancer Series)	CLoc
	'Marcus Graham' (d)	CLoc EBak SLBF WRou
	'Margaret' (d) ♀H4	CLoc CTri EBak EPts SLBF SVic WFar WRou
	'Margaret Brown' ♀H4	CLoc CTri EHyd LRHS NRHS SLBF SVic WRou
	'Margaret My Own'	EPts
	'Margaret Roe'	EBak MJac
	'Margaret Susan'	EBak
	'Margaret Viscountess Thurso'	SLBF
	'Margarite Dawson' (d)	SVic
	'Maria Landy'	MJac SLBF
	'Maria Mathilde' (d)	SLBF
	'Maria Shaw'	EPts
	'Marin Glow' ♀H3	CLoc EBak SVic
	'Marina Kelly'	WRou
	'Marinka' ♀H2	CLoc EBak EPts MBros MJac
	MARISKA ('Bf01' PBR) (Bella Series)	CLoc LCro LOPS
	'Marlies de Keijzer' (E)	EPts NWad SLBF SVen
	'Martha Adcock'	SLBF WRou
	'Martin's Yellow Surprise' (T)	SLBF
	'Marty' (d)	EBak
	'Mary' (T) ♀H1c	CLoc EPts SLBF WCot
	'Mary Lockyer' (d)	CLoc EBak
	'Mary Thorne'	EBak
	'Mauve Beauty' (d)	SLBF
	'Mauve Wisp' (d)	SVic
	'Mavis Enderby'	MJac SLBF
	'Max Cobi'	MJac SLBF WRou
I	'Maxima'	CLoc EPts SLBF WRou
	'Maxine's Smile'	MJac SLBF
	'Meditation' (d)	CLoc
	'Melody Ann' (d)	EBak
	'Melting Moments' (d)	SCoo WRou
	'Mephisto' ♀H2	LRHS
	'Mercurius' ♀H4	LRHS XLum
	'Merry Mary' (d)	EBak
	'Mersty' (d)	SLBF WRou
I	'Mexicali Rose' Machado	CLoc
	'Michael' (d/v)	EPts
	'Michael Wallis' (T)	SLBF
	michoacanensis misapplied	see *F. microphylla* subsp. *aprica*
	michoacanensis Sessé & Moç. (E) B&SWJ 9148	WCru
	'Micky Goult' ♀H2	CLoc EPts MJac
	microphylla (E)	CBcs CBod CElw CExl CLoc CTsd EBak EBee EHyd ELon GBin GQue IDee MGil SDix SMHy SVic WAbe XSte
	- B&SWJ 10331	WCru

§	- subsp. ***aprica*** (E) B&SWJ 9101	WCru
	- - 'Dolly's Dress' (E)	WCru
§	- subsp. ***hemsleyana*** (E)	CExl SVic
	- - B&SWJ 10478	WCru
	- - 'Silver Lining' (E)	CCCN CMil CTsd EPPr EShb MHer NCou NLar SDix SWvt WCot WCru WFar WNPC XSte
	- 'Variegata' (E/v)	EWes
§	'Mieke Meursing' ♀^{H2}	CLoc EBak MJac SVic
	'Millennium'	CLoc EBak EPts MJac SCoo SVic WRou
	'Millfield Alpha'	EPts
	'Millfield Bravo'	EPts
	'Millfield Charlie'	EPts
	'Millfield Delta'	EPts
	'Millfield Echo'	EPts WRou
	'Millfield Foxtrot'	EPts
	'Ming'	CLoc
	'Miniature Jewels' (E)	SLBF
	minimiflora misapplied	see *F.* × *bacillaris*
	'Minipani'	SLBF
	'Minirose'	EPts SLBF
	'Minnesota' (d)	EBak
	'Miranda' (Bella Series) **new**	WRou
	'Mischief'	SVic
	'Misha Charlotte' **new**	SLBF
	'Miss California' (d)	CLoc EBak
	'Miss Lye'	EHDe
	'Miss Muffett' (d)	EPts
	'Miss Vallejo' (d)	EBak
	'Mission Bells'	CLoc EBak EPts SVic
	'Misty Mease'	MJac
	'Molesworth' (d)	MJac
	'Money Spinner'	CLoc
	'Mood Indigo' (d)	CLoc
	'Moody Blues'	WRou
	'Moonbeam' (d)	CLoc
	'Moonglow' (d)	MJac
	'Moonlight Sonata'	CLoc
	'More Applause' (d)	CLoc
	'Morning Light' (d)	CLoc
	'Morrells' (d)	EBak
	'Moth Blue' (d)	EBak
	'Mountain Mist' (d)	SVic
	'Mr A. Huggett'	CLoc EPts SLBF
	'Mr W. Rundle'	EBak
§	'Mr West' (v)	CEme MCot SCob WFar XSte
	'Mrs Audrey Berkley' (d) **new**	SLBF
	'Mrs B.' (E)	MJac
	'Mrs Churchill'	CLoc
	'Mrs Grant'	EHDe
	'Mrs Hobhouse' (d)	EHDe
	'Mrs J Bright'	EHDe
	'Mrs Lee Belton' (E)	SLBF
	'Mrs Lovell Swisher' ♀^{H4}	EBak
	'Mrs Marshall'	EMal SLBF
	'Mrs Popple' ♀^{H4}	Widely available
	'Mrs W. Castle'	SVic
	'Mrs W.P. Wood' ♀^{H4}	CBod CLoc EHDe ELon MSCN SVic WRou
	'Mrs W. Rundle'	CLoc SLBF
	'Mrs Wilks' ♀^{H1c}	SLBF WRou
	'Multa'	WRou
	'Muriel' (d)	CLoc
	'My Charlotte' **new**	SLBF
	'My Dad'	SLBF
	'My Fair Lady' (d)	EBak
	'My Grandchildren'	SLBF WRou
	'My Little Cracker'	MJac WRou

	'My Little Dream' (d) **new**	WRou
	'My Little Fairy' **new**	WRou
	'My Little Gem'	WRou
	'My Little Sparkler'	WRou
	'My Mum'	SLBF
	'My Pat'	SLBF
	'My Sacha'	SLBF
	'Myriad' **new**	SLBF
	'Nancy Lou' (d)	CLoc MJac SLBF SVic
	'Natasha Sinton' (d)	CCCN MJac
	'Nathan Rhys'	EPts
	'Neapolitan' (d)	SLBF
	'Nell Gwyn'	CLoc
	'Nellie Nuttall' ♀^{H2}	CLoc EBak EPts
	'Neopolitan' (E)	CLoc EHDe EPts SVic
	'Nephele'	EPts WRou
	'Nice 'n' Easy' (d)	MJac WRou
	'Nicki Fenwick-Raven' (E)	SLBF
	'Nicki's Findling'	EPts MJac WRou
	'Nicola'	EBak
	'Nicola Jane' (d)	EBak EPts MJac SHar SLBF SVic WRou
	'Nicola Storey'	WRou
	'Nicolette'	MJac
§	***nigricans*** B&SWJ 10664	WCru
	'Nora'[PBR] (Bella Series)	WRou
	'Norman Welton'	SLBF
	'Normandy Bell'	EBak
	'Northern Jewel'	EPts SLBF
	'Northilda'	SVic
	'Northway'	CLoc
	'Norvell Gillespie' (d)	EBak
	'O Sole Mio'	SVic
	'Obcylin' (E)	EPts MHer
	'Ocean Beach'	EPts
	'Oetnang' (d)	CTri SCoo
	'Old Somerset' (v)	CCCN SLBF
	'Olga Storey'	EHyd LRHS NRHS
	'Olive Smith'	EHDe EPts MJac
	OLIVIA ('Bf06') (Bella Series) **new**	WRou
	'Olympic Sunset'	SVic
	'Opalescent' (d)	CLoc
	'Orange Crush'	CLoc EBak
	'Orange Crystal'	MJac SLBF SVic
	'Orange Drops'	CLoc EBak EPts WRou
	'Orange Flare'	CLoc EBak SLBF
	'Orange King' (d)	CLoc
	'Orange Mirage'	CLoc
	'Orange Star' (E)	SLBF WRou
	'Orangeblossom'	SLBF
	'Orient Express' (T) ♀^{H1c}	CLoc
	'Ornamental Pearl' (v)	CLoc SLBF
	'Other Fellow'	EBak EPts MJac SLBF
	'Oulton Empress' (E)	SLBF WRou
	'Oulton Fairy' (E)	SLBF
	'Oulton Painted Lady' (E)	WRou
	'Oulton Red Imp' (E)	SLBF
	'Oulton Travellers Rest' (E)	SLBF WRou
	'Our Carol'	SLBF WRou
	'Our Claire'	WRou
	'Our Hilary'	SLBF
	'Our Michelle' **new**	SLBF
	'Our Nan' (d)	MJac
	'Our Spencer'	SLBF
	'Our Ted' (T)	EBak
	'Over the Waves' (d) **new**	CLoc
	'Overbecks'	see *F. magellanica* var. *molinae* 'Sharpitor'
	'P.E. King' (d)	SLBF
	'Pacific Queen' (d)	EBak

'Pacquesa' (d)	EBak
'Padre Pio' (d)	EBak
'Pam and Ted Love'	SLBF WRou
'Pam Plack'	SLBF
'Pamela Knights' (d)	EBak
paniculata (T) ♀H2	CCCN CRHN EBak EGrI EHDe ELan EPts MCot MHer SLBF WCot WCru
'Papa Bleuss' (d)	EBak
'Papoose' (d)	EBak SLBF SVic WRou
'Party Frock'	CLoc EBak
parviflora misapplied	see *F.* × *bacillaris*
'Pat Meara'	CLoc EBak
'Pathétique' (d)	CLoc
'Patience' (d)	EBak SLBF
'Patio Princess' (d)	CLoc EPts SCob WRou
'Patricia Hodge'	WRou
'Patty Sue' (d)	EPts WRou
'Paul Cambon' (d)	EBak
'Paula Jane' (d) ♀H2	MJac MPri SLBF SVic WRou
'Pauline Rawlins' (d)	CLoc
'Paulus'	WRou
'Pavilion Princess'	SLBF WRou
'Peachy' (California Dreamers Series) (d)	CLoc SCoo WRou
'Peachy Keen' (d)	EBak
'Peacock' (d)	CLoc
'Peasholm'	WRou
'Pee Wee Rose'	EBak EHDe SVic WRou
PEGGY ('Goetzpeg'PBR) (Shadowdancer Series)	SCoo
'Peggy King'	EBak
'Peloria' (d)	CLoc EBak
'Peper Harow'	EBak
'Pepi' (d)	EBak
'Peppermint Candy' (d)	MJac
'Peppermint Stick' (d)	CLoc EBak
'Perky Pink' (d)	EBak EPts
'Perogers 70' **new**	WRou
'Perry Park'	MJac SVic
'Perry's Jumbo'	NPer
perscandens	CExl
'Peter Meredith'	MJac WRou
petiolaris B&SWJ 10675	WCru
'Pharaoh'	CLoc
'Phénoménal' (d)	EBak
'Phryne' (d)	SVic
'Phyllis' (d) ♀H4	CLoc EBak EHyd EPts LRHS MJac NRHS SLBF SVic WRou XLum
'Piet van der Sande'	SLBF WRou
'Pinch Me' (d)	EBak
'Pink Aurora'	CLoc
'Pink Ballet Girl' (d)	CLoc SVic
'Pink Bon Accord'	CLoc SVic
'Pink Cloud'	CLoc EBak
'Pink Darling'	CLoc EBak
'Pink Dessert'	EBak
'Pink Elephant' (d)	CLoc WRou
'Pink Fandango' (d)	CLoc
'Pink Fantasia' ♀H2	CLoc EBak EPts MJac SLBF SVic
'Pink Galore' (d) ♀H2	CLoc MJac
'Pink Goon' (d)	SLBF SVic
'Pink Haze'	SVic
'Pink Ice' (d)	MBros
'Pink la Campanella'	EBak
'Pink Marshmallow' (d) ♀H4	CLoc EBak MJac SLBF
'Pink Pearl' Bright (d)	EHDe
'Pink Profusion'	EBak
'Pink Quartet' (d)	CLoc EBak WCot
'Pink Rain'	MJac
'Pink Slippers'	CLoc

	'Pink Spangles'	see *F.* 'Mieke Meursing'
	'Pink Temptation'	CLoc
	'Pinwheel' (d)	CLoc EBak
	'Piper's Vale' (T)	MJac
	'Pixie'	CLoc EBak EHDe MJac SLBF SVic
	'Playboy' (d)	SVic
	'Playford'	EBak
	'Plenty'	EBak
	'Popsie Girl' (v)	SLBF WRou
	'Port Arthur' (d)	EBak
	'Postiljon'	EBak
	'Powder Puff' Hodges (d)	CLoc
	'Prelude' Blackwell	CLoc
	'President'	EBak
	'President Arthur Phillips' (d) **new**	WRou
	'President Barrie Nash'	CLoc
	'President George Bartlett' (d) ♀H2	CLoc EPts MJac SLBF WRou
	'President Joan Morris' (d)	SLBF
	'President John Porter'	MJac SLBF WRou
	'President Leo Boullemier'	MJac
	'President Margaret Slater'	CLoc
	'President Moir' (d)	SLBF
	'President Peter Holloway'	EPts SLBF WRou
	'President Stanley Wilson' (d)	EBak EPts
	'Preston'	CMac
	'Preston Guild' ♀H3	CLoc EBak NPer SDys SRms SVic WFar WRou
	'Prince of Orange'	CLoc SVic
	'Princess Dollar'	see *F.* 'Dollar Prinzessin'
	'Princessita'	EBak
	procumbens	CBcs CBod CCCN CExl CLoc EBak EHDe ELon EPfP EPts EWld IDee MHer SIvy SLBF WAbe WKor WRou
	- 'Argentea'	see *F. procumbens* 'Wirral'
	- grey-leaved	ESwi SBrt
	- 'Variegata'	see *F. procumbens* 'Wirral'
§	- 'Wirral' (v)	CLoc CTsd EHDe EShb ESwi MHer
	'Prodigy'	see *F.* 'Enfant Prodigue'
	'Prosperity' (d) ♀H3	CKel CLoc EBak EHyd EPts LRHS MAsh MJac NRHS SLBF SPoG SVic
	'Pumila'	CExl CMac EPfP LRHS SDix SVic
	'Purperklokje'	EBak
	'Purple Emperor' (d)	CLoc
	'Purple Heart' (d)	CLoc EBak
	'Purple Lace'	SVic
	'Purple Prince' (d)	SVic
	'Purple Rain'	EPts WRou
	'Pussy Cat' (T)	CLoc EBak
	'Putney Pride'	EPts
	'Put's Folly' ♀H2	EBak MJac
	putumayensis	EBak
	'Quasar' (d)	CLoc EPts MBros MJac SLBF WRou
	'Queen Mary'	CLoc EBak EHDe
	'Queen of Bath' (d)	SVic
	'Queen of Mercia' (d)	MJac
	'Queen Victoria' Smith (d)	EHDe
	'Queen's Park' (d)	EBak
	'Query'	SVic
	'R.A.F.' (d)	CLoc EBak EPts
	'Radings Gerda' (E)	SLBF WRou
	'Radings Karin'	WRou
	'Radings Michelle' (E)	WRou
	'Rambling Rose' (d)	CLoc
	'Raspberry' (d)	CLoc EBak
	'Reading Ruby'	EPts MJac SLBF
	'Reading Show' (d)	EPts SLBF
	'Rebecca Ward' **new**	SLBF
	'Rebeka Sinton' (v)	EBak

'Red Jacket' (d)	EBak
'Red Rover'	SLBF
'Red Shadows' (d)	CLoc EBak
'Red Spider'	CLoc EBak SCoo
'Red Wing'	CLoc
'Reflexa'	see *F.* × *bacillaris* 'Reflexa'
'Reg Gubler'	SLBF
'Regal'	CLoc
regia	SLBF WMal
– subsp. ***regia***	XLum
– subsp. ***reitzii***	XLum
– subsp. ***serrae***	WPGP
'Remember Carole Anne' (d)	SLBF WRou
'Remembering Claire'	EPts MHer SLBF
'Remembrance' (d)	EPts SLBF WRou
'Rhapsody' ambig.	SVic
'Riccartonii' 🏆H6	Widely available
'Riccartonii Variegated' (v)	EHDe
'Richard John' (v)	SVic
'Ridestar' (d)	CLoc
'Rijs 2001' (E)	SLBF
'Ringwood Market' (d)	SCoo SLBF
'Rita May' (E) **new**	WRou
'Rivendell'	EPts WRou
'Rocket Fire' (California Dreamers Series) (d)	SVic
'Roger de Cooker' (T)	CLoc EPts MJac SLBF SVic
'Rohees New Millennium' (d)	SLBF
'Rolla' (d)	EBak
'Roman City' (d)	CLoc
'Romany Rose'	CLoc
'Ronald L. Lockerbie' (d)	CLoc
'Roos Breytenbach' (T)	MJac WRou
'Rosalien' **new**	CLoc WRou
'Rosamunda' (d)	CLoc
'Rose Aylett' (d)	EBak
'Rose Bradwardine' (d)	EBak
'Rose Churchill' (d)	MJac
'Rose Fantasia' 🏆H2	CLoc EPts MJac SLBF
'Rose of Castile'	CLoc EBak EHDe EPts MJac SLBF SVic WRou
'Rose of Castile Improved' 🏆H4	LRHS MJac SLBF
'Rose of Denmark'	CLoc EBak EHDe MJac SCoo SLBF
'Rose Winston' (d)	SCoo
rosea misapplied	see *F.* 'Globosa'
'Rosecroft Beauty' (d/v)	EBak EHDe
'Rosemarie Higham' (v)	MJac SCoo
'Rosemary Day'	CLoc
'Roswitha'	SAll
'Rosy Frills' (d)	MJac
'Roualeyn's White Gold' (d) 🏆H2	WRou
'Rough Silk'	CLoc EBak
'Royal Academy' (d)	EPts
'Royal Mosaic' (California Dreamers Series) (d)	MJac
'Royal Purple' (d)	EBak
'Royal Velvet' (d) 🏆H2	CLoc EBak EHyd EPts LRHS SLBF SVic WRou
'Rubra Grandiflora'	SIvy WRou
'Ruby Tuesday' (d)	MJac
'Ruby Wedding' (d)	SLBF
'Rufus' 🏆H4	CLoc CMac EBak EPts MJac SLBF SVic WRou
'Ruth'	SVic
'Ruth King' (d)	EBak
'Ryan'	SLBF
'S'Wonderful' (d)	CLoc EBak
'Saartje' **new**	WRou

'Sabrina'	WRou
'Sailor'	EPts
'Salmon Cascade'	EPts MJac SLBF
'Salt 'n' Pepper' (E) **new**	SLBF WRou
'Sam Sheppard'	SLBF
'Samantha's Smile' (d)	SLBF
'San Mateo' (d)	EBak
'Sandboy'	EBak
'Santa Cruz' (d)	CMac SLBF SVic
'Santa Lucia' (d)	CLoc
'Santa Monica' (d)	EBak
'Sapphire' (d)	EBak
'Sappho Phaoon' (T)	EPts WRou
'Sara Helen' (d)	CLoc EBak
'Sarah'PBR (Bella Series)	LCro LOPS WRou
'Sarah Brightman' (d)	CLoc
'Sarah Eliza' (d)	SCoo
'Sarah Jane' (d)	EBak
'Sarcoma UK' **new**	WRou
'Satellite'	CLoc EBak
'Saturnus' 🏆H4	CRos EBak LRHS SPoG WMal WRou
'Scarcity'	EBak EHDe SVic
'Scarlet Jester'	EPts SLBF WRou
'Schneeball' (d)	EBak
'Schneewitcher'	EPts
'Sealand Prince'	SVic
'Seattle Blue' (T/d)	SLBF
'Sebastopol' (d)	CLoc
serratifolia Ruíz & Pav.	see *F. denticulata*
'Seventh Heaven' (d)	CLoc MJac SCoo WRou
'Sharpitor'	see *F. magellanica* var. *molinae* 'Sharpitor'
'Shatzy B'	EPts SLBF WRou
'Sheila Crooks' (d)	EBak
'Shelford'	CLoc EBak EPts MJac SCob SLBF SVic
'Shell Pink'	SVic
'She's a Beauty' (d)	MJac
'Shirley'PBR (Shadowdancer Series)	SCoo
'Shirley Teece'	EPts
'Showfire'	EBak
'Shrimp Cocktail'	CKel CLoc LRHS WSMil
'Siberoet' (E)	SLBF
'Sid Garcia'	SLBF
'Sierra Blue' (d)	CLoc EBak
'Silver Chime' **new**	WRou
'Silver Surfer'	EPts MJac SLBF
'Silverdale'	EPts
simplicicaulis	EBak EHDe
'Sincerity' (d)	CLoc
'Siobhan Evans' (d)	SLBF
'Sir Alfred Ramsey'	EBak
'Sir Matt Busby' (d)	EPts MJac WRou
'Sister Ann Haley'	EPts
'Sister Sister' (d)	SLBF
'Skater's Waltz' (d)	CLoc
'Sleepy'	EPts SVic
'Sleigh Bells'	CLoc EBak SVic
'Sneezy'	EPts SVic
'Snow Burner' (California Dreamers Series) (d)	CLoc MBros
'Snowbird' (d)	SLBF
§ 'Snowcap' (d) 🏆H4	CBod CCCN CChe CLoc EBak EHDe EHyd ELon EPfP EPts GKin MGos MJac NPer NRHS SCob SCoo SGBe SGol SLBF SLim SPoG SVic WFar WRou
'Snowdrift' Colville (d)	CLoc
'Snowdrift' Kennett (d)	EBak
'Snowfire' (d)	CLoc

	'Snowflake' (E)	EPts WBor WRou
	'Soila'PBR (Bella Series)	CLoc WRou
	'Son of Thumb' ♀H4	CLoc CRos EHyd EPts LRHS MJac NRHS SGol SLBF SLim SPer SVic WRou
	'Sonata' (d)	CLoc
	'Sophia'PBR (Bella Series)	CLoc LCro LOPS WRou
	'Sophie Louise'	EPts MJac SLBF WRou
	'Sophisticated Lady' (d)	EBak EPts
	'South Gate' (d)	CLoc EBak SVic
	'Space Shuttle'	CLoc
	SPARKLING SILVER ('Lowssil') (d/v) **new**	LRHS SGBe
	'Sparky' (T)	CLoc EHDe EPts MHer SLBF WRou
	'Speciana'	EPts
§	'Speciosa'	EBak EGrI WRou
§	***splendens*** ♀H2	CCCN CLoc EBak IDee MCot NPer SLBF WRou
	- B&SWJ 10469	WCru
	'Sporting Chance'	WRou
	'Spring Bells' (d)	EHyd LRHS NRHS
	'Squadron Leader' (d)	EBak EPts
	'Squirtie'	SLBF
	'Stanley Cash' (d)	CLoc
	'Star Wars'	CLoc EHDe EPts MJac WRou
	'Stardust'	WRou
	'Stella Ann' (T)	EPts
	'Stoke Poges Jewel'	WRou
	'Stokie' **new**	WRou
	'Straat Futami' (E)	EPts
	'Strawberry Delight' (d)	CLoc MJac
	'Strawberry Split'	CDoC EPfP LRHS
	'Strawberry Sundae' (d)	CLoc EBak
	'String of Pearls'	CLoc MJac SLBF SVic
	'Stuart Lockyer' (d)	CLoc
	'Sue'	SLBF
	'Sue Kylymnik' **new**	WRou
	'Suffolk Splendour' (d)	EPts WRou
	'Sugar Plum Fairy' (E)	WRou
	'Sunray' (v)	CBcs CEnd CKel CLoc CMac CRos EBak EHDe EHyd EPfP LBuc LRHS MAsh MGos NCou NRHS SCoo SGBe SLBF SPoG SVen WCot WRou
	'Sunset'	CLoc
	'Susan Green'	EBak MJac
	'Susan Hampshire'	SLBF
	'Susan McMaster'	CLoc
	'Susan Olcese' (d)	EBak
	'Susan Travis'	CLoc EBak SVic
	SUSANNA ('Bf02'PBR) (Bella Series)	WRou
	'Swanley Beauty'	EHDe
	'Swanley Gem' ♀H2	CLoc EBak SLBF SVic
	'Swanley Pendula'	CLoc
	'Swanley Yellow'	EBak
	'Sweet Sarah' (E)	EPts
	'Sweet Willow'	EPts
I	'Sweetheart' van Wieringen	EBak
	'Swingtime' (d) ♀H2	CLoc EBak EPts MBros MJac SLBF WRou
	sylvatica misapplied	see *F. nigricans*
	'Sylvia Barker' ♀H2	SLBF
	'Sylvia's Choice'	EBak WRou
	'Symphony'	CLoc
	'Syreme' (d)	SLBF
	'T.I.S. Herentals'	SLBF WRou
	'Taddle'	SLBF
	'Taffeta Bow' (d)	CLoc SLBF
	'Tamerus Nandoe'	WRou
	'Tamworth'	CLoc EBak MJac SVic
	'Tangerine'	CLoc SVic

	'Tanya Bridger' (d)	EBak
	'Tarra Valley'	EHDe
	'Tausendschön' (d)	WRou
	'Ted Ness' **new**	WRou
	'Ted's Tribute'	SLBF
	'Temptation' Peterson	CLoc EBak
	'Ten Cents' **new**	SLBF
	'Tennessee Waltz' (d) ♀H2	CLoc EBak EPts SLBF SVic
	'Tess'	EPts
	tetradactyla misapplied	see *F.* × ***bacillaris***
	'Texas Longhorn' (d)	CLoc EBak
	'Thalia' (T) ♀H1c	CCCN CLoc CWCL EBak EPts LSRN MHer MJac SCob SGBe SIvy SLBF SPlb SPoG WLov WRou
	'Thamar'	CLoc EPts SVic WRou
	'That's It' (d)	SVic
	'The Aristocrat' (d)	CLoc EBak
§	'The Doctor'	CLoc EBak
	'The Jester' (d)	EBak
	'The Tarns'	EBak SVic WRou
	'Thelma Copestake'	MJac SLBF
	'Thomas' (d)	EPts
	'Thompsonii'	see *F. magellanica* 'Thompsonii'
	'Thornley's Hardy'	SVic
	'Three Cheers'	CLoc
	'Three Counties'	EBak
	'Thumbelina'	EHyd
	thymifolia (E)	CKel EHyd LRHS MHer SDys SEND SGro WCot WKif
	- subsp. ***thymifolia*** (E)	CDoC SEle
	'Tia Clements'	MJac WRou
	'Tiara' (d)	EBak
	'Tickled Pink'	WRou
	'Tillingbourne' (d)	SLBF
	'Time After Time'	CLoc MBros SLBF WRou
	'Timlin Brened' (T)	EBak WRou
	'Timothy Titus' (T) ♀H1c	EHDe SLBF
	'Ting-a-ling'	CLoc EBak SVic
	'Tinker Bell' Hodges	EBak SVic
	'Tinytobes'	MJac
	'Tip Toes'	SLBF
	'Toby Bridger' (d)	CLoc EBak
	'Toby Foreman'	SLBF
	'Toby S' (d)	SLBF
	'Tolling Bell'	EBak
	'Tom Knights'	EBak
	'Tom Thumb' ♀H4	Widely available
	'Tom West' misapplied	see *F.* 'Mr West'
	'Tom West' ambig.	CBod CKel SVic
	'Tom West' Meillez (v) ♀H2	CChe CDoC CLoc CSBt CWCL EBak EHDe EHyd EPts LRHS MAsh MBros MHer MJac MRav MSCN NRHS SGol SLBF WFar WRou
	'Tom Woods'	WRou
	'Tony Talbot'	MJac
	'Tony's Treat' (d)	EPts
	'Torch' (d)	CLoc EBak
	'Torchlight'	EPts
	'Torvill and Dean' (d)	CLoc EPts MJac SLBF
	'Tracid' (d)	SVic
	'Trail Blazer' (d)	CLoc MJac
	'Trailing Queen'	MJac
	'Trase' (d)	EBak SVic
	'Traudchen Bonstedt' (T) ♀H1c	CLoc
	'Traviata'	see *F.* 'La Traviata' Blackwell
	'Treasure' (d)	EBak
	'Tricolor'	see *F. magellanica* var. *gracilis* 'Versicolor'
	'Trientje'	SLBF
	'Trimley Bells'	SLBF

triphylla (T)	EBak MHer
'Tristesse' (d)	CLoc EBak
'Tropicana' (d)	CLoc
'Troubador' Waltz (d)	CLoc
'Trudi Davro'	MBros SCoo
'Trudy'	EPts SVic
'True Love'	CLoc
'Truly Treena' (d)	SLBF
'Trumpeter' Reiter (T)	CLoc EPts MJac
'Tuonela' (d)	CLoc
'Tupence' **new**	WRou
'Turkish Delight'	WRou
'Tutti-frutti' (d)	CLoc
'Twinkling Stars'	MJac
'Ullswater' (d)	EBak
'Uncle Charley' (d)	EBak
'University of Liverpool'	CLoc MJac
'Upward Look'	EBak
'Valerie Ann' (d)	EBak
'Valerie Bradley'	EPts
'Valerie Jane'	SLBF
'Vanessa Jackson'	CLoc MJac SVic
'Vanessa Wright'	EHyd LRHS NRHS
'Vanity Fair' (d)	EBak
'Variegated Procumbens'	see *F. procumbens* 'Wirral'
'Veenlust'	EBak MJac
'Velvet Crush'	EPts WRou
'Venus Victrix'	EBak EHDe
venusta	EBak EHDe
'Vera'^{PBR} (Bella Series)	WRou
'Vera Garcia'	EPts MJac SLBF WRou
'Versicolor'	see *F. magellanica* var. *gracilis* 'Versicolor'
'Vicky J' **new**	WRou
'Violet Bassett-Burr' (d)	CLoc EBak
'Violet Gem' (d)	CLoc
VIOLETTA ('Goetzviol') (Shadowdancer Series)	SCoo
'Viva Ireland'	EBak
'Vivien Colville'	CLoc SVic
'Voodoo' (d)	CLoc EBak EPts MBros SCoo
'Wagtails White Pixie'	EBak
'Wake the Harp'	SLBF
'Waldfee' (E)	WRou
'Waldis Grafin'	WRou
'Waldis Maja'	WRou
'Walton Jewel'	EBak
'Walz Freule'	MJac
'Walz Jubelteen' ♀H2	CLoc CWCL ELan ELon EPts MJac SAdn SEle SGBe SLBF SVen SVic WCot WRou
'Walz Lucifer'	SLBF
'Walz Luit'	WRou
'Wapenveld's Bloei'	EPts SLBF
'Water Color'	SLBF
'Water Nymph'	CLoc MHer SLBF SVic WRou
'Wattenpost'	SLBF
'Waveney Gem'	CLoc EBak MJac SLBF
'Waveney Sunrise'	MJac
'Waveney Waltz'	EBak
'Welsh Dragon' (d)	CLoc EBak
'Wendy' Catt	see *F.* 'Snowcap'
'Wendy Bendy'	EPts MJac
'Wendy Jane Webster'	EPts
'Wendy's Beauty' (d)	CLoc EBak EPts MJac
'Westminster Chimes' (d)	CLoc SLBF
'Whaley Thorns' (d)	MJac
'Wharfedale' ♀H4	EHyd ELon EPts LRHS MJac NRHS SLBF SVic WRou
'What's-it' (E)	SLBF
'Whirlaway' (d)	CLoc
'Whispering Dawn'	WRou
'White Academy'	EPts
'White Ann'	see *F.* 'Heidi Weiss'
'White Clove' (E)	SVic WRou
'White Joy'	EBak
'White King' (d)	CLoc EBak WRou
'White Pixie' ♀H4	EPPr EPts MJac SLBF SVic
'White Queen' ambig.	EHDe
'White Spider'	CLoc EBak
'Whiteknights Amethyst'	SVic
'Whiteknights Blush'	CExl CKel EBee EPfP EWes LRHS SMrm
'Whiteknights Cheeky' (T)	EBak EPts SVic
'Whiteknights Glister' (v)	WRou
'Whiteknights Pearl' ♀H4	ECha EPts SDys SEND SGol SLBF SVic
'Whiteknights Ruby' (T)	SLBF
'Whoopee' (d)	EPts MJac SLBF WRou
'Wicked Queen' (d)	SVic
'Widnes Wonder'	MJac SLBF WRou
'Wigan Peer' (d)	EPts MJac WRou
'Wight Magic' (d)	MJac
'Wilson's Colours'	EPts
'Wilson's Joy'	MJac
'Wilson's Pearls' (d)	SLBF
'Wilson's Sugar Pink'	EPts MJac
'Win and Walt'	WRou
'Windhapper'	SLBF
'Wine and Roses' (d)	EBak
'Winifred Glass'	EHDe
'Winston Churchill' (d) ♀H2	CLoc EBak EPts MBros MJac SCob SCoo
'Winter's Tale'	SLBF
'Woodside' (d)	SVic
'Wyre Light' (E)	SLBF
'Yattendon Lady'	SLBF
'Zifi'	SLBF

Fumaria (*Papaveraceae*)

capreolata	WSFF
lutea	see *Corydalis lutea*

Furcraea (*Asparagaceae*)

bedinghausii	see *F. parmentieri*
§ ***foetida***	CCCN
§ – var. ***mediopicta*** (v)	WSMil
longaeva misapplied	see *F. parmentieri*
longaeva ambig.	CBcs CDoC CTsd EShb LRHS NCft NGKo WSMil
macdougalii	SPlb
§ ***parmentieri***	CCCN CDTJ CExl GBin LEdu SChr SPlb SVen XSte
selloa var. ***marginata*** (v)	NCft SIvy

G

Gahnia (*Cyperaceae*)

sieberiana	SPlb

Gaillardia (*Asteraceae*)

'Apricot Honey' **new**	SHar
aristata Pursh 'Maxima Aurea'	EHyd EPfP SPhx
GOBLIN	see *G.* × *grandiflora* 'Kobold'
× ***grandiflora*** 'Amber Wheels'	ELan
– 'Arizona Apricot'	EHyd MBNS SCob SGBe
– 'Arizona Red Shades'	EAJP EHyd GPSL SCob SGBe WCav

- 'Arizona Sun' — EAJP EHyd MNHC NLar SCob SGBe SVic WCav
- 'Bijou' — EBou SWvt
- 'Burgunder' — CMac CSBt CSpe EAJP EHyd ELan EPfP LRHS LSou MBow SBls SGbt SMrm SPer SPhx SPoG SWvt WGwG
- 'Celebration'PBR — CRos EHyd LRHS MPri NLar SCoo
- 'Dazzler' ♈H5 — CSBt EBee EHyd ELan EPfP LRHS SGbt SPer SPoG
- 'Fanblaze'PBR — CBod EHyd LRHS NRHS SCob WFar
- 'Fanfare'PBR — CWGN EHyd EPfP LRHS NRHS SCoo
- 'Frenzy'PBR (Commotion Series) — SPad
- (Gallo Series) GALLO DARK BICOLOR ('Kiegaldab'PBR) — LRHS
- - GALLO PEACH ('Kiegalpea'PBR) — NRHS
- - GALLO YELLOW ('Kiegalyel') — LRHS
- § - 'Kobold' — CBcs CMac CRos CSBt EBee EHyd ELan ELon EPfP GMaP LBuc LRHS NRHS SCob SGbt SHar SPer SPlb SPoG SWvt
- (Mesa Series) MESA BRIGHT BICOLOUR ('Pas888652') (Mesa Series) **new** — CBod
- - MESA PEACH ('Pas907056') — CBod
- - MESA RED ('Pas953516') — CBod NLar
- - MESA YELLOW ('Pas888653') — CBod
- Monarch Group — WFar
- § - 'Oranges and Lemons'PBR — SHar
- 'Red Sun'PBR — CWGN
- SUNBURST BURGUNDY (Sunburst Series) — WFar
- (Sunset Dwarf Series) 'Sunset Cutie' — LRHS MPri NRHS SPoG
- - 'Sunset Flash' (Sunset Dwarf Series) — LRHS MPri SPoG
- - 'Sunset Snappy' (Sunset Dwarf Series) — SPoG
- - 'Sunset Sunrise' (Sunset Dwarf Series) — EPfP LRHS SPoG
- (Sunset Medium Series) 'Sunset Mexican' **new** — LRHS
- - 'Sunset Popsy' **new** — LRHS
- - 'Sunset Spice' **new** — EPfP LRHS
- 'Tokajer' — EBee EHyd ELan EPfP EWTr LRHS NRHS SBls SPhx

'Naomi Sunshine' — SHar
pinnatifida **new** — EAJP
SAINT CLEMENTS — see *G.* 'Oranges and Lemons'
SPINTOP RED SUNBURST (SpinTop Series) **new** — SPad

Galactites (*Asteraceae*)

tomentosa — CPla EGrI EWTr SPhx
- white-flowered — SPhx

Galanthus ✿ (*Amaryllidaceae*)

'Acton Pigot No. 3' — CElw
'Ailwyn' (d) ♈H5 — GEdr MAsh NDry
'Alison Hilary' — CAvo CTtf GEdr LEdu MCor
× ***allenii*** — EPot EPri GKev
alpinus var. ***bortkewitschianus*** — GKev
'Amy Doncaster's Double' (d) **new** — MCor
'Anne of Geierstein' — CAvo MHCG
'Ann's Millennium Giant' — CBro GEdr
'Armine' — CElw EPfP LRHS WCot
'Art Nouveau' — CElw CTtf
'Atkinsii' ♈H5 — CAvo CBro CElw CMea CRos ECha EHyd EMor EPot EWoo GAbr GEdr GKev LRHS MAsh MRav NBir NRHS SDir SDix WCot WFar WHoo WShi
'Autumn Beauty' — EHyd LRHS NRHS
'Autumn Belle' — LRHS
'Babraham Scented' — GBin GEdr
'Backhouse Spectacles' — GEdr
'Ballerina' (d) — GEdr MAsh NDry WCot
'Barbara's Double' (d) — EWes GEdr
'Basisgrüner' — NDry
'Baylham' **new** — MCor
'Benhall Beauty' — CBro CElw EWes GAbr GEdr
'Benton Magnet' — EPot MCor
'Bertram Anderson' ♈H5 — CAvo EPot GEdr MAsh WCot
'Bess' — CElw GEdr MAsh
'Betty Hansell' (d) — CAvo MCor
'Big Eyes' — CAvo
'Bill Bishop' — CBro CElw ECha GBin GEdr WCot
'Bitter Lemons' **new** — CAvo
'Bitton' ambig. — GEdr NPol
'Blewbury' — ECha LEdu
'Bloomer' **new** — MCor
'Brenda Troyle' — CBro CElw CRos ECha EHyd EMor EPot EPri GAbr GBin GEdr GKev LRHS MAsh NPol NRHS WCot WFar
'Brigadier Mathias' — EPot
'Bright Eyes' **new** — MAsh
'Bungee' — CTtf GEdr
'By Gate' — GEdr
'Byfield Special' — MCor
byzantinus — see *G. plicatus* subsp. *byzantinus*
'Caryl Baron' — CAvo
caucasicus misapplied — see *G. elwesii* var. *monostictus*
caucasicus ambig. — GKev NPol
- 'Comet' — see *G. elwesii* 'Comet'
- var. ***hiemalis*** Stern — see *G. elwesii* Hiemalis Group
- 'John Tomlinson' — see *G. elwesii* 'John Tomlinson'
'Chequers' — GEdr
'Cicely Hall' — CTtf GEdr NDry
cilicicus — GBin
'Cinderella' **new** — MCor
'Cliff Curtis' — GEdr MAsh
corcyrensis spring-flowering — see *G. reginae-olgae* subsp. *vernalis*
- winter-flowering — see *G. reginae-olgae* subsp. *reginae-olgae* Winter-flowering Group
'Cordelia' (d) — CElw GAbr GEdr MCor
'Corrin' — GEdr
'Cotswold Beauty' **new** — CAvo
'Cowhouse Green' — GEdr MAsh MCor NDry
'Curly' — CAvo CElw CTtf EWes GEdr
'Daglingworth' — EPri GEdr
'Daphne's Maximus' **new** — MCor
'Das Gelbe vom Ei' **new** — MAsh
'David Baker' — EPot GEdr
'Desdemona' (d) — EPot GEdr GMaP ITim WCot WFar
'Ding Dong' — CTtf GEdr MAsh MHCG
'Dionysus' (d) — CExl ECha ELon EMor EPot EWes GEdr GKev ITim NBir NWad SDeJ WBrk WFar WShi
'Dodo Norton' — GEdr MAsh
'Dragonfly' — CAvo MAsh
'Dryad Artemis' — NDry
'Dryad Gold Bullion' — NDry
'Dryad Gold Charm' — NDry
'Dryad Gold Medal' — NDry
'Dryad Gold Sovereign' — NDry

	'Dryad Gold Star'	NDry
	'Eilys Elisabeth Hartley' **new**	NDry
	'Eliot Hodgkin'	GEdr
§	***elwesii*** ♀H5	CRos CTri EGrI EHyd ELan EMor EPot GWyn ILea LCro LRHS NBir NPol NRHS NRog SDeJ SDir SPer SRms WCot WFar WHoo WShi
	- 'Abington Green'	ELon EPot
	- 'Athenae'	CBro
	- 'Beany'	CAvo MAsh NDry
	- 'Beluga'	GKev LRHS
	- 'Benjamin Britten'	GKev
	- 'Bo Bette'	GEdr NRog
	- 'Broadwell' **new**	MAsh
	- 'Byrkley'	CAvo
	- 'Cedric's Prolific'	CElw ECha EMor EWoo GEdr MCor NRya WBrk WFar
	- 'Chantry Green Twins'	GEdr MAsh
§	- 'Comet' ♀H5	CElw CTtf GEdr MAsh MCor MNrw WFar
	- 'Daphne's Scissors'	CElw GEdr
	- 'David Shackleton'	CElw GEdr
	- 'Deer Slot'	CAvo CTtf MAsh
	- 'Early Twin'	WCot
	- 'Echoes'	WCot
	- (Edward Whittall Group) 'Phil Bryn' **new**	MAsh
	- - 'Two Eyes'	GEdr
	- 'Elmley Lovett'	CAvo CElw
	- var. ***elwesii*** 'Big Boy'	GEdr MCor
	- - 'Fenstead End'	CAvo GEdr MAsh
	- - 'Fred's Giant'	GMaP
	- - 'Kite'	ELon EWoo GEdr
	- - 'Maidwell L'	CBro EPot MAsh
	- - 'Paradise Giant'	GEdr ITim
	- - 'Pat Mason'	MCor
	- - 'Sibbertoft Magnet'	GEdr
	- - 'Spring Greens'	GEdr
*	- 'Flore Pleno' (d)	NPol
	- 'Godfrey Owen' (d) ♀H5	CAvo CElw CFis CTtf EPot GEdr MAsh MCor NDry WBrk
	- 'Green Brush'	CAvo CBro CTtf EWes LRHS
	- 'Grumpy'	CAvo GEdr
	- 'Helen Tomlinson'	SHar
§	- Hiemalis Group	CBro ECha EPri GKev WCot
	- - 'Barnes' ♀H5	CFis ECha GBin MCor WCot
	- - 'Earliest of All'	CBro
	- - 'Highdown'	GKev
	- - 'Hollis'	CAvo NDry
	- 'Jack-in-the-Green'	CAvo
	- 'Jessica'	CAvo EWoo GEdr
§	- 'John Tomlinson'	GEdr MAsh
	- 'Jonathan'	MAsh
	- 'Jubilee Green'	CAvo
	- 'Kencot Kali'	CAvo CTtf
	- 'Kyre Park'	GEdr
	- 'Ladybird' **new**	MAsh
	- late-flowering	GEdr
	- 'Long 'drop'	GEdr
	- 'Louise Ann Bromley'	CAvo MCor
	- 'Maidwell'	GEdr MAsh MCor
	- 'Mandarin'	CElw EWes
	- 'Margaret Biddulph' **new**	MCor
	- 'Margaret Owen'	MCor MNrw
	- 'Marjorie Brown'	CAvo CElw CFis CTtf ECha EPot GEdr ITim MCor
	- 'Marlie Raphael'	CAvo
	- 'Milkwood'	see *G. elwesii* 'Mrs Macnamara'
	- 'Miss Mowcher'	WCot
§	- var. ***monostictus*** ♀H5	CBro ECha EHyd GKev LRHS MAsh NRHS WBrk WFar
	- - 'B. Britten'	LRHS
	- - 'G. Handel'	LRHS
	- - 'Grayswood'	GEdr
	- - 'H. Purcell'	EMor GEdr LRHS
	- - 'Kryptonite'	CAvo
	- - 'Lord Monostictus'	EWoo
	- - 'Mozart'	LRHS
	- - 'Rogers Rough'	SDys
	- - 'Smaragdsplitter'	CAvo
	- - 'Warwickshire Gemini'	MAvo MHCG
	- aff. var. ***monostictus***	WFar
	- 'Moses Basket' **new**	CTtf
	- 'Moya's Green'	CAvo
	- 'Mr Blobby' **new**	MCor
	- 'Mr Omer'	WCot
	- 'Mr Peggotty'	WCot
§	- 'Mrs Macnamara' ♀H5	CElw CFis ECha ELon EPri EWoo GEdr MCor WBrk WFar
	- November-flowering	WCot
	- 'Penelope Ann'	ECha GEdr NRya
	- 'Peter Gatehouse'	CTtf ELon MCor
	- poculiform	CTtf
	- 'Polar Bear'	CAvo CElw CTtf GKev LRHS
	- 'Pyramid' **new**	CTtf MCor
§	- 'Ransom's Dwarf'	GEdr MCor
	- 'Remember, Remember'	CTtf GEdr MAsh
*	- 'Robustus Praecox'	GKev
	- 'Rosemary Burnham'	CAvo CElw MAsh MCor NDry
	- 'Ruth Birchall'	MCor
	- 'Selborne Green Tips'	CTtf NDry
	- 'Sickle'	MAsh
	- 'Sir Edward Elgar'	GKev LRHS
I	- 'Snowwhite'	NDry
	- 'The Bride'	NDry
	- 'Three Leaves'	CElw
	- 'Yashmak'	CAvo
§	- 'Yvonne Hay'	GEdr NDry
	- 'Zwanenburg'	CTtf MAsh
	'Elworthy Bumble Bee' (d)	CElw
	'Ermine House' (d)	GEdr MCor
	'Ermine Lace'	CAvo
	'Erway'	CTtf GBin
	'Falkland House'	CElw EPot GEdr
	'Fanny'	CAvo
	'Faringdon Double' (d)	CTtf EPot EPri
	'Feodora' Yellow single	CAvo
	'Fieldgate Forte'	CAvo
	'Fieldgate Prelude'	CFis EWoo GEdr MAsh NDry
	'Fieldgate Superb'	CAvo NDry
	'Fly Fishing'	CAvo CTtf GEdr MCor NDry
	'Forge Double' (d)	GEdr MCor
	fosteri	CTtf GEdr GKev NDry NRog
	fosteri × ***koenenianus***	NDry
	'Franz Josef'	CAvo
	'Friar Tuck' **new**	MCor
	'G71' (d)	MCor
	'Gabriel'	EPot GEdr
	'Galadriel'	GEdr
	'Galatea'	CBro ECha EMor EPri EWes GAbr ITim MAsh MCor NRya SDys WBrk WFar
	'George Elwes'	CAvo CTtf GEdr
	'George Proverbs' **new**	MAsh
	'Gill Gregory'	GEdr
	'Ginns'	WBrk
	'Glenchantress'	GEdr MAsh
	(Gold Group) 'Ronald Mackenzie'	GEdr NDry
§	***gracilis***	CExl GEdr GKev LRHS NPol WCot
	- 'Highdown'	CElw CTtf
	- Kew	CElw

- 'Vic Horton'	CElw CTtf GEdr WThu
graecus misapplied	see *G. gracilis*
graecus Orph. ex Boiss.	see *G. elwesii*
'Gravity'	CAvo
'Grayling'	see *G. plicatus* 'Percy Picton'
'Green Comet'	CAvo
'Green Eyes' **new**	MAsh
'Green Man'	CAvo GEdr WFar
'Green Necklace'	CTtf EWes GEdr
'Green Ribbon'	MCor
'Greenfields'	CAvo GEdr ITim WBrk
'Greenfinch'	MCor
green-tipped double (d)	GEdr
'Haconby Green'	NDry
'Hans Guck in die Luft'	NDry
'Headbourne'	ECha MCor
'Heffalump' (d)	ELon EPri GEdr MAsh MCor
'Hercule'	CAvo MCor
'Hill Poë' (d)	CBro CElw CTtf GBin GEdr MCor WHoo
'Hippolyta' (d)	CBro CElw CTtf ECha EMor EPot GEdr GKev LEdu LRHS MAsh MAvo MCor NPol WCot WShi
'Hobson's Choice'	GEdr
'Homersfield'	CElw ELon EPri
'Honeysuckle Cottage'	CAvo MCor
'Hörup'	GEdr
'Hoverfly' **new**	MCor
× ***hybridus*** 'Merlin' Υ^{H5}	CBro CElw CTtf EPri GEdr WCot WFar
- 'Robin Hood'	GEdr GKev NRog
'Icicle'	CElw GEdr
§ ***ikariae*** Bak.	GEdr ITim
- 'Emerald Isle' **new**	NDry
- subsp. ***ikariae*** Butt's form	NPol
- Latifolius Group	see *G. platyphyllus*
- subsp. ***snogerupii***	see *G. ikariae* Bak.
'Imbolc'	CTtf GEdr MCor
(Imperial Group) 'Shepton Merlin'	CElw NDry
'Ivy Cottage Corporal'	GEdr MAsh NDry
'Jacquenetta' (d)	CBro CElw EWes GBin GEdr GKev ITim LRHS MAsh
'Jade'	CAvo
'James Backhouse'	ECha EMor MCor WShi
'Jennifer Hewitt'	CElw
'John Gray' Υ^{H5}	EPri EWes GBin GEdr GQue
'June Boardman'	CAvo
'Kath Dryden'	EPot
'Kersen'	CAvo
'Ketton'	CBro CElw CTtf GEdr MAvo NRya
'Kildare'	CAvo GEdr LEdu
'Kingston Double' (d)	GBin GEdr MAsh
'Kinn McIntosh'	WCot
'Lady Beatrix Stanley' (d) Υ^{H5}	CAvo CBro CElw ECha EHyd EPot GEdr GKev MAsh NWad WCot WFar
lagodechianus	CBro GEdr GKev MCor NRog
'Lapwing'	CTtf EPot GEdr MAsh MCor
latifolius Rupr.	see *G. platyphyllus*
'Lavinia' (d)	CElw CTtf EWes GEdr WFar
'Limetree'	CElw EPri EWes GEdr MAvo NPol WFar
'Little Ben'	CAvo CElw GEdr GMaP MAsh MCor
'Little Dorrit'	GEdr MAsh
'Little John'	EPot GEdr WBrk
'Little Magnet'	CAvo
'Long John Silver' **new**	CAvo
'Longnor Hall' (d) **new**	MCor
'Longstowe'	MAsh

'Lord Lieutenant'	GEdr
'Lucy'	CAvo
lutescens	see *G. nivalis* Sandersii Group
'Lyn'	CBro EMor GEdr NBir
'Magnet' Υ^{H5}	CAvo CBro CElw CMea CTtf CWCL EHyd ELon EMor EPot EWoo GAbr GEdr GKev LEdu LRHS MAsh MCor MNrw NBir NPol NRHS WBrk WCot WFar WHoo WShi
aff. 'Magnet'	GMaP SDir WFar
'Matt Bishop'	CAvo
'Megan'	GEdr
'Melanie Broughton'	CElw EPot EWes GEdr MAsh MCor
'Midas'	CAvo
'Midwinter'	CAvo
'Mighty Atom'	CBro GBin WBrk
'Mill House'	CTtf
'Miss Prissy' (d) **new**	NDry
'Moby Dick'	EWes
'Moccas'	CElw CFis
'Modern Art'	CAvo CTtf EPot GEdr MCor MHCG
'Moortown'	CAvo GEdr
'Mothering Sunday'	CAvo
'Mr Stinker'	CAvo
'Mr Thompson'	EPot
'Mrs Backhouse No 12'	MCor
'Mrs Thompson'	CAvo CElw CTtf ECha GEdr GKev MAsh MNrw
'Mrs Wrightson's Double' (d)	GBin GEdr
'Muku' (d)	NDry
'Natalie Garton'	CAvo CFis CTtf GEdr MCor
'Neill Fraser'	EPri GEdr
'Nerissa' (d)	EPfP GEdr LRHS
nivalis Υ^{H5}	Widely available
- 'Courteenhall' Wyatt	CTtf EPri
- 'Alan's Treat'	CAvo GEdr MCor
- 'Anglesey Abbey'	CElw EWes EWoo GEdr MCor
- 'Ballynahinch'	GEdr ITim
- 'Bitton'	GBin GEdr
- 'Blonde Inge'	CAvo CTtf EPot GEdr MAsh MCor
- 'Chedworth'	CAvo CElw GEdr WBrk
- 'Christmas Wish'	NDry
- 'Cornwood'	GEdr NDry
- dwarf	ITim
- 'Egret'	CAvo
- 'Elfin'	CAvo CElw CTtf EWes GEdr WCot
- Estonian Spirit Group	NDry
- 'Flocon de Neige'	CAvo
- 'Fuzz'	MCor
- 'Gloucester Old Spot'	GEdr
- 'Green Diamond'	CElw
- 'Green Tear'	GEdr MCor
- 'Greenish'	CTtf GKev MCor NDry
- subsp. ***imperati***	CExl WBrk
- 'Kullake'	NDry
- 'Llo 'n' Green'	NDry
- 'Lutescens'	see *G. nivalis* Sandersii Group
- 'Margery Fish'	NDry
- 'Melvillei'	CAvo EWoo
- 'Munchkin' **new**	CTtf
- 'Pewsey Vale'	WBrk
- f. ***pleniflorus*** (d)	GKev MPri SPoG
- - 'Bagpuize Virginia' (d)	GEdr
- - 'Blewbury Tart' (d)	CAvo CBro CElw CTtf ELon EPri EWes GEdr MCor WBrk WCot WFar WHoo
- - 'Doncaster's Double Charmer' (d)	GBin MAsh
- - 'Flore Pleno' (d) Υ^{H5}	CArg CBro CExl CWCL EGrI EMor EPfP EPot EWoo GBin GWyn LCro LOPS LRHS MMuc NHpl NRog

		NRya SDeJ SEND SPer SRms WBrk WCot WHoo WShi
	- - 'Lady Elphinstone' (d)	CBro CElw ELon GBin GEdr MCor NPol NRya WCot
	- - 'Octopussy' (d)	GEdr MAsh MCor
	- - 'Pusey Green Tips' (d)	CElw CTtf EPot NPol WCot
	- - Scharlockii Group double (d)	CTtf
	- - 'Walrus' (d)	ELon GEdr WBrk
	- Poculiformis Group	CElw
	- - 'Angelique'	CTtf NDry
	- - 'Francesca de Grammont'	NDry
	- - 'Henry's White Lady'	GEdr MCor
	- - 'Moreton Mill'	CAvo
	- cf. Poculiformis Group	CElw
	- 'Puck'	CAvo GEdr
	- 'Rosemary Mitchell'	MAvo
§	- Sandersii Group	GBin GEdr GMaP MCor NDry WFar
	- - 'Lowick'	CTtf
	- - 'Norfolk Blonde'	CTtf GEdr
	- - 'Spetchley Yellow' **new**	MCor
§	- Scharlockii Group	CElw ECha ELon MCor NRog WBrk
	- - 'Selina Cords' **new**	CElw
	- 'Sibbertoft White'	EPri WBrk
	- 'Tiny'	GEdr WFar
	- 'Tiny Tim'	EPot GEdr ITim MCor NRya WFar
	- 'Tippy Green'	CElw
	- 'Virescens'	NDry
	- 'Viridapice' ♀H5	CAvo CBro CElw CExl CTtf CWCL ECha EGrI EMor EPot GAbr GKev GMaP MCor NBir NPol NRog NWad SDeJ WCot WFar WHoo WShi
	- 'Warei'	CElw EPri GBin
	- 'White Cloud'	GKev
	- 'White Dream'	CElw GEdr
	aff. ***nivalis***	SDir
	'North Star' (d)	CElw
	'One Drop or Two'	CAvo
	'Ophelia' (d)	CBro ECha GEdr MCor NPol WBrk WFar WHoo
	'Orion'	CFis
	'Peardrop'	GEdr
	'Peg Sharples'	GEdr
	peshmenii	LEdu
	- 'Kastellorizo'	NDry
	'Phantom'	CAvo
	'Philippe André Meyer'	CAvo MCor
§	***platyphyllus***	CExl EPfP
	plicatus ♀H5	CBro CElw EHyd EMor GKev LRHS MCot NPol NRHS WBrk WCot WShi
	- from Coton Manor	MCot
	- 'Amy Doncaster'	CAvo CTtf
	- 'Augustus' ♀H5	CBro CElw ELon EPot EWes GEdr MAsh WCot WHoo
	- 'Barbara Buchanan's Late'	CElw
	- 'Baxendale's Late'	GEdr GKev
	- 'Beth Chatto'	EPot MCor
§	- subsp. ***byzantinus***	CBro MHCG WThu
	- - 'Ariadne' **new**	CAvo
	- - 'Conquest'	CBro
	- - 'Patricia Ann'	CElw
	- - 'Richard Blakeway-Phillips'	NDry
	- 'Clun Green Plicate'	CElw
	- 'Colossus'	CBro CElw EWes GKev LRHS MAsh WCot
	- 'Diggory' ♀H5	CAvo CTtf EPri GEdr MAsh MCor MHCG NDry
	- 'Duckie'	GEdr WFar
	- 'E.A. Bowles' ♀H5	CAvo GEdr MAsh NDry
	- 'Florence Baker'	GEdr

	- 'Gerard Parker'	GEdr MAsh
	- 'Glenorma'	GEdr
	- 'Gold Edge'	EPot
I	- 'Grave Concern'	CAvo
	- 'Green Hayes'	MCor
	- 'Green Teeth'	CElw GEdr
	- 'John Long'	EPot GEdr MCor
	- 'Josie'	GEdr
	- 'Lambrook Greensleeves'	MCor
	- 'Madeleine'	CAvo CElw CTtf MCor NDry
§	- 'Percy Picton'	CAvo EWes EWoo GEdr
	- 'Phil Cornish'	CAvo MAsh
	- 'Sally Pasmore'	CAvo
	- 'Sarah Dumont'	CFis
	- 'Seraph'	CAvo
	- 'Sibbertoft Manor'	CElw
	- 'Sophie North'	CElw CTtf GEdr NDry
	- 'The Pearl'	GEdr MCor NDry
	- 'Three Ships' ♀H5	GBin GEdr MCor NDry NHar
	- 'Trimmer'	CAvo GEdr NDry
	- 'Trym'	CElw CTtf EPri GEdr NDry NPol WFar
	- 'Trymlet'	CAvo EPot EWoo GEdr NDry
	- 'Trympostor'	CAvo CElw GBin GEdr NDry
	- 'Walter Fish'	CAvo
	- 'Warham'	CBro CElw EPot GAbr ITim WCot
	- 'Wendy's Gold'	CAvo CBro CTtf EPot EPri EWes GEdr LRHS MAsh MCor NDry NRHS WBrk WFar
	'Pride o' the Mill'	CTtf GEdr MAsh
	'Primrose Warburg'	CElw EPot EWes GEdr MAsh MCor NDry WFar
	'Ransom's Dwarf'	see *G. elwesii* 'Ransom's Dwarf'
	reginae-olgae	GKev LRHS MAsh NDry
	- 'Blanc de Chine'	NDry
	- subsp. ***reginae-olgae*** 'Cambridge'	NDry
	- - 'Eleni'	NDry
	- - 'Tilebarn Jamie'	NDry WCot
§	- - Winter-flowering Group	CBro
§	- subsp. ***vernalis***	LEdu WCot
	- - 'Christine'	CElw
	'Reverend Hailstone'	CAvo CTtf EWes GEdr MCor
	'Richard Ayres' (d)	CElw EHyd ELon EPri GEdr MCor NDry NRHS
	Richard Nutt's green-leaved hybrid **new**	NDry
	rizehensis	CAvo CBro GKev
	- Baytop 34474	GEdr NDry
	'Rodmarton'	EPot EPri GEdr MAsh NDry
	'Rodmarton Arcturus' **new**	CElw
	'Rodmarton Regulus'	GEdr
	'S.Arnott' ♀H5	CAvo CBro CElw CExl CMea EBee ECha EHyd EPfP GAbr GBin GKev GMaP LCro LOPS LRHS MCor NBir NPol NRHS NRog NRya NSla SDeJ WBrk WCot WFar WHoo WShi
	'Saint Anne's'	CAvo CElw GEdr
	'Sally Wickenden'	CTtf EPot
	'Sally's Double' (d) **new**	MCor
	'Scharlockii'	see *G. nivalis* Scharlockii Group
	'Seagull'	CElw CFis GEdr MCor MNrw
	'Sentinel'	CAvo CElw EPot GEdr
	'Shaggy'	NDry
	'Shropshire Queen'	GEdr
	'Silverwells'	GEdr
	'Sir Henry B-C'	MAsh
	'Sir Herbert Maxwell'	GEdr
	'Snow Angel'	CAvo
	'Snow Fox'	GKev LRHS SDir
	'South Hayes' ♀H5	CAvo EPot GEdr

'Spindlestone Surprise' ♀H5	GEdr ITim NDry
'Sprite'	CAvo CElw
'Starling'	CAvo
§ 'Straffan' ♀H5	CAvo CBro CElw ECha EMor EPot EPri GEdr MCor NPol WBrk WCot WFar
'Sutton Court'	CAvo
'Sutton Courtenay'	GEdr
'The Apothecary'	CElw
'The Linns'	GEdr
'The O'Mahoney'	see *G.* 'Straffan'
'The Wizard'	CAvo
'Titania' (d)	CElw CTtf ELon GEdr MCor WHoo
§ ***transcaucasicus***	GEdr
'Trotter's Merlin'	CElw CFis
'Trumpolute' **new**	MAsh MCor
'Trumps' ♀H5	CAvo GEdr MAsh MCor NDry
'Trym Baby'	GEdr
'Trymming'	GEdr
'Tryzm'	CAvo
'Tubby Merlin'	CElw MAsh
'Turncoat' **new**	CAvo
'Under Cherry Plum'	CAvo
× ***valentinei*** **new**	MCor
- 'Compton Court'	CBro GEdr ITim
'Veronica Cross'	CAvo
Warburg No 1	GBin
§ 'Washfield Colesbourne'	CElw ECha EWoo
'Washfield Warham'	CElw ECha EPri EWoo MCor
'Wasp'	CAvo CTtf EPot EPri GEdr MAsh MCor NDry WCot
'Welshway'	GEdr
'White Dreams'	GEdr
'White Swan' Ballard (d)	CElw EWes GEdr MCor WBrk
'William Thomson'	EWes
'Winifrede Mathias'	CElw MCor
'Wisley Magnet'	MCor
woronowii ♀H5	CArg CBro CElw CTri CTtf EPot EWoo GBin GKev ILea LCro LEdu LRHS MCor NBir NRog SDeJ SDix WBrk WCot WFar WShi
- 'Elizabeth Harrison'	GEdr
- 'Rodmarton Capella' **new**	MCor

Galatella (*Asteraceae*)

§ ***linosyris***	CBod EBee EWes MAvo MHol NLar SPer SPhx WFar
- 'Goldilocks'	see *G. linosyris*
§ ***sedifolia***	CBod CTtf ECtt EHyd ELon EPPr LEdu LRHS LSou MAvo NBid NRHS NSti SEND SPoG SSal WCot
- subsp. ***dracunculoides*** RCB AM 5	WCot
§ - 'Jean Polignier'	LPla
- 'Nana'	CExl EBee MRav NBir NLar NWsh SPer WCot WFar XLum

Galax (*Diapensiaceae*)

aphylla	see *G. urceolata*
§ ***urceolata***	IBlr MNrw NHar WSHC

Galega (*Fabaceae*)

bicolor	NBir SRms
'Duchess of Bedford'	ELon WCot
× ***hartlandii***	CExl LShi
- 'Alba' ♀H7	ELon EWes GBin LRHS MArl MCot MRav WCAu WCot WHoo WSHC
- 'Lady Wilson' ♀H7	ECtt ELon EMor EWes GBin MArl MAvo MHol MMrt SRms WCot WFar WKif
'Her Majesty'	see *G.* 'His Majesty'
§ 'His Majesty'	EBee ELon LEdu MAvo MCot MRav SMrm WCot
officinalis	Widely available
- 'Alba'	CBod CCBP ECtt ELan EMor EPfP LEdu LRHS MACG MAvo MBrN MHer SBut SEND SMrm SPer SPhx SRms WCAu WHrl WKif WSpi WTre
- COCONUT ICE ('Kelgal') (v)	SGBe SPoG
orientalis	EBee ECtt EWes LEdu MArl MAvo MCot MRav SBrt WPGP WSHC
- PAB 6771	WPGP

Galeobdolon see *Lamium*

Galeopsis (*Lamiaceae*)

tetrahit	WSFF

Galium (*Rubiaceae*)

glaucum	SPhx
mollugo	CHab
§ ***odoratum***	Widely available
verum	CHab EBee EBou ENfk GJos GPoy GQue LCro LOPS MHer MMuc MNHC NAts NGrd NMir SEND SPhx SRms SVic WFar WWild

Galtonia (*Asparagaceae*)

candicans ♀H4	Widely available
- 'Moonbeam' (d)	GKev
princeps	ECha EHyd LRHS NRHS WPGP
regalis	CExl WPGP
viridiflora	CBro CTtf ECha EGrl EShb EWoo GBin GKev GQue LRHS MHol MNrw SDeJ SDir SGBe

Galvezia (*Plantaginaceae*)

speciosa	CCCN

Gamblea (*Araliaceae*)

ciliata B&SWJ 13907	WCru
pseudoevodiifolia B&SWJ 11707	WCru

Garcinia (*Clusiaceae*)

mangostana	CCCN

Gardenia (*Rubiaceae*)

augusta	see *G. jasminoides*
florida L.	see *G. jasminoides*
grandiflora	see *G. jasminoides*
§ ***jasminoides*** ♀H1c	CBcs CCCN EBak SGsty
- 'Crown Jewel'PBR (d)	CBcs EHed EHyd EPfP LCro LOPS LRHS MAsh NRHS SPoG WCot XSte
- 'Kleim's Hardy'	Widely available
- PINWHEEL ('Piiga-I')	LCro LOPS
'Perfumed Petticoats'	XSte

garlic see *Allium sativum*; also AGM Vegetables Section

garlic, elephant see *Allium ampeloprasum* 'Elephant'

Garrya ✿ (*Garryaceae*)

elliptica	CBcs CBod CDoC CKel CMac CRos EBee EPfP ERom LMil LRHS LSRN MAsh MGos MPri NRHS SCob SGsty WAvo
- (f)	MSwo SGbt SWvt WSpi
- (m)	CTri NLar SGol WSpi
- 'James Roof' (m) ♀H4	Widely available

× ***issaquahensis*** 'Glasnevin Wine' (m) ♀H4	CRos ELan EPfP IArd LRHS NRHS SCoo SPoG WSpi
- 'Pat Ballard' (m)	WSpi
× ***thuretii***	CBcs EBee MMuc NLar SGol WFar WSpi

× *Gasteraloe* (*Asphodelaceae*)

beguinii **new**	NCft
'Flow' **new**	NCft
'Green Ice' **new**	NCft
'Grey Ghost' **new**	NCft
'Thaise' **new**	NCft
'Tiki Zilla'PBR **new**	SPad
'Wonder' **new**	NCft

Gasteria ✿ (*Asphodelaceae*)

acinacifolia **new**	SPlb
batesiana ♀H2	NCft SEND
bicolor	NCft SPlb
var. ***liliputana*** ♀H1c	
carinata var. ***verrucosa***	EShb SEND SPlb SSim
disticha **new**	SPlb
'Dragon Skin'	SPad
'Little Warty' ♀H2	NCft SPad SSim
nitida var. ***nitida*** variegated (v)	WCot
rawlinsonii **new**	NCft
'Rumpelstiltskin' **new**	NCft
'Salad Cream' **new**	NCft
'Smokey'	EShb

× *Gaulnettya* see *Gaultheria*

Gaultheria ✿ (*Ericaceae*)

antarctica	WThu
cuneata	EHyd LRHS MAsh NRHS WThu
forrestii	CExl
- BWJ 7809	WCru
furiens	see *G. insana*
§ ***insana***	WPav
itoana	GKev
'Jingle Bells'	SCoo
'John Saxton'	WAbe
miqueliana	GEdr NLar WThu
mucronata	CDoC EGrI EPfP GKev MAsh NWea SCob WFar
- (f) **new**	CKel
- (m)	CBod CMac CSBt CTri EPfP MGos NWad SPer SRms WFar WPav
- 'Alba' (f)	WPav
- 'Bell's Seedling' (f/m) ♀H6	CBcs CBod CBrac CKel CTri ELan EPfP MAsh NBir NLar SGbt SPer SPoG
- 'Cherry Ripe' (f)	WPav
- 'Crimsonia' (f) ♀H6	CBcs CMac EPfP SPer SRms
- 'Indian Lake'	NWad
- 'Lilacina' (f)	CMac MAsh
- 'Lilian' (f)	CSBt EPfP NWad
- MOTHER OF PEARL	see *G. mucronata* 'Parelmoer'
- 'Mulberry Wine' (f) ♀H6	CBcs CBod CBrac CSBt ELan NHol SGbt SPer
§ - 'Parelmoer' (f)	CSBt ELan
- 'Pink Pearl' (f) ♀H6	CEme SRms
- pink-berried (f)	GAbr
- 'Rosea' (f)	WPav
§ - 'Signaal' (f)	CBcs ELan MAsh NLar NWad SPer
- SIGNAL	see *G. mucronata* 'Signaal'
§ - 'Sneeuwwitje' (f)	CBcs CBod ELan EPfP LRHS MAsh SPer
- SNOW WHITE	see *G. mucronata* 'Sneeuwwitje'
- 'Thymifolia' (m)	ELan EPfP
- white-berried (f)	SCob
- 'Wintertime' (f) ♀H6	CMac SRms
§ ***myrsinoides***	GKev WThu
nummularioides	NHar
'Pearls'	EPot GArf NWad WAbe
phillyreifolia	MGil
procumbens ♀H5	CAgr CBcs CDTJ CDoC CMac CRos EGrI EHyd ELan EPfP GBin GEdr GKev LRHS MAsh MBlu MGos NRHS NWea SCob SPer SPlb SPoG SRms SWvt WFar
- BIG BERRY ('Gaubi'PBR)	CDoC LCro LOPS LRHS SCoo
- VERY BERRY ('Kieverber')	EShb NWad
prostrata	see *G. myrsinoides*
pyroloides	GArf
schultesii	WThu
shallon	CAgr CBrac EPfP GDam MCoo NLar NWea SCob SPer SRms SWvt WFar
sinensis	GArf NHar
- lilac-berried	GEdr
tetramera	CExl
thymifolia	NWad
trichophylla	GArf NHar
× ***wisleyensis***	CRos EHyd GKev LRHS NRHS SLon SRms
- 'Pink Pixie'	CRos EHyd LRHS MAsh NRHS
- 'Ruby'	CMac
- 'Wisley Pearl'	NLar SCoo WFar
yunnanensis	CExl

Gaura (*Onagraceae*)

'Flamingo White' **new**	SEdd
§ GAUDI PINK ('Florgaucompi'PBR)	CRos EHyd EPfP LRHS NRHS
'Ice Cool Rosy'	EBee SHar
'Lime Green' **new**	LRHS
lindheimeri ♀H4	CBar CBcs CMea CSBt CSpe EBee ECha EHyd ELan EPau EPfP EWoo LCro LOPS LRHS MBow MGos MHer NRHS SBut SDix SPer SPoG SRot SWvt WCAu WHoo XLum XSen
- Belleza Series	CKel CWCL EHyd EPfP LRHS NRHS
- 'Blaze'PBR	EHyd
- CHERRY BRANDY ('Gauchebra'PBR)	EBee ECtt ELan EPfP LRHS SWvt
- 'Chiffon'	SHar
- compact pink-flowered	SRot XLum
- compact red	XSen
- 'Cool Breeze'	CDor EAJP EWTr LSun MAvo SPhx WHoo
- 'Corrie's Gold' (v)	EBee ECha ECtt EHyd ELan EPfP LRHS MHer NRHS
- 'Crimson Butterflies'PBR	CWGN ECtt EHyd ELan EPfP LRHS
- 'Dwarf White' **new**	LRHS
- 'Elurra' **new**	LRHS
- 'Elurra White'	LRHS
- FREEFOLK ROSY ('Harrfolk') (v)	CDor CRos EHyd EPfP LCro LOPS LRHS LSou MSCN NRHS SEdd SGBe SHar SIvy SMrm XLum
- 'Gambit Rose Bicolor' **new**	EAJP
- GAUDI RED ('Florgaured')	CRos EHyd EPfP LRHS NRHS
- GAUDI ROSE ('Florgaucomro'PBR)	EHyd LRHS NRHS SCob
- (Geyser Series) GEYSER PINK ('Gaudros'PBR)	EBee EPfP LSou
- - GEYSER WHITE ('Gaudwwhi'PBR)	EBee EPfP LSou
- 'Jo Adela' (v)	ECha EPfP

	- KARALEE PETITE ('Gauka')	CWCL EPfP SEle
	- KARALEE PETITE IMPROVED	see *G. lindheimeri* LILLIPOP PINK
	- KARALEE WHITE ('Nugauwhite'PBR)	CBod CWCL EHyd ELan EPfP LRHS NLar NRHS SCoo SEdd SPoG
§	- LILLIPOP PINK ('Redgapi'PBR)	CWCL EHyd EPfP MBrN NLar SEdd SMrm SPoG
	- 'Little Janie'	CBod
	- 'My Melody'PBR (v)	CWCL
	- PAPILLON ('Nugaupapil'PBR)	CRos EHyd LRHS NRHS SEdd SPoG
	- 'Passionate Blush'PBR	CBcs CChe CWCL ECtt EHyd EPfP LRHS MGos NRHS SCoo SGBe SLon SPoG SRms
	- 'Passionate Rainbow'PBR (v)	CWCL EHyd EPfP LRHS NRHS SCob SCoo SGBe SPeP SRms
	- 'Pink Dwarf'	EBee
	- PINK FOUNTAIN ('Walgaupf')	EHyd LRHS NRHS
	- 'Pink Gin'	SPoG
	- ROSYJANE ('Harrosy'PBR)	Widely available
	- RUBY RUBY ('Harruby'PBR)	SHar
	- short	XLum
	- 'Siskiyou Pink'	CBar CBcs CSBt CWCL EBee ECha ECtt EHyd ELan EPfP EWoo LCro LOPS LRHS MPie SAdn SCob SGbt SPer SWvt WCFE WKif XLum
	- SNOW FOUNTAIN ('Walsnofou')	EHyd EPfP LRHS MNrw NRHS SMrm WNPC
	- 'Snowbird' **new**	MNrw
	- 'Sparkle White'	CBod EAJP EBee EHyd EPfP LRHS LSou LSun SBea WFar
	- 'Summer Breeze'	CDor EAJP EHyd EPfP GPSL LRHS MACG NGBl NRHS SPhx
	- 'Summer Emotions'	CBod LSou
	- 'The Bride'	CBcs CBod CTri CWCL EBee EHyd ELan EPfP GQue LRHS LSRN MBel MPie MRav NRHS SAdn SGbt SMrm SWvt WCav
	- 'Val's Pink'	WAvo
	- 'Vanilla'	LSou
I	- 'Variegata' (v)	CWCL SRms
	- 'Whirling Butterflies'	CBod CKno CSpe CWCL ECtt ELan EPfP EWoo LBuc LCro LOPS LRHS MNHC SCob SCoo SEdd SGBe SMrm SPer SPhx SPoG SWvt WCAu
	- 'Whiskers Deep Rose'	WFar
	- 'White Dove'	EHyd EWTr SEdd
	- 'White Heron'	MNrw
	'Rosy Shimmers'	EWTr SHar
	sinuata	CFis SHar WMal
	STRATOSPHERE PINK PICOTEE	see *G.* GAUDI PINK

Gazania (*Asteraceae*)

	'Aztec' ♀H2	CCCN
	'Bicton Orange'	CCCN ECtt SCoo SVen
	'Big Kiss White Flame' (Kiss Series)	CRos LBuc
	'Big Kiss Yellow Flame' (Kiss Series)	CRos LBuc
	'Blackberry Ripple'	CCCN SCoo WCav
	'Christopher'	SCoo
	'Christopher Lloyd'	CCCN WCav
	'Cornish Pixie'	CCCN
	'Cream Beauty'	MCot
	Daybreak Series	MBros
	- 'Daybreak Rose Stripe'	SCob
	- 'Daybreak Red Stripe'	SCob
	FROSTY KISS MIXED (Kiss Series)	SCob
	'Katua' (Sunbathers Series) **new**	ELan
	Kiss Series	MBros
	krebsiana	CCCN
	'Lemon Beauty'	ECtt
	linearis 'Colorado Gold'	SGBe
	'Magic'	CCCN ELan SCoo WCav
	NAHUI ('Suga119') (Sunbathers Series)	CCCN
	rigens 'Variegata' (v) ♀H2	CCCN
	RUMI ('Suga116') (Sunbathers Series)	CCCN
	Sunbathers Series	SCob
	Sunburst Series	LCro LOPS
	SUNSET JANE LEMON SPOT ('Sugajale') (Sunbathers Series)	CCCN EHyd NRHS
	SUNSET JANE ('Sugaja'PBR) (Sunbathers Series)	CCCN
	Talent Series ♀H3	LCro LOPS
	TIGER EYE ('Gazte') (v)	CCCN ELan
	TIGER STRIPES MIXED	MBros
	TIKAL (Sunbathers Series)	SCob
	TOPTOKAI ('Suga407') (Sunbathers Series)	CCCN EHyd NRHS
	TOTONACA ('Suga212') (Sunbathers Series)	CCCN EHyd ELan NRHS

Geissorhiza (*Iridaceae*)

	aspera	CPbh
	inflexa	WHil
	radians	WHil
	tulbaghensis	CPbh

Gelsemium (*Gelsemiaceae*)

	rankinii	WCot
	sempervirens ♀H3	CBcs CCCN CRHN EBee EShb LSRN MGil SBrt SPoG WCot

Genista (*Fabaceae*)

	aetnensis ♀H5	EWes LRHS SArc SBrt SPer SPtp SRms WLov WSpi
§	***canariensis*** ♀H3	CExl CSBt
	cinerea	WCFE
	decumbens	see *Cytisus decumbens*
	'Emerald Spreader'	see *G. pilosa* 'Yellow Spreader'
	hispanica	CBcs CBrac CDoC CSBt ELan EPfP MAsh MMuc NLar SCob SPer SRms SWvt WCFE
	horrida	NLar
	humifusa	see *G. pulchella*
	lydia ♀H5	Widely available
	pilosa	MAsh SRot
	- 'Goldilocks'	MMuc
	- 'Lemon Spreader'	see *G. pilosa* 'Yellow Spreader'
	- var. ***minor***	NLar WAbe
	- 'Procumbens' ♀H5	CBrac GEdr
	- 'Vancouver Gold'	CMac ELan EPfP SPer SRms
§	- 'Yellow Spreader'	MAsh MSwo
§	'Porlock' ♀H3	CBcs CBod CDoC CEme CExl CKel CMac CRos CSBt CTri EBee EHyd EPfP LRHS MAsh MMuc MRav NRHS SEND
§	***pulchella***	WAbe
	sagittalis	SBrt SPer
§	× ***spachiana*** ♀H1c	CEnd CTri SPoG
	tinctoria	CCBP CHab GPoy MMuc NAts WHer
§	- 'Flore Pleno' (d) ♀H6	EBtc GEdr

- 'Humifusa'	EPot GEdr
- 'Moesiaca'	WAbe
- 'Plena'	see *G. tinctoria* 'Flore Pleno'
- 'Royal Gold' ♀H6	MRav NLar NWad SPer SPlb
villarsii	see *G. pulchella*

Genlisea (*Lentibulariaceae*)

hispidula	CHew

Gentiana ✿ (*Gentianaceae*)

§ ***acaulis*** ♀H5	CRos EHyd EPot GArf GEdr GKev GMaP ITim LRHS MAsh NGdn NHar NLar NRHS NSla SPlb SRms WAbe WHoo
- 'Arctic Fanfare'	GEdr
- 'Coelestina'	WThu
- 'Krumrey'	EPot GEdr GKev GRum
- 'Luna'PBR	NLar WIce
I - 'Maxima Enzian'	GEdr GRum
- 'Rannoch'	EPot GEdr GKev NLar
- 'Stumpy'	GEdr
- 'Trotter's Variety'	GArf WAbe
- 'Undulatifolia'	EPot
- 'Velkokvensis'	EPot GEdr
alba new	GKev
'Alex Duguid'	CRos EHyd GEdr LRHS NHar
'Amethyst'	CRos EHyd GEdr LRHS WAbe
angulosa misapplied	see *G. verna* 'Angulosa' hort.
angustifolia	GAbr GKev WAbe
I - 'Alba'	EPot
- Frei hybrid	NSla
'Ann's Special'	GEdr
asclepiadea ♀H5	CSpe EBee ECha EHyd ELan EMor GAbr GEdr GKev GMaP GQue LEdu LRHS MBel MNrw NBid NBir NFav NHar NLar NRHS SBls SPer SRms WBor WCAu WCFE WHoo WKif
- 'Alba'	EBee EHyd EMor GEdr GKev GMaP LEdu NBid NFav NRHS SPer SRms WCFE WHoo
- dark blue-flowered	WPGP
- 'Knightshayes'	EBee GKev LEdu
I - 'Nana'	EBee GKev
- 'Phyllis'	EBee GKev
- 'Pink Cascade'	WHil
- 'Pink Swallow'	GEdr
- 'Rosea'	GEdr GKev
- 'White Swallow'	GEdr
- 'Whitethroat'	GKev
atuntsiensis	GKev
'Balmoral'PBR	GMaP NHar
'Barbara Lyle'	WAbe
bavarica var. ***subacaulis***	SPlb
'Berrybank Dome'	CRos EHyd GMaP LRHS
'Berrybank Sky'	CRos EHyd GEdr GMaP LRHS NHar
'Berrybank Snowflakes'	GMaP
'Berrybank Star'	CRos GEdr LRHS SPer
bisetaea	SRms
'Blauer Diamant'	GEdr
'Blauer Kobold'	GEdr
'Blauer Zwerg'	GEdr
'Blue Flame'	GEdr
'Blue Heaven'	GEdr
'Blue Magic'PBR	NLar
'Blue Sea'	CRos EHyd LRHS
'Blue Silk' ♀H5	CRos CSma EHyd EPfP GEdr GKev LRHS NHar NRHS SPoG WAbe
brachyphylla	WAbe
'Braemar'PBR	GMaP NHar
* ***burrowthii***	GEdr
'Cairngorm'	CRos EHyd GEdr LRHS
calycosa	GArf
'Carmen'	GEdr
× ***caroli***	WAbe
clusii	CPla GKev
'Compact Gem'	GEdr NHar WAbe
§ ***cruciata***	ELan GEdr NLar
§ ***dahurica***	EBee GLog NGdn NLar
'Dark Hedgehog'	GEdr
David Sturrock's dark seedling	NHar
decumbens	GKev
depressa	CPla EPot GKev WAbe
'Devonhall'	GEdr NHar
'Diana'PBR	NLar
dinarica 'Colonel Stitt'	WThu
- 'Frocheneite'	EPot
'Dumpy'	GEdr
'Elehn'	GEdr NHar
'Elizabeth'	GEdr
'Ettrick'	GEdr
'Eugen's Allerbester' (d)	CRos CSma EHyd GEdr GKev GMaP LRHS NHar NHol NLar SPer WAbe WFar
'Eugen's Bester'	NHar
farreri	WAbe
- Silken Star Group	WAbe
'Faszination'	GEdr
'Gellerhard'	GEdr
georgei	EPot
'Gewahn'	GEdr
I 'Glamis Strain'	CRos EHyd GEdr LRHS NHar SPer
'Glen Moy'	GEdr
'Glendevon'	GEdr
§ ***gracilipes***	GEdr SPlb SRms
grossheimii	GKev
'Hamburg'	GEdr
'Henry'	GEdr
hexaphylla	EPot
Inshriach hybrids	EHyd LRHS
'Inverleith'	GEdr NHol SPlb
'Iona'PBR	NHar
'Joan Ward'	CRos EHyd LRHS SPer
'John Aitken'	GEdr
'Juwel'	GEdr
'Kobold'	GEdr
kochiana	see *G. acaulis*
kurroo var. ***brevidens***	see *G. dahurica*
lagodechiana	see *G. septemfida* var. *lagodechiana*
ligustica	EPot
'Little Diamond'PBR	NLar
loderi	GKev
'Lucerna'	EHyd GEdr GKev LRHS
lutea	CBod EBee EMor GAbr GKev GPoy NFav NHar NLar SRms WCAu
× ***macaulayi*** 'Blue Bonnets'	GEdr
- 'Kidbrooke Seedling'	GEdr GKev WAbe
- 'Kingfisher'	EHyd GEdr GKev WAbe
§ - 'Praecox'	EBou
makinoi 'Marsha'PBR	NLar SPoG
'Margaret'	GEdr
'Maryfield'	GEdr
'Melanie'	GEdr
'Moonlight' new	GKev
'Multiflora'	EHyd
newberryi new	GArf
nipponica	GKev
'Oban'PBR	GMaP NHar
occidentalis	CPla EPot GKev WAbe
ornata	GArf WAbe
'Orva'	LRHS

pannonica	GKev
paradoxa ♀H5	EPot GKev NSla SBrt
- 'Blauer Herold'	GKev
paradoxa* × *septemfida	GKev MNHC
phlogifolia	see *G. cruciata*
phyllocalyx	GKev
pneumonanthe	NLar SPlb
prolata	GArf
pumila subsp. ***delphinensis***	WAbe
purdomii	see *G. gracilipes*
robusta CC 7494	EBee GKev
'Sapphire Blue'	EBee GEdr
saxosa	GWyn LRHS NBir NHpl NRHS NSla WAbe
scabra 'Little Pinkie'PBR	GEdr
'Selektra'	GEdr
septemfida ♀H5	CRos EBou EHyd EPot GAbr GKev LRHS MAsh NBir NHpl NRHS NSla SPlb SRms WHoo WIce WKif
- 'Alba'	GKev
* - var. ***kuznetzovii***	GKev
§ - var. ***lagodechiana*** ♀H5	GEdr GKev SRms WFar XLum
'Serenity'	CSma EHyd GEdr NHar WAbe
'Shot Silk' ♀H5	CRos EHyd EPfP GEdr LRHS MGos NHol NHpl SPer SPoG WAbe WIce
sikokiana	GArf
'Silken Giant'	GEdr WAbe
'Silken Glow'	WAbe
'Silken Night'	GEdr WAbe
'Silken Seas'	CSma GEdr NHar WAbe
'Silken Skies' ♀H5	GEdr WAbe
'Silken Surprise'	WAbe
sino-ornata ♀H5	CSma EBou EPfP GKev GMaP GQue LCro LRHS MAsh NHpl NRHS SEdd SRms WAbe WIce
- SDR 5127	MGos
- 'Angel's Wings'	GEdr
- 'Bellatrix'	GEdr
- 'Blautopf'	GEdr
- 'Brin Form'	SRms
- 'Downfield'	EHyd GKev
- 'Edith Sarah'	GEdr
- 'Gorau Glas'	WAbe
- 'Mary Lyle'	GEdr
- 'Oha'	GEdr
- 'Praecox'	see *G.* × *macaulayi* 'Praecox'
- 'Purity'	EHyd GEdr WAbe
- 'Starlight'	GEdr GKev NHar
- 'Weisser Traum'	CRos EHyd GEdr LRHS NHar NHol NLar
- 'White Wings'	GEdr
'Sir Rupert'	GEdr NHar
'Stardust' **new**	GKev
'Sternschuppe'	GKev
× ***stevenagensis***	EHyd
§ - 'Bernardii'	GEdr
- dark-flowered	WAbe
straminea	EBee GKev
'Strathmore' ♀H5	CRos CSma EHyd GEdr GKev GMaP LRHS NBir SPlb WIce
'Suendermannii'	GKev
'Surprise'	GEdr
syringea	WAbe
ternifolia 'Cangshan'	GEdr
- 'Dali'	GEdr
'The Caley'	CRos GEdr GMaP LRHS NHar
tibetica	GPoy WCAu XLum
- PAB 2357	LEdu WPGP
Tough's form	GEdr
triflora	GKev
'Troon'	GMaP NHar
veitchiorum	EPot GArf GKev WAbe
verna	CRos CSma EDAr EHyd EPfP EWes GKev LCro LOPS LRHS NHpl NRHS NSla SPlb SPoG WAbe WHoo
- 'Alba'	GEdr NLar NSla WAbe
§ - 'Angulosa' ♀H5	MAsh
§ - subsp. ***pontica***	WIce
'Violette'	CRos EHyd GEdr LRHS
waltonii	EWes
wilsonii	GKev
zekuensis	WCot

Gentianopsis (*Gentianaceae*)

paludosa	GKev

Geranium ✿ (*Geraniaceae*)

aconitifolium misapplied	see *G. palmatum*
aconitifolium L'Hér.	see *G. rivulare*
'Alan Mayes'	CBod CMac ECtt EHyd EPPr EWoo GBin GKin LHGe LRHS MBel NGdn NRHS WCra WFar WPnP
'Alan's Blue'	EBee
albanum	CElw EPPr GLog GPSL GWyn SRGP
albiflorum	EBee
'Allendale Gem'	EBee
anemonifolium	see *G. palmatum*
'Ann Folkard' ♀H7	Widely available
'Ann Folkard' × ***psilostemon***	GWyn LSRN
'Anne Thomson' ♀H7	Widely available
'Ant Chilly'	EBee
× ***antipodeum*** 'Chocolate Candy'PBR	LBuc SPoG
- 'Pink Spice'PBR	CWGN GKin LBuc SPoG SRms
- 'Purple Passion'PBR	LBuc SPoG
- 'Stanhoe'	MHCG
- (*G. sessiliflorum* subsp. *novae-zelandiae* 'Nigricans' × *G. traversii* var. *elegans*)	SRms
argenteum	NSla
aristatum	EBee EPPr EWes MNrw MRav NBir SGbt SPhx WCru
armenum	see *G. psilostemon*
asphodeloides	CElw EHyd MNrw NBid NBir SGbt WBrk WFar
- subsp. ***sintenisii***	EPPr
- 'Starlight'	NBid
atlanticum Hook. f.	see *G. malviflorum*
'Azure Rush'	Widely available
'Azurro'	EBee
'Baby Blue'	see *G. himalayense* 'Baby Blue'
'Bertie Crûg'	ECtt ELon GKev GPSL GWyn LLWG NBir NLar SEdd SRms SRot SWvt
biuncinatum	SBrt
'Bloomtime' **new**	CBod ECtt LRHS
'Blue Boy'	NLar
'Blue Cloud' ♀H7	Widely available
'Blue Pearl'	EPPr MAvo NBir NSti
§ BLUE SUNRISE ('Blogold'PBR) ♀H7	Widely available
'Blue Thunder'	EPPr
'Blushing Turtle'PBR	CBod CKel ECtt ELan EPfP LBuc LHGe LRHS MAvo MHol NDov NLar SCoo SPoG WCAu WCra WNPC
'Bob's Blunder'	CBod CRos ECtt LLWG LPot LRHS MBNS MBel MHol MNrw MSCN SAko SPeP SPoG SRms SWvt WCot WCra WFar WHoo
bohemicum	WHer

	- 'Orchid Blue'	SWvt
	'Brookside' ♀H7	Widely available
	'Buckland Beauty'	CExl EWes SGro
	'Buxton's Blue'	see *G. wallichianum* 'Buxton's Variety'
	caeruleatum	NLar
	canariense	see *G. reuteri*
§	× ***cantabrigiense***	CMac CRos EBee EBou ECtt EHyd LRHS MHer MNrw NBir NBro NLar NPer NRHS NSti SCob SRms WBor WBrk WCru
	- 'Berggarten'	EBee EPPr GBin NLar SAko SRGP WBrk WCra
	- 'Biokovo'	Widely available
	- 'Cambridge'	CBod EBee ECha ECtt EGrI ELan EPPr EPfP GAbr GKin LHGe LRHS MBow MCot MRav MSwo NRHS SCob SPer SPoG SRms SWvt WBrk WCra WFar WFib WPnP
	- CRYSTAL ROSE ('Abpp')	EBee EHyd EPPr EPfP LRHS NRHS NSti SRGP WCot
	- 'Hanne'	CDor EBee ECha ECtt EPPr EWes WCra
	- 'Harz'	CDor EPPr SAko WCra
	- 'Hilary Rendall'	EBee ECtt EPPr
	- 'Karmina'	CBod CDor EBee EBlo EHyd EPPr EPfP GBin GPSL LRHS NFav NLar NRHS WCra WFar WHoo WSpi XLum
	- 'Rosalina'	EPPr
	- 'Show Time'	EPPr
	- 'St Ola'	Widely available
	- 'Vorjura'	EBee EPPr SAko
	- 'Westray'PBR	CDor CMac ECtt GJos GLog LCro LOPS LSou MBel MHol MMuc NCou NGdn NLar NRya NSti SEND SRms SWvt WCra WFib WIce
	'Chantilly'	EBee ECtt EHyd EPPr EWTr LHGe MAvo NBir NChi NLar WCru WFib WGwG
	'Chipchase Castle'	NChi
	christensenianum B&SWJ 8022	WCru
	cinereum	NSla
	- 'Apple Blossom'	see *G.* × *lindavicum* 'Apple Blossom'
	- 'Elizabeth'	LSRN
	- 'Sateene'PBR	CBor CSma GMaP MSCN NLar SRms WCra
	(Cinereum Group) 'Alice'PBR	CBor CSma EBee LHGe LRHS NLar SRms WFar
	- 'Ballerina' ♀H5	Widely available
	- 'Carol'	CBor CSma CWGN EWes GKin LSRN MRav NLar NRHS SWvt WCra WFar
I	- 'Heather'	CBor CSma WFar
	- 'Janette'	CBor NRHS
	- JOLLY JEWEL CORAL ('Noortjjcor')	WCot
	- JOLLY JEWEL HOT PINK ('Noortjjhpi')	LCro LOPS
	- JOLLY JEWEL LILAC ('Noortlil'PBR)	CWGN NSti WCot WCra
	- JOLLY JEWEL NIGHT ('Noortnight'PBR)	CWGN ECtt GEdr LRHS MAvo MPnt MThu SEdd SHeu WCAu WCot WCra
	- JOLLY JEWEL PURPLE ('Noortpur'PBR)	CBod CWGN LCro LOPS LRHS NHar SHeu WCot WHil
	- JOLLY JEWEL RASPBERRY ('Noortjjrab')	CWGN WCot
	- JOLLY JEWEL RED ('Noortimpred')	EMor LHGe MPnt NCou NHar NSti SHeu WCAu WCot WCra WHil
	- JOLLY JEWEL SALMON ('Noortsal'PBR)	CBcs CKno CMil CWGN GEdr LCro LOPS MBNS MCot MHol MSCN MThu NHar NSti SHeu WCot WCra WTor
	- JOLLY JEWEL SILVER ('Noortjjsil')	LRHS NSti WCot WCra
	- JOLLY JEWEL VIOLET ('Noortvio')	WCot
	- 'Lambrook Helen'	CBor CExl CFis
	- 'Laurence Flatman'	CExl CSpe ECtt EHyd EPfP EPri EWoo GMaP LHGe LRHS MCot MPnt NBid NChi NQui NRHS NSla SPoG SRms WCra
	- 'Lizabeth'PBR	CBor NLar WCot
	- 'Melody'PBR	CBor CSma CWCL NLar WCra
	- 'Pandora'	CBor
	- 'Penny Lane'PBR	CBor MHol
	- 'Purple Pillow'	CBor CWGN EGrI ELan LSRN NChi NFav SAko SPer SRms SWvt WCra WFar
	- ROTHBURY GEM ('Gerfos'PBR) ♀H5	ECtt EGrI IPot MRav SWvt WCra
	- 'Signal'	EPot LHGe MPnt WCra
	- 'Sophie'PBR	CBor CSma EHyd LHGe LRHS NRHS
§	- 'Thumbling Hearts'	CBor CWGN EBee EGrI EHed GPSL LCro LHGe SAko SMrm WCot WCra WFar
	- THUMPING HEART	see *G.* 'Thumbling Hearts'
	'Claridge Druce'	see *G.* × *oxonianum* 'Claridge Druce'
	clarkei	SBut
§	- 'Kashmir White'	Widely available
	- 'Mount Stewart'	CExl EBee EPfP WCru
	- Purple-flowered Group	WCav
	- - 'Kashmir Purple'	Widely available
	- Raina 82.83	MNrw
	clarum B&SWJ 10246	WCru
	collinum	EPPr NBir
	'Color Carousel'	EBee GBin
	'Coombland White'	CExl EBee ECtt EHyd EWTr EWoo LHGe LSun MAvo NRHS SPer SPoG SRGP WCot WCra WFar WMal WSpi
	'Copper Tiger'	LEdu
	'Coquet Island'	EPPr
	'Criss Canning'	EPPr
	'Curly Girly'	EBee
	'Daily Purple' **new**	CBod
	dalmaticum ♀H5	Widely available
	- 'Album'	EBee ECtt EHyd EPfP EPot GDam MRav NRHS SRGP SRms WAbe WCra
	- 'Bressingham Pink'	ECtt EPPr
	- 'Bridal Bouquet'	ECtt EPot NSla
	- 'Stade's Hellrosa'	EPPr
	dalmaticum × ***macrorrhizum***	see *G.* × *cantabrigiense*
	'Danny Boy' ♀H7	EBee
	'Deep Purple'	CTtf EBee
	delavayi misapplied	see *G. sinense*
	'Deux Fleurs'	IPot MAvo MNrw
	'Devon Pride'	CElw EBee EPPr
	'Dilys' ♀H7	CFis EBee ELan EPPr LHGe MAvo MNrw NBir NChi NDov NGdn NGrd NLar NSti WCra WFar WHal WPnP WSpi
	'Distant Hills'	EBee EPPr
	'Diva'	EBee ELan EPPr
	'Doctor Geert Lambrecht'	EBee
	'Double Jewel'	see *G. pratense* 'Double Jewel'
	DRAGON HEART ('Bremdra'PBR)	CBod CSpe EBee ECtt ELan EPfP EWoo IPot LCro LOPS LPla LSRN

	MAvo MNrw MPnt NDov NLar NRHS NSti SCoo SGBe WBor WCAu WCra WFar WHil WNPC WPnP WSpi WWtn
drakensbergense	WFar
DREAMLAND ('Bremdream'^{PBR})	CDor CSpe CWGN EBee ECtt EMor EPfP GMaP LCro LHGe LOPS LPla LRHS MAvo MBNS MBel NLar SEdd SGBe WCAu WCot WCra
'Dusky Crûg'	ECtt EHyd ELan ELon EMor EPfP EShb GDam GMaP LHGe LRHS MBel MPie NFav NHpl NSti SDix SEdd SGBe SPoG SRot SWvt WCot WCra WFar WSpi
'Dusky Rose'	CDor ECtt EWoo GJos GKev GPSL GWyn NLar SEdd SRGP WFar
'Dylis'	WCAu
'Elke'	Widely available
'Elworthy Eyecatcher'	CDor CElw MNrw
'Elworthy Tiger'	CElw EBee MAvo
endressii ♀H7	CWCL ECha EPfP GMaP LHGe LPot LShi MBNS MCot MHer MMuc NBro NPer NPol SEND SPlb SRms SWvt WCra WFar XLum
- 'Album'	see *G.* 'Mary Mottram'
- 'Wargrave Pink'	see *G.* × *oxonianum* 'Wargrave Pink'
erianthum	GLog GMaP NLar WCru
- 'Axeltree'	WCot
- 'Blues in the Night'	EBee
- 'Calm Sea'	WCru
- 'Neptune'	WCru
- 'Pale Blue Yonder'	EBee EWes
eriostemon Fischer	see *G. platyanthum*
'Eureka Blue'	CRos ECha ECtt EHyd EPfP LPla LRHS MACG MAvo MHol NLar NRHS NSti SEdd SPoG WCot WCra WPnP
'Expression'	see *G.* 'Tanya Rendall'
'Extravaganza'	EWes
'Farncombe Cerise Star'	CElw
§ ***farreri***	CBor CExl EHyd EPot GGro LRHS NBir NRHS NSla
'Fay Anna'	CBct CBod CWGN EMor EPPr EPfP GBin LHGe MBros MHol MMrt MPnt SCob SMrm SPeP SPoG WCra WFar
'Finnish Pink'	NGrd
'Foundling'	CBct IPot LHGe
gracile	EBee EHyd EPfP GMaP LRHS MNrw NBir NChi NRHS WBrk WCru
- 'Blanche'	EHyd EPPr MNrw
- 'Blush'	EPPr EWes
- 'Golden Gracile'	see *G.* 'Mrs Judith Bradshaw'
grandiflorum	see *G. himalayense*
'Grasmere'	ECtt
gymnocaulon	CMac EBee EPfP LRHS NLar WCru
gymnocaulon* × *platypetalum	EBee
'Harmony'	EBee EPPr
harveyi	EWes EWld NChi SPhx WKif
§ ***hayatanum***	EHyd
- B&SWJ 164	NLar WCru
'Hexham Velvet'	ECtt LHGe MHol SMrm WSpi
'Hilary'	WWtn
§ ***himalayense***	CBod ECha EHyd ELan EPfP LRHS MBNS MMuc MRav NBir NBro NGrd NRHS SEND SPlb SRms WCav WCra WFar XLum
- CC 1957 from Tibetan border	CExl EPPr
- HPA 1347 **new**	GGro
- ***alpinum***	see *G. himalayense* 'Gravetye'
§ - 'Baby Blue'	CElw CRos EBee ECtt EHyd ELon EPPr LHGe LRHS MAvo MBel MNrw NGdn NLar NRHS NSti SRGP WBrk WCAu WCra WCru WFib WPnP
- 'Birch Double'	see *G. himalayense* 'Plenum'
- 'Derrick Cook'	CBod CElw CMea EBee ECha ECtt EPPr EPfP EWTr EWoo GAbr GBin LHGe LPla LRHS MAvo MBel MNrw NGrd NLar NSti WBrk WCAu WCra WHal WHoo WPnP WSpi
- 'Devil's Blue'	EPPr MAvo SRGP WCAu
§ - 'Gravetye'	Widely available
- 'Irish Blue'	CDor CElw EBee EHyd EPPr EWoo GMaP NLar NPol NSti SRGP WCra WFib WPnP
- ***meeboldii***	see *G. himalayense*
- 'Pale Irish Blue'	EBee EPPr
§ - 'Plenum' (d)	Widely available
'Hola Guapa'	GBin IPot
ibericum misapplied	see *G.* × *magnificum*
ibericum ambig.	NFav SRms
ibericum Cav.	CTri EHyd LRHS NRHS
§ - 'Ushguli Grijs'	EPPr MAvo NLar WCot
- 'Black and Blue'	EBee
- subsp. ***ibericum***	CMac WCra
- subsp. ***jubatum***	EPPr MNrw SGbt SRms
- - 'White Zigana'	ECtt NLar SRms WGwG WWtn
- subsp. ***jubatum* × *renardii***	SWvt
- var. ***platypetalum*** misapplied	see *G.* × *magnificum*
- var. ***platypetalum*** Boiss.	see *G. platypetalum* Fisch. & C.A.Mey.
ibericum* × *libani	EBee
incanum	CCht CSpe EBee ELon EWes LLWG NBir NHpl SRGP SVen WCFE WSpi
- var. ***incanum***	SGro
'Ivan' ♀H7	CBod CElw CWCL EBee ECha ECtt EHyd EPPr LPla LRHS MBel NChi NLar NRHS WCot WCra WCru WFib WWtn
'Jean Armour'	CBod ECtt EHyd EPPr GBee LRHS LSou MAvo MBel NDov NRHS SPoG WFar WGwG
× ***johnsonii***	WFib
- 'Johnson's Blue'	Widely available
'Jolly Bee'	see *G.* ROZANNE
'Joy'	CDor CRos CTtf EBee ECtt EHyd EPPr GWyn LHGe LSun MAvo MCot MRav NBir NDov NLar NRHS NSti NWad SRGP SRms WCot WCra WFib WGwG WHil WMal WPnP
'JS Matu Vu'	CBod CDor ECtt GPSL NDov SPoG WCAu WSpi
§ 'Kanahitobanawa'	EBee MAvo
'Karen Wouters'	EPPr
'Kashmir Blue'	CExl CRos ECtt EHyd ELan EPfP GMaP LRHS NLar NRHS SWvt WCAu WCra WFar WKif
'Kashmir Green'	LHGe
'Kashmir Pink'	Widely available
§ 'Khan'	CElw EPPr EWes EWoo MAvo NEoE NLar SDys SMHy SRGP SSal WCru
'Kirsty'	EBee EWes NChi
kishtvariense	GGro MRav NSti WCru
koraiense	WFar
- B&SWJ 797	WCru
- B&SWJ 878	CExl EBee WCru
koreanum misapplied	see *G. hayatanum*
koreanum ambig.	NLar
- B&SWJ 602	CExl WCru WHoo

	Name	Suppliers
	krameri	NLar
	– B&SWJ 1142	CExl WCru
	'Lakwijk Star'	CBod ECtt EMor EPPr EPfP ILea LHGe LRHS NLar SPoG SRms WCra WMal
	libani	CDor EPPr MCot NBid NSti WBrk WCot WSHC
	– RCB RL B-2	WCot
	– 'Kew Gardens'	EPPr
	'Light Dilys'	EBee EPPr LCro LHGe LOPS NDov STPC
	'Lilac Ice'	CBod CWGN EBee ECtt EHyd EPfP GMaP LCro LOPS LPla LRHS MNrw NDov NLar NRHS NSti SGbt WCra
§	× ***lindavicum*** 'Apple Blossom'	CMea EBee EPot LRHS NSla WFar
	linearilobum	CBod CCht CWGN IPot SCoo SRGP
	subsp. ***transversale*** 'Foundling's Friend'	WCot WSpi
I	– – 'Laciniatum'	WCot
§	'Little David'	CBod ECtt EPPr LHGe MBel NLar WCra
	'Little Devil'	see *G.* 'Little David'
	'Little Gem'	CRos EBee ECtt EHyd GPSL LHGe LRHS MAvo NDov NRHS SGro WFar WHoo
	lucidum	WSFF
	'Lydia'	SRGP XSen
§	***macrorrhizum***	CBod CSBt EGrI GBin GJos GKev GKin GWyn LCro LEdu LOPS LRHS LSun MCot MRav MSCN NBro SRms WCAu WFar WSFF XLum
	– 'Album'	CBod CDor CMea ECha EHyd EPPr EWoo GMaP LRHS MBel MSwo NBid NBro NChi NRHS SAko SRGP WBrk WCAu WCot WCra WCru WFar WFib
	– 'Bevan's Variety'	Widely available
	– 'Bulgaria'	EPPr
	– 'Cham Ce'	ECtt EPPr
	– 'Czakor'	CBod CDor CMac EBee ECtt EHyd ELan ELon EPPr EPfP LHGe MCot MRav MSpe NGdn NLar SAko SCob SEdd SRGP SRms SWvt WBrk WCot WCra WCru WFar XLum
I	– 'De Bilt'	EPPr EWes
	– 'Freundorf'	EPPr EWes GQue SAko
	– 'Glacier'	ECha EPPr EWes
	– 'Ingwersen's Variety' 🏆H7	Widely available
	– 'Lohfelden'	EPPr EWes WBrk WCru
	– 'Montasch'	NLar
	– 'Morris Minor' new	EWes
	– 'Mount Olympus'	see *G. macrorrhizum* 'White-Ness'
	– 'Mytikas'	EPPr
	– 'Olympos'	EPPr NLar
	– 'Pastis'	SPoG
	– 'Pindus'	CWCL EBee EHyd EPPr EWes GAbr LRHS NLar NRHS NSti SPtp SRGP WCru WFar
	– 'Prionia'	EBee EPPr NLar SAko
	– 'Purpurrot'	EPPr WBrk
	– 'Ridsko'	EPPr SRGP WBrk WCru
	– ***roseum***	see *G. macrorrhizum*
	– 'Rotblut'	EPPr WBrk
	– 'Sandwijck'	EPPr WBrk
	– 'Snow Sprite'	CMea EPPr GJos GKev MHer NEoE NLar WBrk WHrl WPnP XLum
	– 'Spessart'	CBar CBod CCBP EBee EBlo EHyd ELan ELon EPPr EPfP EWoo GBin GMaP GQue LHGe LRHS MMuc NLar NRHS SCob SEND SGbt SPer SPhx SPoG SWvt WCra WFar WFib XLum

	Name	Suppliers
	– 'Variegatum' (v)	CFis ELan GMaP LPot MBriF NBir SRGP SRms WCot WFar
	– 'Velebit'	EPPr WCru XLum
	– 'Vitalis' new	CBod
§	– 'White-Ness' 🏆H7	Widely available
	macrostylum	WCot
	– 'Leonidas'	EPPr
	– 'Talish'	EPPr
	– 'Uln Oag Triag'	EPPr
	maculatum	EHyd LRHS MCot MMrt MNrw MRav NLar NRHS NSti SRGP WCru WHal
	– from Kath Dryden	EPPr
	– f. ***albiflorum***	CElw EBee EHyd ELan ELon EMor EPPr EWTr EWoo LHGe LRHS MBel MNrw NChi NLar NSti SRGP SSut WBrk WCra WCru WFar WPnP
	– 'Beth Chatto'	CBod CCBP CDor CElw CTtf EBee ECha ELan ELon EPPr EPfP GMaP LEdu LHGe MBel MMuc NBid NDov NLar SBut SPtp WBor WBrk WCAu WCra WFar WFib WHoo WPnP
	– 'Elizabeth Ann'PBR 🏆H7	CWGN EBee ECtt EWoo GBin LHGe LSou MBel MHol MNrw NGdn NLar NSti NWad SDix SEdd WCot WCra WFar WFib WPnP
	– 'Espresso'	Widely available
	– 'Putnam County'	EBee EPPr
	– 'Schokoprinz' new	SAko
	– 'Shameface'	EBee EBlo EHyd EPPr EPfP LRHS NRHS
	– 'Silver Buttons'	EBee
	– 'Smoky Mountain'	EPPr
	– 'Spring Purple'	CDor CElw EBee EPPr MAvo NChi NLar WFar
	– 'Sweetwater'	EPPr
	– 'Vickie Lynn'	CCBP EBee EPPr MAvo MBel NDov NLar WCAu WCra
	maderense 🏆H3	Widely available
	– 'Guernsey White'	CBod CCCN CPla CSpe CTrC CTsd LRHS SPhx WKif
§	× ***magnificum*** 🏆H7	Widely available
I	– 'Anemoniflorum'	WCra
	– 'Blue Blood'	CBod CKel EBee ECtt EHyd EPPr EPfP GAbr LHGe MBNS NGdn NSti SCob SEdd SRms SWvt WCot WCra WFar
	– 'Ernst Pagels'	CBod CDor GBin
	– 'Rosemoor'	CBod CElw CRos CWCL ECtt EHyd ELan EPPr EPfP LCro LOPS LRHS NLar NRHS SPer SPtp WBor WCra WFar WFib WHoo WSpi XLum
	– 'Vital'	LHGe XLum
	magniflorum	EBee EWes GKev NBid
	– LA VETA LACE ('P0135') new	LRHS
	'Maître Hugo'	EBee NChi
§	***malviflorum***	ECha EPPr NSti WCot
	– from Spain	EWes
	– pink-flowered	EPPr WSHC
§	'Mary Mottram'	CElw MAvo
	'Mavis Simpson' 🏆H6	Widely available
	'Maxwelton'	EBee
	'Melinda'	CDor EBee ECtt WCot WFib
	'Memories'PBR	CBor CSma LSRN NLar SRms
	'Menna Bach'	MAvo WFar
	'Midnight Star'	EBee EPPr EWes
	molle	WSFF

	× ***monacense***	CCBP EBee EHyd LEdu LRHS NRHS WCru WFar WGwG WPnP WWtn
	- var. ***anglicum***	CDor EHyd EPPr EPfP LRHS NLar NRHS
	- 'Anne Stevens'	EBee
	- 'Claudine Dupont'	CDor CElw EPPr NWad WCot WFib
	- dark-flowered	WFar
	- 'Emma White'	EBee EPPr NChi NGrd
	- 'Jackie'	EBee EPPr NChi
	- var. ***monacense*** 'Breckland Fever'	EBee EPPr
§	- - 'Muldoon'	NBir SRGP WChS WFar WPnP
	- 'Spotted in the Pass'	EBee
	'Mourning Widow'	see *G. phaeum* 'Lady in Mourning'
	'Mrs Jean Moss'	EBee EPPr EWes MAvo NChi
§	'Mrs Judith Bradshaw'	EPPr
	napuligerum misapplied	see *G. farreri*
	'Natalie'	EBee EHyd LSRN MAvo NChi SWvt
	nepalense	SRGP SRms
	'Nicola'	CElw CRos EBlo EHyd EPPr EPfP LRHS MAvo NLar NRHS SRGP
	'Nimbus' ♀H7	Widely available
	nodosum	Widely available
	- 'Blueberry Ice'	CDor CElw MAvo
	- 'Clos de Coudray'	EAJP EBee EPPr GPSL ILea LRHS MAvo NFav NLar NSti SHar SRGP WCAu WCra WFar WHil WPnP
	- 'Dark Heart'	MCot
	- dark-flowered	see *G. nodosum* 'Swish Purple'
	- 'Darkleaf'	EBee
	- 'Eton Mess' **new**	WCot
	- 'Fielding's Folly'	CElw CMea
	- 'Hexham Big Eye'	CDor CElw EBee EWes LPla MAvo WBrk WFar
	- 'Hexham Face Paint'	EBee
	- 'Hexham Feathers'	CDor CElw
	- 'Hexham Freckles'	EBee EPPr
	- 'Hexham Lace'	CDor CElw EPPr
	- 'Hexham Whitethroat'	EBee
	- 'Julie's Velvet'	CElw LEdu SGro WHoo
	- lilac-flowered **new**	EGrI
	- pale-flowered	see *G. nodosum* 'Svelte Lilac'
	- 'Pascal'	EPPr
	- 'Silverwood'	Widely available
	- 'Simon'	NLar WCra
§	- 'Svelte Lilac'	CBod CRos ECtt EHyd EPPr EPfP EWoo LPla LRHS LSou NBro NHol NRHS NSti SPhx SPoG SRGP WBrk WChS WCru WFar WFib WPnP
§	- 'Swish Purple'	EHyd EPPr NLar WCru WPnP
	- 'Tony's Talisman'	EBee MAvo
	- 'Whiteleaf'	CDor CElw CFis CMac CMea EHyd EPPr GBin LRHS NChi NRHS SBut SRGP WCru WFar WHal
	- 'Wreighburn House White'	EBee EPPr MAvo
	'Nora Bremner'	EBee
	'Nunwood Purple'	EBee EPPr MAvo
	'Old Rose'	EHyd LRHS NRHS WCru
	onaei f. ***yezoense*** **new**	GGro
	oreganum	EBee
§	***orientalitibeticum***	CExl CSpe EBee EHyd GKev MBow MCot MMuc NBid NRya SBrt SEND SMad WCot
	'Orion' ♀H7	Widely available
	'Orkney Blue'	CElw EPPr NChi WCru
	ORKNEY CHERRY ('Bremerry'[PBR])	CMac CTsd EMor EPfP GJos GPSL LCro LHGe LOPS LRHS MBel MNrw SCob SEdd SGBe SHeu SRkn SRms WCra WNPC
	'Orkney Flame'	EBee EPPr NChi
	'Orkney Pink'	EBou ECtt EHyd EPfP WCra
	× ***oxonianum***	EGrI GQue
	- 'A.T. Johnson' ♀H7	Widely available
	- 'Alice'	SRGP
	- 'Ankum's White'	EBee EPPr EWes
	- 'Beholder's Eye' ♀H7	EPPr GWyn MMuc NLar WPnP
	- 'Breckland Sunset'	EBee EPPr NLar SRGP
	- 'Bressingham's Delight'	CRos EBlo EHyd EPfP LRHS NRHS SRGP
I	- 'Cally Seedling'	EWes
	- 'Cam Beauty'	WHoo
	- 'Chocolate Strawberry'	EBee EPPr
§	- 'Claridge Druce'	CMac CTri ECha ELan EPfP GKin GMaP LHGe LPot MBow MRav NBir NGdn NGrd NLar NRHS SPer SRms WCra WFar WWtn XLum
	- 'Cream Chocolate'	EPPr
	- 'David Rowlinson'	CDor EPPr
	- 'Dawn Time'	CDor
	- 'Ella'	CWGN
	- 'Elworthy Misty'	CElw CFis EPPr SRGP
	- 'Frank Lawley'	NBid NChi WFar
§	- 'Fran's Star' (d)	WCru
	- 'Frilly Gilly'	EBee
	- 'Glynis'	SRGP
	- 'Hexham Pink'	EBee EWes
	- 'Hexham White'	EBee EPPr
	- 'Hollywood'	EPPr NLar NPer SAko SRms WCra WFar
	- 'Iced Green Tea'	EBee
	- 'Irene Hatwell'	EPPr
	- 'Julie Brennan'	EBee EHyd
	- 'Kate Moss'	EWes NSti
	- 'Katherine Adele'	CKel CKno CMea CSpe ECha ECtt EMor EPPr EPfP EShb EWes GBee LHGe LSou MMuc MPnt NLar NSti SBut SEND SRGP SRms WCAu WFar WFib
§	- 'Kingston'	EPPr
	- 'Königshof'	EPPr EWes
	- 'Kurt's Variegated'	see *G.* × *oxonianum* 'Spring Fling'
	- 'Lace Time'	CBod CKel CRos ECtt EHyd EPPr EPfP GKin LRHS LSRN NRHS SPer SPoG SRGP SRms WCAu WCra WPnP WTyc
	- 'Lady Moore'	EPfP LHGe LRHS SRGP
	- 'Lambrook Gillian'	CFis SRGP
	- 'Lasting Impression'	EPPr
	- 'Laura Skelton'	CElw EBee
	- 'Little John'	EPPr EWes
	- 'Maurice Moka'	EBee ECtt MSpe NLar
	- 'Miriam Rundle'	WCru
	- 'Miss Heidi'	LCro LOPS LRHS
	- 'Music from Big Pink'	EBee EPPr EWes
	- 'Patricia Josephine'	WCAu
	- 'Phantom'	EBee EPPr
	- 'Phoebe Noble'	CRos EBee EHyd EPPr LRHS MNrw NRHS WFib
	- 'Phoebe's Blush'	NChi
§	- 'Prestbury Blush'	CElw
	- 'Raspberry Ice'	EBee EWes
	- 'Rebecca Moss'	CBod ECha ECtt EHyd ELan GAbr GPSL LRHS LSRN NChi NRHS NSti SAko SBut SMrm WCru WFar WFib WGwG
	- 'Red Sceptre'	EBee
	- 'Rose Clair'	CBod EHyd ELan LHGe LRHS NBir NRHS SRGP WCAu WCru
	- 'Rosenlicht'	CBod EBee EHyd GKin MRav WCru XLum
	- 'Rothbury Sarah'	EBee EPPr
	- 'Sandy'	EBee EPPr

- 'Something Special' EBee EPPr
§ - 'Spring Fling' (v) CDor ECtt EWes MSpe NWad WFar
- 'Stillingfleet Keira' EBee EPPr NSti
- 'Summer Surprise' EPPr EWes WCru
- 'Susan' EPPr EWes
- 'Susie White' EPPr WCru
- 'Tess' CBod ECtt LHGe MHol WHoo
§ - f. ***thurstonianum*** CMac ECtt EHed EHyd EPPr EPfP EPri EWoo GAbr GBin GKev LRHS MRav NBid NBir NBro NRHS SBut SPoG SRms WBrk WCot WCru WFar WSHC WSpi XLum
- - 'Armitageae' SRGP
- - 'Breckland Brownie' EBee EPPr EWes SRGP
- - 'Crûg Star' WCru
- - 'David McClintock' EBee EPPr SRGP WFar
- - 'Robin's Ginger Nut' EBee EWes
- - 'Sherwood' CSde EPPr GBee LHGe LPot MSpe NSti WCra WFar
- - 'Southcombe Double' (d) ECtt ELan SRGP SRms WCra WFar
§ - - 'Southcombe Star' EBee EBlo EPPr GAbr NGdn WCru
- - 'Sue Cox' (d) EPPr
- - 'White Stripes' EBee EPPr
- 'Trevor's White' CDor EBee EHyd EPPr LRHS WCAu WCru WPnP
- 'Tyne Salmon' EBee
- 'Venus' **new** EWes
- 'Wageningen' ♀H7 EBee EHyd LRHS NGdn NLar NRHS SEND WCot WCru WGwG
- 'Walter's Gift' CBod ECtt EHyd EMor EPPr EPfP EPri EShb LRHS LSou MAvo MPie MRav NBir NChi NLar NPer NRHS SAko SRGP WChS WCra WCru WFar WHoo WPnP WWtn
§ - 'Wargrave Pink' Widely available
- 'Waystrode' EBee SRGP
- 'Westacre White' ECha EPPr EWes
- 'Whiter Shade of Pale' EBee
- 'Winscombe' EPfP NChi
§ ***palmatum*** ♀H4 Widely available
palustre EBee EPPr EPfP GLog LHGe LRHS MMuc MNrw NLar SBut WCot WCra
'Pastel Clouds' GWyn WFar
PATRICIA ('Brempat') ♀H7 Widely available
peloponnesiacum EWes MNrw NLar NWad
phaeum Widely available
- 'Advendo' EPPr
- 'Album' Widely available
- 'Alec's Pink' EBee NSti SHar WCAu WCra WPnP
- 'All Saints' LEdu
- 'Angelina' EBee EPPr EWoo WBrk
- 'Ann Logan' EBee
- 'Aureum' see *G. phaeum* 'Golden Spring'
- 'Basket of Lavender' EBee
- 'Blauwvoet' EPPr NChi
- 'Blue Shadow' EPPr LEdu LPla
- 'Brown Sugar' EBee
- 'Calligrapher' EPPr NChi
- 'Chocolate Biscuit' EBee EPPr
- 'Chocolate Chip' EPPr
- 'Conny Broe' (v) CDor EShb WSHC
- 'Dark Angel' EBee
- 'Dark Dream' EBee NGrd
- 'David Bromley' NChi WCru
- 'David Martin' EPPr
- 'Enid' EPPr
- 'Garage Door' EBee
- 'George Stone' NChi NGrd
- 'Golden Samobor' CElw EPPr WCot
§ - 'Golden Spring' EPPr LHGe NChi NEoE NLar SRGP WFar
- 'Green Ghost' EBee EPPr
- 'Hector's Lavender' EBee
- 'Hexham Halo' EBee
- var. ***hungaricum*** EBee EPPr
- 'James Haunch' CDor EPPr
- 'Jenson's Purple' EBee
- 'Joseph Green' (d) EBee MAvo
- 'Judith's Blue' EBee NChi
- 'Klepper' EPPr GBin LHGe
§ - 'Lady in Mourning' CExl EBee NChi SRms WCra WCru WFar WPnP
- 'Lavender Pinwheel' CDor GPSL LHGe MSpe NEoE SPer WCot
* - 'Lilacina' ECha
- 'Lily Lovell' Widely available
- 'Lisa' (v) CDor CElw ECha EPPr EWoo MAvo MBriF MNrw SPtp WCot WFar WHoo
- 'Little Boy' EPPr NEoE
- var. ***lividum*** EBlo GMaP LRHS MACG MRav SRms WFar WPnP XLum
- - 'Joan Baker' CDor CFis EBee MBriF MNrw MSpe NChi NGdn NSti SDys WCru WFar WFib
- - 'Majus' EBee EHyd ELan EMor EPPr EPfP LRHS NRHS WFar
- 'Lustige Witwe' (v) WCot
- 'Margaret Wilson' (v) CElw CWGN EMor EShb EWes LEdu LHGe MSpe NBir NEoE NGdn NLar NSti WCot WFar WSHC
- 'Mierhausen' CElw EBee EPPr EWoo
- 'Misty Samobor' CKel ECha
- 'Mojito' (v) ECha WCot
- 'Moorland Dylan' WFar
- 'Mottisfont Rose' CDor CElw SGro
- 'Mourning Widow' see *G. phaeum* 'Lady in Mourning'
- 'Mrs Charles Perrin' CFis
- 'Night Time' EBee EPPr
- 'Nightshade' EBee EPPr
- 'Our Pat' ♀H7 EBee EPPr NGrd WCot
- var. ***phaeum*** 'Langthorns Blue' CRos EBee EBlo EHyd ELan EPPr EPfP LEdu LRHS MNrw NRHS SWvt
- - 'Samobor' Widely available
- 'Phantom of the Opera' (v) CElw EBee EPPr
- 'Pink Palava' LEdu
I - 'Ploeger de Bilt' EBee
- 'Purple Moon' EPPr
- 'Rachel's Rhapsody' EBee EPPr MSpe
- 'Raven' CBod CDor ECtt EMor EPPr EWoo LHGe LRHS MACG MBel MNHC NChi NGrd NLar SCob SPer WCAu WCra WFar
- 'Ray of Light' EPPr
- 'Rise Top Lilac' EBee
- 'Robin's Angel Eyes' EBee ECha
- 'Rose Air' WFar
- 'Rose Madder' CCBP CDor CElw CMea LEdu MBriF MNrw NChi NLar SPhx WCru
- 'Rothbury Ruby' EBee EPPr
- 'Saturn' EPPr
- 'Séricourt' MAvo MSpe WCot WFib
- 'Shadowlight' ECtt EPPr NEoE NLar
- 'Springtime' PBR CDor EBee EMor GPSL LHGe MSpe NGdn NLar WCAu WCra WFib
- 'Stillingfleet Ghost' EBee LEdu MBriF MNrw MSpe NChi NSti
- 'Taff's Jester' (v) NHol WCot
- 'Tyne Mist' EBee EPPr
§ - 'Variegatum' (v) CMac EBee ELan GMaP MSpe NBir WFar WHer

- 'Walküre'	EMor EPPr EWes EWoo LHGe MBriF MSpe NChi NGrd NLar WCra
- 'Waterer's Blue'	CDor ECha
'Philippe Vapelle'	Widely available
'Pink Delight'	CElw MAvo SGro WMal
'Pink Penny'	CBct CBod CDor CWCL ECtt EPfP LHGe LPla LRHS LSRN MHol MNrw NLar NSti SCob SCoo SGBe SPoG SRms WCAu WCav WCra WFar WNPC WPnP
'Pink Petticoats' **new**	NCou
§ ***platyanthum***	EPPr GGro MNrw WCru
- 'Ankum'	EBee
- var. ***reinii***	WCru
- 'Russian Giant'	EPPr
platypetalum misapplied	see *G.* × *magnificum*
platypetalum Franch.	see *G. sinense*
§ ***platypetalum*** Fisch. & C.A. Mey.	EHyd EPPr LRHS NBir NRHS WCru XLum
- 'Dark Side of the Moon'	EBee EPPr MAvo
- 'Genyell'	EBee EPPr NChi
- 'Turco'	EBee EPPr EPfP NLar WCAu WCra
§ ***pogonanthum***	GLog NBir
- BO 16-049 **new**	GGro
polyanthes	EWes GGro NChi
pratense	CCBP CHab CMac EPPr EWoo GJos GMaP MBow MHer MNHC NAts NMir SCob SPer SPlb SPoG SRms WCot WCra WFar WSFF WShi XLum
- 'Akaton'	NLar
- 'Algera Double'	CBod ECtt ELan EPfP IPot LRHS MAvo SEdd WCAu WCot
- 'Bittersweet'	EPPr
- 'Black 'n' White'	ELan LRHS MAsh SHeu
- 'Blue Lagoon'	EPPr WCra
* - 'Blue Skies'	WFar
- 'Blue Sky Thinking'	EBee
- 'Catforth Cadenza' (v)	MAvo
- 'Cloud Nine' (d)	CWCL CWGN GBin MBel WPnP WTyc
- 'Cluden Sapphire'	EBee EPPr LHGe NHol WCAu WCra WCru
- 'Delft Blue'	CBod WWtn
- 'Delft Blue Butterfly'	WCra
§ - 'Double Jewel' (d)	CWGN EPfP NBir NLar SMrm WBor WFar
- 'Else Lacey' (d)	CElw EBee NSti WCot
- 'Flore Pleno'	see *G. pratense* 'Plenum Violaceum'
- 'Hexham Spook'	EBee
I - 'Himalayanum'	NLar
- 'Hocus Pocus'	CRos CWGN EHyd ELan EWoo LRHS MBNS MNrw NBro NLar NRHS NSti SCob SGBe WCra WFar
- 'Hoo House'	WHoo
- 'Ilja'	EPPr MNrw
- 'Janet's Special'	WHoo
- 'Juliana' (d) **new**	NGrd
- 'Marshmallow'	CDor EBee ECtt EPPr EPfP GPSL LPla MBriF NLar NSti SEdd SPoG WCAu WCot WCra WMal
- 'Milou'	NLar WCra
- 'Moondance'	CBor
- 'Mrs Kendall Clark' ♀H7	Widely available
- 'Painter's Palette' (v)	MACG
- 'Pink Splash'	WFar
- 'Plenum Caeruleum' (d)	CTtf MRav NBid NChi WSHC
§ - 'Plenum Violaceum' (d) ♀H7	CMiW CTri CWCL ECtt EHyd ELan GMaP LRHS MRav NBir NChi NRHS NSti SGbt SRms SWvt WCru WFar WPnP WSHC
- 'Pope's Purple'	see *G. pratense* (Victor Reiter Group) BLACK BEAUTY
- var. ***pratense*** f. ***albiflorum***	EHyd EPPr EWoo GMaP LRHS MNrw NBid SDix SGbt SPer WCra WFar WSpi
- - - 'Galactic'	EAJP ECtt GPSL LRHS LSun MBriF NBir NLar SEdd SPoG WCot WCru WFib WPnP
- - - 'Laura'PBR (d)	CExl EBee ECtt EPfP EWes LHGe LSRN MBel MHol NGdn NLar NSti WCra WFar WPnP WTyc
- - - 'Plenum Album' (d)	CBod EBee ECtt EHed ELan EMor EPPr EWes GWyn LRHS MNrw MRav NGdn NLar SGbt SRms SWvt WCot WFar WGwG WSpi
- - - 'Silver Queen'	EBee ECtt EHyd EPPr GPSL LRHS NBir NRHS SPoG WGwG WPnP
- 'Purple Ghost'	CAbb CBcs CWCL CWGN EHed EHyd EPfP GPSL LRHS LSou MBel MMrt NEoE NLar NRHS NSti SCob SMrm SPoG WCra WFar WSpi
- 'Rectum Album'	see *G. clarkei* 'Kashmir White'
- 'Robin's Grey Beard'	EBee EPPr
§ - 'Rose Queen'	NBir SGbt WCru
- 'Roseum'	see *G. pratense* 'Rose Queen'
- 'Southease Celestial'	SMHy WGoo
- 'Splish-splash'	see *G. pratense* 'Striatum'
- 'Stanton Mill'	NBid
- var. ***stewartianum***	MRav
- - 'Elizabeth Yeo'	ECtt EHyd EPPr WCru
- - 'Raina'	EPPr
§ - 'Striatum'	Widely available
- variegated, white-flowered (v)	WCot
§ - (Victor Reiter Group) BLACK BEAUTY ('Nodbeauty'PBR)	CExl CPla CWGN EBee EPfP EWes LBuc LRHS MAvo MGos MPnt NHpl NLar SGBe SPoG SRkn WCra WFar WSpi
- - 'Kaya'	CBod ECtt LHGe NLar WCot WCra
- - 'Midnight Blues'	CWGN
- - 'Midnight Clouds'	CWGN EBee EPfP WFar
- - MIDNIGHT GHOST ('Midnightlyona'PBR)	EPfP MAsh NLar WSpi
- - 'Midnight Reiter'	CExl CWGN EBee EGrI EHed ELan EPfP GPSL GWyn LRHS MACG MBel MBow NBro NChi NHpl NLar NQui SBls SCob SDys SWvt WCAu WCra WFar
- - 'New Dimension'	NLar WFib WSpi
- - 'Purple Heron'	NRHS
- - 'Purple-haze'	GWyn NLar WFar
§ - - 'Victor Reiter'	CDor CSpe EPPr LEdu NBir NChi NHpl WCot WCra
- 'Wisley Blue'	EPPr WHal
- 'Yorkshire Queen'	NGdn NSti WCru
'Prelude'	CDor CElw EBee ELon EPPr LPla NBir NEoE NLar SHar WCAu WFib WMal
procurrens	CTri GAbr WBrk WCru
§ ***psilostemon*** ♀H7	Widely available
- 'Bressingham Flair'	CTri EBlo ECtt EHyd LHGe LRHS MRav NBid NChi NLar SRms WCra WCru WFar
- 'Catherine Deneuve'PBR	CBod CWGN EBee EPfP EWTr EWes GPSL ILea NLar NSti WCAu WCra
- 'Coton Goliath'	EBee EPPr EWes
- 'Jason Bloom'	CRos EBlo EHyd EPPr LRHS NRHS NLar
- 'Madelon'	NLar
- 'Rosefinch'	EBee EPPr
- 'Snowfinch' **new**	CDor
pulchrum	CDor EWes GWyn
punctatum hort.	see *G.* × *monacense* var. *monacense* 'Muldoon'

- 'Variegatum'	see *G. phaeum* 'Variegatum'
'Purple Rain'	EBee EPPr NChi WCra
pylzowianum	NBid NRya
pyrenaicum	GAbr MBow NSti
- f. ***albiflorum***	GAbr MNrw NBir SPhx SRGP WBrk WCot WFar
- 'Barney Brighteye'	SRGP
- 'Bill Wallis'	CSpe EHyd ELan EPPr EPfP EWoo GQue LRHS LSRN LSun MBrN MBriF MMuc MRav NBir NDov NHpl NPer NRHS SBut SEND SPhx SPtp SWvt WCFE WCot WCra WFar WHoo WSpi
- 'Isparta'	EPPr MNrw SHar SPhx SRGP WBrk WGoo
- 'Summer Sky'	SRGP SWvt
- 'Summer Snow'	GPSL GWyn WFar
'Rainbow'PBR	MBNS WCra
Rambling Robin Group	ECre EWes
* - 'Silver Shadow'	SPhx
rectum	EPPr NLar WCru
- 'Album'	see *G. clarkei* 'Kashmir White'
'Red Admiral'	Widely available
'Red Propellers'	CElw CPla
reflexum	EHyd
- 'Katara Pass'	NChi
refractoides	GGro WCot
refractum	CExl
regelii	EPfP GWyn WCru
renardii ♀H6	Widely available
- 'Beldo'	MAvo
- 'Tcschelda'	ECha ECtt EPPr LRHS NBir NLar SRms WCra WFar
- 'Zetterlund'	CBod EBee EHyd EPPr EPfP EPri LRHS NQui NSti WFar
§ ***reuteri***	SAng SChr WCru WPnP
'Richard Nutt'	EBee
richardsonii	CBod EBee EHyd EWoo GKev LRHS MNrw NBir NRHS NWad SPoG WCra WCru WGwG
- white-flowered	NChi
× ***riversleaianum*** 'Russell Prichard' ♀H4	Widely available
§ ***rivulare***	GLog NLar
robertianum	ENfk EPPr SPhx SRms WSFF
§ - 'Album'	EPPr SHar SPhx SRms WHer
- f. ***bernettii***	see *G. robertianum* 'Album'
- 'Celtic White'	EPPr MMuc
'Robin's Black Heart'	EBee
robustum	EPri GLog NBir SBut SPlb WGoo WKif
'Rosetta'PBR	CBod MSCN WCAu
'Rosie Crûg'	SWvt
Rosie's *sanguineum* hybrid **new**	LPar
'Rothbury Red'	EBee NChi
§ ROZANNE ('Gerwat'PBR) ♀H7	Widely available
rubescens	see *G. yeoi*
rubifolium	WCru
SABANI BLUE ('Bremigo'PBR)	CMac CWGN EBee ECtt EWes EWoo LCro LOPS MHol NLar NSti SMHy SPer WCot WCra WNPC WSHC WSpi
'Salome'	CBcs CBod CDor EBee ECtt GLog GWyn LHGe LRHS NBir NLar NSti SRms SWvt WCot WCra WGwG WKif
'Sandrine'PBR	CSpe CWGN LRHS MBriF MNrw NSti SPoG SRms WCot WCra WPnP
sanguineum	Widely available
- ALAN BLOOM ('Bloger')	EBee EHyd LRHS NLar NRHS WCra WFib
- 'Album' ♀H7	Widely available
- 'Alpenglow'	EBee ELon EPPr WBrk
- 'Ankum's Pride' ♀H7	CDor EHyd EPPr EPfP LHGe LRHS LSou MBel MBros NChi NGdn NLar NRHS NSti SGro SRGP WBrk WCra WCru WFib WPnP XSen
- 'Apfelblüte'	CCBP ELon EPPr LHGe MCot NLar WCAu WCra
- 'Aviemore' ♀H7	EPPr GBin NLar
- 'Barnsley'	EPPr NBro
- 'Belle of Herterton'	EPPr MAvo NChi NEoE WBrk WCru
- 'Bloody Graham'	EHyd EPPr LRHS SPhx WBrk
- 'Canon Miles'	ECtt EPPr IPot LHGe NLar SRms WHoo WSpi
- 'Catforth Carnival'	EPPr
- 'Cedric Morris'	CElw ECha ELon EPPr MAvo MBel NLar SGro WBrk WCra WCru WPnP
- 'Compactum'	EPPr WCra XLum
- dark purple-flowered	SSut
- dwarf	WAbe
- 'Elsbeth'	CElw CRos EBee ECha ECtt EHyd ELan ELon EPPr EPfP EWes GBin LRHS LSou NGdn NLar NRHS NSti SMrm SPoG WBrk WCru WFar WFib WHal WPnP XLum XSen
- 'Feu d'Automne'	EBee ELon EPPr NLar WBrk WCra
- 'Fran's Star'	see *G.* × *oxonianum* 'Fran's Star'
- 'Glenluce'	CDor ECtt EHyd ELon EPPr EPfP EShb LHGe LRHS MAsh MRav NChi NDov NGrd NLar NRHS NWad SPoG SRms WBrk WCra WFar WHal WPnP
- 'Hampshire Purple'	see *G. sanguineum* 'New Hampshire Purple'
- 'Hannelore'	EBee
- 'Holden'	ELon EPPr WBrk
- 'Inverness'	EBee EPPr WCra XLum
- 'Joanna'	ELon EPPr MAvo WBrk
- 'John Elsley'	EBee ECtt EHyd EPPr GPSL LRHS LSou NBro NEoE NGdn NRHS NSti WCra WPnP
- 'John Innes'	EPPr
- 'Jubilee Pink'	WCru
- 'Kristin Jacob'	EPPr
- var. ***lancastrense***	see *G. sanguineum* var. *striatum*
§ - 'Little Bead' ♀H7	EPPr NHpl NWad WBrk XLum
- 'Max Frei'	Widely available
- 'Nanum'	see *G. sanguineum* 'Little Bead'
§ - 'New Hampshire Purple'	EBee ECtt EHyd ELon EPPr EWTr GAbr LHGe LRHS MAvo MBel NBro NDov NLar SRGP SRms WBrk WCra WFib
- 'Nyewood'	EBee ECtt EHyd EPPr LRHS SEND WBrk WCra WCru WFib
- 'Pink Pouffe'	CBct CBod CWGN EBee ECtt EHyd ELon GPSL LHGe LRHS NCou NLar NRHS SCob SCoo SHeu WCra
- 'Pink Summer'	EBee EWTr SGBe WCra
- 'Prado'	XLum
- var. ***prostratum*** (Cav.) Pers.	see *G. sanguineum* var. *striatum*
- 'Purple Flame'	see *G. sanguineum* 'New Hampshire Purple'
- 'Red Robin'	EBee EPPr
§ - 'Rod Leeds'	EBee ELon
- 'Sandra'	SRGP
§ - 'Shepherd's Delight'	ECtt EPPr
- 'Shepherd's Warning' misapplied	see *G. sanguineum* 'Shepherd's Delight'
- 'Shepherd's Warning' ♀H7	CMea CTri ECtt IPot MMuc MRav NBir NLar SEND WCru WFib WHoo WIce

- 'Shooting Star'	EPPr IPot NLar
- 'South Nutfield'	CElw NChi
§ - var. ***striatum*** ♀H7	Widely available
- - deep pink-flowered	CSBt MSwo SWvt
- - 'Mottisfont'	SGro
- - 'Reginald Farrer'	WCru
- - 'Splendens' ♀H7	CRos EHyd EPPr LRHS NBid NChi NRHS SAko WCru
- (Vision Series) 'Vision Light Pink'	CBod EPPr MHol WBor WFar
- - 'Vision Violet'	CBod CSpe EBee EBou LRHS MAvo NGrd SRms SWvt WBrk WCra WFar WPnP
'Sanne'	CBod EWes LRHS LSou SEdd STPC WCot WCra WFar WFib
saxatile	EPPr
'Scapa Flow'	EPPr GAbr MAvo NChi WSHC
schlechteri	EWes MMuc SEND WBrk WMal
'Sea Pink'	EBou
'Sea Spray'	CTri
sessiliflorum subsp. ***novae-zelandiae***	GAbr
I - - 'Nigricans'	ECha EPfP GAbr LPot SCob WFar
§ - - 'Porters Pass'	EWes NHpl SPlb WFar
- - red-leaved	see *G. sessiliflorum* subsp. *novae-zelandiae* 'Porters Pass'
'Sheilah Hannay'	SHar
shikokianum	GArf GLog GWyn NLar WPnP
- var. ***kaimontanum***	WCru
- var. ***quelpaertense***	CFis EBee MAvo
- - 'Crûg's Cloak'	WCru
'Shocking Blue'	NLar WFib
'Shouting Star'	see *G.* 'Kanahitobanawa'
'Simonside'	EBee EPPr
§ ***sinense***	CExl EHyd GGro LSou XLum
'Sirak' ♀H7	Widely available
soboliferum	CFis CPla NBir NDov NLar WCru WFar
- Cally strain	EBee EPPr LPla WHoo
- var. ***kiusianum***	CElw
- 'Rothbury Star'	EBee
- 'Starman'	EWoo NLar WCra WSHC WSpi
'Solitaire'	EBee MAvo WCot
'Southcombe Star'	see *G.* × *oxonianum* f. *thurstonianum* 'Southcombe Star'
'Spinners'	CElw CMac EBee ECtt EHyd EPPr GMaP LHGe LRHS MAvo MRav NBid NBir NGdn NLar NRHS NSti SPer WCru WFar WFib
stapfianum var. ***roseum***	see *G. orientalitibeticum*
'Stephanie'	CCBP CElw EHyd EPPr EWes LHGe LPla LRHS LSRN MBNS MNrw MRav MSpe NChi NGdn NLar NRHS NSti WBor WCAu WCra WPnP WSHC
'Storm Chaser'	EBee IPot LRHS MMrt NSti
subcaulescens ♀H4	CMea CWCL EBee EHyd ELan EPfP LRHS LSRN NBid NLar NRHS NRya SBut SPhx SRms SWvt WAbe WCFE WCav WFar WIce
- 'Giuseppii' ♀H5	CExl CRos ECtt EGrI EHyd ELon EPfP EPot EWoo GAbr LHGe LRHS LSou NBir NDov NRHS SWvt WCra WGwG WHoo WKif WSpi
- 'Splendens' ♀H5	CTri ECtt EHyd LRHS MHer NRHS NSla SRms WCra WFar
'Sue Crûg'	CEme EBee ECtt EHyd ELan LRHS NChi NRHS WCra WCru
'Sue's Sister'	WCru
'Summer Cloud'	EPPr
SUMMER SKIES ('Gernic'PBR) (d)	CDor CExl CMiW CTtf CWCL EBee ECtt EHyd ELan EMor EPfP GAbr LCro LHGe LOPS LRHS MNrw MRav NBro NCou NLar NSti SPer SRkn SWvt WCot WCra WSHC WSpi
suzukii B&SWJ 016	CExl
- NMWJ 14518	WCru
'Sweet Heidy'PBR	CBod CDor EBee ECtt EPfP EWTr LPla MHol MNrw MPnt NLar NSti SGBe WBor WCAu WCra WFar WPnP
sylvaticum	MBow NGdn NGrd NMir SBut WFar WShi
- f. ***albiflorum***	NSti WCru
- - 'Cyril's Superb White'	EBee EPPr
- 'Album' ♀H7	Widely available
- 'Amanda'	EBee
- 'Amy Doncaster'	CBod CDor CElw CExl EBee ECtt EHyd ELan EPPr LRHS MRav NBir NLar NRHS NSti SPer WCot WCra WCru WFar WFib WHoo WPnP
- 'Angulatum'	CElw EPPr NChi
- 'Birch Lilac'	CElw EBee EPPr EPri LHGe NLar WCra WFib
- 'Bridget Lion'	WCra
- 'Coquetdale Lilac'	CDor EBee EPPr
- 'Greek Fire'	EBee MAvo NSti
- 'Ice Blue'	EPPr EWTr NChi WCAu
- 'Immaculée'	EPPr MRav
- 'Jonah P'	EBee
- 'Kanzlersgrund'	CElw EPPr
- 'Lilac Eyes'	EBee
- 'Lilac Time'	EPPr
- 'Master Charles Wilson'	EBee
- 'Master Niall Lawson'	EBee WFar
- 'Mayflower' ♀H7	Widely available
- 'Miss Connie Wilson'	EBee
- f. ***roseum***	NLar
- - 'Baker's Pink'	EPPr MNrw MRav NBir WCAu WCru WFar WPnP
- 'Silva'	MRav WCru
- subsp. ***sylvaticum*** var. ***wanneri***	WCru
§ 'Tanya Rendall'PBR	ECtt ELan NLar SRGP SRms WCot WCra WFar WFib WPnP
'Terre Franche'	EPPr LHGe MAvo NLar SPhx WCAu WCra
§ ***thunbergii***	EWes SRGP WFar XLum
- 'Jester's Jacket' (v)	MNrw WFar
- pink-flowered	EPPr
- white-flowered	EPPr
thurstonianum	see *G.* × *oxonianum* f. *thurstonianum*
'Tinpenny Mauve'	MAvo MNrw
'Tiny Monster'	Widely available
'Tod the Whippet'	NChi
transbaicalicum	EPPr XLum
traversii var. ***elegans***	EHyd LRHS NRHS
tuberosum	CCBP CDor CElw ECha MBow MRav NBir NGdn NQui SPhx WCra WFar
- subsp. ***linearifolium***	EPPr
- 'Richard Hobbs'	EPPr
- 'Rosie's Mauve'	EPPr MAvo
'Ushguli Grijs'	see *G. ibericum* Cav. 'Ushguli Grijs'
'Vectis'	CElw
'Verguld Saffier'	see *G.* BLUE SUNRISE
versicolor	CEme CMea EBee EPPr EPfP GAbr GPSL LRHS MHer NLar SRms WCAu WCra WFar WPnP
- 'Kingston'	see *G.* × *oxonianum* 'Kingston'
§ - 'Snow White'	EPPr SBut WCru WFib
- 'White Lady'	see *G. versicolor* 'Snow White'
'Victor Reiter'	see *G. pratense* (Victor Reiter Group) 'Victor Reiter'

violareum	see *Pelargonium* 'Splendide'
viscosissimum	WFib
wallichianum	CFis EBee GKev NBir NChi NSti
- HPA 1373 **new**	GGro
§ - 'Buxton's Variety'	Widely available
- 'Crystal Lake'PBR	CWGN EBee ECtt EPfP EWoo LHGe MBNS MHol MNrw NBir NDov NGdn NSti SCob WCAu WCra WFar WHil WPnP
- 'Happy Buxton' **new**	MHol SMrm
- HAVANA BLUES ('Noorthava'PBR)	EBee ECha ECtt EPfP ILea IPot LCro LHGe LOPS LRHS MBel NLar NSti SCob SDix SEdd WCot WCra WFar
- 'Pink Buxton'	EWes NLar
- pink-flowered	WCru
- 'Rise and Shine'PBR	CWGN EBee ECtt ELan EWTr LCro LOPS LRHS MBriF NSti SEdd SRms WCAu WCot WCra
- 'Rosie'	SRGP
- 'Syabru'	EBlo MNrw
- 'Sylvia's Surprise'PBR	EBee ECtt EHyd LRHS NRHS SCob WCAu WCra
'Wednesday's Child'	WFar
'White Doves'	MAvo NDov
wilfordii misapplied	see *G. thunbergii*
Wisley hybrid	see *G.* 'Khan'
wlassovianum	Widely available
- from Crûg Farm	NLar WCra
- 'Blue Star'	MRav NEoE SBut SRGP WCra WFar
- 'Martyn and Emma'	SRGP
- 'Zeppelin'	LHGe NLar WCra
§ ***yeoi***	NSti WCru
yesoense	GGro NSti WFar
yoshinoi misapplied	see *G. thunbergii*
yunnanense misapplied	see *G. pogonanthum*

Gerbera (*Asteraceae*)

(Garvinea Sweet Series) GARVINEA SWEET DREAMS ('Gardreams'PBR)	SPad
- GARVINEA SWEET GLOW ('Garglow'PBR)	LRHS NRHS SPad SPeP
- GARVINEA SWEET HEART ('Garheart') **new**	LRHS
- GARVINEA SWEET HONEY ('Garhoney')	SGBe SPeP
- GARVINEA SWEET LOVE ('Garswlove') **new**	LRHS
- GARVINEA SWEET MEMORIES ('Garsweetmemo')	LRHS
- GARVINEA SWEET SMILE ('Garsmile') **new**	LRHS SGBe
- GARVINEA SWEET SUNSET	see *G.* (Garvinea Sweet Series) 'Sweet Sunset'
- GARVINEA SWEET SURPRISE ('Garsurprise') **new**	LRHS SPeP
§ - 'Sweet Sunset' **new**	LRHS

Gerrardanthus (*Cucurbitaceae*)

macrorhizus	NCft

Gesneria (*Gesneriaceae*)

cardinalis	see *Sinningia cardinalis*

Geum ✿ (*Rosaceae*)

'Abendsonne'	CElw MNrw MRav MSpe NEoE
'Alabama Slammer' (Cocktails Series)	Widely available
alpinum	see *G. montanum*
'Apricot Beauty'	CWCL
'Apricot Crush'	MNrw
'Apricot Delight'	CTtf NEoE NWad
'Apricot Pearl' (Censation Series) (d)	CBod CWGN ECtt EWTr MHol
'Baked Beans'	NEoE
'Banana Daiquiri' (Cocktails Series)	CRos CWCL EBee ECtt ECul EGrI EHyd ELan EPfP LRHS MBriF MHost NRHS SCob SHeu SPalm WFar
'Beech House Apricot'	CDor CWCL ECtt EHyd EWes ILea LRHS MAvo MHost MNrw MPie MRav NBro NEoE NHol NLar NWad WGrn
'Beech's Double'	EWes MAvo
'Bell Bank'	Widely available
'Birkhead's Creamy Lemon'	EBee MHCG NBir
'Blazing Sunset' (d)	Widely available
'Blood Orange'	CTtf ECtt EHyd EPPr EPfP GKev LRHS MAvo MBriF MCot MHost NEoE NRHS SPoG WFar
'Borisii'	Widely available
'Bremner's Nectarine'	CElw EPPr MNrw NChi NEoE SHar
'Broomrigg Beauty'	NEoE
'Brown Sugar'	NEoE
bulgaricum	EBee NBir NLar NRya WFar XLum
'Can-can' (d)	CDor CElw CMea MACG MAvo MHost WHoo
'Cantamos'	NEoE
capense	NLar SPlb
'Centurion'	NEoE
chiloense 'Red Dragon'	SBut SWvt
'Chipchase'	CElw NChi NWad
coccineum ambig.	GArf GKev
coccineum Sibth. & Sm.	GLog WHoo
- 'Ann'	EPri
- 'Cooky'	EHyd GPSL LPot LRHS MBriF NBro NGrd NLar NRHS SRms SWvt WFar
- 'Eos'	CSpe CTtf CWCL EBee ECtt ELon EWes LEdu LRHS MBriF MHol MNrw MPnt MRav MSCN MSpe NGdn NLar NSti SHeu SMrm SPoG SRms WGwG
- 'Koi'	CBod EAJP EBee ELon EPfP GBin GPSL GWyn LEdu LRHS LSun MACG MBros MHol MSCN NEoE NGrd SNig STPC WFar
- 'Queen of Orange'	CRos CSBt ECul LRHS MHost NGrd SRms WFar
- 'Werner Arends'	ELon GAbr MAvo MNrw MRav WCot WFar
'Copper Pennies'	CElw NEoE
'Coppertone'	CElw CWCL EGrI ELan EPri LPot MHost MRav NBir NChi WCav
'Coral Pearl' (Censation Series) (d)	LCro LOPS
'Coral Supreme' **new**	MAvo
'Cosmopolitan' (Cocktails Series)	Widely available
'Cotton Candy'	MHost NEoE
'Country Rock'	NEoE
'Country Rock Star'	WFar
'Cream Crackers'	NEoE WBrk
'Cumbrian Candy'	NEoE
'Cumbrian Cheddar'	NEoE
'Cumbrian Cherrypie'	NEoE WFar
'Cumbrian Cherrytart'	NEoE
'Cumbrian Cream'	NEoE
'Custard Tart'	NEoE
'Dark and Stormy' (Cocktails Series)	LRHS MAvo NEoE
'Dawn'	NEoE SMHy

'Deano's Delight'	NEoE
'Diamond White'	EWhm
'Diana'	ELon MNrw NLar
'Dingle Apricot'	ECtt GAbr MNrw MRav NBir
'Dolly North' (d)	CElw CWCL EPPr EWhm GWyn MBel MHol MHost MRav MSpe NBro NGdn SHar WBrk WCAu WHal
'Double Sunrise' (d)	WFar
'East of Eden'	LPot NEoE
'Eden Apricot'	NEoE
'Eden Rising'	NEoE
'Eden Valley Angel'	NChi NEoE WWtn
'El Wano'	NEoE
'Elworthy Amber'	CElw
'Elworthy Coppernob' **new**	CElw
'Emory Quinn'	EPPr EWes LRHS NEoE NSti WHrl
'Fancy Frills'	CElw ECtt MAvo WHoo
'Farmer John Cross'	CElw CTtf EBee ECtt ELon EPPr EPri EShb GBin MBriF MHol NLar WFar WHal WWtn
'Feuermeer'	CElw NLar
'Fire Opal' (d) ♀H7	CElw CWCL EAJP GWyn MAvo MHost MNrw NBir
'Fire Storm'PBR	CBod CMea CWGN EBee ECtt EHyd EPfP GAbr GBin LRHS LSun MHol MNrw MPnt MSCN NDov NEoE NGBl NLar SPad SPalm SPoG SRms WCot WFar WGrn WMal WNPC
'Fireball'	CWCL ECtt EShb LRHS MArl MBNS MHost MMuc NLar
'Firefinch'	NEoE
'Flame'	NLar
'Flames of Passion'PBR	Widely available
'Flower of Darkness'	NEoE
'Georgenberg'	CRos ECtt EPfP GMaP LRHS MACG MBel MHer MNrw NBir NFav NGdn NHol NLar NRHS NWad SPer SRms SWvt WCAu WFar
'Gimlet' (Cocktails Series)	CWGN ECtt ELon EMor EPri EShb GBin GPSL LRHS NLar WTyc
'Golden Joy'	CDor CElw MAvo MNrw NEoE WHoo
'Goldfinch'	WFar
'Hannay's'	EBee MHCG MNrw MPie MSpe NEoE SHar SPtp
'Harvest Moon'	NEoE
'Hearts in Amber'	NEoE WFar
'Herterton Lemon'	CElw WCot
'Herterton Primrose'	CCBP CElw CWCL ECtt EPPr LLWG MHost MNrw NBid NSti WFar WHal
'Hilltop Beacon' (d)	CDor CElw CTtf EBee NEoE NLar SGro WFar WGoo WHoo
* ***hybridum luteum***	NSti
× ***intermedium***	GPSL NGdn NLar
- 'Diane'	NChi
- 'Hofrennydd'	NWad
'Jolly Roger'	EBee MHost NEoE NWad
'Karlskaer'	CBod CWCL ECtt EHyd EWes EWoo GQue LPla LRHS MBel MBow MCot MHost MNrw NGdn NLar NRHS WFar WGwG WWtn
'Lady Stratheden' (d) ♀H7	Widely available
'Lemon Delight'	CDor CElw LEdu MAvo WMal
'Lemon Drops'	Widely available
'Lemon Frilled'	CTtf
'Limoncello'	LRHS SHeu
'Lionel Cox'	CWCL ELan GAbr GMaP MBow MHost MRav NBir NBro NChi NGdn NLar SRms WFar
'Lipstick Sunset'	NEoE
'Lisanne'	CElw CWCL EAJP EBee GBin GKev IPot MACG MAvo MHost MNrw NDov NLar SHar SMHy SPtp WCAu WFar
'Little Lottie'	NEoE
'Little Twister'	NEoE
'Maddy Prior'	NEoE
magellanicum	CSpe EWes NLar WMal
'Magic Toybox'	NEoE
'Mai Tai'PBR (Cocktails Series)	Widely available
'Mandarin' (d)	CDor SHar WMal
'Mango'	CBod MBros NDov
'Mango Lassi'	CElw CTtf ECtt EMor EShb GBin MSCN NEoE NLar SHar WCAu
'Marmalade'	CTtf ECtt EHyd EWhm GAbr LLWG LPla LRHS MNrw MRav NFav NLar NRHS SHar SMHy SSut WFar WHrl WKif
'McClure's Magic'	NEoE
§ ***montanum*** ♀H6	CRos EBee EHyd GKev GLog LRHS MMuc NBir NRHS NSla SRms XLum
'Moonlight Serenade'	CBod CWCL EBee ECtt EHyd EPPr EPfP LRHS MHost NEoE NRHS WFar WGwG WWtn
'Moorland Sorbet'	WFar
'Mr Mojo'	NEoE
'Mrs J. Bradshaw' (d) ♀H7	Widely available
'Mrs W. Moore'	CElw CWCL EBee EShb GAbr GQue MNrw MRav NBir NBro NChi NLar NQui
'Nonna' **new**	MAvo WHil
'Nordek'	CElw ECha ECtt GAbr GQue MCot MNrw MRav NGdn SPoG WFar WWtn
'Norwell Lemon Lamp'	MNrw WMal
'Orangeman'	WHal
'Peach Daiquiri' (Cocktails Series)	ECul
pentapetalum	see *Sieversia pentapetala*
'Pink Fluffy' (Censation Series)	IPot MBros MHol
'Pink Frills'	CBod CElw CWCL ECtt EPPr EPri EWTr EWes EWhm GAbr GBin GQue LEdu LLWG MHost MPie MRav NLar SGbt SMHy SMrm SPtp
'Pink Petticoats'	CBod MAvo MBNS SPad WHoo
'Poco'	CRos CWCL EBee ECtt EHyd EPfP EWes EWhm GBin LRHS MAvo MNrw MSpe NEoE NRHS WFar
'Prairie Dancer'	NEoE
'Present'	ECtt NChi
PRETTICOATS PEACH ('Tngeupp') (Petticoats Series) **new**	SPad
'Primrose'	EWhm NBro NEoE NGdn NLar
'Primrose Cottage'	EBee GQue LRHS SCoo
'Prince of Orange' (d)	CElw CRos EHyd GAbr LRHS MNrw MRav NRHS SWvt WFar
'Prinses Juliana'	Widely available
'Proud's Pearl'	NEoE WMal
* ***pseudococcineum***	EHyd
pyrenaicum	GKev
I 'Rearsby Hybrid'	CElw MRav SPlb
'Red Wings' (d)	CWCL EWTr GMaP GWyn ILea LRHS MBel MCot MHost MNrw MRav NBir SHar WGwG
'Rijnstroom'	EPPr MNrw SHar WFar
'Rise and Shine'	NEoE
rivale	CBen CCBP CHab CRos CWat EBou ELan EPfP MBow MCot MHer MHol

MHost MMuc MNHC MWts NAts NBro NGrd NMir NPer NRHS SEND SPlb SRms WCAu WChS WFar WMAq WShi
- 'Album' Widely available
- 'Barbra Lawton' LEdu SHar
- 'Cream Drop' LLWG MCot NChi SHar
- 'Leonard's Variety' Widely available
- 'Marika' EBee GBin
- 'Marmalade' CElw CWCL IPot MBriF MPnt NChi WCav
I - 'Nana' **new** CBor
- pink-flowered **new** EGrI
- 'Snowflake' CDor CElw MAvo MSpe NChi NEoE NLar

'Roger's Ragamuffin' NEoE
'Roger's Rebellion' ECtt NEoE WFar
'Rubin' EBee GBin NDov NSti SGro
'Rusty Young' CBod CWCL EAJP EBee ECtt EPPr EPfP EWes GBee LRHS MBel MHost MNrw NEoE NRHS SGbt WWtn
'Savanna Sunrise' MNrw
'Savanna Sunset' EBee ECtt EHyd EPPr EWes EWoo LRHS MBel MHer MHost NEoE NRHS WHrl
SCARLET TEMPEST ('Macgeu001') CBod CKel CKno CRos CSpe CWCL CWGN EHyd EMor EPfP LBuc LCro LOPS LRHS MAvo MBel MHol MHost MNrw MPri NLar NRHS NSti SCoo SHar SPoG SRkn WNPC WTor XSte
'Sea Breeze' (Cocktails Series) LRHS
'Shannara' (d) CElw NEoE
'Sigiswang' ELon LEdu MNrw MRav WFar
'Snowdrop' MHost NEoE
'Spanish Fly' (Cocktails Series) LRHS LSou NEoE
'Spellbound' NEoE
'Spider Muffin' NEoE
'Stacey Proud' NEoE
'Stacey's Sunrise' CBod ECtt EHyd EPPr EWes GAbr LRHS MBel MHCG MNrw NEoE NLar NRHS SPoG WFar
'Star of Bethlehem' NEoE
'Starker's Magnificum' MAvo WCot
'Stevie Nicks' MBriF NEoE
'Strawberries and Cream' NEoE
'Sundrud Star' NEoE
'Sunkissed Lime'[PBR] CBod ECtt EMor LRHS LSou MHost MPnt NEoE
'Sunrise' (d) CBod EHyd LRHS MHol MHost MSCN NRHS
'Sweet Angel Dar' NEoE
'Sweet Stacey' MHost NEoE
'Tangerine' EPri MRav
'Tangerine Dream' **new** LRHS
'Tequila Sunrise' (Cocktails Series) CBcs CElw CRos CWGN EAJP EBee ECtt EHyd ELan EMor EPPr EPfP EWTr GBin ILea LRHS MHost MNrw MPnt MSCN NEoE NGdn NHpl NRHS SCob SPad SPalm WCAu WNPC
'The Giant Peach' NEoE
'Tinkerbell' NEoE
× ***tirolense*** EBee
'Toast of Cumbria' NEoE
'Toffee Apples' NEoE
'Tosai' CBor LRHS NEoE
'Totally Tangerine'[PBR] Widely available
triflorum CSpe CWCL EWes GEdr GGro LEdu MHer MNrw NDov NGrd SHar SPhx
- SDR 8121 GKev
- var. ***campanulatum*** NEoE
- 'Peace Pipe' MNrw
'Turbango' NEoE
'Turbango Twister' NEoE
'Turnpike Tales' NEoE
'Turnpike Troubadour' NEoE
'Tutti Frutti' MAvo
'Two Tone Pearl' (Censation Series) (d) CWGN NLar
urbanum ENfk NMir WHer
- 'Corinne Tremaine' WHer
'Wet Kiss' (Cocktails Series) LRHS NDov SHeu
'Wyn's Wish' NEoE

Gevuina (*Proteaceae*)

avellana WPGP

Gilia ✿ (*Polemoniaceae*)

achilleifolia SPhx

Gillenia (*Rosaceae*)

stipulata IPot LEdu LRHS MNrw SHar SPhx WPGP
trifoliata ♀H7 Widely available
- 'Pink Profusion' CBod CMiW CSpe CWCL EBee EHed ELan GBin IPot LPla LRHS MBel MNrw NDov NLar SCob WCAu WCot WFar WGrn WHil XSte

Gingidia (*Apiaceae*)

montana WHil

Ginkgo ✿ (*Ginkgoaceae*)

biloba Widely available
- B&SWJ 8753 WCru
- 'Anny's Dwarf' MAsh MBlu
- 'Autumn Gold' (m) ♀H6 CBcs CEnd CMCN ELan MBlu MGos MPkF SLim WMat
- 'Baldii' **new** NLar
- 'Barabits' Fastigiata' LRHS MBlu SMad
- 'Barabits' Nana' CAco MBlu
- 'Beijing Gold' MBlu MPkF NLar SAko SMad
- 'Blagon' LRHS SGol
- 'Buddy' SLim
- 'California Sunset' MBlu SLim
- 'Chase Manhattan' MPkF
- 'Chotek' MBlu SMad
- 'Chris's Dwarf' LRHS NLar
- 'Clica' **new** NLar
- 'Conica' **new** CAco
- 'David' SLim
- 'Eastern Star' (f) CAgr
- 'Eiffel' LPar
- 'Everton Broom' CMac CMen MBlu SLim SRms WHwl
- 'Fabulous Underwear' SLim
- 'Fairmount' (m) MBlu
- 'Fastigiata' (m) CAco CMCN EPfP MBlu
- 'Fastigiata Blagon' CCVT ERom LMaj LRHS
- 'Finger' SLim
- 'Globosa' CAco MBlu SMad
- 'Gnome' LSRN MPkF
- 'Goethe' **new** MBlu
- 'Golden Dragon' MBlu
- 'Golden Globe' MPkF
- 'Gresham' MPkF
- 'Horizontalis' CAco MBlu SGsty
- 'Jade Butterflies' ♀H6 MBlu NLar SLim
- 'Jehosaphat' MBlu
- 'Jerry Vercade' MPkF

- 'King of Dongting' (f)	CAco CAgr MBlu SLim
- 'Lakeview' (m)	CAco MPkF
- 'Landliebe'	MBlu
- 'Lil' Matthew'	SLim
- 'Long March'	CAgr
- 'Magyar'	MBlu
- 'Majestic Butterfly'	NLar
- 'Mariken' 🏆H6	CAco CWGN EHed ELan EPfP LMaj LPar LRHS MGil MPkF NLar SGsty SLim
- 'Mayfield' (m)	CAco MBlu NLar
- 'McFarland'	CAgr
- 'Menhir'[PBR]	CBcs EBee ELan EPfP ILea LRHS MPkF MTrO WCot WHwl WMat
- 'Obelisk'	CAco NLar SGsty SLim
- Ohazuki Group (f)	CAgr
- 'Palo Alto' **new**	CAco
- Pendula Group	CEnd CMCN EBee MBlu MPkF SGol WMat
- 'Princeton Sentry' (m) 🏆H6	ELan EPfP IPap MBlu
- 'Pyramidalis'	CAco
- 'Robbie's Twist'	MPkF NLar SLim
- 'Roswitha' (v) **new**	NLar
- 'San José' **new**	CAco
- 'Santa Cruz'	CAco
- 'Saratoga' (m) 🏆H6	CAco CAgr CBcs CEnd CLnd CMCN EBee EPfP ESwi MBlu MPkF NOrn SLim SRms WMat
- 'Shangri-La' (m)	MBlu
- 'Sinclair'	MPkF
- 'Survivor'	SMad
- 'Talon Variegated' (v)	MBlu
- 'Thelma'	SLim
- 'Tit'	CEnd CMCN EPfP LPar MBlu MPkF SLim WLea
- 'Todd' **new**	MBlu
- 'Tremonia'	CMCN EPfP MBlu MPkF SAko
- 'Troll' 🏆H6	CAco EPfP LRHS MAsh MBlu MGil SCoo SLim SMad SPoG WHwl
- 'Tubifolia'	CMCN ESwi MBlu MPkF NLar SLim SMad WPGP
- 'Umbrella'	SLim
- Variegata Group (v)	MPkF
- - 'Variegata' (v) **new**	CAco
- 'W.B.'	MPkF

ginseng see *Panax ginseng*

Gladiolus (*Iridaceae*)

'Adi'	WCot
'Ajax'	WPhe
alatus	NRog
'Alba' (N)	WPhe
'Amanda Mahy' (N)	GKev WMal WPhe
'Antica' (L)	WPhe
'Astarte' (L)	WPhe
'Atom' (S/P)	CAvo CBro GKev SDeJ WPhe
aurantiacus	WCot
'Avalanche' (B)	SDeJ
'Azurro'	WPhe
'Bach'	WPhe
'Black Jack' (L)	SDeJ
'Black Surprise'	WPhe
'Blue Frost' (L)	SDeJ
'Blue Mountain'	WPhe
'Bocelli' (M)	WPhe
'Bonfire' (G)	WPhe
'Boone'	GBin SMrm
'Brahms' (L)	WPhe
byzantinus	see *G. communis* subsp. *byzantinus*
callianthus	see *G. murielae*
cardinalis	CPrp IBlr WCru
'Careless' (L)	WPhe
carinatus	NRog
carinatus* × *orchidiflorus	WCot
'Carine' (N)	GKev NRog SDeJ WPhe
carmineus	NRog WCot
carneus	CBro EPot GKev NRog SDeJ
'Carolina Primrose'	GBin
'Casablanca'[PBR] **new**	LRHS
caucasicus	GKev
'Charm' (N/Tub)	EShb SDeJ WPhe
'Charming Beauty' (Tub)	NRog SDeJ WPhe
'Charming Lady' (Tub)	GKev NRog WPhe
'Chopin' (L)	WPhe
citrinus	see *G. trichonemifolius*
'Columbine' (P)	SDeJ
× ***colvillei*** 'Galaxian'	GKev WHil
communis	WCot
§ - subsp. ***byzantinus*** 🏆H5	Widely available
'Coral Lace' (L)	SDeJ
'Côte d'Azur' (G)	SDeJ
crassifolius	CPbh
'Cream Perfection' (L)	SDeJ WPhe
cruentus	WCot
§ ***dalenii***	CDor CExl CPbh IBlr
- 'Apricot Delight' (v)	IBlr
- 'Boone'	LPla WCot
- 'Citrone Spectrum' (v)	IBlr
§ - subsp. ***dalenii***	CBor CPbh CPrp IBlr WCot
- - 'Spinners'	IBlr
- 'Guardsman' (v)	IBlr
'Dark Ruby' (*papilio* hybrid)	LEdu WMal
'David Hills' (*papilio* hybrid)	CAvo CBor CBro CDor CMea CPrp CTtf ECha LPla SMHy WCot WHoo WSHC
ecklonii	CPbh CTtf
'Elvira' (N)	GKev WPhe
'Emerald Spring' (S)	WCot
'Espresso'[PBR] (S)	ERCP
'Esta Bonita' (G)	WPhe
'Evergreen'	ERCP
'Far West' (L)	ERCP
'Farandole' (S)	SDeJ
'Fergie' (B) **new**	ERCP
'Fidelio' (L)	SDeJ
'Fiorentina' (L)	ERCP SDeJ
'Flame'	WPhe
flanaganii	CBor CBro CExl CPbh CSpe CTtf EBee EPot EPri GArf GEdr GKev MNrw NHpl NSla SBrt WAbe WMal WPav
'Flevo Bambino' (S)	EPri
'Flevo Cool' (S)	CAvo
'Flevo Vito' (Min)	CAvo
floribundus hort.	NRog
'Fortarosa' (L)	WPhe
× ***gandavensis*** hort.	WCot
garnieri	see *G. dalenii* subsp. *dalenii*
geardii	WCot
grandis	see *G. liliaceus*
'Green Star' (L)	LCro LOPS SDeJ WPhe
'Greyhound' (L)	WPhe
griseus	NRog
'Halley' (N)	GKev NLar NRog WPhe
'Hansnett'	WCot WSHC
'Happy Weekend' (L)	SDeJ
'Haydn' (L)	WPhe
'Himalaya' (L)	WPhe
'Holland Pearl' (B)	SDeJ
huttonii	NRog

huttonii* × *tristis
var. ***concolor*** WCot
illyricus GKev SPlb
imbricatus GKev MHer
'Imperialis' IBlr
'Impressive' (N) GKev NLar NRog SDeJ WPhe
'Indian Summer'PBR (L) ERCP WPhe
'Invitation' SDeJ
§ ***italicus*** CKel EBee GKev
'Jacksonville Gold' (L) SDeJ
'Jester' (L) SDeJ
'Judy'PBR (M) WPhe
'Karaoke' (L) WPhe
'Kazimir' (L) WPhe
'Lakeland'PBR (L) WPhe
'Las Vegas' (P) WPhe
'Lennon' (L) WPhe
§ ***liliaceus*** NRog
'Little Vintage' GKev
'Lucifer'PBR (L) WPhe
'Mademoiselle de Paris' CBro
'Magma' (L) WPhe
'Mantovani' WPhe
'Marina' (P) WMal
'Matanzas' (M) WPhe
'Match Point' (L) SDeJ
meliusculus NRog
'Messina' (M) WPhe
'Mexico' (L) SDeJ
miniatus NRog
'Mirella' (N) CAvo GKev WPhe
'Modena' (M) WPhe
'Mon Amour'PBR (L) LRHS SDeJ WPhe
'Monsieur Piquet' (P) EPri WCot
'Mount Everest' WPhe
§ ***murielae*** ♀H3 CAvo CBod CBro CCBP CMea CRos CTtf EGrI EHyd ERCP EShb GBin GKev GWyn LCro LOPS LRHS MACG MCot MHol NRHS SCoo SDeJ SDir SPer SPlb SRms WCFE WHal
'Mylena' (M) WPhe
natalensis see *G. dalenii*
'Natan' (L) WCot
'Nathalie' (N) CAvo NRog SDeJ WPhe
'Nijmegen' (L) WPhe
'Nova Lux' (L) SDeJ SDir
'Nymph' (N) CAvo GKev LCro LOPS MBow NBir SDeJ WPhe
§ ***oppositiflorus*** CPbh CSpe EBee IBlr LEdu SPlb WSHC
- subsp. ***salmoneus*** see *G. oppositiflorus*
'Orangerie' (L) WPhe
'Oscar' (G) ERCP SDeJ
palustris WAbe
papilio Widely available
- 'Peachy' new CTtf
§ - Purpureoauratus Group CBro SRms WSHC
- yellow-flowered CMea CTtf SMad
'Passos'PBR (S) ERCP
'Peach Blossom' (N) IBlr WCot
'Penny Lane' (M) WPhe
'Pescara' (M) WPhe
'Peter Pears' (L) ERCP SDeJ SDir
Pilbeam hybrids WCot
'Pink Lady' (L) SDeJ
'Plum Tart' (L) LCro LOPS LRHS MBros SDeJ
'Pop Art' SDeJ
'Prima Verde' (L) WPhe
primulinus see *G. dalenii*
'Prins Claus' (N) EShb GKev SDeJ SDir WPhe
priorii NRog
'Priscilla' (L) MBros SDeJ SDir
'Purple Flora' ERCP
'Purple Mate' LCro LOPS
purple-striped WHil
purpureoauratus see *G. papilio* Purpureoauratus Group
'Raspberry Sorbet' (S) WPhe
'Rigoletto' (L) WPhe
'Robinetta' (*recurvus* hybrid) ♀H3 GArf GKev LCro LOPS MBow SDeJ WPhe
'Rosalina' (L) WPhe
'Rosiebee Red'PBR (G) new LRHS
'Rotary'PBR (L) WPhe
'Roussel' WPhe
'Ruby' (*papilio* hybrid) Widely available
'Salmon Star' (L) WPhe
'San Siro'PBR (M) WPhe
saundersii EBee LEdu
scullyi NRog
segetum see *G. italicus*
'Sogno' (M) WPhe
'Sourire' (S) SDeJ
'Spic and Span' (L) SDeJ
splendens NRog
'Sugar Plum' ERCP
'Thalia' WPhe
'That's Love' (L) SDeJ
'The Bride' CAvo CBro EBee EWoo GBin GWyn ITim LCro LOPS MPie NLar SDeJ SDir
§ ***trichonemifolius*** GKev
tristis CAvo CBor CBro CElw CSpe ELon GKev MHer SMHy WAbe
- var. ***concolor*** CPbh CPrp WCot
- var. ***tristis*** new NRog
undulatus NRog WCot
'Vasto' (M) WPhe
'Venezia' (M) WPhe
venustus CPbh NRog
'Vesuvio' (L) WPhe
virescens NRog
'Vivaldi' (L) WPhe
'Volcano' (N) WPhe
'Wagner' (L) WPhe
watermeyeri CPbh WHil
watsonius NRog
'White Prosperity' (L) ERCP LCro LOPS
'Wine and Roses' (L) SDir
woodii WCot
'Yellow Star' (L) WPhe
'Ziporra' (S) EPri
'Zizanie' (L) SDeJ

Glandularia (*Verbenaceae*)

'Abbeville' WCot WMal
§ (Aztec Series) AZTEC PEARL ('Balazpearl'PBR) SCoo
- AZTEC RED ('Balazred') SCoo
- AZTEC SILVER MAGIC ('Balazsilma'PBR) ♀H2 MBros SCoo
BABYLON PINK ('Morena') (Babylon Series) MTrO
'Boughton House' SBut
§ 'Claret' ♀H3 CBod CMac CRos EBee ECtt EHyd ELan EPfP LCro LOPS LRHS NRHS SBut SCoo SPhx SPoG
corymbosa CBod ECha EPPr LRHS MACG SPer SPhx WSHC
- 'Gravetye' LPot
'Diamond Merci' WMal

'Edith Eddleman'	CMac CRos EHyd EPfP LRHS NRHS SPoG
elegans	NDov
ENCHANTMENT RED (Enchantment Series) **new**	MPri
ESTRELLA VOODOO RED STAR ('Wesverevoo'PBR)	LSou
'Hammerstein Pink'	EBee EHyd EPfP
'Homestead Purple'	CMac CMea CRos EBee EBlo EHyd ELan EPfP EShb GBin LCro LOPS LRHS NRHS SDix SIvy SRkn SRms SWvt
'Jennys'Wine'	see *G.* 'Claret'
'La France'	CRos ECha EHyd EPfP LRHS NRHS SMHy SPhx SPoG
'Little Annie'	WGrn WNPC
'Lois' Ruby'	see *G.* 'Claret'
'Merci'	NDov
§ ***peruviana***	EBou EHyd LRHS NRHS SRms XLum
'Pink Parfait'	EPfP
§ Quartz Series ♀H2	MBros MPri
- 'Quartz Red Polka Dot'	EPfP
(Samira Series) SAMIRA PURPLE WING **new**	LSou
- SAMIRA ROSE **new**	LSou
SEABROOK'S LAVENDER ('Sealav'PBR)	EHyd EPfP NRHS SCoo SHar SRkn SRms SWvt
(Showboat Series) 'Showboat Magenta'	LSou
- 'Showboat Midnight'	LSou
- 'Showboat Salmon'	LSou
- 'Showboat White'	LSou
§ 'Sissinghurst' ♀H3	ECtt SAng SDix SEdd SRms
'Strawberry Kiss'	EPfP SPoG
'Tenerife'	see *G.* 'Sissinghurst'
VECTURA LAVENDER (Vectura Series)	EHyd LRHS LSou NRHS
VEPITA BLUE VIOLET ('Invebluvio'PBR) (Vepita Series)	MHol

Glaucidium (*Ranunculaceae*)

palmatum ♀H5	CExl CPla EWld GEdr GGro GKev NHpl NSla WCru WFar
- 'Album'	see *G. palmatum* var. *leucanthum*
§ - var. ***leucanthum***	GEdr GKev NHpl

Glaucium (*Papaveraceae*)

§ ***corniculatum***	CSpe EHyd EPfP LRHS NRHS SPhx
flavum	CKel CSpe ECha LRHS MHer NFav SPhx WHer XSen
- ***aurantiacum***	see *G. flavum* f. *fulvum*
§ - f. ***fulvum***	CKel ECha MNrw WHil
- orange-flowered	see *G. flavum* f. *fulvum*
- red-flowered	see *G. corniculatum*
grandiflorum	SPhx
phoenicium	see *G. corniculatum*

Glaucosciadium (*Apiaceae*)

cordifolium	WCot
- PAB 9003	LEdu
- from Hatay, Turkey	WCot

× *Glebianthemum* (*Asteraceae*)

§ GRANDAISY YELLOW ('Bonmax 1228') (Grandaisy Series)	MBros SCob

Glebionis (*Asteraceae*)

coronaria	MNHC SRms
§ ***segetum***	CHab LCro LOPS MBow NBir SVic

Glechoma (*Lamiaceae*)

hederacea	GPoy NMir SPhx WHer
§ - 'Variegata' (v)	EShb MPri SPer XLum

Gleditsia (*Fabaceae*)

caspia	LEdu
- NJM 13.019	WPGP
japonica	NLar
koraiensis	LEdu
triacanthos	CMCN LPar NRog SPlb WTSh
- 'Calhoun'	CAgr
- 'Elegantissima' (v)	LMaj SPer
- 'Emerald Cascade'	CEnd
- f. ***inermis***	LPar
- - SPECTRUM ('Speczam')	MAsh
- - 'Sunburst'	Widely available
- 'Millwood'	CAgr
- 'Rubylace'	CBod CCVT CEnd CMCN CMac EBee ELan LMaj MAsh MBlu MRav MSwo NRog SGol SPer WMat
- 'Skyline'	LMaj LPar SGsty

Globba ✿ (*Zingiberaceae*)

racemosa var. ***hookeri*** HWJCM 471	ESwi WCru WSHC
radicalis	MHid WPGP

Globularia (*Plantaginaceae*)

alypum	CKel
bellidifolia	see *G. meridionalis*
bisnagarica	WCot
cordifolia ♀H5	CSma EBou EHyd EPot GEdr GKev LRHS MMuc NBir NHpl NRHS SHar SRms
- RCB UA 30	WCot
incanescens	GEdr
§ ***meridionalis***	CBod EPot EWes
- 'Blue Bonnets'	GEdr
- 'Hort's Variety'	CTri NSla WAbe
nana	see *G. repens*
nudicaulis	CMea EPot GEdr GKev SWvt
punctata	GKev MACG SRms WFar
pygmaea	see *G. meridionalis*
§ ***repens***	GEdr WAbe
trichosantha	GEdr GKev MACG SRms XSen
valentina	CPla GEdr
vulgaris	XSen

Gloriosa (*Colchicaceae*)

lutea	see *G. superba* 'Lutea'
§ ***modesta***	GKev
rothschildiana	see *G. superba* 'Rothschildiana'
superba ♀H1c	GKev SDeJ SDir
- 'Carsonii'	GKev SDeJ
- 'Greenii'	GKev SDeJ SDir
§ - 'Lutea'	GKev SDeJ
§ - 'Rothschildiana'	CBcs CDoC GKev LCro LOPS SDeJ SDir SRms
- 'Rothschildiana Salmon'	SDir
- 'Sparkling Striped'	GKev
- 'Tricolor'	SDir

Gloxinella (*Gesneriaceae*)

§ ***lindeniana***	WDib

Gloxinia (*Gesneriaceae*)

'Defiance'	SDeJ
lindeniana	see *Gloxinella lindeniana*
nematanthodes	see *Seemannia nematanthodes*
sylvatica	see *Seemannia sylvatica*

Glumicalyx (*Scrophulariaceae*)

flanaganii	CPbh GArf SPlb
goseloides	CPbh
nutans	CPbh SPlb

Glyceria (*Poaceae*)

aquatica variegata	see *G. maxima* var. *variegata*
maxima	CPud NPer SPlb
§ - var. ***variegata*** (v)	CPud CWat ECha EHyd ELan EPfP GMaP LLWG LRHS MMuc NBir NRHS SRms SVic WMAq XLum
spectabilis 'Variegata'	see *G. maxima* var. *variegata*

Glycyrrhiza (*Fabaceae*)

echinata	CAgr SBls
§ ***glabra***	CAgr CBod CCCN CHby CLau CSpe EMor ENfk GPoy MHer MNHC SPlb SRms WJek
glandulifera	see *G. glabra*
uralensis	CAgr ELan EPPr SPhx
yunnanensis	CSpe MHer SBls SDix SMHy

Glyptostrobus (*Cupressaceae*)

pensilis	CExl IDee LRHS WPGP
- 'Wooly Mammoth'	LRHS SMad

Gmelina (*Lamiaceae*)

hystrix	CCCN

Gnaphalium (*Asteraceae*)

'Fairy Gold'	see *Helichrysum thianschanicum* 'Goldkind'

Godetia see *Clarkia*

Goeppertia (*Marantaceae*)

§ ***concinna*** new	CDoC
§ ***crocata*** ♀H1a	CDoC
- 'Tassmania'	LCro LOPS
'Freddie'	CDoC
lancifolia new	CDoC
§ ***makoyana*** ♀H1a	CDoC
'Maui Queen'	CDoC
rufibarba 'Wavestar'	CDoC
§ ***truncata***	CDoC
veitchiana 'Medaillon'	LCro LOPS
warscewiczii	CDoC
'Whitestar'	LCro LOPS
§ ***zebrina*** ♀H1a	CDoC

goji berry see *Lycium barbarum*, *L. chinense*

Gomphocarpus (*Apocynaceae*)

§ ***fruticosus***	SVen
§ ***physocarpus***	CBod

Gompholobium (*Fabaceae*)

scabrum	SPlb

Gomphostigma (*Scrophulariaceae*)

virgatum	CBod CCCN CExl CSpe EPPr EPfP GMaP LLWG MPie SEND SMad SMrm SPhx SPlb WCFE WCot WFar WSHC
- 'White Candy'	GBin LRHS MGil MPkF SVen XSte

Gomphrena (*Amaranthaceae*)

globosa	CCCN
- 'Lizard Light'	CCCN

Goniolimon (*Plumbaginaceae*)

collinum	GEdr
- 'Sea Spray'	EDAr NFav
incanum 'Blue Diamond'	GJos NFav NHpl WCot
§ ***tataricum***	EBee GJos MMrt
§ - var. ***angustifolium***	SRms

Goodia (*Fabaceae*)

lotifolia	CCCN

Goodyera (*Orchidaceae*)

repens new	NLAp

gooseberry see *Ribes uva-crispa*; see also AGM Fruit Section

× *Gordlinia* (*Theaceae*)

grandiflora	MPkF XSte

Gordonia (*Theaceae*)

axillaris	see *Polyspora axillaris*

Gorgonidium (*Araceae*)

intermedium	WCot

Gossypium (*Malvaceae*)

herbaceum	XAbr

granadilla see *Passiflora quadrangularis*

granadilla, purple see *Passiflora edulis*

granadilla, sweet see *Passiflora ligularis*

grape see *Vitis*; see also AGM Fruit Section

grapefruit see *Citrus* × *aurantium* Grapefruit Group

Graptopetalum (*Crassulaceae*)

filiferum	SPlb
§ ***paraguayense***	SEdd SVen
- subsp. ***bernalense***	NWad SChr
suaveolens new	SPlb

Graptopetalum × *Echeveria* see × *Graptoveria*

Graptopetalum × *Sedum* see × *Graptosedum*

× *Graptosedum* (*Crassulaceae*)

'Darley Sunshine'	NWad SIvy

× *Graptoveria* (*Crassulaceae*)

'Abbey Brook' new	SEdd
'Ghostly'	WCot

Gratiola (*Plantaginaceae*)

officinalis	EHyd LLWG MHer

Greenovia (*Crassulaceae*)

aizoon	SPlb
§ ***aurea***	SPlb
diplocycla 'Gigantea'	SPlb

Grevillea (*Proteaceae*)

* ***alba***	SEle
alpina	EGrI WPGP
banksii 'Canberra Hybrid'	see *G.* 'Canberra Gem'
- var. ***forsteri***	SPlb
'Bon Accord' new	CTsd

'Bronze Rambler'	CBcs CCCN XSte
§ 'Canberra Gem' ♀H4	Widely available
'Clearview David'	CBod CCCN CDoC CKel LEdu LRHS MMuc SGBe SVen
'Coconut Ice' new	CTsd
crithmifolia	SPlb
'Cvd White'	CCCN
'Ivanhoe'	CCCN
juniperina	CBcs CCCN CEme CExl CMac EPfP LPar SCoo SEle SGsty SLim SVen
- 'Molonglo'	CTsd
- f. ***sulphurea***	CBod CCCN CExl CKel CTsd EGrl ELon MGil MMuc SEdd SEle SPer SPlb WLov
- - prostrate	CTrC
'Lady O'	CCCN
lanigera 'Mount Tamboritha'	CBcs CCCN CDoC CExl CMac CPbh CSde CTsd EBee EGrl EPfP LRHS SEle SPad SPoG WCot WFar XSte
- prostrate	WAbe WGrn
lavandulacea 'Black Range'	WCot
- 'Penola'	CCCN
leucopteris	SPlb
'Little Robyn' new	CTsd
'Mason's Hybrid'	CTsd
miqueliana	CTsd
subsp. ***moroka*** new	
'Murray Valley Queen'	WCot WPGP
'New Blood'PBR new	CBcs XSte
'Olympic Flame'	CBcs CBrac CCCN CCht CDoC CEnd CExl CKel CSBt CTrC EBee EPfP LRHS MGos MMuc SAko SCob SEle SGBe SIvy SPoG WGrn
paniculata	SPlb
'Pink Lady'	CBcs CCCN CKel ELon EPfP
'Poorinda Constance'	WCot
'Poorinda Queen'	CCCN
robusta ♀H2	EShb SPlb
'Robyn Gordon'	CCCN
'Rondeau'	CCCN
rosmarinifolia ♀H4	CBcs CCCN CEme CExl CMac CSBt CTri ELan GKin SArc SEle SLon SPer SPlb SSta WFar
§ - 'Desert Flame'	CExl
- 'Jenkinsii'	CCCN CCht CDoC CExl CKel CMac CSBt CTsd EGrl ELan EPfP LRHS SEle SGBe SIvy SLim
- 'Scarlet Sprite'	CTrC
§ × ***semperflorens***	CCCN CSde CTsd EHyd SPlb
'Spider Man'	CCCN
thelemanniana 'Baby' new	CTsd
tolminsis	see *G.* × *semperflorens*
victoriae	CBcs CCCN CCht CDoC CJun CTsd EBee EPfP LRHS MBlu MHtn SAko SChF SEdd SEle WCot WPGP
- subsp. ***victoriae***	CExl
williamsonii	CBcs CBod CCht CTsd SIvy

Grewia (*Malvaceae*)

occidentalis	LRHS XSte

Greyia (*Melianthaceae*)

sutherlandii	SPlb

Griffinia (*Amaryllidaceae*)

espiritensis new	NRog
liboniana new	NRog
rochae	GKev

Grindelia (*Asteraceae*)

§ ***camporum***	SPlb
chiloensis	SMad
integrifolia	EBee XLum
robusta	see *G. camporum*

Griselinia ✿ (*Griseliniaceae*)

littoralis ♀H5	Widely available
- 'Bantry Bay' (v)	CCCN CSde EBee EHyd ELan LRHS MAsh NLar SPer SPoG SWvt WFar
- 'Brodick Gold'	CExl ELon GKin
- 'Dixon's Cream' (v)	CBcs CCCN CMac CRos CSBt EHyd EPfP LRHS MRav SGBe SLon SRms SVen
- 'Emerald' new	SGsty
- 'Green Favor'	EBee
- GREEN HORIZON ('Whenuapai'PBR)	CBod CKel ELan IBal LPar LRHS SCob SCoo SPer SPoG
- 'Green Jewel' (v)	CBod CCCN EPfP NLar
- 'Variegata' (v) ♀H4	Widely available
ruscifolia	CBcs EBee LEdu
scandens	CCCN SEND WCot

guava, common see *Psidium guajava*

guava, purple or strawberry see *Psidium littorale* var. *longipes*

Guichenotia (*Sterculiaceae*)

macrantha	SPlb

Gunnera ✿ (*Gunneraceae*)

cordifolia	LLWG
densiflora	GEdr
hamiltonii	CBct ECha EPot LEdu NBir SRms XLum
killipiana	WFar
- B&SWJ 9009	WCru
magellanica	Widely available
- (f)	SRms
- 'Osorno'	EBee
manicata	Widely available
perpensa	CBcs CBen CCCN EBee ESwi WCot WFar
prorepens	CBct CBod CExl CMac EBee ECha ELan EPot ILea NWad SRms WFar
saint-johnii B&SWJ 14708	WCru

Guzmania (*Bromeliaceae*)

dissitiflora	NCft

Gymnadenia (*Orchidaceae*)

conopsea	NLAp

Gymnocarpium (*Woodsiaceae*)

dryopteris ♀H5	CLAP EFer EShb GArf GKev GMaP GWyn LRHS WCot WFib WPGP WShi
- PAB 1757	LEdu
- PAB 8351	LEdu
- 'Plumosum' ♀H5	CBod CLAP CRos CWCL EBee EHed EHyd EMor GEdr LEdu LRHS MAsh NHar NLar NRHS WFar WFib WHal
oyamense ♀H5	EShb GKev SPlb
robertianum	EFer EWld LEdu

Gymnocladus (*Fabaceae*)

chinensis	WPGP
dioica	CBcs CLnd CMCN ELan EPfP LEdu LMaj MBlu SMad SPer WPGP WTSh

Gymnospermium (*Berberidaceae*)

	darwasicum new	GKev

Gynandriris see *Moraea*

Gynerium (*Poaceae*)

	argenteum	see *Cortaderia selloana*

Gynostemma (*Cucurbitaceae*)

	pentaphyllum	CAgr LEdu SRms WCot WJek
	- B&SWJ 570	WCru

Gynura (*Asteraceae*)

§	***aurantiaca*** 'Purple Passion' ♀H1b	EShb

Gypsophila (*Caryophyllaceae*)

	acutifolia	EBee
	aretioides	EHyd EPot LRHS NRHS SPlb SRot WAbe
	cerastioides	Widely available
	- 'Pixie Splash' new	LRHS
	- 'Rosy Stripe'	GKev WAbe
	dubia	see *G. repens* 'Dubia'
	elegans	SVic
	fastigiata 'Silverstar'	EHyd EPfP LRHS NRHS
	(Festival Series) 'Festival'	SGbt
	- 'Festival Pink Lady'	WFar
	gracilescens	see *G. tenuifolia*
	'Jolien' (v)	WIce
	muralis 'Garden Bride'	SWvt
	- 'Gypsy Deep Rose'	EHyd ELan EPfP LRHS NRHS
	- 'Gypsy Pink' (d)	SWvt
	NEW LOVE ('Dangypfirm'PBR)	WTyc
	pacifica	GQue
	paniculata	CBod LShi MRav SRms XLum
	- 'Bristol Fairy' (d)	CSBt ECha ELan EPfP EWoo GMaP LRHS NLar SCob SPad SPoG SWvt WCAu WFar XLum
	- 'Compacta Plena' (d)	ECtt EPfP GMaP LRHS MRav NDov NGdn SGbt SRms
	- double white-flowered (d)	XLum
	- 'Flamingo' (d)	CBcs ECha EHyd MACG NLar SCob SPer SWvt WFar XLum
	- MY PINK ('Dangypink')	SMad
	- 'Pacific Pink'	EBee
	- 'Perfect Alba'	LRHS
	- 'Perfekta'	CBcs SPer
	- 'Pink Star' (d)	ECtt
§	- 'Schneeflocke' (d)	CBod CSpe EBou LBuc MACG SRms
	- SNOWFLAKE	see *G. paniculata* 'Schneeflocke'
	- SUMMER SPARKLES ('Esm Chispa'PBR)	CRos EHyd LRHS NRHS
	- WHITE FIRE ('Dangypwhifa')	EBee
§	***petraea***	GKev
	'Pink Festival' (Festival Series) (d)	CDor ECha ECtt EHyd EPfP LRHS NRHS SPoG
	repens ♀H5	ECtt GBin GJos GKev MAsh SPlb SWvt WFar XLum XSen
	- 'Dorothy Teacher'	CMea CSma ECtt WFar
§	- 'Dubia'	EBou ECha EPot MAsh MHer SLee SRms WIce WSHC
	- 'Filou Rose'	CBod EBou EDAr GJos LRHS MACG
	- 'Filou White'	LBuc LRHS MACG
	- 'Fratensis'	WIce
	- PINK BEAUTY	see *G. repens* 'Rosa Schönheit'
§	- 'Rosa Schönheit'	CMea ECha ECtt EPot NDov SPer WFar XLum
	- 'Rosea'	CTri EBee EBou ECtt EDAr ELan EPfP GArf GJos GMaP ITim MMuc NDov NGdn NHpl NSla SBut SEND SLee SPer SPoG SRms SWvt WFar WHoo WIce XLum
	- 'Ruby Gems'	CBor WFar
	- 'Silver Carpet' (v)	EBee ELan
	- white-flowered	CMea NGdn SWvt WFar
§	'Rosenschleier' (d) ♀H6	CBod CDor CMea EBee ECha ECtt ELan EPfP GMaP LCro LOPS LRHS MBel MRav NDov NGdn SGbt SPer SRms SWvt WCAu WSHC XLum
I	'Rosenschleier Variegata' (v)	EBee ELan EPfP
	'Rosy Veil'	see *G.* 'Rosenschleier'
§	***tenuifolia***	EPot GArf GKev GMaP ITim NHpl WAbe
	transylvanica	see *G. petraea*
	VEIL OF ROSES	see *G.* 'Rosenschleier'
	'White Festival'PBR (Festival Series) (d)	EHyd EPfP LRHS NRHS SHar SPoG WTor

H

Habenaria (*Orchidaceae*)

	tridactylites new	GKev

Haberlea (*Gesneriaceae*)

	ferdinandi-coburgii	see *H. rhodopensis*
§	***rhodopensis*** ♀H5	ELan EPPr GArf GEdr NHar NHpl NSla SRms WAbe WThu XLum
	- 'Connie Davidson'	GEdr GKev
	- 'Virginalis'	CElw GEdr NSla WThu

Hablitzia (*Amaranthaceae*)

	tamnoides	CAgr

Habranthus (*Amaryllidaceae*)

	andersonii	see *H. tubispathus*
	brachyandrus	SRms WCot
	gracilifolius	CPla WAbe
§	***robustus*** ♀H2	CBor CCCN CExl EPot EShb GKev
§	***tubispathus*** ♀H2	GKev SBrt

Hacquetia (*Apiaceae*)

	epipactis	see *Sanicula epipactis*

Haemanthus (*Amaryllidaceae*)

	albiflos ♀H2	CPrp ELan EPri EShb GKev NGKo NSti SDir SRms
	amarylloides	WCot
	barkerae	WCot
	carneus	WCot
	coccineus ♀H2	EPri WCot
	humilis	WCot
	- subsp. ***hirsutus***	WCot
	kalbreyeri	see *Scadoxus multiflorus* subsp. *multiflorus*
	katherinae	see *Scadoxus multiflorus* subsp. *katherinae*
	natalensis	see *Scadoxus puniceus*
	nortieri	WCot
	pubescens	WCot
	sanguineus	WCot

Hakea (*Proteaceae*)

	baxteri	SPlb
§	***drupacea***	CPbh
	epiglottis	CTrC

	laurina	CCCN CPbh SPlb
§	***lissosperma***	CBcs EBee EPfP SPlb WPGP
	nodosa	CCCN
	oleifolia	CPbh
	platysperma	SPlb
§	***salicifolia***	CCCN SPlb
	saligna	see *H. salicifolia*
	sericea misapplied	see *H. lissosperma*
	- pink-flowered	SPlb
	suaveolens	see *H. drupacea*
	teretifolia	CTrC
	victoriae	SPlb XSte

Hakonechloa ✿ (*Poaceae*)

	macra 🏆H7	Widely available
§	- 'Alboaurea' (v) 🏆H7	CExl CKno CRos CSde EHyd ELan EPfP GArf LCro LOPS LRHS LSRN MGos MHol NRHS SCob SCoo SRms
	- 'Albovariegata' (v)	CAbb CDoC CKno EBee EHed EMor LCro LEdu LOPS NLar SCob WAvo
§	- 'All Gold'	Widely available
	- 'Aureola' 🏆H7	Widely available
	- 'Beni-kaze'	CBod CKno CMiW EBee ECtt EHed ELan ELon MNrw NDov NLar SCob SCoo WPnP
	- 'Fubuki' (v)	EBee
	- 'Mediovariegata' (v)	EBee ECha
	- 'Naomi' (v)	CMiW EBee EHed ELan EMor GArf LPla SMea SPer WFar WHwl WPnP XSte
	- 'Nicolas'	CBod CExl CMiW EBee ECtt EHed ELan ELon EMor EPfP EWes GAbr LCro LEdu LOPS LPla LRHS LSRN LSou MACG NLar SEle SPer WFar WHwl WNPC WPnP XSte
	- 'Ogon'	see *H. macra* 'All Gold'
	- 'Samurai' (v)	CKno EPPr EPfP LRHS WHwl
	- 'Stripe It Rich' (v)	CCht CKno EBee ECtt EWes LPla NLar
	- SUNFLARE ('Habsfl007')	CBcs CBct CBod CKno CMiW CWGN EBee LCro LOPS LPla NPol SEdd WNPC
	- 'Sunny Delight' (v)	EBee
	- 'Variegata'	see *H. macra* 'Alboaurea'

Halenia (*Gentianaceae*)

	elliptica	GKev

Halesia ✿ (*Styracaceae*)

§	***carolina***	Widely available
	- Monticola Group	CBcs CCVT CLnd CMac ELan EPfP LSRN MMuc NLar SPer SWvt
	- - 'Arnold Pink' **new**	EHed
I	- - 'Variegata' (v)	EPfP MBlu NLar SSta
	- 'Uconn Wedding Bells'	CJun MBlu WTSh
	- Vestita Group 🏆H5	CAco CJun EPfP MAsh MBlu MGil MRav NLar SPer SSta WLov
	- - 'Rosea'	CJun EPfP MBlu NLar
	diptera	MBlu
	- Magniflora Group	CJun EPfP MBlu SSta
	macgregorii	MBlu
	tetraptera	see *H. carolina*

× *Halimiocistus* (*Cistaceae*)

	algarvensis	see *Halimium ocymoides*
§	'Ingwersenii' 🏆H4	ELan EWes SPer SRms XLum
	revolii misapplied	see × *H. sahucii*
§	***sahucii*** 🏆H4	CBcs CBod CDoC CRos CSBt CTri ECha ELan EPfP LRHS MAsh MBNS MPri MRav MSwo SGBe SPer SPoG SRms SWvt XLum
	- ICE DANCER ('Ebhals'[PBR]) (v)	EBee MAsh SCob SPer SWvt WFar
	'Susan'	see *Halimium* 'Susan'
§	***wintonensis*** 🏆H4	CBcs CBod CRos EGrI EHyd ELan EPfP LRHS MAsh MGil MMrt SLon SPer SRms
§	- 'Merrist Wood Cream' 🏆H4	CBcs CBod CBrac CDoC CKel CMac CSBt CSde EBee EGrI ELan EPfP LSRN MAsh MGil MMrt MRav MSwo SCob SGBe SPer SPoG SRkn SWvt WFar WLov WSHC

Halimione (*Amaranthaceae*)

§	***portulacoides***	CEls

Halimium (*Cistaceae*)

§	***calycinum***	CBcs CBod CDoC CKel CRos EGrI EHyd ELan EPfP LRHS MAsh MMuc NRHS SCob SCoo SGBe SPer SPoG SWvt WCav
	commutatum	see *H. calycinum*
	halimifolium misapplied	see *H.* × *pauanum*
§	***halimifolium*** Willk.	WMal
§	***lasianthum***	CMac CSBt MRav
	- 'Concolor' 🏆H4	MAsh MSwo SWvt
	- subsp. ***formosum*** 'Sandling' 🏆H4	EHyd ELan EPfP LRHS MAsh SChF SLon SPoG SRms
	libanotis misapplied	see *H. calycinum*
§	***ocymoides***	LRHS MSwo SGBe WFar
§	× ***pauanum***	EHyd LRHS NRHS
§	'Susan' 🏆H4	CBcs CBod EBee EHyd ELan EPfP LRHS MMrt NRHS SCoo SGBe SPer WAbe WLov
§	***umbellatum***	EPfP
	wintonense	see × *Halimiocistus wintonensis*

Halleria (*Stilbaceae*)

	lucida	CBcs CCCN EBee EGrI SEle SPlb SVen WKor

Haloragis (*Haloragaceae*)

	erecta	SPlb SVen XLum
	- 'Rubra'	WCot
	- 'Wellington Bronze'	CBod CExl CPla CSpe EBee EGrI ELan EWld LEdu SBls SGBe WHer XLum

Hamamelis ✿ (*Hamamelidaceae*)

	'Amethyst'	CJun MBlu
	'Brevipetala'	CEnd CJun LMaj
	'Danny'	CJun
	'Dishi'	CJun
	'Fire Blaze'	CJun MBlu NLar
	× ***intermedia*** 'Advent' 🏆H5	CJun MAsh
	- 'Allgold'	SCob
	- 'Amanda'	NLar
	- 'Andre'	WPGP
	- 'Angelly' 🏆H5	CJun EHed MBlu NLar
	- 'Anne' 🏆H5	WPGP
	- 'Aphrodite' 🏆H5	CBcs CJun CRos EHyd EPfP LRHS MAsh MBlu MGos MRav NLar NOra NRHS SPer
	- 'Arnold Promise' 🏆H5	Widely available
	- 'Aurora' 🏆H5	CBcs CJun EPfP LRHS MBlu NOra WPGP
	- 'Barmstedt Gold' 🏆H5	CDoC CJun CRos EHyd EPfP LRHS LSRN MGos MRav NLar NOra NRHS NWea SAko SPer SPoG SRms

- 'Bernstein' CJun
- 'Birgit' NLar
- 'Carmine Red' CJun CMac LRHS
- 'Copper Beauty' see *H.* × *intermedia* 'Jelena'
- 'Cyrille' MMuc
- 'Diane' ♀H5 Widely available
§ - 'Feuerzauber' CEnd CTri EBee EGrI EPfP LMaj LRHS MAsh NLar NOrn SGsty SMad SPer SWvt WFar
- FIRE CRACKER see *H.* × *intermedia* 'Feuerzauber'
- 'Foxy Lady' MAsh MBlu
- 'Frederic' ♀H5 CJun EPfP MAsh
- 'Gingerbread' ♀H5 CJun EPfP MAsh
- 'Glowing Embers' CJun
- 'Harry' ♀H5 CJun LSRN MAsh NLar
- 'Heinrich Bruns' CJun
- 'Hiltingbury' LRHS
§ - 'Jelena' ♀H5 Widely available
- 'John' LSRN MAsh
- 'Limelight' CJun MBlu MMuc
- 'Livia' CJun CRos EHyd EPfP LRHS MAsh NRHS SCoo WPGP
- MAGIC FIRE see *H.* × *intermedia* 'Feuerzauber'
- 'Moonlight' CJun
- 'Nina' EBee EPfP LRHS MAsh
- 'Orange Beauty' CBcs CBod CJun CRos EGrI EHyd LRHS MBlu MGos NLar NOrn NRHS SAko SCoo SPer WPGP
- 'Orange Peel' CJun EBee EHed EPfP NLar
- 'Ostergold' CJun
- 'Pallida' ♀H5 Widely available
- 'Primavera' CJun CLnd
- 'Ripe Corn' CJun MBlu
- 'Robert' ♀H5 CJun CRos EHyd EPfP LRHS LSRN NRHS
- 'Rubin' ♀H5 CJun CRos EHyd EPfP LRHS MGos NLar NRHS SCoo SPer
- 'Rubinstar' CJun
- 'Ruby Glow' CRos EHed EHyd LRHS LSRN MAsh MGos NLar NRHS NWea SCoo SPer SPoG SWvt
- 'Savill Starlight' CJun
- 'Spanish Spider' CJun MBlu NLar
- 'Strawberries and Cream' CJun
- 'Sunburst' CJun CRos EHyd EPfP LRHS MBlu MGos NLar
- 'Swallow Hayes' new LRHS
- 'Twilight' CJun NLar
- 'Vesna' ♀H5 CJun CMac EPfP MAsh MBlu SCoo
- 'Westerstede' CJun CLnd LMaj LRHS LSRN MGos NHol NLar NWea SCoo SEWo SGsty WFar
- 'Wiero' CJun
- 'Zitronenjette' CJun

japonica 'Pendula' MBlu
- 'Rubra' EGrI
- 'Zuccariniana' NLar

mollis Widely available
- 'Boskoop' MMuc
- 'Coombe Wood' CJun LRHS NOra
- 'Imperialis' CJun MAsh
- 'Iwado' CJun
- 'Jermyns Gold' ♀H5 CJun CRos EHyd EPfP LRHS MAsh NRHS
- 'Kort's Yellow' CJun
- var. ***pallida*** CBrac SEWo SWvt
- 'Wisley Supreme' ♀H5 CJun ELan EPfP LRHS MGos

'Rochester' CJun

vernalis purple-flowered MBlu
- 'Quasimodo' MBlu
- 'Sandra' CMCN EPfP MAsh MBlu MGos MRav NOra SLon

virginiana CAgr CMCN EGrI GPoy IDee LMaj LPar MMuc NLar NWea
- 'Green Thumb' (v) NLar
- 'Mohonk Red' CJun

'Yamina' CDoC CRos LRHS NLar SGol

Hamelia (*Rubiaceae*)

patens CCCN

Hanabusaya (*Campanulaceae*)

§ ***asiatica*** WFar

Haplocarpha (*Asteraceae*)

rueppellii NHpl SRms

Haplopappus (*Asteraceae*)

coronopifolius see *H. glutinosus*
§ ***glutinosus*** ECha EDAr EPot MMuc SLee SPlb SRms

Hardenbergia (*Fabaceae*)

comptoniana ♀H3 CExl
violacea ♀H3 CBod CCCN CRHN CTsd ELan MHer SEND SPer WCot
- f. ***alba*** CBod ELan SEND WLov
- - 'White Wanderer' CCCN
- 'Happy Wanderer' CCCN SIvy
- f. ***rosea*** CCCN

Hasteola (*Asteraceae*)

§ ***suaveolens*** LEdu

Hastingsia (*Asparagaceae*)

alba WSHC

Haworthia ✿ (*Asphodelaceae*)

attenuata EShb NCft
- 'Super Zebra' new WCot

'Black Prince' EShb
coarctata ♀H2 SEND
cooperi NCft
cymbiformis NCft
- variegated (v) new NCft
fasciata EPfP SEND
- 'Concolor' CDoC SSim
glabrata var. ***concolor*** EShb
'Jack Brown' new NCft
limifolia EShb NCft
- SPIDER WHITE ('Lock01'PBR) EShb LCro LOPS
- var. ***ubomboensis*** new NCft
margaritifera NCft SSim
marumiana new NCft
- var. ***batesiana*** new NCft
- var. ***reddii*** new NCft
pumila ♀H2 SEND
reinwardtii var. ***brevicula*** new NCft
retusa 'Grey Ghost' new NCft
× ***revendettii*** new NCft
starkiana new NCft
tortusa NCft
truncata ♀H2 NCft
variegata var. ***modesta*** new NCft
§ ***venosa*** subsp. ***tesselata*** ♀H2 SEND

hazelnut see *Corylus*; see also AGM Fruit Section

Hebe ✿ (*Plantaginaceae*)

	albicans Y^{H4}	CBcs CBrac CCoa CDoC CSde EHyd ELan EPfP GDam GJos GKin LCro LOPS LRHS LSRN MAsh MGos MRav NRHS NWea SCob SCoo SGBe SGbt SPer SRms SWvt WCFE WSpi XLum
	- prostrate	see *H. albicans* 'Snow Cover'
*	- 'Snow Carpet'	CBrac
§	- 'Snow Cover'	EWes
	- 'Snow Drift'	see *H. albicans* 'Snow Cover'
	'Amanda Cook' (v)	NPer
	'Amethyst Mist'	GDam
§	'Amy'	EHyd ELon EShb LRHS NPer SPer SWvt WCot
	× ***andersonii***	CDoC
§	- 'Andersonii Variegata' (v)	SRms
§	***armstrongii***	MMuc
	armstrongii* × *selaginoides new	WKif
	'Autumn Glory'	CBrac CDoC EHyd ELan EPfP LCro LOPS LRHS LSRN MAsh MRav MSwo NBir NRHS SCob SGBe SPer SPlb SPoG SRGP SWvt WSpi XLum
	'Autumn Joy'	SWvt
	'Baby Boo' (v)	CDoC LRHS SCob SLon
	'Baby Marie'	CDoC CSBt EHyd ELan EPfP GJos GKin LBuc LRHS LSRN MAsh MSwo NLar NPer NRHS SCoo SGBe SPoG SRms SWvt WFar
	'Beverley Hills'^{PBR}	CSBt EHyd
	'Bicolor Wand'	CCCN
	bishopiana	EPfP
	'Black Beauty'	EHyd EPfP GDam LRHS MAsh NRHS SCob
	'Black Panther'	ELon
	'Blue Clouds' Y^{H4}	CBrac CRos EHyd EPfP LRHS MSwo NRHS NWad SPer WCFE WMal
	BLUE ELEGANCE ('Lowgeko'^{PBR}) (Garden Beauty Series)	LRHS SGBe
§	'Blue Gem'	CDoC CMac LPar NLar SGBe SGsty
	BLUE HAZE ('Lowchi'^{PBR}) (Garden Beauty Series)	SGBe
	BLUE ICE ('Lowapb') (Garden Beauty Series)	LRHS SGBe
	'Blue Shamrock'	SWvt
	BLUE STAR ('Vergeer 1'^{PBR})	CDoC CRos EPfP GJos LBuc LRHS MAsh NRHS SLon SPoG SRms
	'Boscawenii'	WHer
	'Bouquet'^{PBR}	LSou
§	'Bowles's Hybrid'	CBrac MRav MSwo SCob SEND SRms
	brachysiphon	CTri SEND SPer SRms SVen
	brevifolia	SGBe
	BRONZE GLOW ('Lowglo') (Garden Beauty Series)	CDoC LBuc LRHS SGBe
	'Bronzy Baby'^{PBR} (v)	SPoG
	buchananii	MHer NPer
§	- 'Fenwickii'	WHoo
	- 'Minor' ambig.	GQue
	'Burgundy Blush'	LBuc SPoG
	'Burning Heart' (v)	LBuc LRHS
	buxifolia	see *H. odora*
§	'Caledonia' Y^{H4}	CBcs CDoC CRos EGrl EHyd ELan EPfP LCro LOPS LRHS LSRN MAsh MGos NPer NRHS SCoo SGBe SPoG SRms SWvt WCav XLum
	'Carl Teschner'	see *H.* 'Youngii'
	'Carnea Variegata' (v)	EHyd LRHS NRHS SPer SRms
	carnosula	SPer
	catarractae	see *Parahebe catarractae*
	'Celebration'^{PBR} (v)	LRHS
	'Celine'	CCoa EHyd EPfP LRHS NRHS
	'Champagne'	CBrac CDoC EHyd ELan EPfP LCro LOPS LPar LRHS LSRN MBlu NLar NRHS NWad SCoo SRms XLum
	'Champagne Ice'	LBuc
	CHAMPION ('Champseiont'^{PBR})	GBin MSwo NLar SCoo
	'Charming White'	CChe CEme LSRN
	cheesemanii	WAbe
	'Claret Crush'^{PBR}	SCoo SPoG
	'Clear Skies'^{PBR}	SRms
	'Cobb Valley'	LRHS
	'Conwy Knight'	SRms
	corstorphinensis	EBtc
	'County Park'	EWes GAbr
	cupressoides 'Boughton Dome'	ELan GAbr GEdr GJos MAsh MHer WAbe WHoo
	- 'Golden Dome'	SGsty
	'Dark Angel'	LBuc SCoo
	DARK STAR ('Lowgamma') (Garden Beauty Series) new	SGBe
	darwiniana misapplied	see *H. glaucophylla*
	decumbens	EWes GArf GBin
	'Diamond'	LSRN SCob SLon SRms
	dieffenbachii	SVen
	diosmifolia	CBod CDoC NRHS NWad
	- 'Wairua Beauty'	CDoC LRHS SGBe
	'Dorothy Peach'	see *H.* 'Watson's Pink'
	'E.B.Anderson'	see *H.* 'Caledonia'
	'Edington'	SPer WCFE
	'Ellie'	CBrac
	elliptica	CDoC
	- 'Variegata'	see *H.* 'Silver Queen'
	'Emerald Dome'	see *H.* 'Emerald Gem'
§	'Emerald Gem' Y^{H4}	CRos CTri EGrl EHyd ELan EPfP GDam GJos GWyn LPar LRHS LSRN MAsh MGos MHer MMuc MSwo NRHS SCob SPer SPlb SPoG SRot WLov
	'Emerald Green'	see *H.* 'Emerald Gem'
§	'Eveline'	CRos CSBt CTri LRHS WSpi
	'Evelyn'	SPer
	'Eversley Seedling'	see *H.* 'Bowles's Hybrid'
	'Eyecatcher'^{PBR} (v)	LSou MAsh
	'Fairfieldii'	WAbe WAvo WMal
	'First Light'^{PBR}	CDoC LSou NLar SRms
	'Fragrant Jewel'	SEND
	× ***franciscana***	CBod NCou WSMil
	- 'Blue Gem' ambig.	CBrac EHyd ELan LRHS MAsh MMuc MRav NBir NPer NRHS SCob SEND SPer SPlb SPoG SRms WSpi XLum
	- 'Foreness Pink'	SEND
	- lime variegated (v)	SEND
	- 'Purple Tips' misapplied	see *H. speciosa* 'Variegata'
	- 'Variegata'	see *H.* 'Silver Queen'
I	- 'White Gem'	SRms
	'Frozen Flame' (v)	ELan LBuc MAsh SPoG WMal
	(Garden Beauty Series) GARDEN BEAUTY BLUE ('Cliv'^{PBR})	CDoC CSBt LBuc LCro LOPS LRHS LSou MAsh SCoo SGBe SRms WSpi
	- GARDEN BEAUTY PINK ('Lowpito')	CDoC SGBe SRms
	- GARDEN BEAUTY PURPLE ('Nold'^{PBR})	CSBt EHyd LBuc LCro LOPS LRHS LSou MAsh NRHS SGBe WSpi
	- GARDEN BEAUTY WHITE ('Lowhi')	LRHS SGBe
	(Garden Elegance Series) 'Garden Elegance Blush'	LRHS SGBe

	- 'Garden Elegance Rose'	LRHS
	'Gauntlettii'	see *H.* 'Eveline'
§	***glaucophylla***	XLum
I	- 'Variegata' (v)	EHyd LRHS NRHS SCoo SPer WKif
§	'Gloriosa'	SCob
	'Gold Beauty' (v)	SRms
	'Gold Pixie'	LBuc
	GOLDEN ANNIVERSARY ('Lowag'PBR)	LRHS
	'Goldrush'PBR (v)	SPoG
	gracillima	SEle
	'Great Orme' ♀H4	CBrac CRos EHyd ELan EPfP GBin GLog LSRN MAsh MRav MSwo NPer NRHS SCob SEND SPer SPlb SPoG SRms SWvt WCFE WSFF
	'Green Globe'	see *H.* 'Emerald Gem'
	'Greensleeves'	EHyd
	'Grethe'	EHyd NRHS SCob SEND
	'Hadspen Pink'	CBrac CDoC
	'Hanne'	EHyd LRHS NRHS
§	'Hartii'	CBrac MRav
	'Headfortii'	EBtc EGrI
	'Heartbreaker'PBR (v)	CDoC CRos EHyd ELan EPfP LBuc LCro LOPS LRHS MAsh MGos MPri NRHS SCob SCoo SGBe SPoG SWvt
	'Helena' (Addenda Series)	CDoC
	'High Voltage'PBR	GJos MHtn NEoE WSpi WTyc
	'Hinderwell'	NPer
	hookeriana	see *Parahebe hookeriana*
	hulkeana	MGil MHer SMHy WAbe WKif
§	'Imposter'	SRms
	'Inspiration'	EHyd NWad SCob SRms
	'James Stirling'	see *H. ochracea* 'James Stirling'
	'Jane Holden'	EHyd
	'Jewel of the Nile'PBR (v)	MMrt NFav SCob SGBe SPoG
	'Joan Mac' new	SCoo
	'John Collier'	GAbr SEND
	'Karna'	SCob
	'Katrina' (v)	CDoC
	'Kirkii'	ELan EPfP MSwo NLar XLum
	'Knightshayes'	see *H.* 'Caledonia'
	'Lady Ann'PBR (v)	CRos EHyd EPfP LBuc LRHS MAsh NRHS SCob SPoG
	'Lady Ardilaun'	see *H.* 'Amy'
	latifolia	see *H.* 'Blue Gem'
	'Lavender Spray'	see *H.* 'Hartii'
	LEOPARD ('Lowand') (Garden Beauty Series)	LRHS MPri SGBe
	'Leopard Spot' (v) new	LRHS SCoo SGBe
	'Lilac Fantasy'	LRHS SGBe
	'Linda'	SEND
	'Lisa'	EHyd LRHS NRHS
	'Liz'	LBuc SPoG
	'Louise'	SCob
	lyallii	see *Parahebe lyallii*
	mackenii	see *H.* 'Emerald Gem'
	macrantha ♀H4	EHyd GArf GBin GWyn SRms
	macrocarpa	CBod LRHS SGBe
	- var. ***latisepala***	LRHS SGBe
	'Magic Summer'PBR	LBuc MAsh NRHS SPoG
§	'Maori Gem'	MRav
	'Margret' ♀H4	CBrac CDoC CSBt EBee EHyd EPfP GArf LRHS LSRN MAsh MGos NRHS SCoo SGBe SPer SPoG SRms WSpi
	'Maria'	SCob
	'Marie Antoinette'	CBod
	'Marilyn Monroe'PBR	CBod LSou WTyc
	'Marjorie'	CMac ELan EPfP GBin LRHS LSRN MSwo NPer NRHS NWea SCob SPer SPoG SRms SWvt WFar
	'Marshmallow' new	SCoo
	matthewsii 'Turkish Delight'PBR	NEoE
	MATTY BROWN ('Tull 303'PBR)	LSou
	'McKean'	see *H.* 'Emerald Gem'
	'Merlot Memories'PBR new	SCoo
	MIDNIGHT SKY ('Lowten'PBR) (Garden Beauty Series)	CDoC LBuc LCro LOPS LRHS MPri SCoo SGBe SPoG
	'Midsummer Beauty' ♀H4	EHyd EPfP GBin GDam LRHS LSRN MRav NBir NRHS SCob SEND SPer SPlb SPoG SRms SWvt WSFF XLum
	'Milmont Emerald'	see *H.* 'Emerald Gem'
§	'Mohawk'PBR	GJos MAsh NRHS SCoo SPoG WSpi
§	'Mrs Winder' ♀H4	CBrac CMac EHyd ELan EPfP GDam GJos GWyn LPar LRHS LSRN MAsh MGos MRav MSwo NPer NRHS SCob SCoo SGBe SGbt SGsty SPer SPoG SRGP SWvt WSpi
	'Nantyderry'	CDoC MGil
§	'Neil's Choice' ♀H4	EHyd ELon LRHS
	'New Zealand'	GDam GWyn XLum
	'Nicola's Blush' ♀H4	CDoC CMac CRos EBee EHyd ELon EPfP EShb GBin GWyn LRHS LSRN MCot MRav MSwo NLar NRHS SCob SEND SPer SPoG SRGP SRms SWvt SavN WMal
	ochracea	EHyd EPfP LRHS NRHS
§	- 'James Stirling' ♀H4	CBcs CMac CSBt ELan GArf GJos LCro LOPS LSRN MAsh MGos MSwo NLar NWad SCob SCoo SPlb SPoG SWvt WSpi
§	***odora***	ELan NWea WSpi XLum
I	- 'Nana'	MMuc
	- 'New Zealand Gold'	CRos EHyd EPfP GJos LRHS MAsh MMuc NRHS NWad
	- prostrate	SRms
	- 'Summer Frost'	CBrac CDoC CSde
	'Oratia Beauty' ♀H4	CDoC EHyd LSRN MRav SEND
	'Orphan Annie' (v)	CBrac CDoC
	'Pacific Paradise'PBR	SPoG
	parviflora misapplied	see *H.* 'Bowles's Hybrid'
	- var. ***angustifolia***	see *H. stenophylla*
	- 'Holdsworth'	CBod
	'Pascal' ♀H4	EHyd ELan EPfP LCro LOPS LRHS LSRN MAsh MGos NRHS SCoo SGBe SLon SPer SPoG SRms SWvt WFar
	'Pastel Blue'	LRHS
	'Patti Dossett'	see *H. speciosa* 'Patti Dossett'
	pauciramosa	SRms
	'Pearl of Paradise'PBR	LBuc NRHS NWad SPoG
	perfoliata	see *Parahebe perfoliata*
	'Perry's Rubyleaf'	NPer
	'Petra's Pink'	EHyd
	'Pewter Dome' ♀H4	CSde EPfP MGos MRav SCob SDix SRms SWvt XLum
	pimeleoides 'Glauca'	NPer
	- 'Quicksilver' ♀H4	CBrac CRos CSBt EHyd ELan EPfP GArf GJos LRHS LSRN MGil MGos MRav NPer NRHS SCob SCoo SGBe SLee SPer SRms WAvo WSpi XLum
	pinguifolia	NLar SPlb
	- 'Pagei' ♀H5	Widely available
	- 'Sutherlandii'	CBcs CBrac CDoC EHyd EPfP LPar LRHS LSRN MAsh MGos NRHS NWea SCob SCoo SGsty SWvt WFar XLum
	PINK CANDY ('Tulpink'PBR)	CBod WTyc
	'Pink Elephant' (v) ♀H4	CDoC LBuc LRHS SGBe SPoG
	'Pink Fantasy'	NWad SGbt

	'Pink Goddess'	CBrac EHyd EPfP LRHS NRHS SEND
	'Pink Lady'PBR	ELan SPoG
	'Pink Paradise'PBR	ELan EPfP NRHS NWad SPoG SRms
	'Pink Payne'	see *H.* 'Eveline'
	'Pink Pixie'	LBuc MAsh SCoo SPoG SRms
	'Pinocchio' (v)	LRHS
	poppelwellii	NLar
	'Porlock Purple'	see *Parahebe catarractae* 'Delight'
I	'Prostrata'	CSBt
	'Purple Paradise'PBR	LSou NLar SPoG
	'Purple Pixie'	see *H.* 'Mohawk'
	'Purple Princess'	EHyd LRHS NRHS
	PURPLE SHAMROCK ('Neprock'PBR) (v)	CDoC CRos EHyd EPfP GJos LRHS LSou MAsh NLar NRHS SCoo SGBe SPer SPoG SRms SWvt
	'Purple Tips' misapplied	see *H. speciosa* 'Variegata'
§	***rakaiensis*** ♀H4	Widely available
	- 'Golden Dome'	see *H. rakaiensis*
	ramosissima	GAbr GBin
	raoulii	SRms WAbe
	'Raven'	CBrac CDoC
	recurva	CCoa CSde CTri SRms
	- 'Boughton Silver' ♀H4	CEme LRHS LSRN MMuc SGBe
	'Red Edge' ♀H4	Widely available
	'Red Ruth'	see *H.* 'Eveline'
	RHUBARB AND CUSTARD ('Tull 302'PBR)	LBuc MAsh MMrt SCoo SPoG WCot
	'Rose Elegance'	SGBe
	'Rosie'	CGrG LBuc LSRN NRHS SCoo SPer SRot SWvt
	'Royal Blue'	SCob
	'Ruby Port'PBR **new**	SCoo
	salicifolia	CMac EHyd ELan EPfP GAbr IDee LRHS MRav NRHS NWad SEND SPer SPlb SRms WFar WSpi XLum
	- pale blue-flowered	SEND
	'Sandra Joy'	CBrac LSRN
	'Sangria Sensation'PBR **new**	SCoo
	'Santa Monica'	LSou
	'Sapphire' ♀H4	EHyd EPfP LRHS MAsh NRHS SCoo SRms SWvt
	'Shiraz'	EHyd
	'Silver Dollar' (v)	CBcs GArf GBin LRHS LSou NRHS NWad SCob SGBe SPer SPoG SRms
§	'Silver Queen' (v) ♀H3	CBcs CBrac CCoa CDoC CEme CMac CSBt EHyd ELan LCro LOPS LRHS MMuc NLar NPer NRHS SEND SGBe SGsty SPer SPoG SRms
	'Simon Délaux'	SEND
	'Sparkling Sapphires'	LBuc LRHS SGBe SPoG
	speciosa	CPla
	- 'La Séduisante'	CTri LRHS SEND WSpi
§	- 'Patti Dossett'	CDoC
	- 'Red Hugh'	SEND
§	- 'Variegata' (v)	CRos EHyd LRHS NPer NRHS SCob
	'Spender's Seedling' misapplied	see *H. stenophylla*
	'Spender's Seedling' ambig.	MCot MMuc MSCN WSpi
	'Spender's Seedling' Hort.	LRHS MRav SEND SPoG SRms
	'Spring Glory'	CRos EHyd EPfP LRHS NRHS
	'Starlight' (v) **new**	SGBe
§	***stenophylla***	EShb LRHS LSRN NLar SArc SDix SPer SPlb
	stricta	SEND
	- var. ***macroura***	CBrac
	- var. ***stricta***	CDoC
	subalpina	CSBt
	'Summer Blue'	MBlu
	'Sunset Boulevard'PBR	LSou
	'Super Red'	CEme CSBt SGBe
	'Sweet Kim' (v)	LBuc LRHS NRHS SGBe SPoG
	tetrasticha	GRum
	'Tiptop' (v)	LSou
	topiaria ♀H4	CAgr CBod CDoC CEme CMac CSBt EBou EPfP LRHS MBrN MMuc MRav MSwo NBir NFav NLar NWad SCoo SEND SGbt SPer SPoG WSpi XLum
	- 'Doctor Favier'	SRms
	'Tricolor'	see *H. speciosa* 'Variegata'
	'Trixie'	WSpi
	'Trudi'	SCob
	'Valentino'PBR	SCoo
§	***venustula***	MMuc
	vernicosa ♀H4	CCoa CDoC CEme EHyd EPfP GDam MGos MHer NFav NWad NWea SCob SCoo SGsty SPer SPlb SPoG SWvt WSpi
	'Waikiki'	see *H.* 'Mrs Winder'
§	'Warley'	CBrac CDoC EHyd LRHS NRHS WSpi
	'Warleyensis'	see *H.* 'Warley'
§	'Watson's Pink'	SPer WKif
	'White Gem' (*brachysiphon* hybrid) ♀H4	GWyn NLar NPer SPer
	'White Heather'	CRos EHyd EPfP LRHS NRHS
	'White Paradise'PBR	SPoG
	'White Spritzer'PBR **new**	SCoo
	'Wild Romance'	CDoC LBuc MAsh SPoG
	'Willcoxii'	see *H. buchananii* 'Fenwickii'
	'Wingletye' ♀H4	EHyd LRHS WAbe XLum
	'Wiri Blush'	CBrac SWvt
	'Wiri Charm'	CBcs CBrac CDoC CMac CRos CSBt EBee EGrI EHyd ELon EPfP GArf LRHS MSwo NLar NRHS SEND SPer
	'Wiri Cloud' ♀H4	CBcs CDoC CEme CMac EGrI EHyd EPfP LRHS MMuc MSCN MSwo NRHS SCob SEND SRms
	'Wiri Dawn' ♀H4	EGrI EHyd ELan EPfP NRHS SRms SWvt XLum
	'Wiri Icing Sugar'	CBrac
	'Wiri Image'	CBcs CSBt EHyd MRav NRHS SEND
	'Wiri Joy'	EHyd EPfP LRHS NRHS SEND
	'Wiri Mist'	CBcs EHyd ELan EPfP LPar LRHS NRHS XLum
	'Wiri Prince'	SCob
	'Wiri Splash'	CRos EHyd LRHS NRHS
	'Wiri Vision'	CBrac CSBt SEND
§	'Youngii' ♀H4	CBcs CDoC CRos CSBt CTri EHyd ELan EPfP GArf GBin GJos LCro LOPS LRHS MGil MHer MRav NRHS SCob SEND SGBe SPer SPlb SPoG SRms SWvt WCFE WHoo WMal WSpi

Hechtia (*Bromeliaceae*)

	sp.	WCot

Hedeoma (*Lamiaceae*)

	ciliolata	WAbe

Hedera ✿ (*Araliaceae*)

§	***algeriensis***	SArc WFib
	- 'Bellecour'	WFib XLum
§	- 'Gloire de Marengo' (v) ♀H5	CArg CBcs CBod CDoC CMac CRos CTri EBee EHyd ELan EPfP GKin LPar LRHS LSRN MAsh MGos MSwo NRHS SCob SDix SEND SGsty SNig SPer SPoG SRms SWvt WFar WFib
	- 'Marginomaculata' (v)	EHyd EPfP EShb LRHS MAsh SMad SPoG WFib

	- 'Montgomery'	EHyd LRHS LSRN NRHS
	- 'Ravensholst' ♀H5	CMac EShb MRav SCob WFib
§	***azorica***	EShb WCot WFib
	- amber-fruited	MPie WCot
	- 'Pico'	EShb WFib
	- 'Saiga'	WCot
	- 'Variegata' (v)	WCot
	canariensis misapplied	see *H. algeriensis*
	- 'Variegata'	see *H. algeriensis* 'Gloire de Marengo'
	canariensis Willd. var. ***azorica***	see *H. azorica*
	chinensis	see *H. nepalensis*
	- typica	see *H. nepalensis*
§	***colchica***	NWea WFib
	- 'Arborescens' **new**	NWea WCot
*	- 'Arborescens Variegata' (v)	WCot
	- 'Batumi'	MBNS WFib
	- 'Dendroides'	EWTr
	- 'Dentata' ♀H5	CBod MRav WFar WFib
	- 'Dentata Aurea'	see *H. colchica* 'Dentata Variegata'
§	- 'Dentata Variegata' (v) ♀H5	Widely available
	- 'Dentata Variegata' arboreal (v) **new**	WCot
	- 'My Heart'	see *H. colchica*
	- 'Paddy's Pride'	see *H. colchica* 'Sulphur Heart'
§	- 'Sulphur Heart' (v) ♀H5	Widely available
	- 'Variegata'	see *H. colchica* 'Dentata Variegata'
	cristata	see *H. helix* 'Parsley Crested'
	helix	CCVT CMac LCro LOPS LPar NWea SCob SWeb WSFF XLum
	- 'Adam' (v)	LSRN WFib
	- 'Amber Waves'	WFib
	- 'Anita'	GBin WFib
§	- 'Anna Marie' (v)	WFib
	- 'Arborescens'	EShb LPar WGrn WSFF
	- 'Arborescens Variegata' (v)	EShb
	- 'Ardingly' (v)	WFib
	- 'Atropurpurea'	GBin MMuc SEND WFib
	- (Aureovariegata Group) 'Chrysophylla' (v)	MSwo
	- 'Baltica'	WFib
	- 'Bettina' (v)	WCot
	- 'Bill Archer'	GBin WFib
	- 'Bird's Foot'	see *H. helix* 'Pedata'
	- 'Boskoop'	WFib
	- 'Bredon'	MRav
	- 'Brimstone' (v)	WFib
§	- 'Brokamp'	WFib
	- 'Buttercup' ♀H5	CBod CMac CRos ELan EPfP GQue LRHS LSRN MAsh MGos MMuc NLar SCob SEND SPoG SRms SWvt WCFE WFib
	- 'Caecilia' (v) ♀H5	EPfP MSwo SWvt WFib
	- 'Caenwoodiana'	see *H. helix* 'Pedata'
	- 'Caenwoodiana Aurea'	WFib
§	- 'Calico' (v)	WFib
	- 'Calypso' (v)	WFib
	- 'Carolina Crinkle'	GBin
	- 'Cathedral Wall'	WFib
	- 'Cavendishii'	see *H. helix* Cavendishii Group
§	- Cavendishii Group (v)	SRms WFib
§	- 'Ceridwen' (v) ♀H5	SCob SPlb WFib
	- 'Cheeky'	WFib
	- 'Cheltenham Blizzard' (v)	CNat
	- 'Chester' (v)	WFib
	- 'Chicago'	WFib
	- 'Chicago Variegated' (v)	WFib
§	- 'Classy Lassie' (v)	WFib
	- 'Clotted Cream' (v)	CDoC CRos LRHS MAsh WFib
	- 'Cockle Shell'	EPPr WFib
	- 'Colin'	GBin
§	- 'Congesta' ♀H5	CMac CTsd SRms WFib
	- 'Conglomerata'	ELan SRms WFib
	- 'Courage'	WFib
	- 'Crenata'	WFib
	- 'Crispa'	MRav
	- 'Cristata'	see *H. helix* 'Parsley Crested'
	- 'Curleylocks'	see *H. helix* 'Manda's Crested'
	- 'Curley-Q'	see *H. helix* 'Dragon Claw'
	- 'Curvaceous' (v)	WCot WFib
	- 'Cyprus'	see *H. pastuchovii* subsp. *cypria*
	- 'Dealbata'	see *H. hibernica* 'Dealbata'
	- 'Deltoidea'	see *H. hibernica* 'Deltoidea'
	- 'Discolor'	see *H. helix* 'Minor Marmorata'
§	- 'Donerailensis'	MBlu WFib
	- 'Don's Papillon'	CNat
§	- 'Dragon Claw'	WFib
	- 'Duckfoot' ♀H5	EShb GBin WCot WFib
	- 'Dyinnii'	ELan EPot LShi NLar SPtp WAbe WCot
	- 'Eileen' (v)	WFib
§	- (Elegantissima Group) 'Marginata Elegantissima' (v)	SGsty
	- - 'Tricolor' (v)	CMac CTri EPfP LRHS SPoG WCFE WFib
	- 'Elfenbein' (v)	WCot WFib
	- 'Erecta'	EHyd ELan EPPr GAbr IDee MBlu MHer NHol NWad SDix SPer SPlb WCFE WFib XLum
	- 'Ester' (v)	SCob
	- 'Eva' (v)	WFib
	- 'Fantasia' (v)	WFib
	- 'Feenfinger'	WFib
	- 'Filigran'	WFib
	- 'Flashback' (v)	WFib
	- 'Flavescens'	WFib
	- 'Fluffy Ruffles'	GKev WFib
	- 'Francis'	WFib
	- 'Frosty' (v)	WFib
	- 'Garland'	WFib
	- 'Gavotte'	WFib
	- 'Gilded Hawke'	WFib
	- 'Glache' (v)	MRav WFib
	- 'Glacier' (v) ♀H5	CArg CBcs CMac CTri EHyd ELan EPfP GDam GKev LCro LOPS LRHS MAsh MGos MMuc MRav MSwo NHol NRHS SCob SEND SPer SPoG SRms SWvt WFar WFib
	- 'Glymii'	GBin WFib
	- 'Gold Harald'	see *H. helix* 'Goldchild'
	- 'Gold Ripple'	see *H. helix* 'Golden Starlight'
§	- 'Goldchild' (v) ♀H5	CBcs CMac EBee EHyd EPfP EShb LCro LOPS LRHS MAsh MGos MMuc MRav MSwo NBir NHol NRHS SCob SLim SNig SPer SPoG SWvt WFib
	- 'Golden Ann'	see *H. helix* 'Ceridwen'
	- 'Golden Arrow'	see *H. helix* 'Goldfinger'
§	- 'Golden Curl' (v)	CMac EHyd EPfP LRHS WFib
	- 'Golden Ester'	see *H. helix* 'Ceridwen'
	- 'Golden Gate' (v)	WCot
	- 'Golden Girl' (v)	WFib
§	- 'Golden Ingot' (v) ♀H5	EHyd LRHS WFib
	- 'Golden Jytte'	see *H. helix* 'Classy Lassie'
	- 'Golden Kolibri'	see *H. helix* 'Midas Touch'
§	- 'Golden Starlight' (v)	ELan EShb NLar SEND WFib
	- 'Goldfinch'	WFib
§	- 'Goldfinger'	EHyd LRHS WFib
	- 'Goldheart'	see *H. helix* 'Oro di Bogliasco'
	- 'Goldstern' (v)	MRav WFib
	- 'Gracilis'	see *H. hibernica* 'Gracilis'

	– 'Green Finger'	see *H. helix* 'Très Coupé'
	– 'Green Man'	WFib
	– 'Green Ripple'	CBcs CBod CRos EHyd ELan EPfP GDam LRHS MBlu MGos MMuc MSwo MWht NRHS NWea SCob SEND SGsty SNig SPer SPlb SRms SWvt WFib
	– 'Halebob'	WFib
	– 'Hamilton'	see *H. hibernica* 'Hamilton'
	– 'Harald' (v)	WFib
	– 'Hazel' (v)	WFib
	– 'Heise' (v)	WFib
	– 'Heise Denmark' (v)	WFib
	– 'Helvig'	see *H. helix* 'White Knight'
	– 'Henriette'	WFib
	– 'Hispanica'	see *H. iberica*
	– 'Hite's Miniature'	see *H. helix* 'Merion Beauty'
	– 'Hullavington'	CNat
	– 'Humpty Dumpty'	CExl
	– 'Hunlaf's Winter Red'	CNat
	– 'Ice Cream' (v)	GKev WCot
	– 'Imp'	see *H. helix* 'Brokamp'
	– 'Ingrid' (v)	SRms
	– 'Ivalace'	EPPr EShb MSwo SCob SRms WFib XLum
	– 'Jake'	WFib
	– 'Jane's Findling' (v)	CNat
	– 'Jara' arboreal	WCot
	– 'Jasper'	WFib
	– 'Jersey Doris' (v)	WFib
	– 'Jerusalem'	see *H. helix* 'Calico'
	– 'Jubilee' (v)	WFar WFib
	– 'Kaleidoscope' (v)	WFib
	– 'Kevin'	WFib
	– 'Kolibri' (v)	SCob SRms WFib
	– 'Königer's Auslese'	WFib
	– 'Lalla Rookh'	MRav WFib
	– 'Leo Swicegood'	WFib
	– 'Lightfinger'	WFib
	– 'Little Diamond' (v)	CMac CTri ELan SCob SLon SRms SWvt WFib
	– 'Little Luzii' (v)	WFib
	– 'Lopsided'	CNat
§	– 'Lucida'	SDix
	– 'Luzii' (v)	WFib
	– 'Maculata'	see *H. helix* 'Minor Marmorata'
§	– 'Manda's Crested' 🏆H5	ELan NLar WFib
	– 'Maple Leaf' 🏆H5	EShb WFib
	– 'Marginata Elegantissima'	see *H. helix* (Elegantissima Group) 'Marginata Elegantissima'
I	– 'Marmorata' Fibrex	WFib
	– 'Mathilde' (v)	EHyd WFib
	– 'Melanie'	ECha WCot WFib
	– 'Meon'	WFib
§	– 'Merion Beauty'	WFib
§	– 'Midas Touch' (v) 🏆H5	CBod ELan NWea WFib
	– 'Minikin' (v)	WCot
*	– 'Minima' misapplied <u>**new**</u>	GQue
	– 'Minima' Hibberd	see *H. helix* 'Donerailensis'
	– 'Minima' M.Young	see *H. helix* 'Congesta'
§	– 'Minor Marmorata' (v)	EPPr XLum
	– 'Minty' (v)	WFib
	– 'Misty' (v)	WFib
	– 'Needlepoint'	XLum
	– 'Niagara Falls'	LRHS
	– 'Nigra Aurea' (v)	WFib
	– 'Obovata'	WFib
	– 'Oro di Bogliasco' (v)	Widely available
	– 'Ovata'	WFib
§	– 'Parsley Crested' 🏆H5	CDoC ELan WFib
	– 'Patent Leather'	WFib
	– 'Pedata'	MSwo SRms WFib
	– 'Perkeo'	WCot WFib
	– 'Peter' (v)	WFib
	– 'Pink 'n' Curly'	WCot WFib
	– 'Pink 'n' Very Curly'	WCot
§	– 'Pittsburgh'	WFib
	– 'Plume d'Or'	WFib
	– f. ***poetarum***	MBlu WCot WFib
	– – 'Poetica Arborea'	EShb
	– 'Raleigh Delight' (v)	WCot
	– 'Ray's Supreme'	see *H. helix* 'Pittsburgh'
	– subsp. ***rhizomatifera***	see *H. helix* 'Rhizomatifera'
§	– 'Rhizomatifera'	WFib
	– 'Richard John'	see *H. helix* 'Golden Curl'
	– 'Ritterkreuz'	WFib
	– 'Romanze' (v)	WCot WFib
	– 'Russelliana'	EPPr WCFE WFib
*	– 'Sagittifolia' ambig.	LRHS MAsh MBlu SPoG
	– 'Sagittifolia Variegata' (v)	WFib
	– 'Saint Agnes'	see *H. helix* 'Golden Ingot'
	– 'Sally'	WFib
	– 'Salt and Pepper'	see *H. helix* 'Minor Marmorata'
	– 'Schäfer Three' (v)	WFib
	– 'Seabreeze'	WFib
	– 'Shamrock' 🏆H5	WFib
	– 'Shannon'	WFib
	– 'Silver Ferney' (v)	EPPr EShb WFib
	– 'Silver King' (v)	WCot WFib
§	– 'Snow Cap' (v)	WFib
	– 'Spetchley'	see *H. hibernica* 'Spetchley'
	– 'Splashes' (v)	WFib
	– 'Sunrise'	WFib
	– 'Suzanne'	see *H. nepalensis* 'Suzanne'
	– 'Tanja'	WFib
	– 'Teardrop'	WFib
	– 'Telecurl'	WFib
	– 'Temptation' (v)	WFib
	– 'Teneriffe' (v)	WFib
	– 'Topazolite' (v)	WFib
§	– 'Très Coupé'	MMuc SArc SEND
	– 'Trinity'	WFib
	– 'Tripod'	WFib
	– 'Triton'	WFib
	– 'Troll'	WFib
	– 'Ursula' (v)	WFib
	– 'Very Merry'	WFib
	– 'Vitifolium'	see *H. hibernica* 'Vitifolia'
§	– 'White Knight' (v) 🏆H5	WFib
	– 'White Mein Herz'	see *H. helix* 'Snow Cap'
	– 'White Ripple' (v)	CBod SGsty WFib
	– 'White Wonder'	LCro LOPS SPoG
	– 'Williamsiana' (v)	WFib
	– 'Woerneri'	see *H.* × *soroksarensis* 'Woerneri'
	– 'Yellow Ripple'	see *H. helix* 'Golden Starlight'
	– 'Zebra' (v)	WFib
	hibernica	CBcs EPfP EWTr GDam LBuc LRHS MRav MSwo NOrn NWea SCob SEWo SGsty SPer SWeb SWvt WFib
	– 'Angularis Aurea' 🏆H5	WFib
	– 'Anna Marie'	see *H. helix* 'Anna Marie'
	– 'Arbori Compact'	LPar
	– 'Betty Allen'	WFib
§	– 'Crûg Gold'	WCru
§	– 'Dealbata' (v)	CMac SRms WFib
§	– 'Deltoidea' 🏆H5	MWht WCFE WFib
	– 'Digitata Crûg Gold'	see *H. hibernica* 'Crûg Gold'
	– 'Ebony'	see *H. hibernica* (Hibernica Group) 'Ebony'
	– 'Glengariff'	WFib
§	– 'Gracilis'	WFib
§	– 'Hamilton'	WFib

§	– (Hibernica Group) 'Ebony'	WFib
§	– – 'Rona' (v)	GQue WFib
	– – 'Sulphurea' (v)	WFib
	– – 'Variegata' (v)	WFib
	– 'Lobata Major'	SRms
	– 'Palmata'	WFib
	– 'Rona'	see *H. hibernica* (Hibernica Group) 'Rona'
	– 'Sagittifolia'	CTri EPfP SCob
§	– 'Spetchley' 🏆H5	CMac GKev MRav NLar NPer NWad SLee WCot WFib WGrn
I	– 'Vitifolia'	WFib
§	***iberica***	WFib
	maderensis	WFib
	maroccana 'Morocco'	WFib
	– 'Spanish Canary'	WFib
§	***nepalensis***	WFib
	– KWJ 12345	WCru
	– 'Marbled Dragon'	WFib
§	– 'Suzanne'	WFib
	pastuchovii	EShb WFib
	– from Troödos, Cyprus	see *H. pastuchovii* subsp. *cypria*
	– 'Ann Ala' 🏆H5	EPPr MBlu WAvo WCot WFib
§	– subsp. ***cypria***	WFib
	– 'Lagocetti'	see *H. pastuchovii* 'Lagodekhi'
§	– 'Lagodekhi'	WFib
§	***rhombea***	WCot WFib
	– 'Japonica'	see *H. rhombea*
	– 'Variegata' (v)	WFib
§	× ***soroksarensis*** 'Woerneri'	NLar WFib

Hedychium ✿ (*Zingiberaceae*)

	W/O 7118 **new**	GGro
	W/O 7120 **new**	GGro
*	from Ziyadum, Myanmar	WPGP
	'Anne Bishop'	SEND
	aurantiacum	CBcs CBct CCCN CDTJ CTsd GKev LEdu SPalm XLum
	aureum	LEdu WPGP
	brevicaule B&SWJ 7171	WCru
	'C.P. Raffill'	see *H.* × *moorei* 'Raffillii'
	chrysoleucum	CCCN
*	'Clarkei'	CCCN
	coccineum	CDTJ CTsd GKev MHid
	– B&SWJ 5238	WCru
	– from Mizoram, India	WPGP
	– var. ***angustifolium***	WPGP
	– 'Disney'	CDTJ
	– 'Hungphung Stripe'	LEdu WPGP
	– 'Khangkhui Tall Boy'	LEdu MHid WPGP
	– 'Khonoma Silver'	LEdu WPGP
	– 'Shillong Ghost'	LEdu WPGP
	coronarium 🏆H1c	CAbb CAvo CBct CCCN CDTJ CExl CSpe CTsd ETod GKev MHid XLum
	– B&SWJ 3745	WCru
	– 'Gold Spot'	CCCN CDTJ CTsd GKev
	– var. ***urophyllum***	see *H. flavum* Roxb.
	deceptum **new**	LRHS XSte
	densiflorum	CAbb CCCN CDTJ CExl CTsd ECha GKev LCro LEdu LOPS MHid SPalm SRms WCot WCru WPGP XLum
	– EN 562	CExl
	– LS&H 17393	CExl
	– 'Assam Orange'	CAvo CCCN CExl CTsd IDee LEdu MHid SEND SPlb WCru WPGP WSMil
	– 'Sorung'	CDTJ CExl LEdu SChr WPGP
	– 'Stephen'	CAvo CBct CCCN CDTJ CExl EBee IPot LEdu LRHS MNrw SPlb WPGP XSte
	'Devon Cream'	CCCN CDTJ CExl CTsd LRHS SChr WSMil XSte
	'Doctor Moy' (v)	CDTJ MHid NGKo XSte
	ellipticum	CAbb CCCN CDTJ CTsd GKev SDir SPalm XLum
	– B&SWJ 8354	WCru
	– PAB 7867	LEdu WPGP
	'Filigree'	CExl
§	***flavescens***	CBct CCCN CDTJ CTsd EBee GKev LCro LOPS
	flavum misapplied	see *H. flavescens*
§	***flavum*** Roxb.	CAbb CBcs XLum
	– HWJ 604	WCru
	forrestii misapplied	see *H.* 'Helen Dillon'
	forrestii Diels	CSpe CTsd IDee SPlb
	– KWJ 12314	WCru
	gardnerianum 🏆H2	CAbb CDTJ CExl CTsd EBee GKev LCro LEdu LOPS LRHS MHid MNrw MSCN NGKo SArc SChr SDeJ SDir SPlb WCru WSMil XLum XSte
	– B&SWJ 12533	WCru
	– NJM 13.079	WPGP
	'Giant Yellow'	CDTJ
	'Gold Flame'	EBee
	gomezianum	LEdu
	gracile	WCru
	greenii	CBcs CBct CCCN CDTJ CSpe CTsd EWld GKev LEdu MNrw MPie SDir SPalm SPlb SSal WBor WCru XLum
	– 'Mhui Fang'	WPGP
	griffithianum	CCCN CDTJ XLum
	– white-flowered	CCCN
§	'Helen Dillon'	CCCN CDTJ CExl ESwi ETod LEdu LRHS WCru WPGP
	'Keneggy'	SVen
	'Luna Moth'	WPGP
	luteum	CTsd
	maximum	CDTJ SChr SMad WPGP
	– B&SWJ 8261A	WCru
	– HWJ 810	WCru
§	× ***moorei*** 'Raffillii'	WCru
	'Pink Princess'	CDTJ
	'Pink V'	LRHS
	pink-flowered	WSMil
	'Samsheri'	CCCN
	spicatum	CAbb CAvo CCCN CDTJ CExl CTsd GKev GPoy LEdu MNrw MRav SMHy WPGP
	– B&SWJ 7231	WCru
	– CC 1705	CExl
	– P. Bon. 57188	CExl WPGP
	– PAB 13.0718	LEdu
	– from Ciaojiang	SBrt
	– from Salween Valley, China	CExl
	– 'Himalayan Lipstick'	GKev
	– 'Huani'	LEdu
	– 'Liberty'	WCru
	– 'Shirui Steps'	LEdu
	– 'Singalila'	LEdu WCru WPGP
	– 'Troglodyte'	LEdu WPGP
	'St Martin's'	CCCN
	stenopetalum	MHid
	– B&SWJ 7155	WCru
	'Tahitian Flame' (v)	XSte
	'Tara' 🏆H4	CAvo CBct CCht CDTJ CExl EPfP LEdu LRHS MGil MNrw SArc SMHy SMad SPad SPlb WCru WPGP WSMil XSte
	tengchongense 'Trum Trom'	WCru
	– 'Y Tý'	WCru

thyrsiforme	CDTJ CTsd GKev WCru XLum
villosum	CDTJ
- var. ***tenuiflorum***	CDTJ MHid WPGP
- - KWJ 12305	WCru
wardii	CDTJ CExl CTsd ESwi LRHS MHid WCot WCru WPGP
yunnanense	LEdu SBrt SPlb WPGP
- B&SWJ 7900	ESwi
- BWJ 7900	WCru
- L 633	CExl
- 'Iago'	WCru

Hedysarum (*Fabaceae*)

coronarium	CSpe ELan LShi SPhx SPoG WKif
hedysaroides	GArf
multijugum	MBlu WSHC

Heimia (*Lythraceae*)

salicifolia	EBee ECre MGil SBrt SMad WPGP

Helenium (*Asteraceae*)

'Adios'	WFar
'Amber'	ECtt MAvo MSpe WFar
'Amber Dwarf' **new**	SAko
autumnale	CExl CSBt CTri EPfP LSRN MNHC NChi SWvt WFar XLum
- 'All Gold'	SWvt
- 'Bandera'	CBod ECtt MSCN NRHS SPad
§ - Helena Series	CRos SBls SWvt WFar
§ - - 'Helena Gold'	CBod EPfP MACG
- - 'Helena Rote Töne'	CBod CChe CSpe EHyd EPfP LRHS LSun MACG MHol NRHS SCoo WBor
- - 'Helena Yellow'	EHyd LRHS NRHS WCav
- (Mariachi Series) 'Fuego' PBR	CBod CMac CRos CWGN ECtt EHyd LCro LOPS LRHS LSou MAvo MBel MHol MNrw MPri NRHS SCob SRms SWvt WCAu WNPC XSte
- - 'Ranchera' PBR	LRHS MBel NLar NRHS SPad
- - 'Salsa' PBR	CBod CKno CMac CRos EHyd ELan ILea LCro LOPS LRHS LSou MAvo MNrw NLar NRHS SPad SRms SWvt WNPC
- - 'Siesta' PBR	CRos EHyd LRHS MNrw MPri NLar NRHS SRms WHil
- - 'Sombrero' PBR	CBod ECtt EHyd LCro LOPS LRHS MPri NEoE SPoG WNPC XSte
- 'Short and Sassy' PBR	EHyd ELan LRHS LSou MBros MNrw MPri NLar NRHS SCoo SPoG SRms WNPC
'Baudirektor Linne' ♀H7	EHyd ILea WCAu WPGP
'Betty'	CBod ECtt LSou MSCN MSpe
'Biedermeier'	ECtt MNrw MSpe SAko
bigelovii	XLum
'Blütentisch' misapplied	see *H.* 'Riverton Beauty'
'Blütentisch' Foerster ♀H7	CMea EHyd GMaP LRHS NLar NRHS
'Bressingham Gold'	EHyd MHCG MNrw MSpe WAvo WHrl
'Bruno'	CRos EBlo EHyd LRHS MArl NRHS SHar SMrm
'Butterpat' ♀H7	CDor EBlo ECtt EHyd GMaP LRHS MArl MNrw MRav MSpe NRHS WCav
'Can Can'	CRos ECtt EHyd ELon EPfP IPot LRHS MAvo MHer MNrw NGdn NRHS SPer SRms WCAu WFar WGoo
'Carmen' (UFO Series)	CBod EBlo MSpe
'Chelsey'	ECtt ELan EPfP GQue LCro LOPS LRHS LSRN MNrw MRav MSpe NLar NSti SPer SPoG SRms
'Chipperfield Orange'	CTtf ECtt GMaP MArl NBir NGdn
'Coppelia'	EHyd MACG NBir NGdn WFar
COPPER SPRAY	see *H.* 'Kupfersprudel'
DARK BEAUTY	see *H.* 'Dunkle Pracht'
'Dauerbrenner'	MAvo MSpe SHar
'Die Blonde'	MAvo SMHy
'Doktor Hartmann'	MSpe
'Double Trouble' PBR	CBod ECtt EHyd GBin LRHS MBNS MHol NFav NGdn NHpl NRHS SGbt SPer SRms WCot WFar
§ 'Dunkle Pracht' ♀H7	EBee ECtt EWTr LSRN MSpe NLar WFar
'El Dorado'	CMea CRos EBee EBlo ECtt EHyd ELon EWoo IPot LEdu LRHS MAvo MSpe NDov NRHS NSti SHar SRms WCot WFar
'Fancy Fan' **new**	MSpe
'Fata Morgana'	CBod ECtt MAvo MHer MSpe
'Festival'	ECtt
'Feuersiegel' ♀H7	CRos ECtt EHyd LRHS MSpe NRHS SAko
'Fiesta'	ECtt MAvo WFar
'Flamenco'	MSpe WFar
'Flammendes Käthchen'	CRos EBee ECtt EHyd LRHS NRHS SAko SHar SMrm
'Flammenrad'	EBee SAko
'Flammenspiel'	ECtt EHyd MNrw
flexuosum	SPhx
'Gartensonne' ♀H7	LPla MAvo SMrm WAvo
'Gay-go-round'	MAvo
'Gelbe Waltraut'	MAvo MSpe
'Gold Doubloons'	EBee
GOLD FOX	see *H.* 'Goldfuchs'
'Gold Intoxication'	see *H.* 'Goldrausch'
GOLDEN YOUTH	see *H.* 'Goldene Jugend'
§ 'Goldene Jugend'	ECtt ELon WCot
§ 'Goldfuchs'	WCot
§ 'Goldlackzwerg'	EHyd IPot LRHS WMal
§ 'Goldrausch'	EBee ECtt EPfP GBin MMrt MNrw MSpe NGdn SAko WCAu WFar
'Goldreif'	CMea
'Helena' misapplied	see *H. autumnale* 'Helena Gold'
'Herbstgold'	MSpe
hoopesii	see *Hymenoxys hoopesii*
'Hot Lava'	CBod CWGN ECtt MNrw MSpe
'Indianersommer'	CDor ECtt GMaP GWyn MNrw MSpe NLar SPer SPhx SSut WCFE WGoo WSpi
'Julisamt'	LEdu
'Kanaria'	CBar CBod CDor CRos EBee ECtt EHyd EPfP GBin GWyn LPot LRHS MAvo MBel MRav MSpe NLar NRHS NSti SMrm WHil
'Karneol' ♀H7	EHyd EPfP LRHS NRHS
'Königstiger' ♀H7	CRos ECtt EHyd GBee GBin LRHS MHCG MNrw NRHS SAko WFar
'Kugelsonne'	GBin NLar SAko WCAu
§ 'Kupfersprudel'	MAvo SAko
'Kupferzwerg'	EAJP ELan MSpe SAko
'Lambada'	SMHy
'Lemon Queen'	WSpi
'Little Orange'	WGoo
'Loysder Wieck'	EBee ECtt LRHS MBel MSpe NGdn SPeP WCAu
'Luc' ♀H5	ECha ELon GBin MAvo WCot
§ 'Mahagoni'	IPot
MAHOGANY	see *H.* 'Mahagoni'
'Mahogany'	see *H.* 'Goldlackzwerg'
MARDI GRAS ('Helbro')	EBee ECtt EHyd ELan EMor EPfP GAbr LRHS LSou MBel MCot MHol MSpe NRHS SPoG SRms SWvt WCAu WNPC
'Margot'	MSpe

'Marion Nickig'	WFar
'Meranti'	CMea MSpe NDov SWvt WCot
'Moerheim Beauty' ♀H7	Widely available
'Monique' (UFO Series)	CBod
'Oldenburg'	WCot
'Pat's Promise'	CMea SWvt
PIPSQUEAK ('Blopip')	EBee EBlo LRHS SRms
'Poncho'	LRHS SRms
'Potter's Wheel'	CBod EBee ECtt MACG MSpe NLar SRms
puberulum	EHyd LRHS NBir NGrd NRHS
'Pumilum Magnificum'	EHyd ELan EPfP GQue MSpe NFav NRHS SMad SPer WFar XLum
'Ragamuffin'	ECtt SWvt WCot
'Rauchtopas'	GWyn ILea IPot LCro LEdu LOPS LPla LSou MBel MMrt MSpe NDov NLar SAko SMrm SSal WGoo WPGP
RED AND GOLD	see *H.* 'Rotgold' Foerster
'Red Army'	CMea ECha ECtt EHyd ELon EMor GBee LEdu MAvo MSpe NGdn SRkn SRms SWvt
'Red Jewel'	CRos EBee ECtt EHyd ELon EWTr LRHS MAvo MBriF MHol MNrw MPie NGdn NLar NRHS SAko SCob SEdd WCAu WCFE WCot WHoo WPGP
'Ring of Fire' ♀H7	SMHy
§ 'Riverton Beauty'	ECha ECtt MNrw NChi SDix WCot WHoo
'Riverton Gem'	ECtt GBee GQue MHCG MSpe
'Rotgold' misapplied	see *H. autumnale* Helena Series
§ 'Rotgold' Foerster	ECtt IPot SRms
'Rouge Foncé'	WCot WFar
'Rubinzwerg' ♀H7	Widely available
'Ruby Charm'	ECtt EPfP MBros MNrw WCot WFar
§ 'Ruby Thuesday'	Widely available
'Ruby Tuesday'	see *H.* 'Ruby Thuesday'
'Sahin's Early Flowerer' ♀H7	Widely available
'Septemberfuchs'	LEdu SAko SPhx
'Sophie zur Linden'	ECha ECtt MSpe
'Sunshine Superman'	CMea MSpe
'The Bishop'	EBee ECtt EHyd EPfP GAbr LCro LOPS LRHS MRav NHol NRHS SCob SGbt SPer SWvt WFar
'Tie Dye'	CBod EBee ECtt EPfP MAvo MSpe NGdn SPoG WFar
'Tijuana Brass'	ECtt IPot NLar
'Tip Top'	EHyd EPfP LRHS SGBe
'UFO Tom' (UFO Series)	MSpe
'Vicky'	MHCG SHar
'Vivace'	ELon LEdu MSpe WCot WPGP
'Wagon Wheel'	WFar
'Waldhorn'	WPGP
'Waltraut' ♀H7	CElw CRos EBee ECtt EHyd ELan EMor EPfP GWyn LCro LOPS LPot LRHS MArl MCot MNrw MPie MRav MSpe NBir NDov NLar NRHS SCob SPer SRms SWvt WCAu WFar
'Wesergold' ♀H7	CRos EBee EBlo EHyd LRHS NDov NRHS NSti SPoG WCAu
'Westerstede'	EBlo LRHS
'Wyndley'	CBcs CDor CMea CRos EAJP ECtt EHyd ELan EMor EPfP EShb ETod GMaP LPot LRHS MBel MHer MRav NBir NGdn NLar NRHS SGbt SPer SRms WCAu WCav WFar WHoo
'Zimbelstern'	ECha ECtt MAvo MCot MSpe NLar WCot WFar WPGP
'Zonnedam'	ECtt

Heliamphora (*Sarraceniaceae*)

nutans	SHmp

Helianthella (*Asteraceae*)

§ ***quinquenervis***	EBee EBlo EHyd EPfP LRHS NLar NRHS WFar

Helianthemum (*Cistaceae*)

'Albert's Brick'	NRush
'Alice Howorth'	NRush WIce
'Amabile Plenum' (d)	GBin LShi NRush
'Amy Baring' ♀H5	CRos CTri ECtt EHyd LRHS NRHS NWad SRms WHoo
'Annabel' (d)	CRos ECtt EHyd GBin LRHS NRHS WFar
apenninum	EPPr LPla SBut SEND SRms WAbe XSen
'Apricot'	CTri ECtt
'Apricot Blush'	WAbe
'Baby Buttercup'	CMea NRush
'Beech Park Red'	CSma CTri ECtt EPot NRush WAbe WFar WHoo WIce WKif
'Ben Afflick'	CRos ECtt EHyd LRHS MAsh NRHS NRush NSla SRms
'Ben Alder'	ECtt
'Ben Dearg'	CMea ECtt SRms
'Ben Fhada'	Widely available
'Ben Heckla'	CRos ECtt EHyd GAbr LRHS NRHS SRms XLum
'Ben Hope'	CRos CTri EAJP ECtt EHyd ELan EPfP EWTr EWoo LRHS NRHS SCob SRms WHoo WIce XLum XSen
§ 'Ben Ledi'	CBcs CBod ECtt ELan GAbr GJos GMaP LRHS MAsh NHol SCob SGbt SPoG SRms SRot WAbe WFar
'Ben Lomond'	GAbr
'Ben More'	CAvo CBcs CKel CRos ECtt EHyd ELan EPfP GAbr GJos GMaP LRHS MAsh MBros MRav MSwo NBir NRHS NRush SCob SPoG SRms WFar WHoo WIce
'Ben Nevis'	CTri NRush SRms
'Ben Vane'	CRos ECtt EHyd LRHS NRHS NRush SRms
'Boughton Double Primrose' (d)	WAbe WFar
'Broughty Sunset'	ECtt GAbr NRush
'Bunbury'	ECtt ELon EPfP GJos GQue NBir NRush SEdd SPoG SRms WFar
I 'Butter and Eggs'	SRms
'Captivation'	ECtt NHol NRush
'Cerise Queen' (d)	CTri ECha ECtt EPfP GKev LRHS MSwo NRush SEND SPer SRms WFar
chamaecistus	see *H. nummularium*
'Cheviot'	ECha NBir WHoo XLum
'Chocolate Blotch'	CRos EHyd LRHS NRHS NRush NWad SEND SRms
'Coachman's Salmon Coral'	NRush
'Cornish Cream'	ECtt GAbr NHol NRush SRms
cupreum	GAbr GKev
'David'	NHol
'David Ritchie'	WHoo
'Diana'	CMea ECtt EPot WIce
double apricot-flowered (d)	CBod CPla LRHS
'Elfenbeinglanz'	WFar
'Etna'	NRush
'Everton Ruby'	see *H.* 'Ben Ledi'
'Fairy'	EHyd ELan EPfP NRush
§ 'Fire Dragon' ♀H4	CAvo CMea CRos ECha ECtt EHyd ELan EPfP GAbr GMaP LRHS MAsh NBir NRHS NRush SGbt SRms WAbe XLum XSen

	'Fireball'	see *H.* 'Mrs C.W. Earle'
	'Georgeham'	CAvo CMea CSma EBou ECtt ELon GAbr NBir NHol NRush SPhx SRms WHoo XLum
§	'Golden Queen'	CBod EBou ECtt EPfP MAsh MSwo NRush SRms WFar
	'Hampstead Orange'	CTri
	'Hartswood Ruby'	CRos EHyd GMaP LRHS NRHS NRush SAko SRms WAbe WFar
	'Henfield Brilliant' ♀^{H4}	CExl CRos ECha ECtt EHyd ELan ELon EPfP EWoo GAbr LRHS MRav NBir NHol NRHS NSla SBut SMad SPoG SRms WCav WCot WHil WHoo WSHC WSMil XLum
	'Highdown'	SRms
	'Highdown Apricot'	CRos ECtt EHyd ELon LRHS NRHS NRush SPoG SRms
	'Honeymoon'	ECtt NRush NWad
	'Jubilee' (d) ♀^{H4}	CTri ECtt GJos MAsh MHol NBir NChi NHol SPoG SRms WCav
	'Karen's Silver'	WAbe
	'Kathleen Druce' (d)	ECtt NWad
	'Kathleen Mary'	CMea WIce
	'Lawrenson's Pink'	CBod CRos CSma ECtt EHyd EWoo GJos LRHS NRHS SRms WCAu WFar XSen
	'Lemon Queen'	ECtt NRush
	'Lucy Elizabeth'	ECtt
	lunulatum	CRos EHyd LRHS NRHS SRms WAbe
	'Mead Sunset'	CMea ECtt
§	'Mrs C.W. Earle' (d) ♀^{H4}	CTri ECtt EHyd ELan EPfP GKev LRHS MBow MBros NRHS NRush SRms
	'Mrs Clay'	see *H.* 'Fire Dragon'
	'Mrs Croft'	SRms
	'Mrs Hays'	ECtt
	'Mrs Lake'	GAbr NRush
	'Mrs Mold'	NRush
	'Mrs Moules'	SRms
	mutabile	SPlb SVic WFar
	'New Moon'	CSma NRush
§	***nummularium***	CBee ENfk GPoy GQue MBow MHer MNHC NAts NMir SPhx SRms WAbe WIce WSFF WWild
	oelandicum	NSla SRms WAbe
	- subsp. ***alpestre***	EBou
	- subsp. ***incanum***	WAbe
	- subsp. ***italicum***	WAbe
	- subsp. ***piloselloides***	EPot WAbe
	'Old Gold'	ECtt SRms WAbe
	'Orange Phoenix' (d)	ECtt NRush NWad
	'Ovum Supreme'	NHol
	pannosum new	WAbe
	'Peach'	CTri
	'Pershore Orange'	NRush
	'Pink Angel' (d)	CBod CSma NRush SRms WAbe WFar
	'Praecox'	CMea CTri SRms
	'Prima Donna'	EHyd ELan EPfP
	'Prostrate Orange'	NRush SRms
	'Raspberry Ripple'	CRos CSma EBou ECtt EHyd ELan EPfP EPot LRHS NRHS NRush SPoG SRms
	'Razzle Dazzle' (v)	NRush SRms
	'Red Dragon'	EPot NRush WAbe
	'Red Orient'	see *H.* 'Supreme'
	'Regenbogen' (d)	ECtt SEND
§	'Rhodanthe Carneum' ♀^{H4}	CMea CRos EBou ECha ECtt EHyd ELan EPfP EWTr EWoo GDam GJos GMaP LRHS MMrt MRav MSwo NBir NRHS NRush SCob SEND SPer SPhx SPoG SRms WAbe WCav WKif
§	'Rosakönigin'	EBou ECtt GAbr NHol NRush SEND WAbe
	'Rose of Leeswood' (d)	CBod ECtt GJos MHol SPoG SRms WHoo WKif XLum
	ROSE QUEEN	see *H.* 'Rosakönigin'
	'Roxburgh Gold'	NRush SRms
	'Saint John's College Yellow'	EHyd LRHS NRHS SRms
	'Salmon Queen'	CRos ECtt EHyd LRHS NRHS NRush SEND SRms
	'Shot Silk'	CSma ECtt EWes NRush SRms
	'Snow Queen'	see *H.* 'The Bride'
	'Southmead'	GAbr
	'Sterntaler'	GAbr SRms WFar
	'Strawberry Fields'	ECtt NSla
	'Sudbury Gem'	CRos CTri ECha ECtt EHyd GAbr LRHS NRHS NRush SRms
	'Sulphur Moon'	CRos EHyd LRHS NRHS SRms
	'Sunbeam'	ECtt NRush SRms
§	'Supreme'	ECtt ELan EPfP EWes GArf NRush SRms
	'Tangerine'	ECtt
§	'The Bride' ♀^{H4}	Widely available
	'Tigrinum Plenum' (d)	EWes
	'Tomato Red'	ECtt NRush
	umbellatum	see *Halimium umbellatum*
	'Voltaire'	ECtt NRush NWad
	'Welsh Flame'	ECtt NHol WAbe
	'Whenday'	CMea
	'Wisley Pink'	see *H.* 'Rhodanthe Carneum'
	'Wisley Primrose' ♀^{H4}	Widely available
	'Wisley Rose'	EHyd NRHS
	'Wisley White'	CTri ECha ECtt ELan SHar
	'Wisley Yellow'	ECtt NRush WCav
	'Yellow Queen'	see *H.* 'Golden Queen'

Helianthus (*Asteraceae*)

	angustifolius	SDix
	'Anne'	ELon LPla NDov
	annuus	LRHS SVic
	- 'Claret' ♀^{H4}	LCro LOPS
	- 'Garden Statement'	LCro LOPS
	- 'Lemon Queen'	WCav
	- 'Moonbright'	SVic
	- 'Ring of Fire'	SVic
	- 'Sonja'	SVic
	- SUNBELIEVABLE BROWN EYED GIRL ('Sunbeliv01') (Sunbelievable Series) new	CRos
	- 'Sunbright' ♀^{H4}	SVic
	- 'Sunrich Orange' (Sunrich Series)	SVic
	atrorubens	MHol MRav NBro
	'Bitter Chocolate'	LEdu WPGP
	'Capenoch Star' ♀^{H5}	ECtt EHyd GMaP LEdu MArl MAvo MRav NBro NLar SDix SWvt WCAu
	'Capenoch Supreme'	ECtt EHyd
	'Carine'	ELon GBin LEdu MNrw NLar WCot WFar
	'Cotswold Queen' new	WCot
	debilis subsp. ***cucumerifolius***	SVic
	- - 'Italian White' new	SSal
	- 'Vanilla Ice'	LCro LOPS
*	***decapetalus*** 'Kastle Kobena'	CDor
	- MORNING SUN	see *H.* 'Morgensonne'
	'Dorian Roxburgh'	ECha ECtt LPla MAvo MHol WCot
	× ***doronicoides***	GWyn
	'Double Whammy' (d)	ECtt WTyc

'Flying Saucers' CBod CKno ECtt
giganteus CMea ECha SHar
- 'Sheila's Sunshine' CElw CTtf EBee ECtt EHyd EPPr EWes GBin ILea LEdu LPla LRHS MNrw NDov NRHS SAko SHar SMHy SPhx WFar
'Gullick's Variety' 🏆H5 ECtt NBro NChi NLar SPhx SWvt WFar XLum
'Happy Days' 🏆H5 CTtf ECtt EPfP EWes GBin LSou MAvo MHol NGBl NSti SBea SPeP SRms WCot WFar WHoo
'Hazel's Gold' EHyd
× ***kellermanii*** EBee MAvo SPhx
§ × ***laetiflorus*** EPPr GPSL MACG NLar SEND
- 'Daniel Dewar' MMuc
§ 'Lemon Queen' 🏆H4 Widely available
'Limelight' see *H.* 'Lemon Queen'
'Loddon Gold' 🏆H5 ECtt EHyd ELan EPfP EShb LRHS MArl MBel MHer MRav NBir NFav NRHS SMad SWvt WBor WCot WFar
§ ***maximiliani*** CBod ELan ELon EPPr MMuc SBls SMad SPhx SPtp
microcephalus EBee ELon MMuc NDov
- 'JS Straffe Prairie Gast' MNrw WFar
'Miss Mellish' 🏆H5 EBee ECtt EPPr LEdu LPla SMad WBor WBrk WCot WFar WHoo
mollis CBod MACG SBrt SPhx WFar
'Monarch' 🏆H5 CMea EBee EWhm MBel MHol MRav NLar SMad SMrm WCot WFar WHal
§ 'Morgensonne' WCot
× ***multiflorus*** 'Meteor' EBlo EHyd
'O Sole Mio' WCot WFar
occidentalis EPPr SPhx
orgyalis see *H. salicifolius*
§ ***pauciflorus*** EBee
quinquenervis see *Helianthella quinquenervis*
'Razzmatazz' SAko
rigidus misapplied see *H.* × *laetiflorus*
§ ***salicifolius*** CBod EBee ECtt EHyd ELan ELon EWoo GBin LEdu LRHS LSun MBel MBriF MCot MHol MMuc NBir NRHS SDix SEND SMad SPad SPoG SWvt WCot WFar WPGP XLum
- 'Low Down'[PBR] SCob SWvt
- 'Table Mountain'[PBR] LRHS SWvt
- very fine-leaved WCot
scaberrimus see *H.* × *laetiflorus*
'Soleil d'Or' ECtt SRms WFar WHal
strumosus MHol WCot
'Triomphe de Gand' NDov WFar
tuberosus EBee GPoy
- 'Bleu Patate' LEdu
- 'Drago' LEdu
- 'Dwarf' LEdu
- 'Fuseau' LCro LOPS SVic
- 'Garnet' LEdu
- 'Sakhalinski' LEdu
- 'Sugarball' LEdu

Helichrysum (*Asteraceae*)

adenocarpum SPlb
alveolatum see *H. splendidum*
amorginum 'Amber Cluster'[PBR] **new** SCoo
- RUBY CLUSTER ('Blorub'[PBR]) EHyd NRHS SCob
angustifolium from Crete see *H. microphyllum* (Willd.) Cambess.
§ ***arwae*** WAbe
bellidioides see *Anaphaloides bellidioides*
bellum GBin
bracteatum see *Xerochrysum bracteatum*
coralloides see *Ozothamnus coralloides*
'County Park Silver' see *Ozothamnus* 'County Park Silver'
'Elmstead' see *H. stoechas* 'White Barn'
frigidum WAbe
heldreichii WMal
hookeri see *Ozothamnus hookeri*
§ ***hypoleucum*** SDix
'Icicles' ELan GBin LRHS SEdd
italicum CBod CCBP CKel EBou ECha ENfk GBin GMaP GPoy GQue GWyn LShi MHer MNHC SArc SEND SPoG SRms SVen SVic WCav WHer XLum XSen
- 'Dartington' ENfk GBin SRms
§ - subsp. ***italicum*** SEdi
- 'Korma'[PBR] CBod CKel CPla CRos EHyd ELan EPfP EWTr EWhm GBin LRHS MAsh MHol NRHS SLon SRms
- subsp. ***microphyllum*** see *H. microphyllum* (Willd.) Cambess.
§ - subsp. ***serotinum*** CBcs EPfP GPoy LCro LOPS MRav SPer SRms SWvt
lanatum see *H. thianschanicum*
ledifolium see *Ozothamnus ledifolius*
marginatum misapplied see *H. milfordiae*
microphyllum ambig. SRms
§ ***microphyllum*** (Willd.) Cambess. CCBP ENfk MNHC SEND
§ ***milfordiae*** 🏆H4 GArf ITim SPlb SRms
orientale EPot GKev XSen
pagophilum GKev WAbe
petiolare 🏆H3 EBak ECtt MCot SPer SPoG
- 'Aureum' see *H. petiolare* 'Limelight'
- 'Goring Silver' 🏆H3 SPoG
§ - 'Limelight' 🏆H3 ECtt MCot SPer SPoG
- 'Variegatum' (v) 🏆H3 ECtt MCot SPoG
rosmarinifolium see *Ozothamnus rosmarinifolius*
§ 'Schwefellicht' EBee ECha EPfP MRav SPer WSHC
selago see *Ozothamnus selago*
serotinum see *H. italicum* subsp. *serotinum*
sessilioides EPot WAbe
§ ***splendidum*** 🏆H4 EPPr NBro SLon XSen
stoechas XSen
- 'Silverball' LRHS
§ - 'White Barn' ECha EPPr MAvo WCot WMal WSHC XLum
SULPHUR LIGHT see *H.* 'Schwefellicht'
§ ***thianschanicum*** SRms XLum
- GOLDEN BABY see *H. thianschanicum* 'Goldkind'
§ - 'Goldkind' NBir XLum
- 'White Wonder' EHyd EPfP LRHS NRHS SEdd
trilineatum misapplied see *H. splendidum*
tumidum see *Ozothamnus selago* var. *tumidus*
witbergense GKev
woodii see *H. arwae*

Helicodiceros (*Araceae*)

§ ***muscivorus*** NGKo WCot

Heliconia ✿ (*Heliconiaceae*)

psittacorum CCCN
rostrata CCCN

Helictotrichon (*Poaceae*)

planiculme EPPr
pratense CHab
§ ***sempervirens*** 🏆H5 Widely available
I - 'Pendulum' CBod CEme GBin XSen

- 'Saphirsprudel'	CBod EBee EHyd EPfP NRHS NSti WCot WPGP

Heliophila (*Brassicaceae*)

coronopifolia	CSpe

Heliopsis (*Asteraceae*)

helianthoides	CPla CRos LRHS WCav WFar
- 'Limelight'	see *Helianthus* 'Lemon Queen'
- LORAINE SUNSHINE ('Helhan'PBR) (v)	CBod CWGN LRHS MHol NWsh SIvy SPoG WCot WFar
- var. ***scabra***	NHol
- - 'Asahi'	CBod EBee ECtt MHol
- - BALLERINA	see *H. helianthoides* var. *scabra* 'Spitzentänzerin'
- - 'Benzinggold' 🏆H6	EHyd MRav SMrm
- - 'Bleeding Hearts' **new**	SBls
- - 'Bressingham Doubloon' (d)	LRHS
- - 'Burning Hearts'	CWGN LRHS MCot NLar SBea SRms
§ - - 'Goldgefieder' 🏆H6	MSpe WFar
- - 'Hohlspiegel'	EHyd GBin
- - 'Light of Loddon' 🏆H6	EHyd
- - 'Mars'	WFar
- - 'Patula'	EBee ECtt
- - 'Prairie Sunset'PBR	CBod EBee ECtt MHol
§ - - 'Sommersonne'	CSBt ECtt EHyd ELan EPfP LRHS NGBl NPer SPer SRms
§ - - 'Spitzentänzerin' 🏆H6	EBee ECtt MSpe
- - 'Summer Nights'	EBee ELan EPfP LCro LOPS MNrw NSti SBut SDix SPhx WFar
- - SUMMER SUN	see *H. helianthoides* var. *scabra* 'Sommersonne'
- - 'Sunburst' (v)	CRos EHyd LRHS NRHS
- - 'Venus'	CBod EBee ECtt EHyd LRHS MAsh SRms
- 'Summer Pink' (v)	CBod CWGN SIvy SPoG WCot WFar WWtn
- 'Sunstruck'	ECtt
- 'Tuscan Sun'PBR	EBee

Heliotropium ✿ (*Boraginaceae*)

§ ***amplexicaule***	SDys SMHy
anchusifolium	see *H. amplexicaule*
§ ***arborescens***	ENfk EPfP EShb MCot
- 'Chatsworth' 🏆H1c	CCCN ECre ECtt WABo
- 'Dame Alice de Hales'	ECtt
- 'Gatton Park'	ECtt
- 'Lord Roberts'	ECtt WMal
- MARINO BLUE ('Kleha07520'PBR)	LSou MBros
- 'Mary Fox'	ECtt
- 'Mrs J.W. Lowther'	ECtt
- 'Princess Marina' 🏆H1c	LCro LOPS NLar WBor
- 'Reva'	ECtt
- SCENTROPIA BLUE ('Heliovi') **new**	MPri
- 'White Lady'	CCCN CSpe ECtt SAng
- 'White Queen'	ECtt
- 'Woodcote'	ECtt
'Butterfly Kisses'	CRos SPoG
peruvianum	see *H. arborescens*

Helipterum see *Syncarpha*

Helleborus ✿ (*Ranunculaceae*)

abruzzicus	GKev MAsh
- WM 0227	MPhe
abschasicus	see *H. orientalis* Lam. subsp. *abchasicus*
ANGEL GLOW ('B11-02')	CRos LRHS MAsh NRHS SGBe
§ ***argutifolius*** 🏆H5	Widely available
- HGC SNOW FEVER ('Coseh 900'PBR)	SCoo
- mottled-leaved	see *H. argutifolius* 'Pacific Frost'
§ - 'Pacific Frost' (v)	CDor
- 'Silver Lace'	ELan EPfP GKev LRHS LSRN NBir NLar SGBe SPoG
atrorubens misapplied	see *H. orientalis* Lam. subsp. *abchasicus* Early Purple Group
atrorubens ambig.	MAsh
atrorubens Waldst. & Kit.	MRav
- WM 9028 from Slovenia	MPhe
- WM 9805 from Croatia	MPhe
- spotted	MPhe
× ***ballardiae***	EPfP GKev
- 'Candy Love'PBR	CRos EHyd EPfP LCro LEdu LOPS LRHS NRHS SCob
- HGC CAMELOT ('Coseh 940'PBR)	CRos ECtt EHyd EPfP LRHS MAsh NLar NRHS
- HGC CHAMPION ('Coseh 730'PBR)	EHyd LRHS
- HGC MAESTRO ('Coseh 890'PBR)	CRos EHyd EPfP LRHS NRHS
- HGC MERLIN ('Coseh 810'PBR)	CRos EShb LRHS MAsh NLar SCoo SPoG
- HGC SNOW DANCE ('Coseh 800'PBR)	CRos EHyd EPfP LRHS NRHS SPoG
× ***belcheri*** 'Pink Ice'	MAsh
bocconei WM 1332 from Sicily	MPhe
- WM 1334 from Calabria, Italy	MPhe
- WM 9719 from Italy	MPhe
- WM 9905 from Sicily	MPhe
colchicus	see *H. orientalis* Lam. subsp. *abchasicus*
corsicus	see *H. argutifolius*
- 'Marble' (v)	CSpe
croaticus	GKev
- WM 9810	MPhe
'Crystal Love' **new**	LRHS
dumetorum	GKev MAsh
- WM 1306 from Hungary	MPhe
- WM 1309 from Slovenia	MPhe
- WM 9209	MPhe
- WM 9627 from Croatia	MPhe
§ × ***ericsmithii***	CExl EPfP LRHS LSRN MAsh WSpi
- 'Bob's Best'	CExl EPfP SRms SWvt
- HGC JOKER ('Coseh 740'PBR)	EShb LRHS SPoG
- HGC MARLON CREAM ('Coseh 980'PBR)	LRHS NRHS
- HGC MONTE CRISTO ('Coseh 860'PBR)	CRos EHyd EPfP LRHS NRHS SCoo
- HGC SHOOTING STAR ('Coseh 790'PBR)	CRos EHyd EPfP LRHS NRHS SCoo
- 'HGC Silvermoon'PBR	LRHS NLar
- 'Pink Beauty'PBR	CEnd EPfP LSun NLar SEdd SLon SPoG WCot
- 'Pirouette'PBR	ECre EPfP EShb LCro LOPS LRHS MAsh NRHS
- RUBY GLOW ('Blt01')	EHyd EPfP
- 'Snow Love'PBR	CRos EHyd EPfP LBuc LRHS NLar NRHS
- 'Winter Moonbeam'PBR	CEnd ECre ECtt EPfP LBuc LRHS LSRN LSou LSun NRHS SEdd SGBe SLon SPoG SRms WCot
- 'Winter Sunshine'PBR	EGrI EPfP LBuc LRHS NRHS SGBe SPoG SRms
foetidus 🏆H7	Widely available

- 'Chedglow'	CNat
- 'Chedglow Variegated' (v)	CNat
- 'Gold Bullion'	CSpe SPoG
- 'Harvington Pewter'	EHyd LRHS NRHS
- 'Miss Jekyll'	MAsh
- 'Ruth'	EWoo MAsh
- Wester Flisk Group	CExl CNat EPfP GWyn LEdu LRHS NHol NPer SPoG SPtp WAvo WSpi
Gold Collection	see *Helleborus* with names starting HGC
'Golden Sunrise' (Winter Jewels Series)	CBod
'Harvington Rebekah'PBR	EHyd NRHS
HGC CINNAMON SNOW ('Coseh 700'PBR)	ECre EShb LRHS MAsh NLar NRHS SCoo
HGC ICE 'N' ROSES RED ('Coseh 4100')	CRos LRHS MAsh
HGC ICE 'N' ROSES ROSE ('Coseh 4200') **new**	LRHS MAsh
HGC ICE 'N' ROSES WHITE ('Coseh 4500')	CRos LRHS
HGC MADAME LEMONNIER ('Lem 100'PBR)	CRos EHyd ELan EPfP LRHS MAsh MPri NRHS
HGC PARADENIA ('Coseh 960'PBR)	CRos LRHS MAsh
HGC PINK FROST ('Coseh 710'PBR)	CRos ECtt EHyd EPfP LRHS MAsh MPri NLar NRHS SCoo SPoG
× ***hybridus***	CBod CBro CMac CMea ECha EHyd ELan EPfP GMaP LCro LOPS LRHS MCot MGos MRav NBid NRHS SCob SMrm SPer SRms WAvo WBrk WCAu WCot
- anemone-centred	EGrI LEdu MNrw WFar
- - yellow	LRHS
- - bicolour **new**	EWTr
- 'Angellier' **new**	MAsh
- 'Apple Blossom'	WFar
- 'Apricot Blush' (Winter Jewels Series)	CWGN
- apricot-flowered	WFar
- 'Ashwood Blushing Bride'	MAsh
- 'Ashwood Elegance Pearl'	MAsh
- (Ashwood Evolution Group) 'Ashwood Yellow Hammer' **new**	MAsh
- - 'Lunar Neon'	MAsh
- 'Ashwood Fascination'	MAsh
- Ashwood Garden hybrids	ELan EPfP MAsh MRav SRms
- - anemone-centred	MAsh
- - double-flowered (d)	MAsh
- - - green-spotted (d) **new**	EGrI
- 'Ashwood Neon Star'	MAsh
- Ballard's Group	EHyd WFar
- Barnhaven hybrids, anemone-centred	XBar
- - apricot	XBar
- - dark purple	XBar
- - double (d)	XBar
- - green	XBar
- - picotee	XBar
- - pink	XBar
- - red and green	XBar
- - slate	XBar
- - spotted	XBar
- - white	XBar
- - yellow	XBar
- BLACK BEAUTY ('Blck1'PBR)	GKev WSpi
- black-flowered	GMaP WFar
- 'Blue Lady' (Lady Series)	CBcs GDam GKev LRHS MBNS NCou NGdn SPer
- 'Blue Metallic Lady' (Lady Series)	CBod CExl EHyd EPfP GAbr LRHS MBNS MHol NRHS SPer WSpi
- Bradfield hybrids	MCot
- - anemone-centred	MCot
- - double-flowered (d)	MCot
- - picotee	MCot
- 'Burgundy'	CBod EGrI
- 'Cherry Blossom' (Winter Jewels Series)	CWGN
- 'Cherry Frost'	MAsh
- 'Chocolate Truffle'	CBor
- 'Cinderella'PBR (d)	LRHS SPoG
- 'Circe'	EBee
- 'Clare's Purple'	CBod EWTr
- 'Cosmos'	MBNS
- cream-flowered	WFar
- 'Dark as Night'	CBor WTyc
- dark picotee	WFar
- dark-flowered	WFar
- - purple-flowered	WFar
- deep red-flowered	MHol WFar
- double-flowered (d)	MNrw WFar
- - black-flowered (d)	CExl LEdu WFar
- - pink-flowered (d)	EMor WCAu WFar
- - spotted (Lady Series) (d) **new**	EGrI
- - white picotee (d)	CBod EPfP LRHS NRHS
- - yellow, cream-speckled (d)	CBod EHyd LRHS NRHS
- - dark purple-flowered (d)	EGrI WFar
- - green-flowered (d)	CBod EGrI WFar
- - picotee (d)	WFar
- - purple-flowered (d)	CBod EPfP WFar
- - red-flowered (d)	CExl WFar
- - white-flowered (d)	CExl LRHS WCAu WFar
- - yellow-flowered (d)	CExl CWCL WFar
- 'Double Black' (d)	EGrI EPfP EWTr
- 'Double Ellen Picotee' (d)	CWGN EGrI LCro LOPS
- 'Double Ellen Pink' (d)	EGrI LCro LOPS
- 'Double Ellen Pink Spotted' (d)	EGrI LCro LOPS
- 'Double Ellen Purple' (d)	LCro LOPS
- 'Double Ellen Red' (d)	EGrI LCro LOPS
- 'Double Ellen Red Splash' (d) **new**	EGrI
- 'Double Ellen White' (d)	CWGN EGrI EPfP LCro LOPS SCob
- 'Double Ellen White Spotted' (d)	EGrI LCro LOPS SCob WCAu
- 'Double Ellen Yellow' (d)	EGrI
- 'Elegance Flare' (d) **new**	MAsh
- 'Elegance Ice' (d) **new**	MAsh
- 'Enchantment'	MAsh
- 'Farmyard Appleblossom'	WFar
- Farmyard anemone-centred	WFar
- - apricot	WFar
- - black	WFar
- - cream	WFar
- - - spotted	WFar
- - dark pink	WFar
- - double apricot (d)	WFar
- - - black (d)	WFar
- - - cream (d)	WFar
- - - - spotted (d)	WFar
- - - pink (d)	WFar
- - - - spotted (d)	LRHS WFar
- - - primrose (d)	WFar
- - - - spotted (d)	WFar
- - - red (d)	WFar
- - - slate-grey (d)	EGrI WFar
- - - waterlily (d) **new**	EGrI
- - - white (d)	WFar

- - - - spotted (d)	WFar
- - green	WFar
- - - spotted	WFar
- - picotee	WFar
- - pink	WFar
- - - spotted	WFar
- - plum	WFar
- - primrose	WFar
- - - dark-eyed	WFar
- - - spotted	WFar
- - red	WFar
- - slate-grey	WFar
- - - spotted	WFar
- - white	WFar
- - - dark-eyed	WFar
- - - splash	WFar
- - - spotted	WFar
- 'Farmyard Woodland'	WFar
- 'Gold Red Star'	WSpi
- 'Golden Lotus' (d)	CWGN
- 'Green Ripple'	WFar
- green-flowered	WFar
- Harvington apricot	CRos EHyd LCro LOPS NBir NLar NRHS SLon
- - double apricot (d)	CRos EHyd LRHS NRHS
- - - blush (d)	CRos EHyd LRHS NRHS
- - - chocolate (d)	CRos EHyd LCro LOPS LRHS NRHS
- - - cream speckled (d)	CRos EHyd LRHS NRHS SPoG
- - - dark purple (d)	EHyd NRHS
- - - lilac speckled (d) **new**	LRHS
- - - lime-green (d)	EHyd LCro LOPS LRHS NRHS
- - - pink (d)	CRos EHyd LCro LOPS LRHS NRHS SLon SPoG
- - - - speckled (d)	CRos EHyd LCro LOPS LRHS NRHS
- - - purple (d)	EHyd GAbr GBin LRHS NBir NLar NRHS SPoG
- - - - cascade (d)	CRos EHyd EPfP LRHS NRHS
- - - red (d)	CRos EHyd LCro LOPS LRHS NBir NLar NRHS SLon
- - - speckled (d)	SPoG
- - - yellow (d)	CRos EHyd LRHS NBir NLar NRHS SLon
- - - - speckled (d)	CRos EHyd GAbr LRHS NRHS
- - - white (d)	CRos EHyd LCro LOPS LRHS NBir NLar NRHS SLon SPoG
- - - - speckled (d)	EHyd LRHS
- - dusky	CRos EHyd LRHS NRHS
- - lime	EHyd LCro LOPS NRHS
- - picotee	CRos EHyd LRHS NBir NLar NRHS SLon SPoG
- - pink	CRos EHyd LRHS NLar NRHS SLon
- - - speckled	LCro LOPS NLar SLon SPoG
- - red	CRos EHyd LCro LOPS LRHS NLar NRHS SLon SPoG
- - speckled	CRos EHyd LRHS NRHS SLon
- - white	CRos EHyd LCro LOPS LRHS NLar NRHS SLon SPoG
- - - speckled	LCro LOPS SLon
- - yellow	CRos EHyd LRHS NLar NRHS SLon SPoG
- - - speckled	CRos EHyd EPfP LCro LOPS LRHS NLar NRHS SLon SPoG
- 'Harvington Black'	EHyd EPfP LRHS NRHS
- 'Harvington Blush Picotee'	SRms
- 'Harvington Chocolate'	EHyd
- 'Harvington Petticoat'	LRHS NRHS
- 'Harvington Shades of the Night'	CRos EHyd EPfP LCro LOPS LRHS NLar NRHS SLon SPoG
- 'Harvington Smokey Blues'	CRos LCro LRHS SLon
- 'Harvington Special'	LRHS

- Hillier hybrids anemone-centred, pink	EGrI
- - - spotted pink	EHyd
- - burgundy	EHyd LEdu
- - slate	EHyd LRHS
- - spotted, double yellow (d)	EHyd EPfP
- - - - -pink (d)	EHyd EPfP
- - - pink	EHyd
- - - white	EHyd
- - - yellow	EHyd
- - white	EHyd
- - yellow, magenta eye	EHyd LRHS NRHS
- 'Kingston Cardinal'	MAsh
- Lady Series	EPau
- 'Lucy Black'	LRHS
- maroon-flowered	WFar
- mauve freckled, double (d)	WFar
- 'Moorcroft Legacy' **new**	MAsh
- 'Mrs Betty Ranicar' (d)	ILea SRms
- nearly black-flowered	WFar
- 'Onyx Odyssey'	CWGN
- pale pink-flowered	WFar
- 'Pamina'	SMHy
§ - Party Dress Group (d)	ELon GBin LSRN NLar WFar
- 'Phoebe'	MAsh
- 'Phoenix'	MAsh
- Picotee Group	NLar WFar WHoo
- pink freckled, double (d)	WFar
- 'Pink Lady' (Lady Series)	CBcs CBod CSBt EGrI EHyd EPau EPfP GKev LRHS NCou NRHS SPer
- 'Pink Lady Spotted' (Lady Series)	EGrI SCob
- pink-flowered	MBNS SDeJ WHoo
- pink-red-flowered	WFar
- plum-flowered	MMuc SEND
- 'Pluto'	WFar
- 'Pretty Ellen Pink'	GBin LCro LOPS
- 'Pretty Ellen Purple'	EGrI
- 'Pretty Ellen Red'	LCro LOPS SCob
- 'Pretty Ellen White'	LCro LOPS
- 'Primrose Picotee'	WFar
- primrose-flowered	MCot
- 'Purity'	MAsh
- purple-flowered	WFar
- (Queen Series) 'Queen of the Night'	CExl EGrI WSpi
- - dark red-flowered	GBin
- - double white-flowered (d)	GBin
- - - yellow-flowered (d)	GBin
- - picotee	GBin
- - pink-flowered	GBin
- - white-flowered	GBin
- - yellow-flowered	GBin
- 'Red Lady' (Lady Series)	CBcs CBod CExl EGrI EHyd EPfP LRHS LSRN MBNS NHol NRHS SPer
- red-flowered	LEdu WFar WHoo
- 'Rose Quartz' (Winter Jewels Series)	CBod
- 'Single Black Pearl' **new**	MAsh
- slaty blue-flowered	EGrI LEdu SEND
- 'Smokey Blue'	EHyd ELan LRHS NRHS
- smokey purple-flowered	LSRN SGbt
- 'Speckled Draco'	CExl
§ - spotted	EPfP WCot WFar WHoo
- - cream	NBir WFar
- - double, pink (d)	CBod EGrI WFar
- - - white (d)	CBod WFar
- - - yellow (d)	CBod EGrI WCot WFar
- - green	WFar
- - ivory	WFar
- - light purple	WFar

- - pink	EHyd LEdu LRHS MBNS NBir NRHS SCob SEND WFar WHoo
- - primrose	ELan SGbt WFar
- - white	MMuc NBir SCob SEND WBor WCAu WFar
- - yellow	SCob WFar
- (Spring Promise Series)	SCoo
SP ALICE ('Hlr 270') (d) **new**	
- - SP ANJA OUDOLF ('Hlr 200')	CRos LRHS
- - SP CONNY ('Hlr 160'PBR)	CRos EHyd EPfP LRHS MBNS NRHS SCoo
- - SP ELLY ('Hlr 190'PBR) (d)	SCoo
- - SP FRILLY ISABELLE (d) **new**	SCoo
- - SP FRILLY KITTY (d)	SCoo
- - SP JOHN HOPKINS ('Hlr 220')	CRos EHyd LRHS NRHS SCoo
- - SP LILY ('Hlr 210') (d)	EPfP LRHS MBNS
- - SP MARY LOU ('Hlr 150'PBR)	EHyd LRHS SCoo
- - SP RACHEL	EHyd EPfP SCoo
- - SP REBECCA **new**	LRHS
- - SP SALLY ('Hlr 250')	EPfP LRHS SCoo
- - SP SOPHIE ('Hlr 260') **new**	NLar SCoo
- - SP SUE **new**	SCoo
- - SP TIFFANY	EHyd
- 'Stained Glass'	MAsh
- 'Tutu'PBR	EPfP LBuc NRHS SGBe SPeP SPoG SRms
- Washfield double-flowered (d)	CBod EGrI LEdu SCob SPer SRkn WBor WHil
- 'White Lady' (Lady Series)	CBcs CBod CExl GAbr GKev MBNS NCou SPer
- 'White Lady Spotted' (Lady Series)	CBar CBod EGrI EHyd ELon EPfP GKev LRHS NHol NRHS SPer
- white-flowered	EPfP EWTr GMaP WFar WHoo
- white-veined	WFar
- Wilgenbroek hybrids black	EWoo
- - double white (d)	EWoo
- - red	EWoo
- - slaty blue	EWoo
- - white	EWoo
- 'Wine Chiffon' **new**	MAsh
- Winter Emotions Series **new**	GBin
- 'Yellow Lady' (Lady Series)	CBar CBcs CBod EGrI EHyd LRHS MBNS NRHS SPer WTor
- yellow-flowered	GMaP MCot SEND WFar WHoo
- - freckled, double (d)	LEdu
- Zodiac Group	CBod LRHS MBNS
§ 'Ivory Prince'PBR	CRos EHyd EPfP LRHS MAsh NRHS SPoG
liguricus	GKev MAsh
- WM 0230	MPhe
lividus	CRos EBee EHyd EPfP EWes GKev LRHS NBir NRHS SBrt SDeJ SDir SRms
- subsp. ***corsicus***	see *H. argutifolius*
- 'Purple Ear'	LRHS
- 'Purple Marble'	EPfP
- 'Purple Rose'	SRms
- 'Rose Green'	CSpe MHtn
- 'Silver and Rose'	CSpe
- 'White Marble'	GKev LRHS MAsh
- white-flowered	GKev
lividus × niger	GKev
'Marshmallow'	CBcs MHol MNrw WCot
'Moonshine'PBR	NHol NLar SLon

multifidus	NBir
- WM 1316	MPhe
- subsp. ***hercegovinus*** WM 0020	MPhe
- - WM 0622	MPhe
- subsp. ***istriacus***	CBro MAsh
- - WM 9322	MPhe
- - WM 9324	MPhe
- subsp. ***multifidus***	MAsh
- - WM 9529	MPhe
- - WM 9833 from Croatia	MPhe
niger	Widely available
- Ashwood strain	MAsh
- Blackthorn Group	NLar
- 'Christmas Carol'	CBod EHyd EPfP EWoo LRHS NRHS SCoo
- double-flowered (d)	CDor
- Harvington hybrids	EHyd LRHS MAsh NRHS
- - double-flowered (d)	LCro LOPS SPoG
- HGC GOLDMARIE ('Coseh 2020'PBR)	ELan
- 'HGC Jacob'PBR	ELan LSRN NRHS SRms
- HGC JACOB ROYAL ('Coseh 240'PBR)	EBee
- HGC JASPER ('Coseh 1010'PBR) **new**	ELan MAsh
- HGC JESKO ('Coseh 1000'PBR) **new**	ELan
- HGC JOEL ('Coseh 210'PBR)	CRos ECtt EHyd EPfP LRHS NLar NRHS SCoo
- HGC JONAS ('Coseh 220'PBR)	CRos ECtt EHyd EPfP LRHS NRHS SCoo
- 'HGC Josef Lemper'PBR	GKev LRHS LSRN NLar SRms
- 'HGC Joshua'PBR	EHyd
- HGC SNOW FRILLS ('Coseh 230'PBR)	ECtt EHyd LRHS MAsh NLar NRHS SCoo
- HGC WINTERGOLD ('Coseh 2010'PBR)	CRos ECtt EHyd EPfP EShb LRHS NRHS SCoo
- 'Ivory Prince'	see *H.* 'Ivory Prince'
- 'Mini Blanc'	CRos EHyd LRHS NRHS
- 'Mini Star' **new**	LRHS
- 'Mont Blanc'	EPfP LRHS WCot
- pink-flowered	LSun MAsh
- 'Potter's Wheel'	CRos EHyd EPfP GKev LRHS NBir NRHS
- 'Praecox'	EHyd ELon EPfP
SNOW BIRD ('Hilnelsnobi') **new**	CBod
SNOW CRYSTAL ('Hilnelsncr')	LRHS LSou
- 'Snow Moon'	CBor
- 'White Magic'	LSun
× ***nigercors*** 'Emma'PBR	CEnd CMil CRos ECtt EHyd EPfP EWoo GMaP LRHS MAvo MHol NRHS SEdd SHar SPoG WCot
- 'HGC Green Corsican'	NRHS
- HGC ICE BREAKER FANCY ('Coseh 820')	EHyd EPfP LRHS NRHS SCoo
- HGC ICE BREAKER MAX ('Coseh 750'PBR)	EHyd EPfP LRHS MAsh NRHS SCoo
- HGC ICE BREAKER PICO ('Coseh 840')	ECre EPfP
- HGC ICE BREAKER PRELUDE ('Coseh 830'PBR)	NRHS
- 'Morning's Pride'PBR	EHyd
- 'Pink Beauty'	NLar
- 'Winter Passion'PBR **new**	EPfP
× ***nigristern***	see *H.* × *ericsmithii*
odorus	CBro EBee MPhe XLum
- WM 0312 from Bosnia	MPhe

- WM 9415	MPhe
- WM 9728 from Hungary	MPhe
- subsp. ***cyclophyllus***	MAsh MPhe
odorus × ***orientalis*** **new**	GDam
orientalis misapplied	see *H.* × *hybridus*
orientalis ambig.	CBar CTsd EGrI EWoo GKev MPri WHil
orientalis Lam.	CBcs CEme EHyd EWes LRHS MPhe MSwo NRHS XLum
§ - subsp. ***abchasicus*** (A. Braun) B. Mathew	CBro EBee MAsh WSpi
§ - - Early Purple Group	CTri MRav SRms
- subsp. ***guttatus*** misapplied	see *H.* × *hybridus* spotted
- subsp. ***guttatus*** (A. Braun & Sauer) B. Mathew	SRkn
purpurascens	CBro GKev LCro LOPS MAsh MRav NBir
- WM 0815 from Romania	MPhe
- WM 9211 from Hungary	MPhe
- WM 9412	MPhe
(Rodney Davey Marbled Group) ANNA'S RED ('Abcrd02'PBR)	CRos EBee ECtt EPfP LCro LOPS LRHS MAsh NRHS SCoo SPoG
- CHARMER ('Epb 21') **new**	MAsh
- CHERYL'S SHINE ('Epb 31') **new**	LRHS MAsh NLar
- DANA'S DULCET ('Epb 30') **new**	MAsh WCot
- 'Dorothy's Dawn' (Frost Kiss Series)	SPoG
- MOLLY'S WHITE ('Epbrd01'PBR)	CRos LRHS MAsh MPri
- MOONDANCE ('Epb 20') **new**	LRHS MAsh
- PENNY'S PINK ('Abcrd01')	CBcs CRos ECtt EHyd EPfP LRHS LSRN LSun MAsh MHol SPoG WCot
- PIPPA'S PURPLE ('Rd09') **new**	LRHS
- REANNA'S RUBY ('Epb 32') **new**	MAsh
- SALLY'S SHELL ('Epb 12') (Frost Kiss Series)	MAsh SPoG
× ***sahinii*** 'Winterbells'PBR	CBod EBee EGrI LCro LOPS LRHS LSou MAsh NRHS SCoo SPoG SRms
'Snow White'	LBuc
× ***sternii***	CBcs CBod CKel CRos CTri EHyd ELan EPfP EWoo GKev GMaP LCro LRHS MNrw NLar NRHS SPoG WBrk
- Aberconwy strain	MAsh
- 'Ashwood Silver'	MAsh
- Ashwood strain	MAsh NLar
- Blackthorn Group	EHyd ELon EPfP LRHS SWvt
- 'Boughton Beauty'	EBee ELan WSpi
- pewter-flowered	CSpe
- 'Silver Dollar'	EBee EPfP GKev LRHS LSRN SGBe SPoG SRms
thibetanus	CExl MAsh WAbe
torquatus	CBro MAsh MAvo MPhe
- WM 0609 from Montenegro	MPhe
- WM 0617 from Serbia	MPhe
- WM 9106 from Montenegro	MPhe
- WM 9820 from Bosnia	MPhe
- 'Dido' (d)	CExl WFar
- double-flowered, WM 0621 from Montenegro (d)	MPhe
- Party Dress Group	see *H.* × *hybridus* Party Dress Group
'Verboom Beauty'	CDoC EHyd LCro LOPS LRHS MAsh NRHS
viridis	EBee LEdu MAsh SRms WAbe XLum
- WM 0444 from Italy	MPhe
- WM 1303 from Slovenia	MPhe
- WM 9723 from Italy	MPhe
- subsp. ***occidentalis***	CBro MAsh
- - WM 1340 from Germany	MPhe
- - WM 1344 from Spain	MPhe
- - WM 9501 from Wales	MPhe
WALBERTON'S ROSEMARY ('Walhero'PBR) H7	CRos EHyd EPfP LRHS MAsh NRHS SHar SPoG WSpi
'White Beauty'PBR	EPfP NLar NRHS SGBe SPoG WCot

Helminthotheca (*Asteraceae*)

§ ***echioides***	WHer

Heloniopsis (*Melanthiaceae*)

acutifolia B&SWJ 218	WCru
- B&SWJ 6817	WCru
- B&SWJ 6836	WCru
japonica	see *H. orientalis*
§ ***kawanoi***	CTtf
leucantha B&SWJ 11148	WCru
§ ***orientalis***	CBct CTtf
- B&SWJ 6278	WCru
- var. ***breviscapa***	EPfP GEdr LEdu SMad WCru
- - B&SWJ 5635	WCru
- - B&SWJ 5873	WCru
- - B&SWJ 5938	WCru
- - 'A-so'	LEdu WCru
- 'Dark Single'	GEdr
- var. ***flavida*** 'Snow White'	GEdr
- var. ***yakusimensis***	see *H. kawanoi*
tubiflora	GEdr
- B&SWJ 822	WCot
- 'Temple Blue'	CBct EBee WCru
umbellata	EBee EPfP WSHC
- B&SWJ 1839	WCru

Helosciadium (*Umbelliferae*)

§ ***nodiflorum***	CPud

Helwingia (*Helwingiaceae*)

chinensis	CBcs CCCN CKel CTsd ESwi EWTr EWld GBin MGil MHtn MPie MVil NLar SBrt SEND SPoG WBor WLov WPGP XSte
- broad-leaved	EBee EHed NLar SIvy SMad WPGP
- narrow-leaved	ESwi
himalaica	CExl ESwi MVil SBrt SMad XSte
japonica	EWld MVil NLar
- broad-leaved	WPGP

Helxine see *Soleirolia*

Hemerocallis ✿ (*Hemerocallidaceae*)

'A Bodacious Pattern'	EStr
'A Groovy Kind of Love'	EStr
'A Lady Named Hank'	EStr
'A Small Multitude' **new**	EStr
'Aabaa'	EWoo
'Aabachee'	CBgR EStr
'Aaron Brown'	EStr
'Ablazing Rimfire' **new**	SDay
'Above the Clouds'	EWoo
'Absolute Ripper'	EStr
'Absolute Treasure'	EStr
'Absolute Zero'	SDay
'Addie Branch Smith'	SDay
'Admiral'	WNHG
'Admiral's Braid'	EWoo
'Adoration'	SPer
'Aerea'	MHol

'Aerial Display'	EStr
'African Chant'	ELan
'After the Riot' (d) **new**	EStr
'Ageless Beauty'	EStr SDir
'Ahoy Matey'	EStr
'Ahoya'	CBgR EStr
'Airs and Graces'	SDay
'Alabama Jubilee'	WNHG
'Alan'	CRos EHyd LRHS MRav NRHS
'Alan Adair'	CSpe SDay
'Alaqua'	WSMil
'Alayne Clare'	EStr
'Alec Allen'	SDay
'Aleta Everett Adams'	EStr
'Alexander the Great'	WHrl
'Alien DNA'	EStr
'Alien Fingerprint'	EStr
'Aliens in the Garden'	EStr
'All American Baby'	EStr
'All American Chief' ♀H6	EStr SDay
'All American Plum'	WHrl
'All American Tiger'	SDay
'All American Windmill'	CBgR EStr WHrl
'All Fired Up'	EStr SDay
'All the Magic'	SDay
'Allegheny Skyline'	EStr
'Allegiance'	WNHG
'Alli Sheldon'	ECha
'Alluring Peach'	EStr
'Almond Puff'	SDay
'Alternate Universe'	EStr
altissima	EStr MNrw SDix SPhx XLum XSen
'Always Afternoon' ♀H6	CBgR CBod EGrI EPfP EStr MNrw SDay WCAu WHrl XSen
'Amadeus'	EStr SCob SDay
'Amazon Amethyst'	WCAu
'Ambassador'	CBgR
'Amber Classic'	ELon
'American Freedom'	SDay
'American Revolution'	CBgR EGrI ELon EStr EWoo GBin LSun MBNS MHol NChi SBea SDys SEdd SMad SPoG WCot WHrl WPnP WSMil WSpi XLum XSen
'America's Most Wanted'	EStr SDay
'Amerstone Amethyst Jewel'	EStr
'Amerstone Saffron Jewel' **new**	SDay
'Amy Michelle' (d)	EStr
'Amy's Rainbow'	EStr
'Anastasia'	SDay
'Angel Artistry'	SDay
'Angel in Oz'	EStr
'Angel Rodgers'	EStr
'Angels in America'	EStr
'Angelus Runaway'	EStr
'Angelwalker'	EStr
'Anna Rubinina'	EStr
'Anna Warner'	ELon MMuc SEND
'Annabelle's Ghost'	CBgR
'Annie Golightly'	SDay
'Annie Welch'	EHyd ELon
'Antique Lavender'	WCAu
'Antique Rose'	EStr
'Anzac'	CBro ECha ECtt EStr GArf NGdn SWvt
'Apache Uprising'	SDay
'Apollodorus'	SDay WHrl WNHG
'Apple Court Chablis'	EStr
'Apple Court Damson'	EStr MAvo
'Apple Court Ruby'	ELon
'Apple Swirl'	EStr

'Apple Tart'	SDay
'Applique'	EStr
'Après Moi'	NLar
'Apricot Beauty' (d)	WSpi
'Apricot Velvet'	CBgR
'April Fools'	EStr
'April in Paris'	SDay
'Aquamarine'	SDay
'Aquarelle'	EStr
'Arabian Magic'	EStr
'Arctic Snow' ♀H6	CBgR CBro CMac ECtt EHyd EStr GJos LPar LRHS MCot MNrw NRHS SDay SDir
'Arles Sultry Eyes'	EStr
'Armed and Dangerous'	EStr
'Arpeggio'	EStr SDay
'Art Gallery Curly-Q'	EStr
'Art Gallery Quilling'	EStr
'Arthur Moore'	SDay
'Artificial Evolution'	EStr
'Asheville Pink Lady'	EStr
'Asheville White Winged Dove'	EStr
'Ashton's Giggles'	EStr
'Asian Artistry'	WNHG
'Asterisk' ♀H6	EStr SDay
'Astolat'	EBee
'Aten'	CBgR SDay
'Atlanta Bouquet'	SDay
'Atlanta Cover Girl'	SDay
'Atlanta Fringe Benefit'	SDay
'Atlanta Full House'	SDay
'Atlas'	WGwG
'Augenstern'	EStr
'August Frost' ♀H6	EStr SDay
'August Morn'	CBgR
'Autumn Minaret'	EStr
'Autumn Prince'	EWoo
'Autumn Red'	CBcs CBgR EStr GKin MHost MMuc MNrw NBir SCob SEND WCot
'Autumn Wood'	SDay
'Ava Michelle'	SDay
I 'Avant Garde' Moldovan	EStr
'Avant Garde' Russell	EStr WCAu
'Avon Crystal Rose'	WNHG
'Awakening Dream'	SDay
'Awash With Color'	EStr SDay
'Awesome Blossom'	EStr GBin MBNS MNrw WHrl
'Awesome Candy'	EStr
'Aztec Beauty'	EStr
'Aztec Furnace'	EStr SDay
'Aztec Gold'	EStr
'Baby Betsy'	EStr
'Baby Blues'	SDay
'Baby Red Eyes'	EStr WFar
'Bad Medicine'	EStr
'Baja'	WFar
'Bakabana'	CBod EHyd LRHS NRHS
'Bald Eagle'	EStr MNrw
'Bali Hai'	EStr SRms WHrl WSpi
'Bali Watercolor'	EStr
'Bama Bound'	EStr
'Bamboo Blackie'	CBgR
'Banana Cream Beauty'	SDeJ WSpi
'Banana Man'	EStr
'Banana Smoothie' **new**	EStr
'Bandit Man'	EStr SDay
'Barbara Alsop'	EStr SDay
'Barbara Mitchell'	EStr EWTr EWoo SDay SDeJ WCAu WNHG
'Barbary Corsair'	EStr SDay

'Baroni'	ECha LShi
'Bas Relief'	EStr
'Bat Signal'	EWoo
'Batgirl'	EStr
'Battle Hymn'	WCAu
'Bayou Bride'	SDay
'Be Bop a Lula'	EStr
'Bea'	EStr
'Beautiful Design'	EStr
'Beautiful Edgings'	EStr SDay
'Beauty to Behold' 🏆H6	SDay
'Becky Lynn'	ECtt EStr
'Bed of Nails'	EStr
'Bed of Roses'	EStr
'Bedarra Island'	SDay
'Bee's Big Ben' **new**	SDay
'Before You Accuse Me'	EStr
'Beijing'	SDay
'Bela Lugosi'	CBgR CMac EHyd ELon EPfP EStr EWoo GQue ILea LRHS LSRN LSun MBNS MNrw NBro NChi NQui NRHS SCob SDay SPer WHrl WNHG
'Believe It'	WNHG
'Bella Isabella'	EStr
'Belladonna Starfish'	EStr
'Belly Button Slipknots'	EStr
'Beloved Deceiver'	SDay
'Ben Adams'	SDay
'Ben Bachman'	EStr
'Benchmark'	SDay
'Bengal Fire'	WNHG
'Berlin Lemon Crepe'	GBin
'Berlin Red'	ECha ELon GBee MNrw SDay SSut WFar
'Berlin Red Velvet'	GBin
'Berlin Yellow'	EStr
'Berliner Premiere'	EStr
'Bernard Thompson'	SDay
'Berry Blitz'	EStr
'Berry Patch'	EStr
'Berrylicious'	CBod
'Bertie Ferris'	EStr EWoo NLar SDay
'Beside Still Waters'	EStr
'Best Seller'	CBod WCAu
'Bette Davis Eyes'	CBgR CWat EStr SDay
'Betts Allen'	EStr
'Betty Benz'	SDay
'Betty Jenkins'	EStr
'Betty Warren Woods'	SDay
'Bettylen'	EStr
'Beyond Riches'	EStr
'Beyond Thunder Dome'	EStr
'Bi-colored Blues'	EStr
'Big Apple'	EStr SDay
'Big Beautiful Babe'	EStr
'Big Bird'	EStr MBNS SDay
'Big Blue'	EStr SDay
'Big Honking Bahama Richie'	EStr
'Big Ogeeche'	EStr
'Big Red Wiggles'	EStr
'Big Smile'	MBNS MNrw SDeJ
'Big Snowbird'	SDay
'Big Time Happy'	CBod EHyd LRHS SCob SEdd SPoG STPC
'Big World'	CBgR
'Birthday Honours'	SDay
'Bitsy'	ELon
'Black Adder'	SDay
'Black Ambrosia'	EStr SDay
'Black Arrowhead'	EStr MACG WCAu
'Black Emanuelle'	CExl LSun MNrw NLar
'Black Eye'	SDay WNHG
'Black Eyed Belle'	EWoo WNHG
'Black Eyed Stella'	WSpi
'Black Eyed Susan'	CBod ECtt EStr
'Black Friday'	EStr
'Black Handlebars'	EWoo
'Black Ice'	ELon SDay
'Black Knight'	EWoo NLar SRms
'Black Magic'	CBro CTri ECtt EHyd ELan EPfP EStr GBin GKin GMaP LRHS LSRN MHer MRav NBir NGdn NRHS SPer WHrl WNHG
'Black Plush'	EWoo
'Black Prince'	CBgR EShb MBNS
'Black Stockings'	EBee ELon EPfP EStr EWes MHol MNrw SCob SDeJ SDir SMrm
'Blackberries and Cream'	EStr
'Blackberry Candy'	ECtt EHyd EStr GKin LRHS MHol MNrw NHol NRHS NWad WCAu
'Blackberry Sherbert'	WFar
'Blackberry Sundae'	EStr
'Blacky'	EStr
'Blazing Cannons'	EStr
'Blazing Romance' **new**	EStr
'Blessed Again'	SDay
'Blessing'	EStr
'Blessing in Disguise'	EStr
'Blizzard Bay'	CBod EStr WFar
'Blizzard Blast'	EStr
'Blonde is Beautiful'	SDay
'Blood Spot'	SDay
'Blue Balloon'	EStr
'Blue Deva'	EStr
'Blue Sheen'	CBgR CMac ECtt EStr GMaP MHol WFar WSpi
'Blue Stardust'	EStr
'Blue Wrangler'	EStr
'Blueberry Breakfast'	EStr WNHG
'Blueberry Candy'	ECtt EStr ILea
'Blueberry Cream'	MNrw
'Blueberry Frost'	CBgR
'Blueberry Sundae'	CWat
'Bluethroat'	EStr
'Blufftop Volunteer'	EStr
'Blushing Belle'	NBro
'Bob Faulkner'	EStr
'Bobby's Lavender Eyes'	EStr
'Bobo Anne'	EStr
'Bogeyman' **new**	CBod
'Bohemian Rhapsody'	EStr
'Boitzer Helicopter'	EStr
'Bold Courtier'	CBgR
'Bonanza'	CBcs CBgR CBro CRos CTri ECha ECtt EGrl EHyd EPfP EStr LLWG LPot LRHS MHost MRav NBir NBro NGdn NLar NRHS SCob SEND SPer SWvt WCAu WCot WFar
'Bone China'	WNHG
'Boney Maroney'	CBgR
'Bonfire Heart'	EStr
'Bonibrae Blue-eyed Baby'	EStr
'Bonibrae Heartbreaker'	EStr
'Bonibrae Maggie Anne'	EStr
'Bonibrae Smoke and Mirrors'	EStr
'Bonnie Boy'	XLum
'Booger'	SDay
'Booroobin Magic'	EStr EWoo
'Border Baby'	ECtt
'Border Lord'	EStr EWoo

'Border Music'	EStr
'Borgia Queen'	EStr SDay
'Boss Hogg'	EStr
'Both Sides Now'	ECtt
'Boulderbrook Serenity'	SDay
'Bourbon Kings'	EHyd SDeJ WHrl WWtn
'Bowl of Cream'	EStr
'Bowl of Roses'	EStr WCAu
'Brass Buckles'	see *H.* 'Puddin'
'Breath of Blue Air'	EStr
'Breathing in Snowflakes'	EStr
'Breathless Beauty'	WNHG
'Breathless Charm'	EStr
'Brenda Newbold'	EStr SDay
'Bridget'	ELan
'Bright and Morning Star'	EStr
'Bright Eyed and Bushy Tailed'	EStr
'Bright Side'	CBgR
'Bright Spangles'	SDay
'Brilliant Circle'	ECtt
'Broadway Last Mohican'	EStr
'Brocaded Gown'	ELan SDay
'Brookgreen Plantation' **new**	EStr
'Brooklyn Twist'	EStr
'Brown Billows'	EWoo
'Brown Witch'	ELon EWoo
'Browns Ferry Royalty'	EStr WFar
'Bruce'	EStr
'Brutus'	WHrl
'Bubbling Brown Sugar'	EStr SDay
'Bucksport'	EStr
'Bud Producer'	CBgR
'Buddy's Wild and Wonderful'	EStr
'Buffys Doll'	SDay
'Bug's Hug'	EStr
'Bumble Bee'	CBod ECtt EStr SDay
'Burgundy Love'	EStr LLWG
'Burlesque'	SDay WCot
'Burmese Buddha' **new**	SDay
'Burning Daylight' ♀H6	CBgR CRos EBlo ECtt EHyd EPfP EStr LRHS MNrw MRav NRHS SCob SPer SRms WCAu WCot WFar
'Burning Inheritance'	SDay
'Burning so Brightly' **new**	EStr
'Burnished Ruffles'	EStr
'Bursting Bubble' **new**	SDay
'Butterfly Love' **new**	EStr
'Butterscotch'	WFar
'Butterscotch Ruffles'	SDay
'Buzz Bomb'	ECtt EHyd ELon EMor EStr GBee GKin LRHS LSRN MCot MHol NGdn NRHS SPer WFar
'By Myself'	SDay
'Byzantine Emperor'	EHyd LRHS NRHS
'Caballero'	EStr
'Cabbage Butterfly'	EStr
'Cabbage Flower'	SDay
'Cajun Gambler'	EStr
'Calgary Stampede'	EStr
'Calico Jack'	EStr SPad
'Calico Spider'	EStr
'California Sunshine'	SDay
'Caliph's Robes'	SDay
'Call Girl'	SDay
'Calligraphy'	EStr
'Camden Ballerina'	SDay
'Camden Gold Dollar'	SDay
'Camelot Green'	WNHG
'Cameroons'	EStr SDay
'Campfire Embers'	EStr
'Canadian Border Patrol'	EStr MNrw NLar SCob SPer
'Canary Chaos'	EStr
'Canary Glow'	CTri WFar
'Canary Wings'	CBgR
'Candide'	SDay
'Candor'	SDay
'Candy Cane Dreams'	EStr
'Candy Gram'	EStr
'Can't Fault Ya'	EStr
'Cape Breton'	EStr MHol
'Cape Cod' **new**	SDay
'Captain America' **new**	EStr
'Capulina'	EWoo
'Cara Mia'	CBgR EHyd EStr NBir WFar
'Caramba'	CBgR
'Caramel Taffy'	WHrl
'Caribbean Frank League'	SDay
'Caribbean Purple Spires'	EStr
'Carlotta'	SDay
'Carmine Monarch'	EStr
'Carnal Emporium'	EStr
'Carolicolossal'	ELon SDay
'Carolina Cool Down'	EStr
'Carolina Cranberry'	ELan
'Carolina Dynamite'	EStr
'Carolina Lemon Squeezer'	EStr
'Caroline Taylor'	WHrl
'Carrick Wildon'	CBod EBee EPfP MBros WFar
'Carrot'	SDay
'Cartwheels'	ECha EGrI EHyd EShb EStr GBee GKin GMaP LRHS MRav NBro NRHS SCoo SPer SRms SSut WCAu WFar
'Casino Gold'	SDay
'Catawampus'	EStr
'Catherine Neal'	EStr SDay
'Catherine Woodbery'	Widely available
'Cathy's Sunset'	ECtt EHyd EWhm GBee GKin LRHS LSRN MBNS NBro NGdn NRHS NWad
'Cause for Pause'	EStr
'Caviar'	SDay
'Cedar Waxwing'	MNrw
'Celebration of Angels'	EStr MHol
'Celestial City'	SDay
'Celestial Eyes' **new**	SDay
'Cerulean Warbler'	EStr
'Challenger'	SDay
'Chance Encounter'	NHol
'Changing Latitudes'	WHrl
'Chantilly'	EStr
'Charles Johnston'	CBgR EPfP EStr EWoo MSpe SDay WSMil
'Charleston Strong' **new**	EStr
'Charlie Pierce Memorial'	EStr SDay
'Charm Alarm'	EStr
'Charming Manners' **new**	EStr
'Chartwell'	EWoo
'Checkerboard Curls'	EStr
'Cheerful Note'	WNHG
'Cheese and Wine'	MHol
'Cherokee Star'	EStr
'Cherry Cheeks'	ECtt EHyd ELan ELon EStr LRHS MHol MNrw MRav NRHS WCAu WCot WFar WWtn
'Cherry Eyed Pumpkin' ♀H6	EStr SDay WCAu
'Cherry Grove Beach'	EStr
'Cherry Peacock'	EStr
'Cherry Stripes'	EStr
'Cherry Tiger'	EStr
'Cherry Valentine'	ELon GWyn SPad

'Cherrystone'	EStr
'Chesapeake Crablegs'	EStr
'Chesières Lunar Moth'	CBgR ELon
'Chestnut Mountain'	SDay
'Chevron Spider'	EStr
'Chicago Antique Tapestry'	SDay
'Chicago Apache'	ELon EPfP EStr EWoo LLWG MHer NBir SCob SDay SPer WSpi
'Chicago Aztec'	ELon
'Chicago Blackout'	ECtt WCot
'Chicago Cardinal'	EStr
'Chicago Cherry'	WNHG
'Chicago Fire'	EPfP
'Chicago Firecracker'	XLum XSen
'Chicago Heirloom'	WCAu
'Chicago Jewel'	ELon NSti
'Chicago Knobby'	EStr MNrw SDay
'Chicago Knockout'	EHyd ELan EPfP EWoo
'Chicago Peach'	NBir WCAu
'Chicago Petticoats'	WFar
'Chicago Picotee Memories'	SDay
'Chicago Picotee Promise'	WNHG
'Chicago Picotee Queen'	WNHG
'Chicago Queen'	SDay WNHG
'Chicago Rainbow'	CBgR
'Chicago Royal Blue'	CTri
'Chicago Royal Crown'	ECtt EHyd EMor
'Chicago Royal Robe'	CWCL EBlo ELon LRHS NBid SDay SPer SRms WCot WWtn
'Chicago Silver'	SDay SMrm
'Chicago Star'	WNHG
'Chicago Sugarplum'	SDay
'Chicago Sunrise'	CBgR CBod CRos EHyd ELon GMaP LRHS MRav NGdn NRHS SDay SWvt WCot WNHG
'Chick Flick'	EStr
'Chick Magnet'	EStr
'Chicken Coop Madonna'	EStr
'Chief Four Fingers'	EWoo
'Chief Sequoia'	EStr
'Child of Fortune'	SDay
'Children's Festival'	CMac CRos ECtt EStr GMaP LPot LRHS MRav NLar SWvt WFar
'China Bride'	EStr
'China Lake'	SDay
'Chinese Autumn'	EStr
'Chinese Cloisonne'	EStr SDay
'Chinese Coral'	EWoo
'Chinese Imp'	NLar
'Chinese New Year'	EStr
'Chinese Temple Flower'	SDay
'Chiricahua Warrior'	EWoo
'Chocolate Candy'	EStr
'Chocolate Splash'	SDay
'Chokecherry Mountain'	EStr EWoo
'Chorus Line'	WNHG
'Christina's Pink Parasol'	EStr
'Christine Lynn'	WNHG
'Christmas Is'	CBgR CMac CPar CWGN ECtt EHyd ELon EStr GBin GKin LPot NHol NRHS SDay WCot WHrl WNHG
'Christmas Ornament'	EStr
'Christmas Wishes'	EStr
'Ciarra Vonnie'	SDay
'Cimarron Knight'	CBgR
'Cindy's Eye'	EStr WCot
'Cinnamon Stick'	EStr
'Cinnamon Sunrise'	EStr
citrina 🏆H6	CBgR CEme CExl CMac EBee EStr EWoo MBel MCot WCAu WCot WHoo WHrl XLum XSen XSte
citrina × (× ***ochroleuca***)	WCot
'Civil Law'	SDay
'Civil Rights'	SDay
'Classic Caper'	WNHG
'Classic Edge'	SDay
'Claudine'	ELon
'Claudine's Charm'	EStr
'Clearly a Thrill'	EStr
'Cleopatra'	ELon MSpe
'Clothed in Glory'	EStr WCot
'Clownfish'	EStr
'Cobraskin Necktie'	EStr
'Coburg Fright Wig'	EWoo
'Cocktail Party'	EStr
'Colonel Joe'	WNHG
'Colonel Mustard'	EStr
'Comanche Eyes'	SDay
'Coming Up Roses'	CBod CPar ELon SCoo
'Concorde Nelson'	ELon SDay
'Condilla' (d) 🏆H6	EStr SDay
'Conspicua'	CBgR
'Contessa'	CBro EBlo EHyd LRHS NRHS
'Conway Red Light'	EStr
'Cool It'	EStr LPot MPie MSpe NLar SCob SDeJ WHrl
'Cool Jazz'	EStr SDay
'Cooler Than Me'	EStr
'Copper Dawn'	EStr NChi
'Copper Windmill'	CBgR ELon EStr SDay WNHG
'Copperhead'	EStr
'Coral Majority'	EStr
'Coral Sparkler'	WNHG
'Corinthian Pink' **new**	SDay
'Corky'	CBro ECha EHyd ELan EMor EPfP GBin GMaP GWyn LSRN MBel MHost MNrw NGdn NLar SMrm SPer SPhx SSut WCAu WFar WSpi XLum
'Cornwall'	EStr
'Cosmic Blast'	EStr
'Cosmic Hummingbird'	ECtt EHyd EStr NRHS
'Cosmic Legacy' **new**	EStr
'Cosmik Debris'	EStr
'Cosmopolitan'	GBin
'Country Club'	GMaP
'Country Melody'	SDay
'Court Magician'	EStr EWoo SDay
'Court Troubadour'	ELon
'Coyote Moon'	EStr SDay
'Crackling Fire'	EStr
'Cranberry Baby'	ECtt EStr LRHS MHol MTin SCoo WHoo WNHG
'Cranberry Coulis'	CWat
'Crayola Violet'	EStr SDay
'Crazy Awesome'	EStr
'Crazy Ivan'	EStr
'Crazy Larry'	EStr
'Crazy Mr Jim'	EStr
'Crazy Pierre'	EWoo WHrl
'Cream Drop'	ECtt EPPr GMaP GQue LPot LRHS MBriF MCot MRav NBro NGdn NLar NRHS NSti SPer WCot WFar WHrl
'Crimson Icon'	SDay
'Crimson Pirate'	CBgR CMac ELon EPfP EStr EWoo GBin GKev GLog GQue ILea LPar LPot LRHS LSRN NBir NEoE NQui NRHS SCob SPer SPlb WCAu WFar WHrl WWtn XLum
'Crimson Wind'	EStr
'Cripple Creek'	EStr

'Croesus'	SRms
'Crooked Smile'	EStr
'Crystal Pinot'	ELon EStr
'Cumulus Sunset'	EStr
'Cupid's Gold'	SDay
'Curls'	CBgR SDay
'Curly Cinnamon Windmill' ♀H6	EStr SDay
'Curt's Gift'	EStr
'Custard Candy' ♀H6	CBod CWCL CWGN ECtt EHyd EPfP EStr EWoo GKin LRHS MBriF MHost NHol NRHS WCAu WNHG
'Cute as Can Be'	EStr
'Cyber Zone'	EStr
'Cyclone Twister'	EStr
'Cyclone Whirlaway'	EStr
'Cynthia Lucius'	EStr
'Cynthia Mary'	ECtt GKin SRGP
'Czarina'	EStr
'Daddeeo Segrest'	EStr
'Daddy's Catfish Stew'	EStr
'Dad's Best White'	EStr
'Daily Dollar'	NGdn
'Dallas Spider Time'	SDay
'Dallas Star'	EStr SDay WHrl
'Dan Mahony'	EStr
'Dan Tau'	SDay
'Dance Ballerina Dance'	SDay
'Dance Fever' **new**	SDay
'Dance with Somebody'	EStr
'Dances with Giraffes'	EStr
'Dancing Crab'	CBgR
'Dancing Dreams'	EStr
'Dancing Elf'	EStr
'Dancing for Dixie' **new**	EStr
'Dancing in the Rain'	EStr
'Dancing on Air'	ECtt SMrm SPeP
'Dancing on Ice'	EStr
'Dancing Shiva'	SDay
'Dancing Summerbird'	ELon EStr SDay
'Dancing with Linda'	EStr
'Daring Deception'	ECtt EGrI EHyd ELon EPfP LRHS MNrw NRHS SDeJ
'Daring Dilemma'	EStr SDay
'Daring Reflection'	SDay
'Darius'	WNHG
'Dark Angel'	NRHS
'Dark Magician'	EStr
'Dark Monkey'	EStr
'Dark Sprite'	EWoo
'Darker Shade'	EStr
'Darrell'	SDay
'Dash Dash' **new**	EStr
'David Holman'	WNHG
'David Kirchhoff'	EStr SDay
'Davidson Update'	WNHG
'Davi's Dilemma'	EStr
'Daylight'	WNHG
'De Colores'	EStr
'Dearest Mahogany' **new**	EStr
'Debussy'	EStr
'Decatur Ballerina'	WNHG
'Decatur Captivation'	WNHG
'Decatur Dictator'	WNHG
'Decatur Festival'	WNHG
'Decatur Imp'	SDay WHrl
'Decatur Jewel'	WNHG
'Decatur Piecrust'	EStr
'Decatur Rhythm'	WNHG
'Decatur Supreme'	WNHG
'Decatur Treasure Chest'	WNHG

'Decidedly Happy'	EStr
'Defuniak Peach Blossom'	EStr
'Delicate Design'	SDay
'Delightsome'	SDay
'Deloris Gould'	SDay
'Demetrius'	CWat EStr
'Desdemona'	EStr XLum
'Desert Dreams'	WCot
'Desert Icicle'	SDay
'Designer Gown'	EStr SDay
'Designer Jeans'	EStr SDay
'Designer Rhythm'	EStr
'Desirable Duchess'	EStr
'Desire of Nations' **new**	EStr
'Desperate Housewife'	EStr
'Destined to See'	CBro ECtt ELon EStr EWhm LPot MNrw NBir NBro SPad SPer WCot WHrl
'Devon Cream'	SPer
'Devon Ruby' **new**	SDay
'Devonshire'	EStr
'Diamond Dust'	ECtt LSRN NLar SPer WSpi
'Diana Grenfell'	CBgR
'Dick Kitchingman'	CBgR
'Different for Girls' **new**	EStr
'Digital Dynamics'	EStr
'Dipped in Ink'	EStr
'Dipped in Pink' **new**	EStr
'Discarded Beauty'	EStr
'Disco Inferno'	EStr
'Distant Galaxy'	EStr WCAu
'Diva Bride'	EStr
'Diva in Zebra'	EStr
'Diva's Choice'	EStr
'Divertissment'	CBgR ELon EWoo SDay WHrl
'Dizzy Miss Lizzy'	EStr
'Do You Know Doris'	SDay
'Doc Holliday'	EStr
'Doctor Doom'	EStr
'Doctor Freckles Mr Hyde'	EStr
'Doctor McGregor's Garden'	EStr
'Doctor Strangelove'	EStr
'Dominic'	CBgR EWoo MACG SDay WFar
'Don Stevens'	WHrl
'Don's Wild Heather'	EStr
'Don't Leave Empty-handed'	EStr
'Dorethe Louise'	CBgR SDay
'Dorothy McDade'	EWoo MNrw
'Dory's Big Heart' **new**	EStr
'Dot Paul'	ELan
'Double Action' (d)	ELon SDay
'Double Cream' (d)	WCot
'Double Cutie' (d)	EHyd EStr LRHS NLar NRHS SDay SRms
'Double Delicious' (d)	WCot
'Double Doubloon' (d)	XLum
'Double Dream' (d)	EGrI EStr WHrl
'Double Firecracker' (d)	MBNS NBro NLar
'Double Gardenia' (d)	EStr WNHG
'Double Honey' (d)	EStr
'Double Oh Seven' (d)	ELon
'Double Pompon' (d)	EStr
'Double Red Royal' (d)	EGrI EPfP EStr
'Double River Wye' (d)	CBgR ECtt EHyd EShb EStr GBee MACG MHer MNrw NGdn WBrk WCot WFar WHoo WHrl
'Dowager Queen'	WNHG
'Dragon Fire Breath'	EStr
'Dragon Flight'	LLWG
'Dragon King'	SDay
'Dragon Lore'	EStr

'Dragon Seeker'	EStr
'Dragon's Eye'	EHyd EWoo LRHS NRHS SDay WNHG
'Dragon's Orb'	SDay
'Dream Awhile'	SDay
'Dream Keeper'	EWoo
'Dream Legacy'	SDay
'Dreamliner' **new**	EStr
'Dresden Doll'	SPer
'Driving Me Wild'	SDay
'Drooling Lizard'	EStr
'Droopy Drawers'	ELon
'Drop Cloth'	EStr
'Druid's Chant'	EWoo
'Duke of Durham'	EStr EWoo MSpe
'Duke of Earl'	CBgR
dumortieri	CAgr CBro EBee ECha EWhm GGro MMuc MRav NBid NBir NSti SCob SEND SPer WCot WWtn XSen
- B&SWJ 1283	WCru
'Dumpy'	EStr
'Dune Needlepoint'	EStr WHrl
'Dunkle Prinzessin' **new**	GBin
'Dutch Beauty'	WFar
'Dutch Gold'	MHCG MNrw
'Earl of Warwick'	CBgR
'Earlianna'	EStr
'Earnest Yearwood'	SDay
'Easter Star'	EStr
'Easy Ned'	ELon EWoo
'Eat Our Wake Pintaheads'	EStr
'Echo Echo'	EStr
'Ed Brown'	SDay
'Ed Kirchhoff'	XLum
'Ed Murray'	EStr SDay SHar WCAu
'Edgar Brown'	WCot
'Edge Ahead'	CMac ECtt EHyd GKin LRHS NHol NRHS SDay WCAu WHrl
'Edge of Darkness'	CWGN NLar NSti SDay WFar
'Edith Marie'	EStr
'Edith Vaughan'	EStr SDay
'Edna Spalding'	CRos EHyd LRHS NRHS SDay
'Eenie Allegro'	CBro ECtt SPer
'Eenie Fanfare'	EStr NBir
'Eenie Weenie'	CBro ECtt EHyd ELon EStr GKev NBro SRms WWtn
'Eenie Weenie Non-stop'	ECha EGrI EPPr
'Eggplant Electricity'	EWoo
'Eggplant Escapade' ♀H6	CBgR ELon EStr SDay WHrl
'Egyptian Ibis'	EWoo WNHG
'Egyptian Queen'	CBgR
'Eight Miles High'	EStr
'Eighteen Karat'	EStr
'El Desperado'	CBgR ECtt EHyd ELon EStr EWoo GQue ILea LRHS MBNS MHol MNrw NRHS WCAu WCot WHrl
'El Glorioso'	CWat EStr
'Elaine Farrant'	SDay
'Elaine Strutt'	SDay SWvt WCot WSpi
'Electric Marmalade Magic'	SDay
'Elegant Candy' ♀H6	CBgR CMac EPfP EStr EWoo WCAu
'Elegant Girls'	EStr
'Eleonor'	WFar
'Elfin Illusion'	EStr
'Elizabeth Salter'	CWCL EStr NLar SDay
'Eloquent Silence'	SDay
'Elsie Stelter'	EStr
'Elva White Grow'	SDay
'Elven Elegance'	EStr
'Emerald Dew'	SDay
'Emerald Empress'	EStr

'Emerald Eye'	SDay
'Emerald Starburst'	EStr
'Eminent Domain' **new**	SDay
'Emperor's Choice'	SDay
'Emperor's Dragon'	EStr SDay
'Enchanted Empress' **new**	SDay
'Enchanted Forest'	EStr WCAu
'Enchanter's Spell'	SDay
'Enchanting Blessing'	EStr SDay
'English Cameo'	SDay
'English Skies'	EStr
'Entrapment'	CBod ECtt EStr SDeJ WFar WSMil
'Entwined in the Vine'	EStr
'Envoyé Spécial'	XSen
'Erica Nichole Gonzales'	SDay
'Erin Prairie'	EStr
esculenta	SMad
'Etched Eyes'	EWoo
'Eternal Blessing'	SDay
'Eternity Road'	EStr
'Etruscan Tomb'	EStr
'Evelyn Claar'	CMac
'Evelyn Lela Stout'	SDay
'Evening Enchantment'	EStr SDay
'Ever So Ruffled'	EStr SDay
EVERYDAYLILY CREAM ('Ver00112'^{PBR})	EStr
'Exotic Love'	SDay
'Exotic Spider'	EStr
'Exotic Star'	EStr
'Exotic Treasure'	EStr
'Exploded Pumpkin'	EBee EStr
'Exploding Galaxy'	EStr
'Explosion in the Paint Factory'	EStr
'Eye of the Hurricane'	EStr
'Eye on a String'	EStr
'Eye on America'	EBee ELon EStr
'Eyes are Mosaics'	EStr
'Eyes Bright' **new**	EStr
'Ezekiel'	SDay WHrl
'Fabergé'	SDay
'Facemaker'	EStr
'Fairest Love'	MNrw WHrl
'Fairest of Them'	CBgR
'Fairy Charm'	SDay
'Fairy Summerbird'	SDay
'Fairy Tale Pink'	EStr SDay
'Fall Farewell'	WNHG
'Fall Guy'	SDay
'Fama'	EStr
'Fandango'	SPer
'Fantasia'	EWoo
'Farmer's Daughter'	CBgR
'Father James Foster'	EStr
'Feather Down'	SDay
'Fellow'	EStr
'Femme Fatale'	SDay
'Femme Osage'	EStr SDay
'Ferengi Gold'	SDay
'Ferris Wheel'	EWoo
'Fiestaville'	EStr
'Final Touch'	CBgR CBod EStr MSwo NBro
'Finders Keepers'	EBee EStr
'Fire and Fog'	EStr
'Fire Bird Suite'	EStr
'Fire Dance'	ELon
'Fire from Heaven'	WHrl
'Fire Tree'	CBgR ELon EStr
'Firestorm'	EStr
'First Formal'	SPer

'First Knight'	EStr SDay
'Flaming Firebird'	EStr
'Flaming Sword'	WBrk
'Flamingo Parade'	EStr
'Flash Mob'	EStr
flava	see *H. lilioasphodelus*
'Fleeting Fancy'	SDay
'Flight of the Dragon'	SDay
'Flip Fiasco'	EStr
'Florentine Silk'	EStr
'Florissant Miss'	EStr
'Flower Basket' (d)	EStr
'Flower Pavilion'	SDay
'Floyd Cove'	SDay
'Fly Catcher'	CBgR SDay
'Flying Saucer Blues' **new**	SDay
'Flying Trapeze'	EStr
'Fooled Me' ♀H6	ECtt EHyd EPfP EStr LRHS NRHS SDay
'For the Good Times'	EWoo
'Forbidden Desires'	EStr
'Forest Phantom'	EStr
'Forever Red'	EStr
'Forever Redeemed'	EStr SDay
forrestii	CExl GKev
'Forsooth'	CBgR
'Forsyth Ace of Hearts'	CBgR
'Forsyth Evening Glow'	EStr
'Forsyth White Buds'	EStr
'Fortress of Solitude'	EStr
'Fortune's Dearest'	SDay
'Forty Second Street'	EStr
'Fragrant Bouquet'	EStr
'Fragrant Pastel Cheers'	SDay
'Fragrant Reflections'	EStr
'Fragrant Returns'	CKel ECtt EGrI LEdu SPoG
'Frankly Scarlet'	EStr
'Frans Hals'	Widely available
'Fred Manning'	EStr
'Free Wheelin''	EPfP EStr SCob
'French Connection'	SDay
'French Fare' **new**	EStr
'French Lingerie'	EStr
'French Pavilion'	SDay
'French Porcelain'	SDay
'Fresh Air'	MNrw
'Fried Green Tomatoes'	EStr
'Friends with Benefits'	EStr
'Frills and Furbelows'	SDay
'Frilly Bliss'	EStr
'Fritz Schroer'	CBgR
'Froggy'	EStr
'Frosted Encore'	SDay
'Frosted Vintage Ruffles'	EBee EStr EWes MNrw WCAu
'Frozen Arrowhead'	EStr
'Frozen Jade'	EBee EHyd LRHS NRHS SDay
'Full Grown'	EStr
'Fully Blessed'	EStr
fulva	CTri GPSL LPot MMuc NBir SEND SRms WBrk WHrl XSen
- B&SWJ 8647	WCru
- 'Flore Pleno' (d)	CAvo CMac CTri ECtt ELan GBin LPot MBriF MHer MRav NBir NBro NGdn NSti SMad SPer SRms SSal WBrk WCAu WSMil XSen
- 'Green Kwanso' (d)	CBgR CExl ECha EHyd ITim LRHS NRHS WFar WPnP WWtn
- var. ***kwanso***	WWtn
- - B&SWJ 6328	WCru
- 'Kwanso' ambig. (d)	EHyd
- var. ***littorea***	CMac XLum
- var. ***rosea***	EBlo LRHS WCot
§ - 'Variegated Kwanso' (d/v)	ELon MRav NBir SMad WCot WFar WHer WHrl
- yellow-variegated (v)	WCot
'Fun Fling'	EStr
'Funicular'	EStr
'Furgalisus' **new**	EStr
'Gadsden Light'	EStr SDay
'Galaxy Ranger'	EStr
'Gale Storm'	WNHG
'Galena Holiday'	EWes
'Galileo'	EStr
'Garden Butterfly'	EStr
'Garden Crawler'	CBgR
'Garden Portrait'	EWoo SDay
'Garrett Allen'	EStr
'Gary Colby'	EStr
'Gaudy Grasshopper' **new**	EStr
'Gay Octopus'	CBgR EStr MSpe WHrl
'Gay Rapture'	SPer
'Gay Troubadour'	EWoo
'Gemini'	SDay
'Gender Equality'	EStr
'Geneva Firetruck'	EStr WHrl
'Gentle Country Breeze'	SDay
'Gentle Rose'	EStr SDay
'Gentle Shepherd'	Widely available
'Gentle Thoughts' **new**	SDay
'George Cunningham'	ECtt EGrI EHyd ELan LPot LRHS MRav NBir NRHS SDay WFar
'George David'	WHrl
'Georgette Belden'	ECtt EHyd GKin NHol SPeP
'Georgia Cream' (d)	NLar
'Gerda Brooker'	EStr
'Get All Excited'	ELon
'Ghost Pattern'	EStr
'Giant Moon'	CBgR CRos ECtt EHyd ELan EStr LRHS NRHS SDay SRms
'Giddy Go Round'	EWoo SDay
'Ginger Twist'	EStr
'Give Me Eight'	EWoo
'Glacier Bay'	CBgR EWoo
'Glazed Heather Plum'	EStr
'Gleber's Top Cream'	EStr
'Gleeman Song'	CBgR
'Glendevon'	EStr
'Glittering Treasure'	SDay XLum
'Glow Appeal'	EStr
'Go Seminoles'	EStr
'Going Bananas' PBR	WCot
'Gold Elephant'	SDay
'Gold Fever'	SDay
'Golden Bell'	NGdn
'Golden Chimes'	Widely available
'Golden Compass'	EStr
'Golden Firefly'	SDay
'Golden Ginkgo'	LPot SDay WNHG
'Golden Prize'	NGdn SDay WCot XSen
'Golden Scroll'	SDay
GOLDEN ZEBRA ('Malja' PBR) (v)	CEme CWGN EHyd ELan EPfP MRav NLar SRms
'Goldie Hicks' **new**	SDay
'Golliwog'	CBgR EStr
'Gorgeous Smile'	EStr
'Got Milk'	EStr
'Gothic Butterfly'	EStr
'Gothic Window'	SDay
'Grace and Favour'	SDay
'Graceful Eye'	SDay
'Graceland'	SDay WHrl
'Grand Masterpiece'	EStr NGdn SDay WFar

'Grand Palais' SDay
'Granite City Towhead' ELon
'Granny's Smokehouse' EStr
'Grape Arbor' WNHG
'Grape Harvest' WNHG
'Grape Magic' WCot
'Grape Velvet' CSpe EStr EWoo MHer NSti SRms WCAu WNHG WWtn
'Grapes of Wrath' EStr
'Great Auntie Picklebottom' EStr
'Green Arrow' EStr
'Green Dolphin Street' SDay
'Green Dragon' SDay
'Green Eyes Wink' MHol
'Green Flutter' CBgR EStr GBee GBin GQue LPla NBir NGdn NSti SPhx WSpi
'Green Fringe' SDay
'Green Goddess' XLum
'Green Icon' EStr
'Green Lines' EStr
'Green Mystique' EBee EStr SDay
'Green Nautilus' EStr
'Green Spider' CBgR SDay
'Green Widow' EWoo SDay
'Greenland' EBee ECtt EHyd EStr LRHS NRHS
'Greywoods Cowgirl Casanova' EStr
'Greywoods Fashionista' EStr
'Greywoods Fingers Malone' EStr
'Greywoods Katz Kando' EStr
'Greywoods Nautical Nellie' EStr
'Groove-billed Ani' EStr
'Groovy Green' SDay
'Grumbly' ELan WPnP
'Gryphon Hankow Legacy' EStr
'Gryphon Prague Gothic' EStr
'Guardian Angel' WCFE
'Gwen Leman' EStr
'Gypsy Sweetheart' WNHG
'Hail Mary' SDay
'Halloween Green' EStr
'Hamlet' SDay WNHG
'Handsome Devil' **new** EStr
'Happy Apache' EStr
'Happy Medium' EStr
'Happy Returns' CBgR CRos CSBt CTri ECha EHyd ELan EPfP EStr EWoo GBin LCro LOPS LPot LRHS LSRN MBel MHost NGdn NHol NRHS SRms WCAu XLum
'Harbor Blue' SDay
'Harbor Gate' **new** SDay
'Harrods' EStr
'Harry Barras' XLum
'Harvest Hue' SDay
'Having Fun' EStr
'Hawaiian Nights' WNHG
'Hawk' ELon SDay
'Hawkwoman' EStr
'Hazel' EStr
'Hazmatter's Ball' EStr
'Heady Wine' EStr SDay
'Heart Wishes' EStr
'Heartless' EStr
'Heavenly Angel Ice' ELon EPfP MACG
'Heavenly Beginnings' EStr
'Heavenly Black Bird' EStr
'Heavenly Curls' EStr SDay
'Heavenly Fire and Ice' EStr
'Heavenly Flight of Angels' EStr SMrm
'Heavenly Mr Twister' EStr
'Heavenly Orange Blaze' **new** EStr
'Heavenly Pink Butterfly' EStr
'Heavenly Thunderbird' EStr
'Heavenly Treasure' SDay
'Heavenly United We Stand' EStr
'Heavenly Way Big' EStr
'Heidi Eidelweiss' CExl EWoo
'Heirloom Lace' SDay WCAu
'Helen Sever' EStr
'Helen Shooter' EStr
'Helena Seabird' EStr
'Helix' EPfP EStr MBros SDay
'Helle Berlinerin' SDay SEdd
'Hello Screamer' EStr
'Helter Skelter' SDay
'Heman' EStr
'Henry D. Allnutt' EStr
'Her Majesty's Wizard' CBgR ELan ELon
'Here Lies Butch' EStr
'Hermitage Newton' SDay
'Hexagon' EStr
'Hiding Place' EStr
'High Profile' EStr
'High Tor' ELon EStr SDay WHrl
'High Water Mark' EStr
'Highland Lord' (d) EStr SDay WCAu
'Highland Summerbird' SDay
'Hold Your Horses' SDay
'Holiday Delight' EStr
'Holiday Mood' ELan
'Holly Dancer' ♀H6 EStr
'Homeward Bound' SDay
'Honeysuckle Rose' EStr
'Honor Flight' EStr
'Hooked on Romance' EStr
'Hope Diamond' SDay
'Hope Floats' EStr
'Hoping for Hugs' EStr
'Hornby Castle' CBro CRos EBlo EHyd LRHS NRHS
'Hortensia' SDay
'Hot Pink Fury' EStr
'Hot Tamales and Red Hots' EStr
'Hot Town' ELan
'Hot Wheels' CBgR
'Hot Wire' SDay WNHG
'Houdini' WCAu
'House of Lords' **new** SDay
'House of Orange' EStr
'Humdinger' EStr SDay WCot
'Hummingbird' EStr
'Humungousaur' EStr
'Hunker Down' EStr
'Huntress' EStr
'Hybridizer's Truffle' EStr
'Hymn' SDay
'Hyperion' CBgR CBod CMac CTri ECha ECtt ELon EShb EStr EWoo GKin LEdu LRHS MACG MHol MRav NBid NGdn SDay SMrm SPer SWvt WCot WWtn
'I Gotta be Me' **new** EStr
'I Love to Tell the Story' EStr
'Ice Carnival' EStr NGdn NLar SCob SWvt WSpi
'Ice Castles' CTri SDay
'Ice Cool' SCob
'Ice Planet' **new** SDay
'Icecap' CBgR
'Icy Lemon' EStr SDay

'Ida Duke Miles'	SDay
'Ida Mae Norris'	EStr
'Ida Wimberly Munson'	SDay
'Ida's Magic'	EStr SDay
'Identity Crisis'	EStr
'Iditarod'	EStr
'Ikebana Star'	EStr
'Iktomi'	EStr
'Illini Jackpot'	SDay
'I'm a King Bee'	EStr
'Imperial Lemon'	GBin
'Impromptu'	SDay
'In Depth' (d)	EWoo NBro NLar WCot WHrl
'In Her Shoes'	EStr
'In Search of Angels'	EStr
'In Strawberry Time'	WNHG
'Inca Puzzle'	SDay
'Inchon'	EStr
'Increased Complexity'	EStr
'Indian Paintbrush'	ELon NBir WNHG
'Indy Heart Stopper'	EStr
'Inner View'	ECtt EStr SDay
'Innocent Blush'	EStr
'Inspired Word'	SDay
'Invitation to Immortality'	EWoo LSun
'Iridescent Jewel'	SDay
'Irish Elf'	ELon GBin SDay SHar
'Irish Mixup'	EStr
'Irish Veil'	EStr
'Iron Gate Glacier'	EBee EPPr EStr LRHS MBNS SDay XLum
'Irresistible You'	EStr
'Irving Schulman' **new**	SDay
'Isaac'	EStr
'Isabelle Rose'	EStr SDay
'Isle of Dreams'	SDay
'Isle of Wight' **new**	SDay
'Islesworth'	EWoo SDay
'Isolde'	CBgR EStr
'It's Soul Time'	EStr
'Itsy Bitsy Spider'	CBgR EWoo
'Itza Mirage'	EStr
'Ivelyn Brown'	EStr SDay
'Ivory Cloud' (d)	EStr
'Ivory Coast'	SDay
'J.T. Davis'	EStr
'James Marsh'	CBgR EWoo MNrw NSti SDay WCAu WCot WFar WNHG
'Jane's Prism'	EStr
'Janice Brown'	CWCL ECtt EGrI EMor EStr EWoo GBee NHol NLar NRHS SDay WHrl
'Janie Wilson'	WNHG
'Jan's Twister'	EStr MNrw SDay WHrl
'Jason Salter'	EStr SDay
'Jay Turman'	SDay
'Jealous Sky'	EStr
'Jean'	EStr SDay
'Jean Swann'	EStr
'Jedi Codie Wedgeworth' **new**	SDay
'Jedi Dot Pierce'	EStr SDay
'Jellyfish Jealousy' ♀H6	EStr SDay
'Jennie Sivyer' **new**	EStr
'Jenny Wren'	EPPr EWoo NBro
'Jerry Hyatt'	EStr
'Jersey Breeze'	EStr
'Jerusalem'	SDay
'Jeune Tom'	CBgR
'Jewel Case'	WNHG
'Jim McKinney'	EStr
'Joan Derifield'	EStr

'Joan Senior'	CBgR ECha ECtt EHyd ELan EMor EPfP EShb EStr GBin GKin LRHS LSRN MNrw MRav NGdn NHol NRHS NSti SCob SDay SPer SRms WCAu WCFE WCot WPnP WSpi WWtn
'Job Creator'	EStr
'Jockey Club' (d)	ECtt EStr WHrl
'Jogolor'	EStr
'John R. Pike'	EStr
'Johnny Come Lately'	EStr
'Joie de Vivre'	EWoo
'Jolly Lad' **new**	SDay
'Jordan'	LSRN SWvt
'Jordan's Jazz'	EStr
'Josephine Marina'	EStr
'Journey to Oz'	EWoo
'Journey's End'	SDay
'Jovial'	EStr SDay
'Joyful Occasion' **new**	SDay
'Joyful Participation'	EStr
'Juanita's Picotee Delight'	SDay
'Judah'	SDay
'Judge Roy Bean'	EStr SDay WHrl
'Judy Davidson'	WNHG
'Judy Farquhar'	EStr
'June Melody'	WNHG
'June Wine'	SDay
'Jungle Beauty'	CBgR SDay
'Just Celebrate'	SDay
'Just My Size'	EStr
'Just Whistle'	EStr
'Justin George'	SDay
'Justin June'	WHrl
'Kaleidoscopic Intrigue'	EStr
'Kansas Kitten'	EStr
'Karen's Curls' ♀H6	SDay
'Kasia'	WHrl
'Kate Carpenter'	EStr SDay
'Kathleen Salter'	EStr EWoo SDay
'Katie Elizabeth Miller'	SDay
'Katisue Herrington'	EStr
'Kazuq'	SDay
'Kecia'	SDay
'Kempion'	CBgR
'Kermit's Scream'	EStr
'Key to my Heart'	CBgR
'Key West Sunset'	EStr
'Kharma Police'	EStr
'Kickin' Chicken'	EStr
'Killer Purple'	SDay
'Kimberly Sue'	EStr
'Kindly Light'	EWoo
'King Crab'	EStr
'King George'	EStr
'King Kahuna' (d)	EStr
'King of Anything'	EStr
'King's Gold'	EStr
'King's Throne'	WNHG
'Kiowa Sunset'	SDay
'Kirsten My Love'	EStr
'Kiss Kiss Kiss' **new**	EStr
'Kiss the Sky'	EStr
'Kissed by Moonlight'	EStr
'Knights in White Satin'	EStr
'Kokomo Queen'	EStr
'Kristin Dalton' **new**	EStr
'Kung Fu Panda' **new**	EStr
'Kwanso Flore Pleno'	see *H. fulva* 'Green Kwanso'
'Kwanso Flore Pleno Variegata'	see *H. fulva* 'Variegated Kwanso'
'La Fenice'	EStr

'La Peche'	SDay
'Lacy Doily'	EStr WCAu WSMil
'Lacy Marionette'	ELon EWoo
'Lady Betty Fretz'	EBee EStr
'Lady Fingers'	CBgR
'Lady Inara'	EStr
'Lady Liz'	SDay WNHG
'Lady Mischief'	EStr SDay
'Lady Neva' ♀H6	CBgR ELon
'Lady Tiger'	WNHG
'Ladybug Hawk'	EStr
'Ladybug's Two Moons' (d)	EStr
'Ladykin'	ELon SDay
'Lambada'	EStr
'Lamplighter's Circle'	EStr
'Land of Enchantment'	EStr
'Land's End'	EStr
'Lark Song'	EBlo EHyd LRHS NRHS WFar WHrl
'Larry's Candy Stripe Swizzle'	EStr
'Last Song'	EStr
'Late Report'	EStr
'Late Summer Rose'	WNHG
'Laughing Giraffe'	EStr WCot
'Laughton Tower'	SMHy
'Lauradell'	SDay
'Lauren Leah'	SDay
'Lava Burst'	EStr
'Lava Stream'	EStr
'Lavender Blue Baby'	CBod EPfP EStr MHol SPer
'Lavender Bonanza'	SDay
'Lavender Deal'	MNrw WNHG
'Lavender Handlebars'	SDay
'Lavender Memories'	EStr SDay WNHG
'Lavender Showstopper'	WCAu
'Lavender Spider'	CBgR
'Lavender Stardust'	SDay
'Lavender Tonic'	WNHG
'Lavender Tutu'	ECtt EStr MBros
'Lazy Hazy Days'	EStr
'Leading Edge'	SDay
'Ledgewood's Frequent Flyer'	EStr
'Ledgewood's Irish Spirit'	EStr
'Ledgewood's Sunday Dessert'	EStr
'Lee Reinke'	EStr
'Leila Mantle'	CBgR
'Lemon Bells'	CWat ECha EHyd EPfP EStr GKev GKin GMaP LEdu LRHS NBro SHar WCAu WSpi
'Lemon Custard'	EStr
'Lemon Dessert'	ELon
'Lemon Fellow'	EWoo
'Lemon Madeline'	EStr
'Lemon Mint'	ELon
'Lemon Soldier' **new**	EStr
'Lemonora'	SDay
'Lenox'	SDay
'Leonard Bernstein'	EStr SDay
'Leprechaun's Curls'	EStr
'Let it Rip'	EWoo
'Let Loose'	EStr
'Let Love Rejoice'	EStr
'Lies and Lipstick'	EStr
'Life is a Highway'	EStr
'Life Unlimited'	EStr
'Light the Way'	GBin SEdd SPoG WCot
'Light Years Away'	ELon MBNS MNrw
'Lightning Strikes Twice' **new**	EStr
'Like a Gee Six'	EStr
'Lilac Lady'	EStr
'Lilac Wine'	WBor
§ ***lilioasphodelus***	Widely available
'Lillian's Good Intentions'	EStr
'Lilly Dache'	EStr EWoo
'Lilting Lady'	EStr
'Lilting Lavender'	ELon WCAu
'Lily Munster'	EStr
'Lime Frost' ♀H6	CBgR EStr SDay
'Lime Painted Lady'	CBgR
'Limetree'	CBgR EStr
'Limited Edition'	EWoo
'Lin Wright'	EWoo
'Linda'	MRav
'Linda Sierra'	EStr
'Linda the Green Eyed Lady'	EStr
'Lines of Splendor'	EWoo
'Lip Smack'	EStr
'Lipstick on a Pig' **new**	EStr
'Litchfield Plantation'	EStr
'Little Anna Rosa'	ECtt EStr
'Little Audrey'	EStr
'Little Big Man'	SDay
'Little Bumble Bee'	LRHS WWtn
'Little Business'	SDay
'Little Cadet'	XLum
'Little Cranberry Cove'	GBin
'Little Deeke'	SDay WHrl
'Little Fantastic'	ELon SDay WWtn
'Little Fat Cat'	EStr
'Little Fellow'	EStr
'Little Girl'	ELon
'Little Grapette'	ELon EPfP EStr GQue LLWG LPla NLar NSti SCob
'Little Greenie'	SDay
'Little Gypsy Vagabond'	CBgR CWat EStr
'Little Heavenly Angel'	EStr
'Little Isaac'	EStr
'Little Kiki'	SDay
'Little Lassie'	CBgR
'Little Maggie'	SDay
'Little Men'	WCAu
'Little Miss Lucy'	EStr
'Little Miss Manners'	EStr NLar
'Little Missy'	CBgR EStr WNHG
'Little Monica'	SDay
'Little Music Maker' (d)	EStr
'Little Paul'	EStr
'Little Red Hen'	EHyd GKin LRHS NBir NBro NGdn SDay WFar
'Little Show Stopper'	NBro NLar
'Little Showoff'	SDay
'Little Surfer Girl'	EStr
'Little Swain'	SDay
'Little Sweet Talk'	ELon
'Little Swirling Shadows'	EStr
'Little Tawny'	ELon
'Little Toddler'	SDay
'Little Velma'	EStr
'Little Violet Lace'	SDay
'Little Wart'	CBgR SDay WHrl
'Little William'	EStr
'Little Wine Cup'	CMac CRos ECtt ELon EStr GKin GMaP LPot LRHS MRav NBir NGdn NRHS SCoo SMrm SPer SRms
'Little Women'	SDay WHrl
'Little Zinger'	SDay
'Littlest Angel'	SDay
'Littlest Clown'	SDay
'Living in Amsterdam'	EStr

'Lobo Lucy'	ELon EStr
'Loch Ness Monster'	EStr
'Lochinvar'	MRav
'Loco Bo'	EStr
'Lois Burns'	EWoo SDay
'Lola Branham'	EWoo
'Lonely Heart'	EStr
'Long John Silver'	ELon EStr
'Long Stocking'	EStr WCot
'Long Tall Sally'	EStr
'Longfields Anwar'	EGrl EWoo
'Longfields Bandit'	EWoo
'Longfields Beauty'	EWoo MSpe
'Longfields Dress Pink'	EStr
'Longfields × Factor'	EStr
'Longfields Glory'	EHyd ITim LRHS NRHS
'Longfields Maxim' (d)	EStr MHol SDeJ
'Longfields Pearl'	EStr ITim
'Longfields Pride'	EStr SRms WBor
'Longfields Purple Eye'	NLar
'Longfields Think Pink'	EStr
'Longfields Tropica'	EStr
'Longfields Twins'	MBNS WCot WFar
'Longfields Whoopy'	EGrl ELon EPfP MNrw SDir
longituba B&SWJ 4576	WCru
'Look at Me'	ELan
'Look Lucky'	EStr
'Lost in the Toy Store'	EStr
'Lost in the Translation'	EStr
'Loth Lorien'	EHyd EStr LRHS NRHS
'Lots of Hoopla'	EStr
'Lotta Dotta'	EStr
'Lotus Land'	SDay
'Lotus Position'	EBee
'Louis McHargue'	SDay
'Lourice Abdallah'	EStr
'Love Those Eyes'	EStr
'Lovely Margie'	EStr
'Lovely Miss Laucius' **new**	EStr
'Lovely Rita'	EStr
'Loverboy'	EStr
'Loving Memories'	SDay
'Lowcountry Gem'	EStr
'Lucille Lennington'	WNHG
'Lullaby Baby'	ELan NLar WNHG
'Luminous Jewel' **new**	SDay
'Lunar Sea'	EStr
'Lupita Vindaz'	EStr
'Luscious Honeydew'	WNHG
'Lusty Lealand'	SDay
'Lusty Little Lulu' **new**	SDay
'Luxury Lace'	CAgr EBee ECtt EHyd ELan EStr GBin GKin LRHS LSRN MACG MHost NBir NGdn NHol NWad SPer WFar WHrl WWtn XLum
'Lydia Bechtold'	EStr SDay
'Lynn Hall'	EHyd NLar WSpi
'Mabel Fuller'	CBgR MRav SPer WHrl
'Mabel Nolen'	EStr
'Mable Lewis Nelson'	EStr
'Macbeth'	EGrl EStr MNrw SDir
'Mad Max'	EStr EWoo SDay
'Madeline Nettles Eyes'	EBee ELon EStr
'Madmoiselle Constanza'	SDay
'Mae Graham'	SDay
'Maggie Fynboe'	CBgR
'Magic Amethyst'	CBgR
'Magic Carpet Ride'	EStr
'Magic Dancer'	CBod EStr
'Magic Lace'	EStr
'Magic of Oz'	EStr
'Magical Messenger'	EStr
'Mahogany Magic' ♀H6	ELon EStr
'Majestic Dark Eyes'	EStr
'Malachite Prism'	EStr
'Malaysian Monarch'	EStr SDay WNHG
'Malaysian Spice'	WNHG
'Maleny Canary'	EStr
'Maleny Chantilly Lace'	EStr
'Maleny Debutante'	EStr
'Maleny Kiwi Dazzler'	EStr
'Maleny Mite'	EWoo
'Maleny Tiger'	SDay
'Mallard'	CBgR ECtt EStr LRHS MHer MRav NBir SPer WCot
'Malmaison Plum'	EStr SDay
'Mama Sophia'	EStr
'Mama's Pajamas'	EStr
'Man on Fire'	WNHG
'Manchurian Apricot'	SDay
'Marble Faun'	SDay
'Margaret Perry'	MNrw NLar
'Margaret Seawright'	EStr
'Margo Reed Indeed'	EStr SDay WNHG
'Marietta Charmer'	SDay
'Marietta Delight'	EStr
'Marilyn Lee Bock'	EStr
'Marilyn Morss Johnson'	EStr
'Marion Vaughn'	ECtt ELan EPfP GKin GMaP MBel MRav NSti SDix SPer SRGP SWvt WCAu WCot WFar WHoo WSHC
'Mariska'	EStr SDay WNHG
'Marked by Lydia'	ELon
'Marshall McLuhan'	EStr
'Martie Everest'	EWoo
'Martina Verhaert'	CWGN EStr
'Mary Alice Stokes'	EStr
'Mary Ethel Anderson'	EStr
'Mary Todd'	EBee XSen
'Mary's Baby'	EStr
'Mary's Gold' ♀H6	SDay
'Masada'	WNHG
'Mask of Time'	EStr
'Mask of Zorro'	EStr
'Mata Hari'	SDay
'Matchless Fire'	EStr
'Maude's Valentine'	SDay
'Mauna Loa'	CSBt ELon EStr GQue LPot MNrw NLar SDeJ SWvt WCot
'May May'	CBgR ELon
'Mayan Poppy'	EStr
'Meadow Mist'	CBgR ELon
'Meadow Sprite'	WCot
'Mean Mister Mustard'	EStr
'Medieval Guild'	EStr
'Mema's Dingaling'	EStr
'MeMe's Alter Ego' **new**	EStr
'MeMe's Guilty Pleasure'	EStr
'MeMe's Indulgence' **new**	EStr
'MeMe's Lovin' the Limelight'	EStr
'MeMe's Merlot'	EStr
'MeMe's Pink Flamingo'	EStr
'Memory Number One'	EStr
'Mephistopheles'	EWoo
'Merry Jo's Delight'	EStr
'Merry Moppet'	EStr EWoo
'Merry Witch'	EStr
'Metaphor'	ECtt MHol SDay
'Michael Poliga'	EStr
'Michael's Sword'	EStr

'Michele Coe'	ECtt GKin NBro NGdn WCAu WFar WHrl
'Mico'	ELon
middendorffii	CMac EStr GGro GKev GMaP LPla NSti WHrl WSpi WThu
'Middle of Nowhere'	EStr
'Midnight Confession'	EStr
'Midnight Magic'	SDay
'Midnight Raider'	EWoo
'Midnight Rambler'	SDay
'Midnight Rendezvous'	EStr
'Mighty Shogun' **new**	SDay
'Mikado'	CBgR CMac EStr
'Mike Reed'	EStr
'Milady Greensleeves'	EStr EWoo SDay WHrl
'Milanese Mango'	EStr SDay
'Mildred Mitchell'	CBgR ELon EStr GKev NLar WHrl
'Military School'	EStr
'Mimosa Umbrella'	EStr
'Ming Lo'	SDay
'Ming Porcelain'	SDay WCAu WNHG
'Mini Pearl'	ECtt ELon EStr LRHS MPie NRHS SDay SPer
'Mini Stella'	CBro ECtt SDay WFar
'Minnie Wildfire'	EStr
minor	EBlo EHyd EPPr LRHS NRHS SPhx SRms
– B&SWJ 8841	WCru
'Miracle Maid'	WNHG
'Miss Atomic Bomb'	EStr
'Miss Jessie'	EStr EWoo
'Miss North Carolina'	EStr
'Miss Piggy'	EStr
'Missenden'	CBgR EStr MNrw
'Missouri Beauty'	SWvt
'Mister Lucky'	EStr
'Mojave Sunset'	EStr
'Mokan Butterfly'	SDay
'Monica Marie'	EStr SDay
'Mont Royal Demitasse'	ELon
'Moon Snow'	SDay
'Moonlight Masquerade'	CBgR ECtt ELon NLar SRms
'Moonlight Mist'	SDay
'Moonlight Orchid'	WHrl
'Moonlit Caress'	CBgR EBee ECtt NBro SDay
'Moonlit Crystal'	EStr
'Moonlit Masquerade' ♀H6	CWGN EStr MBNS MNrw SDay SEND WHrl
'Moonlit Summerbird'	EStr
'Moontraveller'	WCot
'Morgen le Fay'	EStr
'Mormon Spider'	EStr
'Morning Face'	EStr
'Morning Sun'	WCot
'Morocco Red'	CBro ELan MHCG
'Morphin Time'	EStr
'Morpho Butterfly'	EStr
'Mosel'	SDay
'Moses' Fire'	ECtt EStr MHol NLar SPeP WFar
'Mossy Glade'	CBgR
'Mount Echo Sunrise'	EWoo
'Mount Joy'	EStr
'Mountain Laurel'	ECtt EHyd EStr GKin LRHS MRav NRHS WFar WGwG
'Moussaka'	CBod CWGN EStr WCAu WFar
'Move Over Moon'	EStr SDay
'Mr and Mrs Bubbs' **new**	EStr
'Mrs Hugh Johnson'	CChe EShb LPot NFav WHrl
* 'Mrs Lester'	SDay
'Muddy Creek Magic'	EStr
'Muffet's Little Friend'	WHrl
'Multiple Multiplications'	EStr
'Mumbo Jumbo'	SDay
'Muriel Rhem'	EStr
'Murphy's Law'	EStr
'Muscle Man'	EStr
'My Belle'	SDay
'My Darling Clementine'	EStr SDay WNHG
'My Friend Kammy' **new**	EStr
'My Happy Valentine' **new**	SDay
'My Heart Belongs to Daddy'	EStr
'My Melinda'	SDay
'My Place or Yours'	EStr
'My Reggae Tiger'	EStr
'Mynelle's Starfish'	WHrl
'Mystical Rainbow'	SDay
'Nacogdoches Lady'	SWvt
'Nagasaki' (d)	SDay
'Nanuq'	ELon SDay
'Naomi Ruth'	EStr
'Nashville'	CBro ELan WHrl
'Nashville Lights'	CBgR EStr
'National Memento'	EStr
'Native Reflection'	EStr
'Natty Man'	EStr
'Naughty Red'	EStr
'Navajo Jewel'	EStr
'Navajo Pony'	EStr
'Navajo Princess'	MNrw SDay
'Neal Berrey'	EStr SDay
'Nefertiti'	CBgR ELon NBir WCAu
'Neon Flamingo'	EStr
'Neon Sunshine'	EStr
'Neon Yellow'	EStr
'Neutron Star'	EStr
'Never Ending Fantasy'	EStr
'Never Get Away'	EStr
'New Design' **new**	EStr
'New Wine'	WNHG
'New York Follies'	EStr
'Neyron Rose'	EHyd GKin LRHS NGdn NRHS WWtn XLum
'Night Beacon'	CBgR ECtt EGrI ELon EStr EWoo GKin MNrw MPie NLar SCob SDay SDeJ WCAu WHrl
'Night Embers'	ECtt ELon EPfP EStr EWoo MBel NLar SDir WCAu WHrl
'Night Raider'	CBgR EStr SDay WNHG
'Nile Crane'	CBgR ELon EStr MNrw SDay SPer
'Nile Plum'	EStr SDay
'Nina Winegar'	EStr
'Ninja Storm'	EStr
'Nivia Guest'	SDay
'Nob Hill'	ELon EStr LRHS WHrl XLum
'Nona's Garnet Spider'	ELon
'Nordic Night'	CBgR SDay
'North Wind Dancer' ♀H6	EWoo
'North Wind Drifter'	EStr
'Norton Beauté'	WCot
'Norton Eyed Seedling'	WNHG
'Norton Orange'	EStr
'Not Forgotten'	WNHG
'Nothing is Easy'	EStr
'Notify Ground Crew'	EStr
'Nova'	ELon SDay
'Nowhere to Hide'	EStr
'Nuit Parisienne'	EStr
'Nuka'	XLum
'Nutmeg Elf'	CBgR
'Oakes Love'	EWoo MNrw
'O'Bannon Orchid' **new**	EStr

'Obsidian'	SCoo
'Ocean Rain'	EStr SDay WNHG
'Ocean Spirit'	EStr
'Octopus Hugs'	EStr
'Ojo de Dios'	EWoo
'Oke-She-Moke-She-Pop'	EStr
'Old San Juan'	EStr
'Old Tangiers' ♀H6	EStr SDay WNHG
'Olive Bailey Langdon'	EStr SDay WCot
'Olive's Odd One'	ELon EStr
'Oloroso'	CBgR
'Olympic Gold'	EStr
'Olympic Showcase'	EStr
'Omomuki'	SDay
'On and On'	EStr GBin GQue MBros MNrw
'On Pointe'	EStr
'On Silken Thread'	SDay
'One Above You'	EStr
'One Strange Cookie' **new**	EStr
'Oodles'	WHrl
'Open Hearth'	EStr WHrl
'Open my Eyes'	EStr
'Orange Dream'	SDay
'Orange Empire'	SDay
'Orange Exotica'	CBgR EStr
'Orange Fizz' (d) **new**	EStr
'Orange Nassau'	EStr WCAu WFar
'Orange Velvet'	SDay
'Orangeman' misapplied	NGdn
'Orchid Candy'	EStr NBir
'Orchid Corsage'	ELon EStr
'Orchid Lady Slipper'	EStr
'Oriental Impressions'	EStr
'Oriental Ruby'	SDay
'Osterized'	EStr
'Ostrich Plume'	EStr
'Ouachita Beauty'	CBgR ELon
'Our Kirsten'	EStr SDay
'Out of Balance'	EStr
'Outrageous'	CBgR EStr SDay WNHG
'Outrageous Ramona'	WNHG
'Oy Vey'	EStr
'Paige's Pinata'	EStr
'Painted Lady'	EGrI WNHG
'Painted Pink'	SDay
'Palace Garden Beauty'	EWoo
'Palace Pagoda'	WNHG
'Panda Bear'	EStr
'Pandora's Box'	CExl CTri CWat ECtt EGrI ELan EStr MNrw NBir NGdn NLar SDeJ SWvt WBor WFar
'Pantherette'	ELon
'Papa Goose'	EStr
'Papa Goose Gets Jiggy' **new**	EStr
'Paper Butterfly'	EStr SDay
'Papilion'	EStr
'Papoose'	XLum
'Paprika Flame'	EStr MHol
'Parade of Peacocks'	CBgR
'Paradise Bar and Grill'	EStr
'Paradise Lost'	EStr
'Pardon Me'	CBro ECtt EGrI EHyd ELan ELon EStr GJos GKin GMaP LRHS MPie NGdn NLar NRHS SCoo SDeJ SWvt WCAu WFar
'Parfait'	CBgR EStr EWoo WHrl WNHG
'Parrot Tattoo'	EStr
'Parson's Robe'	SDay
'Part-time Princess'	EStr
'Party Pants'	EStr
'Party Queen'	SDay

'Passion for Red'	SDay
'Passive Aggressive'	EStr
'Pastel Ballerina'	SDay
'Pat Mercer'	SDay
'Patchwork Puzzle'	EStr EWoo
'Patricia Gentzel Wright'	EWoo
'Patrick Starfish'	EStr
'Patriotic Flavor'	EStr
'Patsy Bickers'	ELon EWoo
'Pattern Breaker'	EStr
'Patterns'	WNHG
'Patti Neyland'	EStr
'Paul Weber'	SDay
'Paula Goes Prime Time' **new**	EStr
'Paula Nettles'	EStr
'Paw Print'	EStr
'Pawn of Prophecy'	EStr
'Peach Float'	EWoo
'Peach Jubilee'	EStr
'Peach Magnolia' (d)	EStr
'Peach Margarita'	EStr
'Peach Whisper'	EStr SDay
'Peacock Maiden'	EStr EWoo WHrl
'Pear Ornament'	SDay
'Pearl Anniversary'	EStr
'Pearl Jam'	SDay
'Pearl Lewis'	EStr SDay
'Peggy Jeffcoat'	EStr
'Penelope Vestey'	CBgR EStr NBir SDay
'Pennypurrs'	EStr
'Penny's Worth'	CRos LEdu LRHS WCot WFar XLum
'Peppermint Ice'	EStr
'Persian Melon Plus'	WCAu
'Persian Ruby'	EStr SDay WNHG
'Petite Ballerina'	SDay
'Phill Warbasse'	EStr
'Photon Torpedo'	MACG
'Phyllis Cantini'	SDay
'Piano Man'	EStr WNHG
'Piccadilly Princess'	EStr
'Pickin' and Grinnin''	EStr
'Piece of the Action'	EStr
'Pigment of Imagination'	EStr
'Pinhill Navajo Beauty'	EStr
'Pink Ambrosia'	ECtt EStr
'Pink Charm'	CEme CMac ECha ECtt EHyd EPPr GKin GMaP NBro NRHS
'Pink Circle'	SDay
'Pink Cotton Candy'	SDay
'Pink Damask' ♀H6	Widely available
'Pink Dazzler'	WNHG
'Pink Delight'	MPie
'Pink Dream'	CBgR NBir
'Pink Flirt'	SDay
'Pink Lady'	GDam MNrw MRav SRms
'Pink Monday'	SDay WNHG
'Pink Puff'	NBir NLar
'Pink Stripes'	EStr
'Pink Sundae'	WHrl
'Pink Super Spider'	EWoo
'Pink Thunderbird'	EStr
'Pink Whip Tips'	EStr
'Pink Windmill'	ELon
'Pinky Promise'	EStr
'Pirate Treasure'	EStr SDay
'Pirate's Patch'	EWoo SDay WCot
'Pixie Dragon' **new**	EStr
'Pixie Parasol'	WNHG WSpi
'Pixie Princess'	EStr
'Pizza'	SDay
'Playing with Crayons'	EStr

'Pleated Petticoats'	EStr
'Plum Beautiful'	EStr
'Plum Beauty'	NLar
'Plumas Lake'	WNHG
'Poetic Pattern' **new**	EStr
'Poinsettia'	EStr
'Point of View'	EStr
'Pojo'	EStr SDay
'Polar Vortex'	EStr
'Polka Dot Bikini'	EStr
'Pony'	ELon
'Porcelain Pleasure'	SDay
'Possum in a Sack'	CBgR
'Post Time'	EStr
'Powerpuff Girls'	EStr
'Prague Spring'	EStr WCAu WHrl WNHG
'Prairie Belle'	GKev NLar
'Prairie Blue Eyes'	EStr SDay SPlb WCot WHrl
'Prairie Charmer'	SEND WHrl
'Prankster'	EStr
'Precious d'Oro'	GQue NFav SCob
'President Hadley'	SDay
'Pretty Face Nice Legs'	EStr
'Pretty Miss'	ECtt EStr WGwG
'Pretty, Pretty Please' **new**	EStr
'Preview Party'	WNHG
'Primal Scream' ♀H6	EStr GAbr LSun MHol SDay SMad SPoG WCot
'Prince of Midnight'	SDay
'Prince of Purple'	ELon
'Prince Poppycock'	EStr
'Prince Redbird'	SDay
'Princess Charming'	EStr
'Princess Summerbird' **new**	SDay
'Princeton Eye Glow'	SDay
'Princeton Silky'	ELon
'Printmaker'	EStr
'Prize Picotee Deluxe'	SDay
'Prize Picotee Elite'	SDay
'Protocol'	ELon SDay
'Proud Mary'	SDay
'Ptarmigan'	CBgR EStr
'Pterodactyl Eye'	EStr SDay
§ 'Puddin'	SDay
'Pueblo Dancer'	EStr
'Pug Yarborough'	EStr SDay
'Pullin' Strings'	EStr
'Pumpkin Kid'	SDay
'Pumpkin Prince'	EStr
'Punxsutawney Phil'	EStr
'Puppet Show'	SDay
'Pure and Simple'	SDay
'Purple Avenger'	SDay
'Purple Bicolor'	WHrl
'Purple Flame'	CBod EStr
'Purple Oddity'	SDay
'Purple Passion's Promise'	EStr
'Purple Penguin'	EStr
'Purple Rain'	CWat MPie SDay SWvt
'Purple Waters'	MHost WPnP
'Purpleicious'	EStr NLar
'Pursuit of Excellence'	SDay
'Pushamataha' **new**	SDay
'Putting on the Ritz'	EStr
'Pygmy Plum'	SDay
'Pyrotechnics'	EStr
'Quality of Mercy'	SDay
'Quartzitic Scintillation'	EStr
'Queen Charlotte'	EStr
'Queen Empress'	WNHG
'Queen Lily'	WNHG
'Queen of Green'	EStr
'Queen of May'	MNrw WCot
'Queen of Spades' **new**	SDay
'Quick Results'	SDay
'Quiet Riot'	EStr
'Quietly Awesome'	SDay
'Quietness'	SDay
'Quilt Patch'	EStr
'Quinn Buck'	SDay
'Ra Hansen'	EStr
'Radiant Moonbeam' ♀H6	CBgR EStr
'Raging Bull'	EStr
'Raging Tiger'	SDay WHrl
'Rainbow Candy'	CWGN
'Rainbow Maker'	EStr
'Rajah'	CBgR CMac EHyd EStr NBro SPer WHrl
'Raspberry Candy'	CBro EStr MNrw SRms WHrl
'Raspberry Star'	EStr
'Raspberry Wine'	ECha
'Raspberry Winter'	EStr
'Razzle'	EStr
'Reach for the Heavens'	EStr
'Real Life Drama'	EStr
'Real Wind'	EStr
'Red Admiral'	EHyd
'Red Bull'	EStr
'Red Grace'	EStr
'Red Pennant'	SDay
'Red Precious' ♀H6	MNrw SMHy WCot
'Red Rain'	EStr EWoo WHrl
'Red Ribbons'	ELon EWoo
'Red Rum'	CBgR LSun MSwo NBro NRHS
'Red Suspenders'	ECtt EStr MBNS
'Red Tallboy'	EStr
'Red Twister'	ELon EStr
'Red Volunteer'	EStr SDay
'Redheaded Hussy'	EStr
'Regal Giant'	EStr
'Regency Dandy'	SDay
'Regency Heights'	EStr
'Regency Masquerade'	SDay
'Renee'	MNrw
'Renie's Delight' **new**	SDay
'Respighi'	EStr
'Rest Beyond the River' **new**	EStr
'Return Trip'	ELon
'Rhubarb Wine'	EStr
'Rhythm of Love'	EStr
'Ribbonette'	EStr
'Rich Girls'	EStr
'Richfield Wonder' **new**	SDay
'Ricky Rose'	SDay
'Riley Barron'	SDay
'Rise of the Phoenix'	EStr
'Rock Solid'	SDay
'Rocket Booster'	EStr
'Rocket City'	ELan EStr WNHG
'Roger Grounds'	CBgR LRHS SDay
'Roll with It' **new**	EStr
'Rolling Raven'	EStr
'Roman Toga'	CBgR SDay
'Romanian Rendevous'	EStr
* 'Romantic Rose'	MBNS NLar WHrl
'Romeo is Bleeding'	EStr
'Ron Azzanni'	EStr
'Root Beer'	GQue WCAu WHrl
'Rorschach Test'	EStr
'Rose'	SDay
'Rose Corsage'	SDir
'Rose Emily'	CBgR EStr SDay

'Rose F. Kennedy'	EStr
'Rose Fever'	EWoo
'Rose Tattoo'	EStr
'Roseate Spoonbill'	EWoo
'Roses in Snow'	EStr SDay
'Rosewood Snowflakes'	SDay
'Roswitha'	EStr
'Rosy Returns'	EPfP LRHS NLar WNHG
'Roy Likes Em Hot'	EStr
'Royal Braid'	NLar SPer WCot
'Royal Celebration'	WCot
'Royal Diana' **new**	SDay
'Royal Elk'	EWoo
'Royal Heritage'	EHyd EStr LRHS NRHS SDay
'Royal Parade'	SDay
'Royal Robe'	CTri
'Royal Saracen'	SDay
'Royal Thornbird'	CBgR
'Ruby Corsage'	EStr
'Ruby Sentinel'	SDay WNHG
'Ruby Spider' ♀H6	ELon EStr
'Ruby Storm'	EStr
'Ruby Sullivan' **new**	SDay
'Ruffled Apricot'	LPot WNHG
'Ruffled Carousel'	WNHG
'Ruffled Dude'	EStr
'Ruffled Ivory'	SDay
'Ruffled Lemon Lace'	EStr
'Ruffled Magic'	SDay
'Rumble Seat Romance'	WNHG
'Running for the Border'	EStr
'Russian Easter'	EStr SDay
'Russian Ragtime'	ELon EStr
'Russian Rhapsody' ♀H6	SDay
'Ruth Love'	WNHG
'Ruth Oliver'	EStr
'Sabie'	EStr
'Sabine Baur'	EStr MNrw WFar
'Sabra Salina'	EStr SDay WNHG
'Sacred Drummer'	SDay
'Saffron Glow'	SDay
'Sahara Sand Storm'	EStr
'Sahara Song'	EStr
'Saintly'	EWoo
'Sallie Brown'	EStr SDay
'Salmon Sheen'	SPer
'Sammy'	EStr WHrl
'Sammy Russell'	Widely available
'Samuel Bell'	EWoo
'Sandra Elizabeth'	SDay
'Sandy Beckman'	EStr
'Santa's Little Helper'	EStr SDay
'Saratoga Belle'	EStr
'Sariah'	SDay
'Satin Glass'	CRos EBlo EHyd LRHS NRHS
'Satin Glow'	ECha
'Saved Soul'	EStr
'Say Yes'	EStr
'Scarlet Flame'	ECha
'Scarlet Oak'	SDay
'Scarlet Orbit'	EWoo
'Scarlet Prince'	WNHG
'Scarlet Ribbons'	EStr
'Scarlock'	SDay
'Schnickel Fritz'	EBee
'School Girl'	EHyd LRHS NRHS
'Scorchio'	EStr
'Scorpio'	CBgR SDay WHrl
'Screamcicle'	EStr
'Screaming Demon'	EStr WCot
'Sea Swept Dreams'	SDay
'Seal of Approval'	EBee EStr
'Seal the Deal'	EStr
'Sebastian'	SDay
'Seductive Fairy Tale'	EStr
'Self Determination' **new**	SDay
'Selma Longlegs' ♀H6	EStr SDay
'Seminole Blood'	SDay
'Seminole Wind'	EWoo SDay
'Semiramide'	CBgR WNHG
'Serena Lady'	SDay
'Serena Sunburst' ♀H6	EHyd EStr LRHS NRHS
'Serene Madonna'	ELan ILea
'Serenity Bay'	EStr
'Serenity Morgan'	CBgR EWoo
'Serge Rigaud'	WHrl
'Seuss on the Loose' **new**	EStr
'Shadow Cabinet'	EStr
'Shadowed Pink'	WNHG
'Shady Lady'	SDay WNHG
'Shaggy Pumpkin'	EStr
'Shaman' Gates'	SDay
'Shards of Kryptonite'	EStr
'Shark Attack'	EStr
'Sharky' (d) **new**	EStr
'She Devil'	EStr
'Shelly Victoria'	SDay
'Sherry Lane Carr'	EStr SDay
'Sherwood Gladiator'	WNHG
'She's So Outrageous'	EStr
'Shimek September Morning'	EStr
'Shinto Etching'	EStr
'Shinto Shrine'	WNHG
'Shotgun'	EStr
'Shreddy'	EStr
'Shuffle the Deck'	EStr
'Sigudilla'	WNHG
'Silent Sentry'	EStr
'Silent Thunder'	EStr
'Silken Fairy'	CBgR SDay
'Silken Touch'	CBgR EStr SDay
'Silly Wabbit'	EStr
'Silly Whimsey'	EStr
'Siloam Amazing Grace'	SDay
'Siloam Angel Blush'	ECtt MHol SDay
'Siloam Baby Talk'	ELon NBir WPnP
'Siloam Bo Peep'	SDay
'Siloam Button Box'	SDay WHrl
'Siloam Bye Lo'	SDay
'Siloam Cinderella'	SDay
'Siloam Doodlebug'	CBgR
'Siloam Double Classic' (d)	EStr SDay
'Siloam Dream Baby'	ELon
'Siloam Ethel Smith'	SDay
'Siloam Fairy Ruffles'	WNHG
'Siloam Fairy Tale'	SDay
'Siloam Flower Girl'	SDay
'Siloam French Doll'	NLar
'Siloam French Marble'	SDay
'Siloam Frosted Mint'	SDay
'Siloam Gold Coin'	SDay
'Siloam Helpmate'	WNHG
'Siloam John Yonski'	SDay
'Siloam June Bug'	CBgR ELan WCot
'Siloam Little Girl'	ECtt
'Siloam Mama'	SDay
'Siloam New Toy'	EStr WHrl
'Siloam Nugget'	EStr
'Siloam Paul Watts'	EGrI EStr SDay
'Siloam Peewee'	ELon
'Siloam Pink Glow'	SDay

'Siloam Pocket Size'	SDay
'Siloam Red Toy'	EHyd LRHS NRHS SMHy
'Siloam Ribbon Candy'	SDay WNHG
'Siloam Ruffled Infant'	SDay
'Siloam Show Girl'	CWGN GKin
'Siloam Space Age'	WNHG
'Siloam Spizz'	EStr SDay
'Siloam Sugar Time'	ELon
'Siloam Tiny Mite'	SDay WHrl
'Siloam Tom Thumb'	CBgR
'Siloam Ury Winniford'	CBro CMac NLar WHoo WHrl
'Siloam Virginia Henson'	WWtn
'Silver Ice'	SDay
'Silver Lance'	EStr SDay WNHG
'Silver Sides'	EStr
'Silver Sword'	EStr
'Silver Veil'	SDay
'Simmons Overture'	ECtt EStr MNrw
'Simple Twist of Fate'	EStr
'Sinbad Sailor'	NLar
'Singapore Sunrise' **new**	EStr
'Sings the Blues'	SDay
'Sink Into Your Eyes'	EStr WHrl
'Sips of Sin' **new**	EStr
'Sir Blackstem'	ELon
'Sir Galahad'	EStr
'Sir Modred' ♀H6	EStr SDay WNHG
'Sissy Pants'	EStr
'Sister Grace'	SDay
'Sitting on a Rainbow'	EStr
'Skinny Dipper' **new**	EStr
'Skinwalker'	EStr
'Skylight'	EStr
'Slapstick'	EStr SDay
'Sleepy'	ECha
'Sleepy Hollow'	EStr
'Slender Lady'	ELon
'Slipping Into the Abyss'	EStr
'Small World Eye of the Cat' **new**	EStr
'Smith Brothers'	ELon
'Smoke on the Water'	EStr
'Smoke Scream'	EStr
'Smoking Gun' **new**	SDay
'Smoky Mountain Autumn'	EStr SDay WHrl
'Smoky Mountain Bell'	SDay
'Smooch Hollow'	CBgR EStr
'Smuggler's Gold'	ECtt EStr GJos SDay
'Smurfette'	EStr
'Snaggle Tooth'	EStr
'Snake in the Grass Boo' **new**	EStr
'Snowed In'	EWoo
'Snowy Apparition'	ECtt EHyd EMor EStr GBin GKev GKin LRHS NRHS NWad SWvt
'Snowy Eyes'	GKin WHrl
'Snowy Morning' **new**	SDay
'So Cold'	EStr
'So Excited'	SDay
'So Lovely'	EWoo XLum
'Soft Cashmere'	XLum
'Solid Geometry'	EStr
'Solid Scarlet'	EStr
'Solomon's Robes'	SDay
'Sombrero Way'	EHyd LRHS NRHS SDay
'Someone Special'	EStr SDay
'Somerset Fandango'	CBgR
'Song Sparrow'	CBro
'Sonic Duck'	EStr
'Soraya Seline'	CBgR
'Sound of Color'	EStr
'South Carolina Peach'	EStr
'South Seas'	EStr
'Southern Cotton'	EStr
'Southern Shiner' **new**	EStr
'Southern Wind'	SDay
'Sovereign Queen'	WNHG
'Spacecoast Dream Catcher'	EStr
'Spacecoast Freaky Tiki'	EStr
'Spacecoast Irish Illumination'	EStr
'Spacecoast Rose Queen' **new**	EStr
'Spacecoast Scrambled'	NLar
'Spacecoast Starburst'	EStr WCot
'Spacecoast Sweet Eye'	EStr
'Spacecoast The Green Mile' **new**	EStr
'Spanish Fandango'	EStr
'Sparkling Dawn'	EStr
'Sparkling Orange'	SDay
'Spartan Warrior'	EStr
'Spartanburg' **new**	EStr
'Spider Breeder'	CBgR ELon EStr
'Spider Man' ♀H6	ELon EStr MSpe SDay WCAu
'Spider Miracle'	EWoo MSpe SDay
'Spider Red'	CWGN EWTr
'Spider Web'	EStr
'Spin Master'	EStr
'Spindazzle'	CBgR SDay
'Spinne in Lachs'	EStr
'Spinneret'	EStr
'Spiral Nebula'	EStr
'Spiral Sun' **new**	EStr
'Spirit Folk'	EStr
'Splatter'	EStr
'Splendid Touch'	SDay
'Splittin' Hairs'	EStr
'Spooner'	CBgR
'Spoons for Escargot'	EStr
'Spotted Fever'	EStr
'Spring Willow Song'	SDay
'Springfield Clan'	EStr
'Springmaid Beach'	EStr
'Spunky Monkey'	EStr
'Stack the Deck'	EStr
'Stafford' ♀H6	Widely available
'Staghorn Sumac'	GKin NHol WCAu
'Star of India'	EStr
'Star of Kryptonite'	EStr
'Star Poly'	EStr
'Stargate Portal'	EStr
'Starling'	EWes EWoo NChi WSpi WWtn
'Starman's Quest'	EStr
'Starstruck'	WNHG
'Startle'	ELon EStr MNrw WCot WHrl
'Statuesque'	EWoo
'Steely Blue Eyes'	EStr
'Stella de Oro'	Widely available
'Stella in Purple'	EPfP
'Stella in Red'	CBod
'Stella Russell' **new**	LRHS
'Stellar Masquerade'	WNHG
'Stewart Mandel'	EStr
'Stoke Poges'	CBgR CBro EBee ELon EPPr EPfP EShb EStr GBin LPot MMuc WHrl WNHG
'Stop the Car'	EStr
'Stop the Insanity'	EStr
'Stoplight'	CBgR EHyd ELon EStr LRHS SMHy WHrl
'Storm Damage'	EStr
'Storm of the Century'	CBod

'Strasbourg'	CMac
'Strawberry Candy' 🏆H6	CBgR CMac CSBt ECtt EHyd ELon EPfP EStr EWoo LRHS MPie NGdn NLar NRHS SDay SDir SPer WCAu WHrl WNHG WSpi
'Strawberry Fields Forever'	EStr EWoo SDay
'Strawberry Lemonade'	EStr
'Strider Spider'	EStr
'Strikingly Dramatic'	EStr
'String Bikini'	EStr
'Strutter's Ball'	EStr EWoo MCot NGdn SDay SHar SPer WCAu WHrl
'Stupid in Love'	EStr
'Stupidville USA'	EStr
'Stu's Old Pink Spider'	CBgR
'Suburban Golden Eagle'	EStr
'Sue Strickfaden'	EStr
'Sugar Cookie'	EWoo SDay
'Sugar Magnolia'	EStr
'Summer Dragon'	EStr
'Summer Interlude'	WFar
'Summer Star'	EStr
'Summer Wine'	CBgR CRos CSBt EBee ECtt EGrI ELon EPfP EWTr GMaP LRHS MBel MCot NBir NChi NHol NLar NRHS NSti SCob SPer SSut SWvt WCAu WCot WHoo WHrl WSpi XLum
'Sun Dazzle' **new**	EStr
'Sun Dial'	EStr
'Sun Scream'	EStr
'Sunday Gloves'	WNHG
'Sunday Morning'	SDay
'Sungold Candy'	EStr
'Sunray Brilliance'	EWoo
'Sunset Lagoon'	EStr
'Sunset Rays' **new**	EStr
'Sunshine on My Shoulders'	EStr
'Superlative'	EStr
'Supermodel'	EStr
'Susan Weber'	SDay
'Svengali'	SDay
'Swagger and Style' **new**	EStr
'Swallow Tail Kite'	SDay
'Swan Dance'	EStr SDay
'Sweet Country Luvin''	EStr
'Sweet Goldoni'	EStr
'Sweet Home Louisiana'	EStr
'Sweet Hot Chocolate'	LRHS MNrw
'Sweet Pea'	EStr
'Sweet Sugar Candy'	ECtt SDeJ
'Swirling Spider'	CBgR EWoo
'Symphony of Praise'	EStr
'Tachibana'	SDay
'Taj Mahal'	ELon EWoo GQue SDay
'Tangerine Tango'	EWoo
'Tangerine Twist'	EStr
'Tani'	SDay
'Taos'	EStr SDay
'Tar and Feather'	EStr
'Tarantula'	ELon
'Taruga'	EWoo SDay
'Tasmania'	SPer
'Tattooed Lady'	SDay
'Techny Peach Lace'	EStr
'Techny Spider'	EStr
'Teenie Girl'	EStr
'Tejas'	ELon SPer
'Tennessee Afterglow'	EStr
'Tennessee Flycatcher'	EWoo
'Tennyson'	SDay
'Tequila and Lime'	CBod EStr MACG SPeP
'Tet Set'	WNHG
'Tetraploid Stella de Oro'	SDay
'Tetrina's Daughter'	CBgR EPfP LRHS SDay
'Texas Blue Eyes'	EStr WNHG
'Thank Your Lucky Stars'	EStr
'The Bird is the Word'	EStr
'The Blessing of Freedom'	EStr
'The Color of Wonderful'	EStr
'The Future of Desire'	EStr
'The Ghosts of Boyfriends Past'	EStr
'The New Normal'	EStr
'The Senator'	EStr
'The Ultimate Sacrifice'	EStr
'Thelma Douglas'	EStr
'Thelma Perry'	LEdu
'There's a Place'	EStr
'Thermal Overload'	EStr
'Thin Man'	EStr SDay
'Think Pink'	EBee
'This World Aflame'	EStr
'Thomas Tew'	EStr
'Thorhalla'	EStr
'Thousand Voices'	EStr
'Thumbelina'	ECha EGrI XLum
§ ***thunbergii***	ECha XLum
'Thunder and Lightning'	EStr
'Thundercat'	EStr
'Thundering Ovation'	CWGN
'Thy True Love'	SDay
'Tidewater Snowflake' **new**	EStr
'Tie-dye Illusion' **new**	EStr
'Tiger Blood'	EPfP EStr LLWG SDir
'Tigereye Spider'	EStr
'Tigerling'	EStr
'Tigger'	EGrI EStr GJos SDeJ SPad WCAu
'Tiki God'	EStr
'Till I Turn Purple'	EStr
'Time Lord'	SDay
'Time of Angels'	EStr
'Time Together'	EStr
'Time Window'	EStr
'Tiny Talisman'	SDay
'Tiny Temptress'	SDay
'Tip of the Iceberg'	EStr
'Tis Midnight'	WNHG
'Tixie'	EStr
'Tom Barnes'	EStr
'Tom Collins'	SDay
'Tom Wise'	EStr
'Tone Poem'	WNHG
'Tonia Gay'	SDay
'Tooth'	EStr
'Toothpick'	EWoo WHrl
'Topguns Aztec Vision'	EStr
'Topguns Bandit's Bandana'	EStr
'Topguns Cactus Jack'	EStr
'Torpoint'	CBgR MRav SDay
'Touch of Magic'	EStr
'Towhead'	MRav SDay WCot
'Toyland'	NBir NGdn NLar
'Trahlyta'	CBgR EStr EWoo SDay WHrl
'Tramps Like Us'	EStr
'Trance'	EStr
'Transatlantic Flutter'	EStr
'Treasure Map'	EStr
'Treasure that I Seek'	EStr
'Triade'	EStr
'Tribute to Joe'	EStr
'Trickster'	EStr
'Tripped Out'	EStr

'Trog'	EStr
'Trond'	SDay
'Trooping the Colour' **new**	SDay
'Tropic Sunset'	SDay
'Tropical Depression'	EWoo
'Tropical Fusion'	EStr
'Tropical Hot Flash'	EStr
'Tropical Passion'	EStr
'Troubled Sleep'	EWoo
'Troubled Waters' **new**	SDay
'True Gertrude Demarest'	WHrl
'Trump Card'	EStr
'Tune the Harp'	EStr
'Tupac Amaru'	EStr
'Turkish Tapestry'	CBgR
'Turkish Turban'	SDay
'Turn the Other Cheek'	EStr
'Turtle Island'	EStr
'Tuscawilla Charlie Baker' **new**	SDay
'Tuscawilla Princess'	EStr
'Tuscawilla Tigress'	EStr GKin MNrw SDay WHrl
'Tutankhamun'	EStr SDay
'Tuxedo Junction' 🏆H6	EStr
'Tuxedo Whiskers'	EStr
'Twenty Nine Flags over Conway'	EStr
'Twilight Swan'	WNHG
'Two Part Harmony'	WHrl
'Ultra Persuasion'	SDay
'Umbrella Parade'	EStr
'Unchartered Waters'	SDay
'Uncle Bryan' **new**	SDay
'Uncle Lurch'	EStr
'Undefinable'	EStr
'Unforgetable Fire'	SDay
'Unlock Your Dreams'	EStr
'Up the Wazoo'	EStr
'Upper Class Peach'	EStr SDay
'Uptown Girl'	EStr SDay
'Valiant'	WHrl
'Valley Monster'	SDay
'Valley Sprite'	EStr
'Vanilla Fluff'	EStr
'Vanishing Mist'	EStr
'Varsity'	CExl EHyd LRHS NBir NRHS SPer
'Vectis Amy Hiscock'	EStr
'Vectis Jean Merritt'	EStr
'Vectis Jean Peirce'	EStr
'Vectis Joan Morey'	EStr
'Vectis Nora Malone'	EStr
'Vegas Show Girl'	EStr
'Veins of Truth'	CBgR EBee EStr WCAu
'Velvet Eyes'	EStr
'Velvet Shadows'	CBgR SDay
'Velvet Web'	EStr
'Vendetta'	WNHG
'Venusian Mirage'	EStr
'Vera Biaglow'	EStr SDay
'Vernal Tutone'	WNHG
'Very Berry Ice'	EStr
vespertina	see *H. thunbergii*
'Vesuvian'	SDay
'Vi Simmons'	EStr SDay
'Vicountess Byng'	WWtn
'Victoria Aden'	CBro
'Victoria Elizabeth Barnes'	WNHG
'Victorian Lace'	SDay
'Victorian Violet'	SDay
'Video'	SDay
'Vie en Rose'	EStr
'Viewpoint'	SDay
'Villa Vanilla'	EStr WFar
'Vino di Notte'	EStr
'Vintage Bordeaux'	ELan SDay
'Vintage Burgundy'	CBgR WNHG
'Vintage Passion'	EStr
'Vintage Wine'	WNHG
'Violent Thunder'	EStr
'Violet Cuckoo'	EStr
'Violet Hour'	EStr SDay
'Violet Patch'	SDay
'Violet Stained Glass'	WNHG
'Viracocha'	WNHG
'Virgin's Blush'	SPer
'Vohann'	SDay
'Volcanic Eruption'	EStr
'Volcano Queen'	EPfP EStr WFar
'Voodoo Dancer'	EGrl EPfP EStr
'Waggle Dance'	EStr
'Waiting in the Wings'	SDay
'Walking on Sunshine'	EStr WCot
'Walnut Hill'	EStr
'Walt Disney'	GKin
'Walter Kennedy'	EStr
'Wanda Evans'	EStr
'War Paint'	EStr SDay
'Warp Drive'	SDay
'Watch Tower'	CBgR
'Watchyl Dancing Spider'	EStr
'Water Witch'	CWat
'Watermelon Man'	CBgR
'Waxen Splendor'	EStr
'Wayne Johnson'	WNHG
'Wayside Green Imp'	MNrw
'Web Browser'	EStr
'Web Crawler'	EStr
'Webster's Aggie'	EStr
'Webster's Pastel Beauty'	EStr
'Webster's Pinched Peach'	EStr
'Webster's Pink Wonder'	EStr
'Wedding Band'	SDay
'Wee Willie Winkie'	WNHG
'Wesley Lee Kirby'	EStr
'What a Day for a Daydream'	EStr
'When I Dream'	EStr
'When You Get to Asheville'	EStr
'Which Way Jim'	SDay
'Whichford'	CBgR CBro CMea EBee EBlo ECha ECtt EHyd ELan EPfP EWoo GKin LRHS NRHS SDay SPer SPhx SSut WGwG WHrl
'Whip City Fancy Free'	EStr
'Whipped Chocolate' **new**	EStr
'Whirling Fury'	ELon
'Whisper my Name' **new**	EStr
'White Coral'	EHyd LSRN NBro NRHS SCoo
'White Edged Madonna'	WHrl
'White Ensign'	SDay
'White Eyes Pink Dragon'	EStr
'White Ibis' **new**	SDay
'White Magician'	EStr
'White Pansy'	SDay
'White Temptation'	EBee EPfP EStr ILea LSun SDay WNHG XSen
'White Tie Affair'	SDay
'White Zone'	SDay
'Whiter Shade' **new**	SDay
'Whooperee'	SDay
'Whoopie'	SPad WHrl
'Wicked Ways' **new**	EStr
'Wideyed'	XLum

'Wiggle Butt'	EStr
'Wigglesworth'	EStr
'Wild and Wonderful'	LSun SDay WFar
'Wild at Heart'	EStr
'Wild Horses'	EWes MNrw NLar SCob SMad WHrl
'Wild Mustang'	EStr
'Wild Planet'	EStr
'Wild Wookie'	SDay
'Wildfire Tango'	SDay
'Wilson Spider'	EStr
'Wind Frills'	EStr
'Wind Song'	ELon SDay
'Wind Storm'	EStr
'Windblown Sands' new	SDay
'Windham Blueberry Mojito'	EStr
'Windmill Yellow'	EWoo SDay
'Window Dressing'	EWoo SDay
'Wineberry Candy'	EStr NLar
'Winged Migration'	EStr
'Winnie'	EStr
'Winsome Lady'	ECtt GKin WBor WHrl
'Winter Dreams' new	SDay
'Winter Masquerade' new	SDay
'Winter Wolf'	EStr
'Winyah Eye'	EStr
'Wired'	EStr
'Wisest of Wizards'	SDay WHrl
'Wishful Dreaming'	EStr
'Wishing Well'	WCot
'Wisk me Away' new	EStr
'Wispy Rays'	EStr
'Witch Hazel'	WCAu WWtn
'Witch Hollow'	EStr
'Witch Stitchery'	EStr SDay
'Witches Brew'	CBgR
'Witches Coven'	SDay
'Without Warning'	CBgR
'Womanizer'	EStr
'Wonder of it All'	EStr
'Wonders Never Cease'	SDay
'Wood Duck'	EStr
'Woodside Ruby'	WNHG
'Wounded Heart'	SDay
'Wyatt's Cameo'	SDay
'Wyoming Wildfire'	CBgR
'Xia Xiang'	SDay
'Xochimilco'	WNHG
'Ya Ya Girl'	EStr
'Yabba Dabba Doo'	EStr
'Yankee Pinstripes'	EStr
'Yazoo Elsie Hintson'	EStr
'Yazoo Wild Violet'	EStr
'Yellow Angel'	ELon WCot
'Yellow Green Monarch' new	SDay
'Yellow Rain'	WCot
'Yellow Ribbon'	EStr
'Yellow Submarine'	EPfP MHol
'Yes Man'	EStr
'Yesterday Memories'	SDay
yezoensis	EBtc
'You Angel You'	SDir
'You are Mine'	EStr
'You Had Me at Woof'	EStr
'You Social Thing' new	EStr
'Yum Yum Plum'	EStr SDay
'Yuma'	WNHG
'Zachary S. Hickey'	EStr
'Zagora'	EStr WCAu
'Zampa'	CBgR EStr SDay
'Zappa'	SDay
'Zara'	EStr SPer
'Zenobia'	EStr
'Zero Dark Thirty'	EStr
'Zig Zag Jazz' new	EStr
'Zip Boom Bah'	EStr
'Zuni Mountains'	WNHG

Hemiboea (*Gesneriaceae*)

bicornuta PB 07-1108 new	GGro
strigosa new	SBrt
- PB	GGro
- PB 374338 new	GGro
subcapitata	SBls SBrt WFar

Hemionitis (*Pteridaceae*)

arifolia	SPlb

Hemipilia (*Orchidaceae*)

§ ***graminifolia***	GKev SDir
- white-flowered	SDir

Hemiptelea (*Ulmaceae*)

davidii	SMad

Hemisteptia (*Asteraceae*)

lyrata B&SWJ 12710 new	WCru

Henckelia (*Gesneriaceae*)

§ ***speciosa*** 'Crûg Cornetto'	WCru

Hepatica ✿ (*Ranunculaceae*)

acutiloba	CWCL EMor EPot GAbr GEdr GKev MAsh NBir SDir WPnP
- blue-flowered	MAsh
- white-flowered	MAsh NLar
americana	EMor GEdr MAsh NBir
- Eco Group seedlings new	MAsh
- var. ***obtusa*** 'Ashwood Marble'	MAsh
- Pink Shades seedlings new	MAsh
angulosa	see *H. transsilvanica*
falconeri	MAsh
(Forest Series) 'Forest Pink'	GBin GKev
- 'Forest Purple'	EBee GKev LCro
- 'Forest Red'	GBin GKev LCro
- 'Forest White'	GBin GKev LCro
* 'Gerani' × ***nobilis*** var. ***glabrata*** new	MAsh
henryi	GEdr MAsh
- blushed pink-backed-flowered new	MAsh
henryi × ***transsilvanica*** new	MAsh
insularis	GEdr MAsh
maxima	GEdr MAsh MBriF NDry
× ***media*** 'Ballardii'	GEdr NDry
- 'Blaue Stunde'	GEdr
- Dryad Blush Group	NDry
- 'Harvington Beauty'	GEdr NBir NDry WSHC
- 'Holzdorfe Silver'	GEdr
- 'Kim'	GEdr NDry
- 'Millstream Merlin'	GEdr NHpl
- 'Silberprinzessin'	GEdr
§ ***nobilis*** ♀H6	Widely available
- 'Alabaster' seedlings new	MAsh
- 'Baby Rosa'	GEdr
- 'Bavarian Blue' new	MAsh
- 'Bibo'	EWld MAsh
- 'Bibo' seedlings, red-flowered new	MAsh
- blue-flowered	MAsh NSla SPlb WAbe

- 'Brockman' (d) GEdr
- 'Cobalt' GEdr NSla
- compact evergreen NDry
- 'Cremar' GEdr NDry
- 'Crenatiloba' **new** MAsh
- dark-blue-flowered NDry
- dwarf white-flowered NSla
- 'Elkofener Heidi' GEdr
- 'Papillion' seedlings **new** MAsh
- 'Flamingo' GEdr
* - var. ***glabrata*** MAsh
- - dwarf white-flowered NDry
- var. ***glabrata* × *nobilis*** red-flowered MAsh
- indigo-flowered **new** MAsh
- var. ***japonica*** EWes GEdr ITim NBir NDry NSla
- - 'Aikawa' (5/d) GEdr
- - 'Akane' (1) GEdr
- - 'Akanezora' (6/d) GEdr
- - 'Akebono' (9/d) GEdr
- - 'Anjyu' (9/d) GEdr
- - 'Aozora' (1) GEdr
- - 'Asahi' (7/d) GEdr
- - 'Asahizuru' (6/d) GEdr
- - 'Benifusya' (1) GEdr
- - 'Benihagure' (9/d) GEdr
- - 'Benikanzan' (1) GEdr
- - 'Benikujyaku' (7/d) GEdr
- - 'Benioiran' (3) GEdr
- - 'Benisuzume' (1) GEdr
- - 'Benitaiko' (9/d) GEdr
- - 'Bojyou' (5A/d) GEdr
- - 'Daishihou' (9/d) GEdr
- - 'Dewa' (9/d) GEdr
- - 'Ebisu-no-hana' (5A/d) GEdr
- - 'Echigobijin' (1) GEdr NDry
- - 'Fukujyu' (9/d) GEdr
- - 'Gosho-zakura' (5A/d) GEdr
- - 'Gyousei' (1) GEdr
- - 'Hakurin' (6/d) GEdr
- - 'Hakusetsu' (9/d) GEdr
- - 'Hanagoromo' (9/d) GEdr
- - 'Haruka' (2) GEdr
- - 'Harumo-no-Gatari' (8/d) GEdr
- - 'Haruno-awajuki' (9/d) GEdr
- - 'Hatsune' (5/d) GEdr
- - 'Hidamari' (5/d) GEdr
- - 'Hohobeni' (9/d) GEdr
- - 'Hokutosei' (7/d) GEdr
- - 'Hoshizora' (2) GEdr
- - 'Hosyun' (1) GEdr
- - 'Isaribi' (1) GEdr NDry
- - 'Junissen' (6/d) GEdr
- - 'Kagura' (5A/d) GEdr
- - 'Kansashi' NDry
- - 'Kasumino' (1) GEdr
- - 'Kiko' (9/d) GEdr
- - 'Kimon' (9/d) GEdr
- - 'Koshi-no-maboroshi' (7/d) GEdr
- - 'Kotobuki-hime' (5/d) GEdr
- - 'Kouen' (6/d) GEdr
- - 'Kougyoku' (9/d) GEdr
- - 'Kurotaiyou' (d) GEdr
- - 'Kuukai' (8/d) GEdr
- - f. ***magna*** MAsh
- - - 'Murasaki-shikibu' (9/d) GEdr
- - 'Manazuru' (9/d) GEdr
- - 'Minamo' (5/d) GEdr
- - 'Miwaku' (1) GEdr
- - 'Miyoshino' (1) GEdr NDry
- - 'Miyuki' (9/d) GEdr
- - 'Murasaki-sakama' (9/d) GEdr
- - 'Nanakubo' (1) GEdr
- - 'Notaniyama' GEdr
- - 'Noumurasaki' (1) GEdr
- - 'Oboryo' (1) GEdr
- - 'Odoriko' (9/d) GEdr
- - 'Okesabayashi' GEdr
- - 'Okina' (9/d) GEdr
- - 'Ō-murasaki' (1) GEdr
- - 'Orihime' (9/d) GEdr NDry
- - 'Reeka' (1) GEdr
- - 'Ryokurei' (5A/d) GEdr
- - 'Ryokusetsu' (9/d) GEdr
- - 'Ryokuun' (9/d) GEdr NDry
- - 'Sadobeni' (1) GEdr
- - 'Saichou' (7/d) GEdr
- - Sandan Group (7/d) GEdr
- - 'Satsuma' (5A/d) GEdr
- - 'Sayaka' (1) GEdr
- - 'Seizan' (9/d) GEdr
- - 'Senhime' (9/d) GEdr
- - 'Sen-nin' (6/d) GEdr
- - 'Sennin-buraku' (8/d) GEdr
- - 'Setsudu' (7/d) GEdr
- - 'Shikouden' (9/d) GEdr
- - 'Shikouryuu' (9/d) GEdr
- - 'Shio' (9/d) GEdr
- - 'Shirayuki' (9/d) GEdr
- - (Shiun Group) 'Shihou' (9/d) GEdr
- - 'Shoujyouno-homare' (9/d) GEdr
- - 'Sougetsu' (6/d) GEdr NDry
- - 'Souhou' (1) GEdr
- - 'Soushyunka' (9/d) GEdr
- - 'Subaru' (9/d) GEdr
- - 'Suien' (9/d) GEdr
- - 'Syouchikubai' (7/d) GEdr
- - 'Syunryuu' (9/d) GEdr
- - 'Taeka' (9/d) GEdr
- - 'Takase' (9/d) GEdr
- - 'Takumi' (9/d) GEdr NDry
- - 'Tamahime' (8/d) GEdr
- - 'Tamakujyaku' (6/d) GEdr
- - 'Tamasaburou' (1) GEdr
- - 'Tenjinbai' (1) GEdr NDry
- - 'Tenjin-ume' (1) GEdr
- - 'Tennyonomai' (6A/d) GEdr
- - 'Toki' (9/d) GEdr
- - 'Tori-no-saezuri' NDry
- - 'Touen' (9/d) GEdr
- - 'Touhou' (9/d) GEdr
- - 'Touryoku' (9/d) GEdr
- - 'Toyama-chiyo-iwai' (7/d) GEdr
- - 'Umezono' (1) GEdr
- - 'Unabara' (9/d) GEdr
- - 'Usugesyou' (9/d) GEdr
- - 'Wakakusa' (9/d) GEdr
- - 'Yaegoromo' (6/d) GEdr NDry
- - 'Yahiko' (5/d) GEdr
- - 'Yahikomurasaki' (1) GEdr
- - 'Yamahibiki' (9/d) GEdr
- - 'Yellow Shades' GEdr
- - 'Yukishino' (2) GEdr
- - 'Yumes' (7/d) GEdr
- - 'Yuunagi' (9/d) GEdr
- - 'Yuunami' (1) GEdr
- - 'Yuuzen' (5/d) GEdr
- - 'Yuzuru' (9/d) GEdr
- var. ***japonica* × *nobilis*** var. ***nobilis*** NDry

– large, pale blue-flowered	NSla
– lavender-flowered new	MAsh
– 'Lilac Picotee'	NSla
– 'Oeland's Nacht'	GEdr
– Ohleila Group new	MAsh
– pale pink-flowered new	MAsh
– patterned leaf	NSla
– pink-flowered	EPot GAbr
– var. ***pubescens***	MAsh NSla
– Pygmy Group new	MAsh
* – var. ***pyrenaica***	LEdu MAsh NSla WAbe WThu
* – – 'Apple Blossom'	GEdr MAsh NBir
– – 'Harold Bawden'	GEdr
– – 'Harold Bawden' seedlings	MAsh
* – – 'Pyrenean Princess'	MAsh
* – – white-flowered	NBir
– 'Pyrenean Marbles'	NBir
– 'Rosa Elite'	GEdr MAsh
– 'Rubra Plena' (d)	GEdr MAsh NDry NSla
– 'Stained Glass'	EWld GKev
– 'Tabby'	NDry
– violet-flowered	MAsh
– 'White Sands'	ELan GBin GEdr
– white-flowered	CWCL EPot GAbr LRHS MAsh
– 'Woodside White'	GBin
– 'Zartila' new	MAsh
'Noubeni'	GEdr
'Professor Friedrich Hildebrandt' new	GEdr
× ***schlyteri***	MAsh NDry
– Ashwood hybrids	MAsh
– Blue Marble Group new	MAsh
– blue-flowered	MAsh NDry
– Silver Shadow Group new	MAsh
– 'The Bride'	GEdr MAsh
× ***schlyteri*** 'The Bride' × ***transsilvanica*** new	MAsh
§ ***transsilvanica*** ♀H5	CBro CTtf GEdr MAsh MCot WCot
– 'Ada Scott'	GEdr
– 'Blue Eyes'	GBin GEdr GKev
– 'Blue Jewel'	ELan GBin GEdr GKev
– blue-flowered	MAsh
– 'Buis'	GEdr NLar
– 'Connie Greenfield'	GEdr NSla
– 'Donner Wolke'	GEdr
– 'Eisvogel'	GEdr NDry
– 'Elison Spence' (d)	GEdr IBlr
– 'Grethe' seedlings	GEdr
– 'Fuchs'	GEdr
– 'Karpati Krönen'	GEdr
– 'Lilacina'	GEdr MAsh NDry
– 'Loddon Blue'	GEdr MAsh NDry
– 'März'	GEdr
– 'Praecox'	GEdr
– 'Supernova'	GEdr
– white-flowered	GEdr MAsh
triloba	see *H. nobilis*
aff. ***yamatutai***	MAsh

Heptacodium (*Caprifoliaceae*)

jasminoides	see *H. miconioides*
§ ***miconioides*** ♀H7	Widely available
– TIANSHAN ('Minhep'PBR)	LRHS MPkF SGol WCot

Heptapleurum see *Schefflera*

Heptaptera (*Apiaceae*)

triquetra	CKel CSpe

Heracleum (*Apiaceae*)

dulce	EBee
sphondylium	WSFF
– pink-flowered	SBls
stevenii	SBrt WCot
wallichii B&SWJ 13931	WCru

Herbertia (*Iridaceae*)

§ ***lahue***	SBrt WAbe

Hereroa (*Aizoaceae*)

glenensis	CSma EBou EDAr EHyd LRHS NRHS SLee SPlb

Hermannia (*Malvaceae*)

flammea	SPlb
stricta	WAbe

Herminium (*Orchidaceae*)

monorchis new	NLAp

Hermodactylus see *Iris*

Herniaria (*Caryophyllaceae*)

glabra	CBod GPoy GQue

Hertia (*Asteraceae*)

§ ***cheirifolia***	CCCN CSde EWes EWld NBir SEND WSHC XLum

Hesperaloe (*Asparagaceae*)

campanulata	WCot
engelmannii	WCot
malacophylla	EBee
'New Blue'	WCot
parviflora	CPla EAJP ELan LEdu SPlb WSMil XSen
– creamy yellow-flowered	WCot

Hesperantha ✿ (*Iridaceae*)

§ ***baurii***	CPbh GArf GBin GKev NHpl WThu
coccinea	CBcs CBen CMac CPla CTri EAJP EBee EPfP GBin GKev IBlr LRHS MBow MWts NChi NFav NGdn NHol NLar SCob SDeJ SDir SGbt WFar WMAq XLum
– f. ***alba***	Widely available
– 'Anne'	NLar WFar
– 'Autumn's Dawn'	ECtt WFar
– 'Ballyrogan Giant'	ECtt IBlr WFar WHer WSHC
– 'Big Moma'	WFar
– 'Cardinal'	NHol WFar
– 'Caroline'	ECtt WFar
– 'Cindy Towe'	CAbb CKno ELon LSou SPoG WFar
– 'Elburton Glow'	WFar
– 'Eric's Early'	ELon WFar
– 'Fenland Daybreak'	CBcs CBod CChe CDor CKno CMac ECtt EGrI EHyd ELan ELon EPfP GWyn LLWG LRHS LSou MBros MGos NGrd NLar NRHS SBea SCob SEdd SGBe SGbt SPoG SRms SWvt WFar
– 'Gigantea'	see *H. coccinea* 'Major'
– 'Good White'	NBir SMHy WFar
– 'Grandiflora'	see *H. coccinea* 'Major'
– 'Hilary Gould'	CMea ECtt WAvo WHal
– 'Ice Maiden'	CAbb CTtf ECtt GWyn LRHS LSou MAvo NSti SGBe SPoG
– 'Jack Frost'	EBee ECtt WFar

	– 'Jennifer' ♀H4	CBro CDor CElw CMac CTri CTtf EBee ECha ECtt EHyd ELon EPfP GAbr GArf LPot LRHS MCot MMuc MRav NLar NWad SRms SWvt WAvo WFar WSHC
	– 'Maiden's Blush'	ECtt LEdu NLar SRms WFar
§	– 'Major' ♀H4	Widely available
	– 'Marchants Seedling'	SMHy
	– 'Marietta'	WFar
	– 'Mollie Gould'	CAvo CBod ECtt EHyd EPfP LRHS MAvo MNrw MPie NHol NWad SCoo SGbt SRms WAvo WBrk WFar
	– 'Mrs Hegarty'	CEme ECtt EHyd ELon EPfP GDam GMaP GWyn MACG MGos MHer NBid NBir NFav NHol NLar NQui SDeJ SPer SPlb SPoG SRms SWvt WFar WPnP
	– 'November Cheer'	CMac ECtt IBlr NBir NLar
	– 'Oregon Sunset'	CBcs CBod CKno CPla ECtt ELon LLWG LRHS LSou SGBe SPad SPeP WFar WHil WHoo WKif
	– 'Pallida'	CMil ECtt NBir WFar
	– 'Pink Marg'	ECtt ITim WFar
	– 'Pink Princess'	see *H. coccinea* 'Wilfred H. Bryant'
	– pink-flowered	MBel
	– 'Professor Barnard'	CCCN EBee ECtt ELon EPfP EPri GWyn MBNS MNrw NBir NFav NLar WBrk WFar
	– 'Red Arrow'	EWes
	– 'Red Dragon'	ECtt NHol WHoo
I	– 'Rosea'	GKev MPie SDeJ WFar
	– 'Ruth'	ECtt WFar
	– 'Salmon Charm'	ECtt EHyd WFar
	– 'Salmon's Leap'	WFar
	– 'Salome'	CDor ECtt WFar WMal
	– 'Scarlet Queen'	WFar
	– 'Simply Pink'	SPad
	– 'Snow Drift'	WFar
	– 'Snow Maiden'	CBod CElw EBee ECtt EShb LRHS WFar WMal
	– 'Strawberry'	WFar
§	– 'Sunrise' ♀H4	CBcs CBro CExl CSBt CWCL EBee ECha EHyd ELan EPfP GAbr GKev IBlr LRHS MCot MHer MRav NBir NGdn NRHS NWad SGbt SPer SWvt WFar WHoo WKif
	– 'Sunset'	see *H. coccinea* 'Sunrise'
	– 'Tambara'	ECtt WFar XLum
	– 'Vibrant Scarlet'	WFar
	– 'Viscountess Byng'	CTri EBee MNrw NBir
*	– 'White Admiral'	WFar
§	– 'Wilfred H. Bryant' ♀H4	Widely available
	– 'Zeal Salmon'	CBro CElw ECha ECtt EGrI GAbr NBir WFar
	cucullata	CPbh
	huttonii	EPPr GEdr ITim NBir WFar
	mossii	see *H. baurii*
	pauciflora	CPbh
	vaginata	CPbh

Hesperis (*Brassicaceae*)

	matronalis	Widely available
	– ***alba***	see *H. matronalis* var. *albiflora*
§	– var. ***albiflora***	CCBP CLau CSpe CTtf ELan EPfP EWTr EWoo GMaP GQue LCro LEdu LOPS MACG MNHC NGdn NLar SBut SPer SPhx WBrk WCFE WHil
	– – 'Alba Plena' (d)	CRos EBee GWyn LRHS LSun MSCN NBir SSal WCAu WCot
	nivea	LEdu
	steveniana	LRHS SPhx

Hesperochiron (*Boraginaceae*)

	californicus	SBrt

× *Hesperotropsis* see × *Cuprocyparis*

Heteromeles (*Rosaceae*)

	arbutifolia	see *H. salicifolia*
§	***salicifolia***	GKev LEdu

Heteromorpha (*Apiaceae*)

	arborescens	CExl SPlb SVen

Heteropolygonatum (*Asparagaceae*)

	'Mikinori Ogisu'	EBee
	roseolum	EWld
	urceolatum	WCru

Heteropterys (*Malpighiaceae*)

	glabra	WCru

Heterotheca (*Asteraceae*)

	subaxillaris	WCot

Heuchera ✿ (*Saxifragaceae*)

	'Alan Davidson'	MPnt
	'Alison'	MPnt
	'Amber Waves' PBR	CBod CExl LRHS MBros MPnt NBir SCob SWvt
§	***americana***	LRHS MRav NBir SHar SHeu SSut SWvt
	– var. ***americana***	MPnt
	– Dale's strain	GPSL MPnt NLar SBls SHeu SPlb SWvt
	– 'Harry Hay'	EPPr EPri LEdu LPla MPnt SHeu WPGP WSHC
	– 'Jet Black' **new**	GJos
	– 'Marvellous Marble'	EShb LRHS MPnt SHeu
	– 'Ring of Fire'	MPnt SHeu SRms SWvt
	'Amethyst Myst'	CBod EHyd EPfP LSRN MCot MPnt SCob SCoo SHeu WSMil
	'Apple Crisp' PBR	CBod ECtt EPfP LCro LOPS LRHS MPnt MTin NLar SCob SHeu SWvt WNPC
	'Apple Souffle'	MPnt SHeu
	'Apple Twist' PBR (Dolce Series) **new**	SHeu
	'Apricot'	CWGN MPnt
	'Autumn Glow' (Seasonal Selection Series)	CRos EHyd LRHS MPnt NRHS SHeu WCot WNPC
	'Autumn Haze' PBR	MPnt SHeu
	'Autumn Leaves' PBR	ECtt EHyd ELan LCro LOPS MPnt NLar SCoo SEdd SHeu SPoG SWvt
	'Baby's Breath'	MPnt
	'Bardot'	MPnt
	'Beaujolais' PBR	EHyd MNrw MPnt NBir SEdd SHeu WCot WNPC
	'Beauty Colour'	ELan EPfP GMaP MRav NGdn NRHS SHeu SWvt WSMil
	'Bella Notte' PBR	MPnt NLar SHeu WNPC
	'Berry Marmalade' PBR	EBee EPfP LRHS MAsh MPnt NDov SHeu SWvt WNPC
	'Berry Smoothie' PBR	CBod CPla CRos CWGN EBee EHyd ELan EPfP LRHS LSRN MBNS MCot MGos MHol MPnt NHol NLar NPer NRHS SCob SCoo SEdd SHeu SPoG SWvt
	'Berry Timeless' **new**	SHeu
	(Big Top Series) 'Big Top Bronze'	SHeu
	– 'Big Top Burgundy'	SHeu

- 'Big Top Gold'	CWGN SHeu
'Bilberry' (Indian Summer Series)	MPnt SHeu
'Binoche'^{PBR}	CBod CRos EBee EHyd ELan LRHS MPnt NRHS SCob SHeu WCot WNPC
'Birkin'	CBod LRHS MPnt
'Black Cherry' (Heucheraholics Series)	SHeu
'Black Pearl'	CBod CPla CSpe CWCL LCro LOPS LRHS MAvo MBros MPnt SCoo SEdd SHeu SPad WTor
'Black Sea'	ECtt EPfP LRHS MPnt MSCN SEdd WCot WNPC
'Black Taffeta'^{PBR}	CBod CWGN EBee EPfP LBuc MPnt SHeu SPad WNPC
'Blackberry' **new**	SHeu
'Blackberry Crisp'^{PBR}	EBee LBuc MPnt SHeu WNPC
'Blackberry Jam' 🏆H6	CRos EHyd ELan EPfP LRHS LSou MPnt NBir NHol NRHS SCoo SGBe SHeu SWvt WFar
'Blackbird'	MPnt SHeu SWvt WFar WSpi
'Blackout'	ECtt MNrw MPnt SHeu
'Blondie in Lime' (Little Cutie Series) 🏆H6	CBod CRos EHyd EPfP LRHS MPnt MPri NLar NRHS SHeu WNPC
'Blondie'^{PBR} (Little Cutie Series)	CBcs CBod CWGN ECtt EHyd EPfP GJos LRHS MPnt MPri MSCN NLar NRHS SEdd SHeu SPad SPoG WCot WNPC
'Blood Red'	SHeu
'Blood Vein'	MPnt SHeu
'Blushing Dawn' **new**	LRHS
'Blushing Down'	MPnt
'Bouquet'	MPnt SHeu
'Boysenberry'^{PBR} (Indian Summer Series)	EBee ELan LRHS MPnt SHeu
bracteata	MPnt XLum
'Bressingham Glow'	MPnt SHeu
Bressingham hybrids	CSBt SRms SVic
'Bressingham Spire'	MPnt
'Bright and Breezy' (Seasonal Selection Series)	CBod CRos EHyd EPfP LRHS MPnt NRHS SHeu WNPC
'Bronze Beauty'	MPnt SHeu WBrk WCot
'Brown Sugar'	MPnt SHeu
'Brownfinch'	CElw LPla MPnt SBrt SHeu SMHy WCot
'Brownies'	MPnt SHeu WHrl
'Burgundy Bill' (Fox Series) **new**	MPnt
'Burgundy Frost'	MPnt SHeu
'Café Olé' 🏆H6	ECtt MPnt SHeu WHer
'Cajun Fire'^{PBR}	CWGN ELan MPnt SHeu
'Can-can' 🏆H6	CBod CRos CTri EHyd ELan EPfP LRHS MNrw MPnt NBir NRHS SCob SCoo SHeu SWvt WCAu WSpi
'Candy Honey' **new**	LRHS
'Canyon Duet'	MPnt SHeu
'Cappuccino'	EBee EHyd ELan EPfP MPnt MRav SCob SHeu SWvt
'Caramel'^{PBR}	CMac CRos CWGN EBee ECtt EHyd ELan GDam GMaP LCro LOPS LRHS MAsh MNrw NRHS SCob SGbt SHeu SPer SPoG SWvt WCot
'Carmen'	MPnt SHeu
'Carmencita'	SHeu
(Carnival Series) CARNIVAL BLACK OLIVE **new**	LRHS
- CARNIVAL COCOMINT ('Balcarcint'^{PBR})	SHeu
- CARNIVAL COFFEE BEAN ('Balcarcean'^{PBR})	EHyd LRHS NRHS

- CARNIVAL LIMEADE ('Balcarmade'^{PBR})	ELan LRHS SHeu
- CARNIVAL PEACH PARFAIT ('Balcarpait')	EHyd LRHS NRHS SHeu
- CARNIVAL PLUM CRAZY ('Balcarulm'^{PBR})	SHeu
- CARNIVAL ROSE GRANITA	LRHS SHeu
- CARNIVAL WATERMELON ('Balcarmelo')	LRHS MHol
'Cascade Dawn'	EBee MPnt NBir SWvt
'Cassis'	LRHS MPnt SHeu WCot WNPC
'Celtic Sea' **new**	LRHS
'Cézanne' (Master Painters Series)	MPnt SHeu
'Champagne Bubbles'	CWGN MPnt SHeu
CHAMPAGNE ('Tnheucha'^{PBR})	MPnt SHeu WNPC
CHARLES BLOOM ('Chablo')	EHyd MPnt SHeu
'Chatterbox'	MPnt SHeu
'Cherries Jubilee'^{PBR}	GMaP MPnt SHeu
'Cherry Cola'^{PBR} 🏆H6	CBcs CPla CRos EBee EHyd ELan EPfP LRHS MAsh MAvo MBros MCot MPnt MPri NLar NRHS SCob SCoo SEdd SHeu SPad SPoG SRkn WCot WFar WNPC WTor
'Cherry Truffles' (Dolce Series) **new**	SHeu WTor
'Chiqui'	MPnt SHeu
chlorantha	MPnt
'Chocolate Limes'	MPnt SHeu WNPC
'Chocolate Ruffles'^{PBR}	CBcs CRos ECha ELan EPfP EShb EWoo GDam GMaP LRHS LSRN MCot MGos MHol MRav NRHS SCob SPer SPoG SRms SWvt WCav WFar WSpi
'Chocolate Veil'	MPnt
'Christa'	MPnt SHeu
'Cinnabar Silver'^{PBR}	LSun MPnt
'Circus'^{PBR}	MPnt SHeu WNPC
'Citronelle'	CWGN ECtt EGrI EHyd EPfP LRHS MPnt NRHS SHeu SWvt WCot
'City Lights'	SHeu
'Coco'^{PBR} (Little Cutie Series)	EBee EHyd EPfP LRHS MPnt MPri MTin NRHS SHeu WNPC
'Color Dream'^{PBR}	MPnt SHeu
'Cool Dude' (Fox Series) **new**	MPnt
coral bells	see *H. sanguinea*
'Coral Bouquet'	MPnt SHeu
'Coral Cloud'	MPnt SHeu
'Coral Frost' **new**	LRHS
'Coral Sea'	WCot
'Coralberry'^{PBR} (Indian Summer Series)	ELan LRHS MPnt SHeu
'Corallion'	MPnt
'Cranberry' (Indian Summer Series)	ELan EPfP LRHS LSou MHol MPnt SHeu WNPC WTor
'Crazy Rasta' **new**	WNPC
CRÈME BRÛLÉE ('Tnheu041') (Dolce Series)	CChe CExl CRos EHyd ELan EPau EPfP GDam LRHS MGos NBir NCou NLar NRHS SCoo SEdd SHeu SPoG SWvt
'Crème Caramel'	CExl MPnt
'Creole Nights'^{PBR}	MPnt SHeu
'Crimson Curls'	CBod EHyd ELan EPfP LBuc LRHS MPnt NRHS SHeu SRms SWvt WNPC
'Crispy Curly'	MPnt SHeu
cylindrica	EPfP GKev GWyn MPnt SHeu
- var. ***alpina***	GKev
- 'Cream'	MPnt
- 'Francis'	MPnt

– 'Greenfinch'	ELan GLog GMaP GWyn LRHS MPnt MRav NBir SHar SHeu SWvt XLum
– 'Hyperion'	EHyd MPnt SHeu
'Da Vinci' (Master Painters Series)	MPnt SHeu
'Damask'	EHyd MPnt SHeu
'Dark Beauty'[PBR]	CBod NLar SCob SHeu SPer WNPC
'Dark Magic' **new**	SHeu
'Dark Secret'[PBR]	EBee LRHS MPnt SHeu
'Dark Storm' (Seasonal Selection Series)	CRos EHyd EPfP LRHS MPnt NRHS SHeu WNPC
'David'	MPnt SHeu WBrk
'Delta Dawn'[PBR]	CPla CWGN EBee EPfP LRHS MPnt NSti SCoo SGBe SHeu SPoG SWvt WNPC
'Dew Drops' (v)	SHeu
'Dizzi Blonde'	SHeu
'Earth Angel'	MPnt SHeu
EBONY AND IVORY ('E and I'[PBR])	EBee EHyd EShb GMaP MPnt NWad SHeu SRms SWvt WSpi
'Eden's Aurora'	MPnt
'Eden's Mystery'	NLar
'Electra'[PBR]	CMea LRHS MPnt NLar SHeu SWvt
'Electric Lime'	ELan MPnt SHeu SPoG WHoo WNPC
'Elworthy Rusty'	CElw
'Emperor's Cloak'	GLog SHeu SWvt
'Emperor's Cloak' green-leaved	EWTr
'Encore'[PBR]	MPnt SHeu
'Fairy Dance'	MPnt
'Fantasia'	SHeu
'Fire Alarm'[PBR]	CWGN EHyd ELan EPfP LBuc LRHS MPnt NRHS SCob SHeu WNPC
'Fire Chief'[PBR]	CBcs CBod CRos CWGN EBee EHyd ELan EPfP EWoo LRHS LSou MAvo MPnt NBir NHol NRHS SCob SCoo SEdd SGBe SHeu SPer SPoG SRkn SWvt
'Firebird'	EHyd MPnt
FIREFLY	see *H.* 'Leuchtkäfer'
'Fireworks'[PBR]	MPnt MRav NLar SCob SHeu
'Fleur' (Fox Series)	CBod MPnt WNPC
'Florist's Choice'	SHeu
(Forever Series) 'Forever Purple'	CBod CWGN EBee EHyd EPfP GPSL LBuc LRHS LSou MHol MPnt NLar NRHS SCoo SHeu SPoG WNPC WTor
– 'Forever Red'	CBod MPnt SHeu WNPC
'French Quarter'	MPnt SHeu
'Frilly Lizzie' (Fox Series)	WNPC
'Frost' (Little Cutie Series)	CBod EPfP MPnt SHeu WNPC
'Frosted Violet'	see *H.* 'Frosted Violet Dream'
§ 'Frosted Violet Dream'[PBR]	EPfP LRHS LSRN MPnt SHeu SWvt WNPC
'Galaxy'[PBR]	CWGN MPnt SHeu
'Gauguin' (Master Painters Series)	MPnt MSCN SHeu
'Georgia Peach'[PBR]	CPla CWGN EBee ELan EPfP MNrw MPnt NBir NLar SHeu SWvt WFar WNPC
'Georgia Plum'	CWGN EBee EHyd ELan EPfP LRHS MPnt NRHS SHeu WNPC
'Ginger Ale'[PBR]	CWGN EBee EHyd ELan EPfP EWes EWoo LRHS MHol MPnt NHol NLar NRHS NSti SGBe SHeu SPer SPoG SWvt
'Ginger Peach'[PBR]	EPfP MPnt SCob SHeu WNPC
'Ginger Snap'[PBR] (Little Cutie Series)	LRHS MPnt SHeu WNPC
glabra	MPnt SHeu
glauca	see *H. americana*
'Glitter'[PBR] ♀H6	CBod CWGN EBee ECtt EPfP MPnt NDov SHeu SPoG WNPC
'Gloire d'Orléans'	MPnt XLum
'Gloriana'	EHyd
'Gojiberry' (Indian Summer Series)	EBee MPnt SHeu
'Gotham'[PBR]	MPnt SHeu WNPC
(Grande Series) GRANDE AMETHYST ('Tnhega') **new**	SHeu
– GRANDE BLACK ('Tnheugb') **new**	SHeu
'Grape Soda'[PBR] (Soda Series)	CWGN MPnt SHeu WNPC
'Green Goddess' (Heucheraholics Series)	SHeu
'Green Ivory'	MPnt SHeu XLum
'Green Sashay'	MPnt SHeu
'Green Spice' ♀H6	CBod CPla CRos EBee ELan EPfP EWoo GBin LCro LOPS LRHS MPnt NBir NHol NRHS SCob SCoo SHar SHeu SPer SPoG SWvt WCav
'Guacamole' ♀H6	MPnt SHeu
'Guardian Angel'	MPnt SHeu SRGP
'Gypsy Dancer'[PBR] (Dancer Series)	MPnt SHeu
'Hailstorm' (v)	MPnt
hallii	MPnt SPlb
'Happy Autumn' **new**	LRHS
'Happy Flames' **new**	SHeu
'Happy Moon'	WCot
HARVEST BURGUNDY ('Balheubur')	EHyd MPnt SHeu
HARVEST SILVER ('Balheusil')	EHyd EPfP MPnt SHeu
'Havana'[PBR]	EHyd LRHS MPnt NRHS SHeu
'Helen Dillon' (v)	EShb GMaP MPnt SHeu SWvt WSMil
'Hercules'[PBR]	MPnt SHeu
'High Hopes' **new**	MPnt SHeu
hispida	MPnt
'Hocus Pocus'	SHeu
'Hollywood'[PBR]	EBee GJos LRHS MGos MPnt NBir NHol SHeu SPoG
'Hot Stuff'	SHeu
'Huckleberry' (Indian Summer Series)	SHeu
§ 'Huntsman'	EHyd MPnt MRav SHeu
Indian Summer Series **new**	LRHS
'Iron Maiden'	SHeu
'Isabella' (Fox Series)	CBod LRHS MPnt WNPC
'Isla' (Heucheraholics Series) **new**	SHeu
'Jade Gloss'[PBR]	EHyd EPfP MPnt SHeu SWvt WNPC
'Jooles Green Giant' (Heucheraholics Series) **new**	SHeu
'June Bride'	MPnt
'Kadastra'	MPnt SHeu
'Kassandra'[PBR]	EHyd LRHS MPnt NRHS SHeu SWvt
KEY LIME PIE ('Tnheu042'[PBR]) (Dolce Series)	CBod CExl CWGN ECtt EHyd LRHS MGos NHol NRHS SCoo SHeu SRms SWvt WFar
'King Kong'	MPnt
Kira Series	MPnt
– 'Kira Purple Rain Forest'	SHeu
'Lady Romney'	XLum
'Lemon Chiffon'[PBR]	EHyd LRHS MPnt NRHS SHeu
'Lemon Love' **new**	MPnt SHeu

§ 'Leuchtkäfer'	EBou EHyd EPfP EWTr GMaP GWyn MHer MPnt MRav NBir NMir SBls SCob SHeu SPlb SRms XLum
LICORICE ('Tnheu044'PBR) (Dolce Series)	CRos ECtt EHyd LRHS MBNS MGos MPnt NRHS SHeu SPoG SWvt WFar
'Lily the Pink'	SHeu
'Lime Marmalade' ♀H6	Widely available
'Lime Rickey'PBR	CWGN EHyd LRHS LSun MGos MSCN NGBl SCob SHeu SWvt WCot
'Lime Ruffles'PBR	LBuc MPnt SHeu WNPC
'Lipstick'PBR ♀H6	CWGN EBee MPnt SHeu SWvt
'Little Tinker'	MPnt SHeu
'Lune Rousse'	MPnt SHeu
'Madison Bride' (Fox Series) ♀H6	CBod LRHS MPnt WCot WNPC
'Magic Color'PBR	GKev
'Magic Flute'	SHeu
'Magic Wand' ♀H6	SHeu
'Magma'	SHeu
'Magnum'	CWGN MPnt SHeu
'Mahogany'PBR	CBod LRHS LSou MPnt MPri SHeu SWvt WHoo
'Mahogany Monster' (Primo Series) **new**	SHeu
'Malachite'	CRos EHyd EPfP LRHS MPnt NRHS SHeu
'Mango'	MPnt SHeu
'Marmalade'PBR ♀H6	Widely available
'Maroon Blush'PBR	SHeu
'Mars'	CRos EHyd EPfP LRHS MPnt NRHS SHeu
'Mary Rose'	MPnt SHeu
maxima	MPnt SHeu
'Mega Caramel'	MPnt SHeu
'Mega Citronelle'	MPnt
'Megan' (Heucheraholics Series)	SHeu
'Melting Fire'	CChe EHyd GPSL LRHS MPnt SBls SHeu
'Mercury'	SHeu
'Metallic Shimmer' (Fox Series) ♀H6	CBod MPnt WNPC
'Metallica'	GJos SHeu
micans	see *H. rubescens*
micrantha	MPnt SHeu SRms
- var. ***diversifolia*** misapplied	see *H. villosa*
- 'Martha's Compact'	MPnt
§ - 'Ruffles'	ECha MPnt SHeu
'Midas Touch'	CWGN MPnt
'Midnight Bayou'	CPla ELan EPfP MPnt NLar NPer SHeu SWvt
'Midnight Rose'	Widely available
'Midnight Rose Select'	MPnt SHeu
'Midnight Ruffles'PBR	LSun MPnt SHeu WFar WNPC
'Milan'PBR	EHyd ELan LRHS MPnt NRHS SHeu WNPC
'Mini Caramel'	MPnt
'Mini Mouse'	MPnt SHeu
'Mint Frost'PBR	ELan LRHS MPnt SHeu SWvt
'Mint Julep'PBR	SHeu
'Miracle'PBR	MPnt SHeu
'Mocha'PBR	MNrw MPnt SHeu SWvt
'Molly Bush'	SHeu
'Morello'	MPnt SHeu WNPC
'Morning Mist'	WNPC
'Mother of Pearl'	MPnt SHeu
'Mulberry' (Indian Summer Series)	EPfP LRHS SHeu WTor
'Muscat'	MPnt SHeu
'Mysteria'PBR	MPnt SHeu
'Mystic Angel'	MPnt SHeu
'Neptune'	MPnt SHeu
(Northern Exposure Series) NORTHERN EXPOSURE AMBER ('Tnheunea')	MPnt SHeu
- NORTHERN EXPOSURE BLACK ('Tnheuneb') **new**	SHeu
- NORTHERN EXPOSURE LIME ('Tnheunel')	MPnt SHeu
- NORTHERN EXPOSURE PURPLE ('Tnheunep') **new**	SHeu
- NORTHERN EXPOSURE RED ('Tnhheuner')	MPnt SHeu
- NORTHERN EXPOSURE SILVER ('Tnheunes')	SHeu
'Oakington Jewel'	MPnt
'Obsidian'PBR ♀H6	Widely available
'Orange Dream'	MPnt SHeu
'Orangeberry' **new**	MPnt SHeu
'Orphée'	MPnt NChi
'Paprika'PBR	CMea CRos CWGN EBee EHyd LRHS MBNS MPnt NRHS SCob SHeu WCot WFar WNPC
'Paris'PBR ♀H6	CDoC CRos CWGN EHyd EPfP LRHS LSRN MAsh MGos MPnt NHol NRHS SGBe SHeu SPer SPoG STPC WCot WNPC
parishii NNS 93384	MPnt
parvifolia var. ***nivalis***	MPnt
- var. ***utahensis***	MPnt
'Pauline' (Fox Series)	CRos CWGN EHyd LBuc LRHS MPnt NRHS SHeu WNPC
'Peach Crisp'PBR	CWGN MPnt SHeu SRkn WNPC
'Peach Flambé'PBR	CBod CPla CRos CWGN EGrI EHyd ELan EPfP LRHS MBNS MCot MGos MHer MPnt NRHS SCob SCoo SHeu SPoG SWvt WHer
PEACH MELBA ('Tnheu043'PBR) (Dolce Series)	MPnt SHeu
'Peach Pie'	MPnt
'Peachberry Ice' (Dolce Series) **new**	SHeu
'Peachy Keen'	SHeu
'Pear Crisp'PBR	MPnt SHeu
'Penelope'	LRHS MPnt SHeu
'Peppermint' (Little Cutie Series)	CBod EPfP LBuc MPnt MSCN SHeu WCot WNPC
'Peppermint Spice'PBR (21st Century Collection Series)	MPnt SHeu
'Persian Carpet'	LRHS MPnt NBir NRHS SHeu SWvt
(Petite Series) 'Petite Marbled Burgundy'	MPnt SHeu SWvt
- 'Petite Pearl Fairy'	EGrI MPnt SHeu SWvt
- 'Petite Pink Bouquet'	MPnt SHeu
'Pewter Moon'	GMaP MPnt NBir SHeu WFar
'Pewter Veil'	MPnt SHeu
'Phoebe's Blush' (Fox Series)	MHtn MPnt WNPC
'Picasso' (Master Painters Series)	MPnt SHeu WNPC
'Pilley Pink'	SHeu
'Pilley Pumpkin'	SHeu
pilosissima	XLum
'Pink Panther' (Heucheraholics Series)	MPnt SHeu
'Pink Pearls'PBR	CBod CWGN EHyd EPfP LRHS MPnt NRHS SHeu WCot WNPC
'Pinot Bianco'	MPnt SHeu
'Pinot Gris'PBR	CWGN MPnt SHeu WNPC

'Pinot Noir'	MPnt SHeu
'Pistache'	LBuc MPnt SHeu WCot WNPC
§ 'Pluie de Feu'	EShb MPnt MRav SHeu XLum
'Plum Pudding'^{PBR}	Widely available
'Plum Royale'^{PBR}	EHyd ELan EPfP GKev LRHS MGos MPnt SHeu SWvt
'Pretty Perinne'^{PBR}	MPnt SHeu
'Pretty Polly'	EHyd MPnt SHeu
'Prince'	EHyd ELan LRHS MPnt NRHS SHeu SWvt
'Prince of Orange'	SHeu
'Prince of Silver'	EHyd MPnt SHeu
pringlei	see *H. rubescens*
pubescens	MPnt SHeu XLum
- 'Alba'	MPnt
pulchella	CBod EBou EDAr GKev GLog MHer MPnt SHeu SPlb SRms
'Purple Crinkle'	MPnt SHeu WNPC
'Purple Petticoats' Υ^{H6}	CBcs ELan LRHS MGos MPnt SCoo SHeu SPoG
'Quick Silver'	EHyd MPnt NBir NRHS SWvt
§ 'Quilter's Joy'	MPnt
'Rachel'	EHyd EPfP GMaP LRHS LSRN MPnt MRav NGdn NRHS SHeu SWvt XLum
RAIN OF FIRE	see *H.* 'Pluie de Feu'
'Raspberry' (Fox Series)	MPnt
'Raspberry Ice'^{PBR}	MPnt SHeu
'Raspberry Regal'	MPnt MRav NBir SHeu SWvt WCot
'Raspberry Sea' **new**	LRHS
'Rave On'^{PBR}	CWGN EBee ELan MPnt NHol SHeu SPer SWvt
'Red Dress'	MPnt SHeu
'Red Lightning'^{PBR}	CWGN MPnt SHeu
'Red Pearls'	LRHS MPnt SHeu
'Red Sea'	ECtt EHyd EPfP LRHS MPnt NRHS SHeu WCot WNPC
'Red Spangles'	EHyd MPnt NBir SHeu
'Regina' Υ^{H6}	EHyd EPfP MPnt NRHS SHeu SWvt
'Renoir' (Master Painters Series)	CWGN MPnt SHeu
'Rex Lime'	SPad
'Rhapsody'	EHyd
richardsonii	MPnt SHeu XLum
'Rickard'	MPnt
'Rio'^{PBR}	CWGN MHtn MPnt SHeu WNPC
'Robert'	MPnt
'Root Beer'^{PBR}	EHyd EPfP MHol MPnt NRHS SHeu WNPC
ROSEMARY BLOOM ('Heuros')	EHyd SHeu
§ ***rubescens***	GKev NBro
- var. ***versicolor***	GKev
'Sanbrot'	MPnt
§ ***sanguinea***	CMac EGrI MMrt MPnt MRav NBir
- 'Alba'	EShb LPot MPnt SMHy
- 'Coral Forest' **new**	CBod
- 'Coral Petite'	EDAr EHyd LRHS NRHS SHeu
- 'Frosty'	EHyd LRHS NRHS
- 'Geisha's Fan'	GArf MPnt SHeu SWvt
- 'Monet' (v)	MPnt SHeu
- var. ***pulchra***	GKev
- 'Ruby Bells'	EHyd LSRN MPnt NRHS SHeu SRms
- 'Sioux Falls'	GPSL SHeu
- 'Snow Storm' (v)	ELan MPnt SHeu SRms
- 'Splendens'	MPnt XLum
- 'Taff's Joy' (v)	MPnt
- 'White Cloud' (v)	EPfP EWTr GQue MPnt SHeu SRms XLum
'Sashay' Υ^{H6}	CBod GBin LPla MPnt SHeu WCot WNPC
'Saturn'	MPnt SHeu SWvt
'Schneewittchen'	EShb MPnt MRav SHeu
'Scintillation'	MPnt
'September Morn' (Seasonal Selection Series)	CRos EHyd EPfP LRHS MPnt NRHS SHeu WNPC
'Shanghai'^{PBR}	CWGN EBee EHyd EPfP LRHS LSRN MAsh MPnt NRHS SHeu SWvt WFar WNPC
'Shenandoah Mountain'	MPnt
'Shere Variety'	EHyd MPnt
'Silver Celebration' (Fox Series) Υ^{H6}	CBod MPnt WNPC
'Silver Dollar'	CWGN EBee MPnt SHeu
'Silver Gilt'	SHeu
'Silver Gumdrop' (Dolce Series)	CPla MPnt SHeu WNPC
'Silver Heart'	EBee EHyd LRHS MPnt NRHS
'Silver Indiana'	MPnt SHeu
'Silver Light'^{PBR}	MPnt SHeu
'Silver Lode'^{PBR}	MPnt SHeu
'Silver Scrolls'^{PBR}	CMac CRos EHyd EPfP GMaP LCro LOPS LRHS LSRN LSun MBel MGos MPnt MRav NRHS SCob SCoo SPoG SRkn SWvt WCot
'Silver Shadows'	MPnt SHeu
'Silver Streak'	see × *Heucherella* 'Silver Streak'
'Sioux Falls'	MPnt
'Slater's Pink' (Fox Series)	MPnt WCot WNPC
'Sloeberry' (Indian Summer Series)	SHeu
'Snow Angel'	CWGN MPnt NGBl SEdd SHeu SPoG WCot WNPC
'Snowfire' (v)	MPnt SHeu
'Southern Comfort'^{PBR}	CPla CWGN EBee MPnt NHol NLar NPer SCoo SHeu SPoG SWvt
'Sparkler'	MPnt
'Sparkling Burgundy'	ELan LRHS MPnt SHeu SWvt
'Spellbound'^{PBR}	CWGN EPfP MPnt SHeu SPoG SRkn WNPC
'Starry Night'	MPnt
'Steel City'	MPnt SHeu
'Stormy Seas'	EBee EGrI EHyd ELan EPfP EWTr LRHS MPnt MRav NBir NRHS SCob SHeu SRGP SWvt WCAu
'Strawberries and Cream' (v) Υ^{H6}	MPnt SHeu
'Strawberry Candy'^{PBR}	CWGN MPnt NLar SCob SHeu WWtn
'Strawberry Swirl'	CElw ELan EPfP EWTr GMaP MPnt MRav NBir NDov SHeu SWvt WCAu
'Sugar Berry'^{PBR} (Little Cutie Series)	EHyd EPfP LBuc LRHS LSun MPnt NRHS NSti SEdd SHeu WCot WNPC
SUGAR FROSTING ('Pwheu0104'^{PBR})	CRos EHyd ELan EPau GJos GKev LRHS LSRN MCot MGos MPnt MPri NCou NHol NRHS SEdd SHeu SWvt
'Sugar Plum'^{PBR}	CWGN EBee ELan EPfP LBuc LRHS LSRN MCot MPnt MPri SHeu WHoo WNPC
'Sunrise' (Seasonal Selection Series)	MPnt SHeu WNPC
'Sweet Berry'	MPnt
'Sweet Caroline' (Fox Series)	CBod MPnt WNPC
'Sweet Tart'^{PBR} (Little Cutie Series)	CBod CRos EHyd EPfP LRHS MPnt MTin NLar NRHS SHeu SPer SPoG WNPC
'Swirling Fantasy'^{PBR}	EGrI MPnt SHeu WFar
'Tangerine Wave' (Fox Series) Υ^{H6}	LRHS MPnt SHeu WNPC
'Tara'	MPnt SHeu
'Tayberry' (Indian Summer Series)	LRHS SHeu
'Thomas' (Fox Series) Υ^{H6}	CBod MPnt SHeu WCot WNPC

	'Tiramisu'PBR	CBod CWGN EHyd MPnt SHeu SPer SWvt WNPC
	'Tokyo'PBR (City Series)	CWGN LRHS MPnt SHeu SPoG
	'Topaz Jazz'	MPnt SHeu WNPC
	'Van Gogh' (Master Painters Series)	MPnt SHeu
	'Vanilla Spice'	MPnt SHeu
	'Velvet Night'	MPnt NBir SHeu SPlb
	'Venus' 🏆H6	CWGN EHyd LRHS MPnt NRHS SHeu SPer WCot WHoo
	'Vesuvius'	MPnt SHeu
	'Vienna'PBR (City Series)	MPnt SHeu WNPC
§	***villosa***	LEdu MPnt MRav WPGP XLum
	- 'Autumn Bride'	EWTr MPnt SDix SHeu SMHy
	- BRESSINGHAM BRONZE ('Absi'PBR)	EHyd MPnt SHeu
	- 'Chantilly'	MPnt SHeu
	- var. ***macrorhiza***	EShb GKev MPnt XLum
	- 'Palace Purple'	Widely available
	- 'Palace Purple Select'	CMac CTri GDam LSun MBow MCot SWvt WSpi
	- 'Plumpower'PBR	SHeu
	- Purpurea Group	LRHS
	'Violet Shimmer' (Fox Series) **new**	CBod MPnt WNPC
	'Virginale'	MPnt
	'Walnut' (Fox Series) 🏆H6	MPnt SHeu WNPC
	'White Marble'	MPnt SHar SHeu
	'White Spires'	EHyd MPnt SHar SHeu
	'White Swirls'	MPnt
	'Wild Rose' (Primo Series)	CBod LRHS LSou MAvo MPnt SHeu WNPC WTor
	'Wildberry' (Dolce Series) **new**	MPnt SHeu
	'William How'	MPnt SHeu
	'Winter Joy' (Seasonal Selection Series)	CRos EHyd LRHS MPnt NRHS SHeu WNPC
	'Winter Red'	EHyd MPnt SHeu
	WORLD CAFFÉ AMERICANO ('Jmb 14/11') (World Caffé Series) **new**	SPad
	'XXL'	MPnt SHeu
	'Zabeliana'	MPnt SHeu
	'Zipper'PBR	CWGN LBuc MPnt SHeu WNPC

Heuchera × *Tiarella* see × *Heucherella*

× *Heucherella* ✿ (*Saxifragaceae*)

	'Alabama Sunrise'PBR	CRos CTsd ELan EPfP EWhm LRHS MPnt NLar NPer NRHS SHeu SWvt WFar
	alba 'Bridget Bloom'	EHyd EPfP GMaP LPot LRHS MPnt MRav SEdd SHeu SRms WCAu WFar XLum
§	- 'Rosalie'	MPnt MRav SHeu SPlb WSHC
	'Art Deco'	MPnt SHeu
	'Art Nouveau'	CBod LRHS LSou MPnt SHeu WNPC
	'Autumn Cascade'PBR (Cascade Series)	MPnt SHeu
	'Berry Fizz'	MPnt SHeu SWvt
	'Birthday Cake'	MPnt SHeu
	'Blue Ridge'	LSou MPnt WTor
	'Brass Lantern'PBR 🏆H6	CBod CPla CRos CSpe EMor EPfP LRHS LSou MAsh MPnt MPri MSCN NHol NRHS SCob SHeu SRms SWvt WCot WNPC
	'Burnished Bronze'PBR	EPfP MPnt NLar NWad SCob SHeu SWvt
	'Buttered Rum'PBR	EBee MPnt SHeu WNPC
	'Catching Fire'	MPnt SHeu
	'Chocolate Lace'PBR	MPnt SHeu
	'Cinnamon Bear'	MPnt SHeu
	'Citrus Shock'	EMor MPnt SHeu
	'Copper Cascade'PBR (Cascade Series)	ELan LRHS LSou MPnt SHeu WNPC
	'Cracked Ice'PBR	LRHS MPnt SCob SHeu
	'Dayglow Pink'PBR	GMaP LSRN LSou MPnt NLar SHeu
	'Eye Spy' (Fun and Games Series) **new**	SHeu WTor
	'Fan Dancer'	MPnt SHeu
	'Fire Frost'PBR	LSou MPnt SHeu
	'Glacier Falls'PBR (Falls Series)	SHeu WNPC
	'Gold Cascade'PBR (Cascade Series)	ELan LRHS MPnt WNPC
	GOLD STRIKE ('Hertn041')	EMor MBNS MPnt SHeu
	'Golden Zebra'PBR	CWGN EMor MPnt NLar SHeu SWvt
	'Great Smokies'	MPnt SHeu
	'Gunsmoke'PBR	EMor LSou MPnt NWad SCob SHeu SWvt WFar
	HAPPY HOUR LIME ('Tnherhhl')	MPnt SHeu WNPC
	'Heart of Darkness'PBR	MPnt SHeu
	'Honey Rose'PBR	EBee LSou MPnt SCob SHeu WNPC
	'Hopscotch' (Fun and Games Series)	SHeu
	'Hot Spot'PBR	MPnt SHeu
	'Infinity'PBR	LSou SHeu
	'Kimono'PBR 🏆H6	CBod CRos EHyd ELan EMor EPfP EWoo GKev GMaP GWyn LRHS LSRN MBel MPnt NLar NRHS NSti NWad SCob SCoo SHeu
	'Leapfrog' (Fun and Games Series) **new**	CBod SHeu
	'Mojito'	MPnt SHeu WNPC
	'Ninja'	see *Tiarella* 'Ninja'
	'Onyx'	SHeu WNPC
	'Party Time'PBR	SHeu
	'Pink Fizz' **new**	MPnt SHeu WTor
	PINK WHISPERS ('Hertn042')	LSou MPnt SHeu
	'Plum Cascade'	MPnt SHeu SPeP WNPC
	'Quicksilver'	CBcs EPfP GMaP MPnt SHeu SWvt
	'Red Rover' (Fun and Games Series)	MPnt SHeu
	'Redstone Falls'PBR (Falls Series)	EBee EPfP MNrw MPnt MSCN NWad SHeu SPoG SWvt WCot WNPC
	'Ring of Fire'	SWvt
§	'Silver Streak'	EHyd LRHS MPnt NRHS SHeu SWvt
	'Solar Eclipse'	CBcs CRos CTsd EBee EHyd EMor LCro LOPS LRHS MAsh MPnt NLar NRHS NSti SCob SHeu SPad SPer SPoG SWvt WFar WNPC
	'Solar Power'PBR	CRos CWGN EBee EHyd ELan EMor EPfP LRHS MPnt NRHS SHeu SWvt WFar WNPC
	'Stoplight'PBR	CRos CWGN ELan EMor EPfP GMaP LRHS MGos MPnt MRav NBir NDov NHol NSti SCob SHeu SRkn SWvt WFar WNPC
	'Summer Snowflake'	SHeu
	'Sunrise Falls'PBR (Falls Series)	EBee MNrw MPnt MSCN SHeu SWvt WFar WNPC
	'Sunspot'PBR (v)	EMor NBro SHeu SRms WHer
	'Sweet Tea'PBR	Widely available
	'Tapestry'PBR 🏆H6	CRos EHyd ELan EMor EPfP GDam GMaP LRHS MBNS MBel MHol MPnt NDov NHol NRHS NSti NWad SCob SHeu SPoG SRkn SRms SWvt WFar WNPC
	tiarelloides	SRms

'Twilight'PBR LSou MPnt SHeu
§ 'Viking Ship' MPnt NBir SHeu
'Yellowstone Falls'PBR 🏆H6 MPnt MSCN NCou NWad SHeu SWvt WNPC

Hexastylis see *Asarum*

Hibanobambusa see × *Phyllosasa*

Hibbertia (*Dilleniaceae*)

aspera CAbb CBcs CCCN CKel CRHN CTsd LRHS WCot WFar WKif WSHC
§ ***cuneiformis*** CCCN
pedunculata WAbe
procumbens ITim WAbe
§ ***scandens*** 🏆H1c CBcs CBod CCCN CRHN EShb
'Spring Sunshine' SEle
volubilis see *H. scandens*

Hibiscus (*Malvaceae*)

coccineus EShb LRHS SBrt SMad SPlb XSte
– white-flowered SBrt
'Cranberry Crush'PBR CWGN ELan MNrw
'Fireball'PBR SPoG
hamabo CCCN IPap SGbt SNig
huegelii see *Alyogyne huegelii*
'Jazzberry Jam'PBR ELan MNrw SPoG
'Kopper King'PBR MBNS MNrw SPoG
moscheutos SBrt SVic XLum
– CAROUSEL JOLLY HEART ('Tahi56'PBR) LCro LOPS
– CAROUSEL PINK CANDY ('Tahi12'PBR) CWGN SPad
– CAROUSEL PINK PASSION ('Tahi16'PBR) LCro LOPS
– 'Old Yella'PBR ELan SPoG
– PLANET GRIOTTE ('Tangri'PBR) MPkF XSte
– 'Royal Gems'PBR ELan
'Newbiscus Pink' CCCN
'Newbiscus Red' CCCN
'Newbiscus White' CCCN
paramutabilis EWes
rosa-sinensis CDoC EBak SPre
– 'Apple Blossom' WFib
– 'Arcadian Spring' WFib
§ – 'Bari' (Sunny Cities Series) CCCN
– 'Blues Man' WFib
§ – 'Bordeaux'PBR (Sunny Cities Series) CCCN
– 'Byron Metts' WFib
– 'Cajun Cocktail' see *H. rosa-sinensis* 'Jambalaya'
– 'Candy Floss' (d) WFib
– 'Carmen Keene' WFib
– 'China Town' WFib
– 'Cloud Nine'PBR WFib
– 'Cockatoo' WFib
– 'Cooperi' (v) 🏆H1b WFib
– 'Courier Mail' WFib
– 'Dorothy Brady' WFib
– 'Enid Lewis' (d) WFib
– 'Fifth Dimension' WFib
– 'Gabriel' WFib
– 'Georgia Peach' WFib
– 'Gwen Mary' WFib
– 'Holly's Pride' WFib
– 'Hot Bikini' WFib
§ – 'Jambalaya' WFib
– 'Jayella' WFib
– 'June's Joy' WFib
– 'Key West Thunderhead' (d) WFib
– 'Lemon Chiffon' WFib
– 'Linda Pear' (d) WFib
– 'Madame Dupont' WFib
– 'Me Oh My Oh' WFib
– 'Mrs Andreasen' (d) WFib
– 'Rhinestone' WFib
– 'Roman Candle' WFib
– 'Rose Flake' WFib
– 'Rum Runner' WFib
– 'Soft Shoulders' WFib
– 'Spanish Lady' WFib
– 'Sprinkle Rain' WFib
– (Sunny Cities Series) SUNNY CANCUN ('Hican'PBR) CCCN
– – SUNNY TORINO ('Hirio'PBR) CCCN
– 'Susan Schlueter' WFib
– 'Tahitian Christmas' WFib
– 'Tahitian Desert Sands' WFib
– 'Tarantella' WFib
– 'The Path' WFib
– 'Vermillion Queen' WFib
– 'Weekend' WFib
– 'White Swan' WFib
ROSE MOON ('Walhirosmo'PBR) CRos EHyd LBuc LRHS NRHS SPoG
sabdariffa XAbr
schizopetalus 🏆H1b WFib
sinosyriacus 'Lilac Queen' CExl CKel EHyd EPfP LRHS WPGP
– 'Ruby Glow' CExl CKel EMil EPfP LRHS LSRN WPGP
'Sunny Premiere' CCCN
syriacus CCCN LMaj SChr SWeb SavN
§ – 'America Irene Scott'PBR SPoG
– 'Aphrodite' EHyd MAsh SSta
– 'Ardens' (d) CEnd EBee LPar SPoG WFar
§ – AZURRI BLUE SATIN ('Dvpazurri'PBR) SSta
– 'Azzurri' see *H. syriacus* AZURRI BLUE SATIN
– BLUE BIRD see *H. syriacus* 'Oiseau Bleu'
– BLUE CHIFFON ('Notwood3'PBR) (d) 🏆H5 CSBt EHyd ELan EPfP LCro LOPS LPar LRHS NRHS SPoG
– 'Bredon Springs' SSta
– CHINA CHIFFON ('Bricutts') (d) EHyd LPar MMuc SEND SGol SPer SPoG
– 'Diana' 🏆H5 CBcs CDoC CRos EHyd ELon EPfP EWTr LRHS LSRN MAsh NRHS SCob SCoo SLon SPer SSta
– 'Dorothy Crane' CKel LRHS SSta
– 'Duc de Brabant' (d) CCCN CSBt LPar MBlu
– 'Elegantissimus' see *H. syriacus* 'Lady Stanley'
– 'Freedom' (d) LRHS
– 'Gandini van Aart'PBR LPar LRHS SGol
– 'Hamabo' 🏆H5 CBod CBrac CRos CSBt CTri EBee EHyd ELan ELon EPfP LRHS LSRN MAsh MGos MMuc NLar NRHS SCoo SEND SGol SPer SPoG SWvt WFar WLov
– 'Helene' EHyd LRHS LSRN MBlu SSta
– 'Honghwarang' SSta
– 'Jeanne d'Arc' (d) SGol
§ – 'Lady Stanley' (d) CBod CCCN CDoC CMac CSBt EHyd SCoo SNig
– LAVENDER CHIFFON ('Notwoodone'PBR) (d) 🏆H5 CSBt EHyd ELan EPfP EWes LCro LOPS LPar LRHS LSRN MMuc NRHS SCoo SEND SGol SPer SPoG WTyc
– 'Leopoldii' (d) EBee

- MAGENTA CHIFFON ('Rwoods5'PBR)	EHyd LCro LOPS LRHS NRHS SPoG
- 'Marina'	CBod CCCN CDoC EHyd ELan ELon EPfP LPar MBlu MRav SGol SNig SPer WFar WLov
- 'Mathilde'	SSta
- 'Mauve Queen'	SSta
- 'Meehanii' misapplied	see *H. syriacus* 'Purpureus Variegatus'
- 'Meehanii' (v) 🏆H5	CEnd EBee EPfP LRHS SCoo SPer SPoG SSta
- 'Melrose'	SSta
- 'Monstrosus'	EBee LPar NLar
§ - 'Oiseau Bleu' 🏆H5	Widely available
- PINK CHIFFON ('Jwnwood4'PBR) (d)	EHyd ELan LCro LOPS LPar LRHS NRHS
- PINK GIANT ('Flogi')	EPfP LPar SPer SSta
- PINKY SPOT ('Minspot'PBR)	MMrt
- PURPLE PILLAR ('Gandini Santiago'PBR)	LCro LOPS LPar LRHS SCoo SGol SWeb
- PURPLE RUFFLES ('Sanchoyo') (d)	CDoC EPfP SPoG
§ - 'Purpureus Variegatus' (v)	CMac EHyd
- 'Red Heart' 🏆H5	CBod CEnd CMac CRos CSBt CTri EHyd ELan EPfP LPar LRHS MAsh MGos MMuc NRHS SCob SEND SGbt SNig SPer SPoG SRms SSta SWvt WCFE XSen
- ROSALBANE ('Minrosa')	SGol
- RUSSIAN VIOLET ('Floru')	CEnd CKel EPfP LRHS
- 'Shintaeyang'	EHyd
- 'Snowdrift'	SSta
I - 'Speciosus' (d)	LPar SPoG WFar
- STARBURST CHIFFON ('Rwoods6')	CRos LCro LOPS LRHS SCoo
- SUGAR TIP	see *H. syriacus* 'America Irene Scott'
- SUP'HEART ('Minomb'PBR)	EPfP SGsty
- 'Totus Albus'	LPar SSta
- ULTRAMARINE ('Minultra'PBR)	CDoC EPfP SGsty
- 'Variegatus'	see *H. syriacus* 'Purpureus Variegatus'
- WHITE CHIFFON ('Notwoodtwo'PBR) (d) 🏆H5	CSBt EHyd ELan EPfP EWes LCro LOPS LPar LRHS LSRN MAsh MRav SCoo SPer SPoG
- 'William R. Smith' 🏆H5	LPar MSwo SSta
- 'Woodbridge' 🏆H5	Widely available
trionum	CSpe WKif
- 'Sunny Day'	ELan

hickory, shagbark see *Carya ovata*

Hieracium (*Asteraceae*)

aurantiacum	see *Pilosella aurantiaca*
intybaceum new	SPhx
laevigatum subsp. ***nivale***	MMuc
§ ***lanatum***	GJos NBir NWad
maculatum Sm.	see *H. spilophaeum*
scullyi	EPPr WFar
§ ***spilophaeum***	GGro MMuc NBid NPer
- 'Blue Leaf'	WCot
- 'Leopard'	GJos NDov
villosum	GJos WHer
waldsteinii	WMal
welwitschii	see *H. lanatum*

Hierochloe (*Poaceae*)

odorata	CBod EPPr GPoy LEdu SBls XLum

Himalayacalamus (*Poaceae*)

asper	CDTJ
§ ***falconeri***	SDix WCot
§ ***hookerianus***	CExl EPfP SChr
- 'Himalaya Blue'	CDTJ

Himantoglossum (*Orchidaceae*)

robertianum	GKev

× *Hippeasprekelia* (*Amaryllidaceae*)

'Durga Pradhan'	WCot
'Red Beauty'	GKev WCot
'Red Star'	CCCN

Hippeastrum ✿ (*Amaryllidaceae*)

× ***acramannii*** 🏆H2	CAvo WCot
'Baby Star' 🏆H2	GKev SDeJ
'Black Pearl'	LCro LOPS
(Butterfly Group) 'Exotic Star'PBR	WPhe
- 'Santa Rosa'	GKev
(Colibri Group) 'Balentino'PBR	GKev
- 'Rapido'	LCro LOPS
- 'Veneto'	GKev SDeJ
'Daphne'	WPhe
(Diamond Group) 'Charisma' 🏆H2	SDeJ WPhe
- 'Fairytale' 🏆H2	LCro LOPS SDeJ
- 'Lemon Star'	WPhe
- 'Picotee' 🏆H2	GKev LCro LOPS SDeJ
- 'Red Fire'	GKev
- 'Très Chic'	WPhe
(Double Diamond Group) 'Alasca'PBR (d)	GKev
- 'Alfresco'PBR (d)	GKev SDeJ
(Double Galaxy Group) 'Aphrodite' (d)	WPhe
- 'Blossom Peacock' (d)	WPhe
- CHERRY NYMPH ('Chernym'PBR) (d)	GKev WPhe
- 'Clown' 🏆H2	SDeJ WPhe
- 'Double Delicious' (d)	WPhe
- 'Double Dream'PBR (d)	GKev
- 'Double Record' (d)	SDeJ
- 'Elvas' (d)	WPhe
- 'Ice Queen' (d)	WPhe
- 'Lady Jane' (d)	SDeJ
- 'Nymph' (d)	GKev WPhe
- 'Red Peacock' (d)	SDeJ
(Galaxy Group) 'Ambiance'	WPhe
- 'Apple Blossom' 🏆H2	GKev LCro LOPS SDeJ WPhe
- 'Apricot Parfait'	GKev
- 'Barbados'	WPhe
- 'Benfica'	WPhe
- 'Christmas Gift'	GKev LCro LOPS WPhe
- 'Desire'	WPhe
- 'Flamenco Queen' 🏆H2	WPhe
- 'Gervase'	GKev WPhe
- 'Grand Diva'	GKev
- 'Hercules'	SDeJ
- 'Lagoon'PBR 🏆H2	LCro LOPS
- 'Liberty'	SDeJ
- 'Limona'PBR	LCro LOPS
- 'Luna'	WPhe
- 'Minerva'	SDeJ WPhe
- 'Mont Blanc'	SDeJ
- 'Monte Carlo'PBR 🏆H2	WPhe
- 'Orange Souvereign'	WPhe
- 'Park Red'	GKev
- 'Pink Surprise'	GKev WPhe
- 'Popov'PBR	WPhe
- 'Purple Rain'	WPhe
- 'Red Lion' 🏆H2	GKev LCro LOPS WPhe

- 'Red Pearl'PBR	WPhe
- 'Rilona'	GKev SDeJ WPhe
- 'Royal Velvet' 🏆H2	WPhe
- 'Showmaster'	WPhe
- 'Spartacus'PBR	WPhe
- 'Susan'	SDeJ WPhe
- 'Tosca'	WPhe
× ***johnsonii*** 🏆H2	CExl WCot
papilio	CPla GKev LCro LOPS SDeJ
'Royal Red'	LCro LOPS
'San Antonio Rose'	WCot
'Snow Queen'	LCro LOPS
(Sonatini Group) 'Eye Catcher'	GKev
- 'Pink Rascal'	GKev
- 'Red Rascal'	GKev
- 'Sonatini Valentino'	WCot
- 'White Rascal'	GKev
(Spider Group) 'Bogota'	GKev LCro LOPS
- 'Carmen'	WPhe
- 'Chico' 🏆H2	GKev
- 'Emerald'	WCot
- 'Evergreen' 🏆H2	LCro LOPS WPhe
- 'Rio Negro'	GKev
- 'Sumatra'PBR	LCro LOPS
striatum	WCot
stylosum	WCot
'Toughie'	EBee EWoo
(Trumpet Group) 'Swan Lake'PBR	SDeJ
vittatum	GKev

Hippeastrum × *Sprekelia* see × *Hippeasprekelia*

Hippocrepis (*Fabaceae*)

§ ***comosa***	EDAr SPhx WAbe
§ ***emerus***	CBcs CCCN CDoC CExl CKel CMac ELan EPfP IArd LPar MAsh MGil MGos MMuc SEND SVen WSpi

Hippophae (*Elaeagnaceae*)

rhamnoides	CArg CBcs CCVT CEme CHab CLnd CMCN CMac CSpe CTri ELan EPfP EPom LBuc LEdu LMaj LPar MBlu MCoo MMuc NWea SCob SEND SEWo SGol SPlb WKor WTSh XSen
- (m)	EPom
- 'Askola' (f/F)	CAgr
- 'Dorana' (f/F)	CAgr
- 'Freisendorf Orange' (f/F)	CAgr
- 'Frugna' (f/F)	CAgr NLar
- 'Hergo' (f/F)	CAgr
- 'Hikul' (m)	CAgr LPar NLar
- 'Juliet' (f/F)	CAgr
- 'Leikora' (f/F) 🏆H7	CAgr ELan EPfP MBlu MCoo SPer
- ORANGE ENERGY ('Habego'PBR) (f/F)	CAgr MCoo
- 'Pollmix' (m) 🏆H7	CAgr ELan EPfP MBlu MCoo SPer
- 'Pollmix 3' (m)	MCoo
- 'Sirola' (f/F)	CAgr MCoo
salicifolia	CAgr WKor
- 'Streetwise'	EHyd LRHS
sinensis LS&E 15724	WPGP

Hippuris (*Plantaginaceae*)

vulgaris	CBen CPud CWat EWat LLWG NPer WMAq XLum

Hirpicium (*Asteraceae*)

armerioides	SPlb

Histiopteris (*Dennstaedtiaceae*)

incisa	LEdu SPlb WPGP

Hoheria ✿ (*Malvaceae*)

'Ace of Spades'	CAbb CDoC CKel EHyd ELan ELon EPfP LRHS MGil MMrt NLar SEND SPer SWvt WSpi
§ ***angustifolia***	EBee EPfP IDee MVil SVen WPGP
angustifolia × ***sexstylosa***	WPGP
'Borde Hill'	CAbb CBcs CDoC CJun CKel CMac CTrC EBee EGrI EHed EHyd ELan ELon EPfP LRHS MAsh MGil SEND SMad SPer SWvt WCFE WPGP WSpi
glabrata	CMac CTrC EPfP GBin IDee NBir
'Glory of Amlwch' 🏆H4	CAbb CBcs CDoC CJun CKel ELan EPfP GGGa LRHS LSRN SChF SPoG SWvt WKif WPGP WSpi
§ ***lyallii*** 🏆H4	CCCN CExl CKel LSRN SVen WSpi
microphylla	see *H. angustifolia*
populnea	CCCN CTsd
- 'Sunshine' (v)	CDoC SPoG
sexstylosa	CAbb CTri EPfP LEdu LRHS LSRN SMad SPer SPlb SVen SWvt WFar WSpi
- 'Crataegifolia'	CCht EBee MGil NLar WSpi
- 'Pendula'	CMac
- 'Stardust' 🏆H4	CBcs CCCN CDoC CEnd CJun CMCN CRos CSBt CTsd EBee EHyd ELan ELon EPfP LRHS LSRN MAsh MBlu MGil NLar SDix SEND SPer SPoG SWvt WBor WPGP WSpi
'Snow White'	LRHS MGos MNic MTrO NOra SPoG WMat

Holarrhena (*Apocynaceae*)

pubescens 'Snowflake'	CDoC

Holboellia (*Lardizabalaceae*)

FMWJ 13055	WCru
angustifolia	WCru
- subsp. ***angustifolia***	WCru
- - H&M 1504	WPGP
- subsp. ***linearifolia*** BWJ 8004	WCru
- subsp. ***obtusa*** DJHC 506	WCru
brachyandra HWJ 1023	WCru WPGP
aff. ***chapaensis*** B&SWJ 7250	WCru
coriacea	CBcs CBod CCCN CKel CRHN EBee EHyd EPfP IDee LEdu LRHS MGil MRav NLar NQui SEND SIvy SPer WCFE WCru
- B&SWJ 2818	WCru
aff. ***grandiflora*** FMWJ 13333	WCru
latifolia	CBcs CCCN CKel CMac CRHN CRos CTri EBee EGrI EHyd ELan EPfP LEdu LRHS MGil NLar SAdn SArc SNig SPer SPoG SWvt WBor WCru WPGP WSHC
- DJHC 98442	WCru
- HWJCM 008	WCru
- HWJK 2014	WCru
- subsp. ***chartacea*** dark-flowered HWJK 2213D	WCru
- - pale-flowered HWJK 2213C	WCru
- lanceolate-leaved	WPGP
- - HWJK 2419	WCru

Holcus (*Poaceae*)

	lanatus	SPhx WSFF
	mollis 'Albovariegatus' (v)	CWCL EBou ECha EPPr GMaP GWyn NBid NBro NPer NSti SPlb SRms XLum
	- 'White Fog' (v)	CBod MMuc NWad

Holmskioldia (*Lamiaceae*)

*	***lutea***	CCCN
	sanguinea	CCCN

Holodiscus (*Rosaceae*)

	discolor	CBcs EBee EHyd ELan EPfP EWes LRHS MBlu MGil MMuc MRav NLar NQui NRHS SLon SPer SPlb

Homalocladium (*Polygonaceae*)

§	***platycladum***	EShb

Homeria (*Iridaceae*)

	breyniana var. ***aurantiaca***	see *Moraea collina*

Homoglossum see *Gladiolus*

Hordeum (*Poaceae*)

	jubatum ♀^{H6}	CDor CKel CKno CSpe CTtf CWCL EAJP EWes GBee LEdu MAsh NGdn NGrd SEdd SMrm SPhx
	- 'Early Pink'	NDov
	secalinum	CHab WWild

Horkelia (*Rosaceae*)

	hendersonii	GEdr

Hormathophylla (*Brassicaceae*)

§	***spinosa*** 'Roseum' ♀^{H5}	CMea CTri ECha ELan EPot GArf WAbe XLum
*	- 'Roseum Variegatum' (v)	EPot

Horminum (*Lamiaceae*)

	pyrenaicum	MHol MMuc SBut SEND SRms
I	- f. ***alboviolaceum***	EWhm SBrt SBut
	- dark-flowered	SBrt WSHC
	- white-flowered	GKev

Hornungia (*Brassicaceae*)

	alpina	GEdr MACG NSla XLum

horseradish see *Armoracia rusticana*

Hosta ✿ (*Asparagaceae*)

	AGSJ 302	WCot
	'A Many-Splendored Thing'	IBal
	'Abana' (v)	IBal
	'Abba Dabba Do' (v)	CDor ECtt ELon EMic IBal MHost NSue SSien
	'Abba Showtime'	IBal
	'Abby' (v)	EMic IBal MHost NSue SSien WFar
	'Abiqua Ariel'	EMic
	'Abiqua Blue Crinkles'	IBal NBir
	'Abiqua Blue Edger'	IBal MHost SSien
	'Abiqua Blue Madonna'	IBal
	'Abiqua Blushing Recluse'	SSien
	'Abiqua Delight' (v)	EMic
	'Abiqua Drinking Gourd' ♀^{H7}	CBdn CDor ECtt ELon EMic GBin GMaP IBal MHost NLar NSue SSien XSte
	'Abiqua Elephant Ears'	IBal
	'Abiqua Ground Cover'	IBal
	'Abiqua Moonbeam' (v)	EMic IBal MHost NGdn SSien
	'Abiqua Recluse'	EMic IBal
	'Abiqua Trumpet'	EMic IBal LRHS NGdn NLar NNor SSien
	'Abraham Lincoln'	IBal
	'Academy Flora'	IBal
	'Academy Mavrodaphne'	EMic
	'Ada Reed'	IBal
	'Adorable'	CBdn IBal NSue SSien
	aequinoctiiantha	EMic IBal SSien
	'Afterglow' (v)	IBal SSien
	'Alabama Gold'	EMic
	'Alakazaam' (v)	EMic IBal SSien WFar
	'Alan Titchmarsh'	IBal MHost
	albomarginata	see *H.* 'Paxton's Original' (*sieboldii*)
§	'Albomarginata' (*fortunei*) (v)	CBcs CMac EMic NBir NGdn NNor SSien SWvt WFar
	'Alex Summers'	EMic IBal SSien WFar
	'Alice in Wonderland' (v) **new**	IBal
	'All That Jazz' (v)	IBal
	'Allan P. McConnell' (v)	EMic IBal LRHS MHost MNrw NSue SSien WFar WHal
	'Allegan Emperor' (v)	IBal SSien
	'Allegan Fog' (v) ♀^{H7}	EShb GEdr IBal LRHS NHpl NSue SSien
	'Alligator Alley' (v)	EMic IBal SSien
	'Alligator Shoes' (v) ♀^{H7}	EMic IBal
	'Almost'	IBal
	'Alpine Aire'	EMic IBal
	'Alpine Dream'	IBal
	'Alternative'	IBal
	'Alvatine Taylor' (v)	EMic IBal NGdn SSien
	'Amalia'^{PBR} (v)	IBal NSue SSien
	'Amanuma'	EMic IBal NSue
	'Amazing Grace' (v)	EMic IBal
	'Amber Tiara'	EMic IBal MHost NSue SSien
	'American Choo Choo' **new**	EMic
	'American Dream' (v)	EMic IBal SSien
	'American Gothic' (v)	IBal
	'American Halo'	CBdn EMic IBal MHost NLar NSti NSue SPalm SSien
	'American Icon'	IBal
	'American Sweetheart'	EMic IBal SSien
	'Americana' (v)	IBal SSien
	'Amethyst Gem'	IBal NSue
	'Amos'	IBal SSien
	'Amy Elizabeth' (v)	EMic IBal
	'Andorian'	IBal NSue
	'Andrew'	SSien
	'Andy Murray' (v)	MHost
	'Angel Falls' (v) **new**	NSue SSien
	'Angel Feathers' (v)	IBal SSien
	'Angelique' (v)	IBal
	'Anglo Saxon' (v)	IBal
	'Ani Machi' (v) ♀^{H7}	NSue
	'Ann Kulpa' (v)	CBdn EMic IBal MHost NGdn SSien
	'Annabel Lee'	IBal
	'Anne' (v)	IBal LSRN NSue SSien
	'Ansly' (v)	IBal
	'Antioch' (*fortunei*) (v)	EMic GLog IBal MRav NLar NNor SSien
	'Aoki' (*fortunei*)	EMic IBal
	'Aoki Variegated' (v) **new**	EMic
	'Aomori Select' **new**	EMic
	'Aphrodite' (*plantaginea*) (d)	EPfP EWTr SMad SMrm SSien
	'Apollo'	NNor
	'Apple Candy' (v)	IBal NSue SSien
	'Apple Green'	EMic GKev IBal
	'Apple Pie'	IBal MHost
	'Appletini'	IBal NSue
	'Aqua Velva'	IBal

'Arc de Triomphe'	ECtt EMic EMor IBal MHost NLar SSien
'Arch Duke'	IBal SSien
'Arctic Blast'	EMic IBal
'Arctic Circle' (v)	EMic
'Argentea Variegata' (*undulata*)	see *H. undulata* var. *undulata*
'Aristocrat' (Tardiana Group) (v)	EMic EMor IBal NGdn NNor SSien WFar
'Asian Pearl' (v)	IBal
'Aspen Gold' (*tokudama* hybrid)	EMic
'Astral Bliss'	IBal
'Athena' (v)	SSien
'Atlantis'^{PBR} (v) ♀^{H7}	CBod EMic EMor IBal NGdn NSue SSien
'Atom Smasher'	NSue
'Atomic Elvis'	CBdn IBal NSue
'August Beauty'	EMic IBal SSien
'August Moon'	Widely available
'Aureafolia'	see *H.* 'Starker Yellow Leaf'
'Aureoalba' (*fortunei*)	see *H.* 'Spinners'
'Aureomaculata' (*fortunei*)	see *H. fortunei* var. *albopicta*
'Aureomarginata' ambig. (v)	CEme EHyd SCoo SSien
'Aureomarginata' (*montana*) (v) ♀^{H7}	CBod CMac ELan EMic GMaP IBal MMuc NGdn NLar NSue WFar
'Aureomarginata' (*ventricosa*) (v) ♀^{H7}	EMic IBal NBir NGdn WFar
'Aureostriata' (*tardiva*)	see *H.* 'Inaho'
'Austin Dickinson' (v)	ECtt EMic IBal SSien
'Autumn Frost' (Shadowland Series) (v)	EMic EMor IBal NSue
'Avalanche'	SSien
'Avocado'	CBdn ELon EMic EWTr IBal NLar NSue SSien WFar
'Ayesha' (v) **new**	SSien
'Azure Snow'	IBal
'Azuretini'	IBal NSue
'Babbling Brook'	IBal NSue
'Baby Blue' (Tardiana Group)	EMic
'Baby Blue Eyes'	EMic IBal NSue
'Baby Booties' (v)	IBal NSue
'Baby Bunting' ♀^{H7}	IBal MHost NBro NLar NNor NSue
'Baby Doll' (v)	IBal
'Baby Kim'	EMic
'Backyard Monster' (v)	IBal
'Bailey's Cream' (v)	IBal
'Baja White'	IBal SSien
'Bali-Hai'	IBal
'Ballerina'	IBal
'Bam Bam Blue'	IBal
'Banana Muffins'	IBal
'Band of Gold'	CBdn EMic IBal MHost SSien
'Banyai's Dancing Girl'	EMic IBal
'Barbara Ann' (v) ♀^{H7}	CBdn EMic IBal ITim MHost NGdn SSien
'Barbara May'	IBal
'Barney Fife'	IBal
'Battle Star' (v)	IBal NSue SSien
'Beach Boy' (v)	IBal MHost MNrw NLar NSue SSien
'Bea's Colossus'	IBal
'Beauty Little Blue'	IBal NSue
'Beauty Substance'	IBal NNor SSien
'Beckoning'	EMic IBal MHost NSue SSien
'Bedazzled' (v)	IBal SSien
'Bedford Blue'	CBdn EMic IBal MHost SSien
'Bedford Rise and Shine' (v)	EMic ESwi IBal LRHS MHost
'Bedford Wakey-Wakey'	IBal MHost
'Behemoth'	IBal NSue
'Bell Bottom Blues'	IBal

	bella	see *H. crassifolia*
	'Bells of Edinburgh'	IBal SSien
	'Ben Vernooij' (v)	CBdn IBal SSien
	'Bennie McRae'	IBal
	'Best of Twenty'	IBal NSue
	'Betcher's Blue'	EMic IBal
	'Betsy King'	CMac MRav NLar
	'Bette Davis Eyes'	IBal
	'Betty'	IBal MHost NSue
	'Beyond Glory' (v)	EMic
	'Biddy's Blue'	IBal
	'Big Beauty' (v) **new**	ESwi IBal
	'Big Boy' (*montana*)	IBal LRHS NSue
	'Big Daddy' (*sieboldiana* hybrid) (v) ♀^{H7}	Widely available
	'Big John' (*sieboldiana*)	IBal NSue
	'Big Mama'	EMic IBal MBNS MNrw NGdn NSue SSien
	'Big Performer' (v) **new**	IBal
	'Big Top'	IBal SSien
	'Bigfoot'	IBal
	'Biggie'	IBal
	'Bill Brinka' (v)	IBal SSien
	'Bill Dress's Blue'	EMic SSien
	Binny sport (*sieboldii*) **new**	GBin
	'Birchwood Blue Beauty'	IBal
	'Birchwood Gem'	IBal
§	'Birchwood Parky's Gold'	EBee ECtt EMic EPfP GMaP IBal MHost NGdn NHol NLar NNor SMrm SSien
	'Birchwood Ruffled Queen'	EMic SSien
	'Bitsy Gold'	EMic
	'Bitsy Green'	NSue
	'Bix Blues'	IBal
	'Bizarre'	EMic
	'Black Beauty'	IBal
	'Black Hills'	EMic IBal
	'Blackfoot'	IBal
	'Blackjack' (*sieboldiana*)	IBal SSien WFar
	'Blarney Stone'	IBal SSien
	'Blaue Venus'	IBal
	'Blaze of Glory'	IBal
	'Blazing Saddles' (v)	CBdn EMic IBal SSien
	'Blonde Elf'	EMic IBal NGdn NHol NNor
	'Blue Angel' misapplied	see *H. sieboldiana* var. *elegans*
	'Blue Angel' (*sieboldiana*) ♀^{H7}	Widely available
	'Blue Arrow' ♀^{H7}	IBal LRHS NNor NSue
	'Blue Baron'	EMic IBal
	'Blue Belle' (Tardiana Group)	EMic IBal MHost NEoE NGdn
	'Blue Blush' (Tardiana Group)	EMic IBal MHost NGdn
	'Blue Boy'	EMic NNor SSien
	'Blue Cadet'	CMac CRos EBee EMic EShb GKev GQue LRHS MACG MHost NBir NGdn NLar NRHS NSue NWad SCoo SSien WFar
	'Blue Canoe'	IBal MHost
	'Blue Cascade'	EMic IBal NSue
	'Blue Chip'	EMic
	'Blue Circle'^{PBR}	EMic IBal
	'Blue Clown'	IBal
	'Blue Cup' (*sieboldiana*)	MRav SRms
	'Blue Danube' (Tardiana Group)	ECha EMic IBal MHost
	'Blue Diamond' (Tardiana Group)	EMic NNor NSue WFar
	'Blue Dimples' (Tardiana Group)	ECtt IBal MHost
	'Blue Dolphin'	IBal SSien

	'Blue Edger'	IBal MHost NBir SSien
	'Blue Eyes'	EMic NSue
	'Blue Flame'	ECtt EMic IBal
	'Blue Frost'	IBal
	'Blue Haired Lady'	IBal
	'Blue Hawaii'	CBdn IBal NSue SSien
	'Blue Heart' (*sieboldiana*)	ECha EMic IBal
	'Blue Ice' (Tardiana Group)	NSue SSien
	'Blue Impression'	EMic
	'Blue Ivory' (v)	EBee ECtt EHed ELon EMor NSue SPad WWtn
	'Blue Jay' (Tardiana Group)	EMic IBal
	'Blue Lady'	EMic IBal
	'Blue Magic'	MHost
	'Blue Mammoth' (*sieboldiana*)	CBdn EMic EMor IBal NLar NSue SEdd SSien
	'Blue Maui'	IBal
	'Blue Monday'	EMic SSien
	'Blue Moon' (Tardiana Group)	EMic GKev IBal MHost NGdn NLar SSien
	'Blue Mountains'	IBal
	'Blue Mouse Ears' ♀H7	Widely available
	'Blue River' (v)	EMic IBal
	'Blue Seer' (*sieboldiana*)	EMic SSien
	'Blue Shadows' (*tokudama*) (v)	ESwi NLar SSien WFar
	'Blue Skies' (Tardiana Group)	EMic IBal MHost
	'Blue Sliver'	SSien
	'Blue Splendor' (Tardiana Group)	IBal
	'Blue Umbrellas' (*sieboldiana* hybrid)	ECtt ELan EPfP GMaP IBal MHost NGdn NLar NNor SSien
	'Blue Vision'	ECtt IBal
	'Blue Wedgwood' (Tardiana Group)	EMic GQue IBal LRHS MHost NGdn SCob SSien
	'Blue Wonder'	IBal
	'Blue Wu'	EMic IBal
	'Blueberry à la Mode'	IBal
	'Blueberry Cobbler'	IBal MHost
	'Blueberry Muffin'	CBdn EMic MHost NSue
	'Blueberry Tart'	IBal
	'Bluetooth'	IBal
	'Blushing Blue' **new**	CBdn
	'Bob Deane' (v)	EMic IBal SSien
	'Bob Olson' (v)	ESwi IBal MHost SSien WFar
	'Bobbie Sue' (v)	IBal SSien
	'Bobcat'	IBal
	'Bogie and Bacall' (v)	IBal
	'Bold Edger' (v)	EMic IBal
	'Bold Intrigue' (v)	IBal
	'Bold Ribbons' (v)	EMic SSien
	'Bolt out of the Blue'	EMic
	'Bonanza'	EMic
	'Bonfire'	EMic
	'Boracay'	IBal
	'Border Bandit' (v)	EHyd IBal
	'Border Favorite'	EMic
	'Border Street' (v)	SSien
§	'Borwick Beauty' (*sieboldiana*) (v)	ELon EMic IBal LSou NGdn NLar SPer SSien
	'Bottom Line' (v)	IBal
	'Bountiful'	EMic IBal NSue
	'Boyz Toy'	EMic IBal NSue
	'Branching Out' **new**	IBal
	'Brandywine'	IBal
	'Brash and Sassy'	IBal
	'Brave Amherst' (v)	IBal
	'Brenda's Beauty' (v)	EMic IBal
	'Bressingham Blue'	CRos ECtt ELon IBal LRHS MHost MRav NLar NNor SPer SSien SWvt WFar

	'Bridal Falls'PBR (v)	CBdn EMic ESwi IBal NSue SSien
	'Bridal Veil'	EMic IBal
	'Bridegroom'	EMic ESwi IBal SSien
	'Bridgeville'	IBal
	'Brigadier'	IBal
	'Brigham Blue'	IBal
	'Bright Glow' (Tardiana Group)	EMic IBal
	'Bright Lights' (*tokudama*) (v)	EMic NGdn SSien WFar
	'Bright Star' (v)	CBdn IBal NSue SSien
	'Brim Cup' (v)	CDor ECtt ELon EPfP EShb GAbr MACG MBNS MNrw NBro NGdn NNor SMrm SPer SSien
	'Broadband' (v)	GBin IBal
	'Broadway' (v)	EMic EMor IBal
	'Bronx Bomber' (v)	IBal NSue
	'Brooke'	EMic IBal
	'Brother Ronald' (Tardiana Group)	EMic IBal LRHS MHost
	'Brother Stefan'	CBdn EMic IBal MHost NSue SSien
	'Brutus'	IBal
	'Buckshaw Blue'	EMic EMor IBal MHost NBir NEoE NGdn NNor SSien WHrl
	'Bulletproof'	CBod IBal
	'Bumblebee'	CBdn SSien
	'Bunchoko'	IBal NNor
	'Burke's Dwarf'	IBal
	'Butter Rim' (*sieboldii*) (v)	IBal
	'Buttered Popcorn' (v)	SSien
	'Cally Atom'	GBin IBal MHost
	'Cally Colossus'	IBal MHost
I	'Cally Strain' (*nigrescens*)	MHer
	'Cally White' (*nigrescens*)	IBal MHost
	'Calypso' (v)	EHyd EMic IBal MNrw NGdn NSue WFar
	'Camelot' (Tardiana Group)	IBal MHost NGdn NSue
	'Cameo'	NSue
	'Camouflage'	EMic IBal MHost
	'Canadian Blue'	ECtt EMic IBal LSou NLar NNor NSue SPeP SSien WFar
	'Candle Wax'	IBal MHost
	'Candy Dish'	IBal NSue
	'Candy Hearts'	EMic IBal NNor SSien
	capitata	NNor
	– B&SWJ 588	WCru
	'Captain Kirk' (v) ♀H7	CBdn EHyd EMic ESwi IBal MHost NGdn NSue SSien WFar
	'Captain's Adventure' (v)	EMic EMor IBal LCro LOPS NSue SSien WFar
	caput-avis	see *H. kikutii* var. *caput-avis*
	'Carder Blue'	EMic IBal
	'Carl'	SSien
	'Carnival' (v)	EHyd EMic IBal NGdn NHpl SPoG SSien
	'Carol' (*fortunei*) (v)	IBal MHost NGdn NLar NNor NSue SSien
	'Carolina Blue'	IBal
	'Carolina Sunshine' (v)	SSien
	'Carousel' (v)	EMic IBal SSien
	'Carrie' (*sieboldii*) (v)	EMic
	'Cascades' (v)	EMic IBal NGdn SSien
	'Cathedral Windows' (v) ♀H7	CLAP EMic IBal MHost NSue SSien
	'Catherine'	CBdn ELon EMic EMor IBal NLar NSue SSien WFar
	'Cat's Eyes' (*venusta*) (v)	IBal SSien
	'Cavalcade' (v)	EMic
	'Celebration' (v)	ELan EMic IBal
	'Celestial'	IBal
	'Celtic Dancer'	EMic IBal SSien

	'Celtic Uplands'	EMic IBal
	'Center of Attention'	EMic EMor IBal NGdn SSien
	'Centerfold'	NSue
	'Cha Cha Cha'	IBal
	'Chabo-unazuki' (*kikutii* var. *caput-avis*)	EMic
	'Chain Lightning' (v)	EMic IBal MHol NSue
	'Challenger'	EMic
	'Chameleon' (v)	EMic
	'Champagne for All' (v) **new**	IBal
	'Champagne Toast' (v)	IBal NSue
	'Change of Tradition' (*lancifolia*) (v)	EMic
	'Chantilly Lace' (v)	EMic IBal
	'Chariots of Fire' (v)	IBal
	'Chartreuse Waves'	IBal
	'Cheatin' Heart'	EMic IBal MHost NSue WFar
	'Chelsea Babe' (*fortunei*) (v)	IBal MHost SSien
	'Cherish' ♀H7	NGdn NHpl WFar
	'Cherokee' (v)	CBdn IBal SSien
	'Cherry Berry' (v)	CLAP CWGN EBee ECtt EHed EShb ESwi GBin IBal LRHS MBNS MHost MNrw NBro NEoE NGdn NLar NNor NRHS NSue NWad SCob SPeP SPoG SSien WFar WWtn
	'Cherry Flip'	SSien
	'Cherry Tart'	IBal NSue SSien
	'Cherub' (v)	EMic IBal SSien
	'Chesapeake Bay'	CBdn EMic IBal
	'Chesterland Gold'	IBal
	'Chief Sitting Bull'	IBal
	'Childhood Sweetheart' (v)	IBal NSue
	'China Girl'	EMic ESwi IBal
	'Chinese Sunrise' (v) ♀H7	CWCL EMic GBin GWyn IBal NNor SRms SSien
	'Chionea' (v)	IBal
	'Chiquita'	IBal
	'Chi-town Classic' (v)	IBal
	'Chodai Ginba'	IBal
§	'Chōkō-nishiki' (*montana*) (v)	CDor EHyd IBal LRHS NGdn NNor NRHS SSien
	'Choo Choo Train'	EMic SSien
	'Chopsticks'	EMic SSien
	'Christmas Candy'PBR	ECtt EMic IBal MHost NSue SSien
	'Christmas Charm' (v)	IBal
	'Christmas Cookies'	IBal SSien
	'Christmas Island'	NSue
	'Christmas Pageant' (v)	EMic IBal
	'Christmas Tree' (v) ♀H7	ECtt EHyd EMic EMor ESwi IBal MHost NGdn NLar NRHS NSue SSien
	'Church Mouse'	CBdn EMic IBal NSue SSien
	'Cinderella'	IBal MHost SSien
	'Cinnamon Sticks'	IBal NSue
	'Citation' (v)	IBal
	'City Lights'	ECtt EHyd EMic LRHS NRHS
	'City Slicker' (v)	IBal
	clausa	EMic
	- var. ***normalis***	IBal NBir NGdn NLar
	'Clear Fork River Valley'	EMic IBal SSien
	'Cleopatra' (v)	SSien
	'Clifford's Forest Fire'	ECtt EHyd EMic IBal NLar SSien WFar
	'Clifford's Stingray' (v)	EMic IBal NSue SSien
	'Climax' (v) ♀H7	CBdn EMic EPfP IBal SSien
	'Cloudburst'	EMic IBal
	'Clovelly'	IBal
	'Clown's Collar' (v)	EMic IBal SSien
	'Coal Miner'	IBal SSien
	'Coast to Coast' (Shadowland Series)	SSien
	'Coastal Treasure' (v) **new**	IBal
	'Coconut Custard'	EMic
	'Cody'	IBal NSue
	'Cold Heart'	EMic IBal
	'Collector's Banner'	IBal
	'Collector's Choice'	IBal
	'Color à la Mode' (v)	IBal
	'Color Festival' (v)	CDor ELon EMic IBal NLar NNor NSue SSien WFar
	'Color Glory'	see *H.* 'Borwick Beauty'
	'Colored Hulk' (v)	EMic IBal SSien
	'Colossal'	EMic IBal
	'Columbus Circle' (v)	EMic IBal
	'Con Te Partiro' (v)	MHost NSue SSien WFar
	'Confused Angel' (v)	IBal
	'Cookie Crumbs' (v)	EMic IBal NNor NSue
	'Cool as a Cucumber' (v)	CBdn IBal NSue
	'Coquette' (v)	EMic GAbr IBal
	'Corkscrew'	EMic NSue
	'Corn Belt' (v)	EMic IBal
	'Corn Muffins'	EMic
	'Corona' (v)	EMic
	'Corryvreckan'	IBal MHost
	'Cotillion' (v)	EMic GEdr IBal NSue
	'Count Your Blessings' (v)	EMic IBal
	'Country Mouse' (v)	EMic GBin GEdr IBal NHpl NSue SPoG SSien WFar WPnP WTor
	'County Park'	EMic IBal MHost
	'Cowrie' (v)	IBal
	'Cracker Crumbs' (v) ♀H7	CBdn EMic GEdr IBal LRHS MNrw NHpl NNor NSla NSue SSien WAbe WCot WFar
	'Craig's Temptation'	EHyd IBal NRHS NSue
	'Cranberry Wine'	IBal
§	***crassifolia***	EMic IBal XLum
	'Cream Cheese' (v)	IBal
	'Cream Delight' (*undulata*)	see *H. undulata* var. *undulata*
	'Cream Edger' (v) **new**	MHost
	'Crepe Soul' (v)	IBal
	'Crepe Suzette' (v)	IBal NNor SSien
	'Crested Reef'	EMic SSien
	'Crested Surf' (v)	EMic IBal
	'Crinoline Petticoats'	IBal
§	***crispula*** (v)	CDor EHyd IBal LRHS MCot MRav NChi NRHS
	'Crocodile Socks' (v)	IBal
	'Crown Prince' (v)	IBal NGdn
	'Crown Royalty'	EMic IBal
§	'Crowned Imperial' (*fortunei*) (v)	EMic IBal
	'Crumples' (*sieboldiana*)	IBal MHost
	'Crusader' (v) ♀H7	CBdn ELon EMic IBal LRHS SEND WFar
	'Crystal Dixie'	EMic GBin IBal NSue SSien WFar
	'Cumulonimbus'	IBal MHost
	'Cup of Grace'	IBal
	'Curlew' (Tardiana Group)	EMic IBal MHost
	'Curls'	EMic IBal
	'Curly Fries'	IBal MHost NSue SSien
	'Curtain Call'	IBal
	'Cutting Edge'	EMic IBal NSue
	'Cuyahoga' (v)	IBal
	'Dab a Green'	IBal
	'Dance with Me' (v)	EMic IBal NSue
	'Dancing in the Rain' (v)	CWGN NBro WFar
	'Dancing Mouse' (v)	CBdn GEdr IBal NSue WFar
	'Dancing Out of Time' **new**	NSue
	'Dancing Queen'	EMic IBal NSue SSien
	'Danish Mouse' **new**	IBal
	'Dark Shadows'	EMic IBal NGdn NSti WFar
	'Dark Star' (v)	EMic IBal MHost NGdn NSue

'Dark Victory'	EMic
'Dartmoor Forest'	IBal MHost
'Dawn'	EMic IBal MHost NSue NWad
'Dawn's Early Light'	EMic IBal NSue
'Dax'	IBal
'Daybreak' ♀H7	EMic IBal NBro
'Day's End' (v)	EMic IBal SSien
'Deane's Dream'	EMic IBal MHost SSien
'Decorata'	EMic
decorata var. ***normalis***	EMic
'Deep Blue Sea' ♀H7	EMic IBal NNor NSue
'Deep Pockets'	IBal
'Dee's Golden Jewel'	CBdn EMic SSien
'Déjà Blu' (v)	EMic IBal NSue
'Delicious' (v) **new**	IBal
'Deliverance'	EMic IBal NSue
'Delta Dawn' (v)	EMic IBal NGdn
'Delta Desire'	IBal
'Derek Coxs'	EMic IBal
'Desert Mouse'PBR (v)	GEdr IBal NSue
'Designer Genes'	IBal LRHS SSien WFar
'Devil's Advocate'	IBal
'Devon Blue' (Tardiana Group)	CBdn EMic IBal MHost NNor NSue
'Devon Cloud'	CBdn MHost
'Devon Desire' (*montana*)	IBal MHost NLar SSien
'Devon Discovery'	IBal MHost
'Devon Giant'	EMic MHost NNor SSien
'Devon Gold'	EMic GAbr IBal MHost SSien
'Devon Green' ♀H7	Widely available
'Devon Hills'	MHost
'Devon Mist'	IBal MHost NNor SSien
'Devon Tor'	EMic IBal MHost
'Dew Drop' (v)	MHost
'Dewed Steel'	IBal SSien
'Diamond Tiara' (v)	EMic IBal LRHS MHost NBir NGdn NSue SSien
'Diamonds are Forever' (v)	CBdn IBal NSue
'Diana Remembered'	CDor EMic EMor IBal MHost NGdn NNor NSue SSien WFar
'Dick Ward'	EMic IBal
'Dilithium Crystal'	IBal NSue WFar
'Dillie Perkeo'	IBal
'Dilys'	EMic MNrw
'Dimple'	CBdn EMic
'Dinky Donna' (v)	EMic IBal MHost NHpl NSue
'Dinner Jacket' (v)	EHyd EMor IBal LRHS MHost SSien
'Dinner Mint' (v) **new**	IBal
'Dino' (v)	IBal
'Dixie Chick' (v)	EMic IBal LRHS MHost NHpl NNor NSue SSien
'Dixie Chickadee' (v)	EMic NSue SSien
'Dixie Cups'	CBdn IBal
'Dixieland Heat'	IBal
'Doctor Fu Manchu'	IBal
'Domaine de Courson'	EMic IBal MHost NSue WFar
'Don Stevens' (v)	IBal LRHS SSien
'Dorothy'	EMic
'Dorset Blue' (Tardiana Group)	EMic IBal MHost SSien
'Dorset Charm' (Tardiana Group)	EMic MHost
'Dorset Flair' (Tardiana Group)	EMic IBal MHost
'Double D Cup'	SSien
'Doubled Up'	CBdn IBal
'Doubloons'	EMic
'Dracula'	MHost
'Dragon Tails' ♀H7	EHyd EMic GEdr IBal LRHS NHpl NNor NRHS NSue WAbe WFar
'Dragon Warrior' (v)	IBal
'Drake's Tail'	IBal NLar
'Dream Queen' (v)	CBdn CBod CDor ECtt EHed EMic IBal MHost MSCN NLar SPad SPalm SSien
'Dream Weaver' (v) ♀H7	ELon IBal MBrN MNrw NBro NGdn NSue SPoG SSien WFar
'Dress Blues'	CMac EMic IBal
'Drip Drop' (v)	SSien
'Drummer Boy'	EMic IBal MHost
'Duchess' (*nakaiana*) (v)	EMic IBal
'Duke of Cornwall' (v)	IBal
'DuPage Delight' (*sieboldiana*) (v)	EMic IBal NGdn NLar
'Dust Devil' (*fortunei*) (v)	IBal MHost SSien
'Dusty Waters'	IBal
'Dutch Flame' (v)	NSue
'Eagle's Nest' (v)	IBal
'Early Times'	IBal MHost
'Earth Angel'PBR (v) ♀H7	CBdn EMic IBal MHost NGdn NSue
'Eastern Spires' **new**	EMic
'Ebony Towers'	EMic IBal
'Eclipse' (v)	LRHS
'Eco Mirror'	IBal
'Edge of Night'	EMic IBal
'Edwin Bibby'	EMic MHost
'El Capitan' (v)	EHyd EMic IBal
'El Niño'PBR (Tardiana Group) (v) ♀H7	CBdn CDor CWGN EMic EPfP IBal LRHS MHost MNrw NBro NGdn NLar NSue SCoo SPoG SSien WFar
§ 'Elata'	EMic
'Elatior' (*nigrescens*)	IBal SSien
'Elbridge Gerry' (v)	IBal
'Eldorado'	see *H.* 'Frances Williams'
'Eleanor Lachman' (v)	IBal
'Eleanor Roosevelt'	IBal
'Electrocution' (v)	GEdr NSue SSien
'Elegans'	see *H. sieboldiana* var. *elegans*
'Elephant Burgers'	EMic
'Elisabeth'	EMic IBal
'Elizabeth Campbell' (*fortunei*) (v)	EMic IBal MHost SSien
'Elkheart Lake'	EMic IBal SSien
'Ellen'	EMic
'Ellerbroek' (*fortunei*) (v)	EMic
'Elsley Runner'	IBal NSue
'Elvis Lives'	EMic IBal NGdn NLar NNor NSue SSien
'Embroidery' (v)	EMic
'Emerald Carpet'	IBal
'Emerald Charger' (v)	IBal SSien
'Emerald Crown'	EMic IBal
'Emerald Edger'	EMic MHost
'Emerald Emperor'	IBal SSien
'Emerald Necklace' (v)	EMic IBal
'Emerald Paisley'	IBal
'Emerald Ruff Cut'	CBdn EMic IBal SSien
'Emerald Tiara' (v)	EHyd EMic IBal LRHS MHost NLar NSue SSien WFar
'Emeralds and Rubies'	EMic IBal NNor NSue SSien
'Emily Dickinson' (v)	ECtt EMic IBal LRHS NNor
'Emma' (v)	SSien
'Empress Wu'PBR	CBod CDor EBee ECtt EHed ELan EMor EPfP ESwi EWTr IBal ITim LCro LOPS LPla MBel MHol MHost MNrw NGdn NLar NNor NSue SMad SPalm SPoG SSien WCot WFar XSte
'Enchiladas' (v)	SSien
'Encore'	IBal
'Enduring Beacon'	NSue
'English Sunrise' (Tardiana Group)	IBal

'Enterprise' (v)	EMic EMor IBal NGdn NSue SSien
'Eola Sapphire'	EMic IBal
'Eos'	IBal NLar
'Eric Smith' (Tardiana Group)	EMic IBal MHost SHar WFar
'Eric Smith Gold'	GKev
'Eric's Gold'	IBal MHost
'Erie Magic' (v)	EMic IBal SSien
'Eskimo Pie' (v)	WFar
'Essence of Summer'	EMic IBal
'Essence of Sunset' (v) **new**	IBal
'Eternal Flame'	NSue SSien
'Everlasting Love' (v)	EMic IBal
'Excitation'	EMic IBal
'Exotic Presentation' (v)	EMic IBal
'Extasy' (v)	EMic IBal NGdn NSue WFar
'Eye Candy' (v)	IBal
'Eye Catcher'	EMic SSien
'Eye Declare' (v)	IBal
'Fair Maiden' (v)	NHpl
'Faith'	EMic SSien
'Faithful Heart' (v)	EMic IBal MHost NSue
'Fall Dazzler' (v)	IBal SSien
'Fall Emerald'	EMic
'Fallen Angel'	EMic
'Fan Dance' (v)	IBal
'Fantabulous' (v)	IBal SSien
'Fantasy Island' (v)	EMor IBal MHost NSue SSien WFar
'Fat Boy'	IBal
'Fat Cat'	SSien
'Fatal Attraction'	IBal SSien
'Feather Boa'	CBdn EMic IBal LRHS MHost NSue WFar
'Feng Shui'	IBal
'Fenman's Fascination'	EMic IBal
'Fiesta' (v)	IBal SSien
'Final Summation' (v)	EMic IBal NSue
'Final Victory' (v)	IBal
'Finlandia'	IBal
'Fire and Ice' (v) ♀H7	Widely available
'Fire Island' ♀H7	CBdn CDor ECtt EHyd ELan ELon EMic EMor EPfP GBin IBal MHost MNrw NLar NPoe NSue SPeP SSien WCot
'Fire Opal' (v)	IBal
'Firefly' (v)	IBal
'Fireplace' (v)	IBal
'Fireworks' (v) ♀H7	CDor ECtt EHed EMor EPfP EWoo GEdr LBuc MBNS MBel MNrw NBro NCou NNor NSue SMad SSien WCot
'Firn Line' (v)	CBdn EMor IBal SSien
'First Blush'	CBdn IBal NSue
'First Frost' (v) ♀H7	CBdn CRos ECtt EHed EHyd ELon EMic EMor EPfP IBal LRHS MACG MBros MHost MNrw NGdn NLar NRHS NSue SPoG SSien
'First Love' (*montana*)	EMic IBal NSue SSien
'First Mate' (v)	IBal SSien
'Five O'Clock Shadow' (v)	IBal
'Five O'Clock Somewhere' (v)	IBal
'Flamenco Mouse'	CBdn NSue
'Flapjack' (v)	IBal
'Fleet Week'	EMic IBal
'Flemish Angel' (v)	IBal NSue SSien
'Flemish Design'	IBal
'Flemish Gold'	IBal
'Flemish Master' (v)	EMic IBal SSien
'Flemish Sky'	EMic IBal NGdn NLar
'Flemish Steel'	IBal

'Floradora'	EMic IBal MHost NSue
'Floratini'	NSue
'Flower Power'	NNor
'Fluted Fountain'	EMic
'Fog Light'	CBdn IBal
'Fool's Gold' (*fortunei*)	EMic IBal
'Forbidden Fruit'PBR (v)	CBdn ELan EMic EMor IBal MHost NSue SSien
'Forest Fireworks' (v)	SSien
'Forest Shadows'	EMic IBal
'Formal Attire' (*sieboldiana* hybrid) (v) ♀H7	EMic IBal LRHS
'Forncett Frances' (v)	IBal MHost
'Fortis'	see *H. undulata* var. *erromena*
fortunei	EMic GWyn WFar
§ - var. ***albopicta*** (v)	CBcs ECha EGrI ELan EMic EPfP GMaP GWyn LCro LRHS MHost MRav NChi NLar NNor NRHS SPer SRms SSien WBrk WFar WHoo
- - f. ***aurea***	CMac ECha EMic MHost MMuc NLar SRms SSien WFar WHal
- - - dwarf	EMic
- - f. ***viridis***	NNor
§ - var. ***aureomarginata*** (v) ♀H7	CPud CRos CTri ECha ELan ELon EMic EPfP EShb GMaP IBal LRHS MHost MMuc NGdn NLar NNor NRHS SCob SEND SPer SPlb SSien WFar
- var. ***gigantea***	see *H. montana*
- var. ***hyacinthina***	EMic EPfP IBal MRav NGdn NLar XLum
- - variegated	see *H.* 'Crowned Imperial'
- var. ***stenantha***	EMic
'Fountain of Youth' (*kikutii*)	IBal
'Fourteen Carats'	EMic IBal
'Fourth of July'	NSue
'Foxfire Night Skye' (v) **new**	IBal SSien
'Foxfire Palm Sunday' (v)	IBal
'Fragrant Blue'	CTsd EHyd ELan ELon EPfP IBal LBuc MHost NBro NGdn NHpl NNor SPalm SPoG XLum
'Fragrant Blue Ribbons' (v)	EMic IBal
'Fragrant Bouquet' (v) ♀H7	CBdn CDor ECtt ELan EMic IBal LRHS LSRN MHost NGdn NHol NLar NNor NSue SSien WFar
'Fragrant Dream'	EHyd EMic IBal NLar NSue SSien
'Fragrant Fire'	EMic IBal
'Fragrant Gold'	EMic
'Fragrant King'	IBal
'Fragrant Queen'PBR (v)	EMic IBal NSue SSien
'Fragrant Star'	EMic IBal MHost
'Fragrant Surprise' (v)	NSue SSien
'Fran Godfrey'	EMic IBal MHost SSien
'Francee' (*fortunei*) (v) ♀H7	Widely available
§ 'Frances Williams' (*sieboldiana*) (v) ♀H7	Widely available
'Francheska' (v)	EMic IBal
'Frank Lloyd Wright'	IBal
'Free Jazz' (v)	IBal
'Fresh' (v)	CBdn EMic IBal NSue
'Fried Bananas'	CBod CDor EHed EMic IBal ITim MHost SMrm SSien WWtn
'Fried Green Tomatoes'	EMic IBal MHost NLar NNor
'Friends' (v)	EMic SSien
'Fringe Benefit' (v)	EMic MHost SSien
'Frisian Pride'	EMic IBal NSue
'Frisian Waving Steel'	EMic IBal
'Frosted Dimples'	EMic IBal MHost
'Frosted Frolic' (v)	EMic IBal SSien WFar
'Frosted Jade' (v) ♀H7	EMic EPfP IBal LRHS MMuc NLar SEND

'Frosted June'	IBal
'Frosted Lollipop' (v)	IBal
'Frosted Mini Hearts'	CBdn IBal NSue
'Frosted Mouse Ears'PBR	CBdn GEdr IBal NHpl NSue SSien
'Frozen Margarita'	CBdn EMic IBal NLar SSien
'Fruit Punch'	EMic IBal MHost SSien
'Fujibotan' (v)	EMic IBal
'Fukurin-Fu' (*venusta*) (v)	GEdr
'Fulda'	EMic IBal
'Full Moon'	EMic
'Funky Monkey'	EMic IBal SSien
'Funny Bones' **new**	CBdn
'Funny Frolic' (v)	IBal
'Funny Mouse' (v)	CBdn EMic IBal NHpl NSue SSien WFar
'Futura' (v)	IBal
'Gabriel's Wing' (v) **new**	IBal
'Gaiety' (v)	ECtt EHyd EMic IBal
'Gaijin' (v)	EMic IBal NSue
'Garden Party' (v)	IBal NSue SSien
'Garnet Prince'	CBdn IBal
'Gay Blade' (v)	IBal LPla
'Gay Feather' (v)	EMic SSien
'Gay Search' (v)	IBal MHost
'Geisha' (v)	IBal LRHS NEoE NGdn NNor NSue
'Geisha Satin Ripples'	IBal
'Gemstone'	MHost NSue
'Gene's Joy'	EMic
'Gentle Giant'	IBal
'Gentle Spirit' (v)	IBal
'George M. Dallas' (v)	IBal
'George Smith' (*sieboldiana*)	EMic IBal MHost SSien
'Georgia Sweetheart' (v)	IBal SSien
'Ghost Spirit' (v)	EBee IBal NSue SSien WFar
'Ghostmaster' (v)	IBal WFar
'Giantland Mouse Cheese'	IBal NSue
'Giantland Sunny Mouse Ears'	GEdr IBal NSue SSien
'Gig Harbor'	IBal
'Gigantea' (*sieboldiana*)	see *H.* 'Elata'
'Gilded Teacup' (v)	NSue
'Gilt by Association'	EMic IBal
'Gilt Edge' (*sieboldiana*) (v)	EMic
'Gin and Tonic' (v)	NSue
'Gingee'	EMic IBal NSue SSien
'Ginko Craig' (v) ♀H7	CMac CRos EHyd ELan EMic EPfP GKev GMaP IBal LRHS MRav NBir NGdn NLar NRHS NSti SPer SPoG SSien WFar
'Ginrei'	IBal
'Ginsu Knife' (v)	EMic IBal
'Glacial Towers' (v)	IBal SSien
'Glad Rags' (v)	IBal
'Glad Tidings'	IBal
'Glamour'	EMic IBal NSue SSien
'Glass Hearts'	EMic IBal NNor
glauca	see *H. sieboldiana* var. *elegans*
'Glen Triumph' **new**	SSien
'Glitter'	EMic IBal
'Glockenspiel'	EMic IBal MHost
I 'Gloriosa' (*fortunei*) (v)	IBal NSue
'Glory'	CBdn IBal SSien
'Glory Hallelujah'	CBdn EMic IBal
'Goddess of Athena' (*decorata*) (v)	IBal
'Gold Bug'	SSien
'Gold Drop' (*venusta* hybrid)	EMic IBal MHost NHol NSue
'Gold Edger'	CDor CMac EBlo EHyd EMic EPfP EShb GMaP IBal LRHS MHost MRav NBir NGdn NLar NNor NRHS NSti WFar
'Gold Edger Surprise' (v)	EMic
'Gold Flush' (*ventricosa*)	EMic
§ 'Gold Haze' (*fortunei*)	CDor IBal MHost NBir SSien
'Gold Leaf' (*fortunei*)	IBal MHost
'Gold Pressed Latinum'	IBal
'Gold Regal'	EHyd EMic GBin IBal LRHS WFar
'Gold Rush'	EMic MHost SSien
'Gold Standard' (*fortunei*) (v) ♀H7	Widely available
'Goldbrook' (v)	EMic IBal MHost
'Goldbrook Galleon'	IBal
'Goldbrook Gayle' (v)	MHost
'Goldbrook Gaynor'	IBal MHost
'Goldbrook Genie'	IBal MHost
'Goldbrook Girl'	IBal MHost
'Goldbrook Glamour' (v)	IBal MHost SSien
'Goldbrook Gleam' (v)	IBal MHost
'Goldbrook Glimmer' (Tardiana Group) (v)	IBal MHost
'Goldbrook Glory'	IBal MHost SSien
'Goldbrook Gold'	IBal MHost
'Goldbrook Good Gracious' (v)	IBal
'Goldbrook Grace'	IBal MHost
'Goldbrook Gratis' (v)	IBal MHost
'Goldbrook Grayling'	ECtt EMic IBal LRHS MHost NRHS
'Goldbrook Grebe'	IBal MHost
'Goldbrook Greengage' (v)	IBal MHost
'Goldbrook Greenheart'	IBal
'Golden Age'	see *H.* 'Gold Haze'
'Golden Empress' **new**	NSue
'Golden Fountain'	EMic
'Golden Friendship'	SSien
'Golden Gate'	IBal
'Golden Goal'	IBal
'Golden Guernsey' (v)	EMic
'Golden Isle'	EMic IBal MHost
'Golden Meadows'PBR (*sieboldiana*)	CBdn CDor ECtt EMic IBal NGdn NSue SSien WFar
'Golden Medallion' (*tokudama*)	CRos EBee EBlo ECtt EHyd EMic LRHS NGdn NRHS WFar
'Golden Mouse' **new**	NHpl
'Golden Nakaiana'	see *H.* 'Birchwood Parky's Gold'
'Golden' (*nakaiana*)	see *H.* 'Birchwood Parky's Gold'
'Golden Needles' (v)	IBal NSue SSien
'Golden Oriole'	EMic LRHS MHost NNor
'Golden Prayers' (*tokudama*)	ECtt ELan MRav NBir NBro NGdn NLar WFar WHal WSHC
'Golden Regal'	WFar
'Golden Scepter'	EMic IBal LRHS MHost NNor SRms SSien WFar
'Golden Spades'	EMic NSue
'Golden Spider'	EMic MHost NNor SSien
'Golden Sunburst' (*sieboldiana*)	ECtt NGdn NLar XLum
'Golden Sweetie'	EMic
'Golden Tiara' (v) ♀H7	Widely available
'Golden Tusk'	IBal
'Golden Waffles'	ECtt EMic EMor SPeP
'Goldene Woge'	SSien
'Goldpfeil'	MHost
'Goldsmith'	EMic MHost
'Gone Fishin'' (v)	IBal
'Gone with the Wind' (v)	IBal
'Goober'	IBal MHost
'Good as Gold'	CBdn EMic
'Goodness Gracious' (v)	IBal
'Gorgeous George'	IBal
'Gosan' (*tardiva*)	EMic
'Gosan Gold Midget'	EMic
'Gosan Leather Strap'	ESwi IBal

	'Gosan Mina'	EMic
	'Gosan Shining'	EMic
	gracillima	IBal NWad
	'Granary Gold' (*fortunei*)	MHost
	'Grand Canyon'	EMic SSien
	'Grand Finale'	IBal
	'Grand Marquee' (v)	CDor EMic IBal NGdn NLar WFar
	'Grand Master'	IBal
	'Grand Prize' (v)	EMic IBal NSue SSien
	'Grand Rapids'	EMic IBal
	'Grand Slam'	IBal
	'Grand Tiara' (v)	CDor EHyd EMic IBal MHost NGdn NSue SSien
	'Grand Total'	IBal
	'Grant Park'	IBal
	'Grape Fizz'	IBal
	'Gray Cole' (*sieboldiana*)	EMic IBal ITim
	'Great Arrival'	EMic IBal
	'Great Escape'[PBR] (v)	CBdn EMic IBal SSien
	'Great Expectations' (*sieboldiana*) (v)	CChe CDor CMac EBee EGrI EHyd ELan EMic EPfP EWoo LRHS LSRN MBNS MHer MHost MNrw NBro NGdn NHpl NLar NNor NRHS SBea SCob SIvy SPoG SSien WFar WPnP WTyc
	'Great Lakes Gold'	IBal
	'Green Acres' (*montana*)	EMic IBal LEdu WFar
	'Green Angel' (*sieboldiana*)	IBal
	'Green Cheese'	EMic IBal
	'Green Dwarf'	WFar
	'Green Eyes' (*sieboldii*) (v)	IBal WFar
	'Green Fountain' (*kikutii*)	EMic IBal
	'Green Gold' (*fortunei*) (v)	EMic
	'Green Guppy' new	NSue
	'Green Lama'	EMic IBal
	'Green Mouse Ears'	CBdn IBal NHpl NSue SSien WFar
	'Green Piecrust'	EMic
	'Green Platter'	EMic
	'Green Sheen'	EMic
	'Green Sleeve'	EMic
	'Green Velveteen'	CDor IBal
	'Green with Envy' (v) ♀H7	EMic IBal MBrN MHost NNor NSue NWad
	'Greenie Weenie Bikini'	MHost NSue SSien
	'Greenrush' new	SSien
	'Greensleeves' (v)	IBal
	'Grey Ghost'	EMic
	'Grey Glacier' (v)	IBal
	'Grey Goose' (Tardiana Group)	EMic MHost
	'Groo Bloo'	IBal
	'Ground Master' (v)	CMac ECtt EHyd ELan EPfP GMaP MRav NBro NGdn NLar NNor NSti SPer WFar
	'Ground Sulphur'	EMic NSue SSien
	'Grover Cleveland'	IBal
	'Grünherz'	IBal
	'Grunspecht' (Tardiana Group)	IBal
	'Guacamole' (v) ♀H7	CBcs CDor CRos CTsd EBee ECha ECtt EHyd ELon EMic EMor EPfP EWTr GBin IBal LRHS MBrN MHost NGdn NLar NNor NRHS SCob SPoG SSien WFar WPnP
	'Guardian Angel' (*sieboldiana*) ♀H7	EMic IBal NSue SSien
	'Gum Drop'	EMic NNor
	'Gun Metal Blue'	IBal
	'Gunther's Prize' (v)	IBal
	'Gunther's Rim' (v)	IBal
	'Gypsy Rose' ♀H7	EMic EShb IBal NGdn NLar NSue SSien WFar
	'Hacksaw'	EMic IBal MHost SSien
	'Hadspen Blue' (Tardiana Group) ♀H7	CDor CSBt CWCL EBee ELan EMic EPfP GMaP IBal LRHS MBrN MGos MHost MRav NBir NBro NGdn NHol NLar NNor NSti SCob SPer SPoG SSien WSpi XSte
	'Hadspen Hawk' (Tardiana Group)	IBal MHost
	'Hadspen Heron' (Tardiana Group)	EMic IBal MHost NWad XLum
	'Hadspen Honey'	EHyd
	'Hadspen Nymphaea'	IBal MHost
	'Hadspen Rainbow'	EMic IBal
	'Hadspen Samphire'	EMic IBal MHost NBir NBro SSien
	'Hadspen White' (*fortunei*)	EMic IBal MHost NLar
	'Haku-chu-han' (*sieboldii*) (v)	EMic NHpl
	'Hakujima' (*sieboldii*)	IBal NSue
	'Hakumuo' (v)	IBal SSien
§	'Halcyon' (Tardiana Group) ♀H7	Widely available
	'Half and Half'	EMic IBal NSue SSien
	'Halo'	NNor
	'Hampshire County' (v)	EMic IBal SSien
	'Hands Up'[PBR] (v)	CBdn EMic EMor EPfP IBal MHost NNor NSue SSien
	'Hanja's Crazy Mouse' (v) new	IBal
	'Hanky Panky' (v)	EMor IBal NGdn NSti NSue SSien WFar
	'Hannibal Hamlin' (v)	IBal
	'Happily Ever After' (v)	IBal
	'Happiness' (Tardiana Group)	EMic IBal MHost MRav SSien
	'Happy Camper' (v)	IBal
	'Happy Dayz' (v)	IBal SSien
	'Happy Hearts'	EMic MHost
	'Happy Valley' (v)	IBal NSue SSien
	'Harmony' (Tardiana Group)	EMic MHost
	'Harold Read' (v) new	CDor
	'Harpoon' (v)	EMic
	'Harriette Ward'	IBal
	'Harry van de Laar'	EMic IBal MHost SSien
	'Harry van Trier'	CBdn EMic GWyn MHost SSien
	'Hart's Tongue'	IBal
	'Harvest Delight'	EMic
	'Harvest Glow'	IBal
	'Hasta Manana' (v) new	CBdn
	'Hawkeye' (v)	IBal
	'Hazel'	EMic IBal
	'Heart and Soul' (v)	EMic IBal NSue
	'Heart Broken'	IBal MHost
	'Heart of Chan'	IBal
	'Heart Throb'	EMic
	'Heartbeat' (v)	NSue SSien
	'Heartleaf'	EMic
	'Heart's Content' (v)	IBal SSien
	'Heartsong' (v)	CBdn EMic IBal
	'Heat Wave'[PBR] (v)	EMic IBal SSien
	'Heavenly Beginnings' (v)	IBal
	'Heavenly Tiara' (v)	NSue SSien
	'Heavy Duty'	IBal SSien
	'Heideturm'	IBal
	'Helen Doriot' (*sieboldiana*)	EMic IBal
	'Helen Field Fischer' (*fortunei*)	IBal NLar
	helonioides f. ***albopicta*** misapplied	see *H. rohdeifolia*

'Herifu' (v)	EMic
'Hertha' (v)	EMic
'Hida-no-hana' (*montana*) (v)	IBal
'Hidden Cove' (v)	IBal NSue SSien
'Hidden Treasure' (v)	IBal
'Hideout' (v)	IBal
'High Kicker'	IBal
'High Noon'	SSien
'High Society' (v)	EPfP GEdr IBal MNrw NHpl NNor NSue SSien
'High Tide'	IBal
'High Voltage' (v) **new**	IBal
'Hi-ho Silver' (v)	EMic IBal NSue SSien
'Hilda Wassman' (v)	IBal
'Hillbilly Blues' (v)	EMic NSue
'Hippodrome' (v)	EMic IBal
'Hirao Elite'	EMic IBal
'Hirao Majesty'	IBal
'Hirao Supreme'	EMic IBal
'Hirao Tetra'	SSien
'His Honor' (v)	EMic IBal SSien
'Holar Arches Park' **new**	IBal
'Holar Ice Empress' **new**	IBal
'Holar Purple Flash'	IBal
'Holar Wild Side' **new**	IBal
'Hollywood Lights' (v)	EMic IBal NGdn NSue
'Holstein'	see *H.* 'Halcyon'
'Holy Molé' (v)	EMic IBal
'Holy Mouse Ears' PBR	CBdn GEdr IBal NSue SSien
'Honey Moon'	EMic IBal NNor SSien
'Honeybells'	CBcs CDor CMac EBee ECha EHyd ELan EMic EPfP GBin IBal LEdu MBros MCot MHost MRav NBid NGdn NNor NSti SPer SSal WCAu WFar XLum
'Honeysong' (v)	EMic IBal MHost NNor SSien
'Hoosier Dome'	EMic
'Hoosier Harmony' (v)	EMic
'Hope' (v)	EMic NLar
'Hot Air Balloon'	IBal SSien
'Hotcakes'	EMic IBal
'Hudson Bay' (Shadowland Series) (v)	EMic IBal
'Humpback Whale'	EMic IBal NSue SSien
'Hush Puppie'	EMic IBal MBrN MHost MNrw NHpl NSue SSien WFar
'Hyacintha Variegata' (*fortunei*) (v)	CMac NNor
'Hydon Gleam'	EMic IBal MHost NSue
'Hydon Sunset'	CRos EBee ECtt EHyd EMic GEdr IBal LRHS MHost MNrw NBir NLar NNor NRHS NSti NSue SSien WHal
hypoleuca	IBal
'Hyuga-urajiro' (v)	EMic GEdr IBal NSue SSien WFar
'Ice Cream' (*cathayana*) (v)	IBal NGdn NSue
'Ice Cube' (v)	IBal SSien
'Ice Prancer'	EMic IBal
'Iced Lemon' (v)	CBdn EMic GEdr IBal MHost NHpl NNor NSue SSien WFar
'Illicit Affair'	ECtt EMic IBal NHpl NNor NSue SSien
'Imp' (v)	IBal
§ 'Inaho'	LRHS NSue
'Inca Gold'	IBal NSue
'Incoming'	IBal
'Independence' (v)	EBee EMic IBal MHost NBro NSue SPoG SSien WFar
'Independence Day' (v)	EMic
'Inniswood' (v)	CDor CWCL ECtt EMic IBal MBNS NBro NGdn NLar NSti SSien WFar

'Invincible'	CDor ECtt EMic EMor IBal MHost NBid NGdn NLar NNor SSien WFar
'Invincible Spirit'	CDor IBal
'Iona' (*fortunei*)	EMic IBal MHost NNor SSien
'Irische See' (Tardiana Group)	IBal
'Irish Eyes' (v)	EMic IBal SSien
'Irish Luck'	EMic IBal NSue
'Iron Gate Delight' (v)	NNor
'Iron Gate Glamour' (v)	CDor
'Iron Gate Special' (v)	EMic
'Iron Sky'	IBal
'Island Charm' (v) 🏆H7	EHyd EPfP IBal LBuc LRHS NHpl NLar NNor NSue SCob SSien WFar
'Itty Gold'	IBal
'Ivory Coast' (v)	ECtt EHyd EMic EMor IBal LRHS MHol NRHS NSue SSien
'Ivory Necklace' (v)	IBal SSien
'Ivory Queen' (v)	CBdn EMic IBal NSue SSien
'Iwa Yara Moto'	IBal
'Jack Berry' **new**	CBdn
'Jack of Diamonds'	IBal SSien
'Jade Beauty'	EMic
'Jade Cascade'	CDor EMic GBin IBal NBir NLar WFar WHal
'Jade Scepter' (*nakaiana*)	EMic MHost
'Jadette' (v)	NSue
'Jane Ward' (v)	SSien
'Janet' (*fortunei*) (v)	EMic NGdn NNor SSien
'Janet Day' (v)	EMic
'Janet's Green Sox'	EMic
'Japan Boy'	see *H.* 'Montreal'
'Jason and Katie' (v)	EMic IBal
'Jaws'	EMic IBal NSue
'Jaz'	IBal SSien
'Jennifer' (v)	IBal
'Jerry Landwehr'	EMic IBal
'Jewel of the Nile' (v)	CDor IBal
'Jiminy Cricket' **new**	NSue
'Jimmy Crack Corn'	EMic IBal NGdn
'Jingle Bells'	IBal
'John Wargo'	IBal
'Joker' (*fortunei*) (v)	CBdn NNor
'Jolly Green Giant' (*sieboldiana* hybrid)	EMic
'Joseph'	EMic IBal MHost
'Josephine' (v)	SSien
'Joshua's Banner' (v)	SSien
'Journeyman'	EMic IBal MHost
'Journey's End' (v)	EMic IBal NSue
'Joyce Trott' (v)	SSien
'Joyful' (v)	IBal
'Jubilee' (v)	EMic IBal
'Judy Rocco'	IBal
'Juha' (v)	EMic
'Jules'	IBal
'Julia' (v)	CBdn EMic IBal NSue SSien
'Julie Morss'	EMic GMaP IBal MHost SSien
'Jumbo' (*sieboldiana*)	SSien
'June' PBR (Tardiana Group) (v) 🏆H7	Widely available
'June Fever' PBR (Tardiana Group)	CDor EHed ELon EMic EMor ESwi IBal NBro NGdn NLar NSue SPoG SSien WFar
'June Moon' (v)	SSien
'June Spirit' (v)	CBdn EMic IBal NSue SSien
'Jurassic Park'	IBal LLWG LRHS MNrw NLar NNor NSue SSien
'Just So' (v)	EMic IBal NNor SSien
'Justine' PBR	IBal NSue SSien

	'Kabitan'	see *H. sieboldii* var. *sieboldii* f. *kabitan*
	'Kabuki'	IBal NSue
	'Kalamazoo' (v)	CBdn EMic IBal SSien
	'Kaleidochrome' (v)	IBal
	'Kanzi' (v) **new**	NSue
	'Karin'	EMic IBal
	'Katherine Lewis' (Tardiana Group) (v)	EMic IBal LRHS LSRN MHost NHol SSien
	'Kath's Gold'	EMic
	'Katie Q' (v)	EMic IBal SSien
	'Katsuragawa-beni' (v)	EMic IBal SSien
	'Kayak'	IBal
	'Kelly'	CBdn EMic
	'Kelsey'	EMic IBal
	'Kempen Waving Shadow' **new**	IBal
	'Kenzie' (v)	EMic IBal
	'Key Lime Pie'	EMic IBal MHost SSien
	'Key West'	NSue SSien
	'Kifukurin' (*kikutii*)	see *H.* 'Kifukurin-hyuga'
§	'Kifukurin-hyuga' (v)	IBal
	'Kifukurin-kiyosumi'	IBal
	'Kifukurin-ko-mame' (*gracillima*) (v)	NSue
	'Kifukurin-otome' (*venusta*) (v)	EMic NSue SSien
	'Kifukurin-ubatake' (*pulchella*) (v)	EMic IBal
	kikutii	EMic IBal
§	- var. ***caput-avis***	EMic
§	- var. ***yakusimensis***	EMic GArf GEdr IBal SMad
*	'Kimidori Fukurin Otome' (*venusta*) **new**	SSien
	'Ki-nakafu-otome' (*venusta*)	IBal SSien
	'Kinbotan' (*venusta*) (v)	EMic GEdr SSien
	'Kinbuchi Tachi' (*rectifolia*) (v)	IBal
	'King James'	CBdn IBal
	'King Michael'	CBdn
	'King of Spades'	IBal
	'King Tut'	EMic
	'Kingfisher' (Tardiana Group)	LRHS MHost
	'Kingsize'	CBdn IBal NSue SArc SSien
§	'Kirishima'	EMic NHpl NSue NWad
	'Kisuji'	see *H.* 'Mediopicta'
	'Kitty Cat'	IBal MHost WFar
	'Kiwi Black Magic'	IBal
	'Kiwi Blue Baby'	EMic IBal
	'Kiwi Blue Ruffles'	IBal
	'Kiwi Blue Sky'	IBal
	'Kiwi Canoe'	IBal
	'Kiwi Cream Edge' (v)	EMic
	'Kiwi Forest'	IBal
	'Kiwi Full Monty' (v)	CBdn CDor EMic EMor ESwi IBal NLar NSue SSien WFar
	'Kiwi Gold Rush'	CBdn SSien
	'Kiwi Hippo'	IBal NSue
	'Kiwi Jordan'	IBal
	'Kiwi Kaniere Gold'	IBal
	'Kiwi Minnie Gold'	IBal ITim
	'Kiwi Parasol'	IBal
	'Kiwi Skyscraper'	IBal
	'Kiwi Spearmint'	ECtt EMic WFar
	'Kiwi Sunshine'	CBdn IBal
	kiyosumiensis	IBal
	'Klopping Variegated' (v)	EMic
	'Knight's Journey'	IBal SSien
	'Knockout' (v)	MBNS MRav NBro NGdn NLar NNor
	'Kogarashi Nakafu' (*tortifrons*)	NSue
	'Komodo Dragon'	IBal MHost SSien
	'Konkubine'	EMic
	'Korean Snow'	IBal NSue
	'Koriyama' (*sieboldiana*) (v)	EMic
	'Krossa Cream Edge' (*sieboldii*) (v)	IBal
	'Krossa Regal' ♀H7	Widely available
	'La Donna'	IBal
	'Lacy Belle' (v)	CDor EHyd EMic EPfP IBal LRHS NBro NEoE NGdn NSue SSien
	'Lady Godiva'	IBal
	'Lady Guineverre'	EMic IBal SSien
	'Lady Helen'	EMic
	'Lady in Red'	IBal
	'Lady Isobel Barnett' (v) ♀H7	IBal
	'Lady Luck' (v) **new**	IBal
	laevigata	IBal
	'Lake Hitchcock' (v)	IBal
	'Lake Superior'	IBal
	'Lake Tekapo' (v)	IBal
	'Lakeside Accolade'	IBal
	'Lakeside Alex Andra' (v)	IBal
	'Lakeside April Snow' (v)	EMic IBal NGdn SSien
	'Lakeside Baby Face' (v)	EMic ESwi IBal NHpl NSue SSien WFar
	'Lakeside Banana Bay' (v)	IBal NGdn SSien
	'Lakeside Beach Bum'	IBal
	'Lakeside Beach Captain' (v)	EMic SSien
	'Lakeside Black Satin'	NNor WFar
	'Lakeside Blue Cherub'	EMic IBal NNor
	'Lakeside Breaking News' (v)	EMic IBal
	'Lakeside Butter Ball'	IBal
	'Lakeside Cha Cha' (v)	EMic IBal NNor SPeP WFar
	'Lakeside Cindy Cee' (v)	IBal
	'Lakeside Circle O' (v)	IBal
	'Lakeside Coal Miner'	NGdn NLar SSien
	'Lakeside Color Blue'	IBal
	'Lakeside Contender'	IBal SSien
	'Lakeside Cupcake' (v)	CBdn EMic IBal MHost NGdn NSue SSien
	'Lakeside Cupid's Cup' (v)	EMic IBal
	'Lakeside Dimpled Darling' (v)	EMic MHost NSue
	'Lakeside Dividing Line' (v)	IBal
	'Lakeside Doodad' (v)	IBal MHost NSue
	'Lakeside Down Sized' (v)	CBdn EMic IBal MHost MNrw NSue SSien WFar
	'Lakeside Dragonfly' (v)	ECtt ELon EMic EShb IBal MNrw NGdn NLar NSue SSien WFar
	'Lakeside Elfin Fire'	GEdr NSue
	'Lakeside Fancy Pants' (v)	CBdn IBal
	'Lakeside Feather Light' (v)	IBal
	'Lakeside Foaming Sea'	IBal
	'Lakeside Full Tide'	IBal
	'Lakeside Hazy Morn' (v)	IBal
	'Lakeside Hoola Hoop' (v)	IBal
	'Lakeside Iron Man'	IBal
	'Lakeside Jazzy Jane' (v)	IBal
	'Lakeside Kaleidoscope'	CBdn EMic IBal NGdn NSue
	'Lakeside Keepsake' (v)	IBal
	'Lakeside Khum Kaw'	IBal
	'Lakeside Legal Tender'	IBal
	'Lakeside Lime Time'	IBal
	'Lakeside Little Gem'	IBal MHost NSue
	'Lakeside Little Tuft' (v)	EMic IBal MHost NLar NSue SSien
	'Lakeside Lollipop'	EMic IBal SSien
	'Lakeside Looking Glass'	EMic
	'Lakeside Love Affaire'	IBal WFar

'Lakeside Maestro'	IBal NLar
'Lakeside Maverick'	IBal SSien
'Lakeside Meadow Ice' (v)	IBal SSien
'Lakeside Meter Maid' (v)	IBal NSue
'Lakeside Midnight Miss'	IBal
'Lakeside Miss Muffett' (v)	EMic IBal NSue
'Lakeside Missy Little' (v)	IBal
'Lakeside Neat Petite'	IBal LRHS NSue
'Lakeside Ninita' (v)	ECtt EHyd EMic IBal NNor NRHS NSue
'Lakeside Old Smokey'	IBal
'Lakeside Paisley Print' (v)	CBod ECtt EMic EMor EPfP IBal MHol MNrw NSue SSien WFar
'Lakeside Pebbles'	IBal
'Lakeside Premier'	EMic IBal
'Lakeside Prophecy'	IBal
'Lakeside Prophecy Fulfilled' (v)	IBal
'Lakeside Rhapsody' (v)	EMic IBal SSien
'Lakeside Ring Master' (v)	IBal
'Lakeside Ripples'	IBal
'Lakeside Rocky Top' (v)	IBal WFar
'Lakeside Roy El' (v)	IBal SSien
'Lakeside Sapphire Pleats'	EMic
'Lakeside Sassy Sally'	IBal
'Lakeside Scamp' (v)	CBdn EMic GEdr IBal MHost NSue SSien
'Lakeside Shadows' (v)	IBal
'Lakeside Shoremaster' (v)	IBal
'Lakeside Slick Chick' (v)	IBal
'Lakeside Sophistication' (v)	IBal
'Lakeside Sparkle Plenty' (v)	IBal
'Lakeside Spellbinder' (v)	CLAP EMic IBal LRHS
'Lakeside Spruce Goose' (v)	CBdn EMic IBal SCoo
'Lakeside Storm Watch'	EMic IBal NLar SSien
'Lakeside Swan Pon' (v)	IBal
'Lakeside Symphony' (v)	EMic
'Lakeside Tee Ki' (v)	IBal
'Lakeside Whizzit' (v)	IBal NSue
'Lakeside Zesty Zeno' (v)	IBal
'Lakeside Zinger' (v)	EMic IBal MBrN MHost NNor NSue SSien
lancifolia	CMac EBee EMic GMaP IBal MHost MRav NGdn NSti SRms SSien WKif WSHC WThu
'Last Dance' (v)	IBal
'Last Train Home'	MHost SSien
'Laura Lanier'	EMic IBal
'Laura Z'	IBal
'Lavender Doll'	IBal
'Leading Lady' ♀H7	IBal
'Leather Sheen'	EMic
'Leatherneck'	IBal
'Lederhosen'	EMic
'Lemon Delight'	EHyd EMic ESwi IBal LRHS MHost NNor NRHS NSue SSien WFar
'Lemon Drop' **new**	MHost
'Lemon Frost'	EMic IBal NSue
'Lemon Lime'	CDor ECtt EMic EMor EWld IBal LRHS MBrN MHost MNrw NEoE NNor NRHS NSue SIvy SSien WAbe WCot
'Lemon Meringue'	NSue
'Lemon Twist'	CDor
'Lemonade'	GBin IBal
'Lemontini'	MHost NSue
'Leola Fraim' (v)	CBdn IBal MHost NSue
'Let Me Entertain You'	EMic
'Let's Twist Again' (v) **new**	CBdn SSien
'Leviathan'	EMic
'Lewis and Clark'	IBal

'Libby'	EMic IBal MHost NSue
'Liberty'PBR (v) ♀H7	CBcs CBdn CBod CDor CWGN EMic EPfP IBal MHost NBro NGdn NLar NNor NSue SAko SPer SSien
'Light of Zetar'	IBal
'Li'l Abner' (v)	IBal
* ***lilacina***	WFar
'Lily Blue Eyes'	EMic MHost SSien
'Lime Fizz'	CBdn EMic IBal MHost NHpl NSue SSien WFar
'Lime Regal'	MHost
'Lime Shag' (*sieboldii* f. *spathulata*)	IBal MHost NSue SSien WFar
'Limetini'	MHost
'Limey Lisa'	EMic IBal NNor NSue
'Linda Sue' (v)	IBal
'Lionheart' (v)	IBal NSue
'Lipstick Blonde' **new**	SSien
'Little Aurora' (*tokudama* hybrid)	EMic IBal NSue WFar
'Little Bit'	EMic IBal MHost NSue
'Little Black Scape'	EMic IBal NGdn NLar NWad SSien
'Little Blue' (*ventricosa*)	EMic
'Little Bo Beep' (v)	IBal WFar
'Little Boy'	IBal
'Little Caesar' (v)	IBal LRHS NGdn NNor NSue SSien WFar
'Little Devil'	EMic MHost NSue SSien
'Little Doll' (v)	IBal
'Little Hobber' **new**	EMic NSue
'Little Ice Mouse' (v) **new**	NSue
'Little Jay' (v)	NSue
'Little Maddie'	EMic NSue
'Little Miss Magic'	IBal
'Little Miss Muffett'	NSue
'Little Miss Sunshine'	IBal NSue
'Little Prayer'	WFar
'Little Red Joy'	EMic IBal MHost NSue SSien
'Little Red Rooster'	CBdn EMic GEdr IBal MHost NGdn NHpl NLar NNor NSue SSien WFar
'Little Star Struck'	NSue
'Little Stiffy'	IBal
'Little Sunspot' (v)	EMic NSue
'Little Treasure' (v)	EMic IBal NSue SSien WFar
'Little White Lines' (v)	EHyd EMic GKev IBal MHost NRHS NSue SSien
'Little Wonder' (v) ♀H7	EMic LRHS MHost NSue SIvy SSien
'Living Water'	EMic SSien
'Lizard Lick'	EMic IBal NSue
'Lollapalooza' (v)	CBdn IBal
'London Fog' (v)	GBin GEdr IBal
'Lonesome Dove' (v)	SSien
'Long Fellow' (v)	IBal
longipes	SSien
- B&SWJ 10806	WCru
- f. ***hypoglauca***	SSien
longissima var. ***brevifolia***	NSue
'Lost World'	EMic IBal
'Lothar the Giant'	IBal
'Love of Life' **new**	SSien
'Love Pat' ♀H7	ECtt EMic IBal LSRN MRav NGdn NLar NNor NSue NWad
'Love Song'	IBal SSien
'Loyalist'PBR (v)	IBal NGdn NLar NNor SPoG SSien WFar
'Lucky Mouse'PBR (v)	EMic EMor GEdr IBal NSue SSien
'Lucky Number' **new**	CBdn
'Lucy Vitols' (v)	CDor EMic ESwi IBal
'Lullabye'	EMic
'Luna Moth'	CBdn CBod ECtt EMor EPfP IBal NSue

'Lunar Eclipse' (v)	EMic
'Lunar Orbit' (v)	SSien
'Machete'	IBal
'Mack the Knife'	EMic IBal NLar WFar
'Maculata Aurea'	NNor
'Made in Spades' (v) **new**	NSue
'Maekawa'	IBal
'Magic Fire'^{PBR} (v)	ECtt EMic EPfP IBal NLar SSien
'Magic Island'	CBdn IBal MHol MHost NSue SSien
'Magica'	IBal
'Majesty'	EMic IBal MNrw NGdn SSien
'Major Tom'	IBal
'Majordomo'	EMic ESwi
'Malabar' (v)	EMic IBal
'Mama Mia' (v)	EHyd EMic EPfP IBal LSou MBNS NBro NGdn NHol NWad SSien WFar
'Mango Salsa'	IBal
'Mango Smoothie'	MHost SSien
'Mango Tango' (v)	IBal SSien
'Maple Leaf' (*sieboldiana*) (v)	EMic EMor
'Maraschino Cherry'	EMic GBin IBal LPla NGdn NSue
'Mardi Gras' (v)	EMic IBal
'Marge' (*sieboldiana* hybrid)	EMic
'Margie's Angel' (v)	NSue
'Margin of Error' (v)	IBal
'Marginata Alba' misapplied	see *H.* 'Albomarginata' (*fortunei*), *H. crispula*
'Marilyn'	EMic IBal
'Marilyn Monroe'	EMic IBal MHost NSue SSien
'Marmalade on Toast'	EMic MHost
'Marquis' (*nakaiana* hybrid)	IBal
'Marrakech'	EMic IBal NSue
'Marshmallow Sky' (v)	SSien
'Martini' **new**	SSien
'Mary Joe'	EMic
'Mary Marie Ann' (*fortunei*) (v)	CBdn EMic IBal
'Masquerade' (v)	EMic MHost NNor SMHy WAbe WFar WHal WThu
'Mata Hari' (v) **new**	CBdn NSue
'Maui Buttercups'	EMic MHost NSue
'May'	EMic IBal
'Maya' (*fortunei*) (v)	EMic IBal
'Medieval Age' (v)	IBal
§ 'Mediopicta' (*sieboldii*)	EMic IBal
'Mediovariegata' (*undulata*)	see *H. undulata* var. *undulata*
'Medusa' (v)	MHost NGdn NSue
'Megan's Angel' (v) **new**	SSien
'Memories of Dorothy'	EMic IBal MHost
'Mesa Fringe' (*montana*)	EMic NLar
'Metallica'	SSien
'Mid Afternoon'	IBal
'Midas Touch'	NLar
'Middle Ridge'	EMic
'Midnight at the Oasis' (v)	EMic IBal NSue SSien
'Midnight Oil' **new**	ESwi
'Midnight Ride'	IBal SSien
'Midwest Magic' (v)	EMic IBal MHost NLar
'Mighty Mite'	IBal NSue
'Mighty Mouse' (v)	EMor IBal
'Mikawa-no-yuki'	IBal
'Mike Shadrack' (v)	EMic IBal SSien
'Miki'	IBal
'Mildred Seaver' (v)	CBdn EMic IBal
'Milkmaid' (v)	CBdn
'Millennium'	ECtt EMic IBal
'Ming Jade'	CDor EMic
'Mini Skirt'	IBal NSue SSien
I 'Minima Aurea'	IBal
'Minke' (v) **new**	SSien
'Minnesota Wild' (v)	IBal SSien
'Minnie Bell' (v)	IBal
'Minnie Klopping'	EMic
minor misapplied f. ***alba***	see *H. sieboldii* var. *alba*
§ ***minor*** Maekawa	GEdr ITim LShi NWad WFar XLum
- B&SWJ 1209 from Korea	WCru
- B&SWJ 8775 from Korea	WCru
- B&SWJ 11103 from Japan	WCru
- from Japan	EMic LShi
- from Korea	IBal
'Minor' (*ventricosa*)	see *H. minor* Maekawa
'Mint Julep' (v)	IBal
'Minuet' (v)	IBal
'Minuta' (*venusta*)	MHost
'Minuteman' (*fortunei*) (v) ♀H7	CBcs CBdn CDor EHyd ELon EMic EPfP EWoo IBal MBNS MHost MMuc NGdn NHpl NLar NNor SEND SSien WFar
'Minutini'	NSue
'Miracle Lemony'	CBdn EMor IBal NSue
'Miss Linda Smith'	EMic IBal MHost
'Miss Ruby'	EMic IBal SSien
'Miss Saigon' (v)	IBal
'Miss Susie'	IBal
'Miss Tokyo' (v)	EMic IBal SSien
'Mississippi Delta'	EMic
'Mister Watson'	EMic IBal
'Misty Waters' (*sieboldiana*)	EMic
'Misweave' (v)	IBal
'Moerheim' (*fortunei*) (v)	EMic IBal MHost WFar WHal
'Mohegan'	EMic
'Mohrchen'	EMic
'Moi Marleen'	EMic
'Monster Ears'	EMor EPfP IBal NSue
montana	EMic WFar
- B&SWJ 4796	WCru
- B&SWJ 5585	LEdu WCru
- f. ***macrophylla***	IBal NSue
aff. ***montana***	SSien WFar
§ 'Montreal'	SSien
'Moody Blues' (Tardiana Group)	CBdn EMic
'Moon Dance' (v)	IBal
'Moon Lily'	EMic SSien
'Moon River' (v)	EMic IBal
'Moon Split' (v)	EPfP IBal NGdn SSien
'Moon Waves'	IBal
'Moonbeam'	EMic EShb
'Moongate Flying Saucer'	EMic
'Moonlight' (*fortunei*) (v)	EMic GMaP IBal LRHS NNor
'Moonlight Sonata'	CBdn EMic IBal SSien
'Moonstruck'^{PBR} (v)	ECtt EMic IBal NSue SSien
'Morning Light'	ECtt EMor IBal MBNS MHost NBro NGdn NLar SRkn SSien WFar
'Morning Star' (v)	EMic IBal LCro LOPS NSue SSien WFar
'Moscow Blue'	EMic
'Moulin Rouge'	IBal NSue
'Mount Everest'	EMic IBal SSien
'Mount Fuji' (*montana*)	IBal
'Mount Kirishima' (*sieboldii*)	see *H.* 'Kirishima'
'Mount Tom' (v)	IBal SSien
'Mountain Green'	SSien
'Mountain Snow' (*montana*) (v)	EHyd EMic SSien
'Mourning Dove' (v)	EMic IBal SSien
'Mouse Capades' (v) **new**	IBal
'Mouse Party' (v) **new**	IBal
'Mr Big'	IBal NGdn WCot
'Mr Blue'	IBal NSue

'Mrs Minky'	EHyd EMic MHost SSien
'Muffie' (v)	EMic NSue
'Munchkin' (*sieboldii*)	MHost SSien WFar
'My Child Insook' (v)	SSien
'My Claire' (v)	IBal SSien
'My Cup of Tea'	IBal SSien
'My Marianne' (v)	SSien
'My Precious' (v)	IBal NSue
'Mystic Mouse'	IBal
'Mystic Star'	IBal NSue
nakaiana	CDor EMic GWyn
'Nakaimo'	GBin IBal NLar
'Nana' (*ventricosa*)	see *H. minor* Maekawa
§ 'Nancy Lindsay' (*fortunei*)	CDor EMic IBal MHost NGdn NLar
'Nancy Minks'	EMic IBal
'Neat and Tidy'	IBal
'Neat Splash' (v)	CWCL NBir SSien
'Neat Splash Rim' (v)	SSien
'Needlepoint'	IBal
'Neelix'	IBal
'Nemesis' (v)	IBal
'Neptune'	EMic EMor IBal NSue SSien
'Nesmith's Giant'	EMic
'Niagara Falls' ♀H7	EMic IBal NGdn NSue SSien
'Nicola'	CBdn EMic IBal MHost NSue
'Nifty Fifty' (v)	SSien
'Night before Christmas' (v) ♀H7	EMic EMor IBal MBNS MHost MNrw NBro NGdn NHol NLar NNor SPalm SSien WHoo
'Night Life'	EMic IBal NSue
nigrescens	EMic IBal NChi
'Niko' (v)	IBal
'Nippers'	EMic IBal NSue
'None Lovelier' (v)	EMic IBal
'North Hills' (*fortunei*) (v)	EMic IBal NBir NGdn SWvt WFar
'Northern Exposure' (*sieboldiana*) (v)	CDor EHed EMic IBal NGdn NLar SPoG SSien WFar
'Northern Halo' (*sieboldiana*) (v)	CDor
'Norwalk Chartreuse'	IBal
'Number Nine'	IBal
'Nutty Professor' (v)	IBal
'Oberon'	NSue
'Obscura Marginata' (*fortunei*)	see *H. fortunei* var. *aureomarginata*
'Ocean Isle' (v)	IBal
'October Sky'	CBdn EMic IBal SSien
'Oder'	EMic IBal
'Ogon Tsushima'	SSien
'Ogon-chirifu-hime'	EMic IBal
'Ogon-hime-tokudama'	IBal
'Ogon-koba'	IBal
'Ogon-tachi' (*rectifolia*) (v)	EMic IBal
'Oh Cindy' (v)	EMic IBal
'O'Harra'	CBdn EMic NSue
'Old Faithful'	IBal
'Old Glory'^{PBR} (v)	ECtt EMic IBal MHol SSien
'Olga's Shiny Leaf'	EMic
'Olive Bailey Langdon' (*sieboldiana*) (v)	CDor EMic IBal
'Olive Branch' (v)	EMic IBal SSien
'Olympic Edger'	EMic IBal
'Olympic Glacier' (v)	EMic SSien
'Olympic Gold Medal'	EMic IBal MHost SSien
'Olympic Silver Medal'	EMic IBal MHost
'Olympic Sunrise' (v)	EMic IBal SSien
'Olympic Twilight'	CBdn EMic IBal
'On Stage'	see *H.* 'Chōkō-nishiki'
'On the Border' (v)	IBal
'On the Marc'	SSien
'On the Move'	EMic
'One Iota' (v)	IBal
'One Last Dance' (v)	NSue SSien
'One Man's Treasure' ♀H7	EMic IBal LSou MBel MHost NGdn NNor SSien
'Ooh La La' (v)	EMic IBal NSue
'Ophir'	EMic SSien
'Ops' (v)	EMic IBal SSien
'Orange Crush' (v)	IBal
'Orange Marmalade' (v) ♀H7	Widely available
'Orange Star'^{PBR} (v)	EMic IBal NSue SSien
'Oriana' (*fortunei*)	EMic MHost SSien
'Orion's Belt' (v)	IBal MHost
'Osprey' (Tardiana Group)	MHost
'Over the Waves'	IBal MHost NSue
'Oxheart'	EMic IBal
'Oze' (v)	SSien
pachyscapa	CBdn
'Pacific Blue Edger'	EMic MHost NNor SPalm WFar
'Painted Lady' (*sieboldii*) (v)	GKev
'Paisley Border' (v) **new**	NSue
'Pamela Lee' (v)	EMic IBal NGdn SSien
'Pandora's Box' (v)	EMic EMor GEdr NHar NHpl NSue WCot WFar WPnP
'Papa' (v)	IBal
'Paradigm' (v)	CBdn EMic IBal LRHS MBrN MHost NGdn NLar SSien
'Paradise Backstage' (v)	EMic IBal
'Paradise Beach'	EMic IBal WFar
'Paradise Blue Sky'	IBal
'Paradise Expectations' (*sieboldiana*) (v)	EMic IBal SSien
'Paradise Glory'	CBdn EMic IBal
'Paradise Gold Line' (*ventricosa*) (v)	IBal
'Paradise Goldheart' **new**	SSien
'Paradise Island'^{PBR} (*sieboldiana*) (v)	CBdn ECtt EMic EPfP IBal NGdn NSue SSien WFar
'Paradise Joyce'^{PBR}	EMic EMor IBal NNor
'Paradise Ocean'	CBdn EMic IBal SSien
'Paradise on Fire' (v)	IBal SSien
'Paradise Parade' (v)	EMic IBal
'Paradise Passion' (v)	IBal
'Paradise Power'^{PBR}	EMic SSien
'Paradise Puppet' (*venusta*) ♀H7	EMic GKev IBal MHost NNor NSue NWad SSien
'Paradise Red Delight' (*pycnophylla*)	EMic IBal MHost SSien
'Paradise Sandstorm'	IBal SSien
'Paradise Standard' (d)	EMic IBal
'Paradise Sunset'	EMic IBal MHost NHpl NNor NSue SSien WFar
'Paradise Sunshine'	EMic IBal
'Paradise Surprise' (v)	IBal SSien
'Paradise Tritone' (v)	EMic IBal
'Parasol' (v)	IBal
'Parky's Prize' (v)	CBdn IBal MHost NSue SSien
'Party Popper' (v)	MHost NSue
'Pastures Green'	IBal MHost
'Pastures New'	EMic MHost
'Pathfinder' (v)	EMic IBal SSien WFar
'Patricia'	EMic
'Patrician' (v)	IBal MHost
'Patriot' (v) ♀H7	Widely available
'Patriot's Fire' (v)	EHyd IBal NRHS SSien
'Patriot's Green Pride'	IBal
'Paul's Glory' (v) ♀H7	CBdn CDor EMic EPfP GLog GMaP IBal LRHS MBros MHost NBir NGdn NNor NSue SCob SPoG SSien WFar
§ 'Paxton's Original' (*sieboldii*) (v)	SSien
'Peace' (v)	CBdn IBal MHost

'Peacock Strut'	IBal
'Peanut'	IBal NSue SSien
'Pearl Lake'	EMic IBal MHost NBir NGdn NHol NLar NNor
'Peedee Absinth'	EMic
'Peedee Elfin Bells' (*ventricosa*)	CBdn IBal
'Pelham Blue Tump'	EMic MHost SSien
'Peppermint Ice' (v)	EMic NGdn SSien
'Percy'	EMic SSien
'Permanent Wave'	IBal
'Perry's True Blue'	CBdn EMic IBal
'Peter Pan'	EMic IBal SSien
'Pete's Dark Satellite'	EMic IBal NSue
'Pewterware'	EMic IBal
'Phantom'	CBdn IBal
'Philadelphia'	EMic IBal
'Phoenix'	CDor EMic IBal NLar
'Photo Finish' (v)	IBal SSien
'Phyllis Campbell' (*fortunei*)	see *H.* 'Sharmon'
'Picta' (*fortunei*)	see *H. fortunei* var. *albopicta*
'Piecrust Power'	IBal
'Piedmont Gold'	EHyd EMic IBal SSien
'Pilgrim' (v)	CDor EHyd EMic IBal LRHS MHol MHost MMuc NBro NGdn NHpl NRHS SEND SSien WFar
'Pinani Island Surf' (v) **new**	CBdn
'Pineapple Poll'	EMic MHost NNor WFar WHoo
'Pineapple Upside Down Cake' (v)	EMic IBal NBro NLar NSue SSien
'Pinky'	IBal
'Pin-up' (v)	IBal NSue
'Pistache' (v)	IBal NSue
'Pixie Vamp' (v)	EMic IBal SSien
'Pizzazz' (v)	EMic IBal MHost NGdn NHol NLar SSien WFar
plantaginea	EGrl LEdu SSien WFar WSpi WWtn
- var. ***grandiflora***	see *H. plantaginea* var. *japonica*
§ - var. ***japonica*** 🏆H7	CAvo EBee ECha LRHS MNrw MRav SMHy SPhx WCFE WFar WSpi
'Platinum Tiara' (v)	EMic IBal NBir NSue SSien
'Playmate' (v)	IBal
'Plug Nickel'	EMic IBal MHost NSue SSien
'Plum Creek' **new**	SSien
'Pocketful of Sunshine' (v)	CBdn EMic IBal NSue SSien
'Poker'	IBal
'Polar Moon' (v)	IBal
'Pole Cat' (v)	IBal
'Pooh Bear' (v)	EMic NSue SSien
'Popcorn'	CBdn IBal NSue SSien
'Popo' 🏆H7	EMic IBal MHost NHpl NNor NSue SSien
'Porter' (*venusta*)	EMic IBal NSue
'Potomac Pride'	CDor EHyd EMic LRHS MHost NRHS
'Powder Blue' (v)	IBal
'Powder Keg' (v)	IBal
'Prairie Magic' (v) **new**	SSien
'Prairie Moon'	NSue
'Prairie Sky'	CBdn ECtt EMic EMor IBal MACG NGdn NLar SSien WFar
'Prairie Sunset' (v)	NSue
'Prairie's Edge' (v)	SSien
'Praying Hands' (v) 🏆H7	Widely available
'Precious Metal'	IBal
'Prestige and Promise' (v)	IBal
'Pretty Flamingo'	EMic MHost
'Prima Donna'	CBdn EMic
'Prince of Wales'	CRos EHyd EMic IBal LRHS MHost NNor NRHS SPeP SPoG SSien XSte
'Private Dancer'	IBal

'Prom Queen' (v)	EMic IBal
'Proud Dragon' (v)	IBal
'Proud Sentry'	EMic IBal SSien
'Punk Rock'	IBal
'Punky' (v)	EMic IBal SSien
'Purbeck Mist'	MHost SSien
'Purbeck Ridge' (Tardiana Group)	MHost
'Purple and Gold'	EMic SSien
'Purple Boots'	EMic IBal MHost SSien
'Purple Bouquet'	MHost
'Purple Dwarf'	EMic IBal NLar NNor WCru WHal
'Purple Gem' **new**	NNor
'Purple Glory'	CBdn EMic MHost SSien
'Purple Haze'	EMic IBal LPla NGdn WFar
'Purple Heart'	CBcs ECtt EHed EMor EPfP EWoo GBin IBal LCro LOPS LPla LRHS NEoE NHpl NSti NSue NWad SCoo SGBe SPalm SSien WNPC WPnP XSte
'Purple Passion'	EMic IBal NSue
'Purple Profusion'	EMic IBal
'Purple Python'	IBal MHost
'Purple Sensation'	see *H.* 'Stirfry'
'Quarter Note' (v)	IBal
'Queen Josephine' (v)	CDor CRos ECtt EMic EPfP IBal LRHS MBNS MHost NGdn NHpl NNor SSien WFar
'Queen of Islip' (*sieboldiana*) (v)	SSien
'Queen of the Seas'	EMic ESwi IBal NNor NSue
'Quill'	EMic NSue
'Quilting Bee'	EMic EMor IBal NNor NSue
'Radiant Edger' (v)	EHyd EMic IBal MHost NHol NRHS NSue
'Rain Dancer'	CBdn IBal SSien
'Rain Forest'	EMic IBal
'Rainbow's End' (v)	EBee ECtt EPfP IBal MSCN NLar NSue SSien
'Rainforest Sunrise' (v)	CBod ELon EMic IBal LSou NGdn NSue SSien WFar
'Randy Rachel' (v)	LRHS
'Rare Breed' (v)	IBal
'Rascal' (v)	CDor EMic IBal SSien
'Raspberries and Cream' (v)	IBal
'Raspberry Sorbet'	EHyd EMic IBal LRHS MHost NRHS NSue
'Raspberry Sundae' (v)	CBod CMil CTsd CWGN ECtt EMor IBal LRHS MMrt NGdn NHpl NSue NWad SPalm SPoG SSien WNPC
'Raucous Ruffles'	EMic
'Rebel Heart' (v)	IBal
rectifolia	NNor
'Red Alert' (v)	IBal SSien
'Red Cadet'	EMic ESwi IBal MHost NSue SSien WFar
'Red Dog'	EMic NSue
'Red Dragon'	EMic IBal SSien
'Red Hot Flash' (v)	EMic IBal SSien
'Red Hot Poker'	IBal
'Red Neck Heaven' (*kikutii* var. *caput-avis*)	IBal
'Red October'	ECtt EHyd EMic EWTr EWoo GQue IBal LEdu MBNS MHost NGdn NHpl NLar NNor SSien WCAu WFar
'Red Salamander'	EMic ESwi IBal
'Red Sox'	IBal
'Red Stepper'	EMic IBal SSien WFar
'Red Stilts'	IBal
'Red Tubes' (*venusta*)	IBal
'Regal Rhubarb'	EMic IBal

	'Regal Splendor' (v) ♀H7	CBdn CDor ECtt EHyd ELan ELon EMic IBal LCro LOPS LRHS MHost NBro NGdn NNor NRHS NSue SCob SPoG SSien WFar WHoo
	'Regal Supreme' (v)	IBal NSue SSien
	'Regal Tot'	NSue
	'Reginald Kaye'	EMic
	'Rembrandt Blue'	EMic IBal
	'Remember Me'[PBR] ♀H7	CWCL ELan LSRN MBNS MPnt NHol NNor NSue SSien WBor WFar
	'Reptilian'	EMic IBal
	'Resonance' (v)	IBal NGdn NLar
	'Restless Sea'	CBod EMic EMor NGdn NSue
	'Reverend Mac'	IBal MHost
	'Reversed' (*sieboldiana*) (v)	EMic EMor IBal LRHS NBro NGdn NNor WFar WHal
	'Revolution'[PBR] (v) ♀H7	GKev IBal LSRN MACG MHost NBro NGdn NLar NSue SSien WFar
	'Rhapsody' (*fortunei*) (v)	EMic IBal
	'Rhein' (*tardiana*)	EMic IBal
	'Rhinestone Cowboy' (v)	IBal
	'Rhino Hide' (v)	CBdn IBal MHost SSien
	'Rhythm and Blues'	CBdn IBal NSue
	'Rich Uncle'	IBal
	'Richland Gold' (*fortunei*)	EMic MHost
	'Rim Rock'	EMic IBal
	'Ringtail'	EMic IBal NSue
	'Ripple Effect' (v)	CBdn EMic EMor IBal MHost NNor NSue SSien
	'Rippled Honey'	EMic IBal MHost NEoE SPtp SSien
	'Rippling Waves'	EMic
	'Riptide'	EMic NGdn
	'Risa'	IBal
	'Risky Business'[PBR] (v)	CBdn CWGN EMic EMor IBal NLar NSue SSien
	'Robert Frost' (v)	EMic IBal
	'Robin Hood'	IBal NSue
	'Robin of Loxley'	EMic IBal
	'Robusta' (*fortunei*)	see *H. sieboldiana* var. *elegans*
	'Robyn's Choice' (v)	IBal MHost
	'Rock and Roll'	IBal SSien
	'Rock Island Line' (v)	CBdn EMic IBal MHost NSue NWad WFar
	'Rock Princess'	IBal
	'Rocket's Red Glare'	IBal
§	***rohdeifolia*** (v) B&SWJ 10862	WCru
	'Roller Coaster Ride'	IBal
	'Ron Damant'	IBal MHost
	'Rootin'-Tootin'' (v)	IBal
	'Roseann Walter' (v)	EMic IBal
	'Rosedale Knox'	IBal
	'Rosedale Lost Dutchman'	IBal
	'Rosedale Melody of Summer' (v)	IBal
	'Rosedale Misty Magic' (v)	IBal
	'Rosedale Richie Valens'	IBal
	'Rosemoor'	EHyd IBal MHost NSue
	'Rossing's Pride'	EMic SSien
	'Roxsanne'	EMic MHost
	'Roy Klehm' (v)	EMic IBal
	'Royal Charm'	IBal
	'Royal Charmer' (v)	CBdn IBal
	'Royal Flush' (v)	IBal
	'Royal Golden Jubilee'	EMic IBal MHost
§	'Royal Standard' ♀H7	Widely available
	'Royal Tapestry' (v)	IBal
	'Royal Tiara' (*nakaiana*) (v)	IBal
	'Royal Wedding' (v) **new**	SSien
	'Royalty'	IBal MHost NSue
	'Rubies and Ruffles' (v)	IBal
	'Ruffed Up'	EMic
	'Ruffled Mouse Ears'	IBal NSue
	'Ruffled Pole Mouse' (v) **new**	NSue
	'Rufus Rider'	IBal
	rupifraga	IBal SSien
	'Rusty Bee'	IBal MHost
	'Ryan's Big One'	IBal
§	'Sagae' (v) ♀H7	EHyd EMic EWhm IBal LRHS MHost NGdn NNor NRHS NSue NWad SSien WFar
	'Saint Elmo's Fire' (v)	CDor EMic GBin IBal LRHS
	'Saint Fiacre'	EMic
	'Saint John'	IBal
	'Saishu-jima' (*sieboldii* f. *spathulata*)	EMic GEdr ITim NSue WCru
	'Saishu-yahato-sito' (v)	IBal MHost NSue
	'Salute' (Tardiana Group)	EMic SSien
	'Samurai' (*sieboldiana*) (v)	EMor MRav NBir NBro NGdn NLar SSien
	'Sandhill Crane' (v)	EMor LSou
	'Sarah Kennedy' (v)	MHost
	'Sara's Sensation' (v)	IBal NSue
	'Satisfaction' (v) ♀H7	EMic IBal
	'Savannah'	IBal
	'Sazanami' (*crispula*)	see *H. crispula*
	'Scallion Pancakes'	EMic
	'Scarlet Ribbons' (v)	EMic IBal SSien
	'School Mouse' (v)	CBdn NSue SSien
	'Schwan'	GBin
	'Sea Current'	IBal
	'Sea Dream' (v)	CBdn CDor EMic LRHS NGdn NNor SSien
	'Sea Fire'	IBal
	'Sea Gold Star'	CDor
	'Sea Gulf Stream'	EMic NSue
	'Sea Lotus Leaf'	EMic NLar NNor
	'Sea Monster'	IBal
	'Sea Thunder' (v)	CDor EMic EMor IBal LRHS NSue SSien
	'Sea Yellow Sunrise'	EMic IBal SSien
	'Searing Flame' (v)	IBal
	'Second Wind' (*fortunei*) (v)	EMic ESwi MHost SSien
	'Secret Ambition'[PBR] (v)	IBal
	'Secret Love'	EMic IBal
	'Secret Treasure'[PBR] (v)	CBdn IBal NSue SSien
	'Seducer' (v)	EMic ESwi IBal SSien
	'See Saw' (*undulata*)	EMic IBal
	'Semperaurea' (*sieboldiana*)	IBal
	'September Sun' (v)	EMic IBal SSien
	'September Surprise'	SSien
	'Serena' (Tardiana Group)	IBal
	'Serendipity'	CBdn EMic IBal
	'Shade Beauty' (v)	EMic IBal SSien
	'Shade Fanfare' (v)	CDor CRos ECtt EHyd ELan ELon EMic EPfP GQue IBal LRHS MBNS MRav NBir NGdn NLar NNor NRHS NSti SSien WFar
	'Shade Finale' (v)	IBal
	'Shade Master'	EMic
	'Shade Parade' (v)	EMic IBal
	'Shady Affair'	EMic
§	'Sharmon' (*fortunei*) (v)	ELon EMic MBNS MHost NLar SSien
	'Sharp Dressed Man'	IBal
	'Shazaam'	IBal
	'Sheila West'	EMic MHost
	'Shelleys' (v)	IBal
	'Sherborne Profusion' (Tardiana Group)	EMic IBal MHost SSien
	'Sherborne Songbird' (Tardiana Group)	IBal MHost

	'Sherborne Swallow' (Tardiana Group)	EMic IBal MHost SSien
	'Sherborne Swan' (Tardiana Group)	IBal MHost
	'Sherborne Swift' (Tardiana Group)	EMic ESwi IBal LRHS MHost NRHS SSien
	'Shere Khan' (v)	EMic IBal
	'She's got the Moves' **new**	CBdn
	'Shimmy Shake'	EMic SSien
	'Shining Tot' ♀H7	IBal NNor
	'Shiny Penny' (v)	EMic IBal MHost NSue
	'Shiny Sonata'	IBal
	'Shirley Levy'	IBal
	'Showboat' (v)	EMic
	sieboldiana	CAgr CMac CSBt ECha EGrI ELan EMic GMaP MRav MSwo NChi SCob SPlb SRms XLum
§	- var. ***elegans*** ♀H7	Widely available
	- var. ***mira***	EMic
§	- var. ***sieboldiana***	NGdn SSien
	sieboldiana* × *venusta	NGdn
	sieboldii	MRav
§	- var. ***alba***	IBal
§	- var. ***sieboldii*** f. ***kabitan*** (v)	EMic IBal NGdn NSue SSien
	- - f. ***shiro-kabitan*** (v)	EMic LRHS NSue
	- f. ***spathulata***	EMic
	'Sienna Susan' **new**	SSien
	'Silberpfeil'	EMic NSue
	'Silk Road' (v)	IBal NSue
	'Silver Bay' ♀H7	EMic SSien
	'Silver Crown'	see *H.* 'Albomarginata'
	'Silver Lance' (v)	EMic IBal
	'Silver Lode' (v)	IBal
	'Silver Moon'	EMic IBal
	'Silver Serenity'	IBal SSien
	'Silver Shadow' (v)	IBal NBir NGdn NLar NNor NWad SSien
	'Silver Spray' (v)	IBal SSien
	'Silver Star' (v)	IBal
	'Silver Threads and Gold Needles' (v)	IBal NHpl NSue SSien
	'Silverado' (v)	IBal
	'Silvery Slugproof' (Tardiana Group)	IBal LRHS MHost
	'Simply Sharon' (v)	IBal
	'Singin' the Blues'	IBal
	'Singing in the Rain' (v)	IBal NSue
	'Sitting Pretty' (v)	IBal
	'Sizzle'	IBal NSue SSien
	'Sky Dancer'	ECtt EMic IBal NSue
	'Sleeping Beauty'	CWGN ECtt EMic IBal NGdn NSue SSien
	'Sleeping Star'PBR (v)	IBal NSue SSien
	'Slick Willie'	EMic
	'Slim and Trim'	EMic IBal MHost NHpl NSue SIvy
	'Small Parts'	CBdn ECtt EMic IBal MHost NNor NSue SSien
	'Small Sum'	IBal
	'Smash Hit' (v)	IBal NSue
	'Smiley Face'	NSue
	'Smiling Mouse' (v)	CBdn IBal NSue
	'Smoke Signals'	IBal
	'Snake Eyes' (v)	CBdn ELon EMic EMor IBal MBel NSue SSien
	'Snow Boy' (v)	IBal NSue
	'Snow Bunting' (v)	MHost
	'Snow Cap' (v)	CDor ECtt EMic EMor IBal NEoE NGdn NLar NNor SPoG WFar
	'Snow Crust' (v)	EMic SSien
	'Snow Flakes' (*sieboldii*)	CMac NBro NEoE NGdn NLar SCob
	'Snow Mouse' (v)	IBal NHpl SSien WFar
	'Snowden' ♀H7	ECha EMic EWTr GMaP IBal LRHS MHost NBir NGdn NNor NRHS SPhx SSien WCru
	'Snowy Lake' (v)	IBal SSien
	'So Sweet' (v)	CRos EBee ECtt EHed EHyd ELan ELon EMic EMor EPfP EWoo GEdr GLog LRHS MHost MSwo NBro NGdn NHol NNor NRHS SSien WFar
	'Something Blue'	EMic IBal
	'Something Else'	EMic
	'Southern Gold'	EMic
	'Space Odyssey'	IBal NSue SSien
	'Sparkler' (v)	IBal
	'Sparkling Burgundy'	EMic
	'Sparky' (v)	IBal
	'Spartacus' (v)	EMic IBal MHost NSue SSien
	'Spartan Arrow'	NSue
	'Spartan Glory' (v)	IBal SSien
	'Special Blend' (v)	IBal
	'Special Gift'	EMic IBal MHost SSien
	'Spellbound' (v)	CBdn IBal
	'Spilt Milk' (*tokudama*) (v) ♀H7	EMic EMor IBal SSien WHoo
	'Spinach Souffle' (v)	IBal
§	'Spinners' (*fortunei*) (v)	ECha EMic IBal MHost NNor
	'Spock's Ears'	IBal
	'Spring Break' (v)	EMic
	'Spring Fling'	EMic IBal SSien
	'Spring Love'	IBal
	'Spring Morning'	EMor
	'Spritzer' (v)	CBdn CDor EMic MNrw NSue SSien
	'Squash Casserole'	IBal
	'St. Paul'	EMic IBal MNrw NSue
	'Stag's Leap' (v) **new**	IBal
	'Stained Glass' (v) ♀H7	CBcs CDor ECtt EHyd ELon EMic EMor EPfP IBal MHost NGdn NNor NSue SSien WFar
	'Stand by Me' (v)	CBdn EMic IBal MHost NSue SSien
	'Stand Corrected' (v)	IBal SSien
	'Star Kissed'	IBal
	'Star Light Star Bright'	EMic IBal
	'Star Wars'	NSue
	'Starburst' stable (v)	IBal
	'Stardust'	IBal
	'Stargate'	IBal
§	'Starker Yellow Leaf'	EMic
	'Starship' (v)	EMic IBal
	'Steffi' (v)	CBdn IBal
	'Step Sister'	EMic IBal
	'Stepping Out' (v)	EMic IBal
	'Stetson' (v)	EMic IBal
	'Stiletto' (v)	ELon EMic GEdr GKev IBal LRHS MBNS MHost MNrw NBro NEoE NGdn NHpl NLar NNor NSue SPalm SPoG SSien SWvt WFar WSHC
	'Stimulation'	IBal
	'Sting' (v)	EMor LCro LOPS SEdd
	'Stir it Up' **new**	SSien
§	'Stirfry'	CBod EHed EMic SSien
	'Stone's Valentine'	EMic
	'Strawberry Surprise' (v)	EMic IBal
	'Strawberry Yoghurt'	NSue
	'Striker' (v)	IBal NSue
	'Striptease' (*fortunei*) (v) ♀H7	CBdn CDor CMac EMic EMor EPfP GLog IBal LRHS MBNS MHost MNrw NGdn NHol NLar NSue SSien WFar
	'Stuck in Time'	CBdn IBal SSien

'Subcrocea'	SSien
'Sugar and Cream' (v)	EMic IBal NGdn NNor
'Sugar and Spice' (v)	CBdn CBod ELon EMic EPfP IBal MHost SSien
'Sugar Babe' (v)	EMic
'Sugar Daddy'	EMic EMor IBal MHost SSien
'Sugar Mama' (v)	SSien
'Sugar Plum'	IBal
'Sugar Snap' (v) **new**	SSien
'Sulphur Glory'	SSien
'Sultana' (v)	EMic IBal SSien
'Sum and Substance' ♀H7	Widely available
'Sum and Subtle' (v)	IBal
'Sum Cup-o-Joe' (v)	EMic
'Sum of All' (v)	EMic NSue
'Summer Breeze' (v)	EMic IBal NGdn NSue
'Summer Dress'	GBin NSue
'Summer Fragrance'	ECtt EMic GBin IBal
'Summer Gold'	EMic
'Summer Joy'	CDor
'Summer Lovin'' (v)	IBal
'Summer Music' (v) ♀H7	CDor CWCL EMic IBal SSien
'Summer Serenade' (v)	EMic NGdn NSue SSien
'Summer Squall'	IBal
'Sumsational' (v)	EMic IBal
'Sun Catcher'	EMic
'Sun Mouse'	CBdn IBal NSue SSien
'Sun Power'	EHyd ELon EMic MBNS NBro NLar SSien
'Sun Worshipper'	IBal
'Sundance' (v)	IBal
'Sunlight Child'	CBdn EMic IBal MHost NSue
'Sunny Delight'	CBdn
'Sunny Disposition'	SSien
'Sunny Smiles' (v)	EMic
'Sunnybrook' (v)	SSien
'Sunset Grooves' (v)	EMic IBal
'Sunshine Glory'	CDor EMic IBal NSue
'Super Bowl'	IBal
'Super Nova' (v)	EMic IBal SSien
'Super Sagae'	CDor EMic IBal MHost SSien WFar
'Surfer Girl'	NSue
'Surprised by Joy' (v)	IBal MHost NHpl NNor NSue SSien
'Susan' (v) **new**	NSue
'Susy'	IBal
'Sutter's Mill'	IBal
'Suzuki Thumbnail'	EMic
'Swamp Thing' (v)	IBal
'Sweet Bo Beep'	EMic IBal
'Sweet Bouquet'	EMic
'Sweet Home Chicago' (v)	EHyd EMic IBal SSien
'Sweet Innocence' (v)	EMic IBal SSien
'Sweet Marjorie'	IBal
'Sweet Susan'	CRos EBee EHyd EMic LRHS MBNS NNor NRHS SPer SSien SWvt
'Sweet Tater Pie'	EMic IBal
'Sweetheart'	EMic
'Sweetie' (v)	CDor EMic IBal
'Sweetness'	IBal
'Swirling Hearts'	IBal
'Swizzle Sticks'	EMic
'T Dawg' (v)	EMor NLar
'T. Rex'	CBod CDor ELon EMic EMor IBal NSue SSien WFar
takudama	see *H. sieboldiana* var. *sieboldiana*
'Tall Boy'	GBin IBal NBir NNor
'Tamborine' (v)	EMic EMor IBal LRHS
'Tango'	EMic IBal
'Tappen Zee' (v)	EMic IBal SSien
Tardiana Group	GWyn NGdn NNor
tardiflora	CExl IBal LRHS
tardiva	EMic NLar
'Tattle Tails'	CBdn EMic IBal NHpl NSue SSien
'Tattoo'PBR (v)	CWGN LSRN MBNS NLar SSien
'Tea and Crumpets' (v)	NSue
'Tea at Bettys' ♀H7	CBdn EMic IBal MHost NSue SSien
'Teacher's Pride'	IBal MHost NSue
'Tears of Joy'	NSue WFar
'Teaspoon'	EMic IBal MHost NHpl NNor NSue SSien
'Teatime' (v)	EMic IBal NSue
'Teeny-weeny Bikini' (v)	NSue SSien WFar
'Templar Gold'	IBal SSien
'Temple Bells'	IBal
'Temptation'	EMic IBal
'Tequila Sunrise'	IBal
'Terpsichore'	EMic
'Terry Wogan'	IBal MHost
'Thank You' **new**	SSien
'The Devil's Edge' (v) **new**	SSien
'The King' (v)	IBal NSue SSien
'The Leading Edge' (v)	IBal
'The Razor's Edge'	IBal WFar
'The Right One' (v)	IBal
'The Shining'	IBal
'The Twister'	EMic
'Theo's Blue'	EMic IBal SSien
'Theo's Red'	IBal
'Thomas Hogg'	see *H. undulata* var. *albomarginata*
'Thumb Nail'	EMic IBal MHost NNor NSue NWad SMHy
'Thumbelina'	EHyd EMic IBal LRHS NGdn NRHS NSue SSien
'Thunderbolt'PBR (*sieboldiana*)	ECtt EMor IBal MBNS MHol NGdn NLar SPeP SSien WFar WNPC
tibae	IBal
'Tick Tock' (v)	CBdn ECtt EMic IBal NSue SSien
'Tickle Me Pink'	EMic IBal NSue WFar
'Tidewater'	IBal
'Tilt-a-Whirl'	IBal
'Time Tunnel' (*sieboldiana*) (v)	EMic IBal
'Timeless Beauty' (v)	EMic EMor IBal MHost NSue SSien WFar
'Timothy' (v) **new**	IBal
'Tiny Tears'	SSien
'Titanic'PBR	EMic IBal SSien
'Titanium'	CBdn IBal NSue SSien
'Toasted Waffles'	WFar
tokudama	EMic IBal NBir NGdn WFar XLum
§ - f. ***aureo-nebulosa*** (v)	EMic IBal MHost NGdn SRms SSien
- f. ***flavocircinalis*** (v) ♀H7	CBod ELon EMic EPfP GMaP IBal MHost NBro SSien WFar WHoo
'Tokyo Smog' (v)	NSue
'Toledo'	IBal
'Tom Schmid' (v)	CBdn EMic IBal MHost NSue SSien
'Tom Thumb'	EMic IBal MHost NNor NSue SSien
'Tongue of Flame' (v) **new**	NSue
'Tongue Twister'	IBal
'Topaz'	IBal
'Topscore'	NNor
'Torchlight' (v) ♀H7	CBdn IBal LRHS NSue
tortifrons	EMic IBal SSien
'Tortilla Chip'	IBal WFar
'Tot Tot'	EMic IBal MHost NSue
'Totally Twisted'	EMic IBal NSue
'Touch of Class'PBR (v) ♀H7	CBdn CDor ECtt EGrI EMor GBin IBal MHost NGdn NHol NNor NSue SSien WFar WTyc
'Touchstone' (v)	SWvt
'Toy Soldier'	EMic IBal MHost NGdn NLar NSue SSien

'Trail's End'	EMic
'Tranquility' (v)	EMic
'Tremors'	EMic IBal
'Triple Ripple' (v) **new**	SSien
'Trixi' (v)	IBal
'Tropical Dancer'	IBal
'Tropical Storm' (v)	IBal SSien
'Tropicana' (v) **new**	SSien
'True Blue'	ECtt EMic
'Tsugaru Komachi'	EMic
'Tsugaru Komachi Kifukurin' (v)	IBal
'Tugaux' (v)	IBal
'Turnabout' (v)	IBal
'Turning Point'	IBal
'Twiggie'	EMic MHost
'Twilight' (*fortunei*) (v)	ECtt EGrI EHyd EMic EMor EShb IBal LRHS MBNS MHol MHost NGdn NLar NRHS NSue SSien SWvt WFar
'Twilight Time'	IBal
'Twinkle Toes'	EMic IBal NSue
'Twist of Green'	MHost
'Twist of Lime' (v)	EHyd EMic GKev IBal LRHS MHost NGdn NNor NRHS NSue SSien WCot
'Twitter'	IBal
'Tycoon' (v)	SSien
'UFO'	EMic IBal NSue WFar
'Ultramarine'	IBal
'Ultraviolet Light'	IBal SSien
'Ulysses S. Grant'	IBal
'Unchained Melody'	IBal
undulata (v)	NNor WFar
§ - var. ***albomarginata*** (v)	CMac EHyd EMic EPfP GMaP LRHS LSRN MHost MRav NBid NBir NGdn NLar NRHS SCob SPer SRms SWvt WFar XLum
§ - var. ***erromena***	CRos EHyd GMaP LRHS NNor NRHS XLum
§ - var. ***undulata*** (v) ♀H7	CBod CDor EHyd EMic GMaP IBal LRHS MCot MRav NGdn NLar NNor NRHS SPer
- var. ***univittata*** (v)	ECha EMic GKev NBir NEoE SRms WFar
'Unforgettable'	EMic IBal SSien
'Unruly Child'	ESwi IBal NSue
'Upper Crust' (v)	IBal
'Uprising' (v)	IBal SSien
'Urajiro' (*hypoleuca*)	IBal
'Urajiro-hachijo' (*longipes* var. *latifolia*)	IBal
'Valentine Lace'	EMic IBal
'Valley's Blue Curaçao'	IBal
'Valley's Cathedral'	IBal
'Valley's Chute the Chute'	EMic IBal MHost SSien
'Valley's Glacier' (v)	IBal WFar
'Valley's Lemon Squash'	IBal
'Valley's Paparazzi' (v)	CBdn IBal
'Valley's Sushi' (v)	IBal SSien
'Valley's Vanilla Sticks'	EMic IBal MHost SSien
'Van Wade' (v)	EMic IBal MHost
'Vanilla Cream' (*cathayana*)	EHyd EMic IBal NNor NRHS NSue WFar
'Variegata' (*gracillima*)	see *H.* 'Vera Verde'
'Variegata' (*tokudama*)	see *H. tokudama* f. *aureo-nebulosa*
'Variegata' (*undulata*)	see *H. undulata* var. *undulata*
'Variegata' (*ventricosa*)	see *H.* 'Aureomarginata' (*ventricosa*)
'Variegated' (*fluctuans*)	see *H.* 'Sagae'
'Velvet Moon' (v)	ECtt EMic IBal SSien
'Venetian Skies' (v)	IBal
ventricosa ♀H7	CMac EMic IBal WFar XLum
- BWJ 8160 from Sichuan	WCru
ventricosa × ***venusta*** **new**	NWad
'Venus' (d)	ECtt EMic ITim LEdu NGdn WCot WFar
'Venus Star'	EMic MHost
venusta ♀H7	CRos EBee EHyd EMic EPfP GBin GEdr IBal LRHS MHost MRav NBid NBir NNor NRHS NRya NSue NWad SSien WFar
- B&SWJ 4389	WCru
- dwarf	IBal SSien
- ***yakusimensis***	see *H. kikutii* var. *yakusimensis*
§ 'Vera Verde' (v)	NBir NSue
'Verdi Valentine'	EMic IBal
'Verkade's One'	IBal NSue
'Vermont Frost' (v)	IBal NSue
'Verna Jean' (v)	EBee ECtt EHyd EMic IBal LRHS NRHS NSue
'Veronica Lake' (v)	ECtt EHyd EMic IBal LRHS MHost NNor NRHS NSue SSien WHal
'Vibrant Hope'	SSien
'Victory' ♀H7	EHyd IBal LRHS MHost NRHS NSue SSien
'Viking Ship'	EMic IBal SSien
'Vilmoriniana'	EMic
'Vim and Vigor'	EMic IBal SSien
'Vina'	IBal
'Virginia Reel' (v)	IBal NSue
'Viridis Marginata'	see *H. sieboldii* var. *sieboldii* f. *kabitan*
'Volcano Island'PBR (v)	CBdn EMic IBal NSue SSien
'Vulcan' (v)	CBdn EMic EMor IBal SSien
'Wagtail' (Tardiana Group)	IBal MHost NNor SSien
'Wahoo' (*tokudama*) (v)	IBal
'War Paint' ♀H7	EMic IBal ITim NNor NSue SSien WFar
'Warwick Comet' (v)	EMic IBal SSien
'Warwick Curtsey' (v)	EMic IBal
'Warwick Delight' (v)	NSue
'Warwick Edge' (v)	EMic IBal SSien
'Warwick Essence'	EMic IBal
'Warwick Sheen'	IBal
'Watermark' (v)	EMic
'Waterslide' **new**	CBdn
'Waukon Glass'	EMic IBal
'Waukon the Moon'	CBdn
'Waukon Thin Ice'	EMic IBal
'Waukon Water'	EMic IBal
'Waving Winds' (v)	EMic IBal
'Waving Wuffles'	EMic
'Wayne' (v)	EMic
'Wayside Blue'	EMic
'Wayside Perfection'	see *H.* 'Royal Standard'
'Weihenstephan' (*sieboldii*)	EMic IBal
'Well Shaked' (v)	IBal
'Weser'	IBal
'Wheaton Blue'	EMic
'Wheaton Thunder' (v)	EMic
'Wheee!' (Shadowlands Series)	IBal NSue SSien
'Whirligig' (v)	EMic SSien
'Whirling Dervish' (v)	IBal
'Whirlwind' (*fortunei*) (v) ♀H7	CBdn CDor ELan EMic EPfP IBal MBros MHost MNrw MRav NBro NGdn NLar NNor NSue SPoG SPtp SSien WCAu WFar
'Whirlwind Tour' (v)	IBal
'Whiskey Sour'	IBal
'White Bikini' (v)	IBal NNor SSien
'White Ceiling'	IBal

'White Christmas' (*fortunei*) (v)	NGdn SSien
'White Christmas' (*undulata*) (v)	SSien
'White Dove' (v)	EPfP IBal
'White Edger'	EMic
'White Elephant' (v)	IBal
'White Fairy' (*plantaginea*) (d)	EMic
'White Feather' (*undulata*)	CWGN EHyd EPfP LCro LOPS LSou MNrw NBir NEoE NGdn NLar SMad SPeP SPoG SSien WFar
'White Gold'	EMic SSien
'White Jewel' (v)	CBdn IBal
'White Knight'	IBal
'White On' (*montana*)	EMic
'White Triumphator' (*rectifolia*)	IBal
'White Trumpets'	EMic
'Wide Brim' (v) ƳH7	Widely available
'Wiggles and Squiggles' **new**	ESwi
'William Lachman' (v)	IBal NLar
'Wily Willy'	IBal SSien
'Wind River Gold'	EMic
'Windsor Gold'	see *H.* 'Nancy Lindsay'
'Winfield Blue'	EMic IBal NBir
'Winfield Gold'	EMic MHost
'Winfield Mist' (v)	IBal
'Winsome' (v)	EMor IBal LRHS NSue SSien
'Winter Lightning' (v)	NNor
'Winter Snow' (v)	CDor EMic IBal NSue SPalm SSien WFar XSte
'Winter Warrior' (v)	EMic IBal SSien
'Wintergreen' (v)	SSien
'Wishing Well'	SSien
'Wogon' (*sieboldii*)	EMic GKev GMaP ITim NNor
'Wogon's Boy'	CDor EMic LRHS
'Wolverine' (v) ƳH7	CBod ECtt EHyd EMic EMor MBNS NGdn NNor NSue SSien SWvt WFar
'Wonderful'	NSue
'Wonderful Life' (v) **new**	IBal
'Woodland Elf' (v)	IBal NSue
'Woolly Mammoth' (v)	IBal
'Woop Woop' (v)	IBal
'World Cup'	IBal SSien
'Worldly Treasure'	IBal
'Wrinkles and Crinkles'	EMic
'Wu-La-La' (v) **new**	ESwi
'Wunderbar' (v) **new**	SSien
'Wylde Green Cream'	IBal NGdn SSien
'Xanadu' (v)	IBal
'X-rated' (v)	NSue
'X-ray' (v)	NSue SSien
'Yakushima-mizu' (*gracillima*)	EMic IBal
'Yankee Blue'	IBal NSue SSien
'Yellow Boa'	EMic IBal NSue
'Yellow Edge' (*fortunei*)	see *H. fortunei* var. *aureomarginata*
'Yellow Edge' (*sieboldiana*)	see *H.* 'Frances Williams'
'Yellow Polka Dot Bikini' (v)	CBdn EMic EPfP IBal SSien
'Yellow River' (v)	EBee EHyd EMic IBal MHost NGdn NNor NSue SSien WFar
'Yellow Splash' (v)	EMic NNor
'Yellow Splash Rim' (v)	EMic SSien
'Yellow Waves'	SSien
'Yesterday's Memories' (v)	EMic IBal SSien
'Yin' (v)	EMic IBal SSien
yingeri	WPGP WSHC
- B&SWJ 546	LEdu WCru
'You're so Vein' **new**	IBal
'Yucca Ducka Do' (v)	EMic IBal SSien
'Zager Blue'	EMic
'Zager Green'	EMic
'Zager White Edge' (*fortunei*) (v)	CBdn EMic IBal SSien
'Zebra Stripes' (v)	IBal
'Zig Zag' (v) **new**	IBal
'Zion's Hope'	EMic
'Zitronenfalter'	IBal
'Zodiac' (*fortunei*) (v)	IBal
'Zorro'	CBdn IBal
'Zounds'	EBee ECtt EHyd EMic EPfP EShb IBal LRHS MRav NGdn NLar NSue SRms SSien WFar
Hottonia (Primulaceae)	
palustris	CBen CPud LCro LLWG LOPS NPer
Houstonia (Rubiaceae)	
caerulea misapplied	see *H. michauxii*
caerulea L.	EBou SPlb SRot
- var. ***alba***	EWes SPlb
- 'Millard's Variety'	GQue WIce
§ ***michauxii***	GAbr
- 'Fred Mullard'	EWes
Houttuynia (Saururaceae)	
cordata	CAgr CMac GKev GPoy LEdu LLWG LPot NSti SDix WFar WWtn XLum
§ - 'Boo-Boo' (v)	CMac CWat WSMil
§ - 'Chameleon' (v)	Widely available
- 'Fantasy' (v)	LLWG
- 'Flame' (v)	CPla EBee LLWG LRHS MBNS MHol SMrm WFar WSMil
- 'Flore Pleno' (d)	CBen CBod CMac CPla CWat ECha EPfP EWld LCro LLWG LOPS MRav MSCN NBir NPer SBls SPer SPlb SRms XLum
- 'Joker's Gold'	ECtt ELan EMor EPPr EPfP WFar
- 'Pied Piper' (v)	NBir SPad SPtp
- 'Terry Clarke'	see *H. cordata* 'Boo-Boo'
- 'Tricolor'	see *H. cordata* 'Chameleon'
- Variegata Group (v)	LLWG LPot NBro
Hovea (Fabaceae)	
celsii	see *H. elliptica*
§ ***elliptica***	SPlb
montana	SPlb
Hovenia (Rhamnaceae)	
dulcis	CAgr CBcs EBee EPfP LEdu MBlu MVil NLar WKor
- B&SWJ 11024	WCru
- NJM 11.003	WPGP
Howea (Arecaceae)	
§ ***forsteriana*** ƳH1a	CCCN LCro LOPS SArc SPlb
Hoya (Apocynaceae)	
§ ***australis***	EShb
bella	see *H. lanceolata* subsp. *bella*
carnosa ƳH2	CRHN CTtf EBak EOHP EShb WWFP
- 'Compacta Regalis' (v)	NPer
- HINDU ROPE	see *H. carnosa* 'Compacta Regalis'
- 'Krinkle 8'	NPer
- 'Tricolor' (v)	CCCN CDoC NCft NPer
- 'Variegata' (v)	EShb
* ***compacta*** 'Tricolor'	NPer
gracilis	CCCN EShb
kerrii	CDoC

	lacunosa	CCCN
§	***lanceolata***	CCCN CDoC EShb
	subsp. ***bella*** ♀^{H1c}	
	linearis	CDoC EShb
	pubicalyx **new**	EShb
	tsiangiana	EShb

Humata (*Davalliaceae*)

tyermanii ♀^{H3}	CCCN CDoC CMen EShb LEdu SBrt SPlb WCot WFib
- 'Bunny'	CCCN LCro LOPS
- 'Selcka'	CMen

Humea see *Calomeria*

elegans	see *Calomeria amaranthoides*

Humulus ✿ (*Cannabaceae*)

	lupulus	CBcs CDoC EPfP GPoy GQue MBow NLar NMir SRms WHer WSpi
	- 'Aureus' ♀^{H6}	Widely available
	- 'Aureus' (f)	CRHN GKev MGil SPoG WCot
	- 'Bramling Cross' (f) **new**	SEsH
	- 'Brewer's Gold' (f) **new**	SEsH
	- 'Bullion' (f) **new**	SEsH
	- 'Cascade' (f) **new**	SEsH
	- 'Centennial' (f) **new**	SEsH
	- 'Chinook' (f) **new**	SEsH
*	- ***compactus***	GPoy
	- 'Early Choice' (f) **new**	SEsH
	- 'Fuggle'	CAgr GPoy SEsH
	- 'Galena' (f) **new**	SEsH
	- 'Glacier' (f) **new**	SEsH
	- 'Golden Tassels' (f)	CBod EHyd ELon MGil MGos MMuc MNHC NLar SEND SNig SPer SPoG SRms WBor WFar
	- (Goldings Group) 'Amos' Early Bird' (f) **new**	SEsH
	- - 'Calais Golding' (f) **new**	SEsH
	- - 'Cobbs'	SEsH
	- - 'Eastwell Golding' (f) **new**	SEsH
	- - 'Mathons'	SEsH
	- - 'Redsell's Eastwell' (f) **new**	SEsH
	- - 'Whitbread Golding' (f) **new**	SEsH
	- 'Hallertau' (f) **new**	SEsH
	- 'Hallertau Tradition' (f) **new**	SEsH
	- 'Hersbrucker' (f) **new**	SEsH
	- 'Late Cluster' (f) **new**	SEsH
	- 'Liberty' (f) **new**	SEsH
	- 'Magnum' (f)	LCro LOPS SEsH
	- 'Mount Hood' (f) **new**	SEsH
	- 'Northern Brewer' (f)	CAgr EBee SEsH
	- 'Nugget' (f) **new**	SEsH
	- 'Omega' (f) **new**	SEsH
	- 'Perle' (f) **new**	SEsH
	- 'Phoenix' (f) **new**	SEsH
	- 'Prima Donna'	CAgr CMac LEdu MGil NLar SEsH SPer SPoG SWvt
	- 'Progress' (f) **new**	SEsH
	- 'Record' (f) **new**	SEsH
	- 'Saaz' (f) **new**	SEsH
	- 'Santium' (f) **new**	SEsH
	- 'Styrian Golding' (f) **new**	SEsH
	- 'Tettnanger' (f) **new**	SEsH
	- 'Willamette' (f) **new**	SEsH
	- 'Wye Challenger'	CAgr GPoy MHer SEsH
	- 'Wye Northdown'	CAgr SEsH
	- 'Wye Target' (f) **new**	SEsH
	- 'Yeoman' (f) **new**	SEsH
	- 'Zenith' (f) **new**	SEsH

Hunnemannia (*Papaveraceae*)

fumariifolia	CSpe

Huodendron (*Styracaceae*)

biaristatum	IDee

Huperzia (*Lycopodiaceae*)

lucidula **new**	CBrP

Hutchinsia see *Hornungia*

Hyacinthella (*Asparagaceae*)

glabrescens	WCot
leucophaea	WCot

Hyacinthoides (*Asparagaceae*)

	aristidis	WCot
	'Bakkum Blue'	GKev WHil
	ciliolata	CBro GKev SGro WAbe WCot
§	***hispanica***	NBir SEND WCot
	- 'Alba'	EHyd NRHS
	- subsp. ***algeriensis***	WCot
	- 'Dainty Maid'	GKev NRog WCot
	- 'Excelsior'	GKev NRog
	- 'Miss World'	GKev WCot
	- 'Queen of the Pinks'	GKev NRog WCot
	- 'White City'	GKev NRog WCot
§	***italica*** ♀^{H6}	GKev WCot WShi
	lingulata	NDry WAbe WCot
	mauritanica	GKev NRog
§	***non-scripta***	Widely available
	- 'Alba'	CAvo EGrI MMuc NBir NRog SDir SEND SRms WHil
	- 'Backkum's Blue'	SDir
	- 'Bracteata'	CNat WCot
	- 'Chedglow Weeping'	CNat
	- cleistogamous	CNat
	- double-flowered, blue (d)	WCot
	- - pink (d)	WCot
	- - white (d)	WCot
	- long-bracteate, white-flowered	WCot
	- 'Rosea'	EGrI ILea NRog
	- 'Wavertree'	GKev NRog WCot
	reverchonii	NRog WCot
§	***vincentina***	GKev

Hyacinthus ✿ (*Asparagaceae*)

amethystinus	see *Brimeura amethystina*
azureus	see *Muscari azureum*
comosus 'Plumosus'	see *Muscari comosum* 'Plumosum'
orientalis	NRog
- 'Aida' ♀^{H4}	ERCP
- 'Aiolos'	GKev SDeJ SDir
- var. ***albulus*** 'Roman Blue'	CAvo GKev
- - 'Roman White'	CAvo GKev
- 'Amsterdam'	NRog
- 'Anastasia'	CAvo
- 'Anna Liza'	NRog SDeJ
- 'Anna Marie' ♀^{H4}	NRog SDeJ
- 'Apricot Passion'	ERCP GKev NRog SDeJ
- 'Blue Eyes'	SDeJ
- 'Blue Festival' ♀^{H4}	GKev SDeJ SDir
- 'Blue Giant'	SDeJ
- 'Blue Jacket' ♀^{H4}	ECul GKev NRog SDeJ
- 'Blue Magic'	SDeJ
- 'Blue Pearl'^{PBR}	GKev LCro LOPS SDeJ

	- 'Blue Star'	SDeJ SDir
	- 'Blue Tango'	ERCP
	- 'Carnegie'	CArg CAvo EPfP ERCP GKev LCro LOPS NRog SDeJ
	- 'Chestnut Flower' (d)	NRog SDeJ SDir
	- 'China Pink'	CRos EHyd LRHS NRHS SDeJ
	- 'City of Haarlem' ♀H4	CArg CRos EHyd GKev LCro LOPS LRHS NRHS NRog SDeJ
	- 'Crystal Palace' (d)	NRog SDeJ
	- 'Dark Dimension'	ERCP SDir
	- 'Delft Blue' ♀H4	CArg CAvo CRos EHyd EPfP GKev LCro LOPS LRHS NRHS NRog SDeJ SPer WShi
	- 'Distinction'	SDir
	- 'Eros'	SDeJ
§	- 'Fairly'PBR ♀H4	SDir
	- 'Fondant'	CArg EHyd LCro LOPS LRHS NRHS SDeJ
	- 'General Köhler' (d)	SDeJ
	- 'Gipsy Queen' ♀H4	CAvo GKev NRog SDeJ SDir WCot
	- 'Hollyhock' (d) ♀H4	NRog SDeJ SDir
	- 'Jan Bos' ♀H4	CArg EHyd GKev LCro LOPS LRHS NRHS NRog SDeJ
	- 'Lady Derby'	SDeJ
	- 'Madame Sophie' (d)	SDeJ
	- 'Miss Saigon' ♀H4	ECul ERCP LRHS NRog SDeJ
	- multi-flowered	ERCP SDeJ
	- 'Odysseus'	SDeJ
	- 'Paul Hermann' ♀H4	NRog SDeJ
	- 'Peter Stuyvesant'	ERCP LCro LOPS NRog SDeJ SDir
	- 'Pink Festival' ♀H4	GKev SDeJ
	- 'Pink Pearl'	CAvo CRos EHyd GKev LCro LOPS LRHS NRHS NRog SDeJ
	- 'Pink Surprise'	ERCP
	- 'Prince of Love'PBR (d) **new**	ERCP
	- 'Purple Sensation'PBR	LCro LOPS NRog SDeJ
	- 'Purple Star'	LCro LOPS
	- 'Red Magic'	SDeJ
	- 'Rosette' (d)	SDeJ
	- 'Royal Navy' (d) ♀H4	ERCP SDeJ
	- 'Sky Jacket'	LCro LOPS NRog
	- 'Snow Crystal' (d)	ERCP
	- 'Splendid Cornelia'	EPfP ERCP NRog SDeJ
	- 'White Festival' ♀H4	GKev SDeJ
	- 'White Pearl'	CAvo CRos EHyd GKev LCro LOPS LRHS NRHS NRog SDeJ SPer
	- 'Woodstock'	CAvo EPfP ERCP GKev LCro LOPS NRog SDeJ SDir
	- 'Yellow Queen' ♀H4	NRog
	- 'Yellowstone'	SDeJ

Hydrangea ✿ (*Hydrangeaceae*)

	angustipetala	see *H. scandens* subsp. *chinensis* f. *angustipetala*
	anomala subsp. ***anomala*** BWJ 8052 from China	WCru
	- - HWJK 2065 from Nepal	WCru
§	- - 'Winter Glow'	CWit EBee ELan EPfP ESwi LBuc MRav SGol WCru WFar WPnP
	- subsp. ***glabra***	LRHS
	- - B&SWJ 6804	WCru
	- - 'Crûg Coral'	SGol SMad SNig SPoG WCru
§	- subsp. ***petiolaris*** ♀H5	Widely available
	- - B&SWJ 5996 from Yakushima	WCru
	- - B&SWJ 6337	WCru
§	- - var. ***cordifolia***	CBcs NBro NFav NLar
	- - - B&SWJ 6081	WCru
	- - - B&SWJ 11487	WCru
§	- - - 'Brookside Littleleaf'	IDee MGos NBro NLar WFar
	- - dwarf	see *H. anomala* subsp. *petiolaris* var. *cordifolia*
	- - 'Early Light' (v)	SGbt
	- - 'Flying Saucer' **new**	LRHS
	- - var. ***megaphylla*** B&SWJ 4400	WCru
	- - - B&SWJ 8497	WCru
*	- - var. ***minor*** B&SWJ 5991	WCru
	- - 'Mirranda' (v)	CBcs CRHN ELan EPfP LPar MGos NBro NLar SGol SNig SPer SPoG SRms SWvt
§	- - var. ***ovalifolia***	CRHN ESwi SEdd
	- - - B&SWJ 8799	WCru
	- - - B&SWJ 8846	WCru
	- - 'Silver Lining'PBR	CBcs CBod CCCN CKel CRos CWGN EBee EHyd EMil EPfP LCro LOPS LRHS MGos NRHS SGol SGsty SMad SPoG SRms
	- - 'Summer Snow' (v)	EHyd LRHS NRHS SPoG
	- - var. ***tiliifolia***	see *H. anomala* subsp. *petiolaris* var. *ovalifolia*
	- - 'Yakushima'	WCru
	- subsp. ***quelpartensis***	see *H. anomala* subsp. *petiolaris* var. *ovalifolia*
	- 'Winter Surprise'	see *H. anomala* subsp. *anomala* 'Winter Glow'
§	***arborescens***	CExl MRav WPGP
	- 'Annabelle' ♀H6	Widely available
	- 'Bounty'	MAsh MBlu SGol WLov
	- CANDYBELLE LOLLIPOP ('Grhyar1407') **new**	SGol
	- CANDYBELLE MARSHMALLOW ('Grhyar1406') **new**	SGol
§	- subsp. ***discolor***	GBin
	- - 'Sterilis'	NLar WLov WPGP
	- 'Eco Pink Puff'	SEdd WPGP
	- 'Emerald Lace'	CMil IArd MBlu SEdd SGol WLov XSte
	- 'Golden Annabelle' (v) **new**	SGol
	- 'Grandiflora'	CBcs CEme EPfP LRHS NBro WPGP
	- 'Hayes Starburst'PBR	CDoC CMil CRos EBee EHyd ELan EPfP LRHS MAsh MMrt SGol SPoG SWvt WBor WPGP XSte
	- 'Hills of Snow'	NLar
	- INCREDIBALL	see *H. arborescens* STRONG ANNABELLE
	- INCREDIBALL BLUSH	see *H. arborescens* SWEET ANNABELLE
	- INVINCIBELLE SPIRIT	see *H. arborescens* PINK ANNABELLE
	- LIME RICKEY ('Smnhalr')	LCro LOPS LRHS NLar SGol
	- MAGICAL PINKERBELL ('Kolpinbel')	LRHS NLar SGol
	- 'Picadilly'	NLar
§	- PINK ANNABELLE ('Ncha1'PBR)	Widely available
	- 'Pink Pincushion'	NBro NLar WFar
	- 'Puffed Green'	NLar
	- subsp. ***radiata***	EHyd LRHS MRav SGol WFar WPGP
	- - 'Samantha'	EBee EPfP LRHS SPoG WLov WPGP
	- RUBY ANNABELLE ('Ncha3')	LBuc LCro LOPS NLar
	- 'Ryan Gainey'	LEdu WSpi
	- 'Sheep Cloud'	MBlu
§	- STRONG ANNABELLE ('Abetwo'PBR)	CBcs CDoC CEme CRos EHyd ELan EPfP LCro LRHS LSRN MAsh MBlu NLar NRHS SCob SGol SGsty SLon SPoG WHwl WSpi XSte
§	- SWEET ANNABELLE ('Ncha4')	LCro LOPS LRHS NLar

	- 'Vasterival'	NLar
	- 'Visitation'	CTsd MACG
	- WHITE DOME ('Dardom'PBR)	NBro
	aspera	CMac SLon SSta WCru WKif WPGP
	- HWJCM 452	WCru
	- from Gongshan, China	CExl CMil WPGP
	- 'Anthony Bullivant' ♀H5	CBcs CDoC CKel EPfP IArd IDee LRHS MAsh NLar SGol SHyH SWvt WKif WLov XSte
	- 'Bellevue'	IArd MBlu NLar WPGP XSte
	- Farrell form	EPfP MBlu WPGP
	- HOT CHOCOLATE ('Hpopr012')	CBcs CBod CDoC CKel CMil CTsd EBee EHed ELan EPfP LPar LRHS MBlu MGos MRav NSti SCob SGol SPoG
	- Kawakamii Group	CExl CKel CSpe EPfP ESwi NLar SGol SWvt WCru WPGP
	- - B&SWJ 3456	WCru
	- - B&SWJ 3527	WCru
	- - B&SWJ 6702	WCru
	- - B&SWJ 6714	WCru
	- - B&SWJ 6827	WCru
	- - B&SWJ 6996	WCru
	- - B&SWJ 7101	WCru
	- - 'August Abundance'	WCru
	- - 'Formosa'	WCru
	- - 'Maurice Mason'	CExl
	- - 'September Splendour'	WCru
	- Kawakamii Group × ***involucrata***	EPfP WPGP WSpi
	- 'Koki'	LRHS WPGP
	- 'Macrophylla' ♀H5	EBee ELan EPfP GKin MBlu MGil MGos MRav NLar SPer SWvt WCru WPGP WSpi
	- 'Mauvette'	CKel EHyd EPfP GKin LRHS MBlu NBro SGol SHyH SPer WCru
	- 'Peter Chappell' ♀H5	CExl CMac MBlu NLar WLov WPGP
§	- subsp. ***robusta***	CExl LRHS WPGP WSpi
	- - B&SWJ 13999	WCru
	- - GWJ 9430	WCru
	- - KR 10735	WPGP
	- - WWJ 11888	WCru
	- 'Rocklon'	ESwi NLar SGol
	- 'Rosthornii'	see *H. aspera* subsp. *robusta*
	- 'Sam MacDonald'	CExl EHyd EPfP LRHS NLar WPGP WSpi
	- 'Sapa'	EPfP WPGP
§	- subsp. ***sargentiana***	Widely available
	- - GOLD RUSH ('Giel') new	CRos LRHS
	- - 'La Fosse'	MBlu WPGP
	- - large-leaved	CExl WCru
	- 'Spinners'	NLar
	- subsp. ***strigosa***	CExl CKel CSde EHyd EPfP SWvt WCru WPGP
	- - B&SWJ 8201	WCru
	- - KWJ 12151 from northern Vietnam	WCru
	- - from Gong Shan, China	CExl
	- - 'Elegant Sound Pavilion'	WPGP
	- - 'Gongshan'	WPGP
	- 'Taiwan Pink'	NLar SGol
	- 'The Ditch'	ESwi NLar
	- 'Titania'	WPGP
§	- Villosa Group	Widely available
	- - 'Trelissick'	WPGP
	- - 'Velvet and Lace' ♀H5	EPfP MGos NLar WPGP WSpi XSte
	asterolasia B&SWJ 10481	WCru
§	'Blue Deckle' (L)	CMac MAsh MGos MRav NBro NLar SDys SGol WBor WLov XSte
	cinerea	see *H. arborescens* subsp. *discolor*
	davidii B&SWJ 8307	WCru
	- B&SWJ 11692	WCru
	- B&SWJ 11717	WCru
	- f. ***purpurascens*** KWJ 12233B	WCru
	'Dharuma'	GKin LRHS SCoo SGol
	EARLY SENSATION ('Bulk'PBR)	CBcs CCVT CDoC CEme CEnd CKel EBee EHed EHyd EPfP EShb GBin GKin LRHS MSwo NRHS SGol SPoG WFar WGrn WPGP XSte
	'First Red'	CEnd
	'Garden House Glory'	CExl CMil SAko WPGP
	glabrifolia	see *H. scandens* subsp. *chinensis*
	glandulosa B&SWJ 4031	WCru
	'Glyn Church'	EPfP MAsh SAko SChF WPGP
	aff. ***gracilis*** B&SWJ 3942	WCru
§	***heteromalla***	CMCN LEdu NBro WPGP
	- B&SWJ 2142 from India	WCru
	- BWJ 7657 from China	WCru
	- HWJ 526 from Vietnam	WCru
	- HWJ 938 from Vietnam	WCru
	- HWJCM 180	WCru
	- HWJK 2127 from Nepal	WCru
	- GWJ 9337 from Sikkim	WCru
	- KR 9913 from India	WPGP
	- Bretschneideri Group	EBee EPfP GKin SHyH WCru
	- 'Fan Si Pan'	WCru
	- 'Jermyns Lace'	NLar
	- 'June Pink'	NLar
	- 'Long White'	NLar
	- 'Morrey's Form'	WCru
	- 'Nepal Beauty'	EBee EPfP ESwi NLar SGol WPGP
	- 'Snow in June'	GGGa
	- 'Snowcap'	NLar
	- f. ***xanthoneura*** NJM 11.009	WPGP
	- - 'Wilsonii'	WCru WKif
	- 'Yalung Ridge'	WCru
	aff. ***heteromalla***	SGol WSpi
	'Hidcote Pink'	see *H. macrophylla* 'Juno'
	hirta	GEdr MBlu
	- B&SWJ 5000	WCru
	- B&SWJ 11022	WCru
	indochinensis	CExl
	- B&SWJ 8307	WCru
	- WWJ 11609	WCru
*	- f. ***purpurascens***	MGil
	integerrima	see *H. serratifolia*
	integrifolia	WPGP
	- B&SWJ 022	WCru
	- B&SWJ 6967	NLar WCru
	involucrata	CSde EPfP LRHS SGol WSpi
	- B&SWJ 4790	WCru
	- B&SWJ 11578	WCru
	- dwarf	CExl
	- 'Hortensis' (d)	CMac NLar SMad WCru WKif WPGP WSpi
	- var. ***idzuensis***	WCru
	- 'Late Love' new	XSte
	- 'Mihara-kokonoe'	CMil SGol WPGP
	- 'Multiplex'	ESwi MBlu WCru
	- 'Oshima'	WPGP
	- 'Plena' (d)	CKel EPfP NLar WLov WPGP WSpi
	- 'Plenissima' (d)	WCru
	- 'Sterilis'	EPfP WCru WSpi
	- 'Tokada Yama'	CMil IArd IDee NLar
	- 'Viridescens' ♀H4	CBcs NLar WCru WPGP
	- 'Yohraku-tama' ♀H4	EPfP NLar SGol WPGP
	- 'Yokudanka' (d)	IArd IDee NLar WPGP
	- 'Yoraku' (d)	WCru XSte

kawagoeana WCru
var. ***grosseserrata*** B&SWJ 11500
- - B&SWJ 11511 WCru
lobbii see *H. scandens* subsp. *chinensis*
longifolia CWJ 12413 WCru
longipes CExl WCru
- var. ***fulvescens*** B&SWJ 8188 WCru
- var. ***longipes*** CExl
- - NJM 11.084 WPGP
luteovenosa EBee WCru
- B&SWJ 5647 WCru
- B&SWJ 5929 WCru
- B&SWJ 6220 WCru
- B&SWJ 6317 WCru
macrophylla 'AB Green Shadow'[PBR] (H) MAsh MMrt SGol
- 'Adria' (H) NLar SGol
- 'Aduarda' see *H. macrophylla* 'Mousmée'
- ADULA ('H211901'[PBR]) (H) **new** LRHS
- 'All Summer Beauty' (H) CSBt ELan ELon GBin GGGa MAsh MNHC SHyH
- ALPEN GLOW see *H. macrophylla* 'Alpenglühen'
§ - 'Alpenglühen' (H) CBcs CExl CSBt NLar
- 'Altona' (H) 🏆[H5] CBcs CBrac CCVT EHyd EPfP IArd LCro LOPS LRHS MAsh MGos MRav NBir NLar SHyH SPer SRms
- 'Amethyst' (H/d) LRHS XSte
- 'Ami Pasquier' (H) CBcs CDoC CEme CKel CMac CSBt CSde CTri EGrI EHyd ELan EPfP EShb LRHS LSRN MRav MSwo SAko SCob SCoo SHyH SPoG SRms SWvt WLov
- 'Amor' (H) SCob SCoo SGol
- 'Amour Toujours' (Rendez-vous Series) (H) **new** LRHS
- 'Angélique' (Rendez-vous Series) (H) LRHS MAsh
* - 'Aureomarginata' (v) WCot
- 'Ave Maria' (H) GBin MAsh NLar
§ - 'Ayesha' (H) Widely available
- 'Bachstelze' (Teller Series) (L) GEdr MAsh WLov WPGP
- 'Baron Pourpre' (H) **new** MAsh
- 'Bavaria'[PBR] (H) GKin SGol WFar
- 'Beauté Vendômoise' (L) CMil LRHS NLar SHyH XSte
- 'Bela'[PBR] (H) MAsh XSte
- 'Benelux' (H) CBcs
- 'Benxi'[PBR] (L) **new** LRHS SCoo
- 'Bergfink' (Teller Series) (L) NLar
- BERLIN ('Rabe'[PBR]) (City-line Series) (H) MAsh SGol
- BIANCO ('Hbabia'[PBR]) (H) **new** LRHS
- 'Bicolor' see *H. macrophylla* 'Harlequin'
- Black Steel Series (H) LRHS NRHS
- - 'Black Steel Zambia' (H) LCro LOPS SGol WCot
- - 'Black Steel Zaza' (H) EPfP
- - 'Black Steel Zebra' (H) SGol
- 'Black Trombone' (H) SGol
- BLACKBERRY PIE ('Makz') (Flair & Flavours Series) (L) EHyd EPfP LRHS SPoG
§ - 'Blanc Bleu' (L) EPfP LSRN WFar
§ - 'Blauer Prinz' (H) NLar SHyH SRms
§ - 'Bläuling' (Teller Series) (L) 🏆[H5] CDoC GKin LSRN MAsh MNHC SGbt SGol XSte
§ - 'Blaumeise' (Teller Series) (L) 🏆[H5] CDoC CSBt ELon EPfP EShb GGGa LRHS MAsh MGil MGos MRav NChi NLar SCob SCoo SDix SGol SGsty SHyH SLon SPoG SWvt WFar WLov WPGP WPnP WSpi XSte
- 'Blue Bonnet' (H) EPfP LRHS LSRN MRav SCob SHyH SPer
- BLUE BUTTERFLY see *H. macrophylla* 'Bläuling'
- BLUE PRINCE see *H. macrophylla* 'Blauer Prinz'
- BLUE SKY see *H. macrophylla* 'Blaumeise'
- BLUE TIT see *H. macrophylla* 'Blaumeise'
- 'Blue Wave' see *H. macrophylla* 'Mariesii Perfecta'
- BLUEBIRD see *H. macrophylla* 'Bläuling'
- 'Bluebird' misapplied see *H. serrata* 'Bluebird'
§ - 'Blushing Bride' (H) LCro LOPS
- 'Bodensee' (H) CCVT CMac MAsh NLar SGsty WFar WSpi XSte
- 'Bottstein' (H) CCVT
- 'Bouquet Rose' (H) ECtt MMuc NLar SHyH
- 'Brestenburg' (H) MAsh
- 'Brügg' (H) LRHS MAsh SAko SGol SPer
- 'Buchfink' (Teller Series) (L) XSte
- CAIPIRINHA ('H212907'[PBR]) (H) SCoo SGol
- 'Cameroun' (H) SGol
- 'Camilla'[PBR] (H) SGol WFar
- 'Camino' (L) EPfP SGol
- CARDINAL see *H. macrophylla* 'Kardinal' (Teller Series)
§ - 'Cardinal Red' (H) CRos ECre EHyd EPfP LRHS NRHS WFar
- 'Charm' (H) LRHS SGol
- CHARMING CLAIRE (H) **new** LRHS
- CHARMING LISA (H) **new** LRHS
- CHIQUE ('Hbachi'[PBR]) (H) NRHS
- 'Choco Chic' (L) LRHS SGol
- 'Choco Pur' (Rendez-vous Series) (H) MAsh XSte
- CLARISSA ('Hba 208901'[PBR]) (H) SCoo
- 'Cocktail' (H) LRHS SGol
- 'Coco' (Beautensia Series) (H) NRHS
- 'Coco Blanc' (H/d) SGol
- COLOR FANTASY (H) MBrN
- 'Cotton Candy Two' (L) CMil EPfP LRHS MMrt NRHS
- CURLY SPARKLE ('H213901'[PBR]) (H) **new** LRHS
- 'Dark Angel' (L) ELan LCro LOPS LPar MAsh MGil NRHS SCoo SGol
- 'Dark Angel Purple' (Black Diamonds Series) (L) LCro LOPS LPar
- DEEP PURPLE DANCE ('Schrolla02'[PBR]) (Music Collection) (H) EPfP LRHS MGos
- 'Deutschland' (H) CTri
- 'Doctor Jean Varnier' (L) CKel EMil EPfP NLar
- 'Dolce Chic' (Rembrandt Series) (H) SGol
- DOLCE FARFALLE ('Dolfarf'[PBR]) (H) WCot
- DOLCE GIPSY ('Dolgip'[PBR]) (L) EPfP MGos SGol
- DOLCE KISS ('Dolkis'[PBR]) (L) EHed EPfP MGos SGol
- 'Doppio Bianco' see *H. macrophylla* 'Wedding Gown'
- 'Doppio Rosa' (L/d) LCro LOPS SGol
- 'Doris' (H) SCob SGol
- DRAGONFLY see *H. macrophylla* 'Libelle'
- EARLY BLUE ('Hba 202911'[PBR]) (H) CDoC EHyd LRHS MAsh SCob SCoo SGol SPoG XSte

§ - 'Early Sensation' (Forever and Ever Series) (H) CMac GKin
- 'Elbtal'^{PBR} (H) **new** LRHS
- 'Eldorado' (H) CBod MGil SHyH SNig WLov WSpi
- 'Elégance' (L) LRHS MAsh SGol
- 'Elegant Rosa' (Rembrandt Series) (H) SGol
- ENDLESS SUMMER ('Bailmer') (H) ELan SEWo SGsty
§ - 'Enziandom' (H) CBcs CExl CSBt MAsh SGol
- 'Etoile Violette' (L) CDoC SGol XSte
- 'Eugen Hahn' (H) SGsty XSte
- 'Europa' (H) ♀^{H5} CBcs CBrac CDoC CExl NLar SHyH
- EXPRESSION ('Youmesix') (H/d) SGol
- 'Fanfare'^{PBR} (H) SGol
§ - 'Fasan' (Teller Series) (L) MAsh NBro SGol WFar XSte
- FIRELIGHT see *H. macrophylla* 'Leuchtfeuer'
- FIREWORKS see *H. macrophylla* 'Hanabi'
- FIREWORKS BLUE see *H. macrophylla* 'Jōgasaki'
- FIREWORKS PINK see *H. macrophylla* 'Jōgasaki'
- FIREWORKS WHITE see *H. macrophylla* 'Hanabi'
- FIRST WHITE ('Hba 202903'^{PBR}) (H) MAsh XSte
- FOREVER & EVER see *H. macrophylla* 'Early Sensation'
- FOREVER & EVER DOUBLE PINK ('Rie 09') (Forever and Ever Series) (H/d) SGol
- FOREVER & EVER PEPPERMINT ('Rie 13'^{PBR}) (Forever and Ever Series) (H) CBod CSBt MBros SGol
- FOREVER & EVER TOGETHER ('Rie 05') (Forever and Ever Series) (H/d) CSBt EHyd LRHS MAsh SCoo SGol SPoG
- 'Forever Pink' (H) MAsh NLar SGol
- FOREVER ('Youmeone'^{PBR}) (H/d) CBod CSBt EPfP LRHS SCoo
§ - 'Frau Fujiyo' (Lady Series) (H) CExl
§ - 'Frau Katsuko' (Lady Series) (H) SPer
§ - 'Frau Mariko' (Lady Series) (H) MRav SGol
§ - 'Frau Nobuko' (Lady Series) (H) XSte
§ - 'Frau Taiko' (Lady Series) (H) SPer
- 'French Cancan' (Rendez-vous Series) (L) LRHS MAsh SGol
- 'Freudenstein' (H) XSte
- 'Frillibet' (H) MRav NLar
- FRISBEE ('H211903'^{PBR}) (L) ELan SGol
- 'Ganku Bo Chokens' (H) WCot
- 'Gartenbaudirektor Kühnert' (H) SHyH
- GEMINI ('Stramini'^{PBR}) (H) **new** SGol
§ - 'Générale Vicomtesse de Vibraye' (H) ♀^{H5} CBcs CBod CChe CDoC CEnd CKel CSde CTri EBee EHyd ELan ELon EPfP GBin LRHS MAsh MGil NBir NRHS SHyH SNig SPer SPoG WBor WFar WPnP XSte
- GENTIAN DOME see *H. macrophylla* 'Enziandom'
- 'Geoffrey Chadbund' see *H. macrophylla* 'Möwe'
- 'Gerda Steiniger' (H) SHyH
- 'Gertrud Glahn' (H) SHyH
- 'Gimpel' (Teller Series) (L) MAsh

§ - GLAM ROCK ('Horwack'^{PBR}) (H) CBcs CBod CDoC EGrI LCro LOPS MPkF SCoo SGol SGsty XSte
- 'Glowing Embers' (H) IArd
- GOLDRUSH ('Nehyosh') (L/v) CBcs CEme NHol SRms WCot
- 'Gräfin Cosel' (H) LRHS SGol XSte
§ - 'Grant's Choice' (L) NBro
- GREAT STAR see *H. macrophylla* 'Blanc Bleu'
- 'Green Lips' (H) SGol
- 'Grünes Gewölbe' (H) SGol
- 'Hamburg' (H) CBcs CTri ECtt EPfP SDix SHyH WFar
§ - 'Hanabi' (L/d) ♀^{H5} CBcs CEnd MBlu MGil NLar SGol WSpi XSte
§ - 'Harlequin' (H) CMac SGol
- 'Hatsu-shime' (L) CMil NLar
- 'Heinrich Seidel' (H) CBcs CTri
- 'Hercule Poirot' (H) SGol
- 'Holehird Purple' (H) MAsh
- (Hovaria Series) 'Hobella'^{PBR} (L) CBcs SGol WFar
- - 'Hobergine'^{PBR} (H) SGol XSte
- - 'Holibel'^{PBR} (H) SGol
- - 'Homigo'^{PBR} (H) SGol
- - 'Hopaline'^{PBR} (H) WPGP
- 'Hopcorn'^{PBR} (H) SGol XSte
§ - 'Hörnli' (H) XSte
- HOT RED ('Agrihydradrie'^{PBR}) (H) CDoC EHyd LCro LOPS LRHS MAsh NRHS SCoo SPoG XSte
- 'Inspire'^{PBR} (H) SGol XSte
- 'Izu-no-hana' (L/d) CAbb CBcs CBod CMil EHed ELan EPfP GBin MBlu MGil NLar SGol SHyH SPoG WPnP WSpi
- 'Izu-no-odoriko' (L) **new** SGol
- 'James Grant' see *H. macrophylla* 'Grant's Choice'
- JIP ('H213910') (H) LRHS SGol
- 'Jofloma' (H) NLar
§ - 'Jōgasaki' (L/d) CBcs CExl CSde MAsh MBlu NLar SDys SHyH WPGP
- 'Jomari' (Fireworks Series) (L/d) SGol
- 'Joseph Banks' (H) CBcs CTri EWld
- 'Julisa' (H) MPkF XSte
§ - 'Juno' (L) CKel SGol XSte
- KANMARA SPLENDOUR IN CHAMPAGNE (H) CRos LRHS MBNS SCoo
- KANMARA SPLENDOUR IN LILAC (H) CRos LRHS MBNS SCoo
- KANMARA SPLENDOUR IN ROSE (H) **new** LRHS
- KANMARA SPLENDOUR IN STRONG PINK (H) CRos LRHS SCoo
- KANMARA SPLENDOUR IN WHITE (H) CRos LRHS MBNS SCoo
- 'Kardinal' see *H. macrophylla* 'Cardinal Red' (H)
§ - 'Kardinal' (Teller Series) (L) ♀^{H5} MAsh MPri SGol SPoG WLov
- 'Kardinal Violet' (L) LCro LOPS MAsh
- 'King George' (H) CBar CBcs CBod CBrac CDoC CEme CKel CRos CSBt ECtt EHyd ELon EPfP LRHS MGil MGos MMuc NHol NRHS SAdn SAko SGol SHyH SNig SPer SPoG SWvt WFar
§ - 'Klaveren' (L) ♀^{H5} CMil MAsh NBro XSte
- 'Kluis Superba' (H) CTri SHyH
- 'Koria'^{PBR} (L) CKel CRos EMil LRHS MPkF NRHS SCoo SGol SPoG
§ - 'Kumico' (H) SCob SGol
- 'L.A. Dreamin' (H) SGol
- 'La France' (H) CBod CTri EHyd LRHS MGil SHyH SNig SPoG

- 'La Marne' (H) — LRHS XSte
- 'La Vie en Rose' (H) — LRHS SCob SGol XSte
- 'Lady in Red' (L) — EHyd EPfP LRHS NRHS SPoG
- LADY KATSUKO — see *H. macrophylla* 'Frau Katsuko'
- 'Lady Nobuko' — see *H. macrophylla* 'Frau Nobuko'
- 'Lady Oshie' (Teller Series) (L) — SGol
- 'Lady Taiko Blue' — see *H. macrophylla* 'Frau Taiko'
- 'Lady Taiko Pink' — see *H. macrophylla* 'Frau Taiko'
- 'Lanarth White' (L) 🏆H5 — Widely available
- 'Lemon Wave' (L/v) — NLar
- § 'Leuchtfeuer' (H) — ELon MGil SGol SHyH WLov XSte
- § 'Libelle' (Teller Series) (L) 🏆H5 — CBcs CMac EHyd ELan ELon EPfP EShb GDam LMil LPar LRHS MGos MMuc MRav NBir NLar NRHS SCob SEND SGol SGsty SPer SPoG WSpi XSte
- 'Lilacina' — see *H. macrophylla* 'Mariesii Lilacina'
- LITTLE LIME — see *H. paniculata* LITTLE LIME
- LOVE ('Youme H1917'[PBR]) (H/d) — CRos EPfP LOPS LRHS SGol SPer SPoG
- 'Love You Kiss'[PBR] (Hovaria Series) (L) 🏆H5 — CBcs CDoC CEnd LRHS NLar NRHS SCoo SGol SPoG WCot
- 'Lutin'[PBR] (L) — CDoC
- § 'Maculata' (L/v) — WGwG
- 'Madame A. Riverain' (H) — EPfP NLar SHyH
- 'Madame Emile Mouillère' (H) 🏆H5 — Widely available
- 'Madame Plumecocq' (H) — LRHS XSte
- 'Mademoiselle' (Rendez-vous Series) (H) **new** — LRHS
- (Magical Series) MAGICAL AMETHYST ('Hokomathyst'[PBR]) (H) — CBcs CDoC MPkF SGol XSte
- - MAGICAL BRIDE ('Hortmabrid'[PBR]) (H) **new** — CBod
- - MAGICAL CLEOPATRA ('Hortmaclepa') (H) — SGol
- - MAGICAL CORAL ('Hokomac'[PBR]) (H) — CBcs SGol XSte
- - MAGICAL CRYSTAL ('Ankong'[PBR]) (H) — SGol
- - MAGICAL GREENFIRE ('Qufu') (H) — SGol
- - MAGICAL HARMONY ('Hortmahar'[PBR]) (H) — NLar XSte
- - MAGICAL JADE ('Hortmaja'[PBR]) (H) — EPfP MBlu MPkF WCot XSte
- - MAGICAL NOBLESSE ('Hokomano'[PBR]) (H) — CBcs SGol XSte
- - MAGICAL OCEAN ('Hortmoc'[PBR]) (H) — NLar
- - MAGICAL RED AMETHYST ('Hokomareda') (H) **new** — SGol
- - MAGICAL REVOLUTION ('Hokomarevo') (H) — CBcs CDoC SGol XSte
- - MAGICAL RHAPSODY ('Hortmarahso') (H) **new** — CBod
- - MAGICAL RUBY RED ('Kolmaru'[PBR]) (H) — CBod SGol
- - MAGICAL RUBY TUESDAY (H) — SGol
- - MAGICAL WINGS ('Hortmawin'[PBR]) (H) — MBlu
- 'Maréchal Foch' (H) — CTri NLar
- 'Mariesii' (L) — CBod CTri ELan GBin MGil MSwo NLar SCob SHyH SPer
- § 'Mariesii Grandiflora' (L) — CMac EHyd EPfP MMuc NBro SCob SGol SGsty SPer SRms WFar
- § 'Mariesii Lilacina' (L) 🏆H5 — MMuc SEND SPer WFar WSpi
- § 'Mariesii Perfecta' (L) — Widely available
- 'Marina' (H) **new** — LRHS MAsh
- 'Masja' (H) — CBar CBcs CCVT EGrl ELon GKin IArd MAsh MGos MMuc MRav MSwo NBro NLar SAko SGol WBor
- 'Mathilde Gütges' (H) — CCVT SCob SGsty XSte
- 'Merveille' (H) — NBro
- 'Merveille Sanguine' (H) — Widely available
- 'Messalina' (L) — MAsh
- 'Mini Hörnli' — see *H. macrophylla* 'Hörnli'
- 'Mini Penny'[PBR] (H) — SGol
- MINTY ICE ('Es11'[PBR]) (Flair & Flavours Series) (H) — SGol
- 'Mirai'[PBR] (H) — CBcs EPfP ESwi NRHS SEdd WCot WPGP
- 'Miss Belgium' (H) — CMac CTri GKin
- 'Moritzburg' (H) — CBcs
- § 'Mousmée' (L) — SHyH XSte
- 'Mousseline' (H) — LRHS
- § 'Möwe' (Teller Series) (L) 🏆H5 — CBcs CExl ECtt EGrl ELon EPfP GBin MAsh MGil MMuc NLar SCob SCoo SDix SEdd SGol SHyH SPer SRms WLov WPnP WSpi
- 'Mrs W.J. Hepburn' (H) — CSBt SPer
- § 'Nachtigall' (Teller Series) (L) 🏆H5 — EPfP MAsh SHyH WLov WPGP
- 'Nadeshiko-gaku' (L) — SHyH
- 'Nanping'[PBR] (Sturdy Series) (L) — SPoG
- 'Niedersachsen' (H) — CTri MRav SHyH
- NIGHTINGALE — see *H. macrophylla* 'Nachtigall'
- 'Nigra' (H) — CBcs CBod CExl CKel CMac EHyd ELan ELon EPfP GBin LRHS MGil MGos MMuc MRav NBro NLar NRHS SAdn SDix SEND SHyH SPer WGrn WGwG WLov XSte
- 'Nikko Blue' (H) — CBcs GKin NLar SHyH
- var. ***normalis*** (L) — CExl
- § 'Nymphe' (H) — SGsty
- 'Oregon Pride' (H) — EPfP MAsh WFar
- 'Otaksa' (H) — CMil NLar
- 'Papagei' (Teller Series) (L) — SPer
- 'Pax' — see *H. macrophylla* 'Nymphe'
- 'Pfau' (Teller Series) (L) 🏆H5 — ELon MAsh MGil WSpi XSte
- PHEASANT — see *H. macrophylla* 'Fasan'
- 'Pia' (H) — CExl CMac CMil EHyd ELon EShb ESwi GBin MAsh MRav NLar SPer SRms WLov WSpi
- PIGEON — see *H. macrophylla* 'Taube'
- 'Pink Lollipop' (Flair & Flavours Series) (H) — SGol
- 'Pink Sensation'[PBR] (H) **new** — MAsh
- 'Pirate's Gold' (L/v) — WFar
- PRINCESS DIANA ('H213') (H) — SGol
- 'Prinses Beatrix' (H) — SHyH
- 'Purple Prince' (H) **new** — EGrl
- 'Quadricolor' (L/v) 🏆H5 — CDow CExl CMac CMil MRav SAdn SDix SHyH SPlb SRms WCot
- 'Queen Elizabeth' (H) — GKin
- 'R.F. Felton' (H) — CBcs SHyH
- 'Radiant' (H) — SRms
- 'Rathen' (H) — SGol
- 'Red Ace' (H) — SCob
- 'Red Angel' (Black Diamonds Series) (H) — MAsh NRHS SCoo SGol

	- 'Red Baron'	see *H. macrophylla* 'Schöne Bautznerin'
	- 'Red Beauty'PBR (H)	EHyd SGol
	- 'Red Red' (H)	MAsh
	- 'Red Riding Hood' (H) **new**	EGrI
	- REDBREAST	see *H. macrophylla* 'Rotkehlchen'
	- 'Regula' (H)	SHyH
	- 'Renate Steiniger' (H)	CBrac MRav SGol WSpi XSte
	- ROMANCE ('Youmenine'PBR) (H/d)	CRos EHyd LRHS MAsh NRHS SCob SCoo SGol SPoG WCot
	- 'Romantique' (H) **new**	MAsh
	- 'Rosita' (H)	CBrac MAsh NBir SGol SGsty XSte
	- 'Rosso Glory' (Rembrandt Series) (H)	SGol
	- 'Rotdrossel' (Teller Series) (L)	GBin
§	- 'Rotkehlchen' (Teller Series) (L)	GArf NLar SGol SPlb SWvt
	- 'Rotschwanz' (Teller Series) (L) 🏆H5	CDoC CMil GBin MAsh NLar SCob SHyH WBor WLov WPGP XSte
	- 'Rouge Baiser' (H)	SGol
	- 'Royal Red' (H)	LRHS SGol XSte
	- 'Royal Red Lilac' (Teller Series) (L) **new**	MAsh
	- 'Sabrina' (H)	CBcs CBod CChe CEnd CRos EGrI EHyd LRHS NRHS SCob SGol SHyH SRkn WFar
	- 'Saint Claire' (H)	CBcs
	- 'Salsa' (H)	CBrac CRos EHyd LRHS MMrt NRHS SCob SCoo SGol
	- 'Sandra' (Dutch Ladies Series) (L)	CBcs CRos LRHS MBros WFar
	- 'Saskia' (Dutch Ladies Series) (H)	SCob SGol
	- SAXON STYLE PINK (H) **new**	LRHS
	- SCHLOSS WACKERBARTH	see *H. macrophylla* GLAM ROCK
	- 'Schneeball' (H)	MAsh SCoo SGol WLov XSte
§	- 'Schöne Bautznerin' (H)	CCVT CDoC EGrI LRHS WFar WLov WSpi
	- 'Sea Foam' (L)	NLar
	- 'Selina' (Dutch Ladies Series) (L)	CBcs EHyd EPfP LSRN SCoo SGol WLov
	- 'Selma'PBR (Dutch Ladies Series) (L)	CBcs EPfP SGol
	- 'Semperflorens' (H)	XSte
	- 'Sensation' (H)	CBcs
§	- 'Setsuka-yae' (L/d)	SGol
	- 'Shakira' (H)	SGol
	- 'Shamrock' (L)	SHyH
	- 'Sheila' (Dutch Ladies Series) (L)	CBcs EPfP EShb LCro LOPS LSRN
	- 'Shin-ozaki' (H)	NLar
	- 'Shooting Star'PBR (L)	LRHS
	- 'Sibilla' (H)	SGol SHyH SPlb WFar
	- SISTER THERESE	see *H. macrophylla* 'Soeur Thérèse'
	- SO LONG EBONY ('Monmar') (H) **new**	SGol
	- SO LONG ROSY ('Coumont') (H) **new**	SGol
	- SO LONG SUNNY ('Tk02') (H) **new**	SGol
§	- 'Soeur Thérèse' (H)	CBar CBcs CSBt EPfP LPar MAsh MMuc NLar SGol SGsty SWvt WGwG XSte
	- Speedy ('Hba215911') (H) **new**	LRHS
	- 'Spike'PBR (H)	NRHS
	- STAR GAZER ('Kompeito'PBR) (Double Delight Series) (L/d)	SGol XSte
	- STRAWBERRIES 'N' CREAM ('Mak2') (L)	CRos EPfP LRHS SPoG
	- subsp. ***stylosa***	WCru WFar WPGP
	- - MF 942115	WPGP
*	- 'Sunset' (L)	CBcs
	- 'Sweet Fantasy' (Hovaria Series) (H)	ELan EPfP SGol
	- 'Tandem' (H)	LRHS XSte
§	- 'Taube' (Teller Series) (L)	CBcs CExl ELan MAsh SGol SHyH SWvt
	- 'Teller Pink'	see *H. macrophylla* 'Taube'
	- 'Teller Red'	see *H. macrophylla* 'Rotkehlchen'
	- Teller Series (L)	CDoC
	- Teller variegated	see *H. macrophylla* 'Tricolor'
	- Teller Weiss	see *H. macrophylla* 'Libelle'
	- THREE SISTERS (mixed) (H) **new**	LPar
	- TIFFANY ('H211902'PBR) (Flair & Flavours Series) (L)	SCoo SGol
	- 'Tivoli'PBR (H)	EHyd LCro LOPS MAsh NRHS SCoo SGol WFar
	- TIVOLI BLUE	see *H. macrophylla* 'Tivoli'
	- TIVOLI PINK	see *H. macrophylla* 'Tivoli'
	- 'Tokyo Delight' (L) 🏆H5	CExl CMac ESwi MAsh SDys SHyH
	- 'Tovelit' (H)	SGol XSte
§	- 'Tricolor' (L/v)	CBcs CTri EShb MGos MPkF NLar SHyH SLon SPer WAvo WFar XSte
	- 'Variegata'	see *H. macrophylla* 'Maculata'
	- 'Veitchii' (L) 🏆H5	CBcs CExl CMil CSBt ECre EHyd EPfP MGos MRav MSwo SDix SHyH SPer
	- 'Vibrant Verde' (Rembrandt Series) (H)	SGol
	- 'Vicomte de Vibraye'	see *H. macrophylla* 'Générale Vicomtesse de Vibraye'
	- 'Warabe'	see *H. serrata* 'Warabe'
§	- 'Wedding Gown'PBR (L/d)	MPkF SGol
	- 'Weisse Königin' (H)	SHyH
	- 'Westfalen' (H) 🏆H5	CMac SDix SHyH
	- 'White King'PBR (H)	SGol
	- 'White Spirit' (L)	SGol
	- 'White Wave'	see *H. macrophylla* 'Mariesii Grandiflora'
	- 'Wudu'PBR (H)	SCoo SGol
	- 'Xian'PBR (Sturdy Series) (H)	SGol
	- 'Yamato' (H) **new**	XSte
	- 'Yola' (H)	NBro WFar
	- YOU & ME TOGETHER ('Youmefive'PBR) (H/d)	EMil LCro LOPS
	- 'Zebra'PBR (H)	ELan ESwi LCro LOPS WCot
	- 'Zhuni Hito' (L)	NLar
	- 'Zorro'PBR (L) 🏆H5	CBcs CBod CDoC CRos CTsd CWGN EGrI EHed EHyd ELan EPfP ESwi GAbr GGGa LRHS LSun MAsh MGos NCou NRHS SCoo SHyH SLon SPer SPoG WBrk WCot WSpi WTyc XSte
	aff. ***mangshanensis*** BWJ 8120	WCru
	MISS SAORI ('H20-2') (H/d)	CBcs CBod CKel CRos CWGN EBee EGrI EMil EPfP LCro LOPS LRHS MBros MPkF NRHS SPoG XSte
	paniculata	CMCN GDam SavN
	- B&SWJ 3556 from Taiwan	WCru WFar
	- B&SWJ 5413 from Japan	WCru
	- B&SWJ 8894 from Japan	WCru
	- ANGEL'S BLUSH	see *H. paniculata* 'Ruby'
	- BABY LACE ('Piihp-1')	SGol
	- 'Big Ben' 🏆H5	CRos EHed EHyd EPfP GGGa LRHS NRHS SGol

- BOBO ('Ilvobo'PBR)	CDoC EBee ECul EHyd EPfP LPar LRHS MGos MPkF NRHS SCob SEdd SGol XSte
- 'Bombshell'PBR	CKel EMil LCro LOPS NLar NRHS SCob SGol WSpi
- 'Brussels Lace'	CKel EHed EMil EPfP GWyn LRHS LSRN MRav NLar NRHS SCoo SGol SHyH SLon SSta WLov WPnP
- 'Burgundy Lace'	MBlu NLar
- CANDLELIGHT ('Hpopr013'PBR)	CMil NLar SGol
- 'Chantilly Lace'	CKel EBee
- CONFETTI ('Vlasveld 02'PBR)	LCro LOPS SCoo SGol
- DART'S LITTLE DOT ('Darlido'PBR)	GBin LSRN NLar WFar WPGP
- DENTELLE DE GORRON ('Rencri'PBR) **new**	SGol
- DIAMANT ROUGE ('Rendia'PBR)	CCVT ECul EGrI EHed ELan LCro LOPS LPar LRHS MGos MPkF NRHS SCob SGol XSte
- DIAMANTINO ('Ren101'PBR)	SGol
- 'Dolly'	CRos EHyd EPfP LRHS LSRN SGol SPoG
- EARLY HARRY ('Hpopr018') **new**	CTsd
- 'Everest'	CCVT CRos EHyd EPfP LRHS NLar NRHS SPoG
- FIRE LIGHT ('Smhpfl')	LCro LOPS
- 'Floribunda'	CRos EHyd ELan EPfP LRHS NRHS SChF WFar
- FRAISE MELBA ('Renba')	MPkF SGol XSte
- 'Grandiflora'	Widely available
- 'Great Escape'	NLar
- GREAT STAR	see *H. paniculata* 'Le Vasterival'
- 'Greenspire'	CRos EHyd EPfP LRHS MBlu MRav NRHS WFar
- 'Harry's Souvenir'	NLar
- 'Kyushu'	Widely available
- 'Last Post'	NRHS
§ - 'Le Vasterival'PBR	CDoC CEnd CKel EHed MMrt SCob WSpi
- 'Levana'PBR	EHed EWTr NLar SGol SHar SHyH WFar
- 'Limelight'PBR ♀H5	Widely available
- LITTLE FRAISE ('Rou201306') **new**	SGol
§ - LITTLE LIME ('Jane'PBR)	CBcs CBod CCVT CDoC CKel CWGN EMil EPfP LCro LOPS LPar LRHS LSRN MAsh MMrt MPri NLar NRHS SCob SEdd SGol SGsty SHyH SPoG XSte
- LITTLE QUICK FIRE ('Smhplqf'PBR)	LCro LOPS SGol
- LITTLE SPOOKY ('Grhp08') **new**	SGol
- (Magical Series) MAGICAL CANDLE ('Bokraflame'PBR)	CDoC ELan EPfP NRHS SGol
- - MAGICAL FIRE ('Bokraplume'PBR)	MPkF NLar NRHS SGol WSpi
- - MAGICAL FLAME ('Bokratorch'PBR)	ELan EPau
- - MAGICAL HIMALAYA ('Kolmahima'PBR)	MGos NLar SGol
- - MAGICAL MATTERHORN **new**	NLar
- - MAGICAL MONT BLANC ('Kolmamon'PBR)	EBee SGol
- - MAGICAL MOONLIGHT ('Kolmagimo'PBR)	SCoo SGol
- - MAGICAL SUMMER ('Bokrathirteen')	SGol
- - MAGICAL VESUVIO ('Kolmavesu'PBR)	EBee MGos NLar SGol
- 'Mathilde'	SGol
- MEGA MINDY ('Ilvomindy'PBR)	SGol
- 'Melody'	NLar
- 'Mount Aso'	NBro SGol
- 'October Bride'	CEnd NLar WPGP
- 'Papillon'	WPGP
- PASTELGREEN ('Renxolor') **new**	MPkF SGol
- 'Pee Wee'	NLar
§ - PERLE D'AUTOMNE ('Degustar')	SGol
- 'Phantom' ♀H5	Widely available
- PINK DIAMOND ('Interhydia') ♀H5	Widely available
- 'Pink Lady'	NBro
- PINKY-WINKY ('Dvppinky'PBR) ♀H5	CDoC CKel CRos CTsd CWGN EHyd EPfP ESwi GKin IArd LBuc LCro LOPS LPar LRHS MBlu MGos MPkF NLar NRHS SCob SCoo SEdd SGol SHyH SLim SPoG SSta WFar XSte
- 'Polar Bear'PBR	CBcs CBod CWGN EBee NLar SCob SEdd SGol
- POLESTAR ('Breg14')	NLar
- 'Praecox'	MRav WCru
- PRIM'WHITE ('Dolprim')	MBlu
- 'Rosy Morn'	CRos EHyd LRHS
§ - 'Ruby'	EPfP LSRN NLar SGol
- 'Silver Dollar' ♀H5	CDoC CKel CRos EHed EHyd EPfP GBin IArd LCro LOPS LRHS LSRN MAsh MBros MGos NRHS SCob SEdd SGol SHyH SNig SWvt WCot WFar WSpi
- SKYFALL ('Frenne') **new**	SGol
- 'Sparkling'	SGol
- 'Starlight'	MPkF
- SUNDAE FRAISE ('Rensun'PBR)	CCVT CChe CDoC CEme CEnd CWGN EBee EHed EHyd EPfP EShb GGGa LPar LRHS MAsh MGos MPkF NRHS SCob SEdd SGol SGsty XSte
- 'Tardiva'	CBcs CBod EBee EPfP GKin LCro LOPS MGos NBro SDix SGol SHyH SPer SRms SWvt WFar WLov WPGP
- 'Tender Rose'	NLar
- 'The Slooten Rocket' **new**	ESwi
- 'Unique'	CBcs CBod CCVT CKel CRos EBee EHyd ELan EPfP LRHS LSRN MAsh MRav MSwo NBro NLar NRHS SCoo SEdd SGol SHyH SPer SSta WAvo WFar WLov WPGP
- VANILLE FRAISE ('Renhy'PBR)	Widely available
- 'White Goliath'	NLar
- 'White Lace'	NLar
- 'White Lady'	CBcs NRHS SGol
- 'White Moth'	GGGa NBro NLar
- 'Wim's Red'PBR	CBcs CBod CTsd ECul EGrI ELan EPfP EShb ESwi GAbr LCro LEdu LOPS LPar LRHS MMrt MPkF MThu NLar SCob SGol SSta WSpi XSte
- 'Yuan-Yang'	WCru
peruviana var. ***oerstedii*** B&SWJ 10750	WCru
peruviana × ***seemannii***	CEnd GKin IArd SSta
peruviana × ***serratifolia***	CRHN

	Name	Suppliers
	petiolaris	see *H. anomala* subsp. *petiolaris*
	'Preziosa' ♀H4	Widely available
	quercifolia	Widely available
	- 'Alice'	CDoC CKel CMac EBee EHyd ELan EPfP ESwi LMil LRHS LSRN MAsh NLar SChF SGol SHyH WPGP
	- 'Alison'	SGol
I	- 'Amethyst' Dirr	CJun NLar SGol
	- 'Applause'	EBee EHyd ELan EPfP LRHS NLar SGol WPGP
	- 'Back Porch'	NLar SGol
	- 'Burgundy'	CBcs CJun EBee EPfP ESwi IArd LRHS MBlu NLar SGol WPGP WSpi
	- 'Flore Pleno'	see *H. quercifolia* SNOWFLAKE
	- 'Harmony'	CKel EBee EHyd ELan EPfP ESwi IDee LRHS MGos NLar NRHS SGol SHyH SSta WLov WPGP XSte
	- ICE CRYSTAL ('Hqopr010'PBR)	CBod CDoC CKel EBee ELan EPfP ESwi LRHS NLar NSti SGol SGsty WAvo WPGP WSpi
	- 'Lady Anne'	WPGP
	- 'Little Honey'PBR	XSte
	- LITTLE HONEY ('Brihon')	MAsh NLar SGol WPGP
	- 'Munchkin'	CDoC LRHS MGos SGol XSte
	- 'Pee Wee'	CBcs CDoC CKel EBee EHyd ELan EPfP LRHS MAsh MMrt SAko SGol SHyH SLon SPoG SSta SWvt WLov WPGP
	- 'Queen of Hearts'	ESwi LRHS MGos
	- 'Ruby Slippers'	CDoC ESwi LRHS MGos MThu NLar SCoo SEdd SGol WSpi
	- 'Sike's Dwarf'	ELan MPkF MRav NLar SGol WCFE WLov
	- 'Snow Giant'	SGol
	- SNOW QUEEN ('Flemygea') ♀H5	CBcs CDoC CMCN CRos EHyd ELan EPfP LCro LOPS LRHS LSRN MAsh MGos MPkF MRav MSwo NLar SCob SEdd SGol SHyH SLim SPer SPoG SWvt WFar WPGP WSpi
	- 'Snowdrift'	CJun
§	- SNOWFLAKE ('Brido') (d) ♀H5	CBcs CDoC CEnd CKel CMac CRos CSde CWGN EHed ELan EPfP LCro LOPS LRHS MAsh MGos MPkF MRav NLar NRHS SCoo SGol SHyH SLon SPer SPoG WLov WPGP WSpi XSte
	- 'Tennessee Clone'	EBee LRHS NLar SGol
	'Renatea'	CSBt
	RUNAWAY BRIDE SNOW WHITE ('Ushyd0405') **new**	LRHS SGol XSte
	sargentiana	see *H. aspera* subsp. *sargentiana*
	scandens	NBro
	- B&SWJ 5448	WCru
	- B&SWJ 5481	WCru
	- B&SWJ 5496	WCru
	- B&SWJ 5523	WCru
	- B&SWJ 5602	WCru
	- B&SWJ 5725	WCru
	- B&SWJ 5893	WCru
	- B&SWJ 6159	WCru
	- B&SWJ 6317	WCru
§	- subsp. ***chinensis***	CExl
	- - B&SWJ 1488	WCru
	- - B&SWJ 3214	WCru
	- - B&SWJ 3410 from Taiwan	WCru
	- - B&SWJ 3420	WCru
	- - B&SWJ 3423 from Taiwan	WCru
	- - B&SWJ 3487 from Taiwan	WCru
	- - B&SWJ 3869	WCru
	- - BWJ 8000 from Sichuan	WCru
	- - BWJ 8035	WCru
§	- - f. ***angustipetala***	WPGP
	- - - B&SWJ 3454	WCru
	- - - B&SWJ 3553	WCru
	- - - B&SWJ 3667	WCru
	- - - B&SWJ 3733	WCru
	- - - B&SWJ 3814	WCru
	- - - B&SWJ 6038 from Yakushima	WCru
	- - - B&SWJ 6041 from Yakushima	WCru
	- - - B&SWJ 6056 from Yakushima	WCru
	- - - B&SWJ 6787	WCru
	- - - B&SWJ 6802	WCru
	- - - B&SWJ 7121	WCru
	- - - B&SWJ 7128	WCru
§	- - - 'Golden Crane'	CBcs EBee EPfP WCru WFar WPGP
	- - - 'Monlongshou'	see *H. scandens* subsp. *chinensis* f. *angustipetala* 'Golden Crane'
	- - 'Big White'	EBee WPGP
	- - f. ***formosana***	CMil SBrt
	- - - B&SWJ 1488	WCru
	- - - B&SWJ 7097	WCru
	- - f. ***macrosepala*** B&SWJ 3423	ESwi WCru
	- - - B&SWJ 3476	WCru
	- - - CWJ 12441	WCru
	- - f. ***obovatifolia*** B&SWJ 3487b	WCru
	- - - B&SWJ 3683	WCru
	- - - B&SWJ 3869 from the Philippines	WCru
	- - - B&SWJ 7121	WCru
	- subsp. ***liukiuensis***	WCru
	- - B&SWJ 6022	WCru
	- - B&SWJ 11471	WCru
	- 'Mine-no-yuki' **new**	SGol
	seemannii	Widely available
	- 'Roger Grounds' (v)	WCot
	aff. ***seemannii***	CBod CEnd GKin WHwl WSpi
	SEMIOLA ('Inovalaur'PBR)	CBcs EBee EHyd EPfP LRHS NRHS SGol
	serrata	CExl CTri
	- B&SWJ 6184	WCru
	- B&SWJ 6241	WCru
	- PAB 4757	LEdu
	- 'Acuminata'	see *H. serrata* 'Bluebird'
	- 'Aigaku' (L)	CExl CMil
	- 'Akabe-yama' (L)	NBro NLar
	- 'Aka-tsanayama' (L)	LRHS
	- 'Akishino-temari' (L)	WPGP
	- Amacha Group (L)	SGol
	- - 'Amagi-amacha' (L)	CMil NBro NLar
	- - 'Ō-amacha' (L)	WPGP
	- 'Amagyana' (L)	CExl
	- subsp. ***angustata***	WCru
	- 'Ao-yama' (L)	WPGP
	- AVELROZ ('Dolmyf'PBR) (L)	SGol
	- 'Belladonna' (L)	LRHS NBro
	- 'Belle Deckle'	see *H.* 'Blue Deckle'
	- 'Beni-gaku' (L)	CExl ECre EHyd LRHS MAsh MBlu NBro NLar NRHS SGol
	- 'Beni-temari' (L)	LRHS NBro
	- 'Beni-yama' (L) ♀H4	CMil
	- 'Betu-ko-temari' (L) **new**	LRHS
	- 'Bleuet' (L)	XSte
	- 'Blue Billow' (L)	GKev NBro NLar SGol
	- BLUEBERRY CHEESECAKE	see *H. serrata* TUFF STUFF
§	- 'Bluebird' (L) ♀H4	Widely available
I	- 'Boothii' (L)	CMac
	- 'Cap Sizun' (L)	SChF SGol WPGP XSte
	- 'Chiba Cherry-lips' (L)	ESwi WCru

- 'Chiri-san Sue' (L/d) CMil WCru
- COTTON CANDY see *H. serrata* TUFF STUFF
- 'Crûg Bicolor' (L) WCru
- 'Crûg Caerulean' (L) WCru
- 'Crûg Cobalt' (L) ESwi WCru
- 'Crûg Sõ Cool' (L) ESwi WCru
- 'Diadem' (L) ♀H4 CAbb CBod CExl CSde EHed ELon EPfP GKev LRHS NBro SEdd
- 'Forget Me Not' (L) NBro
- 'Fuji Waterfall' see *H. serrata* 'Fuji-no-taki'
- 'Fuji-no-shirayuki' (L/d) LRHS
§ - 'Fuji-no-taki' (L/d) ♀H4 CMil GEdr WPGP
- 'Golden Showers' (L) NBro
- 'Golden Sunlight'PBR (L) SGol SWvt
- 'Graciosa' (L) XSte
- 'Grayswood' (L) ♀H4 CBcs CBod CDoC CExl CKel CMac CSBt EHyd ELan EPfP LRHS MAsh MGil MRav NBro NRHS SCob SDix SGol SHyH SPer WKif WLov WPGP WPnP XSte
- 'Hakucho' (L/d) CMil NBro WPGP
- 'Hallasan' misapplied see *H. serrata* 'Maiko', 'Spreading Beauty'
- 'Hallasan' R. & J. de Belder (L) CMil WPGP
- 'Hime-benigaku' (L) CMil MBlu WFar
- 'Hoshi-kuzu' (L) SGol
- 'Impératrice Eugénie' (L) LRHS NLar XSte
- 'Intermedia' (L) CExl NBro
- 'Kiyosumi' (L) ♀H5 CBcs CBrac CEnd CExl CKel EBee ECre ELon EPfP NBir NLar SBrt WCru WLov WPGP
- 'Klaveren' see *H. macrophylla* 'Klaveren'
- 'Koreana' (L) SAko SGol
- 'Kujuusan' (L) **new** CMil
- 'Kurenai' (L) EBee EPfP NBro NLar WFar WPGP
- 'Kurohime' (L) EBee NBro WFar WPGP
- 'Macrosepala' (L) WPGP
§ - 'Maiko' (L) IArd
- 'Midori' (L) CExl
§ - 'Mikanba-gaku' (L) SGol
- 'Mikata Yae' (L) WPGP
- 'Miranda' (L) ♀H4 CExl CMil EHyd EPfP LRHS MAsh NBro NLar SDys SGol WFar
- 'Miyama-yae-murasaki' (L/d) ♀H4 CExl CMil SGol SRms WPGP
- 'Momobana' (L) **new** CMil
- 'Momo-beni-yama' (L) CMil NBro
- 'Mont Aso' (L) IArd NLar
- 'Niji' (L) WPGP
- 'Odoriko-amacha' (L) SChF WPGP
- 'Otsu-hime' (L) NLar
- 'Pretty Maiden' see *H. serrata* 'Shichidanka'
- 'Ramis Pictis' (L) NBro NLar
- 'Rosalba' (L) ♀H4 CExl ECre NBro
- 'Santiago'PBR (L) EPfP SGol WPGP
- 'Sekka' (L) EBee SChF SEdd WPGP
§ - 'Shichidanka' (L/d) CMil EPfP NBro
- 'Shichidanka-nishiki' (L/d/v) CExl
- 'Shinonome' (L/d) CExl
- 'Shirahuzi' (L/d) SGol
- 'Shirofuji' (L/d) ♀H4 CMil
- 'Shiro-gaku' (L) CMil NBro NLar
- 'Shiro-maiko' (L) WPGP
- 'Shirotae' (L/d) CExl LRHS SGol
- 'Shōjō' (L) ♀H4 CMil EBee MAsh MBlu NBro SGol WPGP XSte
- subsp. ***sinensis*** GKev
§ - 'Spreading Beauty' (L) WPGP
- 'Suzukayama-yama' (L) WPGP
- 'Tessa' (L) **new** CMil
* - var. ***thunbergii*** 'Plena' (L/d) WCru
- 'Tiara' (L) ♀H4 CAbb CExl CKel CMil EBee EHyd EPfP GGGa GKev LSRN NBir NBro NLar NRHS SDix SDys SEdd SGol SHyH SPoG WPGP XSte
§ - TUFF STUFF ('Mak 20'PBR) (L) EPfP LPar LRHS NRHS SGol SPoG XSte
- 'Veerle' (L) CBod CMil EHed NBro NLar SGol
- 'Vicomte de Kerlot' (L) XSte
§ - 'Warabe' (L) CMil SGol
- 'Yae-no-amacha' (L/d) CBcs CExl NBro NLar
- subsp. ***yezoensis*** NLar SGol

§ ***serratifolia*** CBcs CExl IArd IDee SSta WPGP
- HCM 98056 WCru

sikokiana B&SWJ 5035 WCru
- B&SWJ 5855 WCru
- B&SWJ 11174 WCru
- B&SWJ 11381 WCru

'Silver Slipper' see *H. macrophylla* 'Ayesha'

steyermarkii B&SWJ 10501 WCru

tiliifolia see *H. anomala* subsp. *petiolaris* var. *ovalifolia*

villosa see *H. aspera* Villosa Group

xanthoneura see *H. heteromalla*

aff. ***zhewanensis*** MF 93117 WCru

Hydrastis (*Ranunculaceae*)

canadensis GPoy LEdu

Hydrocharis (*Hydrocharitaceae*)

morsus-ranae CBen CHab CPud CWat EWat LLWG MWts NPer WPnP

Hydrocotyle (*Araliaceae*)

asiatica see *Centella asiatica*

sibthorpioides 'Crystal Confetti' (v) LLWG WHil

vulgaris CWat EWat

Hydrophyllum (*Boraginaceae*)

virginianum LEdu WHal WPGP

Hylomecon (*Papaveraceae*)

hylomeconoides EWld WCru

§ ***japonica*** CMiW EBee EHyd ELan EPot EWld GArf GEdr GGro GKev GLog LEdu LRHS NBir NHar NHpl NQui NRHS NRya WCot WPGP

Hylotelephium (*Crassulaceae*)

§ 'Abbey Dore' CBod EBee ECtt ELan ELon EPfP LRHS NBir SPhx WCAu

AMBER ('Florseamb') WCot

§ ***anacampseros*** GQue MMuc NDov NRya NWad XLum

'Aquarel' GBin GWyn

'Autumn Charm' see *H.* (Herbstfreude Group) 'Lajos'

§ 'Bertram Anderson' ♀H7 Widely available

'Birthday Party' (Birthday Party Series) CBod SPoG

'Blade Runner' LRHS

'Blue Elf'PBR (SunSparkler Series) **new** CSpe XSte

'Blue Pearl'PBR (SunSparkler Series) CBod EBee LCro LOPS MPnt MSCN SPoG

§ 'Carl' ♀H7 Widely available

§ ***cauticola*** ♀H5 EPot MAsh MRav NWad SRms WIce XLum

	- 'Coca-Cola'	Widely available
	- 'Lidakense' 🏆H5	CMea CSpe CTri ECha ECtt EGrI EPot MAsh MAvo MHer NHol NLar NWad SPlb SRot XLum XSen
	- 'Robustum'	see *H.* 'Ruby Glow'
	'Cherry Tart'PBR (SunSparkler Series)	CSpe LRHS
	'Chocolate Cherry'	CKno LRHS LSou NDov SHeu
	'Chocolate Drop'PBR	CWGN MAvo NLar SHeu SRms
	'Class Act'PBR	ECtt EHyd LRHS MNrw NDov NLar NRHS SPoG SRms
	'Cloud Walker'PBR	ECtt SPoG WFar
	'Crazy Ruffles'	WCot
	cyaneum 'Sakhalin'	CRos EHyd LRHS NRHS
	'Dark Jack'	ECtt GQue NGdn SMrm WCot
	'Dazzleberry'PBR (SunSparkler Series)	EPfP IPot LCro LOPS LRHS
§	***erythrostictum***	GBin XLum
	- B&SWJ 11384	WCru
	- 'Frosty Morn' (v)	Widely available
§	- 'Mediovariegatum' (v)	CDor ELan LPot LRHS MHer SWvt WFar XLum
§	***ewersii***	ECtt MAsh NBro NLar SPhx SPlb SRot
	- CC 5288	GKev
	- var. ***homophyllum*** 'Rosenteppich'	CDoC EHyd EPPr EPfP GWyn LRHS MAsh NBir NRHS SPoG SRms SWvt WAvo
	'Firecracker'PBR (SunSparkler Series)	CSpe LOPS LRHS LSou MPnt MSCN SCoo WNPC
	'Frosted Fire'	CBod MACG MAsh SRms WFar WHil
	'Green Expectations'	MRav
§	Herbstfreude Group	EHyd EWoo GQue LRHS NWsh SGbt SMrm WCav WMal
	- 'Autumn Fire'	EBee MAsh
	- 'Beka' (v)	NFav
	- 'Elsie's Gold' (v)	CTtf EBee ECtt EPfP MNrw SRms
§	- 'Herbstfreude' 🏆H7	Widely available
	- 'Jaws'PBR	CKno EBee ECtt LSou NLar WCot WFar XLum
§	- 'Lajos' (v)	CBod LRHS MAsh NFav WCot WFar WHoo
	- 'Mini Joy'	ELon MNrw
	'Ice Ruffles' (v)	CBod SPoG WFar
	'Jade Tuffet' (SunSparkler Series) **new**	LRHS
	'José Aubergine'PBR	CBod CKno CTtf EAJP EBee ECha ECtt EHyd EPfP EWoo IPot LCro LOPS LPla LRHS MAsh MAvo MBel MRav NDov NHol NLar NRHS NSti SCob SHeu SPoG SRms WCAu
§	'Joyce Henderson'	CDor CElw EHyd ELan EPfP GBin LRHS MCot MRav NChi NLar SPer SRGP SRms WAvo WBrk WCot XSen
	'Lac d'Oô'	GBin
	'Lime Zinger'PBR (SunSparkler Series)	CPla CRos LCro LOPS LRHS LSou SEdd WNPC
I	'Marchants Best Red' 🏆H7	MNrw MRav SPhx WCot WMal
§	'Matrona' 🏆H7	Widely available
§	'Mr Goodbud'PBR 🏆H7	CBct ECtt GPSL LRHS MAsh MAvo MNrw NBir NLar NRHS SAko SCob SHeu SPoG SRms WCAu WCot WSpi WTor
	'Munstead Purple'	MCot
§	'Munstead Red'	CBod CDor CRos CWCL EBee ECha ECtt EGrI EHyd EPfP LRHS MACG MAvo MNHC MNrw MRav NDov NLar NRHS SCob SMrm SPer SPhx SRms WCAu WFar WKif WMal
§	'Oriental Dancer'	LRHS MThu
	'Pinky'	EBee
	PLUM DAZZLED ('Pldaz2018') (SunSparkler Series) **new**	CSpe
§	***pluricaule***	CDor EHyd EPot LRHS NBro NHol NRHS NWad SPlb SRms WCav
	'Pool Party'PBR (Party Hardy Series)	CRos EHyd EPfP NLar NRHS SRms
§	***populifolium***	ECha GQue MHer MMuc NLar WMal XLum
§	'Red Cauli' 🏆H7	Widely available
	'Red Rum'	GWyn
	'Red Setter'	SAko SPhx WMal
	'Red Sparkle' **new**	LRHS
	'Roy Lancaster' **new**	LShi
§	'Ruby Glow' 🏆H5	CDor CRos CSBt CTri EBee ECha ECtt EGrI EHyd ELan EPfP GMaP GWyn LCro LOPS LRHS MAvo MCot MHer MRav MSwo NDov NGdn NRHS SMrm SPer SWvt WBrk WSpi XLum
	sieboldii 'Dragon'	MHCG
	- 'Mediovariegatum'	see *H. sieboldii* 'Misebaya-nakafu'
§	- 'Misebaya-nakafu' (v) 🏆H3	MHer MRav SPlb XLum
§	***spectabile*** 🏆H7	CBod CTri EHyd ELan EPfP GJos LRHS MCot MHer MRav NGdn NRHS SGbt SPlb SRms WBor WBrk WFar WSFF
	- BLACK BEAUTY ('Florseblab')	ECtt NLar
	- Brilliant Group	CBar CRos EGrI LRHS SCob SRms WCAu
	- - 'Abendrot'	ECha
	- - 'Brilliant' 🏆H7	CBcs CBod CSBt CTri ECha ECtt EHyd ELan EPfP LCro LOPS LRHS MAvo MGos MHol MRav NFav NGdn NLar NWsh SCob SPer SPoG SWvt WFar WSpi
	- - 'Carmen'	NBir XLum
	- - 'Hot Stuff'	CBod ECtt EHyd ELan EPau EPfP LRHS NCou NRHS SPoG SRms WCot
	- - 'Lisa'	ECha GWyn NLar
	- - 'Meteor'	MRav NLar SMrm
	- - 'Neon'	EHyd EPfP LRHS MAsh MAvo MBros
	- - 'Pink Fairy'	MNrw
	- - 'Rosenteller'	SMrm WBrk
§	- - 'Septemberglut'	CRos EHyd LRHS NRHS WSpi XLum
	- - 'Steven Ward'	EWes
	- 'Crystal Pink'PBR	LRHS MNrw NLar
	- 'Humile'	XLum
	- 'Iceberg'	CBod CTtf EBee ECha ECtt EGrI EHyd EPfP GBin LPot LRHS LShi MAsh MGos MRav NGdn NLar NRHS SPhx SWvt WCAu WFar WSFF WSpi XLum XSen
	- 'Nordlicht'	GWyn
	- 'Pink Chablis' (v)	WCot
	- SEPTEMBER GLOW	see *H. spectabile* (Brilliant Group) 'Septemberglut'
	- 'Stardust'	CDor CRos CTri EBee EHyd EPfP GBin GKev GMaP LCro LRHS LSou MBNS NFav NRHS SCob SRms WBrk WFar XLum
	- 'Variegatum'	see *H. erythrostictum* 'Mediovariegatum'
	- WALBERTON'S PIZAZZ	EHyd EPfP LRHS NRHS SPoG
§	'Stewed Rhubarb Mountain'	CKno EBee ECha ECtt EHyd ELan EPfP MBNS MRav NLar NRHS SGbt SMrm WCAu
	'Sunset Cloud'	EWes LPla LPot MRav

§ ***tatarinowii***	WCot
§ ***telephium***	NBir SIvy SRms WSFF XLum
§ - Atropurpureum Group	MRav NLar SWvt
- - 'African Pearl'	EGrl GWyn
- - 'Arthur Branch'	EHyd GWyn LRHS NChi
- - 'Bon Bon'	EPfP MBros NLar SPoG
- - 'Bressingham Purple'	CRos EBee EHyd LRHS NRHS
- - 'Chocolate'	GPSL NLar
- - 'Dark Knight'	CRos EHyd EPfP GPSL LRHS NRHS
- - 'El Cid'	EWes
- - 'Karfunkelstein' 🏆H7	CDor CKno EBee ECha ECtt EHyd GBee GBin GLog LCro LOPS LPot LRHS NBir NDov SPhx WCot XLum
- - 'Lynda Windsor'	ECtt EPfP NLar SWvt
- - 'Möhrchen'	EGrl GMaP MRav NGdn NLar
- - 'Picolette'	ECtt EHyd EPfP LRHS NGdn NRHS SPoG SRms WCot
- - 'Postman's Pride'PBR	CWGN ECtt EPfP GWyn NGdn
§ - - 'Purple Emperor' 🏆H7	Widely available
- - 'Ringmore Ruby'	MNrw SPhx WCot
- - 'Xenox'PBR 🏆H7	CBct CWGN EBee ECtt EHyd EPfP EShb GBin IPot LRHS MAsh MAvo MCot MNrw NLar NRHS NWad SPoG SRms WAvo WCAu
- 'Cherry Truffle'PBR	SHeu
- 'Dark Magic'PBR **new**	CBod LRHS LSun SIvy
- 'Desert Black'PBR	LSou MBNS NLar SEdd
- 'Desert Blonde'PBR **new**	MACG
- Emperor's Waves Group	ELan MNHC NGdn NWad SBls
§ - subsp. ***fabaria***	ECtt MRav NWsh SMrm WCot
- - var. ***borderei***	ECha LPla SPhx
- 'Jennifer'	EBee ECtt GQue LSun SGro WCAu WCot
- 'Marina'PBR	NLar
- subsp. ***maximum*** 'Atropurpureum'	see *H. telephium* Atropurpureum Group
- - 'Gooseberry Fool'	CMea EBee ECtt ELan EPfP GMaP LRHS LSou MACG MBriF NEoE NLar SPhx SRms WCAu
- 'Moonlight Serenade'PBR	EBee ECtt EHyd EPfP SRms
- 'Orange Xenox'PBR	EPfP
- 'Raspberry Truffle'	EPfP LRHS SHeu
§ - subsp. ***ruprechtii***	CDor ECha ECtt EGrl EHyd EPfP GMaP LRHS MCot MRav NLar NRHS SPer SPhx WWtn
- - 'Citrus Twist'	ECtt LPla LRHS MRav
- - 'Hab Gray'	CSpe EBee ECtt EWes EWld LRHS NLar SGro SMrm SRms
- - 'Pink Dome'	ECha LPla
- 'Strawberries and Cream'	CMac EBee ECha ECtt EHyd ELan ELon EPfP EShb EWTr GMaP LCro LRHS MAsh MBNS MBel MMuc MRav NGdn NLar NRHS SGbt SMrm SPer WHil
- 'Sunkissed'PBR	ECtt NLar WHil
- (Touchdown Series) 'Touchdown Breeze'PBR **new**	CKno
- - 'Touchdown Flame'PBR	SHeu
- - 'Touchdown Teak'PBR	CKno CTtf EBee ECha EHyd EPfP IPot LEdu LRHS MAsh NRHS SCob SHeu WTor
- 'Twinkling Star'PBR	MNrw
- YELLOW MATRONA ('Eline'PBR)	CKno ECtt LCro LOPS LRHS MAsh MBNS MSCN NDov
- 'Yellow Xenox'PBR	ECtt EHyd IPot NLar
'Thundercloud'PBR	EPfP GJos NWad SCob SRms
'Thunderhead'PBR	NLar SHeu
§ ***ussuriense***	EPfP GBin GPSL NBir
- 'Chuwangsan'	EWld WCru
'Veluwse Wakel'	ECtt GBin GWyn
§ 'Vera Jameson' 🏆H5	CRos ECha ECtt EHyd ELan EPfP EShb GKev LRHS LSRN MBel MCot MRav NBir NHol NRHS NWsh SMrm SPer SRms SWvt WHoo WKif WSMil WSpi WWtn
§ ***verticillatum***	LShi
§ ***viviparum***	NLar
- B&SWJ 8662	WCru
WALBERTON'S PINK WHISPER	EHyd EPfP LRHS NRHS SPoG
'Washfield Purple'	see *H. telephium* (Atropurpureum Group) 'Purple Emperor'

Hymenanthera see *Melicytus*

Hymenocallis (*Amaryllidaceae*)

× ***festalis***	see *Ismene* × *deflexa*
harrisiana	CCCN GKev SDeJ
longipetala	see *Ismene longipetala*
'Sulphur Queen'	see *Ismene* 'Sulphur Queen'

Hymenolepis (*Asteraceae*)

parviflora	see *Athanasia parviflora*

Hymenosporum (*Pittosporaceae*)

flavum	EShb

Hymenoxys (*Asteraceae*)

grandiflora	see *Tetraneuris grandiflora*
§ ***hoopesii***	CMac EHyd EPfP GDam GMaP GWyn LPot LRHS LShi NBir NGrd NLar NRHS SRms WFar XLum

Hyoscyamus (*Solanaceae*)

niger	GPoy WSFF XAbr

Hypericum ✿ (*Hypericaceae*)

CC 4131	CExl
CC 4544	CExl
aegypticum	CTri EPot MHer SLee SPlb WAbe WThu
androsaemum	CBod ECha ELan GAbr MMuc MSwo NPer SCob WFar
§ - 'Albury Purple'	ELan EShb ESwi XLum
- 'Autumn Blaze'	CBcs
- 'Excellent Flair'	NLar
§ - f. ***variegatum*** 'Mrs Gladis Brabazon' (v)	CMac EShb NBir WCot
'Archibald'	EWes NWad
athoum	SLee WThu
balearicum	MMuc SBrt WIce XSen
§ ***beanii***	WCFE
bellum	SPtp
calycinum	CBod CBrac CMac CTri ELan EPfP GDam LBuc MGos MRav NWea SCob SEND SNig SPer SRms SWvt WFar XLum
- 'Brigadoon' 🏆H5	MAsh SGol
- CARNIVAL	see *H. calycinum* FIESTA
§ - FIESTA ('Crowthyp'PBR) (v)	LRHS LSou NEoE
cerastioides	CSma CTri EDAr EWes GJos NGdn SRms WCot
coris	EWes SRms
× ***cyathiflorum*** 'Gold Cup'	CMac EHyd LRHS MAsh
'Daybreak'	CRos EHyd LRHS MAsh NEoE SGol SPoG
× ***dummeri*** 'Peter Dummer'	NLar WSpi
'Eastleigh Gold'	CMac
elodes	CWat LLWG
'Fancy Pants'	LEdu WPGP
forrestii 🏆H5	MMuc SEND
fragile misapplied	see *H. olympicum* f. *minus*

frondosum 'Sunburst'	EPfP
grandiflorum	see *H. kouytchense*
grandifolium	EDAr
henryi L 753	SRms
'Hidcote'	see *H.* × *hidcoteense* 'Hidcote'
§ × ***hidcoteense*** 'Hidcote' 🏆^{H5}	Widely available
- 'Hidcote Variegated' (v)	MAsh SRms
hirsutum	CHab NMir
× ***inodorum*** 'Albury Purple'	see *H. androsaemum* 'Albury Purple'
- 'Autumn Surprise'^{PBR}	NWad
- 'Dream'	NLar
- 'Elstead'	EPfP MRav NWad NWea WSpi
- GOLDEN BEACON ('Wilhyp'^{PBR}) 🏆^{H5}	CEnd CSpe EHyd ESwi MAsh MHer MMuc MNrw NBir NWad SEND WCot
- MAGICAL CHERRY ('Kolmcherrip'^{PBR})	ELan SCob
- MAGICAL GRACE ('Kolmagrace'^{PBR})	CBod LRHS LSou MMrt SCob
- MAGICAL LIGHTNING ('Kolmligh'^{PBR})	CBod LRHS LSou MMrt NEoE NLar
- MAGICAL PUMPKIN ('Kolmapuki'^{PBR})	CBod LRHS LSou NEoE SCob
- MAGICAL SUNSHINE ('Kolmasun'^{PBR})	NEoE SCob
- MAGICAL UNIVERSE ('Kolmuni'^{PBR})	CBod GDam LRHS LSou NEoE NLar
- MAGICAL WHITE ('Kolmawhi'^{PBR})	CBod ELan EPfP LSou MMrt NEoE SPoG
- 'Rheingold'	MAsh NLar
- 'Ysella'	MRav
kalmianum	IDee SBrt
kamtschaticum	XLum
kazdaghense	EWes
§ ***kouytchense*** 🏆^{H5}	CRos EHyd EPfP EWes GBin LRHS MAsh MMuc MRav SEND SPoG SWvt WKif WSpi
lancasteri	CRos EHyd EPfP ESwi LRHS MAsh SPoG SPtp
leschenaultii misapplied	see *H.* 'Rowallane'
'Little Misstery'	CDoC CKel CRos EHyd EMil EPfP LBuc LRHS MAsh NEoE NRHS SCob SPoG
maclarenii	EWes
MAGICAL BEAUTY ('Kolmbeau'^{PBR})	CBod EPfP NEoE NLar SGbt SPoG
MAGICAL RED FLAME ('Kolmaref'^{PBR})	EPfP
MAGICAL RED ('Kolmred')	EPfP NEoE NLar SPoG
MIRACLE ATTRACTION ('Alldiablo'^{PBR})	CDoC CRos LRHS MGos SRms
MIRACLE BLIZZ ('Allblizz')	CRos EHyd LRHS MGos NLar NRHS
MIRACLE BLOSSOM ('Allblossom'^{PBR})	CRos EHyd LRHS MBNS NRHS
MIRACLE MARVEL ('Allmarvel'^{PBR})	CDoC MGos
MIRACLE NIGHT ('Allmadne'^{PBR}) <u>**new**</u>	MBNS
MIRACLE SUMMER ('Hymirsum')	NEoE NLar
MIRACLE WONDER ('Hymirwon')	LRHS MBNS NLar
× ***moserianum*** 🏆^{H5}	CMac CRos EHyd EPfP EWes LRHS NPer SCob SLon SPer SRms WFar
§ - 'Tricolor' (v)	CBcs CBod CBrac CKel CMac CSBt CTri EBee EHyd ELan ELon EPfP LCro LOPS LRHS MAsh MGos MRav MSwo NRHS SCob SGol SNig SPer SPlb SPoG SWvt WFar WSMil
- 'Variegatum'	see *H.* × *moserianum* 'Tricolor'
'Mr Bojangles'	SCob
'Mrs Brabazon'	see *H. androsaemum* f. *variegatum* 'Mrs Gladis Brabazon'
oblongifolium	CExl
olympicum 🏆^{H4}	CBod CRos CTri ECha EHyd ELan GJos LRHS MAsh NRHS SEND SPer SRms SWvt WIce XLum XSen
- 'Grandiflorum'	see *H. olympicum* f. *uniflorum*
§ - f. ***minus***	CSma CTri ECtt EPfP GRum MAsh NGdn NHpl SPlb SRms
§ - - 'Sulphureum'	CBod CChe CRos EHyd ELon EWes GMaP LRHS NBir NRHS SHar SPer SRms SWvt WCFE WFar
- - 'Variegatum' (v)	EWes NBir SWvt
§ - f. ***uniflorum***	EBou MMuc NBro SLee WIce
- - 'Citrinum' 🏆^{H5}	CBcs CMea CSpe ECha ECtt EPfP LPla MHol MMuc MRav NLar SEND SMad SPad WAbe WCot WHoo WKif XSen
orientale	EWes GLog
patulum	SPtp
- var. ***henryi*** Rehder & hort.	see *H. pseudohenryi*
- var. ***henryi*** Veitch ex Bean	see *H. beanii*
perforatum	CCBP CHab CHby ENfk EPfP GJos GPoy IRos MGil MHer MNHC NGrd NLar NMir SEND SRms SVic WHer WSFF XAbr
- 'Topaz'	GJos
polyphyllum misapplied	see *H. olympicum* f. *minus*
- 'Citrinum'	see *H. olympicum* f. *minus* 'Sulphureum'
- 'Grandiflorum'	see *H. olympicum* f. *uniflorum*
§ ***pseudohenryi***	MMrt SPtp
quadrangulum L.	see *H. tetrapterum*
reptans misapplied	see *H. olympicum* f. *minus*
reptans Hook.f. & Thomson ex Dyer	EWes NWad
revolutum PAB 3861	LEdu
§ 'Rowallane' 🏆^{H4}	CTri LRHS NLar SDix SPoG SWvt
subsessile	CExl
'Sungold'	see *H. kouytchense*
'Sweet Lion'	CMac
§ ***tetrapterum***	CPud
trichocaulon	EWes ITim
uralum	ESwi SPtp
- HWJ 520	WCru
- NJM 10.097	WPGP
wilsonii	WCFE

Hypocalyptus (*Fabaceae*)

sophoroides	SPlb

Hypochaeris (*Asteraceae*)

radicata	CHab NMir

Hypocyrta see *Nematanthus*

Hypoestes (*Acanthaceae*)

aristata	CExl EShb SVen

Hypolepis (*Dennstaedtiaceae*)

ambigua	SPlb
glandulifera <u>**new**</u>	LEdu
millefolium	CBrP LEdu LRHS SPlb WCot WPGP

Hypoxis (*Hypoxidaceae*)

hemerocallidea	NWad
hirsuta	CBor CCCN GKev
krebsii	CBor
longifolia	MAsh
parvula	CBor XLum
- var. ***albiflora***	NWad

§ – – 'Hebron Farm Biscuit' CCCN EWes GEdr NWad WAbe WFar
villosa GKev

Hypoxis × *Rhodohypoxis* see × *Rhodoxis*

H. parvula* × *Rhodohypoxis baurii see × *Rhodoxis hybrida*

Hypsela (*Campanulaceae*)

longiflora see *H. reniformis*
§ ***reniformis*** CBor EBou ITim LLWG MAsh MSCN NHpl SLee

Hyssopus ✿ (*Lamiaceae*)

officinalis Widely available
– f. ***albus*** ECha ENfk EPfP GPoy MHer MNHC SBls SRms WHer XLum XSen
– subsp. ***aristatus*** CBod EBou ELon ENfk EPfP GPoy LCro LOPS MHer MNHC SPoG WHoo XLum XSen
– subsp. ***officinalis*** XSen
– 'Roseus' CBod EBou ECha ENfk EPfP GPoy MHer MNHC SPer SPoG SSal WHer XLum XSen
– f. ***ruber*** CLau
– white-flowered CBod SEdi

Hystrix (*Poaceae*)

patula CBod EMor EPPr EShb MNrw SBls SPlb XLum

Iberis (*Brassicaceae*)

ABSOLUTELY AMETHYST ('Ib2401') CBod ELan EWTr GBin LRHS SPoG WFar WIce
amara SVic
commutata see *I. sempervirens*
DWARF FAIRY (mixed) LCro LOPS
gibraltarica SRms
– 'Betty Swainson' 🏆H4 CElw CSpe SMrm SPhx
jordanii see *I. violacea*
'Masterpiece'^{PBR} CBod CDoC EHyd ELan EPfP LRHS NPer NRHS SCoo SEdd SPoG WFar
'Pink Ice' CBod CRos EHyd ELan EPfP LRHS NRHS SCob SEdd WFar WIce WTor
pruitii see *I. violacea*
saxatilis CRos EHyd ITim LRHS NRHS SRms WThu
semperflorens WAvo WBrk WCFE
§ ***sempervirens*** CCBP CMea CTri EBou ELan EPfP MAsh MCot MMuc NBro SAdn SBut SCob SEND SHar SRms WCFE XSen
– 'Appen-Etz' CRos EHyd EPfP GMaP LRHS NRHS NWad SRms WFar
– 'Fischbeck' MMrt SRms SRot
– 'Golden Candy' CSma CTri ECtt MHer NHpl SPoG SRms WFar WIce XSen
– 'Little Gem' see *I. sempervirens* 'Weisser Zwerg'
– 'Nevina' **new** CBod
– 'Pygmaea' WHil
– SCHNEEFLOCKE see *I. sempervirens* 'Snowflake'
– 'Snow Cushion' EPfP
§ – 'Snowflake' 🏆H5 EBou EPfP EPot GKev GMaP LCro LOPS LRHS MACG MHer SCob SPer SPoG SRms SWvt WBrk WIce XLum
§ – 'Weisser Zwerg' CMea EBou ECha ELan GMaP MHer MRav SRms WThu
– 'Whiteout' CBod MACG
'Snowball' SRms
§ ***violacea*** NSla SPlb
§ – Candolleana Group GEdr

Ichthyoselmis (*Papaveraceae*)

§ ***macrantha*** ECha EPot LEdu NLar WCru WFar WSHC

Idesia (*Salicaceae*)

polycarpa CBcs EBee EGrI EPfP SChF WKor WPGP
– CWJ 12837 WCru

Ilex ✿ (*Aquifoliaceae*)

× ***altaclerensis*** 'Balearica' (f) CJun
§ – 'Belgica Aurea' (f/v) 🏆H6 CBcs CJun EPfP MSwo NHol NLar WAvo
– 'Camelliifolia' (f) 🏆H6 CBcs CJun LPar MBlu SGol SPer WSpi
– 'Camelliifolia Variegata' (f/v) CMac
– 'Golden King' (f/v) 🏆H6 Widely available
– 'Hodginsii' (m) CTri
– 'Howick' (f/v) CJun
– 'Lawsoniana' (f/v) 🏆H6 CBod CBrac CCVT CJun CMac CRos CSBt CTri EBee EHyd EPfP EShb LRHS MAsh MBlu MMuc NHol NRHS NWea SCob SEND SGol SLon SPer SPoG SRms WFar
– 'Purple Shaft' (f) CJun CMCN MRav
– 'Ripley Gold' (f/v) CBrac CJun CMac CRos LRHS MAsh MRav NWea WAvo
– 'Silver Sentinel' see *I.* × *altaclerensis* 'Belgica Aurea'
– 'W.J. Bean' (f) CJun
– 'Wilsonii' (f) NLar
aquifolium 🏆H6 Widely available
– 'Alaska' (f) CBrac CCCN CCVT CJun CLnd CMCN CRos EHyd EPfP ETod ILea IPap LBuc LPar LRHS MAsh MNic MTrO NLar NOra NRHS NWea SCob SGsty SWvt SavN WAvo WFar WMat WMou
– 'Amber' (f) 🏆H6 CJun NLar
– 'Ammerland' (f) CJun
– 'Angustifolia' (f) CJun EHyd
– 'Angustifolia' (m or f) CRos EPfP LRHS SPoG
– 'Angustimarginata Aurea' (m/v) MTrO
§ – 'Argentea Marginata' (f/v) 🏆H6 Widely available
§ – 'Argentea Marginata Pendula' (f/v) CMac CRos CTri ELan EPfP LRHS MAsh NOra SRms WFar
– 'Argentea Pendula' see *I. aquifolium* 'Argentea Marginata Pendula'
– 'Argentea Variegata' see *I. aquifolium* 'Argentea Marginata'
– 'Atlas' (m) CBcs LBuc SWvt
– 'Aurea Marginata' (f/v) CMac EPfP MGos NOra NWea SCob SEWo WCFE WFar WMat
– 'Aurea Marginata Pendula' (f/v) WLov
– 'Aurifodina' (f) CJun WAvo
– 'Bacciflava' (f) CBcs CJun CMac CTri ELan ELon EPfP IArd MBlu MRav NLar SPer SRms SWvt WFar
– 'Chris Whittle' LRHS
– 'Crassifolia' (f) EBee
– 'Crispa' (m) CBod
– 'Elegantissima' (m/v) CBrac CJun

	- 'Fastigiata Sartori'	NLar
	- 'Ferox' (m)	CJun CRos EHyd ELan EPfP LRHS
	- 'Ferox Argentea' (m/v) ♀H6	Widely available
	- 'Ferox Aurea' (m/v)	CBrac CJun ELon MAsh
§	- 'Flavescens' (f)	MBlu
	- 'Frogmore Silver' (m/v)	CJun
	- 'Glanzzwerg'	SAko
	- 'Gold Flash' (f/v)	CJun NLar
	- 'Golden Milkboy' (m/v)	CBrac CJun CMac EPfP MAsh WAvo WCot WLov
§	- 'Golden Queen' (m/v) ♀H6	SRms
	- 'Golden Tears' (f/v)	CJun
	- 'Golden van Tol' (f/v)	CBcs CJun CSBt CTri EBee ELan ELon EPfP EShb ETod MAsh MBlu MGos MSwo MTrO NLar SCoo SGol SPer SRms WFar
	- 'Green Minaret'	SAko
§	- 'Green Pillar' (f)	LRHS
	- 'Handsworth New Silver' (f/v) ♀H6	Widely available
	- 'Harpune' (f)	IArd SAko
	- 'Hastata' (m)	IArd IDee
	- HECKENZWERG ('Hachzwerg'PBR)	SAko
	- 'Heterophylla Aureomarginata' (m/v)	CDoC
	- 'Ingramii' (m/v)	CJun
	- 'J.C. van Tol' (f) ♀H6	Widely available
	- 'Latispina' (f)	CJun
	- 'Lichtenthalii' (f)	CJun IArd
	- 'Madame Briot' (f/v) ♀H6	CDoC CJun CMac CRos CTri EBee EHyd ELan EPfP LBuc LRHS MAsh MRav MSwo NHol NRHS NWea SCob SEND SGol SPer SPoG SRms SWvt WFar
	- 'Monstrosa' (m)	CJun
	- moonlight holly	see *I. aquifolium* 'Flavescens'
	- 'Myrtifolia' (m)	CBod CDow CJun CMac ELan EPfP NLar SWvt WPav
	- 'Myrtifolia Aurea' (m/v)	SWvt
	- 'Myrtifolia Aurea Maculata' (m/v)	CBod CDoC CJun CRos CTri EHyd ELan LRHS MAsh MRav SPoG SWvt WCot WLov
	- 'Northern Lights' (v)	MSwo SGsty
	- 'Pendula' (f)	MRav
	- 'Pyramidalis' (f) ♀H6	CBcs CJun CMac CRos CTri ELan LRHS MAsh MGos NLar NWea SCob SGol SRms WFar
	- 'Pyramidalis Aureomarginata' (f/v)	NLar
	- 'Pyramidalis Fructu Luteo' (f) ♀H6	MAsh
	- 'Recurva' (m)	CJun CMac
	- 'Rubricaulis Aurea' (f/v)	CJun NLar
	- 'Scotica' (f)	CJun NWea
	- SIBERIA ('Limsi'PBR) (f)	LMaj
	- 'Silver King'	see *I. aquifolium* 'Silver Queen'
	- 'Silver Lining' (f/v)	CJun
	- 'Silver Milkboy' (f/v)	MBlu WFar
	- 'Silver Milkmaid' (f/v)	CJun CRos EHyd LRHS MAsh NRHS SLim SWvt
§	- 'Silver Queen' (m/v) ♀H6	CBar CBcs CCVT CDoC CEnd CLnd EPfP LCro LOPS LRHS MAsh MGos MRav MSwo MTrO NHol NLar NOra NWea SAko SGbt SLim SLon SPer SPoG SWvt WLov WMat
	- 'Silver Sentinel'	see *I.* × *altaclerensis* 'Belgica Aurea'
	- 'Silver van Tol' (f/v)	CBod CDoC CJun CLnd EBee ELan EPfP EShb ETod MAsh MRav NLar NPer WFar
	- 'Somerset Cream' (f/v)	CJun CTri
*	- 'Variegata' (v)	SArc SWeb
	- 'White Cream' (m/v)	SAko
	- 'Zig Zag' (f)	CJun
	× ***aquipernyi*** DRAGON LADY ('Meschick') (f) ♀H6	CBod IArd LRHS NLar
	- 'San Jose' (f)	CJun
	× ***attenuata***	WFar
	- 'Sunny Foster' (f/v)	CBcs CMCN SAko WFar
	× ***beanii***	CJun
§	***bioritsensis***	CMCN
	cassine L.	CMCN
	chapaensis HWJ 946	WCru
	'Clusterberry' (f)	CJun
	colchica	CMCN IArd
	cornuta	EPfP ESwi LMaj
	- B&SWJ 8756	WCru
	- 'Anicet Delcambre' (f)	CJun
	- 'Burfordii' (f)	NLar
§	- 'Dazzler' (f)	CJun
	- 'D'Or' (f) **new**	IArd
	- 'Ira S. Nelson' (f)	CJun IArd
	- 'Mercury' (f)	CJun
	- 'O. Spring' (f/v)	CJun CMac WSpi
	crenata	CAco CDoC CMCN CTri EPfP ERom GDam LCro LOPS LPar LRHS MGos NHol NWea SArc SCob SGsty SPer SWeb WFar
*	- 'Akagi'	WFar
	- 'Aureovariegata'	see *I. crenata* 'Variegata'
	- 'Blondie'PBR (f)	LPar SWeb
	- 'Carolina Upright' (m)	EBee LPar SEWo
	- 'Cherokee' (m) **new**	LMaj
	- 'Convexa' (f) ♀H6	CJun EHyd EPfP LPar LRHS MAsh MRav NRHS NWea SGsty SJap SWeb
	- 'Convexed Gold' (f/v)	EPfP NLar NWad SPoG WFar
	- DARK GREEN ('Icoprins11'PBR)	CDoC CLnd ELan EPfP LBuc LCro LMaj LOPS LRHS LSRN NWea SCob SGsty SVic SWeb
	- 'Dwarf Pagoda' (f)	SAko
	- 'Eden's Paradise'PBR	SGsty
	- Fastigiata Group	CRos LRHS SCob WFar
	- - 'Fastigiata' (f) ♀H6	CAco CBod CRos EHyd EPfP LRHS LSRN MAsh MGos NLar SPer SPoG
	- - 'Sky Pencil' (f)	CMCN
	- 'Glorie Gem' (m)	SJap
*	- 'Glory Gem' (f)	CBcs LRHS LSRN SGsty
	- 'Golden Gem' (f/v) ♀H6	CJun CMac CRos CTri ELan EPfP GArf LRHS MAsh MGos MSwo NLar NRHS NWad NWea SAko SJap SPer SPoG SWvt WFar
	- 'Green Hedger' ♀H6	CLnd EPfP LMaj MGos NLar SGsty
	- 'Green Lustre' (f)	LPar LSRN
	- 'Hetzii' (f)	CBod
	- 'Kinme' (f)	LRHS SGsty SWeb
	- 'Luteovariegata'	see *I. crenata* 'Variegata'
	- LUXUS GLOBE ('Annys5'PBR) (m)	NLar
	- 'Mariesii' (f)	CMac EBee MBlu
I	- 'Pyramidalis' (f)	CMac MRav NWea
§	- 'Shiro-fukurin' (f/v)	CJun CMCN CRos EHyd ELan EPfP LRHS NRHS SLon SPoG
	- 'Snowflake'	see *I. crenata* 'Shiro-fukurin'
	- 'Stokes' (m)	CBod CDoC LPar MSwo NLar NWad
§	- 'Variegata' (v)	CMCN CMac CRos EHyd EPfP LRHS NLar NRHS
	'Dazzler'	see *I. cornuta* 'Dazzler'
	dimorphophylla 'Somerset Pixie' (f)	CJun

dipyrena	SAko
'Doctor Kassab' (f)	CMCN
'Elegance' (f)	MBlu WFar
excelsa	CMCN
fargesii	IArd
- subsp. ***fargesii*** var. ***fargesii***	WPGP
aff. ***gagnepainiana*** FMWJ 13168	WCru
glabra	CJun
- f. ***leucocarpa*** 'Snow White' (f)	CJun
'Good Taste' (f)	CJun NLar WFar
'Hohman' (f)	CJun
'Indian Chief' (f)	CJun
× ***koehneana***	CCVT LPar MMuc SDix SEND
- 'Chestnut Leaf' (f) ♀H5	CBcs CBod CCVT CDoC CJun CLnd CMCN ELan EPfP LMaj LRHS MRav NLar NSti SMad SSta WFar WGrn
laevigata	CMCN
latifolia	CJun NLar
'Leonardo'	EBee
'Mary Nell' (f)	CJun
§ × ***meserveae*** 'Anny's Dwarf' (m)	LRHS
- BLUE ANGEL ('Conang') (f)	CBod CBrac CCCN CDoC CMac CSBt EBee ELan EPfP LMaj LPar LRHS MRav NFav NLar NRHS NWea SPer SPoG SRms WAvo WFar
- BLUE MAID ('Mesid') (f)	CCCN CDoC LMaj LOPS LPar LRHS MGos NLar NRHS SWeb
- BLUE PRINCE ('Conablu') (m) ♀H7	CBcs CBrac CCCN CDoC CMCN CMac CRos ELan EPfP LBuc LPar MBlu NHol NLar NWea SCob SPer WFar
- BLUE PRINCESS ('Conapri') (f) ♀H7	CBcs CBod CBrac CCVT CMCN CMac ELan EPfP GBin LBuc LPar MBlu MGos MRav NLar NWea SCob SCoo SPer WFar
- CASTLE SPIRE ('Hachfee'PBR) (f)	CLnd LRHS SEWo SWeb WFar
- CASTLE WALL ('Hecken Star'PBR) (m)	CLnd LMaj LRHS NLar SEWo WFar
- GOLDEN GIRL ('Mesgolg') (f)	SGsty
- 'Goliath' (f)	WFar
- 'Heckenpracht'PBR (m)	LMaj LPar WFar
- LITTLE RASCAL ('Mondo') (m)	CRos EHed EPfP LRHS MGos MPkF NLar SGsty XSte
- 'Little Sensation'	LRHS MBlu SPoG
myrtifolia	CDoC MAsh MRav NHol
'Nellie R. Stevens' (f)	CCVT CJun CLnd CRos EBee ELan EPfP ILea LMaj LPar LSRN NLar SEWo SGsty SWeb WAvo WMat
opaca	CMCN
pedunculosa	MBlu NLar
perado subsp. ***azorica*** B&SWJ 12526	WCru
- subsp. ***platyphylla***	CMCN EBee MBlu SArc
pernyi	CJun CMCN MAsh
- var. ***veitchii***	see *I. bioritsensis*
rotunda	LEdu WPGP
rugosa	CMCN
'September Gem' (f)	CJun CMCN
serrata	CMac CMen
- 'Leucocarpa' (f)	CMac
sikkimensis	LEdu
spinigera	CBcs NWea
sugerokii	WCru
var. ***longipedunculata*** B&SWJ 10856	
'Tanager' (f)	CJun
triflora var. ***kanehirae***	NLar
verticillata	CMCN EBee NFav NWea WFar
- (f)	CBcs EPfP MMrt NLar
- (m)	EPfP MMrt NLar
- f. ***chrysocarpa*** (f)	NLar
- 'Compacta'	see *I. verticillata* 'Nana'
- 'Maryland Beauty' (f)	CJun NLar
§ - 'Nana' (f)	CJun
- 'Red Sprite'	see *I. verticillata* 'Nana'
- 'Scarlett O'Hara' (f) **new**	CJun
- 'Southern Gentleman' (m)	CJun MBlu
- 'Sunset'PBR (f)	CJun
- 'Winter Gold' (f)	CJun MBlu
- 'Winter Red' (f)	CJun CMCN MBlu
vomitoria	CMCN EBtc
× ***wandoensis***	CJun WFar
'Washington' (f)	IArd WFar
'William Cowgill' (f)	CJun
yunnanensis	EBee IArd IDee

Iliamna see *Sphaeralcea*

Illicium (*Schisandraceae*)

anisatum	CBcs CCCN CExl EPfP LEdu SSta WLov WPGP
- B&SWJ 8411	WCru
floridanum	CBcs CCCN SBrt SSta WLov
- 'Halley's Comet'	CExl NLar
aff. ***griffithii*** WWJ 11911	WCru
- WWJ 11971	WCru
- WWJ 11974	WCru
henryi	CExl EBee EPfP LRHS NLar WPGP
aff. ***henryi***	CBcs
jiadifengpi	NLar
lanceolatum	CExl
- KWJ 12245	WCru
macranthum B&SWJ 11809	WCru
majus WWJ 11919	WCru
aff. ***majus***	WCru
- WWJ 12017	WCru
merrillianum HWJ 1015	WCru
mexicanum	CExl
oligandrum	CBcs CExl NLar WPGP
philippinense CWJ 12466	WCru
simonsii	CExl MBlu WPGP
- BWJ 8024	WCru
tashiroi CWJ 12468	WCru
'Woodland Ruby'	EPfP WPGP

Ilysanthes see *Lindernia*

Impatiens (*Balsaminaceae*)

CC 4980	CExl
from China, Darrell Probst collection	GGro WFar
apiculata	WFar
arguta	CExl EBee EWld SBrt WBor WFar
- 'Alba'	CExl CSpe EPPr GGro MPie MSCN WFar
- big blue-flowered	EPPr ESwi
- big form	GGro WFar
auricoma × ***bicaudata***	CDTJ MPie WDib
balansae	CDTJ
bicaudata	CSpe SPlb SSal
congolensis	CCCN
DIVINE LAVENDER ('Pas425593') (Divine Series) (NG)	MBros
ernstii	CExl
flanaganae	CDTJ ESwi SBrt SIvy SSal WFar WPGP

forrestii	GGro
gomphophylla	CDTJ WFar
hawkeri Divine Series	MBros
hochstetteri	WFar
insignis	EBee EPPr EWld GGro SBrt
keilii	WDib
kilimanjari subsp. ***kilimanjari***	CDTJ CSpe ECre MPie
kilimanjari × ***pseudoviola***	CSpe ECre MPie WDib WFar
- -, dark pink-flowered	WFar
- -, pale pink-flowered	ECre MPie WFar
langbianensis HWJ 1054 new	GGro WCru WFar
macrophylla	WFar
- B&SWJ 10157	WCru
mengtszeana PB 02-519	GGro WFar
- trailing	GGro SBrt WFar
namchabarwensis	CCCN
niamniamensis 🏆^{H1b}	EBak EShb NCft WDib
- 'Congo Cockatoo'	CDTJ NPer SRms
- 'Golden Cockatoo' (v)	CDTJ EBak EShb
noli-tangere	WSFF
omeiana	CCCN CDTJ CPla CSpe EBee ELan EPPr ESwi EWld GEdr GGro GWyn ILea LEdu MNrw MSCN NFav NLar SPtp WCru WFar WPGP
- DJHC 98492	WCru WFar WMal
- 'High Voltage'	GGro WFar
- 'Ice Storm'	CDTJ EBee EPPr ESwi EWld GEdr GGro IPot LEdu NBro NLar WCot WCru WFar WPGP
- long-leaved	WFar
- 'Pink Nerves'	CTsd EBee ESwi GGro LEdu MPie WFar
- 'Red Leaf'	EPPr ESwi
- 'Sango'	CPla CSpe GGro LEdu WFar WMal
- 'Silver Pink' new	GGro
- variegated (v)	GEdr
oxyanthera new	GGro
- 'Milo'	GGro SBrt WFar
P1961	EPPr ESwi
parasitica	WDib
pritzelii	CDTJ
- 'Sichuan Gold'	CDTJ EPPr ESwi LEdu WFar
puberula	GGro WFar
- HWJK 2063	EBee ESwi EWld SBrt WCru
qingchengshanica 'Emei Dawn'	CExl EBee EPPr ESwi WCru WFar
repens 🏆^{H1b}	WDib
rhombifolia new	GGro
rothii	EBee ESwi WCot WPGP
rupestris	CDTJ
scabrida	CSpe
§ 'Secret Love'	CCCN CDoC
sodenii 🏆^{H1c}	CDTJ EShb ESwi SSal WDib WFar
- 'Flash'	WFar
- white-flowered	WFar
- white-flowered, red eye	WFar
stenantha	EBee ESwi EWld GEdr SBrt WFar
(SunPatiens Series)	MBros
- SUNPATIENS VIGOROUS BLUSH PINK ('Sakimp023'^{PBR}) (NG)	MBros
- SUNPATIENS VIGOROUS LAVENDER ('Sakimp006') (NG)	MBros
- SUNPATIENS VIGOROUS MAGENTA ('Misato Fg3') (NG)	MBros
- SUNPATIENS VIGOROUS ORANGE ('Misato Fg2') (NG)	MBros
- SUNPATIENS VIGOROUS WHITE IMPROVED ('Sakimp010'^{PBR}) (NG)	MBros
tinctoria	CAbb CDTJ CExl CSpe EBee EPPr ESwi EWld IPot SBrt
- from Cherangani, Kenya	EPPr
tuberosa	WDib
uniflora	GGro SBrt WBor
VELVETEA	see *I.* 'Secret Love'
walleriana DeZire Series	MBros MPri
- - 'DeZire Red'	MBros
- - 'DeZire White'	MBros
- 'Salsa Red' (Fiesta Series) (d)	SCob
- Imara Series new	CRos
- (Xtreme Series) 'Xtreme Lavender' new	MBros
- - 'Xtreme Pink'	MBros
- - 'Xtreme Red'	MBros
- - 'Xtreme White'	MBros

Imperata (*Poaceae*)

cylindrica	CMen XLum
- 'Red Baron'	see *I. cylindrica* 'Rubra'
§ - 'Rubra'	Widely available

Incarvillea (*Bignoniaceae*)

arguta	XLum
- W/O 7122 new	GGro
brevipes	see *I. mairei*
'Brighton Pride' new	SBrt
compacta	GKev
- BWJ 7620	WCru
delavayi	CBcs CSBt CTsd ECha EDAr EGrI EHyd ELan EPfP GArf GKev LRHS MGos MSCN NRHS SDeJ SGBe SRms SVen SWvt WAvo WFar XLum
- 'Alba'	see *I. delavayi* 'Snowtop'
- 'Bees' Pink'	EPfP GEdr LPla
§ - 'Snowtop'	CBcs CTsd EBee EDAr EHyd ELan EPfP GBin SDeJ SWvt WBor WCot WFar
cf. ***delavayi***	CEme
forrestii	GKev
grandiflora	EBee GKev
himalayensis 'Frank Ludlow'	GKev
lutea	EBee GKev
§ ***mairei***	CRos EBee EHyd GKev GWyn LRHS NRHS SRms
- var. ***mairei*** f. ***multifoliata***	see *I. zhongdianensis*
olgae	EBee ELan GKev WPGP
'Snowdrop'	EMor
§ ***zhongdianensis***	EBee EDAr EPri GArf GEdr GKev
- BWJ 7692	WCru
- BWJ 7978	WCru
- W/O 7127 new	GGro

Indigofera (*Fabaceae*)

NJM 9166	WPGP
§ ***amblyantha***	CBcs CCCN CExl EHed EHyd EPfP GKev LRHS LShi MAsh MBlu MGil NLar NRHS NSti SPlb WCFE WSHC WSpi
aff. ***amblyantha***	MMrt
balfouriana Craib BWJ 7851	WCru
cassioides	WCru

§ 'Claret Cascade' ♀H5	EPfP LRHS WSHC
decora **new**	SBrt
dielsiana	CCCN EHyd ELan EPfP WSpi
'Dosua'	SEND
gerardiana	see *I. heterantha*
hancockii	CExl EPfP SChF WSHC
hebepetala	EPfP SBrt WCFE WSHC
§ ***heterantha*** ♀H5	Widely available
heterophylla	CCCN
himachalensis	EBee
- H&M 1818	WPGP
himalayensis	CExl EBee MGil WCFE
- Yu 10941	CExl
- 'Silk Road'	CCCN CKel CRos EBee EHed EHyd ELan EPfP GKev LRHS MBlu MGil MGos MNHC MSCN NLar NRHS SPoG SPtp WSpi
§ ***howellii*** 'Reginald Cory' ♀H5	CExl EBee EPfP ESwi LRHS WCru WPGP WSHC
kirilowii	CCCN EHyd ELan EPfP EWTr GKev LRHS MBlu NLar WPGP WSHC WSpi
- var. ***alba***	CKel EBee EPfP LRHS WPGP WSHC
§ ***pendula***	CCCN CExl CMac CRos CSde CWGN EBee EHyd ELan EPfP ESwi LRHS MGil SPoG WCFE WKif WPGP WSHC WSpi
- B&SWJ 7741	WCru
potaninii misapplied	see *I. howellii* 'Reginald Cory', *I. amblyantha*, *I.* 'Claret Cascade', *I. pendula*
potaninii ambig.	CBcs CExl CMac MMrt WHer
pseudotinctoria	CCCN MGil MHer SRms
aff. ***pseudotinctoria***	CCCN
subverticillata misapplied	see *I. howellii* 'Reginald Cory'
szechuensis	CKel CSde IDee LPla LRHS MGil NLar WSpi
tinctoria	CCCN

Indocalamus (*Poaceae*)

latifolius	MWht
solidus	see *Bonia solida*
§ ***tessellatus*** ♀H5	CAbb CBcs ELon MWht NGdn SMad
- f. ***hamadae***	MWht

Inula (*Asteraceae*)

acaulis	GKev WCot
conyzae	WSFF
dysenterica	see *Pulicaria dysenterica*
ensifolia	CBcs EHyd ELan EPfP MSCN WCav WHoo XLum
- 'Gold Star'	EBee MHol MRav NBid NBir WAvo WCot WFar
glandulosa	see *I. orientalis*
helenium	CBod CCBP CHab CHby EBou ENfk GGro GPoy ILea LCro LEdu LOPS MHer MNHC NBid NBir NGrd NLar SRms WGwG WHer WShi XAbr
hirta	XLum
hookeri	CChe CMea ECha ELan EShb GBin GMaP GWyn ILea LEdu LLWG LShi MBel MHer MHol MMuc MSpe NBid NChi NDov NPer NSti SAdn SBls SDix SEND WBrk WCAu WCav WWtn
- GWJ 9033	WCru
- 'Mude'	EBee
macrocephala misapplied	see *I. royleana*
magnifica	Widely available
- 'Sonnenstrahl' ♀H6	EPPr LEdu NLar SPhx
oculus-christi	EBee EWes WCot
§ ***orientalis***	CRos EBee EHyd EPfP GJos ILea LRHS MHol NGBl NLar NRHS SPad SPer SRms XLum
- 'Grandiflora'	EBlo
- B&SWJ 15379 **new**	WCru
racemosa	EBee EHyd EPPr EWes GBin GGro GJos GQue LRHS MACG MNrw NRHS SPlb SRms WBor
- 'Sonnenspeer'	CBod NBid NLar SBls
§ ***royleana***	MNrw MRav
salicina	EBee

Inulanthera (*Asteraceae*)

calva	WCot WFar

Iochroma (*Solanaceae*)

australe	see *Eriolarynx australis*
cyaneum	CCCN CDow ECre SPlb SVen
- purple-flowered	CCCN NGKo
§ - 'Trebah'	NGKo
fuchsioides	NGKo
gesnerioides 'Coccineum'	CCCN
grandiflorum	see *Trozelia grandiflora*
violaceum hort.	see *I. cyaneum* 'Trebah'

Ipheion (*Alliaceae*)

'Alberto Castillo' ♀H5	Widely available
'Alice'	WCot WMal
'Diana'	WCot
hirtellum	see *Nothoscordum hirtellum*
'Jessie'	CBor CBro CMea CPrp CTtf EBee ECha EHyd EPot ERCP EWes GKev LHWs LRHS NHpl NRHS SDeJ WBrk WMal WTor WTyc
'Judy'	WCot
'Rolf Fiedler' ♀H4	CBro CPrp CTri EBee EHyd ELan EPot ERCP EWes GKev LRHS NRHS NRog NRya SDeJ SRms WFar WHil
sellowianum	CTtf
'Tessa'PBR	EBee ECha EHyd ERCP EWes GKev LHWs NHpl
§ ***uniflorum***	CBor CBro CTri ECha EGrI GKev ITim NRog SEND SRms WBrk WCav WCot WShi WTyc XLum
- f. ***album***	CBro CPrp EBee ECha EHyd EWes GArf LRHS NRHS NRog WBrk WCot WHil WMal
- 'Charlotte Bishop'	CAvo CBro CPrp CRos EBee ECha EGrI EHyd ELon ERCP EWes GKev LHWs LRHS MNrw MPie NBir NHpl NRHS NRog NRya SDeJ SRms WBrk WCav WCot WHil WHoo WMal WTyc
- 'Froyle Mill' ♀H5	CAvo CBro CPrp EHyd ELon EPot ERCP EWes GKev LRHS MNrw NHpl NRHS NRog SDeJ SRms WCot WHoo
- 'Hoo House'	WHoo WMal
- 'Miss Hannah'	WMal
- subsp. ***tandiliense***	EBee EPPr
- 'Wisley Blue' ♀H5	CBod CBro CExl CPrp CRos CTri CWCL ECha EHyd ELan ELon EPot ERCP GKev LRHS MBros MRav NRHS NRog NRya SDeJ SPoG SRms WCot
- 'Wisley Star'	GKev

Ipomoea (*Convolvulaceae*)

acuminata	see *I. indica*
alba	CCCN EShb

batatas	CCCN
- 'Beauregard'	SVic
- 'Bonita'	LRHS
- (Bright Ideas Series) BRIGHT IDEAS BLACK	EShb
- - BRIGHT IDEAS LIME ('Fripalligr')	EShb
- 'O'Henry'	SVic
cairica	WCot
carnea	CCCN
§ ***hederifolia***	CCCN
× ***imperialis*** 'Sunrise Serenade'	CCCN
§ ***indica*** ♀H1c	CCCN CRHN ECre EShb SPer
learii	see *I. indica*
lindheimeri	SMad
§ ***lobata*** ♀H1c	CSpe LCro LOPS WHil
mauritiana	CCCN
'Milky Way'	CCCN
muellerii	CCCN
× ***multifida***	CSpe
purpurea 'Kniola's Black Night'	CSpe
quamoclit	CSpe
tricolor 'Heavenly Blue' ♀H1c	LCro LOPS
versicolor	see *I. lobata*

Iresine (*Amaranthaceae*)

BLAZIN' LIME	see *I.* 'Lime'
herbstii ♀H1c	SSal
§ 'Lime'	SSal

Iris ✿ (*Iridaceae*)

AGSJ	EPPr
KR 3739	GEdr
'Abbey Chant' (IB)	XSen
'About Town' (TB)	WCAu
'Absolute Treasure' (TB)	WCAu
'Acacia Rhumba' (La)	LLWG
'Action Front' (TB)	CBod CEnd CKel CRos ECtt EHyd EIri EPfP ESgI EShb EWoo GBin LRHS MCot MGos NRHS SDeJ WGwG
'Actress' (TB)	CRos ECtt EHyd EPfP ETod LRHS LSRN MCot MGos NRHS WGwG
acutiloba × ***afghanica***	GKev
'Adobe Rose' (TB)	SIri XSen
'Adventuress' (TB)	XSen
'Afternoon Delight' (TB)	ESgI
'Afternoon in Rio' (TB)	WCAu
'Agatha Christie' (IB)	CKel WCAu
'Agnes James' (CH)	CBro MAvo
'Ahwahnee Princess' (SDB)	ELon
'Aichi-no-kagayaki' (SpH)	WCot XLum
'Alabaster Unicorn' (TB)	ESgI
albicans ♀H5	CBro EPot GKev LEdu
'Alcazar' (TB)	EWoo GDam
'Alice Harding' (TB)	ESgI
'Alida' (Reticulata)	EHyd EPot ERCP EShb EWoo GKev LCro LOPS LRHS NBir NRHS NRog SDeJ WBrk
'Alien Mist' (TB)	EIri
'Alizes' (TB) ♀H7	CKel ESgI LRHS WViv XSen
'Ally Oops' (SpH)	CDor LLWG
'Amadora' (TB)	EIri
'Amanda Jane' (AB) **new**	EWld
'Amas' (TB)	EWoo
'Amazing Grace' (TB)	EWoo
'Amber Beauty' (Dut)	NRog
'Amber Queen' (SDB)	CKel ECtt EHyd ELan NBir SCob SDeJ WGwG
'Ambroisie' (TB) ♀H7	ESgI
'Amethyst Flame' (TB)	SRms
'Amherst Blue' (IB)	EIri
'Amherst Caper' (SDB)	EIri
'Amherst Glacier' (IB)	WCAu
'Amphora' (SDB)	CBro
'Ancient Echoes' (TB)	ESgI
'Andalou' (TB) ♀H7	CWCL WViv XSen
anglica	see *I. latifolia*
'Ann Chowning' (La)	CPud GAbr LCro MWts SDir WHil WPnP
'Annabel Jane' (TB)	ELon WCAu
'Anne Elizabeth' (SDB)	CBro
'Annemarie Troeger' (Sib) ♀H7	ELon
'Annick' (Sib)	EHyd MMrt XSen
'Antarctique' (IB)	ESgI
'Antiope' (Rc)	GKev
'Aphrodisiac' (TB)	XSen
aphylla	GBin SBrt WAbe
- 'Aslet's Purple' **new**	GBin
'Apollo' (Dut)	CAvo NRog
'Appointer' (SpH)	NChi
'Apricorange' (TB)	SRms WCot
'Apricot Blaze' (TB)	ESgI
'Apricot Drops' (MTB) ♀H7	ESgI EWoo WCAu
'Apricot Frosty' (BB)	XSen
'Apricot Silk' (IB)	CKel NQui WCot
'Aquamarine' (IB)	MHol
'Archie Owen' (Spuria)	WCAu
'Arctic Night' (IB)	WCAu
'Arctic Sunrise' (TB)	CKel ESgI
arenaria	see *I. humilis*
'Argus Pheasant' (TB)	ESgI
'Around Midnight' (TB)	EHyd
'Arpège' (TB)	CKel GWyn LCro LOPS XSen
'Arrows' (La)	LLWG
'Art Deco' (TB)	SIri XSen
'As de Coeur' (TB)	XSen
'Ascension Crown' (TB)	ESgI
'Ask Alma' (IB)	SIri XSen
'Astro Flash' (TB)	ESgI
'Attention Please' (TB)	SBea
attica	CBro CMea GEdr GKev WThu
- blue-flowered	GKev
- lemon-flowered	EPPr GKev WAbe WThu
- violet-flowered	GKev
§ ***aucheri*** ♀H4	EPot GKev NRog XSen
- 'Leylek Ice'	NRog
- 'Olof'	GKev
'Audition' (La)	LLWG
'Aunt Josephine' (TB)	ESgI
'Aurélie' (TB)	WViv
'Austrian Sky' (SDB)	CKel CMac ECtt EHyd ELon EPfP SDeJ WCot
'Autumn Circle'	WCAu
'Autumn Echo' (TB)	ESgI LRHS XSen
'Autumn Encore' (TB)	CKel SRms
'Autumn Princess' (Dut)	GKev SDeJ
'Autumn Riesling' (TB)	WCAu
'Autumn Tryst' (TB)	ESgI WCAu
'Avalon Sunset' (TB)	EIri
'Avanelle' (IB)	GBin
'Awesome Blossom' (TB)	ESgI
'Az Ap' (IB)	ELon WCAu
babadagica	GEdr WAbe
'Babbling Brook' (TB)	CKel ESgI GWyn XSen
'Baby Bengal' (BB)	XSen
'Baby Blessed' (SDB)	CBro WCAu
'Baby Sister' (Sib)	EBlo EHyd ELon EWoo GBin LSRN NBro WFar

'Badlands' (TB)	WCAu
'Baie Rose' (IB)	SIri
'Bal Masqué' (TB)	ESgI WViv XSen
'Ballerina Pink' (BB)	WCAu
'Ballet Lesson' (SDB)	ESgI
'Ballyhoo' (TB)	XSen
'Baltic Star' (TB)	WCAu
'Banbury Beauty' (CH) ♀H4	NLar
'Banbury Gem' (CH)	MAvo NLar
'Banbury Ruffles' (SDB)	ESgI LRHS NLar WCAu
'Bangles' (MTB) ♀H7	WCAu
'Banish Misfortune' (Sib)	EPri LLWG WGob
'Bar de Nuit' (TB)	ESgI EWoo
'Barbara May' (TB)	WCAu
'Barbara My Love' (TB)	WCAu
barbatula	SBrt
– BWJ 7663	WCru
'Barcoo' (La)	LLWG
'Batik' (BB)	WCot XSen
'Bayberry Candle' (TB)	CKel
'Beauty Becomes Her' (TB)	WCAu
'Bedtime Story' (IB)	XSen
'Before the Storm' (TB)	CKel CTsd ELan ELon ESgI LRHS WCAu WLov XSen
'Being Busy' (SDB)	ESgI
'Bel Azur' (IB)	ESgI LRHS
'Belgian Princess' (TB)	SIri WCAu
'Belise' (Spuria)	WCot
'Belle de Nuit' (TB)	WViv
'Benbow' (TB)	WMil
'Benton Ankaret' (TB)	EMal
'Benton Apollo' (TB)	ECha EMal WMal
'Benton Argent' (TB)	ECha ESgI
'Benton Arundel' (TB)	EGrI EMal ESgI EWoo SIri
'Benton Bluejohn' (TB)	EMal
'Benton Caramel' (TB)	CMil ECha ECtt EMal EPfP ETod EWoo LRHS MBriF NRHS
'Benton Cordelia' (TB)	ECha ECtt EMal EPfP EWoo MBriF MCot WMal
'Benton Daphne' (TB)	EMal ESgI
'Benton Dierdre' (TB)	CCBP CMil ECha ECtt ELan ELon EMal EPfP ESgI EWoo LRHS MBriF NRHS SRms
'Benton Duff' (TB)	CMil ECha ESgI NRHS
'Benton Evora' (TB)	ECha EMal ESgI
'Benton Farewell' (TB)	ECha
'Benton Judith' (TB)	ECha WMal
'Benton Lorna' (TB)	CMil ECha ECtt ELan EMal EPfP EWoo GBin MBriF MHol NRHS
'Benton Menace' (TB)	ECha EMal
'Benton Nigel' (TB)	CMil ECha ECtt ELan EMal EWoo LRHS MBriF SBea WGwG WMal
'Benton Nutkin' (TB)	EMal
'Benton Old Madrid'	ECha EMal
'Benton Olive' (TB)	ECha EMal NRHS
'Benton Opal' (TB)	ECha EMal ESgI WGwG
'Benton Pearl' (TB)	ECha EMal ESgI
'Benton Primrose' (TB)	CEnd CMil ECha EMal ESgI ETod NRHS SBea WGwG
'Benton Sheila' (TB)	CCBP CKel CMil ECha ELan ELon EWoo
'Benton Susan' (TB)	CMil ECha ECtt EMal ESgI ETod EWoo MBriF MCot NRHS WGwG
'Berkeley Gold' (TB)	CRos CSBt ECtt ELan EWes LRHS NRHS SCob SDeJ SPer WGwG
'Berlin Bluebird' (Sib)	SMHy
'Berlin Purple Wine' (Sib)	EPri ESgI WGob
'Berlin Ruffles' (Sib) ♀H7	EWes
'Berlin Sky' (Sib)	EWes
'Berlin Tiger' (SpH) ♀H7	CBen EPPr EWoo LLWG MSCN NLar SDix SMHy

'Berlin Violetta' (SpH) **new**	GBin
'Best Bet' (TB)	ESgI MNHC WCAu
'Bethany Claire' (TB)	ESgI WCAu
'Better Believe It' (La)	LLWG
'Better Together' (TB)	WCAu
'Betty Cooper' (Spuria)	WCAu
'Betty Simon' (TB)	XSen
'Beverly Sills' (TB)	CKel CRos ECtt EHyd EIri EPfP LCro LRHS MRav NRHS SBls SDeJ WLov XSen
'Bewilderbeast' (TB)	XSen
'Bianco' (TB)	EWoo GWyn WCAu WHil
'Bickley Cape' (Sib)	GBin
'Big Blue' (Sib)	WFar
'Big Heart' (Sib)	EIri
'Big Squeeze' (TB)	SIri
biglumis	see *I. lactea*
biliottii	CBro
'Bishop's Robe' (TB)	CKel LCro LOPS LRHS
'Black as Night' (TB)	XSen
'Black Aura'	NWad
'Black Cherry Delight' (SDB)	ESgI
'Black Dragon' (TB)	CKel EGrI GWyn WSpi XSen
'Black Flag' (TB)	XSen
'Black Gamecock' (La)	CPud CWCL ECtt EGrI EShb GKev LCro LLWG LOPS MHer MNrw MSCN MWts NLar SBls WCAu WFar WMAq WPnP
'Black is Back' (TB)	WCAu
'Black Joker' (Sib)	ELon EPfP LLWG MHol WGob
'Black Knight' (TB)	EGrI LRHS MRav NQui SCob WKif WSpi
'Black Magic' (IB)	EWoo
'Black Suited' (TB)	SIri
'Black Swan' (TB)	CBor CEme CKel CMac ECha ECtt EHyd ELan EPfP ESgI EShb EWTr LCro LOPS LRHS LSRN MCot NQui NRHS SBea SCob SPeP SPer SPoG SRms WCot XSen
'Black Taffeta' (TB)	WSpi
'Black Tie Affair' (TB)	CBod CEnd CKel ECtt EHyd ELan EPfP ESgI LRHS MAsh MCot NRHS XSen
'Black Watch' (IB)	CKel GWyn LCro LOPS LRHS
'Blackbeard' (BB) ♀H7	WCAu
'Blackbeard's Ghost' (AB)	WCAu
'Blackberry Tease' (TB)	WCAu
'Blackberry Towers' (TB)	ESgI
'Blackcurrant' (IB)	WCAu
'Blackout' (TB)	ESgI
'Blatant' (TB)	ESgI XSen
'Blaue Milchstrasse' (Sib)	GBin GWyn MMrt
'Blaues Schweben' (Sib)	GBin
'Blazing Light' (TB)	XSen
'Blenheim Royal' (TB)	ESgI XSen
bloudowii	WAbe
'Blue Admiral' (TB)	GBin
'Blue Bird' (Sib)	ECtt MBros SCoo SPoG WFar WGob
'Blue Boy' (IB)	EWoo
'Blue Burgee' (Sib)	ECha
I 'Blue Butterfly' (Sib)	EPfP NGdn
'Blue Denim' (SDB)	CMea ECtt ELon EPfP GMaP MHol MRav NBir NLar SCob WCot
'Blue Eyed Blond' (IB)	CKel MBriF SBea
'Blue Eyed Brunette' (TB)	ESgI
'Blue Gown' (TB)	EWoo
'Blue Hendred' (SDB)	NBir
'Blue Hill' (Reticulata)	ERCP GKev NRog
'Blue Ice' (Reticulata) **new**	ERCP GKev
'Blue King' (Dut)	EHyd SCob

'Blue King' (Sib)	CBod CDor CKel ELan EPfP GMaP LSun MRav NBro NGdn SPer
'Blue Magic' (Dut) ♀H5	CAvo
'Blue Mere' (Sib)	MCot MHol
'Blue Moon' (Sib)	ELon WFar
'Blue Mountain Mist' (La)	LLWG
'Blue my Mind' (TB)	WCAu
'Blue Note' (Reticulata)	EHyd EPfP EPot ERCP EWoo GKev LRHS NRHS NRog SPer
'Blue Note Blues' (TB)	WCAu
'Blue Pigmy' (SDB)	CBod CWat ECtt EGrI EHyd EPfP MRav MTin NLar SDeJ SPer
'Blue Reverie' (Sib)	ELon
'Blue Rhythm' (TB)	CEnd EHyd ELan ELon EPfP EWoo GBin GMaP LRHS MCot MRav NRHS SCoo SDeJ SPer
'Blue Sapphire' (TB)	CKel ESgI
'Blue Sapphire' (Dut)	MHol
'Blue Shimmer' (TB)	CMac EBee ECha ECtt ELan EPfP ESgI EShb EWoo LRHS LSRN MCot NRHS SDeJ SPer SRms WGwG
'Blue Splash' (IB)	WCAu
'Blue Staccato' (TB)	ESgI WCAu XSen
'Blue Suede Shoes' (TB)	ESgI LSRN XSen
'Blue Trill' (TB)	WCAu
'Blueberry Fair' (Sib)	CDor
'Bluebird Wine' (TB)	CKel
'Blushing Pink' (TB)	CKel
'Bold Encounter' (TB)	WCAu
'Bold Pretender' (La)	CBod ECtt EGrI ELon EPfP MBros MHol NLar WHil
'Bold Print' (IB)	CBod CKel CRos ECtt EHyd ELon GMaP IPot LRHS LSRN MCot MGos MHer NRHS SMad SPoG WCAu WLov
'Boo' (SDB)	WCAu XSen
'Border Town' (Spuria)	WCAu
'Bottled Sunshine' (IB)	LRHS
'Bound for Glory' (La)	LLWG
'Bournemouth Beauty' (Sib) ♀H7	CDor
'Bouzy Bouzy' (TB)	ESgI XSen
bracteata	EBee
'Braithwaite' (TB)	CKel CRos CWGN EHyd ELan EPfP ESgI EShb LRHS NRHS SBea SCob SDeJ SPer SRms WGwG
'Brannigan' (SDB)	NBir NSti
'Brasilia' (TB)	NBir
'Brassie' (SDB)	CBro XSen
'Breakers' (TB) ♀H7	ESgI WCAu
'Brenchley' (IB)	SIri
§ 'Bride' (DB)	NLar
'Bride's Halo' (TB)	XSen
'Bright Button' (SDB)	ESgI
'Bright Vision' (SDB)	ESgI
'Bright White' (MDB)	CBro
'Bright Yellow' (DB)	MRav
'Brighteyes' (IB)	SRms
'Brindisi' (TB)	XSen
'Brise de Mer' (TB)	XSen
'Bristo Magic' (TB)	XSen
'Bristol Gem' (TB)	XSen
'Broadleigh Angela' (CH)	CBro
'Broadleigh Carolyn' (CH) ♀H5	CElw WMal WSHC
'Broadleigh Dorothy' (CH)	MAvo
'Broadleigh Lavinia' (CH)	CBro CPla
'Broadleigh Nancy' (CH)	CBro
'Broadleigh Peacock' (CH)	CElw MAvo NLar WHil WMal WSHC
'Broadleigh Penny' (CH)	NLar
'Broadleigh Rose' (CH)	CBro CElw CTtf EGrI EPri MAvo MBrN WSHC

'Broadway Baby' (IB)	ESgI
'Broadway Star' (TB)	CKel
'Bronzaire' (IB)	EIri WCAu WGwG
'Bronze Beauty' (Dut)	ERCP NRog
'Bronze Beauty' (TB)	SDeJ
'Bronze Beauty' van Tubergen (*boogiana* hybrid)	NBir SDeJ
'Brother Carl' (TB)	XSen
'Bruno' (TB)	EWoo LSRN NLar WMil
'Brussels' (TB)	ESgI
bucharica misapplied	see *I. orchioides* Carrière
bucharica ambig.	CAvo ECha EWoo GKev MBow MNrw NHpl SDeJ XSen
§ ***bucharica*** Foster ♀H5	CBro EPot WHil
- 'Princess'	NRog
* - 'Top Gold' (J)	GKev
'Buckwheat' (TB)	SIri
'Buisson de Roses' (TB)	XSen
bulleyana	CBro GKev SRms
- BWJ 7912	WCru
- black-flowered	CExl GKev
- - SDR 1792	EBee
'Bumblebee Deelite' (MTB) ♀H7	CBor CKel WCAu WMal
'Bundle of Joy' (Sib)	ECtt WGob
'Bundle of Love' (BB)	WCAu
'Burgermeister' (TB)	XSen
'Burgundy Party' (TB)	XSen
'Burka' (TB)	ESgI
'Burmese Dawn' (TB)	CKel
'Burnt Toffee' (TB)	ESgI SIri XSen
'Buto' (TB)	EWoo
'Butter and Sugar' (Sib)	Widely available
'Buttermere' (TB)	SRms
'Butterpat' (IB)	ESgI
'Butterscotch Kiss' (TB)	CMac EHyd ELan ELon EPfP LRHS MGos MRav NBir NLar NRHS SDeJ SPeP SPer WHoo WLov
'Bye Bye Blues' (TB)	ESgI XSen
'Cabaret Royale' (TB)	ESgI XSen
'Cable Car' (TB)	CKel ESgI
'Caesar' (Sib)	SRms
'Caesar's Brother' (Sib)	CKel CRos EHyd ELan EWoo GBee GWyn LCro LOPS LRHS MGos NHol NLar NRHS SHar SPer WBrk WFar WWtn
'Cajun Rhythm' (TB)	CKel XSen
'Calaeno' (Reticulata) **new**	GKev
'Caldron' (TB)	CKel
'Caliente' (TB)	MRav WCAu XSen
'California Style' (IB)	CKel XSen
§ Californian hybrids	CElw CMac NBir WCot
'Calm Stream' (TB)	WCAu
'Calypso Beat' (TB)	SIri
'Calypso Mood' (TB)	XSen
'Cambridge' (Sib) ♀H7	EHyd EIri EPfP LRHS NRHS WFar WGob WWtn
'Camelot' (TB) **new**	WMil
'Camelot Rose' (TB)	XSen
'Cameo Blush' (BB)	XSen
'Cameo Wine' (TB)	ESgI MNrw XSen
'Cameroun' (TB)	ESgI EWoo
'Campbellii'	see *I. lutescens* 'Campbellii'
canadensis	see *I. hookeri*
'Canadian Streaker' (TB/v)	EWoo
'Canary Bird' (TB)	ESgI
'Candy Rock' (IB)	WCAu
'Cannington Ochre' (SDB)	CBro
'Cantab' (Reticulata)	EHyd GKev LRHS NBir NRHS SDeJ
'Canterbury' (TB)	LRHS
'Cape Cod Boys' (Sib)	CDor WGob

	'Captain Indigo' (IB)	ESgI
	'Captive Sun' (SDB)	CKel ECtt EHyd EPfP MAsh SIri WGwG WTor
	'Caramel' (TB)	XSen
	'Cardinal' (TB)	WMil
	'Care to Dance' (TB)	WCAu
	'Carfax' (TB)	WMil
	'Caribbean Dream' (TB)	NLar XSen
	'Carnaby' (TB)	CBod CEnd CKel EHyd ELon EPfP ESgI EShb LRHS MRav NRHS SDeJ WGwG XSen
	'Carnival Time' (TB)	CBod CKel CMac CRos CWGN ECtt EHyd EPfP ESgI ETod LRHS MBriF MCot MHer NRHS WHoo WLov XSen
	'Carolina' (Reticulata)	EHyd NRHS
	'Carolina Gold' (TB)	CKel XSen
*	'Caronte' (IB)	ESgI
	'Carriage Trade' (TB)	LRHS
	'Cartouche' (BB)	SIri
	'Casbah' (TB)	XSen
	'Cascade Springs' (TB)	XSen
	'Cascade Sprite' (SDB)	SRms
	'Casque d'Or' (TB)	LCro LOPS
	'Catalyst' (TB)	XSen
	'Cat's Eye' (SDB)	SIri
	'Catwalk Idol' (La)	LLWG
	caucasica	CMac
	'Cayenne Capers' (TB)	ESgI
*	'Cedric Morris'	EWes
	'Cee Cee' (TB)	XSen
	'Cee Jay' (IB) ♀H7	EWoo
	'Celebration Song' (TB)	ESgI SIri WCAu XSen
	'Celestial Glory' (TB)	XSen
	'Cerdagne' (TB)	XSen
	'Champagne Elegance' (TB)	CKel EIri EPfP NBir XSen
	'Champagne Encore' (IB)	ELon
	'Champagne Frost' (TB)	XSen
	'Champagne Waltz' (TB)	XSen
	'Chance Beauty' (SpH) ♀H7	GBin
	'Change of Pace' (TB)	ESgI XSen
	'Chanted' (SDB)	XSen
	'Chantilly' (TB)	ELan EWoo LRHS MRav NBir NGdn NLar NRHS SPer
	'Chapeau' (TB)	ESgI WCAu
	'Charlotte's Tutu' (La)	LLWG
	'Charmaine' (TB)	XSen
	'Charming Billy' (Sib)	ECtt MHol NLar WGob
	'Chartreuse Bounty' (Sib)	CDor ECtt ELan EPri EWes GMaP MHol MMrt NLar WFar WGob
	'Chasing Rainbows' (TB)	WCAu
	'Cheap Frills' (TB)	WCAu
	'Cherished' (TB)	CKel
	'Cherished One' (La)	LLWG
	'Cherry Blossom Song' (TB)	SIri
	'Cherry Garden' (SDB)	CBro CWat ECtt EGrI EHyd ELan ELon EPfP EShb EWes GKev GMaP MBNS MRav MTin NBir NGdn NLar SCob SDeJ WCot WGwG
	'Cherub's Smile' (TB)	XSen
	'Chicken Little' (MDB)	CBro
I	'Chieftain' (SDB)	MRav
	'Childhood Sweetheart' (La)	LLWG
	'Chilled Wine' (Sib)	ELan ELon LRHS
	'China Dragon' (TB)	XSen
	'Chinese Coral' (TB)	XSen
	'Chinese Treasure' (TB)	XSen
	'Chinook Winds' (TB)	ESgI
	'Chivalry' (TB)	ESgI
	'Chou Bleu' (TB)	SIri
	'Christine Mullins' (Sib)	WBor
	'Christmas Angel' (TB)	NLar
	chrysographes ♀H6	CBcs CBod CBro CDor CEme CKel CTsd EBlo EGrI EHyd EPfP EPri EWhm EWoo GDam GJos GKev LCro LOPS LRHS MHer MRav NRHS SDir SPeP SPoG WFar WPnP XSen
	- BWJ 7930	WCru
I	- 'Black Beauty'	EWoo
	- 'Black Gold'	CPla ECtt EPri ESgI LRHS MHol NLar
I	- 'Black Knight'	CExl EHyd EPfP GBin MCot NChi NFav NLar SChF SMad
I	- 'Black Velvet'	GEdr WSpi
	- black-flowered	CExl EBee ELan GAbr GKev GKin LCro LOPS LRHS LShi MNrw NGdn NHpl NLar NRHS SBls SCob SPer WCru WFar WGwG WPGP WPnP WSHC WSpi
	- 'Bob's Fancy'	SDeJ
	- dark-flowered	GKev WFar
	- hybrid	ESgI WFar
	- 'Kew Black'	CExl GKev LEdu NBir
	- 'Mandarin Purple'	GBin GQue SPer
	- yellow-flowered	WFar
	chrysographes* × *forrestii	NBir
	'Château d'Auvers-sur-Oise' (TB)	SIri WViv
	'Ciel et Mer' (TB)	WViv
	'Cimarron Rose' (SDB)	ESgI
	'Cimarron Strip' (TB)	CKel EPfP WCot XSen
	'Cinque Terre' (TB)	WCAu
	'Circle of Light' (TB)	WCAu
	'Circus Stripes' (TB)	XSen
	'Citoyen' (TB)	XSen
	'Citronnade' (TB)	ESgI
	'City of Paradise' (TB)	ESgI
	'Clairette' (Reticulata)	CRos EHyd EPot GKev LRHS NRHS NRog SDeJ
	'Clarence' (TB)	ESgI MHol XSen
	clarkei	MHol
	- B&SWJ 2122	WCru
	- CC 2751	CExl
	- SDR 3819	GKev
	'Class Ring' (TB)	WCAu
	'Classic Look' (TB)	ESgI SIri
	'Classic Navy' (BB)	ESgI
	'Clear Blue Sky' (SDB)	WCAu
	'Clematis' (TB)	WMil
	'Cleo' (TB)	NSti
	'Cleo Murrell' (TB)	ESgI EWoo
	'Cleve Dodge' (Sib)	EPri EWoo WGob XLum
	'Cliffs of Dover' (TB)	CKel EIri ESgI LCro LOPS MCot SCob SCoo SRms
	'Cloudcap' (TB)	SRms
	'Clownerie' (TB)	WViv
	'Clyde Redmond' (La) ♀H5	WMal
	'Coal Face' (TB)	WCAu
	'Coal Seams' (TB)	WCAu
	'Coalignition' (TB)	WCAu
	'Codicil' (TB)	ESgI WViv XSen
	colchica	LEdu
	'Colette Thurillet' (TB)	CKel WViv XSen
	'Colin's Pale Blue' (Sib)	SMHy
	'Color Glory' (TB)	SIri
	'Color Me Blue' (TB)	WCAu
	'Color Splash' (TB)	XSen
	'Color Strokes' (TB)	WCAu
	'Colorific' (La)	WGob
	'Colortart' (TB)	XSen
	'Coming Up Roses' (TB)	XSen

'Con Fuoco' (TB) XSen
'Concertina' (IB) WCAu
'Concord Crush' (Sib) WGob WPnP WTor WTyc WWtn
confusa 🏆H4 ESwi MACG MBriF SArc SMad SPlb XSen XSte
§ - 'Martyn Rix' CAbb CBct CMac CWCL EGrI ELon EPPr EPfP ESwi LRHS MACG MBriF MPie SBrt SEND SRms WGwG
'Conjuration' (TB) CKel SIri WCAu
'Constant Wattez' (IB) CKel ESgI NLar
'Constantine Bay' (TB) ESgI
'Contrast in Styles' (Sib) ECtt EPri MNrw MSCN NQui SDir WFar WGob WWtn
'Cool Change' (TB) WCAu
'Copatonic' (TB) ESgI WCAu
'Copper Capers' (TB) ESgI
'Copper Classic' (TB) ELon ESgI LSRN WCAu
'Coquet Waters' (Sib) NBid
'Coraband' (TB) NLar
'Coral Sunset' (TB) XSen
'Cordoba' (TB) WCAu XSen
'Coronation Anthem' (Sib) EPri EWoo
'Côte d'Azur' (Sib) CBor
'Côte d'Or' (TB) XSen
'Country Charm' (TB) WCAu
'Country Kisses' (TB) WCAu
'County Town Red' (TB) SIri
'Coup de Soleil' (TB) WViv
'Cracklin' Burgundy' (TB) XSen
'Crackling Caldera' (TB) MMrt
'Cranapple' (BB) 🏆H7 EIri ESgI WCAu
'Cranberry Ice' (TB) ELon XSen
'Cranberry Sauce' (TB) SIri
'Cranbrook' (IB) 🏆H7 SIri
'Crathie' (TB) ECha EHyd EMal
'Cream Beauty' (Dut) LCro LOPS SDeJ
cretensis see *I. unguicularis* subsp. *cretensis*
'Crimson King' (IB) EWoo
'Crinoline' (TB) CKel XSen
cristata EPot GEdr NHpl SGro SMad
- 'Abbey's Violet' CBod SMad
- 'Alba' SGro WAbe WHil
§ - 'Captain Collingwood' WAbe
cristata × lacustris GArf
crocea 🏆H6 GBin SPtp
'Croftway Lemon' (TB) ELon WSpi
'Crowned Heads' (TB) WCAu XSen
'Crushed Ice' (La) LLWG
'Crystal Gazer' (TB) WCAu
'Crystal Glitters' (TB) ESgI
'Cumulus' (TB) SIri
'Cup Race' (TB) XSen
'Curlew' (IB) WCAu
'Currier' (Sib) **new** CBod
'Cute or What' (SDB) SIri
'Cyanea' (DB) EGrI GKev
'Cyclamint' (La) LLWG
cycloglossa EPot GKev NRog
'Daedalus' (Rc) GKev
'Daemon Imp' (MTB) EIri WCAu
'Dainty Lace' (La) LLWG
'Dale Dennis' (DB) XSen
'Dance Ballerina Dance' (Sib) CBod CWCL EBee EPri GWyn MRav NFav NLar WFar WGob
'Dance for Joy' (TB) XSen
'Dance the Night Away' (TB) WCAu
'Dancer's Veil' (TB) CKel CMac EBee ECtt EHyd ELon EPfP LRHS MRav NRHS SPer WHoo
'Dancing Lilacs' (MTB) ESgI
'Dancing Nanou' (Sib) ECtt
danfordiae EHyd EPot GKev LCro LOPS LRHS NHpl NRHS NRog SDeJ
'Daphne' (TB) WMil
'Dardanus' (Rc) EPot ERCP GKev NRog SDeJ WCot
'Dark Circle' (Sib) EBee WFar
'Dark Crystal' (SDB) ESgI
'Dark Desire' (Sib) MRav
'Dark Vader' (SDB) ESgI
'Darkness' (IB) SIri
'Darkside' (TB) XSen
'Dating a Royal' (TB) WCAu
'Daughter of Stars' (TB) ELon
'Dauntless' (TB) CCBP ESgI
'Dawn of Fall' (TB) ESgI
'Dawn Waltz' (Sib) ELon WFar WGob
'Dawning' (TB) 🏆H7 ESgI
'Dazzling Gold' (TB) CKel ESgI XSen
'Dear Delight' (Sib) ELon MNrw NLar WFar
'Death by Chocolate' (SDB) SIri
'Decadence' (TB) WCAu
§ ***decora*** WAbe
'Deep Black' (TB) CKel CRos CWGN EBee ECha ELan EPfP ESgI ETod EWoo GBin GMaP LRHS LSRN MBNS MBriF MCot MRav NLar NRHS NWad SDeJ SPer SPoG WGwG
'Deft Touch' (TB) XSen
delavayi 🏆H6 EWes GGro
- SDR 50 CExl GKev
- 'Didcot' CRos EHyd LRHS NRHS
'Delirium' (IB) WCAu
'Delta Butterfly' (La) WMAq
'Demon' (SDB) SMrm XSen
'Demure Illini' (Sib) MNrw
'Depth of Field' (TB) EGrI
'Derwentwater' (TB) SRms WCAu
'Desert Echo' (TB) XSen
'Desert Song' (TB) EGrI
'Devil May Care' (IB) ESgI
'Dewful' (Sib) WFar
'Diabolique' (TB) 🏆H7 XSen
'Dirigo Black Velvet' (Sib) ELon
'Disco Jewel' (MTB) ESgI
'Discovered Treasure' (TB) WCAu
'Discovery' PBR (Dut) GKev SDeJ
'Disguise' (TB) WCAu
'Distant Music' (La) LLWG
'Ditzy' (SDB) SIri
'Diversion' (TB) ESgI
'Dividing Line' (MTB) WCAu
'Dixie Darling' (TB) ESgI XSen
'Dixie Pixie' (SDB) WCAu
'Dogrose' (TB) EWoo
'Dolce' (SpH) WCAu
dolichosiphon GKev
subsp. ***orientalis*** **new**
§ ***domestica*** CBro CPla EHyd EPPr MACG SMad SPlb SRms WSHC
- 'Freckle Face' CWCL MHol
'Dominion' (TB) WMil
'Dotted Swiss' (TB) XSen
'Double Byte' (SDB) XSen
'Double Espoir' (TB) XSen
'Double Lament' (SDB) CBro
'Double Standards' (Sib) EPri NLar SDir WFar WGob
'Double Vision' (TB) XSen
'Douce Reverie' (TB) WViv
douglasiana GKev
'Dover Beach' (TB) SIri
'Dover Castle' (BB) 🏆H7 SIri
'Downtown Brown' (TB) WCAu

	'Draco' (TB)	ECtt EPfP ESgI IPot SBea XSen
	'Dream Indigo' (IB)	EWoo XSen
	'Dreaming Green' (Sib)	EBee ECha
	'Dreaming Orange' (Sib)	ECtt EPri SDir
	'Dreaming Spires' (Sib)	GBin
	'Dreaming Yellow' (Sib)	CBar CKel CPud ECha EHyd EPri ESgI EWhm GBin GKin LRHS MRav NGdn NRHS SPer WCAu WGob WGwG WWtn
	'Duke of Bedford' (TB)	WMil
	'Dunkler Wein' (Sib)	EWes
	'Dunlin' (MDB)	CBro NBir SBut
	'Dusky Challenger' (TB)	CBod CKel EBee ECtt EPfP ESgI LCro LOPS LRHS MMrt SRms WCAu XSen
	'Dusky Evening' (TB)	XSen
	'Dutch Chocolate' (TB)	EWes LCro LOPS XSen
	'Dynamite' (TB)	XSen
	'Dyonisos' (TB)	SIri
	'Eagle's Flight' (TB)	XSen
	'Earl of Essex' (TB)	XSen
	'Early Light' (TB) ♀H7	EIri ESgI
	'Easter' (SDB)	SIri
	'Eastertime' (TB)	ESgI
	'Eastman Winds' (La)	LLWG
	'Easy' (MTB)	EIri
	'Échassier' (TB)	SIri
	'Echo de France' (TB)	ESgI SRms XSen
	'Eden's Paradise Blue' (Sib)	ELon
	'Edge of Winter' (TB)	XSen
	'Edith Wolford' (TB)	CKel GWyn MMrt SBea SCob XSen
	'Edna Grace' (La)	LLWG
	'Ed's Blue' (DB)	ELan
	'Edward' (Reticulata)	EPfP NRog SDeJ
	'Edward of Windsor' (TB)	ELan EWoo GMaP LRHS NLar
	'Ego' (Sib)	ECha ELon EPfP EPri EWTr EWoo GMaP WFar
	'Eileen Louise' (TB) ♀H7	WCAu
	'Elaine's Wedding' (La) **new**	LLWG
	'Eleanor Roosevelt' (IB)	EWoo
	'Eleanor's Pride' (TB)	SRms
	elegantissima	see *I. iberica* subsp. *elegantissima*
	'Elizabeth Poldark' (TB)	ESgI XSen
	'Elsa Sass' (TB)	ESgI
	'Elsie Petty' (IB)	SIri
	'Elvinhall'	CBro
	'Emperor' (Sib)	CWat LRHS NSti
	'Empress of India' (TB)	EWTr EWoo
	'Endless Love' (TB)	EIri
	'English Charm' (TB)	ESgI XSen
	'English Cottage' (TB)	CKel CTsd ELon EWoo GBin LSRN MHer NLar SMrm SRms WCAu WSpi XSen
	'Ennerdale' (TB)	SRms
	'Enriched' (MTB) ♀H7	WCAu
§	***ensata***	CBcs CBro CRos CTri EGrI ELan EPfP GArf LRHS LSun MMuc MNrw NLar NRHS SCob SPlb SRms WBor WPnP WWtn
	- 'Activity'	ELon WFar
	- 'Alba'	ECha MMuc WCFE
	- 'Angel Mountain'	IPot LLWG MBNS WFar WGob
	- 'Angelic Choir'	LLWG
	- 'Asian Warrior'	WFar
	- 'August Emperor'	MBel
	- 'Azuma-kagami'	MNrw
	- 'Azure'	SDir WFar
I	- 'Blue King'	NHol
	- 'Blue Mandarin'	ECtt
	- 'Blue Spritz'	LLWG
	- 'Carnival Prince'	WFar
	- 'Cascade Crest'	WFar
	- 'Celestial Emperor'	LLWG WGob
	- 'Center of Interest'	NBir
*	- 'Charm'	EHyd
	- 'Christina's Gown'	WFar WGob
	- 'Crepe Paper'	WFar
	- 'Crystal Halo' ♀H6	EPfP MNHC WWtn
	- 'Dace'	GBin
I	- 'Darling'	EPfP WFar WGob
	- 'Dirigo Editor'	LLWG
	- 'Dirigo Maiden's Blush'	LLWG
	- 'Dramatic Moment'	WFar WSpi
I	- 'Dresden China'	WFar
	- 'Eden's Paintbrush'	EShb SPer
	- 'Eileen's Dream'	ECtt EPfP LLWG SPeP
	- 'Electric Rays'	ELon LLWG SDir WFar
I	- 'Emotion'	CMac WFar
	- 'Flying Tiger'	GBin
I	- 'Fortune'	GBin MSCN SDir
	- 'Freckled Geisha'	CBrac CMac ECtt ELon EPfP EShb IPot MACG NBir NQui SRms WFar
	- 'Frilled Enchantment' ♀H6	IPot WFar WGob
	- 'Galatea Marx'	CBod CExl WFar
	- 'Gipsy'	CKel CMac LRHS
	- 'Gold Bound'	ECtt ELon SDir WGob
	- 'Good Omen'	ECtt WGob
	- 'Gracieuse'	CMiW CTsd NLar
	- 'Greywoods Catrina'	WFar WGob
	- 'Gusto'	CMac ELon EPfP MNrw SRms WFar
	- 'Harlequinesque'	ECtt IPot SMad WFar WGob
	- 'Harpswell Chantey'	IPot
	- 'Hercule'	CExl NBir WFar
	- Higo white	SPer
	- 'Hoshi-akari'	WFar
	- 'Ike-no-sazanami'	LLWG
	- 'Imperial Velvet'	WFar
	- 'Indigo Delight'	LLWG
*	- 'Innocence'	NLar SRms WFar
	- 'Iso-no-nami'	WFar
	- 'Japanese Plum'	LLWG
	- 'Jocasta'	WFar
	- 'Jodlesong'	WFar
	- 'Jupiter' **new**	EGrI
	- 'Kalamazoo'	WFar
	- 'Katy Mendez' ♀H6	IPot
	- 'Kogesho'	NLar
	- 'Koh Dom'	SPer
	- 'Kongo-san'	NLar WFar
	- 'Kuma-funjin'	CExl
	- 'Kumo-no-obi'	CExl CFis CPud EHyd ESgI GBin MCot NHol WFar WWtn
	- 'Lady in Waiting'	ECtt EPfP LRHS SDir WGob WWtn
	- 'Laughing Lion'	ECtt EWoo WFar WGob
	- 'Light at Dawn'	MBel
	- 'Lilac Blotch'	SPer
	- 'Loyalty'	CExl EWoo WFar
	- 'Momogasumi'	ECtt LLWG MNrw NQui SGro WHil
§	- 'Moonlight Waves'	CExl CKel CMac CPud CRos EBee ECha EHyd ELan EPfP EWoo GBin GKin GMaP IPot LRHS LShi MACG MCot MHer MHol MRav NGdn NHol NRHS SRms WFar WGob WSpi WWtn
	- 'Murasame' ♀H6	EShb
	- 'Neptune's Trident'	LLWG
	- 'Oase'	ECtt
	- 'Ocean Mist'	ECtt
	- 'Oku-banri'	CExl WFar
	- 'Oriental Eyes'	NGdn
	- pale mauve-flowered	NBir
	- 'Pin Stripe'	WFar
	- 'Pink Frost'	CFis EPfP ESgI MHer WFar WGob WWtn

- 'Pleasant Earlybird'	WFar
- 'Pleasant Journey'	ECtt
- 'Prairie Frost'	NLar
- 'Pure Emotion'	LLWG
- 'Purple Parasol'	ECtt LLWG WGob
- purple-flowered	EWoo SPer
- 'Queen's Tiara'	ECtt ELon IPot WBor WGob WTyc
- 'Rakka-no-utage'	NLar
- 'Red Tessa'	LLWG
- 'Returning Tide' 🏆H6	GBin
- 'Rivulets of Wine'	LLWG
- Rodionenko hybrids	WMal
§ - 'Rose Queen' 🏆H6	CDor CExl CMac CRos CTtf ECha EHyd ELan EPfP EWoo GBin GKin GMaP MCot MRav NBir NGdn NHol NRHS SPer SRms WFar WGob WWtn XLum
- 'Rowden King'	NChi
- 'Rowden Mikado'	NChi
I - 'Royal Banner'	ECtt EWoo WFar
- 'Royal Crown'	XLum
- 'Ruffled Dimity'	IPot
I - 'Sensation'	ECtt GBin NLar SRms WWtn
- 'Snowy Hills'	XLum
- 'Sorcerer's Triumph'	WFar
- 'Splish Splash'	GKev
- var. ***spontanea*** B&SWJ 1103	WCru
- - B&SWJ 8699	WCru
- 'Stippled Ripples'	IPot
- 'Strut and Flourish'	EWoo
- 'Sugar Dome'	LLWG
- 'Sunrise Ridge'	LLWG
- 'Taketori-hime' (v)	XLum
- 'Topas'	WFar WGob
- 'Umi-kaze'	NLar
- 'Variegata' (v) 🏆H6	CBct CEme CMac CRos EBee ECha EHyd EIri ELon EPfP GBin GMaP LRHS MHer MHol MMuc NLar NRHS SEND SMad SPoG SRms WFar WMal WPnP WWtn
- 'Velvety Queen'	ECtt
- 'Waka-murasaki-uyeki'	EGrI
- 'Wave Action'	EWTr IPot
I - 'White Ladies'	CSBt EShb LRHS SPeP WBor WCAu WGob WSpi
- 'Yako-no-tama'	WFar
- 'Yedo-yeman'	WFar
'Epicenter' (TB)	XSen
'Eramosa Skies' (SDB)	WCAu
'Eric the Red' (Sib)	ELon
'Erste Sahne' (Sib)	GBin
'Evadne' (TB)	WMal WMil
'Evening Drama' (TB)	SIri
'Evening Gown' (TB)	XSen
'Ever After' (TB)	XSen
'Ever Again' (Sib)	ELon EWoo
'Everything Plus' (TB)	ESgI XSen
'Ewen' (Sib)	EWoo GKin GLog GMaP NGdn WCot
'Exotic Isle' (TB)	EPPr ESgI XSen
'Exotic Star' (TB)	CKel
'Experiment' (SDB)	EIri
'Extra Dazzle' (La)	LLWG
'Eye Catcher' (Reticulata)	EPot ERCP GKev IPot NRog
'Eye Magic' (IB)	XSen
'Eye of Tiger'	see *I.* 'Tigereye'
'Eyebright' (SDB) 🏆H7	CBro
'Fabiola' (Reticulata)	EHyd EPot ERCP GKev NRHS SDeJ
'Fabuleux' (TB)	SIri WViv
'Face of an Angel' (TB)	WCAu
'Fall Fiesta' (TB)	XSen
'Fanciful Whimsy' (IB)	WCAu
'Fanfaron' (TB)	ESgI XSen
'Farleigh Damson' (SDB)	SBdl SIri
'Fashion Lady' (MDB)	CBro
'Fathom' (IB)	WCAu
'Faubourg-St John' (La)	LLWG
'Feather and Fan' (La)	LLWG
'Feminine Charm' (TB)	MRav
'Festival's Acadian' (La)	LLWG
'Feu du Ciel' (TB) 🏆H7	CKel ESgI XSen
'Few Are Chosen' (La)	LLWG
'Fiesta Time' (TB)	XSen
'Film Festival' (TB)	ECtt EPfP ESgI LRHS
'Finalist' (TB)	XSen
'Finola' (Reticulata)	ERCP GKev
'Firebug' (IB)	XSen
'Firecracker' (TB)	MRav
'First Interstate' (TB)	ESgI XSen
'First Movement' (TB)	ESgI
'First Violet' (TB)	ESgI
'Five Star Admiral' (TB)	XSen
'Flaming Dragon' (TB)	XSen
'Flaming Victory' (TB)	XSen
flavescens	EWoo XSen
'Fleece of White' (BB)	WCAu
'Flibbertigibbet' (SDB)	SIri
'Flight of Butterflies' (Sib) 🏆H7	Widely available
'Flirting Again' (SDB) 🏆H7	SIri
'Floorshow' (TB)	XSen
§ 'Florentina' (IB/TB) 🏆H6	CBro CHby CKel GPoy LRHS MHer MNHC MRav NBid NBir NLar SAko SEND SRms WCAu WLov XAbr XSen
'Florentine Silk' (TB)	WCAu
'Flumadiddle' (IB)	CBro
'Flûte Enchantée' (TB)	XSen
'Focus' (TB)	XSen
foetidissima 🏆H6	Widely available
- 'Aurea'	WCot
- ***chinensis***	see *I. foetidissima* var. *citrina*
§ - var. ***citrina***	EPPr EPri EWld GAbr GKev LEdu LRHS NLar WGwG
- 'Fructu Albo'	WCot
- var. ***lutescens***	NSti
- 'Variegata' (v) 🏆H6	NBir NPer
'Fogbound' (TB)	WCAu
'Foggy Dew' (TB)	EHyd EPfP LRHS NRHS SDeJ
'Folie Douce' (TB)	WViv
'Fond Kiss' (Sib)	CDor WGob
'Fondation Van Gogh' (TB)	XSen
'Foolish Fancy' (TB)	SIri
'Footloose' (TB)	XSen
'Forecasting Rain' (SDB)	SIri
'Foreign Legion' (TB)	WCAu
'Forest Light' (SDB)	CBro ESgI
'Forever Blue' (SDB)	WCAu
'Forever Gold' (TB)	XSen
* 'Forever Trevor' (CH)	MAvo
'Forge Fire' (TB)	ESgI
formosana B&SWJ 3076	WCru
'Forrest Hills' (TB)	EHyd EPfP
forrestii 🏆H6	CBro CExl CMac EPfP GAbr GGro GKev GLog LRHS NBir SPtp
- black-flowered **new**	GRum
'Fort Apache' (TB)	EWes
'Fortunata' (TB)	XSen
'Fortunate Son' (TB)	WCAu
'Fourfold Blue' (SpH)	GBin
'Fourfold Lavender' (Sib)	EWes NLar
'Fourfold White' (Sib)	ESgI

'Framboise' (TB)	XSen
'Francina' (TB)	WMil
'Frank Elder' (Reticulata)	EHyd EPot ERCP LRHS NRHS NRog SDeJ WAbe
'Frans Hals' (Dut)	NBir
'Frappe' (TB)	CKel
'French Can Can' (TB)	GWyn SIri
'Fresno Calypso' (TB)	CKel ESgI XSen
'Friends' Song' (La)	LLWG
'Frigiya' (Spuria)	GBin
'Frimousee' (TB)	WViv
'Frison-roche' (TB)	WViv
'Frisounette' (TB)	ESgI
'From this Moment' (La)	LLWG
'Frontier Marshall' (TB)	XSen
'Frost and Flame' (TB)	CEnd CKel EBee ECtt EHyd ELan GBin GKev LCro LRHS MAsh MRav NBir NLar NRHS SDeJ SPer SPoG WGwG
'Frosted Angel' (SDB)	CBro
'Frosted Velvet' (MTB)	WCAu
'Frosty Jewels' (TB)	XSen
'Frozen Planet' (Reticulata) **new**	ERCP
'Fruit Cocktail' (IB)	XSen
'Full Sun' (Spuria)	EWoo
fulva ♀H5	EBee EGrI EPPr EPri EWat EWhm MMrt NBir NSti SBrt WCAu WCot
- 'Marvell Gold' (La)	EWat
× ***fulvala*** ♀H5	NBir NSti
- 'Violacea'	EHyd
'Funambule' (TB)	EWoo
'Furnaceman' (SDB)	CBro
'Futuriste' (TB)	SIri WViv
'Fuzzy' (MDB)	EPot
'Gai Luron' (TB)	CKel
'Gallant Moment' (TB)	ESgI SIri XSen
'Galway' (IB)	XSen
'Gandalf the Grey' (TB)	ESgI
'Garnement' (TB)	WViv
'Garnet Storm Dancer' (La)	LLWG
'Gay Parasol' (TB)	CKel
'Gelbe Mantel' (Sino-Sib)	NBir
'Gemstone Walls' (TB)	ESgI
'George' (Reticulata) ♀H7	CAvo CWCL EHyd EPot ERCP EWoo GKev IPot LRHS NRHS NRog SDeJ WBrk
'George Smith' (TB)	ECtt EPfP
'Gerald Darby'	see *I.* × *robusta* 'Gerald Darby'
§ ***germanica***	MMuc SEND WCot WGwG
- var. ***florentina***	see *I.* 'Florentina'
§ - 'Nepalensis'	WCAu
- 'The King'	see *I. germanica* 'Nepalensis'
'Ghost Train' (TB)	CKel ESgI SIri
'Ginger Twist' (Sib)	CDor ELon WGob
'Gingerbread Man' (SDB)	CBro CMea EPot ESgI EWld GEdr MBrN NSla SMrm SWvt WCAu
'Ginny's Choice' (La)	LLWG
'Girly Girl' (TB)	WCAu
'Glacier Gold' (TB)	XSen
'Glad Rags' (TB)	XSen
'Gladys Austin' (TB)	XSen
'Glenthorn' (TB)	SIri
'Glowing Embers' (TB)	ESgI
'Gnu' (TB)	XSen
'Goddess of Green' (IB)	EWoo
'Godfrey Owen' (TB)	WCAu
'Godinton' (TB)	SIri
'Going Home' (TB) ♀H7	SIri
'Going My Way' (TB)	CKel ESgI SBea SIri XSen
'Gold Burst' (TB)	XSen
'Gold Country' (TB)	XSen
'Gold Galore' (TB)	SIri
'Golden Alps' (TB)	SRms
'Golden Beauty' (SpH)	GKev NRog SDeJ
'Golden Child' (SDB)	XSen
'Golden Edge' (Sib)	CBod ECtt GBin GQue LLWG NLar SMrm WFar WGob
'Golden Encore' (TB)	WCAu
'Golden Fireworks' (La)	LLWG
'Golden Immortal' (TB)	EIri
'Golden Muffin' (IB)	CKel
'Golden Violet' (SDB)	ESgI
'Golden Zebra' (TB)	LCro LOPS MBros MHol
'Good Looking' (TB)	ESgI
'Good Show' (TB)	ESgI XSen
'Good Vibrations' (TB)	XSen
'Gordon' (Reticulata)	CAvo EHyd ERCP LRHS NRHS NRog
'Gossip' (SDB)	CBro
'Got Milk' (TB)	MACG
'Goudhurst' (SDB)	SIri
'Gracchus' (TB)	EWoo
'Grace Sturtevant' (TB)	WMil
gracilipes 'Alba'	GArf GEdr
graeberiana	EPot GKev NRog SDeJ
graminea ♀H6	CBro CFis CMac EGrI EIri ELan EPri GKev NBir NChi NSti WCot
- var. ***pseudocyperus***	GBin
graminifolia	see *I. kerneriana*
'Granada Gold' (TB)	SRms XSen
'Grand Amiral' (TB)	WViv
'Grand Canari' (TB)	WMal
'Grand Waltz' (TB)	XSen
'Grandis' (Sib)	GBin
'Great Lakes' (TB)	ESgI
'Grecian Skies' (TB)	ESgI
'Green Eyed Lady' (TB)	ESgI
'Green Ice' (TB)	LRHS MRav
'Green Spot' (SDB) ♀H7	CBod CBro CKel ECha ECtt EHyd ESgI LRHS MBriF MRav NBir NLar NRHS SDeJ SPer
'Greensand Way' (TB)	SIri
'Grenade' (TB)	SIri WViv
grey-flowered (Sib)	ELon
'Grooving' (BB)	ESgI
'Grosser Wein' (Sib)	GBin
'Gull's Wing' (Sib)	EPfP LLWG LRHS MBel MHol NLar SMrm SPoG WGob WPnP
'Gypsy Beauty' (Dut)	CAvo ELan GKev LCro LOPS MNrw NRog SDeJ
'Gypsy Jewels' (TB)	XSen
'Gypsy Lord' (TB)	WCAu
'Gypsy Romance' (TB) ♀H7	SIri
'Gypsy Tart' (SDB)	SIri
'Habit' (TB)	WCAu
'Hail Mary' (La)	LLWG
halophila	see *I. spuria* subsp. *halophila*
'Happenstance' (TB)	WCAu
'Happiness' (Reticulata)	GKev
'Happy Mood' (IB)	EIri
'Harbor Blue' (TB)	CKel EWoo NLar WCAu
'Harlow Gold' (IB)	ESgI
'Harmony' (IB)	EHyd
'Harmony' (Reticulata)	CAvo EHyd EPfP EPot EWoo GKev LCro LOPS LRHS NBir NRHS NRog SDeJ SPhx WBrk
'Harpswell Happiness' (Sib) ♀H7	CKel EBee ELon EPfP EPri GBin SDir WGob
'Harpswell Haze' (Sib)	ECha
'Harpswell Velvet' (Sib)	GBin
'Harriette Halloway' (TB)	CBod CWGN EHyd EPfP EShb EWoo LSRN NLar WCot

'Harvest Home' (BB) SIri
'Harvest King' (TB) XSen
'Harvest of Memories' (TB) ESgI GWyn SPoG
'Haut les Voiles' (TB) WViv
'Haute Couture' (TB) XSen
'Haviland' (TB) XSen
'Having Fun' (Sib) CDor
'Headcorn' (MTB) 🏆H7 SIri
'Headline Banner' (BB) WCAu
'Heather Carpet' (SDB) WCAu
'Heather Stream' (La) ELon
'Helen Astor' (Sib) CDor ELon MRav
'Helen Collingwood' (TB) ESgI
'Helen McGregor' (TB) EWoo
'Helen Proctor' (IB) ESgI WCot XSen
'Helena Terry' (TB) ESgI
'Helene C.' (TB) WViv XSen
'Helga' **new** EGrI
'Hello Darkness' (TB) 🏆H7 ESgI WCAu WCot XSen
'Hell's Fire' (TB) ELan ELon WSpi
henryi GKev
'Her Royal Highness' (TB) LCro LOPS
'Here Be Dragons' (Sib) CDor WGob
'Here Comes the Night' (TB) WCAu
'Here Comes the Sun' (TB) WCAu
'Hester Prynne' (TB) WMil
'Heure Bleue' (TB) WViv
'Hey True Blue' (TB) WCAu
'High Blue Sky' (TB) WCAu
'Highland Mist' (La) LLWG
'Hildegarde' (Dut) SDeJ
'Hindenburg' (TB) CKel
'Hippolyta' (Rc) GKev
'His Royal Highness' (TB) WCAu
histrio EPot
- subsp. ***aintabensis*** NRog
histrioides GKev
- 'Halkis' EHyd EPot ERCP EShb GKev LRHS NRHS SDeJ
- 'Lady Beatrix Stanley' CAvo CRos EHyd EPot ERCP GKev LHWs LRHS MNrw NBir NRHS NRog SDeJ WBrk WHoo
- 'Major' NRog
'Hoar Edge' (Sib) EPri NChi
'Hocus Pocus' (SDB) CKel CWGN ECtt EHyd LRHS NRHS SPer WGwG
'Hohe Warte' (Sib) 🏆H7 EWoo GBin
'Höhenflug' (Sib) GBin
'Holden Clough' (SpH) 🏆H7 CExl CPla EBee ELan EPPr EPfP GBin LEdu MBriF MMuc MNrw MRav NBir NChi NFav NGdn NSti NWad WBrk WFar WSHC
'Holden's Child' (SpH) CWat LLWG
'Holidaze' (IB) 🏆H7 EIri
× ***hollandica*** EShb
'Hollywood Ending' (La) LLWG
'Holy Night' (TB) ESgI SRms
'Honey Glazed' (IB) ELon
'Honey Stars' (La) LLWG
'Honeyplic' (IB) 🏆H7 SIri
'Honington' (SDB) WCAu
'Honky Tonk Blues' (TB) ESgI MAvo
hoogiana 🏆H5 GKev MBow
I - 'Amphion' GKev
- 'Purpurea' GKev
- 'Zethos' **new** GKev
§ ***hookeri*** CFoA CSma CTsd GArf GKev GMaP MACG MHol NHpl NSla SPtp SRms WAbe WIce
'Hopelessly Devoted' (La) LLWG
'Horned Rosyred' (TB) EWoo
'Hortensia Rose' (TB) SIri WViv
'Hot' (SDB) ESgI
'Hot and Spicy' (La) LLWG
'Hot Spiced Wine' (TB) SIri
'Hot to Trot' (TB) ESgI
'How Audacious' (Sib) ECtt MBros
'Howard Weed' (TB) EGrI
'Hubbard' (Sib) EPri LLWG MNrw SPoG WFar WGob
'Huckleberry Fudge' (TB) XSen
§ ***humilis*** LShi WAbe
'Humors of Whiskey' (Sib) WGob
'Huntress' (Sib) **new** CDor
hyrcana GKev NRog WCot
'I Repeat' (TB) XSen
§ ***iberica*** GKev
subsp. ***elegantissima***
'Ice Blue' (TB) **new** NRog
'Ice Capades' (TB) WCAu
'Ila Crawford' (Spuria) 🏆H7 XSen
'Illini Charm' (Sib) WFar
illyrica see *I. pallida*
'I'm Back' (TB) WCAu
'Immortality' (TB) CBod CKel CRos CWGN EPfP GKev GWyn LRHS MHol SCob SRms STPC WCAu XSen
'Imperative' (IB) SIri
'Imperator' (TB) ELan
'Imperial Opal' (Sib) ECtt NGdn WFar WGob
I 'Imperial Velvet' (Sib) ELon WFar
'Imprimis' (TB) WCAu XSen
'In Full Sail' (Sib) CDor WGob
'In Love' (TB) XSen
'In Town' (TB) XSen
'Indeed' (IB) ESgI
'Indian Chief' (TB) CWCL ELan EPfP ESgI EWoo LCro LOPS MCot MHer MRav
'Indian Hills' (TB) EWoo
'Indigo Princess' (TB) XSen
'Ink Patterns' (TB) WCAu
'Inn-Keeper' (La) LLWG
'Innocent Pink' (TB) ESgI
innominata EHyd GArf GKev LRHS NBir NBro NRHS NSla SRms WAbe
I - 'Clotted Cream' EGrI
- 'Peacock' EGrI
- 'Spinners' MAvo
- yellow-flowered NRya
'Inspired' (TB) WCAu
'Interpol' (TB) ESgI XSen
'Intrepid' (TB) WViv
'Invicta Celebration' (BB) SIri
'Invicta Daybreak' (IB) SIri
'Invicta Gold' (SDB) SIri
'Invicta Reprieve' (IB) SIri
'Invicta Sapphire' (TB) SIri
'Irisades' (TB) SIri WViv
'Irish Harp' (SDB) ESgI
'Isabelle' (Sib) ELon LSRN XSen
'Island Sunset' (TB) SIri
'Isobel Rose' (TB) SIri
'Italian Ice' (TB) EIri
'Italian Velvet' (TB) WCAu
'It's Amazing' (IB) WCAu
'J.S. Dijt' (Reticulata) EHyd EPfP EPot ERCP EWoo GKev LCro LOPS LRHS MGos NRHS NRog SDeJ
'Jack Attack' (La) WWtn
'Jac-y-do' (Sib) EWes
'Jamie Roo' (TB) SIri
'Jane Phillips' (TB) 🏆H7 Widely available

'Japanese Pinwheel' WGob
japonica ♀H4 CExl EWTr NLar NPer SPlb WCot WFar XLum XSen
- B&SWJ 8921 WCru
- 'Bourne Graceful' CExl
- 'Ledger' CExl CMac ECha MRav SIvy SMad WWFP
- 'Monty' WWFP
- 'Rudolph Spring' EPPr WSHC
§ - 'Variegata' (v) ♀H4 CBcs CBct CBro ECha ELan ESwi NPer NSti SArc WBrk WFar WWFP XSen
'Jasper Gem' (MDB) EPot
'Java Bleue' (TB) SIri
'Jazz Festival' (TB) SIri WCAu XSen
'Jazz Hot' (La) LLWG
'Jazzed Up' (TB) XSen
'Jean Band' (CH) <u>**new**</u> GBin
'Jean Cayeux' (TB) ESgI
'Jean Guymer' (TB) ESgI
'Jeanne Price' (TB) ESgI
'Jerry Murphy' (Sib) ECtt EPfP WGob
'Jesse's Song' (TB) XSen
'Jewel Baby' (SDB) CBro
'Jiansada' (SDB) CBro
'Jigsaw' (TB) XSen
'Joanna' (TB) LSRN NLar
'Joie de Vivre' (La) LLWG
'Joyce' (Reticulata) CRos EHyd GKev LRHS NRHS SDeJ
'Joyful Skies' (TB) WCAu
'Jubilant Spirit' (Spuria) EWes
'Jubilé Rainier III' (TB) WViv
'Juliet' (TB) ESgI
'June Prom' (IB) EHyd ELan EPfP ESgI LRHS NRHS
'June Rose' (IB) CKel ELan
'Jungle Shadows' (BB) ELon ESgI EWoo MRav NBir
'Jurassic Park' (TB) CKel WCAu XSen
'Just Dance' (IB) ESgI
'Just Imagine' (La) LLWG
'Just Jennifer' (BB) WCAu
'Kabluey' (Sib) EBee ECtt MWts WFar WGob
'Kaboom' (Sib) MHol WFar
kaempferi see *I. ensata*
'Kasim' (J) GKev
'Katharine Hodgkin' (Reticulata) ♀H7 CAvo CRos EBee ECha EHyd EPfP EPot ERCP EWoo GAbr GKev LCro LHWs LOPS LRHS MNrw MRav NBir NHpl NLar NRHS NRog SDeJ WBrk WCot WFar WHoo
'Katharine's Gold' (Reticulata) EPfP EPot ERCP GKev NRog WBrk
'Katy Petts' (SDB) ESgI
kemaonensis PAB 8473 LEdu
'Kent Compote' (IB) SIri
'Kent Pride' (TB) CBod CEnd CKel CSBt ECha ECtt ELan EPfP ESgI ETod EWoo GBin IPot LCro LOPS LRHS MCot MRav NBir NLar NRHS SCob SCoo SIvy SPeP SPer SPoG SRms WHoo
'Kent Skylark' (IB) SIri
Kenta No Se129 (Sib) EPri
'Kentish Icon' (SDB) SIri
'Kentish Lad' (IB) SIri
'Kentucky Derby' (TB) ESgI XSen
§ ***kerneriana*** ♀H5 CBro GKev NBir
'Kharput' (IB) EWoo
'Kimzey' (TB) CKel
'Kinshikou' (SpH) LLWG
kirkwoodii GKev
'Kiss of Summer' (TB) ♀H7 ESgI
'Kissing Circle' (TB) ESgI
'Kita-no-seiza' (Sib) CDor ECtt NGdn WFar
'Kiwi Slices' (SDB) CWat
'Knick Knack' (MDB) CBro CKel ECtt EHyd ELan ELon EPfP GKev GMaP LRHS MRav MTin NRHS SDeJ SPoG
koreana EPPr
korolkowii GKev
'Kuh-e-Abr' (Reticulata) GKev NRog
'La Meije' (TB) SIri WViv
'La Senda' (Spuria) WCot
'Lace Legacy' (TB) LSRN
'Laced Cotton' (TB) XSen
§ ***lactea*** SBrt SMHy XSen
- CC 7174 GKev
lacustris GKev WAbe WCot
- 'Captain Collingwood' see *I. cristata* 'Captain Collingwood'
'Lady Belle' (MTB) ESgI
'Lady Byng' (TB) WMil
'Lady Friend' (TB) WCAu XSen
'Lady in Red' (SDB) ESgI WCAu
'Lady Mohr' (AB) WMal
'Lady of the Night' (BB) WCAu
'Lady Vanessa' (Sib) EBee ELon MRav NSti WGob
laevigata CPud CRos EPfP EWat ITim MRav NBro NPer SRms WFar WMAq WShi
- var. ***alba*** LLWG LRHS SRms
- 'Atropurpurea' LLWG
- blue-flowered LLWG
- 'Colchesterensis' CPla CPud EWat NGdn NPer WMAq
I - 'Dorothy' NGdn
- 'Dorothy Robinson' EPfP MRav
* - 'Elgar' WMAq
- 'Liam Johns' LLWG
- 'Midnight' see *I. laevigata* 'Weymouth Midnight'
- 'Monstrosa' EWat
- 'Richard Greaney' EWat LLWG
- 'Rose Queen' see *I. ensata* 'Rose Queen'
- 'Rowden Starlight' LLWG
- 'Royal Cartwheel' LLWG
I - 'Snowdrift' CPud EWat LLWG NBir NGdn NLar NPer WCAu WFar WMAq
- 'Variegata' (v) ♀H6 CBen CPud CWat ECha ELon EPfP EWat LLWG MWts NBro NGdn NPer SCob WMAq WWtn
- 'Weymouth' see *I. laevigata* 'Weymouth Blue'
§ - 'Weymouth Blue' EWat LLWG
§ - 'Weymouth Midnight' LLWG
- 'Weymouth Purity' EWat
laevigata × versicolor WCAu
- -, Tamberg hybrid LLWG
§ 'Lake Niklas' (Sib) ELon MHol
'Langport Chapter' (IB) ESgI
'Langport Claret' (IB) ESgI
'Langport Curlew' (IB) ESgI
'Langport Duchess' (IB) ESgI
'Langport Fairy' (IB) ESgI
'Langport Flame' (IB) ESgI
'Langport Lord' (IB) ESgI
'Langport Minstrel' (IB) ESgI
'Langport Star' (IB) ESgI
'Langport Storm' (IB) EHyd ELon EPfP ESgI LRHS MBriF MRav NRHS SDeJ
'Langport Sun' (IB) ESgI
'Langport Violet' (IB) ESgI
'Langport Wren' (IB) ♀H7 CBro CCBP CKel ECtt EHyd ELon EPfP EPri ESgI EShb LRHS MBel MCot NBir NGdn NRHS
'Langthorns Pink' (Sib) ELan MRav
'Lark Ascending' (TB) MACG

§	***latifolia***	EGrI WShi
	– ***alba***	WCot
	– 'Duchess of York'	EBee
	– 'Isabella'	GKev NRog SDeJ
	– 'King of the Blues'	EBee GKev SDeJ
	– 'Mansfield'	MNrw
	– 'Montblanc'	GKev NRog SDeJ
	– 'Queen of the Blues'	SDeJ
	'Latin Lark' (TB)	ESgI
	'Laura Louise' (La)	LLWG WGob
	'Laurenbuhl' (Sib)	CExl
	'Lavender Bounty' (Sib)	GBin
	lazica ♀H5	CBct CBod CBro CMac EBee EIri ELan EPPr EPfP EPot EPri EWoo GBin GKev IBlr LRHS MMrt MPie MRav NBir NChi NSti SEND SPer SPlb SRms WGwG
	– 'Joy Bishop'	CJun
*	– 'Richard Nutt'	CJun ELon WCot WSHC
	– 'Turkish Blue'	CJun IBlr
	'Legato' (TB)	ESgI
	'Lemon Flare' (SDB)	MRav SRms
	'Lemon Ice' (TB)	ECha EHyd GBin SDeJ SPer WGwG WLov
	'Lemon Pop' (IB)	WCAu
	'Lemon Puff' (MDB)	CBro
	'Lemon Veil' (Sib)	SDir WGob
	'Lena' (SDB)	CBro
	'Lenora Pearl' (BB)	XSen
	'Leo Hewitt' (Sib)	ELon
	leptophylla	GKev
	'Let's Elope' (IB)	WCAu
	'Licorice Stick' (TB)	XSen
	'Light Beam' (TB)	XSen
	'Light Cavalry' (IB)	ESgI
	'Lilli-white' (SDB)	CKel CWat EHyd ELon EPfP ESgI LRHS MRav NRHS SPoG WCAu
	'Lilting' (TB)	XSen
	'Limbo' (SpH)	LLWG
	'Lime Fizz' (TB)	XSen
	'Limelight' (TB)	SRms
	lineata	GKev
	'Lion King' (Dut) ♀H6	CAvo GAbr LCro LOPS MNrw
	'Little Black Belt' (SDB)	LRHS
	'Little Blackfoot' (SDB)	WCot
	'Little Blue-eyes' (SDB)	ESgI
	'Little Bluets' (SDB)	ESgI
	'Little Episode' (SDB)	CBro ELon
	'Little Nutkin' (La)	LLWG
	'Little Rosy Wings' (SDB)	CBro
	'Little Ruby Slippers' (La) **new**	LLWG
	'Little Shadow' (IB)	CWGN MRav SRms
	'Little Showoff' (SDB)	ESgI
	'Little Tilgates' (CH)	WCot WMal WSHC
	'Little Twinkle Star' (Sib)	MHer WFar
	'Living Waters' (TB)	ESgI
	'Local Color' (TB)	ESgI SIri XSen
	'Lodore' (TB)	SRms
	'Lohengrin' (TB)	EWoo
	'Lollipop' (SDB)	ESgI
	longipetala	EPPr NBir
	'Looking Forward' (TB)	ESgI
	'Loop the Loop' (TB)	CKel CMac SPoG SRms
	'Loose Valley' (MTB) ♀H7	SIri
	'Lord Warden' (TB)	ECtt EHyd EPfP WGwG
	'Lorilee' (TB)	ESgI
	'Lost in Love' (TB)	WCAu
	'Lottie Lou' (TB)	SIri
	'Lotus Land' (TB)	WCAu
	'Louvois' (TB)	CKel ESgI EWoo NLar
	'Love Me Do' (La) **new**	LLWG
	'Love the Sun' (TB)	ESgI XSen
	'Lovely Again' (TB)	GKev MRav WCAu
	'Lovely Combination' **new**	EBlo
	'Lovely Leilani' (TB)	ESgI
	'Lovely Señorita' (TB)	WCAu
	'Love's Tune' (IB)	CRos ECtt EHyd EPfP LRHS NRHS WTor
	'Loyalist' (TB)	SIri
	'Lucky Devil' (Spuria) ♀H7	WCAu
	'Lullingstone Castle' (Kent Castles Series) (IB)	SIri
	'Lumarco' (TB)	WViv
	'Lumière d'Automne' (TB)	XSen
	'Lurline' (TB)	WMil
	lutescens ♀H7	EPot GArf GKev MHid WAbe
§	– 'Campbellii'	GArf
§	– subsp. ***lutescens***	XSen
	'Ma Mie' (IB)	WViv
	maackii	GGro
	'Mabel Coday' (Sib)	EBee EPri
	'Mad Magenta' (Sib)	GBin
	'Madeira Belle' (TB)	ECtt EHyd EPfP ESgI LRHS NRHS SPeP WGwG
	'Magharee' (TB)	ESgI
	'Magic Man' (TB)	XSen
	'Magical Encounter' (TB)	SIri
	magnifica ♀H5	GKev NRog
	– 'Alba'	GKev
	'Mahogany Lord' (Spuria)	WCAu
	'Maid of Orange' (BB)	CKel WCAu
	'Maisie Lowe' (TB)	ESgI
	'Majestic' (TB)	WMil
	'Majestic Overtures' (Sib)	LLWG
	'Making Eyes' (SDB)	ELon
	'Mallow Dramatic' (TB)	CKel
I	'Mandarin' (TB)	ESgI
	'Mango Smoothy' (BB)	ESgI
	'Man's Best Friend' (IB)	SIri
	'Maranatha'	EWoo
	'Margot Holmes' (Cal-Sib)	WFar
	'Margrave' (TB)	XSen
	'Marilyn Holmes' (Sib)	GLog WCot
	'Mariposa Autumn' (TB)	EWoo SIri
	'Marjaneh' (J)	GKev
	'Marjorie' (TB)	SRms
	'Marksman' (SDB)	SIri
	'Marmalade Skies' (BB)	WCAu
	'Mars Landing' (Reticulata)	EPot ERCP GKev
	'Marsh Marigold' (TB)	WMil
	'Martyn Rix'	see *I. confusa* 'Martyn Rix'
	'Mary Frances' (TB)	CKel XSen
	'Mary McIlroy' (SDB) ♀H7	CBro
	'Marybill' (TB)	SIri
	'Master Touch' (TB)	ELon WLov XSen
	'Matinata' (TB)	ELan EWoo XSen
	'Maui Moonlight' (IB) ♀H7	ESgI NLar WCAu
	'Meadow Court' (SDB)	CBro GEdr
	'Medallion' (Spuria)	EWoo
	'Media Luz' (Spuria)	WCAu
	'Medici Prince' (TB)	WCAu
	'Medway Valley' (MTB) ♀H7	SIri
	'Mellow Yellow' (TB)	CEme
	'Melon Honey' (SDB)	ELon WCAu
§	'Melton Red Flare' (Sib)	EHyd ESgI EWoo GBin LRHS MBNS NRHS WAvo
	'Memphis Memory' (Sib)	EBee ELan ELon LRHS MHol NLar WFar WGob
	'Mer du Sud' (TB) ♀H7	CEnd ECtt EIri EPfP ESgI LCro LRHS MACG MCot SCob WCot WViv XSen

*	'Merebrook Blue Lagoon' (La)	WMAq
	'Merebrook Jemma J' (La)	WMAq
	'Merebrook Purpla' (La)	WMAq
	'Merebrook Rum 'n' Raisin' (La)	WMAq
*	'Merebrook Rusty Red' (La)	WMAq
	'Merebrook Sunata' (La) **new**	WMAq
	'Merebrook Sunnyside Up' (La)	WMAq
	'Merebrook Symphony' (La)	WMAq
	'Mesa Pearl' (Sib)	CDor
	mesopotamica	see *I. germanica*
	'Mezza Cartuccia' (IB)	ESgI
	'Miami Beach' (TB)	WCAu
	'Midhurst White' (TB)	SIri
I	'Midnight Blue' (MDB)	CBro
	'Midnight Caller' (TB)	ESgI XSen
	'Midnight Tryst'	WCAu
	'Midwest Star' (IB) **new**	CKel
	'Mighty Mouse' (MDB)	ELon
	milesii ♀H3	CExl EPri GBin GKev NBir SBrt
	'Millennium Sunrise' (TB)	WCAu
	'Mini-Agnes' (SDB)	CBro
	'Minisa' (TB)	ESgI
	'Miss Apple' (Sib)	CBod EPfP WGob
	'Miss Nellie' (BB)	CKel
	'Mission Ridge' (TB)	MHol
	'Missouri Autumn' (Spuria)	WCAu
	missouriensis	CMac EPPr GKev
	'Moby Grape' (TB)	GKev
	'Monsieur-Monsieur' (TB)	ESgI
	Monspur Group	WCot
	'Moon Silk' (Sib)	CBro ECtt ELon EPri EWes GBin MBel SCob WCot WFar WGob WHil
	'Moonlight Masquerade'	WCAu
	'Moonlight Waves'	see *I. ensata* 'Moonlight Waves'
	'Moonlit Water' (TB)	WCAu
	'Morning Show' (IB)	CKel
	'Morwell' (TB)	WMil
	'Morwenna' (TB) ♀H7	ESgI
	'Mother Earth' (TB)	ESgI
	'Mount Everest'[PBR] (TB)	GKev SDeJ
	'Mountain Lake' (Sib)	EBee EHyd EPfP EShb GBin LRHS MPie NRHS WFar WGob WSpi
	'Mr Peacock' (Sib)	WGob
	'Mrs Horace Darwin' (TB)	EWoo
	'Mrs Rowe' (Sib)	EIri ELon EPri ESgI MRav NFav WCAu WFar
	'Mrs Tait' (Spuria)	NChi
	'Mrs Valerie West' (TB)	WMil
	'Muggles' (SDB)	SIri
	'Music' (SDB)	SIri
	'Music Maker' (TB) **new**	EGrI
	'My Cher' (SDB)	WCAu
	'My Cher of Happiness' (BB)	WCAu
	'My Kayla' (SDB)	ESgI
	'My Seedling' (MDB)	CBro
	'Myra' (SDB)	XSen
	'Mysterieux' (TB)	SIri
	'Mystic' (TB)	WMil
	'Mystic Beauty' (Dut)	SDeJ
	'Nada' (SpH)	WCot
	'Nancy Hardy' (MDB)	CBro
	'Naples' (TB)	SIri
	'Nassak' (TB)	EWoo
	'Natascha' (Reticulata)	EPot GKev NRog SDeJ
	'Natchez Trace' (TB)	CKel EPri LCro LOPS LRHS XSen
	'Navajo Jewel' (TB)	XSen
	'Navy Brass' (Sib)	EPri
	'Needlecraft' (TB)	XSen

	'Needlepoint' (TB)	ESgI
	'Neige de Mai' (TB)	ESgI
*	'Nel Jupe' (TB)	LRHS NLar
	nepalensis	see *I. decora*
	'New Centurion' (TB)	XSen
	'New Face' (TB)	WCAu
	'New Idea' (MTB)	CBro ESgI WCAu
	'New Leaf' (TB)	WCAu
	'Nibelungen' (TB)	CBro ELan EWoo XSen
	'Nickel' (IB)	WCAu
	nicolai 'Hissar' **new**	NRog
	'Night Breeze' (Sib)	EPri
	'Night Edition' (TB)	ESgI XSen
	'Night Game' (TB)	XSen
	'Night Owl' (TB)	CKel CTsd EGrI ELon ESgI MHer MNHC SBls WLov
	'Nightfall' (TB)	EBee NLar
	'Nights of Gladness' (TB)	ESgI
	'Ninja Turtles' (SDB)	SIri
	'Noctambule' (TB) ♀H7	SIri WViv
	'Noon Siesta' (TB)	ESgI
§	× ***norrisii***	EHyd LRHS NRHS
	– KIBA GIANTS (mixed) **new**	SBls
	'North Downs' (BB)	SIri
	'North Star' (TB)	GKev
	'Not Quite White' (Sib) **new**	CBod
	'Now and Forever' (La)	LLWG
	'Nuit Blanche' (TB) **new**	ESgI
	'Nuit de Noces' (TB)	SIri
	'Oblivion' (IB)	WCAu
	'Ochre Doll' (SDB)	CBro
	ochroleuca	see *I. orientalis* Mill.
	'October' (TB)	ESgI
	'October Sun' (TB)	CKel ELan
	'Oh Happy Day' (La)	LLWG
	'Oh Jamaica' (TB)	XSen
	'Oh So Cool' (MTB)	ESgI
	'Oklahoma' (TB)	EWoo
	'Oklahoma Bandit' (IB)	CKel
	'Oktoberfest' (TB)	XSen
	'Ola Kalá' (TB)	CRos EHyd ESgI EWTr EWoo GMaP LRHS MGos NLar NRHS SPeP SPer XSen
	'Old Black Magic' (TB)	ESgI XSen
	'Old Flame' (TB)	XSen
	'Olympiad' (TB)	ESgI XSen
	'Olympic Challenge' (TB)	ESgI MRav
	'Ominous Stranger' (TB)	ESgI MMrt
	'Once Again' (TB)	XSen
	'One Desire' (TB)	XSen
	'Open Sky' (SDB)	LRHS XSen
	'Orageux' (IB)	ESgI SIri WMal
	'Orange Caper' (SDB)	CKel CMac ECtt EHyd ESgI LRHS MRav MTin NRHS SCob WCot
§	'Orange Chariot' (TB)	MBros
	'Orange Glow' (TB)	GKev
	'Orange Harvest' (TB)	ESgI XSen
	orchioides misapplied	see *I. bucharica* Foster
§	***orchioides*** Carrière	ELan
	'Oregon Skies' (TB)	ESgI
	'Oriental Beauty' (TB)	SDeJ
	orientalis ambig.	ELan EWes MNrw
§	***orientalis*** Mill. ♀H6	GBin GKev MMuc SEND WCot WCru XSen
	'Orinoco Flow' (BB) ♀H7	ESgI WCAu
	'Orloff' (TB)	ESgI
	'Orville Fay' (Sib)	GWyn WBor WCot
	'Ottawa' (Sib)	CWat EHyd MMuc WFar
	'Oulo' (TB)	XSen
	'Our House' (TB)	ESgI
	'Our Marcus' (TB)	SIri

	'Our Sassy' (La)	LLWG
	'Out of the Dark' (TB)	WCAu
	'Overjoyed' (TB)	XSen
	'Owyhee Desert' (TB)	WCAu
	Pacific Coast hybrids	see *I.* Californian hybrids
	'Pacific Panorama' (TB)	ESgI XSen
	'Pagan Pink' (TB)	XSen
	'Pageant' (TB)	WFar
I	'Pageant' (Sib)	WCot WFar
	'Paint It Black' (TB)	XSen
	'Painted Lady' (Reticulata)	EPot ERCP GKev LCro LOPS WBrk
	'Painted Woman' (Sib)	CBod CDor LLWG MBros
	'Pale Shades' (IB)	CBro
§	***pallida***	CBro CMac CPla GMaP LSun MRav SEND SRms XSen
§	- 'Argentea Variegata' (TB/v)	Widely available
	- 'Aurea'	see *I. pallida* 'Variegata' Hort.
	- 'Aurea Variegata'	see *I. pallida* 'Variegata' Hort.
	- subsp. ***cengialtii***	GKev
	- var. ***dalmatica***	see *I. pallida* subsp. *pallida*
§	- subsp. ***pallida***	CCBP CExl CKel ECha EHyd ELan EPfP LRHS MHid NRHS SCob SCoo SHar SPer
	- 'Variegata' misapplied	see *I. pallida* 'Argentea Variegata'
§	- 'Variegata' Hort. (v) ♀[H7]	CBcs CBct CBro CEnd CKel CMac CWat ECha ELan EPfP LRHS MAsh MHol MRav NRHS SDix SPeP SPer SPlb SPoG SRms SWvt WBrk XSen
	'Palm Springs' (IB)	EHyd EPot LHWs SDeJ
	'Palm Springs' (Reticulata)	GKev LRHS NRHS SDeJ
	'Pamplemousse' (IB)	SIri
	'Pansy Purple' (Sib)	LRHS MNrw WHil
	'Panther' (SDB)	WCAu
	'Papillon' (Sib)	CTri ECtt EHyd ELan ELon EPri EWes EWoo GWyn LRHS NBir NGdn NRHS NSti SCob SDeJ SPer WFar WWtn
	'Paprikash' (Sib)	LLWG
	paradoxa	GKev
	'Paris Lights' (TB)	XSen
	'Parisian Dawn' (TB)	WCAu
	'Parting Glances' (IB)	WCAu
	'Party Dress' (TB)	CMac EBee ECtt EHyd ELan ESgI EShb LRHS MRav NBir NLar NRHS NWad SCob SPer SPoG SRms WGwG
	'Party's Over' (TB)	WCAu
	'Pastel Accent' (La)	LLWG
	'Patina' (TB)	EIri EWoo LRHS
	'Patterdale' (TB)	NBir
	'Pauline' (Reticulata)	CAvo EPot ERCP EWoo GKev LRHS NRHS NRog SPhx
	'Pauline' (TB)	EHyd
	'Pause' (SDB)	WCAu
	'Peaceful Waters' (TB)	XSen
	'Peach Eyes' (SDB)	CBro
	'Peach Picotee' (TB)	ESgI XSen
	'Peaches in Wine' (La)	LLWG
	'Peachy Face' (IB)	XSen
	'Pearl Queen' (Sib)	MCot
	'Pearly Dawn' (TB)	ECtt
*	'Pêche Melba' (TB)	XSen
	'Pelion Hills'	LRHS SGBe
	'Penny a Pinch' (TB)	CKel
	'Pennywhistle' (Sib)	NLar
	'Percheron' (Sib)	EPri EWoo
	'Perfect Interlude' (TB)	EIri XSen
	'Perfect Vision' (Sib) ♀[H7]	MHCG
	'Performer' (MTB)	EIri
	'Perry's Blue' (Sib)	CBcs CKel CMac CSBt EBee EHyd EPfP EPri EWTr GKin GMaP LCro LOPS LRHS LSun MBel MGos MHol MRav NBir NGdn NPer NRHS SPer SRms WFar WWtn
	'Perry's Pigmy' (Sib)	ELon
	'Persian Berry' (TB)	XSen
	'Persimmon' misapplied	see *I.* 'Tycoon'
	'Persimmon' ambig. (Sib)	CDor CKel ECtt EHyd EShb GKin GQue LRHS MHer NRHS WFar WGwG WWtn
	'Peter Hewitt' (Sib) ♀[H7]	EPri MAvo
	'Peter's Heir' (La)	LLWG
	'Pétillant' (TB)	EWoo
	'Petit Tigre' (IB)	SIri
	'Petite Charm' (IB)	WCAu
	'Petite Monet' (MTB)	ESgI
	'Petite Polka' (SDB)	NLar
	'Petticoat Shuffle' (TB)	WCAu
	'Pharaoh's Daughter' (IB)	EWoo
	'Phyllis Bliss' (TB)	WMil
	'Picasso Moon' (TB)	SIri
	'Pigeon' (SDB)	XSen
	'Pinewood Amethyst' (CH)	MAvo
	'Pinewood Charmer' (CH)	CElw
	'Pinewood Sunshine' (CH)	MAvo
	'Pink Attraction' (TB)	ESgI XSen
	'Pink Bubbles' (BB)	XSen
	'Pink Charm' (TB)	ECtt EHyd ELan EPfP LRHS MHer NRHS SDeJ SPlb SPoG
	'Pink Confetti' (TB)	XSen
	'Pink Empress' (IB)	CKel
	'Pink Horizon' (TB)	SPeP XSen
	'Pink Kitten' (IB)	WGwG XSen
	'Pink Lavender' (TB)	ELon SRms
	'Pink Parfait' (Sib)	MBNS NGdn WFar WGob WTor
	'Pink Pele' (IB)	CKel ESgI
	'Pink Quartz' (TB)	ESgI
	'Pink Swan' (TB)	XSen
	'Pink Taffeta' (TB)	XSen
	'Pinnacle' (TB)	EWoo
	'Pioneer' (TB)	WMil
	'Pipes of Pan' (TB)	ESgI MRav
	'Pirate Ahoy' (TB)	WCAu
	'Pirate Prince' (Sib)	NPer
	'Pirate's Quest' (TB)	ECtt MHer XSen
	'Piroska' (TB)	XSen
	'Pixie' (DB)	EHyd GKev
	'Pixie' (Reticulata) ♀[H7]	CAvo ELan EPot ERCP LRHS NRog SDeJ
	'Pleasures of May' (Sib)	ELon WGob
	'Pledge Allegiance' (TB)	ESgI
	'Plickadee' (SDB)	CBro
	'Plissée' (Sib) ♀[H7]	GBin GWyn
	'Poesie' (TB)	WViv
	'Pogo' (SDB)	CKel CMac CRos ECtt EHyd LRHS MHer MRav MTin NBir NRHS SDeJ SRms
	'Polar Ice' (Reticulata)	LHWs WBrk
	'Polar Ice' (TB)	EPot ERCP GKev LRHS
	'Polvere di Stelle' (TB)	ESgI
	'Poodle Parade' (TB)	WCAu
	'Pop Culture' (IB)	WCAu
	'Port of Call' (Spuria)	EWoo
	'Post Master' (La)	LLWG
	'Potpourri Rose' (La)	LLWG
	'Pounsley Purple' (Sib)	EPri
	'Power Point' (TB)	WCAu
	PRETTY IN BLUE (mixed) (Dut)	SDeJ
	'Pretty Please' (TB)	ESgI
	'Pretty Polly' (Sib) **new**	CDor
	'Pretty Reward' (MTB)	WCAu

'Primrose Cream' (Sib)	GBin WCot
'Primrose Drift' (TB)	ESgI
'Prince Indigo' (TB)	MRav
'Prince of Tuscany' (DB)	CBor
'Princess Bride' (BB) ♀H7	WCAu
'Princess Leia' (La)	LLWG
'Princess Osra' (TB)	WMil
'Princesse Caroline de Monaco' (TB)	CKel WViv
prismatica	GArf GKev MHid
'Private Eye' (TB)	WCAu
'Professor Blaauw' (Dut) ♀H5	CAvo CWCL
'Prosper Laugier' (IB)	WLov
'Proud Tradition' (TB)	SIri XSen
'Provençal' (TB)	CKel ELon ESgI WCAu XSen
'Prussian Blue' (Sib) ♀H7	GBin SMHy
pseudacorus	Widely available
- B&SWJ 5018 from Japan	WCru
- 'Alba'	CPud CWat MWts NGdn SRms
- var. ***bastardii***	CWat ECha EGrI ELon EPfP LCro LLWG LOPS NPer SLon SPer WBrk WFar WPnP WWtn XLum
- 'Clotted Cream'	GLog
- 'Come in Spinner'	LLWG
- cream-flowered	NBir
- 'Crème de la Crème'	ELon EPfP EWoo GBin LLWG NLar NSti NWad WFar
- 'Dragonfly Dance'	LLWG
- 'Esk'	EPPr
- 'Flore Pleno' (d)	NLar NPer SRms WBrk WCot WFar WPnP WWtn
I - 'Golden Fleece'	SPer
- 'Golden Queen'	EWat LLWG
- 'Ivory'	LLWG
- 'Kelis Choice'	LLWG
- 'Krill'	CDor EPPr EWoo LLWG
- 'Mini Mart'	LLWG
- 'Roccapina'	GBin
- 'Roy Davidson' ♀H7	CBro LLWG MWts NLar WCot WFar WHil WWtn
- 'Spartacus'	EBee
- 'Sulphur Queen'	GBin LLWG NLar WCot
- 'Sun Cascade'	GBin
- 'Tiger Brother'	CBro LLWG WBrk
- 'Turnipseed'	WCot
- 'Variegata' (v) ♀H7	Widely available
pumila	CRos EGrI EHyd ITim LRHS MBros MCot NRHS NSla
- f. ***atroviolacea***	WAbe
* - 'Gelber Mantel'	NBir WFar
- 'Violacea' (DB)	SRms
- yellow-flowered	WAbe
'Pure as Gold' (TB)	CWCL EIri ESgI WCot XSen
'Purple Gem' (Reticulata)	EHyd LRHS NRHS NRog
'Purple Hill' (Reticulata)	GKev
'Purple Mere' (Sib)	MHCG
'Purple Sensation' (Dut)	SDeJ
'Pussycat Pink' (SDB)	ESgI WCAu
'Quaker Lady' (TB)	ESgI
'Quark' (SDB)	CBro
'Quechee' (TB)	EHyd EPPr EPfP ESgI ETod EWoo GMaP IPot LBuc LRHS MBriF MCot MRav NLar NRHS NWad SCob SCoo SDeJ SPer WGwG
'Queen Adelaide' (La)	LLWG
'Queen in Calico' (TB)	ESgI
'Queen Jeanne' (La)	LLWG
'Queen of Angels' (TB)	WCAu
'Queen of Hearts' (TB)	XSen
'Queen of the Mist' (TB)	WCAu
'Queen's Circle' (TB) ♀H7	WCAu
'Rabbit's Foot' (SDB)	SIri
'Radiant Apogee' (TB)	EIri
'Radiant Burst' (IB)	SIri
'Rain Dance' (SDB) ♀H7	ESgI
RAINBOW GRAND MIXTURE	SDeJ
'Rainbow Rim' (SDB)	ESgI WCAu
'Rajah' (TB)	CBod CEnd CRos EHyd ELan ESgI EWoo GMaP LRHS LSRN MCot MHer MNrw MRav NRHS SBea SCob SCoo SDeJ SPer SPoG WGwG WLov WSpi
'Rambunctious' (Sib) **new**	CDor
'Rameses' (TB)	ESgI EWoo
'Rancho Rose' (TB)	XSen
'Ranman' (Sib) **new**	CDor
'Rare Edition' (IB)	CKel NBir XSen
'Rare Quality' (TB)	XSen
'Rare Treat' (TB)	XSen
'Raspberry Acres' (IB)	MRav
'Raspberry Blush' (IB) ♀H7	CBod CKel ECtt EGrI EHyd EIri EPfP GBin LRHS MCot MRav NBir NRHS SBea SDeJ WGwG WHoo WTor XSen
'Raspberry Tiger' (SDB)	WCAu
'Ravissant' (TB)	WViv
'Re La Blanche' (TB)	SIri
'Recurring Delight' (TB)	WCAu
'Red Echo' (La)	LLWG
'Red Ember' (Dut)	CAvo ERCP GKev LCro LOPS MNrw MPie WHil
'Red Enigma' (TB)	SIri
'Red Flare' (TB)	WFar
'Red Flash' (TB)	ESgI
'Red Heart' (SDB)	ELon ESgI MRav XSen
'Red Orchid' (IB)	ELan EWoo LRHS SRms
'Red Revival' (TB)	MRav WCAu
'Red Rufus' (TB)	CKel
'Red Velvet Elvis' (La)	LLWG
'Red Zinger' (IB)	CMac EWoo LRHS
'Reddy Maid' (Sib)	LRHS
'Redelta' (TB)	XSen
'Reflets Safran' (TB)	XSen
'Regal Surprise' (SpH) ♀H7	EWat LLWG SBrt
'Regality' (Sib)	MHer MMuc
'Regard Sombre' (TB) **new**	SIri
'Regards' (SDB)	CBro XSen
'Regency Belle' (Sib) ♀H7	GBin
'Regency Buck' (Sib)	WFar
§ ***reichenbachii***	GKev WAbe
'Rendez-Vous' (Dut)	SDeJ
'Renee Fleming' (La)	LLWG
'Repartee' (TB)	XSen
reticulata	ELan GKev NRog SDeJ
- var. ***bakeriana***	NRog
'Rhapsody' (Reticulata)	EHyd EPot GKev LRHS NRHS SDeJ
'Rheingauperle' (TB)	ESgI
'Rhinelander' (TB)	SIri
'Rigamarole' (Sib)	MWts WFar WGob
'Rikugi-sakura' (Sib)	ELon EPri NLar SHar WCot WGob WHil
'Rimfire' (TB)	ELan MHol
'Ringo' (TB)	EGrI LSRN MRav
'Rio de Oro' (TB)	WViv
'Rio Rojo' (TB)	WCAu
'Rip City' (TB)	ESgI
'Rive Gauche' (TB)	ESgI
'Riveting' (SDB)	WCAu
'Roanoke's Choice' (Sib)	CBro CElw ELon EWes MNrw SDir WFar
'Roaring Jelly' (Sib)	CDor EPri EWes NLar WCot WGob

	'Robe d'Été' (TB)	WViv
§	× ***robusta*** 'Dark Aura' ♀H7	LLWG LRHS MAvo MWts WCot WHil
§	- 'Gerald Darby'	Widely available
	- 'Mountain Brook'	LLWG
	- 'Purple Fan'	LLWG
	'Rochester Castle' (Kent Castles Series) (IB)	SIri
§	'Rocket' (TB)	ECtt EHyd ESgI GMaP LBuc LRHS MRav NBir NRHS SDeJ SPer
	'Roku Oji' (Sib)	CDor
	'Romantic Evening' (TB)	EIri WCAu XSen
	'Romney Marsh' (IB)	SIri
	'Romola' (TB)	WMil
	'Roryu' (SpH)	LLWG
	'Rosace' (Sib)	EWoo
	'Rosalie Figge' (TB)	CMac EIri ESgI MHol WCot
	'Rose Queen'	see *I. ensata* 'Rose Queen'
	'Rosebud Melody' (Sib)	GBin GWyn
	'Roseplic' (TB)	LRHS
	'Rosette Wine' (TB)	ESgI
	'Rosy Bows' (Sib)	WCAu WFar
	'Rosy Veil' (TB)	ESgI
	'Rosy Wings' (TB)	ESgI
	'Roucoulade' (TB)	SIri
	'Rouge Gorge' (TB)	SIri WViv
I	'Royal Blue' (Sib)	EBee ECha
	'Royal Crusader' (TB)	XSen
	'Roy's Repeater' (SpH)	EWoo LLWG
	'Ruby Chimes' (IB)	ESgI WCAu
	'Ruby Contrast' (SDB)	CKel WCAu
	'Ruby Eruption' (SDB)	EIri
	'Ruby Wine' (Sib)	EPri NLar
	rudskyi	see *I. variegata*
	'Ruffled Velvet' (Sib) ♀H7	CBcs CDor CElw CKel ECtt ELan EPfP EPri GBee GBin GDam GLog GMaP LRHS MCot MRav NChi NLar SCob SPeP SPer WCAu WFar WWtn
	'Ruffles and Flourishes' (Sib)	LLWG
	'Ruffles Plus' (Sib)	EPri WGob
	'Rumor Has It' (TB)	WCAu
	'Russian Kavelguard' (J) **new**	CWCL
	'Rusty Beauty' (Dut)	NRog SDeJ
	'Ruth Margaret' (TB)	CKel
	'Ruth Rowlands' (TB)	ESgI
	ruthenica	GArf
	- var. ***nana***	CExl GEdr GKev
	'Sable' (TB)	CKel CRos EHyd ELan EPfP ESgI ETod EWoo GMaP LRHS MRav NLar NRHS SCob SCoo SDeJ SHar SPer WGwG
	'Sable Night' (TB)	ESgI
	'Saint Crispin' (TB)	ECtt EHyd EPfP EWoo GMaP LRHS MRav NRHS SPer SPoG WGwG
	'Salonique' (TB)	NLar
	'Saltwood' (SDB)	CBro
	'Saltwood Castle' (Kent Castles Series) (IB)	SIri
	'Sam Carne' (TB)	WCAu
	× ***sambucina***	XSen
	'San Diego' (TB)	ESgI
	'San Francisco' (TB)	ESgI EWoo
	'Sanctification' (TB) ♀H7 **new**	ESgI
	sanguinea 'Nana Alba'	GBin
§	- 'Snow Queen'	CBcs CEme CKel EGrI ELan EPfP EPri EWTr GBin GKev GWyn LRHS NBid NLar NQui NRHS NSti SPer WCot WFar WWtn
	'Sapphire Beauty' (Dut)	GKev NRog SDeJ
	'Sapphire Gem' (SDB)	ESgI LSRN
	'Sapphire Hills' (TB)	LRHS XSen
	'Sasha Borisovich' (TB)	ESgI
	'Savoir Faire' (Sib)	ECha
	'Scent Sational' (Reticulata)	EPot ERCP GKev SPhx
	'Scented Wonder' (TB)	WCAu
	schachtii	GArf
	- purple-flowered	GArf WAbe
	'Scramble' (Sib)	WCot WFar
	'Scribe' (MDB)	CBro NBir
	'Sea Breeze' (Reticulata)	EPot ERCP GKev
	'Sea Fret' (SDB)	CBro
	'Sea of Joy' (TB)	XSen
	'Sea Shadows' (Sib)	EGrI EPri NBir
	'Season Ticket' (IB)	XSen
	'Second Look' (TB)	MBow XSen
	'Second Wind' (TB)	WCAu
	'Secret Melody' (TB)	XSen
	'Semola' (SDB)	ESgI
	'Senlac' (TB)	ELan EWoo NLar WMil
	serbica	see *I. reichenbachii*
	setosa ♀H7	CMac CTri EAJP EGrI EHyd EPPr EPot EWTr GBin GKev LRHS MNrw NHpl NRHS SGBe WFar
	- var. ***arctica***	GKev LEdu
I	- 'Baby Blue'	EHyd EPfP LRHS MACG MBNS NRHS
	- subsp. ***canadensis***	see *I. hookeri*
	- dark violet-flowered	EPri
	- var. ***nana***	see *I. hookeri*
	- - ink-black seed pods **new**	GGro
	'Shaker's Prayer' (Sib) ♀H7	ELon GBin MNrw SDir WGob
	'Shall We Dance' (Sib) ♀H7	CDor
	'Shampoo' (IB)	EWoo
	'Share the Spirit' (TB)	WCAu
	'Sharp Dressed Man' (TB)	WCAu
	'Sharrie Carrie' (TB)	SIri
	'Sheila Ann Germaney' (Reticulata)	CRos EHyd EPot ERCP GKev LHWs LRHS NRHS WBrk
	'Sherbet Lemon' (IB) ♀H7	WCAu
	'Shirley Chandler' (IB) ♀H7	SIri
	'Shirley Pope' (Sib) ♀H7	EWes GBin GWyn LRHS NSti WFar WGob WPnP WSpi
	'Shirley's Choice' (Sib)	ELon EPri
	'Shiryukyo' (SpH)	WMal
	'Showdown' (Sib)	ECtt EHyd GMaP LRHS NRHS
	shrevei	see *I. virginica* var. *shrevei*
	'Shurton Inn' (TB)	SRms WCAu
	sibirica	CCBP CTri CTsd GAbr GArf GBin GKev MBros MCot MHid MMuc NChi SBls SCob SPlb WBrk WCFE WFar WGwG WHer WShi
	- PAB 6119	LEdu
	'Sibirica Alba' (Sib)	ECha EPfP EPri SRms WBrk WFar
	sibirica 'Niklas Sea'	see *I.* 'Lake Niklas'
	- 'Redflare'	see *I.* 'Melton Red Flare'
	- 'Snow Queen'	see *I. sanguinea* 'Snow Queen'
	sichuanensis	CExl SPlb
	'Side Effects' (TB)	WCAu
	'Sierra Blue' (TB)	ESgI
	'Sierra Grande' (TB)	XSen
	'Sierra Nevada' (Spuria)	XSen
	'Sign of Leo' (TB)	CKel EWoo XSen
	'Silver Edge' (Sib) ♀H7	Widely available
	'Silver Peak' (TB)	CKel
	'Silverado' (TB)	ESgI GBin LRHS WCAu WSpi
	'Silvery Beauty' (Dut) ♀H6	CAvo ELan GAbr GKev LCro LOPS MPie NBir NRog SDeJ
	'Silvery Princess' (Dut)	SDeJ
	'Simply Coral' (TB)	WCAu
	'Simply Irresistible' (La)	LLWG
	sindjarensis	see *I. aucheri*

	'Sinfonietta' (La)	LLWG WCot
	'Sing to Me' (TB)	WCAu
	'Sinister Desire' (IB)	SIri
	sintenisii ♀H6	GKev WAbe XSen
	'Sir Michael' (TB)	ESgI
	'Siva Siva' (TB)	CKel ESgI ETod MRav
	'Skating Party' (TB)	ESgI XSen
	'Skiers' Delight' (TB)	ESgI
	'Sky Beauty' (Dut)	SDeJ
	'Sky Hooks' (TB)	XSen
	'Sky Wings' (Sib)	ECha MArl WFar
	'Skydancer' (SDB)	WCAu
	'Skyfire' (TB)	CKel
	'Skylark's Song' (TB)	EIri
	'Small Sky' (SDB)	CBro
	'Smart' (SDB)	WCAu
	'Smart Aleck' (TB)	ESgI
	'Smart Move' (TB)	ESgI
	'Smiling Faces' (TB)	WCAu
	'Smooth Orange'	see *I.* 'Orange Chariot'
	'Snow Prince' (Sib)	EPri
	'Snow Season' (SDB)	ESgI
	'Snow Tracery' (TB)	ECtt EHyd EPfP LRHS NRHS
	'Snowcrest' (Sib)	CPud EBee EHyd ESgI GBin LRHS MRav NRHS WGob WWtn
	'Snowmound' (TB)	CKel ESgI
	'Snowy Owl' (TB)	WCAu
	'Snugglebug' (SDB)	WCAu
	'Social Event' (TB)	ESgI XSen
	'Soft Blue' (Sib) ♀H7	ELon EPri
	'Solid Mahogany' (TB)	MRav
	'Song of Norway' (TB)	EIri EWoo XSen
	songarica	MHid
	sophenensis	EPot GKev
	'Sopra il Vulcano' (BB)	ESgI
	'Sorbonne' (TB)	WCAu
	'Sordid Lives' (TB)	WCAu
	'Sostenique' (TB)	ESgI
	'Southcombe White' (Sib)	SMHy
	'Souvenir de Madame Gaudichau' (TB)	ESgI EWoo
	'Sparkling Rose' (Sib)	Widely available
	'Sparkling Waters' (TB)	ESgI
	'Spartan' (TB)	EWoo
	'Speckled Hen' (La)	LLWG
I	'Speckles' (Sib)	EPPr
	'Speeding Star' (Spuria)	WCAu
	'Spellbreaker' (TB)	ELon SIri
	'Spice Lord' (TB)	WCAu
	'Spiced Custard' (TB)	EIri ESgI
	'Spicy Cajun' (La)	WHil
	'Spindazzle' (Sib)	ECtt
	'Spirit of Memphis' (TB)	XSen
	'Splashacata' (TB)	XSen
	'Spot On' (Reticulata)	EPot GKev LRHS WBrk
	'Spreckles' (TB)	CKel ESgI
	'Spree' (SDB)	WCAu
	'Spring Blush' (MTB) ♀H7	EIri
	'Spring Madness' (TB)	WCAu
	'Spring Time' (Reticulata)	SDeJ
	spuria	CMac EWoo SBls
§	- subsp. ***halophila***	GKev
	- subsp. ***notha*** CC 725	WCot
	- subsp. ***ochroleuca***	see *I. orientalis* Mill.
	'St Louis Blues' (TB)	ESgI XSen
	'Stairway to Heaven' (TB)	ESgI WCAu
	'Stapleford' (SDB)	CBro
	'Staplehurst' (MTB) ♀H7	SIri
	'Star Cluster' (Sib)	WFar
	'Star in the Night' (TB)	WCAu
	'Star Shine' (TB)	WCAu
	'Starring' (TB)	EIri
	'Starship' (TB)	XSen
	'Starwoman' (IB) ♀H7	WCAu
	'Staten Island' (TB)	ESgI SRms WCAu
	'Stella Polaris' (TB)	ELon
	'Stellar Lights' (TB)	EIri EWoo WCAu
	'Stephen Wilcox' (Sib)	CDor EPri
	'Stepping Out' (TB) ♀H7	CBod CKel CMac CRos ECtt EHyd EPfP ESgI ETod GBin LRHS NRHS SCob SDeJ SHar WTor
	'Steve' (Sib)	CPar EWes
	'Steve Varner' (Sib)	EPri
	'Stingray' (TB)	ESgI
	'Stitch in Time' (TB)	EIri
	stolonifera	GKev NRog
	- 'Augustus'	GKev
	- 'Caligula' (Rc)	GKev
	- 'Claudius'	GKev
	- 'George Barr'	GKev
	- 'Tiberius' **new**	GKev
	- 'Trajanus' **new**	GKev
	- 'Vespasianus' **new**	GKev
	'Stop the Music' (TB)	XSen
	'Storrington' (TB)	CEnd ECha ECtt ELan EMal EPfP
	'Strathmore' (TB)	ECha EMal
	'Strawberry Fair' (Sib) ♀H7	GBin
	'Strike it Rich' (TB)	ESgI
	'Strozzapreti' (TB)	ESgI
	'Strut your Stuff' (TB)	WCAu
	'Study in Black' (TB)	XSen
	'Stylish Socialite' (La)	LLWG
	stylosa	see *I. unguicularis*
§	***suaveolens***	GEdr NHpl NWad
	- var. ***flavescens***	see *I. suaveolens* yellow-flowered
	- Hevolvus Group **new**	WCot
§	- purple-flowered	GEdr GKev SGro WAbe
	- var. ***violacea***	see *I. suaveolens* purple-flowered
§	- yellow-flowered	GArf GKev WAbe
	'Succès Fou' (TB)	WViv
	'Sugar' (IB)	NSti WCAu
	'Sugar Magnolia' (TB)	SIri
	'Sugarmouse' (BB)	SIri
	'Sultan's Palace' (TB)	CKel EBee ECtt EPfP EWoo LCro LRHS MCot MHer WSpi XSen
	'Sultry Mood' (TB)	CKel
	'Summer Holidays' (TB)	XSen
	'Summer Olympics' (TB) **new**	CKel
	'Summer Revels' (Sib)	EPri EWes WGob
	'Summer Sky' (Sib)	CDor ELon LEdu MHCG MSCN WCot
	'Sunadokei' (SpH)	LLWG
	'Sunlit Shores' (La)	LLWG
	'Sunny Delight' (TB) **new**	ESgI
	'Sunny Disposition' (TB)	XSen
	'Sunnyside Up' (TB)	GKev
	'Sunset Sky' (TB)	CKel CWGN
	'Sunshine' (TB)	GKev
	'Sunshine' (Reticulata)	EPot ERCP SDeJ
	'Superact' (Sib)	ELon
	'Superstition' (TB) ♀H7	CKel CWGN EIri ELan EWes LCro LOPS LRHS MRav WCAu XSen
	'Supreme Sultan' (TB)	ESgI SCob WCAu XSen
I	'Surprise' (Dut)	MNrw
	'Susan Bliss' (TB)	ELan EPfP ESgI WMal WMil
	'Swain' (TB)	ESgI
	'Swan Ballet' (TB)	ESgI
	'Swazi Princess' (TB)	ELon SEdd SRms WSpi
	'Sweet Kate' (SDB)	ESgI
	'Sweet Lavender' (TB)	WMil
	'Sweet Lena' (TB)	ESgI
	'Sweet Musette' (TB)	SChr SRms WCAu

'Sweet Surrender' (Sib)	EPri
'Sweeter than Wine' (TB)	MRav
'Swingtown' (TB)	WCAu
'Swirling Waters' (La)	LLWG
'Swiss Majesty' (TB)	WCAu
'Swizzle' (IB)	XSen
'Sybil' (TB)	GBin
'Sylvan' (TB)	XSen
'Symphony' (Dut)	NBir SDeJ
'Syncopation' (TB)	ELon ESgI XSen
'Syrian Hills' (TB)	WCAu
'Tabac Blond' (TB)	EWoo
'Tact' (IB)	SIri
'Taking Chances' (TB)	WCAu
'Tamberg' (Sib)	CKel EWoo
'Tan Tingo' (IB)	XSen
'Tangerine Sky' (TB)	LRHS MBriF
'Tantara' (SDB)	XSen
'Tantrum' (IB)	XSen
'Tanz Nochmal' (Sib)	GBin
'Tarn Hows' (TB)	ESgI SRms
'Taubenblau' (Sib)	SAko
'Teal Velvet' (Sib)	ECha ELon EPfP EPri EWes EWoo GLog LRHS MCot SCob WFar WGob
'Tealwood' (Sib)	GBin WMal
'Teapot Tempest' (BB)	WCAu
'Teasaucer Hill' (MTB) ♀H7	SIri
tectorum	GKev LRHS SGBe WCot WMal XLum XSen
- BWJ 8191	WCru
- from Yunnan	MHid
- 'Alba'	GKev WThu XSen
- 'Cruella'	GWyn MHol MSCN WSpi
- 'Variegata' misapplied	see *I. japonica* 'Variegata'
- 'Variegata' (v)	SRms
'Tell Fibs' (SDB)	CBro
'Teller of Tales' (La)	LLWG
'Temper Tantrum' (Sib)	CBrac EGrI
'Temple Gold' (TB)	NPer
'Temple Meads' (IB)	ESgI WCAu
'Tempting Fate' (TB)	SIri
§ ***tenax***	EHyd
'Tenebrae' (TB)	WMil
'Tenterden' (BB)	SIri
'Teven' (La)	LLWG
'Teverlae' (Sib)	EBee EHyd LRHS NRHS
'Thaïs' (TB)	ESgI
'That's Red' (MTB)	EIri
'The Bride'	see *I.* 'Bride'
'The Citadel' (TB)	ELon
'The Rocket'	see *I.* 'Rocket'
'Third Charm' (SDB)	CBro
'Third World' (SDB)	CBro
'Thornbird' (TB) ♀H7	EIri ESgI SRms WCAu
'Three Part Harmony' (TB)	WCAu
'Three Quarters' (Sib)	ELon EWoo NChi
'Thriller' (TB)	ESgI WCAu XSen
'Thunder Echo' (TB)	SIri
'Thundering Ovation' (TB)	WCAu
'Tickety Boo' (SDB)	ECtt MBros
§ 'Tigereye' (Dut)	ERCP GBin GKev LCro LOPS MNrw SDeJ
* 'Tiger's Eye' ambig.	CKel
tigridia	CExl
'Time Zone' (TB)	WCAu
'Timescape' (TB) **new**	EGrI
tingitana	GKev
'Tinkerbell' (SDB)	EBee ECtt EHyd ESgI GMaP LRHS NBir NRHS SDeJ WTor
'Titan's Glory' (TB) ♀H7	CKel CMac ECtt EPfP IPot LEdu MPie MRav SRms WCot WHoo WSpi

'Tollong'	ILea
'Tom Tit' (TB)	WMil
'Tomato Bisque' (La)	LLWG
'Top Flight' (TB)	EHyd ELan SRms
'Top Gun' (TB)	ESgI
'Torero' (TB)	SIri
'Total Eclipse' (TB)	SRms
'Touch of Mahogany' (TB)	WCAu
'Trapel' (TB)	ESgI
'Trencavel' (TB)	ESgI
'Trenwith' (TB)	ESgI
'Triple Whammy' (TB)	ESgI XSen
'Tristram' (TB)	WMil
'Tropic Night' (Sib)	Widely available
tuberosa	CAvo CBor CBro CFis CTri ECha ELan ERCP EWoo LPot MHer SDeJ SSal WShi
- MS 76	WCot
- MS 964	WCot
- PB	GKev WCot
'Tulip Festival' (TB)	CKel
'Tumble Bug' (Sib)	CDor ECtt WGob
'Tumultueux' (TB)	WViv
'Tuxedo' (TB)	XSen
§ 'Tycoon' (Sib)	EHyd EShb EWoo GBin LCro LOPS NChi SPer
typhifolia	GKev
'Ultimate' (SDB)	WCAu
'Unbuttoned Zippers' (Sib)	CDor NLar
'Uncorked' (Sib)	ECtt EPfP LLWG MSCN
'Undercurrent' (TB)	WCAu
§ ***unguicularis***	Widely available
- from Karpathos, Greece	GKev
- 'Abington Purple'	EIri
- 'Alba'	CAvo CExl XSen
- subsp. ***angustifolia***	WSHC
§ - subsp. ***cretensis***	GKev
- - white-flowered	WSHC
- 'Marondera'	CAvo CBct
- 'Mary Barnard' ♀H5	CAvo CBro EGrI EHyd MHer WHoo
- 'Peloponnese Snow'	CJun GEdr
- 'Speciosa' **new**	CBro
§ - 'Walter Butt'	CAvo EBee
'Up in Flames' (TB) **new**	SIri
'Vague à l'Âme' (TB)	EWoo
'Val de Loire'	MAvo
'Valda' (Sib)	ELon EWoo
'Vamp' (IB)	EWoo GBin XSen
'Vanilla Mist' (La)	LLWG
'Vanilla Skies' (TB)	WCAu
'Vanity' (TB)	XSen
'Vanity's Child' (TB)	WCAu XSen
§ ***variegata*** ♀H7	CDor EBee GBin SCob XSen
- from Podyjí, Moravia	SBrt
I - var. ***reginae*** 'Davidowii'	MAvo
'Velvet King' (TB)	ESgI
'Venus Vortex' (La)	LLWG
versicolor	CBen CPud GBin GKev GMaP GPoy MMuc MNHC MWts SEND SPlb SRms WFar WMAq WPnP WShi
- 'Algonquin'	LLWG
- 'Bellerive Harmony'	LLWG
- 'Between the Lines'	LLWG
- 'Candystriper'	LLWG
- 'China West Lake'	LLWG
- 'Claret Cup'	EWoo SHar
- 'Kermesina'	CEme CPud ECha ELan EWoo LCro LLWG LOPS MACG NPer NSti SBls SRms WFar WMAq WPnP
- 'Mint Fresh'	LLWG
- 'Mysterious Monique'	CWat LLWG MWts

– 'Party Line'	CBen
– purple-flowered	EWat
– 'Raspberry Slurp'	LLWG
– 'Rowden Allegro'	LLWG
– 'Rowden Aria'	LLWG
– 'Rowden Cadenza'	EWat LLWG
– 'Rowden Calypso'	LLWG
– 'Rowden Cantata'	LLWG
– 'Rowden Concerto'	LLWG
– 'Rowden Electro'	LLWG
– 'Rowden Lyric'	LLWG
– 'Rowden Melody'	LLWG
– 'Rowden Pastorale'	LLWG
– 'Rowden Sonata'	LLWG
– 'Rowden Waltz'	LLWG
'Vi Luihn' (Sib)	ECha ELon SAko WFar
'Vibrations' (TB)	ESgI WCAu
vicaria	NRog
'Victoria Falls' (TB)	CKel ESgI MHol
'Victorian Secret' (Sib)	EBee ELon
'Viel Creme' (Sib)	ESgI
'Viel Schnee' (Sib)	ELon
'Vin Nouveau' (TB)	XSen
'Vino Rosso' (SDB)	ESgI
'Violet Beauty' (Reticulata)	EHyd NRHS NRog
'Violet Harmony' (TB)	ESgI
virginica	LLWG
– 'De Luxe'	see *I.* × *robusta* 'Dark Aura'
– 'Lavender Lustre'	LLWG
– 'Orchid Purple'	LLWG
– 'Pale Lavender'	LLWG
– 'Pink Perfection'	LLWG
§ – var. ***shrevei***	LLWG
– 'Slightly Daft'	LLWG
'Vitafire' (TB)	ESgI
'Vitality' (IB)	ELon ESgI
'Vitrail' (IB)	WViv
'Voilà' (IB)	CMea ESgI
'Volts' (SDB)	XSen
'Voyage' (SDB)	XSen
'Wabash' (TB)	CKel XSen
'Waihi Wedding' (La)	LLWG
'Walmer Castle' (Kent Castles Series) (IB)	SIri
'Walter Butt'	see *I. unguicularis* 'Walter Butt'
'War Chief' (TB)	EPfP ESgI MBriF MRav SPeP WCAu
'War Sails' (TB)	SIri WCAu
warleyensis	NRog
'Warlsind' (J)	GKev
wattii	CExl EPPr WGwG
– KWJ 12172	WCru
'Wealden Mystery' (Sib)	EPri
'Wearing Rubies' (TB)	ESgI WCAu
'Webelos' (SDB)	MRav
'Wedding Candles' (TB)	CKel
'Wedding Vow' (TB)	EIri
'Wedgwood' (Dut)	GBin
* 'Wedgwood Blue' (Sino-Sib)	GBin
'Weisse Etagen' (Sib)	ELon
'Welcome Return' (Sib)	LLWG MMuc SDir WGob
'Welfenfürstin' (Sib)	GBin SAko
'Westwell' (SDB)	GEdr
'What Again' (SDB)	XSen
'What It's Worth' (TB)	WCAu
'What's New Pussycat' (BB)	WCAu
'White Amber' (Sib)	ECtt WGob
'White Caucasus' (Reticulata)	EPot ERCP GKev WBrk
'White City' (TB)	CKel EHyd EPfP ESgI EWoo GMaP LRHS MRav NPer NRHS SDeJ SPer SRms
'White Gem' (SDB)	ESgI
'White Knight' (TB)	EBee WSpi
'White Reprise' (TB)	XSen
I 'White Swan' (Sib)	EPri
'White Swirl' (Sib)	CBar CBro CTri EBee ECha ECtt ELon EPfP ESgI GBin GLog GMaP GWyn LCro LRHS MRav NBro NLar NRHS NSti SCob SPer SRms WFar WGob WPnP
'White Triangles' (Sib)	ELon
'White Umbrella' (La)	ECtt LLWG MBros
'White van Vliet' (Dut)	SDeJ
'Wild' (BB)	WCAu
'Wild Wings' (TB)	LRHS MCot SGbt
willmottiana 'Alba'	GKev
wilsonii ♀H7	CExl GArf GKev NRya WGob
'Wine Wings' (Sib)	LRHS WGob
'Winesap' (TB)	ESgI EWoo
winogradowii ♀H7	EHyd EPot GKev NRHS NRog WAbe
'Winter Olympics' (TB)	CKel CRos ECtt EHyd ELan LRHS MRav NRHS SPer WGwG
'Winterfest' (TB)	WCAu
'Wintry Sky' (TB)	WCAu
'Wishful Thinking' (TB)	SIri
'Wizard's Return' (SDB)	SIri
'Wondrous' (TB)	ECtt EPfP ESgI IPot
'Word of Warning' (La)	LLWG
'Wrangler' (IB)	SIri
xiphioides	see *I. latifolia*
xiphium var. ***lusitanica***	GKev
'Yankee Consul' (Sib)	EPri
'Yaquina Blue' (TB)	ESgI WCAu
'Yarai' (SpH)	LLWG
'Yasha' (SpH)	LLWG
'Yellowtail' (Sib)	CBod EPfP MSCN
'Yeoman' (TB)	WMil
'Yes' (TB)	ESgI
'Yukiyanagi' (SpH)	LLWG
'Zakopane' (Sib)	EWes
'Zantha' (TB)	XSen
'Zero' (SDB)	SIri
'Zinger' (BB)	WSpi
'Zweites Hundert' (Sib)	WFar WKif

Isatis (*Brassicaceae*)

glauca	SPhx
tinctoria	CBod CHab CHby CKel ENfk GJos GPoy MHer MNHC SRms WSFF XSen
– subsp. ***athoa***	WCot

Ismene (*Amaryllidaceae*)

'Advance'	GKev
§ × ***deflexa*** ♀H1c	CCCN EShb GKev LCro LOPS SDeJ
– 'Zwanenburg'	GKev
§ ***longipetala***	GKev
§ 'Sulphur Queen' ♀H1c	CBor GKev SDeJ

Isodon (*Lamiaceae*)

calycinus	SPlb
effusus	MHol MNrw WPGP
excisus	EWld LPla
longitubus	LEdu MHol
– B&SWJ 11027	WCru
rubescens	SMad

Isolepis (*Cyperaceae*)

§ ***cernua***	CBen CPud CWat EWat LCro LLWG LOPS LRHS MWts SCoo WCot WMAq
'Live Wire'	see *I. cernua*
nodosa (Rottb.) R. Br.	see *Ficinia nodosa*

Isoloma see *Kohleria*

Isomeris see *Cleome*

Isoplexis see *Digitalis*

Isopogon (*Proteaceae*)

anemonifolius CCCN SPlb
anethifolius SPlb
formosus LRHS MPkF XSte

Isopyrum (*Ranunculaceae*)

biternatum LEdu
nipponicum GGro
thalictroides EBee EPot LEdu NRya WCot

Isotoma (*Campanulaceae*)

sp. SWvt
§ ***axillaris*** CSpe NPer SCoo
- 'Fairy Carpet' CBod LLWG LRHS NCou NHpl SLee SRms
- 'Lauren Blue' **new** MPri
- 'Lauren Pink' **new** MPri
fluviatilis NLar

Itea (*Iteaceae*)

chinensis CExl
ilicifolia 🏆H5 Widely available
* - 'Rubrifolia' ELan SLon
virginica CBcs CMCN EGrI LRHS MMrt MRav SLon
§ - 'Henry's Garnet' 🏆H5 CBod CDoC CEme CEnd CKel CMCN CMac EBee EGrI EHyd EPfP EShb EWhm GArf GBin MGil MGos NLar SCob SEle SGol SMad SPad SPer SPoG SRms SWvt WLov WPGP
- LITTLE HENRY ('Sprich'PBR) CBcs CKel CMac CSBt EBee EPfP ILea LRHS LSRN NLar XSte
- 'Long Spire' NLar
- 'Merlot' CBod ELon MBlu NLar SGol SIvy
- 'Sarah Eve' CMCN NLar
- 'Saturnalia' NLar
- Swarthmore form see *I. virginica* 'Henry's Garnet'
yunnanensis CExl MBlu NLar

Ixeris (*Asteraceae*)

stolonifera XLum

Ixia (*Iridaceae*)

bellendenii **new** NRog
'Blue Bird' NRog SDeJ
'Castor' EGrI NRog
'Giant' CBor EShb GKev NRog SDeJ
'Hogarth' GKev NRog
'Holland Glory' NRog
'Jesse' GKev SDeJ
latifolia CPbh
lutea NRog
'Mabel' CAvo CBor CWCL GKev NRog
'Marquette' CBor GKev
paniculata NRog
- 'Eos' CBor GKev NRog
'Panorama' NRog
polystachya CPbh GKev NRog
'Rose Emperor' ECha GKev NRog SDeJ
scillaris CPbh
'Spotlight' CAvo EShb GKev NRog
'Venus' CBor CWCL EGrI EShb GKev NRog SDeJ
viridiflora NRog SPlb WHil
'Vulcan' NRog
'Yellow Emperor' CBor GKev NRog SDeJ

Ixiolirion (*Ixioliriaceae*)

pallasii see *I. tataricum*
§ ***tataricum*** EBee NRog SDeJ

J

Jaborosa (*Solanaceae*)

integrifolia CExl EBee LEdu SVen XLum

Jacaranda (*Bignoniaceae*)

acutifolia misapplied see *J. mimosifolia*
§ ***mimosifolia*** 🏆H1c CBcs CCCN EShb SPlb WCFE

Jacobaea (*Asteraceae*)

candida WCot
§ ***maritima*** SCob SEND
- 'Ramparts' ECre
- 'Silver Dust' 🏆H4 MBros

Jacobinia see *Justicia*

Jamesia (*Hydrangeaceae*)

americana CBcs CMCN GEdr NLar SBrt WCru

× *Jancaemonda* (*Gesneriaceae*)

vandedemii NHar

Jasione (*Campanulaceae*)

§ ***heldreichii*** NBir SRms
jankae see *J. heldreichii*
§ ***laevis*** EHyd EPfP GAbr GArf SRms
§ - 'Blaulicht' CBor ECha EHyd EPfP GJos MHol NRHS SPlb WFar
- BLUE LIGHT see *J. laevis* 'Blaulicht'
montana MNHC SPhx SRms WWild
perennis see *J. laevis*

Jasminum ✿ (*Oleaceae*)

CC 4728 CExl
CW&T 6374 CMCN
affine see *J. officinale* f. *affine*
angulare 🏆H2 CExl CRHN EShb SEND WFib
azoricum 🏆H2 CBcs CCCN CRHN CTsd EPfP EShb SEND SPalm SPre WFib
beesianum Widely available
blinii see *J. polyanthum*
dispermum CRHN NLar
fruticans CMac EBee ELon GAbr SBrt SEND WCru WGob
- RCB UA 22 WCot
grandiflorum misapplied see *J. officinale* f. *affine*
grandiflorum L. 'De Grasse' 🏆H2 CRHN EShb WFib
humile CExl MGil NLar SEND SPtp WKif
§ - f. ***farreri*** Farrer 867 WPGP
- var. ***glabrum*** see *J. humile* f. *wallichianum*
- 'Pershore Purple' WAvo
§ - 'Revolutum' 🏆H5 CBcs CEme CMac CRHN CRos CSBt CWCL EBee EHyd ELan EPfP EShb LPar LRHS MGos MRav NLar SEND SGbt SLon SPer SPoG SRms SWvt
§ - f. ***wallichianum*** B&SWJ 2559 WCru
- - PAB 2534 LEdu

- - PAB 9962	LEdu
humile* × *parkeri	SEle
§ ***laurifolium* f. *nitidum*** ♀H2	SMad
§ ***mesnyi*** ♀H3	CBcs CCCN CExl CMac CRHN CTri EBak EPfP EShb SEND SGol SGro SPer SVen WCFE WSHC
multiflorum	CCCN
multipartitum	CCCN EShb
§ ***nudiflorum*** ♀H5	Widely available
- 'Argenteum'	see *J. nudiflorum* 'Mystique'
- 'Aureum'	CMac CRos ELan LRHS MAsh MRav NLar SPer SPoG SRms
§ - 'Mystique' (v)	CRos EHyd ELan LRHS MRav NRHS SLon
odoratissimum	WFib
officinale	Widely available
§ - f. ***affine***	CBcs CCCN CRHN CRos CTri EHyd ELan EPfP LRHS MAsh MRav NRHS SCoo SDix SRms
§ - 'Argenteovariegatum' (v) ♀H5	CBod CKel CMac CWGN ELan EPfP LRHS LSRN MAsh MGos MHer MMuc MRav SEND SMad SPer SPoG SWvt WLov WSHC
- 'Aureovariegatum'	see *J. officinale* 'Aureum'
§ - 'Aureum' (v)	CBcs CBod CMac CWCL ELan EPfP LRHS LShi MAsh MHer MNHC NFav SCoo SLon SRms
- 'Clotted Cream'	see *J. officinale* 'Devon Cream'
- 'Crûg's Collection'	WCru
§ - 'Devon Cream'PBR	Widely available
- FIONA SUNRISE ('Frojas'PBR) ♀H5	CBcs CKel CMac CRos CWGN EBee EHyd ELan ELon EPfP LRHS LSRN LSou MAsh MGos MHer MRav NLar NRHS SCoo SGol SPad SPer SPoG SPtp SWvt WFar
- 'Grandiflorum'	see *J. officinale* f. *affine*
- 'Inverleith' ♀H5	CBod CCCN CRos EBee ECtt ELan EPfP LRHS MAsh MBNS MGil MGos MNHC MRav NRHS SCoo SMad SNig SPad SPer SPoG WGrn
- SUNBEAM ('Lobeam')	CBod CDoC CRos EBee EHyd LRHS NRHS SCoo
- 'Variegatum'	see *J. officinale* 'Argenteovariegatum'
parkeri	CBcs CCCN CMac CTri EBee EHyd ELon GMaP MGil NLar SEle SNig
- 'Bychan'	WAbe
§ ***polyanthum*** ♀H2	CBcs CExl CKel CRHN CSBt CSde CTri EBak ELan EPfP EShb ETho LCro LOPS SEND SGsty SPer SPre SRms SWeb
- dark red-leaved	CCCN CExl CKel EBee EPfP
primulinum	see *J. mesnyi*
reevesii hort.	see *J. humile* 'Revolutum'
sambac ♀H2	CCCN CRHN ELan SPre WFib
- 'Grand Duke of Tuscany' (d)	CCCN
- 'Maid of Orleans' (d)	CCCN EShb
sieboldianum	see *J. nudiflorum*
§ ***simplicifolium*** subsp. ***suavissimum***	CRHN
stenalobium	WCot WFib
× ***stephanense***	Widely available
suavissimum	see *J. simplicifolium* subsp. *suavissimum*

Jatropha (*Euphorbiaceae*)

cinerea	SPlb
integerrima	CCCN
multifida	CDoC SPlb
podagrica ♀H1b	CDoC SPad

Jeffersonia (*Berberidaceae*)

diphylla	CRos EBee EHyd EMor EPPr EPot EPri EWld GBin GKev LEdu LRHS MBel MNrw NBir NChi NRHS WCru WFar WPnP WThu
dubia	CRos EHyd EPot EWes EWld GBin GKev LEdu LRHS MNrw NBir NChi NRHS SBrt WAbe WCot WThu
- 'Sunago-fu' (v)	GEdr
- variegated (v) **new**	EPot

jostaberry see *Ribes* × *nidigrolaria*

Jovellana (*Calceolariaceae*)

punctata	CBcs CCCN CExl CTsd EBee EWld IArd SPlb WLov
sinclairii	CExl CTsd
violacea ♀H3	CAbb CBcs CCCN CExl CKel CMac CPla CTrC CTsd CTtf EBee EHyd EPfP EWld LRHS MGil SEle SPad SVen WPGP WPav

Jovibarba ✿ (*Crassulaceae*)

§ ***allionii***	CBod CMea CTri EBou EDAr EPot LRHS MHer MSCN NFav NHpl SRms SSim WCav WFar WHal WHoo
- 'Oki'	CRos EHyd LRHS NRHS SRms
allionii* × *hirta	SDys SPlb
allionii* × *sobolifera	LRHS
§ ***arenaria***	GAbr NMen XLum
'Autumn Fires'	SSem
* ***echiniformis***	XLum
'Emerald Spring'	GFgr
§ ***heuffelii***	CRos EHyd GArf LRHS NFav NHpl NRHS WFar XLum
- 'Achisia'	NMen
- 'Adagdak'	NMen
- 'Agaffa'	NMen
- 'Aiolos'	NHol
- 'Aldicia'	NMen
- 'Alena'	NMen
- 'Almkroon'	NHol NWad
- 'Ambassadeur'	NMen
- 'Angel Wings'	SRms WHoo
- 'Ardysia'	NMen
- 'Arnia'	NMen
- 'Askja'	NMen
- 'Atoll'	NMen
- 'Atria'	NMen
- 'Bandana'	NMen
- 'Barbel'	NMen
- 'Baripper'	NMen
- 'Beacon'	NMen
- 'Beacon Hill'	NMen
- 'Belcore'	NMen XLum
- 'Bermuda'	NMen
- 'Biapho'	NMen
- 'Bibiana'	NMen
- 'Big Brother'	NMen
- 'Big Red'	NHol NWad
- 'Bolero'	NMen
- 'Bora'	NWad
- 'Brandaris'	SDys
- 'Brocade'	MSCN NHol NMen NWad
- 'Bronze Ingot'	NMen
- 'Bulgarien'	NMen
- 'Burgharis'	NMen
- 'Cauvery'	NMen
- 'Centaurus'	NMen
- 'Charell'	NMen

§ – 'Cherry Glow' NMen
– 'Chocoleto' NMen
– 'Cimmanon' NMen
– 'Comanchero' NMen
I – 'Compacta' NMen
– 'Copper King' NMen
– 'Corbierie' NMen
– 'Coutanche' NMen
– 'Cover Girl' NMen
– 'Crill' NMen
– 'Deciso' NMen
– 'Dream' NMen
– 'Drechter Gem' NMen
– 'Dynosia' NMen
– 'Elmo's Fire' NMen
* – 'Emerald and Ruby' WFar
– 'Enicia' NMen
– 'Eos Moment' NMen
– 'Ernest' NMen
– 'Etysia' NMen
– 'Fan Joy' NMen
– 'Fandango' NMen
– 'Geronimo' NHol NMen
– 'Ghaysia' NMen
– 'Giuseppi Spiny' NMen
– var. ***glabra*** WHoo
– – from Anaba Kanak, Bulgaria NHol
– – from Treska Gorge, Macedonia SRms
§ – – 'Cameo' NMen
– 'Gladiator' NMen
– 'Gold Rand' NHol NWad
* – 'Golden Touch' WFar
– 'Grand Slam' NMen
– 'Green Land' NMen
– 'Greenstone' NHol NMen NWad
– 'Harmony' NHol
– 'Henry Correvon' NMen
– var. ***heuffelii*** NMen
– 'Heulin' NMen
– 'Hot Bikini' NMen
– 'Hot Chocolate' NMen
– 'Hot Lips' NMen
– 'Idylle' NMen
– 'Ikaros' NHol
– 'Inferno' NMen NWad
– 'Ithaca' NHol NWad
– 'Iuno' NHol
– 'Jackpot' NMen
– 'Jade' NMen
I – 'Jovi King' NMen
– 'June's Choice' NMen
– 'King Sunny' NMen
– 'Konrada' NMen
– var. ***kopaonikensis*** NMen NWad
– 'Lorelei' NMen
– 'Lucky Bell' NMen
– 'Machon' NMen
– 'Madera' NMen
– 'Major' NMen
– 'Mary Ann' NMen
– 'Miller's Violet' NMen
– 'Mink' NMen
– 'Minuta' NMen
– 'Misty' NMen
– 'Mystique' NMen WHoo
– 'Nannette' NMen
– 'Olivia' NMen
– 'Orion' NMen XLum
– var. ***patens*** NMen
– 'Penponds' NMen
– 'Pink Skies' NMen
– 'Pink Star' NMen
– 'Prisma' NMen
– 'Pronker' NMen
– 'Purple Haze' XLum
– 'Purple Heide' NMen
– 'Quennevalis' NMen
– 'Red Rose' NMen
– 'Red Start' NMen
– 'Rhapsody' NMen
– 'Samares' NMen
– 'Sarabande' NMen
– 'Serenade' NMen SRms
– 'Silex' NMen
– 'Springael's Choice' NMen
– 'Summer King' NMen
* – 'Sun and Silver Edge' WFar
– 'Sungold' NHol NWad
– 'Suntan' NWad
– 'Superduper' NMen
– 'Sylvan Memory' NMen
– 'Tancredi' NMen
– 'Torrid Zone' MBrN NMen
– 'Trinity' NMen
– 'Troon' NMen
– 'Try Me' NMen
– 'Tuxedo' NHpl NMen
– 'Violet' NMen SDys
– 'Yuppy Alone' NMen
§ ***hirta*** EDAr GAbr GKev SLee WFar XLum
– from Wintergraben, Austria SPlb SRms
– 'Belansky Tatra' NMen SRms
– subsp. ***glabrescens*** from High Tatra, Slovakia/Poland XLum
– – from Smeryouka, southern Carpathians NMen
– var. ***neilreichii*** CRos EHyd LRHS MHer NRHS SRms
– 'Purpurea' XLum
§ ***sobolifera*** EDAr EGrI EPot GArf GKev SPlb WHal XLum
– 'Green Globe' CRos EHyd LRHS NRHS SDys SSem
– 'Miss Lorraine' XLum

Jubaea (*Arecaceae*)

§ ***chilensis*** ♀H2 CPHo ETod SArc SPalm SPlb
spectabilis see *J. chilensis*

Juglans ✿ (*Juglandaceae*)

§ ***ailanthifolia*** CMCN IDee
– B&SWJ 11026 WCru
– var. ***cordiformis*** 'Brock' (F) CAgr
– – 'Campbell Cw3' (F) CAgr
– – 'Fodermaier' seedling (F) CAgr
– – 'Imshu' (F) CAgr
– – 'Rhodes' (F) CAgr
– – 'Simcoe' (F) CAgr
ailanthifolia* × *cinerea see *J.* × *bixbyi*
§ × ***bixbyi*** CAgr
cinerea 'Beckwith' (F) CAgr
– 'Booth' (F) CAgr
– 'Booth' seedling (F) CAgr
– 'Chamberlin' (F) CAgr
– 'Craxezy' (F) CAgr
– 'Kenworthy' seedling (F) CAgr
– 'Myjoy' (F) CAgr
hindsii CMCN
mandshurica (F) CMCN
– B&SWJ 12550 from Korea WCru
– BWJ 8097 from China WCru

- RWJ 9905 from Taiwan	WCru
microcarpa* × *nigra	CDoC LPar MTrO NRog
nigra (F) ♀H6	Widely available
- 'Beineke 10'PBR (F) new	CAco
- 'Bicentennial' (F)	CAgr
- 'Emma Kay' (F)	CAgr
- 'Laciniata'	EPfP MBlu
- 'Potsdam' (F)	CAgr
- 'Thomas' (F)	CAgr
- 'Weschke' (F)	CAgr
regia (F)	Widely available
- 'Apollo' new	MTrO
- 'Axel' (F)	CAgr WMat
- 'Broadview' (F)	CAgr CArg CBrac CEnd CMac ELan EPom LBuc LCro LOPS LPar LRHS MBlu MGos MTrO NOra NWea SCoo SEWo SKee SPoG SSFT SVic WMat
- 'Buccaneer' (F)	CAgr CArg CDoC CMac ELan EPom LPar MTrO NOra SCoo SKee WMat
- 'Chandler' (F)	CAgr
- 'Corne du Périgord' (F)	CAgr
- 'Excelsior of Taynton' (F)	WMat
- 'Ferjean' (F)	CAgr
- 'Fernette'PBR (F)	CAgr MTrO NOra WMat
- 'Fernor' (F)	CAgr MTrO WMat
- 'Franquette' (F) ♀H6	CAgr MTrO NOra WMat
- 'Hansen' (F)	CAgr
- 'Hartley' (F)	CAgr
- 'Jupiter' (F)	ELan MTrO
- 'Laciniata' ♀H6	CMCN
- 'Lara' (F) ♀H6	CAgr NOra WMat
- 'Mars' (F) new	ELan MTrO
- 'Mayette' (F)	CAgr
- 'Meylannaise' (F)	CAgr
- 'Mini Multiflora 14' (F)	CAgr
- number 16 (F)	WMat
- 'Parisienne' (F)	CAgr SGol
- 'Plovdivski' (F)	WMat
- 'Proslavski' (F)	WMat
- 'Purpurea'	CMCN MBlu
- 'Rita' (F)	LBuc
- 'Ronde de Montignac' (F)	CAgr
- 'Saturn' (F)	ELan MTrO
- 'Sychrov' (F)	MTrO WMat
sieboldiana	see *J. ailanthifolia*
sigillata	LEdu

jujube see *Ziziphus jujuba*

Juncus (*Juncaceae*)

articulatus	LLWG XLum
bulbosus	CNat
§ ***decipiens*** 'Curly-wurly'	CDoC EHyd EPfP LRHS NRHS NWad
- 'Spiralis'	see *J. decipiens* 'Curly-wurly'
effusus	CBen CPud LRHS NPer WMAq XLum
- 'Carman's Japanese'	NSti
- 'Gold Strike' (v)	LLWG
§ - f. ***spiralis***	CBen CPud CRos CSpe CTtf CWat EHyd EPfP EWat GQue LCro LOPS LPot LRHS MAsh NBir NFav NRHS SBls SCob SPlb SVic WCot WMAq XLum
ensifolius	CWat EWat EWes LLWG MMrt MWts NPer NSti WMAq
- 'Flying Hedgehogs' new	MACG
inflexus	CBen CPud CWat LLWG WSMil XLum
- 'Afro'	NBro NWsh SPlb WSMil
pallidus	EPPr
patens 'Carman's Gray'	CKno CWCL EHyd
- 'Elk Blue'	CKno
subnodulosus	LLWG
'Swarm of Hedgehogs'	NWsh
TWISTED ARROWS (mixed) new	LRHS
'Twister' new	LRHS

Junellia (*Verbenaceae*)

azorelloides	WAbe
congesta	WAbe
coralloides new	WAbe
§ ***micrantha***	WAbe
odonnellii	WAbe
§ ***succulentifolia***	WAbe
thymifolia	WAbe

Juniperus ✿ (*Cupressaceae*)

ashei new	CAco
bermudiana new	CAco
chinensis	CAco CMen NWea
- 'Aurea' ♀H6	SEND
§ - 'Blaauw' ♀H6	CMac CMen LRHS SLim
- 'Blue Alps' ♀H6	CAco LRHS MGos MMuc SCoo SEND SLim
- 'Bokor'	CAco
- 'Echiniformis'	CKen
- 'Expansa Aureospicata' (v)	CMac EPfP SCoo SEND SPoG SRms
§ - 'Expansa Variegata' (v)	SLim
- 'Itoigawa'	CAco CMen
§ - 'Kaizuka' ♀H6	SLim
- 'Kaizuka Variegata'	see *J. chinensis* 'Variegated Kaizuka'
- 'Kék' new	CAco
- 'Keteleeri'	CAco
- 'Kuriwao Gold'	see *J.* × *pfitzeriana* 'Kuriwao Gold'
- 'Plumosa'	SLim
- 'Plumosa Aurea' ♀H6	CAco
- 'Plumosa Aureovariegata' (v)	CKen
- 'Pyramidalis' ♀H6	CBrac CEme EPfP MAsh SCob SCoo
- 'San José'	CMen
§ - var. ***sargentii***	CMen
- 'Shimpaku'	CKen CMen
- 'Stricta'	CAco CSBt LRHS NOrn SLim
- 'Sulphur Spray'	see *J.* × *pfitzeriana* 'Sulphur Spray'
- 'Torulosa'	see *J. chinensis* 'Kaizuka'
§ - 'Variegated Kaizuka' (v)	SLim
- 'Wilson's Weeping'	LRHS NLar
communis	CAco CHab GPoy NWea SCob SPre WKor WTSh
- 'Arnold Sentinel'	CKen
- 'Barton'	NWad
- 'Barton Gem'	NWad
- 'Brien'	CKen
- 'Brynhyfryd Gold'	CKen GKev SLim
- 'Compressa' ♀H7	CBcs CEme CKen CMac CSBt CTri EPfP GEdr LBee LRHS MAsh MGos NHol NWea SCob SCoo SLim SPer SPoG WIce
- 'Corielagan'	CKen
- 'Cracovia'	CKen
- var. ***depressa***	GPoy SEND
- 'Depressa Aurea'	CBrac CKen CSBt LBee
- 'Depressed Star'	SPoG
- 'Effusa'	CKen
- 'Gold Cone'	CBrac CEme CKen ELan EPfP LBee MAsh MGos SLim SPoG
- 'Goldschatz'	CKen EPfP LRHS SCoo SLim SPoG
- 'Green Carpet' ♀H7	CKen ELan EPfP GKin LBuc LRHS MAsh MGos SCoo SGsty SLim SPoG SVic

- 'Greenmantle' LPar LRHS MTrO WMat
- 'Haverbeck' CKen
- 'Hibernica' ♀H7 CBrac CSBt ELan EPfP EWTr LRHS MGos NWea SCob SGsty SLim SPer SPoG
- 'Hibernica Aurea' CMac
- 'Hornibrookii' NWea SRms
- 'Horstmann' SMad
I - 'Horstmann's Pendula' NLar
- 'Kenwith Castle' CKen
- 'Meyer' CMac
- 'Repanda' ♀H7 CAco CBcs CBrac CMac CSBt EPfP LRHS MGos NLar NWea SCob SCoo SLim SPer SPoG WFar
- 'Sentinel' SLim
- 'Sieben Steinhauser' CKen NLar
- 'Silver Mist' CKen
- 'Spotty Spreader' (v) SLim
- Suecica Group NWea
- - 'Suecica Nana' SLim
- 'Zeal' CKen

conferta see *J. rigida* subsp. *conferta*
- 'Blue Lagoon' CAco
convallium **new** CAco
davurica 'Expansa Albopicta' see *J. chinensis* 'Expansa Variegata'
- 'Expansa Variegata' see *J. chinensis* 'Expansa Variegata'
deppeana var. ***zacatecensis*** **new** CAco
drupacea **new** CAco
excelsa **new** CAco
- subsp. ***polycarpos*** CAco
foetidissima CAco
- 'Karaca Blue' **new** CAco
formosana **new** CAco
× ***gracilis*** 'Blaauw' see *J. chinensis* 'Blaauw'
'Grey Owl' ♀H7 CAco CBod CBrac ELan LRHS MMuc NWea SCob SEND SGsty SLim SRms
horizontalis NWea
I - 'Andorra Variegata' (v) CKen SCoo
- 'Bar Harbor' CMac
§ - 'Blue Chip' CAco CKen ELan EPfP LBee MGos SCob SCoo SGsty SLim SPoG WLea
- 'Blue Moon' see *J. horizontalis* 'Blue Chip'
- 'Glauca' CBrac NWea SCob
- 'Golden Carpet' ♀H7 CBod ELan LBuc LCro LOPS LPar LRHS NLar
- 'Grey Pearl' CKen
- 'Hughes' LBee MRav NWea
- ICEE BLUE ('Monber') ♀H7 CKen ELan EPfP LRHS NLar SPoG
- 'Limeglow' ♀H7 CAco CBrac ELan EPfP SCoo SPoG
- 'Mother Lode' CKen LPar
- 'Neumann' CKen
- 'Plumosa' CAco
- 'Prince of Wales' MAsh NWea WLea
- 'Turquoise Spreader' CSBt NWea
- 'Villa Marie' CKen SPoG
§ - 'Wiltonii' LRHS NWea
- 'Yukon Belle' CKen
× ***media*** see *J.* × *pfitzeriana*
navicularis **new** CAco
occidentalis **new** CAco
oxycedrus XSen
§ × ***pfitzeriana*** CMac GDam NWea SCob WFar
- 'Arctic' NLar
- 'Blaauw' see *J. chinensis* 'Blaauw'
- 'Blue and Gold' (v) CKen SPoG
§ - 'Carbery Gold' ♀H6 CBcs CBrac CMac CSBt EPfP GKin LRHS MAsh MGos NOrn SCoo SLim SPoG
- 'Gold Coast' CBod CBrac CKen CSBt LBee LRHS MAsh MGos
- GOLD SOVEREIGN ('Blound') LBee
- 'Gold Star' LRHS MAsh WLea
* - 'Golden Joy' SLim
- 'Golden Saucer' MAsh
- 'Goldkissen' LRHS
- 'King of Spring' SLim
§ - 'Kuriwao Gold' GKin SEND
- 'Mint Julep' CAco CBrac CSBt EPfP LRHS SCob SCoo SGsty SLim
- 'Old Gold' ♀H6 CEme EPfP GKin LBee LCro LOPS LPar LRHS MGos MMuc NWea SCob SCoo SEND SGsty SPer SPlb SVic WFar
- 'Old Gold Carbery' see *J.* × *pfitzeriana* 'Carbery Gold'
- 'Pfitzeriana Aurea' CBrac CEme CMac NWea SCob
§ - 'Sulphur Spray' ♀H6 LRHS MMuc SCob SEND SLim WCFE

phoenicea CKel XSen
- subsp. ***turbinata*** XSen
pinchotii **new** CAco
§ ***pingii*** 'Glassell' NLar
- 'Hulsdonk Yellow'PBR LPar SPoG
§ - var. ***wilsonii*** CKen
procumbens 'Nana' ♀H7 CEme CKen CMac EPfP LBee LPar LRHS MAsh MGos NHol NLar SCoo SGsty SLim SPoG SavN
pseudosabina Fisch. & C.A.Mey. **new** CAco
recurva IDee
- 'Castlewellan' MGil NLar WFar
- var. ***coxii*** CMac LRHS MBlu NHol NLar SMad SRms
§ - 'Densa' CKen
- 'Nana' see *J. recurva* 'Densa'
rigida CAco CMen
§ - subsp. ***conferta*** CMac SEND
- - 'All Gold' ♀H6 LRHS SLim SPoG
* - - 'Blue Ice' CKen
- - 'Blue Pacific' CEme CKen LRHS SGsty SPoG SWeb
- - 'Blue Tosho' NLar
- - 'Schlager' ♀H6 SLim
- - 'Silver Mist' CKen
sabina NWea
- 'Hicksii' NWea
- 'Skandia' CKen
- 'Tamariscifolia' GKin LBee MAsh MGos NOrn NWea SArc SCob SEND SGsty SLim SPer SPoG
saltuaria **new** CAco
scopulorum 'Blue Arrow' ♀H6 Widely available
- 'Blue Banff' CKen
- 'Moonglow' LPar SGsty
- 'O'Connor' CAco
- 'Skyrocket' CBcs CBod CCVT CMac CSBt EPfP IPap LMaj MGos MRav NWea SCob SPad SRms SWeb
- 'Springbank' WCFE
- 'Wichita Blue' CCVT EPfP
semiglobosa **new** CAco
§ ***squamata*** SavN
- 'Blue Carpet' ♀H7 CAco CBcs CBod CEme CKen CMac CSBt EPfP LBuc LPar LRHS MAsh MGos NHol NLar NOrn NWea SCob SCoo SEND SGsty SLim SPer SPoG WFar
- 'Blue Star' ♀H7 CBod CBrac CEme CKen CMac CSBt ELan EPfP LBee LCro LOPS

	LRHS MAsh MGos NHol NLar NWea SCob SCoo SGsty SLim SPer SPoG WFar
- 'Blue Star Variegated'	see *J. squamata* 'Golden Flame'
- 'Chinese Silver'	CAco
- 'Dream Joy'	CBod NLar
- 'Filborna'	LBee NLar
- 'Floreant'	SPoG
- 'Glassell'	see *J. pingii* 'Glassell'
§ - 'Golden Flame' (v)	CKen
- 'Holger' 🏆H7	CAco CEme CMac EPfP LBee LRHS MAsh MGos NHol NLar SCoo SLim SPoG WFar
§ - 'Hunnetorp'	WFar
- 'Tropical Blue'	SPoG
- 'Wilsonii'	see *J. pingii* var. *wilsonii*
§ ***taxifolia***	CSBt
thurifera	XSen
tibetica new	CAco
virginiana	CAco
- 'Burkii'	SArc
- 'Frosty Morn'	CKen
- 'Golden Spring'	CKen
- 'Pendula'	CAco
- SILVER SPREADER ('Mona')	CKen
- 'Sulphur Spray'	see *J.* × *pfitzeriana* 'Sulphur Spray'

Jurinea (*Asteraceae*)

mollis	SBrt SPhx

Jurinella see *Jurinea*

Jussiaea see *Ludwigia*

Justicia (*Acanthaceae*)

adhatoda new	EShb
americana	LLWG SBrt
aurea	EShb SPlb
§ ***brandegeeana*** 🏆H1b	CCCN EShb
- variegated (v)	EShb
§ - 'Yellow Queen'	EShb
- yellow-flowered	EShb
§ ***carnea***	EMdy EShb SSal WFar
- 'Alba'	CCCN
- dark-leaved	EShb
- 'Radiant'	SMad
'Penrhosiensis'	EShb
pohliana	see *J. carnea*
rizzinii 🏆H1b	CBcs CCCN MNHC SEle WLov
spicigera	CCCN EShb
suberecta	see *Dicliptera sericea*

K

Kadsura (*Schisandraceae*)

coccinea B&SWJ 11793	WCru
- FMWJ 13489	WCru
heteroclita FMWJ 13385	WCru
- WWJ 11947	WCru
japonica	CBcs
- B&SWJ 1027	WCru
- B&SWJ 4463 from Korea	WCru
- B&SWJ 11109 from Japan	WCru
- B&SWJ 14672	ESwi WCru
- 'Fukurin' (v)	IDee NLar
- 'Variegata' (v)	CCCN CKel EBee EHyd EPfP LRHS
- white fruit	NLar
aff. ***japonica*** NMWJ 14550	WCru

Kaempferia ✿ (*Zingiberaceae*)

pulchra	CDTJ
rotunda	CCCN SDir

Kageneckia (*Rosaceae*)

oblonga	SPlb

Kalanchoe (*Crassulaceae*)

beauverdii	EShb
beharensis 🏆H1b	CCCN CDTJ CDoC ELan EShb WCot
- 'Fang' 🏆H1b	CDTJ ELan EShb WCot
- 'Rusty'	CDTJ CSpe EShb
daigremontiana	EShb
§ ***delagoensis***	CCCN CDoC EShb SPlb
'Dorothy'	EShb
fedtschenkoi 'Variegata' (v)	EShb WCot
hildebrandtii	EShb
humilis	CDoC EShb WCot
× ***kewensis***	EShb
laciniata	EShb
laetivirens	SSim
luciae 🏆H1b	CDoC
manginii 🏆H1b	EShb
'Oak Leaf'	EShb
orgyalis	EShb WCot
pinnata	EShb
'Prebella'	EShb
pumila 🏆H1b	CDoC EShb SGro
rosei var. ***variifolia*** new	EShb
scandens 'Kalahari Survivor'	EShb
serrata	EShb
sexangularis	EShb
'Tessa' 🏆H1b	WCot
thyrsiflora	CDoC EShb
- 'Bronze Sculpture'	CAbb CBod MCot SEdd SIvy SSim
- RED LIPS ('Ubilips')	LCro LOPS
- 'Variegata' (v)	EShb
tomentosa 🏆H1b	CDoC EShb WCot XAbr
tubiflora	see *K. delagoensis*

kale, curly see AGM Vegetables Section

Kalimeris (*Asteraceae*)

altaica	EPPr
§ ***incisa***	CFis CFoA CMea EBee MMuc
- 'Alba'	CKno EBee ECha ELon GMaP NLar WCAu WFar
- 'Blue Star'	CBod CKno EBee ECha ECtt ELon GMaP GQue MNrw MSpe NLar SIvy SPad WCAu WFar WSHC
- 'Charlotte'	EWes LPla MACG MNrw NDov NHol SAko SDix SPoG WFar WGoo
- 'Edo Murasaki'	GGro SBrt
- 'Jürgen Wever'	LPla
- 'Madiva'	EBee ECha ELon GBee LPla NDov SAko WGoo
- 'Nana Blue'	EBee ECha NDov SPoG
integrifolia 'Daisy Mae'	NDov
'Mon Jardin'	WCot
§ ***mongolica***	ECha EPPr LEdu MMuc SAko SBut WFar WGoo WSHC
- 'Antonia'	ECha LPla NDov WCot
- variegated (v) new	WCot
§ ***pinnatifida***	EHyd MHol
- 'Hortensis'	MACG MHol MNrw WSHC

§ ***yomena*** 'Shogun' (v) — CBod CDor CKel CMac EBee ECha ECtt EHyd ELon EMil EPfP LEdu LRHS MACG MBel MHol MNrw MPie NSti SDix SPer SPoG SRms WFar XLum
- 'Variegata' — see *K. yomena* 'Shogun'

Kalmia ✿ (*Ericaceae*)

angustifolia ♀H5 — GKev MGil WSpi
- var. ***angustifolia*** f. ***candida*** — LRHS
- f. ***rubra*** ♀H5 — CBcs CCCN CDoC CRos EBee EHyd EPfP LRHS MAsh NLar SCob SPer WFar WSpi
I - 'Rubra Nana' — CMac
buxifolia subsp. ***hugeri*** — GKev
latifolia — CBcs EBee EGrI EPfP LPar LRHS NWea SPer SWvt
- 'Alpine Pink' — WSpi
- BEACON — see *K. latifolia* 'Leuchtfeuer'
- 'Black Label' new — XSte
- 'Bullseye' — MAsh SAko SPoG
- 'Bumblebee' new — XSte
- 'Carol' — XSte
- 'Carousel' — CBcs CCCN MAsh
- 'Clementine Churchill' — CMac
- 'Freckles' ♀H6 — CMac SCob SPoG
- 'Galaxy' — LRHS SAko
- 'Ginkona' — MAsh SAko XSte
- 'Kaleidoscope' — MAsh SCoo
- 'Latchmin' new — XSte
§ - 'Leuchtfeuer' new — XSte
- 'Minuet' — CBcs CCCN EHyd LRHS MAsh MGil SCoo SPoG SWvt XSte
- 'Mitternacht' — GGGa MAsh
- f. ***myrtifolia*** — EHyd
- - 'Elf' — EHyd LRHS MAsh
- 'Nipmuck' — CMac
- 'Olympic Fire' ♀H6 — CBcs EGrI EHyd GGGa LRHS MGil SAko SWvt WSpi WTSh XSte
- 'Olympic Wedding' — LRHS SPoG
- 'Ostbo Red' — CBcs CMac EHyd LRHS MAsh SCob SPoG SWvt XSte
- 'Peppermint' — GGGa LRHS
- 'Pink Charm' ♀H6 — CMac SAko
- 'Pinwheel' — LRHS MAsh MGil SAko SPoG
- 'Raspberry Glow' — XSte
- 'Tiddlywinks' new — LRHS
- 'Tofka' new — XSte
§ ***microphylla*** — WAbe
polifolia — CBcs CCCN CDoC LCro LOPS LRHS MGil SPer SavN WThu
- 'Alba' — see *K. polifolia* f. *leucantha*
- 'Glauca' — see *K. microphylla*
§ - f. ***leucantha*** — LRHS WAbe
- 'Newfoundland' — CBcs LRHS

Kalmiopsis (*Ericaceae*)

leachiana — EPot

Kalmiopsis × *Phyllodoce* see × *Phylliopsis*

Kalmiopsis × *Rhodothamnus* see × *Kalmiothamnus*

× *Kalmiothamnus* (*Ericaceae*)

'Haytor' — ITim
'Sindelberg' — ITim

Kalopanax (*Araliaceae*)

pictus — see *K. septemlobus*
§ ***septemlobus*** — CBcs EPfP MMuc NLar SEND
- var. ***magnificus*** B&SWJ 10900 — WCru
- f. ***maximowiczii*** — EPfP MBlu NLar

Kaufmannia (*Primulaceae*)

semenovii new — GKev

Keckiella (*Plantaginaceae*)

corymbosa — GAbr

Keiskea (*Lamiaceae*)

japonica — GEdr
- pink-flowered — SBrt

Kelseya (*Rosaceae*)

uniflora — WAbe

Kennedia (*Fabaceae*)

coccinea — CCCN SPhx
nigricans — CCCN
prostrata — SPhx
rubicunda — CCCN

Kentia (*Arecaceae*)

forsteriana — see *Howea forsteriana*

Kentranthus see *Centranthus*

Kerria (*Rosaceae*)

japonica misapplied single — see *K. japonica* 'Simplex'
japonica (L.) DC. — CBod EWld SGbt
- (d) — see *K. japonica* 'Pleniflora'
- 'Albescens' — NLar WCot
- 'Golden Guinea' ♀H5 — CBod CBrac CExl CMac CRos ELan EPfP LCro LOPS LRHS MAsh MGos MRav NLar NRHS SCoo SPer SPoG SRms SWvt WFar WPnP
§ - 'Picta' (v) — CMac EBee MGos MRav MSwo SLon SRms WAvo WFar
§ - 'Pleniflora' (d) ♀H5 — CBar CBod CBrac CEme CExl CMac CPla CRos CSBt EBee ELan EPfP GAbr LRHS MAsh MGos MPri MRav MSwo NLar SCob SEND SGol SPer SPlb SPoG SRms SSal SWvt WFar
§ - 'Simplex' — CExl CMac EShb SRms
- 'Variegata' — see *K. japonica* 'Picta'

Keteleeria (*Pinaceae*)

evelyniana — CAco
fortunei new — CAco

Khadia (*Aizoaceae*)

acutipetala — CCCN

Kiggelaria (*Flacourtiaceae*)

africana — SVen

Kirengeshoma (*Hydrangeaceae*)

palmata — Widely available
- 'Black Style' — EBee
- dwarf — WCot
- Koreana Group ♀H7 — CExl EBee EHyd ELan EPPr GAbr GKev LEdu LRHS MBel MCot MHol MMuc MRav NBid NCou NGBl NHol NLar NRHS NSti SPad SPer WBor WCot WCru WFar WHil WPGP

Kitaibela (*Malvaceae*)

vitifolia — CExl CSpe EWoo ILea LShi NBid SBls SPlb WAvo WFar WHer

Kitchingia see *Kalanchoe*

kiwi fruit see *Actinidia deliciosa*

Klasea (Asteraceae)

§ ***bulgarica***	ECha EPPr ESwi MPie NDov SBls SDix SHar SPhx WGoo
§ ***coronata***	LPla
§ - subsp. ***insularis*** B&SWJ 8698	WCru
§ ***lycopifolia***	WCot WMal
§ ***radiata*** subsp. ***gmelinii***	EHyd EPPr LRHS NRHS

Kleinia (Asteraceae)

abyssinica **new**	SSal
fulgens	ECre
§ ***grantii***	EShb EWld SGro SIvy WCot
neriifolia	EShb SIvy
repens	see *Curio repens*

Knautia (Caprifoliaceae)

§ ***arvensis***	CBod CCBP CElw CFoA CHab EBee EHyd ELan EPfP EWoo GJos GQue LCro LOPS MBow MHer MNHC NAts NLar NMir SPer SPhx SRms WCAu WHer WSFF WShi WWild
- white-flowered	SPhx
dipsacifolia	SBut SHar
'Jardin d'en Face'	LRHS WCav
§ ***macedonica***	Widely available
- 'Crimson Cushion'	CSpe
- 'Mars Midget'	CBod CExl CRos CSpe EBee EHyd ELan ELon EMor EPfP GJos GMaP LRHS MGos NLar NRHS SCob SPhx SPoG SWvt WCAu WCav WFar WHoo WSHC
- Melton pastels	CBod CChe CDor CExl CRos EBee EGrl EHyd ELan EPPr EPfP GJos GMaP LRHS MGos NLar NPer NRHS SBls SCob SCoo SGBe SPhx SPoG SRkn SRms SWvt WCAu WCav WFar
- pink-flowered	SRms
- 'Red Baron'	CChe
- 'Red Knight'	CBod CDor CRos EBee EHyd EPfP GWyn LRHS MBNS NLar NRHS SCoo WCav WSMil
- tall, pale-flowered	SPhx
- 'Thunder and Lightning'[PBR] (v)	CBct CBod CDoC CRos CSpe CWGN EBee ECtt EHyd ELan EPfP EWes LBuc LRHS LSou MAvo MNrw MRav NLar NRHS SCob SCoo SEdd SGBe SPer SPoG SRms WCAu WCot
sarajevensis	MAvo MHol

Knightia (Proteaceae)

excelsa	CBcs LRHS XSte

Kniphofia ✿ (Asphodelaceae)

'Ada'	ELon LRHS
albescens	SPlb
'Alcazar'	CBcs CBod ECtt ELon EPfP EWhm LCro LOPS MAvo MBel MHer SCob SPer SSal SWvt WCAu WCFE WFar WSpi
'Amazing Fun'	CWGN
'Ample Dwarf'	ECtt WCot
'Amsterdam'	GBin
angustifolia	SPlb
'Apricot'	EHyd WCot
'Apricot Souffle'	EPri WCot
'Atlanta'	EHyd
BANANA POPSICLE ('Tnknibp') (Popsicle Series) **new**	CBod LRHS
'Barton Fever' ♀H6	WCot
baurii	CExl SPlb
'Bees' Jubilee'	MAvo NChi
'Bees' Lemon'	Widely available
§ 'Bees' Sunset' ♀H5	CAvo CPrp CRos EBee EBlo ECha ECtt EHyd EPfP EPri LRHS MAvo MBel MMuc NLar NRHS SEND SPoG SWvt WSHC
'Bees' Yellow'	SGro
'Border Ballet'	EHyd LBuc LRHS NBir NGdn NLar NRHS XLum
brachystachya	LEdu SBrt SPlb
'Bressingham Comet'	CRos EBee EBlo ECtt EHyd ELon GKev LRHS NBir NRHS SRms WSpi
'Bressingham Gleam'	EBlo
BRESSINGHAM SUNBEAM ('Bresun')	CRos EBee EBlo ECtt EHyd LRHS NBir NRHS
'Bressingham Yellow'	ECtt
'Brimstone' Bloom ♀H5	CDor CPrp CRos ECtt EPfP EPri LEdu LRHS NBir NRHS SCob SWvt WFar
bruceae	SPlb SVen
'Buttercup' ♀H5	CAvo CPrp LSRN
'C.M. Prichard' misapplied	see *K. rooperi*
'C.M. Prichard' Prichard	WCot
'Candlelight'	ECtt EPri WSHC
caulescens	Widely available
- 'Coral Breakers'	CExl ECtt EHyd ELon GMaP LRHS SEND WCot
- early-flowering	WSpi
- 'John May'	EBee ECtt ESwi MHer SEdd SWvt WCot
- 'Tiny Girl'	ECtt
'Champagne'	WCot
'Chichi'	WCot
'Christmas Cheer'	EBee
citrina	CSpe CTsd GKev GLog MBrN NGBl WCot XLum
'Cobra'	CDor CRos EBee EBlo ECtt EHyd GMaP LRHS NRHS WCot
'Coral Flame' ♀H5	CRos EBlo EHyd LRHS NRHS
'Coral Sceptre'	WCot
'Corallina'	GBin
'Creamsicle'[PBR] (Popsicle Series)	ECtt WCot
'Dingaan'	EBee ECtt MNrw NBir NLar
'Dorset Sentry'	ECtt EHyd ELon EPfP EWoo LRHS MBNS MBel MGos MNrw NBir NLar WCot WFar
'Drummore Apricot'	CKno CPrp CRos EBee ECha ECtt ELon EPfP LRHS LSRN MPie MSpe NBir NRHS NWsh WCot WFar WGwG
'Early Buttercup'	WFar
'Elvira'[PBR]	CRos ECtt EHyd LRHS MHol NRHS SAko SPeP SPoG WCot
EMBER GLOW ('Tneg'[PBR]) (Glow Series)	EBee ECtt LCro LOPS
ensifolia	ECtt NGdn SVen XLum
'Ernest Mitchell'	WCot
Express hybrids	XLum
'Feuerkerze'	SAko
'Fiery Fred' ♀H6	CRos EBee ECtt EHyd ELon EPfP EWhm GBee LRHS MMuc MSpe NRHS NWsh SGbt WCot WHoo WSpi

	'Fire Brand'	WCot
	FIRE GLOW ('Tnfg'PBR) (Glow Series)	NLar
	'First Sunrise'PBR	ECtt
	'Flamenco'	EHyd ELon LRHS NGdn NRHS SCob SRms SVic WFar WLov
	'Florence Bedecked'	WCot
	fluviatilis	GKev
	foliosa Hochst.	LEdu
	'Frances Victoria'	WCot
	galpinii misapplied	see *K. triangularis* subsp. *triangularis*
	galpinii ambig.	EHyd LRHS NRHS SRms XLum
	'Gelbe Flamme'	SAko
	'Gilt Bronze'	WCot
	'Gladness'	MAvo NBir WCot
	'Goldelse'	CRos EBee EHyd LRHS NBir NRHS
	'Green and Cream'	MHCG
	'Green Jade'	CBcs CExl EBee ECha ECtt EHyd GMaP LEdu LRHS MAvo MBros MCot MNrw MRav NBir NGBl NLar NRHS SCob SEND SGbt SPer SRms STPC WCAu WCot WFar WSpi
	'H.E. Beale'	WCot
	'Happy Halloween'	CRos LRHS MAvo
	'Hen and Chickens'	ECtt WCot WFar
	hirsuta	EHyd SRms WSHC
	- 'Fire Dance'	CEme CTsd EBou EHyd GAbr LRHS LSun NLar WFar WSpi
	- 'Traffic Lights'	GDam
	'Ice Queen'	CAvo CBcs CBod CDor EBee ECha ECtt ELon EPPr EPri LRHS MAvo MCot MHer MNrw MRav NChi NLar NSti SCob SEND SEdd SPeP SRms SWvt WABo WCAu WCot WFar
	ichopensis	LEdu SVen WPGP
	'Incandesce' ♀H5	CBod EPPr EWhm MBNS MNrw SPoG WCot WMal
	'Innocence' ♀H4	CRos EBee EBlo EHyd EPfP LRHS NRHS
	'Jane Henry'	CDor LEdu
	'Jenny Bloom'	CPrp CRos ECtt EPfP EWTr EWoo GMaP LEdu LRHS MRav MSpe NLar NRHS NSti SRms WFar WSpi
	'Jess's Delight'	WCot
	'John Benary'	CMac ECtt EHyd GLog GMaP LRHS MBel MSpe NBir NLar NRHS SRms WCAu WCot WGwG WKif
	'Jonathan' ♀H5	WCot
	laxiflora	EPri WPGP
	'Lemon Popsicle'PBR (Popsicle Series)	CAbb CBct CBod CMea CRos CWCL CWGN EHyd ELan LRHS MMrt MPri NFav NRHS SCob SEdd SGBe SRms WABo WFar WNPC XSte
	'Light of the World'	see *K. triangularis* subsp. *triangularis* 'Light of the World'
	'Limelight'	CBod CChe CPar ECtt MBros SPad WCAu
	linearifolia	CExl EBee SPlb WCot WPGP XLum
	'Little Elf'	CDor XLum
	'Little Maid'	CBcs CBod CRos CSBt ECha ECtt EGrl EHyd ELan EPfP EPri EShb GMaP LRHS MHer MRav NBir NLar NRHS SCob SPer SRms SWvt WCAu WCot WFar WSpi
	'Lord Roberts'	MAvo MRav WCot
	'Luna'	WCot
	macowanii	see *K. triangularis* subsp. *triangularis*
	'Mango Popsicle'PBR (Popsicle Series)	Widely available
	'Mermaiden'	ECtt MAvo SEND
	'Minister Verschuur'	CRos EBee ECtt EHyd LRHS NRHS WSpi
	'Moonstone' ♀H5	CWCL ECtt ELon EPPr GBin LRHS LSun MACG MNrw NLar NSti SEND SEdd SPoG WCot WSpi
	'Mount Etna'	WAvo
	multiflora 'November Glory'	WCot WFar WMal
	'Nancy's Red'	Widely available
	nelsonii Mast.	see *K. triangularis* subsp. *triangularis*
	'New Sensation'	WCot
	'No Rhyme nor Reason'	WCot
§	'Nobilis' ♀H5	CBod CExl CRos ECha ECtt ELan ELon EPfP GAbr GMaP LRHS LSRN MAvo MHol MNrw NGdn SArc SDix SEND SPer SRms SWvt WCAu WCot WMal WSpi
	northiae ♀H4	CExl CPla EBee ELan EPfP EPri EWes GKev LRHS MNrw NLar SArc SEND SEdd SPad SPlb SWvt WABo WCot WCru WPGP WSpi XLum
	'Old Court Seedling'	EBee WCot WFar
	'Orange Fackel'	SAko
	'Orange Vanilla Popsicle'PBR (Popsicle Series)	CBct CBod CRos CSBt ECtt EHyd EWTr IPot LEdu LLWG LRHS MBros MPnt MPri MThu NLar NRHS SCob SEdd SPad SPoG WFar WHil WNPC WTyc XSte
§	'Painted Lady'	CDor CTri ECtt GMaP MNrw NLar SEND SWvt WCot
	'Papaya Popsicle'PBR (Popsicle Series)	CBct CBod CRos CWGN EBee ECtt EHyd ELan ELon IPot LLWG LRHS LSou MAvo MNrw MThu NLar NRHS SCob SEdd SPoG SRms WABo WFar WHil WSpi
	parviflora	XLum
	pauciflora	CPbh WCot WMal
	'Penny Rockets' ♀H6	CRos EBlo EHyd EPPr LRHS NRHS
	'Percy's Pride'	Widely available
	'Pfitzeri'	SRms
	'Pineapple Popsicle'PBR (Popsicle Series)	CTsd CWGN ECtt ELon EMor LRHS LSou MPnt NEoE NLar NSti SRms WNPC
	(Poco Series) POCO ORANGE ('Tnknipo'PBR)	NLar
	- POCO YELLOW ('Tnknipy') **new**	CBod
	'Primrose Upward' ♀H6	WCot
I	'Primulina' Bloom	EHyd LRHS NRHS
	'Prince Igor' misapplied	see *K.* 'Nobilis'
	'Prince Igor' Prichard	ECtt NBir
	'Red Rocket'PBR	EGrl EWTr LRHS NLar WCot WHil
	'Redhot Popsicle'PBR (Popsicle Series)	CTsd CWGN EHyd EPfP LRHS MAvo MHol MNrw MPnt SGBe SPoG WCot WNPC
	'Rich Echoes' ♀H5	CAvo CWGN ECtt ELon EPPr ESwi EWhm LEdu MHol MNrw NLar WCot WMal
	ritualis	CExl
§	***rooperi*** ♀H5	Widely available
	'Royal Castle'	CExl CRos CTsd EHyd EPfP GMaP LRHS NBir NGdn NRHS SCob SEND SRms WFar XLum
	'Royal Standard' ♀H5	CBcs CBod CRos EBee ECtt EHyd ELon EPfP GMaP LCro LOPS LRHS NLar NRHS SCob SPer SPoG SWvt WCAu WFar WGwG WSpi

rufa Baker	LEdu MAvo WPGP
- 'Rasta'	CBcs CBod
aff. ***rufa***	SSal
'Safranvogel' 🏆^{H5}	ECtt LRHS WCot
'Samuel's Sensation' misapplied	see *K.* 'Painted Lady'
'Samuel's Sensation' Samuel 🏆^{H5}	EBee EBlo ECtt EHyd LRHS NLar NRHS SWvt WCot
sarmentosa	CExl SPlb SVen WCot
'Saturn'	MAvo
'Scorched Corn'	CBod LEdu
'Sherbet Lemon'	WCot
'Shining Sceptre' misapplied	see *K.* 'Bees' Sunset'
'Shiny Beast' **new**	WCot
'Springtime'	WCot
'Star of Baden-Baden'	NBir SEND SSal WCot
Stark's early perpetual-flowering hybrids	XLum
'Strawberries and Cream'	ECtt EGrI ELon NLar SGbt SWvt
stricta	XLum
'Sunningdale Yellow' 🏆^{H5}	ECha ECtt GMaP MAvo SMHy SRms WHoo WSpi
'Sweet Corn'	CBod SMrm
'Tawny King' 🏆^{H5}	Widely available
'Tetbury Torch'^{PBR}	CExl CWGN EBee ECtt EHyd LRHS MCot MHer NRHS SPtp SWvt WCAu WSpi
thomsonii	CExl
- 'Kichocheo'	EPPr LEdu MAvo WCot
- var. ***snowdenii*** misapplied	see *K. thomsonii* var. *thomsonii*
- var. ***snowdenii*** ambig.	CExl XLum
§ - var. ***thomsonii***	LEdu SMHy WABo WSHC
- - 'Stern's Trip' 🏆^{H4}	EBee WPGP
'Timothy' 🏆^{H5}	Widely available
'Toffee Nosed' 🏆^{H5}	CMac CPrp CRos EBee ECtt EHyd ELon EMor EPPr EPfP EPri EWhm EWoo LRHS MRav MSpe NBir NGdn NLar NRHS NWsh SCob SPer SPtp SSut SWvt WCAu WCot WSHC WSpi
'Torchbearer'	WCot
triangularis	EPfP GKev SGBe WFar XLum
§ - subsp. ***triangularis***	EPfP SRms SVen XLum
§ - - 'Light of the World'	ECtt EHyd GAbr NBir SWvt WCot WFar
'Tuckii' misapplied	SRms
typhoides	NBir SPlb
tysonii	SPlb XLum
uvaria	EBee EHyd EWld GKev LCro LOPS LPar LRHS NBir NRHS SBls SCob SPer SRms WABo WCAu WCot XLum XSen
'Vanilla'	EWTr LRHS MMuc NLar SEND
'Vesta'	CRos EBee EHyd LRHS NRHS
'Vincent Lepage'	NLar
'Wol's Red Seedling'	CAvo ECtt ELon MCot MNrw WCot WGwG
'Wrexham Buttercup' 🏆^{H6}	CDor EBee ECtt ELan EWhm GMaP LSRN MCot MHol MNrw MSpe NLar SCob SEND WCot WFar WHal WSpi
'Yellow Cheer'	WCot WMal
'Yellow Hammer' Slieve Donard	ELon MMuc SEND

Knowltonia (*Ranunculaceae*)

filia	CExl

Koeleria (*Poaceae*)

cristata misapplied	see *K. macrantha*
glauca	CBod CRos EBee ECha EHyd EPfP EShb GMaP LRHS MBNS NGdn NRHS NWsh SCob SPlb SWvt WFar
§ ***macrantha***	EPPr

Koelreuteria (*Sapindaceae*)

bipinnata	IDee LRHS
elegans subsp. ***formosana***	CMCN
paniculata	Widely available
- 'Coral Sun'^{PBR} 🏆^{H5}	CDoC CExl EBee ELan EPfP LPar LRHS MBlu MGos NLar NOra NOrn WMat
- 'Fastigiata'	EBee ELan EPfP MBlu SCoo
- 'Rosseels'	NLar
- 'September'	MBlu

Kohleria (*Gesneriaceae*)

'Ampallang'	WDib
'An's Nagging Macaws'	WDib
'Brazil Gem'	WDib
'Bristol's Evil Storm'	WDib
'Cybele'	WDib
'Dark Velvet'	WDib
digitaliflora	see *K. warszewiczii*
'Flashdance'	WDib
'Hcy's Jardin de Monet'	WDib
'Heartland's Blackberry Butterfly'	WDib
'Jester' 🏆^{H1b}	WDib
'Lilla Gubben'	WDib
lindeniana	see *Gloxinella lindeniana*
'Manchu'	WDib
'Marquis de Sade'	WDib
'Queen Victoria'	WDib
I ***sciadotydaea***	WDib
'Silver Feather'	WDib
§ 'Sunrise'	WDib
'Sunshine'	see *K.* 'Sunrise'
'Texas Rainbow'	WDib
§ ***warszewiczii*** 🏆^{H1b}	WDib
'Yf's Elin' **new**	WDib
'Yf's Emma'	WDib
'Yf's Josse'	WDib
'Yf's Lotta' **new**	WDib
'Yf's Torun' **new**	WDib

kohlrabi see AGM Vegetables Section

Kolkwitzia (*Caprifoliaceae*)

amabilis	CExl CSBt CTri ELan EPfP GBin GDam LPar NWea SGol SPlb SRms SavN WCFE
- DREAM CATCHER ('Maradco')	CMac EPfP MAsh MRav NEoE NLar SGol WSpi
- 'Pink Cloud' misapplied	see *K. amabilis* 'Rosea'
- 'Pink Cloud' 🏆^{H6}	Widely available
§ - 'Rosea'	CBrac

kumquat see *Citrus japonica*

Kunzea (*Myrtaceae*)

ambigua	CBcs SPlb
- pink-flowered	SEle
'Badja Carpet'	SEle
baxteri	CPbh
ericifolia	SPlb
§ ***ericoides***	GPoy
parvifolia	SPlb
pauciflora	SPlb

L

Lablab (Fabaceae)

§ **purpureus**	CLau
- 'Ruby Moon'	CSpe XAbr

+ Laburnocytisus (Fabaceae)

'Adamii'	CMac EBee ELan EPfP LPar LSRN MGos NLar NOrn SMad SPer

Laburnum ✿ (Fabaceae)

alpinum	NRog NWea SPlb SavN
- 'Pendulum'	CAco CBod CCVT ELan LCro LSRN MAsh MGos MRav NOrn NRog SPoG
§ **anagyroides**	IPap LMaj LPar MMuc NWea SEND SRms WMou
- 'Erect'	SPoG WMat
- 'Yellow Rocket'	EBee LRHS MTrO WMat
'Famous Walk'	see *L.* × *watereri* 'Vossii'
vulgare	see *L. anagyroides*
× **watereri**	MTrO
§ - 'Vossii' ♀H6	Widely available
* - 'Vossii Pendulum'	CCVT

Lachenalia ✿ (Asparagaceae)

§ **aloides**	CPbh SDeJ
- var. **aurea**	see *L. flava*
- var. **luteola**	see *L. flava*
- var. **quadricolor**	see *L. quadricolor*
- var. **vanzyliae**	see *L. vanzyliae*
bachmanii	NRog
bifolia	see *L. bulbifera*
§ **bulbifera** ♀H2	WCot
contaminata ♀H2	CPbh NRog
elegans var. **suaveolens**	NRog
ensifolia	WCot
§ - subsp. **maughanii**	NRog
§ **flava** ♀H2	CPbh SGro WCot
'Fransie' (African Beauty Series)	NRog
kliprandensis	NRog
latimerae	NRog
§ **longituba** ♀H2	NRog SGro
mathewsii	NRog
maughanii	see *L. ensifolia* subsp. *maughanii*
mediana	NRog
'Namakwa' (African Beauty Series) ♀H2	NRog
namaquensis	NRog
'Nelsonii'	SGro
obscura	WCot
orchioides var. **glaucina**	NRog
pallida	NRog
I 'Pearsonii'	SPlb
pendula	see *L. bulbifera*
pusilla	CPla
pustulata ♀H2	NRog
§ **quadricolor** ♀H2	NRog WCot
reflexa	NRog
'Robijn' (African Beauty Series)	NRog
'Romaud' (African Beauty Series)	NRog SDeJ
'Romelia' (African Beauty Series)	WCot
'Ronina' (African Beauty Series)	NRog
'Rosabeth' (African Beauty Series)	NRog WCot
'Rupert' (African Beauty Series) ♀H2	NRog SDeJ WCot
tricolor	see *L. aloides*
unicolor	NRog
unifolia	NRog
§ **vanzyliae** ♀H2	NRog
viridiflora ♀H2	NRog
zeyheri	NRog

Lactuca (Asteraceae)

alpina	see *Cicerbita alpina*
perennis	EPPr GGro WHer

Lagarostrobos (Podocarpaceae)

§ **franklinii**	IDee SMad WPGP

Lagenaria (Cucurbitaceae)

siceraria 'Speckled Swan'	SVic

Lagerstroemia (Lythraceae)

BLACK DIAMOND BEST RED **new**	SGsty
indica ♀H3	CBod CCCN EPfP ILea LMaj LPar MGil SCob SEND SEle SPlb SVen WFar
- B&SWJ 12660	WCru
- BERRY DAZZLE ('Gamad VI')	LCro LOPS LRHS
- BRAISE D'ÉTÉ ('Indybra'PBR) (Indya Charms Series)	ILea
- CAMAÏEU D'ÉTÉ ('Indycam'PBR) (Indiya Charms Series) **new**	XSte
§ - 'Cedar Red'	WPGP
- 'Coral Filli'PBR (Fleming Filigree Series) **new**	ELan
- 'Cordon Bleu'	LRHS
- 'Lafayette' **new**	LRHS
- MIMIE FUCHSIA ('Dablage01') **new**	XSte
- 'Nivea'	EBee
- PETITE PINKIE ('Monkie')	CCCN EGrI ELan EShb
- 'Red Filli'PBR (Fleming Filigree Series) **new**	ELan
- 'Red Imperator'	CBcs
- RHAPSODY IN PINK ('Whit VIII')	CBcs ELan LRHS SGsty XSte
- 'Rosea'	CBcs IPap SEND
- 'Rubra'	XSte
- 'Violet Filli'PBR (Fleming Filigree Series) **new**	ELan
- (With Love Series) WITH LOVE BABE ('Milaperl'PBR)	SPoG
- - WITH LOVE CHERIE ('Cov')	SPoG
- - WITH LOVE VIRGIN ('Milabla'PBR)	LCro LOPS
- 'World's Fair'	LRHS
subcostata CWJ 12352	WCru
'Tuscarora'	WPGP
'Tuskegee'	WPGP

Lagotis (Plantaginaceae)

glauca	GEdr WFar
takedana	GEdr

Lagunaria (Malvaceae)

patersonia	LRHS

Lagurus (*Poaceae*)

ovatus	CTtf SAdn SPhx SRot WChS

Lallemantia (*Lamiaceae*)

canescens	WHil
– 'Blue Snap' **new**	SPhx

Lamiastrum see *Lamium*

Lamium (*Lamiaceae*)

album	CHab SMrm
– 'Friday' (v)	NBir
§ ***galeobdolon***	CTri EShb LRHS NAts SPhx SRms WHer WWtn XSen
– 'Emil Tramposch' **new**	LPla
§ – 'Florentinum' (v)	CMac ECha GQue MMuc MRav SCob WCAu WFar WSFF
– 'Hermann's Pride'	CBod EHyd ELan EPfP GMaP LRHS LShi MHol NBir NDov NMir NRHS SCob SPoG SRms SWvt XLum
– 'Kirkcudbright Dwarf'	EPPr EWes GBin WFar XLum
§ – 'Silberteppich'	ECha MRav XLum
– 'Silver Angel'	XLum
– SILVER CARPET	see *L. galeobdolon* 'Silberteppich'
– 'Variegatum'	see *L. galeobdolon* 'Florentinum'
garganicum	EWes
subsp. ***garganicum***	
– subsp. ***pictum***	see *L. garganicum* subsp. *striatum*
– subsp. ***reniforme***	see *L. garganicum* subsp. *striatum*
§ – subsp. ***striatum***	CDor
LAMI DARK PURPLE (Lami Series)	EHyd LRHS NRHS
luteum	see *L. galeobdolon*
maculatum	GJos GKev GWyn MMuc SRms WCot WWtn
– 'Album'	EPfP SHar SPer SRms WWtn
– 'Anne Greenaway' (v)	SCob SMrm
§ – 'Aureum'	ECtt SWvt WFar XLum
– 'Beacon Silver'	CMac EBee ECha ECtt EHyd ELan EMor EPfP EShb GWyn LCro LOPS LPot LRHS MGos MMuc NBir NRHS SCob SPer SPlb SPoG SRms SWvt WFar XLum
– 'Brightstone Pearl'	ELon EWes EWld SHar
– 'Cannon's Gold'	EBee ECtt SWvt
– 'Chequers Board'	GAbr
– 'Dingle Candy'	MHCG
– 'Forncett Lustre'	EWes
– 'Ghost'	CKel ECtt ELon EPPr EPfP LBuc LRHS NLar SCob SRms
– 'Gold Leaf'	see *L. maculatum* 'Aureum'
– GOLDEN ANNIVERSARY ('Dellam'PBR) (v)	EHyd ELan GJos LRHS LSRN MBow NBro NRHS SWvt
– 'Golden Nuggets'	see *L. maculatum* 'Aureum'
– 'Golden Wedding'	SRms
– 'James Boyd Parselle'	WCot
– LAMI MEGA PURPLE (Lami Series)	EBee
– 'Margery Fish'	SRms
– 'Orchid Frost'	EBee ELon GQue
– PINK CHABLIS ('Checkin'PBR)	ELon LRHS MRav NCou NLar SCoo SPer
– 'Pink Nancy'	SWvt
– 'Pink Pearls'	CSBt NLar SHar SMrm
– 'Pink Pewter'	CRos EBee ECha ECtt EHyd ELan EMor EPfP EShb EWoo GMaP GWyn LRHS LShi MBel NRHS SCob SHar SPer SPlb SPoG SRms WWtn
– 'Purple Dragon'	SPoG
– 'Red Nancy'	CBod CRos EHyd ELan EPfP LRHS NLar NRHS SCob SWvt XLum
§ – 'Roseum'	EBee ELan EPfP GWyn MCot MRav SPer XLum
– 'Shell Pink'	see *L. maculatum* 'Roseum'
– 'White Nancy'	Widely available
– 'Wootton Pink'	MHCG NBir SWvt
orvala	Widely available
– 'Album'	CCBP CDor CExl CKel CMiW CTtf EBee EMor EPPr GBin LEdu LPla LRHS MBel MBriF NBir NLar SEND WCAu WHer
– 'Silva'	CExl EPPr EPfP LEdu LRHS WCot WMal
purpureum	GJos WSFF
sandrasicum	SGro

Lampranthus (*Aizoaceae*)

aberdeenensis	see *Delosperma aberdeenense*
apricot-flowered	EHyd LRHS NRHS
aurantiacus	CBcs
blandus	CBcs CCCN
'Blousey Pink'	SVen
§ ***brownii***	CBcs CCCN CRos EHyd ELan EPfP LRHS NRHS SPlb
coccineus	CPla
deltoides	see *Oscularia deltoides*
edulis	see *Carpobrotus edulis*
'Exposure'	CCCN SSim
multiradiatus	SEND
oscularis	see *Oscularia deltoides*
'Pink'	CBod CPla ELan SPlb SSim
purple-flowered	CBen CBod SPlb WABo
roseus	CBod CCCN CRos CSma EHyd LRHS NRHS
'Salmon Pink'	SPlb
'Shanklin'	SPlb SVen
spectabilis	CBcs CCCN CTri GLet SSut
– orange-flowered	CBod SSim WFar
– purple-flowered	CBod CPla ELon SPlb SSim
– 'Tresco Apricot'	CCCN
– 'Tresco Brilliant'	CCCN ELon MBros SSim WABo
– 'Tresco Fire'	CBod CCCN CExl CSma SPlb SRms SVen
– 'Tresco Orange'	CCCN
– 'Tresco Peach'	CCCN
– 'Tresco Purple'	ELan
– 'Tresco Red'	CCCN CPla SEdd SSim
– white-flowered	SPlb SSim SVen WFar
– yellow-flowered	CBod CPla SSim SVen WFar
stipulaceus	SPlb
'Tresco Pearl'	CPla WCav
'Ventnor Red'	SChr SEdd

Lamprocapnos (*Papaveraceae*)

§ ***spectabilis*** ♀H6	Widely available
– 'Alba' ♀H6	Widely available
– 'Gold Heart'PBR	CBcs CPla CWCL EBee ECha ECtt EMor EPfP GDam GLet LRHS LSou MGos MHer MHol MRav MSCN NBid NHpl NLar NRHS NSti SCob SGBe SPeP SPoG WCot WFar WHil WSpi
– 'Valentine' ♀H6	Widely available
– 'White Gold'	CBod GLet LRHS MSCN SPad SPeP
– 'White Heart'	WHil

Lamprothyrsus (*Poaceae*)

hieronymi	CBod CSde SMad
– RCB RA K2-2	CCht CKno EBee ELon MAvo MHol WCot WPGP

Lancea (*Phrymaceae*)

tibetica GEdr

Lantana ✿ (*Verbenaceae*)

BANDANA LEMON ZEST ('Ban Yelbic'PBR) new EMdy
BANDANA RED 09 ('Bant Reda09'PBR) new EMdy
'Calippo Tutti Frutti' LSou
camara EShb SEle
- BANDANA CHERRY ('Bante Cheria') new EMdy
- BANDANA ORANGE SUNRISE ('Bante Oransun'PBR) new EMdy
- BANRAM PINK '07 ('Bante Pinka07') new EMdy
- (Lucky Series) LUCKY PEACH ('Balucpea') SPoG
- - LUCKY PURE GOLD ('Balucpure'PBR) SPoG
- - LUCKY RED FLAME ('Balandimfla') SPoG
- - LUCKY SUNRISE ROSE ('Balandrise'PBR) SPoG
- - LUCKY WHITE ('Balucwite'PBR) SPoG
- orange-flowered CCCN
- pink-flowered CCCN
- red-flowered CCCN
- white-flowered CCCN
'Chapel Hill Gold'PBR EMdy
'Dallas Red' EHyd ELan LRHS NRHS
'Miss Huff' EBee ELan EMdy EPfP
§ **montevidensis** EShb
- f. **albifora** EShb
'Pink Caprice' EPfP
'Radiation' ELan

Lapageria ✿ (*Philesiaceae*)

rosea ♀H3 CCCN CExl CRHN CTsd SAdn SChF SWvt WPav
- var. **albiflora** ♀H3 CRHN SChF
- - 'Hugletts Blush' SChF
- 'Beatrix Anderson' CRHN
- 'Flesh Pink' CExl CRHN
- 'Pink Panther' CRHN WPav

Lapeirousia (*Iridaceae*)

cruenta see *Freesia laxa*
laxa see *Freesia laxa*

Lapsana (*Asteraceae*)

communis 'Inky' CNat

Lardizabala (*Lardizabalaceae*)

biternata see *L. funaria*
§ **funaria** WCru WPav

Larix ✿ (*Pinaceae*)

decidua CAco CCVT CMen ELan EPfP EWTr GDam IPap LRHS MGos MMuc NWea SCob SEND SPlb WTSh
- 'Bükk' new CAco
- 'Corley' CKen
- 'Globus' CAco
- 'Horstmann's Recurved' NLar SLim
- 'Krejci' NLar
- 'Little Bogle' CAco CKen LRHS MBlu NLar SLim
- 'Lucek' NLar SLim
- 'Oberförster Karsten' CAco CKen
- 'Pendula' CAco CMen
- 'Puli' ♀H7 CAco LRHS MAsh MBlu NHol NLar SPer SPoG WMat
gmelinii var. **olgensis** CAco
- var. **principis-rupprechtii** CAco
- 'Tharandt' CAco CKen
§ **kaempferi** CAco CCVT CMen ELan EPfP IPap LBuc LMaj LPar SCob SCoo SEWo WTSh
- 'Bambino' CKen SLim
- 'Bingman' CKen
- 'Blue Ball' CKen
- 'Blue Dwarf' ♀H7 CAco EPfP MAsh SLim
- 'Blue Rabbit' CAco CKen
- 'Blue Rabbit Weeping' CAco SLim
- 'Cruwys Morchard' CKen
- 'Diana' CAco CKen CMen NHol NLar SLim
- 'Elizabeth Rehder' CAco CKen
- 'Grant Haddow' CKen
- 'Grey Green Dwarf' MAsh
- 'Grey Pearl' CKen MAsh SLim
- 'Hobbit' CKen
- 'Jakobsen' LRHS
- 'Jakobsen's Pyramid' MAsh WMat
- 'Magic Gold' new NLar
I - 'Nana' CAco CKen CMen NHol
I - 'Nana Prostrata' CKen
- 'Paper Lanterns' CAco
- 'Pendula' CAco EPfP SPer SPoG
- 'Pulii' CAco SLim
- 'Stiff Weeper' ♀H7 CAco LRHS SLim
- 'Varley' CKen
- 'Wehlen' CKen
- 'Wolterdingen' CAco CKen NLar
laricina CAco
- 'Arethusa Bog' CKen
- 'Bear Swamp' CKen
- 'Bingman' CKen
- 'Blue Sparkler' NLar
- 'Greg Williams' CKen
- 'Hartwig Pine' CKen
- 'Iron Red' NLar
- 'Madie G.' new CAco
- 'Michigan Tower' NLar
- 'Newport Beauty' CKen
- 'Stubby' CKen
leptolepis see *L. kaempferi*
§ × **marschlinsii** NWea
- 'Domino' CKen
- 'Gail' CKen
- 'Julie' CKen
- 'Orvelte' new CAco
occidentalis CAco
'Nowhere' new
'Varied Directions' CAco

Laser (*Apiaceae*)

trilobum SPhx
- PAB 3382 LEdu WPGP

Laserpitium (*Apiaceae*)

gallicum CKel GPSL SPhx
halleri SPhx
latifolium EBee SPhx
§ **siler** CSpe EBee EShb LPla MNrw NDov SPhx SPlb WHil WSHC WSpi

Lasiagrostis see *Stipa*

Lasiospermum (*Asteraceae*)

bipinnatum	SPlb

Lathraea (*Orobanchaceae*)

clandestina	CAvo

Lathyrus ✿ (*Fabaceae*)

	annuus red	SPhx
§	***articulatus***	CSpe
§	***aureus***	CBor CDor CSpe EPPr EWld GEdr LRHS MCot MHer MNrw NBid NBir SBrt SPhx WCAu WFar WHal WHoo WSHC
	chilensis	GWyn LShi WPav WSHC
	cirrhosus	WSHC
	cyaneus misapplied	see *L. vernus*
	davidii	EPPr LEdu SBrt WPav
	fremontii hort.	see *L. laxiflorus*
	gmelinii	SBrt
	grandiflorus ♀H6	CCBP CMea NChi NHpl SMHy WCot
	× ***hammettii*** 'Erewhon'	CArg SPhx
	- 'Turquoise Lagoon' **new**	CArg
	inermis	see *L. laxiflorus*
	japonicus	CEls EBee
	- subsp. ***maritimus***	SPhx WCot
	laevigatus	SBrt
	latifolius ♀H7	CAgr CRHN CSde EPPr EPfP GQue MHol NPer SCob SRms SVic WBrk WCot WFar WHer XLum
§	- 'Albus' ♀H7	CTri SRms WFar WKif XLum
	- PINK PEARL	see *L. latifolius* 'Rosa Perle'
	- 'Red Pearl'	CBcs CBod CKel CRos CTsd CWGN EBee EHyd ELan EPfP GAbr LBuc LRHS LSRN MHer NLar NRHS SPer SPlb SPoG SRms SWvt WFar
§	- 'Rosa Perle' ♀H7	CBcs CBod CEme CKel CRos CTri EBee EHyd ELan EPfP LCro LOPS LRHS LSRN LShi MRav NBir NLar NPer NRHS SNig SPer SPoG SWvt WBor WFar XLum
	- 'Rose Queen'	GJos
	- WEISSE PERLE	see *L. latifolius* 'White Pearl'
	- 'White Pearl' misapplied	see *L. latifolius* 'Albus'
§	- 'White Pearl' ♀H7	Widely available
§	***laxiflorus***	CBor
	linifolius	EBee NLar SBrt
	montanus	GPoy
	nervosus	SRms WMal
	niger	CFoA CSpe EBee EWld LEdu MHer MMrt SBut SHar
	nissolia	SPhx WSFF
	odoratus	XAbr
	- 'Albutt Blue'	CArg CSpe
	- 'Almost Black'	CArg
	- 'America' ♀H3	CArg
	- 'Anniversary'	CArg MCot
	- 'Barry Dare'	CArg
	- 'Beaujolais'	LCro LOPS SPhx
	- 'Beth Chatto'	MCot
	- 'Betty Maiden'	MCot
	- 'Black Knight'	CArg
	- 'Blue Medley'	MCot
	- 'Blue Velvet'	CArg CSpe
	- 'Bobby's Girl' ♀H3	LCro LOPS
	- 'Bouquet Navy' **new**	CArg
	- 'Bristol' ♀H3	CSpe
	- 'Burnished Bronze'	MCot
	- 'Cathy' ♀H3	CArg
	- 'Charlie's Angel' ♀H3	CArg LCro LOPS MCot
	- 'Cupani'	LCro LOPS SPhx
	- 'Daphne'	LCro LOPS
	- 'Dark Passion'	MCot
	- 'Dawn'	MCot
	- 'Ethel Grace'	MCot
	- 'Evening Glow' ♀H3	MCot
	- 'Flora Norton'	CArg CSpe
	- 'Geoff Hamilton' **new**	SSal
	- 'George Priestley'	MCot
I	- 'Gwendoline' ♀H3	CArg LCro LOPS
	- 'Heaven Scent' **new**	CArg
	- 'Henry Eckford'	SPhx
	- 'High Scent' ♀H3	LCro LOPS
	- 'Honey Pink'	MCot
	- 'Honeymoon'	MCot
	- 'Jilly' ♀H3	CArg LCro LOPS MCot
	- 'Just Julia' ♀H3	CArg CSpe
	- 'Karen Louise'	LCro LOPS
	- 'King Edward VII' ♀H3	CArg LCro LOPS
	- 'Lord Nelson'	CArg
	- 'Magnificent Maroon' **new**	CArg
	- 'Marion'	MCot
	- 'Marti Caine'	MCot
	- 'Matucana' ♀H3	CArg CSpe ELan LCro LOPS MNHC SPhx
	- 'Midnight'	LCro LOPS
	- 'Millennium' **new**	CArg
	- 'Milly'	MCot
	- 'Misty Mountain'	MCot
	- 'Mollie Rilstone'	CArg LCro LOPS MCot
	- 'Mrs Bernard Jones' ♀H3	LCro LOPS MCot
	- 'Mrs Collier'	CArg CSpe SPhx
	- 'Noel Sutton' ♀H3	CArg
	- 'Old Spice'	SVic
	- 'Our Harry'	CArg
	- 'Oxford Blue'	LCro LOPS
	- 'Painted Lady'	LCro LOPS SPhx
	- 'Pink Pearl' **new**	CArg
	- 'Pluto'	LCro LOPS
	- 'Promise'	CArg MCot
	- 'Restormel'	CArg MCot
	- 'Richard and Judy'	MCot
	- 'Royal Wedding'	LCro LOPS
	- 'Solitude' **new**	CArg
	- SPENCER MIXED	LCro LOPS SVic
	- 'Valerie Harrod' ♀H3 **new**	CArg
	- 'Wedding Day' ♀H3	MCot
	- 'White Frills'	CArg LCro LOPS
	palustris	EBee LLWG MMuc SPhx SPlb
	pannonicus	CPla
	pratensis	CHab EBee NMir SPhx WSFF
	pubescens	CRHN EBee
	roseus	EBee WSHC
	rotundifolius ♀H6	GLog SMHy SPhx WBor WSHC
	- 'Tillyperone' ♀H7	EBee SPhx WSHC
	sativus	CSpe SPhx
	subandinus	SPlb
	sylvestris	LShi NAts WBrk
	tingitanus	CSpe
	transsylvanicus	GBin SBrt SPhx
	tuberosus	EBee EPPr LEdu WCot WSHC
	'Tubro'	EBee
	venetus	EBee EWes MNrw SPhx WSHC
§	***vernus*** ♀H6	Widely available
	- 'Albiflorus'	MNrw
	- 'Alboroseus' ♀H6	CDor CTtf EBee ELan EMor EPPr EPfP EWTr GArf ILea MBel MNrw NBir NChi NLar SPhx SPoG SWvt WCAu WCot WFar WHoo
	- var. ***albus***	CMea MNrw NChi SRms WCot
	- ***aurantiacus***	see *L. aureus*

- 'Caeruleus' WHoo
* - 'Cyaneus' CDor WCot
- 'Dama Duet' **new** SHar
- 'Dama Emily' SHar
I - 'Filifolius' CSpe
- 'Flaccidus' MNrw WCot WMal
* - 'Gracilis' EBee LEdu NLar SHar
- 'Little Elf' SHar
- 'Madelaine' WCot
- narrow-leaved CTtf
I - 'Pendulus' SHar
- purple-flowered CRos EHyd LRHS MMuc NRHS SEND
- 'Rainbow' CRos EHyd EPfP LRHS NRHS
- 'Rosenelfe' GJos LEdu LSou MHer SBea SHar SPhx WCot WHal WHil
- f. ***roseus*** CRos ECha EHyd LRHS MMuc MRav NBir NRHS SRms WBrk WCot
- 'Sky' **new** MAvo
- 'Spring Melody' EBee MRav SHar WCot
- 'Subtle Hints' SHar WCot

Latua (*Solanaceae*)

pubiflora WPav

Laureliopsis (*Atherospermataceae*)

philippiana CMCN IDee NLar WPGP

Laurentia see *Isotoma*

Laurus (*Lauraceae*)

§ ***azorica*** CBcs
canariensis see *L. azorica*
nobilis ♀^{H4} Widely available
- f. ***angustifolia*** ♀^{H4} CKel CMac LRHS MBlu MHer MMuc MRav NLar SArc SEND SPoG
- 'Aurea' ♀^{H4} CBcs CEme CMac ELan ELon EPfP MHer MMuc NLar SEND SLon SPer SPoG SWvt
- clipped pyramid LSRN
- 'Crispa' MRav
- variegated (v) CMac SRms

Lavandula ✿ (*Lamiaceae*)

'After Midnight' see *L.* 'Avonview'
'Alba' see *L. angustifolia* 'Alba', *L.* × *intermedia* 'Alba'
'Alba' ambig. SPer
§ ***angustifolia*** CBee CCBP CCVT CRos EBee ECul EHyd ENfk EPfP GPoy GWyn LCro LOPS LRHS LSRN MGos MHer MPri NGdn NPer NRHS NWea SCob SDow SEdi SGBe SPlb SPoG XLum XSen
- 'Alba' misapplied see *L. angustifolia* 'Blue Mountain White'
§ - 'Alba' ELan EPfP EWoo GPoy LRHS MHer MSwo SCob SEdi SGsty SLon SPlb SVen SVic WAvo WGwG WJek WLov WSpi XSen
- 'Alba Nana' see *L. angustifolia* 'Nana Alba'
- 'Arctic Snow' CBcs CRos EHyd ENor EPfP LCro LOPS LRHS MAsh MHer MSwo NRHS SDow SFai SPoG SRms WLav WSpi XSen
- AROMATICO BLUE ('Lablusa'^{PBR}) EHyd LRHS NRHS
- AROMATICO FORTE BLUE ('Laa20001') EHyd LRHS NRHS SPoG
- AROMATICO ROSEA **new** LRHS
- AROMATICO SILVER ('Lasila') EHyd
- 'Ashdown Forest' EBee ENfk EWhm SAdn SDow SFai SPer SRGP SRms SSut WLav WSpi XSen
- 'Backhouse Purple' SDow
- 'Beechwood Blue' ♀^{H5} SDow WLav
- 'Betty's Blue' SDow
- BLEU DE GIEN ('Lavval') **new** XSen
- BLUE CUSHION ('Schola'^{PBR}) ELan LCro LOPS MAsh SPoG SRms WLav
- BLUE ICE ('Dow3'^{PBR}) ENor NLar SDow WLav XSen
§ - 'Blue Mountain White' WLav
- 'Blue Rider' NRHS WLav
- BLUE SCENT ('Syngablusc') LRHS MBros
- BLUE SPEAR ('Pas1213799') **new** LRHS
§ - 'Bowles's Early' WGwG
- 'Bowles's Grey' see *L. angustifolia* 'Bowles's Early'
- 'Bowles's Variety' see *L. angustifolia* 'Bowles's Early'
- 'Cedar Blue' EWhm MHer SDow SRms WLav
- 'Coconut Ice' ELan LRHS WLav WSpi XSen
- 'Compacta' SDow WLav
- 'Contrast' GBin
- 'De Lagrasse' XAbr
- 'Dursley White' WLav
- 'Dwarf Blue' CBod CCBP LSRN MHed NWea SRms WFar XSen
- ELIZABETH ('Fair 16'^{PBR}) ENor LSRN SDow SFai SPoG WLav XSen
- (Ellagance Series) 'Ellagance Ice' LSou SRms
- - 'Ellagance Purple' LRHS LSou MBros SRms XSen
- - 'Ellagance Sky' LSou SRms
- - 'Ellagance Snow' **new** LRHS
- 'Essence Purple' CBod LRHS
- 'Folgate' ♀^{H5} CBod EWhm MHer MNHC NGdn SDow SEdi SRms WHoo WLav WSpi
- 'Forever Blue' SFai SGBe
- GARDEN BEAUTY ('Lowmar'^{PBR}) (v) MAsh SGBe
- GRANNY'S BOUQUET ('Lavang38') WSpi XSen
- HAVANA ('Arbelpaso'^{PBR}) ELan LRHS MAsh MHol SGBe SPoG XSen
§ - 'Hidcote' ♀^{H5} Widely available
- 'Hidcote Pink' CBrac EWhm MHer MRav NGdn SCob SDow SEdi SPer SRms
- 'Hidcote Superior' NGdn
- 'Imperial Gem' ♀^{H5} Widely available
- 'Jean Davis' see *L. angustifolia* 'Rosea'
- 'Lady' NPer WSpi
- 'Lady Ann' SDow WLav
- 'Lavenite Magic Blue Chip' NLar
- 'Lavenite Petite'^{PBR} EHyd ENor LSRN WLav WSpi XSen
- LITTLE LADY ('Batlad') ♀^{H5} CMea ENor LCro LOPS LRHS LSRN MAsh MHed MNHC MSwo NLar NRHS SAko SCob SFai SPoG SRms SWvt WCav WHoo WLav WSpi XSen
- LITTLE LOTTIE ('Clarmo') ♀^{H5} EWhm MHer SDow SEdi SPer WLav XSen
- 'Loddon Blue' CRos EHyd ENor EPfP EWhm LRHS MAsh NRHS SDow SFai SRms WLav WSpi XSen
§ - 'Loddon Pink' CRos EHyd ELan ENor EPfP EWhm GMaP LRHS MAsh MMuc MNHC MRav NGdn NRHS SEND SEdi SFai SRms WAvo WLav WLov XSen
- 'Lullaby Blue' SDow
- 'Maillette' NGdn SDow SRms WLav
- 'Melissa' MHol XSen

	- MELISSA LILAC ('Dow4'PBR)	CBcs CRos CSBt EHyd ENfk ENor LCro LOPS LRHS LSRN MAsh MGos MHer MHol MNHC NRHS SCob SDow SFai SGBe SRkn SRms WLav XSen
	- 'Middachten'	EHyd XSen
	- 'Miss Dawnderry'	SDow
	- 'Miss Donnington'	see *L. angustifolia* 'Bowles's Early'
	- 'Miss Katherine'PBR ♀H5	ENor EPfP MAsh MHed NLar SDow SPoG WLav XSen
	- MISS MUFFET ('Scholmis') ♀H5	SDow SRms WLav XSen
	- 'Munstead'	Widely available
§	- 'Nana Alba' ♀H5	CMea EHyd ELan ENfk EPfP EWhm GMaP GPoy MAsh MHer SEdi SRGP SRms SWvt WLov WSpi XSen
	- 'Nana Atropurpurea'	SDow XSen
	- 'Nikita'	XSen
	- 'No 9'	SDow
	- 'Pacific Blue'	LRHS SDow XSen
	- 'Peter Pan'	ECtt ELan GBin MAsh MHer MNHC SCob SDow WLav XSen
	- PLATINUM BLONDE ('Momparler'PBR)	CCht CRos EHyd ENor LRHS LSou MAsh NRHS SCob SCoo SPoG
	- 'Princess Blue'	ENor SEdi WLav
	- 'Princess Rose'	XAbr
	- 'Purity'	SDow
	- 'Purple Treasure'	SDow
§	- 'Rosea'	CSBt ECha EHyd ELan ENfk EPfP EWoo GPoy LCro LOPS LRHS MAsh MNHC MRav NBir SCob SDow SFai SGBe SPer SPlb SPoG SRms SWvt WLav XSen
	- 'Royal Purple'	EWes NGdn SDow SSut SWvt WLav XSen
	- 'Royal Velvet'	SDow
	- 'Saint Jean'	SDow
	- 'Siesta'	GBin XSen
	- 'Silver Blue'	XSen
	- 'Silver Line'	EHyd LRHS NRHS
	- 'Silver Line Blue' **new**	LRHS
	- 'Silver Mist'	CBod CMea SRms WHer XSen
	- 'Thumbelina Leigh'PBR	ENor MAsh SFai SRms WSpi XSen
	- 'Twickel Purple'	CBar CBcs EBee EHyd ELan EPfP LRHS LSRN MAsh MHed MHol MNHC NRHS SCob SDow SEdi SFai SGbt SPer SRms SWvt WLav WSpi XSen
	- 'Walberton's Silver Edge'	see *L.* × *intermedia* WALBERTON'S SILVER EDGE
	- white-flowered **new**	MBros
	aristibracteata	MHer WLav
§	'Avonview'	MHer WLav
	'Ballerina' ♀H4	SDow
§	'Bee Brilliant'PBR	ENfk EWhm WLav
§	'Bee Cool'PBR	ENfk WLav
§	'Bee Happy'	ENfk EWhm WLav
§	'Bee Pretty'	ENfk EWhm
	'Blue Star'	EPfP EWhm MNHC WGwG
	'Bouquet of Roses'	CRos EHyd LRHS NRHS SCoo
	buchii var. ***buchii***	SDow SVen WLav
	'Bulls Cross'	WLav
	canariensis	MHer SDow SVen WLav
	× ***chaytoriae*** 'Bridehead Blue'	SDow
	- 'Gorgeous'	SDow
	- 'Joan Head'	SDow XSen
	- 'Molton Silver'	XSen
	- 'Richard Gray' ♀H4	LRHS LSRN MHed MHer MNHC SDow SRms WAvo WLav XSen
§	- 'Sawyers' ♀H4	CBod CBrac CRos EHyd EPau EPfP EShb GMaP LRHS LSRN MAsh MCot MHed MHer MNHC MRav NBir NPer NRHS SEND SPer SPhx SPoG SRms WMal XSen
	- SILVER SANDS ('Fair 14'PBR)	CBcs ELan ENfk EPfP LRHS MCot SFai SPoG XSen
	× ***christiana***	EHyd ENor MHol SDow SFai SVen WJek WLav
	'Cornard Blue'	see *L.* × *chaytoriae* 'Sawyers'
	dentata	CBrac ENfk EShb SRms WJek XAbr XSen
§	- var. ***candicans***	MHer SDow SRms WJek WLav
	- var. ***dentata*** 'Dusky Maiden'	SDow WLav
	- - 'Ploughman's Blue'	SVen WGwG
	- - f. ***rosea***	SDow
	- - 'Royal Crown' ♀H3	WLav
	- silver-leaved	see *L. dentata* var. *candicans*
	'Devonshire Compact'	CPla CSBt MHol SRms
	'Fathead'	CBcs CBod CBrac CChe EHyd ELan EPfP LRHS LSRN MAsh MGos MHer MNHC NBir NGdn NLar SCob SCoo SDow SFai SGBe SPoG WAvo WLav
	'Flaming Purple'	SDow
	× ***ginginsii*** 'Goodwin Creek Grey' ♀H4	MHer SRms WJek WLav
	'Hazel'	EHyd EPfP LRHS NRHS SGBe
	'Helmsdale'PBR	CBcs CEnd CRos CSBt ELan ENor EPfP GMaP LRHS LSRN MAsh NLar SCoo SFai SGBe
	heterophylla misapplied	see *L.* × *heterophylla* Viv. Gaston Allard Group
§	× ***heterophylla*** Viv. Gaston Allard Group	WLav
	- - 'African Pride'	SVen
	- - 'Meerlo'	CCht MHol SFai
	'Hidcote Blue'	see *L. angustifolia* 'Hidcote'
	× ***intermedia*** 'Abrialii'	SDow
§	- 'Alba' ♀H5	CMea MHed MHer MNHC SEND SEdi SGbt SVen
	- 'Anniversary Bouquet'	SDow
	- 'Arabian Night'	see *L.* × *intermedia* 'Impress Purple', 'Sussex'
	- 'Arabian Night' ambig.	SRms
§	- Dutch Group	CBod CSBt EHyd ENfk EPfP LRHS MAsh MNHC MRav MSwo SArc SCob SCoo SFai SPer SRms SVic XSen
	- 'Edelweiss'	CBcs CBod CSBt ECul EHyd ENfk EPfP EWhm LRHS MAsh MNHC MRav NLar NRHS SDow SEdi SFai SPer SPoG SRms SWvt WGwG WLav WSpi XSen
	- 'Fragrant Memories'	SCoo SDow SRms WLav XSen
	- 'Fred Boutin'	WSpi
	- 'Grappenhall' misapplied	see *L.* × *intermedia* 'Pale Pretender'
	- 'Grappenhall' ambig.	CSBt EWhm WSpi XSen
	- 'Grey Hedge'	SRms WLav
	- 'Gros Bleu'	SDow WLav
	- 'Grosso'	Widely available
	- (Heavenly Series) HEAVENLY ANGEL ('Dowphangel'PBR)	ENor SDow SGBe XSen
	- - HEAVENLY NIGHT ('Dowphnight'PBR)	LSRN SDow XSen
	- - HEAVENLY OLYMPIA **new**	SGBe
	- - HEAVENLY SCENT ('Dowphscent')	ENor SDow XSen
	- 'Hidcote Giant' ♀H5	CRos EHyd EPfP LRHS NPer NRHS SDow WKif WLav WSpi XSen
§	- 'Impress Purple'	SDow WLav XSen
	- 'Lullingstone Castle'	ENfk EWhm SIvy SRGP SRms SSut WAvo WLav

- 'Magnum' **new** — SDow
- 'Old English' misapplied — see *L. × intermedia* 'Seal'
- 'Old English' — CBod CBrac CLau ENfk SDow SRms SWeb
- Old English Group — MMuc SEND WHoo WLav XSen
- OLYMPIA ('Downoly'^{PBR}) — MHol NLar SDow SPoG XSen
- § - 'Pale Pretender' — GQue SPer SRms
- PHENOMENAL ('Niko'^{PBR}) — ENor LCro LOPS LRHS LSRN NDov NLar SEdd SFai WNPC XSen
- 'Provence' — CSBt NLar SDow SFai SRms XSen
- § - 'Seal' — ENfk GMaP MNHC SDow SRms
- § - 'Sussex' 🏆^{H5} — CBod CFis CRos EHyd EPfP LRHS NRHS SDow WLav
- 'Twickel Purple' — ELan EWes
- § - WALBERTON'S SILVER EDGE ('Walvera') (v) — EHyd ELan EPfP LBuc LRHS MGos NRHS SCoo SDow SRms

'Jamboree' — WLav
'Jean Davis' — see *L. angustifolia* 'Rosea'
lanata 🏆^{H3} — ECha SRms WLav XSen
§ ***latifolia*** — XAbr XSen
'Loddon Pink' — see *L. angustifolia* 'Loddon Pink'
'Madrid Blue' — see *L.* 'Bee Happy'
'Madrid Pink' — see *L.* 'Bee Pretty'
'Madrid Purple' — see *L.* 'Bee Brilliant'
'Madrid White' — see *L.* 'Bee Cool'
minutolii — SDow
multifida — WLav
- 'Spanish Eyes' — MBros
officinalis — see *L. angustifolia*
PASSIONNÉ ('Lavsts 08'^{PBR}) 🏆^{H4} — WLav
pedunculata — ENor XSen
- subsp. ***lusitanica*** — EHyd EPfP LRHS NRHS SPoG
- - LUSI PINK ('Wijs02'^{PBR}) — CRos ENfk SFai SGBe
- - 'Lusi Purple' — CRos EHyd LRHS NRHS SFai SGBe SPoG
§ - subsp. ***pedunculata*** — CBar CBrac ECha EHyd ELan EPfP LCro LOPS LRHS LSRN MAsh MBow MGos MNHC MSwo NGdn NRHS SCob SFai SGbt SPer SRms WAvo WSHC WSpi
- - 'James Compton' 🏆^{H3} — CRos ECha EHyd LRHS MAsh NGdn
- subsp. ***sampaiana*** 'Purple Emperor' — CRos EHyd EPfP LRHS NRHS WLav
pinnata — CCBP CCht ENfk ENor LRHS MHol SAng SDow
'Pretty Polly' 🏆^{H4} — CBcs EHyd ELan EPfP LRHS MAsh NLar SDow SFai SGBe SRkn WLav XSen
'Pukehou' — EHyd EPfP LRHS NRHS SCoo WLav
'Regal Splendour'^{PBR} — CBcs CRos CSBt EHyd ELan ENor EPfP LRHS LSRN MAsh MGos MHer MNHC NRHS SCoo SDow SFai SGBe SPoG SRms WLav
ROCKY ROAD ('Fair09'^{PBR}) — CSBt ENor SFai WLav
'Rosea' — see *L. angustifolia* 'Rosea'
rotundifolia — SDow
'Silver Edge' — see *L. × intermedia* WALBERTON'S SILVER EDGE
'Somerset Mist' — WLav
spica nom. rejic. — see *L. angustifolia*, *L. latifolia*
- 'Hidcote Purple' — see *L. angustifolia* 'Hidcote'
stoechas — CBcs CBod CEme CRos CSBt ECha EHyd ELan EPfP GArf GMaP GPoy LRHS LSRN MGil MSwo NRHS SCob SPer SPlb SWeb SWvt WCav
- from Corsica — SGBe
- var. ***albiflora*** — see *L. stoechas* subsp. *stoechas* f. *leucantha*
- 'Anouk'^{PBR} — EBee ELan EPfP SPoG
- 'Antibes' (Provençal Series) — SRms
- 'Bandera' — MBros NBir
- (Bella Series) BELLA LAVENDER ('Bellav') — CRos EHyd LRHS NRHS
- - BELLA ROSE ('Belros') — EHyd EPfP LRHS NRHS
- 'Blueberry Ruffles'^{PBR} (Ruffles Series) — ELan LRHS
- 'Boysenberry Ruffles'^{PBR} (Ruffles Series) — ELan ENfk XSen
- 'Dark Royalty'^{PBR} — ELan SCob
- JAVELIN BLUE ('Jin Bulle') (Javelin Series) — CRos EHyd LRHS NRHS
- (Javelin Forte Series) JAVELIN FORTE DEEP PURPLE ('Labz0004'^{PBR}) **new** — LRHS
- - JAVELIN FORTE DEEP ROSE ('Labz0006'^{PBR}) **new** — LRHS
- LAVENDER LACE ('Colace') — WLav
- LITTLE BEE DEEP PURPLE ('Florvendula Deep Purple') (Little Bee Series) — EHyd
- 'Mulberry Ruffles'^{PBR} (Ruffles Series) — ELan LRHS SCob
- 'Night of Passion' — SCoo SDow
- 'Papillon' — see *L. pedunculata* subsp. *pedunculata*
- subsp. ***pedunculata*** — see *L. pedunculata* subsp. *pedunculata*
- 'Purley' — SRms
- Ruffles Series — ENfk
- 'Sancho Panza'^{PBR} **new** — EGrI
- 'Spring-break Princess' — CRos EHyd LRHS NRHS
§ - subsp. ***stoechas*** f. ***leucantha*** — EPfP MSwo SDow
- - - 'Snowman' — CBcs CSBt EHyd EPfP LRHS MAsh MHer NLar NRHS SCob SCoo SFai SGBe SPoG SWvt
- - LILAC WINGS ('Prolil'^{PBR}) — CRos EHyd ENor EPfP LRHS NRHS SCoo SDow SFai SGBe WLav
- - 'Provençal' — CRos EHyd LRHS NRHS SCoo
- - 'Purple Wings' — EHyd ELan EPfP MAsh MGos
- - f. ***rosea*** — ENor
- - - 'Kew Red' — CBrac CTri ENfk LRHS MGos MHer SFai SRms SWvt WLav
- 'Sugarberry Ruffles'^{PBR} (Ruffles Series) — LRHS
- 'Victory' — CRos EHyd LRHS NRHS SPoG
- 'With Love'^{PBR} — SDow
SUPERBLUE ('Balavurlu') — LSou
TIARA ('Fair 10'^{PBR}) — CBcs CRos CSBt EHyd ENor LRHS MGos NEoE NLar NRHS SCob SCoo SFai SPad SPoG SRms WLav
'Van Gogh' — SDow
vera misapplied — see *L. × intermedia* Dutch Group
vera DC. — see *L. angustifolia*
viridis — CRos EHyd ELan EPfP LRHS MHer NPer NRHS SDow SRms WJek WLav
'Whero Iti' — SDow
'Willow Vale' 🏆^{H3} — EHyd ENor EPfP EWhm LRHS MAsh MHer NRHS SDow SWvt WAvo WJek

Lavatera (*Malvaceae*)

arborea — CPla SChr
- 'Rosea' — see *L. × clementii* 'Rosea'
- 'Variegata' (v) — CPla ELan NPer SEND WCot
bicolor — see *L. maritima*
BLUE BIRD ('Renlav') — LRHS MNrw
cachemiriana — EPPr NPer
CHAMALLOW ('Inovera'^{PBR}) — LSRN

× ***clementii*** 'Barnsley'	Widely available
- 'Barnsley Baby'	CBod CMac CRos EBee EHyd ELan EPfP LBuc LRHS MAsh MTin NLar NPer SChF SCob SEle SGBe SGbt SPer SPoG SRkn SWvt WFar WNPC
- 'Blushing Bride'	EPfP MGos NLar SCob SGBe SPer SWvt
- 'Bredon Springs' ♀H5	CBrac CSBt EBee ECha EHyd ELon EPfP LRHS LSRN MAsh MGos MMuc MSwo NGdn NRHS SCob SEND SGBe SGbt SGol SPer SWvt WAvo XLum
- 'Burgundy Wine' ♀H5	CBcs CBod CBrac CDoC CMac CRos EBee EHyd ELan EPfP GArf LRHS MAsh MGos MPri MSwo NBir NPer NRHS SGBe SGbt SGol SLon SPer SPoG SWvt WAvo WFar WMal
- 'Candy Floss' ♀H5	CBrac NLar NPer SGBe
- 'Eye Catcher'	CBod CBrac EPPr LRHS MSwo NLar SGBe SPer
- 'Kew Rose'	CBod MHtn MMuc MSwo NLar NPer SEND SRms XLum
- 'Lavender Lady'	EPPr NPer SEND
- 'Lisanne'	EHyd MSwo
- 'Mary Hope' ♀H5	CDoC CRos EHyd EPfP LRHS MAsh NRHS SCoo SEle SWvt
- 'Pavlova'	CExl
§ - 'Pink Frills'	CEme SWvt WCot WFar
- RED RUM ('Rigrum'PBR) ♀H5	CBod CDoC CEme CKel CMac CSBt EHyd EPfP GDam LBuc LSRN MAsh MGos MPri NLar NRHS SCob SEdd SPoG SWvt WFar
§ - 'Rosea' ♀H5	CBcs CBod CBrac CDoC CKel CMac CPla CRos EBee EHyd EPfP LCro LOPS LRHS LSRN LShi MAsh MGos MPri NHol NRHS SCob SGBe SGbt SGol SLon SPer SPoG SWvt
- RUBY STAR ('Jostar'PBR)	CKel EBee EHyd LRHS NRHS
- 'Songbird'	CBod NRHS SEle
§ - 'Wembdon Variegated' (v)	NPer
cretica **new**	WHil
'Frederique'	CMac LRHS SWvt WKif WMal
'Grey Beauty'	LRHS SEND
'Magenta Magic'PBR	MHol SEdd SPoG
§ ***maritima*** ♀H3	CBod CDoC CExl CMac CPla CSde ELan EPfP EWoo SEND SEle SGBe SPer SRkn SRms SWvt WCFE WCot WFar WSMil
- 'Princesse de Lignes'	XLum
olbia	SDix SPlb SRms WFar
- 'Lilac Lady'	CBod ECha ELan MGos MMuc WFar WKif
'Peppermint Ice'	see *L. thuringiaca* 'Ice Cool'
phoenicea	WMal
'Pink Frills'	see *L.* × *clementii* 'Pink Frills'
'Rosea'	see *L.* × *clementii* 'Rosea'
thuringiaca 'First Light'	SPhx
§ - 'Ice Cool'	SCob SWvt WKif
- 'Saalestrand'	MNrw
trimestris 'Loveliness' **new**	GJos
- 'Mont Blanc' **new**	GJos
- 'Silver Cup' ♀H3	GJos LCro LOPS
'Variegata'	see *L.* × *clementii* 'Wembdon Variegated'
'White Satin'PBR	NHol

Lawsonia (*Lythraceae*)

inermis	WSFF

Lecanthus (*Urticaceae*)

peduncularis	GGro SBrt

Ledebouria (*Asparagaceae*)

adlamii	see *L. cooperi*
concolor misapplied	see *L. socialis*
§ ***cooperi***	CBor EAJP EHyd ELan EPri EShb GKev LEdu MPie SBrt WBor WPGP WTor XLum
ovalifolia	NWad
§ ***socialis***	EShb LEdu MCot MPie SGro SIvy WCot WFar
- green-leaved	EShb
violacea	see *L. socialis*

Ledum see *Rhododendron*

leek see AGM Vegetables Section

Legousia (*Campanulaceae*)

speculum-veneris **new**	CSpe

Leibnitzia (*Asteraceae*)

anandria	EPPr GGro

Leiophyllum see *Kalmia*

Lembotropis see *Cytisus*

Lemna (*Araceae*)

gibba	NPer
minor	CWat NPer
trisulca	CWat EWat NPer

lemon see *Citrus* × *limon*

lemon balm see *Melissa officinalis*

lemon grass see *Cymbopogon citratus*

lemon, rough see *Citrus* × *taitensis*

lemon verbena see *Aloysia citrodora*

Leonotis (*Lamiaceae*)

leonurus	CCCN CDTJ CPbh ECre EMdy EShb LRHS SGBe SMad SMrm SPlb WCFE XLum
- var. ***albiflora***	CCCN EShb
nepetifolia	CCCN
var. ***nepetifolia*** 'Staircase'	
§ ***ocymifolia***	CCCN CExl

Leontodon (*Asteraceae*)

hispidus	CHab NMir
§ ***rigens***	ELan GEdr GGro MMuc NBid NBir SMrm SPtp WFar
- B&SWJ 12527	WCru WSHC
- 'Girandole'	see *L. rigens*

Leontopodium (*Asteraceae*)

alpinum	see *L. nivale* subsp. *alpinum*
coreanum	GKev
discolor	WAbe
forrestianum **new**	GKev
haastioides	WAbe
himalayanum	GKev
jacotianum	GKev
kurilense	GKev
nanum	GKev SPlb
§ ***nivale*** subsp. ***alpinum***	CTri EBou ELan EPfP GKev MAsh MBel NHpl NSla SLee SPlb SPoG SRms XLum

- - Blossom of Snow ('Berghman') LRHS SCoo
- - 'Everest' EDAr LRHS
- - 'Matterhorn' GEdr GMaP NLar
- - 'Mignon' EPfP EWes GArf GMaP NLar WAbe

§ ***ochroleucum*** var. ***campestre*** NLar XLum
palibinianum see *L. ochroleucum* var. *campestre*
pusillum SPlb WAbe
souliei NSla XLum
wilsonii GKev

Leonurus (*Lamiaceae*)

artemisia see *L. japonicus*
cardiaca CBee CBod CCBP EGrI GGro GPoy LRHS MHer MNHC NGrd SPhx SRms
- 'Grobbebol' EPPr WCot WHer

§ ***japonicus*** SSal
sibiricus misapplied see *L. japonicus*
sibiricus L. CPla SPhx
turkestanicus EBee

Leopoldia (*Asparagaceae*)

caucasica GKev
comosa see *Muscari comosum*
cycladica subsp. ***subsessilis*** GKev
spreitzenhoferi see *Muscari spreitzenhoferi*
tenuiflora see *Muscari tenuiflorum*
weissii GKev

Lepechinia (*Lamiaceae*)

bella SDys
chamaedryoides CExl
hastata CSpe EWld LRHS SPlb WJek
salviae WFar WHer

Lepidium (*Brassicaceae*)

campestre CHab
latifolium CAgr ENfk LEdu

Lepidothamnus (*Podocarpaceae*)

§ ***colensoi*** new SMad

Leptinella (*Asteraceae*)

atrata subsp. ***luteola*** ELan
'County Park' EDAr
dendyi ECtt ELan EWes GEdr NSla WIce
dioica GBin
- 'Minima' WFar

hispida see *Cotula hispida* (DC.) Harv.
§ ***pectinata*** ITim
§ ***potentillina*** CTri ECha GQue MBNS NBro NLar SRms XLum
§ ***pusilla*** MPkF XSte
§ ***pyrethrifolia*** EDAr GEdr
reptans see *L. scariosa*
§ ***scariosa*** GAbr
§ ***squalida*** ECha GBin MBel NSti SLee
* - 'Minima' GQue WFar
§ - 'Platt's Black' Widely available
traillii NBro

Leptodermis (*Rubiaceae*)

oblonga 'Summer Stars' LRHS

Leptopus (*Euphorbiaceae*)

§ ***chinensis*** EWTr WCot

Leptospermum ✿ (*Myrtaceae*)

citratum see *L. petersonii*
'Copper Sheen' CTrC
'County Park Blush' ELon
cunninghamii see *L. myrtifolium*
'Electric Red' (Galaxy Series) CAbb CKel EPfP MGil SEle
ericoides see *Kunzea ericoides*
flavescens misapplied see *L. glaucescens*
flavescens Sm. see *L. polygalifolium*
§ ***glaucescens*** SPlb
§ ***grandiflorum*** CBcs CTrC EPfP SVen
grandifolium LRHS
'Havering Hardy' SEle
humifusum see *L. rupestre*
juniperinum SPlb
'Karo Pearl Star' CBcs CTrC CTsd MGil MPkF WLov
'Karo Spectrobay' CBcs CKel CTsd MGil
laevigatum SVen
§ ***lanigerum*** CExl CTri CTsd EPfP GAbr SPlb SPtp SVen
- 'Cunninghamii' see *L. myrtifolium*

liversidgei SPlb
§ ***myrtifolium*** CMac CTrC EWes SEdd
namadgiensis IDee
nitidum SPlb
§ ***petersonii*** GPoy XAbr
phylicoides see *Kunzea ericoides*
'Pink Cascade' CBcs CMac CTri MPkF SEle XSte
§ ***polygalifolium*** SPlb
prostratum see *L. rupestre*
pubescens see *L. lanigerum*
'Red Cascade' SWvt
rodwayanum see *L. grandiflorum*
rotundifolium CBcs SPlb
- from Jervis Bay EBee

§ ***rupestre*** CTrC CTri SPlb SVen
scoparium CBee CTrC CTsd EGrI GPoy MNHC SPlb SVen WJek WKor XAbr
- 'Adrianne' EHyd EPfP LRHS NRHS
- 'Appleblossom' ♀H4 CBcs CBod CDoC CEnd CKel CTrC EPfP SAko SEle
- 'Autumn Glory' WLov
- 'Blossom' (d) CBcs CMac
- 'Burgundy Queen' (d) CBcs CCCN CEme CMac CTrC CTsd
- 'Chapmanii' CCCN SEdd WPGP
- 'Coral Candy' CBcs CCCN CEnd MGil MPkF SEdd SGbt WFar WLov XSte
- 'Crimson Glory' (d) CBod CSBt
- 'Elizabeth Jane' WFar
- 'Gaiety Girl' (d) CKel CSBt
- var. ***incanum*** new ESwi
- 'Jubilee' (d) CBcs CCCN CMac
- 'Leonard Wilson' (d) CTri
- 'Martini' CAbb CBcs CCCN CDoC CKel CMac CSBt EHyd EPfP LRHS MGil MPkF NRHS SGol SPoG WLov XSte
- (Nanum Group) 'Huia' SCob
- - 'Kea' CBcs MHer
- - 'Kiwi' ♀H4 CBcs CBod CBrac CCCN CEme CKel CRos CSBt EBee EGrI EHyd ELan EPfP LRHS MAsh MMuc SEle SLon SPoG WFar
- - 'Nanum' CCCN
- - 'Tui' CMac CSBt CTrC
- 'Nichollsii' ♀H4 CBcs SVen
- 'Nichollsii Nanum' ♀H4 WAbe WThu
- 'Pink Damask' SWvt
- var. ***prostratum*** misapplied see *L. rupestre*
- 'Red Damask' (d) ♀H4 Widely available
- 'Red Ensign' SPoG
- 'Red Falls' CExl

* - 'Ruby Wedding'	EHyd ELan EPfP LRHS LSRN MAsh SLon SPoG
- 'Snow Flurry'	CBcs CDoC CRos EHyd EPfP LRHS NRHS SGol SVen WFar
- 'Winter Cheer' (d)	CBcs CTrC EGrI EHyd EPfP SGol
- 'Wiri Donna'	CSde
- 'Wiri Kerry' (d)	MPkF XSte
- 'Wiri Linda'	CBcs CMac
'Silver Sheen' ♀H3	CAbb CBcs CCCN CDoC CEnd CKel CSde CTrC CTsd ELan EPfP LRHS MAsh NLar SPer SPoG SVen WPGP

Lespedeza (*Fabaceae*)

bicolor	CAgr CCCN EGrI EHed WCFE WFar WSHC
- 'Yakushima'	NLar
buergeri	EHyd MMrt NLar SHar WSHC
capitata	EBee
japonica	SPlb
thunbergii ♀H5	CBcs CDoC CEme CKel CRos CSde EBee EHyd EPfP LRHS MAsh MBlu MGil NLar NRHS SEdd SLon SMad SPer SPoG SSta WCFE WHil WPGP WSHC
- subsp. ***formosa***	EBee EGrI MGil
- 'Gibraltar'	EBee WPGP
- 'Summer Beauty'	CBcs
- subsp. ***thunbergii*** 'Albiflora'	ELan
- - 'Edo-shibori'	CKel EBee EHed ELan EPfP LRHS NLar SEdd SPer WHil WPGP WSHC
- - 'White Fountain'	CRos EHyd EPfP LRHS MAsh NRHS SPoG WSHC
tiliifolia	see *Desmodium elegans*

Lesquerella (*Brassicaceae*)

arctica var. ***purshii***	GKev

lettuce see AGM Vegetables Section

Leucadendron (*Proteaceae*)

argenteum	CCCN CPbh CTrC SPlb
'Bell's Supreme'	CTrC
'Burgundy Sunset'	CBcs CCCN MPkF
conicum	CPbh
'Cream Delight'	CCCN
daphnoides	SPlb
'Deacon Red'	MPkF
discolor	SPlb
eucalyptifolium	CPbh SPlb
galpinii	CPbh
gandogeri	CPbh
'Highlights'	CCCN
'Inca Gold' ♀H1c	CBcs CPbh
'Jack Harre'	LRHS MPkF
'Jester' (v)	CCCN CPbh
'Jubilee Crown'	MPkF XSte
laureolum	CCCN CPbh
'Maui Sunset'	CTrC
modestum 'Strawberry Fair'	CCCN
'Mrs Stanley'	CTrC
'Pisa'	LRHS MPkF XSte
'Red Dwarf'	CPbh
'Safari Magic'	CCCN
'Safari Sunset' ♀H3	CBcs CCCN CPbh CTrC CTsd MPkF
salicifolium	SPlb
salignum	CCCN CPbh
- 'Fireglow'	CTrC LRHS MPkF
'Sand Dollar' new	CPbh
sessile	CPbh
strobilinum	CPbh
'Summer Sun'	XSte
'Sundance'	MPkF XSte
tinctum	CPbh

Leucaena (*Fabaceae*)

leucocephala	SPlb

Leucanthemella (*Asteraceae*)

§ ***serotina*** ♀H7	Widely available
- 'Herbststern'	NLar

Leucanthemopsis (*Asteraceae*)

§ ***alpina***	NSla
hosmariensis	see *Rhodanthemum hosmariense*

Leucanthemum ✿ (*Asteraceae*)

'Angel'	CBod ELon MBros NCou NLar
atlanticum	see *Rhodanthemum atlanticum*
catananche	see *Rhodanthemum catananche*
hosmariense	see *Rhodanthemum hosmariense*
maximum misapplied	see *L.* × *superbum*
§ ***maximum*** (Ramond) DC.	NBro NPer
- ***uliginosum***	see *Leucanthemella serotina*
nipponicum	see *Nipponanthemum nipponicum*
'Osiris Neige'	ECtt XLum
paludosum 'Snowland'	LRHS
'Real Charmer'PBR	CRos EHyd LRHS MAsh MBros NRHS SGBe SPeP SRms SWvt
'Real Sunbeam'PBR new	LRHS
'Sante'	CBod EHyd ELan EMor EPfP LRHS NRHS
'Sunshine Peach'	EBou EHyd
§ × ***superbum***	CMac MBow MMuc SEND WBrk
- 'Aglaia' (d)	Widely available
- 'Alaska'	CBod CExl CRos EBee EHyd ELan EWoo GAbr GBin GQue LRHS LSun MACG MCot NLar NRHS SCoo SEdd SPer SWvt XLum
- 'Amelia'	EBee EHyd LRHS NLar NRHS
- 'Anita Allen' (d)	ECtt WCot
- 'Antwerp Star'	NLar
- 'Banana Cream'	CBcs CBod CRos CWGN EBee ECtt EHyd EPfP IPot LCro LEdu LRHS MACG MAsh MBriF MBros MSCN NHol NLar NRHS SCob SCoo SEle SPoG WCav WFar WHoo WTor
- 'Barbara Bush' (d/v)	SWvt
§ - 'Beauté Nivelloise'	CElw ECtt EHyd EPfP GWyn LRHS LSou NBir SRms WFar WSpi WTor
- 'Becky'	CElw CMac CRos EBlo ECha EHyd ELan ELon EWTr GBin GWyn ILea LRHS LSRN MBel NEoE NLar NRHS WCAu WCot WSpi
- 'Belgian Lace'	NLar
- 'Bishopstone'	EBee ECtt ELan LEdu MSpe SMrm
- 'Bridal Bouquet'PBR	CRos ECtt EHyd LRHS NRHS
- 'Brightside'	EHyd ELan ELon LRHS LSun NRHS SBls SBut WFar
- BROADWAY LIGHTS ('Leumayel'PBR)	CKel CRos EBee EHyd EPfP EWes GBin GDam LPot LRHS MAsh MRav NFav NRHS SCob SRms WAvo WCAu WFar WGrn WSpi WTor
- 'Christine Hagemann'	CElw ECtt MNrw MRav SHar WBrk WCFE
- 'Cloud Cumulus'	CBod SCoo WHil
- 'Cobham Gold' (d)	CWCL
- 'Crazy Daisy'	CBod CChe CTri EAJP ECtt EHyd EMor EPfP GWyn MACG NFav NRHS SCoo SWvt WFar

- 'Droitwich Beauty'	ECtt MAvo WAvo WCFE WCav WHoo
- 'Dwarf Snow Lady'	SGBe
- 'Edgebrook Giant'	WBrk
- 'Eisstern'	LEdu SHar
- 'Elworthy Sparkler'	CElw MAvo WBrk
- 'Engelina'^{PBR}	EBee ECtt ECul EPfP LRHS MBriF NBir WCAu
- 'Esther Read' (d)	EBee ECtt EHyd EPau EPfP GBin LRHS LSRN MACG NBro NChi NLar NRHS SRms SWvt WBrk WCot WFar
§ - 'Everest'	SRms
- 'Exhibition'	EHyd LRHS NRHS
- 'Fiona Coghill' (d)	CBod CElw CWGN ECtt EHyd EPfP GBee GBin LRHS MHol MNrw MSCN MSpe NBir NFav NGdn NLar NRHS WCot WHoo
- 'Flore Pleno' (d)	MMuc SEND SPlb
- FREAK! ('Leuz0001'^{PBR})	CBcs CRos EHyd EPfP LRHS LSou MHol NRHS SCoo SWvt
- 'Goldfinch'^{PBR}	CBod CMea CWCL CWGN ECtt MACG MAsh MHol MPri NGBl NHpl NLar NWsh SCob SPoG SRms WCot WHil
- 'Goldrausch'^{PBR}	EBee ECtt EHyd ELan EPfP LEdu LRHS MRav NBir NGdn NHol SCob SGbt SRms SWvt WFar
- 'Gruppenstolz'	GBin
- 'H. Seibert'	MArl
- 'Highland White Dream'^{PBR}	EHyd
- 'Horace Read' (d)	CDor CElw CMea ECtt NBir NHol SWvt
- 'Ice Star'	EBee EHyd ELan LRHS NRHS
- 'Jennifer Read'	NLar
§ - 'John Murray' (d)	NBir NWsh WFar
- 'Lacrosse'	CRos EBee EHyd ELon EPfP LRHS NLar NRHS SCob WFar
- 'Laspider'	EHyd GBee LRHS NRHS
- 'Little Miss Muffet'	CSBt CWGN ECtt EHyd LRHS LSou MBNS NRHS
- 'Little Princess'	see *L.* × *superbum* 'Silberprinzesschen'
- 'Luna'^{PBR}	CBod LRHS MACG SPeP
- 'Macaroon'^{PBR}	CBod
- 'Manhattan'	CDor EWes GBin SEdd
- 'Marion Bilsland'	MSpe NChi WBrk
- 'Mayfield Giant'	MACG
- 'Old Court'	see *L.* × *superbum* 'Beauté Nivelloise'
- 'Paladin'^{PBR}	ECtt
- 'Phyllis Smith'	CBod EBee ECtt ELan ELon GWyn LSRN MAvo MHer MPie MRav MSpe NGdn SMad WBrk WCAu WCot WFar
- 'Polaris'	CRos EBlo LRHS NRHS XLum
- 'Rags and Tatters'	ECtt
- 'Real Dream'^{PBR}	EBee EHyd ELan IPot LRHS NRHS SCob SWvt WFar WNPC
- 'Real Galaxy'^{PBR}	CRos EHyd ELan EPfP LBuc LRHS MHol NRHS SGBe SPoG
- 'Real Glory'	CRos ECtt EHyd ELan EPau LRHS LSou MMrt NHpl NRHS SCob SGBe SWvt WCAu WFar WNPC
- 'Real Neat'	CRos EBee ECtt EHyd ELan LRHS MAsh NHpl NRHS SCob SGBe STPC WNPC
- 'Shaggy'	see *L.* × *superbum* 'Beauté Nivelloise'
- 'Shapcott Gossamer'	CBod ECtt NGBl SEdd SPoG SRms WBrk WChS WCot
- 'Shapcott Ruffles'	CBod EBee ECtt WBrk WCot
- 'Shapcott Summer Clouds'	CDor CKno EBee ECtt GAbr GMaP MSCN SEdd SMad SPoG WBrk WCot
§ - 'Silberprinzesschen'	CSBt EBou EHyd EPfP GMaP GWyn LRHS NRHS SPlb SRms XLum
- 'Silver Spoon'	EHyd SCoo
- 'Snehurka'	EHyd WCot WFar WHoo
- 'Snow Lady'	EAJP EHyd EPfP GDam GWyn LPot LRHS NPer SRms WFar
- 'Snow Queen'	GWyn
- 'Snowbound'	EHyd LRHS NEoE NRHS
- 'Snowcap'	EBlo ECha EHyd EPfP LCro LOPS LRHS MRav MTin NRHS SCoo SWvt WCAu WGwG
- 'Snowdrift'	CRos LRHS NLar NRHS WBrk WCot WFar
§ - 'Sonnenschein'	CBod CDor CRos EBee ECha ECtt ELan EPfP EWoo GMaP GQue LRHS LSRN MArl MRav MSpe NBir NGdn NRHS NWsh SPer SRms WCAu WChS
- 'Starburst' (d)	CRos EBlo EHyd ELan LRHS NRHS SRms WFar
- 'Stina'	EBee IPot XLum
- 'Summer Snowball'	see *L.* × *superbum* 'John Murray'
- 'Sunny Side Up'^{PBR}	CBod CWCL EBee ECtt EHyd EWes LRHS LSou NLar NRHS SCob SEdd WFar
- SUNSHINE	see *L.* × *superbum* 'Sonnenschein'
- 'T.E. Killin' (d) 🏆^{H4}	CBod CRos EBee ECha ECtt EHyd ELan EPfP GMaP LCro LRHS MRav NFav NRHS SCoo WCAu WFar
- 'Victorian Secret'^{PBR}	ECtt EHyd GAbr LBuc LRHS LSou MNrw NEoE NRHS SMad SPeP WCot WHil WTor
- WHITE MOUNTAIN ('Gfleuwhmtn'^{PBR})	EHyd LRHS NRHS
- 'Wirral Pride'	EPfP WBrk
- 'Wirral Supreme' (d) 🏆^{H5}	CBcs CBod CRos CSBt EBee EHyd ELan EPfP GJos GMaP ILea LCro LOPS LRHS MNrw MRav NBir NFav NLar NRHS SCob SEdd SRms SWvt WCAu WFar WSpi
'Tizi-n-Test'	see *Rhodanthemum catananche* 'Tizi-n-Test'
§ ***vulgare***	Widely available
- 'Filigran'	EHyd LRHS NRHS WFar
- 'Lollipop'	GWyn
§ - 'Maikönigin'	CRos EBlo EHyd GWyn LRHS NRHS SCob XLum
- MAY QUEEN	see *L. vulgare* 'Maikönigin'
'White Knight'	CBod EHyd LRHS NRHS SCob

Leucocoryne (*Alliaceae*)

'Andes' 🏆^{H3}	CCCN GKev NRog SDeJ WHil
'Dione'	GKev SDeJ
'Double Fantasy'	GKev
* ***ixioides alba***	NRog
- 'Blue Ocean'	GKev SDeJ
pauciflora	NRog
purpurea 🏆^{H2}	NRog
'Spotlight'	GKev
'Sunny Stripe'	GKev
vittata	NRog
'White Dream'	NRog SDeJ

Leucogenes (*Asteraceae*)

grandiceps	GKev WAbe
leontopodium	EPot NSla WAbe
tarahaoa	WAbe

Leucogenes × *Raoulia* see × *Leucoraoulia*

Leucojum ✿ (*Amaryllidaceae*)

aestivum	CBcs CDor CTri EAJP EBee EWTr GKev ILea LRHS MCot NBir NChi NHol NLar NRHS NRog SDeJ SEND SRms WCot WFar WHil WShi
- 'Gravetye Giant' ♀H7	Widely available
autumnale	see *Acis autumnalis*
longifolium	see *Acis longifolia*
roseum	see *Acis rosea*
tingitanum	see *Acis tingitana*
trichophyllum	see *Acis trichophylla*
valentinum	see *Acis valentina*
vernum ♀H5	CBor CBro CExl CWCL EBee EHyd ELan EPfP EPot EWoo GKev LCro LOPS MNrw NBir NHol NHpl NPol NRHS NRog NRya SDeJ SPhx SRms WCot WHer WPnP WShi
- var. ***carpathicum***	EPri GRum
- var. ***vagneri***	ECha SDys WSHC
- var. ***vernum*** 'Green Lantern'	CElw

Leucophyta (*Asteraceae*)

§ ***brownii***	CDoC WSMil
- 'Silver Sand'	LRHS MCot

Leucopogon (*Ericaceae*)

§ ***colensoi***	MGil WThu
ericoides	GKev
§ ***fraseri***	WThu

× *Leucoraoulia* (*Asteraceae*)

§ ***loganii***	WAbe

Leucosceptrum (*Lamiaceae*)

canum	CExl SBrt
- GWJ 9424	WCru
japonicum B&SWJ 10804	WCru
- B&SWJ 10981	WCru
- 'Golden Angel'	SBls
stellipilum	MHol
- var. ***formosanum*** B&SWJ 1926	WCru
- - RWJ 9907	SBrt WCru
- var. ***tosaense*** B&SWJ 8892	WCru

Leucospermum (*Proteaceae*)

(Carnival Series) 'Carnival Copper'	CBcs CCCN
- 'Carnival Red'	CCCN
cordifolium	CCCN CPbh
glabrum	SPlb
'Scarlet Ribbon'	CCCN
'Succession'	CCCN
'Tango'	CPbh
'Vulkano'	CCCN

Leucostegia (*Davalliaceae*)

immersa PAB 7836	LEdu WPGP

Leucothoe (*Ericaceae*)

axillaris	MAsh
- 'Curly Red' PBR	CDoC CMac CRos EBee ELan EPfP LPar LRHS MAsh MGos NLar NRHS SCob SCoo SGol SLon SPoG SWvt SavN WFar
- 'Royal Red'	SavN
- 'Tricolor' (v)	SavN
- TWISTING RED ('Opstal20' PBR)	MBlu
CARINELLA ('Zebekot')	CRos EPfP LRHS NLar NRHS SPoG
davisiae	NLar
§ ***fontanesiana***	CMac
- 'Makijaz' PBR (v)	CBod EBee EPfP LRHS NLar SNig SPoG
- 'Rainbow' (v)	CBcs CBod CBrac CDoC CEme CMac CRos EBee EGrl EHyd EPfP LRHS MGos NLar SCob SGbt SGol SPer SPoG SRms SSta SWvt WFar
- 'Rollissonii' ♀H6	MRav SRms
- WHITEWATER ('Howw' PBR) (v)	CBod CBrac CMac LCro LOPS LRHS MPkF NLar SNig
keiskei BURNING LOVE ('Opstal50' PBR)	LRHS NLar XSte
- HALLOWEEN ('Opstal16' PBR)	EBee MPkF XSte
- 'Royal Ruby'	MAsh MGos MPkF NLar SGbt SGol SPoG SavN WFar
'Little Flames' PBR	LRHS MPkF XSte
LOVITA ('Zebonard')	MRav NLar SCoo
RED LIPS ('Lipsbolwi' PBR)	EPfP SCob
SCARLETTA ('Zeblid') ♀H6	Widely available
walteri	see *L. fontanesiana*
- 'Hokus Pokus' (v)	CBod

Leuzea (*Asteraceae*)

centaureoides	see *Rhaponticum centaureoides*

Levisticum (*Apiaceae*)

officinale	CAgr CBod CCBP CHby CLau EBou ENfk EPfP EWhm GAbr GPoy GQue LEdu MBow MHer MMuc MNHC MPri NGrd SDix SEND SEdi SPhx SPlb SRms SVic WHer WJek XAbr

Lewisia ✿ (*Portulacaceae*)

'Archangel'	EPot NRya
Ashwood Carousel hybrids	NHar
- orange shades	NHpl
- pink shades	NHpl
- yellow shades	NHpl
Birch strain	CBcs
brachycalyx ♀H4	EWes GKev
Brynhyfryd hybrids **new**	GKev
columbiana	MAsh NHpl
- 'Alba'	EPot GKev NSla
- 'Rosea'	MAsh
- subsp. ***rupicola***	NSla
- subsp. ***wallowensis***	MAsh NSla
cotyledon ♀H4	CRos CWCL EHyd EPfP GArf GKev GMaP ITim LCro LOPS LRHS NHpl NRHS NSla SRot SSim WIce
- f. ***alba***	CWCL
- 'Ashwood Ruby'	MAsh
- Ashwood strain	EPfP EWes MAsh NHpl SRms
- 'Brannan Bar'	MAsh
- 'Bright Eyes'	GKev
- ELISE MIXED	CBod LRHS MACG MHol SRot
- var. ***heckneri***	MAsh
- hybrid	EBee GKev NRya SPoG
- 'John's Special'	MAsh
- magenta-flowered	CWCL
- orange-flowered	CWCL
§ - 'Regenbogen'	LRHS MHer
- rose-pink-flowered	CWCL
- salmon-flowered	CWCL
- Sunset Group ♀H4	EPfP NHpl NLar
- 'White Splendour'	MAsh

'George Henley'	EWes MAsh NRya WAbe
glandulosa	GKev
leeana	MAsh
(Little Series) 'Little Mango'	EDAr GEdr NHar NRya NSla SSim
- 'Little Peach'	CWCL EDAr EPot MCot NHpl NRya NSla SEdd SSim
- 'Little Plum'	CMea CPla CTsd EDAr EHyd GEdr MAsh MCot NHpl NLar NRya NSla SSim WHoo WIce
- 'Little Raspberry'	EDAr NSla
- 'Little Snowberry'	EDAr
- LITTLE TUTTI FRUTTI (mix)	CSma NSla
§ ***nevadensis***	CRos EBou EHyd EPot LRHS NRHS NRya WThu
I - 'Alba'	GKev NHpl
- ***bernardina***	see *L. nevadensis*
- 'Rosea'	NHpl NRya NSla
oppositifolia	MAsh
'Pinkie'	GArf NHpl
pygmaea	EHyd EWes GKev LRHS MAsh MHer NBir NRHS NRya NSla SPlb XLum
rediviva	EPot GKev ITim MAsh NHpl NSla
'Trevosia'	MAsh
tweedyi ♀H4	CRos EHyd EPot GKev LRHS MAsh NHar NHpl NRHS SPlb WAbe
- 'Alba'	WAbe
- 'Elliott's Variety'	MAsh
- 'Rosea'	CRos EHyd EPot LRHS MAsh NHar NRHS WAbe

Leycesteria (*Caprifoliaceae*)

crocothyrsos	CBcs EBee GKev ILea NLar SPoG WFar
formosa	Widely available
- from Longstock	SLon
- 'Gold Leaf'	CMac CPla GAbr LShi MGil MHer SHar WFar
- GOLDEN LANTERNS ('Notbruce'PBR) ♀H4	CBcs CBod CDoC CEme CRos CSBt EBee EHyd ELan EPfP LBuc LRHS LSRN MAsh MGos MMrt MMuc MSwo NLar NRHS SCob SCoo SGBe SGsty SPer SPoG SRms SWvt WBor WFar
- 'Purple Rain'	CDoC CRos EBee EHyd EPfP EWes LPar LRHS MAsh MGos NLar NRHS SGsty

Leymus (*Poaceae*)

from the Falkland Islands	ELon EPPr
§ ***arenarius***	CBod CElw CEme CKno EBee ECha ELan EShb GBin GMaP LRHS MMuc NBid NBro SCob SDix SEND SEdd SGbt SPlb SRms WABo WFar WSMil WTre XLum XSen
- 'Blue Dune'	EBee SEdd
cinereus	WCot
hispidus	see *Elymus hispidus*

Lhotzkya see *Calytrix*

Liatris (*Asteraceae*)

aspera	SPhx
cylindracea	SPhx
elegans	GKev SPlb
ligulistylis	SPhx
microcephala	SPhx
mucronata	NLar
pycnostachya	CSpe GBin GQue SAko SRms
scariosa	LRHS SPhx
- 'Alba'	CBcs EBee LSun SAko SPhx
- 'White Spire' **new**	SBls
§ ***spicata***	Widely available
- 'Alba'	CBod CMac CSBt EAJP EBee ECha ELan EMor EPfP GBin LSRN LShi MPri MSCN NLar SCob SPer SPlb WWtn XLum
- ***callilepis***	see *L. spicata*
- 'Floristan Violett'	CMea CRos CSBt CTri EBee EHyd EPfP GMaP LRHS MHer MHol MPri MSpe NLar NRHS SBls SCob SCoo SGbt SPlb SPoG SWvt WFar WGwG XLum
- 'Floristan Weiss'	CExl CRos CTri EBee EHyd EPPr EPfP ERCP GMaP LRHS MACG MBel MHer MPri MRav NLar NRHS SBls SDeJ SGbt SPoG SRms STPC SWvt WFar WGwG
- GOBLIN	see *L. spicata* 'Kobold'
§ - 'Kobold'	Widely available
squarrosa	SPhx

Libanotis see *Seseli*

montana	see *Seseli libanotis*

Libertia ✿ (*Iridaceae*)

'Amazing Grace'	EBee
chilensis ♀H3	Widely available
- Elegans Group	CExl EBee WCru
§ - Formosa Group	CBcs CBod CBro CEme CExl CTri EBee EHyd ELan GKev LRHS NChi NRHS NSti SArc SCob SRms SWvt WHer
- Procera Group	CSpe CTsd EBee EPfP GBin LEdu LRHS SPlb WPGP
§ ***cranwelliae***	CExl WPGP
formosa	see *L. chilensis* Formosa Group
grandiflora ambig.	CBod CCht CDoC CTsd EGrI EWoo GAbr GBin GKev MACG MAvo MBel MBow MMrt MSCN NBro SArc SCob SEdd SGBe SIvy WCAu WSMil
grandiflora (R. Br.) Sweet	EHyd LRHS SDix SVen
'Grasshopper'	CBod GBin LBuc SGBe
ixioides	CBcs ECha EGrI LEdu SGBe SPtp WCFE WPGP
- 'Goldfinger' (v)	CBcs CBod CBor CExl CKno CMac EBee EHyd ELan EMor EPfP LEdu LLWG LRHS MPkF NFav NHol NRHS SBls SCob SEdd SLon SPoG SWvt WFar WGrn WHer XSte
- 'Highlander'	LRHS
- 'Taupo Blaze'	CBct CMac ELan ELon EPfP GBin MRav SCob SIvy SLon SPoG XSte
- 'Taupo Sunset'PBR	CBcs CBct CCCN CExl EPfP LEdu LRHS MBNS MPkF NSti SGBe SPeP SWvt WPGP XSte
- 'Tricolor'	CSde EWld GEdr MRav
'Nelson Dwarf'	EBee ESwi
paniculata	CExl EBee
peregrinans	CAbb CExl CKno CSpe EBee ECha EGrI EHyd ELan EPri EWoo GKev LEdu LRHS MACG MRav NBir NRHS SCob SEdd SGBe SIvy SPer SPtp SRkn SWvt WLov WPGP
- 'Gold Leaf'	CBcs CCCN CTri CTsd EBee ELan EPfP SMad SWvt WFar XSte
- 'Gold Stripe'	SWvt
pulchella misapplied	EHyd LRHS NRHS
pulchella ambig. blue-flowered	GKev
sessiliflora	CExl NBir

– 'Ballyrogan Blue'	EBee GKev WMal
– 'Caerulescens'	CBcs CBod CCCN CCht CExl CMac CSde EGrI EPfP LRHS NBir NGBl SIvy SMad SPer SPtp WFar XSte
'Sunset Strain'	CBod LRHS MHtn WFar

Libocedrus (*Cupressaceae*)

chilensis	see *Austrocedrus chilensis*
decurrens	see *Calocedrus decurrens*
plumosa	CBrP

Libonia see *Justicia*

Ligularia (*Asteraceae*)

aff. ***atkinsonii*** WJC 13663	WCru
'BBQ Banana'	CBod EPfP WWtn
'Bottle Rocket'PBR	CBor NLar SMad
'Britt Marie Crawford'PBR ♀H6	Widely available
clivorum	see *L. dentata*
§ ***dentata***	ECtt NBro SRms
– 'Dark Beauty'	MBNS
– 'Desdemona'	Widely available
– 'Franz Feldweber'	EBee ELon
– 'Midnight Lady'	EHyd ELan EMor GPSL GWyn MHol NLar SBls
– 'Orange Princess'	NPer
– 'Osiris Café Dark'PBR	SCob
– 'Osiris Fantaisie' (v)	CDor CExl EBee ECtt EPfP EWes GBee GWyn MAvo MHol MNrw NLar NSti SPoG WFar WPnP
– 'Othello'	CBod CEme CRos ECtt EHyd EPfP GBee LRHS NGdn NLar NRHS NWad SCob SRms SWvt WCAu
– 'Pandora'	ECtt MHol SMad
– 'Sommergold'	WFar
– 'Twilight'	CBct CBod ECtt MBNS
§ ***fischeri*** B&SWJ 2570	WCru
– B&SWJ 4381	WCru
– B&SWJ 4478	WCru
– B&SWJ 5653	WCru
– B&SWJ 8802	WCru
– var. ***megalorhiza*** 'Cheju Charmer'	ELon WCru
'Garden Confetti'	ECtt
'Gold Torch'	ECtt NLar
§ 'Gregynog Gold' ♀H6	ECha ECtt EHyd GBee GMaP LRHS MRav NBro NLar NRHS
× ***hessei***	EHyd GMaP MMuc WWtn
hodgsonii	EPPr MRav
– B&SWJ 10855	WCru
intermedia B&SWJ 606a	WSHC
japonica	CDor ECha EHyd LEdu NLar WWtn
– B&SWJ 2883	WCru
– 'Rising Sun'	CExl ESwi NLar WCot WCru
'Laternchen'PBR	ECtt NLar SAko
'Little Rocket'PBR	CBct CBod CExl EBee ECtt EPfP MBNS NBro NGdn NLar NRHS SPoG WFar
'Osiris Café Noir'	ECtt MHol NLar WFar
'Osiris Pistache' (v)	EBee ECtt
× ***palmatiloba***	see *L.* × *yoshizoeana* 'Palmatiloba'
pleurocaulis new	GArf
§ ***przewalskii***	Widely available
– SSSE 176	WCot
– 'Dragon Wings'	GBin MAsh MHol NEoE NLar SCob
– 'Dragon's Breath'	ECtt GBin MAsh MHol SCob
sibirica	NLar
– B&SWJ 4383	WCru
– B&SWJ 5841	WCru
– var. ***speciosa***	see *L. fischeri*
smithii	see *Senecio smithii*
speciosa	see *L. fischeri*
stenocephala	EBee EMor MBros NBro NLar WWtn XLum
'Sungold'	CMac CRos EBlo ECtt EHyd LRHS NGdn NRHS
tangutica	see *Sinacalia tangutica*
'The Rocket' ♀H6	Widely available
tussilaginea	see *Farfugium japonicum*
– 'Aureo-maculata'	see *Farfugium japonicum* 'Aureomaculatum'
veitchiana	CBod WWtn
vorobievii	CElw EBee NLar
'Weihenstephan'	EHyd
wilsoniana	EHyd GAbr LRHS MMuc MRav NRHS SEND WFar WWtn
– B&SWJ 14195	WCru
§ × ***yoshizoeana*** 'Palmatiloba'	CRos EHyd EWes LRHS MRav NRHS SPhx WFar WWtn
'Zepter' ♀H6	CBod CRos ECtt EHyd ELan EPfP EShb GBee GQue LRHS MMuc NHol NLar NRHS NWad WCot WWtn

Ligusticum (*Apiaceae*)

hultenii	WCot
lucidum	CDor CMCN EPfP GBin LEdu LPla MBel NSti SMHy SPhx SPtp WBor WCot WPGP
– subsp. ***lucidum***	CSpe
§ ***scoticum***	CBod ELan ELon EShb EWes GBin GLog GPSL GPoy GQue LEdu LPla LRHS MBel MHer NAts SBut SDix SPhx SPtp SRms WFar WHil WJek WPGP
– variegated (v)	LEdu WCot

Ligustrum ✿ (*Oleaceae*)

B&L 12261	WPGP
chenaultii	see *L. compactum*
§ ***compactum***	NLar
§ ***delavayanum***	CBod ELan ERom EShb GKev MNHC NLar SCob SGsty SWeb WPGP
– B&L 12083	CExl
ibota	EBtc
– MUSLI ('Muster'PBR) (v)	LRHS NLar SPoG WCot
ionandrum	see *L. delavayanum*
japonicum	CLnd EBar EHyd LMaj LSRN SCob SEND SGol SGsty SPer SWeb
– B&SWJ 14604	WCru
– 'Coriaceum'	see *L. japonicum* 'Rotundifolium'
– GREEN CENTURY ('Melgreen'PBR)	LRHS WMat
– 'Korea Dwarf'	NLar
§ – 'Rotundifolium'	CBcs CBod CDoC CExl CKel EBee EHyd ELan EPfP GBin LPar LRHS MAsh MRav NLar SPer SPoG SPtp WCFE WCot WFar
§ – 'Silver Star' (v)	NLar SEND SGol
§ – 'Texanum'	CCVT CDoC EPfP LMaj LPar LRHS NLar SArc SGsty SavN WCFE
– 'Texanum Argenteum'	see *L. japonicum* 'Silver Star'
– 'Variegatum' (v)	LMaj LPar SGol SWeb
lucidum ♀H5	CBcs CCVT CSBt CSde CTri ELan IDee LRHS MRav NWea SArc SCob SEND SGol SPer SWvt WFar
– Guiz 296	CExl
– 'Curly Wurly'	EHyd LRHS NRHS
– 'Excelsum Superbum' (v) ♀H5	CCVT CLnd CMac EBar EHyd ELan EPfP LMaj LRHS LSRN MGos SGol SGsty SPoG SWeb WCot
– 'Golden Wax'	CJun MRav

- 'Tricolor' (v) ♀H5	EHyd ELan EPfP LRHS MAsh MGos NLar SPer SWvt
obtusifolium	MMuc NLar
var. ***regelianum***	
ovalifolium	Widely available
§ - 'Argenteum' (v)	CBcs CBod CCVT CMac CTri ELan EShb GArf LRHS MMuc MRav SCob SEND SGol SLim SPer SPoG SWvt WFar
- 'Aureomarginatum'	see *L. ovalifolium* 'Aureum'
§ - 'Aureum' (v) ♀H5	Widely available
- 'Lemon and Lime' (v)	CBod CDoC CEme ELan LSRN MAsh MThu SCoo SRms SWvt WCot
- 'Variegatum'	see *L. ovalifolium* 'Argenteum'
- 'Vicaryi'	ELan EPfP GBin LRHS MGos NWad SDix SGol WFar
quihoui	CKel CTri EBee EHyd ELan EPfP IDee LRHS MBlu NLar SDix SEND SLon SPer SPoG
sinense	CMCN MRav
- 'Multiflorum'	WFar
- var. ***myrianthum***	SPtp
- 'Sunshine'	CRos EHyd LRHS NRHS SPoG
- 'Variegatum' (v)	MRav SPer
- 'Wimbei'	WLov
strongylophyllum	CExl
texanum	see *L. japonicum* 'Texanum'
tschonoskii	MBlu NLar
undulatum 'Lemon Lime and Clippers'	EHyd EShb LRHS NLar NRHS SDix SGBe SPoG WPnP
vulgare	CArg CCVT CHab CMac CTri ELan EPfP LBuc LPar MMuc MNic MSwo NWea SCob SEND SEWo SGsty SWvt WMat WMou WSFF WTSh
- 'Lodense'	EBtc

Lilium ✿ (*Liliaceae*)

'Abbeville's Pride' (Ia/b)	GKev SDeJ
'Acapulco' (VII-/d)	SDeJ
§ 'Acoustic' (Colour Carpet Series) (VIIa/b-c)	EHyd
'Adonis' (Ic/d)	GEdr
African Queen Group (VI-/a) ♀H6	ERCP GKev LCro LHWs LOPS SCoo SDir SRms
- 'African Queen' (VIb-c/a)	SDeJ
African Queen Group × ***sulphureum*** (VI) **new**	EGrI MBros
'After Eight' (VIIa/b) **new**	LHWs
'Agostini' (VIIIa/b) **new**	LHWs
akkusianum (IXc/a) **new**	GKev
'Altari' (VIIIa-b/b)	SDeJ
'Amarossi' (VIIIa-b/b-c) **new**	LHWs
'Anastasia' (VIIIb-c/b-d)	EGrI GKev LCro LHWs LOPS SDeJ SDir
'Annemarie's Dream' (Ia/c)	GKev SDeJ SDir
'Apogee'^{PBR} (VIIa/b) **new**	LHWs
APOLLO (Ia/b)	see *L.* 'Blizzard'
'Apricot Fudge'^{PBR} (VIIIa/b)	GKev IPot SDir
'Arabian Knight' (IIc/d)	CBcs ERCP GKev LHWs SDeJ SDir WFar
'Arena' (VIIa/b)	SCoo
Asiatic hybrids (I)	EHyd LRHS MBros
'Atacama'^{PBR} (VIIIa/b) **new**	LHWs
auratum (IXb/c)	GKev LHWs
- 'Gold Band'	see *L. auratum* var. *platyphyllum*
§ - var. ***platyphyllum*** (IXb/c)	SDeJ
- - B&SWJ 4824	WCru
- - B&SWJ 5041	WCru
- var. ***virginale*** (IXb/c)	SDeJ
'Baferrari' (VIIa/b)	GKev SDeJ
'Bamako' (VIIa-b/b)	SDeJ
'Bandiëra' (VIIa/b-d) **new**	LHWs
'Barbara North' (Ic/d)	GEdr
'Barbaresco' (VIIa-b/b)	SCoo
'Beijing Moon' (VIb-c/a)	GKev LHWs SDeJ SDir
'Belém' (Ia/b-c) **new**	CBod LRHS
'Belgrado'^{PBR} (VIIa/b-c)	SDeJ
'Belladonna'^{PBR} (VIIIb-a/b)	SDeJ
'Belle Epoque' (VIIb/b-c)	SDeJ
'Bergamo' (VIIb/b)	SCoo SDeJ
'Beverly Dreams' (VIIIa/a)	GKev IPot
'Beverly Hills'^{PBR} (VIIIa-b/b)	SDeJ
'Black Beauty' (VIIIb-c/d)	CCBP EGrI GBin GKev IPot LCro LHWs LOPS NHpl SDeJ SDir
§ 'Blizzard' (Ia/b)	SCob SDeJ
'Blushing Joy' (Ia/b)	LRHS
'Boogie Woogie' (VIIIa-b/b)	SDeJ
'Bracelet' (VIIIa-b/b)	SDeJ
'Brasil'^{PBR} (Ia/b)	GKev
BRASILIA ('Zora') (VIIa/b-c)	SDeJ SDir
'Bright Joy' (Ia/c)	LRHS
BRIGHT PIXIE ('Ceb Bright') (Ia/b)	SDeJ
'Broken Heart' (VIIb-a/c)	SDeJ
bulbiferum (IXa/b)	GKev
'Buriano'^{PBR} (VIII a/b) **new**	LHWs
'Butter Pixie'^{PBR} (Ia/b)	SCob SDeJ
'Cali'^{PBR} (VIII a-b/a) **new**	LHWs
§ ***canadense*** (IXc/a)	GEdr GKev WCot
- var. ***flavum***	see *L. canadense*
'Cancun' (Ia/b-c)	SDeJ
candidum (IXb/a)	CAvo CBcs CTri ECha ELan EPot ERCP GKev ILea LCro LHWs LOPS LSun NRog SCob SDeJ SDir SRms WSpi
'Candy Blossom' (Ia/b)	SDeJ
'Carbonero' (VIIIa-b/b) **new**	LHWs
'Casa Blanca' (VIIb/b-c) ♀H6	CAvo CBro GKev LCro LHWs LOPS NBir SCoo SDeJ SDir
'Cavoli' (Ia-b/b) **new**	GKev
'Cecil' (VIIIa/b)	SDeJ
cernuum (IXc/d)	SDeJ
* - 'Album'	SDeJ
'Child in Time' (VIIIa-b/b) **new**	LHWs
'Chill Out' (VIIa/b)	LCro LOPS
§ 'Chocolate Canary' (Ic/b-c)	SDeJ
'Chocolate Event' (Ib-c/c-b) **new**	LHWs
'Christopher'^{PBR} (VIIa/b) **new**	LHWs
Citronella Group (Ic/d)	NHpl SDeJ
'Classic Joy' (Ia/b)	LRHS
'Claude Shride' (IIc/d)	CAvo CBcs EPot ERCP GKev ILea IPot LHWs LRHS NHpl SDeJ WCot WPnP
'Clearwater'^{PBR} (VIIa/b) **new**	LHWs
'Cocktail Twins' (Ia/b)	SDeJ
'Cogoleto'^{PBR} (VIIIa-b/b)	SDir
'Coldplay' (Colour Carpet Series) (VIIa-b/b-c)	EHyd LBuc LRHS NRHS
'Collesium' (VIIa/b) **new**	LHWs
columbianum (IXc/d) B&SWJ 9564	WCru
'Con Amore' (VIIb/b)	SCoo
'Conca d'Or'^{PBR} (VIIIb/b)	LHWs SDeJ
concolor (IXa/c)	GKev
'Corsage' (Ib/b-c)	LHWs
'Creation' (VIa/b)	SDeJ
'Crimson Pixie' (Ia/b)	LCro LOPS NRHS SDeJ
'Curitiba' (Ia/b) **new**	LHWs
'Curly Sue' (VIIa-b/b)	GKev LCro LOPS MHol

	× ***dalhansonii*** (IIc/d)	LRHS MBros SDeJ
§	- Backhouse Group (IIc/d)	WFar
	- 'Guinea Gold' (II)	GKev LHWs SDir
	- 'Mrs R.O. Backhouse' (IIc/d)	GEdr SDeJ
	- 'Sutton Court' (IIc/c)	GEdr
	- Terrace City Group (IIc/d)	GKev LHWs SDeJ
	'Dark Romance' (Romance Series) (VIIb/b)	CRos EHyd LHWs LRHS NRHS
§	***dauricum*** (IXa/b)	GKev
	- f. ***rebunense*** (IXa/b)	CBor
	davidii (IXc/d)	CExl GKev NHpl SDeJ WCru
§	- var. ***willmottiae*** (IXc/d)	WCru
	DAZZLER ('Maru') (Colour Carpet Series) (VIIa/b)	LBuc LRHS
	'Debby' (VIIIa-b/b-c)	GKev LHWs SDeJ
	'Delicate Joy' (Ia/b)	LHWs LRHS
	'Dimension' (Ia/b-c)	LCro LOPS
	'Disco' (Ia)	SDeJ
	distichum (IXb-c/d) B&SWJ 4465	WCru
	- B&SWJ 794	WCru
	'Dizzy' (VIIa-b/b-c)	CBod SDeJ
	'Double Sensation' (Ia/b) (d) **new**	LHWs
	duchartrei (IXc/d)	CExl GEdr GKev WCru
	'Eastern Morn' (VIIIb-c/a) **new**	LHWs
	'Easy Dance' (Ia/b) **new**	LHWs
	'Easy Waltz' (Ia/b) **new**	GKev
	'Electric Yellow'	see *L.* 'Yellow Electric'
	'Elgrado' (Ia/b)	SDeJ
	'Elodie'PBR (Ia/b)	IPot LHWs SDeJ SDir
	'Elusive' (VIIIb/b-d)	GKev LHWs MNrw SDeJ SDir
	'Emani'PBR (VIIa/b) **new**	LHWs
	'Enchantment' (Ia/b)	SDeJ
	'Entertainer' (VIIa/b) **new**	LRHS
	'Eros' (Ic/d)	GEdr
	'Euskadi' (VIIa/b) **new**	LHWs
	'Expression' (VII)	SDeJ
	'Eyeliner'PBR (VIIIa/b)	LHWs
	'Fairy Morning' (IIc/c)	GKev LHWs WFar
	'Fangio' (VIIIa/b)	EGrI
	FANTASIATIC LIPGLOSS (mixed) (I) **new**	MHol
	fargesii (IXc/d)	CExl
	'Fata Morgana' (Ia/b) ♀H6	SCoo SDeJ SDir
	'Fields of Gold' (VIIIb/b) **new**	LHWs
	'Fire King' (Ib/d)	SCoo SDeJ SRms
	'Firebolt' (VIIa/b-c) **new**	LHWs
	'Fopapo' (Ia-b/c)	SDeJ
	'Forever Susan' (Ia/b)	GKev LHWs SDeJ
	'Formia' (VIII a-b/b) **new**	LHWs
	formosanum (IXb/a)	EBee MHol
	- short, from high altitude RWJ 10005 (IXb/a)	WCru
	- var. ***formosanum*** (IXb/a)	LRHS
	- - B&SWJ 1589	WCru
	- var. ***pricei*** (IXb/a)	CEme CKel CRos EBee EBou EDAr EHyd ELan GBin GEdr GKev LEdu LRHS MHer MTin NRHS SCoo SRms WIce
*	- - f. ***album***	SBls
	- - 'Snow Queen' (Vb/a)	EShb SDeJ
	'Foxtrot' (Ia/b)	CBod GKev LRHS SDeJ
	'Fredo'PBR (VIII a/a) **new**	LHWs
	'Friso' (VIIIb/b)	GKev LHWs SDeJ
	'Frosty Wonder' (VIIIa/b-a) **new**	LHWs
	'Fusion' (IV b-c)	LHWs MHol NHpl SDir WCot
	'Garden Party' (VIIb/b) ♀H6	GKev SDeJ SDir
	'Gaybird' (IIc/c)	GKev LHWs
	'Gironde' (Ia/b)	SDeJ
	'Gizmo'PBR (VIIIb-a/b) **new**	LHWs
	'Gold Class' (VIIIb-a/b-c)	GKev LHWs SDeJ
	'Golden Matrix' (Ia/b)	CBod
	'Golden Romance' (Romance Series) (VIIa/b)	LHWs
	Golden Splendor Group (VIb-c/a) ♀H6	GKev LHWs SCoo SDeJ SDir
	'Golden Stone' (VIIIa-b/b)	SDeJ
	'Gran Tourismo' (VIIa/b-c) **new**	GKev
	'Grand Cru' (Ia/b)	SDeJ
	'Hannah North' (Ic/d)	GEdr
	hansonii (IXb-c/d)	CBod CWCL EBee GBin GKev LHWs NHpl SDeJ WPnP
	- B&SWJ 4309	WCru
	- B&SWJ 8506	WCru
	- B&SWJ 8528	WCru
	henryi (IXc/d) ♀H6	CAvo EBee GKev LHWs SDeJ SDir WCru
	'Hit Parade' (VIa-b/b)	SDeJ
	'Honeymoon' (VIIIa-b/b)	EGrI SDeJ
	'Hotel California' (VIIIb/b) **new**	LHWs
	humboldtii (IXc/d)	EBee
	'Ice Breaker' (VIIa/a) **new**	LHWs
	'Ice Pixie' (Ia/b)	SDeJ
	'Inuvik' (Ia/b)	SDeJ
	'Island Joy' (Ia/b-c)	LRHS
	'Ivory Pixie' (Ia/b)	SDeJ
	japonicum (IXb/a)	GKev
	'João Pessoa' (Ia/b-c)	SDeJ
	'Jo's Choice' (VIa-b/a)	SDeJ
	'Josephine' (VIIa/b)	SDeJ SDir
	'Joy'	see *L.* 'Le Rêve'
	'Kamsberg'PBR (VIIIa/b) **new**	LHWs
	'Karen North' (Ic/d)	GEdr
§	***kelleyanum*** (IXc/d)	EBee
	'King Pete' (Ib/b-c)	SDeJ
	'Kingdom'PBR (VIIIa/b-c)	SDeJ
	'Kushi Maya'PBR (VIIIc/b-c)	GKev LHWs SDeJ SDir
	'Lady Alice' ambig. (VI-/d)	GKev LHWs SDeJ SDir
	'Lake Tulare' (IVc/c-d)	GEdr
§	***lancifolium*** (IXc/d)	EPot GBin LHWs XAbr XLum
	- B&SWJ 4352	WCru
	- var. ***flaviflorum*** (IXc/d)	GKev SDeJ WFar
	- 'Flore Pleno' (IXc/d)	EHyd EPPr GKev GQue LHWs NBir SDeJ WCot WCru WHil XLum
	- var. ***fortunei*** (IXc/d)	EGrI EPPr SDix
	- - B&SWJ 539	WCru
	- pink-flowered	SDeJ
	- 'Splendens' (IXc/d)	GKev NBid SDeJ SDir WCot
	'Landini'PBR (Ia/b)	SDeJ
	'Lankon' (VIIIc/a)	LHWs
	lankongense (IXc/d)	CBod CBor CWCL EBee EPot GEdr GGGa GKev LHWs MHol SDir WCru
	- BWJ 7554	WCru
	- BWJ 7691	WCru
	'Late Morning' (VIIIb-c)	SDeJ
	'Latvia' (Ia/b)	SDeJ
	'Lazy Lady'	see *L.* 'Chocolate Canary'
§	'Le Rêve' (VIIa-b/b)	SDeJ
	ledebourii (IXc/d)	GKev
	leichtlinii (IXc/d)	CAvo CCBP EPot GBin NHpl SDeJ
	'Lemon Pixie' (Ia/b)	NRHS SCob
	'Leslie Woodriff' (VIIIb-c/d)	GKev LHWs
	leucanthum var. ***centifolium*** (IXb-c/a)	WCru

	- - BWJ 8130	WCru
	'Levi'^{PBR} (Ia/c)	SDeJ
	lijiangense (IXc/d)	GEdr GKev
	LILY ALLEN	see *L.*'Popstar'
I	'Linda' (Ia/b)	SDeJ
	'Little John' (VIIa-b/b)	SDeJ
	'Little Kiss' (Ia/d)	SDeJ
	LOLLYPOP ('Holebibi') (Ia/b)	SCoo SDeJ
	'Londrina' (Ia/b)	SDeJ
	longiflorum (IXb/a)	SCoo SDir XLum
	- B&SWJ 11376	WCru
	- 'Foliis Variegatis' (Vb/a/v)	MAvo
	- 'Rose' (V)	SDeJ
	- 'White Heaven'^{PBR} (Vb/a)	LCro LHWs LOPS
	'Lotus Beauty' (VIIa/c) **new**	LHWs
	'Lotus Breeze' (VIIb/c) **new**	LHWs
	'Lotus Dream' (VIIa/c) **new**	LHWs
	'Lotus Elegance' (VIIb/c) **new**	LHWs
	'Lotus Queen' (VIIa/c) **new**	LHWs
	'Lotus Wonder' (VIIb-c/c) **new**	LHWs
	'Love Story' (VIIa-b/b) **new**	LRHS
	'Lovely Girl' (VII-/b)	SDeJ
	'Luzia' (VIIa-b/c)	EHyd LRHS NRHS
	mackliniae (IXc/a) ♀H5	EBee EWes GEdr GGGa GKev ITim NBir WHal WPGP WTyc
	- PAB 9327	LEdu WPGP
	- PAB 9668	LEdu WPGP
	- from Nagaland, India	GGGa
	- deep pink-flowered	GGGa
	- 'Naga Pink' (IXc/a) **new**	GKev
	'Magic Star'^{PBR} (VIIa-b/b)	SDeJ
	'Magny Cours' (VIIa/b)	LRHS
	'Manitoba Morning' (IIc/c)	CBod GKev ILea LHWs LRHS MBros NHpl SDeJ SDir
	'Mansfield'^{PBR} (VIIa-b/b) **new**	LHWs
	'Mapira' (VIIIb/b)	GKev SDeJ
	'Marco Polo' ambig.	SCoo SDeJ
	'Marie North' (Ic/d)	GEdr
	'Maroon King' (IIc/d)	WFar
	martagon (IXc/d) ♀H6	CBro CTtf CWCL ECha EMor EPot ERCP GKev GPoy LCro LHWs LOPS NBir NChi NGrd NHpl SDeJ SRms WCAu WPnP WShi WSpi
	- var. ***albiflorum*** (IXc/d)	CTtf LHWs SDeJ
	- var. ***album*** (IXc/d)	CBro CSpe EMor EPot GBin GKev LHWs LRHS MCot NBir NChi NRHS SDeJ SRms WShi
	- var. ***cattaniae*** (IXc/d)	GKev
	- - 'The Moor' (IXb/d)	LHWs
*	- var. ***rubrum***	EGrI MACG
	'Mascara' (Ia-b/b)	GKev
	'Matrix' (Ia-b/b)	SCoo
	medeoloides B&SWJ 4184 (IXc/d)	WCru
	- B&SWJ 4363	WCru
	michiganense (IXc/d)	GKev
	'Miss Feya' (VIIIb/c)	CBod EGrI GKev LHWs MHol MNrw SDeJ SDir
	'Miss France' (VIIb/b-c)	SDeJ
I	'Miss Lily' (VIIIb/b-c)	MNrw SDeJ
	'Miss Lucy'^{PBR} (VIIa-b/b-c)	SDeJ
	MISS RIO	see *L.*'Rio'
	'Mister Cas' (VIIIb/b) **new**	GKev LHWs
	'Mister Job' (VIIIa/c)	LHWs SDeJ
	'Mister Pistache' (VIII b-a) **new**	GKev LHWs
	'Mona Lisa' (VIIb/b-c)	GKev NGdn SCob SDeJ
	monadelphum (IXc/d)	CBor GKev SDeJ

	- pale-flowered	GKev
	'Mont Blanc' (Ia/b-c)	SCob SDeJ
	'Montezuma'^{PBR} (VIIa-b/b)	SDeJ
	'Montreux' (Ia/b-c)	SDeJ
	'Morpho Pink' (VIIIa/b-c) **new**	LHWs
	'Mount Cook' (VIIa/b)	CBod LRHS SDeJ SDir
	'Mountain Joy' (Ia/b)	LHWs LRHS
	'Muscadet' (VIIa-b/b)	CBod GKev LCro LHWs LOPS SDeJ SDir
	'Must See' (Ia/b)	GKev LHWs
	'My Wedding' (VII/b-a/c)	CBod
	'Navona' (Ia/b)	GKev SDeJ
	nepalense (IXc/a)	CBcs CBro CExl CWCL EPot ERCP GKev LCro LOPS MCot SDeJ SDir WCru WPnP WTyc XLum
	- B&SWJ 2985	WCru
	'Netty's Pride' (Ia/b-c)	CAvo GKev SDeJ SDir
	'New Wave' (Ia/b)	SDeJ
	'Night Flyer' (Ib-c/b-c)	GKev LHWs SDeJ
	'Nightrider' (VIIIa/b)	GKev LHWs MBros
	'Nove Cento' (Ia/b)	SDeJ
	'November Rain' (VIIIa/b) **new**	LHWs
	'Nymph'^{PBR} (VIIIa/b-d) **new**	LHWs
	'Orange County' (Ia/b)	SDeJ
	'Orange Electric' (Ia/b)	CBod SDeJ SDir
	'Orange Marmalade' (IIb/c-d)	ERCP GKev LHWs LRHS NHpl SDeJ SDir WPnP
	'Orange Matrix' (Ia/b) **new**	CBod
	'Orange Pixie' (Ia/b)	NRHS SCob SCoo
	'Orange Planet' (VIa/a)	SDeJ
	'Orange Ton' (Ia/b) **new**	GKev
	'Orange Twinkle' (Ib-c/b)	SDeJ
	'Orania'^{PBR} (VIIIb/b)	EGrI SDeJ
	Oriental hybrids (VII)	MACG MBros
*	Oriental Superb Group	NGdn
	oxypetalum var. ***insigne*** (IXb-c/b)	GBin GKev NHpl SDir
	'Pan' (Ic/d)	GEdr
	'Paposo'^{PBR} (VIIIa-b/b) **new**	LHWs
	pardalinum (IXc/d) ♀H6	CWCL EBee ECha GKev SBrt WCot WCru
	- var. ***giganteum*** (IXc/d)	MNrw
	- subsp. ***pardalinum*** (IXc/d)	SDeJ
§	- subsp. ***vollmeri*** (IXc/d)	GKev WCru
§	- subsp. ***wigginsii*** (IXc/d)	GKev WCru
	× ***parkmanii*** 'Rosy Dimple' (VIIa/b)	SDeJ
	parryi (IXb-c/a)	GKev
	'Passion Moon' (VIIb-c/a)	GKev SDeJ SDir
	'Patricia's Pride' (Ia-b/b-c)	GKev SDeJ SDir
	'Peach Butterflies' (Ic/d)	SDeJ
	'Peach Dwarf' (Ia/b-c)	SDeJ
	'Peach Pixie' (Ia/b)	SCob SCoo
	'Pearl Frances' (Ib/b-c) **new**	GKev
	'Pearl Jennifer' (Ib-a/c)	SDeJ
	'Pearl Jessica' (Ib-c/b-c)	SDeJ SDir
	'Pearl Justien' (Ia-b/c)	SDeJ
	'Pearl Loraine' (Ib-c/b-c)	SDeJ SDir
	'Pearl Melanie' (Ib/c)	SDeJ SDir
	'Pearl Sonja' (Ib/b)	SDeJ
	'Pearl Stacey' (Ib-c/c)	GKev SDeJ
	'Pearl White' (Ib/b) **new**	LHWs
	'Peggy North' (Ic/d)	GEdr
	pensylvanicum	see *L. dauricum*
	'Pepard Gold' (IIc/d)	EPot GKev LHWs
	philippinense (IXa-b/a)	SBls SDir WPGP
	'Pieton' (Ia/b-c)	SDeJ
	'Pimento' (VIIa/b)	SDeJ

'Pink Flavour' (Ic/c) SDeJ
'Pink Flight' (Ic/b-c) **new** GKev
'Pink Flush' (Ic/d) **new** LHWs
'Pink Morning' (IIc/c) ERCP GKev LRHS NHpl SDir
Pink Perfection Group (VIb/a) 🏆H6 EGrI ERCP EShb GKev LCro LHWs LOPS SCoo SDeJ SDir
'Pink Pixie'PBR (Ia/b) NRHS SDeJ
'Pink Romance' (Romance Series) (VIIa/b) LHWs
'Pink Zsar' (VIIa/b) LRHS
poilanei misapplied see *L. primulinum*
'Polar Star' (VIIa-b/b) SDeJ
polyphyllum (IXc/d) GKev
pomponium (IXc/d) CBor
§ 'Popstar' (Ia/c) **new** LHWs
'Pretty Woman' (VIIIa-b/b-c) **new** MNrw
§ ***primulinum*** HWJ 681 (IXc/a) WCru
- WWJ 11679 WCru
- aff. var. ***ochraceum*** KWJ 12064 (IXc/a) WCru
'Proud Bride' (VIIa/b) SDeJ
'Prunotto'PBR (Iab/b) SDeJ
§ ***pumilum*** (IXc/d) EPot LHWs MHol SDeJ SDir
'Purple Eye' (Ia-b/b) SDeJ
'Purple Prince' (VIIIa-b/a-b) SDeJ
pyrenaicum (IXc/d) GKev WShi
- subsp. ***carniolicum*** var. ***bosniacum*** (IX) GKev
- - var. ***carniolicum*** (IXc/d) GKev
'Red Carpet' (Ia/b) NBir SCob SDeJ
'Red County' (Ia/c-b) SDeJ
'Red Electric' (Ia/b) SDeJ
'Red Flavour' (Ic/b-c) SDeJ
'Red Hot' (VIIIc-d/b) SDeJ
'Red Life' (Ib-a/c) NHpl
'Red Matrix' (Ia/b-c) **new** CBod
'Red Morning' (VIIIa-b/b) GKev
'Red Twinkle' (Ib-c/b-c) MHol SDeJ
'Red Velvet' (Ic/d) CAvo GKev LHWs SDeJ SDir
regale (IXb/a) 🏆H6 CAvo CBod CBro ECha EGrI ELan EPfP ERCP EShb GKev LCro LHWs LOPS LRHS MCot SCob SDeJ SDir SPer SRms
- 'Album' (IXb/a) CAvo ERCP GKev LCro LHWs LOPS LRHS SCoo SDeJ SDir
'Reinesse' (Ia/b) NRHS SDeJ
§ 'Rio' (VIIb/b-c) SCoo
RIO NEGRO ('Corvara'PBR) (VIIa-b/b-c) SDeJ
'Rising Moon' (VIb/a) **new** GKev
'Robert Griesbach' (VIIIc/b-c) SDir
'Robert Swanson' (VIIIb-c/b) GKev LHWs SDeJ
'Robina' (VIIIa-b/b-c) WCot
'Rose Arch Fox' (IIc/c-d) GKev
ROSELILY AISHA ('DL102085') (VIIa-c/b) **new** LHWs
ROSELILY ANGELA ('DL111421') (VIIa-b/b) **new** LHWs
ROSELILY ANOUSKA ('DL111067') (VIIa/b) **new** LHWs
ROSELILY CAROLINA ('DL044040'PBR) (VIIa-b/b) LHWs SDir
ROSELILY CELINA ('DL041121'PBR) (VIIa-b/b) **new** LHWs
ROSELILY EDITHA ('DL11356') (VIIa-b/b) **new** LHWs
ROSELILY ELENA ('DL04581'PBR) (VIIa-b/b) LHWs MSCN
ROSELILY FELICIA ('DL04881'PBR) (VIIa-b/b) **new** LHWs
ROSELILY ISABELLA ('DL044033'PBR) (VIIa-b/b) LHWs SDir
ROSELILY KENDRA ('DL112077') (VIIa-b/b) **new** LHWs
ROSELILY NATALIA ('DL04544'PBR) (VIIa-b/b) LHWs SDir
ROSELILY ROBERTA ('DL112598') (VIIa-b/b) **new** LHWs
ROSELILY SAMANTHA ('DL112317') (VIIa-b/b) **new** LHWs
'Rosella's Dream' (Ia/b) SDeJ
'Rosemary North' (Ic/d) GEdr
'Rosselini' (VIIIa-b/b) SDeJ
rosthornii (IXc/d) CExl WCru
rubellum (IXb/a) GEdr
sachalinense (IXa/b) GKev
- RBS 0235 EPPr
'Salinas' (VIIa/b) SDeJ
'Salmon Flavour' (Ic/b-c) SDir
'Salmon Star'PBR (VIIa-b/b-c) LHWs
'Salmon Tiger' (Ib-c/b-c) SDeJ
'Salmon Twinkle' (Ib-c/c) SDeJ
'Satisfaction' (VIIIa-b/-) SDeJ
'Scarlet Delight' (VIIb-c/c-d) GKev SDeJ SDir
'Scarlet Morning' (IIc/c) CAvo GKev
'Scheherazade' (VIIIc/d) GKev LHWs SDeJ SDir
'Secret Kiss'PBR (Ia/b) **new** LHWs
'Set Point' (VIIb/b) SDeJ
'Showwinner' (VIIa/b-c) EHyd LRHS NRHS
'Silk Road' (VIIIb-c/b) **new** LHWs
'Slate's Morning' (IIc/c) GKev LHWs WCot
'Smoky Mountain' (VIIIc/d) SDeJ
'Solution' (VIIa-b/b) **new** LHWs
'Souvenir'PBR (VIIa-b/b) SDeJ
'Space Star' (VIIa/b-c) LRHS
'Spark' (Ia-b/b) MHol
'Sparkling Joy' (Ia-b/c) LRHS
'Special News' (VIIa/b) **new** LHWs LRHS
speciosum (IXb-c/d) LHWs
- B&SWJ 4847 WCru
- B&SWJ 4924 WCru
- var. ***album*** (IXb-c/d) LHWs NBir NHpl SDeJ WFar
- 'Ida Uchida' (IX) SDir
- var. ***rubrum*** (IXb-c/d) ECha LCro LOPS NBir SDeJ SRms
§ - - 'Uchida' (IXb-c/d) CExl GKev SDeJ
'Sphinx' (Ia/d) WCot
'Spring Pink' (Ia/-) CAvo GKev SDeJ SDir
'Spring Romance' (Romance Series) (VIIa/b) LHWs
'Stainless Steel' (Ia/b) SDeJ
'Star Gazer' (VIIa/c) CBod CRos EGrI EHyd GKev LCro LHWs LOPS LRHS NRHS SCoo SDeJ SDir

'Star Romance' (Romance Series) (VIIa-b/b)	LHWs
'Starfighter' (VIIa-b/c)	LRHS SDeJ
'Starlight Express' (VIIa-b/b-c) **new**	LRHS
'Sterling Star' (Ia/b)	GKev
'Stonehenge'^{PBR} (VIIIa-b/b) **new**	LHWs
'Stracciatella Event' (Ic-d/b) **new**	LHWs
'Strawberry Event' (Ic-d/b) **new**	LHWs
'Sun Ray' (Ia/b)	SCob
'Sunny Bonaire'^{PBR} (VIIa/b) **new**	LHWs LRHS
'Sunny Grenada' (VIIa-b/b) **new**	LRHS
'Sunny Keys' (VIIa/b) **new**	LHWs
'Sunny Martinique' (VIIa-b/b) **new**	LHWs
'Sunny Morning' (IIc/d)	EPot GKev LHWs
'Sunny Okinawa'^{PBR} (VIIa-b/b) **new**	LHWs
'Sunny Robyn' (VIIa-b/b) **new**	LHWs
'Sunset Boulevard' (VIIIb/b) **new**	LHWs
superbum (IXc/d)	WCru WPGP
'Sweet Desire'^{PBR} (VIIIa-b/b)	LHWs SDir
'Sweet Lord' (Ia/b)	SDeJ
'Sweet Sugar'^{PBR} (VIIIa/b) **new**	LHWs
'Sweet Surrender' (Ib-c/c-d)	GKev LHWs SDeJ SDir
'Sweet Talk'^{PBR} (VIIIa-b/b) **new**	LHWs
'Sweet Zanica'^{PBR} (VIIIa/b) **new**	LHWs
szovitsianum (IXc/d)	GKev
'Tailor Made' (Ia/b)	SDeJ
taliense (IXc/d)	WCru
'Tarragona'^{PBR} (VIIIb/b)	SDeJ
tenuifolium	see *L. pumilum*
'Terrasol' (VIIIa/a) **new**	LHWs
'Terry' (IIc/c-d) **new**	LHWs
Tiger Babies Group (VIIIb-c/c-d)	LHWs SDeJ
'Tigermoon' (VIIa/b)	CBod LHWs
'Tigerwoods' (VIIa/c)	LCro LOPS
tigrinum	see *L. lancifolium*
'Tiny Bee'^{PBR} (Ia-b/b)	LHWs
'Tiny Dino'^{PBR} (Ia-b/b)	LHWs MAsh
'Tiny Double You'^{PBR} (Ia-b/b)	LHWs
'Tiny Epic' (Ia/c) **new**	LHWs
'Tiny Ghost'^{PBR} (Ia-b/b-c)	MAsh SCob
'Tiny Invader'^{PBR} (Ia-b/b-c)	MAsh
'Tiny Nanny'^{PBR} (Ia-b/b-c)	MAsh SCob
'Tiny Nugget' (Ia-b/b) **new**	LHWs
'Tiny Orange Sensation'^{PBR} (Ia/b) **new**	LHWs
'Tiny Padhye'^{PBR} (Ia-b/b-c) **new**	LHWs
'Tiny Parrot' (Ia/b) **new**	LHWs
'Tiny Poems' (Ia-b/b) **new**	LHWs
'Tiny Rocket'^{PBR} (Ia-b/b) **new**	LHWs
'Tiny Skyline'^{PBR} (Ia-b/b)	MAsh
'Tom Pouce' (VIIa/b)	SDeJ
'Top Draw' **new**	LHWs
'Toronto' (Ia-b/b)	SDeJ
'Toscane' (Ia/b-c)	SDeJ
'Tribal Dance' **new**	GKev
TRIUMPHATOR ('Zanlophator'^{PBR}) (VIIIb/a-b)	GKev MCot SDeJ
'True Romance' (Romance Series) (VIIa/b)	LHWs
tsingtauense (IXa/c)	SDeJ
- B&SWJ 519	WCru
- B&SWJ 4263	WCru
- B&SWJ 4698	WCru
'Twyford'^{PBR} (VIIa/b) **new**	LHWs
'Uchida Kanoka'	see *L. speciosum* var. *rubrum* 'Uchida'
'Urandi' (VIIIc/b)	SDeJ
'Val di Sole'^{PBR} (Ia/b)	SDeJ
'Venezuela' (VIIa-b/b-c)	SDeJ SDir
'Visaversa' (VIIIa-b/b)	SDeJ
'Viva la Vida' (VIIIa-b/b) **new**	LHWs
'Vivaldi' (Ia/b)	SDeJ
vollmeri	see *L. pardalinum* subsp. *vollmeri*
wallichianum (IXb/a)	GKev SDeJ XLum
wardii (IXc/d)	CExl EBee
'Whistler' (Ia/c)	SDeJ
'White Paradise' (V-/a)	SCoo
'White Pixels' (Ia/b)	SDeJ
'White Present' (Vb/a)	SDeJ
'White Twinkle' (Ia-b/b)	GKev LHWs SDeJ
wigginsii	see *L. pardalinum* subsp. *wigginsii*
willmottiae	see *L. davidii* var. *willmottiae*
'Wine Electric' (Ia/c)	SDeJ
'World Trade' (Vb-c/a) **new**	LRHS
xanthellum var. ***luteum*** (IXb-c/d)	WCru
'Yang'^{PBR} (VIIIb-c/a) **new**	LHWs
'Yellow Bruse' (Ic/c)	LHWs SDeJ
'Yellow Cocotte' (Ia/c)	SDir
'Yellow County' (Ia/b-c)	SDeJ
§ 'Yellow Electric' (Ia/b-c)	SDeJ
'Yellow Eye' (Ia/b)	SDeJ
'Yellow Space' (VIIIc-b/b-c) **new**	LHWs
'Yeti' (Ia/b)	SDeJ
'Yin'^{PBR} (VIIIb-a) **new**	LHWs
'Zambesi'^{PBR} (VIIIa/b-c) **new**	LHWs
'Zelmira' (VIIIa-b/b) **new**	LHWs

lime see *Citrus* × *aurantiifolia*

lime, djeruk see *Citrus amblycarpa*

lime, Philippine see *Citrus* × *microcarpa*

limequat see *Citrus* × *floridana*

Limnanthes (*Limnanthaceae*)

douglasii ^{H5}	LCro LOPS MNHC MPri NBir
- subsp. ***nivea***	SPhx
- subsp. ***rosea***	CSpe

Limnobium (*Hydrocharitaceae*)

spongia	LLWG

Limonium (*Plumbaginaceae*)

bellidifolium	CFis CFoA CMea EBou EDAr SLee SWvt WHoo
binervosum	NAts
'Blauer Diamant'	EWoo
cosyrense	CMea MHer
gmelinii	SPlb

* - subsp. ***hungaricum***	SBut XLum
latifolium	see *L. platyphyllum*
§ ***platyphyllum***	CBod CMea EPfP EWoo GJos GMaP LRHS LShi LSun MBel MHer MHol MMuc NFav SAng SCob SEdd SGbt SPer SRms SSut WCAu WCot XSen
- 'Blue Cloud'	SRms
- 'Robert Butler'	CBod ECtt GPSL LRHS MRav WCot
- 'Violetta'	CBod CTri ECtt EHyd ELan EPfP GBin LRHS MBel MPie NRHS SEdd SPer SPoG WHoo
'Salt Lake'	LRHS
§ ***sinuatum***	SVic
tataricum	see *Goniolimon tataricum*
vulgare	SGBe XSen

Linaria (*Plantaginaceae*)

aeruginea	CMea SBut
- 'Lindeza Violet'	CSpe
- 'Neon Lights'	CSpe EDAr SPoG WFar
- subsp. ***nevadensis*** 'Gemstones'	SGro
alpina	CSpe LShi NRya NSla SRms WFar
- red-flowered **new**	WFar
anticaria 'Antique Silver'	CExl ECha MMrt MRav
cymbalaria	see *Cymbalaria muralis*
§ ***dalmatica***	CBod EPPr MMuc MPie NBid NGBl NSti SPhx WCot WFar
dalmatica × purpurea	WCot
'Dial Park'	CSpe ECha ECtt LSou MHol SPad WBrk WCot WMal WTor
× ***dominii*** 'Carnforth'	LPla SBut
'Florence Lily Sophia Brown'	WCot WFar
genistifolia	WCot
- W&B BGB-6	WCot WFar
- subsp. ***dalmatica***	see *L. dalmatica*
hepaticifolia	see *Cymbalaria hepaticifolia*
'Lemon Cream'	WCot
* ***lobata alba***	SPlb
* 'Lucy's Pink'	ECha
maroccana Fairy Bouquet Group ♀H6	LCro LOPS
origanifolia	see *Chaenorhinum origanifolium*
pallida	see *Cymbalaria pallida*
'Peachy'	CDor CSpe ECha ECtt GBin LPla LSou MHol SBut SEdd SMHy SPad SPoG WBrk WCot WFar
'Phillant Ruby'	WMal
pilosa	see *Cymbalaria pilosa*
'Pink Kisses'	ECha ECtt LSou MHol MPie MSCN SPad SPoG WBrk WCot WFar WMal
purpurea	CBod CDor CTri EBee EGrI ELan EPfP MBow MHer MNHC NBro NPer NPol SEND SPhx SRms WCot WFar WSFF
- 'Alba'	see *L. purpurea* 'Springside White'
- 'Brown's White Strain'	EPPr WCot
- 'Canon Went'	Widely available
- 'Freefolk Piccolo'	SHar
- pink-flowered	LEdu
- 'Poached Egg'	CMea LEdu WGoo WMal
- 'Radcliffe Innocence'	see *L. purpurea* 'Springside White'
§ - 'Springside White'	CBod CDor CSpe GJos LRHS NBir NGdn SBut SGro SPhx WFar
repens	WCot WHer
× ***sepium***	WCot
triornithophora	SPlb WWFP
- 'Rosea'	CSpe
tristis	LShi
vulgaris	CHab EBou EPfP GQue MBow MHer MMuc MNHC NAts NGrd NMir SRms WHer WShi WWild
- f. ***peloria***	EPPr WAbe

Lindelofia (*Boraginaceae*)

anchusoides (Lindl.) Lehm.	NBid SBrt

Lindera (*Lauraceae*)

aggregata	WPGP
angustifolia	NLar
- FMWJ 13156	WCru
assamica B&SWJ 13984	WCru
benzoin	CBcs CMCN EPfP LRHS MBlu NLar
erythrocarpa B&SWJ 6271	WCru
- B&SWJ 8730	WCru
metcalfiana var. ***dictyophylla*** KWJ 12312	WCru
neesiana B&SWJ 13984	WCru
obtusiloba ♀H5	MBlu WLov WPGP
- B&SWJ 8723	WCru
- B&SWJ 11054	WCru
- B&SWJ 12555 from Korea	WCru
praecox	NLar
- B&SWJ 10802	WCru
- B&SWJ 10953 from north Japan	WCru
- B&SWJ 11125 from south Japan	WCru
reflexa	NLar
sericea B&SWJ 11123	WCru
- B&SWJ 11141	WCru
- var. ***lancea***	NLar
- - B&SWJ 11071	WCru
- - B&SWJ 11118	WCru
tonkinensis FMWJ 13123	WCru
triloba B&SWJ 5570	WCru
- B&SWJ 11121	WCru
- B&SWJ 11466	WCru
umbellata B&SWJ 10881	WCru
- var. ***membranacea*** B&SWJ 10837	WCru

Lindernia (*Linderniaceae*)

grandiflora	CBod LLWG SLee WTor

Linnaea (*Caprifoliaceae*)

borealis	CExl EPot GRum NSla WAbe
- subsp. ***americana***	NWad

Linum (*Linaceae*)

alpinum	SBut
arboreum ♀H4	GKev WThu
austriacum	SPhx WThu
capitatum	EPot
flavum	XSen
- 'Compactum'	CBor CFis CMea EBou GAbr SBls SRms
'Gemmell's Hybrid' ♀H4	EWes WAbe WThu
grandiflorum ♀H4	LCro LOPS SVic
- 'Bright Eyes'	CSpe
- 'Rubrum'	CSpe
hypericifolium	LPla SPhx
lewisii	SBls
narbonense	CKel CSpe SPhx
- 'Heavenly Blue'	LSun
§ ***perenne***	CBod EBee EBou ECha ELan ENfk EPfP GKev MHer MNHC SPer SPhx SPoG SVic WJek XAbr
- 'Album'	EBee ECha ELan EPfP SBut

	- subsp. ***alpinum***	EWTr
§	- 'Blau Saphir'	MBel NHol SBut
	- BLUE SAPPHIRE	see *L. perenne* 'Blau Saphir'
I	- 'Nanum'	NSla
	- 'Nanum Sapphire'	see *L. perenne* 'Blau Saphir'
	rubrum	SPhx SVic
	sibiricum	see *L. perenne*
	suffruticosum	EPot
	subsp. ***salsoloides*** 'Nanum'	
	uninerve	WAbe
	usitatissimum	SVic

Liparis (*Orchidaceae*)

loeselii **new**	NLAp

Lippia (*Verbenaceae*)

sp.	SWvt
canescens	see *Phyla nodiflora* var. *canescens*
chamaedrifolia	see *Glandularia peruviana*
citriodora	see *Aloysia citrodora*
dulcis	ENfk MNHC SRms WFar WJek
nodiflora	see *Phyla nodiflora*
repens	see *Phyla nodiflora*

Liquidambar ✿ (*Hamamelidaceae*)

	acalycina	CBcs ELan EPfP NOra SCoo SGol SLim SSta WHwl WLov WMat WPGP
	- 'Burgundy Flush' ♀^{H5}	CJun NLar SSta
	- 'Spinners'	CBcs CRos EHyd ELan EPfP LMil LRHS WPGP
	formosana	CMCN CMac CWit SGol SSta WPGP
	- 'Afterglow'	CJun MBlu NLar
	- 'Ellen'	CJun NLar
	- Monticola Group	CJun SLim SSta
	orientalis	CJun CLnd CMCN EPfP IDee SSta WPGP
	poilanei B&SWJ 11756	WCru
	styraciflua	Widely available
	- 'Andrew Hewson'	CJun CLnd CRos EBee EHyd EPfP LRHS MBlu NRHS SSta
	- 'Anja'	CJun MBlu SSta
	- 'Anneke'	CJun SSta
	- 'Aurea'	see *L. styraciflua* 'Variegata' Overeynder
	- 'Aurea Variegata'	see *L. styraciflua* 'Variegata' Overeynder
	- 'Aurora'	CJun
	- 'Burgundy'	CJun MBlu SSta
I	- 'Corky'	LRHS MTrO SSta WMat
	- 'Emerald Sentinel'	CJun SSta
	- 'Festeri'	CEnd SSta
	- 'Festival'	CLnd MBlu SGol
	- 'Frosty' (v)	CJun SSta
	- 'Globe'	see *L. styraciflua* 'Gum Ball'
	- 'Golden Sun'^PBR	CBcs LSRN NLar
	- 'Golden Treasure' (v)	CLnd CMCN LPar LSRN MGos SGol SSta
	- 'Granary Sunset'	SSta
§	- 'Gum Ball'	CCVT CEnd CMCN EBee EPfP ERom EWes LPar LRHS NLar NOra SGsty SLim SPoG SSta SWvt WLov
	- 'Jennifer Carol'	SSta
	- 'Kia'	CEnd CJun
	- 'Lane Roberts' ♀^{H6}	Widely available
	- 'Lynn'	SSta
	- 'Manon' (v)	CJun
	- 'Midwest Sunset'	CJun MBlu NLar
	- 'Moonbeam' (v)	CJun SLim SSta
	- 'Moraine'	CJun
	- 'Naree'	SSta WHwl
	- 'Nina'	SSta
	- 'Oconee'	CEnd SSta WHwl
	- 'Paarl' (v)	CLnd
	- 'Palo Alto' ♀^{H6}	CEnd EBee EPfP EWTr LPar MBlu MTrO SCoo SLim SSta WHwl WLov WMat WMou WPGP
	- 'Parasol'	CEnd CJun CLnd SSta
	- 'Pasquali Fastigiata'	CRos ELan LRHS
	- 'Pendula'	CJun MBlu SSta WMou
	- 'Penwood' ♀^{H6}	CJun NLar SSta WLov
	- 'Red Sunset'	SSta
	- 'Rotundiloba'	CJun CMCN EPfP MBlu NLar SGsty WLov WPGP
	- 'Savill Torch'	CJun SSta
	- 'Schock's Gold'	CJun NLar SSta
§	- 'Silver King' (v)	CJun CLnd CMCN CMac CWit LPar LRHS MGos NLar NOrn SCoo SGol SLim SPer SSta
	- 'Simone'	SSta
	- 'Slender Silhouette' ♀^{H6}	Widely available
	- 'Stared'	CEnd CJun CLnd EBee EPfP MBlu MGos MTrO NOra NOrn SCoo SLim SSta WLov WMat
	- 'Teresa'	EBee LRHS
	- 'Thea'	CJun CRos EBee EHyd ELan EPfP LMil LRHS MBlu MTrO NRHS SSta
	- 'Variegata' misapplied	see *L. styraciflua* 'Silver King'
§	- 'Variegata' Overeynder (v)	CJun CMac EBee ELan LPar LRHS SLim SSta
	- 'White Star' (v)	CJun
	- 'Wisley King' **new**	LRHS WPGP
	- 'Woorby Rose'	CJun
	- 'Worplesdon' ♀^{H6}	Widely available

Liriodendron (*Magnoliaceae*)

chinense ♀^{H6}	CLnd CMCN EBee EPfP MBlu WPGP
× ***sinoamericanum*** 'Chapel Hill'	MBlu NLar
- 'Doc Deforce's Delight'	LRHS MBlu NLar
tulipifera ♀^{H6}	Widely available
- 'Aureomarginatum' (v) ♀^{H6}	CBcs CCVT CEme CEnd CMCN CMac EBee ELan EPfP EWTr IPap LMaj LPar MAsh MBlu MGos MSwo MTrO NOrn NWea SGol SMad SPer SPoG SSta WMat
- 'Fastigiatum'	CEnd CLnd CMCN EBee ELan EPfP LMaj MAsh MBlu MGos MTrO NLar NOrn SGol SGsty SPer
- 'Glen Gold'	CEnd MBlu NLar
- 'Purgatory'	MBlu
- 'Roodhaan'	MBlu NLar
- 'Rotundiloba'	MBlu
- 'Snow Bird' (v)	EBee MAsh SPoG WMat

Liriope ✿ (*Asparagaceae*)

	'Big Blue'	see *L. muscari* 'Big Blue'
	exiliflora 'Ariaka-janshige' (v)	EHyd NRHS
	- SILVERY SUNPROOF misapplied	see *L. spicata* 'Gin-ryu', *L. muscari* 'Variegata'
	graminifolia misapplied	see *L. muscari*
	hyacinthifolia	see *Reineckea carnea*
	'Majestic'	SMrm WHoo
	minor	CMac
§	***muscari*** ♀^{H5}	Widely available
	- 'Alba'	see *L. muscari* 'Monroe White'
	- AMETHYST ('Liptp')	CBod CDor NRHS WNPC
§	- 'Big Blue'	Widely available
	- 'Big Pink'	CBod

- 'Christmas Tree'	WHoo
- 'Gold-banded' (v)	CBct EHyd EPfP GWyn LCro LOPS LRHS SBea SCob SMad WFar
- 'Goldfinger'	CExl SMad
- 'Ingwersen'	CExl CKno EBee EPPr EPfP NRHS SCob XLum
- ISABELLA ('Lirf')	EBee EPPr
- 'John Burch' (v)	CBct CExl CMac SCob WGob WSMil
- 'Kindi Pink'	ELan
- 'Lilac Wonder'	EHyd EMor EPPr EPfP GBin LRHS
- 'Moneymaker'	CDor EPPr EPfP GKev LCro LOPS MACG MNrw SCob SCoo SPoG
§ - 'Monroe White'	CBcs CBct CBod CExl CMac ELan EPfP EShb EWoo LCro LOPS MACG MBel MCot MRav NBid NLar SBea SCob SMad SPer SWvt
- 'Okina' (v)	CBod CBro CPla EBee LCro LOPS MBNS MBel MHol MNrw NGBl NLar NSti SEdd SMad SPoG WCot WMal
- 'Pee Dee Ingot'	SPoG
- 'Royal Purple'	CBct CDor EBee ECtt EHyd EPfP LCro LOPS LRHS MAsh NLar NRHS SCob SPer WHoo
- 'Silver Ribbon'	CBro MGos WSMil
- 'Super Blue'	NLar
§ - 'Variegata' (v)	CExl CRos EBee EHyd ELan EWes LCro LOPS LRHS NBir NRHS SCob SCoo SPer SPoG SWvt
- 'Webster Wideleaf'	EBee WCot
platyphylla	see *L. muscari*
'Samantha'	ECha
spicata	CBod EBee EWoo WFar XLum
- 'Alba'	MRav
§ - 'Gin-ryu' (v)	CBct CExl ELan EPfP EShb LPot MAvo MCot MRav NSti SCob SPer WBrk XLum
- 'Silver Dragon'	see *L. spicata* 'Gin-ryu'

Litchi (*Sapindaceae*)

chinensis	CCCN
- 'Mauritius' (F) **new**	SVic

Lithocarpus ✿ (*Fagaceae*)

densiflorus	CMCN
edulis	CExl SArc
fenestratus NJM 13.074	WPGP
§ ***glaber***	SEND

Lithodora (*Boraginaceae*)

diffusa 'Alba'	CBod CWCL GJos SPoG
- 'Compacta'	CSma WAbe
- 'Grace Ward' ♀H5	CBod ECtt ELan EPfP GArf GJos LRHS NRHS SEdd SGbt WIce
§ - 'Heavenly Blue' ♀H5	Widely available
- 'Pete's Favourite'	NWad
- 'Picos'	CMea NLar
- 'Star' PBR	CBod CWCL EHyd ELan EPfP GJos GMaP LLWG LRHS MACG NHpl NLar NRHS SCoo SEdd SPer SPoG SWvt WFar WIce
- 'White Star'	WIce
× ***intermedia***	see *Moltkia* × *intermedia*
§ ***oleifolia*** ♀H4	CBor EHyd LRHS NBir NRHS
rosmarinifolia	EBee EHyd LRHS NRHS WCFE
zahnii	EHyd LRHS NRHS SVen
- 'Azure-ness'	SChF SGro WAbe

Lithophragma (*Saxifragaceae*)

parviflorum	CMiW CTtf EWes LPla

Lithops ✿ (*Aizoaceae*)

sp.	CDoC
hallii ♀H2	SSim

Lithospermum (*Boraginaceae*)

diffusum	see *Lithodora diffusa*
doerfleri	see *Moltkia doerfleri*
'Heavenly Blue'	see *Lithodora diffusa* 'Heavenly Blue'
officinale	GPoy XAbr
oleifolium	see *Lithodora oleifolia*
purpureocaeruleum	see *Buglossoides purpurocaerulea*

Lithraea (*Anacardiaceae*)

caustica	WPav

Litsea (*Lauraceae*)

NJM 13.047	WPGP
glauca	see *Neolitsea sericea*
japonica	CMCN SVen

Littonia (*Colchicaceae*)

modesta	see *Gloriosa modesta*

Livistona (*Arecaceae*)

chinensis ♀H2	CPHo SPalm
decora	SPalm
rotundifolia	CDoC

Llagunoa (*Sapindaceae*)

glandulosa	WPav

Loasa (*Loasaceae*)

triphylla var. ***volcanica***	EWes WSHC

Lobelia ✿ (*Campanulaceae*)

angulata	see *Pratia angulata*
'Bordervale'	WBor
bridgesii	CDTJ CExl EBee ECtt EWes EWld LRHS SPlb WKif WPav
'Bruce Wakefield' **new**	WHil
§ ***cardinalis*** ♀H3	CMac CPud CWat ELon EWld GMaP LCro LOPS NGBl NLar NPer SPer SPlb SRms SWvt WFar WSMil
- 'Bee's Flame'	CBod CEme CNor CWGN ECtt EHyd LRHS MArl MRav MSpe NGdn NRHS SCoo SRkn WWtn
§ - 'Chocolate Truffle' PBR	EBee LSou SRms
§ - 'Elmfeuer'	CWCL EWoo NLar SPlb SPoG SWvt XLum
§ - 'Queen Victoria' ♀H3	Widely available
- 'Russian Princess' misapplied	CBod EHyd EPfP EWoo LLWG LRHS MAsh NGdn NRHS SPoG SRkn SWvt WFar WMal
chinensis	LLWG
'Cinnabar Deep Red'	see *L.* × *speciosa* 'Fan Tiefrot'
COMPLIMENT DEEP RED	see *L.* × *speciosa* 'Kompliment Tiefrot'
COMPLIMENT SCARLET	see *L.* × *speciosa* 'Kompliment Scharlach'
'Compton Pink'	CBcs CBod CNor EAJP ECtt ELan EMor EShb EWTr EWes IPot LBuc LCro LOPS LRHS LSou MPie MSpe NGBl NRHS NSti WFar WWtn
Elizabeth Strangman selection	NDov
erinus 'Cambridge Blue' ♀H2	MBros
- Cascade Series ♀H2	LCro LOPS
- 'Crystal Palace' ♀H2	MBros MPri
- (Fountain Series) 'Fountain Blue'	MBros MPri

- - 'Fountain Rose' MBros
- - 'Fountain White' MBros MPri
- 'Mrs Clibran' ♀H2 LCro LOPS MBros
- Riviera Series MPri
- 'Sapphire' LCro LOPS MBros MPri
- 'String of Pearls' ♀H2 MBros
- WATERFALL BLUE ICE (Waterfall Series) LSou MPri
- 'White Lady' MBros

excelsa CBod SEND WPav
FAN DEEP RED see *L.* × *speciosa* 'Fan Tiefrot'
FAN DEEP ROSE see *L.* × *speciosa* 'Fan Orchidrosa'
FAN SALMON see *L.* × *speciosa* 'Fan Lachs'
'Flamingo' see *L.* × *speciosa* 'Pink Flamingo'
fulgens see *L. cardinalis*
- SAINT ELMO'S FIRE see *L. cardinalis* 'Elmfeuer'
× ***gerardii*** see *L.* × *speciosa*
giberroa CDTJ
'Gladys Lindley' LRHS
'Grape Knee-Hi' ECtt EHyd LRHS NRHS
'Hadspen Purple' see *L.* × *speciosa* 'Hadspen Purple'
inflata GPoy
laxiflora CFis SAdn WFar
- var. ***angustifolia*** CDTJ CPbh CPla CWCL EWld SBrt SRms SVen WCot
linnaeoides SPlb
§ ***montana*** EWld
- B&SWJ 8220 ESwi WCru
pedunculata see *Pratia pedunculata*
polyphylla WPav
'Queen Victoria' see *L. cardinalis* 'Queen Victoria'
sessilifolia CExl EBee NLar
- B&SWJ 8875 WCru
siphilitica Widely available
- f. ***albiflora*** EBee ECtt EWoo LEdu
- - 'Alba' EMor EPfP SBls SRms SWvt WFar
- 'Rosea' MNrw
'Sombre Purple' EBee
§ × ***speciosa*** EGrI SVic WFar XLum
- 'Butterfly Blue' CNor SGbt
- 'Cranberry Crush' ECtt EHyd LRHS NRHS
- CRIMSON PRINCESS ('Gencrim'PBR) (Princess Series) LSou SPoG
- 'Dark Crusader' EBee ECtt EHyd EPfP LRHS MHol MPie MSpe NRHS SGbt SMHy
- Fan Series MRav
- - 'Fan Blau' CKel EHyd ELan EMor EPfP LRHS MHol NLar SCob WFar
- - 'Fan Burgundy' EHyd ELan EMor EPfP LRHS NGdn NLar
§ - - 'Fan Lachs' EHyd EPfP NLar SCob WFar
§ - - 'Fan Orchidrosa' ♀H5 EHyd EPfP
- - 'Fan Scharlach' ♀H5 EHyd EPfP LRHS NLar NRHS SPoG SWvt WFar
§ - - 'Fan Tiefrot' ♀H5 SRms SWvt WBor
§ - - 'Fan Zinnoberrosa' ♀H5 SRms SWvt
§ - 'Hadspen Purple'PBR Widely available
- 'Kimbridge Beet' CMac EBee LRHS
- Kompliment Series WFar
§ - - 'Kompliment Blau' SWvt WFar
* - - 'Kompliment Pale Pink' WFar
§ - - 'Kompliment Purpur' MMuc SWvt
§ - - 'Kompliment Scharlach' ♀H5 EHyd EPfP MNrw NPer NRHS SWvt
§ - - 'Kompliment Tiefrot' EHyd EPfP MNrw SWvt
- 'Monet Moment' CRos EBee ECtt EHyd ELon EWes ILea LRHS NLar NRHS SWvt
- 'Pauline' ECtt
- 'Pink Elephant' ♀H5 CBod ECtt EHyd ELan LRHS NRHS SGbt
§ - 'Pink Flamingo' CKel ELan EPfP LRHS
- ROSE PRINCESS ('Genross'PBR) (Princess Series) SPoG
- 'Ruby Slippers' CMac EBee ELan EPfP
- 'Russian Princess' purple-flowered CRos CWCL ECtt ELan ELon ILea LSou MBel MHer MHol MPie MSpe NGBl NHol SCob SGbt WFar WKif WSMil WWtn
- 'Sparkling Ruby' CBod EBee ECtt EPfP EWTr EWoo LBuc LRHS NDov NRHS SCoo SWvt WWtn
- 'Starship Deep Rose' CBod CRos EHyd LRHS MHol NRHS SBls SCoo
- 'Starship Scarlet' CRos EHyd LRHS LSun MBros MHol MPie NRHS SBls SCob SCoo WHil
- 'Tania' Widely available
§ - 'Vedrariensis' CMac CSpe CWat ECtt EPfP LRHS MBel MMuc MNrw NGBl SRms SWvt WCFE WCav WFar WHoo XLum
'Tania's Sister' EBee ECtt WCot WFar
telekii **new** LShi
treadwellii see *Pratia angulata* 'Treadwellii'
tupa Widely available
- Archibald's form CExl WPGP
valida SWvt
- 'Delft Blue' LRHS
- 'True Blue' SWvt
vedrariensis see *L.* × *speciosa* 'Vedrariensis'

Lobostemon (*Boraginaceae*)

belliformis CPbh

Lobularia (*Brassicaceae*)

maritima 'Carpet of Snow' **new** LRHS
- GOLF BRIGHT MIXED (Golf Series) LCro LOPS
- 'Snow Crystals' MPri
- 'Violet Queen' ♀H3 LCro LOPS
PRINCESS IN PURPLE CPla
SNOW PRINCESS ('Inlbusnopr'PBR) CPla MHol

loganberry see *Rubus* × *loganobaccus*

Loiseleuria see *Kalmia*

Lomandra (*Asparagaceae*)

hystrix SPlb
longifolia LEdu SPlb
- PLATINUM BEAUTY ('Roma13') (v) CBod SPeP SPoG XSte
- TANIKA ('Lm300'PBR) GBin

Lomaria see *Blechnum*

Lomatia (*Proteaceae*)

dentata MRav
ferruginea CBcs CCCN CDTJ CDoC CExl CKel CSde CTsd EPfP LRHS MGil SArc SPoG WCru WPGP XSte
fraseri CCCN CDoC CKel EHyd EPfP LRHS NLar SPoG WPGP
hirsuta MGil
longifolia see *L. myricoides*
§ ***myricoides*** CBcs CCCN CDoC CExl CTsd EHyd EPfP NLar SLon SPoG
tinctoria CBcs CExl CPbh EPfP IDee LRHS XSte

Lomatium (*Apiaceae*)

columbianum	SPhx
grayi	LPla SPhx WHil

Lomatogonium (*Gentianaceae*)

perenne	GKev

Lonicera ✿ (*Caprifoliaceae*)

KR 10106	WPGP
KR 10608	CRHN
§ ***acuminata***	CMCN EBee
- B&SWJ 3480	WCru
- B&SWJ 6743	CRHN WCru
- B&SWJ 6815	WCru
- var. ***acuminata***	WCot
albertii	EPfP MBNS NLar
alseuosmoides	CBcs CBod CKel CRHN EBee EPfP LRHS NLar SEND SLon SPoG WCru WPGP WSHC WSpi
× ***americana*** misapplied	see *L.* × *italica*
americana ambig.	ETho
§ ***americana*** (Mill.) K. Koch	CBcs EPfP LEdu MSwo NLar SEND SRms
§ × ***brownii*** 'Dropmore Scarlet'	Widely available
- 'Fuchsioides' misapplied	see *L.* × *brownii* 'Dropmore Scarlet'
caerulea	CDoC EPom IDee LRHS MRav SEdi SPre SRms SVic WBor WKor WLov
- 'Atut'	NLar
- 'Duet'	NLar
- var. ***edulis***	CAgr EPfP LBuc LEdu MCoo NLar WMat
- var. ***kamtschatica***	EPom IDee LCro LOPS NLar WPGP
- - 'Balalaika' (F)	CAgr MCoo
- - 'Borealis' (F)	CAgr
- - 'Eisbar' (F)	CAgr
- - 'Erin' (F)	LEdu
- - 'Honey Bee' (F)	CAgr
- - 'Indigo Gem' (F)	CAgr
- - 'Indigo Yum' (F) **new**	CAgr
- - 'Kalinka' (F)	CAgr
- - 'Larisa' (F)	LEdu WPGP
- - 'Maistar' (F)	XAbr
- - 'Maries' (F)	LEdu WFar WPGP
- - 'Morena'PBR (F)	EBee EPom
- - 'Rebecca' (F)	LEdu WPGP
- - 'Ruth' (F)	LEdu WPGP
- - 'Sinoglaska' (F)	NLar
- - 'Vicky' (F)	LEdu WFar WPGP
- - 'Wojtek' (F)	CAgr NLar SPre
- - 'Zojka' (F) **new**	CAgr
- 'Kirke'	NLar SMad
* - var. ***longifolia***	NLar
§ ***caprifolium***	CRHN EHyd EPfP LRHS NLar WCot
- 'Anna Fletcher'	CRHN WCFE
- f. ***pauciflora***	see *L.* × *italica*
'Celestial'PBR	CRos EPfP LCro LOPS LRHS
chaetocarpa	CEnd WSHC
ciliosa	CRHN WCFE
'Clavey's Dwarf'	EPPr
crassifolia	CBcs EWld GEdr NLar SBrt WPGP
- 'Little Honey'	GKev LRHS MBNS MMrt MRav NLar SPoG XSte
deflexicalyx	CMCN NLar
dioica red-flowered **new**	GGro
'Early Cream'	see *L. caprifolium*
'Elegant'	see *L. ligustrina* 'Elegant'
elisae	CBcs CMac CRos EHed EPfP GBin LRHS MMuc NLar NRHS SEle SMad SPoG SSta WCot WHwl WLov
etrusca	MRav XSen
- 'Donald Waterer'	CRHN CRos EPfP LRHS NLar WFar
- 'Michael Rosse'	CKel ELan MBNS NLar SNig WLov
- 'Superba' ♀H5	CRHN EBee ELan EPfP LEdu LRHS NLar SEND SNig WSHC
'Fire Cracker'	NLar SLon
flexuosa	see *L. japonica* var. *repens*
fragrantissima	Widely available
giraldii misapplied	see *L. acuminata*
giraldii Rehder	CRHN WSHC
glabrata	SCoo
- B&SWJ 2150	WCru
- 'Damchin La'	WPGP
'Golden Trumpet'	CWGN EPfP MGos SGsty
grata	see *L.* × *americana* (Mill.) K. Koch
× ***heckrottii***	CRHN CSBt NLar
- 'Gold Flame' ambig.	GKin NLar SCob
- 'Gold Flame' hort. ♀H5	CArg CMac CRos EBee EHyd ELan EPfP ETho LBuc LCro LOPS LRHS MAsh MMuc NRHS SCoo SEND SNig SPer SPoG SRms SWvt WFar WLov WSHC
§ ***henryi***	Widely available
- B&SWJ 8109	WCru
- NJM 11.033	WPGP
- 'Copper Beauty'PBR	Widely available
- var. ***subcoriacea***	see *L. henryi*
hildebrandiana ♀H2	CCCN CExl CRHN IKel WPGP
hirsuta	EBee SBrt
hispidula	SBrt
'Honey Baby'PBR	ELon EPfP LCro LOPS NHol NWad WHwl
implexa	CMCN CRHN
insularis	see *L. morrowii*
involucrata	CExl CMCN EBee EPfP MBNS MBlu MMuc SEND
- var. ***ledebourii***	CBcs EHyd EPPr EPfP LRHS MGil NLar
- - 'Vian'	NLar
§ × ***italica***	CRHN CTri EBee MBNS MSwo NPer SCob SCoo SPer
§ - HARLEQUIN ('Sherlite') (v)	CMac EPfP SPlb SRms SWvt
japonica	CMen WFar XSen
§ - 'Aureoreticulata' (v) ♀H5	CMac ELan EPfP EShb MRav NPer SRms WFar WLov
- var. ***chinensis*** **new**	SGsty XSen
- 'Cream Cascade'	MSwo NLar SCoo
- 'Dart's Acumen'	CRHN
- 'Dart's World'	CArg CBod CSBt EBee EHyd LPar LRHS NLar NRHS WLov
- 'Halliana'	Widely available
- 'Hall's Prolific' ♀H5	CArg CBod CDoC CEnd CRos CSBt EBee EHyd ELan EPfP LBuc LCro LOPS LRHS LSRN MAsh MBlu MGos MHer MRav MSwo NRHS SCob SPad SPoG SWvt WFar XSen
§ - 'Horwood Gem' (v)	CDoC ECtt MGos NLar SCoo
- 'Maskerade' (v)	NLar
- 'Mint Crisp'PBR (v)	CBod CDoC CMac CPla CRos CSBt CWGN EBee ECtt ELan EPfP EShb LRHS LSou MGos NLar SCoo SLon SNig SPad SPer SPoG SRms SWvt
- 'Peter Adams'	see *L. japonica* 'Horwood Gem'
- 'Princess Kate'	ELan NLar SRms
- 'Red World'	WLov
§ - var. ***repens*** ♀H5	CMac CRos CSBt CTri ECtt EHyd ELan EPfP EShb GGro LRHS MRav MSwo NLar NRHS SCoo SLon SPad SPer SPoG SRms WFar
- - PINK APERITIF ('Crowthlon') **new**	CKel LRHS

- 'Variegata'	see *L. japonica* 'Aureoreticulata'
korolkowii	EPPr MBNS NBir NLar WAvo WCot
- 'Blue Velvet'	CAgr MCoo NLar
- 'Mayberry Farm'	MCoo
- var. ***zabelii*** misapplied	see *L. tatarica* 'Zabelii'
lanceolata BWJ 7935	WCru
§ ***ligustrina*** 'Elegant'	LBuc MNic SArc
- 'Lemon Beauty' (v)	CBcs CCoa CEme CKel CMac EHyd EShb LRHS LSRN MBNS MGos NLar NWad SCob SGbt SGol SPer SRms SWvt WAvo WFar
- 'Lime Twist' (v)	CBod
§ - var. ***pileata***	CBcs CBrac CCVT CEme CEnd CMCN CMac CSBt CTri EHyd EPfP EShb EWTr EWoo GQue LBuc MGos MSwo NPer NWea SBrt SCob SGol SPer SRms WAvo WCFE WCot WFar WLov
- - 'Moss Green'	CBod EShb
§ - var. ***yunnanensis***	CAco CArg CBar CBcs CBod CBrac CCVT CCoa CDoC CEme CEnd CMac CMen CSBt CTri GDam MHed MSwo NWea SEND SEWo SGbt SGol SGsty SPer WMat WTSh
- - 'Baggesen's Gold' 🏆H5	Widely available
* - - 'Compacta' **new**	SGsty
- - EDMÉE GOLD ('Briloni')	WCot
- - 'Ernest Wilson'	EPPr
- - 'Fertilis'	CBrac
- - 'Golden Glow'PBR	CBod NEoE
- - 'Lemon Queen'	MMuc MSwo SEND
- - 'Maigrün'	CBar CBcs CCVT EHyd ELan EShb GBin GDam LPar LRHS MNHC MSwo NEoE SCob SPer SWvt WFar XSen
- - 'Red Tips'	EShb NLar SCoo SRms
- - 'Silver Beauty' (v)	CCoa CMac LRHS MGos MSwo SPer SPlb SPoG SRms SWvt WFar
- - 'Silver Lining' (v)	WCFE
- - 'Tidy Tips'	CBcs CBod CDoC MTin NEoE SCob
- - 'Twiggy' (v)	CSBt EDAr MHer NHol NLar NWad SCob WAvo WFar
maackii	CMCN CRos EHyd EPPr EPfP LRHS LShi MRav NLar NRHS WCFE
macrantha B&SWJ 11687	WCru
- WWJ 11606	WCru
'Mandarin' 🏆H5	CBcs CKel CRHN LCro LOPS MBlu NLar SCoo SWvt WLov
maximowiczii var. ***sachalinensis***	NLar
§ ***morrowii***	SBrt XSen
- 'Ullung do'	CMCN
myrtillus	NLar SBrt
nitida	see *L. ligustrina* var. *yunnanensis*
- MAYGREEN	see *L. ligustrina* var. *yunnanensis* 'Maigrün'
aff. ***pamirica*** **new**	WPGP
periclymenum	CCVT CTri GPoy MHer MRav NWea SCob SPlb WSFF XSen
- 'Belgica' misapplied	see *L.* × *italica*
- 'Belgica'	Widely available
- CAPRILIA IMPERIAL ('Inov86'PBR)	LCro LOPS
- CHIC ET CHOC ('Inov205'PBR)	CKel SCoo SPoG
§ - 'Chojnów'PBR	ETho
- 'Florida'	see *L. periclymenum* 'Serotina'
- 'Graham Thomas' 🏆H6	Widely available
- 'Harlequin'	see *L.* × *italica* HARLEQUIN
- 'Heaven Scent'	CDoC ETho LBuc LCro LOPS LSRN NLar WFar

- 'Honeybush'	CJun CWGN MAsh MGos NHol NWad WFar WNPC
- 'La Gasnérie'	SCoo
- 'Munster'	WSHC
- 'Purple Queen'	CChe
- 'Red Gables'	CBod CDoC CRHN ELon LSRN MBNS MGos MHtn NLar SCoo SEND SWvt WCot WKif WLov
- 'Rhubarb and Custard'	CBcs CDoC CEnd LCro LOPS LRHS MGos SCoo WHwl WNPC
- 'Scentsation'PBR	CEnd CMac CRos CSBt CWGN EBee EHyd ELan EPfP GBin LCro LOPS LRHS MAsh NLar NRHS SCoo SLon SPoG WHwl WNPC
- 'Serotina' 🏆H6	Widely available
- 'Strawberries and Cream'	CDoC LCro LOPS LRHS WHwl WNPC
- 'Sweet Sue'	CDoC CRHN CRos EBee EHyd ELan ELon EPfP LRHS LSRN MAsh MGos MSwo NLar NRHS SCoo SNig SPoG SWvt WFar
- 'Winchester'	SRms
pileata	see *L. ligustrina* var. *pileata*
pilosa (Kunth) Willd. ex Kunth	CRHN EWld
- F&M 207	WPGP
- F&M 256	WPGP
prolifera	CRHN NLar
× ***purpusii***	CMac CRHN CTri EBee EPfP LMaj MBNS SCob SRms WCFE WFar
- 'Spring Romance'	CMac
- 'Winter Beauty' 🏆H6	Widely available
quinquelocularis	CMCN
ramosissima	NLar
reticulata 'Silver'	NLar
saccata	EPfP
sempervirens	CBcs CRHN CSBt IDee MRav
- 'Blanche Sandman'	EShb
- 'Cedar Lane'	CRHN EHyd LRHS SBrt
- 'Dropmore Scarlet'	see *L.* × *brownii* 'Dropmore Scarlet'
- 'Leo'	CWGN
- f. ***sulphurea***	CMCN WSHC
- - 'John Clayton'	EHyd EPfP LRHS
setifera 'Daphnis'	CJun EPfP WPGP
similis var. ***delavayi*** 🏆H5	CBod CRHN CWGN EHyd ELan EPfP ETho LPar MAsh MRav NLar SCoo SDix SEND SRms SWvt WCot WCru WSHC XSte
'Simonet'	CWCL EBee NLar
'Spring Purple'	NLar
standishii	CTri WFar
- var. ***lancifolia*** 'Budapest'	EHyd ELan ELon EPfP LRHS MBlu MRav NLar SMad SRms WFar
§ ***strophiophora***	WAvo
subaequalis	WHwl
- Og 93.329	CExl WPGP WSHC
syringantha	CBcs CRHN EBee EHed ELan EPPr EPfP EWld IDee MMuc MNrw MRav NLar NWad SBut SDix SEND SPer WCFE WFar
tatarica	CMCN MRav
- 'Alba'	ELan
- 'Arnold Red'	ELan EPfP MBlu NLar SEND
- 'Hack's Red'	CMCN EHed ELan EPfP LRHS NLar SCoo SPer SVen SWvt WGrn
§ - 'Zabelii'	ELan MNrw
× ***tellmanniana*** 🏆H5	CArg CBcs CBod CBrac CExl CMac CRHN CRos CWCL EBee ECtt EHyd ELan EPfP LCro LOPS LRHS LSRN MAsh MBlu MGos MSwo NLar NRHS SCob SCoo SNig SPer SPoG SRms

– 'Joan Sayers'	SCoo WCFE
– 'Pharaoh's Trumpet'	SLon
thibetica	MBlu
tomentella B&SWJ 2654	WCru
tragophylla ♀H5	ELan IDee LRHS MBNS MRav NLar SCoo SWvt
– 'Maurice Foster'	CBcs CRHN EBee EWTr LEdu NLar SNig WLov WSpi
× ***xylosteoides***	NLar
xylosteum	EPPr MMuc NLar

Lophomyrtus ✿ (*Myrtaceae*)

§ ***bullata*** ♀H2	CDTJ SPer
× ***ralphii*** 'Black Pearl'	CDoC CMCN CMac EHyd EShb LRHS SCoo SGBe SGbt WFar
– 'Gloriosa'	CCCN CTrC CWit
– 'Kathryn'	CBcs CCoa CDoC CKel CSde CTrC LRHS NLar
– 'Krinkly'	SVen
– 'Little Star' (v)	CBcs CBod CSde CTrC EHyd SEle SGBe XSte
– Logan's form (v)	CBcs CKel MGil NLar NRHS SGBe
– 'Magic Dragon'PBR (v)	CBod CKel CMac CRos CTsd EGrI EHyd ELan LCro LOPS LRHS NRHS SEle SGBe SGbt SPoG WFar XSte
– 'Multicolor' (v)	CBcs CCoa CDoC CSde EBee LRHS MRav SVen
– 'Pixie'	CBcs CBod CCoa CDoC CKel CSde CTrC LRHS MAsh SEle SGBe SIvy SPoG SVen
– 'Purpurea'	CTrC
– 'Red Dragon'	CBcs CMac EHyd LPar LRHS MAsh MGos NRHS SGBe SIvy WFar XSte
– 'Variegata' (v)	CMCN
– 'Wild Cherry'	CKel

Lophosoria (*Dicksoniaceae*)

quadripinnata	CBdn CDTJ CKel IKel

Lophospermum (*Plantaginaceae*)

'Cream Delight'	CCCN
§ ***erubescens*** ♀H2	CRHN SGro
– white-flowered	EShb SGro
(Lofos Series) LOFOS COMPACT PINK ('Sunlorose'PBR) **new**	LSou
– LOFOS WINE RED ('Sun-asaro')	EShb
§ 'Magic Dragon'	SEND SLim SPlb
§ 'Red Dragon'	CCCN SGro
§ ***scandens***	CCCN
– 'Joan Loraine'	SGro

loquat see *Eriobotrya japonica*

Loropetalum (*Hamamelidaceae*)

chinense	SEle
– BLACK PEARL	see *L. chinense* var. *rubrum* 'Pearl'
– CAROLINA MOONLIGHT ('Nci 002')	SEle
§ – 'Chang Nian Hong'	CDoC EGrI LCro LOPS LRHS SEle XSte
– EVER RED	see *L. chinense* 'Chang Nian Hong'
– HOT SPICE	EGrI SEle
– 'Ming Dynasty'	EGrI MAsh SEle SSta WFar
– var. ***rubrum***	CExl SGsty
– – 'Blush'	CBcs SEle
– – 'Daybreak's Flame'	MGil SEle SNig
– – 'Fire Dance'	Widely available
§ – – 'Pearl'PBR	EGrI SGsty WCot XSte
– f. ***rubrum*** 'Pipa's Red'	EGrI
– 'Tang Dynasty'	CBct CDoC CWit WFar

Lotus (*Fabaceae*)

berthelotii	CCCN CDTJ EShb LPot MCot
– deep red-flowered ♀H2	SWvt
berthelotii × ***maculatus*** ♀H2	CCCN MCot MSCN
corniculatus	CHab EBou GJos LCro LOPS MBow MCoo MHer MMuc MNHC NAts NFav NGrd NMir SEND SPhx SRms WSFF WWild
creticus	SPhx
dorycnium	CKel SPhx XSen
hirsutus ♀H4	CBod CExl CPla EAJP ECha EGrI ELan EPfP LPot MAsh MRav SAdn SEND SLon SPer SPhx SPlb SPoG SWvt WMal XLum XSen
– 'Brimstone' (v)	EPPr MRav SIvy SPer SPoG SWvt
* – var. ***italica***	LSun
– LITTLE BOY BLUE ('Lisbob'PBR)	CRos CSBt EHyd EPfP LRHS NRHS SGBe
– 'Lois'	SIvy SNig SPoG
jacobaeus	MCot
maritimus	NFav XLum
mearnsii	SPlb
pedunculatus	CHab MCoo NAts NMir SPhx WSFF
tetragonolobus	SPhx SVic

lovage see *Levisticum officinale*

Loxostigma (*Gesneriaceae*)

kurzii GWJ 9342	WCru

Ludwigia (*Onagraceae*)

palustris	LLWG

Luetkea (*Rosaceae*)

pectinata	GArf GEdr

Luma ✿ (*Myrtaceae*)

§ ***apiculata*** ♀H4	Widely available
§ – 'Glanleam Gold' (v)	Widely available
– 'Nana'	LEdu WJek WPGP
– 'Penlee'	WJek
– 'Rainbow's Gold' (v)	EShb
– 'Saint Hilary' (v)	CEme CTrC EPfP WJek WPav
– 'Variegata' (v)	CTri WFar
§ ***chequen***	CBcs CCoa CSde EShb LEdu WJek WPGP WPav

Lunaria (*Brassicaceae*)

§ ***annua***	GJos LCro LOPS MNHC WCot WSFF
– var. ***albiflora*** ♀H6	CKel LCro LOPS NBir SEND WCot
I – – 'Alba Variegata' (v) ♀H6	CSpe CTtf SSal WBrk
– 'Chedglow'	CNat GBin LEdu LRHS SGro SPhx SSal WCot
– 'Corfu Blue' ♀H6	CSpe EWes GBin SPhx SPtp SSal WCot
– 'Cynthia'	CNat
– 'Early Autumn' **new**	CNat
– 'Lugbury' **new**	CNat
– 'Marlou's Revenge' **new**	CNat
– 'Munstead Purple' ♀H6	CSpe
– 'Nettleton'	CNat
– 'Purple Emperor' **new**	CTtf
– purple-leaved	CMea
– 'Rosemary Verey'	SSal
– 'Ruth'	CNat
– 'The Optimist'	CNat
– 'Variegata' (v)	CSpe CTtf GJos NBir WCot

biennis	see *L. annua*
rediviva ♀H7	CSpe CTtf EBee ECha EHyd EMor EPPr GAbr GBin GMaP LEdu MAvo MBel MHer MMuc NBid NChi NPer NSti SBrt SEND SPtp SSal WCAu WCot WFar WPGP
- 'Partway White' (v)	CMil MAvo WCot

Lupinus ✿ (*Fabaceae*)

angustifolius	SPhx
arboreus ♀H4	CBcs CEme CSBt CTri CWCL EHyd ELan EPfP LRHS MCoo MGil MHer MNHC MNrw MRav NBir NLar NRHS SBls SCob SEle SIvy SPer SPlb SPoG SRms SVic WFar
- 'Barton-on-Sea'	CDoC ELon SPad
- blue and white-flowered	CEme WFar
- 'Blue Boy'	ELan SWvt
- blue-flowered	CBcs CBod CWCL EHyd LShi NLar NRHS SPer SPlb SPoG SRms SWvt WFar
- 'Chelsea Blue'	EHyd EPfP LRHS NRHS
- 'Lavender Spires'	LCro LOPS
- 'Mauve Queen'	MNrw
- prostrate	WAvo
- 'Snow Queen'	CDoC CWCL LRHS SPer SPoG SWvt
- 'Sulphur Yellow'	SWvt
- white-flowered	CBcs CBod CEme CSpe ELan LEdu LShi MNHC SPlb
- yellow and blue-flowered	NBir SRkn WFar
- yellow-flowered	CBod CDoC CEme ELan GArf SPhx SWvt
arcticus	EBee
Band of Nobles Series	SBls
'Beefeater'	CRos CWCL EHyd ELan EPfP EWes GBee LBuc LRHS LSou MHol MPri NLar NRHS SCoo SPoG SWvt
'Bishop's Tipple'	CWCL
'Blacksmith'	EPfP LRHS LSou MPri
'Blossom'[PBR]	CRos CWCL CWGN EHyd ELan EPfP EWes LRHS LSRN LSou MPri NRHS SPoG SWvt
caespitosus	see *L. lepidus* var. *utahensis*
(Camelot Series) 'Camelot White'	ECul
- 'Camelot Yellow'	ECul GDam
'Cashmere Cream'	CWCL CWGN NRHS
'Chameleon'	LRHS NRHS
chamissonis	CCCN CSpe CWCL EHyd LRHS NRHS SBut SPer
'Chandelier' (Band of Nobles Series)	CBcs CRos CSBt CTri ELan ELon EPfP GMaP GQue LCro LOPS MAsh MCot MPri MSCN NBir NGBl NHol NLar SCob SCoo SGbt SNig SPer SPhx SPoG SWvt WCAu WFar
'Desert Sun'[PBR]	CBcs CRos CWCL EHyd EPfP LRHS LSou MPri NLar NRHS SCoo SPoG SWvt
digitatus	SPhx
'Dwarf Lulu'	see *L.* 'Lulu'
elegans 'Pink Fairy'	SSal
Gallery Series	CSBt MBros SCob SCoo SPlb WFar
- 'Gallery Blue'	CBod CRos EAJP ECtt ECul EHyd ELan EPfP LBuc LCro LOPS LRHS LSRN MACG MBros MHol MPri NLar NRHS SCoo SPoG WFar
- 'Gallery Pink Bicolor'	CBod
- 'Gallery Pink'	CRos EAJP EHyd ELan EPfP LCro LOPS LRHS MACG MHol MPri NLar NRHS SCoo SPoG SRms WFar
- 'Gallery Pink White' **new**	EPfP LRHS
- 'Gallery Red'	CBod CRos EAJP ECtt EHyd ELan EPfP EWTr GPSL LCro LOPS LRHS MACG MBow MBros MHol MPri NLar NRHS SCob SCoo SPoG WFar
- 'Gallery Rose'	LSRN NRHS SPoG WFar
- 'Gallery White'	CBod CRos EAJP ECul EHyd ELan EPfP LCro LOPS LRHS MACG MBros MHol MPri NLar NRHS SCoo SPoG WFar
- 'Gallery Yellow'	CBod CRos EAJP ECtt EHyd ELan EPfP EWoo LCro LOPS LRHS MACG MBros MHol MPri NLar NRHS SCob SPoG WFar
'Gladiator'[PBR]	CRos CWCL ECtt EHyd ELan EPfP EWes LRHS LSou MHol MPri NLar NRHS SCob SCoo SPoG SWvt
hartwegii	SPhx
'Judy Harper'	ECtt GBee
'Jupiter'	LRHS
'King Canute'	CRos CWCL CWGN EHyd ELan EPfP GBee LRHS MPri NLar NRHS
latifolius subsp. ***parishii***	EBee
lepidus	CPbh
§ - var. ***utahensis***	SPlb
§ 'Lulu'	EPfP SGbt SPoG SWvt
'Magic Lantern'	CRos CWCL EHyd EPfP LRHS LSou MHol MPri NRHS SCoo SPoG
'Manhattan Lights'[PBR]	CBcs CRos CWCL CWGN ELan EPfP EWes LRHS LSou MHol MPri NLar NRHS SCob SCoo SGBe SPoG SWvt
'Masterpiece'[PBR]	CBcs CDoC CKel CRos CWCL EHyd ELan EPfP EWes LCro LOPS LRHS LSRN LSou MPri NLar NRHS SCoo SGBe SPoG SWvt WCAu
Minarette Group	CRos EHyd EPfP LRHS MNrw NRHS SRms
montanus	SPhx
mutabilis	SPhx
'My Castle' (Band of Nobles Series)	CBcs CRos CSBt CTri ECtt EHyd ELan EPfP GAbr GMaP GQue LRHS LSRN MAsh MGos MPri NGBl NLar NRHS SCob SGbt SNig SPer SPoG SWvt WFar
'Noble Maiden' (Band of Nobles Series)	Widely available
nootkatensis	GLog
'Pam Ayres'	ECtt GBee
perennis	CBod SPhx
'Persian Princess' **new**	LRHS
'Persian Slipper'[PBR]	CBcs CKel CRos CWCL CWGN EBee ECtt EHyd ELan EPfP EWes LBuc LRHS LSRN LSou MPri NLar NRHS SCob SGBe SPoG SWvt WCAu
'Polar Princess'	CBcs CKel CWCL CWGN ECtt EHyd ELan EPfP EWes GBee LRHS LSou MHol MMrt MPri NRHS SCob SPoG SWvt
'Purple Swirl'	EHyd EPfP GBee LRHS NRHS
'Rachel de Thame'	CRos CWCL CWGN EBee EHyd EPfP EWes LRHS LSou MHol MPri NRHS SCoo SPoG SWvt
'Red Rum'[PBR]	CWCL CWGN EHyd LBuc LRHS LSRN MPri NLar NRHS SCob SCoo SPoG SWvt
§ × ***regalis*** Russell Group	CPla CSBt EPfP MHer SCob SPlb SRms SVic SWvt WFar
'Rote Flamme'	ELon EWes
Russell hybrids	see *L.* × *regalis* Russell Group
'Saffron'[PBR]	EHyd LBuc LRHS NRHS

'Salmon Star'[PBR]	CRos CWCL CWGN EHyd LRHS LSou NLar NRHS SCob
sericeus	SPhx
'Silver Fleece'	CCCN EHyd WFar
'Tequila Flame'[PBR]	CRos CWCL EPfP LBuc LRHS LSou MPri NLar NRHS SCob SPoG SWvt
'Terracotta'	CWCL LRHS NRHS SPoG
texensis	CSpe SPhx WSHC
'The Chatelaine' (Band of Nobles Series)	Widely available
'The Governor' (Band of Nobles Series)	Widely available
'The Page' (Band of Nobles Series)	CBcs CRos EHyd ELan ELon EPfP EWTr EWoo GBin GMaP GQue LCro LOPS LRHS LSRN LSun MAsh MNHC MSCN NLar NRHS SNig SPer SPoG SWvt WBor WFar
'Thundercloud'	EBee
'Towering Inferno'	CRos CWCL EBee EHyd EPfP EWes LBuc LRHS LSou MPri NLar NRHS SPoG
Woodfield hybrids	LRHS

Luzula (*Juncaceae*)

	alpinopilosa	EPPr
	× ***borreri*** 'Botany Bay' (v)	EHyd GBin
	'Engel'	EWes
	luzuloides	LPla
	- 'Schneehäschen'	NWsh WSHC
	maxima	see *L. sylvatica*
	nivalis	GAbr
	nivea	Widely available
	pedemontana	EBee
	pilosa 'Grünfink'	EBee
	- 'Igel'	CBod CKno ELan EShb LEdu LPla NBid WSpi
	purpureosplendens	WCot
	'Snowflake' **new**	CKno
§	***sylvatica***	EBee EGrl ELan EPPr EPfP GBin GDam GQue LRHS MMuc MRav NBro NLar NMir NPol NRHS SCob SCoo SEND SPer WPnP WShi XLum
	- 'A. Rutherford'	see *L. sylvatica* 'Taggart's Cream'
	- from Tatra Mountains, Slovakia	EPPr
	- 'Aurea'	CDoC CKel CKno CRos EBee ECha EHyd EPPr EPfP EWoo GWyn LRHS MMuc MRav NRHS NSti NWsh SEND WCot WFar WGrn WLov
	- 'Aureomarginata'	see *L. sylvatica* 'Marginata'
I	- 'Auslese'	EPPr
	- 'Bromel'	EPPr
	- 'Hohe Tatra' ♀H7	CBod CSpe EPPr EShb EWes GMaP GQue MBNS NFav NGdn SCob SPer SPoG
§	- 'Marginata' (v) ♀H7	CKno EBee ECha ELan EMor EPPr EWoo GBin GMaP MAvo MBNS MMuc MRav NBid NFav NGdn NLar NSti SArc SCob SEND WChS WCot WFar WHoo WPnP
	- 'Mariusz'	EPPr
*	- f. ***nova***	EPPr
	- 'Onderbos'	EBee
	- 'Solar Flair'	CBod CKno EBee GBin GJos NRHS
	- 'Starmaker'	CBod
§	- 'Taggart's Cream' (v)	CRos EBee EHyd EPPr LRHS NHol NRHS NWad WFar
	- 'Tauernpass'	EPPr SPhx
	- 'Thierry's Cream' (v)	EPPr MBNS MHol SPoG WCot WFar
	- 'Wintergold'	EPPr
	ulophylla	GBin GEdr NFav SPlb

Luzuriaga (*Luzuriagaceae*)

polyphylla HCM 98202	WCru
radicans	CCCN CRHN GEdr WCru WPav WSHC
- RH 0602	ESwi WCru

Lychnis (*Caryophyllaceae*)

	alpina	EDAr LRHS NGdn WFar WIce XLum
	- 'Rosea'	NBir
	- 'Snow Flurry'	GKev GQue
§	× ***arkwrightii***	NRHS
	- 'Orange Zwerg'	SGbt
	- 'Vesuvius'	CBcs CMac EBee ECha SBls SCob SPer SRms
	chalcedonica ♀H7	Widely available
	- var. ***albiflora***	EMor EPPr EPfP NBro NLar WCAu WHrl
	- 'Carnea'	EBee EHyd EPPr EPfP EShb NGdn SBls SPhx WCAu
	- 'Dusky Salmon'	WHrl
	- 'Flore Pleno' (d)	EShb WCot
	- 'Pinkie'	GJos MMuc NFav NLar NWad SSal
	- 'Rauhreif'	NLar WHer
	- 'Rosea'	CBod EGrl EMor EPfP NBir WHrl
*	- 'Salmonea'	EMor EPPr GPSL NBir SRms
	- salmon-pink-flowered	MBow
	cognata	GGro
	- B&SWJ 4234	ESwi WCru
§	***coronaria*** ♀H7	Widely available
	- 'Alba' ♀H7	Widely available
	- 'Angel's Blush'	LShi LSun NBir NGrd NLar SBut SRkn WMal
	- Atrosanguinea Group	CBod CDoC CRos EBlo EHyd EPfP GMaP LRHS MBel MRav NGdn NRHS NSti NWad SCob SGbt SPer WTor
	- 'Blood Red'	CSpe LEdu LRHS WBrk
	- 'Cerise'	MArl NBir
	- GARDENERS' WORLD ('Blych') (d)	CBod CCBP CSpe CTtf EBee ECha ECtt EHyd ELan EWes LRHS LSou MAsh MBNS MBel MHol NRHS NSti SAko SCoo SMad SPer SRkn WBrk WCot WHil WSMil
	- MESE 356 **new**	LRHS SPhx
	- Oculata Group	CSpe EBee ELan EPfP LEdu SBls SPlb WFar WKif
§	***coronata*** var. ***sieboldii***	NFav SPhx
	dioica	see *Silene dioica*
	flos-cuculi	Widely available
	- var. ***albiflora***	EWoo NLar WHer WSFF
	- JENNY ('Lychjen') (d)	CRos EBee ECtt EGrl EHyd ELan EMor EPfP LEdu LRHS LSRN MBNS MBel MNrw MSCN NDov NRHS NSti SCob SRkn WCAu WCot
	- 'Little Robin'	EBou SLee
	- 'Nana'	EAJP GJos LLWG NGdn NLar WGwG
	- 'Petit Henri'	LPla LRHS LSou NSti WNPC WTor XSte
	- 'Petite Jenny' (d)	CRos CTtf EBee ECtt EHyd GWyn LRHS LSou MBNS MPri MSCN NDov NRHS SCob SPoG SRms WCAu WCot
	- 'White Robin'	Widely available
	flos-jovis ♀H6	CCBP ECha EHyd GJos LRHS NBir NRHS SPhx SRms WMal XLum
	- 'Hort's Variety'	EBee EBlo EHyd LRHS NBir NRHS
	- 'Minor'	see *L. flos-jovis* 'Nana'
§	- 'Nana'	SCoo

- 'Peggy'	EBee EBou EHyd EPfP NGdn NLar SBut
fulgens W/O 7151 new	GGro
× ***haageana***	SRms
'Hill Grounds'	CElw EBee ECha ECtt ELon GBin NLar SCoo WCot WGoo WSHC
'Molten Lava'	EHyd EPfP LRHS MHol NRHS SRms
nutans	SPtp
I ***sieboldii*** 'Plena' (d)	WFar
§ ***viscaria***	ECha EPPr GJos GPSL
- 'Alba'	ECha EGrI XLum
- ***alpina***	see *L. viscaria*
§ - subsp. ***atropurpurea***	EHyd ELan EPPr EWes GJos MMuc MPie SBut SPhx SRms
- 'Feuer'	EWes MHol NGBl
- 'Firebird'	EWes SPeP
- 'Plena' (d)	CBor NBir SRkn
- 'Schnee'	GJos NGBl NLar
- 'Splendens'	CCBP EGrI NGrd SCob WCav WFar XLum
- 'Splendens Plena' (d) ♀H5	WSMil XLum
wilfordii	NWad
- 'Karafuto' new	GGro
§ ***yunnanensis***	GKev NSti SPhx WBrk
- ***alba***	see *L. yunnanensis*

Lycianthes (*Solanaceae*)

§ ***rantonnetii*** ♀H3	CBcs CCCN ELan EShb SEND SIvy SPoG WAvo WKif
- 'Royal Robe'	EAJP

Lycium (*Solanaceae*)

afrum	SVen
barbarum	CAgr CBcs CCCN CLau CSBt EPom IDee LCro LEdu LOPS MAsh MGil MHtn NLar SEND SEdi SPre SVic SWvt WKor WLov XAbr
- 'Big Lifeberry'	CAgr
- 'Number 1 Lifeberry'	CAgr
- 'Sweet Lifeberry'	CAgr LEdu
chinense	MGil NQui

Lycopodium (*Lycopodiaceae*)

clavatum	GPoy

Lycopsis see *Anchusa*

Lycopus (*Lamiaceae*)

europaeus	CHab CPud GPoy MMuc NAts NMir WSFF

Lycoris (*Amaryllidaceae*)

albiflora	GKev NRog
aurea	GKev NRog SDeJ WHil
caldwellii	NRog
chinensis	NRog
haywardii	NRog
houdyshelii	NRog
longituba	NRog
radiata	CCCN GKev SDeJ WHil
sanguinea	NRog
sprengeri	NRog
straminea	NRog

Lygeum (*Poaceae*)

spartum	XSen

Lygodium (*Lygodiaceae*)

japonicum	WFib

Lygos see *Retama*

Lyonothamnus (*Rosaceae*)

floribundus subsp. ***aspleniifolius***	CCCN CExl EBee SArc WPGP

Lysichiton (*Araceae*)

camtschatcensis ♀H7	CBen CPud CWat ECha GBin LCro LLWG LOPS LRHS NPer SWvt WPnP WShi XLum
× ***hortensis***	ECha EGrI SPer

Lysiloma (*Fabaceae*)

watsonii	SPlb

Lysimachia (*Primulaceae*)

albescens	CExl XLum
§ ***atropurpurea***	CBod CSpe EAJP EBee EHyd ELan LRHS NLar SCoo SPer WHil
- 'Beaujolais'	CBod CChe CExl CKel CRos GGro LCro LOPS LRHS MGos NGBl NRHS SCoo SPeP SPoG WHil
- 'Geronimo'	CSpe
barystachys ♀H6	MArl MBel MRav SHar WCot WFar WHoo XLum
- PAB 8755	LEdu
- 'Huntingbrook'	LEdu MAvo SEdd WPGP WWtn
CANDELA ('Innlyscand')	CBod CChe CSpe ECtt EHyd EPau GPSL GWyn LRHS LSou MHer MHol MMuc NBir NCou NGBl NRHS SCoo SGbt SPoG WCav WCot WTor WWtn
candida	WCot
christinae 'Zixin'	LEdu WPGP
ciliata	CMac ECha EHyd GMaP MNrw NBir NFav NGdn NLar
§ - 'Firecracker' ♀H6	Widely available
- 'Purpurea'	see *L. ciliata* 'Firecracker'
clethroides ♀H6	Widely available
- 'Geisha' (v)	ECha WCot
- 'Lady Jane'	CEme CPla CRos GJos MAvo MNrw SRms
- 'Leigong Storm'	WPGP
§ ***congestiflora***	NPer
- 'Midnight Sun'PBR	CCCN ECtt
- 'Outback Sunset'PBR (v)	ECtt MBros
- 'Persian Chocolate'	WFar WMal
ephemerum ♀H6	Widely available
fordiana	MAvo WPGP
- Og 454	SPtp
fortunei	MACG WFar XLum
japonica	GRum ITim SLee SRot
var. ***minutissima***	
lichiangensis	EHyd GKev NBir
lyssii	see *L. congestiflora*
minoricensis	GKev WSpi XLum
nemorum	NAts
- 'Lola Playle'PBR	WCot
nummularia	CPud CSBt CWat EPfP GPoy LLWG MBow NAts NBir WBrk
- 'Aurea' ♀H5	Widely available
paridiformis	LEdu
var. ***paridiformis***	
- - NJM 11.067	WPGP
- var. ***stenophylla***	CDTJ CExl GBin SPtp WMal WPGP
punctata misapplied	see *L. verticillaris*
punctata L.	CBod CSBt EBou ECha EPfP GAbr MACG MHer MRav NBro NMir NPer SBls SCob SPer SRms WBrk WCAu WCav WFar WMAq
§ - 'Alexander' (v)	Widely available
- dwarf	EWoo

- 'Gaulthier Brousse'	EBee MHCG WCot
- GOLDEN ALEXANDER ('Walgoldalex'PBR) (v)	CChe CKel CTtf LBuc MBNS NHol NLar
- 'Golden Glory' (v)	WCot
- 'Hometown Hero'	EBee NLar
- 'Ivy Maclean' (v)	SWvt
- 'Variegata'	see *L. punctata* 'Alexander'
- ***verticillata***	see *L. verticillaris*
'Purpurea'	see *L. atropurpurea*
serpyllifolia	GJos
SNOW CANDLES ('L9902')	EBee ELon EWes MNrw SIvy WFar
taliensis	GGro
thyrsiflora	CWat EBee NPer WCot WMAq
§ ***verticillaris***	CTri WCot
vulgaris	CBod CHab CPud EWat LLWG
- subsp. ***davurica***	WCot
- - B&SWJ 8632	WCru

Lysionotus (*Gesneriaceae*)

gamosepalus	MVil
- B&SWJ 7241	WCru
kwangsiensis	MVil
- HWJ 625	WCru
pauciflorus	IArd IDee MVil SMad
- B&SWJ 303	WCru
- B&SWJ 335	WCru
- HWJ 643 from Vietnam	WCru
- HWJ 811 from Vietnam	WCru
- dwarf B&SWJ 189	WCru
- 'Lady Lavender'	MVil WFar
serratus	MVil
- HWJK 2426	WCru

Lythrum (*Lythraceae*)

anceps	NLar
'Rose Dream'	NWad
salicaria	CBee CBen CCBP CHab CPud CWat ENfk EWat GJos LLWG MBow MCot MHer MMuc MNHC MWts NAts NBro NGrd NMir SEND SPlb SRms WBrk WHer WPnP WSFF WShi WWtn XLum
- 'Augenweide'	XLum
- 'Blush' ♀H7	Widely available
§ - 'Feuerkerze' ♀H7	CBod CMea CRos EBee ECtt ELan ELon EPfP EShb LRHS MArl MBel MRav MSpe NBir NHol NRHS NSti SCob SGbt SPer WFar WHrl WWtn
- FIRECANDLE	see *L. salicaria* 'Feuerkerze'
- 'JS Pink Tails'	IPot
- 'Lady Sackville'	EBee ECtt ELon GMaP IPot LSou MCot NDov NLar WSHC
- 'Little Robert'	ECtt WFar
- 'Morden Pink'	CTri EBee EHyd ELan ELon MMuc NLar NRHS SCob SEND WFar XLum
- 'Prichard's Variety'	ELon
- 'Red Beauty'	LSun
- 'Robert'	Widely available
- 'Robin'	CBod CRos EBee ECtt EHyd LRHS MAsh MHol MPri NDov NLar NRHS SGbt SWvt
- 'Rose'	NBir SWvt
- 'Stichflamme'	ELon
- 'Swirl'	CMea ECha ECtt EHyd ELan ELon EMor EPfP ILea LEdu LLWG LRHS MACG NDov NLar NRHS NSti SHar WHoo
- 'The Beacon'	CPla CTtf EBee ELon NLar SRms
- 'Zigeunerblut'	ECtt ELon MRav NLar WCAu XLum
virgatum	SMHy SPhx WCFE WSHC
- 'Dropmore Purple'	Widely available
- 'Helene'	NDov
- pale-flowered	NDov
- 'Rose Queen'	ECtt IPot MRav
- 'Rosy Gem'	EBee EPfP GJos GMaP LShi MACG NBro NRHS SCob SDix SRms SWvt WFar
- 'The Rocket'	CBod CTri EHyd EPfP EShb LRHS MBel MPie MRav NBro NDov NRHS SPer SWvt WFar WWtn

M

Maackia (*Fabaceae*)

amurensis	CBcs CMCN EPfP GBin LMaj LPar
hupehensis	MBiu NLar

Macadamia (*Proteaceae*)

integrifolia (F)	SVic
tetraphylla new	CAco

mace, English see *Achillea ageratum*

Macfadyena see *Dolichandra*

Machaeranthera (*Asteraceae*)

sp. new	EBee
coloradoensis new	WHil

Machaerina (*Cyperaceae*)

rubiginosa	LLWG

Machilus see *Persea*

Mackaya (*Acanthaceae*)

§ ***bella*** ♀H1b	EShb

Macleaya (*Papaveraceae*)

cordata misapplied	see *M.* × *kewensis*
§ ***cordata*** (Willd.) R. Br. ♀H6	CRos EBee EWoo LRHS LSun NBir NRHS SPer SPlb SRms WCAu XLum
- NJM 11.002	WPGP
§ × ***kewensis***	GKev SCob SPoG
- 'Flamingo' ♀H6	EBee EBou ECha EHyd GWyn MBNS NLar SPer SWvt WCot WSMil
§ ***microcarpa***	WSMil
- 'Kelway's Coral Plume' ♀H6	CBcs CMac EBee EGrI EHyd ELan EPfP EWoo GAbr GMaP LCro LOPS LRHS LSRN MRav NBid NBro SBls SCob SDix SPeP SPer SPoG SWvt WSMil
- 'Spetchley Ruby'	EBee ECha GBin LRHS MRav NLar SPhx WCot XLum

Maclura (*Moraceae*)

pomifera	CBcs CMCN EWTr IDee MBlu SBrt SEND SPlb
- 'Cannonball'	CDoC LRHS
- 'Naughty Boy'	NLar
- 'Pretty Woman'	NLar
tricuspidata B&SWJ 12755	WCru
- 'Parthenos' (F)	CAgr
- seedless (F)	CAgr

Macrodiervilla see *Weigela*

Macropiper (*Piperaceae*)

§ ***excelsum***	GPoy

Macrothelypteris (*Thelypteridaceae*)

torresiana	WPGP

Macrozamia (*Zamiaceae*)

communis	CBrP
lucida	CBrP
moorei	CBrP

Maddenia (*Rosaceae*)

hypoleuca	IDee MBlu NLar

Maesa (*Primulaceae*)

japonica CWJ 12371	WCru

Magnolia ✿ (*Magnoliaceae*)

acuminata	CBcs CMCN LMaj
- 'Blue Opal'	CBcs LRHS SGsty
* - 'Kinju'	CEnd CJun
- 'Koban Dori'	CBcs CJun
- 'Patriot'	CMCN
- 'Patriot' × (× ***brooklynensis*** 'Yellow Bird')	MAsh
- 'Seiju'	CJun NLar
- var. ***subcordata*** 'Miss Honeybee'	CJun
- - 'Mister Yellowjacket'	CJun
'Advance'	CBcs CDoC CJun NLar
'Albatross'	CBcs CEnd CJun WPGP
'Alex'	CJun LMil SEdd
'Alixeed'	CJun
'Amber'	CJun
'Ambrosia'	CJun
'Amethyst Flame'	XSte
amoena	CBcs
'Angelica'	CJun
'Anilou'	CJun
'Anna'	CJun
'Anticipation'	CBcs CEnd CJun LRHS WPGP
'Antje Zandee' **new**	CBcs
'Aphrodite'	NLar
'Apollo'	CBcs CDoC CJun LSRN WPGP XSte
'Archangel'	CJun
ashei	see *M. macrophylla* subsp. *ashei*
'Asian Artistry'	CDoC CJun LRHS
'Athene' 🏆H5	CBcs CDoC CEnd CJun LMil NLar SAko WPGP
'Atlas'	CBcs CDoC CEnd CJun LEdu WPGP
'Aurora'	CJun XSte
'Avocet'	LRHS
'Banana Split'	LMil LRHS MAsh
'Betty'	CBcs CKel CMac EBee ELon LRHS LSRN MBlu MGos MMuc NLar NWea SGsty SLim SSta SWeb
'Big Dude'	CBcs CEnd CJun EPfP IDee LRHS MTrO NLar SLim WMat
'Binette'	CJun
biondii	MBlu
'Bishop Michael' **new**	CBcs
'Black Beauty'	CBcs CJun LRHS XSte
'Black Swan'	WPGP
BLACK TULIP ('Jurmag1'PBR)	CBcs CMac ELan EPfP GGGa LCro LMil LOPS LPar LRHS LSRN MAsh MGos MTrO NLar NOrn SCoo SLon SPoG WHwl WLea WMat WPGP WTSh XSte
BLACKBERRY ROSE ('Brombeer') **new**	CBcs
'Blushing Belle'	CJun
'Brenda'	CJun
'Brixton Belle'	CBcs WPGP XSte
× ***brooklynensis*** 'Evamaria'	XSte
- 'Golden Joy'	CBcs CJun
- 'Hattie Carthan'	CJun NLar
- 'Woodsman'	CBcs NLar NOra WMat
- 'Yellow Bird'	CBcs CCVT CDoC CEnd CJun CMCN CMac EPfP LMaj LMil LPar LSRN MAsh MBlu MGos MPri MThu MTrO NLar NOra NOrn SCob SLim SPoG SWeb WHwl WMat XSte
BURGUNDY STAR ('Jurmag4')	CBcs LCro LOPS MGos SWeb XSte
'Butterbowl'	CJun
'Butterflies'	CBcs CCCN CDoC CJun EHyd ELan EPfP LPar LRHS LSRN MBlu MGos NLar NOra NRHS SCob SGsty SLim SPer SRms SSta WFar WMat WSpi
'Caerhays Belle' 🏆H5	CBcs CDoC CJun LMil LRHS NLar SAko SPoG WHwl WPGP XSte
'Caerhays Surprise' 🏆H5	CBcs CEnd CJun WPGP
campbellii	CBcs CMCN EPfP WHwl
- Alba Group	WPGP
- - 'Chyverton'	WPGP
- - 'Sir Harold Hillier'	CJun WPGP
- - 'Strybing White'	WPGP
- 'Ambrose Congreve'	WPGP
- 'Betty Jessel'	CBcs CJun IDee WPGP
- 'Darjeeling' 🏆H4	CBcs CJun LRHS WPGP XSte
- 'Lionel de Rothschild'	WPGP
- subsp. ***mollicomata***	LRHS WHwl
- - 'Lanarth'	CBcs WPGP
- - 'Peter Borlase'	WPGP
- - 'Werrington'	CBcs
- 'Queen Caroline'	SBdl WPGP
- (Raffillii Group) 'Charles Raffill'	CBcs CDoC EPfP LMil LRHS SPer SPoG WHwl XSte
- - 'Kew's Surprise'	WPGP
- 'Sidbury'	CBcs
campbellii × ***sargentiana*** var. ***robusta***	LRHS
campbellii × ***sprengeri***	WPGP
'Candy Cane'	CJun
'Carlos'	CBcs CJun NLar
cathcartii	WPGP
- B&SWJ 11802	WCru
- HWJ 874	WCru
caveana	LEdu
- NJM 13.037	WPGP
- NJM 13.044	EBee WPGP
'Cecil Nice'	CBcs CJun
CHAMELEON	see *M.* 'Chang Hua'
§ 'Chang Hua'	CJun NLar
changhungtana × ***insignis***	WPGP
'Charles Coates'	CJun EPfP NLar WPGP
'Charming Lady'	CJun
chevalieri B&SWJ 11802	WCru
- DJHV 06037	WCru
- HWJ 621	WCru
CHINA TOWN ('Jing Ning')	CJun
'Columnar Pink'	LMil LRHS NLar WHwl
compressa	XSte
'Coral Lake'	CJun LMil LRHS
'Cornish Chough'	WPGP
crassifolia hort.	see *M. fansipanensis*
'Crescendo'	CJun
'Crystal Chalice'	CJun
'Cup Cake'	CJun
'Curlew'	WPGP
cylindrica misapplied	see *M.* 'Pegasus'

cylindrica ambig.	CBcs SPtp
cylindrica E.H.Wilson	WPGP
- 'Bjuv'	CJun
'Daphne' ♀H6	CBcs CEnd CJun EPfP EWTr LMil LRHS LSRN MAsh MGos MTrO NLar SLim SPoG WMat WPGP XSte
'Darrell Dean'	CJun
'David Clulow' ♀H5	CBcs CJun SSta WPGP XSte
dawsoniana	CBcs CMCN IDee WSpi
- 'Barbara Cook'	CJun
- 'Chyverton Red'	CBcs WPGP
- 'Ruby Rose'	CJun
- 'Valley Splendour'	CJun
'Daybreak' ♀H6	CBcs CJun ELan EPfP LMil LPar LRHS MBlu MGos MRav MTrO NLar NOra SGol SSta WMat WPGP XSte
'Deborah'	CJun
decidua	CBcs
delavayi	CBcs CBrP CJun CMCN EPfP LRHS SArc SEND WPGP XSte
'Delia Williams'	WPGP
§ ***denudata*** ♀H6	CBcs CMCN ELan EPfP LMaj LMil MBlu SSta
- 'Double Diamond'	CJun
- FESTIROSE ('Minfor')	EHed LRHS
- 'Forrest's Pink'	CBcs
- FRAGRANT CLOUD ('Dan Xin')	CJun EHed
- 'Gere'	CBcs CJun
- 'Ghost Ship'	CJun
- YELLOW RIVER ('Fei Huang')	CDoC CEnd CJun LMaj LPar NLar NOra SCob SPoG WLea WMat
doltsopa	CBcs CCCN CExl EPfP SSta WPGP
- B&SWJ 13996	WCru
- NJM 12.028	WPGP
- NJM 12.047	WPGP
'Early Red' **new**	LRHS
'Early Rose'	CJun
'Elegance'	CJun
'Elisa Odenwald'	LMil LRHS XSte
'Elizabeth' ♀H6	CBcs CDoC CJun CMCN EHyd EPfP LMil LRHS LSRN MAsh MBlu MGos MTrO NLar NOra NOrn NRHS SGsty SPer SPoG SRms SWvt WHwl WMat
'Emma Cook'	CJun
§ ***ernestii***	WPGP
'Eskimo'	CJun EPfP LRHS MTrO WMat
'F.J. Williams'	CBcs WPGP
'Fairy'	MThu
FAIRY BLUSH ('Micjur01'PBR)	CBcs CDoC LCro LOPS LRHS MGos WHwl XSte
FAIRY CREAM ('Micjur02'PBR)	CBcs CCCN LCro LOPS LRHS NLar WHwl XSte
FAIRY MAGNOLIA WHITE ('Micjur05'PBR)	CBcs CCCN LCro LOPS NLar SPoG WHwl XSte
§ ***fansipanensis*** FMWJ 13054	WCru
- FMWJ 13163	WCru
'Felicity'	CJun
FELIX JURY ('Jurmag2'PBR)	CBcs ELan EPfP LRHS MTrO WMat XSte
figo	CBcs CCCN CExl CKel EBee EHed EHyd ELan EPfP EShb MGil NRHS SSta WPGP
'Fireglow'	CJun
'Flamingo'	CJun NLar
floribunda FMWJ 13384 from Tonkin, Vietnam	WCru
- NJM 09.179	WPGP
- WWJ 11874	WCru
- WWJ 11996	WCru
- WWJ 12003	WCru
- WWJ 12011	WCru
- WWJ 11982 from Tonkin, Vietnam	WCru
- 'Fansipan Furry'	WCru
- 'Furry Uok'	WPGP
× ***foggii*** 'Allspice'	CBcs LRHS XSte
fordiana	CExl
'Foster's Late White'	WPGP
§ ***foveolata*** B&SWJ 11749	WCru
- DJHV 06105	WCru
- WWJ 11900	WCru
- WWJ 11929	WCru
- WWJ 11955	WCru
'Frank Gladney'	CJun
fraseri	CBcs CMCN
'Galaxy' ♀H6	CBcs CBrac CDoC CEnd CJun CMac ELon EPfP IDee IPap LMil LPar MAsh MGos MMuc MTrO NLar NOrn SAko SLim SPer SSta SavN WMat
'Genie'PBR	CBcs CCVT CDoC EHed EHyd ELan LMil LPar LRHS MTrO NLar NOra NRHS SCob SEdd SGsty SWeb WMat WPGP XSte
'George Henry Kern' ♀H6	CBcs CBrac CLnd EHyd EPfP LMil LPar MGos NLar SGsty XSte
'Ghislaine'	WPGP
'Gladys Carlson'	CJun
globosa	CExl EHyd LEdu NRHS WPGP
'Gold Crown'	CJun
'Gold Star' ♀H6	CBcs CEnd CJun EHyd LMil LRHS MGos NLar NOra NRHS SPoG SSta WGob WMat WPGP XSte
'Golden Endeavour'	CJun
'Golden Gala'	CJun
'Golden Gift'	CJun LMil LRHS MAsh WPGP
'Golden Pond'	CJun LRHS
'Golden Rain'	CJun
'Golden Sun'	CJun
'Goldfinch'	CBcs CJun
I × ***gotoburgensis*** Chollipo clone	WPGP
grandiflora	CMCN CSBt CTsd EBee EPfP ESwi EWTr LCro LEdu LOPS LPar LSRN MGos MMuc MRav NLar NOrn SArc SEND SEWo SWeb WTSh XSte
- ALTA ('Tmgh'PBR)	LRHS MGos MTrO XSte
- 'Blanchard'	CJun LRHS NLar XSte
- 'Bracken's Brown Beauty'	EHyd LMil NRHS
- 'Charles Dickens'	SVen
- 'Edith Bogue'	LRHS SSta
- 'Exmouth'	CBcs CDoC CEme CEnd CKel CMCN CMac CSBt CTri EHyd ELan EPfP LMil LSRN MAsh MBlu NLar NRHS SCob SPer SPoG SRms SSta SWvt
- 'Ferruginea'	CBcs CBod CJun EPfP LPar NLar SGol SGsty WLov
- 'Flore Pleno' (d)	SGol
- 'Foothills'	CMCN
- 'François Treyve'	CDoC EPfP LSRN NLar WHwl XSte
- 'Galissonnière'	CBcs CCVT CDoC EHyd EPfP ERom LMaj SCob SGol SGsty SWvt WHwl
I - 'Galissonnière Nana'	WHwl
- 'Goliath'	ELan EPfP LMaj LPar SEWo SGsty SSta
- 'Harold Poole'	CJun
- 'Kay Parris' ♀H5	CBcs CJun EHyd EPfP LMil LRHS MAsh NRHS SPoG XSte

– 'Little Gem'	CBcs CBod CCCN CDoC CJun EBee ELan ELon EPfP IDee LCro LOPS LPar LRHS LSRN NLar SGol SPoG SSta WFar WLov XSte
– 'Mainstreet'	CJun LRHS XSte
– 'Monlia'	CJun
– 'Nannetensis' (d)	EHed MHtn NLar
– 'November Fox'	LRHS
– 'Pistoiese'	SGsty
– 'Praecox'	LMaj
– 'Purpan'	NLar
– 'Russet'	CJun
– 'Saint Mary'	CJun
– 'Samuel Sommer'	CJun
– 'Symmes Select'	CJun
– 'Treyvei'	CJun
– 'Victoria' ♀^{H5}	CJun CTri EHyd ELan ELon EPfP LMil LSRN MAsh MBlu NLar NRHS SSta XSte
'Green Bee'	CJun
'Green Diamond' **new**	SGsty
'Hawk'	EBee WPGP
'Heaven Scent' ♀^{H5}	Widely available
'Helen Fogg'	CJun
heptapeta	see *M. denudata*
'Honey Belle'	CJun
'Honey Flower'	CJun
'Honey Liz'	CBcs LRHS
HONEY TULIP ('Jurmag5')	CBcs LRHS MTrO NLar SWeb WMat XSte
§ 'Hong Yun'	CJun
'Hot Flash'	CJun
'Hot Lips'	CJun
hypoleuca	see *M. obovata* Thunb.
'Ian's Red'	CBcs CJun LMil LRHS WMat WPGP
§ ***insignis***	CBcs CExl EBee LEdu LRHS WPGP
– B&SWJ 11810	WCru
– NJM 12.040	WPGP
– WWJ 11854	WCru
insignis × yuyuanensis	WPGP
'Iolanthe'	CBcs CEnd CJun CMCN EPfP LMil LRHS MAsh MGos NOrn WMat WPGP XSte
'Iufer'	CJun
'J.C.Williams'	CBcs CJun SSta WPGP
'Jane'	CJun CMac EHyd EPfP LMil MAsh MGos NOrn NRHS
'Jersey Belle'	CJun
'Joe McDaniel'	CBcs CJun IArd NLar
'John Bond'	LRHS SSta
'John Congreve'	CJun WPGP
'Joli Pompom'	CBcs CJun EPfP LMil LRHS MTrO NLar SSta WMat
'Judy Zuk'	CBcs CJun LRHS
× ***kewensis*** 'Wada's Memory'	see *M. salicifolia* 'Wada's Memory'
'Kim Kunso'	SSta
kobus	CBcs CCCN CCVT CLnd CMCN CTsd EPfP EWTr GKin IPap LMaj LPar MBlu NLar NWea SEWo SGsty SPer WMou
– B&SWJ 12751	WCru
– 'Esveld Select'	CJun
– 'Janaki Ammal'	CJun
– 'Maráczy'^{PBR} **new**	LRHS
§ – 'Norman Gould'	CJun CMCN EPfP LMil
– 'Octopus'	CJun
– pink-flowered	CBcs CJun
– 'White Elegance'	CJun
– 'Wisley Star'	CJun SSta
kwangtungensis	WPGP
laevifolia	CBcs CExl CJun CMCN LPar MGil WPGP XSte
– 'Dali Velvet'	CExl
– 'Gail's Favourite'	CRos EHyd EPfP LMil LRHS MAsh NRHS
– 'Kh-Achteraan'	XSte
– 'Mini Mouse'	EHyd EPfP LMil LRHS MAsh NRHS
– 'Summer Snowflake'	CBcs NLar
– 'Willow Leaf'	NLar
'Laura Saylor'	CJun
'Leda'	CBcs CJun IArd LMil SSta WPGP
'Legacy'	CJun WPGP
'Lemon Star'	CBcs LRHS
'Lennarth Jonsson'	CJun
liliiflora 'Darkest Purple'	CJun
§ – 'Nigra' ♀^{H6}	Widely available
– 'Raven'	LMil WPGP
* 'Limelight'	CBcs CJun EPfP NLar NOra NWea WMat WPGP
'Livingstone' **new**	CBcs
× ***loebneri*** 'Donna' ♀^{H6}	CBcs CDoC CJun EPfP LMil LRHS SSta
– 'Encore'	CJun XSte
– 'Green Mist'	CJun EHyd NRHS
– 'Leonard Messel' ♀^{H6}	Widely available
– 'Lesley Jane'	CJun
– 'Mag's Pirouette' ♀^{H6}	CBcs CJun EMil EPfP LMil LRHS NLar SAko SPoG SSta XSte
– 'Merrill' ♀^{H6}	CBcs CBod CDoC CJun CLnd CMCN CMac EHyd ELan EPfP EWTr LEdu LMaj LMil LPar LRHS MAsh MGos MMuc MRav NLar NOrn NRHS SPer SSta WMou
– 'Neil McEacharn'	CJun
– 'Pink Cloud'	CJun
– 'Powder Puff'	CJun
– 'Raspberry Fun'	CBcs CJun NLar
– 'Snowdrift'	CJun CKel EMil SLim
– 'Spring Snow'	CJun
– 'Star Bright'	CJun
– 'Swansong' **new**	WPGP
– 'White Stardust'	CJun
– 'Wildcat' ♀^{H6}	CBcs CJun LMil NLar SLim SSta XSte
– 'Willow Wood'	CJun
'Lois' ♀^{H6}	CBcs CEnd CJun EGrI EHyd EPfP GGGa LMil LRHS NLar NRHS SSta WPGP
lotungensis	WPGP
'Lotus'	CBcs CJun WPGP
* 'Lu Shan' **new**	LMil
'Lucy Carlson'	CJun
'Luscious'	CJun
macrophylla	CBcs CBrP CMCN CMac EPfP EWTr IDee LRHS MBlu MPkF NLar SMad WPGP XSte
§ – subsp. ***ashei***	CBcs CJun CMCN WPGP
– subsp. ***ashei*** × ***macrophylla*** subsp. ***dealbata***	WPGP
– subsp. ***ashei*** × ***sieboldii***	CJun
– subsp. ***ashei*** × ***virginiana***	CJun WPGP
macrophylla × ***sieboldii***	CJun
'Malin'	CJun
'Manchu Fan'	CBcs CDoC CJun EPfP GBin IArd LMil LRHS LSRN MTrO SChF SLim WMat WPGP
§ 'March til Frost'	CBcs CJun CWit EBee ELan LMil LRHS NLar WPGP
'Margaret Helen'	CBcs CJun WPGP

'Marillyn' **new**	LRHS
'Marj Gossler'	CJun
'Marjorie Congreve'	WPGP
'Mark Jury'	CBcs
'Mary Nell'	CJun
'Maryland'	CJun GGGa NLar
maudiae	CBcs CExl NLar
'Maxine Merrill'	CBcs CJun
'May to Frost'	see *M.* 'March Til Frost'
'Michael Rosse' **new**	IArd
'Milky Way' 🏆H5	CBcs CJun EPfP LRHS MGos WPGP
'Mister Yellowjacket'	CJun
'Moondance'	CJun
'Nimbus'	CJun EHyd NRHS WPGP
nitida	CExl
obovata Diels	see *M. officinalis*
§ ***obovata*** Thunb.	CBcs CMCN EPfP IDee NLar WPGP
- B&SWJ 10821	WCru
- B&SWJ 12626	WCru
- pink-flowered	WPGP
obovata × sargentiana var. ***robusta***	WPGP
§ ***officinalis***	CBcs NLar
- var. ***biloba***	CBcs CMCN EWTr GKev MBlu NLar WPGP
'Old Port'	CBcs
'Olivia'	CBcs CJun EBee WPGP
'Paul Cook'	CDoC CEnd LRHS
'Peaches 'n' Cream'	CBcs CJun
'Peachy'	CBcs CJun LMil LPar LRHS WMat
§ 'Pegasus' 🏆H6	CBcs CEnd CJun LMil LRHS SSta
'Peppermint Stick'	NLar WMat
'Peter Smithers'	CJun
'Petit Chicon'	EBee
'Phelan Bright'	CJun WPGP
'Phillip Tregunna'	CBcs LMil WPGP
'Phil's Masterpiece'	CJun
'Pickard's Sundew'	see *M.* × *soulangeana* 'Sundew'
'Piet van Veen'	CJun
'Pink Delight'	CJun
'Pink Goblet'	EHyd NRHS
'Pink Surprise'	CJun
'Pinkie'	CJun XSte
'Porcelain Dove'	CBcs CJun LMil MGos WPGP
'Premier Cru'	CJun LRHS
'Princess Margaret'	CBcs CDoC CJun LMil LRHS WMat
'Pristine'	EPfP LMil LRHS
× ***proctoriana***	EHyd LMil MBlu MMuc NRHS WPGP
- 'Robert's Dream'	CJun EHyd MAsh NRHS SSta
- 'Slavin's No 44'	CJun
- 'Slavin's Snowy'	CTsd
'Purple Breeze'	CJun LRHS MBlu NLar SAko SLim
'Purple Globe'	CBcs CEnd CJun
'Purple Platter'	CBcs
'Purple Sensation'	CBcs CJun SLim WPGP
'Purple Star'	WPGP
'Raspberry Ice'	CMac EHyd EPfP MAsh NRHS SRms
'Raspberry Swirl'	SSta
'Rebecca's Perfume'	CBcs CJun LRHS MGos MTrO NLar WMat WSpi
'Red as Red'	CBcs CJun NLar
'Red Baron'	CJun
'Red Lion'	CBcs CJun LRHS SEdd
'Ricki'	CEme CJun CKel CMac LSRN MBlu
'Rose Marie' **new**	NLar
'Roseanne'	CJun
rostrata	CBcs CExl NLar WPGP
'Royal Crown'	CBcs EPfP IArd XSte
'Royal Purple' **new**	CBcs
'Ruby'	CBcs CJun
'Ruth'	CBcs NLar
salicifolia	CMCN MMuc WSpi
- 'Aia' **new**	WPGP
- var. ***concolor***	CJun
- 'Garden House Upright'	EBee
- 'Jermyns'	CJun
- 'Louisa Fete'	CJun LMaj
- 'Miss Jack'	CMCN
* - 'Rosea'	CJun
- upright	WPGP
- 'Van Veen'	CJun WPGP
§ - 'Wada's Memory' 🏆H6	CExl CJun CMCN EHyd ELan EPfP LMaj LMil LRHS MAsh MBlu SPer SSta WFar WMat
- 'Windsor Beauty'	CJun SSta
'Sangreal'	NLar
sapaensis	IKel
- FMWJ 13315	WCru
- FMWJ 13330	WCru
- HWJ 533	WCru
- NJM 09.168	WPGP
'Sara Koe'	CJun MTrO WMat
sargentiana	CBcs SSta
- 'Broadleas'	CJun
- var. ***robusta***	CBcs EPfP
- - ***alba***	SavN
- - 'Blood Moon'	CBcs CJun EBee WPGP
- - 'Multipetal'	WPGP
'Satisfaction'	ELon LPar NLar WTSh
'Sayonara' 🏆H6	CBcs CDoC CJun EPfP LMaj LMil LRHS MTrO WMat XSte
'Scented Gem'	SSta
'Schmetterling'	see *M.* × *soulangeana* 'Pickard's Schmetterling'
'Sentinel'	LRHS WMat
'Serene'	CBcs CEnd CJun EPfP IArd LMil NLar
SHIRAZZ ('Vulden')	CBcs CDoC EBee EPfP IArd LMil LRHS MTrO NLar SEdd SLim SPoG WMat WPGP
sieboldii	CBcs CDoC CJun CMCN CMac CTsd EGrI EHed EHyd EPfP EWTr GKin IDee LMaj LMil LPar LRHS LSRN MBlu MGos MPkF MRav NLar NRHS SPoG WHwl WMou WPGP WSpi XSte
- B&SWJ 4127	WCru
- 'Colossus' 🏆H6	CJun MBlu WPGP XSte
- 'Genesis'	CJun NLar
- 'Genesis' × ***tripetala***	CJun
- 'Genesis' × ***virginiana***	CJun
- 'Michiko Renge' (d)	CJun
- 'Min Pyong-gal'	CJun
- 'Pride of Norway'	CBcs CJun
- subsp. ***sieboldii*** B&SWJ 12553 from Korea	WCru
- subsp. ***sinensis***	CJun CMCN EPfP WPGP
I - - 'Grandiflora'	CJun WPGP
- 'White Flounces' (d)	CJun NLar
'Sir Harold Hillier'	CBcs WPGP
'Snow Goose'	CJun
'Solar Flair'	CBcs CJun LPar NLar
× ***soulangeana***	Widely available
- 'Alba Superba'	CBcs CDoC CKel CTsd EPfP LCro LMil LOPS LPar MBlu MMuc MRav NLar SPer SPoG SavN WFar WSpi
- 'Alexandrina'	CBcs CLnd EPfP MBlu
- 'André Leroy'	EPfP LRHS
- 'Beugnon'	IArd LRHS
- 'Brozzonii' 🏆H6	CDoC CMac EPfP LMil SSta
- 'Cleopatra' PBR	CBcs LRHS NLar XSte

- 'Just Jean' CJun
- 'Lennei' CBcs CBrac CKel CMCN CMac CSBt EHyd EPfP IArd IPap LPar MGos MRav NOrn NRHS SCob SPer SPoG SRms WFar WLov
- 'Lennei Alba' CMCN ELan MBlu NLar NOra WFar WMat WSpi XSte
- 'Nigra' see *M. liliiflora* 'Nigra'
§ - 'Pickard's Schmetterling' ♀H6 EPfP LMil MAsh
- 'Pickard's Snow Queen' CJun
- 'Pickard's Sundew' see *M.* × *soulangeana* 'Sundew'
- 'Picture' CBcs NOrn XSte
- 'Purple Rocket' **new** LRHS
- RED LUCKY see *M.* 'Hong Yun'
- 'Rubra' misapplied see *M.* × *soulangeana* 'Rustica Rubra'
§ - 'Rustica Rubra' CBcs CBod CEme CMCN CTri EHyd EPfP LMil LRHS LSRN MAsh NLar NRHS SGol SRms SavN
- 'San José' CJun LMil MAsh WFar
- 'Speciosa' SSta SavN
§ - 'Sundew' EPfP NLar
- 'Superba' CMac LPar LRHS
- 'Sweet Simplicity' **new** CBcs
- 'Verbanica' EPfP LMil MAsh
'Spectrum' ♀H6 CBcs CEnd CJun CKel ELan EPfP IArd IDee LMaj LMil LPar LRHS MBlu MGos MMuc MTrO SSta WMat
sprengeri from Guizhou, China WPGP
- var. ***diva*** CBcs CEnd CExl LMil WPGP
- - 'Burncoose' ♀H6 CBcs
- - 'Copeland Court' ♀H6 CJun LMil LRHS MTrO WMat WPGP
- - 'Dark Diva' CJun
- - 'Diva' LRHS WPGP
- - 'Eric Savill' ♀H6 CJun WPGP
- - 'Lanhydrock' CBcs CDoC CJun LRHS WPGP
- - 'Marwood Spring' CBcs CJun LMil LRHS WPGP
- - 'Westonbirt' WPGP
'Spring Rite' CJun
'Star Wars' ♀H5 CBcs CCVT CDoC CEnd CExl CJun CMCN CMac EHyd ELan EPfP GGGa LMil LRHS MAsh MGos MTrO NOra NOrn NRHS SEWo SPoG SSta WHwl WMat WPGP XSte
'Stellar Acclaim' CJun LMil
stellata Widely available
- 'Centennial' ♀H6 CJun LMil
- 'Chrysanthemumiflora' CJun
- 'Dawn' CJun
- 'Jane Platt' ♀H6 CBcs CJun CRos EGrl EHyd ELan EPfP LEdu LMil LRHS MGos NLar NRHS SSta WPGP
- f. ***keiskei*** CBcs CEnd CJun MGos NHol SLim
- 'Kikuzaki' CJun
- 'King Rose' CBcs CJun CTsd EPfP SPer
- 'Massey' CJun
- 'Norman Gould' see *M. kobus* 'Norman Gould'
- 'Rosea' CBod CJun CKel CLnd CMCN ELan ELon EPfP LMaj LMil MGos MPri MRav MSwo NLar NOrn NWea SCob SWeb WFar
- 'Rosea Massey' CJun
- 'Royal Star' ♀H6 CAco CBcs CBrac CCVT CDoC CEnd CJun CKel CLnd CMCN CRos CTri ELon EPfP EWTr ILea LMil LRHS MBlu MGos MRav NLar NRHS SCob SGol SPer SSta WFar
- 'Rubra' **new** LPar
- 'Scented Silver' CJun LMil
- 'Shi-banchi Rosea' CJun
- 'Water Lily' CBcs CBod CDoC CJun CKel CMCN CMac CRos EHyd ELan ELon EPfP LMil LRHS LSRN MAsh MBlu MGos NRHS SCob SPer SPoG SSta WPGP
'String of Pearls' **new** CJun
'Summer Solstice' CBcs CJun EBee EPfP LMil LRHS SSta WPGP
'Summer Sonnet' WPGP
'Sun Ray' CJun
'Sunburst' CJun SRms
'Sundance' CBcs CJun LRHS MBlu
'Sunrise' LRHS SAko
'Sunsation' CBcs CJun ELan LPar LRHS NLar SLim XSte
'Sunset Swirl' CJun LRHS
'Sunspire' CJun
'Suntown' CJun
'Susan' ♀H6 Widely available
'Susanna van Veen' CBcs CDoC CEnd CJun LMil WPGP
'Swedish Star' CJun
'Sweet Merlot' CBcs CJun
'Sweet Valentine' CBcs CJun NLar WPGP
'Sweetheart' ♀H5 CJun
'Sybille' CMCN SLim WPGP
tamaulipana **new** WPGP
'Theodora' CBcs LMil LRHS SSta
× ***thompsoniana*** CBcs CMCN
- 'Olmenhof' IArd
'Thousand Butterflies' CJun
'Tikitere' CBcs LMil
'Tina Durio' CBcs CDoC NLar WMat
'Todd Gresham' CJun
'Tranquility' CBcs CJun
tripetala CExl CMCN ELan EPfP LMaj LRHS MBlu NLar SSta XSte
- 'Bloomfield' CJun
'Ultimate Yellow' CJun
× ***veitchii*** CBcs
- 'Columbus' CJun LRHS WPGP
- 'Isca' CBcs
'Venus' **new** CBcs
virginiana CBcs CJun CMCN EWTr LRHS XSte
- var. ***australis*** 'Green Shadow' SGol
- - 'Henry Hicks' XSte
I - 'Glauca' **new** CBcs
§ - 'Jim Wilson' CJun MBlu
- MOONGLOW see *M. virginiana* 'Jim Wilson'
'Vulcan' CBcs CDoC CEnd CJun EGrl ELan EPfP LMil LRHS NLar NOrn XSte
× ***watsonii*** see *M.* × *wieseneri*
'Wedding Vows' CJun
'White Mystery' CJun XSte
§ × ***wieseneri*** CBcs CJun CMCN EBee EPfP MBlu NLar NWea SPer WPGP
- 'Aashild Kalleberg' CBcs CJun WPGP
- 'Swede Made' **new** CJun
- 'William Watson' SSta
wilsonii ♀H6 CBcs CCVT CDoC CExl CJun CMCN CTri EBee EHed EHyd ELan EPfP GGro IArd LRHS MBlu MGos MMuc MNrw MTrO NLar NWea SEND SSta WGob WMat WPGP XSte
- 'Gwen Baker' CEnd CJun
'Yellow Fever' CBcs CJun WPGP
'Yellow Garland' CJun
'Yellow Lantern' ♀H6 CBcs CEnd CJun EHed EHyd ELan EPfP GGGa LMil LSRN MAsh MBlu NLar NRHS SPoG SSta WPGP

'Yellow Sea'	CJun
Yuchelia No. 1	CBcs WPGP
yunnanensis	CCCN CDoC CTsd ELon EPfP LRHS MPkF
zenii	CBcs CMCN IArd LRHS
- 'Pink Parchment'	CBcs CJun XSte

× *Mahoberberis* (*Berberidaceae*)

aquisargentii	CBcs CKel CMac EBee EHyd EPfP LRHS MMuc MRav NLar SEND WFar
'Dart's Desire'	NLar
miethkeana	SRms
§ ***neubertii***	NLar

Mahonia ✿ (*Berberidaceae*)

§ ***aquifolium***	CAgr CBcs CBrac GPoy LPar MGos MMuc MRav NWea SCob SEND SGbt SGol SPer SPlb SWvt
- 'Apollo' 🏆H5	CBcs CDoC CMac EBee EHyd ELan EPfP LCro LOPS LRHS LSRN MAsh MBlu MGos MRav NLar SCob SCoo SPoG SRms SWvt WFar WSpi
- 'Atropurpurea'	CMac CRos CSBt CTsd ELan EPfP LRHS MRav SPer
- 'Fascicularis'	see *M.* × *wagneri* 'Pinnacle'
- 'Moseri'	WLov
- 'Smaragd'	CMac ELan EPfP LRHS LSRN MBlu MGos MRav NLar SCob WSpi
- 'Versicolor'	MBlu
'Arthur Menzies'	EHyd LMil LRHS NRHS
§ ***bealei***	CBcs CBod CBrac CDoC CKel CRos CSBt EHyd ELan ELon EPfP LRHS MAsh MGos MRav MSwo NLar NPer SCob SCoo SGol SWvt
- 'Cornish Silver' **new**	EBee
BLACKFOOT ('Bokrafoot'[PBR])	EHyd ELan EPfP LRHS MAsh SLon
bodinieri	WPGP
- Og 93.033	WPGP
chochoco	CExl
confusa* × *gracilipes	WSpi
§ ***duclouxiana***	SPtp
- KR 7692	WPGP
'Esme'	WPGP
eurybracteata	CExl SPtp WCru WPGP
- subsp. ***ganpinensis***	SEND WPGP
- - 'Soft Caress'	CBcs CBod CDoC CMCN CRos EBee EHyd ELan EPfP EWTr LCro LOPS LPar LRHS MGos MRav NLar NRHS SCob SCoo SGol SPad SPer SPoG SWvt SavN WFar WLea WSMil XSte
- 'Minganpi'[PBR]	LSRN
- 'Narihira'	LPar SGsty
- 'Sweet Winter'	CDoC EMil IDee MAsh MMrt SWvt
eutriphylla misapplied	see *M. trifolia*
fortunei	CBcs
- 'Curlyque' **new**	WPGP
gracilipes	CBcs CExl CMCN EBee EPfP ESwi EWes MBlu NLar WAvo WCru WPGP
gracilis	EBee
haematocarpa	WPGP
hartwegii	WPGP
japonica 🏆H5	CAco CBar CBcs CDoC CEme CMac CRos CTri EBee EHyd EPfP LRHS MAsh MGos MMuc MRav MSwo NHol NRHS SCob SEND SGbt SPer SPoG SRms SSta WCFE
- 'Gold Dust'	MBlu
§ - 'Hivernant'	NWea
lanceolata	EPfP MBlu
leschenaultii B&SWJ 9535	WCru
× ***lindsayae*** 'Cantab' 🏆H4	EBee EPfP WPGP
lomariifolia	see *M. oiwakensis* subsp. *lomariifolia*
longibracteata	GKin
× ***media*** 'Buckland' 🏆H5	CMac EPfP SRms WLov
- 'Charity'	Widely available
- 'Lionel Fortescue' 🏆H5	CBcs CBod CMac CRos CSBt EBee EHyd EPfP GKin LRHS MAsh NRHS SPer SWvt
- 'Winter Sun' 🏆H5	Widely available
moranensis	CExl EBee
- T 292	WPGP
napaulensis	NLar
- 'Maharajah'	IArd NLar
nervosa	CMac EPfP MBlu SBrt WPGP
- B&SWJ 9562	WCru
- B&SWJ 13580	WCru
neubertii	see × *Mahoberberis neubertii*
nevinii	SBrt
nitens	EBee SPtp WCru WPGP
- 'Cabaret'[PBR] 🏆H4	CBcs CRos EBee EHyd EPfP LCro LOPS LRHS LSRN MAsh MBlu MGos NRHS SCob SPoG SSta SWvt WSpi
oiwakensis	LRHS WPGP
- B&SWJ 371	WCru
- B&SWJ 3660	LEdu WCru
- PBR 371 from Hong Kong	WCru
§ - subsp. ***lomariifolia*** 🏆H4	CExl CRos EPfP LRHS SArc SPtp
pallida	CExl EBee SPtp WPGP
'Pan's Peculiar'	EBee WPGP
pinnata misapplied	see *M.* × *wagneri* 'Pinnacle'
pinnata (Lag.) Fedde 'Ken S. Howard'	NLar WPGP
- 'Maurice Foster'	NLar
- subsp. ***insularis*** 'Schnilemoon'	WPGP
repens	NLar WKor WSpi
- 'Rotundifolia'	SPlb
× ***savilliana***	EBee IArd NLar WPGP
§ ***sheridaniana*** Og 93033	WPGP
- Og 93056	WPGP
SIOUX ('Bokrasio'[PBR])	EHyd LRHS MAsh NRHS SPoG
§ ***trifolia***	IArd
- EKB 4618	EBee WPGP
volcania B&SWJ 10400	WCru
× ***wagneri***	SWvt
- 'Hastings' Elegant'	NLar
§ - 'Pinnacle' 🏆H5	CRos EHyd ELan EPfP LRHS MAsh MBlu NLar SPoG SWvt WFar
- 'Sunset'	MBlu
- 'Undulata'	MBlu SPer

Maianthemum (*Asparagaceae*)

amoenum B&SWJ 10390	WCru
atropurpureum	WCru
bicolor	LEdu
bifolium	CAvo CBct ESwi GLog GMaP LEdu MAvo MBel MNrw NBro SRms WCru WShi WThu XLum
- from Yakushima, Japan	GRum
§ - subsp. ***kamtschaticum***	CAvo EMor EPPr ESwi LEdu MAvo NLar NRya WCot WPGP
- - B&SWJ 4360	WCru
- - CD&R 2300	WCru
- - var. ***pumilum***	EBee LEdu WCru
canadense	EAJP EBee EPPr EPot ESwi GKev LEdu MNrw NBid SIvy WCru
chasmanthum	see *M. bifolium* subsp. *kamtschaticum*
comaltepecense B&SWJ 10215	WCru

dilatatum	see *M. bifolium* subsp. *kamtschaticum*
flexuosum	LEdu
- B&SWJ 9069	WCru
- B&SWJ 9079	WCru
- B&SWJ 9150	WCru
aff. ***flexuosum*** B&SWJ 9026	WCru WFar
- B&SWJ 9055	WCru
formosanum B&SWJ 349	EPPr WCru WFar
forrestii	WCru
fuscum	GKev WCot WCru WPnP
- var. ***cordatum***	WCru
- 'Shirui Giant'	WPGP
- 'Tangkhul Giant'	LEdu
gigas B&SWJ 10470	WCru
henryi	GKev LEdu WCru WPGP
- BWJ 7616	WCru WFar
japonicum	GKev LEdu
- B&SWJ 1179	WCru
- B&SWJ 4714	WCru
- B&SWJ 7306	WCru
- 'Ki Shiro Fukurin Fu' (v) **new**	WCot
oleraceum	CBct CExl GEdr GKev LEdu SDir WFar WHil WPnP
- B&SWJ 2148	WCru
paniculatum	LEdu SHar
- B&SWJ 9137	WCru
- B&SWJ 9140	WCru
- purple-flowered B&SWJ 9139	WCru
pendent, B&SWJ 10305 from Guatemala	WCru
purpureum	GKev LEdu
- G-W&P 150	EPPr
racemosum 🏆^{H6}	Widely available
- subsp. ***amplexicaule***	ILea
- - 'Emily Moody'	CBct CExl EPPr EPfP IPot WCot WPGP
- 'Major'	EHyd
aff. ***salvinii***	CBct
- B&SWJ 9000	WCru
- B&SWJ 9030	ESwi
- B&SWJ 9088	WCru
- B&SWJ 10402	WCru
scilloideum B&SWJ 10407	WCru
* - var. ***roseum*** B&SWJ 10335	CBct WCru
stellatum	CBct ECha EHed EHyd EMor EPPr EPfP GQue ILea LEdu LRHS NChi NLar NRHS WCru WFar WKor XLum
szechuanicum	WCru
tatsienense	CBct CExl CSpe GEdr GKev LEdu WCot WCru WPGP
- dark-stemmed **new**	WPGP

Maihuenia (*Cactaceae*)

poeppigii	SPlb
- F&W 9670	WCot
- JCA 2.575.600	WCot

Maihueniopsis (*Cactaceae*)

darwinii	SPlb

Mallotus (*Euphorbiaceae*)

japonicus B&SWJ 14613	WCru
- B&SWJ 14679	WCru

Malotigena (*Aizoaceae*)

§ ***frantiskae-niederlovae***	CCCN CSma EBou EPot GEdr NHpl SSim WIce XLum
- 'Album'	see *M. frantiskae-niederlovae* 'White Nugget'
- 'Gold Nugget' 🏆^{H4}	EHyd LRHS NRHS
§ - 'White Nugget'	CCCN CSma ELan EPot EWes GEdr LRHS NHpl NRHS SLee SSim WIce

Malus ✿ (*Rosaceae*)

'Adams' **new**	LMaj
§ 'Adirondack' 🏆^{H6}	CLnd CSBt ELan EPfP EWTr LBuc LCro LOPS LRHS MMuc MPri MTrO NOra SCoo SGol SPoG WMat WMou
'Admiration'	see *M.* 'Adirondack'
× ***adstringens*** 'Almey'	LMaj SBdl
- 'Hopa'	CAgr CLnd
- 'Purple Wave'	SBdl
- 'Simcoe'	EBee SBdl
'Aldenhamensis'	see *M.* × *purpurea* 'Aldenhamensis'
'Allow Super' (D)	WMat
'Amberina'	CLnd
'Appletini' (D)	LCro LOPS
baccata	CLnd CMCN GKev NOra NWea SCoo SEND SPlb WMat
- 'Braendkjaer'	CLnd
- 'Street Parade'	EWTr LMaj
aff. ***baccata***	MTrO
'Barbara'	NOra WMat
'Baskatong' **new**	SBdl
§ ***bhutanica***	SBdl
- 'Mandarin'	SCoo
BRANDYWINE ('Branzam') **new**	SPer
brevipes	CLnd LRHS SCoo
- 'Wedding Bouquet' 🏆^{H6}	CBod EBee EPfP LCro LSRN MAsh MTrO NLar NOra NOrn SGol SPer WMat
'Butterball' 🏆^{H6}	CBod CLnd CSBt EBee EPfP EPom LMaj MNic MTrO NOra NWea SCoo SEdi SGol SLim SPer SPoG SRms SVic WMat WMou WWct
'Candymint Sargent'	CLnd MTrO NOra SGol SLim SPoG WMat
'Cave Hill'	CLnd
'Cheal's Scarlet'	CHab NRog
* 'Cheal's Weeping'	CAco CBod CLnd CMac EWTr SEdi SGsty SRms
CINDERELLA ('Cinzam') **new**	MTrO NOra WMat
COCCINELLA ('Courtarou')	LMaj SGol SMad
'Comtesse de Paris' 🏆^{H6}	CLnd EBee EPfP EWTr LRHS MBlu MTrO NLar NOra NOrn WMat
CORALBURST ('Coralcole')	LCro LOPS MAsh MTrO NOra NOrn SPoG WMat
coronaria	SPtp
- var. ***dasycalyx*** 'Charlottae' (d)	CCVT EWTr SPer
- 'Elk River'	CLnd NOra SBdl SCoo WMat
'Cowichan'	CLnd SBdl SSFr
'Crimson Brilliant'	CLnd
'Dartmouth'	CHab CLnd CSBt CTri NRog
'Directeur Moerlands'	CArg CCVT CDoC CLnd CSBt EPfP MTrO NOra SCoo SPer SWvt WMat
domestica 'A.D.W. Atkins' (C/D) **new**	SBdl
- 'Acklam Russet' (D)	CHab NRog SBdl SKee
- 'Adams's Pearmain' (D)	CArg CEnd CHab CLnd CTri MTrO NOra NRog SKee WMat WWct
- 'Admiral'^{PBR} (D)	EWTr SBdl
- 'Advance' (D)	SBdl
- 'Akane' (D)	NOra
- 'Akerö' (D)	SBdl
- 'Aldenham Blenheim' (D)	SBdl
- 'Alderman' (C)	SBdl

§ – 'Alexander' (C)	NRog SBdl
– 'Alfriston' (C)	CAgr CHab NRog SBdl SKee WMat
§ – 'Alkmene' (D) ♀H6	CAgr LPar NOra NRog SBdl SKee
– 'All Doer' (C/D/Cider)	SEdi
– 'All Red Gravenstein' (D)	SBdl
– 'Allen's Everlasting' (D)	SKee
– 'Allington Pippin' (D)	CArg CHab CSBt CTri MGos NOra NRog SBdl SKee WMat
– AMBASSY ('Dalil'PBR) (D)	SBdl SEdi SSFr
– 'Amber' (D)	SBdl
– 'Ambro'PBR (D) **new**	SBdl
– 'American Beauty' (D)	SBdl
– 'American Golden Russet' (D)	SBdl
– 'American Mother'	see *M. domestica* 'Mother'
– 'Ames' (D)	SBdl
– 'Ananas Reinette' (D)	CHab LPar NRog SBdl SKee
– 'Anna Boelens' (D)	SBdl
– 'Annie Elizabeth' (C)	CAgr CArg CHab MGos MTrO NLar NOra NRog SBdl SKee SSFr SVic WJas WMat WWct
– 'Antonovka' (C)	NOra SBdl
– 'Apache' (F)	SSFr
– 'Apez Zagarra' (D) **new**	SBdl
– 'Api' (D)	LSRN MTrO NOra NWea SBdl SKee WMat
– 'Api Noir' (D)	LPar SBdl SKee
– 'Ard Cairn Russet' (D)	IArd SBdl SKee
– 'Ariwa'PBR (D) **new**	SBdl
– 'Arkansas' (D)	NOra SBdl
– 'Aroma' (D)	SBdl
– 'Aromatic Russet' (D)	NRog SBdl SKee
– 'Arthur Turner' (C) ♀H6	CArg CCVT CHab CTri EPom LBuc MTrO NOra NRog NWea SBdl SKee SSFr WJas WMat
– 'Arthur W. Barnes' (C)	SKee
– 'Ascot' (D)	SBdl
– 'Ashmead's Kernel' (D) ♀H6	CAgr CArg CBod CEnd CHab CLnd CRos CSBt CTri EPfP EPom LBuc LRHS MRav MTrO NOra NRog NWea SBdl SEdi SKee SLim SLon SSFT SSFr SVic WJas WMat WWct
– 'Ashton Bitter' (Cider)	CHab CTri SBdl
– 'Ashton Brown Jersey' (Cider)	CArg SBdl
– 'Astrachan Large Fruited' (D)	SBdl
– 'Auralia' (D) **new**	NRog
– 'Autumn Harvest' (C/D)	NRog SBdl
– 'Autumn Pearmain' (D)	SBdl SKee
– 'Backwell Red' (Cider)	SBdl
– 'Baker's Delicious' (D)	NOra SBdl SKee SSFr WMat
– 'Baldwin' (D)	NOra SBdl
– 'Ballarat Seedling' (D)	SBdl
– (Ballerina Series) 'Ballerina Bolero' (D)	WMat
– – 'Ballerina Polka' (D)	WMat
– – 'Ballerina Samba' (D)	CArg LCro MGos MTrO NLar NOra WMat
– 'Ball's Pippin' (D)	SBdl
– 'Ballyfatten' (C)	SBdl
– 'Ballyvaughan Seedling' (D)	IArd
– 'Balsam'	see *M. domestica* 'Green Balsam'
– 'Banana Pippin' (F)	CEnd
– 'Banns' (D)	SBdl SKee
– 'Barchard's Seedling' (D)	SBdl
– 'Bardsey' (D)	CAgr CArg CEnd CHab EPom MTrO NOra SKee WGwG WMat
– 'Barnack Beauty' (D)	CHab NOra NRog SBdl SKee
– 'Barnack Beauty' sport (D)	SBdl
– 'Barnack Orange' (D)	SBdl SKee
– 'Barnhill Pippin' (D)	SBdl
– 'Baron Ward' (C)	CHab NRog SBdl
– 'Baron Wood' (C)	SBdl
– 'Bascombe's Mystery' (D)	SBdl
– 'Baumann's Reinette' (D)	SBdl
– 'Baxter's Pearmain' (D)	SBdl SKee
– 'Beauty of Bath' (D)	CAgr CArg CBod CCVT CEnd CHab CLnd CTri ELan EPom LBuc LPar MRav MTrO NOra NRog SBdl SEdi SKee SPer SSFr WJas WMat WWct
– 'Beauty of Bedford' (D)	SBdl
– 'Beauty of Blackmoor' (D)	CLnd SBdl
– 'Beauty of Hants' (C/D)	CLnd SBdl
– 'Beauty of Kent' (C)	SBdl SKee
– 'Beauty of Moray' (C)	SBdl
– 'Beauty of Stoke' (C)	NRog SBdl
– 'Bedfordshire Foundling' (C)	SBdl
– 'Bedwyn Beauty' (C)	SBdl
– 'Beeley Pippin' (D)	SBdl SKee
– 'Belgica'PBR (D) **new**	SBdl
– 'Belle de Boskoop' (C/D) ♀H6	CAgr CEnd CHab NOra NRog NWea SBdl SKee
– 'Belle de Pontoise' (D)	SBdl
– 'Belle Flavoise' (F)	SBdl
– 'Belledge Pippin' (C/D)	SBdl
– 'Belle-fille Normande' (C)	SBdl
– 'Belle-fleur de France' (C)	SBdl
– 'Bellefleur Kitika' (D) **new**	SKee
– 'Bellida'PBR (D) **new**	SBdl
– 'Belvoir Seedling' (C/D)	SBdl
– 'Bembridge Beauty' (F)	CHab
– 'Benenden Early' (D)	SBdl SKee
– 'Benoni' (D)	LPar SBdl
– 'Ben's Red' (D)	CAgr CBod CDoC CEnd CTsd SKee WMat
– 'Bess Pool' (D)	CHab NRog SBdl
– 'Betty Geeson' (C)	SBdl
– 'Bewley Down Pippin'	see *M. domestica* 'Crimson King' (Cider/C)
– 'Bielaar'PBR (C/D) **new**	SBdl
– 'Bismarck' (C)	NRog SBdl SKee
– 'Black Dabinett' (Cider)	CArg CEnd MTrO SBdl WMat
– 'Black Tom Putt' (C/D)	MTrO
– 'Black Vallis' (Cider)	SBdl
– 'Blackwell Red' (F) **new**	SBdl
– 'Blanc Sur' (C/D) **new**	SKee
– 'Blaze' (D)	SBdl
– 'Blenheim Orange' (C/D) ♀H6	Widely available
– 'Blood of the Boyne' (D)	IArd
– 'Bloody Butcher' (C)	SBdl
– 'Bloody Ploughman' (D)	CArg CHab CLnd LBuc MTrO NOra NRog SBdl SKee SLon WMat
– 'Blue Moon' (D)	LRHS
– 'Blue Pearmain' (D)	SBdl
– 'Bodil Neergaard' (D)	SBdl
– 'Boiken' (D)	SBdl
– BOLERO	see *M. domestica* 'Tuscan'
– 'Bonum' (D/C)	WMat
– 'Bosbury Pippin' (D)	SBdl
– 'Bossom' (D)	SBdl
– 'Boston Russet'	see *M. domestica* 'Roxbury Russet'
– 'Bountiful' (C)	CAgr CArg CDoC CLnd CMac CSBt CTri EPom LRHS LSRN MAsh MRav MTrO NLar NOra NRog SBdl SKee SSFT SSFr WMat WWct
– 'Bow Hill Pippin' (C)	SBdl
– 'Box Apple' (D)	SBdl
– 'Brabant Bellefleur' (C)	SBdl
– 'Braddick's Nonpareil' (D)	SBdl

- 'Bradley's Beauty' (C/D) NRog NWea
- 'Braeburn' (D) CAgr CArg CLnd CSBt EPom GDam IPap LBuc LEdu LMaj LPar LRHS MTrO NOra NRog NWea SBdl SEND SEWo SEdi SKee SPer SSFr SVic WMat
- 'Braeburn Hillwell' (D) EPom NOra
- 'Braintree Seedling' (D) SBdl
- 'Bramley 20' (C) CSBt LCro LOPS MTrO NOra NWea SBdl SCoo SGbt SPer WMat
- 'Bramley's Seedling' (C) 🏆H6 Widely available
- 'Bramley's Seedling' clone 20 (F) CLnd CSBt CTsd EBee LBuc LSRN MAsh MNHC NLar NOra SCoo SKee SLim SPoG WWct
- 'Bramshott Rectory' (D/C) CLnd SBdl SSFr
- 'Bread Fruit' (C/D) CBod CEnd CTsd
- 'Breakwell's Seedling' (Cider) SBdl
- 'Breitling' (D) SBdl
- 'Brenchley Pippin' (D) SBdl
- 'Bridgwater Pippin' (C) SBdl
- 'Bright Future' (D) CArg EPom NOra WMat WWct
- 'Brith Mawr' (C) WGwG
- 'Broadholme Beauty' (C) CArg EPom MTrO NOra WMat
- 'Brookes's' (D) SBdl
- 'Brown Crofton' (D) IArd NRog SBdl
- 'Brown Snout' (Cider) NRog SBdl
- 'Brown Thorn' (Cider) SBdl
- 'Brownlee's Russet' (D) CAgr CHab CTri NOra NRog SKee SSFr WMat
- 'Brown's Apple' (Cider) CAgr CArg CHab CTri MTrO NOra SBdl WMat
- 'Brown's Seedling' (D) NRog
- 'Broxwood Foxwhelp' (Cider) MTrO SBdl
- 'Budimka' (D) SBdl
- 'Bulmer's Norman' (Cider) SBdl
- 'Burn's Seedling' (D) SBdl SKee
- 'Burr Knot' (C) SBdl
- 'Burrowhill Early' (Cider) SBdl WMat
- 'Byeloborodovka' (C/D) SBdl
- 'Byfleet Seedling' (C) SBdl
- 'Byford Wonder' (C) SBdl
- 'Calville Blanc d'Hiver' (D) NOra SBdl SKee
- 'Calville des Femmes' (C) SBdl
- 'Calville Rouge d'Hiver' (C) **new** SBdl
- 'Cambusnethan Pippin' (D) SBdl SKee
- 'Camelot' (Cider/C) SBdl SEdi

§ - 'Captain Broad' (Cider/D) CDoC CEnd CTsd SBdl

- 'Captain Kidd' (D) EPom NOra SBdl
- 'Captain Tom' (C/D) WMat
- 'Caravel' (D) SBdl
- 'Carlisle Codlin' (C) NOra SBdl WMat
- 'Caroline' (D) SBdl
- 'Carswell's Honeydew' (D) SBdl SKee
- 'Carswell's Orange' (D) SBdl
- 'Carter's Pearmain' (D) **new** SBdl
- 'Castle Major' (C) **new** SBdl
- 'Catherine' (C) SBdl
- 'Catshead' (C) CAgr CArg CDoC CHab CTri NOra NRog SBdl SKee WMat WWct
- 'Caudal Market' (F) SBdl
- 'Cellini' (C) NOra SBdl SKee
- 'Cevaal' (D) WWct
- 'Channel Beauty' (D) SBdl WGwG
- 'Charles Eyre' (C) SBdl
- 'Charles Ross' (C/D) 🏆H6 CAgr CArg CCVT CEnd CHab CLnd CMac CSBt CTri EPom IArd LBuc LPar LSRN MAsh MRav MTrO NOra NRog NWea SBdl SCob SEWo SKee SLim SSFT SSFr WJas WMat WWct
- 'Charlestown Pippin' (F) **new** NRog
- 'Charlotte'PBR (C) SBdl
- 'Chaxhill Red' (Cider/D) SBdl
- 'Cheddar Cross' (D) CAgr CCVT CTri SBdl
- 'Chehalis' (D) **new** SBdl
- 'Chelmsford Wonder' (C) SBdl SKee
- 'Cherry Cox' (D) **new** SBdl
- 'Chips' (F) SBdl
- 'Chisel Jersey' (Cider) CAgr CTri NOra SBdl SKee
- 'Chivers Delight' (D) CAgr CArg CLnd EBee EPom LBuc MCoo MTrO NOra NRog SBdl SSFr
- 'Chorister Boy' (D) SBdl
- 'Christie Manson' (C) **new** SBdl
- 'Christmas Pearmain' (D) CAgr CArg CLnd SBdl SSFr WMat
- 'Christmas Pippin'PBR (D) 🏆H6 CArg CBod CEnd CRos CTri EBee ELan EPom LBuc LCro LRHS MCoo MTrO NLar NOra NRHS SGbt SSFr WMat
- 'Cider Lady's Finger' (Cider) SBdl
- 'Cissy' (D) SBdl WGwG
- 'Cistecké' (D) SBdl
- 'Claygate Pearmain' (D) CAgr CHab CTri NOra NRog SBdl SKee SVic WMat
- 'Cleeve' (D) SBdl
- 'Climax' (D) **new** SBdl
- 'Clopton Red' (D) SBdl
- 'Close' (D) SBdl
- 'Clydeside' (C) SBdl
- 'Coat Jersey' (Cider) SBdl
- 'Cobra' (F) CAgr CArg NOra SKee SPoG SSFr WJas WMat
- 'Cockett's Red' (D) SBdl
- 'Cockle Pippin' (D) CAgr SBdl
- 'Cockpit' (C) CHab SBdl
- 'Coeur de Boeuf' (C/D) SBdl
- 'Colapuy' (D) **new** NRog
- 'Collogett Pippin' (C/Cider) CBod CDoC CEnd CTsd SBdl
- 'Colonel Vaughan' (C/D) SBdl
- 'Colonel Yate' (D) SBdl
- 'Comrade' (D) SBdl
- 'Cooper's Seedling' (C) SBdl
- 'Coo's River Beauty' (D) **new** SBdl
- 'Core Blimey' (D) EPom LBuc MTrO
- 'Cornish Aromatic' (D) CAgr CArg CBod CDoC CTri CTsd MTrO NOra SBdl SKee WMat
- 'Cornish Gilliflower' (D) CAgr CBod CDoC CEnd CHab CTsd MTrO NOra NRog SBdl SKee WMat
- 'Cornish Honeypin' (D) CBod CDoC CEnd CTsd SBdl SKee SSFr
- 'Cornish Longstem' (D) CAgr CEnd
- 'Cornish Mother' (D) CBod CEnd
- 'Cornish Pine' (D) CDoC CEnd CTsd SBdl SKee
- 'Cornish Queen' (C/D) CTsd
- 'Coronation' (D) CHab NRog SBdl
- 'Cortland' (D) NOra SBdl SKee
- 'Costard' (C) CHab SKee
- 'Cottenham Seedling' (C) SBdl
- 'Coul Blush' (D) GBin MTrO SBdl SKee WMat
- 'Court of Wick' (D) CAgr CArg CHab NOra NRog SBdl SKee SVic WMat
- 'Court Pendu Plat' (D) CAgr CArg CHab GQue NOra NRog SBdl SKee SSFT WJas WMat WWct
- 'Court Royal' (Cider) SBdl SKee
- 'Cox Cymraeg' (D) WGwG
- 'Cox's Orange Pippin' (D) Widely available

– 'Cox's Pomona' (C)	LPar NRog SBdl SKee
– 'Cox's Rouge de Flandres' (D)	SKee
– 'Cox's Selfing' (D)	CMac CSBt CTri EBee EPfP LBuc LRHS MAsh MGos MNHC NLar SKee SPer SPoG WJas WMat WWct
– 'Crawley Beauty' (C)	CAgr CArg CHab NRog SBdl SSFT WMat
– 'Crawley Reinette' (D)	CHab NRog SBdl
– 'Crimson Beauty' (D)	SBdl
– 'Crimson Beauty of Bath' (D)	CAgr SBdl
– 'Crimson Bramley' (C)	SBdl
– 'Crimson Cox' (D)	SBdl
§ – 'Crimson King' (Cider/C)	CAgr SBdl
– 'Crimson King' (D)	CAgr CHab CTri SBdl
– 'Crimson Newton' (C) **new**	SBdl
– 'Crimson Peasgood' (C)	SBdl
– 'Crimson Queening' (D)	SBdl
– 'Crimson Superb' (D) **new**	SBdl
– 'Crimson Victoria' (Cider)	SBdl
§ – 'Cripps Pink'^{PBR} (D)	SGsty SSFr
– CRISPIN	see *M. domestica* 'Mutsu'
– 'Croen Mochyn' (D)	WGwG
– 'Croquella' (D) **new**	LRHS
§ – 'Crowngold' (D)	EPom SBdl
– 'Cummy Norman' (Cider)	SBdl
– 'Curl Tail' (D)	SBdl
– 'Cutler Grieve' (D)	SBdl
– 'Dabinett' (Cider)	CAgr CArg CHab CLnd CMac CTri EPom LBuc NOra NRog SBdl SKee WMat WWct
– 'D'Arcy Spice' (D)	CAgr EPfP GQue MTrO NOra SBdl SKee WMat WWct
– 'Dawn' (D)	SBdl
– 'Deacon's Blushing Beauty' (C/D)	CLnd
– 'Decio' (D)	SBdl
– DELBARD JUBILÉ ('Delgollune') (D) **new**	SBdl
– DELBARESTIVALE ('Delcorf') (red) (D)	LPar SBdl
– 'Delicious' (D) **new**	SBdl
– 'Delorgue'^{PBR} (F) **new**	SBdl
– 'Delprim' (D)	SBdl
– 'Delprivale'^{PBR} (F) **new**	SBdl
– 'Devonshire Buckland' (C)	CEnd SBdl
– 'Devonshire Crimson Queen' (D)	SBdl
– 'Devonshire Quarrenden' (D)	CAgr CBod CHab NOra NRog SBdl SKee SVic WMat
– 'Diamond' (D)	WGwG
– 'Diamond Jubilee' (D)	SBdl
– 'Discovery' (D) 🏆^{H6}	Widely available
– 'Discovery NFT' (D)	CEnd
– 'Doctor Clifford' (C)	SBdl
– 'Doctor Harvey' (C)	SBdl
– 'Doctor Hogg' (C)	CLnd NRog SBdl
– 'Doctor Kidd's Orange Red'	see *M. domestica* 'Kidd's Orange Red'
– 'Doddin' (D)	WWct
– 'Dog's Snout' (C/D)	NRog
– 'Domino' (C)	SBdl
– 'Don's Delight' (C)	WMat
– 'Doux Normandie' (Cider)	SBdl
– 'Dove' (Cider)	SBdl
– 'Downton Pippin' (D)	CHab NRog SBdl SKee
– 'Dredge's Fame' (D)	SBdl
– 'Duchess of Bedford' (D)	SBdl
– 'Duchess of Oldenburg' (C)	NOra SBdl SKee
– 'Duchess's Favourite' (D)	SBdl SKee
– 'Duck's Bill' (D)	SKee
– 'Dufflin' (Cider)	CTsd SBdl
– 'Duke of Cornwall' (C)	CBod CDoC
– 'Duke of Devonshire' (D)	CSBt CTri NRog NWea SBdl
– 'Dumeller's Seedling'	see *M. domestica* 'Dummellor's Seedling'
§ – 'Dummellor's Seedling' (C) 🏆^{H6}	CHab NOra NRog SBdl SKee
– 'Dunkerton Late Sweet' (Cider)	CArg CCVT CHab SBdl SEdi WMat
– 'Dunn's Seedling' (D)	SBdl
§ – 'Dutch Codlin' (C)	SBdl
§ – 'Dutch Mignonne' (D)	SBdl SKee
– 'Dymock Red' (Cider)	SBdl
– 'Early Blenheim' (D/C)	CEnd
– 'Early Bower' (D)	CEnd
– 'Early Julyan' (C)	GBin SBdl
– 'Early McIntosh' (D) **new**	SBdl
– 'Early Strawberry' (D) **new**	SBdl
– 'Early Victoria'	see *M. domestica* 'Emneth Early'
– EARLY WINDSOR	see *M. domestica* 'Alkmene'
– 'Early Worcester'	see *M. domestica* 'Tydeman's Early Worcester'
– 'East Lothian Pippin' (C)	SBdl
– 'Easter Orange' (D)	CLnd SBdl
– 'Eccleston Pippin' (D)	SBdl
– 'Ecklinville' (C)	SBdl
– 'Edelborsdorfer' (D)	NRog
– 'Eden' (D)	LRHS MGos MTrO NOra SBdl WMat
– 'Edith Hopwood' (D)	SBdl
– 'Edward VII' (C) 🏆^{H6}	CHab NOra NRog SBdl SKee WMat WWct
– 'Egremont Russet' (D) 🏆^{H6}	Widely available
– 'Elektra' (D) **new**	NRog
– 'Ellis' Bitter' (Cider)	SBdl SKee SVic
– 'Ellison's Orange' (D) 🏆^{H6}	Widely available
– 'Elmore Pippin' (D)	SBdl
– 'Elstar' (D) 🏆^{H6}	CBod CCVT CLnd EPom LPar NOra SBdl SEdi SKee
– 'Elton Beauty' (D)	SBdl
§ – 'Emneth Early' (C) 🏆^{H6}	CAgr CArg CHab NOra NRog SBdl SEdi WMat WWct
– 'Emperor Alexander'	see *M. domestica* 'Alexander'
– 'Empire' (D)	NOra SBdl SKee
– 'Endsleigh Beauty' (D)	SBdl
– 'English Codlin' (C)	CTri
– 'Epicure'	see *M. domestica* 'Laxton's Epicure'
– 'Eros' (D)	SBdl
– 'Esopus Spitzenburg' (D)	NOra SBdl
– 'Etlin's Reinette' (D) **new**	NRog
– 'Evagil' (C) **new**	SBdl
– 'Excelsior' (C)	SBdl
– 'Exeter Cross' (D)	CSBt SBdl
– 'Exquisite' (D)	SBdl SRms SWeb
– 'Eynsham Challenger' (F)	SBdl
– 'Eynsham Dumpling' (C)	SBdl
– 'Fair Maid of Devon' (Cider)	CAgr CArg CEnd WMat
– 'Fairie Queen' (D)	SBdl
– 'Fall Pippin' (D)	SBdl
– 'Fall Russet' (D)	SBdl
– 'Falstaff'^{PBR} (D)	CAgr CTri EPfP EPom LSRN MGos NOra SBdl SCoo SEdi SKee SPer SSFr
– 'Fameuse' (D)	NOra SBdl
– 'Farmer's Glory' (D)	CAgr CBod WMat
– 'Fearn's Pippin' (D)	SBdl
– 'Feltham Beauty' (D)	SBdl
– 'Fiessers Erstling' (C)	SBdl
– 'Fiesta' (D) 🏆^{H6}	Widely available
– 'Filippa' (D) **new**	SBdl

- ‘Fillbarrel’ (Cider) CHab NRog SBdl
- ‘Fillingham Pippin’ (C) CHab NRog SBdl
- ‘Firedance’ (D) LRHS
- ‘Fireside’ (D) SBdl
- ‘Firmgold’ (D) SBdl
- ‘First and Last’ (D) NOra WMat
- ‘Flame’ (D) SBdl
- ‘Flamenco’ see *M. domestica* ‘Obelisk’
- ‘Florina’ (F) **new** NOra SBdl
- § ‘Flower of Kent’ (C) CHab EPom MAsh MTrO NOra NRog NWea SBdl SKee SSFr WMat
- ‘Flower of the Town’ (D) CHab NRog SBdl SKee
- ‘Folkestone’ (D) SBdl
- ‘Forester’ (C) **new** SBdl
- ‘Forfar’ see *M. domestica* ‘Dutch Mignonne’
- ‘Forge’ (D) CAgr CHab NRog SBdl
- ‘Forpear’ (D) **new** SBdl
- ‘Fortosh’ (D) **new** SBdl
- ‘Fortune’ see *M. domestica* ‘Laxton’s Fortune’
- ‘Forty Shilling’ (D) SBdl
- ‘Foster’s Seedling’ (D) SBdl
- ‘Four Square’ (F) SBdl
- ‘Foxwhelp’ (Cider) CArg CHab CLnd NRog NWea SKee
- ‘Francis’ (D) SBdl
- ‘Frederick’ (Cider) CArg CLnd SBdl WMat
- ‘Freiherr von Berlepsch’ (D) SBdl
- ‘French Codlin’ see *M. domestica* ‘Dutch Codlin’
- ‘French Crab’ (C) SBdl
- ‘Freyberg’ (D) NOra SKee
- ‘Friandise’ (D) **new** SBdl
- ‘Frogmore Prolific’ (C) SBdl
- ‘Fuji’ (D) LMaj NOra SBdl SKee
- ‘Gala’ (D) CLnd CSBt CTri EBee EPom IPap MTrO NOra NRog SBdl SCoo SEdi SGbt SGsty SKee SSFr SVic WMat
- ‘Gala Musk’ (D) LPar
- ‘Galaxy’^{PBR} (D) NOra SBdl SEdi
- ‘Galloway Pippin’ (C) GBin MTrO NLar NOra NWea SBdl WMat
- ‘Galton’ (D) **new** SBdl
- ‘Garden Fountain’ (D) LRHS
- ‘Garnet’ (D) SBdl
- ‘Gascoyne’s Scarlet’ (C/D) LMaj NRog SBdl SKee
- ‘Gavin’ (D) CAgr SBdl SKee
- ‘Genet Moyle’ (C/Cider) CTri SBdl WMat
- ‘George Carpenter’ (D) CTri NRog SBdl
- ‘George Cave’ (D) NOra NRog SBdl SEdi SKee SSFr WJas
- ‘George Fox’ (D) **new** NRog
- ‘George Neal’ (C) CAgr NRog SBdl
- ‘Gibbon’s Russet’ (D) IArd SBdl
- ‘Gilliflower of Gloucester’ (D) SBdl
- ‘Gipsy King’ (D) **new** NRog
- ‘Gladstone’ (D) CAgr NOra SBdl WMat WWct
- ‘Glasbury’ (C) SBdl
- § ‘Glass Apple’ (C/D) CEnd SBdl
- ‘Glockenapfel’ (C) SBdl
- ‘Gloria Mundi’ (C) SBdl
- ‘Gloster ’69’ (D) CLnd LPar SBdl
- ‘Gloucester Cross’ (D) SBdl
- ‘Gloucester Royal’ (D) SBdl
- ‘Gold Medal’ (D) **new** SBdl
- ‘Golden Bittersweet’ (D) CAgr SBdl WMat
- ‘Golden Delicious’ (D) CArg CMac ELan EPom IPap LBuc LMaj LPar LRHS MPri MTrO NOra NRog SBdl SEWo SEdi SGsty SKee SSFr SVic WMat
- ‘Golden Gate’ (D) LRHS
- ‘Golden Harvey’ (D) CAgr SBdl
- ‘Golden Jubilee’ (F) CEnd
- ‘Golden Knob’ (D) CTri SBdl SKee
- ‘Golden Noble’ (C) Υ^{H6} CAgr CTri IArd NOra NRog SBdl SKee
- ‘Golden Nugget’ (D) CAgr NRog SBdl SKee
- ‘Golden Pearmain’ (D) LMaj LPar NRog
- ‘Golden Pippin’ (C) CAgr NOra NRog SBdl SKee WMat
- ‘Golden Reinette’ (D) SBdl
- ‘Golden Russet’ (D) CAgr NOra SKee
- ‘Golden Spire’ (C) CHab NOra NRog SBdl SKee
- GOLDRUSH (‘Coop 38’^{PBR}) (F) **new** NOra
- ‘Gooseberry’ (C) SBdl
- ‘Grandpa Buxton’ (C) CHab NRog
- ‘Grange’s Pearmain’ (C) SBdl
- ‘Granny Smith’ (D) CBcs CBod IPap LMaj LPar LSRN MTrO NOra NRog SBdl SEdi SGbt SKee SPer SVic WMat
- ‘Gravenstein’ (D) CHab NOra NRog SBdl SEdi SKee
- ‘Greasy Pippin’ (D/C) SBdl
- § ‘Green Balsam’ (D) CHab CTri NRog
- ‘Green Chisel’ (D) **new** IArd
- ‘Green Harvey’ (D/C) SBdl
- ‘Green Roland’ (C/D) SBdl
- ‘Greenfinch’ (D) LRHS
- ‘Greensleeves’^{PBR} (D) Υ^{H6} CAgr CArg CMac CTri ELan EPfP EPom LPar MAsh MGos MMuc MTrO NOra NRog NWea SBdl SEND SEdi SKee SLim SPer SSFT SSFr WJas WMat WWct
- GREENSTAR (‘Nicogreen’^{PBR}) (D) **new** SBdl
- ‘Greenup’s Pippin’ (D) CHab NRog SBdl
- ‘Grenadier’ (C) Υ^{H6} CAgr CArg CHab CLnd CTri EPom MGos MMuc MTrO NOra NRog NWea SBdl SEND SEdi SKee SLon SPer SSFT SSFr WJas WMat
- ‘Grimes Golden’ (D) **new** NOra NRog SBdl
- ‘Groninger Kroon’ (D) CLnd SBdl
- ‘Grvena Lepogvetka’ (D) SBdl
- ‘Guelph’ (D) **new** SBdl
- ‘Guillevic’ (Cider) CHab NRog
- ‘Guldborg’ (C) **new** SBdl
- ‘Gwell Na Mil’ (D) WGwG
- ‘Halstow Natural’ (Cider) CAgr
- ‘Hambledon Deux Ans’ (C) CLnd SBdl SKee
- ‘Hangy Down’ (Cider) CArg WMat
- ‘Hannan Seedling’ (D) SBdl
- ‘Hanwell Souring’ (C) SBdl
- ‘Haralson’ (D) SBdl
- ‘Harbert’s Reinette’ (D) SBdl
- ‘Harling Hero’ (D) SBdl
- HARMONIE (‘Delorina’) (F) SBdl
- § ‘Harry Master’s Jersey’ (Cider) CAgr CArg CTri EPom MTrO NOra NRog SKee WMat WWct
- ‘Harry Master’s Red Streak’ (Cider) SEdi
- ‘Harry Pring’ (D) SBdl
- ‘Hastings’ (Cider) **new** MTrO NRog
- ‘Hawthornden’ (C) CHab NRog SBdl
- ‘Hector MacDonald’ (C) SBdl
- ‘Helen’s Apple’ (Cider) **new** NRog
- ‘Hereford Cross’ (D) SBdl
- ‘Herefordshire Beefing’ (C) SBdl
- ‘Herefordshire Redstreak’ (Cider) CAgr CArg EPom LBuc NOra WMat
- ‘Herefordshire Russet’^{PBR} (D) CArg CDoC EBee EPom LBuc LRHS MTrO NLar NOra NRHS SBdl SKee SSFr WJas WMat WWct
- ‘Herring’s Pippin’ (C/D) CTri NRog
- ‘Hibernal’ (C) SBdl

- 'Hidala'[PBR] **new**	SBdl
- 'High View Pippin' (D)	SBdl
- 'Histon Favourite' (D/C)	SBdl
- 'Hoary Morning' (C)	SBdl
- 'Hocking's Green' (C/D)	CAgr CEnd CTsd
- 'Holiday' (D) **new**	SBdl
- 'Holland Pippin' (C)	SBdl
- 'Hollandbury' (C) **new**	SBdl
- 'Hollow Core' (C)	CAgr
- 'Holstein' (D)	IPap NOra SBdl SEdi SKee
- 'Honey Pippin' (D)	SBdl
- 'Honeycrisp'[PBR] (D)	MTrO NOra WMat
§ - 'Honeygold' (D)	CEnd SBdl
- 'Hormead Pearmain' (C)	SBdl
- 'Horneburger Pfannkuchen' (C)	SBdl SKee
- 'Hornsea Herring' (D/C)	NRog
- 'Horsford Prolific' (D)	SBdl
- 'Horsham Russet' (D)	SKee
- 'Houblon' (D)	SBdl
- 'Hounslow Wonder' (C)	SBdl
- 'Howgate Wonder' (C) 🏆H6	CAgr CArg CBod CCVT CDoC CHab CLnd CSBt CTri EPfP EPom GDam LBuc MMuc MTrO NOra NRog NWea SBdl SEdi SKee SPer SSFr SVic WJas WMat WWct
- 'Hubbard's Pearmain' (D)	SKee
- 'Hubbardston Nonesuch' (D) **new**	NOra SBdl
- 'Hume' (D) **new**	SBdl
- 'Hunter's Majestic' (D/C)	SBdl
- 'Hunthouse' (D) **new**	NRog
- 'Huntingdon Codlin' (D)	SBdl
- 'Hunt's Duke of Gloucester' (D)	SBdl SKee
- 'Idared' (D)	NOra SBdl SEdi SSFr SVic WMat
- 'Improved Ashmead's Kernel' (D) **new**	SBdl
- 'Improved Cockpit' (C)	NRog SBdl
- 'Improved Dove' (Cider)	SBdl
- 'Improved Keswick' (C/D)	CEnd
- 'Improved Lambrook Pippin' (Cider)	CArg CTri SBdl
- 'Improved Redstreak' (Cider)	SBdl
- 'Ingall's Red' (D)	NRog
- 'Ingrid Marie' (D)	NRog SBdl SSFr
- 'Irish Peach' (D)	CAgr CArg CHab CTri IArd MTrO NOra NRog SBdl SKee SSFr WMat
- 'Isaac Newton's Tree'	see *M. domestica* 'Flower of Kent'
- 'Isle of Wight Pippin' (D)	CLnd SSFr
- 'Jackson's'	see *M. domestica* 'Crimson King' (Cider/C)
- 'Jacques Lebel' (C)	SBdl
- 'James Grieve' (D) 🏆H6	Widely available
- 'James Lawson' (D)	SBdl
- 'Jane' (Cider) **new**	NRog
- JAZZ ('Scifresh'[PBR]) (D)	SSFr
- 'Jeanne Hardy' (C) **new**	SBdl
- 'Jersey Beauty' (C/D)	CLnd SBdl
- 'Jersey Black' (D/Cider)	SBdl SKee
- 'Jerseymac' (D)	SBdl
- 'Jester' (D)	CLnd NRog SBdl SSFr
- 'Joaneting' (D)	CAgr CHab NRog SBdl
- 'John Broad'	see *M. domestica* 'Captain Broad'
- 'John Divers' (C) **new**	SBdl
- 'John Standish' (D)	CAgr CTri NRog SBdl
- 'John Toucher's'	see *M. domestica* 'Crimson King' (Cider/C)
- 'John Waterer' (C) **new**	SBdl
- 'Johnny Andrews' (Cider)	CAgr
- 'Johnny Voun' (D)	CEnd CTsd
- 'Jonagold' (D) 🏆H6	CArg CLnd CTri ELan EPom IArd IPap LMaj LRHS NOra NRog SBdl SEdi SGsty SKee SPer SSFr WWct
- 'Jonagold Crowngold'	see *M. domestica* 'Crowngold'
§ - 'Jonagored'[PBR] (D)	NOra NRog SBdl SEdi WMat
- 'Jonared' (D)	SBdl
- 'Jonathan' (D)	NOra SBdl SKee
- 'Josephine' (D)	SBdl
- 'Joybells' (D)	SBdl
- 'Joyce' (D) **new**	SBdl
- 'Jubilee'	see *M. domestica* 'Royal Jubilee'
- 'Julgrans' (D) **new**	SBdl
- 'Julie's Late Golden' (F)	CTri
- 'Jumbo' (C/D)	MTrO NOra SBdl SKee WJas WMat
- 'Jupiter'[PBR] (D) 🏆H6	CAgr CArg CBod CSBt CTri EPfP LSRN MRav MTrO NLar NOra NRog NWea SBdl SEdi SKee SLon SSFr WJas WMat
- 'Kandil Sinap' (D)	SBdl
- 'Karmijn de Sonnaville' (D)	NOra SBdl SKee
§ - 'Katja' (D)	Widely available
- KATY	see *M. domestica* 'Katja'
- 'Kemp' (D)	IArd SBdl
- 'Kendall' (D)	SBdl
- 'Kenneth' (D)	SBdl WGwG
- 'Kentish Fillbasket' (C)	SBdl SKee
- 'Kentish Quarrenden' (D)	SBdl
- 'Kerry Pippin' (D)	IArd NRog SBdl SKee
- 'Keswick Codlin' (C)	CArg CHab EBee MTrO NLar NOra NRog NWea SBdl SKee SSFr WJas WMat WWct
§ - 'Kidd's Orange Red' (D) 🏆H6	CAgr CArg CBod CEnd CLnd CMac CRos CTri EBee EPfP EPom LBuc LRHS MTrO NOra NRog NWea SKee SLon SSFr WMat WWct
- 'Kilkenny Pearmain' (D)	IArd SBdl
- 'Kim' (C/D)	SBdl
- 'King Albert' (C) **new**	SBdl
- 'King Byerd' (C/D)	CDoC CEnd SBdl
- 'King Charles' Pearmain' (D)	SBdl
- 'King Coffee' (D)	SBdl
- 'King David' (C/D) **new**	NOra SBdl
- 'King George V' (D)	CLnd SBdl
§ - 'King of the Pippins' (D) 🏆H6	CArg CHab CLnd CTri EPom LBuc MTrO NOra SBdl SKee SVic
- 'King of Tompkins County' (D)	NOra SBdl
- 'King Russet' (D) 🏆H6	SBdl
- 'King's Acre Pippin' (D)	MTrO NOra NRog SKee WMat
- 'Kingston Black' (Cider/C)	CAgr CArg CEnd CHab CLnd CMac CTri EPom LBuc MTrO NOra NRog SBdl SKee WMat
- 'Knobby Russet' (D)	SBdl SSFr
- 'Koningin Juliana' (D) **new**	NRog
- 'Korobovka' (D)	SBdl
- 'Lady Henniker' (C)	CEnd CHab MTrO NOra NRog SBdl SKee
- 'Lady Hollendale' (D)	SBdl
- 'Lady Isabel' (D)	SBdl
- 'Lady Lambourne' (C/D)	CHab NRog SBdl SKee
- 'Lady of the Lake' (D)	SBdl
- 'Lady of the Wemyss' (C)	GBin SBdl SKee
- 'Lady Sudeley' (D)	CEnd CHab NRog SKee
- 'Lady Williams' (D)	SBdl
- 'Lady's Finger' (C/D)	CDoC CEnd
- 'Lady's Finger of Lancaster' (C/D)	CHab NRog
- 'Lady's Finger of Offaly' (D)	IArd
- 'Lakeland' (D)	SBdl

- 'Lamb Abbey Pearmain' (D) SBdl
- 'Landsberger Reinette' (D) SBdl
- 'Lane's Prince Albert' (C) ♀H6 CAgr CArg CBod CEnd CHab CLnd CSBt CTri EPfP LRHS MGos MRav MTrO NOra NRog NWea SBdl SCoo SEdi SSFr SVic SWeb WMat
- 'Langley Pippin' (D) SBdl
- § 'Langworthy' (Cider) SBdl
- 'Lass o' Gowrie' (C) SBdl
- 'Lawfam' (D) **new** SBdl
- 'Laxton's Early Crimson' (D) SBdl
- § 'Laxton's Epicure' (D) ♀H6 CAgr CBod CEnd CHab CTri NRog SBdl SKee
- 'Laxton's Favourite' (D) SBdl
- § 'Laxton's Fortune' (D) ♀H6 CArg CHab CMac CSBt CTri IArd MTrO NOra NRog SBdl SEdi SKee SSFr WMat WWct
- 'Laxton's Herald' (D) **new** SBdl
- 'Laxton's Pearmain' (D) SBdl
- 'Laxton's Rearguard' (D) SBdl
- 'Laxton's Reward' (D) SBdl
- 'Laxton's Royalty' (D) SBdl
- § 'Laxton's Superb' (D) CArg CBcs CCVT CHab CLnd CMac CSBt CTri EPom GKin LBuc LRHS MPri MTrO NOra NRog NWea SBdl SEWo SEdi SKee SPer SRms SSFr SVic SWeb WJas WMat WWct
- 'Laxton's Triumph' (D) SBdl
- 'Laxton's Victory' (D) **new** SBdl
- 'Leicester Burton' see *M. domestica* 'Dutch Codlin'
- 'Lemon Pippin' (C) ELan NOra SBdl SKee
- 'Lemon Queen' (D) SBdl
- 'Lewis's Incomparable' (C) SBdl
- 'Liberty' (D) NOra SBdl
- 'Limelight' (D) ♀H6 CArg CBod CDoC EBee MAsh MCoo MTrO NLar NOra NRog NWea SBdl SCoo SKee SSFT SSFr WMat
- 'Limoncella' (D) SBdl
- 'Linda' (D) SBdl SKee
- 'Link Wonder' (D) CEnd
- 'Little Pax' (D) CBod EPom LRHS MTrO NLar NOra SSFT
- 'Llwyd Hanner Goch' (D) WGwG
- 'Lobo' (D) SBdl
- § 'Loddington' (C) SBdl
- 'Lodgemore Nonpareil' (D) SBdl
- 'Lodi' (C) SBdl
- 'London Pearmain' (D) SBdl
- 'London Pippin' (C) CAgr SBdl
- 'Long Bider' (C) **new** SBdl
- 'Longkeeper' (D) CAgr CEnd
- 'Longney Russet' (Cider/D) SBdl
- 'Longstart' (F) SBdl
- 'Lord Burghley' (D) SBdl
- 'Lord Derby' (C) CAgr CArg CBod CHab CLnd CMac EPom MRav MTrO NLar NOra NRog SBdl SEND SEdi SKee SPer SSFT SVic WMat WWct
- 'Lord Grosvenor' (C) SBdl SKee
- 'Lord Hindlip' (D) CHab NOra NRog SBdl WMat WWct
- 'Lord Lambourne' (D) ♀H6 CAgr CArg CEnd CHab CLnd CMac CSBt CTri ELan EPom LSRN MAsh MGos MTrO NOra NRog SBdl SEdi SKee SLon SPer SSFr WJas WMat WWct
- 'Lord Lennox' (D) **new** SBdl
- 'Lord of the Isles' (Cider) CAgr
- 'Lord Peckover' (D) SBdl
- 'Lord Rosebery' (D) SBdl
- 'Lord Stradbroke' (C) SBdl
- 'Lord Suffield' (C) SBdl SKee
- 'Lough Tree of Wexford' (D) IArd
- 'Love Beauty' (D) SBdl
- 'Lucombe's Pine' (D) CAgr CDoC CEnd SVic
- 'Lynn's Pippin' (D) SBdl
- 'Mabbott's Pearmain' (D) SBdl SKee
- 'Machen' (D) WGwG
- 'Maclean's Favourite' (D) SBdl
- 'Macoun' (D) **new** NOra SBdl
- 'Macy' (C/D) **new** SBdl
- 'Madresfield Court' (D) SBdl WWct
- 'Magdalene' (D) SBdl
- 'Maggie Grieve' (D) **new** SBdl
- 'Maggie Sinclair' (D) GBin SBdl
- 'Maid of Kent' (F) SBdl
- 'Maidstone Favourite' (D) SBdl SKee
- 'Major' (Cider) CAgr SBdl WMat
- 'Maldon Wonder' (D) SBdl
- 'Malling Kent' (D) SBdl
- 'Maltster' (D) SBdl
- 'Manaccan Primrose' (C/D) CBod CDoC CEnd CTsd
- 'Mank's Codlin' (C) SBdl
- 'Mannington's Pearmain' (D) NRog SBdl WMat
- 'Marged Nicolas' (D) WGwG
- 'Margil' (D) NOra NRog SBdl SKee
- 'Marriage-maker' (D) SBdl
- 'Marston Scarlet Wonder' (C) **new** SBdl
- 'Maxton' (D) SBdl
- 'May Beauty' (D) SBdl
- 'May Queen' (D) SBdl WWct
- 'Maypole' (D) SBdl SEdi
- 'McIntosh' (D) NOra NRog SBdl SKee
- 'Mead's Broading' (C) SBdl
- 'Measday's Favourite' (C) SBdl
- 'Médaille d'Or' (Cider) CArg SBdl SKee WMat
- 'Medina' (D) SBdl
- 'Megabite' (C/D) EPom
- 'Melba' (D) SBdl
- 'Melon' (D) SBdl
- 'Melrose' (D) LMaj LPar NRog SBdl SGsty
- 'Merchant Apple' (D) SBdl
- 'Mère de Ménage' (C) NRog
- 'Meridian'PBR (D) CAgr MTrO NOra NRog SBdl SEdi SSFr WMat
- 'Merlin's Apple' (D) **new** NRog
- 'Merlyn' (F) **new** SBdl
- 'Merton Beauty' (D) SBdl
- 'Merton Charm' (D) SBdl
- 'Merton Delight' (D) **new** SBdl
- 'Merton Joy' (D) SBdl
- 'Merton Knave' (D) SBdl
- 'Merton Prolific' (D) SBdl
- 'Merton Russet' (D) SBdl
- 'Merton Worcester' (D) SBdl SKee
- 'Michaelmas Red' (D) NRog SBdl
- 'Michelin' (Cider) CAgr CArg CTri MGos MTrO NOra SBdl SKee WMat WWct
- MIEL D'OR see *M. domestica* 'Honeygold'
- 'Miller's Seedling' (D) NOra SBdl SKee
- 'Millet' (D) **new** SBdl
- 'Millicent Barnes' (D) SBdl
- 'Minister von Hammerstein' **new** SBdl
- 'Minshull Crab' (C) SBdl SKee
- 'Missing Link' (D) **new** SBdl
- 'Molleskov' (C/D) **new** SBdl
- 'Mollie's Delicious' (D) SBdl SKee

- 'Monarch' (C) CAgr CBod CTri EPom NRog SBdl SKee SSFr
- 'Monmouthshire Green' (D) WGwG
- 'Montfort' (D) SBdl
- 'Morgan's Sweet' (C/Cider) CArg CEnd CHab CTri NOra NRog SBdl SKee WMat
- 'Morley's Seedling' (C) SBdl
- 'Moss's Seedling' (D) SBdl

§ - 'Mother' (D) ♀H6 CAgr CEnd CLnd CTri SBdl SKee SSFr
- 'Mrs Barron' (D) **new** SBdl
- 'Mrs Lakeman's Seedling' (C) **new** SBdl
- 'Mrs Phillimore' (D) SBdl
- 'Munster Tulip' (D/C) IArd SBdl
- 'Murfitt's Seedling' (C) **new** SBdl
- 'Muscadet de Dieppe' (Cider) SBdl

§ - 'Mutsu' (C/D) CArg CLnd LBuc MRav NOra NRog SBdl SEdi SKee SPer SSFr WMat
- 'Mylor Pike' (D) CEnd
- 'Nancy Jackson' (C) CHab NRog SBdl
- 'Nanny' (D) CLnd SBdl
- 'Nant Gwrtheyrn' (D) WGwG
- 'Nasona' (D) SBdl
- 'Nehou' (Cider) SBdl
- 'Neild's Drooper' (D/C) SBdl
- 'Nemes Szercsika Alma' (C) SBdl
- 'New Bess Pool' (D) NRog SBdl
- 'New German' (D) **new** SBdl
- 'New Hawthornden' (C) **new** SBdl
- 'New Rock Pippin' (D) SBdl
- 'Newport Cross' (D) **new** SBdl
- 'Newton Wonder' (C) CAgr CArg CEnd CHab CSBt CTri EPom LMaj MGos MTrO NOra NRog NWea SBdl SEdi SKee SRms SSFr WJas WMat WWct
- 'Newtosh' (D) **new** SBdl
- 'Newtown Pippin' (D) NOra SBdl
- 'Nigde' (D) SBdl
- 'No Pip' (C) SBdl
- 'Nolan Pippin' (D) SBdl
- 'Nonpareil' (D) NRog SKee
- 'Norfolk Beauty' (C) NRog SBdl
- 'Norfolk Beefing' (C) CArg CHab NOra NRog SBdl SKee WMat
- 'Norfolk Royal' (D) CHab CLnd NOra NRog SBdl SKee
- 'Norfolk Royal Russet' (D) NOra NRog SBdl SKee WMat
- 'Norman's Pippin' (D) SBdl
- 'Northern Greening' (C) SBdl SKee
- 'Northern Spy' (D) **new** NOra SBdl SKee
- 'Northland Seedling' (D) **new** SBdl

§ - 'Northwood' (Cider) SBdl WMat
- 'Nottingham Pippin' (D) NRog SBdl
- 'Nutmeg Pippin' (D) SBdl
- NUVAR CHEERFULL GOLD (D) SKee
- NUVAR FRECKLES (D) SKee
- NUVAR GOLDEN HILLS (D) SKee
- NUVAR HOME FARM (D) SKee
- 'Oaken Pin' (D) CEnd SBdl

§ - 'Obelisk'PBR (D) CArg MGos MTrO NOra SKee WMat
- 'Old Fred' (D) **new** SBdl
- 'Old Pearmain' (D) SBdl SKee
- 'Old Somerset Russet' (D) SBdl
- 'Onibury Pippin' (D) SBdl
- 'Ontario' (C) **new** LPar SBdl
- 'Opal'PBR (D) SBdl
- 'Opalescent' (D) CEnd SBdl
- 'Orange Goff' (D) SBdl
- 'Orangenburg' (D) SBdl
- 'Orin' (D) SBdl
- 'Orleans' (D) **new** SBdl
- 'Orleans Reinette' (D) CAgr CArg CEnd CTri EPom MTrO NOra NRog SBdl SKee SSFr WJas WMat WWct
- 'Ortley' (D) **new** SBdl
- 'Osier' (Cider) SBdl
- 'Oslin' (D) GBin SBdl SKee WMat
- 'Osnabrucker Reinette' (D) **new** SBdl
- 'Otava'PBR (C/D) SKee
- 'Owen Thomas' (D) SBdl
- 'Oxford Beauty' (D) **new** SBdl
- 'Oxford Conquest' (D) SBdl
- 'Oxford Sunrise' (D) **new** SBdl
- 'Oxford Yeoman' (C) **new** SBdl
- 'Ozark Gold' (D) **new** SBdl
- 'P.J. Bergius' (D) **new** SBdl
- 'Paignton Marigold' (Cider) SBdl
- 'Palmer's Rosey' (D) SBdl
- PARADICE GOLD (D) CRos EBee EPom LRHS MTrO
- 'Paroquet' (D) SBdl
- 'Patricia' (D) **new** SBdl
- 'Paulared' (D) SBdl
- 'Payhembury' (C/Cider) CAgr
- 'Peacemaker' (D) SBdl
- 'Pear Apple' (D) CAgr CEnd
- 'Pearl' (D) NOra SBdl WMat
- 'Peasgood's Nonsuch' (C) ♀H6 CAgr CArg CHab EPom IArd LSRN MAsh MTrO NOra NRog SBdl SKee SLon WMat
- 'Peck's Pleasant' (D) SBdl
- 'Pederstrup' (D) **new** SBdl
- 'Pedro' (D) **new** SBdl
- 'Pendragon' (D) CEnd
- 'Pennard Bitter' (Cider) SBdl
- 'Pépin Shafrannyi' (D) SBdl
- 'Peter Lock' (C/D) CAgr CEnd SBdl
- 'Pethyre' (Cider) CCVT SBdl
- 'Petit Pippin' (D) **new** SBdl
- 'Pewaukee' (D) **new** SBdl
- 'Pickering's Seedling' (D) NRog SBdl
- 'Pig Aderyn' (C) CHab WGwG
- 'Pig's Nose Pippin' (D) CEnd SBdl
- 'Pig's Nose Pippin' Type III (D) CAgr
- 'Pig's Snout' (Cider/C/D) CEnd NRog SBdl
- 'Pine Apple Russet' (C/D) CAgr SBdl
- 'Pine Apple Russet of Devon' (D) CEnd
- 'Pine Golden Pippin' (D) SBdl
- PINK LADY see *M. domestica* 'Cripps Pink'
- 'Pinova'PBR (D) CAgr EPom LPar MTrO NOra SSFr
- 'Pitmaston Pine Apple' (D) CArg CHab CLnd CTri EWTr MAsh MTrO NOra NRog SBdl SKee SLon SSFr WMat WWct
- 'Pitmaston Russet Nonpareil' (D) SBdl
- 'Pixie' (D) ♀H6 CDoC CLnd CSBt EPom LRHS MPri MTrO NOra NRog SBdl SKee SLon WWct
- 'Plum Vite' (D) CAgr CTri
- 'Plymouth Cross' (D) SBdl
- 'Plympton Pippin' (C) CEnd CTri
- POLKA ('Trajan') (D) NOra SBdl
- 'Polly' (C/D) SBdl

- 'Polly Prosser' (D) SBdl
- 'Pomeroy of Somerset' (D) CHab CTri NRog SBdl
- 'Ponsford' (C) CAgr SBdl WMat
- 'Pónyik Alma' (C) SBdl
- 'Pope's Scarlet Costard' (D/C) **new** SBdl
- 'Port Allen Russet' (C/D) SBdl
- 'Port Wine' see *M. domestica* 'Harry Master's Jersey'
- 'Porter's Perfection' (Cider) CTri NOra NRog SBdl
- 'Pott's Seedling' (C) SBdl
- 'Present van Holland' (D) **new** SBdl
- 'Prima' (D) SBdl
- 'Prince Alfred' (C) **new** SBdl
- 'Prince Charles' (D) SBdl
- 'Prince Edward' (C) **new** SBdl
- 'Prince George' (C) **new** SBdl
- 'Princesse' (F) CEnd
- 'Priscilla' (D) NOra SBdl
- 'Proctor's Seedling' (D) **new** SBdl
- 'Pumpkin Sunset' SBdl
- 'Purpurroter Cousinot' (D) SBdl
- 'Queen' (C) CAgr NRog SBdl
- 'Queen Alexandra' (C) **new** SBdl
- 'Queen Cox' (D) CEnd CLnd CTri EPom LPar LSRN NOra NRog SBdl SEdi SKee SSFr SWvt WMat WTSh
- 'Queens' (D) CEnd
- 'Radford Beauty' (F) NRog
- 'Rajka'PBR (D) GQue NOra NRog SKee WWct
- 'Rambour Papeleu' (C) **new** SBdl
- 'Rathe Ripe' (D) **new** SBdl
- 'Red Alkmene' see *M. domestica* 'Red Windsor'
- 'Red Astrachan' (D) SBdl
- 'Red Belle de Boskoop' (D) CAgr LMaj NRog SBdl
- 'Red Blenheim' (C/D) SBdl
- 'Red Charles Ross' (C/D) SBdl
- 'Red Delicious' see *M. domestica* 'Starking'
- 'Red Devil' (D) Widely available
- 'Red Ellison' (D) CTri NRog SBdl
- 'Red Elstar' (D) SBdl
- 'Red Falstaff'PBR (D) ♀H6 CAgr CArg CBod CCVT CDoC CEnd CMac CTri EPfP GKin LBuc LRHS LSRN MAsh MTrO NLar NOra NRHS NRog SBdl SCoo SEWo SGbt SKee SLim SLon SPoG SSFT WMat WWct
- 'Red Fortune' (D) **new** SBdl
- 'Red Gravenstein' (D) NRog SBdl SEdi
- 'Red Ingestrie' (D) **new** NRog
- 'Red Jersey' (Cider) SBdl
- 'Red Joaneting' (D) SBdl SKee
- 'Red Jonagold' see *M. domestica* 'Jonagored'
- § 'Red Jonaprince'PBR (D) SBdl WMat
- 'Red Jonaprince Wilton's' (F) **new** MTrO
- 'Red Melba' (D) SBdl
- 'Red Newton Wonder' (C) SBdl
- 'Red Pixie' (D) CArg GQue SBdl WMat
- 'Red Rattler' (D) CTri
- 'Red Roller' (D) CTsd
- 'Red Sauce' (C) SBdl
- 'Red Victoria' (C) NRog SBdl
- § 'Red Windsor' (D) CArg CEnd CLnd CMac CRos CTri EBee ELan EPom LBuc LCro LOPS LRHS MAsh MTrO NLar NOra NRog SCoo SKee SLim SPoG SSFr WJas WMat
- 'Redcoat Grieve' (D) SBdl
- 'Redfree' (D) NOra SBdl
- 'Redsleeves' (D) CAgr CLnd NOra SBdl SKee
- 'Redwing' (D) **new** SBdl
- REGALI ('Delkistar'PBR) (D) SBdl
- 'Reid's Seedling' (C/D) **new** SBdl
- 'Reine de Pommes' (Cider) SBdl
- 'Reine des Reinettes' see *M. domestica* 'King of the Pippins'
- 'Reinette de Champagne' (C) **new** SBdl
- 'Reinette de Mâcon' (D) **new** NRog
- 'Reinette Descardre' (D) SBdl
- 'Reinette Dorée de Boediker' (D) SBdl
- 'Reinette du Canada' (D) SBdl SGsty
- 'Reinette Rouge Etoilée' (D) SBdl
- 'Renora' (D) **new** SBdl
- 'Renown' (D) **new** SBdl
- 'Resi'PBR (C/D) WWct
- 'Reverend W. Wilks' (C) CAgr CArg CBod CEnd CHab CSBt CTri EBee EPom EWTr MTrO NOra NRog SBdl SEdi SKee SSFr WJas WMat WWct
- 'Rhode Island Greening' (C/D) NOra SBdl
- 'Ribston Pippin' (D) ♀H6 CArg CTri LBuc MRav MTrO NOra NRog NWea SBdl SKee SLon SSFr WJas WMat WWct
- 'Richardson' (F) **new** SBdl
- 'Richared Delicious' (D) **new** SBdl
- 'Ringstad' (D) **new** SBdl
- 'Rival' (D) CAgr SBdl
- 'Rivers' Early Peach' (D) **new** SBdl
- 'Rivers' Nonsuch' (D) CHab SBdl
- 'Robert Blatchford' (C) SBdl
- 'Robin Pippin' (D) SBdl
- 'Rock' (C) SBdl
- 'Rogers McIntosh' (D) **new** SBdl
- 'Rokewood' (D) **new** SBdl
- 'Rome Beauty' (D) SBdl
- 'Rosemary Russet' (D) ♀H6 CAgr CArg CHab ELan NOra NRog SBdl SKee SLon SSFr WMat WWct
- 'Rosette' (D) CArg EPfP EPom LRHS MAsh MTrO NLar NOra WMat
- 'Rosmarina Bianca' (D/C) SBdl
- 'Ross Nonpareil' (D) CAgr IArd NOra NRog SBdl SKee WMat
- 'Rossie Pippin' (C) **new** SBdl
- 'Rosy Blenheim' (D) SBdl
- 'Roter Stettiner' (D) **new** SBdl
- 'Rougemont' (D) **new** SBdl
- 'Rough Pippin' (D) CBod CEnd SBdl
- 'Roundway Magnum Bonum' (C/D) CAgr CLnd SBdl
- § 'Roxbury Russet' (D) NOra SBdl
- 'Royal Blush'PBR (D) **new** SBdl
- 'Royal Gala' (D) CMac EPom LBuc LMaj LPar MRav SBdl SLon
- § 'Royal Jubilee' (C) SBdl
- 'Royal Russet' (C) CAgr CEnd SBdl SKee
- 'Royal Somerset' (C/Cider) CTri SBdl WMat
- 'Rubens' (D) SBdl
- RUBINETTE ('Rafzubin') (D) NOra SKee
- RUBINETTE ROSSO ('Rafzubex'PBR) (D) MTrO NOra WMat

– 'Rubinola' PBR (D)	SKee WWct
– 'Ruby' Seabrook (D)	SBdl
– 'Ruby' Thorrington (D)	SBdl
– 'S.T. Wright' (C)	NRog SBdl
– 'Sabaros' (C)	SBdl
– 'Saint Ailred' (D)	SBdl
– 'Saint Albans Pippin' (D)	SBdl SKee
– 'Saint Cecilia' (D)	CHab SBdl
§ – 'Saint Edmund's Pippin' (D) 🏆H6	CHab ELan EPfP MTrO NOra NRog NWea SKee SSFr
– 'Saint Edmund's Russet'	see *M. domestica* 'Saint Edmund's Pippin'
– 'Saint Everard' (D)	SBdl
– 'Saint Martin's' (D)	SBdl
– 'Saltcote Pippin' (D)	SBdl WMat
– 'Sam Young' (D)	CAgr NRog SBdl SKee
– 'Samba' (C/D)	LOPS
– 'Sandew' (C/D)	SBdl
– 'Sandlin Duchess' (D)	NOra WMat
– 'Sandringham' (C)	SBdl
– 'Sanspareil' (D)	CAgr SBdl
– 'Santana' PBR (D) 🏆H6	LPar NOra SBdl WMat
– 'Saturn' (D)	CAgr CArg CBod CCVT MTrO NOra NRog SBdl SKee SSFr WMat WWct
– 'Saw Pits' (D)	CAgr CEnd
– 'Scarlet Crofton' (D)	IArd SBdl
– 'Scarlet Nonpareil' (D)	SBdl SKee
– 'Scarlet Pearmain' (D)	SBdl
– 'Scarlet Pimpernel' (D)	SBdl
– 'Schoolmaster' (C)	NRog SBdl
– 'Schweizer Orange' (F)	SBdl
– 'Scilly Pearl' (C)	SBdl
– 'Scotch Bridget' (C)	CArg CHab EBee GQue MTrO NBid NOra NRog SBdl SKee WMat WWct
– 'Scotch Dumpling' (C)	GBin GKin GQue MTrO NOra SBdl SKee WMat
– 'Scotia' (C/D)	SBdl
– 'Scrumptious' PBR (D) 🏆H6	Widely available
– 'Seabrook's Red' (D)	SBdl
– 'Seaton House' (C)	SBdl
– 'September Beauty' (D)	SBdl
– 'Severn Bank' (C)	SBdl
– 'Sharleston Pippin' (D)	NRog SBdl
– 'Sharon' (D) **new**	SBdl
– 'Sheep's Nose' (C)	CHab
– 'Shenandoah' (C)	SKee
– 'Shoesmith' (C)	SBdl
– 'Siddington Russet' (C/D) **new**	SBdl
– 'Sidney Strake' (C)	CAgr CEnd SBdl
– 'Signe Tillisch' (C/D) **new**	SBdl
– 'Sikulai Alma' (D)	SBdl
– 'Sir Isaac Newton's'	see *M. domestica* 'Flower of Kent'
– 'Sir John Thornycroft' (D)	CLnd SBdl
– 'Sisson's Worksop Newtown' (D)	NRog SBdl
– 'Skovfoged' (C)	SBdl
– 'Slack Ma Girdle' (Cider)	CArg CBod NOra SBdl SKee WMat
– 'Sleeping Beauty' (C) **new**	SBdl
– 'Small's Admirable' (C) **new**	SBdl
– 'Smart's Prince Arthur' (C)	CHab NRog SBdl
– 'Smiler' (D) **new**	SBdl
– 'Smoothee' (D) **new**	SBdl
– 'Snell's Glass Apple'	see *M. domestica* 'Glass Apple'
– 'Somerset Lasting' (C)	CTri
– 'Somerset Redstreak' (Cider)	CAgr CArg CHab CTri MTrO NOra NRog SBdl WMat
– 'Sops in Wine' (Cider/D)	CArg CDoC NOra SBdl SVic WMat
– 'Sour Bay' (Cider)	CAgr
– 'Sour Natural'	see *M. domestica* 'Langworthy'
– 'Sowman's Seedling' (C)	SBdl
– 'Spartan' (D)	Widely available
– 'Spätblühender Taffetapfel' (D) **new**	SKee
– 'Spencer' (D)	SBdl SKee
– 'Splendour' (D) **new**	SBdl
– 'Stable Jersey' (Cider)	SBdl
– 'Stamford Pippin' (D)	NRog
– 'Stanway Seedling' (C)	SBdl
– 'Star of Devon' (D)	CBod CEnd SBdl SKee
§ – 'Starking' (D)	LMaj NOra SBdl SGsty SKee
– 'Starkrimson' (D)	SBdl
– 'Stark's Earliest' (D)	SBdl SVic
– 'Starkspur Golden Delicious' (D)	SBdl
– 'Stembridge Cluster' (Cider)	CTri SBdl
– 'Stembridge Jersey' (Cider)	SBdl
– 'Steyne Seedling' (D)	CLnd NRog
– 'Stibbert' (D)	SBdl
– 'Stirling Castle' (C)	CAgr MTrO NOra SBdl SKee WMat
– 'Stobo Castle' (C)	SBdl
– 'Stoke Edith Pippin' (D)	SBdl
– 'Stoke Red' (Cider)	CArg NOra NRog SBdl WMat
– 'Stone's'	see *M. domestica* 'Loddington'
– 'Stonetosh' (D) **new**	SBdl
– 'Storey's Seedling' (D)	SBdl
– 'Strawberry Pippin' (D)	NRog SBdl
– 'Striped Beefing' (C)	NRog SBdl
– 'Strippy' (C)	SBdl
– 'Sturmer Pippin' (D)	CSBt CTri EBee NOra NRog SBdl SWeb WWct
– 'Summer Golden Pippin' (D)	NRog SBdl
– 'Summerland' (D) **new**	SBdl
– 'Sunburn' (D)	SBdl
– 'Sunrise' PBR (D)	CEnd NOra SKee
– 'Sunrise' (D) **new**	SBdl
– 'Sunset' (D) 🏆H6	Widely available
– 'Suntan' (D)	EWTr NOra NRog SBdl SKee
– 'Superb'	see *M. domestica* 'Laxton's Superb'
– 'Sure Crop' (D)	SBdl
– 'Surprise' (D)	LRHS MTrO SBdl
– SURPRIZE (D)	EPom LBuc NOra
– 'Sussex Mother' (C/D)	CHab NRog SBdl
– 'Swaar' (D)	SBdl
– 'Sweet Alford' (Cider)	CArg SBdl WMat WWct
– 'Sweet Bay' (Cider)	CAgr
– 'Sweet Caroline' (D)	LPar SBdl
– 'Sweet Coppin' (Cider)	CArg CTri SBdl WMat
– 'Sweet Lilibet'	see *M. domestica* 'Red Windsor'
– 'Sweet Merlin' (D/Cider)	SBdl
– 'Sweet Pethyre' (C)	SEdi
– 'Sweet Sixteen' (D)	NOra SBdl
– 'Sweet Society' (D)	NOra SKee WMat
– 'Sylvia' (D)	SBdl
– 'Tale Sweet' (Cider)	SBdl
– 'Tamar Beauty' (D)	CEnd
– 'Tan Harvey' (Cider)	CEnd SBdl
– 'Tare de Ghinda' (F)	SBdl
– 'Tasman Pride' (D) **new**	SBdl
– 'Taunton Cross' (D)	CAgr CArg SBdl WMat
– 'Taylor's' (Cider)	CAgr SBdl
– 'Taylor's Favourite' (F) **new**	NWea
– 'Ten Commandments' (Cider/D)	SBdl WWct
– 'Tenroy' PBR (D) **new**	SBdl
– 'Téton de Demoiselle' (D)	NRog SBdl
– 'Tewkesbury Baron' (D)	SBdl
– 'The Rattler' (Cider)	CEnd

- 'Thoday's Quarrenden' (D) **new** SBdl
- 'Thomas Jeffrey' (D) GBin SBdl
- 'Thomas Rivers' (C) SBdl
- 'Thompson's Apple' (D) **new** SBdl
- 'Thorle Pippin' (D) SBdl
- 'Thorpe's Peach' (D) SBdl
- 'Thurso' (D) SBdl
- TICKLED PINK ('Baya Marisa') (C/D) CArg EPom LBuc LRHS MGos MTrO NOra SPer SSFr WMat
- 'Tidicombe Seedling' (D) WMat
- 'Tiffen' (C) **new** SBdl
- 'Tillington Court' (C) SBdl
- 'Tinsley Quince' (D) SBdl WMat
- 'Tom Putt' (C) CAgr CArg CCVT CHab CLnd CSBt CTri LBuc NOra NRog SBdl SKee WJas WMat WWct
- 'Tommy Knight' (D) CAgr CEnd SBdl
- 'Topaz'PBR (D) ♀H6 LPar MTrO NOra SBdl SKee
- 'Tower of Glamis' (C) CHab NRog SBdl SKee
- 'Transparente de Bois Guillaume' (D) **new** SBdl
- 'Transparente de Croncels' (C) SBdl
- 'Tregonna King' (C/D) CBod CDoC CTsd
- 'Tremlett's Bitter' (Cider) CAgr CArg CHab CTsd MTrO NOra NRog SBdl SKee SVic WMat
- 'Trwyn Mochyn' (C) WGwG
- § - 'Tuscan' (D) SBdl SKee
- 'Twenty Ounce' (C) SBdl
- § - 'Tydeman's Early Worcester' (D) CAgr CBod CHab CLnd LPar NRog SBdl SEdi SKee SRms SSFr WWct
- 'Tydeman's Harvest' (D) **new** SBdl
- 'Tydeman's Late Orange' (D) CArg CHab CTri NOra NRog SBdl SKee WMat
- 'Tyler's Kernel' (C) SBdl
- 'Uland' (C) **new** SBdl
- 'Underleaf' (D) SBdl
- 'Upton Pyne' (C/D) CBod SBdl
- 'Vanda'PBR (F) **new** SBdl
- 'Veitch's Perfection' (C/D) WMat
- 'Venus Pippin' (C/D) CEnd SBdl
- 'Vernade' (F) SBdl
- 'Vicar of Beighton' (D) SBdl
- 'Vickie' (Cider) **new** NRog
- 'Victory' (C) SBdl
- 'Vileberie' (Cider) CTri NRog
- 'Violette' (C) SBdl
- 'Vista-bella' (D) SBdl SEdi
- 'Vitgylling' (D/C) SBdl
- 'Von Zuccalmaglio's Reinette' (D) **new** SBdl
- 'Wadey's Seedling' (D) SBdl
- 'Wadhurst Pippin' (C/D) **new** NRog SBdl
- 'Wagener' (D) CLnd NRog SBdl
- 'Warden' (D) SBdl
- 'Warner's King' (C) ♀H6 CTri MTrO NOra NRog SBdl SKee
- 'Warren's Seedling' (C) **new** SBdl
- 'Washington Strawberry' (D) **new** SBdl
- 'Wealthy' (D) SBdl
- 'Weight' (C) SBdl
- 'Wellington' (C) see *M. domestica* 'Dummellor's Seedling'
- 'Wellington' (Cider) CAgr
- 'Wellington Bloomless' (D) **new** NRog
- § - 'Wellspur' (D) SBdl
- 'Wellspur Red Delicious' see *M. domestica* 'Wellspur'
- 'Werrington Wonder' (D) CEnd
- 'West View Seedling' (D) SBdl
- 'Weston's Seedling' (C) **new** SBdl
- 'Wheeler's Russet' (D) NRog SBdl
- 'White Jersey' (Cider) SBdl
- 'White Melrose' (C) NOra SKee WMat
- 'White Quarrenden' (D) SBdl
- 'White Transparent' (C/D) SBdl SKee
- 'White Winter Pearmain' (D) SBdl
- 'Whitpot Sweet' (Cider) CEnd
- 'William Crump' (D) CEnd CHab MTrO NOra NRog SBdl SKee WMat WWct
- 'William Peters' (D) **new** NRog
- 'Williams Favourite' (D) **new** SBdl
- 'Windsor Early' (D) SSFr
- 'Winesap' (C/D) NOra SBdl
- 'Winston' (D) ♀H6 CAgr CBod CCVT CMac CTri LPar NRog SBdl SKee SRms SVic SWeb WWct
- 'Winter Banana' (D) CArg CHab NOra NRog SBdl SVic WMat
- 'Winter Cockpit' (C) **new** NRog
- 'Winter Gem' (D) CAgr CArg CBod CCVT CEnd CLnd EPom LBuc MTrO NOra NRog SBdl SKee SSFr WJas WMat
- 'Winter Lemon' (C/D) SBdl
- 'Winter Majetin' (C) SBdl
- 'Winter Peach' (D/C) CAgr SBdl
- 'Winter Pearmain' (D) SBdl SKee
- 'Winter Quarrenden' (D) SBdl
- 'Winter Stubbard' (C) SBdl
- 'Withington Fillbasket' (C) **new** SBdl
- 'Wolf River' (D/C) NOra NRog SBdl
- 'Woodbine' see *M. domestica* 'Northwood'
- 'Woodford' (C) SBdl
- 'Woolbrook Pippin' (D) CAgr CEnd SBdl WMat
- 'Woolbrook Russet' (C) CEnd SBdl
- 'Worcester Cross' (D) **new** SBdl
- 'Worcester Pearmain' (D) ♀H6 Widely available
- 'Worcester Woodsil' (F) SBdl
- 'Wyatt's Seedling' see *M. domestica* 'Langworthy'
- 'Wyken Pippin' (D) SBdl WWct
- 'Yarlington Mill' (Cider) CAgr CArg CHab CTri MTrO NOra NRog SBdl SKee SVic WMat WWct
- 'Ye Old Peasgood' (D) **new** SBdl
- 'Yellow Bellflower' (D/C) SBdl
- 'Yellow Ingestrie' (D) CArg CHab CLnd MTrO NOra NRog SBdl SKee WMat WWct
- 'Yorkshire Aromatic' (C) NRog SBdl SKee
- 'Yorkshire Greening' (C) CHab NOra NRog SBdl SKee
- 'Young America' (D) SBdl
- 'Young's Pinello' (D) **new** SBdl
- 'Zabergäu Renette' (D) NOra SBdl SKee

'Donald Wyman' CLnd EPfP MAsh MTrO NLar NOra SCoo WMat
§ 'Echtermeyer' SBdl
'Elise Rathke' CLnd SBdl
'Evelyn' CBcs CLnd MTrO NOra NWea WMat
§ 'Evereste' ♀H6 Widely available
florentina 'Rosemoor' CLnd
× ***floribunda*** ♀H6 Widely available
'Gardener's Gold' CEnd CLnd SRms
'Gibbs' Golden Gage' (D) **new** SBdl

	× ***gloriosa*** 'Oekonomierat Echtermeyer'	see *M.* 'Echtermeyer'
	'Golden Gem'	CLnd GQue MAsh MTrO NLar NOra NOrn SBdl SEWo SKee SPer WMat
	'Golden Hornet'	see *M.* × *zumi* 'Golden Hornet'
	'Gorgeous'	CLnd CMac CSBt EBee EPfP EPom EWTr LBuc LRHS LSRN MPri MRav MSwo MTrO NLar NOra NOrn NWea SBdl SCoo SEWo SEdi SKee SLim SPer SPoG WJas WMat WMou WWct
	'Harry Baker'	CCVT CDoC CEnd CLnd CMac CSBt EPfP EPom EWTr LRHS LSRN MAsh MBlu MRav MTrO NOra SCoo SLim SPer SPoG WMat WWct
	× ***hartwigii***	CLnd
	- 'Katherine' **new**	EWTr
	'Hillieri'	see *M.* × *scheideckeri* 'Hillieri'
	hupehensis ♀H6	CBcs CEnd CLnd CMCN CSBt CTri EPfP EWTr GKev LRHS MBlu MGos MRav MTrO NLar NOra NOrn NRog NWea SCob SDix SPer SPtp WMat WMou WTSh
	'Hyde Hall Spire'	SCoo
	'Hyslop'	CLnd
	'Indian Magic'	CLnd EBee EPfP EWTr LRHS MAsh MTrO NLar NOra SPer WHCr WMat WMou
	'Indian Summer'	CLnd
	ioensis 'Fimbriata' (d) **new**	LRHS MAsh MTrO NOra
	JELLY KING ('Mattfru') ♀H6	CDoC CLnd EBee EPfP EPom EWTr LBuc LCro LOPS LRHS LSRN MAsh MTrO NLar NOra NWea SEWo SGbt SPer SPoG WHCr WMat WMou
	'John Downie' (C)	Widely available
	'Kaido'	see *M.* × *micromalus*
	'Lady Northcliffe'	CLnd SBdl
	'Laura' ♀H6	CLnd EBee ELan EPfP EPom LCro LOPS LRHS LSRN MAsh MTrO NOra SCoo SKee SLim SLon SPer SPoG WJas WMat
	'Louisa'	EBee EPfP LSRN MAsh MTrO NOra NWea SCoo SGbt SGol SLim WMat
	× ***magdeburgensis***	CAco CCVT CLnd
	'Makamik'	SBdl
	'Mariri Red' (D)	WMat
§	× ***micromalus***	CLnd
	× ***moerlandsii*** 'Liset'	CEnd CLnd MRav NOra NRog SBdl SCob SCoo SEdi WFar
§	- 'Profusion'	CBcs CTri ELan EPfP EWTr IPap LCro LOPS LRHS MGos MPri MRav MSwo MTrO NOra NRHS NRog NWea SGol SGsty SKee SPer SRms SWvt WSpi
	'Mokum'	CLnd EWTr LMaj LPar LSRN
	'Molten Lava'	CLnd
	'Montreal Beauty'	CLnd EPom SBdl WJas
	niedzwetzkyana	CLnd SBdl
	NUVAR CARNIVAL	SKee
	NUVAR MARBLE (C)	EBee MTrO NOra NOrn SKee WMat
	'Oporto' (F) **new**	SBdl
	orientalis **new**	SBdl
	PERPETU	see *M.* 'Evereste'
	'Peter's Red'	CLnd LMaj
	'Pink Perfection'	CEnd EPfP LCro LOPS MAsh MTrO NOra NWea SGbt SPoG WMat
	× ***platycarpa*** **new**	SBdl
	'Pond Red'	CLnd
	'Prairifire'	CLnd EBee EGrI LRHS MAsh MTrO NOra SCoo SLim SLon SPer SPoG WMat
	prattii	CLnd GLog WLov
	- 'Pourpre Noir'	CLnd
	'Princeton Cardinal' ♀H6	CLnd CMac EPfP MAsh SCoo SLim SPoG
	'Professor Sprenger'	see *M.* × *zumi* 'Professor Sprenger'
	'Profusion'	see *M.* × *moerlandsii* 'Profusion'
	prunifolia	MBlu
	- var. ***rinkii***	CLnd
	'Purple Prince'	CLnd
§	× ***purpurea*** 'Aldenhamensis'	CLnd NRog
	- 'Eleyi'	EPfP NRog NWea SBdl SEdi
	- 'Lemoinei'	CLnd
	- 'Neville Copeman'	CCVT EPom LRHS SBdl SEdi SSFr WJas
	- 'Pendula'	see *M.* 'Echtermeyer'
	'Ralph Shay'	CLnd
	'Red Barron'	CLnd
	'Red Glow'	CAco CLnd NRog SBdl
	'Red Jade'	see *M.* × *scheideckeri* 'Red Jade'
	RED OBELISK ('Dvp Obel')	CBod CCVT CLnd EBee LBuc MTrO NOra NOrn SCoo SPoG WLov WMat
	'Red Peacock'	CLnd
	'Red Prince'	see *M.* 'Red Jonaprince'
	'Red Topaz' PBR **new**	MTrO
	'Roberts Crab'	MTrO NLar NOra
§	× ***robusta***	CLnd LSRN NRog NWea SBdl SLon SRms
	- 'Dolgo'	CLnd CSBt EPfP EPom LCro LRHS MBlu MTrO NLar NOra NWea SBdl SCoo SKee SPoG WMat
	- 'Red Sentinel' ♀H6	Widely available
	- 'Red Siberian'	SPer
	- 'Yellow Siberian'	CLnd
	'Rosehip'	CEnd CLnd EWTr LCro LOPS MTrO NLar NOra NOrn WMat WMou
	'Royal Beauty'	CLnd EPfP EWTr IPap LRHS MAsh MBlu MGos MPri MSwo MTrO NOra NOrn NWea SBdl SCoo SEdi SLon SPer WMat
	'Royal Burgundy' **new**	NRog
	'Royalty'	Widely available
	'Rudolph'	CCVT CLnd EBar EBee IPap LBuc LMaj LPar LSRN MAsh MGos MPri MTrO NOra NOrn SCob SCoo SEWo SEdi SLim SPer SPoG WJas WMat WMou
	'Ruth Ann'	CLnd
	sargentii	CLnd GKev NOra NRog NWea
	- 'Candy Mint'	MAsh WMat
	- 'Tina'	CLnd LRHS MTrO NOra NOrn SPoG WMat
	'Satin Cloud'	CLnd
§	× ***scheideckeri*** 'Hillieri'	CLnd MBlu NOra
§	- 'Red Jade'	CDoC CTri ELan LRHS MGos MRav MSwo NOrn NRog NWea SBdl SEdi SPer SRms WJas
	Siberian crab	see *M.* × *robusta*
	sieboldii	see *M. toringo*
	sieversii	CLnd NOra
	sikkimensis B&SWJ 2431	WCru
	'Silver Drift'	CLnd
	'Simon'	WMat
	'Snowcloud'	CLnd MAsh NOrn SLim
	'Snowdrift'	CLnd
	'Strathmore'	SBdl
	'Street Parade'	CLnd
	× ***sublobata***	CLnd
	SUGAR TYME ('Sutyzam')	CLnd SGol
	'Sun Rival' ♀H6	CCVT CDoC CEnd CLnd CMac EBee ELan EPfP EPom EWTr LRHS

LSRN MAsh MBlu MPri MRav MTrO NOra NOrn SBdl SCoo SEWo SEdi SLim SPer SPoG SRms WJas WMat WMou

sylvestris CArg CBrac CCVT CHab CLnd EPfP IPap LBuc LMaj LPar MMuc MNic MRav NRog NWea SCob SEND SEWo SEdi SPer SPre WKor WMou WTSh

§ ***toringo*** CLnd EPfP GKev NOra SBdl

I - var. ***arborescens*** CLnd

- 'Aros'PBR EBee ELan EPfP LBuc LCro LOPS LRHS MTrO NOra NOrn SEWo WMat

- 'Browers' LPar

- 'Scarlett' ℽH6 CCVT CEnd CLnd CMac EBee ELan EPfP IArd LMaj LRHS LSRN MAsh MTrO NLar NOra NWea SCoo SEWo SLim SPer SPoG WMat

- 'Wintergold' SBdl

- 'Wooster' CLnd

toringoides see *M. bhutanica*

transitoria ℽH6 CEnd CLnd CMac CSpe ELan EPfP GKin LRHS MAsh MBlu MRav MTrO NLar NOra NWea SCoo SLau SPer WMat WMou WPGP

- 'Roundabarrow Ruby' EBee WPGP

- 'Thornhayes Tansy' NOra SLim SPoG WMat

trilobata EBee ELan EPfP LMaj LPar MBlu MGos SCoo SEND

- 'Guardsman' CLnd CMac EBee EPfP MPri NOra SBdl WMat WMou

tschonoskii CAco CDoC CLnd CMCN CMac CTri ELan GKev LMaj LPar LRHS MBlu MGos MMuc NOrn NRog NWea SBdl SCob SEND SEdi SPer SRms SWvt WJas WMou WTSh

- 'Belmonte' MBlu

'Van Eseltine' CAgr CBod CDoC CMac CSBt EPfP MAsh MMuc SBdl SEdi SPer WJas

'Veitch's Scarlet' CHab CLnd CSBt NRog SBdl

VELVET PILLAR ('Velvetcole') SPer

'Virginia Crab' SBdl

WEEPING CANDIED APPLE ('Weepcanzam') CLnd SGol

'White Angel' CLnd

'White Star' CCVT CLnd CSBt EBee EWTr LRHS NOra SBdl SEWo SLon WMat

'Winter Gold' LMaj SEdi SGol

'Wisley Crab' CBod CLnd SBdl SEdi SGol SKee SLon SRms

yunnanensis EPfP SBdl WPav

× ***zumi*** GLog

- var. ***calocarpa*** CLnd

§ - 'Golden Hornet' Widely available

§ - 'Professor Sprenger' CLnd EPfP LMaj LPar MTrO NOra SCoo

Malva (*Malvaceae*)

alcea CAgr

- var. ***fastigiata*** CMac EPPr LRHS SPer SRms

- 'Royal Flush' NRHS

bicolor see *Lavatera maritima*

crispa see *M. verticillata*

'Gibbortello' GJos

moschata CAgr CBcs CBod CTtf EBee ECha ELan ENfk EPfP GJos GPoy GQue MBow MHer MNHC NAts NLar NMir SPer SPlb SRms SVic WFar WHer WShi WWild

§ - f. ***alba*** ℽH5 Widely available

- 'Appleblossom' EAJP

- 'Romney Marsh' see *Althaea officinalis* 'Romney Marsh'

- 'Rosea' EHyd EPfP GMaP LRHS NPer NRHS SPoG SWvt

- 'Snow White' see *M. moschata* f. *alba*

- 'White Perfection' WFar

pusilla CCCN

sylvestris CBod GJos SRms

- 'Blue Fountain'PBR EBee SRms

- 'Brave Heart' CTtf GJos SWvt

- MARINA ('Dema'PBR) NLar

- var. ***mauritiana*** LCro LOPS NLar NPer

- - 'Bíbor Felhő' CSpe

- - 'Mystic Merlin' GJos

- - 'Primley Blue' CBod EBee ELan EPfP GMaP LRHS MRav NLar NPer SGBe WKif WSpi

- - 'Zebrina' CTtf EPfP GJos MBow NGBl NPer SBut SWvt

- 'Minety Violet' **new** CNat

- 'Perry's Blue' NPer

- 'Poetry'PBR **new** SGBe

- 'Windsor Castle' LShi

§ ***verticillata*** CLau

Malvastrum (*Malvaceae*)

× ***hypomadarum*** see *Anisodontea* × *hypomadara* (Sprague) D.M. Bates

mandarin see *Citrus reticulata* Mandarin Group

mandarin, Cleopatra see *Citrus reticulata*

Mandevilla ✿ (*Apocynaceae*)

§ × ***amabilis*** CCCN

- 'Alice du Pont' ℽH1c CCCN EMdy EShb SPre

- SUNDAVILLE APRICOT ('Sunpapri') (Sundaville Series) **new** LSou

'Audrey'PBR (Vogue Series) CWGN SPoG

boliviensis ℽH1c CCCN CRHN

(Diamantina Series) DIAMANTINA OPALE FUCHSIA FLAMMÉ ('Lanmissouri'PBR) LCro LOPS

- DIAMANTINA OPALE GRENAT ('Lanutah') EMdy

'Ginger' (Vogue Series) CWGN SPoG

§ ***laxa*** ℽH2 CCCN CRHN CSpe ECre ELan EMdy EShb SVen

(Rio Series) RIO DEEP RED ('Fisrix Dered'PBR) CCCN

- RIO PINK ('Fisrix Pinka'PBR) CCCN

- RIO WHITE ('Fisrix Whit'PBR) EMdy

'Ruby' (Vogue Series) CWGN

sanderi CCCN EShb SPre

- 'Pink of Hint' EMdy

- 'Rosea' CCCN

splendens ℽH1c CCCN EMdy

suaveolens see *M. laxa*

Sundaville Series CCCN

- SUNDAVILLE CREAM PINK ('Sunparapibra'PBR) EMdy

- SUNDAVILLE DARK RED ('Sunparabeni') CAbb EMdy

- SUNDAVILLE GIANT RED ('Sunparadai'PBR) **new** LSou

- SUNDAVILLE GRAND RED ('Sunpara15'PBR) EMdy

- SUNDAVILLE IMPROVED WHITE 16 ('Sunparamakuho') EMdy
- SUNDAVILLE PEARL ('Patmandewi') EMdy
- SUNDAVILLE PINK ('Sunmandecripi'PBR) EMdy
- SUNDAVILLE PRETTY ROSE ('Sunparaprero'PBR) EMdy
- SUNDAVILLE RED ('Sunmandecrim'PBR) EMdy
- SUNDAVILLE ROSE STAR ('Sunpararosta'PBR) EMdy

Mandragora (*Solanaceae*)

autumnalis GEdr SPhx WSFF
caulescens GEdr
- BO 15-123 new GGro
§ ***officinarum*** EBee GEdr GGro GPoy SPhx XAbr

Manettia (*Rubiaceae*)

cordifolia SBrt
§ ***luteorubra*** CCCN

Manfreda see *Agave*

× *Mangave* see *Agave*

Mangifera (*Anacardiaceae*)

indica (F) CCCN SPre SVic
- 'Palmer' (F) new SVic

Manglietia see *Magnolia*

yunnanensis see *Magnolia insignis*

mango see *Mangifera indica*

Manihot (*Euphorbiaceae*)

carthaginensis SPlb

Mantisia (*Zingiberaceae*)

saltatoria PAB 4208 LEdu WPGP

Margyricarpus (*Rosaceae*)

§ ***pinnatus*** EWld WAbe WPav
setosus see *M. pinnatus*

Mariscus see *Cyperus*

marjoram, pot see *Origanum onites*

marjoram, sweet see *Origanum majorana*

marjoram, wild, or oregano see *Origanum vulgare*

marrow see AGM Vegetables Section

Marrubium (*Lamiaceae*)

§ ***bourgaei*** var. ***bourgaei*** 'All Hallows Green' ECha ECtt EHyd SRms
* ***cylleneum*** 'Velvetissimum' WCot
§ ***incanum*** XSen
libanoticum ECha
supinum EBou ECha LRHS NFav SGro
vulgare CBee CBod CCBP ENfk GJos GPoy MHer MNHC SRms WJek

Marsdenia (*Apocynaceae*)

oreophila CBcs CKel CRHN LRHS SLon SPoG WPGP WSHC

Marshallia (*Asteraceae*)

grandiflora EBee

Marsilea (*Marsileaceae*)

mutica EWat
quadrifolia LLWG

Massonia (*Asparagaceae*)

depressa ♀H2 SChF WAbe WCot
echinata SChF WAbe WCot
jasminiflora WHil
longipes WCot
pseudoechinata WCot
pustulata ♀H2 SChF WAbe WCot
- purple-leaved WCot
thunbergiana WCot

Mathiasella (*Apiaceae*)

bupleuroides 'Green Dream' CAvo CBcs CBod CSpe EBee EGrI ELan EPfP EWoo GBin GMaP ILea LCro LOPS LRHS MBel MHol MNrw MPnt SCob SEdd SPoG WCAu WCot

Matricaria (*Asteraceae*)

chamomilla see *M. recutita*
maritima see *Tripleurospermum maritimum*
parthenium see *Tanacetum parthenium*
§ ***recutita*** GPoy MBros MNHC SPhx XAbr
tchihatchewii XLum XSen

Matteuccia (*Onocleaceae*)

orientalis ♀H5 CBod CDTJ CLAP CRos CSta CWCL ECha EFer EHed EHyd EMor GArf GMaP IBal LEdu LLWG LRHS MMuc NBid NBro NLar NRHS SCob SPlb WHwl WPGP WPnP XLum
pensylvanica EHyd LRHS NRHS
struthiopteris ♀H5 Widely available
* - 'Depauperata' CLAP
- 'Jumbo' CBdn CCCN EHyd LRHS MAsh NRHS WPGP
- 'The King' EHed LRHS WCot

Matthiola (*Brassicaceae*)

fruticulosa 'Alba' EPfP WPGP
- subsp. ***perennis*** NSti WHal
incana CEls LCro LOPS SVic WKif
- 'Alba' EBee ECha ELan LRHS MHol SMad SPad SPhx
- Cinderella Series ♀H4 LCro LOPS
- dwarf, mixed MBros
- 'Low' WCot
- 'Pillow Talk' ECha LRHS
scapifera WAbe
sinuata CEls WABo
white-flowered perennial CSpe EShb NPer

Maurandya (*Plantaginaceae*)

§ ***barclayana*** CSpe IDee
erubescens see *Lophospermum erubescens*
'Magic Dragon' see *Lophospermum* 'Magic Dragon'
'Red Dragon' see *Lophospermum* 'Red Dragon'

Maytenus (*Celastraceae*)

boaria LEdu SAko SArc SEND
disticha (Hook.f.) Urb. LEdu
magellanica WPGP

Mazus (*Phrymaceae*)

radicans ECha

reptans	CBod EBee EBou ECtt ELan GEdr NLar NPer NQui SPtp WFar WIce XLum
- B&SWJ	CExl
- 'Albus'	CBod EBee ECtt LLWG LRHS NLar SPlb WFar WIce
- 'Blue'	LLWG

Mecardonia (*Plantaginaceae*)

'Goldflake'	CCCN

Meconopsis ✿ (*Papaveraceae*)

§ ***baileyi*** 🏆H5	CBcs CBod CTri EBee EHyd GDam GGGa GKev ITim LCro LOPS NBir NChi SCob WFar WSFF
* - var. ***alba***	EBee EHyd EPot GKev NLar NRHS
- 'Hensol Violet'	EBee EWes GGGa GKev NRHS SBls WTyc
- violet-flowered	ITim
balangensis BO 16-072 new	GGro
Ballyrogan form	GEdr GKev
× ***beamishii***	GKev
betonicifolia misapplied	see *M. baileyi*
'Biggar Park'	GEdr
'Burgundy'	GWyn
cambrica	see *Papaver cambricum*
'Clydeside Early Treasure'	GEdr GKev
× ***cookei***	GKev NHpl
- 'Old Rose'	GGGa GKev GMaP
'Edrom'	GEdr
§ Fertile Blue Group	ITim
- 'Blue Ice'	see *M.* (Fertile Blue Group) 'Lingholm'
- 'Harry Bush'	GEdr
- 'Lingholm'	Widely available
- 'Louise'	GEdr GKev GMaP
- 'Mop-head' 🏆H5	GEdr GKev GMaP
§ George Sherriff Group	MArl
- 'Ascreavie'	GEdr GKev GMaP
- 'Barney's Blue'	GEdr GKev GMaP
- 'Dalemain' 🏆H5	GEdr GKev GMaP
- 'Dorothy Renton' new	GKev
- 'Branklyn' ambig.	CExl GEdr
- 'Huntfield'	GEdr GGGa GKev GMaP
- 'Jimmy Bayne'	GEdr GKev GMaP
- 'Spring Hill'	GKev
- 'Susan's Reward' 🏆H5	GEdr GMaP
grandis misapplied	see *M.* George Sherriff Group
grandis ambig.	ITim
- GS 600	see *M.* George Sherriff Group
- 'Himal Sky'	GEdr GKev
'Great Glen' new	GKev
§ (Infertile Blue Group) 'Bobby Masterton' 🏆H5	GEdr GKev GMaP
- 'Bryan Conway'	GEdr
- 'Crarae'	GEdr GGGa GKev GMaP
- 'Crewdson Hybrid'	GEdr GKev GMaP
- 'Cruickshank'	GKev
- 'Dawyck'	see *M.* (Infertile Blue Group) 'Slieve Donard'
- 'Maggie Sharp'	GEdr
- 'Mrs Jebb' 🏆H5	GArf GEdr GGGa GKev GMaP
- 'P.C. Abildgaard' 🏆H5	GEdr GGGa GKev GMaP
§ - 'Slieve Donard' 🏆H5	CRos EHyd GArf GEdr GGGa GKev GMaP LRHS NRHS
integrifolia	CCCN GEdr
- subsp. ***integrifolia*** W/O 7158 new	GGro
'Inverewe' 🏆H5	GEdr GKev GMaP
'Keillour' 🏆H5	GEdr GMaP
'Keillour Violet'	GKev
'Kilbryde Castle White'	GEdr
'Marit' 🏆H5	GEdr GKev GMaP
'Mervyn Kessell'	GEdr GKev
'Mildred'	GEdr GKev GMaP
napaulensis misapplied	EBee GAbr GKev ITim
napaulensis DC. from Solukhumbu, Nepal	GDam
nudicaulis	see *Papaver nudicaule*
paniculata	GAbr GKev GMaP
'Pride of Angus'	GEdr
punicea	GKev NHpl
- 'Sichuan Silk'	NHpl
quintuplinervia 🏆H5	GKev GRum NHpl NSla
× ***sheldonii*** misapplied (fertile)	see *M.* Fertile Blue Group
× ***sheldonii*** misapplied (sterile)	see *M.* Infertile Blue Group
× ***sheldonii*** ambig.	CBcs EPfP EWoo GAbr LRHS NLar NPer NRHS
'Stewart Annand'	GEdr GKev GMaP
'Strathspey'	GEdr GKev GMaP NHpl
superba	GAbr
'Willie Duncan'	GEdr GMaP

Medeola (*Asparagaceae*)

virginiana	EBee

Medicago (*Fabaceae*)

arborea	SEND SPlb
lupulina	CHab NGrd SPhx SVic
sativa	NGrd SPhx SVic WSFF

Medinilla (*Melastomataceae*)

'Bella'PBR (Florinilla Series)	CDoC
magnifica 🏆H1a	CCCN CDoC

medlar see *Mespilus germanica*; see also AGM Fruit Section

Meehania (*Lamiaceae*)

cordata	EBee
urticifolia	EBee GEdr WPnP
- B&SWJ 1210	WCru

Megaskepasma (*Acanthaceae*)

erythrochlamys	SVen

Melaleuca (*Myrtaceae*)

acuminata	SPlb
alternifolia	CCCN CTsd EShb GPoy MHer NWad SPlb SVen XAbr
armillaris	CCCN CTsd SEND SPlb
cuticularis	SPlb
decussata	CSde SPlb
§ ***diosmatifolia***	CExl
diosmifolia	CPbh
ericifolia	CTri CTsd SEND SPlb
fulgens	SPlb
gibbosa	CExl CKel SEND SVen
hypericifolia	CExl SPlb SVen
linariifolia	CCCN SPlb
nesophila	SPlb
pallida new	GAbr
pungens	SPlb
pustulata	SVen
squamea	GAbr SPlb
squarrosa	CBcs CExl SPlb SVen
thymifolia	SPlb
trichophylla	SPlb
wilsonii	IDee

Melampodium (*Asteraceae*)

§ ***montanum*** AZTEC GOLD ('Starbini'PBR) MBNS MBros
- 'Gold Queen' LSou
- 'Sunbini'PBR CCCN LSou
- 'Sunlight' new LSou MPri

Melandrium see *Vaccaria*

rubrum see *Silene dioica*

Melanoselinum (*Apiaceae*)

§ ***decipiens*** CAbb CPla CSpe EShb GBin LEdu LPla LRHS MHer MNrw SDix SPhx SPtp WPGP WSHC

Melanoseris (*Asteraceae*)

souliei new GKev
taliensis BWJ 7891 WCru

Melanthium (*Melanthiaceae*)

virginicum MNrw

Melasphaerula (*Iridaceae*)

graminea see *M. ramosa*
§ ***ramosa*** CBor NRog

Melia (*Meliaceae*)

§ ***azedarach*** CBcs CCCN SBrt SPlb
- B&SWJ 14625 WCru
- 'Jade Snowflake' new SPtp
- var. ***japonica*** see *M. azedarach*

Melianthus (*Melianthaceae*)

comosus CDTJ CPla ESwi EWes NLar SCoo SPlb WPGP
major ♀H3 Widely available
villosus EBee EWes SPad SPlb SSal WPGP

Melica (*Poaceae*)

altissima 'Alba' EHyd LCro LRHS SWvt
- 'Atropurpurea' CBod CCBP ECha EHyd EPPr LRHS SBls SEND SPlb SPoG
ciliata CBod ELon EPPr XLum XSen
- subsp. ***taurica*** SPhx
cupani EPPr
nutans CWCL EAJP EPPr EShb GMaP GQue LRHS MAsh NWsh SMHy SPhx WCot
persica EPPr
transsilvanica 'Red Spire' LShi SPeP XLum
uniflora EAJP NWsh SPhx
- f. ***albida*** ♀H7 CKno ECha EGrI EHyd GQue LPla MAvo MRav SPhx WCot
- 'Variegata' (v) EShb LPla MAvo WCot

Melicytus (*Violaceae*)

alpinus WThu
crassifolius EBee
obovatus NLar

Melilotus (*Fabaceae*)

albus SPhx
officinalis CHab SPhx WHer
- subsp. ***albus*** SPhx

Melinis (*Poaceae*)

nerviglumis CBod

Meliosma (*Sabiaceae*)

alba new WPGP
dilleniifolia WJC 13819 WCru
- subsp. ***cuneifolia*** CBcs CExl SBrt WPGP
- subsp. ***dilleniifolia*** WPGP
- subsp. ***tenuis*** CExl
myriantha var. ***discolor*** MF 97132 WCru
pinnata var. ***oldhamii*** CExl
simplicifolia subsp. ***pungens*** CExl
veitchiorum CExl NLar SBrt

Melissa ✿ (*Lamiaceae*)

officinalis CBod CCBP CHab CLau EBou ENfk GJos GMaP GPoy GQue LCro LEdu LOPS MBow MBros MGil MHer MMuc MNHC NBir SEND SEdi SPlb SRms SVic WBor WFar XAbr XLum
- 'All Gold' CLau ECha ENfk GQue NBid SPer SPoG SRms SVic WFar WJek
- subsp. ***altissima*** MNHC
§ - 'Aurea' (v) CBod CCBP CExl CLau CTsd EBou ELan GPoy MBow MHer MMuc MNHC MRav NBid NBir NBro NGrd SEND SPer SPoG SRms WFar
- 'Citronella' MGil
* - 'Compacta' GPoy LEdu
- 'Lemona' CAgr SPhx
- 'Lime Balm' LEdu MHer NPol
- 'Variegata' misapplied see *M. officinalis* 'Aurea'

Melittis (*Lamiaceae*)

melissophyllum CMea CTtf EHyd LEdu LRHS MHol MNrw MPie MPnt MRav SGro SHar WCAu WCot
- subsp. ***albida*** EBee EMor LEdu LRHS NSti WCAu WCot WHil WTor
- pink-flowered LEdu WCot
- 'Royal Velvet Distinction'PBR CBod CRos EBee EHyd ELan EMor EPfP GEdr ILea LRHS MHol MPie MRav MSCN NDov NGBl NHpl NRHS SCoo SHar SPoG WCot WHil WTyc
- 'Wit Laag' new SHar

Melliodendron (*Styracaceae*)

xylocarpum CExl SAko WPGP

melon see AGM Vegetables Section

Melothria (*Cucurbitaceae*)

scabra LRHS SVic

Menispermum (*Menispermaceae*)

canadense CTri
dauricum NLar

Mentha ✿ (*Lamiaceae*)

aquatica CBen CBod CHab CPud CWat GPoy MHer MWts NAts NMir NPer NPol SPlb SRms SVic WHer WMAq WPnP WSFF XLum
§ ***arvensis*** MHer
- 'Banana' CBod ENfk LEdu MHer MNHC SEdi SRms SVic WFar WJek
- 'Lemon' LEdu MHer
- var. ***piperascens*** CBod LEdu MHer SRms WJek
§ - - 'Sayakaze' CLau
- 'Thai' ENfk SRms
asiatica MHer
'Berries and Cream' CCBP CLau ENfk LCro LEdu LOPS MHer MNHC SRms

	'Blackcurrant'	MHer
	Bowles's mint	see *M.* × *villosa* var. *alopecuroides* Bowles's mint
	cervina	CBen CPud CWat LEdu LLWG MHer MWts SRms WJek XLum
*	- ***alba***	ENfk LLWG MHer MWts WJek
I	'Chocolate Peppermint'	CLau ENfk EWhm LEdu NBir NLar SPhx WCav
	citrata	see *M.* × *piperita* f. *citrata*
	corsica	see *M. requienii*
	crispa L. (1753)	see *M. spicata* var. *crispa*
	'Eau de Cologne'	see *M.* × *piperita* f. *citrata*
	eucalyptus mint	MHer
	× ***gentilis***	see *M.* × *gracilis*
§	× ***gracilis***	CBod CLau ENfk EWhm GAbr GJos MBow MBros MPri NGrd NLar NSti SEdi SRms SVic WFar
	- 'Aurea'	see *M.* × *gracilis* 'Variegata'
§	- 'Variegata' (v)	CCBP ECha GPoy GQue LEdu MHer MNHC MPri SPlb WHer WJek XLum
*	'Hillary's Sweet Lemon'	ECul ENfk MHer SRms
	'Jessica's Sweet Pear'	ENfk MHer
	'Julia's Sweet Citrus'	MHer
	lavender mint	GPoy LEdu MHer MNHC SRms
§	***longifolia***	ENfk GJos LEdu MBow MMuc SPlb SRms
	- Buddleia Mint Group	CCBP ENfk GAbr LEdu MHer MRav NSti WJek WWFP XLum
	- - variegated (v)	CBod LEdu WJek
	- 'Lake Van'	LEdu
	- subsp. ***schimperi***	LEdu MHer SRms WJek
	- silver-leaved	GAbr LEdu MHer MNHC NBir SEND SRms SVic WFar WJek
*	- 'Variegata' (v)	GAbr SRms
	Nile Valley mint	CLau LEdu SRms
	'Orange Fresh'	CBod
	× ***piperita***	CHby ECha GJos GPoy GQue LCro LOPS MBow MHer MNHC MPri NGrd NPol SPlb SVic WFar XAbr
	- 'After Eight'	ECul ENfk
	- 'Black Mitcham'	CLau SPhx WFar WJek XAbr
	- black peppermint	CAgr CBod CHby CLau ENfk EPfP LEdu LRHS MMuc MNHC NBir NLar SRms SVic
§	- f. ***citrata***	CBod CCBP CHby CLau CTri ECha ENfk GAbr GMaP GPoy GQue LEdu MBow MHer MNHC MPri MRav NBir NLar NPer SEdi SPlb SRms SVic WGwG WJek
	- - 'Basil'	CBod CLau CTsd ECul GJos GLog LCro LEdu LOPS MHer MNHC MRav SEdi SRms SVic WFar WJek
	- - 'Bergamot'	SRms
	- - 'Chocolate'	CBod CCBP ECul EHyd ENfk EPfP EWhm GJos LCro LEdu LOPS MBros MHer MNHC NGrd NPer NRHS SEdi SPlb SRms SVic WFar WGwG WJek XLum
	- - 'Grapefruit'	CBod EWhm LCro LOPS MHer MNHC NWad SRms SVic
	- - 'Kumin'	LEdu
	- - 'Lime'	CLau EMor ENfk EWhm LEdu MBow MHer MNHC NBir SEdi SPlb SRms SVic WFar WJek
	- - 'Orange'	CLau EMor ENfk GJos LEdu MHer MMuc MNHC NGrd NPer SEdi SRms WJek
	- - 'Swiss Ricola'	CLau MHer WJek
	- 'Crispa'	NPol
	- 'Logee's' (v)	WFar
§	- 'Multimentha'	SRms
	- 'Strawberry'	ENfk GJos LCro LOPS MBros SVic WFar
	- 'Swiss'	CBod ENfk GJos LCro LOPS NGrd NLar SRms WHer
	pulegium	CBen CBod CCBP CHby CPud ENfk EWhm GJos GPoy GQue LLWG MHer MNHC SPlb SRms SVic WHer WSFF XAbr
	- 'Cunningham Mint'	WJek
	- 'Upright'	CBod ENfk GPoy MHer SRms WJek
§	***requienii***	CBod CCBP CKel EBou ENfk EPot GAbr GPoy LCro LEdu LLWG LOPS MHer MNHC NBir NWad SDix SPlb SPtp SRms SVic WGwG WJek WNPC
	rotundifolia misapplied	see *M. suaveolens*
	rubra var. ***raripila***	see *M.* × *smithiana*
	sachalinensis	SVic
	'Sayakaze'	see *M. arvensis* var. *piperascens* 'Sayakaze'
§	× ***smithiana***	CLau GPoy LCro LOPS MHer MNHC MRav NBir NGrd SRms SVic WFar WJek
§	***spicata***	CAgr CArg CBod CCBP CTri CTsd ENfk EWoo GJos GPoy GQue LCro LOPS MBow MBros MCot MHer MNHC MPri NPol SCob SPhx SPlb SRms SVic WFar WHer XAbr XLum
*	- var. ***crispa***	ECha ENfk LEdu MHer SPlb SRms SVic WFar WGwG WJek
	- - 'Moroccan'	CCBP CLau EBou ECul ENfk EWhm GAbr GJos GLog GPoy LCro LEdu LOPS MBow MHer MNHC MPri NBir NGrd NLar SEdi SRms SVic XAbr
	- 'Crispula'	XLum
	- 'Erdbeere'	WFar
	- 'Guernsey'	CLau SRms
	- 'Kentucky Colonel'	LEdu
	- 'Mexican'	CLau
	- 'Newbourne'	CLau SRms
	- 'Nile Valley'	WJek
	- 'Russian'	CAgr MHer SVic WFar
	- 'Spanish'	ECul NGrd NLar SRms
	- 'Spanish Furry'	MHer
	- 'Tashkent'	CHby CLau EHyd ENfk EWhm LCro LEdu LOPS LRHS MHer MNHC NGrd NRHS SRms WFar WGwG WHer WJek
I	'Strawberry Mint'	CCBP CLau ECul EWhm LEdu MHer MNHC SEdi SRms WCav WFar WJek
§	***suaveolens***	CAgr CBod CCBP CHby EBou ENfk GJos GMaP GPoy GQue LCro LOPS MBow MBros MHer MNHC NGrd SPlb SRms SVic WFar WSFF
*	- 'Grapefruit'	CAgr CLau ECul GJos LEdu WFar
*	- 'Pineapple'	CBod CLau EBou ECul ENfk EWhm GLog MBow SVic WFar WJek
	- subsp. ***timija***	LEdu MHer SRms WJek
	- 'Variegata' (v)	CCBP CTri ECha GJos GMaP GPoy GQue LEdu LShi MCot MHer MNHC MPri MRav NSti SPlb SRms WHer XLum
	'Sweet Pear'	MHer SRms WJek
	sylvestris L.	see *M. longifolia*
I	'Tangerine Mint'	LEdu
§	× ***villosa***	MMuc SEND
§	- var. ***alopecuroides*** Bowles's mint	CLau GPoy LCro LEdu LOPS MHer MNHC NBir NLar NSti SRms WFar WHer WJek

- 'Jack Green' CLau
viridis see *M. spicata*

Mentzelia (*Loasaceae*)
decapetala CSpe

Menyanthes (*Menyanthaceae*)
trifoliata CBen CPud CWat EWat GPoy LLWG MWts NPer WHal WMAq WSFF WWtn XLum

Menziesia see *Rhododendron*
alba see *Daboecia cantabrica* f. *alba*

Mercurialis (*Euphorbiaceae*)
perennis GPoy WHer WSFF WShi

Merendera (*Colchicaceae*)
attica NRog
filifolia NRog
§ **montana** GKev
pyrenaica see *M. montana*
sobolifera GKev NRog WCot

Merrilliopanax (*Araliaceae*)
alpinus B&SWJ 13906 WCru
- B&SWJ 13939 WCru
membranifolius LEdu WPGP

Mertensia (*Boraginaceae*)
lanceolata EBee GEdr GKev
§ **maritima** CEls CLau CSpe CWCL EBee EHyd EWes GKev GPoy GRum MNHC SPlb SRms WHoo XAbr
- subsp. **asiatica** see *M. maritima*
pterocarpa see *M. sibirica*
pulmonarioides see *M. virginica*
§ **sibirica** CWCL SPlb SPtp
§ **virginica** ♀H4 CBor CMiW CWCL EBee EGrl ELan EPfP EPot GAbr GKev LCro LEdu LOPS MNrw NLar NSti SPhx SRms WFar
viridis SPlb

Merwilla (*Asparagaceae*)
§ **plumbea** WCot

Merxmuellera (*Poaceae*)
cincta see *Capeochloa cincta*

Mesembryanthemum (*Aizoaceae*)
sp. new MAsh
brownii see *Lampranthus brownii*
crystallinum GPoy MPri

Mespilus ✿ (*Rosaceae*)
germanica (F) CHab CLnd CMCN CTri IPap LMaj LPar MGil NLar NRog NWea SGsty SLon WFar
- 'Boom en Vrucht' (F) new NRog
- 'Brabant Giant' (F) IArd
- 'Bredase Reus' (F) ELan NRog SKee
- 'Dutch' (F) SKee
- 'Flanders Giant' (F) CAgr LRHS MTrO WMat
- 'Iranian' (F) ♀H6 CAgr SKee
- 'Large Russian' (F) CAgr
- 'Macrocarpa' (F) NRog SKee
- 'Nottingham' (F) ♀H6 Widely available
- 'Royal' (F) CAgr CBod LRHS MCoo NOra NRog SCoo SKee WMat
- 'Westerveld' (F) CAgr CLnd EPom LPar MTrO NRog SKee

Metapanax ✿ (*Araliaceae*)
davidii SPtp WPGP
delavayi SPtp WPGP

Metaplexis (*Apocynaceae*)
japonica GGro

Metasequoia ✿ (*Cupressaceae*)
glyptostroboides Widely available
- AMBER GLOW ('Wah-08ag') LRHS
- 'Chubby'PBR EPfP
- 'Emerald Feathers' SLim
- 'Fastigiata' see *M. glyptostroboides* 'National'
- GOLD RUSH ('Golden Oji') ♀H7 Widely available
- 'Golden Dawn' NLar
- 'Hamlet's Broom' SLim
- 'Little Creamy' NLar
- 'Little Giant' MBlu
- 'Matthaei' MAsh MBlu SLim
- 'McCracken's White' (v) NLar
- 'Miss Grace' SLim
§ - 'National' MBlu
- 'Schirrmann's Nordlicht' GKev LRHS MAsh SLim
- 'Sheridan Spire' CEnd MBlu
- 'Waasland' MBlu SLim
- 'White Spot' (v) MBlu

Metrosideros (*Myrtaceae*)
carminea CCCN CTsd
§ **excelsa** CTrC ECre ESwi IKel WCFE
- 'Maori Princess' CBcs
- 'Parnell' CBcs CCCN
- 'Vibrance' CCCN
kermadecensis 'Variegata' (v) CBcs
lucida see *M. umbellata*
robusta CBcs CCCN SPlb
- **aureovariegata** (v) CCCN EShb
§ 'Springfire' CCCN
× **subtomentosa** 'Mistral' IDee MPkF
tomentosa see *M. excelsa*
§ **umbellata** CBcs CCCN EBee
- 'Gold Nugget' CBcs CCCN MPkF SSta
- MOONLIGHT ('Lowmoo') CBcs CCCN CKel SEle SIvy SLim

Meum (*Apiaceae*)
athamanticum CSpe EBee EBlo EPPr GPoy GQue LEdu LRHS MHol MRav SMHy SPhx SPtp WJek WSHC

Michauxia (*Campanulaceae*)
campanuloides CSpe GJos SBls
tchihatchewii CDTJ

Michelia see *Magnolia*
fulgens see *Magnolia foveolata*

Microbiota (*Cupressaceae*)
decussata ♀H7 CAco CBcs CMac CSBt LBee LRHS MGos NHol SLim WFar WPav
- 'Gold Spot' (v) CAco LRHS WFar
- 'Jakobsen' CKen
- 'Trompenburg' CKen

Microcachrys (*Podocarpaceae*)
tetragona IDee LRHS WThu

Microlepia (*Dennstaedtiaceae*)

strigosa	CCCN CLAP EBee EHyd EShb LEdu LRHS NRHS WPGP
- 'MacFaddeniae' ♀H4	CLAP CRos EBee EHyd LEdu LRHS NRHS WPGP

Micromeria (*Lamiaceae*)

sp.	SRms
corsica	see *Clinopodium corsicum*
fruticosa	WJek
juliana	XLum
rupestris	see *M. thymifolia*
§ ***thymifolia***	SPlb XSen

Microseris (*Asteraceae*)

ringens hort.	see *Leontodon rigens*

Microsorum (*Polypodiaceae*)

§ ***diversifolium***	CDoC EShb IKel LEdu SPlb WPGP
musifolium	CDoC EShb
'Crocodyllus'PBR	
pustulatum new	CBdn IKel

Microtropis (*Celastraceae*)

petelotii HWJ 719	WCru

Milium (*Poaceae*)

effusum 'Aureum' ♀H7	Widely available
- 'Yaffle' (v)	CBod CKno CNat EBee EPPr EShb

Millettia (*Fabaceae*)

pachycarpa	CMen

Mimetes (*Proteaceae*)

chrysanthus	SPlb
cucullatus	CPbh
- 'Crackerjack Red'	CCCN

Mimosa (*Fabaceae*)

pudica ♀H1b	CCCN CDTJ CDoC EShb

Mimulus (*Phrymaceae*)

'Andean Nymph'	see *M. naiandinus*
§ ***aurantiacus*** ♀H2	CMac CSpe EBak ECtt EShb MGil NPer SPlb SPoG SRms WFar WMal
- 'Primrose'	MGil
cardinalis ♀H4	CWat EBee ELan EPfP EWes EWld GKev WBor
- gold-flowered	EBee
- 'Red Dragon'	CBod MHol
cardinalis* × *lewisii	EWes
cupreus 'Red Emperor'	LCro LOPS
- 'Whitecroft Scarlet' ♀H4	LShi
eastwoodiae	GEdr
'Eleanor'	ECtt EShb
glutinosus	see *M. aurantiacus*
- ***atrosanguineus***	see *M. puniceus*
- ***luteus***	see *M. aurantiacus*
§ ***guttatus***	LCro LOPS MBow NPer WMAq
'Highland Orange'	EPfP GWyn MAsh SPlb SPoG WIce
'Highland Pink'	EPfP GWyn MAsh NHpl SPlb SPoG
'Highland Red' ♀H4	EBou EPfP GWyn MAsh NHpl SPlb SPoG WIce
'Highland Yellow'	GWyn NHpl SPlb SPoG
hose-in-hose (d)	NPer
× ***hybridus*** Mystic Series new	LRHS
langsdorffii	see *M. guttatus*
lewisii ♀H3	EWes MNrw SRms
luteus	CWat GAbr LLWG NPer WBrk XLum
- 'Variegatus' ambig. (v)	NPer
Magic Series	LRHS SVic
MAXIMUS MIXED	LRHS
§ ***naiandinus*** ♀H4	EWes GKev LShi SPlb
'Orange Glow'	LLWG
§ 'Orkney Gold' (d)	ECtt
'Popacatapetl'	CSpe WMal
primuloides	EWes SPlb
§ ***puniceus***	SChF SRkn WFar WMal
RED EMPEROR	see *M.* 'Roter Kaiser'
ringens	CBen CPla CPud CWat EBee LLWG NBir NPer SPlb SRms WMAq
§ 'Roter Kaiser'	ELan
yellow hose-in-hose	see *M.* 'Orkney Gold'

Mina see *Ipomoea*

mint, apple see *Mentha suaveolens*

mint, basil see *Mentha* × *gracilis*

mint, Bowles's see *Mentha* × *villosa* var. *alopecuroides*

mint, curly see *Mentha spicata* var. *crispa*

mint, eau-de-Cologne see *Mentha* × *piperita* f. *citrata*

mint, ginger see *Mentha* × *gracilis*

mint, horse or long-leaved see *Mentha longifolia*

mint (pennyroyal) see *Mentha pulegium*

mint (peppermint) see *Mentha* × *piperita*

mint, round-leaved see *Mentha suaveolens*

mint (spearmint) see *Mentha spicata*

Minuartia (*Caryophyllaceae*)

parnassica	see *M. stellata*
§ ***stellata***	EPot GArf GKev
verna subsp. ***caespitosa***	CTri
- - 'Aurea'	see *Sagina subulata* var. *glabrata* 'Aurea'

Mirabilis (*Nyctaginaceae*)

dichotoma	EShb
jalapa	CExl EPfP GKev SDeJ SRms WHil XAbr
- 'Buttermilk'	CCCN
longiflora	EShb SBrt WHil
multiflora	EBee

Miscanthus (*Poaceae*)

capensis	SPlb
chejuensis B&SWJ 8803	WCru
flavidus	ESwi SRms XLum
- B&SWJ 6749 new	EPPr
floridulus misapplied	see *M.* × *giganteus*
floridulus ambig.	MMuc MNrw SEdd SPlb XLum
§ × ***giganteus***	CKno ELon EPPr GBin GKev MAsh MNrw MWht NWsh SCob SCoo SDix SDys SVic WABo WCot XLum
- 'Aksel Olsen'	SAko
- 'Gilt Edge' (v)	CKno EPPr NWsh WCot
- 'Gotemba' (v)	ELon EPPr
- 'Jubilar' (v)	MWht
- 'Meidl'	SAko

	Name	Suppliers
	lutarioriparius	WPGP
	nepalensis	Widely available
	- NJM 09.141	WPGP
	- 'Shikola'	WCru
	nudipes **new**	EPPr
	oligostachyus	SBls
§	- 'Afrika'	CMea EPPr GBin MNrw WPGP
I	- 'Nanus Variegatus' (v)	ELon LEdu WCot
	'Purpurascens'	CBod CKno ECha EHyd ELan EPPr EPfP LPar LPot LRHS LSRN MAsh MNrw NRHS SCob XLum
	'Red Cloud'	LRHS
	sacchariflorus misapplied	see *M.* × *giganteus*
	sacchariflorus ambig.	CBcs CKno EBee EBou ECha EHyd ELan EPfP LRHS MBrN NRHS
	sacchariflorus (Maxim.) Hack.	LEdu SBls WSpi
	- 'Robustus'	SPeP
	sinensis	CTri GDam WFar XSen
	- CL 1325 **new**	EPPr
	- 'Abundance'	CKel CKno CRos EHyd EPPr EPfP LRHS NRHS
	- 'Adagio' ♀H6	CBod CDor CKno CSde ECtt EHyd ELan ELon EPPr EShb EWhm EWoo GKev LPar LRHS MAsh MNrw NRHS NWad NWsh SCoo SMHy SMea SPoG SRms WABo WCot WHoo XLum XSen
	- 'Afrika'	see *M. oligostachyus* 'Afrika'
	- 'Aldebaran'	EPPr MNrw
	- ALLIGATOR ('Lottum'PBR) (v)	CBod CKno
	- 'Andante'	CKno
	- 'Arabesque'	EPPr XLum
	- 'Augustfeder'	EPPr MAvo SMea XLum
	- 'Autumn Light'	EPPr SMea XLum
	- 'Barney Campbell'	NWsh
	- 'Beth Chatto' **new**	ECha EPPr LEdu
	- 'Blütenwunder'	EBee EPPr NWsh SMea XLum
	- 'Bogenlampe'	EBee EPPr GBin
	- 'China' ♀H4	CKno CPar CRos CTtf EBee EHyd ELon EPPr EPfP EShb EWes GKev IPot LEdu LRHS MAsh MAvo MNrw NRHS NWsh SDys SRms
	- 'Cindy'	CKno EPPr
	- var. ***condensatus*** NJM 11.021	WPGP
	- - 'Cabaret' (v)	CBod CKno EBee EBlo EHyd EPPr EPfP EShb GMaP ILea LEdu LPar LRHS LSRN MNrw NRHS NSti NWsh SBls SMad SPoG WCot WFar WHal WPGP WSpi XLum XSen
	- - 'Central Park'	see *M. sinensis* var. *condensatus* 'Cosmo Revert'
§	- - 'Cosmo Revert'	EPPr NWsh WPGP
	- - 'Cosmopolitan' (v) ♀H6	Widely available
	- - 'Emerald Giant'	see *M. sinensis* var. *condensatus* 'Cosmo Revert'
	- - 'Laigong'	LEdu
	- 'Cute One'	CBct XSte
	- 'David'	ELon EPPr MBNS XLum
	- 'Digestif'	EBee
	- 'Dixieland' (v)	CKno ELan ELon EPPr EWes NLar
	- 'Dreadlocks'	CKno EBee EPPr GBin MAvo MNrw
	- 'Dronning Ingrid'	CKno EPPr LPla LRHS MNrw NDov SBls SMea WHil XLum
	- EARLY HYBRIDS	EBou
	- 'Elfin'	CKno EPPr
	- 'Emmanuel Lepage'	CKno EPPr LPla MAvo NWsh XLum
	- 'Etincelle'	CKno EPPr EWes WSMil
	- 'Federriese'	EBee GBin
	- 'Ferner Osten' ♀H6	Widely available
	- 'Flamingo' ♀H6	Widely available
	- 'Flammenmeer'	EPPr SAko
	- 'Gearmella'	EBee EPPr
	- 'Gewitterwolke' ♀H6	EWes NWsh SMHy XLum
	- 'Ghana' ♀H6	CDor CSpe ECha ELon EPPr EPfP EWoo LEdu MAvo MMrt MNrw SDys SEdd SMHy SMad SPoG SRms SSut XLum
	- 'Giraffe'	CDTJ CKno ELon EWes LEdu XLum
	- 'Gnome'	CKno EHyd EPPr EPfP EShb LRHS MAsh MTin NRHS SRms
	- 'Gold Bar'PBR (v)	CBod CChe CEme CWGN ECha EHyd ELan ELon EPfP LLWG LRHS LSRN LSou MACG MAsh MBNS NGdn NLar NRHS NWad SCob SEle SPad SPeP SPer SPoG WFar WGrn
	- 'Gold Breeze'PBR	CDoC EHyd LRHS NRHS
	- 'Gold und Silber' ♀H6	XLum
	- 'Goldfeder' (v)	EWes XLum
	- 'Goldglanz'	EBee
	- 'Goliath'	CKno ELon EPPr GLog LEdu MACG MBNS WFar XLum
	- 'Gracillimus'	Widely available
	- 'Graziella'	CBod CEnd CKno EHyd EPPr EPfP GBin GWyn LRHS MAsh NRHS SCoo SPer SRms WFar WHoo WSMil XSen
	- 'Grosse Fontäne' ♀H6	ELon EPPr LEdu LRHS LSRN NWsh SCob SEdd SMHy WCot XLum
	- 'Gutenberg Gold'	XLum
	- 'Haiku'	CKno EBee EPPr LEdu XLum
	- 'Helga Reich'	EWes
	- 'Hercules'	EPPr MAvo XLum
	- 'Hermann Müssel'	CRos EBlo EHyd EPPr EWes LEdu LRHS NRHS SMea XLum
§	- 'Hinjo' (v)	ECha ECtt EHyd ELon EPPr EPfP GBin GKev LRHS MAsh NGdn NRHS NWsh WCot
	- 'Ibiza'PBR	CKno EBee SCoo
I	- 'Jubilaris' (v)	ELon EPPr
	- 'Juli'	EHyd EPPr WSpi
	- 'Kaskade' ♀H6	CBod CKno EHyd EPPr GBin LEdu LRHS NDov NLar NRHS
	- 'Kim' **new**	NDov
	- 'Kirk Alexander' (v)	EPPr
	- 'Kleine Fontäne' ♀H6	Widely available
	- 'Kleine Silberspinne' ♀H6	Widely available
	- 'Korea'	EBee EPPr
	- 'Krater'	EHyd EPPr ILea LRHS MBrN NRHS NWsh SDys SMea XLum
	- 'Kupferberg'	SMea XLum
	- 'Kupferzwerg'	EBee EPPr
§	- 'Little Kitten'	EPPr LEdu LRHS SCob SMea SRms XLum
	- 'Little Miss'	CKno CPla EPfP LRHS SPad SPeP
	- LITTLE NICKY	see *M. sinensis* 'Hinjo'
	- 'Little Zebra'PBR (v)	CDoC EBee GMaP LRHS LSRN MGos MPnt NWsh SEdd SEle SMad SRms
	- 'Lorelei' **new**	GBin
	- 'Malepartus'	Widely available
	- 'Memory'	EPPr MAvo
	- 'Morning Light' (v) ♀H6	Widely available
	- 'Mrs Higgins'	NWsh
	- 'München'	EBee
	- 'Navajo'PBR	CBct CBod MBNS
	- 'Nippon'	EHyd EPPr EPfP GBin LEdu LRHS MAsh NGdn NRHS NWsh SCob SDys SPer WSpi XLum
	- 'Nishidake'	EPPr XLum
	- 'November Sunset'	EPPr XLum
	- 'Overdam'	ECtt NGdn

- 'Poseidon'	EPPr MAvo SDys SMad XLum
- 'Positano'	EPPr XLum
- 'Professor Richard Hansen'	CKno EPPr EWes SMHy SMea XLum
- 'Pünktchen' (v)	ECha EHyd ELon EPPr GBin SRms XLum
- 'Purple Fall'	CDor CKno CSpe ECha ECtt EHyd EWes GMaP IPot LEdu LRHS MAvo MNrw SCoo
- 'Red Chief'	CKno CMiW CRos EHyd EPPr EPfP EWes LRHS MACG MAvo MHtn MNrw NDov NLar NRHS SCob SCoo WCot WTor
- RED CLOUD ('Emphis01')	LCro LOPS NDov SCoo SMad
- 'Red Meister'	CKno EHyd EPPr EPfP LRHS NRHS
- 'Red Wine'	MNrw
- 'Roland'	EPPr SMad XLum
- 'Rosi'	EPPr MAvo SSal
- 'Roterpfeil'	EPPr
- 'Rotfeder'	EPPr
- 'Rotfuchs'	CMac MAvo XLum
- 'Rotsilber'	CBod CKno ECha EHyd EPPr GMaP IArd LEdu LRHS MAsh MMuc NRHS NWsh SRms WHoo WPGP XLum
- 'Russia'	NWsh
- 'Samurai'	EPPr GMaP MAvo MNrw SCob
- 'Sarabande' ♀H6	EPPr SMHy SMea WSpi
- 'Septemberrot' ♀H6	EPPr MMuc SEND
- 'Serim'	EPPr
§ - 'Silberfeder' ♀H6	Widely available
- 'Silberpfeil' (v)	NWsh
- 'Silberspinne'	EBee ELon EPPr SCob SMHy SMea SPlb XLum
- 'Silberturm'	EPPr XLum
- SILVER FEATHER	see *M. sinensis* 'Silberfeder'
- 'Silver Sceptre'	MAvo SMHy
- 'Silver Stripe'	EPPr
- 'Sioux'	ECtt EHyd EPPr EPfP EShb GBin LRHS MAsh MBNS NRHS SPer
- 'Sirene'	EPPr MBNS MMuc NBir
- 'Spätgrün'	EPPr
- 'Starlight'	CKno CRos EPPr LRHS NWsh
- 'Strictus' (v) ♀H6	Widely available
- 'Strictus Compactus' **new**	LRHS
- 'Super Stripe' (v)	EPPr
- 'Taiwan'	EBee EPPr
- 'Tiger Cub' (v)	EPPr
- 'Undine' ♀H6	CKel CMea ECha EPPr EPfP MBel MBrN MMuc NWsh XLum
- 'Vanilla Sky'	EBee SCoo
- 'Variegatus' (v)	CBod CEme ECha ECtt EHyd ELan ELon EPPr EPfP EWoo GMaP LPar LRHS LSRN LSun MMuc MRav NGdn NRHS NSti SDix SPer SPoG SRms WCot WSMil WSpi XLum
- 'Vorläufer'	EPPr
- 'Westacre Wine'	EPPr EWes
- 'Wetterfahne'	EPPr
§ - 'Yaku-jima'	CBod ECha ECtt EHyd ELan EPPr LRHS MMuc MWht NRHS SMea WFar
- 'Yakushima Dwarf'	CEnd CExl CRos EHyd ELan ELon EPPr EPfP EWoo GBin LRHS MCot NRHS NSti NWsh SBea SCob SCoo SDys SRms SSut WCot WHoo XLum
- 'Zebrinus' (v) ♀H6	Widely available
- 'Zwergelefant'	EBee MAvo SMHy XLum
***tinctorius* 'Nanus Variegatus' misapplied**	see *M. oligostachyus* 'Nanus Variegatus'
transmorrisonensis	EHyd ELan EPPr LEdu LPla LRHS MAvo MBel NDov NRHS NWsh WCot WPGP
yakushimensis	see *M. sinensis* 'Little Kitten', *M. sinensis* 'Yaku-jima'

Mitchella (*Rubiaceae*)

repens	CBcs CBod EBee EPot GEdr LEdu MNrw WCru
undulata B&SWJ 10928	WCru
* - f. ***quelpartensis*** B&SWJ 4402	WCru

Mitella (*Saxifragaceae*)

acerina	GGro
- B&SWJ 11029	EWld WCru
breweri	CBod CDor CMac EBee ECha EWld GLog MAvo MBriF MPnt MRav NSti WBor WFar WPnP
caulescens	ECha NBro
formosana B&SWJ 125	WCru
furusei var. ***subramosa***	GGro
- - B&SWJ 11097	WCru
× ***inami***	GGro
- B&SWJ 11122	WCru
japonica B&SWJ 4971	WCru
- 'Variegata' (v) **new**	GGro
kiusiana B&SWJ 5401 **new**	GGro
- B&SWJ 5888	WCru
makinoi	EWld GGro
- B&SWJ 4992	CExl WCru
ovalis	CPla GGro
pauciflora B&SWJ 6361	WCru
- B&SWJ 11067 **new**	GGro
stylosa B&SWJ 5669	WCru
- PB 04-301 **new**	GGro
yoshinagae	GGro WFar
- B&SWJ 4893	CExl EPPr WCru

Mitraria (*Gesneriaceae*)

coccinea	CCCN CExl CMac CPbh CRHN CTsd GBin GEdr GKev IDee MBlu NLar SLon SPlb WPav
- Clark's form	LRHS NLar SIvy
- 'Lago Puyehue'	CAbb CBcs CCCN CDoC CExl CKel CSpe EBee EPfP LRHS MAsh MGil SIvy SPlb SVen SWvt WPav WSHC WThu
- 'Lake Caburgua'	CCCN ELon NLar WAbe WPav

Modiolastrum (*Malvaceae*)

lateritium	CRHN CSpe CTri EBee EGrl ELan EPPr EPri NBir SIvy SPhx SPoG SRms WHal WSHC XLum

Moehringia (*Caryophyllaceae*)

muscosa	WCot

Molinia ✿ (*Poaceae*)

altissima	see *M. caerulea* subsp. *arundinacea*
caerulea	CKno EHyd EPPr LRHS MBlu NRHS SCoo
§ - subsp. ***arundinacea***	CFis CKno CSpe CWCL ECha EPPr SSut WChS XLum
- - 'Automne Bronze'	EPPr
- - 'Autumn Charm'	CKno
- - 'Bergfreund'	CKno EPPr GBin MAvo SMHy
- - 'Black Arrows'	MAvo NDov
- - 'Breeze'	CKno EPPr NDov
- - 'Cordoba'	CBod EBee ECha ELan EPPr GQue MAvo NDov SMHy WFar XLum
- - 'Fontäne'	ECha EPPr GQue MAsh MAvo SMea
- - 'Golden Chimes'	EPPr

- - 'Intruder' **new** NWsh
- - 'JS Mostenveld' (v) EPPr
- - 'JS Witches Broom' EPPr GBin
- - 'JS Yellow Pipe' GBin
- - 'Karl Foerster' Widely available
- - 'Les Ponts de Cé' EBee ECha EPPr
- - 'Liebreiz' EPPr
- - 'Skyracer' ♀H7 CBod CKno CRos CSde EHyd ELan ELon EMor EPPr EWoo GBin GLog GMaP GQue LEdu LRHS MAsh MAvo MNrw NRHS SEdd SMHy WCot WGrn WPGP WPnP
- - 'Staefa' EPPr
- - 'Sunbeam' EPPr
- - 'Tears of Joy' EPPr
- - 'Transparent' ♀H7 Widely available
- - 'Windsaule' CKno EPPr MAvo MNrw NDov
- - 'Windspiel' ♀H7 CBod CKno CSde CWCL EBou ECha EHyd ELon EPPr EPfP EShb GBin GQue LRHS MAsh MAvo MNrw NDov NRHS NWsh SCoo SDix SPoG WCAu WCot XLum
- - 'Zuneigung' ECha EHyd EPPr MAvo
- subsp. ***caerulea*** EPPr LRHS
- - 'Carmarthen' (v) EHyd ELon EPPr
- - 'Claerwen' (v) ECha ELon EPPr MAvo
- - 'Coneyhill Gold' (v) EPPr
- - 'Dark Defender' EPPr LEdu MAvo NDov SPhx
- - 'Dauerstrahl' CKno EPPr GQue LEdu MAsh MNrw NBid NDov SEdd
- - 'Edith Dudszus' ♀H7 CBod CKno CMea CWCL EAJP EBou ECha EHyd ELan ELon EPPr EPfP GBin GQue LRHS MAsh MBel MBrN NDov NHol NRHS SCob WGrn WPnP
- - 'Heidebraut' CBod CMea EAJP ECha EHyd ELon EPPr EPfP EWoo GMaP GQue LCro LOPS LPar LRHS MBel MRav NDov NRHS SAko SCob SEdd SPhx WCot
- - 'Heidezwerg' CKno EBee ELon EPPr GBin
- - 'Heinrichs Dauerstrahl' **new** EPPr
- - 'Igel' CKno EBee EPPr GBin
- - 'Moorflamme' ELon MAvo NDov
- - 'Moorhexe' ♀H7 CBod CMea EBee ECha EHyd ELon EPfP EShb EWoo GBin GMaP GQue GWyn LRHS MAvo NBid NDov NGdn NHol NRHS NSti NWsh SCob SCoo SSut WCAu WCot WFar WHoo
- - 'Overdam' CKno EBee EPPr MNrw NDov
- - 'Poul Petersen' ♀H7 CKno EBee EPPr LRHS MBel NDov SCob SPhx WChS
- - 'Rotschopf' EBee
- - 'Strahlenquelle' CBod CFis EHyd EPPr EWhm GQue LRHS NDov NHol NRHS NWsh WCAu
- - 'Variegata' (v) ♀H7 CBod CEme CExl CMac EBee ECha EHyd ELan ELon EMor EPfP EWhm GBin GMaP GQue LEdu LPot LRHS MAsh MBrN MGos NBro NRHS NSti NWad SCob SDys SPlb SRms WHoo
- 'Torch'PBR CKno
- 'Winterfreude' EPPr

litoralis see *M. caerulea* subsp. *arundinacea*

Molospermum (*Apiaceae*)

peloponnesiacum CSpe EBee ELan EPPr GBin LEdu LRHS MHer SBrt SMHy SPhx SPtp WCru WPGP WSHC

Moltkia (*Boraginaceae*)

§ ***doerfleri*** CPla LPla NBir NChi SBrt WSHC
§ × ***intermedia*** ♀H4 CMea CRos EHyd LRHS NRHS SMrm WAbe
petraea CRos EHyd LRHS NRHS

Moluccella (*Lamiaceae*)

laevis CSpe LCro LOPS SPhx SVic

Monanthes (*Crassulaceae*)

laxiflora WCot

Monarda ✿ (*Lamiaceae*)

'Adam' GBee GQue LSRN MRav NGrd NLar WMon WSHC
'André Eve' NDov WMon
'Aquarius' CBod CWCL EHyd GQue LRHS NLar NRHS WCAu WFar WMon XLum
'Baby Spice' LRHS WMon
§ 'Balance' EBee ECtt EHyd GBee LRHS MMrt MPie MRav NGdn NRHS WMon WSHC XLum
'Beauty of Cobham' ♀H4 Widely available
(Bee-You Series) 'Bee-Free' CWGN EBee LRHS NLar SHeu WMon
- 'Bee-Happy' CWGN EBee LEdu LRHS MNrw NLar SHeu SPeP
- 'Bee-Lieve' EBee LRHS MNrw NLar SHeu WMon
- 'Bee-True' CWGN EBee LRHS MNrw NLar SHeu SPeP
'Bergamo' CSpe LCro LOPS
§ 'Blaustrumpf' ECtt EGrI EHyd EPfP EWes GQue LRHS MACG NGrd NLar SPer WFar WMon WSHC XLum
BLUE STOCKING see *M.* 'Blaustrumpf'
BOWMAN see *M.* 'Sagittarius'
bradburyana EBee EShb LRHS SAko SBrt SPhx
- 'Grey Summit' NDov
- 'Maramek' IPot NLar WMon
- 'Ozark' ECha NDov SAko
- Schm. 2004-0076 WMon
'Cambridge Scarlet' Widely available
'Camilla' WGoo WMon
'Capricorn' WMon XLum
'Cherokee' MSpe WMon
citriodora GJos GPoy NSti SRms
'Comanche' EWes NLar WMon
'Croftway Pink' CBcs CBod CEme CRos CSBt ECha ECtt EGrI EHyd ELan EPfP GMaP LCro LOPS LRHS NRHS SCob SPeP SPer SWvt WCAu WFar WMon WSHC XLum
I 'Dark Ponticum' WMon
didyma CBod CLau EBou ENfk EPfP MNHC NBro SRms SVic WFar XAbr
- 'Alba' WMon
- BALMY LILAC ('Balbalmac'PBR) EHyd LRHS MHol NRHS SCob SPoG WHil
- BALMY PINK ('Balbalmink'PBR) CBod LRHS SPoG WHil
- BALMY PURPLE ('Balbalmurp'PBR) EHyd LRHS MHol NRHS SCob SPoG WFar WHil
- BALMY ROSE ('Balbalmose'PBR) SCob SNig WHil
- 'Coral Reef' EHyd WFar
- 'Cranberry Lace'PBR CRos ECtt EHyd EPfP LRHS MBel MHol NRHS SPoG WCAu
- DANCING BIRD ('Allmobird'PBR) **new** IPot
- 'Pardon My Pink' EBee NLar SPad WMon

- 'Pardon My Purple'	EPfP NLar SPoG WHil WMon
- 'Pink Lace' PBR	CBod CPla CRos ECtt EHyd EPfP LRHS LSou LSun MHol MNrw MThu NDov NHol NLar NRHS NSti SCob SPoG WCAu WFar WMon
- 'Sugar Lace' PBR	LBuc
'Earl Grey'	CBod ECtt NChi SCoo SEdi WFar WMon
'Elsie's Lavender'	EBee EHyd EPfP GMaP IPot LRHS NDov NLar NRHS WFar WMon WSHC
'Elworthy'	CElw WWFP
'Eugens Kirschrot'	WMon
'Eugens Purpursamt'	WMon
'Feckenham Danielle'	WMal
'Feckenham Delight'	WMal
§ 'Feuerschopf'	WMon
'Fireball' PBR	Widely available
FIRECROWN	see *M.* 'Feuerschopf'
§ 'Fishes'	CExl CMac EBee ECtt ELan EWes EWoo GQue LEdu LRHS MACG MRav MSpe NDov NGdn SGbt SWvt WFar WGwG WMon
fistulosa	CBod CFis CHby CMac EBou IPot MBow MNHC NDov SRms XAbr XLum
- 'Humdinger'	EBee WMon
- var. ***menthifolia*** 'Mohikaner'	NDov WGoo WMon
- - 'Pummel'	NDov WMon
- tetraploid **new**	IPot
- 'Wahpe Washtemna'	NDov
'Gardenview Scarlet' ♀H4	Widely available
GEMINI	see *M.* 'Twins'
'Gewitterwolke'	ECtt EGrI MNrw NDov WMon
'Hartswood Wine'	EWes LEdu SMrm WFar WMon WPGP
'Häuptling'	WMon
'Heidelerche'	WFar WMon
'Huckleberry'	GBin NDov WMon
'Jacob Cline'	CDor CMea CRos ECtt EHyd EPfP EWes GBin GWyn IPot LEdu LPla LRHS MACG MBel MNrw MPie NLar NRHS SGbt SPhx SRms WCAu WFar WMon WPGP XLum
'Kardinal'	GBin LRHS NDov WMon XLum
'Knight Rose' **new**	WMon
'Knight Violet' **new**	WMon
'Lederstrumpf'	WMon
LIBRA	see *M.* 'Balance'
'Loddon Crown'	ECtt MBNS MHer NHol NLar SHar WCAu WFar WMon WSHC
'Mahogany'	CRos EBee ECtt EHyd ELan EPfP EWTr GBee GKev GMaP IPot LRHS LSou MHol NRHS NSti SPer SPoG WFar WMon XLum
'Marshall's Delight' ♀H4	CRos EBee ECtt EHyd EPfP EWes GQue LRHS MAvo MNrw MRav NDov NRHS SPhx SWvt WCAu WFar WMon
'Melissa'	CRos EHyd EPfP LRHS NLar NRHS WSHC
menthifolia	SRms
'Mohawk'	CBod ECtt EHyd EPfP GQue LRHS MHol MPie MRav NDov NGdn NGrd SGbt WCAu WMon XLum
'Neon'	LRHS NDov SPhx WMon
'On Parade'	CWCL ECtt EHyd ELon GBee GPSL LEdu LPla LRHS MMrt NDov NGdn NRHS WMon
'Othello'	EHyd LRHS NDov NRHS WGoo WMon
'Ou Charm'	EWes NLar SMrm WFar WMon
Panorama Series	SPlb
- 'Panorama Red Shades'	CCBP EPfP WFar WMon
'Pawnee'	GBin WGoo WMon
PETITE DELIGHT ('Acpetdel')	LSou XLum
'Petite Wonder'	WFar WMon
'Pink Supreme' PBR	CBod ECtt EHyd ELan EPfP LRHS MBel NLar SCoo WFar WHil WMon WTor
'Pink Tourmaline'	SMrm WMon
PISCES	see *M.* 'Fishes'
'Poyntzfield Pink'	GPoy LEdu
PRAIRIE NIGHT	see *M.* 'Prärienacht'
§ 'Prärienacht'	Widely available
punctata	MNHC
- 'Bee Bop'	LCro LOPS
'Purple Acres' **new**	ECtt
'Purple Ann'	XLum
'Purple Lace' PBR	EHyd EPfP LRHS NRHS WFar WMon
'Purple Tower'	EWes
'Raspberry Wine'	CBod CDor CRos EBee ECtt EHyd EPPr EPfP EWes LEdu LRHS LSou MACG NRHS WFar WMon WPGP
'Rebecca'	MSpe NDov WMon
'Remie'	WMon
'Ruby Glow'	EHyd GDam GWyn NRHS WMon
§ 'Sagittarius'	EBee EHyd LRHS MSpe NGdn NRHS NSti SPoG WFar WMon
'Saxon Purple'	MBel NDov WMon XLum
§ 'Schneewittchen'	CBod CWCL EBee ECha ECtt ELan EPfP EWoo LRHS MRav NDov NHol SCob SCoo SGbt SPer SPoG SRms SWvt WCAu WFar WMon XLum
'Scorpion'	CRos EBee ECtt EHyd ELan EPfP GBee GBin GQue LCro LOPS LRHS MRav NBir NGdn NRHS NSti SGbt SPoG SWvt WCAu WMon XLum
'Shelley'	ECha WMon
'Snow Maiden'	see *M.* 'Schneewittchen'
'Snow Queen'	EBee ECtt EHyd EShb LRHS MPie SMrm
SNOW WHITE	see *M.* 'Schneewittchen'
'Squaw' ♀H4	Widely available
'Talud' ♀H4	IPot MNrw NDov WMon
'Tante Polly'	WMon
§ 'Twins'	NLar SWvt WFar WMon WSHC
'Vintage Wine'	CElw NDov WMon
'Violacea'	NHol WFar WMon
'Violet Queen' ♀H4	CRos CWCL EBee ECtt EHyd ELan EWes GQue LEdu LRHS MBel MCot MPie MSpe NEoE NRHS SCoo SPhx WCAu WCot WFar WMon WPGP
'Violette'	EBee WFar WMon
'Westacre Purple'	ECha EGrI EPPr EWes

Monardella (*Lamiaceae*)

odoratissima	GEdr MHer SPhx

Monochoria (*Pontederiaceae*)

§ ***hastata***	LLWG

Monstera (*Araceae*)

adansonii **new**	CDoC
deliciosa (F) ♀H1b	CDoC LCro LOPS
obliqua 'Monkey Mask'	LCro LOPS

Montbretia see *Crocosmia*

Montia (*Portulacaceae*)

perfoliata	see *Claytonia perfoliata*
sibirica	see *Claytonia sibirica*

Moraea (*Iridaceae*)

	alticola	GAbr GKev SPlb
§	***aristata***	NRog WHil
	atropunctata	NRog
§	***bellendenii***	NRog
	bipartita	NRog WCot
	britteniae	NRog
	ciliata	NRog
§	***collina***	CBor GKev NRog
	comptonii	WHil
	cookii new	GKev
	flaccida	MBros
	gigandra	NRog
	glaucopsis	see *M. aristata*
	huttonii	CBor CCCN CFis CPbh CSpe EPri GEdr GKev SBrt SMad WKif WSHC
	iridioides	see *Dietes iridioides*
	loubseri	NRog
	lugubris	NRog
	macrocarpa	NRog
	marlothii	NRog
	ochroleuca	CBor GKev MBros NRog
	pavonia var. ***lutea***	see *M. bellendenii*
	polystachya	NRog
	robusta	GKev
	setifolia	NRog
	sisyrinchium	NRog NWad SDeJ
	spathacea	see *M. spathulata*
§	***spathulata***	CExl GKev SBrt WCot
	thomsonii	NRog
	tricuspidata	NRog
	tripetala	NRog
	tulbaghensis	NRog
	vegeta	NRog SBrt
	villosa	NRog

Morella (*Myricaceae*)

	californica	CAgr
	pensylvanica	CAgr NLar

Moricandia (*Brassicaceae*)

	moricandioides	WCot

Morina (*Caprifoliaceae*)

*	***afghanica***	NWad
	alba	GKev
	betonicoides	GKev
	bulleyana	see *M. nepatensis* var. *delavayi*
	longifolia	Widely available
§	***nepatensis*** var. ***delavayi***	GKev
	polyphylla	GPoy

Morinda (*Rubiaceae*)

	umbellata WWJ 11688	WCru

Morisia (*Brassicaceae*)

	hypogaea	see *M. monanthos*
§	***monanthos***	EPfP GEdr SRot WCav WIce
	- 'Fred Hemingway'	ELan GArf NSla WAbe

Morus ✿ (*Moraceae*)

§	***alba***	CBcs CCVT CHab CLnd CMCN ELan EPfP EWTr IPap LBuc LEdu LPar MRav MTrO NRog SPer SPre SVic WFar WLov WMou WTSh
	- 'Agate' (F) new	CAgr
	- fruitless new	EHed
	- 'Laciniata'	EBee ELan
	- 'Macrophylla'	CMCN MBlu SCob
	- 'Pakistan' (F)	CAgr NOra SPoG
	- 'Paradise' (F)	CAgr
	- 'Pendula'	CAco CEnd CMCN CMac ELan LPar MBlu MTrO NOra SCoo SPoG SWeb SWvt WMat
	- 'Platanifolia'	see *M.* 'Macrophylla'
	- var. ***tatarica***	CAgr LEdu NLar
	'Black Tabor' (F)	CAgr
	'Capsrum' (F)	CAgr
	'Carman' (F)	CAgr ELan MTrO NLar NOra
	cathayana	EBee WPGP
	CHARLOTTE RUSSE	see *M.* 'Waisei-kirishima-shikinari'
	'Illinois Everbearing' (F)	CAgr
	'Italian' (F)	CAgr
	'Ivory' (F)	CAgr
	kagayamae	see *M. alba*
	latifolia 'Spirata'	NLar
	macroura	LCro LOPS MTrO WSpi
	'Matsunaga'	see *M.* 'Waisei-kirishima-shikinari'
	MOJO BERRY	see *M.* 'Waisei-kirishima-shikinari'
	nigra (F)	Widely available
§	- 'Chelsea' (F) ♀H6	CEnd CSBt CTri EBee EPfP EPom LRHS MGos MTrO NLar NOra NWea SCoo SEWo SKee SLim SPer SPoG SSFT WMat
	- 'Izvor' (F)	CAgr
	- 'Jerusalem' (F) ♀H6	MTrO NOra WMat
	- 'King James'	see *M. nigra* 'Chelsea'
	- 'Large Black' (F)	EPom
	- 'Repsime' (F)	CAgr
	- 'Sham Dudu' (F)	CAgr
	rubra	EBtc
§	'Waisei-kirishima-shikinari' (F) new	LRHS MTrO NOra SSFT
	'Wellington' (F)	CBod CCVT CEnd CLnd EBee ELan EWTr LRHS LSRN MTrO NOra SSFT WMat

Muehlenbeckia ✿ (*Polygonaceae*)

	astonii	EBee SIvy WPGP
	axillaris misapplied	see *M. complexa*
§	***axillaris*** (Hook. f.) Endl.	CBcs CTri EBee EShb GBin MGil XLum
§	***complexa***	Widely available
	- (f)	CDoC LPar
	- 'Nana'	see *M. axillaris* (Hook. f.) Endl.
	- 'Spotlight'PBR (v)	EShb
	- 'Texture Big Leaf'	EBee WPGP
	- var. ***trilobata***	CTrC EShb ESwi SSta WBor XLum
	volcanica B&SWJ 14913	WCru

Muhlenbergia (*Poaceae*)

	capillaris	CBod CSpe CWit EBee LSRN MBNS MBel NGBl SDix SMad WSpi
	dumosa	CKno SMad WCot WPGP
	lindheimeri	CKno EBee WCot
	mexicana	SRms
	reverchonii UNDAUNTED ('Pund01s') new	SBls
	rigens	CKno WSpi XLum

Mukdenia (*Saxifragaceae*)

	acanthifolia	GEdr LEdu WPGP
	rossii	CTtf EBee ECha ELon GBin LEdu LPla MBel MNrw NBid NLar SBut SIvy WCAu WFar WPGP XLum
	- 'Crimson Fans'	see *M. rossii* 'Karasuba'
	- dwarf	MNrw
§	- 'Karasuba'	Widely available
	- 'Shishiba'	GEdr LEdu

× *Mukgenia* (*Saxifragaceae*)

§	'Flame'	CBcs CBct EBee EHed ELan EWoo GBin GEdr IBal LEdu LSou MHol MPnt NHar SPoG XSte
	NOVA	see × *M.* 'Flame'

mulberry see *Morus*

Murraya (*Rutaceae*)

	koenigii	see *Bergera koenigii*
§	***paniculata***	EShb

Musa ✿ (*Musaceae*)

§	***acuminata*** 'Dwarf Cavendish' (AAA Group) (F) ♀H1b	CAbb CBod CCht CDoC ELan SIvy SPlb
	- 'Zebrina' ♀H1b	CDTJ EHyd LRHS
	basjoo ♀H2	Widely available
I	- 'Rubra'	CCCN
	- 'Sakhalin'	LRHS
	'Cavendish Super Dwarf'	SMad
	cavendishii	see *M. acuminata* 'Dwarf Cavendish'
	ensete	see *Ensete ventricosum*
	hookeri	see *M. sikkimensis*
	lasiocarpa ♀H2	CDTJ IKel LCro LOPS LRHS MGos MPkF SArc SPalm SPlb XSte
	nana misapplied	see *M. acuminata* 'Dwarf Cavendish'
	ornata ♀H1b	CCCN
	× ***paradisiaca*** 'Ney Poovan' (AB Group) (F)	CCCN
§	***sikkimensis*** ♀H2	CDTJ CTsd SGsty SPlb
	- 'Red Tiger'	CCCN CDTJ SPalm
	velutina ♀H1b	CCCN CTsd WTyc

Muscari ✿ (*Asparagaceae*)

	adilii	GKev NRog
	'Aleyna'	NRog
	ambrosiacum	see *M. muscarimi*
	anatolicum	NRog WCot
	- giant	GKev
	armeniacum ♀H6	CArg CRos CTri ECul EWoo GKev GWyn LCro LOPS LRHS NRHS NRog SPer SRms WCot WShi
	- PAB 6748	LEdu
	- 'Alida'	GKev
	- 'Argaei Album'	NRog
	- 'Artist'	GKev NRog SDeJ
	- 'Atlantic'	EHyd EShb GKev LRHS NRHS NRog
	- 'Big Smile' **new**	NRog
	- 'Blue Pearl'	NRog
	- 'Blue Spike' (d)	GKev NBir NRog SDeJ WBrk
	- 'Cantab'	SDeJ XLum
	- 'Carola'	GKev
	- 'Christmas Pearl' ♀H6	GKev
	- 'Cupido'	GKev
	- 'Dark Eyes'	GKev SDeJ
	- 'Early Giant'	SDeJ
	- 'Fantasy Creation'	GKev NRog SDeJ
	- 'Gül'	WCot
	- 'Helena'	ERCP
	- 'Lady Blu'	LRHS
	- 'Peppermint'	CRos EHyd GKev LRHS NRHS SDeJ SPer SPhx
	- 'Saffier' ♀H6	WCot
	- 'Siberian Tiger'	CDoC CRos ECul EHyd EPfP EPot ERCP LHWs LRHS NHpl NRHS SPer WTor
	- 'Touch of Snow'	GKev LCro LOPS LRHS SPhx
	- 'Valerie Finnis'	CAvo EPfP EPot EWoo GKev MBNS NLar NRog SDeJ SMad SPer WBrk WCot
	aucheri ♀H6	GKev NRya
*	- var. ***bicolor***	WCot
	- 'Blue Magic'	CAvo ECul EPot GKev LRHS NRog SDeJ
	- 'Ocean Magic'	CAvo GKev LCro LOPS MBriF NHpl NLar
	- 'White Magic'	CAvo EPot EWoo GKev LCro LOPS LRHS NHpl SDeJ WBrk WFar
§	***azureum*** ♀H6	CAvo ELan EPfP ERCP GKev GMaP NBir NLar NRog SPhx WCot WFar
	- 'Album'	NRog SPhx WCot
	- 'Bling Bling'	LRHS SDeJ WCot
	'Baby's Breath'	see *M.* 'Jenny Robinson'
	'Big Smile'	CRos EHyd EPfP GKev LRHS NRHS WCot
	'Blue Eyes'	WCot
	botryoides	GKev NRog WCot
	- 'Album'	CAvo CTri EPfP EShb GKev LCro LOPS NRog SDeJ SRms WCot WShi
	bourgaei	GKev NRog
	caucasicum	WCot
	chalusicum	see *M. pseudomuscari*
	coeleste	GKev WCot
	commutatum	GKev NRog
	- white-flowered	GKev
§	***comosum***	CBro CKel ERCP GKev NRog WCot WFar
	- 'Epirus Giant' **new**	GKev
	- 'Monstrosum'	see *M. comosum* 'Plumosum'
§	- 'Plumosum'	GKev NRog SDeJ
	dionysicum	NRog
	discolor	NRog
	inconstrictum	GKev
	'Ivor's Pink'	WCot
§	'Jenny Robinson' ♀H5	CAvo LHWs SDys SMad WCot WHoo
	'Joyce Spirit'	ECul ERCP GKev LRHS
	kerkis	GKev
	latifolium ♀H6	CDoC CRos EHyd ERCP EShb GKev LCro LOPS LRHS MBow NLar NRHS NRog SDeJ WCot
*	- 'Blue Angels'	NBir
	- 'Grape Ice'	CRos GKev LRHS
§	***macrocarpum***	ECha GKev NRog WShi
	- 'Golden Fragrance'PBR	CAvo CBro CExl EPot ERCP GKev MNrw NRog SDeJ
	'Memory of Gary Fisher'	WCot
	mirum	NRog WCot
	'Morgenhimmel'	GKev
	moschatum	see *M. muscarimi*
	'Mount Hood'	NRog SDeJ SPhx
	'Mountain Lady'	GKev
§	***muscarimi***	CAvo GKev NRog SDeJ WCot
	- var. ***flavum***	see *M. macrocarpum*
§	***neglectum***	CKel GKev NLar NRog SEND WCot WShi
	pallens	GKev NRog
	paradoxum	see *Bellevalia paradoxa*
	parviflorum	GKev WCot
	'Pink Sunrise'	EPot ERCP GKev NHpl NRog SDeJ WCot
§	***pseudomuscari*** ♀H5	GKev WCot
	pulchellum	GKev
	subsp. ***clepsydroides***	
	- subsp. ***pulchellum***	GKev
	racemosum	see *M. neglectum*
	'Rosy Sunrise'	GKev WCot
	'Sky Blue'	WCot

§ ***spreitzenhoferi***	NRog
'Superstar'	GKev NRog
§ ***tenuiflorum***	WCot
aff. ***tenuiflorum*** JCA 0.691.251	WCot
'Venus'	GBin GKev WCot
'White Beauty'	LRHS SPhx WCot
'Winter Amethyst'	WCot

Muscarimia see *Muscari*

ambrosiacum	see *Muscari muscarimi*

Musella see *Musa*

Mussaenda (*Rubiaceae*)

'Tropic Snow'	CCCN

Musschia (*Campanulaceae*)

wollastonii	CAbb

Mutisia (*Asteraceae*)

oligodon	GKev
retrorsa	GKev

Myoporum (*Scrophulariaceae*)

acuminatum	see *M. tenuifolium*
laetum	CExl IDee SPlb SVen
§ ***tenuifolium***	SPlb SVen

Myosotidium (*Boraginaceae*)

§ ***hortensia***	CBcs CBct CExl CPla CTsd ELan GAbr GBin GKev IBal ITim LRHS NBid NRHS SEdd SIvy
nobile	see *M. hortensia*

Myosotis (*Boraginaceae*)

arvensis	MBow
australis	WCot
glabrescens	EPot
MY OH MY ('Myomark'PBR)	CBod
palustris	see *M. scorpioides*
pulvinaris	GArf SPlb
rakiura	CPla EWes
§ ***scorpioides***	CHab CPud CWCL CWat LCro LLWG LOPS MMuc MWts NAts SCoo SPlb SRms SVic WBrk WMAq WPnP XLum
- 'Alba'	CPud LLWG MWts
- 'Ice Pearl'	ECha
- MAYTIME ('Blaqua') (v)	NBir
- 'Mermaid'	CBen CWat ECha EWat LLWG SRms
- 'Pinkie'	LLWG
- 'Snowflakes'	CWat EWat
sylvatica	LCro LOPS MMuc NMir WWild
- 'Bluesylva' (Sylva Series) ♀H6	SPhx
- 'Indigo'	ELan
- 'Rosylva' (Sylva Series) ♀H6	GJos
- 'Ultramarine' ♀H6	LCro LOPS
'Sylvia Blue'	LCro LOPS

Myrceugenia (*Myrtaceae*)

ovata var. ***nannophylla***	WPGP

Myrica (*Myricaceae*)

gale	CAgr GPoy NLar WSpi

Myricaria (*Tamaricaceae*)

germanica	NLar

Myriophyllum (*Haloragaceae*)

propinquum	LLWG
spicatum	CBen EWat MWts WMAq
verticillatum	CWat SCoo

Myrmecodia (*Rubiaceae*)

beccarii 'Adventure'	SPad

Myrrhis (*Apiaceae*)

odorata	Widely available
- 'Forncett Chevron'	LEdu SPhx

Myrsine (*Primulaceae*)

africana	CCht EShb MHer
australis	SVen
divaricata	GBin SVen
salicina	CTsd

Myrteola (*Myrtaceae*)

§ ***nummularia***	GAbr GArf GRum ITim WPav WThu
- from Falkland Islands **new**	GRum

Myrtus ✿ (*Myrtaceae*)

apiculata misapplied	see *Luma apiculata*
bullata	see *Lophomyrtus bullata*
chequen	see *Luma chequen*
communis ♀H4	Widely available
- 'Flore Pleno' (d)	MHer
- 'Jekka's All Gold'	WJek
- 'Jenny Reitenbach'	see *M. communis* subsp. *tarentina*
- 'Lumi' **new**	LRHS
- 'Merion'	WJek
- 'Microphylla'	see *M. communis* subsp. *tarentina*
- 'Nana'	see *M. communis* subsp. *tarentina*
- 'Pyewood Park'	SRms WJek
§ - subsp. ***tarentina*** ♀H4	Widely available
- - 'Compacta'	SCoo SLon
- - 'Microphylla Variegata' (v)	EShb MNHC SPer SRms WJek
I - - 'Variegata' (v)	CBod CEme EPfP
- 'Tricolor'	see *M. communis* 'Variegata'
§ - 'Variegata' (v)	CBod CCoa CMac CSBt CTri EBee EHyd ELan ENfk EPfP EShb LEdu LRHS MGil MHer MSwo NLar NRHS SCob SGBe SGbt SGol SLon SPer SPoG WAvo WFar WHer WJek
'Glanleam Gold'	see *Luma apiculata* 'Glanleam Gold'
lechleriana	see *Amomyrtus luma*
luma	see *Luma apiculata*
nummularia	see *Myrteola nummularia*
* ***paraguayensis***	EBee
ugni	see *Ugni molinae*

N

Nabalus (*Asteraceae*)

albus	see *Prenanthes alba*

Nandina (*Berberidaceae*)

BRIGHTLIGHT ('Selten004'PBR)	EBee LRHS SGol
domestica	Widely available
- B&SWJ 4923	WCru
- B&SWJ 11113	WCru
- BLUSH PINK ('Aka'PBR)	CDoC CMac EPfP LRHS LSRN MAsh MPkF MThu SPoG SWvt

- 'Filamentosa'	EPfP LRHS MPkF NLar SGol XSte
- 'Fire Power'	Widely available
- FLIRT ('Murasaki'PBR)	MAsh MPkF SGol SMad XSte
- 'Gulf Stream'	CRos EGrI EHyd ELan ELon EPfP ERom LBuc LPar LRHS LSRN MAsh MBNS MGos MPkF NRHS SGsty SMad SavN XSte
- 'Harbour Dwarf'	CEnd WFar
- var. ***leucocarpa***	NLar
- MAGICAL LEMON AND LIME ('Lemlim'PBR)	CBcs CBod EBee ELan LCro LOPS LRHS SGol SGsty SavN WHwl XSte
- OBSESSED	see *N. domestica* 'Seika'
- PLUM PASSION ('Monum')	EHyd EPfP MAsh MGos SavN
§ - 'Pygmaea'	CMen ELon SGol
- 'Red Dragon'	MPkF
- 'Richmond' ♀H5	CBcs CDoC CEme CKel CRos EBee EHyd ELan ELon EMil EPfP LPar LRHS MAsh MGos NLar NRHS SCob SEdd SJap SPer SPoG SWvt WCFE WFar WHwl WLov
§ - 'Seika'PBR	Widely available
- SIENNA SUNRISE ('Monfar')	LRHS MPkF NLar SGol
- 'Sunset'PBR	CAbb CBcs EBee EHed GKev LRHS LSRN MMrt NLar SCob SPad
- 'Twilight'PBR (v)	CBod CKel CMac CRos CWGN EBee EMil EPfP LRHS MPkF SGsty SMad SWvt
- 'Wood's Dwarf'	CBcs EGrI WFar

Nannorrhops (*Arecaceae*)

arabica	see *N. ritchieana*
§ ***ritchieana***	SPlb
- blue-leaved	SPlb

Napaea (*Malvaceae*)

dioica	LEdu SPhx WCot WPGP

Narcissus ✿ (*Amaryllidaceae*)

'Abba' (4) ♀H6	CQua
'Aberfoyle' (2) ♀H6	CQua
'Abstract' (11a)	CQua
'Accent' (2)	CQua
'Achentoul' (4)	CQua
'Achnasheen' (3)	CQua
'Acropolis' (4)	CQua GKev LHWs NRog SDeJ
'Actaea' (9) ♀H6	CBro CQua GBin GCro LCro LOPS NRog SDeJ
'Acumen' (2)	CQua
'Admiration' (8)	CQua
'Adversane' (3)	CQua
'Advocat' (3)	CQua
'Ahwahnee' (2)	CQua
'Ainley' (2)	CQua
'Aintree' (3)	CQua
'Aircastle' (3)	CQua
'Albatross' (3)	CQua WShi
'Albus Plenus Odoratus'	see *N. poeticus* 'Plenus' ambig.
'Alex Jones' (2)	CQua
alpestris (13)	NDry
'Altruist' (3)	CQua ERCP NRog SDeJ
'Altun Ha' (2)	CQua GKev
'Amabilis' (3)	CQua
'Amadeus Mozart' (2)	CQua
'Amazing Grace' (2)	CQua
'Amber Castle' (2)	CQua
'Ambergate' (2)	CQua GKev NRog SDeJ WPhe
'American Dream' (1)	CQua
'American Goldfinch' (7)	CQua
'American Heritage' (1)	CQua
'Amstel' (4)	CQua
'Andrew's Choice' (7) ♀H6	CQua
'Androcles' (4)	WPhe
'Andy Blanchard' (5)	NDry
'Angel' (3)	CQua
'Angel Face' (3)	CQua
'Angelina' (6) **new**	NDry
'Angel's Breath' (5) ♀H6	CAvo EPot GKev
'Angel's Flight' (6) **new**	NDry
Angel's tears	see *N. triandrus* subsp. ***triandrus*** var. ***triandrus***
'Angel's Whisper' (5)	CQua GKev LHWs WShi
'Angel's Wings' (2)	CQua
'Angkor' (4)	CQua
'An-gof' (7)	CQua
'Annequin' (3)	CQua
'Apollo Gold' (10)	NHpl
'Apotheose' (4)	SDeJ
'Apricot' (1)	GCro
'Apricot Whirl' (11a)	CQua GKev LRHS
'April Tears' (5)	WShi
'Ara' (6)	CQua GKev
'Arctic Gem' (3)	CQua
'Arctic Gold' (1) ♀H6	CQua
'Ard Righ' (1)	GCro
'Areley Kings' (2)	CQua
'Argent' (4)	CQua
'Argosy' (1)	CQua
'Ariel'PBR (8)	GKev NRog
'Arish Mell' (5)	CQua
'Arkle' (1) ♀H6	CQua GKev SDeJ
'Arleston' (2)	CQua
'Armada' (2)	CQua
'Armidale' (3)	CQua
'Armoury' (4)	CQua
'Arndilly' (2)	CQua
'Arpege' (2)	CQua
'Arthurian' (1)	CQua
'Articol' (11a)	CQua NRog
'Arwenack' (11a)	CQua
'Ascot' (4)	GKev SDeJ
'Ashmore' (2)	CQua
'Ashton Wold' (2)	CQua
'Aspasia' (8)	GKev
§ ***assoanus*** (13)	EPot GKev NRog WCot WShi
'Astropink' (11a)	CQua
§ ***asturiensis*** (13)	GKev NDry NRog WShi
- giant	see *N. asturiensis* 'Wavertree'
§ - 'Wavertree' (1)	CQua
asturiensis* × *cyclamineus	NDry
'Audubon' (2)	CQua GKev SDeJ
'Auntie Eileen' (2)	CQua
'Aureolin' (7) **new**	NDry
'Ava Grace' (2)	CQua
'Avalanche' (8) ♀H4	CQua ELan GKev LCro LOPS NRog SDeJ
'Avalanche of Gold' (8)	CQua
'Avalon' (2)	CQua ERCP GKev SDeJ WPhe
'Baby Boomer' (7)	CQua ERCP GKev LHWs WPhe
'Baby Moon' (7)	CCBP CQua EPot GKev LRHS NRog SDeJ SDir
'Back Flash' (2)	CQua
'Badbury Rings' (3) ♀H6	CQua
'Badgeworth' (3)	CQua
'Bahama Beach' (7)	CQua
'Bala' (4)	CQua
'Balalaika' (2)	CQua
'Balanced Equation' (11a)	CQua
'Baldock' (4)	CQua
'Ballyrobert' (1)	CQua
BALMACARA BEAUTY (2)	GCro

	'Balvenie' (2)	CQua
	'Banana Daiquiri' (11a)	WPhe
	'Bandesara' (3)	CQua
	'Bandit' (2)	CQua
	'Banker' (2)	CQua
	'Banstead Village' (2)	CQua
	'Bantam' (2) ♀H6	CQua CRos LRHS SDeJ
	'Barbara Hunt' (7)	CQua
	'Barbara's Passion' (1)	CQua
	'Barbary Gold' (2)	CQua
	'Barn Dance' (3)	CQua
	'Barnham' (1)	CQua
	'Barnsdale Wood' (2)	CQua
	'Barrett Browning' (3)	GKev MBros NRog SDeJ
	'Barrii' (3)	CQua
	'Bath's Flame' (3)	CAvo CQua GCro GKev WShi
	'Bear's Gold' (4)	CQua
	'Beaulieu' (1)	CQua
	'Beautiful Dream' (3)	CQua
	'Beautiful Eyes' (7)	GKev
	'Beauvallon' (4)	SDeJ
	'Bebop' (7)	CBro
	'Bedruthan' (2)	CQua
	'Beersheba' (1)	CQua
	'Belcanto' (11a)	CQua NRog SDeJ
	'Belisana' (2)	SDeJ
	'Belize' (2)	CQua
	'Bell Rock' (1) ♀H6	CQua
	'Bell Song' (7)	CBro CQua EShb LRHS NRog SDeJ WShi
	'Bella Estrella' (11a)	ERCP
	'Berceuse' (2)	CQua
	'Bere Ferrers' (4)	CQua
	'Bernardino' (2)	CQua GCro
	'Beryl' (6)	CQua NRog WShi
	'Best Friend' (3)	CQua
	'Best Seller' (1)	CArg
	'Bethal' (3)	CQua
	'Bethan-Sîan' (2)	CQua
	'Biffo' (4)	CQua
	BIGGAR BOUNTIFUL (2)	GCro
	'Bilbo' (6)	CBro
	'Billy Graham' (2)	CQua
	'Binkie' (2)	CQua
	'Biondina' (1)	NDry
	'Bionic' (2)	CQua
	'Birchwood' (3)	CQua
	'Birma' (3)	SDeJ
	'Bittern' (12)	CBro CQua GKev NRog SDeJ
	'Black Prince' (9)	CQua
	'Blackstone' (2)	CQua
	'Blarney' (3)	CQua
	'Blisland' (9)	CQua
	'Blossom Lady' (4)	CQua
	'Blue Danube' (1)	CQua
	'Bluntington' (3)	CQua
	'Blushing Maiden' (4)	CQua
	'Bobbysoxer' (7)	CBro CQua LEdu
	'Bobolink' (2)	CQua
	'Boconnoc' (2)	CQua
	'Bodelva' (2)	CQua
	'Bolton' (7)	GCro
	'Bonython' (1)	GCro
	'Bosbigal' (11a)	CQua
	'Boscastle' (7)	CQua
	'Boscoppa' (11a)	CQua
	'Boslowick' (11a) ♀H6	CQua
	'Bossa Nova' (3)	CQua
	'Bossiney' (11a)	CQua
	'Brackenhurst' (2)	SDeJ
	'Bravoure' (1) ♀H6	GBin SDeJ SDir
	'Breezand Tristar' (11a) ♀H6	CBro
	'Brentswood' (8)	CQua
	'Bridal Crown' (4) ♀H6	CDoC GKev LCro LOPS LRHS NRog SDeJ
	'Bright Flame' (2)	CQua
	'Bright Spangles' (8)	CQua
	'Bright Spot' (8)	CQua
	BRIGHTERWELL (2)	GCro
	'Brilliancy' (3)	CQua
	'British Gamble' (1) **new**	GKev
	'Broadway Star' (11b)	SDeJ
	'Brodick' (3)	CQua
	'Brooke Ager' (2) ♀H6	CBro CQua GKev
	'Broomhill' (2) ♀H6	CQua
	'Broughshane' (1)	CQua
	broussonetii (13)	EPot GKev NRog
	- from Morocco	WPGP
	'Brunswick' (2)	SDeJ
	'Bryanston' (2) ♀H6	CQua
	'Buckshead' (4)	CQua
	'Budock Water' (2)	CQua
	'Bugle Major' (2)	CQua
	bulbocodium (13) ♀H4	CBro CWCL EHyd GKev LCro LOPS LRHS NRHS SRms WCot
	- 'Arctic Bells' (10) **new**	LHWs
§	- subsp. ***bulbocodium*** (13)	CBro
§	- - var. ***citrinus*** (13)	CRos EHyd LRHS NRHS SPlb
	- - var. ***conspicuus*** (13)	CBro CQua EGrI ERCP GKev NHpl NRog SDeJ SDix WCot WShi XLum
*	- - var. ***filifolius*** (13)	CBro
§	- - var. ***graellsii*** (13)	NSla
	- - var. ***nivalis*** (13)	EPot GKev NDry NRog
§	- Golden Bells Group (10)	CQua CRos CWCL EHyd EPfP EPot GBin LHWs LRHS NHol NRHS NRog SDeJ
	- subsp. ***obesus*** (13)	GKev NDry NRog
	- - JW 90-13	GKev
§	- - 'Diamond Ring' (10)	CQua CRos EHyd EPot GKev LRHS MNrw NRHS
	- - 'Lee Martin' (10)	NDry
	- subsp. ***praecox*** (13)	CRos EHyd NRHS
	- - var. ***paucinervis*** (13)	GKev NRog
	- - - Rrw84.18	NDry
	- subsp. ***tananicus***	see *N. cantabricus* subsp. *tananicus*
	- subsp. ***vulgaris***	see *N. bulbocodium* subsp. *bulbocodium*
	'Bundle' (7) **new**	NDry
	'Bunting' (7) ♀H6	CQua
	'Burntwood' (4)	CQua
	'Burravoe' (1)	CQua
	'Busbie' (12)	NDry
	'Bute Park' (4)	CQua
	'Butter and Eggs' (4)	CAvo GKev
	'Cadgwith' (2)	CQua
	'Cairngorm' (2)	NRog SDeJ WPhe
	'Cairntoul' (3)	CQua
	'Calamansack' (2)	CQua
	calcicola (13)	NDry
	'Calgary' (4)	CQua GKev MBriF WCot
	'Callisto' (10)	NDry
	'Camaraderie' (2)	CQua
	'Camborne' (1) **new**	NDry
	'Camelot' (2) ♀H6	CQua SDeJ
	'Cameo Angel' (2)	CQua
	'Cameo Baron' (2)	CQua
	'Cameo Frills' (2)	CQua
	'Cameo Gem' (1)	CQua
	'Cameo Joy' (2)	CQua
	'Cameo King' (2)	CQua
	'Cameo Magic' (4)	CQua
	'Cameo Marie' (3)	CQua

'Cameo Mist' (2)	CQua
'Campernelli' (7)	CQua
'Campernelli Plenus'	see *N.* 'Double Campernelle'
'Campion' (9)	CQua
'Can Can Girl' (2) **new**	LHWs
'Canaliculatus' (8)	CArg CQua CTri EHyd ERCP GBin GKev LCro LOPS NRog SDeJ SPer
canaliculatus Gussone	see *N. tazetta* subsp. *lacticolor*
canariensis (13)	CQua
'Canary' (7)	CQua
'Canarybird' (8)	CQua
'Canasta' (11a)	CQua
'Candlepower' (1)	CQua NDry
'Canoodle' (2)	CQua
'Cantabile' (9) ♀H6	CQua
cantabricus (13)	CQua GKev LCro LOPS NDry
- subsp. ***cantabricus*** (13)	GKev
- - var. ***eu-albidus*** (13)	NDry
- - var. ***foliosus*** (13) ♀H4	NDry
I - subsp. ***monophyllus*** var. ***laciniatus*** (13)	NDry
§ - subsp. ***tananicus*** (13)	GKev
cantabricus* × *romieuxii (13)	NDry
cantabricus* × *romieuxii subsp. ***albidus*** var. ***zaianicus*** f. ***lutescens*** (13)	NDry
'Canterbury' (5)	CQua
'Capability Brown' (9)	CQua
'Capax Plenus'	see *N.* 'Eystettensis'
'Cape Cornwall' (2)	CQua
'Cape Point' (2)	CQua
'Capisco' (3)	CQua
'Carbineer' (2)	CQua GCro SDeJ
'Cargreen' (9)	CQua
'Carib Gipsy' (2) ♀H6	CQua
'Carlton' (2) ♀H6	CArg GKev LCro LOPS NRog SDeJ
'Carn Brea' (3)	CQua
'Carnkief' (2)	CQua
'Carole Lombard' (3)	CQua
'Carwinion' (2)	CQua
'Casiah' (2)	CQua
'Cassandra' (9)	GCro
'Cassata' (11a)	GKev LHWs NBir NRog SDeJ
'Casterbridge' (2)	CQua
'Castle Rings' (4)	CQua
'Casual Elegance' (10) **new**	LHWs
'Cavalli King' (4)	CQua
'Caye Chapel' (3)	CQua
× ***cazorlanus*** (13)	NDry
'Cedar Hills' (3)	CQua
'Cedric Morris' (1)	ECha MCor WCot WSHC
'Celestial Fire' (2)	CQua
'Celtic Gold' (2)	CQua
'Centannées' (11a)	NRog
'Centenary Gold' (2)	CQua
'Cha-cha' (6)	CBro GKev
'Changing Colors' (11a)	GKev NRog SDeJ
'Chanterelle' (11a)	NRog SDeJ
'Charity May' (6)	CQua
'Charleston' (2)	CQua
'Charlie Connor' (1)	CQua
'Chaste' (1)	CQua
'Chat' (7)	CQua
'Cheeky Chappie' (6)	NDry
'Cheep' (1)	NDry
'Cheer Leader' (3)	CQua
'Cheerfulness' (4) ♀H6	CArg CQua ELan GKev LCro LOPS MBros NPer NRHS NRog SDeJ WPhe
'Cheetah' (1)	CQua
'Chelsea China' (2)	CQua
'Chelsea Girl' (2)	CQua
'Chemeketa' (2)	GKev
'Chérie' (7)	CQua
'Cherish' (2)	CQua
'Cherry Ice' (2)	CQua
'Cherry Spot' (3)	CQua
'Cherrygardens' (2)	CQua
'Chesapeake Bay' (1)	CQua
'Chesterton' (9) ♀H6	CQua
'Chickadee' (6)	CQua
'Chicken Hill' (1)	CQua
'Chief Inspector' (1)	CQua
'Chiloquin' (1)	CQua
'Chinita' (8)	CQua
'Chirp' (1)	NDry
'Chit Chat' (7) ♀H6	NRog SDeJ SPlb
'Chitter' (2)	NDry
'Chobe River' (1)	CQua
'Chortle' (3)	CQua
'Chorus Line' (8)	CQua
'Christelle' (4)	CQua
'Chromacolor' (2) ♀H6	GKev LHWs NRog WPhe
'Churchfield Bells' (5)	CQua
'Cisticola' (3)	CQua
citrinus	see *N. bulbocodium* subsp. *bulbocodium* var. *citrinus*
'Citron' (3)	CQua
'Citronita' (3)	CQua
'Clare' (7)	CQua
'Classic Garden' (1) **new**	GKev LHWs
'Classic Gold' (10) ♀H6	CQua
'Claverley' (2)	CQua
'Cloth of Gold' (8)	CQua
'Cloud Nine' (2)	CBro CQua
'Clovelly Ayr' (9)	CQua
'Codlins and Cream'	see *N.* 'Sulphur Phoenix'
'Coker's Frome' (9)	CQua
'Colblanc' (11a)	GKev NRog
'Colin's Joy' (2)	CQua
'Colley Gate' (3)	CQua
'Colorama' (11a)	CQua
'Colville' (9)	CQua
'Come to Good' (2)	CQua
'Compressus'	see *N.* × *intermedius* 'Compressus'
'Conestoga' (2)	CQua
confusus (13) **new**	GKev
'Congress' (11a)	LHWs
'Conowingo' (11a)	CQua
'Content' (1)	GCro
'Coo' (12)	NDry
'Cool Crystal' (3)	CQua
'Cool Evening' (11a)	CQua
'Cool Shades' (2)	CQua
'Corbiere' (1)	CQua
'Corbridge' (2)	CQua
'Corby Candle' (2)	CQua
'Corky's Song' (2)	CQua
'Cornish Chuckles' (12) ♀H6	CQua
'Cornish Gold' (1)	LCro LOPS
'Cornish King' (1)	GKev LHWs WPhe
'Corofin' (3)	CQua
'Coromandel' (2)	CQua
'Corozal' (3)	CQua
'Cosette' (6) **new**	NDry
'Cotinga' (6)	CBro CQua EShb NRog SDeJ
'Cottrell' (1)	CQua
'Countdown' (2)	CQua
'Crackington' (4) ♀H6	CQua
'Cragford' (8)	GKev SDeJ

'Craig Stiel' (2)	CQua
'Craigton Chorister' (13)	NDry
'Craigton Clumper' (13)	NDry
'Creag Dubh' (2)	CQua
'Cream Satin' (2) **new**	NDry
Crème Fraîche Group (3)	NDry
'Crenver' (3)	CQua
'Crill' (7)	CQua
'Crimson Chalice' (3)	CQua
'Cristobal' (1)	CQua
'Croesus' (2)	CQua
'Crofty' (6)	CQua
'Croila' (2)	CQua
'Crowndale' (4)	CQua
'Crugmeer' (11a)	CQua
'Crystal Star' (2)	CQua
cuatrecasasii (13)	NDry
- var. ***segimonensis*** (13)	GKev
'Cudden Point' (2)	CQua
'Cul Beag' (3)	CQua
'Culmination' (2)	CQua
'Cultured Pearl' (2)	CQua
'Cum Laude' (11a)	SDeJ
'Curlew' (7) 🏆H6	CQua GKev LCro LOPS NRog SDeJ WShi
'Curly' (2)	NRog SDeJ
'Cuscarne' (8)	CQua
cyclamineus (13) 🏆H6	CAvo CBro CExl CRos CTtf EHyd EPot GKev LEdu LRHS NDry NRHS NRog SRms
cypri (13)	CQua
'Cyros' (1)	CQua
'Dailmanach' (2)	CQua
'Dalcharn' (2)	LRHS
'Dallas' (3)	CQua
'Dalmeny' (2)	CQua
'Damson' (2)	CQua
'Dan du Plessis' (8)	CQua
'Danehill' (1)	CQua
'Danger Zone' (2)	CQua
'Daphnis' (10)	NDry
'Dateline' (3)	CQua
'Dawn Brooker' (2)	CQua
'Dawn Cloud' (2)	CQua
'Dawn Duel' (12)	NDry
'Dawn Sky' (2)	CQua
'Daydream' (2)	CQua NRog
'Daymark' (8)	CQua
'Dayton Lake' (2)	CQua
'De Lacey' (11a)	CQua
'Dean' (2)	CQua
'Dear Love' (11a)	CQua
'Dear Me' (2)	CQua
'Debutante' (2)	CQua
'December Bride' (11a)	CQua
'Dell Chapel' (3)	CQua
'Delnashaugh' (4)	CQua ERCP GKev NHol NRog SDeJ
'Delos' (3)	CQua
'Delta' (11a)	CQua
'Delta Flight' (6)	CQua
'Demand' (2)	CQua
'Demmo' (2)	CQua
'Denali' (1)	CQua
'Derek Tangye' (2)	CQua
'Derringer' (7)	GKev
'Descant' (1)	CQua
'Desdemona' (2) 🏆H6	CQua GKev SDeJ
'Desert Bells' (7)	CQua
'Desert Orchid' (2)	CQua
'Desert Storm' (2)	CQua
'Despera' (6) **new**	NDry
'Diamond Ring'	see *N. bulbocodium* subsp. *obesus* 'Diamond Ring'
'Dick Wellband' (2)	GCro
'Dick Wilden' (4)	GKev NRog SDeJ
'Dickcissel' (7) 🏆H6	CQua ERCP GKev NRog
'Dimple' (9)	CQua
'Dispatch Box' (1) 🏆H6	CQua
'Disquiet' (1)	CQua
'Diversity' (11a)	CQua
'Doctor Hugh' (3) 🏆H6	CQua
'Doctor Jazz' (2)	CQua
'Doctor Who' (4)	CQua
'Dolcoath' (2)	CQua
'Doll Baby' (7)	GKev
'Dolly Mollinger' (11b)	NRog
'Don Stead' (10)	NDry
'Doombar' (1)	CQua
'Dorchester' (4)	CQua
'Dorothy Yorke' (2)	GCro
§ 'Double Campernelle' (4)	CQua GKev SDeJ WShi
'Double Fashion' (4)	NRog SDeJ
double pheasant eye	see *N. poeticus* 'Plenus' ambig.
double Roman	see *N.* 'Romanus'
'Double White' (4)	CQua
'Doublet' (4)	CQua
'Dove Wings' (6)	CQua
'Dover Boy' (11a)	CQua
'Downing College' (2)	CQua
'Downlands' (3)	CQua
'Dragon Run' (2)	CQua
'Drama Queen' (11a)	CQua
'Dream Castle' (3)	CQua
'Dream Catcher' (2)	CQua
'Dreamlight' (3)	CQua GKev
dubius (13)	EPot NRog
'Duchess of Westminster' (2)	GCro
'Dunkeld' (2)	CQua
'Dunkery' (4)	CQua
'Dunley Hall' (3)	CQua
'Dunskey' (3)	CQua
'Dunstan's Fire' (1)	CQua
'Dutch Lemon Drops' (5) 🏆H6	CQua EPot
'Dutch Master' (1) 🏆H6	EPfP GKev LCro LOPS NRog SDeJ SDir
'Early Bride' (2)	CQua
'Early Sensation' (1)	EHyd NRHS
'Early Splendour' (8)	CQua
'Earthlight' (3)	CQua
'Eastbrook Sunrise' (1)	CQua
'Easter Moon' (2)	CQua
'Eastern Dawn' (2)	CQua SDeJ
'Eastern Promise' (2)	CQua
'Eaton Song' (12) 🏆H6	CQua GKev
'Ebony' (1)	CQua
'Edge Grove' (2)	CQua
'Edinburgh' (11a)	NRog
'Editor' (2)	CQua
'Edna Earl' (3)	GKev NRog SDeJ
'Edward Buxton' (3)	CQua
'Edward Hart' (2)	GCro
'Egard' (11a)	CQua
'Egmont King' (2)	CQua
'Egmont Star' (2)	CQua
'Eira Hibbert' (3)	CQua
'El Camino' (6)	CQua
'Eland' (7)	CQua
'Elara' (10) **new**	NDry
'Elegance' (2)	CQua
elegans (13)	NRog
'Elf' (2)	CQua

	Name	Suppliers
	'Elfin Gold' (6)	CQua
	'Elite' (8)	GKev
	'Elizabeth Ann' (6)	CQua
	'Elka' (1) ♀H6	CAvo CBro CQua ECha EPot ERCP GKev LHWs LRHS SPhx WShi
	'Ellen' (2)	CArg
	'Elphin' (4)	CQua
	'Elusive' (3)	CQua
	'Elven Lady' (2)	CQua
	'Elvin's Voice' (5) **new**	LHWs
	'Elvira' (8)	CQua WShi
	'Emerald Green' (2)	SDir
	'Emerald Pink' (3)	CQua
	'Emily' (2)	CQua
	'Empire' (2)	GCro
	'Empress of Ireland' (1)	CQua
	'Englander' (6)	EPot LRHS
	'Epona' (3)	CQua
	'Éponine' (6) **new**	NDry
	'Erin' (3)	CQua
	'Erlicheer' (4)	CQua GKev LCro LOPS NRog SDeJ WCot
	'Estrella' (3)	CQua
	'Estremadura' (2)	CQua
§	***eugeniae*** (13)	GKev WCot
	'Euryalus' (1)	CQua
	'Evangeline' (3)	GCro
	'Eve Robertson' (2)	CQua
	'Evelyn Roberts' (11a)	CQua
	'Evesham' (3)	CQua
	'Exotic Beauty' (4)	CQua NRog
	'Exotic Mystery' (11a)	GKev LHWs
	'Extravaganza' (4)	SDeJ
§	'Eystettensis' (4)	IBlr NDry WFar
	'Fair Head' (9)	CQua
	'Fair Prospect' (2)	CQua
	'Fairlawns' (3)	CQua
	'Fairmile' (3)	CQua
	'Fairy Chimes' (5)	CQua EPot
	'Fairy Island' (3)	CQua
I	'Faith' (1)	SDeJ
	'Falaise' (4)	CQua
	'Falconet' (8) ♀H6	CQua GKev NRog SDeJ
	'Falmouth Bay' (3)	CQua
	'Falstaff' (2)	CQua
	'Fantine' (6) **new**	NDry
	'Far Country' (2)	CQua
I	'Fashion' (11b)	CQua
	'Fastidious' (2)	CQua
	'Fat Rascal' (12)	NDry
	'February Gold' (6) ♀H6	CArg CAvo CBro CQua CRos CTri EHyd ELan EPfP EPot ERCP GKev LCro LOPS LRHS NBir NRHS NRog SDeJ SRms WPhe WShi
	'February Silver' (1)	CBro EPot ERCP NRog SDeJ
	'Feeling Lucky' (2)	CQua
	'Felindre' (9)	EPot
	'Feock' (3)	CQua
	fernandesii (13)	EPot ITim NRog WCot
	– from Spain	ITim
	– var. ***cordubensis*** (13)	CAvo CBro CQua EPot GKev ITim NDry
	– var. ***cordubensis*** × ***jonquilla*** (13)	NRog
	'Ferndown' (3)	CQua
	'Fertile Crescent' (7)	CQua
	'Ffitch's Ffolly' (2)	CQua
	'Fiery Maiden' (2)	CQua
	'Filoli' (1)	CQua
	'Filskit' (2)	CQua
	'Finchcocks' (2)	CQua
	'Fine Gold' (1)	CQua
	'Fine Romance' (2)	CQua
	FINTRY BEAUTY (2)	GCro
	'Fiona MacKillop' (2)	CQua
	'Fire-Blade' (2)	CQua
	'Firebrand' (3)	CQua WShi
	'Firehills' (2)	CQua
	'Firetail' (3)	CQua
	'First Born' (6)	CQua
	'Five Ashes' (2)	CQua
	'Flambards Village' (4)	CQua
	'Fletching' (1)	CQua
	'Fling' (6)	NDry
	'Flirt' (6)	CQua
	'Flora Brava' (2)	CQua
	'Flower Drift' (4)	NRog SDeJ
	'Flying High' (3)	CQua
	'Foff's Way' (1)	CQua
	'Folkestone Girl' (11a)	CQua
	'Foresight' (1)	CQua
	'Fortissimo' (2)	GKev NRog SDeJ
	'Fortune' (2)	CArg CQua SDeJ
	× ***fosteri*** (2) **new**	NDry
	'Foxhunter' (2)	CQua
	'Fragrant Breeze' (2)	NRog SDeJ
	'Fragrant Rose' (2)	CQua GKev NRog
	'Frances Delight' (11a)	CQua
	'Frank Miles' (2)	CQua GCro
	'Freedom Rings' (2)	CQua
	'Freedom Stars' (11a) ♀H6	GKev
	'Fresco' (11a)	CQua
	'Fresh Field' (2)	CQua
	'Fresh Lime' (1)	CQua
	'Frigid' (3)	CQua
	Fringella Group (6)	NDry
	'Frostkist' (6)	CBro CQua
	'Fruit Cup' (7)	NRog SDeJ
	'Full House' (4)	SDeJ
	'Fulwell' (4)	CQua
	'Furbelow' (4)	CQua
	'Gabriella Rose' (4)	CQua
	gaditanus (13)	CBro
	gaditanus × ***rupicola*** subsp. ***watieri*** (13)	GKev
	Galantoquilla Group (12)	NDry
	'Gale Force' (6)	NDry
	'Gallipoli Dawn' (2)	CQua
	'Gamebird' (1)	CQua
	'Garden Princess' (2)	CQua
	'Gay Kybo' (4) ♀H6	CQua
	'Gay Swain' (4)	CQua
	'Gay Time' (4)	SDeJ
	gayi (13)	CQua WShi
	'Gee Tee' (2)	CQua
	'Geevor' (4)	CQua
	'Gellymill' (2)	CQua
	'Gemini Girl' (2)	CQua
	'Gentle Giant' (2)	LHWs SDeJ
	'Georgie Girl' (6)	CQua
	'Georgie May' (2)	CQua
	'Geranium' (8) ♀H6	CBro CQua ERCP GKev LCro LOPS LRHS NRHS NRog SDeJ WShi
	'Gigantic Star' (2)	NRog SDeJ
	'Gillan' (11a)	CQua
	'Gilly Drummond' (1)	CQua
	'Gin and Lime' (1)	CQua
	'Gipsy Moon' (2)	CQua
	'Gipsy Queen' (1)	CBro ECha EPot GKev NDry WCot WFar WShi
	'Gipsy Vale' (1)	NDry
	'Giselle' (10)	NDry

'Glapthorne' (2)	CQua
'Glasnevin' (2)	CQua
'Glasney' (3)	CQua
'Glen Cassley' (3)	CQua
'Glen Clova' (2)	CQua
'Glendurgan' (2)	CQua
'Glenfarclas' (1)	CQua
'Glenside' (2)	CQua
'Glissando' (2)	CQua
'Gloaming Hill' (1)	CQua
'Gloria Townsin' (4)	CQua
'Gloriana Fair' (2)	CQua
'Gloriosus' (8)	CQua
'Glorious' (8)	CQua
'Glory of Lisse' (9)	WShi
'Glover's Reef' (1)	CQua
'Glowing Phoenix' (4)	CQua
'Glowing Red' (4)	CQua
'Goblet' (1)	SDeJ
'Golant' (2)	CQua
'Gold Bond' (2)	CQua
'Gold Charm' (2)	CQua
'Gold Convention' (2) ♀H6	CQua
'Gold Disc' (11a) **new**	GKev
'Gold Ingot' (2) ♀H6	CQua
'Gold Medallion' (1)	CQua
'Gold Sails' (2)	CQua
'Gold Top' (2)	CQua
'Golden Amber' (2)	CQua
'Golden Anniversary' (2)	CQua
'Golden Aura' (2) ♀H6	CQua
'Golden Bear' (4)	CQua
'Golden Bells'	see *N. bulbocodium* Golden Bells Group
'Golden Cheer' (2)	CQua
'Golden Cycle' (6)	CQua
'Golden Dawn' (8) ♀H4	CQua LRHS NRog SDeJ
'Golden Ducat' (4)	CArg NBir NRog SDeJ
'Golden Echo' (7)	CQua GKev SDeJ WPhe
'Golden Flute' (2)	CQua
'Golden Harvest' (1)	NPer NRog
'Golden Incense' (7)	CQua
'Golden Jewel' (2) ♀H6	CQua
'Golden Joy' (2)	CQua
'Golden Mary' (3)	GCro
'Golden Orbit' (4)	CQua
'Golden Perfection' (7)	CQua
'Golden Phoenix' (4)	CQua WShi
'Golden Rain' (4)	GKev
'Golden Sheen' (2)	CQua
'Golden Spur' (1)	CQua GCro
'Golden Torch' (2)	CQua
'Golden Trumpet' (1)	CQua
'Golden Twins' (7)	CQua
'Golden Vale' (1)	CQua
'Golden Years' (6)	CQua
'Goldfinger' (1) ♀H6	CQua SDeJ
'Goldhanger' (2)	CQua
'Golitha Falls' (2)	CQua
'Good Fella' (2)	CQua
'Good Measure' (2)	CQua
'Good Success' (11a)	CQua
'Goonbell' (2)	CQua
'Gorran' (3)	CQua
'Gossamer' (3)	GBin
'Gossmoor' (4)	CQua
graellsii	see *N. bulbocodium* subsp. *bulbocodium* var. *graellsii*
'Grand Monarque' (8)	CQua
'Grand Primo' (8)	LCro LOPS
'Grand Primo Citronière' (8)	CQua
'Grand Prospect' (2)	CQua
'Grand Soleil d'Or' (8)	CQua GKev LCro LOPS NRog SDeJ SDir SPer
'Great Expectations' (2)	CQua
'Greatwood' (1)	CQua
'Green Howard' (3)	CQua
'Green Island' (2)	GKev SDeJ
'Green Lawns' (9)	CQua
'Greenodd' (3)	CQua
'Grenoble' (2)	CQua
'Gresham' (4)	CQua
'Gribben Head' (4)	CQua
'Guiding Spirit' (4)	CQua
'Gulliver' (3)	CQua GCro
'Gunwalloe' (11a)	CQua
'Gwawr' (2)	CQua
'Gwendoline Rae' (3)	CQua
'Gwenllian' (3)	CQua
'Gwennap' (1)	CQua
'Gwinear' (2)	CQua
'Gylly Glow' (6)	CQua
'Hacienda' (1)	CQua
'Half Moon Caye' (2)	CQua
'Halley's Comet' (3)	CQua
'Halloon' (3)	CQua
'Hampton Court' (2)	CQua
'Hannah Jesse' (7)	CQua
'Happy Fellow' (2)	CQua
'Happy Valley' (2)	CQua
'Harmony Bells' (5)	CQua
'Harpers Ferry' (1)	CQua
HARTLAND'S IRVING (1)	GCro
'Hartlebury' (3)	CQua
'Harvard' (2)	CQua
'Havelock' (2)	GCro
'Hawera' (5) ♀H6	CArg CAvo CBro CQua CTri EPfP EPot ERCP EShb GKev GQue LCro LOPS NRog SDeJ WShi
'Heamoor' (4) ♀H6	CQua GKev
hedraeanthus (13)	EPot NDry
- subsp. ***luteolentus*** (13)	NDry
'Helene' (10)	NDry
'Helford Dawn' (2)	CQua
'Helford Sunset' (2)	CQua
'Helios' (2)	CQua
hellenicus	see *N. poeticus* var. *hellenicus*
henriquesii	see *N. jonquilla* var. *henriquesii*
'Henry Irving' (1)	CQua GCro
'Hero' (1)	CQua
'Hesla' (7)	CQua
'Heslington' (3)	CQua
'Hexameter' (9)	CQua
'High Society' (2) ♀H6	CQua GKev LCro LOPS NRog SDeJ
'Highfield Beauty' (8) ♀H6	CQua
'Highgrove' (1)	CQua
'Highlite' (2)	CQua
'Hilda's Pink' (2)	CQua
'Hillstar' (7) ♀H6	CQua GKev NRog SDeJ
'Hindenburg' (1)	CQua
hispanicus (13)	NRog
'Holme Fen' (2)	CQua
'Home Fires' (2)	CQua
'Honeybird' (1)	CQua
'Honeybourne' (2)	CQua
'Hoopoe' (8) ♀H6	CQua NRog
'Horace' (9)	CQua GCro
'Horn of Plenty' (5)	GKev WPhe
'Hors d'Oeuvre' (1)	CBro
'Hospodar' (2)	CQua GCro
'Hot Gossip' (2)	CQua
HOWICK BEAUTY (2)	GCro

HOWICK'S HALF NELSON (2)	GCro
'Hugh Town' (8)	CQua
'Hugus' (7)	CQua
humilis misapplied	see *N. pseudonarcissus* subsp. *pseudonarcissus* var. *humilis*
'Hummingbird' (6)	EPot
'Hungarian Rhapsody' (11a) 𝕐H6	LHWs WPhe
'Hunting Caye' (2)	CQua
'Huntley Down' (1)	CQua
'Huon Pride' (4)	CQua
'Ice Dancer' (2)	CQua
'Ice Diamond' (4)	CQua
'Ice Follies' (2) 𝕐H6	CArg CQua EPfP GBin LCro LOPS LRHS NBir NRog SDeJ
'Ice King' (4)	MBros NBir NRog SDeJ SPer
'Ice Wings' (5) 𝕐H6	CQua EPot GKev NRog SDeJ
'Immaculate' (2)	CQua
'Impeccable' (2)	CQua
'Inara' (4)	CQua
'Inbal'^{PBR} (8)	GKev
'Inca' (6)	CQua
'Inchbonnie' (2)	CQua
§ × ***incurvicervicus***	NDry
'Indian Maid' (7) 𝕐H6	CQua
'Indora' (4)	CQua
'Inglescombe' (4)	NRog
'Innovator' (4)	CQua
'Insulinde' (4)	CQua
'Interim' (2)	CQua SDeJ
× ***intermedius*** (13)	CBro CQua
§ - 'Compressus' (8)	CBro CQua NPoe WShi
'Intrigue' (7) 𝕐H6	CQua
'Invercassley' (3)	CQua
'Inverpolly' (2)	CQua
'Ipi Tombi' (2)	GKev
'Ireland's Eye' (9)	CQua
'Irene Copeland' (4)	CQua GKev
'Irish Cream' (3)	CQua
'Irish Fire' (2)	CQua
'Irish Light' (2)	CQua
'Irish Linen' (3)	CQua
'Irish Luck' (1)	CArg
'Irish Minstrel' (2) 𝕐H6	CQua
'Irish Wedding' (2)	CQua
'Isambard' (4)	CQua
'Isenhurst' (2)	CQua
'Island Pride' (8)	CQua
'Isobel Salt' (8)	CQua
italicus (13)	GKev
'Itzim' (6) 𝕐H6	CBro CQua GKev NRog SDeJ
'Jabberwocky' (11a)	CQua
'Jack Snipe' (6) 𝕐H6	CBro CQua ELan EPot ERCP GKev LCro LOPS NHol NRog SDeJ SPer WCot WShi
'Jack Wood' (11a)	CQua
'Jacob Maurer' (6)	CQua
'Jamage' (8)	CQua
'Jambo' (2)	CQua
'Jamboree' (2)	CQua
'Janelle' (3)	CQua
'Jantje' (11a)	CQua
'Jazz' (11b)	CQua
'Jeanne Bicknell' (4)	CQua
'Jeannie Tangye' (2)	CQua
'Jenna' (3)	CQua
'Jenny' (6) 𝕐H6	CBro CQua EMor EPot ERCP GKev LCro LOPS NBir NRog SDeJ SPhx WShi
'Jersey Lace' (2)	CQua GKev LHWs WPhe
'Jersey Roundabout' (4)	CQua
'Jersey Star' (4)	CQua LHWs
'Jersey Torch' (4)	CQua
'Jessie Jane' (8)	CQua
'Jetfire' (6) 𝕐H6	CArg CQua CRos EHyd EPfP EPot ERCP EShb GKev LCro LOPS LRHS NHol NRHS NRog SDeJ SPer WShi
'Jim Lad' (2)	NDry
'Jimmy Noone' (1)	CQua
'Jim's Gold' (2)	CQua
'Johanna' (5)	CBro
'John Daniel' (4)	CQua
'John Evelyn' (2)	CQua GCro
'John Lanyon' (3)	CQua
'John's Delight' (3)	CQua
jonquilla (13)	CBro CQua EPot NRog WShi
§ - var. ***henriquesii*** (13)	CQua EPot GKev NRog
'Joy Bishop'	see *N. romieuxii* 'Joy Bishop'
'Juanita' (2)	LCro LOPS NPer SDeJ
'Julia Jane'	see *N. romieuxii* 'Julia Jane'
'Jumblie' (12) 𝕐H6	CBro CQua CRos EHyd EPfP EPot LRHS NRHS SDeJ
'Jump Start' (1)	CQua
juncifolius Req. ex Lag.	see *N. assoanus*
'June Christy' (2)	CQua
'June Lake' (2)	CQua
'Kabani' (9)	CQua
'Kalyke' (10) **new**	NDry
'Kamms' (1)	CQua
'Kapiti Talisman' (8)	CQua
'Karamudli' (1)	CQua
'Kari' (10) **new**	NDry
'Kate Davies' (2)	CQua
'Katherine Jenkins' (7) 𝕐H6	CQua
'Kathy's Clown' (6)	CQua
'Katie Heath' (5)	ERCP NRog SDeJ SDir WBrk WPhe
'Katrina Rea' (6)	CQua
'Kaydee' (6) 𝕐H6	CQua EMor ERCP GKev NRog SDeJ SDir WShi
'Kea' (6)	CQua
'Keats' (4)	CQua
'Kebaya' (2)	CQua
'Kedron' (7)	ERCP GKev SDeJ
'Kelly Bray' (1)	CQua
'Ken Sunshine Johnson' (2)	CQua
'Kerryteuila' (8)	CQua
'Kidling' (7)	CQua
'Killara' (8)	CQua
'Killearnan' (9)	CQua
'Killigrew' (2)	CQua
'Killivose' (3)	CQua
'Kilndown' (2)	CQua
'Kilworth' (2)	CQua
'Kimmeridge' (3)	CQua
'King Alfred' (1)	CArg CQua GCro LCro LOPS SDeJ SPer
'Kingham' (1)	CQua
'Kinglet' (7)	CQua
'King's Grove' (1)	CQua
'Kings Pipe' (2)	CQua
'Kingscourt' (1)	CQua
'Kingsleigh' (1)	CQua
'Kingsmill Lake' (2)	CQua
'Kissproof' (2)	NRog SDeJ
'Kit Hill' (7)	CQua
'Kitten' (6)	CQua
'Kiwi Magic' (4)	CQua
'Kiwi Ruler' (3)	CQua
'Kiwi Sunset' (4)	CQua
'Knightsbridge' (1)	CQua
'Knocklayde' (3)	CQua

'Kokopelli' (7) ♀^{H6}	CBro CQua GKev NRog SDeJ
'Kuantan' (3)	CQua
'La Belle' (7)	SDeJ
'La Fiancée' (8)	CQua
'La Riante' (3)	CQua
'Lady Be Good' (2)	CQua
'Lady Hilaria' (2)	CQua
'Lady Margaret Boscawen' (2)	CQua GCro
'Lady Moore' (3)	GCro
'Lady Serena' (9)	CQua
'Ladymeads' (2)	CQua
'Lake Alabaster' (2)	CQua
'Lake District' (2)	CQua
'Lakeland Fair' (2)	CQua
'Lalique' (3)	CQua
'Lamanva' (2)	CQua
'Lanarth' (7)	CQua
'Lancaster' (3)	CQua GKev
'Landewednack Lady' (4)	CQua
'Lara Lovely' (1)	NDry
'Larkwhistle' (6)	GKev NRog SDeJ
'Las Vegas' (1)	GKev NRog SDeJ
'Latchley Meadows' (2)	CQua
'Laura Webb' (4)	CQua
'Laurens Koster' (8)	CQua
'Lavender Lass' (6)	CQua
'Lavender Mist' (2)	CQua
'Leedsii' (3)	CQua
'Lemon Beauty' (11b)	CQua NRog SDeJ
'Lemon Brook' (2)	CQua
'Lemon Drizzle' (2)	CQua
'Lemon Drops' (5)	CQua EPot ERCP GKev NRog SDeJ SPhx WShi
'Lemon Haze' (2)	CQua
'Lemon Silk' (6)	CBro CQua ELan
'Lemon Spice' (3)	CQua
'Lemonade' (3)	CQua
'Lennymore' (2)	CQua
'Letsee' (2)	CQua
'Lezant' (3)	CQua
'Liberty Bells' (5)	CQua GQue
'Liebeslied' (3)	CQua
'Lieke' (7)	EPot ERCP GKev LCro LOPS SDeJ
'Lilac Mist' (2)	CQua
'Limbo' (2)	CQua GKev
'Lincolnshire Lady' (3)	CQua
'Lindsay Joy' (2)	CQua
'Lingerie' (4) ♀^{H6}	CQua
'L'Innocence' (8)	CQua
'Little Beauty' (1)	CQua
'Little Becky' (12)	WShi
'Little Dancer' (1)	CBro CQua
'Little Emma' (12) **new**	LHWs
'Little Frills' (1) **new**	NDry
'Little Jewel' (3)	CQua
'Little Meg' (7)	CQua
'Little Oliver' (7)	GKev LRHS SDeJ
'Little Racer' (6)	NDry
'Little Rusky' (7)	CBro CQua
'Little Sentry' (7)	CAvo CBro CQua
'Little Soldier' (10)	CQua EPot
'Little Spell' (1)	NDry
'Little Sunray' (5) **new**	GKev LHWs
'Little Tweet' (6)	NDry
'Little Tyke' (2)	CQua
'Little Witch' (6)	CQua GKev NRog SDeJ WShi
'Littlefield' (7)	CQua
'Liverpool Festival' (2)	CQua
'Living Colour' (3)	CQua
'Lizard Beacon' (2)	CQua

	'Lobularis'	see *N. lobularis* (Haw.) Schult. & Schult. f.
	lobularis misapplied	see *N. nanus*
§	***lobularis*** (Haw.) Schult. & Schult. f. (13)	CAvo CBro CQua CTri EHyd EPot ERCP GKev LCro LHWs LOPS LRHS NRHS NRog SDeJ SPer
	'Loch Assynt' (3)	CQua
	'Loch Brora' (2)	CQua
	'Loch Coire' (3)	CQua
	'Loch Fada' (2)	CQua
	'Loch Fyne' (2)	GCro
	'Loch Hope' (2)	CQua
	'Loch Leven' (2)	CQua
	'Loch Loyal' (2)	CQua
	'Loch Lundie' (2)	CQua
	'Loch Maberry' (2)	CQua
	'Loch Naver' (2)	CQua
	'Logan Rock' (7)	CQua
	'Lord Kitchener' (2)	GCro
	'Lordship' (1)	CQua
	'Lorikeet' (1)	CQua
	'Lough Gowna' (1)	CQua
	'Louise de Coligny' (2)	ERCP
	'Lubaantun' (1)	CQua
	'Lucie Nottingham' (4)	CQua
	'Lucifer' (2)	CQua GCro WShi
	'Ludo' (1)	NDry
	'Lundy Light' (2)	CQua
	'Lynher' (2)	CQua
	'Lyric' (9)	CQua
	'Lysander' (2)	CQua
	'M.J. Berkeley' (1) **new**	GCro
	'Machan' (2)	CQua
	'Madam Speaker' (4)	CQua
	'Madame Plemp' (1)	GCro
	'Madison' (4)	CQua GKev
	'Magic Moment' (3)	CQua
	'Magician' (2)	CQua
	'Magnificence' (1)	CQua GCro
	'Maker's Mark' (1)	CQua
	'Mallee' (11a) ♀^{H6}	CQua
	'Malpas' (3)	CQua
	'Manaccan' (1)	CQua
	'Mangaweka' (6)	CQua
	'Manly' (4) ♀^{H6}	CQua ERCP NRog SDeJ
	'Manon Lescaut' (2)	NRog
	'March Sunshine' (6)	CQua
	'Margaret Herbert' (7)	CQua
	'Marguerite Patten' (8)	CQua
	'Marie Curie Diamond' (7) ♀^{H6}	CQua
	'Marieke' (1)	SDeJ
	'Marilyn Anne' (2)	CQua
	'Marjorie Hine' (2)	CQua
	'Marjorie Treveal' (4)	CQua
	'Market Merry' (3)	GCro
	'Marlborough' (2)	CQua
	'Marshfire' (2)	CQua
	'Martha Washington' (8)	CQua
	'Martinette' (8)	CAvo CQua GKev NRog SDeJ
	'Mary Bohannon' (2)	NRog SDeJ
	'Mary Copeland' (4)	CQua
	'Mary Jose' (2)	CQua
	'Mary Kate' (2)	CQua
	'Mary Moore' (2)	CQua
	'Mary Poppins' (10) **new**	WShi
	'Mary Rosina' (4)	CQua
	'Mary Veronica' (3)	CQua
	'Matador' (8)	CQua
	'Mawla' (1)	CQua
	'Max' (11a)	CQua

'Maximus Superbus' (1)	CQua
'Maya Dynasty' (2)	CQua
'Mayor's Choice' (11a)	CQua
'Maywood' (11a)	CQua
'Mazzard' (4)	CQua
× ***medioluteus*** (13)	CBro CQua GCro
'Medway Gold' (7)	CQua
'Mega' (9)	CQua
'Meldrum' (1)	CQua
'Memento' (1)	CQua
'Mên-an-Tol' (2)	CQua
'Menehay' (11a) ♀H6	CQua
'Merlin' (3) ♀H6	CQua SDeJ SDir
'Merrymeet' (4)	CQua
'Mersing' (3)	CQua
'Merthan' (9)	CQua
'Midas Touch' (1)	CQua
'Midget'	see *N. nanus* 'Midget'
MIDTOWN AEROLITE (2)	GCro
MIDTOWN ALFIE (1)	GCro
MIDTOWN AMBER (2)	GCro
MIDTOWN BRIGADIER (2)	GCro
MIDTOWN LAURIE (1)	GCro
MIDTOWN NOBLE (1)	GCro
MIDTOWN SPARKLER (2) **new**	GCro
'Mike Pollock' (8)	CQua
'Milan' (9)	CQua
'Millennium Gold' (1)	CQua
'Millennium Sunrise' (2)	CQua
'Millennium Sunset' (2)	CQua
'Milly's Magic' (2)	CQua
Minicycla Group (6)	NDry
minimus misapplied	see *N. asturiensis*
'Minionette' (6) **new**	NDry
'Minnow' (8) ♀H6	CArg CAvo CBro CQua CRos EHyd ELan EPfP ERCP EShb GKev LCro LOPS LRHS NBir NRHS NRog SDeJ
'Minnowlet' (11a)	CQua
minor (13) ♀H5	CQua ECha MCor NRog WFar WShi
- 'Douglasbank' (1)	ITim
- 'Little Gem' (1) ♀H6	CBro CQua CTri GKev NRog SDeJ SDir
- var. ***pumilus*** 'Plenus'	see *N.* 'Rip van Winkle'
- Ulster form (13)	IBlr
'Mint Julep' (3) ♀H6	GKev SDeJ
'Mirar' (2)	CQua
'Mirror Lake' (2)	CQua
'Misquote' (1)	CQua
'Miss Diddles' (7)	CQua
'Miss Mabel' (6)	CQua
'Miss Muffit' (1)	CQua
'Mission Bells' (5) ♀H6	CQua
'Mission Impossible' (11a)	CQua
'Mist of Avalon' (4)	CQua
'Mistress Mine' (2)	CQua
'Misty Glen' (2) ♀H6	CQua GKev SDeJ SPhx
'Mite' (6) ♀H6	CAvo CBro CQua EPot GKev NDry NHpl NRog WShi
'Mitimoto' (10)	NDry
'Mitzy' (6)	NDry
'Modern Art' (2)	CQua NRog SDeJ
'Modulation' (2)	SDeJ
'Monal' (2)	GKev
'Mondragon' (11a)	GKev NRog
'Mongleath' (2)	CQua
'Monks Wood' (1)	CQua
'Monksilver' (3)	CQua
'Montego' (3)	CQua
'Moon Ranger' (3)	CQua
'Moon Shadow' (3)	CQua
'Moonlight Sensation' (5)	CAvo GKev LHWs
'Morab' (1)	CQua
'Moralee' (4)	CQua
'More and More' (7)	CAvo EPot GKev LHWs LRHS NHpl SDir
'Mortie' (6)	NDry
moschatus (13) ♀H6	CAvo CBro CQua EPot GKev NRog WShi
'Mother Duck' (6)	GKev
'Motmot' (8)	CQua
'Mount Fuji' (2)	CQua
'Mount Hood' (1) ♀H6	CArg GKev NBir NRog SDeJ SDir
'Mountain Poet' (9)	CQua
'Mousehole' (3)	CQua
'Mowser' (7)	CQua
'Mrs Ernst H. Krelage' (1) **new**	GCro
'Mrs Iwasa Masako' (2) ♀H6 **new**	GKev
'Mrs Langtry' (2)	CQua GCro GKev WShi
'Mrs R.O. Backhouse' (2)	CQua WShi
'Mullion' (3)	CQua
'Mulroy Bay' (1)	CQua
'Murlough' (9)	CQua
'My Story' (4) ♀H6	GKev LHWs SDeJ SDir WPhe
'My Sunshine' (2)	CQua
'My Sweetheart' (3)	CQua
'Mystic' ambig. (3)	CQua
'Namraj' (2)	CQua
'Nancegollan' (7)	CQua
'Nangiles' (4)	CQua
'Nanpee' (7)	CQua
'Nansidwell' (2)	CQua
'Nanstallon' (1)	CQua
§ ***nanus*** (13)	CQua
§ - 'Midget' (1)	CQua EPot NHpl WShi
'Neahkahnie' (1)	CQua
'Nelly' ambig.	CQua
× ***neocarpetanus*** var. ***romanensis*** (13)	NDry
'Nessa' (7)	CQua
nevadensis (13)	NDry
'New Hope' (3)	CQua
'New Life' (3)	CQua
'New Penny' (3)	CQua
'New World' (2)	CQua
'New-Baby' (7)	CQua GKev LRHS MMrt NRog SDeJ SDir
'Newcomer' (3)	CQua
'Nickelodeon' (8)	CQua
'Night Life' (2)	CQua
'Night Music' (4)	CQua
'Nightcap' (1)	CQua
'Nightflight' (1)	CQua
'Niphetos' (2)	GCro
'Nirvana' (7)	CQua
'Niveth' (5)	CAvo CQua GCro WShi
'No Worries' (3)	CQua
§ ***nobilis*** (13)	EPot GCro GKev NDry
- var. ***leonensis*** (13)	NRog
- var. ***primigenius*** (13)	GKev
'Nonchalant' (3)	CQua
'Norma Jean' (2)	CQua
'North Rim' (2)	CQua
'Notre Dame' (2) ♀H6	CQua
Nylon Group (10)	EPot EPri GKev
'Nynja' (2)	CQua
'Oadby' (1)	CQua
'Obdam' (4)	GBin NRog SDeJ
'Obsession' (2)	CQua
obsoletus (13)	GKev WCot

obvallaris (13) ♀H6	CAvo CBro CQua EPot ERCP GCro GKev LCro LHWs SDeJ WBrk WShi
'Odd Job' (12)	CQua
× ***odorus*** (13)	CQua NRog WShi
- 'Plenus' (4)	CQua ERCP WPhe WShi
old pheasant's eye	see *N. poeticus* var. *recurvus*
'Oliver Carne' (4)	CQua
'Ombersley' (1)	CQua
'Omri' (8)	GKev
'Orange Comet' (6)	CQua
'Orange Phoenix' (4)	CQua WShi
'Orange Progress' (2)	NRog SDeJ
'Orange Queen' (3)	GKev
'Orange Queen' (7) **new**	NRog
'Orange Supreme' (2)	CQua
'Orangery' (11a)	GKev LHWs NRog SDeJ
'Oregon Cedar' (2)	CQua
'Orkney' (2)	CQua
'Ornatus' (9)	CQua GCro
'Oryx' (7) ♀H6	CQua
'Otaki Lights' (1)	CQua
'Ouma' (1)	CQua
'Oundle' (2)	CQua
'Oxford Gold' (10) ♀H6	CAvo CQua GKev LHWs LRHS MNrw
'Ozan' (2)	CQua
pachybolbus (13)	CQua NRog
'Pacific Coast' (8) ♀H6	CQua LCro LOPS
'Pacific Mist' (11a)	CQua
'Pacific Rim' (2)	CQua
'Pacific Waves' (3)	CQua
'Paean' (1)	CQua
'Painted Desert' (3)	CQua
pallidiflorus (13)	ECha
- var. ***pallidiflorus*** (13)	GKev
'Palmares' (11a)	CQua SDeJ
'Pamela Hubble' (2)	CQua
'Pamela Joan' (2)	CQua
'Pampaluna' (11a)	CQua
'Panache' (1)	CQua
panizzianus (13)	CQua
'Paper White'	see *N. papyraceus*
'Paper White Grandiflorus' (8)	CQua EPfP NRHS SDeJ SPer
'Papillon Blanc' (11b)	GKev NRog
'Papua' (4)	CQua
§ ***papyraceus*** (13)	CQua GKev MHtn NRog
- subsp. ***polyanthos*** (13)	GKev
- 'Ziva' (8)	CAvo ELan GKev LCro LOPS NRog SDeJ SPhx
'Parcpat' (7)	CQua
'Parisienne' (11a)	GKev NRog SDeJ
'Park Springs' (3)	CQua
'Parkdene' (2)	CQua
'Passionale' (2) ♀H6	CQua GKev NBir NRog
'Pastiche' (2)	CQua
'Pat Redman' (3)	CQua
'Patois' (9)	CBro CQua
'Paujen Gold' (7)	CQua
'Pawating' (4)	CQua
'Pay Day' (1)	CQua
'Peach Prince' (4)	CQua
'Pearl Wedding' (3)	CQua
'Pearlshell' (11a)	CQua
'Peeping Jenny' (6)	ERCP SDeJ
'Peeping Tom' (6) ♀H6	CBro CQua ERCP GKev NRog SDeJ SRms
'Peggy Irene' (3)	CQua
'Pemboa' (1)	CQua
'Pencrebar' (4)	CQua EPot GKev NHol NRog SDeJ WShi

'Pend Oreille' (3)	CQua
'Penjerrick' (9)	CQua
'Penkivel' (2) ♀H6	CQua
'Pennine Way' (1)	CQua
'Penny Perowne' (7)	CQua
'Pennyfield' (2)	CQua
'Penpol' (7)	CQua
'Penril' (6)	CQua
'Penselwood' (2)	CQua
'Pensioner' (2) **new**	LHWs
'Penstraze' (7)	CQua
'Pentewan' (2)	GCro
'Pentire' (11a)	CQua
'Penvale' (7)	CQua
'Percuil' (6)	CQua
'Perdredda' (3)	CQua
'Perfect Lady' (2) **new**	GKev
'Perfect Peace' (2)	CQua
'Peridot' (2)	GKev
'Peripheral Pink' (2)	CQua
'Perpetuation' (7)	CQua
'Personable' (2)	CQua
'Peter Chown' (11a)	CQua
'Petit Four' (4)	NRog SDeJ
'Petrel' (5)	CQua ERCP GKev NRog SDeJ WShi
'Phantom' (11a)	CQua
'Philomath' (7)	CQua
'Phil's Gift' (1)	CQua
'Phoenician' (2)	CQua
'Pickwick' (2)	CQua
'Picoblanco' (2)	CBro CQua
'Pimpernel' (2) ♀H6	GKev WPhe
'Pinafore' (2)	WFar
'Pink Angel' (7)	CQua
'Pink Champagne' (4)	CQua
'Pink Charm' (2)	CQua GKev LHWs LRHS NBir NRog SDeJ WPhe
'Pink Chimes' (5)	CQua
'Pink China' (2)	CQua
'Pink Formal' (11a)	CQua
'Pink Gilt' (2)	CQua
'Pink Glacier' (11a)	CQua
'Pink Ice' (2)	CQua
'Pink Pageant' (4)	CQua
'Pink Paradise' (4)	CQua NRog
'Pink Parasol' (1)	SDeJ
'Pink Pride' (2)	CArg
'Pink Silk' (1)	CQua GKev SDeJ
'Pink Smiles' (2)	CQua
'Pink Surprise' (2)	CQua
'Pink Tango' (11a)	CQua
'Pinza' (2) ♀H6	CQua SDeJ
'Pipe Major' (2)	CQua NRog
'Pipers Barn' (7)	CQua
'Piper's Gold' (1)	CQua
'Pipestone' (2)	CQua
'Pipit' (7)	CAvo CBro CQua EPot ERCP EShb GBin GKev NBir NRog SDeJ WPhe WShi
'Pismo Beach' (2)	CQua
'Pistachio' (1) ♀H6	GKev LHWs NRog
'Pitchroy' (2)	CQua
'Pitt's Diamond' (3)	CQua
'Pixie's Sister' (7) ♀H6	CQua
'Pledge' (1)	CQua LRHS
'Plymouth Hoe' (1)	CQua
§ ***poeticus*** var. ***hellenicus*** (13)	CBro CQua
- old pheasant's eye	see *N. poeticus* var. *recurvus*
- var. ***physaloides*** (13)	CQua GKev NRog

	- 'Plenus' misapplied	see *N. poeticus* 'Spalding Double White', *N.* 'Tamar Double White'
§	- 'Plenus' ambig. (4)	CBro CQua ERCP GKev LHWs SDeJ WShi
§	- var. ***recurvus*** (13) 𝕐H6	CAvo CBro CQua ELan ERCP EShb GKev LCro LHWs LOPS MBros NBir NPoe NRog SDeJ SDir SPer SPhx WPhe WShi
§	- 'Spalding Double White' (4)	CQua GCro
	- white-flowered (13)	SDeJ
	'Poet's Way' (9)	CQua
	'Pol Crocan' (2)	CQua
	'Pol Voulin' (2)	CQua
	'Polar Ice' (3)	CQua GKev NRog SDeJ
	'Polgooth' (2)	CQua
	'Polindra' (2)	GCro
	'Polly's Pearl' (8)	CQua
	'Polmenor' (2)	CQua
	'Polnesk' (7)	GCro
	'Polonaise' (2)	CQua
	'Polruan' (7)	CQua
	'Polyphant' (2)	CQua
	'Pomona' (3)	GCro
	'Pooka' (3)	CQua
	POOLEWE PINTUCK (2)	GCro
	'Poppy's Choice' (4)	CQua
	'Port Noo' (3)	CQua
	'Porthchapel' (7)	CQua
	'Portloe Bay' (3)	CQua
	'Portrush' (3)	CQua
	'Posai' (2)	CQua
	'Postulate' (2)	CQua
	'Praecox' (9)	CBro
	'Prairie Fire' (3)	CQua
	'Preamble' (1)	CQua
I	'Precocious' (2) 𝕐H6	CQua GKev SDeJ
	'Presidential Pink' (2)	CQua
	'Pretty in Yellow' (11a)	SDeJ
	'Pride of Cornwall' (8)	CQua
	'Primrose Beauty' (4)	CQua
	'Princeps' (1)	CQua GCro
	'Printal' (11a)	NRog SDeJ
	'Prism' (2)	CQua
	'Probus' (1)	CQua
	'Professor Einstein' (2)	CQua GKev NRog SDeJ
	'Prologue' (1)	CQua
	'Prom Dance' (11a) 𝕐H6	CQua
	'Proska' (2)	CQua
	pseudonarcissus (13)	CArg CHab CQua LCro LOPS MMuc NPoe WBrk WShi
	- subsp. ***eugeniae***	see *N. eugeniae*
	- subsp. ***nobilis***	see *N. nobilis*
	- var. ***porrigens*** (13)	GCro
	- subsp. ***pseudonarcissus*** (13) 𝕐H6	MBow
	- - double-flowered (4)	CQua
§	- - var. ***humilis*** (13)	NRog
	'Ptolemy' (1)	GCro
	'Pueblo' (7)	CQua GKev LRHS NRog SDeJ
	'Pukenui' (4)	CQua
	pumilus ambig. (13)	CQua SDeJ
	'Punchline' (7) 𝕐H6	CQua GKev
	'Punk' (1)	NDry
	'Puppet' (5)	CQua SDeJ
	'Purbeck' (3) 𝕐H6	CQua
	'Quail' (7) 𝕐H6	CQua GKev NRog SDeJ
	'Quasar' (2) 𝕐H6	CQua
	Queen Anne's double daffodil	see *N.* 'Eystettensis'
	'Queen Bess' (2)	CQua
	'Queen of Spain' (5)	CQua
	'Queen of the North' (3)	CQua GCro LRHS WShi

	'Quetta' (3)	GCro
	'Quick Step' (7)	CQua
	'Radiant Gem' (8)	CQua
	radiiflorus (13)	EPot NRog
	- var. ***poetarum*** (13)	CQua GCro
	- var. ***radiiflorus*** (13)	GCro
	'Radjel' (4)	CQua
	'Raffles' (4)	CQua
	'Rager' (4)	CQua
	'Rainbow' (2) 𝕐H6	CQua NRog SPer
	'Rainbow of Colors' (11a)	LCro LOPS
	'Raj' (2)	CQua
	'Rame Head' (1)	CQua
	'Rameses' (2)	CQua
	'Raoul Wallenberg' (2)	SDeJ
	'Rapture' (6) 𝕐H6	CQua ERCP GKev NRog SPhx
	'Rashee' (1)	CQua
	'Raspberry Ring' (2)	CQua WPhe
	'Rathowen Gold' (1)	CQua
	'Ravenhill' (3)	CQua
	'Rebekah' (4)	CQua
	'Red Beacon' (3)	GCro
	'Red Coat' (2)	CQua
	'Red Devon' (2)	CArg LCro LOPS LRHS NRog SDeJ
	'Red Ember' (3)	CQua
	'Red Era' (3)	CQua
	'Red Mantle' (2)	CQua
	'Red Reed' (1)	CQua
	'Refrain' (2)	CQua
	'Regal Bliss' (2)	CQua
	'Regeneration' (7)	LHWs
	'Reggae' (6) 𝕐H6	LRHS NRog SDeJ
	'Rembrandt' (1)	CQua
	'Rendezvous Caye' (2)	CQua
	'Renovator' (1)	CQua
	'Replete' (4)	CQua GKev NRog SDeJ
	requienii	see *N. assoanus*
	'Resolute' (2)	GCro
	'Reverse Image' (11a)	CQua
	rifanus	see *N. romieuxii* subsp. *romieuxii* var. *rifanus*
	'Rijnveld's Early Sensation' (1) 𝕐H6	CAvo CBro CQua ECha ERCP GKev LCro LOPS NRog SDeJ WShi
	'Rikki' (7)	CBro
	'Rimmon' (3)	CQua
	'Rimski' (2)	CQua
	'Ring Fence' (3)	CQua
	'Ringing Bells' (5)	CQua
	'Ringleader' (2)	CQua
§	'Rip van Winkle' (4)	CBro CQua CRos EHyd EPfP EPot ERCP GKev LRHS NHol NHpl NRHS NRog SDeJ SPer WBrk WShi
	'Rippling Waters' (5)	CQua GKev
	'Rival' (6)	CQua
	'River Queen' (2)	CQua
	'Rockall' (3)	CQua
	'Roger' (6)	CQua
	'Rogue' (2)	CBro
§	'Romanus' (4)	CQua
	'Romeo' (8)	CQua
	romieuxii (13) 𝕐H4	EHyd EPri GArf NDry NRHS WCot
	- SF 370	WCot WMal
	- subsp. ***albidus*** (13)	EPot GKev
	- - SF 110	NDry WCot
§	- - var. ***zaianicus*** (13)	GKev NRog
	- - - SB&L 82 from Morocco	WCot
	- - - M168	NDry
§	- 'Joy Bishop' (10)	NDry WCot
§	- 'Julia Jane' (10)	CAvo CBor CQua ERCP GKev LCro LHWs LOPS LRHS NRog SDir WCot
	- 'Mrs McGee' (10)	NDry

* - subsp. ***pallidus*** (13) SB&L 237 WCot
- subsp. ***romieuxii*** (13) NRog
§ - - var. ***rifanus*** (13) NRog
- - B 8929 WCot
'Rongoiti Gem' (4) CQua
'Rosannor Gold' (11a) CQua
'Rose Lake' (2) CQua
'Rose of May' (4) CQua WShi
'Rose Royale' (2) CQua
'Rose Villa' (2) CQua
'Rosemary Pearson' (2) CQua
'Rosemerryn' (2) CQua
'Rosemoor Gold' (7) 🏆H6 CQua
'Rosemullion' (4) CQua
'Rosevine' (3) CQua
'Roulette' (2) GKev SDeJ
'Round Oak' (1) CQua
'Roundita' (1) **new** LRHS
'Royal Connection' (8) CQua
'Royal Marine' (2) CQua
'Royal Princess' (3) CQua
'Royal Regiment' (2) CQua
'Rubilina' (2) NDry
'Ruby Red' (2) CQua
'Rubythroat' (2) CQua
'Ruddynosey' (1) CQua
'Rugulosus' (7) CQua
rupicola (13) CBro CQua NDry NRog NSla
§ - subsp. ***marvieri*** (13) NDry
- subsp. ***rupicola*** (13) 🏆H4 **new** GKev
§ - subsp. ***watieri*** (13) CBro CQua ERCP NDry SDir
'Rushlake Green' (2) CQua
'Rustom Pasha' (2) CQua GCro
'Saberwing' (5) CQua
'Sabine Hay' (3) CQua EPot GKev
'Sabrosa' (7) 🏆H6 CBro CQua GKev LCro LHWs LOPS WShi
'Sagana' (9) CQua
'Sailboat' (7) 🏆H6 CAvo CBro CQua GKev LCro LOPS LRHS NRog SDeJ SPhx WBrk
'Saint Agnes' (8) CQua
'Saint Budock' (1) CQua
'Saint Day' (5) CQua
'Saint Keverne' (2) 🏆H6 CQua SDeJ
'Saint Keyne' (8) CQua
'Saint Olaf' (3) GCro
'Saint Patrick's Day' (2) CQua GBin SDeJ
'Saint Peter' (4) CQua
'Saint Petroc' (9) CQua
'Saint Piran' (7) CQua
'Salakee' (2) CQua
'Salcey Forest' (1) CQua
'Salome' (2) 🏆H6 CQua LCro LOPS MBros NBir NPer NRog SDeJ
'Salute' (2) CQua
'Sandra's Diamond' (3) CQua
'Sandycove' (2) CQua
'Sarchedon' (9) GCro
'Sargeant's Caye' (1) CQua
'Satchmo' (1) CQua
'Saturn' (3) CQua
'Saxby' (11a) CQua
'Saxonbury' (2) CQua
'Scarlet Chord' (2) CQua
'Scarlet Elegance' (2) CQua
'Scarlet Gem' (8) SDeJ
'Scilly White' (8) CQua WShi
'Scorrier' (2) CQua
'Scrum Half' (1) NDry
'Scrumpy' (2) CQua
'Sea Dream' (3) CQua
'Sea Green' (9) CQua
'Sea Princess' (3) SDeJ
'Seagrave' (4) CQua
'Seagull' (3) CQua
'Sealing Wax' (2) CQua
'Segovia' (3) 🏆H6 CAvo CBro CQua EHyd ELan ERCP GKev NRHS NRog SDeJ SPhx
'Sempre Avanti' (2) CArg NRog SDeJ
'Sentinel' (2) GKev SDeJ
'Seraglio' (3) CQua
'Serena Lodge' (4) 🏆H6 CQua
serotinus (13) NRog
'Sharnden' (1) CQua
'Sharon's Champagne' (3) CQua
'Shauna Rose' (8) CQua
'Shepherd's Hey' (7) CQua SDeJ
'Sherborne' (4) 🏆H6 CQua
'Sherpa' (1) CQua
'Shining Light' (2) CQua
'Shockwave' (2) CQua
'Shrike' (11a) 🏆H6 CQua GKev
'Shurdington' (3) CQua
'Shykowski' (4) CQua
'Sidley' (3) CQua
'Sidora' (1) NDry
'Silk Cut' (2) CQua
'Silver Chimes' (8) CAvo CBro CQua EPfP GKev LCro LOPS NBir NRog SDeJ
'Silver Kiwi' (2) CQua
'Silver Smiles' (7) LHWs NRog SPhx
'Silver Surf' (2) CQua
'Silversmith' (2) CQua
'Silverwood' (3) CQua
'Sinopel' (3) GKev LHWs NRog SDeJ
'Sir Samuel' (2) CQua
'Sir Watkin' (2) CQua GCro
'Sir Winston Churchill' (4) 🏆H6 CAvo CQua LCro LOPS LRHS NRog SDeJ SPer
'Sirius' (2) GCro
'Sissy' (6) CQua
'Skerry' (2) CQua
'Skilliwidden' (2) 🏆H6 CQua
'Skookum' (3) CQua
'Sleek' (6) NDry
'Small Fry' (1) CQua
'Small Talk' (1) 🏆H6 CQua
'Smiling Sun' (2) **new** GKev
'Smiling Twin' (11a) CQua SDeJ
'Smokey Bear' (4) CQua
'Smooth Sails' (3) CQua
'Snipe' (6) CQua WShi
'Snook' (6) NDry
'Snow Baby' (1) CBro CQua CRos EPfP ERCP GKev ITim LHWs LRHS
'Snowball' (4) GKev NRog
'Snowcrest' (3) CQua
'So Sweet' (3) CQua
'Solar Tan' (3) CQua
'Soleil d'Or' (8) CQua
'Solferique' (2) CQua
'Solveig's Song' (12) EPot
'Sonata' (9) CQua
'Songket' (2) CQua
'Sophie Girl' (2) GKev
'Soprano' (2) CQua
'Sorbet' (11b) CQua NRog SDeJ
'Sorcerer' (3) CQua
'Southease' (2) CQua
'Southern Gem' (2) CQua GCro

	'Spaniards Inn' (4)	CQua
	'Sparkling Tarts' (8)	CQua
	'Special Envoy' (2)	CQua
	'Speedie' (6)	NDry
	'Spellbinder' (1)	CQua SDeJ
	'Spirit of Rame' (3)	CQua
	'Split Vote' (11a)	CQua
	'Spoirot' (10) ♀H6	CQua ERCP GBin GKev LRHS MNrw MPie NHpl SDeJ
	'Sportsman' (2)	CQua
	'Spring Dawn' (2)	LCro LOPS SPer WBrk
	'Spring Morn' (2)	CQua
	'Spun Honey' (4)	CQua
	'Squinney' (12)	NDry
	'Stainless' (2)	NRog SDir SPhx WPhe
	'Standard Value' (1)	NRog
	'Stann Creek' (1)	CQua
	'Stanway' (3)	CQua
	'Star Glow' (2)	CQua
	'Starfire' (7)	CQua
	'Starlight Sensation' (5)	ERCP LHWs SPhx
	'Starlit' (1)	NDry
	'State Express' (2)	CQua
	'Stella' (2)	GCro
	'Step Child' (6)	CQua
	'Step Forward' (7)	CQua
	'Steren' (7)	CQua
	'Stilton' (9)	CQua
	'Stint' (5) ♀H6	CQua GKev SDeJ SDir SPhx
	'Stoke Charity' (2)	CQua
	'Stoke Doyle' (2)	CQua
	'Stratosphere' (7) ♀H6	CQua SDeJ
	'Strines' (2) ♀H6	CQua
	'Suave' (3)	GKev SDeJ
	'Suda' (2)	GCro
	'Sugar and Spice' (3)	CQua
	'Sugar Cups' (8)	CQua
	'Sugar Loaf' (4)	CQua
	'Sugar Rose' (6)	CQua
	'Suisgill' (4)	CQua
§	'Sulphur Phoenix' (4)	CQua WShi
	SULPHUR STAR (2)	GCro
	'Sumo Jewel' (6)	CQua
	'Sun Bronze' (2)	CQua
	'Sun Disc' (7) ♀H6	CBro CQua CTri GKev LCro LOPS MBros NRog SDeJ WPhe WShi
	'Sundial' (7)	CBro NRog
	'Sunlight Sensation' (5)	LHWs
	'Sunny Girlfriend' (11a)	SDeJ WPhe
	'Sunnyside Up' (11a) ♀H6	SDeJ
	'Sunrise' (3)	CQua
	'Sunstroke' (2)	CQua
	'Suntory' (3)	CQua
	'Surfside' (6) ♀H6	CQua GKev NRog SDeJ SPhx
	'Suzy' (7)	CQua SDeJ
	'Swallow' (6)	CQua SDeJ
	'Swan of Avon' (1)	CQua
	'Swedish Sea' (2)	CQua
	'Sweet Blanche' (7)	CQua
	'Sweet Georgia' (2)	CQua
	'Sweet Lorraine' (2)	CQua
	'Sweet Memory' (2)	CQua
	'Sweet Pepper' (7)	CQua
	'Sweet Pomponette' (4)	GKev SDeJ
	'Sweet Smiles' (7)	GKev LHWs
	'Sweet Sue' (3)	CQua
	'Sweetness' (7) ♀H6	CAvo CQua EShb GCro LCro LOPS NRog SDeJ WShi
	'Swift Arrow' (6) ♀H6	CQua
	'Swing Wing' (6)	CQua
	'Swoop' (6)	SDeJ

	'Sydling' (5)	CQua
	'Taffeta' (10)	EPri
	'Tahiti' (4) ♀H6	CQua ELan LCro LOPS NRog SDeJ
	× ***taitii*** (13)	GKev WShi
	'Talgarth' (2)	CQua
§	'Tamar Double White' (4)	CBro CQua
	'Tamar Fire' (4) ♀H6	CQua
	'Tamar Lad' (2)	CQua
	'Tamar Lass' (3)	CQua
	'Tamar Snow' (2)	CQua
	'Tamara' (2)	CArg
	'Tangent' (2)	CQua
	'Tao' (3)	CQua
	'Tasgem' (4)	CQua
	'Taslass' (4)	CQua
	tazetta (13)	CQua GKev
§	- subsp. ***lacticolor*** (13)	CQua ERCP NRog SDeJ SDir
	- subsp. ***ochroleucus*** (13)	CQua
*	- var. ***odoratus*** (13)	CQua LHWs WShi
	- subsp. ***tazetta*** (13)	CQua
	'Teal' (1)	CQua
	'Tehidy' (3)	CQua
§	'Telamonius Plenus' (4)	CQua GBin GCro GKev NRog SEND WShi
	× ***tenuior*** (13)	GKev WShi
	'Terminator' (2)	CQua
	'Terracotta' (2)	CQua
	'Tête Bouclé' PBR (4)	CBro CQua SDir WPhe
	'Tête Deluxe' (4)	LRHS
	'Tête Rosette'	LCro
	'Tête-à-tête' (12) ♀H6	CArg CAvo CBro CQua CRos CWCL EGrI EHyd EPfP EPot ERCP GAbr GKev GQue LCro LOPS LRHS MBow MBros NHpl NRHS NRog SDeJ SDir SPer WBrk WPhe WShi
	'Tethys' (10)	NDry
	'Texas' (4)	GCro
I	'Thalia' (5)	CArg CAvo CBro CQua ELan EPfP ERCP GKev LCro LOPS MBriF NBir NHol NRog SDeJ SPer SPhx WShi
	'The Alliance' (6) ♀H6	CQua
	'The Caley' (2)	CQua
	'The Grange' (1)	CQua
	'The Little Gentleman' (6)	CQua
	'Themisto' (10)	NDry
	'Thomas Kinkade' (2)	CQua
	'Three Oaks' (1)	CQua
	'Thriplow Gold' (1)	CQua
	'Tickled Pinkeen' (2)	WPhe
	'Tidebrook' (3)	CQua
	'Tideford' (2)	CQua
	'Tiercel' (1)	CQua
	'Tiffany Jade' (3)	CQua
	'Timolin' (3)	CQua
	'Tinhay' (7)	CQua
	'Tino Pai' (9)	CQua
	'Tintagel Lady' (4)	CQua
	'Tiny Bubbles' (12)	CBro CQua ERCP GKev LHWs LRHS
	'Tiritomba' (11a)	CQua
	'Tittle-tattle' (7)	CQua
	'Tiwi' (2)	CQua
	'Toby' (2)	SDeJ
	'Toby the First' (6)	CQua
	'Tommy White' (2)	NRog
	'Top Hit' (11a)	CQua
	'Topolino' (1) ♀H6	CBro CQua CRos EHyd EPfP EPot ERCP GKev LCro LOPS LRHS NRHS NRog

'Topsy Turvy' (4)	CQua
'Torianne' (2) ♀H6	CQua
'Torridon' (2)	CQua
'Toto' (12) ♀H6	CAvo CBro CQua ERCP GKev LCro LHWs LOPS LRHS MBriF SDeJ SDir SPhx
'Transmitter' (4)	CQua
'Trebah' (2) ♀H6	CQua
'Treble Two' (7)	CQua
'Trecara' (3)	CQua
'Tregarrick' (2)	CQua
'Trelawney Gold' (2)	CQua
'Trelissick' (7)	CQua
'Tremough Dale' (11a)	CQua
'Trena' (6) ♀H6	CQua ERCP NRog SDeJ
'Trenwith' (1)	CQua
'Trepolo' (11b)	SDeJ
'Tresamble' (5)	CBro CQua GCro GKev LCro LOPS NBir NRog SDeJ
'Tresserve' (1)	GCro
'Treviddo' (2)	CQua
'Trevithian' (7)	CQua GCro GKev NRog SDeJ
triandrus var. ***albus***	see *N. triandrus* subsp. *triandrus* var. *triandrus*
- subsp. ***triandrus*** (13)	NDry
§ - - var. ***triandrus*** (13)	CBor GBin NRog
'Tricollet' (11a)	NRog SDeJ
'Trigonometry' (11a) ♀H6	CQua
'Tripartite' (11a) ♀H6	CQua GKev NRog SDeJ
'Triple Crown' (3) ♀H6	CQua
'Tristar' (11a)	CQua
'Tristram' (2)	CQua
'Tropic Isle' (4)	CQua
'Trousseau' (1)	CQua
'Tru' (3)	CQua
'Truculent' (3)	CQua
'Trumpet Voluntary' (1)	NDry
'Trumpet Warrior' (1) ♀H6	CQua
'Tryst' (2)	CQua
'Tudor Minstrel' (2)	CQua
'Tuesday's Child' (5) ♀H6	CQua
'Tunis' (2)	GCro
'Turncoat' (6)	CQua
'Twicer' (2)	CQua
'Twin Cam' (12)	NDry
'Twink' (4)	CQua GCro
'Twinkling Yellow' (7) ♀H6	CBro CQua GKev LHWs
'Twirl' (1) **new**	NDry
'Tyrone Gold' (1) ♀H6	CQua
'Ulster Bank' (3)	CQua
'Ultimus' (2)	CQua
'Uncle Duncan' (1)	CQua
'Unique' (4) ♀H6	GKev NRog SDeJ
'Unsurpassable' (1)	CQua GCro
'Upalong' (12)	CQua
'Upshot' (3)	CQua
'Utiku' (6)	CQua
'Val d'Incles' (3)	CQua
'Valdrome' (11a)	CQua
'Valinor' (2)	CQua
'Valjean' (6) **new**	NDry
'Van Sion'	see *N.* 'Telamonius Plenus'
'Vanilla Peach' (11a)	GKev LRHS SDeJ WPhe
'Vantage' (2)	CQua
'Vanya Noeletta' (2)	CQua
vardulienisis (13) **new**	GKev
'Vaticaan' (1)	SDeJ
'Velocity' (6)	LRHS
'Verdin' (7)	CQua
'Verger' (3)	EPfP SDeJ
'Vernal Prince' (3) ♀H6	CQua
'Verona' (3) ♀H6	CQua
'Vers Libre' (9)	CQua
'Victoria' (1)	GCro
'Viking' (1) ♀H6	CQua
'Vineland' (6)	CQua
'Violetta' (2)	CQua
'Vitrina' (5)	NDry
'Voltage' (2)	CQua
'Vulcan' (2)	CQua
'W.P. Milner' (1)	CAvo CBro CQua EMor EPfP ERCP GKev LCro LOPS LRHS NRog SDeJ SPer SPhx WBrk WShi
'Walden Pond' (3)	CQua
'Waldorf Astoria' (4)	CQua
'Walton' (7)	CQua
'Waltz' (11a)	LHWs
'War Dance' (3)	CQua
'Warbler' (6) ♀H6	CQua GKev NRog SDeJ
'Watership Down' (2)	CQua
'Watersmeet' (4)	CQua
watieri	see *N. rupicola* subsp. *watieri*
'Wave' (4)	CQua LHWs NRog SDeJ
'Wavertree'	see *N. asturiensis* 'Wavertree'
'Waxwing' (5)	CQua
'Wee Bee' (1)	CQua
'Wee Dote' (1)	NDry
'Welcome' (2)	CQua
'Welsh Rugby Union' (1)	CQua
'Welsh Warrior' (1)	CQua
'Westward' (4)	CQua NRog WPhe
'Wheal Coates' (7) ♀H6	CQua
'Wheal Jane' (2)	CQua
'Wheal Kitty' (7)	CQua
'Whetstone' (1)	CQua
'Whipcord' (7) ♀H6	CQua
'Whippet' (6)	NDry
'White Emperor' (1)	GCro
'White Empress' (1)	CQua
'White Lady' (3)	CAvo CQua GCro GKev WShi
'White Lion' (4) ♀H6	NRog SDeJ SDir
'White Marvel' (4)	CQua GKev NRog SDeJ
'White Medal' (4)	GKev NRog SDeJ
'White Nile' (2)	CQua GCro
'White Petticoat' (10)	ERCP NHpl
'White Plume' (2)	CQua
'White Tea' (2)	CQua
'White Tie' (3)	CQua
'Whitewell' (2)	GCro
'Wicklow Hills' (3)	CQua
'Widgeon' (2)	CQua
'Wild Carnival' (2)	LHWs WPhe
willkommii (13)	CBro CQua EPot EPri GKev NRog
'Wimbledon County Girl' (2) ♀H6	CQua
'Windy City' (2)	CQua
'Winholm Jenni' (3)	CQua
'Winifred van Graven' (3)	CQua
'Winning Shot' (2) **new**	NDry
'Winter Waltz' (6)	CQua GKev LHWs
'Wisley' (6) ♀H6	ERCP GKev LRHS
'Witch Doctor' (3)	CQua
WOODCROFT GOLD (2)	GCro
'Woodland Prince' (3)	CQua
'Woodland Star' (3)	CQua
'Woodley Vale' (2)	CQua
'Woodstar' (5)	CQua EPot
'Woolaroo' (4)	CQua
'Woolsthorpe' (2)	CQua
'World Class' (5)	CQua
'Wychbold' (3)	CQua
'Xit' (3)	CBro CQua EPot

'Xunantunich' (2)	CQua
'Yellow Cheerfulness' (4) ♀H6	CArg CQua ELan GKev LCro LOPS NRHS NRog SDeJ WPhe
'Yellow River' (1) ♀H6	NRog
'Yellow Xit' (3)	CQua
'York Minster' (1)	CQua
'Young American' (1)	CQua
'Young Blood' (2)	CQua
'Your Grace' (2)	CQua
zaianicus	see *N. romieuxii* subsp. *albidus* var. *zaianicus*
'Zeekie' (2)	NDry
'Zekiah' (1)	CQua
'Zion Canyon' (2)	CQua
'Zoë's Pink' (3)	CQua
'Zonk' (11a)	CQua

Nardostachys (*Caprifoliaceae*)

grandiflora	see *N. jatamansi* 'Grandiflora'
§ ***jatamansi*** 'Grandiflora'	GPoy

Nardus (*Poaceae*)

stricta	LPla

Nassauvia (*Asteraceae*)

darwinii	WAbe
digitata	SPlb
gaudichaudii	GArf SPlb
lagascae	WAbe

Nassella (*Poaceae*)

cernua	EPPr
tenuissima	see *Stipa tenuissima*
trichotoma	WHal
- 'Palomino'	EHyd

Nastanthus (*Calyceraceae*)

caespitosus new	SPlb

Nasturtium (*Brassicaceae*)

officinale	CPud CWat MWts SVic WMAq

Natal plum see *Carissa macrocarpa*

nectarine see *Prunus persica* var. *nectarina*

Nectaroscordum (*Alliaceae*)

§ ***siculum***	CArg CAvo CBod CBro CSpe CTri EPfP ERCP EShb EWoo GKev LCro LEdu LHWs LOPS LRHS NBir NChi NSti SCob SDeJ SDir SDix SPer SPoG WBor
§ - subsp. ***bulgaricum***	CKel CRos EBee ECha EGrI EHyd EPot EWhm LRHS MNrw NRHS NRog SPhx WBrk WCot XLum
- subsp. ***bulgaricum*** × ***tripedale***	NRog

Neillia (*Rosaceae*)

affinis	CExl CKel EBee EHyd EPfP EWTr IDee LRHS MGil NBid NLar SLon SPoG SWvt WLov
longiracemosa	see *N. thibetica*
sinensis	NLar
§ ***thibetica***	CBcs CBod CDoC CExl CMCN CMac EGrI EHyd ELan EPfP GBin GKin LEdu LRHS MAsh MBlu MGil MMuc NLar SCob SLon SPer SRms SSta SWvt WAvo WBor WFar WGrn WLov
thyrsiflora	EBee
- PAB 3267	LEdu
- var. ***tunkinensis*** HWJ 505	WCru

Nelumbo (*Nelumbonaceae*)

'Pink 'n' Yellow'	EWat
'Yu Ta Jiugui' new	CBen

Nematanthus (*Gesneriaceae*)

'Apres'	WDib
'Black Magic'	WDib
'Christmas Holly'	WDib
'Freckles'	WDib
§ ***gregarius*** ♀H1b	WDib
§ - 'Golden West' (v)	WDib
- 'Variegatus'	see *N. gregarius* 'Golden West'
'Lemon and Lime'	WDib
radicans	see *N. gregarius*
'Tropicana' ♀H1b	WDib

Nemesia (*Scrophulariaceae*)

§ AMELIE ('Fleurame'PBR)	CRos LBuc SPoG
(Aroma Series) AROMA BANANA SPLIT	CRos MPri
- AROMA PLUMS AND CUSTARD	SCob
- AROMA RHUBARB AND CUSTARD	CRos LSou MBros MPri SCob
BERRIE WHITE ('Fleurow'PBR)	LSou
BERRIES AND CREAM ('Fleurbac'PBR)	CRos ECtt LBuc LSou MBow MCot SPoG
BLUE LAGOON ('Pengoon'PBR) (Maritana Series)	SCoo
'Bordeaux'	CRos SPoG
caerulea 'Joan Wilder' (clonal)	WAvo
CANDY GIRL ('Pencand') (Maritana Series)	SCoo
'Cream Surprise' new	CRos
§ ***denticulata*** ♀H3	EWoo MHer SCoo
- 'Confetti'	see *N. denticulata*
'Easter Bonnet' (French Connection Series)	CRos MPri SCob SPoG
'Evening Dusk' new	CRos
'Fairy Kisses Pink Lemonade' (Fairy Kisses Series) new	LSou
'Fleurie Blue'	LBuc SPoG
FRAMBOISE ('Fleurfram'PBR)	CRos LBuc MPri
HONEY GIRL ('Penhon') (Maritana Series)	SCoo
'Innocence' ♀H3	SCoo
(Karoo Series) KAROO BLUE ('Innkablue'PBR)	SCoo
- KAROO PINK ('Innkapink'PBR)	LRHS
- KAROO SOFT BLUE ('Innkarsofb'PBR)	LRHS
- KAROO WHITE ('Innkarwhi'PBR)	MCot
'Lady Penelope' new	CRos
'Lyric Copper' (Lyric Series)	LSou MCot
MARITANA SKY LAGOON ('Pensky') (Maritana Series)	SCoo
'Mirabelle'	LBuc SPoG
MYRTILLE ('Fleurmyr'PBR)	CRos LBuc MPri SPoG
NESIA SNOW ANGEL (Nesia Series)	LRHS
OPAL INNOCENCE	see *N.* AMELIE

RASPBERRIES AND CREAM ('Fleurrac') LBuc SPoG
'Sugar Almond' CMac
'Sundrops' MBros MPri
(Sunsatia Series) SUNSATIA BANANA ('Intraibana') SPoG
- SUNSATIA BLACKBERRY ('Inuppink'PBR) SCoo
- SUNSATIA CRANBERRY ('Intraired'PBR) SCoo
- SUNSATIA LEMON ('Intraigold'PBR) SCoo
- SUNSATIA PEACH ('Inupcream') CWCL SCoo
(Sunsatia Plus Series) SUNSATIA PLUS CHERRY ON ICE CPla LRHS SPoG
- SUNSATIA PLUS LYCHEE CRos LRHS
- SUNSATIA PLUS POMELO ('Innemsunpo'PBR) CRos LRHS
sylvatica CSpe
'Vanilla Lady' ECtt
'Wisley Vanilla' CRos EHyd LBuc LRHS LSou MBros MPri NRHS SCob SPoG

Nemophila (*Boraginaceae*)

menziesii SPhx
var. ***menziesii*** - 'Penny Black' CSpe SPer

Neodypsis (*Arecaceae*)

decaryi see *Dypsis decaryi*

Neolepisorus (*Polypodiaceae*)

lancifolius CExl

Neolitsea (*Lauraceae*)

glauca see *N. sericea*
polycarpa B&SWJ 11705 WCru
- KWJ 12309 WCru
§ ***sericea*** CBcs CCCN EBee LRHS MPkF NLar WPGP XSte
- B&SWJ 12738 WCru
- CWJ 12800 WCru
- yellow-fruited CWJ 12830 WCru

Neomarica (*Iridaceae*)

caerulea CPla WCot

Neopanax (*Araliaceae*)

§ ***arboreus*** CAbb CDTJ CTrC CTsd EBee LEdu SArc
colensoi CTsd
§ ***laetus*** ♀H3 CTrC CTsd IKel WPGP XSte

Neoregelia ✿ (*Bromeliaceae*)

'Atlantis' NCft
'Fireball' ♀H1b NCft
'Grace' **new** NCft
lilliputiana NCft
'Magali' **new** NCft
'Narciss' NCft
pauciflora NCft
I ***paulinae*** 'Paulinae' NCft
'Pink Sensation' **new** NCft
'Royal Burgundy' **new** NCft
I ***schultesiana*** NCft
I - 'Variegata' (v) NCft

Neoshirakia (*Euphorbiaceae*)

japonica MBlu WPGP

Nepenthes ✿ (*Nepenthaceae*)

sp. SRms
alata × ventricosa ♀H1a SHmp
'Bloody Mary'PBR CDoC LCro LOPS SHmp
bongso SHmp
burbidgeae × robcantleyi SHmp
× ***burkei × hamata*** SHmp
× ***burkei × singalana*** SHmp
(***copelandii × truncata***) × ***spathulata*** SHmp
densiflora SHmp
diatas SHmp
dubia × singalana SHmp
dubia × spathulata SHmp
fusca SHmp
fusca × maxima SHmp
glabrata × spathulata SHmp
× ***hookeriana*** ♀H1a SHmp
jacquelineae × spectabilis SHmp
'Linda'PBR SHmp
'Louisa' SHmp
lowii SHmp
macfarlanei SHmp
maxima × (× ***mixta***) SHmp
maxima × talangensis SHmp
mira × spathulata SHmp
ovata SHmp
ovata × ventricosa SHmp
petiolata × veitchii SHmp
platychila × spathulata SHmp
ramispina SHmp
'Rebecca Soper' ♀H1a SHmp
robcantleyi SHmp
robcantleyi × spathulata SHmp
robcantleyi × talangensis SHmp
sanguinea SHmp
sibuyanensis SHmp
singalana SHmp
spectabilis SHms
talangensis SHmp
talangensis × veitchii SHmp
truncata highland form SHmp
- 'King of Spades' × ***truncata*** 'Queen of Hearts' SHmp
ventricosa SHmp

Nepeta ✿ (*Lamiaceae*)

badachschanica LEdu
'Blue Beauty' see *N. sibirica* 'Souvenir d'André Chaudron'
'Blue Dragon' CBod CCBP CKel CKno CNor CSde ECha ECtt EHyd GBin GPSL GQue GWyn LRHS LSou MACG MAvo MHol MPie MSpe NLar NRHS SGBe SPad SPoG SRms WCot WFar WHoo
* ***buddlejifolium*** NLar
* - 'Gold Splash' NLar
camphorata WSpi
cataria CBee CBod CLau CTsd EBou ENfk GJos GPoy LCro LOPS MHer MNHC NBro NGrd SBls SRms SVic WSpi XAbr
§ - 'Citriodora' CBod CLau ENfk NGrd SRms SVic
'Chettle Blue' CDor ECha MAvo
citriodora Dum. see *N. cataria* 'Citriodora'
clarkei GMaP MRav WSpi
curviflora SPhx SPtp

	'Dropmore'	EBee ECha EHyd GWyn LPla LRHS NLar NRHS WSpi
	'Early Bird'	MAvo
§	× ***faassenii*** ♀H7	Widely available
	- 'Alba'	EBee ECtt EHyd ELan EPfP EWhm LPot LRHS NLar SRms WSpi
	- 'Blauknirps'	EBee NLar
	- 'Blue Wonder'	CRos EBee EBlo EHyd ELan EPfP LRHS LSou NDov NLar NRHS WCAu WFar WSpi
	- 'Crystal Cloud'	CBod CKno CRos ECtt EHyd LRHS LSou MBriF MHol NDov NRHS SHar WCAu
	- 'Gletschereis'	EBee ECha NLar WCAu
	- JUNIOR WALKER ('Novanepjun'PBR)	CBod CRos EBee EBlo EHyd EPfP GMaP LCro LOPS LRHS LSRN MBel MMrt NDov NLar NRHS SCob SCoo SEdd SWvt WCot XSen
	- 'Kit Cat'	CBod CRos EBee EBlo ECtt EHyd EPfP GBin GWyn LRHS LSRN MAsh MBel NRHS SCob SEdd SWvt WAvo WCAu XSen
	- 'Purrsian Blue'PBR	CBod CRos ECtt LRHS NCou NLar SGbt SPad SPoG WCav WTor
	- 'Senior'	XLum
	glechoma 'Variegata'	see *Glechoma hederacea* 'Variegata'
	govaniana	Widely available
	grandiflora	CDor MRav
	- 'Blue Danube'	EBee GBee GBin GWyn SDix XLum
	- 'Blue Elf'	LPla MAvo NDov
	- 'Bramdean' ♀H6	CBod CCBP CDor CMac CMea CRos CSde EBee ECtt EHyd EPfP EWes GBin GWyn LRHS LSou MCot MHol MRav NRHS SPhx SRms WCAu WCot XLum
	- 'Dawn to Dusk'	Widely available
	- 'Pool Bank'	EBee ECtt EWes NLar SMrm XLum
	- 'Summer Magic'PBR	CBod CKno CRos EBee ECha EHyd EPfP LRHS LSou MBel MHol NLar NRHS SCob SEdd SHar SPoG SRkn SWvt WCAu WFar WNPC WTor
	- 'Wild Cat'	WCAu
	- 'Zinser's Giant'	EBee LPla SAko
	hederacea 'Variegata'	see *Glechoma hederacea* 'Variegata'
	'Hill Grounds'	CKno EBee ECha GBin LPla LSun MAvo MHol SPhx SRkn WCot
	italica	EBee LRHS SPhx
	'Joanna Reed'	GBin NLar WSpi
	kubanica	CBod CSpe EBee EHyd GBin LRHS MBel MRav NBir NLar NRHS SAng SDix SPhx SPtp WCot WSHC
	'Lamendi'	NDov
§	'Leeds Castle'	CBod CCBP EBee ECtt EHyd EPfP LRHS MHol NGdn NRHS NSti SCoo SHar SPoG WAvo WHal
	'Limelight'	NLar
	LITTLE TRUDY ('Psfike') **new**	LRHS
	longipes hort.	see *N.* 'Leeds Castle'
	macrantha	see *N. sibirica*
	'Maurice'	LPla
	mussinii misapplied	see *N.* × *faassenii*
	mussinii Spreng.	see *N. racemosa*
	NEPTUNE ('Bokratune')	CBod CKno LCro LOPS WNPC
	nervosa	CDor CSpe ECha ELan EPfP LRHS NBro NLar NSti SHar SPer
	- 'Blue Carpet'	CSpe
	- 'Blue Moon'	CFis EBee EHyd EPfP EWes GBee GJos LRHS LShi MACG MBNS MHol MMrt MPnt NDov NLar NQui NRHS SRms WFar WHil WSpi
	- 'Forncett Select'	MRav
	- 'Pink Cat'	CDor CRos EHyd EPfP GBee GJos LRHS MACG NLar NRHS WFar
	- 'Schneehäschen'	SAko WSpi
§	***nuda***	ECha EWes GQue LPla LShi MAvo MRav SBut SHar SMHy WGoo
	- 'Accent'	IPot
	- 'Alba'	SBut
	- subsp. ***albiflora***	ECha
	- 'Lake Sevan'	LEdu
	- 'Purple Cat'	EBee EPfP IPot
	- 'Romany Dusk'	ECha LEdu LPla MAvo SMHy SWvt
	pannonica	see *N. nuda*
	parnassica	EPPr GKev GLog GQue MBel MCot MHol MMuc SMrm
	'Pink Candy'	SPhx SRms
	'Porzellan'	LPla
	'Poseidon'	MAvo MHol
§	***prattii***	NLar
	'Purple Haze'PBR	ECtt EHyd ELan EPfP EWTr LRHS LSou MHol NRHS
§	***racemosa*** ♀H7	CEme CHby CMac EBou EHyd EPfP EWhm GJos GWyn MCot MNHC
	- RCB AM 3	WCot
	- 'Alba'	CDor SBut XLum
	- 'Amelia'	CBod CCBP CElw CKel EBee ECha EPfP LPla MBriF MHer SSal WAvo WCAu WCav WGoo WTor
	- 'Felix'	ELan LRHS WFar
	- 'Grog'	CBod EBee EWTr GBin GWyn LRHS NLar SBut SEdd SPoG
	- 'Little Titch'	CBod EBee ECha ECtt EHyd EPfP GWyn LRHS LSRN LShi MAsh MTin NGdn NLar SCob SCoo WHoo
	- 'Snowflake'	Widely available
	- 'Superba'	XSen
	- 'Toria'	NDov
	- 'Walker's Low' ♀H7	Widely available
	'Rae Crug'	EWes
	recta	see *Stachys recta*
	reichenbachiana	see *N. racemosa*
§	***sibirica***	CCBP ECha EHyd ELan EPfP LRHS NBid NBro NRHS SRkn WCAu WCot XLum
§	- 'Souvenir d'André Chaudron' ♀H6	CDor CRos CWCL EBee ELan EPfP GMaP GWyn LRHS MBel MCot MHol MRav NLar NRHS SCob SPer SPoG WCAu WSpi
	'Six Hills Giant'	Widely available
	'Six Hills Gold' (v)	CDor EBee LBuc LShi MAsh WCAu WCot WFar WSpi
	stenantha	WCot
	stewartiana	EAJP MRav
	aff. ***stewartiana*** W/O 7173 **new**	GGro
	subsessilis	CBod CKel CRos ECtt EHyd ELan EPfP GJos GLog GMaP LRHS LSou MBel MRav NBid NBir NGdn NLar NRHS NSti SPhx SPoG SRms WCAu WCru
	- 'Blue Dreams'	GQue GWyn LRHS MACG MHol NLar SBut SHar SPhx SRkn WSpi XLum
	- 'Candy Cat'	MCot NLar
	- 'Cool Cat'	EBee EPfP LSRN
	- NIMBUS ('Yanim')	MPnt
	- 'Pink Dreams'	CBod EHyd ELan EPfP GJos GWyn LRHS MHer SHar XLum
	- pink-flowered	ECha SMrm SPhx
	- 'Sweet Dreams'	EHyd EMor EPfP EShb LRHS MRav NLar NRHS XLum
	- 'Washfield'	EBee NLar SAko
	transcaucasica	SDix

– 'Blue Infinity'	GMaP NGrd WFar
tuberosa	CTsd ECha EPPr LShi XSen
'Veluws Blauwtje'	ECha NLar WSpi
'Weinheim Big Blue'	ECha MAvo MHol
'Weinheim Summer Blues'	EBee GBin
* ***yunnanensis***	EBee EPPr NBid SMrm SPhx WPGP

Nephrolepis (*Lomariopsidaceae*)

cordifolia	CDTJ
duffii	EShb
exaltata ♀H1b	LCro LOPS SEND
– 'Bostoniensis' ♀H1b	EShb
– 'Marisa'	EShb
– 'Smithii'	EShb
– 'Verona'	WCot

Nephrophyllidium (*Menyanthaceae*)

crista-galli	GGro

Nerine ✿ (*Amaryllidaceae*)

'Afterglow'	WCot
'Alexandra'	WCot
alta	see *N. undulata* Alta Group
angustifolia	SPtp WAbe
'Aurora'	WCot
'Baghdad'	SChr WCot
'Belladonna'	CWCL WCot
'Bennett-Poë'	WCot
'Berlioz'	SGro WCot
'Blanchefleur'	WCot
bowdenii ♀H5	Widely available
– 'Alba' ambig.	EBee ELan EPot ERCP SCoo SMHy
– 'Alba'	CBro CTsd CWCL EPfP EPri GBin GKev LRHS MNrw NHoy SDeJ SDir SPeP WCot WFar
– 'Albivetta'	ELon EPri GKev MNrw NHoy NRog
– 'Bicolor' **new**	SMad
– 'Blanca Perla' ♀H5	CAvo CBro ELan EPri EShb GKev LRHS NHoy WCot WHil
– 'Castlewellan'	IBlr
– 'Codora'	see *N.* 'Codora'
– 'Edelweiss'	GKev LEdu NHoy WHil
– 'Ella K'	EPfP EPot EPri LCro LOPS NHoy SPer WFar
– 'Emma' **new**	WCot
– 'Eric Smith'	WCot
– 'Gletsjer'	NHoy WCot
– Irish clone	WCot
– 'Isabel' ♀H4	CAvo CBro CMac CTsd CWCL ECha ELan EPot EPri ERCP EShb EWes GKev LSou NHoy NWad SDeJ SPeP WBor WCot WHoo
– 'Kathleen Pollock'	WCot
– 'Linda Vista'	WCot
– 'Lipstick'	LRHS NHoy
– 'Marjorie'	EHyd EMal LRHS NRHS
– 'Mark Fenwick'	CBro WCot
– 'Marney Rogerson'	CBro SMHy WCot
§ – 'Mollie Cowie' (v)	IBlr WCot WCru
– 'Mount Stewart' ♀H5	IBlr WCot
– 'Nikita'	EPri ERCP GKev LRHS MNrw NHoy NWad SDeJ WCot
– 'Ostara'	ELan EPot EPri GKev LCro LOPS MNrw NHoy NWad SPer WCot WFar WHil
– 'Patricia'	EGrI EPot EPri GKev LRHS MNrw NHoy
– 'Pink Frostwork'	EPri
– 'Pink Surprise' ♀H5	EPri WCot WMal
– 'Pink Waveline'	SMHy
§ – 'Quinton Wells' ♀H5	WCot WMal
– 'Quinton Wells' pale yellow-leaved	WCot
– 'Richard Blakeway-Phillips'	WCot WHil
– 'Robert Smith'	WCot
– 'Rowie'	EPri
– 'Sheila Owen'	WCot WMal
– 'Sofie'	EBee
– 'Stam 63' ♀H5	CWCL EPot ERCP GKev LRHS NWad WCot WHil
– 'Stefanie' ♀H5	EBee ELan EPri EShb GKev NHoy SDeJ SPeP
– 'Stewart Gilkison' **new**	SHar
– Ted Allen No 2	WCot
– 'Tess Allen'	WCot WHil
– 'Variegata'	see *N. bowdenii* 'Mollie Cowie'
– 'Vesta K'	EBee EPot EPri GKev LRHS NHoy
– 'Wellsii'	see *N. bowdenii* 'Quinton Wells'
– Wellsii pale form **new**	SHar
bowdenii* × *sarniensis	WFar
'Canasta'	WCot
'Caryatid'	WCot WFar
'Catkin'	WCot
'Clent Charm'	WCot
§ 'Codora'	CCCN EPfP WCot WFar
'Corlette'	WCot
'Countess of Mulgrave'	WCot
'Cranfield'	WCot
crispa	see *N. undulata* Crispa Group
'Cynthia Chance'	WCot
'Diana Oliver'	WCot
'Doris Vos'	WCot
Elegance Series	GKev LRHS NHoy WCot
– 'Elegance Red'	CBro ELan
'Elspeth'	WCot
'Exbury Red'	WCot
'Falaise'	WCot
filamentosa misapplied	see *N. filifolia* Baker
filamentosa ambig.	CBro
§ ***filifolia*** Baker	WAbe
'Firelight'	WCot
gaberonensis	WAbe
'Giraffe'	WCot
'Glacier'	EBee
'Glensavage Gem'	CBro
gracilis	WCot
'Harlequin'	WCot
'Helena'	WCot
'Hera'	CBro ELon
'Hertha Berg'	WCot
* ***hirsuta***	WCot
humilis ♀H2	CBro WAbe
– from Bredasdorp, South Africa	WCot
– Breachiae Group	SAng
'Iman'	WCot
'Isobel'	EGrI LEdu LRHS SDir SHar WFar
'Janet'	WCot
'Jenny Wren'	WCot
'Judith'	SChr
'King Leopold'	WCot WFar
'Kinn McIntosh'	EPri WCot
krigei	WCot
'Kyle'	WCot
'Lady Cynthia Colville'	WCot
'Lady Downe'	WCot
'Lady Eleanor Keane'	WCot
'Lady Havelock-Allen'	WCot
'Lady Llewellyn'	WCot
'Lady St Aldwyn'	WCot
'Lambourne'	WCot

laticoma	WCot
'Lawlord'	WCot
'Leila Hughes'	WCot
'Long Island Beauty'	WCot
'Lucinda'	WCot
'Lyndhurst Salmon'	WCot
'Malvern'	WCot
'Maria'	WCot
masoniorum ♀H2	EPot SGro WAbe
'Meadowbankii'	WCot
'Miss E. Cator'	WCot
'Miss Florence Brown'	WCot
'Miss Frances Clarke'	WCot
'Mr John'	CBro CWCL EBee EGrI ELan EPri ERCP EShb GKev LRHS LSou NHoy SDir SMad WCot WHil
'Mrs Cooper'	WCot
'Mrs Dent Brocklehurst'	WCot
'Natasha'	WCot
'Nena'	WCot
'Oberon'	WCot
'Ophelia'	WCot
'Owslebury'	WCot
'Pink Triumph'	CBcs CMac CWCL EBee EHyd ELan EPot ERCP EShb GKev NHoy NRHS NWad SDeJ SPeP WCot WHoo
'Plymouth'	SChr
pudica pink-flowered	WCot
'Quivotina'	WCot
'Red Pimpernel'	NHoy
'Red Surprise'	SDir
'Regina' ♀H5	WCot
'Rembrandt'	WCot
'Rose Princess'	WCot
'Rushmere Star'	SChr WCot
'Ruth'	WCot WFar
sarniensis	CBro CWCL ECha EPot EPri EShb GKev SDeJ SDir WCot WFar
* - 'Alba'	NHoy
* - 'Borde Hill White'	WCot
- var. ***corusca*** 'Major'	EGrI WCot
- var. ***curvifolia***	CBro
- - f. ***fothergillii***	WCot
- 'Hanley Castle'	WCot
- 'Lydia'	NHoy
- 'Mother of Pearl'	WCot
- 'Mottistone'	WCot
- red-flowered	NHoy
- rose-pink-flowered	NHoy
- var. ***sarniensis***	CBor
'Snowflake'	WCot
'Stephanie'	CCCN EShb LEdu LRHS MBros MNrw WCot WHoo
'Susan Norris'	WCot
'Sweet Sixteen' **new**	SGro
'Tweedledee'	WCot
undulata	CCCN CWCL ECha EGrI EPri GKev MPie NHoy NRog SDeJ SDir SPer WMal
§ - Alta Group	WCot
§ - Crispa Group	EPfP WFar
§ - Flexuosa Group	MRav
- - 'Alba' ♀H3	CAvo CBro ECha EPri GKev MRav NRog WCot WMal
× ***versicolor*** 'Mansellii'	CBro
'Vestal'	SDir
'Vicky'	WCot
'Winter Sun'	SRms
'Zeal Giant' ♀H3	CAvo CBro EPri IBlr LPla WCot WFar
'Zeal Grilse'	WCot
'Zeal Salmon'	IBlr
'Zennor'	WCot

Nerium (*Apocynaceae*)

§ ***odoratum*** 'Miss Agnes Campbell'	SEND
oleander L.	CAbb CTri EBak EShb SPer SPlb SPoG
- from Morocco	WPGP
- 'Album'	CTri EShb SEND
- 'Album Plenum' (d)	XSen
- 'Alsace'	SEND
* - 'Atlas'	XSen
* - 'Barcelona'	SEND
- 'Cavalaire' (d)	XSen
* - 'Claudia'	SEND
- 'Commandant Barthélemy' (d)	XSen
- double apricot (d)	SEND
- 'Emile Sahut'	ELan
- 'Flavescens Plenum' (d)	EShb XSen
- 'Hardy Red'	XSen
* - 'Harriet Newding'	XSen
- 'Italia'	XSen
- 'Madame Allen' (d)	EShb
- 'Magaly'	SEND
- 'Margaritha'	SEND XSen
- 'Minouche'	SEND
- subsp. ***oleander***	SEdd
- 'Petite Red'	XSen
- 'Professeur Granel' (d)	EShb
- 'Provence' (d)	XSen
- 'Red Beauty'	XSen
- red-flowered	SPad
- 'Roseum Plenum' (d)	CRHN SEND
§ - 'Soeur Agnès'	XSen
- 'Soleil Levant'	XSen
- 'Splendens Giganteum' (d)	EShb
- 'Tito Poggi'	XSen
- 'Variegatum' (v) ♀H2	ELan EShb
- 'Villa Romaine'	XSen

Neviusia (*Rosaceae*)

alabamensis	NLar

Nicandra (*Solanaceae*)

physalodes	CHby ELan ENfk NBir SMrm SSal WSFF XAbr
- ***alba***	CSpe
- 'Splash of Cream' (v)	CCCN GJos MNHC
- 'Violacea'	CSpe GJos GLog SRms SWvt

Nicotiana ✿ (*Solanaceae*)

alata	CSpe LCro LOPS WSFF
- 'Grandiflora'	LCro LOPS
glauca	CCCN CDTJ EWld NGKo SPlb SSal
knightiana	CDTJ CSpe
langsdorffii ♀H2	CSpe LCro LOPS SPhx SSal
- 'Cream Splash' (v)	CTtf SSal
- 'Hot Chocolate'	CSpe
'Lime Green' ♀H2	CSpe LCro LOPS SPhx
mutabilis	CCBP CSpe LCro LOPS SDys SPhx WBor
quadrivalvis	SPhx
rustica	CSpe SPhx
× ***sanderae*** Avalon Series	MBros
- Cuba Series	MPri
- (Perfume Series) 'Perfume Deep Purple'	CSpe SPhx

- - 'Perfume Antique Lime' **new**	SPhx
solanifolia	SPlb
suaveolens	SPhx
sylvestris ♀H2	CBod CDTJ CRos CSpe ELan EPfP EWoo GJos LCro LOPS MPri NFav SEND SPhx SPoG SWvt
tabacum	SSal XAbr
'Tinkerbell'	CSpe
WHISPER MIXED	SPhx

Nidularium (*Bromeliaceae*)

billbergioides	NCft

Nierembergia (*Solanaceae*)

§ ***repens***	NLar WCot XLum
rivularis	see *N. repens*

Nigella (*Ranunculaceae*)

damascena	CKel
- 'Albion Green Pod'	LCro
- 'Miss Jekyll' ♀H3	LCro LOPS MNHC SPhx
- 'Miss Jekyll Alba' ♀H3	CSpe LCro LOPS
- 'Oxford Blue'	LCro LOPS
- Persian Jewels Group	SVic
hispanica L.	CKel SPhx
papillosa 'African Bride'	CSpe MNHC SPhx
- 'Delft Blue'	LCro SPhx
- 'Midnight'	CSpe SPhx
sativa	XAbr

Nigritella see *Gymnadenia*

Niphidium (*Polypodiaceae*)

crassifolium	EShb LEdu WCot

Nipponanthemum (*Asteraceae*)

§ ***nipponicum***	EBee ELon GBin GWyn MMuc NLar NSti SAko SPoG SRms XLum
- 'Hama-giku'	NWad

Noccaea see *Thlaspi*

Nolina (*Asparagaceae*)

hibernica	EBee
lindheimeriana	WCot
microcarpa	XSen
nelsonii	CCht CDoC LRHS SArc SPlb XSen XSte
parviflora	XSen
texana	WCot

Nomocharis (*Liliaceae*)

aperta	CExl EBee GGGa GKev NHpl WTyc
farreri	EBee GKev
mairei	see *N. pardanthina*
meleagrina	GEdr NHpl
§ ***pardanthina***	GKev NHpl
- f. ***punctulata***	GGGa GKev
saluenensis	GGGa

Nonea (*Boraginaceae*)

lutea	EPPr MMrt NSti WHal

Nothaphoebe (*Lauraceae*)

cavaleriei **new**	CExl

Nothochelone see *Penstemon*

Nothofagus ✿ (*Nothofagaceae*)

§ ***alpina***	NWea SCob WPav
antarctica	CAco CBcs CMCN EBee ELan EPfP GKin LMaj LPar MBlu MMuc MTrO NOra NOrn NWea SAko WMat
betuloides	GBin IArd SAko SPlb WPGP
cunninghamii	CBcs CBrP EPfP IArd IDee SAko SPlb
dombeyi ♀H5	EPfP IArd IDee MBlu SArc WPGP WSpi
fusca	SAko WPGP
menziesii	WPGP
moorei	WPGP
nervosa	see *N. alpina*
obliqua	GAbr IPap WMou WPav
procera Oerst.	see *N. alpina*

Notholaena see *Cheilanthes*

Notholirion (*Liliaceae*)

bulbuliferum	EBee GKev
campanulatum	EBee GKev MNrw
macrophyllum	GArf GBin GKev
thomsonianum	CBor GKev

Nothoscordum (*Alliaceae*)

dialystemon	EPot NHpl NRog WAbe
§ ***hirtellum***	NRog
montevidense	WCot
neriniflorum	see *Allium neriniflorum*
ostenii	WCot

Nothotsuga (*Pinaceae*)

longibracteata	SPtp

Nuphar (*Nymphaeaceae*)

japonica	LLWG
lutea	CBen CHab LCro LLWG LOPS
- subsp. ***advena***	LLWG
pumila	LLWG

Nuytsia (*Loranthaceae*)

floribunda	SPlb

Nylandtia (*Polygalaceae*)

spinosa	SPlb

Nymphaea ✿ (*Nymphaeaceae*)

alba (H)	CBen CHab CPud CWat LCro LOPS MWts NBir SVic WCAu WMAq
'Albatros' misapplied	see *N.* 'Hermine'
§ 'Albatros' Latour-Marliac (H)	CWat LLWG NPer WMAq
'Albatross'	see *N.* 'Albatros' Latour-Marliac, *N.* 'Hermine'
* 'Albida'	LLWG WMAq
'Almost Black' (H)	CBen EWat LCro LLWG LOPS
'Amabilis' (H)	CBen WMAq
'American Star' (H)	CBen
'Andreaa Berthold' (H)	LLWG
'Andreana' (H)	EWat LLWG
'Angelique' (H)	LLWG
'Anna Epple' (H)	LLWG
'Arc-en-ciel' (H)	CBen LLWG WMAq
'Atropurpurea' (H)	CBen LLWG NPer WMAq
'Attorney Elrod' (H)	LLWG
'Attraction' (H)	CBen CPud LLWG MWts NPer SVic WMAq XLum
'Aurora' (H)	CBen CPud LCro LLWG LOPS MWts SVic WMAq
'Barbara Davies' (H)	LLWG
'Barbara Dobbins' (H)	CBen EWat LCro LLWG LOPS
'Bateau' (H)	LLWG
'Bernice Ikins' (H)	LLWG

	'Betsy Sakata' (H)	LLWG
	'Black Cherry' (H)	LLWG
	'Black Princess' (H)	CBen CPud EWat LLWG
	'Blushing Bride' (H)	LLWG
	'Bua Rapee' (H)	LLWG
	'Burgundy Princess' (H)	CBen CWat EWat LLWG NPer
	candida (H)	CBen CPud MWts NPer WMAq
	'Candidissima' (H)	CBen
	'Carolina Sunset' (H)	LLWG
	'Caroliniana Nivea' (H)	CBen
	'Caroliniana Perfecta' (H)	CBen
	'Celebration' (H)	LLWG
	'Charlene Strawn' (H)	EWat LLWG WMAq
	'Charles de Meurville' (H)	CBen LCro LLWG LOPS NPer SVic WMAq
	'Chompoo Pairat' (H)	LLWG
	'Chrysantha' (H)	LLWG
	'Château le Rouge' (H)	CBen LLWG
	'Chubby' (H)	LLWG
	'Citrus Twist' (H)	LLWG
	'Cliff Tiffany' (H)	CBen LLWG
	'Clyde Ikins' (H)	EWat LLWG
	'Colonel A.J. Welch' (H)	CBen NPer WMAq
	'Colorado' (H)	CBen EWat LLWG NPer
	'Colossea' (H)	CBen CWat NPer
	'Comanche' (H)	CBen LLWG NPer WMAq
	'Concordia' (H)	LLWG
	'Conqueror' (H)	CBen CWat LLWG NPer SVic
	'Cranberry Cup'	LLWG
	'Crazy Pom Pom' (H)	LLWG
	'Curly Purple' (H)	LLWG
	'Cynthia Ann' (H)	LLWG
§	'Darwin' (H)	CBen CWat LLWG MWts NPer SLon WMAq
	'David' (H)	CBen EWat LLWG
	'Debbie June' (H)	LLWG
	'Denver' (H)	CPud EWat LLWG
	'Dwarf Beauty' (H)	LLWG
	'Ellisiana' (H)	CPud LLWG NPer
	'Erhard Van Oldehoff' (H)	LLWG
	'Escarboucle' (H) ♀H5	CBen CPud CWat EWat LLWG NPer SVic WMAq
§	'Fabiola' (H)	NPer WMAq
	'Fiesta' (H)	CBen
	'Fire Cracker' (H)	LLWG
	'Fire Crest' (H)	CBen CPud LLWG NPer SVic WMAq
	'Fireball' (H)	LLWG
	'Flore de Cologne' (H)	LLWG
	'Frezzby' (H)	LLWG
	'Fritz Junge' (H)	CBen
	'Froebelii' (H)	CBen CPud CWat EWat LLWG NPer WMAq
	'Frosted Pink' (H) **new**	LLWG
	'Fuchsia Pom-pom' (H)	LLWG
	'Galatée' (H)	CBen
	'Georgia Peach' (H)	LLWG
	'Gladstoniana' (H) ♀H5	CBen CPud MWts NPer WMAq
	'Gloire du Temple-sur-Lot' (H)	CBen LLWG NPer WMAq
	'Gloriosa' (H)	LLWG MWts NPer
	'Gold Medal' (H)	CBen LLWG
	'Golden Goblet' (H)	LLWG
	'Golden Star' (H)	LLWG
	'Gonnère' (H) ♀H5	CBen CWat EWat LLWG MWts NPer SLon WMAq
	'Graziella' (H)	WMAq
	'Gregg's Orange Sunset' (H) **new**	LLWG
	'Guava Chiffron' (H)	LLWG
	'Gypsy' (H)	LLWG

	'Hal Miller' (H)	LLWG
	'Hassell' (H)	LLWG
	'Haunting Beauty' (H) **new**	LLWG
	'Hawaiian Gold' (H)	LLWG
	'Hazorea Dagan White' (H)	LLWG
	'Heart Beat' (H)	LLWG
	'Helen Fowler' (H)	WMAq
	'Helen Hariot' (H)	LLWG
	× ***helvola***	see *N.* 'Pygmaea Helvola'
§	'Hermine' (H)	CBen NPer WMAq
	'Hidden Violet' (H)	LLWG
§	'Highlight' (H)	LLWG
	'Hilite'	see *N.* 'Highlight'
	'Hollandia' misapplied	see *N.* 'Darwin'
	'Honeycup' (H) **new**	LLWG
	'Indiana' (H)	CBen LLWG NPer WMAq
	'Inner Light' (H)	EWat LLWG
	'Irene Heritage' (H)	CBen
	'J.C.N. Forestier' (H)	CBen
	'James Brydon' (H) ♀H5	CBen CPud CWat EWat LLWG MWts NPer SLon SVic WMAq
	'Jean de Lamarsalle' (H)	LLWG
§	'Joanne Pring' (H)	CBen
	'Joey Tomocik' (H)	CBen CWat EWat LLWG WMAq
	'Kiss the Sky' (H)	LLWG
	'Lactea' (H)	CBen LLWG
	'Laydekeri Fulgens' (H)	CBen EWat LLWG MWts WMAq
	'Laydekeri Lilacea' (H)	CBen LLWG WMAq
	'Laydekeri Purpurata' (H)	WMAq
	'Laydekeri Rosea' misapplied	see *N.* 'Laydekeri Rosea Prolifera'
§	'Laydekeri Rosea Prolifera' (H)	CBen EWat
	'Lemon Cup' (H)	LLWG
	'Lemon Drop' (H) **new**	LLWG
	'Lemon Meringue' (H)	LLWG
	'Lemon Mist' (H)	LLWG
	'Lily Pons' (H)	CBen LLWG
	'Liou' (H)	LLWG
	'Little Champion' (H)	LLWG
	'Little Sue' (H)	CPud LLWG
	'Lucida' (H)	LLWG WMAq
	'Lucky Red' (H)	LLWG
	'Madame Bory Latour-Marliac' (H)	CBen
	'Madame Wilfon Gonnère' (H)	CBen CWat LLWG MWts NPer SVic WMAq
	'Manee Red' (H)	LLWG
	'Manee Siam' (H)	LLWG
	'Mangkala Ubol' (H)	CBen
	'Marliacea Albida' (H)	CBen CPud EWat LCro LLWG LOPS MWts NPer WMAq XLum
	'Marliacea Carnea' (H)	CBen CPud LCro LOPS MWts NPer WMAq
§	'Marliacea Chromatella' (H) ♀H5	CBen CPud CWat EWat SVic WMAq XLum
	'Marliacea Rosea' (H)	CBen WMAq XLum
	'Martha' (H)	EWat
	'Mary' (H)	LLWG
	'Masaniello' (H)	CBen WMAq
	'Maurice Laydeker' (H)	CBen LLWG
	'Maxima'	see *N.* 'Odorata Maxima'
	'Mayla' (H)	CBen LLWG NPer
§	'Météor' (H)	CBen EWat WMAq
	mexicana (H)	CBen LLWG
	'Millennium Pink' (H)	CBen
	'Miss Siam' (H)	LLWG
	'Moon Dance' (H)	LLWG
	'Moorei' (H)	CBen MWts WMAq
	'Mrs Richmond' misapplied	see *N.* 'Fabiola'
	'Mrs Richmond' Latour-Marliac (H)	CBen MWts

'Munkala Ubon' (H) LLWG
'Myra' (H) LLWG
'Neptune' (H) LLWG
'Newchapel Beauty' WMAq
'Newton' (H) LLWG WMAq
'Nigel' (H) LLWG
'Norma Gedye' (H) CBen WMAq
§ ***odorata*** (H) CBen LLWG WMAq
§ - var. ***minor*** (H) CBen CPud WMAq
- 'Pumila' see *N. odorata* var. *minor*
- subsp. ***tuberosa*** (H) CBen
'Odorata Alba' see *N. odorata*
'Odorata Juliana' (H) CBen
§ 'Odorata Maxima' (H) WMAq
'Odorata Sulphurea' (H) LLWG
'Odorata Sulphurea Grandiflora' (H) LLWG
'Odorata William B. Shaw' see *N.* 'W.B. Shaw'
'Ori Flame' (H) LLWG
'Ori Oruba' (H) LLWG
'Patio Joe' (H) LLWG
'Paul Hariot' (H) CPud EWat LLWG MWts NPer WMAq
'Peace Lily' (H) LLWG
'Peach Glow' (H) EWat LLWG
'Peach Sunrise' (H) LLWG
'Peaches and Cream' (H) LLWG
'Perry's Baby Red' (H) CBen CPud CWat EWat LLWG MWts NPer WMAq
'Perry's Deepest Red' (H) LLWG
'Perry's Double White' (H) LLWG NPer
'Perry's Double Yellow' (H) LLWG
'Perry's Dwarf Red' (H) LLWG
'Perry's Fire Opal' (H) EWat LLWG NPer
'Perry's Orange Sunset' (H) LLWG
'Perry's Pink' (H) WMAq
'Perry's Red Bicolor' (H) CBen
'Perry's Red Glow' (H) LLWG
'Perry's White Star' (H) LLWG
'Perry's Yellow Sensation' see *N.* 'Yellow Sensation'
'Peter Slocum' (H) CBen
'Phoebus' (H) CBen
'Pia Stella Berthold' (H) LLWG
'Picciola' (H) LLWG
'Pink Beauty' (H) LLWG
'Pink Dawn' (H) LLWG
'Pink Grapefruit' (H) LLWG
'Pink Lemonade' (H) LLWG
'Pink Opal' (H) LLWG
'Pink Pom-pom' (H) LLWG
'Pink Pumpkin' (H) LLWG
'Pink Ribbon' (H) LLWG
'Pink Sensation' (H) CBen EWat LLWG NPer SLon WMAq
'Pink Sparkle' (H) LLWG
'Pink Sunrise' (H) LLWG
'Pink Tulip' (H) LLWG
'Pinwaree' (H) LLWG
'Pöstlingberg' (H) LLWG
'Prakeisap' (H) LLWG
'Princess Elizabeth' (H) LLWG
'Purple Fantasy' (H) LLWG
'Pygmaea Alba' see *N. tetragona*
§ 'Pygmaea Helvola' (H) $\mathbb{Y}^{H5}$ CBen CPud CWat EWat LCro LLWG LOPS MWts NPer SLon SVic WMAq
'Pygmaea Rubis' (H) WMAq
'Pygmaea Rubra' (H) CPud CWat EWat LCro LLWG LOPS MWts NPer SVic WMAq
'Queen of the Whites' (H) CBen LLWG
'Rattana Ubol' (H) LLWG
'Ray Davies' (H) CBen LLWG
'Razzberry' (H) LLWG
'Red Paradise' (H) LLWG
'Red Queen' (H) LLWG
'Red Spider' (H) LLWG NPer SVic
'Reflected Flame' (H) LLWG
'Rembrandt' misapplied see *N.* 'Météor'
'René Gérard' (H) CBen CPud LLWG MWts NPer WMAq
'Rosanna Supreme' (H) LLWG
'Rose Arey' (H) CBen LCro LOPS NPer SVic WMAq
'Rosennymphe' (H) CBen NPer WMAq
'Rosy Morn' (H) CBen LLWG
'Ruby Star' (H) LLWG
'Savanlamp' (H) LLWG
'Seignoureti' (H) LLWG
'Shady Lady' (H) CPud LLWG
'Siam Angel' (H) LLWG
'Siam Beauty' (H) LLWG
'Siam Jasmine' (H) LLWG
'Siam Purple 1' (H) LLWG
'Siam Purple 2' (H) LLWG
'Siam Rose' (H) **new** LLWG
'Siam Sunset' (H) LLWG
'Sioux' (H) CBen LLWG NPer SVic WMAq
'Sirius' (H) LLWG
'Snow Princess' (H) CPud EWat MWts
'Snowflake' (H) LLWG
'Solfatare' (H) EWat LLWG
'Splendida' (H) WMAq
'Starbright' (H) LLWG
'Steven Strawn' (H) LLWG
'Strawberry Milkshake' (H) LLWG
'Sunfire' (H) LLWG
'Sunny Pink' (H) CBen LLWG
'Sunrise' (H) LCro LOPS
'Sunset Dawn' (H) **new** LLWG
'Superba' (H) CBen
'Sweet Pea' (H) LLWG
'Tangerine Pink' (H) LLWG
'Tan-khwan' (H) LLWG
§ ***tetragona*** (H) CPud EWat LCro LLWG LOPS NPer WMAq
- 'Alba' see *N. tetragona*
- 'Johann Pring' see *N.* 'Joanne Pring'
'Texas Dawn' (H) CBen CWat LLWG SLon WMAq
'Thomas O'Brian' (H) LLWG
'Thongsup' (H) LLWG
'Tony's Starlike' LLWG
'Tuberosa Flavescens' see *N.* 'Marliacea Chromatella'
'Tuberosa Richardsonii' (H) CBen NPer
'Turtle Island Tropic Star' (H × T) LLWG
'Turtle Island Violicious' (H × T) LLWG
'Vésuve' (H) LLWG
'Virginalis' (H) CBen LLWG NPer WMAq
'Virginia' (H) LLWG
§ 'W.B. Shaw' (H) CBen CPud NPer
'Walter Pagels' (H) EWat LLWG WMAq
'Wanvisa' (H) CBen LCro LLWG LOPS
'Weymouth Red' (H) CBen
'White 1000 Petals' (H) **new** LLWG
'White Star' (H) LLWG
'White Sultan' (H) LCro LLWG LOPS
'William Falconer' (H) CBen LLWG NPer
'Wow' (H) LLWG
'Yellow Princess' (H) CWat
'Yellow Queen' (H) LLWG
§ 'Yellow Sensation' (H) CBen
'Yellow Watermelon' (H) LLWG
'Yul Ling' (H) EWat LLWG

Nymphoides (*Menyanthaceae*)

	peltata	CBen CBod CHab CPud CWat EWat LCro LLWG LOPS NPer SVic WMAq WPnP XLum

Nyssa ✿ (*Nyssaceae*)

	aquatica	CBcs IDee MBlu SMad SSta
	leptophylla	NLar WPGP
	ogeche	CJun
	shweliensis FMWJ 13122	WCru
	sinensis	CBcs CLnd CMCN CRos EGrI EHyd ELan EPfP LRHS MAsh MBlu MPkF NLar SPer WFar
	- 'Inferno'	CRos EPfP LRHS MTrO NLar NWea SPoG WMat
	- 'Jim Russell' ♀H5	EBee LRHS WPGP
	- 'Volcano'	CRos LRHS
	sylvatica	Widely available
	- 'Autumn Cascades'	CJun EHyd EPfP LRHS MAsh MBlu
	- var. ***biflora***	CMCN SSta
	- 'Haymen's Red'	see *N. sylvatica* RED RAGE
	- 'Isabel Grace'	CRos EHyd EPfP LRHS MAsh
	- 'Jermyns Flame'	CRos EHyd EPfP LRHS MAsh NLar
	- JOLLY ('Yiping') (v)	MPkF
	- 'Lakeside Weeper'	CRos ELan LRHS
	- 'Miss Scarlet' (f)	NLar WPGP
§	- RED RAGE ('Haymanred')	ELan EPfP LMil LRHS MAsh MBlu MPkF
	- 'Sheffield Park'	MAsh SLim
§	- 'Valley Scorcher'	CRos EHyd LRHS MAsh NLar
	- 'Wildfire'	LRHS NLar
	- 'Windsor'	see *N. sylvatica* 'Valley Scorcher'
	- 'Wisley Bonfire' (m) ♀H6	CBcs CJun CRos EBee EHyd ELan EPfP LMil LRHS MAsh MTrO NLar NRHS NWea SPoG SSta WMat WPGP

O

Oakesiella see *Uvularia*

Ochagavia (*Bromeliaceae*)

	carnea	NCft
	elegans	WCot
§	***litoralis***	SArc SMad
*	***rosea***	SPlb

Ochna (*Ochnaceae*)

	serrulata	CCCN

Ocimum (*Lamiaceae*)

	'African Blue'	CBod CSpe ENfk EWhm GPoy LCro LOPS MBros MHer MHol SPoG SRms
§	× ***africanum***	ENfk MNHC
	- 'Lesbos'	MHer
	- 'Lime'	ENfk MNHC
§	- 'Perpetuo'PBR (v)	ENfk
	- PESTO PERPETUO	see *O.* × *africanum* 'Perpetuo'
	- 'Siam Queen'	MHer SRms
	basilicum	EWhm GPoy LCro LOPS MPri SRms
	- 'Anise'	see *O. basilicum* 'Horapha'
	- 'Ararat'	SRms
	- 'Aristotle'	MHer SRms
	- 'Aroma 2' ♀H1c	LCro LOPS MCtn
	- 'Blue Spice'	SEdi
I	- 'British Basil'	MBros SRms
	- ***camphorata***	see *O. kilimandscharicum*
	- 'Christmas'	SEdi SRms
	- 'Cinnamon'	ENfk MNHC SEdi SRms WJek
	- 'Crimson King'PBR	SRms
	- 'Dark Opal'	ENfk SEdi SRms
	- 'Genovese'	CLau MHer MNHC SEdi
	- 'Glycyrrhiza'	see *O. basilicum* 'Horapha'
	- 'Green Globe'	SRms
	- 'Green Ruffles'	SRms
	- 'Holy'	see *O. tenuiflorum*
	- 'Holy Tulsi'	see *O. tenuiflorum*
§	- 'Horapha'	CLau ENfk LCro LOPS MNHC SEdi WJek XAbr
*	- 'Horapha Nanum'	ENfk SRms
	- large-leaved	XAbr
	- 'Lemonade' ♀H1c	SRms
	- lettuce leaf	SEdi
	- 'Magic Mountain'	SPoG
	- 'Magic White'	SPoG
	- 'Medinette'	CLau
	- 'Mrs Burns' Lemon' ♀H1c	EKin MCtn SRms WJek
	- 'Napoletano'	ENfk LCro LOPS SRms
	- 'Pluto' ♀H1c	LCro LOPS
	- 'Puck'	SRms
	- var. ***purpurascens*** 'Purple Ruffles'	EHyd LCro LOPS SRms
	- - 'Red Rubin'	MHer NRHS SRms WJek
	- var. ***purpurascens*** × ***kilimandscharicum***	CSpe GPoy WJek
	- 'Sweet Genovese'	SVic
	- 'Thai'	see *O. basilicum* 'Horapha'
	× ***citriodorum***	see *O.* × *africanum*
	gratissimum	SEdi
§	***kilimandscharicum***	CLau GPoy
	minimum	ENfk LCro LOPS LRHS MNHC SRms
	sanctum	see *O. tenuiflorum*
	'Spice'	ENfk
§	***tenuiflorum***	GPoy MNHC SPre SVic WJek XAbr

Odontonema (*Acanthaceae*)

	schomburgkianum	CCCN
	tubaeforme	CCCN

Oemleria (*Rosaceae*)

	cerasiformis	CBcs CJun CTri CWit ELan ELon EPfP EWes LEdu MGil MMuc WBor WCot WGwG

Oenanthe (*Apiaceae*)

	fistulosa	LLWG
	javanica	LEdu
	- 'Flamingo' (v)	CBen CBod CWat EBee ELan LEdu LLWG MWts SRms WMAq XLum
	pimpinelloides	CHab SPhx

Oenothera ✿ (*Onagraceae*)

§	***acaulis***	CSpe EBee GKev MNrw WCot
§	- 'Aurea'	XLum
	- 'Lutea'	see *O. acaulis* 'Aurea'
	'Apricot Delight'	MACG SGbt
§	***biennis***	EBou ELan ENfk GAbr GJos GPoy GQue LCro LOPS MBow MHer MNHC NBro SPhx SRms WBrk WHer WSFF
	'Blood Orange'	GEdr GJos
	caespitosa	GArf
	- pink-flowered **new**	GJos
	childsii	see *O. speciosa*
	cinaeus	see *O. fruticosa* subsp. *glauca*
	'Crown Imperial'	CChe CMac MACG MArl NHol SHar SLon
§	***elata*** subsp. ***hookeri***	EWes GJos
	erythrosepala	see *O. glazioviana*

	'Finlay's Fancy'	WCru
§	***fruticosa***	NLar SPlb
	- 'African Sun'	ECtt MMrt SGBe
	- 'Camel' (v)	XLum
	- FIREWORKS	see *O. fruticosa* 'Fyrverkeri'
§	- 'Fyrverkeri'	CBcs CMea ECtt EHyd GJos GMaP GWyn ILea LRHS MRav NRHS SCob SPer SWvt WCAu XLum
§	- subsp. ***glauca***	CElw ILea MHer NLar SMrm SRms
	- - 'Erica Robin' (v)	CChe CDor ECtt EHyd GBin MNrw MRav NGdn SCob SMad SWvt WCav WCot WHoo
	- - 'Longest Day'	MBrN
	- - SOLSTICE	see *O. fruticosa* subsp. *glauca* 'Sonnenwende'
§	- - 'Sonnenwende'	CElw EHyd ILea MMrt NEoE NLar XLum
	- HIGHLIGHT	see *O. fruticosa* 'Hoheslicht'
§	- 'Hoheslicht'	EBee NLar
	- 'Lady Brookeborough'	MRav
	- 'Yellow River'	CElw EBee
	'Give-me-Sunshine'	SLon
	glabra Miller	see *O. biennis*
	glabra misapplied	ECha
§	***glazioviana***	NBir SVic
	hookeri	see *O. elata* subsp. *hookeri*
	kunthiana	EBou ECha GJos
	- 'Glowing Magenta'	SPoG
	lamarckiana	see *O. glazioviana*
	'Lemon Sunset'	ECha EGrI EWTr
	linearis	see *O. fruticosa*
	longituba <u>**new**</u>	GJos
§	***macrocarpa*** ♀H5	CBod CHab CSBt EBee EBou ECha EHyd ELan EPfP EShb GJos LRHS MBel MHer SEND SPer SPhx SPlb SPoG SRms SVic SWvt WCAu XLum XSen
	- subsp. ***fremontii*** 'Silver Wings'	ELan SPhx
	- subsp. ***incana***	CSpe SPhx WHoo
	missouriensis	see *O. macrocarpa*
	oakesiana	SPhx
	odorata misapplied	see *O. stricta*
	odorata Hook. & Arn.	see *O. biennis*
	odorata Jacquin	XLum
	- cream-flowered	CSpe
	organensis	EBee MNrw
	pallida 'Innocence'	LCro
§	***perennis***	MPie SRms XLum
	pilosella 'Mella Yella'	EBee
	- 'Yella Fella'	ELan NWad
	pumila	see *O. perennis*
	rosea	XLum
§	***speciosa***	SRms XLum
*	- 'Alba'	EBee SCob
	- var. ***childsii***	see *O. speciosa*
	- 'Pink Petticoats'	ECha GJos LSun MACG NPer SBut
	- 'Rosea'	SPlb
	- 'Siskiyou'	CBcs CBod CMea EBee ECha ECtt EHyd ELan EPfP ILea LEdu LRHS MAvo MNrw NRHS SCob SCoo SGBe SMad SPer SPoG SSut WGwG WMal XLum
	- TWILIGHT ('Turner01'PBR) (v)	EBee EHyd ELan EPfP ILea LRHS LSou NEoE NHol NLar WNPC
	- 'Woodside White'	SMrm
§	***stricta***	CMea EPPr MNrw
	- 'Sulphurea'	CDor CMea EAJP EHyd ELan EPPr EPfP LCro LRHS NPer SMrm SPhx
	'Summer Sun'	CBod EHyd LRHS MPie NRHS SGbt WCAu
	'Sunny Delight'	CBod
	taraxacifolia	see *O. acaulis*
	tetragona	see *O. fruticosa* subsp. *glauca*
	- var. ***fraseri***	see *O. fruticosa* subsp. *glauca*
	versicolor	CKel
	- 'Sunset Boulevard'	CSpe EHyd GJos SPer WHil XLum

Olea (Oleaceae)

	europaea (F)	Widely available
§	- 'Cipressino' (F)	IDee
	- 'El Greco' (F)	CBcs
	- 'Leccino' (F)	LMaj SWeb
	- 'Pyramidalis'	see *O. europaea* 'Cipressino'

Olearia ✿ (Asteraceae)

	algida	GBin
	arborescens 'Moondance' (v)	CBcs CBod LRHS SGBe
	argophylla	CExl
	avicenniifolia	CMac CTrC
	× ***capillaris***	EBee
§	***cheesemanii***	CExl CTrC NLar SPer SVen
	erubescens	CTrC
	erubescens × ***ilicifolia***	SVen
	fragrantissima	GBin
	gunniana	see *O. phlogopappa*
	× ***haastii***	Widely available
	- FAIRLIE FRAGRANT ('Hutfair')	GBin
	- 'McKenzie'	ELon
§	'Henry Travers'	CCCN CExl EPfP SVen
	ilicifolia	EPfP WPGP
	insignis	see *Pachystegia insignis*
	lacunosa	IDee WPGP
	macrodonta ♀H4	Widely available
	- 'Major'	CCCN CTrC EBee SCob
	- 'Minor'	CCCN CDoC CKel CMac CTrC EBee ELan ELon EPfP SPlb SRms WPGP WSpi
§	× ***matthewsii***	SPer
	× ***mollis*** misapplied	see *O.* × *matthewsii*
	× ***mollis*** (Kirk) Cockayne	CMac EHyd
	- 'Zennorensis' ♀H4	CCCN EBee ELan
	myrsinoides	CSde
	nummularifolia	CBcs CCCN CDoC CKel CTrC CTri CWit ELan EPfP GBin LRHS NLar SEND SPer SVen SWvt
	× ***oleifolia*** 'Waikariensis'	CBcs CCCN CExl EHyd SEND SLon
	paniculata	CBod CCCN CCoa CDoC CSde CTri EHyd EPfP LRHS SEND SRms SVen
§	***phlogopappa***	CTri SVen
	- 'Comber's Blue'	CBcs CCCN EHyd ELan EPfP LRHS SAko SNig SPer WLov
§	- 'Comber's Pink'	CBcs CCCN CExl CKel ELan EPfP LRHS MAsh NPer SAko SEle SGBe SPer SPoG
	- 'Rosea'	see *O. phlogopappa* 'Comber's Pink'
I	- var. ***subrepanda*** (DC.) J.H.Willis	CTrC GBin
	ramulosa	CCCN CExl CSde
	- 'Blue Stars'	CMac SRms
	rani misapplied	see *O. cheesemanii*
	× ***scilloniensis*** misapplied	see *O. stellulata* DC.
	× ***scilloniensis*** ambig.	CBcs CBod CCoa CDoC CKel CTrC EWld LRHS MAsh SGBe SPoG WKif
	× ***scilloniensis*** Dorrien-Smith ♀H4	CCCN
	- 'Master Michael' ♀H4	CBcs CCCN CTri EHyd ELon EPfP EWld LRHS SGBe SNig SPer SPoG WLov
	semidentata misapplied	see *O.* 'Henry Travers'

solandri CBod CCCN CCoa CMac CSde CTrC EPPr NLar SDix SEND
- 'Aurea' CBcs
'Stardust' SPlb SVen
stellulata misapplied see *O. phlogopappa*
§ *stellulata* DC. CExl CMac CSBt EPfP MAsh SPer
- 'Michael's Pride' CExl
traversii CBcs CBod CCCN CCoa CDoC CSBt CSde CTrC CTsd EHyd EPfP LRHS SArc SEND SRms WHer
- 'Compacta' CCCN CTrC
- dwarf CBod EBee
- 'Tweedledee' (v) SEND
- 'Tweedledum' (v) CBcs CBod CCCN CCoa CSde
virgata CCCN CWit IDee NLar
- var. *laxiflora* WHer
- var. *lineata* CCoa CSde MMuc NLar SEND WHer
- - 'Dartonii' CBcs CBod GBin NLar SPlb SSta SVen

Oligoneuron see *Solidago*

Oligostachyum (*Poaceae*)

lubricum see *Semiarundinaria lubrica*
§ *oedogonatum* MWht

olive see *Olea europaea*

Olsynium (*Iridaceae*)

biflorum GEdr
§ *douglasii* ♀H5 CBor CBro CMea EBee EPot GAbr GArf GEdr NHar NHpl NRya NSla
- 'Album' CBor EBee EPot EWes MNrw NHar NRya NSla WFar
- var. *inflatum* EWes
§ *junceum* CBor CSpe SPlb WKif
trinerve B&SWJ 10459 WCru

Omphalodes ✿ (*Boraginaceae*)

'Blue Eyes' NLar SEdd WCot
cappadocica ♀H5 CDor CMac EPfP EPot EWld GKev LRHS MRav NBro NPer NSla SRms WMal
- 'Alba' SPoG
- 'All Summer Blues' new CSpe
- 'Cherry Ingram' ♀H5 Widely available
- 'Lilac Mist' EBee SRms SWvt
- 'Starry Eyes' Widely available
§ *linifolia* ♀H3 CSpe ELan GWyn LCro LOPS MCot SPhx SSal
- *alba* see *O. linifolia*
nitida CSpe EWes EWld GWyn MMuc MNrw NQui WMal
verna Widely available
- 'Alba' CDor CMac EBee ECha EGrI ELan EMor EPPr EPfP GAbr GBin GMaP LRHS MBel MBriF MCot MNrw NBid NChi NGdn NLar SCob SPer SRms SWvt WBor WBrk WGwG WMal WPnP
- 'Elfenauge' EBee EPPr GMaP NBir NLar WCot
I - 'Grandiflora' WCot

Omphalogramma (*Primulaceae*)

delavayi GEdr
tibeticum new GKev

Oncostema see *Scilla*

onion see *Allium cepa*; also AGM Vegetables Section

Onixotis (*Colchicaceae*)

stricta see *Wurmbea stricta*

Onobrychis (*Fabaceae*)

montana SPhx
viciifolia NGrd SPhx

Onoclea (*Onocleaceae*)

sensibilis ♀H6 Widely available
- copper-leaved CJun EBee EPfP EWes WPGP
- var. *interrupta* new LEdu WPGP
* - var. *minima* LEdu WPGP
- 'Rotstiel' EBee

Ononis (*Fabaceae*)

natrix SPhx
repens NAts
spinosa CDor MHer WSpi

Onopordum (*Asteraceae*)

acanthium CDor CRos CTtf EBee ECha EHyd ELan ENfk EPfP GAbr GGro GPoy LRHS NGBl NRHS SCob SEND SHar SPhx SPtp WSpi
cyprium SPhx
illyricum SPhx
§ *nervosum* ♀H7 CSpe

Onosma (*Boraginaceae*)

alborosea EBee ECha ECre ELan GKev SEND WKif
conferta W/O 208636 new GGro
nana EDAr EPot
rigida GKev SPhx

Onosmodium (*Boraginaceae*)

molle GKev

Onychium (*Pteridaceae*)

contiguum LEdu WCot
japonicum CExl CLAP CRos EFer EHed EHyd LEdu LRHS MRav NRHS SPlb WAbe WCot
- 'Dali' CLAP WSHC

Ophiopogon ✿ (*Asparagaceae*)

BWJ 8244 from Vietnam WCru
NJM 11.018 WPGP
'Black Dragon' see *O. planiscapus* 'Kokuryū'
bodinieri EShb EWes LEdu SEND
- B&L 12505 EBee EPPr
caulescens B&SWJ 8230 WCru
- B&SWJ 11813 WCru
aff. *caulescens* B&SWJ 11287 WCru
- HWJ 590 WCru
chingii EBee EPPr EPfP EWes LEdu WCot
* - 'Crispum' EBee
clavatus KWJ 12267 WCru
formosanus B&SWJ 3659 ESwi WCru
'Gin-ryu' see *Liriope spicata* 'Gin-ryu'
graminifolius see *Liriope muscari*
'Hosoba Kokuryu' CBod EShb GGro LRHS MAsh MPie NEoE XSte
intermedius CSpe EPPr EShb ESwi LPla WCot
- GWJ 9387 WCru
§ - 'Argenteomarginatus' (v) EWes
- 'Variegatus' see *O. intermedius* 'Argenteomarginatus'
§ *jaburan* CMac EBee LEdu

	- 'Variegatus'	see *O. jaburan* 'Vittatus'
§	- 'Vittatus' (v)	EBee EWes LEdu WCot
	japonicus	CMac EBee EShb ESwi LEdu SCob XLum
	- B&SWJ 1871	WCru
	- 'Albus'	EPri
	- 'Comet' (v) **new**	EPPr
	- 'Compactus'	WPGP
	- 'Gyoku-Ryu'	EBee
	- 'Kigimafukiduma'	CExl CMac MRav NGdn
	- 'Kyoto'	ESwi
	- 'Lengteng Giant'	LEdu
	- 'Minor'	CBod CKno EBee ELon EPPr GMaP LRHS NLar NWsh SCob WAbe WPGP XLum
	- 'Nanus' **new**	CBod
	- 'Nanus Variegatus' (v)	EBee ESwi
	- 'Nippon'	EPPr LPot NGdn
	- 'Silver Dragon' (v)	EPPr
	- 'Tama-ryu'	WAbe
	- 'Tama-ryu Number Two'	ESwi
*	- 'Variegatus' (v)	CDTJ CMac CPla SRms
	aff. ***latifolius*** KWJ 12031	WCru
	longifolius FMWJ 13278	WCru
	malcolmsonii B&SWJ 7271	WCru
	megalanthus FMWJ 13118	WCru
	parviflorus GWJ 9387	WCru
	- HWJK 2093	WCru
	planiscapus	CCBP CExl CKno CSde CSpe ECha EGrI EPPr GArf NBro NWsh SPtp
*	- 'Albovariegatus' (v)	WFar
	- 'Black Beard'	CBod CKno GWyn MAsh NRHS SCob SHar SPoG WFar
	- 'Nigrescens'	see *O. planiscapus* 'Kokuryū'
	- 'Black Needle'	EBee
	- 'Black Smaragd'	EBee
§	- 'Kokuryū' ♀H5	Widely available
	- f. ***leucanthus***	CDor EPPr WCot
	- 'Little Tabby' (v)	CBen CMil EBee EBlo EShb ESwi MAsh WCot WGrn WHal WHoo WSHC
	scaber B&SWJ 1842	ESwi WCru
	- B&SWJ 3655	WCru
	'Spring Gold'	EShb ESwi LEdu

Oplopanax (*Araliaceae*)

	horridus	GGro
	- B&SWJ 9551	WCru
	japonicus	WCru

Opopanax (*Apiaceae*)

	chironium	SPhx
	- PAB 845	LEdu WPGP
	- PAB 872	WPGP
	hispidus **new**	SPhx

Opuntia (*Cactaceae*)

	angustata	see *O. phaeacantha*
	camanchica	see *O. phaeacantha*
	compressa	see *O. humifusa*
	elata	SChr
	erinacea var. ***utahensis***	see *O. polyacantha* var. *erinacea*
§	***ficus-indica***	SPlb WKor
	fragilis	SPlb XSen
§	***humifusa***	CDTJ SChr WKor XLum XSen
*	- subsp. ***littoica***	SPlb
	joconostle	see *O. ficus-indica*
	microdasys ♀H2	CBen
	monacantha	SEND
§	***phaeacantha***	SChr
	- NNS 99-264	WCot
	- var. ***major*** NNS 95-285	WCot
	pollardii	see *O. humifusa*
	polyacantha	SChr SPlb
	- 'Carmin'	XSen
§	- var. ***erinacea***	SChr WCot
	salmiana	SEND
	spinosior	see *Cylindropuntia spinosior*

orange, sour or Seville see *Citrus* × *aurantium* Sour Orange Group

orange, sweet see *Citrus* × *aurantium* Sweet Orange Group

Orbea (*Apocynaceae*)

§	***variegata*** ♀H2	CBen EShb WSMil

Orbexilum (*Fabaceae*)

	pedunculatum var. ***psoralioides***	SBrt SPhx

Orchis (*Orchidaceae*)

	elata	see *Dactylorhiza elata*
	foliosa	see *Dactylorhiza foliosa*
	fuchsii	see *Dactylorhiza fuchsii*
	laxiflora	see *Anacamptis laxiflora*
	maculata	see *Dactylorhiza maculata*
	maderensis	see *Dactylorhiza foliosa*
	majalis	see *Dactylorhiza majalis*
§	***mascula***	NLAp WHer
	militaris	NLAp
	morio	see *Anacamptis morio*

oregano see *Origanum vulgare*

Oreocharis (*Gesneriaceae*)

	aurea B&SWJ 11718	WCru
§	'Calliantha'	NHar WAbe
	convexa B&SWJ 6624	WCru
	- B&SWJ 7182	WCru

Oreopanax ✿ (*Araliaceae*)

	cecropifolius B&SWJ 14761	WCru
	dactylifolius	WCot
	floribundus	see *O. incisus*
	hypargyreus B&SWJ 14870	WCru
§	***incisus*** B&SWJ 10669	WCru
	mutisianus B&SWJ 14912	WCru
	sectifolius B&SWJ 14805	WCru
	xalapensis B&SWJ 10444	WCru

Oreopolus (*Rubiaceae*)

	glacialis **new**	GKev

Oresitrophe (*Saxifragaceae*)

	rupifraga	CTtf LEdu

Origanum ✿ (*Lamiaceae*)

	from Kalamata, Greece	SEND
	amanum ♀H4	EWes NBir NSla WAbe
	- var. ***album***	WAbe
	'Amethyst Falls'	CBod CWCL XSen XSte
	'Barbara Tingey'	ELan EPot EWes SRms WAbe WIce
	'Bellissimo'	IPot
	'Bristol Cross'	EBee ECha ECtt EPot MHer SBut WFar WGoo XSen
	'Buckland'	ECtt WSHC
	caespitosum	see *O. vulgare* 'Nanum'
	creticum	see *O. vulgare* subsp. *hirtum*

	dictamnus	EPot GPoy MHer WAbe WJek
	'Dingle Fairy'	EBee ECha ECtt EPot EWes GJos MCot MHer NBir SGro SWvt WIce WSpi XSen
	'Emma Stanley'	EPot WAbe WMal
	'Frank Tingey'	ELan
	'French'	CLau SRms WJek
	'Golden Narrow'	EHyd
	heracleoticum L.	see *O. vulgare* subsp. *hirtum*
	'Hot and Spicy'	CBod CLau ENfk EWhm SRms WFar WJek XSen
	'Jekka's Beauty'	WJek
	'Kent Beauty' ♀H4	Widely available
	laevigatum ♀H6	EWhm NBro NPer WCot WKif WSHC XSen
	- 'Dingle'	NLar
	- 'Herrenhausen' ♀H6	Widely available
	- 'Hopleys' ♀H6	CBod CCBP CDor CMea CRos CTri EBee ECha EHyd ELan EPfP LEdu LRHS MCot MHer MHol MRav NBir NDov NLar NRHS SCob SEND SEdd SPer SPhx SPoG WSHC XSen
	- 'Purple Charm'	EDAr SRms
	libanoticum	SPhx
	majorana	CHab ENfk GQue MHer MNHC SRms SVic WJek
I	- 'Aureum'	GKev
	- Italian	SEdi
	- PAGODA BELLS ('Lizbell'PBR)	IPot
	- var. ***tenuifolium***	WJek
	× ***majoricum***	WJek
	'Norton Gold'	ECtt NPer
	'Nymphenburg'	XSen
	onites	CBod CCBP CHby CLau CTsd EBou ENfk GQue LEdu MHer MNHC SPlb SRms
	- 'Limelight'	NWad
	'Rosenkuppel' ♀H7	CBar CBod CDor CMea EBee ECha ECtt ELan EPPr EWhm GQue LCro LOPS LRHS MHer MHol NDov SCob SPer SPhx SPlb SRms SWvt WCAu XSen
	'Rotkugel'	ELon WCFE
	rotundifolium ♀H4	CMea LEdu MHer NBir
	- 'Jan's Pink' **new**	ECha
	scabrum subsp. ***pulchrum*** 'Newleaze'	SGro
	syriacum	WJek
	'Teddy'	EBee
	vulgare	Widely available
	- 'Acorn Bank'	CBod EBou ECtt ENfk EWes LEdu MHer MNHC SPoG SRms WFar WJek
	- 'Aureum' ♀H6	Widely available
	- 'Aureum Crispum'	CBod ENfk GBin GQue GWyn NBid SRms WFar
	- 'Compactum'	CBod CCBP CLau CMea EBee EBou ECha ECtt ENfk EWhm GBin GPoy LEdu MHer MNHC NBir NPol NRHS NSla SPlb SRms WJek XLum
	- 'Corinne Tremaine' (v)	WHer
	- 'Country Cream' (v)	Widely available
	- 'Curly Gold'	CLau CTsd MBow
	- GENTLE BREEZE ('All120506'PBR) **new**	LPla
§	- 'Gold Tip' (v)	CBod CMea EBou ENfk EWhm GJos MHer MNHC SCob SPlb SRms WFar WHer
	- 'Golden Shine'	EWes EWhm SEdi
	- 'Greensleeves'	WFar
	- 'Himal' **new**	GPoy
§	- subsp. ***hirtum***	CHby GPoy LCro LOPS SPlb XAbr XSen
	- - 'Greek'	CArg CBod CCBP CLau ECul ENfk EWhm MHer MNHC SEdi SRms SVic WJek
§	- 'Nanum'	SRms WJek
	- 'Pink Mist'	MNrw NWad SRms WHoo
	- 'Pink Thumbles'	ECha
	- 'Polyphant' (v)	SRms
	- 'Thumble's Variety'	CBod CMea CRos EBee ECha ECtt EHyd EPfP LRHS MHer MRav NDov NRHS NWad SRms SWvt WCFE WFar XLum XSen
	- 'Tomintoul'	GPoy
	- 'Variegatum'	see *O. vulgare* 'Gold Tip'
	- 'Waddow Delight'	NWad
	- 'White Charm'	EBee NWad SEdi
	'Z'Attar'	MNHC

Orixa (*Rutaceae*)

	japonica	CExl EBee NLar WPGP
	- 'Variegata' (v)	NLar

Orlaya (*Apiaceae*)

	grandiflora ♀H7	CAvo CKel CMiW CSpe EPfP LCro LEdu LOPS LRHS MAvo MCot SPhx WHal

Ornithogalum (*Asparagaceae*)

	arabicum	CBro CCCN EShb GKev MBros NRog SDeJ SRms
	arcuatum	WCot
	atticum	GKev
	baeticum	GKev
	balansae	see *O. oligophyllum*
	caudatum	see *O. longibracteatum*
	creticum	GKev
	cuspidatum	GKev
I	***dictaeum***	GKev
	dubium ♀H2	CBor CPla SDeJ
	- hybrids	GKev
	- yellow-flowered **new**	CBor
	fimbriatum	GKev NRog
	lanceolatum	GKev WCot
§	***longibracteatum***	GKev NGKo SChr WHer
	magnum	CBro CKel CWCL ERCP GBin MCot MNrw NRog SDeJ WCot
	- 'Moskou' **new**	CAvo
	- 'Saguramo'	NRog
	montanum	GKev
	'Mount Fuji'	GKev
	'Namib Gold'	SDeJ
	nanum	see *O. sigmoideum*
	narbonense	GKev NRog WCot
	nutans ♀H5	CAvo CMea CWCL EAJP EHyd ELan EPot EWoo GKev LRHS LShi MNrw NBir NRog SDeJ SEND SPer SPhx WFar WShi
§	***oligophyllum***	EBee EPot GKev MNrw NRog SDeJ
	ponticum	WCot
	- 'Sochi'	ERCP GKev MBow
	pyramidale	EBee GKev NRog
	- short	SMHy
	pyrenaicum	CAvo CSpe ECha EPPr WCot WShi
	reverchonii	EBee ERCP GKev WShi
	saundersiae	GKev MPtr NGKo
	sibthorpii	see *O. sigmoideum*
§	***sigmoideum***	GKev
	sintenisii	GKev NRog
	thyrsoides ♀H2	CCCN GKev LCro LOPS SDeJ

umbellatum	CAvo CHab CRos CTri EGrI EHed EHyd ELan GKev GPoy LRHS MBow MCot MNrw NRHS NRog SDeJ SEND SRms WShi
'White Trophy' **new**	GKev

Orontium (*Araceae*)

aquaticum	CBen CPud CWat EWat LCro LLWG LOPS NPer WMAq

Orostachys (*Crassulaceae*)

furusei	WFar WHal
iwarenge	CBod SPlb SSim
§ ***spinosa***	CRos EDAr EHyd EWes LRHS NFav NRHS SPlb WAbe WFar

Orthophytum (*Bromeliaceae*)

gurkenii	WCot

Orthrosanthus (*Iridaceae*)

chimboracensis JCA 13743	EBee
laxus	CAbb CBod CWCL EGrI MACG NBir SMad WCAu
multiflorus	CBor CPbh CSde EBee EPri SBls
polystachyus	CTsd LPla MHer WSHC

Orychophragmus (*Brassicaceae*)

violaceus	CCCN CSpe

Oryzopsis (*Poaceae*)

hymenoides 'Rimrock'	EAJP
lessoniana	see *Anemanthele lessoniana*
miliacea	CSpe EPPr MAvo NSti SDix SEND WCot WPGP
paradoxa	EPPr

Osbeckia (*Melastomataceae*)

stellata NJM 13.058	WPGP

Oscularia (*Aizoaceae*)

copiosa **new**	SEdd
§ ***deltoides*** ♀H2	CCCN EShb SVen WFar

Osmanthus (*Oleaceae*)

armatus	CBcs CJun CKel CMac EBee EPfP LMaj LSRN NLar SEND SGol
× ***burkwoodii*** ♀H5	Widely available
§ ***decorus***	CBcs CBrac CMac CTri EBee EPfP MGos MRav NLar SBrt SGol SPer WPav
- 'Angustifolius'	NLar
delavayi ♀H5	Widely available
- 'Frank Knight'	EPfP LRHS MAsh
- 'George Gardner'	CMac SRms
- 'Heaven Scent'	SPoG
- 'Latifolius'	CExl CJun CRos EHyd LRHS MAsh SLon SWvt
forrestii	see *O. yunnanensis*
× ***fortunei***	CBcs CCVT CExl CKel EBee EHyd EPfP LMaj LPar LRHS
fragrans	LPar SLon SWeb SWvt WCFE
- f. ***aurantiacus***	XSte
§ ***heterophyllus***	CBcs CDoC CMac EBee ELan EPfP ERom GDam LMaj LPar MGos MRav NLar SArc SCob SGol SPer SRms SSta SWeb WCFE
§ - all gold	CKel EBee ELan EMil EPfP LRHS SPer SPoG
- 'Argenteomarginatus'	see *O. heterophyllus* 'Variegatus'
§ - 'Aureomarginatus' (v)	CBcs CMac CTsd ELon MHtn SLon SRms
- 'Aureus' misapplied	see *O. heterophyllus* all gold
- 'Aureus' Rehder	see *O. heterophyllus* 'Aureomarginatus'
§ - 'Goshiki' (v) ♀H5	Widely available
- 'Gulftide'	CRos EGrI EHyd EPfP LRHS MAsh MGos NLar NRHS
- 'Kembu' (v)	NLar
- 'Myrtifolius'	CMac NLar
- 'Ōgon'	NLar
- 'Purple Shaft' ♀H5	CRos EHyd ELan EPfP LRHS MAsh NRHS
- 'Purpureus'	CBcs CBod CKel CMac CTsd EBee EGrI ELon EShb LPar MGos MRav MSwo NLar SCoo SEND SGol SLon SNig SPer
- 'Rotundifolius'	CMac NLar SMad
- 'Sasaba'	NLar SMad
- TRICOLOR	see *O. heterophyllus* 'Goshiki'
§ - 'Variegatus' (v) ♀H5	CBcs CBrac CDoC CEme CKel CMac CRos CSBt EHyd ELan ELon EPfP LRHS LSRN MAsh MGil MGos MRav MSwo NLar SCob SEND SGbt SGol SNig SPer SPoG SRms SVen WSHC
ilicifolius	see *O. heterophyllus*
serrulatus	EPfP LRHS NLar WPGP
suavis	NLar
§ ***yunnanensis*** ♀H5	CBcs CMCN EBee EPfP LSRN MBlu MRav NLar SArc WPGP

× *Osmarea* see *Osmanthus*

Osmaronia see *Oemleria*

Osmorhiza (*Apiaceae*)

aristata B&SWJ 1607	WCru
claytonii	SPhx

Osmunda ✿ (*Osmundaceae*)

sp.	CCCN
asiatica	EBee WCru
cinnamomea ♀H6	CBdn CBod CCCN CLAP CRos CWCL EBee EFer EHyd ELan EWes LEdu LRHS NBro NLar NRHS SPlb SRot
claytoniana	CBdn CLAP CRos CSta EBee EFer EHyd LRHS NBro NLar NRHS SMad WCot XLum
japonica	CLAP CSta EBee NBro
regalis ♀H6	Widely available
- from southern USA	CLAP
- 'Cristata' ♀H6	EHyd NRHS SWvt WFib
- 'Purpurascens'	Widely available
- var. ***spectabilis***	CBdn CCCN CLAP EHyd NRHS
- 'Undulata'	WFib

Osteomeles (*Rosaceae*)

subrotunda	WPGP

Osteomeles × *Pyracantha* see × *Pyracomeles*

Osteospermum (*Asteraceae*)

3D Series	SPoG
- 3D PURPLE ('Kleoe12198'PBR)	MBros
- 3D VIOLET ICE ('Kleoe14223')	CWCL MBros
'African Queen'	see *O.* 'Nairobi Purple'
BANANA SYMPHONY ('Sekiin47') (Symphony Series)	CCCN
barberae misapplied	see *O. jucundum*

barberae (Harv.) Norl. 'Compactum' GArf WFar
BLUE EYED BEAUTY ('Balostlueye'PBR) CWCL LCro LOPS MBros MPri
'Blue Streak' CCCN CMac
'Buttermilk' 🏆H3 CCCN ELan
'Cannington John' CCCN
'Cannington Joyce' CCCN
'Cannington Roy' CBcs CCCN CEnd CMac CSma EBee ECtt ELan ELon EPfP EWoo GBee LRHS MACG NRHS SGBe WFar WMal
caulescens misapplied see *O.*'White Pim'
'Dwarf Pink' **new** CTtf
ecklonis CBcs CCCN CDTJ CTri NBro
- var. ***prostratum*** see *O.* 'White Pim'
(Erato Series) 'Erato Lemon Pink' **new** LRHS
- 'Erato Pink Eye' **new** LRHS
- 'Erato Purple' **new** LRHS
- 'Erato Purple Stripe' **new** LRHS
- 'Erato Yellow' **new** LRHS
Flowerpower Double Series (d) LBuc
FLOWERPOWER ICE WHITE ('Kleo06123') (Flowerpower Series) LCro LOPS
'Giles Gilbey' (v) CCCN
'Gweek Variegated' (v) CCCN
'Hopleys' 🏆H3 SEND
'In the Pink' CBod LCro LOPS LRHS MHol SCoo SGBe
'Irish' CTtf ECtt ELon EPPr EPot SMrm WIce WMal
§ ***jucundum*** 🏆H3 CCht CMea CTri CWCL ECha EHyd EPPr EPfP GAbr LCro LOPS LRHS LSRN NBir NPer NRHS SGBe SPlb SRms WIce WThu
- 'Blackthorn Seedling' 🏆H3 CBor CCCN CMea CWGN ECha SPtp
- var. ***compactum*** CBod CMac CRos CTsd EHyd ELan ELon EPfP GBee GLog GMaP LRHS LSRN MBow MPri NPer NRHS SCoo SIvy SPer SPtp SWvt WABo WFar WHil WHoo
- 'Elliott's Form' WHoo
- 'Langtrees' 🏆H3 SMrm
- 'Nanum' EDAr
'Keia' (Springstar Series) CCCN
§ 'Lady Leitrim' 🏆H3 Widely available
'Lisa Traxler' SVen
MILK SYMPHONY ('Seiremi') (Symphony Series) CCCN
§ 'Nairobi Purple' CBcs CBod CCCN CCht CDoC EBee ECtt EHyd ELan EPfP EShb LRHS MPri NRHS SGBe SWvt WABo WFar WHil
NASINGA CREAM ('Aknam'PBR) (Cape Daisy Series) CCCN
ORANGE SYMPHONY ('Seimora'PBR) (Symphony Series) CCCN MBNS
'Pale Face' see *O.* 'Lady Leitrim'
'Peggyi' see *O.* 'Nairobi Purple'
'Pink Gem' MHer WFar
'Pink Whirls' 🏆H3 CCCN
'Port Wine' see *O.* 'Nairobi Purple'
(Serenity Series) SERENITY BLUSHING BEAUTY ('Balostush') MBros
- SERENITY RED ('Balsered') MBros WBor
- SERENITY ROSE MAGIC ('Balseroma') **new** CWCL
'Silver Sparkler' (v) 🏆H3 CCCN CDTJ MHer SVen
'Snow Pixie' CBod CWGN ECtt ELan LCro LOPS LRHS MPri SPoG SWvt WFar WHil WIce
SONJA see *O.*'Sunny Sonja'
'Sparkler' CCCN
'Stardust' CRos ECtt EHyd LRHS NPer NRHS SCoo
(Sunny Series) 'Sunny Bronze' CSpe
- 'Sunny Carlos'PBR SPoG
- 'Sunny Cherry' SPoG
- 'Sunny Mary'PBR LCro LOPS SPoG
§ - 'Sunny Sonja'PBR SPoG
- 'Sunny Victoria'PBR SPoG
- 'Sunny Xena'PBR SPoG
I 'Superbum' CBod MACG WFar
'Tresco Peggy' see *O.*'Nairobi Purple'
'Tresco Pink' CCCN
'Tresco Purple' see *O.* 'Nairobi Purple'
'Upright Purple' CDoC
VOLTAGE YELLOW ('Balvoyelo') (Voltage Series) MBros
'Weetwood' 🏆H3 CCCN CEnd CMea ECtt ELan EPPr EPot EWoo GLog LRHS MHer SPoG SWvt WFar
'Westwood White' EDAr
§ 'Whirlygig' 🏆H3 CCCN
§ 'White Pim' 🏆H3 CDTJ NPer SEND SMrm
'Wine Purple' see *O.* 'Nairobi Purple'
'Zaurak' (Springstar Series) CCCN
'Zulu' (Cape Daisy Series) CCCN

Ostrowskia (*Campanulaceae*)

magnifica EPot GKev

Ostrya (*Betulaceae*)

carpinifolia CBcs CCVT CMCN EBee ELan EPfP IPap LMaj LPar MBlu MMuc MTrO NOra NOrn NWea SCob SEND SGol SWvt WMat WTSh
japonica MVil
virginiana SBrt

Otacanthus (*Plantaginaceae*)

caeruleus 'Atlantis' CDoC

Otholobium (*Fabaceae*)

glandulosum EBee

Othonna (*Asteraceae*)

cheirifolia see *Hertia cheirifolia*
coronopifolia SVen

Othonnopsis see *Hertia*

Ourisia (*Plantaginaceae*)

× ***bitternensis*** 'Cliftonville Canary' WAbe
- 'Cliftonville Crimson' WAbe
- 'Cliftonville Old Rose' WAbe
- 'Cliftonville Pink' WAbe
- 'Cliftonville Roset' WAbe
caespitosa GAbr GArf WAbe
- var. ***gracilis*** GKev
coccinea EBee EWes EWld GArf GBin GKev GQue NBir NHpl WAbe WHal

	fragrans	GKev
	'Loch Ewe'	CExl EBee GKev NFav
	macrophylla	GKev
	microphylla	WAbe
	- f. ***alba***	WAbe
	- 'Hollowcliffe'	WAbe
	polyantha 'Cliftonville Scarlet'	WAbe
	'Snowflake' ♀H4	GAbr GArf NHpl

Ovidia (*Thymelaeaceae*)

	andina	MGil

Oxalis (*Oxalidaceae*)

	acetosella	GPoy GQue MHer NQui WHer WShi
	- var. ***rosea***	GRum
	- var. ***subpurpurascens***	MMrt WCot
	adenodes	NRog
	adenophylla ♀H4	CExl CMiW CRos EHyd ELan EPfP GAbr GBin GKev GMaP LRHS NFav NHol NHpl NLar NRHS NRog SDeJ SPoG SRms WBrk WCav
	adenophylla × ***enneaphylla***	see *O.*'Matthew Forrest'
	'Anne Christie'	NRya NSla
	arenaria F&W 10584	WCot
§	***articulata***	ELan NPer SEND WCav WSHC XLum
	- 'Alba'	ELan WCot XLum
	- f. ***crassipes*** 'Alba'	WCot
	- 'Jill'	CMea
§	- subsp. ***rubra***	SDeJ
	'Autumn Pink'	GKev
	bowiei	WCot
*	- ***purpurea***	CBor
	brasiliensis	CBor EPPr GKev
	compressa	NRog
	convexula	NRog
	'Dark Eye'	EPot
	dentata 'Pot of Gold'	GKev
	deppei	see *O. tetraphylla*
§	***depressa***	EPot EWes GKev LShi NBir NRya NSla SDeJ SGro
	'Double Trouble' (d)	CBor GKev
	dregei new	NRog
	eckloniana var. ***sonderi***	NRog
	enneaphylla ♀H4	CElw CRos EHyd GBin GEdr GMaP LRHS MNrw NRHS NRya SGro SPlb
	- 'Alba'	CElw GArf NRya NSla
	- subsp. ***ibari***	EPPr GEdr NRya WFar
	- 'Minutifolia'	GEdr GQue NRya NWad
	- 'Rosea'	CBor EPot GKev ITim NLar NRog NRya NSla SGro
	- 'Sheffield Swan'	GEdr NSla NWad
	- 'Ute'	EPPr GEdr NRya NWad
	'Fanny'	GKev
	flava	CPla NRog SChr
	- white-flowered	EPot GKev
	floribunda misapplied	see *O. articulata*
	foveolata	NRog
	gracilis	CBor EPot GKev
	griffithii double-flowered (d)	CMiW GGro
	- 'Pink Charm'	GEdr
	- 'Snowflake'	CMiW GEdr
	'Gwen McBride'	GArf GEdr
	hedysaroides Kunth	CCCN
	'Hemswell Knight'	EPPr
	hirta	SGro
	- 'Gothenburg'	EPPr EPri EShb GKev ITim NRog
	inops	see *O. depressa*
	'Ione Hecker' ♀H4	CBor CMiW EPot GArf GKev GMaP ITim NHpl NLar NRog NRya
	'Irish Mist' (v)	GKev
	'Jay'	NSla
*	***karroica***	NHpl WCot
	laciniata hybrid	GEdr
	lactea double-flowered	see *O. magellanica* 'Nelson'
	lasiandra	CCCN GKev
§	***latifolia***	GKev
	magellanica	GAbr SPlb
	- 'Flore Pleno'	see *O. magellanica* 'Nelson'
§	- 'Nelson' (d)	GBin NBir NPer SMad
	magnifica	GKev
	massoniana ♀H2	ECha EPot WAbe WCot
§	'Matthew Forrest'	WCot
§	***megalorrhiza***	NWad SChr
	melanosticta	EPot GEdr SDeJ WCot
§	- 'Ken Aslet' ♀H3	GKev ITim NBir NHpl SDeJ
	obtusa	ECha EPot
	- apricot-flowered	SDeJ
	oregana	CMac EPPr EWld MNrw SPhx WCot WCru
	- 'Bob Haszeldine'	GEdr
	- 'Klamath Ruby'	EWld WSHC
	- f. ***smalliana***	EWld GEdr MNrw NBro NLar WCot WCru
	- white-flowered	WCot
	perdicaria	EHyd EPot EWes GKev LRHS NRHS NRog WAbe WIce
	- 'Citrino'	WAbe WCot
	'Pink Pillow'	CBod
	polyphylla var. ***heptaphylla***	GEdr
§	***purpurea***	NRog
*	- 'Alba'	GKev
	- 'Garnet'	GKev
	- 'Ken Aslet'	see *O. melanosticta* 'Ken Aslet'
	regnellii	see *O. triangularis* subsp. *papilionacea*
	rosea misapplied	see *O. articulata* subsp. *rubra*
	semiloba	EPPr
	Slack Top hybrids	NSla
	'Slack's Hummingbird' new	WFar
	'Slack's Peacock'	NSla WFar
	'Snipe'	NSla
	speciosa	see *O. purpurea*
§	***spiralis*** subsp. ***vulcanicola***	CCCN
	- - 'Sunset Velvet'	WCot
	squamata	SPlb
	succulenta ambig.	CSpe
	'Sunny'	GKev
§	***tetraphylla***	CExl CPla GKev NPer
	- 'Iron Cross'	ELan EPPr GKev LCro LOPS NLar SDeJ SPlb WHil
	triangularis	CCCN CExl EWld MHer NPer WBrk
	- 'Birgit'	GKev SDeJ
	- BURGUNDY WINE ('JR Oxburwi') (Xalis Series)	CWGN NPer SBls
	- 'Mijke'	GKev
§	- subsp. ***papilionacea*** ♀H3	GKev WCot
	- - 'Atropurpurea'	CSpe SDeJ
	- subsp. ***triangularis***	GKev MBow
	tuberosa	CLau EPfP GPoy LEdu SPoG WKor
	'Ute'	NSla
	valdiviensis	NWad
	versicolor ♀H3	CBor EPot GKev ITim NBir NRog SDeJ WHil
	- 'Golden Cape'	CBor EPot GKev

vespertilionis Zucc. see *O. latifolia*

virginea NRog

I 'Waverley Hybrid' GKev GRum

zeekoevleyensis NRog

Oxycoccus see *Vaccinium*

Oxydendrum ✿ (*Ericaceae*)

arboreum CBcs CEnd CMCN EBee EGrI EHyd EPfP IArd LPar LRHS MAsh MBlu MGil MPkF SCob SPoG SSta XSte

Oxypetalum (*Apocynaceae*)

caeruleum see *Tweedia coerulea*

Oxyria (*Polygonaceae*)

digyna CAgr GGro WKor

Oxytropis (*Fabaceae*)

campestris var. ***gracilis*** GKev WSHC

podocarpa SPlb

purpurea SPlb

Ozothamnus (*Asteraceae*)

§ ***coralloides*** EPot SPlb WAbe

§ 'County Park Silver' GEdr GKev LShi

§ ***hookeri*** CDoC SPer SVen WCFE WPGP

§ ***ledifolius*** CBcs CBod CCoa CDoC ELan EPfP LRHS MGil SPer

§ ***rosmarinifolius*** CBcs CDoC CRos EHyd ELan EPfP GBin LRHS MAsh MSwo SEdd SGBe SPer SVen

- 'Silver Jubilee' CBcs CBod CCht CKel CRos CSBt ECre ELan EPfP LRHS MAsh MHtn MRav MSwo NRHS SLon SPer SPlb

§ ***selago*** ELan EPot WCot

- 'Major' SPlb

§ - var. ***tumidus*** ITim WThu

'Threave Seedling' CBod CCht CDoC CKel EHyd ELan LRHS MAsh SPer

P

Pachira (*Malvaceae*)

insignis <u>new</u> XSte

Pachyphragma (*Brassicaceae*)

§ ***macrophyllum*** EBee ECha ELon EWld IBlr LEdu MBel MMuc MRav NLar NSti SDix WCAu WCot WCru WPGP WPnP WSHC

Pachyphytum (*Crassulaceae*)

bracteosum CBod CDoC SEdd SIvy

hookeri SIvy

Pachypodium (*Apocynaceae*)

lamerei 𝕐H1a SPad SPlb

Pachysandra (*Buxaceae*)

axillaris SGBe WCot WPGP

- BWJ 8032 WCru

- 'Crûg's Cover' ESwi EWld GBin SMad WCru WFar

- var. ***stylosa*** MRav

procumbens EBee GKev MNrw NLar WCot

- 'Angola' (v) WCot

terminalis Widely available

- 'Green Carpet' CBcs CBod CChe CDoC CExl CRos CSBt EBee EHyd ELan EPfP GDam GMaP LRHS LSRN MAsh MGos MSwo NHol NLar NRHS SCob SJap SMad SNig SPer SPoG SWvt WCAu XLum

- 'Green Sheen' 𝕐H5 CBod ECha EHyd ELan EPPr EPfP GWyn LPar LRHS NRHS SCob WCAu

- 'Silver Edge' (v) EBee

- 'Variegata' (v) 𝕐H5 Widely available

Pachystachys (*Acanthaceae*)

lutea 𝕐H1b CCCN EShb

Pachystegia (*Asteraceae*)

§ ***insignis*** CTsd LRHS MPkF SGBe

× *Pachyveria* (*Crassulaceae*)

sp. CBod CDTJ NCft SEdd SIvy SSim

scheideckeri CDoC

Paederia (*Rubiaceae*)

scandens SBrt

Paederota (*Plantaginaceae*)

§ ***bonarota*** GEdr GKev WAbe

lutea GEdr GKev WCot

Paeonia ✿ (*Paeoniaceae*)

albiflora see *P. lactiflora*

'America' LPmr WCAu

§ ***anomala*** subsp. ***anomala*** EPot GKev ILea LPmr MPhe NLar SPtp

§ - subsp. ***veitchii*** CExl CJun CKel GAbr GBin GKev GMaP ILea LPla NBid NLar NWad WCAu WCot WPGP WSpi WThu

- subsp. ***veitchii*** × ***tenuifolia*** CJun

'Apricot Queen' <u>new</u> LPmr

arietina W&B BG A-4 WCot

'Armani' EPfP LRHS

'Athena' EHyd GBin LPmr LRHS WCAu

'Avant Garde' WCAu

'Bai Xue Ta' (S) NTPC

'Ballarena de Saval' ILea

banatica see *P. officinalis* subsp. *banatica*

§ 'Bartzella' (d) 𝕐H6 CBod CKel CRos EHed EHyd ELan EPfP GBin ILea LCro LOPS LPla LRHS MNrw NLar NRHS SEdd SHar SMad SPeP SPoG WCAu WCot

'Berry Garcia' GBin LRHS

beresowskii see *P. anomala* subsp *veitchii*

'Blaze' CKel EHyd GMaP ILea LPmr LRHS NLar NRHS SPeP WCAu WCot

'Blushing Princess' (d) <u>new</u> GBin

'Border Charm' CKel GBin ILea SDir

'Bridal Icing' CKel GBin LPmr WCAu

'Bride's Dream' GBin

'Buckeye Belle' (d) CBod CKel EBee EGrI ELan EPfP EWoo GBin GMaP ILea LCro LOPS LPmr LRHS LSRN MBel NLar SCob SMad SPoG WCAu WCot

'Burma Joy' WCAu

'Burma Midnight' GBin WCAu WKif

'Callie's Memory' CKel EGrI EPfP GBin ILea LRHS WCAu

cambessedesii 𝕐H3 CBro CRos CSpe EHyd EPot GEdr GKev LRHS NBir NRHS NSla WAbe

cambessedesii × ***daurica*** subsp. ***mlokosewitschii*** CRos EHyd LRHS NRHS

'Canary Brilliant'PBR CKel GBin

'Carol' ILea LPmr LSRN

	caucasica	see *P. daurcia* subsp. *coriifolia*
	× ***chamaeleon***	GKev
	'Chocolate Soldier'	WCAu
	'Christmas Velvet' (d)	LPmr WCAu
	'Claire de Lune'	CKel EWoo GBin GKev GMaP ILea IPot LPmr LRHS MGil WCAu WCot WKif
	'Claudia'	GBin
	'Color Magnet'	GBin WCAu
	'Command Performance'	GBin ILea IPot LPmr WCAu
	'Convoy' (d)	GBin WCAu
	'Copper Kettle' (d)	CKel ELan GBin ILea
	'Cora Louise'	CKel ELan GBin ILea LRHS MBros MHol SMad WCAu
	'Coral Beach' **new**	LRHS MPri
	'Coral Charm' ♀H6	CKel EBee EGrI EPfP GBin GMaP ILea LCro LOPS LPmr LRHS LSRN MHol MMrt MPri NLar SDeJ SPeP WCAu WCot WHoo XSen
	'Coral Fay'	GBin MPri
	'Coral 'n' Gold'	LRHS MPri WCAu
	'Coral Sunset'	CKel EGrI EWTr GBin ILea LCro LOPS LPmr LRHS MACG MMrt MPri NLar SCob SDeJ SMad SPer WCot WTyc
	'Coral Supreme'	GBin LPmr MPri
	corallina	see *P. mascula* subsp. *mascula*
	'Court Jester'	ELan GBin ILea
	'Cytherea'	GBin LPmr LRHS WCAu
§	***daurica***	EPot GKev WCot
§	- subsp. ***coriifolia***	WCot
	RCB UA 12	
§	- subsp. ***mlokosewitschii*** ♀H6	CBro CExl CKel CMea CRos EBee ECha EHyd EPot GEdr GKev ILea LEdu LPmr LRHS MBel MNrw NBir NRHS SLon SWvt WAbe WCAu WCot WHoo WKif WSpi
	- - hybrids	GKev
§	- subsp. ***wittmanniana***	EBee GEdr MBel WCAu
	- - PAB 3673	LEdu
	- - 'Rosea'	WCAu
	'Dearest'	GBin
	decora	see *P. peregrina*
	delavayi (S)	CPla CRos CTsd EHyd ELan EPfP GKev GMaP LCro LRHS MAsh MGil MGos NBir SCob SDix SPer SPoG SRms WCot
	- BWJ 7775	WCru
	- from China (S)	MPhe
	- var. ***angustiloba*** f. ***alba*** (S)	CExl
§	- - f. ***angustiloba*** (S)	CBcs GKev SEND
§	- - f. ***trollioides*** (S)	CExl SPtp
	- cf. var. ***angustiloba*** BO 15-142 **new**	GGro
§	- var. ***delavayi*** f. ***lutea*** (S)	CCVT CDoC CJun CRos EHyd EPfP GKev GLog GMaP LEdu LRHS MAsh MGos NBir SCob SIvy SLon SNig SPoG SRms WHoo
	- var. ***lutea***	see *P. delavayi* var. *delavayi* f. *lutea*
	- 'Mrs Sarson' (S)	SPtp
	- Potaninii Group	see *P. delavayi* var. *angustiloba* f. *angustiloba*
	- 'Tapestry' (S)	CSpe
	'Diana Parks'	GBin ILea LPmr NLar
	'Early Daybreak'	GBin
	'Early Glow'	GBin
	'Early Scout'	GBin
	'Early Windflower'	CKel ELan GBin ILea LPmr WCAu
	'Eden's Perfume'	CKel EPfP SPer
	'Eliza Lundy' (d)	GBin WCAu
	'Ellen Cowley'	WCAu
	emodi	CAvo CKel CMiW GKev ILea LPmr LRHS MCot WCAu WCot
	'Etched Salmon'	GBin LPmr WCAu
	'Fairy Princess'	GBin WCAu
§	× ***festiva*** 'Alba Plena' (d)	CKel EHyd EPfP GMaP ILea LPmr LRHS MRav NLar NRHS SCob SPer SWvt WFar
§	- 'Mutabilis Plena' (d)	LPmr
§	- 'Rosea Plena' (d) ♀H6	ECtt ELan EPfP GMaP LRHS SCob SPer SWvt WCAu WCot WFar
	- 'Rosea Superba Plena' (d)	LPmr
§	- 'Rubra Plena' (d) ♀H6	CKel CTri EBee ECtt EGrI ELan EPfP GMaP ILea LPmr LRHS LSun MBel MRav NGdn NLar SCob SPer SRms SWvt WBor WCAu WCot
	'Firelight'	GBin
	'First Arrival'	CKel GBin ILea LRHS MHol WCAu
	'First Dutch Yellow'	see *P.* 'Garden Treasure'
	'Flame'	EHyd EPfP EWTr GMaP ILea LPmr LRHS MBel MNrw NRHS NSti SDeJ SMad SPeP WCAu WCot
§	Gansu Group (S)	MPhe NTPC
	- 'Bai Bi Lan Xia' (S)	MPhe
	- 'Bai Zhang Bing' (S)	NTPC
	- 'Bing Xin Zi' (S)	NTPC
	- 'Dan Feng Ling Kong' (S)	NTPC
	- 'Er Long Nao Hai' (S)	MPhe
	- 'Fen Guan Yu Zhu' (S)	NTPC
	- 'Fen He' (S)	MPhe NTPC
	- 'Fen Jin Yu' (S)	NTPC
	- 'Gan Lan Yu' (S)	NTPC
	- 'Hei Feng Die' (S)	MPhe
	- 'Hei Xuan Feng' (S)	MPhe NTPC
	- 'Hei Yuan Shuai' (S)	MPhe
	- 'Hui He' (S)	MPhe
	- 'Jiao Rong' (S)	MPhe
	- 'Lan He' (S)	MPhe
	- 'Lan He Qi Ming' (S)	NTPC
	- 'Lan Tian Meng' (S)	MPhe
	- 'Lan Yu San Cai' (S)	NTPC
	- 'Long Yu Er Qiao' (S)	NTPC
	- 'Long Yuan Hong' (S)	MPhe
	- 'Mo Hai Yin Bo' (S)	MPhe
	- 'Ren Mian Tao Hua' (S)	NTPC
	- 'Ri Yue Tong Hui' (S)	MPhe
	- 'San Hua Nu' (S)	MPhe
	- 'Shu Sheng Peng Mo' (S)	MPhe
	- 'Tie Mian Wu Si' (S)	MPhe
	- 'Wu Kong Xiu Xing' (S)	NTPC
	- 'Xiong Mao' (S)	MPhe
	- 'Xue Hai Bing Xin' (S)	MPhe NTPC
	- 'Xue Lian' (S)	NTPC
	- 'Xue Yuan Yu Hui' (S)	NTPC
	- 'Ye Guang Bei' (S)	MPhe NTPC
	- 'Yi Du Chun Qiu' (S)	NTPC
	- 'Yin Yang Shan' (S)	MPhe
	- 'Yuan Yang Pu' (S)	MPhe
	- 'Zi Ban Bai' (S)	NTPC
	- 'Zi Die Ying Feng' (S)	MPhe NTPC
	- 'Zi Yan' (S)	NTPC
	- 'Zong Ban Bai' (S)	MPhe NTPC
	Gansu Mudan Group	see *P.* Gansu Group
	'Garden Peace'	GBin WCAu
§	'Garden Treasure'	CKel EHyd EPfP GBin LRHS MHol NRHS SDeJ SPoG WCAu
	'Going Bananas'	CKel LRHS
	'Golden Dream'	see *P.* 'Bartzella'
	'Golden Thunder'	CKel
	'Goldenball' (S) **new**	CKel
	'Hélène Martin'	GBin LPmr

	'Henry Bockstoce' (d)	CBod GMaP ILea LPmr LRHS MGil NLar WCAu
	'Hillary'	CKel GBin ILea WCAu
	'Hoki'	EHyd NRHS
	'Hong Bao Shi' (S)	NTPC
	'Honor'	WCAu
	'Huo Lian Jin Dan' (S)	NTPC
	'Illini Warrior'	CKel GBin ILea WCAu
	japonica misapplied	see *P. lactiflora*
	japonica (Makino) Miyabe & Takeda	see *P. obovata*
	japonica ambig.	GEdr
	'Jay Cee'	GBin
	'Jin Ge' (S)	NTPC
	'Joanna Marlene'	GBin ILea WCAu
	'Joseph Rock'	see *P. rockii*
	'Joyce Ellen'	LPmr
	'Julia Rose'	CKel EHyd EPfP GBin ILea LRHS NRHS SHar SMad SPoG WCAu
	'Kasagayama'	CKel
	'Kinkaku'	see *P.* × *lemoinei* 'Souvenir de Maxime Cornu'
	'Kinko'	see *P.* × *lemoinei* 'Alice Harding'
	'La Donna' (d)	GBin
§	***lactiflora***	SSal
	- 'Abalone Pearl'	GBin
	- 'Adolphe Rousseau'	ILea LCro LOPS LRHS WCAu
	- 'Agida'	ECtt EHyd LRHS MRav NRHS
	- 'Albert Crousse'	CBcs CKel LPmr MRav NBir WCAu
	- 'Alertie'	CKel GBin LPmr LRHS
	- 'Alice Harding'	LPmr WCAu
	- 'Allan Rogers'	WCAu
	- 'Amabilis'	LPmr
	- 'Amalia Olson'	WCAu
	- 'Angel Cheeks'	CKel GBin LCro LOPS LPmr WCAu
	- 'Ann Cousins'	CKel LPmr MGil WCAu
	- 'Antwerpen'	CRos EHyd LRHS NRHS
	- 'Argentine'	WCAu
	- 'Auguste Dessert'	WCAu
§	- 'Augustin d'Hour'	CKel LPmr LRHS NLar SHar
	- 'Aureole'	MRav
	- 'Avalanche'	CKel EPfP ILea LPmr LRHS NLar NRHS
	- 'Avalon'	WCAu
	- 'Ballerina'	MRav
	- 'Barbara'	WCAu
	- 'Baroness Schröder'	CKel EBee GBin LPmr MGil WCAu
	- 'Barrington Belle'	CKel ECtt EHyd EPfP GBin LPmr LRHS MBros NRHS WCAu WFar
	- 'Bess Bockstoce'	WCAu
	- 'Best Man'	LPmr WCAu
	- 'Better Times'	WCAu
	- 'Big Ben'	CKel EPfP LPmr LRHS NLar SMrm
	- 'Black Beauty'	EHyd IPot LPmr LRHS NRHS SCob SDeJ
	- 'Blush Queen'	CKel GBin WCAu
	- 'Border Gem'	CRos EHyd LRHS MRav NRHS WCAu
	- 'Bouchela'	LPmr NSti
	- 'Boule de Neige'	CKel ILea LPmr
	- 'Bouquet Perfect'	EHyd LRHS NRHS WCAu
	- 'Bowl of Beauty' ♀H6	Widely available
	- 'Bowl of Cream'	CKel GBin ILea LPmr LRHS SCob SWvt WCAu
	- 'Bridal Gown'	GBin LPmr WCAu
	- 'Bridal Shower'	GBin
	- 'Bright Knight'	WCAu
	- 'Bunker Hill'	CBod CKel CRos ECtt EHyd EWTr GBin LPmr LRHS NRHS SPer SWvt WCAu
	- 'Butter Bowl'	CBod GBin WCAu

- 'Candy Stripe'	GBin LPmr
- 'Catharina Fontijn'	CBod CKel EHyd GBin ILea LPmr LRHS NRHS WCAu
- 'Celebrity'	CKel LPmr
- 'Charles Burgess'	EPfP GBin ILea LPmr WCAu
- 'Charlie's White'	GBin ILea LPmr LRHS NLar SDeJ SPer WCAu
- 'Charm'	EGrI WCAu
- 'Cheddar Cheese'	CKel LPmr
- 'Cheddar Gold'	WCAu
- 'Cherry Hill'	GBin SMad WCAu
- 'Claire Dubois'	EHyd LRHS NRHS
- 'Class Act'	GBin
- 'Cora Stubbs'	CKel GBin SPer WCAu
- 'Cornelia Shaylor'	WCAu
- 'Couronne d'Or'	GBin ILea WCAu
- 'Cringley White'	SRms
- 'Dawn Pink'	EPfP WCAu
- 'Daystar'	MRav
- 'Dinner Plate'	CKel GBin LPmr MGil WCAu
- 'Do Tell'	CKel EPfP ILea LPmr NLar SPer WCAu
- 'Doctor Alexander Fleming'	CKel EGrI EHyd EPfP EWoo GBin ILea LRHS MACG MBNS MGil MNrw MPri NBir NRHS SDeJ SWvt WCAu WFar
- 'Doreen'	CKel EBee EHyd EPfP GBin LPmr LRHS NRHS SHar WCAu
- 'Drumline'	SDeJ
- 'Dublin' **new**	LPmr
- 'Duchesse de Nemours' ♀H6	Widely available
- 'Edulis Superba'	CRos EBee ECtt EHyd GBin ILea LEdu LPmr LRHS MBNS MRav NPer NRHS SPer WCAu
- 'Elaine'	MRav
- 'Elsa Sass'	CKel GBin ILea LPmr WCAu
- 'Emma Klehm'	CKel GBin WCAu
- 'Evelyn Tibbets'	GBin
- 'Fairy's Petticoat'	CKel LPmr WCAu
- 'Félix Crousse' ♀H6	CBcs CKel CTri EBee EGrI ELan EPfP GBin GMaP ILea LPmr LRHS LSRN MBNS MPri MRav NBir NLar SDeJ SPer WCAu WFar XSen
- 'Felix Supreme'	GBin
- 'Festiva Maxima' ♀H6	Widely available
- 'Firebelle'	WCAu
- 'Florence Ellis'	WCAu
- 'Florence Nicholls'	CKel ELan EPfP ILea LPmr WCAu
- 'Foxtrot'	GBin
- 'François Ortegat'	EPfP LRHS
- 'Garden Lace'	SDeJ WCAu
- 'Gardenia'	CKel CRos EHyd ELan EPfP GBin LPmr LRHS NRHS SDeJ WCot WKif
- 'Gay Paree'	CKel GBin ILea LPmr MGil MHol MRav WCAu
- 'Gayborder June'	WCAu
- 'Général Joffre'	MRav
- 'Général MacMahon'	see *P. lactiflora* 'Augustin d'Hour'
- 'Germaine Bigot'	CKel GBin MRav WCAu
- 'Gilbert Barthelot'	WCAu
- 'Golden Frolic'	WCAu
- 'Goldilocks'	CKel WCAu
- 'Goldmine'	SMrm SPeP
- 'Great Lady'	GBin
- 'Great Sport'	MRav
- 'Green Halo'	GBin LPmr WCot
- 'Green Lotus'	LPmr NLar
- 'Happy Days'	WCAu
- 'Hari-ai-nin'	ILea
- 'Helen Hayes'	CKel WCAu

– 'Henry Sass' **new**	CKel
– 'Hermione'	LPmr WCAu
– 'High Adventure'	GBin
– 'Highlight'	LPmr
– 'Hit Parade'	WCAu
– 'Honey Gold'	CKel EWoo GBin ILea IPot LPmr SMad SPoG WCAu WSpi
– 'Hot Chocolate'	WCAu
– 'Immaculée'	CKel EHyd EWoo GBin ILea LCro LOPS LPmr LRHS MRav SCob SPer SPoG WKif
– 'Inspecteur Lavergne'	CKel ECtt EHyd EPfP ILea LPmr LRHS MACG NGdn NRHS SPer WCAu WCot
– 'Instituteur Doriat'	WCAu
– 'Jacorma'	ILea LPmr NLar
– 'Jadwigha'	ILea
– 'James Kelway'	CKel
– 'Jan van Leeuwen'	CKel EPfP GBin GMaP LCro LOPS LPmr LRHS SEdd WCAu WCot WKif
– 'Joker'	GBin WCAu
– 'Jubilee'	LRHS
– 'Judith Eileen'	WCAu
– 'June Rose'	WCAu
– 'Kansas'	CKel CWCL EBee EHyd ELan EPfP GBin ILea LPmr LRHS MPri NBir NGdn NLar NRHS SCob SPeP SPoG WCAu WCot WFar
– 'Karen Gray'	GBin WCAu
– 'Karl Rosenfield'	CBcs CKel CRos EBee EHyd EPfP EWoo GBin ILea LCro LOPS LPmr LRHS LSRN LSun MGil MNrw MPri MRav NLar NRHS SCob SPer SPoG SRms SWvt WCAu WFar WHoo XSen
– 'Kelway's Glorious'	CKel ECtt EHyd EPfP EWTr LPmr LRHS MBNS MHol MRav NLar NRHS WCAu WGwG WHoo WKif
– 'Kelway's Majestic'	MRav
– KIEV	EHyd LPmr LRHS NRHS
§ – 'Koningin Wilhelmina'	MNrw
– 'Krinkled White'	CBod CKel CRos EBee EHyd EPfP EWTr EWoo GBin GMaP ILea LPmr LRHS MPri MRav NLar NRHS SDeJ SPeP SPoG WCAu WKif
– 'Lady Alexandra Duff' ♀H6	CKel GBin ILea LPmr LRHS MRav NBir NGdn SWvt WCAu WKif
– 'Lady Anna'	LPmr
– 'Lady in Red' **new**	MHol
– 'Lady Orchid'	EPfP WCAu
– 'Lancaster Imp'	GBin WCAu
– 'Largo'	WCAu
– 'Laura Dessert' ♀H6	CKel GBin ILea LCro LOPS LPmr LRHS WCAu WKif
– 'Le Cygne'	CKel
– 'L'Éclatante'	LRHS
– 'Liebchen'	WCAu
– 'Lilac Times'	WCAu
– 'Lillian Wild'	WCAu
– 'Little Medicineman'	EHyd
– 'Lois Kelsey'	WCAu
– LONDON	EHyd LPmr LRHS NRHS
– 'Lord Kitchener'	CRos ECtt EHyd EPfP GBin LPmr LRHS NRHS WGwG
– 'Lotus Queen'	ECtt
– 'Louis van Houtte'	EGrI
– 'Love's Touch'	GBin
– 'Lowell Thomas'	GBin LPmr WCAu
– 'Ma Petite Cherie'	GBin
– 'Madame Calot'	CKel EHyd LPmr LRHS NRHS WCAu
– 'Madame Claude Tain'	LPmr WCot
– 'Madame Edouard Doriat'	WCAu
– 'Madame Emile Debatène'	MBNS MHol WCAu WFar
– 'Madame Gaudichau'	MAvo WCot
– MADRID	EHyd LPmr LRHS NRHS
– 'Margaret Truman'	LPmr WCAu
– 'Marie Crousse'	WCAu
– 'Marie Lemoine'	CKel ILea LPmr LRHS MACG WCAu WCot
– 'Mischief'	MRav
– 'Miss America' ♀H6	CKel EPfP GBin LPmr MMrt NLar WCAu WKif
– 'Miss Eckhart'	WCAu
– 'Mister Ed'	WCAu
– 'Monsieur Jules Elie' ♀H6	CKel ELan EPfP EWTr EWoo GBin ILea LCro LOPS LRHS MHol NGdn NLar SPer WCAu
– 'Monsieur Martin Cahuzac'	GBin LRHS
– 'Moon of Nippon'	ILea LPmr LRHS WCAu
– 'Moon River'	CKel EPfP GBin LPmr NLar WCAu
– 'Morning Kiss'	EPfP LPmr
– 'Moscow' (d) **new**	LPmr
– 'Mother's Choice'	CKel EWoo GBin LCro LOPS LSRN NGdn NLar WCAu WCot
– 'Mr G.F. Hemerik'	CKel EGrI GBin WBor WCAu WCot
– 'Mrs Edward Harding'	WCAu
– 'Mrs Livingston Farrand'	GBin
– 'My Pal Rudy'	GBin
– 'Myrtle Gentry'	WCAu
– 'Nancy Nora'	SPer WCAu
– 'Neon'	LPmr LRHS
– 'Nice Gal'	GBin LPmr WCAu
– 'Nick Shaylor'	WCAu
– 'Nippon Beauty'	EGrI ILea LPmr LRHS NLar SCob SDeJ WCAu WCot WFar WTor
– 'Noémie Demay'	CKel LPmr LRHS
– 'Nymphe'	CKel LPmr MBel MRav NLar SDeJ WCAu
– OSLO	LPmr LRHS
– 'Paul M. Wild'	CKel ELan ILea NLar WCAu
I – 'Peaches and Cream'	LPmr
* – 'Pecher'	EHyd EPfP LRHS NLar NPer NRHS SDeJ
– 'Peter Brand'	CKel ECtt ELan GBin ILea IPot LPmr LRHS LSRN NLar
– 'Petite Elegance'	GBin WCAu
– 'Petite Porcelain'	WCAu
– 'Philippe Rivoire'	CKel WCAu
– 'Philomèle'	CKel WCAu
– 'Pietertje Vriend Wagenaar'	GBin
– 'Pillow Cases'	WCAu
– 'Pillow Talk'	ELan ILea LPmr LRHS NLar SPoG WCAu
– 'Pink Cameo'	WCAu WCot WFar
– 'Pink Dawn' Kelways	WCAu
– 'Pink Delight'	GBin
– 'Pink Giant'	WCAu
– 'Pink Parfait'	CKel ILea LPmr SCob SPer WCAu
– 'Pink Princess'	GBin
– 'President Franklin D. Roosevelt'	ECtt EHyd LRHS NRHS
– 'Président Poincaré'	MRav
– 'President Taft'	see *P. lactiflora* 'Reine Hortense'
– 'Primevère'	CKel ECtt LPmr NBir NLar SPer WFar
– 'Princess Bride'	GBin
§ – 'Purple Spider'	LPmr SPeP
– 'Queen of Sheba'	WCAu
– 'Raspberry Sundae'	CKel EHyd ELan EPfP ILea LPmr LRHS MRav NLar NRHS SPer SPoG WCAu WCot

	- 'Red Queen'	CKel GBin
	- RED SARAH BERNHARDT	EPfP GBin ILea LPmr SDeJ SPer
	- 'Red Satin'	WCAu
	- 'Red Spider'	see *P. lactiflora* 'Purple Spider'
§	- 'Reine Hortense'	CKel ECtt GBin LPmr LRHS MRav
	- 'Renato'	EHyd MHol
	- 'Roland'	WCAu
	- ROME	EHyd EPfP LPmr LRHS NRHS SCoo
	- 'Salmon Dream'	GBin WCAu
	- 'Santa Fe'	CKel EHyd EPfP LRHS NRHS WCAu
	- 'Sarah Bernhardt' ♀H6	Widely available
	- 'Sea Shell'	CKel GMaP ILea SPeP WCAu
	- 'Sebastiaan Maas'	ILea LPmr
	- 'Serene Pastel'	CKel WCAu
	- 'Shawnee Chief'	GBin
	- 'Shirley Temple'	CKel CRos EBee EHyd ELan EPfP EWoo GBin ILea LCro LOPS LPmr LRHS MBNS MGos MPri MRav NBir NGdn NRHS SCob SCoo SDeJ SEdd SPoG WCAu WCot WFar
	- 'Silver Rose'	GBin
	- 'Sir Ernest Shackleton'	MRav
	- 'Snow Mountain'	CKel LPmr
	- 'Soft Salmon Joy'	EGrI GBin WCAu
	- 'Solange'	CKel ILea LPmr LRHS
	- 'Sorbet'	CKel EPfP LPmr LRHS MHol NBir NLar NPer SDeJ SMad WCAu WFar
	- 'Surugu'	WCAu
	- 'Sweet Sixteen'	GBin LPmr WCAu
	- 'Sword Dance'	CKel CRos EGrI EHyd EPfP GDam ILea LPmr LRHS NRHS SDeJ WCAu WSpi
	- 'The Fawn'	CKel EPfP ILea LPmr WCAu
	- 'The Nymph'	LRHS NBir
	- 'Thérèse'	WCAu
	- 'Tom Eckhardt'	CKel GBin WCAu
	- 'Top Brass'	CKel ECtt GBin ILea LPmr MRav SDeJ WCAu WTor
	- 'Ursa Minor'	WCAu
	- 'Victoire de la Marne'	CKel ILea LPmr
	- 'Victoria Blush'	WCAu
	- 'Vivid Rose'	WCAu
	- 'Vogue'	CKel EHyd EPfP LPmr LRHS MRav NRHS SWvt WCAu
	- 'West Elkton'	GBin
	- 'Westerner'	GBin WCAu
	- 'White Angel'	SPer
	- 'White Cap'	CKel GBin ILea IPot LPmr MMrt NLar WCAu
	- 'White Grace'	GBin
	- 'White Sands'	GBin
	- 'White Wings'	CBcs CKel CRos CTri ECtt EHyd ELan EPfP EWTr GBin GMaP ILea LPmr LRHS MBel MNrw NLar NRHS NSti SMad SPer SWvt WCAu WCot
	- 'Whitleyi Major' ♀H6	WCot
	- 'Wilbur Wright'	CKel WCAu
	- 'Wine Red'	GBin
	- 'Władysława'	CKel LPmr LRHS NLar SHar WCot
§	- 'Zi Yu Nu'	NRHS SMad
	- 'Zuzu'	GBin
	× ***lagodechiana***	see *P. daurica* subsp. *mlokosewitschii*
	'Late Windflower'	GBin GKev LPla LPmr WCAu
	'Lavender Baby'	GBin
	× ***lemoinei*** (S)	WHal
§	- 'Alice Harding' (S)	CKel
	- 'High Noon' (S) ♀H5	CKel GMaP LRHS MPhe WCAu
§	- 'Souvenir de Maxime Cornu' (S)	CKel EHyd NRHS
	'Lemon Chiffon'	CKel GBin LPmr WCAu WCot
	'Lemon Dream'PBR	CKel ELan GBin ILea WCAu
	lobata 'Fire King'	see *P. peregrina*
	'Lollipop' (d)	CKel ELan GBin ILea LRHS
	'Lorelei' (d)	GBin
	'Love Affair'	ELan WCAu
	'Lovely Rose'	GBin WCAu
	ludlowii (S)	Widely available
	ludlowii × (× ***suffruticosa***) 'Hakuojisi' (S)	EHyd
	lutea	see *P. delavayi* var. *delavayi* f. *lutea*
	'Mackinac Grand'	WCAu
	'Magenta Gem'	GBin
	'Magical Mystery Tour'	GBin LRHS
	'Mahogany'	GBin
	'Mai Fleuri'	WCAu
	mairei	CExl GGGa SPtp WMal
	'Many Happy Returns'	CKel GBin ILea LPmr WCAu
	'Martha Bulloch'	CKel
	mascula	CBro GEdr GKev GLog NBir WCot
§	- subsp. ***mascula***	GKev
	- subsp. ***russoi*** 'Reverchoni'	EPot WAbe
	- subsp. ***triternata***	see *P. daurica*
	'Merry Mayshine'	GBin GKev
	'Mikuhino-akebono'	CKel SDeJ
	mlokosewitschii	see *P. daurica* subsp. *mlokosewitschii*
	mollis	see *P. officinalis* subsp. *officinalis*
	'Moonrise'	CKel GBin LPmr MMrt WCAu
	'Morning Lilac'	CKel ILea LRHS SPeP WCAu
	'My Love'	CKel GBin LPmr WCAu
	'Norwegian Blush'	CKel GBin ILea WCAu
	'Nova'	GBin
§	***obovata*** subsp. ***obovata***	GKev SPtp
	- - 'Alba' ♀H5	CExl GEdr GKev WAbe WSHC WSpi
	- subsp. ***willmottiae***	CExl GKev
	officinalis	GKev MCot WCot
	- WM 9821 from Slovenia	MPhe
	- from NW Croatia	LEdu
	- 'Alba Plena'	see *P.* × *festiva* 'Alba Plena'
	- 'Anemoniflora Rosea' ♀H6	EHed EHyd EPfP ILea LRHS NRHS SMad SPer SWvt WCAu
§	- subsp. ***banatica***	MPhe
§	- subsp. ***huthii***	LPmr LRHS SEND WCAu
	- 'James Crawford Weguelin'	WCot
	- 'Mutabilis Plena'	see *P.* × *festiva* 'Mutabilis Plena'
§	- subsp. ***officinalis***	GKev
	- 'Rosea Plena'	see *P.* × *festiva* 'Rosea Plena'
	- 'Rubra Plena'	see *P.* × *festiva* 'Rubra Plena'
	- subsp. ***villosa***	see *P. offinalis* subsp. *huthii*
	'Old Faithful'	GBin LPmr
	'Old Rose Dandy'	CKel ELan GBin ILea NLar
	'Oriental Gold'	WHil
	ostii (S)	CExl GKev
	'Oukan' (S)	CKel
	'Paladin'	GBin
	'Paris'	EHyd LRHS
	'Pastel Splendor'	CKel CRos EHyd ELan GBin ILea LRHS NRHS SMad WCAu
	'Patio Moscow Deep' (Patio Series)	LRHS
	'Paula Fay'	EPfP GBin GMaP ILea LPmr MGil MRav NLar SDeJ WCAu WCot
	'Pehrson's Violet Frisbee'	GBin
§	***peregrina***	CBro EPot GEdr GKev LEdu MPhe WCAu
	- 'Fire King'	WCAu
§	- 'Otto Froebel' ♀H6	CKel LPmr WCAu WCot WKif

	– 'Rosabella'	EHyd LRHS NRHS
	– 'Sunshine'	see *P. peregrina* 'Otto Froebel'
	'Picotee'	GBin
	'Pink Ardour'	GBin
	'Pink Double Dandy' (d)	GBin
	'Pink Hawaiian Coral'	CKel GBin ILea LPmr MPri NLar WCot WTor
	potaninii	see *P. delavayi* var. *angustiloba* f. *angustiloba*
	'Prairie Charm'	CKel EPfP ILea LRHS
	'Prairie Moon'	CKel GBin
	'Raggedy Ann'	ELan GBin
	'Raspberry Charm'	SDir
	'Red Charm'	CKel EPfP EWTr GBin ILea LPmr LRHS SPer WCAu WFar WKif WSpi
	'Red Grace' (d)	GBin LPmr
	'Red Magic'	EPfP WFar WSpi
§	***rockii*** (S)	CSpe GKev LRHS MPhe SPtp WSpi
	– from Tianshui, Gansu	MPhe
§	– subsp. ***atava*** (S)	GKev
	– hybrid	see *P.* Gansu Group
	– subsp. ***taibaishanica***	see *P. rockii* subsp. *atava*
	'Roman Gold'	CKel
	romanica	see *P. peregrina*
	'Rose Garland'	GBin
	'Rosedale'	GBin WCAu
	'Roselette'	GBin WCAu
	'Roy Pehrson's Best Yellow'	GBin
	'Salmon Beauty' (d)	WCAu
	'Salmon Chiffon'	GBin
	'Scarlet Heaven'	CKel ELan GBin ILea LRHS MMrt MNrw WCAu
	'Scarlet O'Hara'	EWoo NLar SPer WCAu WCot
	'Scrumdidleumptious' (d)	GBin
	'Sebastian Maas' (d) **new**	LPmr
	'Sequestered Sunshine'	CKel ILea LRHS NLar WCAu
	'Serebrenyi Velvet'	GBin
	'Shikoh' (S) **new**	CKel
	'Shimano-fuji' (S)	WCAu
	'Show Girl'	LPmr WCAu
	'Silver Dawn'	GBin
	sinensis	see *P. lactiflora*
	'Singing in the Rain'	CKel ILea NLar
	sinjianensis	see *P. anomala* subsp. *anomala*
	× ***smouthii***	EHyd GEdr LRHS NRHS
	'Soft Salmon Saucer' **new**	GBin
	'Sonoma Amethyst'	CKel ELan
	'Sonoma Apricot'	WCAu
	'Sonoma Kaleidoscope'	CKel ILea
	'Sonoma Sun'	CKel
	'Sonoma Velvet Ruby'	GBin LRHS
	'Soshi'	GBin LRHS SHar
	'Stardust'	WCAu
	'Starlight'	LCro LOPS LPmr LRHS WCAu WCot
	sterniana	CExl
	suffruticosa	see *P.* × *suffruticosa*
	– subsp ***atava***	see *P. rockii* subsp. *atava*
	× ***suffruticosa***	CDoC MGil MGos SSal
	– 'Akashigata' (S)	CKel
	– BIRD OF RIMPO	see *P.* × *suffruticosa* 'Rimpo'
	– 'Cardinal Vaughan' (S)	CKel
	– dark lavender-flowered (S)	ILea
	– dark pink-flowered (S)	ILea
	– dark red-flowered (S)	ILea
	– 'Dou Lu' (S)	NTPC
	– 'Duchess of Kent' (S)	CKel
	– 'Duchess of Marlborough' (S)	CKel
	– ETERNAL CAMELLIAS	see *P.* × *suffruticosa* 'Yachiyo-tsubaki'
	– FLIGHT OF CRANES	see *P.* × *suffruticosa* 'Renkaku'
	– 'Gekkyu-den' (S)	LRHS
	– 'Hai Huang' (S)	NTPC
§	– 'Hakuo-jisi' (S/d)	LRHS
	– 'Hana-asobi' (S) **new**	LRHS
§	– 'Hana-daijin' (S)	LRHS
§	– 'Hana-kisoi' (S)	EBee EHyd LRHS NRHS
	– 'Hei Hai Sa Jin' (S)	NTPC
§	– 'Hei Hua Kui' (S)	NTPC
	– JEWEL IN THE LOTUS	see *P.* × *suffruticosa* 'Tama-fuyo'
	– 'Jin Jiang Hong' (S)	NTPC
	– 'Joseph Rock'	see *P. rockii*
§	– 'Kamada-fuji' (S)	CKel
§	– 'Kaow' (S)	EHyd NRHS WCAu
	– KING OF FLOWERS	see *P.* × *suffruticosa* 'Kaow'
	– 'Kinkaku'	see *P.* × *lemoinei* 'Souvenir de Maxime Cornu'
	– 'Kinshi'	see *P.* × *lemoinei* 'Alice Harding'
	– 'Koshino-yuki' (S)	LRHS
	– 'Lan Bao Shi' (S)	NTPC
	– light pink-flowered (S)	ILea
	– light red-flowered (S)	ILea
	– 'Mrs William Kelway' (S)	CKel
	– 'Nigata Akashigata' (S)	CKel
	– purple-flowered (S)	EWTr ILea
§	– 'Renkaku' (S)	CKel LRHS
§	– 'Rimpo' (S)	WSpi
	– 'Rou Fu Rong' (S)	WSpi
	– 'Sakurajishi' (S)	CKel
	– 'Seidai' (S)	LRHS
	– 'Shikōden' (S) **new**	LRHS
	– 'Shimadaijin'	EHyd LRHS NRHS WCAu
	– 'Shimane-chōjuraku' (S)	CKel
	– 'Shimanishiki' (S)	CKel
	– SNOWY PAGODA	see *P.* × *suffruticosa* 'Xue Ta'
§	– 'Taiyo' (S)	EBee EHyd LRHS NRHS
§	– 'Tama-fuyo' (S)	CKel
	– white-flowered (S)	EWTr ILea
	– WISTERIA AT KAMADA	see *P.* × *suffruticosa* 'Kamada-fuji'
	– 'Wu Long Peng Sheng' (S)	LPar WSpi
§	– 'Xue Ta' (S)	LPar
§	– 'Yachiyo-tsubaki' (S)	CKel
§	– 'Yae-zakura' (S)	LRHS
	– 'Yatsu-kazishi' (S)	EBee
	– yellow-flowered (S)	ILea
	– 'Yin Hong Qiao Dui' (S)	NTPC
	– 'Yu Ban Bai' (S)	EGrI
	– 'Zhao Fen' (S)	NPer NTPC SRms
	'Sugar 'n' Spice'	GBin
	'Summer Glow' (d)	LPmr WCAu
	'Sunny Girl'	WCAu
	'Sunshine'	see *P. peregrina* 'Otto Froebel'
	'Syukiden'	CKel
*	***szowitsianum***	GKev
	'Tama-usagi'	CKel
	'Tango'	WCAu
	tenuifolia	CBro CJun CPla CSpe EPot EWes GBin GEdr GKev MBel NSti SMad WCAu WSpi
	'Terrific Gal'	GBin
	'Unique'	ILea
	veitchii	see *P. anomala* subsp. *veitchii*
	– var. ***woodwardii***	see *P. anomala* subsp. *veitchii*
	'Viking Full Moon'	CKel ILea NLar
	'Walter Mains'	WCAu
	'Watermelon Wine'	CKel ILea WCAu
	wendelboi **new**	GKev
	'White Charm'	GBin
	'White Emperor'	CKel ELan GBin ILea LRHS WCAu
	'White Innocence'	GBin
	'White Towers'	WFar
	'Whopper'	GBin

wittmanniana	see *P. daurica* subsp. *wittmanniana*
'Yankee Doodle Dandy' (d)	LRHS WCAu
'Yellow Crown'	LRHS MHol SCob SDir WCAu
'Yellow Waterlily'	CKel

Paesia (*Dennstaedtiaceae*)

scaberula	CBdn CBrP LEdu NBir WCot WPGP

pak choi see AGM Vegetables Section

Pallenis (*Asteraceae*)

§ ***maritima***	CCCN

Pamianthe (*Amaryllidaceae*)

peruviana	WMal

Panax (*Araliaceae*)

ginseng	GPoy
japonicus	WCru
- BWJ 7932	WCru

Pancratium (*Amaryllidaceae*)

canariense	NRog
maritimum	GKev SDeJ WCot

Pandorea (*Bignoniaceae*)

jasminoides ♀H1c	CCCN CDoC CRHN CTri EBak EShb
- 'Alba'	CRHN EShb
§ - 'Charisma' (v)	CBcs CCCN CKel ECre EPfP EShb SEND SPer WAvo
- 'Lady Di'	CCCN
- 'Rosea'	CCCN WAvo
- 'Rosea Superba' ♀H1c	CBcs CRHN SEND SPer WLov
- 'Variegata'	see *P. jasminoides* 'Charisma'
lindleyana	see *Clytostoma calystegioides*
pandorana	CRHN MGil WAvo
- 'Golden Showers'	CBcs CCCN CRHN MRav WLov
- 'Snowbells'	IArd IDee

Panicum (*Poaceae*)

amarum	CBod EPPr
- var. ***amarulum***	CKno
- 'Dewey Blue'	SMHy
bulbosum	EBee EPPr
clandestinum	EHyd EPPr EShb EWes
'Frosted Explosion'	CSpe LRHS SSal
miliaceum	EHyd SVic
- 'Violaceum'	SPhx
virgatum	CKno EPPr LRHS XLum
- 'Black and Blue'	MNrw
- 'Black and Light'	MNrw
- 'Blue Tower'	CKno EHyd ELon EPPr SMea XLum
- 'Cardinal'	CKno ECha EPPr MNrw WFar WHoo
- 'Carthage'	EPPr
- 'Cave-in-Rock' **new**	EPPr
- 'Cheyenne Sky'	EBee ECha EPPr
- 'Cloud Nine' ♀H5	CKno EBee EPPr LRHS MAvo SMea WHal
- 'Dallas Blues' ♀H5	CBod CKno EAJP EBee ECha EHyd ELan ELon EPPr EShb EWes GBee LRHS MAvo MSpe NLar NRHS NWsh SCob SGbt SMHy SPeP SPer SPoG WFar XLum XSte
- 'Emerald Chief'	CBod EHyd LSun SBls
- 'Farbende Auslese'	EPPr
- 'Hänse Herms'	CBod CKno EHyd ELon EMor EPPr LRHS NLar NRHS SMea WFar
- 'Heavy Metal' ♀H5	Widely available
- 'Heiliger Hain'	EHyd ELon EPPr LRHS NRHS WCot WFar WHoo
- 'Hot Rod' **new**	IPot NDov
- 'JS Blue Darkness'PBR **new**	IPot LRHS MAvo
- 'JS Dark Night'PBR **new**	MAvo
- 'Külsen Moor'	EBee IPot WCot
I - 'Kupferhirse'	CMea ECha EPPr MAvo WFar
- 'Kurt Bluemel'	EBee EPPr
- 'Nican'	EPPr MAvo
- 'Northwind' ♀H5	CBod CKno CRos CSde EBee EHyd ELon EPPr EPfP LRHS MACG MAvo NRHS SCob SEdd SMHy SMad SMea SPeP SRms WFar
- 'Prairie Fire'	ECtt
- 'Prairie Sky'	CBod CKno CRos EAJP EBee EBlo EHyd ELon EPPr EWTr EWhm EWoo GMaP LEdu LRHS MACG MAsh MAvo NBro NLar NRHS NWsh SCob SCoo SEdd SGbt SMHy SMad SMea SRms
- PURPLE BREEZE ('Joz276'PBR)	CBod CKno CPar EShb LCro LOPS LRHS SPad SPeP
- 'Purple Haze'	EBlo EHyd EPPr
- 'Red Cloud'	CKno ELon MAvo
- 'Rehbraun'	CBod CSde EHyd ELan EPPr EPfP LCro LOPS LRHS LSRN NRHS SCob SRms WCAu WChS WSMil XLum
- 'Rotstrahlbusch'	CBod CKno ELan EPPr GMaP LRHS LSun MAvo SPer SRms WCot XLum
- 'Rubrum'	EPfP LRHS MAvo SRms
- 'Sangria'PBR	CBod CSpe LEdu SPoG
- 'Shenandoah' ♀H5	Widely available
- 'Squaw'	Widely available
- 'Straight Cloud'	EPPr WFar
- 'Strictum'	CBod EPPr EWes GQue LRHS SCob SMHy SPer SPhx
I - 'Strictum Compactum'	CBod
- 'Sunburst' **new**	EPPr
- 'Thundercloud'	CKno
- 'Warrior'	CBod CKno CRos CTri ECtt EHyd ELan ELon EPPr EPfP EWhm LRHS MAsh MAvo NFav NLar NRHS NWsh SBls SCob SCoo SEdd SPer WCAu WFar WHoo
- 'Wood's Variegated' (v)	WCot

Papaver (*Papaveraceae*)

from Tajikistan **new**	GGro
alboroseum	EHyd GArf LRHS NRHS
alpinum	CSpe EHyd GQue MAsh NRHS
atlanticum	EBou NBro SPlb
- 'Flore Pleno' (d)	CSpe GAbr NBro
bracteatum	see *P. orientale* var. *bracteatum*
burseri	SRot
§ ***cambricum***	CBod CCCN CExl CMac CTri CTtf EHyd ELan EPfP LEdu LRHS NAts NRHS SPer WBrk WCot WFar WHer
- var. ***aurantiacum***	WCot
§ - 'Frances Perry'	CSpe
carmeli	SPhx
'Cherry Glow'	SPhx
commutatum ♀H5	CSpe LCro LEdu LOPS SPhx
- 'Ladybird' ♀H5	GAbr SPoG SVic
dubium	CSpe GPoy SPhx
- subsp. ***lecoqii*** 'Albiflorum'	CSpe LRHS SDix SPhx
'Faucett Moon' **new**	LRHS
glaucum	CSpe SPhx
guerlekense W&B BG-K-5	WCot
'Heartbeat' (Super Poppy Series)	CBod EPfP MHol WFar

heldreichii — see *P. pilosum* subsp. *spicatum*
lateritium — SRms
'Matador' PBR 🏆H6 — EHyd NRHS
'Medallion' (Super Poppy Series) — MPie
§ ***miyabeanum*** — CSpe EHyd LRHS NRHS
'Moondance' — CBcs CRos EHyd LRHS MACG NRHS SVic
§ ***nudicaule*** — LCro LOPS SVic
- Champagne Bubbles Group — CBod CSBt EHyd LRHS NRHS WFar
- DELUXE MIXED — CSpe
- Garden Gnome Group — see *P. nudicaule* Gartenzwerg Group
§ - Gartenzwerg Group 🏆H7 — EHyd EPfP LRHS NRHS SPoG SRot SWvt
- 'Kelmscott Giant' — SVic
- 'Pacino' — LRHS
(Oriental Group) — CBcs CDor LRHS NGdn SPhx
'Aglaja' 🏆H7 — WCAu WSpi
- 'Allegro' — CSBt EHyd GMaP LRHS LSun NGdn SCob SCoo SPlb SPoG SVic SWvt WFar
- 'Baby Kiss' PBR — WFar
- 'Beauty of Livermere' — CBod CDor CWCL EAJP ECha EHyd ELan EShb EWoo LCro LOPS LRHS LSun MACG MAvo MBel MCot MNHC MPri NGdn NLar SBls SCoo SGbt SPer SPoG SRms WCAu WFar
- 'Beauty of Livermere' clonal — WCot
- 'Beauty Queen' — CDor NGdn
- 'Bolero' — EPri MACG MHol
- 'Bonfire Red' — SCob
- 'Brilliant' — CTsd EHyd GQue LRHS NGdn NRHS SCoo WFar
- 'Brooklyn' (New York Series) — EGrI LRHS
- 'Burning Heart' — CWGN NLar
- 'Carneum' — EHyd EPfP LRHS NRHS SPoG SRms
- 'Cedric Morris' 🏆H7 — ECha EPPr
- 'Central Park' (New York Series) — CBod EHyd LRHS NLar WFar
- 'Charming' red-flowered — EHyd
- 'Coral Reef' — GJos
- 'Curlilocks' — EHyd SRms SWvt WFar
- Double Red Shades (d) — NGdn
- 'Doubloon' (d) — WFar
- 'Dwarf Allegro' — LRHS MPri
- 'Dwarf Allegro Vivace' — EHyd
- 'Fiesta' — ELon
- 'Flamenco' — WFar
- 'Forncett Summer' — NLar SPer SPoG WCAu WCot
- 'Garden Glory' — LSRN
- 'Goliath' — ELan NBro SRms WFar
- HAREMSTRAUM (mixed) — WFar
- 'Harlem' (New York Series) — CBcs CBod CElw CRos EHyd EPfP LRHS MNrw NLar STPC
- 'Harvest Moon' (d) — CBod EHyd LRHS NPer NRHS SPeP
- 'Indian Chief' — NPer SCob WFar
- 'John III' 🏆H7 — SPhx
- 'Karine' 🏆H7 — EHyd NLar SCob
- 'King Kong' — MBNS MBel WFar
- 'Kleine Tänzerin' — CBod NLar SEND WFar
- 'Ladybird' — EHyd LRHS
- 'Little Patty Plum' PBR — MHol NLar WTyc
- 'Louvre' (Parisienne Series) — WFar
- 'Manhattan' (New York Series) — CElw EHyd EPfP LRHS MNrw NRHS NSti SGbt SPeP WFar
- 'Marlene' — LRHS WCAu
- 'May Queen' (d) — EWes WCot WFar
- 'Miss Piggy' PBR — SGbt WFar
- 'Mrs Perry' — EHyd LRHS NPer SGbt SRms WBrk WFar
- 'Papillon' PBR — CBcs EHyd NLar NRHS
- 'Patty's Plum' — Widely available
- 'Perry's White' — CBcs EHyd MBel NChi SCob SRkn SWvt WCAu WSpi
- 'Picotée' — ECtt LRHS SCob SWvt WFar
- 'Pink Ruffles' PBR — EHyd SGbt WFar
- 'Pinnacle' — WFar
- 'Pizzicato' — CBod CRos EAJP EHyd LRHS NPer WFar WHil
- 'Plum Pudding' — EHyd EPfP LRHS
- 'Prince of Orange' — SWvt
- 'Prinz Eugen' — WFar
- 'Prinzessin Victoria Louise' — CDor CKel CRos EHyd ELan EPfP EWoo GJos GMaP LRHS MPri NGdn NRHS SEND SPoG SRms WBrk
- 'Queen Alexandra' — CDor EHyd EPfP LRHS NChi SCoo
- 'Raspberry Brûlée' — EHyd LRHS NRHS
- 'Raspberry Queen' — CBod CDor ECtt EHyd MAvo NChi
- 'Rembrandt' — EWoo WCot
- 'Royal Chocolate Distinction' — CBod ECtt ELan EPfP LRHS MHol WFar
- 'Royal Wedding' — Widely available
- 'Ruffled Patty' PBR — ECtt ELan MSCN SGbt WCot
- 'Salmon Glow' (d) — WFar
- 'Scarlett O'Hara' PBR (d) — ECtt WFar
- 'Snow Goose' — CDor CWGN ECtt EHyd EPfP GAbr ILea LRHS LSun NLar NRHS SCob SPoG WKif WTyc
- 'Springtime' — WCav
- 'Staten Island' (New York Series) — MNrw
- 'Sweet Sensation' **new** — MHol
- 'Tiffany' — ECtt
- 'Türkenlouis' — CBod ECtt EHyd NQui SPoG WBrk WCAu WFar
- 'Turkish Delight' — EHyd EWoo MAvo MBel NBir SWvt WCAu
- 'Walking Fire' — MNrw
- 'Watermelon' — SCob SPoG
- 'White Ruffles' PBR — CBod EPfP MSCN SGbt
orientale — CBcs EGrI EPfP GArf SRms SVic
§ - var. ***bracteatum*** — GGro
- 'Guardsman' — see *P.* (Oriental Group) 'Beauty of Livermere' clonal
- 'Mrs Marrow's Plum' — see *P.* (Oriental Group) 'Patty's Plum'
- PRINCESS VICTORIA LOUISE — see *P.* (Oriental Group) 'Prinzessin Victoria Louise'
pavoninum — SPhx
§ ***pilosum*** subsp. ***spicatum*** — CSpe ECha LPla NBir WCot
popovii **new** — GGro
rhoeas — CHab LCro LOPS LRHS MBow MNHC SPhx SVic
- 'Bridal Silk' — CSpe LCro
- 'Bridal White' — LOPS SPhx
- Mother of Pearl Group — CSpe LRHS SPhx
- 'Paradise' — CSpe
rupifragum — CBod CKel ECha LShi SPhx WCot
- 'Double Tangerine Gem' — see *P. rupifragum* 'Flore Pleno'
§ - 'Flore Pleno' (d) — CDor CSpe CWCL EPPr GBin MAsh MBNS SVic WBrk
- 'Tangerine Dream' — GPSL
'Shasta' (Super Poppy Series) — LRHS WFar
somniferum — CLau ENfk GPoy SVic
- var. ***album*** — LRHS XAbr
- 'Blackcurrant Fizz' (d) — LCro LOPS SPhx
- 'Boudoir Babe' (d) — CSpe
- 'Drama Queen' — CSpe
- 'Lauren's Grape' — CSpe LCro LOPS LRHS SPhx

- 'Lilac Pompom' (d) LCro LOPS
- (Paeoniiflorum Group) 'Black Beauty' (d) CSpe GJos SDeJ SPhx SVic
I - - 'Black Paeony' (d) CKel LCro LOPS LRHS SPhx
- - 'Schwarzer Drachen' (d) LRHS
I - - 'Yellow Paeony' (d) **new** GJos
- 'Persian White' CSpe SPhx
- 'Rye Beaner' GJos SVic
- single black-flowered CSpe SPhx
- - white-flowered CSpe
- 'White Cloud' (d) CSpe
'Spring Fever Red' **new** LRHS
thianschanicum SPhx
triniifolium GGro SPhx WCot

papaya (pawpaw) see *Carica papaya*

Parabenzoin see *Lindera*

Parachampionella see *Strobilanthes*

Paradisea (*Asparagaceae*)

liliastrum misapplied see *P. lusitanica*
liliastrum (L.) Bertol. ♀H5 EBee EPri LRHS NBid NChi
§ ***lusitanica*** CAvo CNor CSpe EBee EGrI EPri GBin GKev LEdu MHol SPhx WCot

Parahebe (*Plantaginaceae*)

× ***bidwillii*** GJos SRms
- 'Kea' ECtt
§ ***catarractae*** CExl ECha EHyd ELan EPfP EWld ITim LRHS MSCN NBir NRHS SLee SRms WCav WKif
- 'Avalanche'PBR CWGN EHyd EPfP GDam GMaP LRHS MAsh MSCN NRHS SGBe SGbt SPoG WHer WNPC XSte
- 'Baby Blue' EHyd LRHS NRHS
- blue-flowered GJos SGbt SPer
§ - 'Delight' ♀H4 CExl EHyd GMaP GQue LRHS MHer NPer NRHS SCob WLov
- subsp. ***diffusa*** NPer SRot
- 'Miss Willmott' ECtt SPer SPlb
- 'Porlock' CBod CDoC EBee EPfP GDam GKev GWyn SBut SDix SGBe SRms SRot SWvt WCav WHoo
- 'Porlock Purple' see *P. catarractae* 'Delight'
- 'Rosea' SRms WTyc
- white-flowered EGrI GAbr SRms
- 'Whittallii' GBin
densifolia see *Chionohebe densifolia*
§ ***formosa*** SPlb SVen
'Greencourt' see *P. catarractae* 'Delight'
§ ***hookeriana*** GKev
'Jean' GBin
'Kenty Pink' MMuc
linifolia 'Blue Skies' ECtt EPot GBin
§ ***lyallii*** CTri EBee ELan EPfP GDam GMaP MHer MMuc MRav MSwo NQui SLee SPlb SRms WIce WKif
- 'Julie-Anne' ♀H4 LRHS SGBe SLee
- 'Snowcap' EBee LRHS MRav SGBe SPlb SRms
'Mervyn' CNor CTri
§ ***perfoliata*** CDor CExl CMea CSde EBee ECha EGrI GMaP LEdu MAsh MNrw MRav SBrt SBut SDix SEND SPer SPlb SRms WSHC WWFP XLum
'Snow Clouds' CBar CBod CMea CSpe CTsd EBee ECtt EHyd ELan EPfP EWoo GKev LRHS NEoE NHpl NRHS SBut SDix SEdd SGBe SGro SPad SRot WFar WHoo WTor

Parajubaea (*Arecaceae*)

torallyi LRHS SPalm

Parakmeria see *Magnolia*

Paramongaia (*Amaryllidaceae*)

weberbaueri WMal

Paranomus (*Proteaceae*)

reflexus SPlb

Paraquilegia (*Ranunculaceae*)

adoxoides see *Semiaquilegia adoxoides*
§ ***anemonoides*** CExl GKev WAbe
grandiflora see *P. anemonoides*

Parasenecio (*Asteraceae*)

delphiniifolius B&SWJ 5789 WCru
- B&SWJ 10885 WCru
- B&SWJ 11189 WCru
- B&SWJ 11415 WCru
farfarifolius WCru
- var. ***acerinus*** B&SWJ 11549 WCru
- - B&SWJ 11554 WCru
- var. ***bulbifer*** WCru
hastatus var. ***farfarifolius*** see *P. maximowiczianus*
- subsp. ***orientalis*** variegated (v) GGro
§ ***maximowiczianus*** B&SWJ 11468 WCru
mortonii GWJ 9419 WCru
- HWJK 2214 WCru
tebakoensis B&SWJ 11167 WCru
- B&SWJ 11536 WCru

Paraserianthes (*Fabaceae*)

distachya see *P. lophantha*
§ ***lophantha*** ♀H2 CExl CTsd EBak EShb MVil SPlb

Parastyrax (*Styracaceae*)

BWJ 15185 from Northern Vietnam WCru

Parasyringa see *Ligustrum*

Parathelypteris (*Thelypteridaceae*)

beddomei LEdu WCot WPGP
- crested **new** LEdu

Pardanthopsis see *Iris*

Parietaria (*Urticaceae*)

judaica GPoy WHer WSFF

Paris (*Melanthiaceae*)

chinensis WCru
forrestii WCru
incompleta CTtf ESwi GEdr GKev LEdu WCru
japonica GEdr
lancifolia B&SWJ 3044 from Taiwan WCru
polyphylla CMiW ECha EGrI GKev MNrw NBid NFav NHpl NLar SDir SDix SPalm WCru WPnP
- B&SWJ 2125 WCru
- HWJCM 475 WCru
- var. ***alba*** GEdr

- var. ***stenophylla***	WCru
quadrifolia	CSpe CTtf EBee EMor EPfP GEdr GKev GPoy LEdu MNrw MVil NGrd NLar SPhx WCru WFar WHer WPnP WShi
thibetica	EBee GKev
- var. ***thibetica***	SDir

Parkinsonia (*Fabaceae*)

aculeata	SPlb

Parnassia (*Celastraceae*)

cabulica	GKev
foliosa	NHar
gansuensis	NHar
- SDR 5128	EBee GKev
nubicola	GKev
palustris	GKev WHer
- var. ***yakushimensis***	NHar

Parochetus (*Fabaceae*)

communis ambig.	CExl EWld MSCN NPer
- subsp. ***africanus*** 🏆H2	CPla WHil
* - 'Blue Gem'	CCCN

Parolinia (*Brassicaceae*)

ornata	WCot

Paronychia (*Caryophyllaceae*)

§ ***capitata***	CTri SRms
kapela	SPlb XSen
§ - subsp. ***serpyllifolia***	XLum
- - 'Binsted Gold' (v)	XLum
nivea	see *P. capitata*
serpyllifolia	see *P. kapela* subsp. *serpyllifolia*

Parrotia ✿ (*Hamamelidaceae*)

persica	Widely available
- PAB 13.046	LEdu
- 'Bella'	CJun EBee MBlu MTrO NLar WMat WMou
- 'Biltmore'	CJun SSta
- 'Burgundy'	CJun EPfP NLar
- 'Cobhay Upright'	CJun
- fastigiate	CJun
- 'Felicie'	CJun EPfP IArd NLar
- 'Het Plantsoen'	NLar
- 'Horizontalis'	CJun
- 'Jodrell Bank'	CJun MBlu NLar
- 'Pendula'	CJun CMCN EPfP MBlu SSta
- 'Persian Carpet'	NLar
- PERSIAN SPIRE ('Jlpn01'PBR)	CBcs LCro LOPS LPar LRHS SGol SGsty SMad
- 'Summer Bronze'	CJun EHyd ELan EPfP LRHS MAsh
- 'Vanessa' 🏆H6	Widely available
subaequalis	CJun MBlu NLar SGol WPGP

Parrotia × *Sycopsis* see × *Sycoparrotia*

Parrotiopsis (*Hamamelidaceae*)

jacquemontiana	CBcs CJun GBin LMaj LPar MBlu NLar

Parrya (*Brassicaceae*)

pulvinata new	GKev

parsley see *Petroselinum crispum*

parsnip see AGM Vegetables Section

Parsonsia (*Apocynaceae*)

heterophylla	CTsd

Parthenium (*Asteraceae*)

integrifolium	GPoy LPla SPhx

Parthenocissus (*Vitaceae*)

§ ***henryana*** 🏆H5	Widely available
- 'Malene'	EShb
himalayana 'Purpurea'	see *P. himalayana* var. *rubrifolia*
§ - var. ***rubrifolia***	CMac ELan GBin MAsh MRav SLon SPtp WCru
inserta misapplied	see *P. quinquefolia*
inserta ambig.	CMac NLar
laetevirens	NLar
§ ***quinquefolia***	Widely available
- var. ***engelmannii***	CBcs EBee EPfP EShb LBuc SEND WCFE
- 'Guy's Garnet'	WCru
- RED WALL ('Troki')	CRos EHyd EPfP LPar LRHS NRHS
- STAR SHOWERS ('Monham') (v)	EBee NLar
- 'Yellow Wall'PBR	CRos EHyd LRHS NRHS
semicordata B&SWJ 6551	WCru
striata	see *Cissus striata*
thomsonii	see *Cayratia thomsonii*
§ ***tricuspidata***	CCVT CMCN EPfP MAsh MGos SArc SPer
- 'Beverley Brook'	CRHN ELon LSRN MGos NLar SNig SPer SRms
- 'Crûg Compact'	WCru
- 'Fenway Park'	EBee ELan MRav
- 'Green Spring'	CBcs ELan IArd MGos NLar
- 'Lowii'	CDoC CMac EHyd ELan EPfP MBlu MRav NLar SLon SNig SPoG
- 'Robusta'	EBee
§ - 'Veitchii' 🏆H5	Widely available

Pasithea (*Hemerocallidaceae*)

caerulea	CBod CMea EPri MHol SMHy WCot WGob WPGP WSHC

Paspalum (*Poaceae*)

glaucifolium	MNrw
quadrifarium RCB RA S-5	WCot

Passiflora ✿ (*Passifloraceae*)

actinia	CCCN SPlb
'Adularia'	CCCN
alata (F) 🏆H1c	CCCN
× ***allardii***	CCCN
ambigua	CCCN
§ 'Amethyst' 🏆H3	CBcs CCCN CRHN CSBt LSRN MAsh SPoG
amethystina misapplied	see *P.* 'Amethyst'
§ ***amethystina*** Mikan	ECre EHyd LRHS NRHS
'Anastasia'	CCCN
'Andy'	CCCN
'Anemona'	CCCN
'Annika'	CCCN
antioquiensis misapplied	see *P.* × *exoniensis*
antioquiensis ambig.	CBcs CCCN SEND
antioquiensis H. Karst.	CRHN
× ***parritae***	
'Ariane'	CCCN
× ***atropurpurea***	CCCN
§ ***aurantia***	CCCN
§ × ***belotii***	CCCN
- 'Perfume Passion'PBR	CCCN
'Betty Myles Young'	CCCN CRHN ECre ELan EPfP LPar LRHS
'Blue Bouquet'	CCCN
'Blue Crown'	CCCN

	'Blue Moon'	CCCN
	'Blue Stripper'	CCCN
	'Blue Velvet'	CCCN
	bogatensis B&SWJ 14951	WCru
	'Byron Beauty'	CCCN
	'Byte'	CCCN
§	***caerulea*** 𝕐^{H4}	Widely available
	- 'Chinensis'	CCCN
	- 'Clear Sky'^{PBR}	CBod CCCN ELan EPfP LPar LRHS SRms
	- 'Constance Eliott' 𝕐^{H4}	CAgr CBar CBcs CBod CBrac CCCN CMac CRHN CRos EBee EHyd ELan EPfP LCro LOPS LPar LRHS MAsh MGos MNHC NLar NRHS SCob SPer SWvt
	- 'Pierre Pomié'	CCCN
I	- 'Rubra'	CBod CCCN CDoC CSBt
	- WHITE LIGHTNING ('Yanpas'^{PBR})	CCCN EHyd ELan EPfP EShb LRHS NRHS SCoo SPoG SWvt
	× ***caeruleoracemosa***	see *P.* × *violacea*
	× ***caponii***	CCCN
	- 'John Innes'	CCCN
	'Cary' <u>**new**</u>	CCCN
	'Celine'	CCCN
	chinensis	see *P. caerulea*
	citrifolia	CCCN
	citrina	CCCN
*	***classica*** × ***coccinea***	CCCN EShb
	× ***colvillii***	CCCN
	'Coordination'	CCCN
	'Coral Glow' <u>**new**</u>	CCCN
§	***coriacea***	CCCN
	'Crimson Tears'	CCCN
	cuatrecasasii B&SWJ 14834	WCru
§	'Damsel's Delight'	CCCN CPla CWGN ECre EHyd ELan LRHS NRHS SGsty SNig SPeP
	'Daylight'	CCCN
	'Debby'	CCCN
	× ***decaisneana*** (F)	CCCN
	'Divertido'	CCCN
	EDEN ('Hil Pas Eden') 𝕐^{H3}	CCCN SRkn
	edulis (F)	CBcs CCCN SPre SVic
	- 'Byte' (F)	CCCN
§	- f. ***edulis*** (F)	CCCN
	- f. ***flavicarpa*** (F)	CCCN WHil
	- 'Lilikoi' (F) <u>**new**</u>	CAgr
	- 'Norfolk' (F)	CCCN
	'Elizabeth' (F)	CCCN
	'Evatoria'	CCCN
§	× ***exoniensis*** 𝕐^{H2}	CCCN CRHN CSBt ECre
	'Fantasma'	CCCN
	'Fata Confetto'	CCCN
	'Fledermouse'	CCCN
	'Flying V'	CCCN
	gracilens	CRHN
	'Grand Duchess'	CCCN
	gritensis	CCCN
	'Guglielmo Betto'	CCCN
	'Hetty Nicolaas'	CCCN
	'Hildegard'	CCCN
	incarnata (F)	CAgr CCCN GPoy SPlb
	'Incense' (F) 𝕐^{H2}	CCCN SPlb
	'Inspiration'	CCCN
	'Jara'	CCCN
	'Jelly Joker'	CCCN
	'Justine Lyons'	CCCN
	karwinskii	CCCN
	× ***kewensis***	CCCN
	'Lady Margaret'	CCCN
	'Lambiekins'	CCCN
§	***ligularis*** (F)	CCCN SVic
	'Livie'	CCCN
	lowei	see *P. ligularis*
	lutea	CCCN
	'Manapany'	CCCN
	manicata (F)	CCCN
	- B&SWJ 14284	WCru
	- B&SWJ 14868	WCru
	'Maria'	CCCN
	'Marijke'	CCCN
	'Mary Jane'	CCCN
I	***matthewsii*** 'Alba'	CRHN
	mayana	see *P. caerulea*
	membranacea (F)	CCCN
	'Michael'	CCCN
	'Mini Lamb'	CCCN
	mixta (F)	CCCN SEND
	- B&SWJ 14832	WCru
	- clone 2	CCCN
	- red-flowered	CCCN
	aff. ***mixta*** B&SWJ 14302	WCru
	mollissima misapplied	see *P. tarminiana*
	mollissima ambig. (F)	CBcs CCCN EShb SPlb
	mollissima (Kunth) L.H.Bailey (F) 𝕐^{H2}	CAgr CRHN
	- B&SWJ 14876	WCru
	'Monika Fischer'	CCCN
	mucronata	CCCN
	murucuja	CCCN
	'New Incense'	CCCN
	'Nightshift'	CCCN
	onychina	see *P. amethystina* Mikan
	'Panda'	CCCN
	'Party Animal'	CCCN ECre ELan
	'Pink Festival'	CCCN
	'Pink Nightmare'	CCCN
	'Pink Passion'^{PBR}	CCCN
	'Pinky'	CCCN
	× ***piresiae***	CCCN
	'Poppet'	CCCN
	'Precioso'	CCCN
	'Pura Vida'	CCCN
	'Purple Companion'	CCCN
	'Purple Haze'	CCCN CDoC EHyd ELan LCro LOPS LRHS NRHS SCoo WFar
	'Purple Pendulum'	CCCN
	'Purple Rain'	CCCN
	quadrangularis (F) 𝕐^{H1a}	CCCN
	quinquangularis	CCCN
	racemosa 𝕐^{H1a}	CCCN
	- 'Blushing Bride'	CCCN
	- 'Buzios'	CCCN
	- 'Diva'	CCCN
	- pink-flowered	CCCN
	'Red Inca'	CCCN
	reitzii	CCCN
	riparia	CCCN
	semiciliosa B&SWJ 14824	WCru
	'Silly Cow'	see *P.* 'Damsel's Delight'
	'Silvie'	CCCN
	'Simply Red'	CCCN
	'Snow Queen'	CBod CCCN CRos CWGN ELan EPfP LRHS MNHC SCoo SGsty SNig SPeP WHil
	'Star of Kingston'	CCCN
	'Star of Surbiton'	CCCN ELan LRHS
	'Sunburst'	CCCN
	'Surprise'	CCCN
§	***tarminiana*** (F)	CCCN CRHN CSBt
	- B&SWJ 14960	WCru
	- white-flowered	CCCN

'Temptation'	CCCN
tetrandra	CExl
trifasciata	CCCN
tripartita B&SWJ 14768	WCru
- B&SWJ 14807	WCru
tucumanensis tetraploid	CCCN
tulae	CCCN
§ × ***violacea*** ♀H2	CCCN CRHN CRos
- 'Eynsford Gem'	CCCN
§ - 'Tresederi'	CCCN
- 'Twin Star'	CCCN
- 'Victoria'	CCCN CSBt
'Violetta' new	CCCN
vitifolia (F)	CCCN
- 'Innocentiae'	CCCN
'White Queen'	CCCN
'White Surprise'	CCCN
'White Wedding'	CCCN
'Wilgen Heintje'	CCCN
'Wilgen K Verhoeff'	CCCN
'Wilgen Marieke'	CCCN
'Winterland'	CCCN

passion fruit see *Passiflora*

passion fruit, banana see *Passiflora mollissima* (Kunth) L.H. Bailey

Pastinaca (*Apiaceae*)

sativa	CHab CKel SPhx SVic WCot
- subsp. ***sylvestris***	NGrd

Patersonia (*Iridaceae*)

occidentalis	SGBe SPlb

Patrinia ✿ (*Caprifoliaceae*)

gibbosa	CSpe EBee GGro MMrt NLar SBut SPhx WFar WPnP
- B&SWJ 874	ESwi WCru
heterophylla	GGro GKev
intermedia	EBee
cf. ***monandra***	EBee ESwi
punctiflora	CSpe EShb SDix WSHC
aff. ***punctiflora***	ECha NDov WGoo
rupestris B&SWJ 12654	WCru
scabiosifolia	CKno CMiW CSpe ECha ECtt EShb ESwi GGro LRHS MAvo MHol NBir NLar SBls SBut SDix SMrm SPhx SPtp WFar WHoo
- B&SWJ 8740	WCru
- 'Nagoya'	MNrw
triloba	CBod CMiW CSpe EHyd EMor GEdr MMrt NLar SBut WFar
- var. ***palmata***	EBee GKev
- var. ***triloba***	EHed
villosa	CExl GGro SBut SPhx

Paulownia (*Paulowniaceae*)

catalpifolia	EBee NLar
elongata	CBcs IDee NLar WLov
fargesii misapplied	see *P. tomentosa* 'Lilacina'
fargesii ambig.	WCot
fortunei	MBlu SPlb
- NMWJ 14533	WCru
- FAST BLUE ('Minfast') ♀H5	CExl LRHS LSRN
kawakamii	CBct CMCN EPfP ESwi MVil SChF WPGP
- NMWJ 14552	WCru
- RWJ 9909	WCru
'Purple Spendour'	EPfP SPer
taiwaniana NMWJ 14529	WCru
tomentosa ♀H5	Widely available
- W 769	WPGP
- 'Coreana'	ESwi WCru
§ - 'Lilacina'	EPfP ESwi

Pauridia (*Hypoxidaceae*)

canaliculata new	NRog
serrata	NRog
subsp. ***serrata*** new	

Pavonia (*Malvaceae*)

multiflora ambig.	CCCN
praemorsa	CCCN
strictiflora	CCCN
* ***volubilis***	CCCN

pawpaw (false banana) see *Asimina triloba*

pawpaw (papaya) see *Carica papaya*

pea see AGM Vegetables Section

peach see *Prunus persica*

pear see *Pyrus communis*; see also AGM Fruit Section

pear, Asian see *Pyrus pyrifolia*

pecan see *Carya illinoinensis*

Pelargonium ✿ (*Geraniaceae*)

'A.M. Mayne' (Z/d)	WFib
'Aaron West' (St)	WFib
'Abba' (Z/d)	WFib
'Abbie Hillier' (R)	WFib
'Abel Carrière' (I/d)	WFib
abrotanifolium (Sc)	CSpe ENfk EPPr EWoo MHer SPet SVen WFib WGwG
acetosum	EPPr EWoo MHer SMrm WFib
acraeum	EWoo
'Ada Green' (R)	WFib
'Ada Sutterby' (Dw/d)	WFib
'Ade's Elf' (Z/St)	WFib
'Ainsdale Beauty' (Z)	WFib
alchemilloides	EWoo WFib
'Aldwyck' (R) ♀H1c	WFib
'Alex Kitson' (Z)	WFib
'Algenon' (Min/d)	WFib
I 'Alice' (Min)	WFib
'Alison March' (Dw/Z/d/v)	WFib
'Allesley Shadow' (Dw/d)	WFib
'Allwoods Lemon Drizzle' (Z/Min)	SAll
'Alma' (Dw/C)	SSea
alpinum	MHer
'Amari' (R)	WFib
'Ambrose' (Min/d)	WFib
AMELIT ('Pacameli'PBR) (I/d)	SSea
'American Prince of Orange' (Sc)	SPet
'Amethyst' (R)	SCoo WFib
I 'Amy' (Dw)	WFib
(Angeleyes Series)	MCot
ANGELEYES BICOLOR ('Pacbicolor'PBR) (A)	
- ANGELEYES ORANGE ('Paccrio'PBR) (A)	EWoo
- ANGELEYES RANDY ('Pacra') (A)	SSea
'Angelique' (Dw/d)	WFib
'Ann Hoystead' (R) ♀H1c	WFib

'Annabelle Stephenson' (Dw/d) WFib
'Annsbrook Beauty' (A/C) SPet WFib
'Annsbrook Jupiter' (Z/St) WFib
(Antik Series) ANTIK ORANGE ('Tikorg'PBR) (Z) ♀H1c SPoG
- ANTIK PINK ('Tikpink'PBR) (Z) SPoG
- ANTIK SCARLET ('Tikscarl'PBR) (Z) SPoG
- ANTIK VIOLET ('Tikvio'PBR) (Z) SPoG
'Antoine Crozy' (I × Z/d) WFib
'Apache' (Z/d) WFib
appendiculatum MHer
'Apple Betty' (Sc) EPPr EWoo NWsh WFib
'Apple Blossom Rosebud' (Z/d) ♀H1c CBod ECre ECtt EShb EWoo MHer SMrm WFib
'Apricot Fool' (U/Sc) WFib
'Apricot Glace' (U/Sc) MHer WFib
'April Hamilton' (I) LCro LOPS WFib
'April Showers' (A) WFib
'Arctic Frost' (I) WFib
§ 'Arctic Star' (St) ♀H1c CSpe WBrk WFib
'Ardens' ♀H1c CBod CDow CNor CPbh CSpe CTsd CWCL EBee ELan EWoo LCro LOPS MCot MHer SWvt WCAu WCot WFib WWFP
'Ardwick Cinnamon' (Sc) ENfk EWoo MHer NWsh SPet SRms WFib
'Arnside Fringed Aztec' (R) MHer WFib
'Ashby' (Dec/Sc) ♀H1c ECtt ENfk EPPr EWoo MHer SPet WFib
'Ashfield Jubilee' (Z/C) WFib
'Ashfield Serenade' (Z) ♀H1c WFib
'Askham Fringed Aztec' (R) ♀H1c WFib
asperum Ehr. ex Willd. see *P.* 'Graveolens'
§ 'Atomic Snowflake' (Sc/v) ECtt ENfk EWoo MNHC NWsh SPet SRms WFib
'Atrium' (U) MHer NWsh WFib
'Attar of Roses' (Sc) ♀H1c CCBP CCht CLau CSpe ECtt ENfk EPPr EWoo LCro LOPS MCot MHer MNHC NCou NWsh SAng SEdi SGro SPet SPoG SRms WBrk WFib WGwG
'Aurora' (Z/d) ECtt
australe EWoo MCot MHer NWsh WFib
'Australian Mystery' (R/Dec) ♀H1c CSpe ECtt WFib
'Aztec' (R) ♀H1c MHer WFib
'Baby Bird's Egg' (Min) WFib
'Baby Harry' (Dw/v) WFib
'Ballerina' (R) see *P.* 'Carisbrooke'
I 'Ballerina' (Min) WFib
'Barbara Eldridge' (Z) WFib
§ 'Barbe Bleu' (I/d) ♀H1c LCro LOPS WFib
barklyi WFib
'Baronne A. de Rothschild' (Z/d) WFib
'Bath Beauty' (Dw) CSpe EPri
'Beatrice Cottington' (I/d) WFib
'Beauty of Calderdale' (Z/C) WFib
'Beauty of Eastbourne' misapplied see *P.* 'Lachskönigin', *P.* 'Eastbourne Beauty'
BELLADONNA ('Fisopa') (I/d) SCoo
'Bembridge' (Z/St/d) CDow WFib
'Ben Matt' (R) WFib
§ 'Bergpalais' (Z/d) SSea
'Berkswell Bolero' (A) WFib
'Berkswell Carnival' (A) ELan
'Berkswell Lace' (A) MHer
'Berkswell Pixie' (A) SPet
'Beromünster' (Dec) ECtt EWoo MHer WFib
'Bert Pearce' (R) WFib
'Beryl Gibbons' (Z/d) WFib
'Beryl Reid' (R) WFib
'Betty Catchpole' (Z) EWoo
betulinum CPbh EWoo WFib
'Betwixt' (Z/v) WFib
'Big Apple' (Sc) EWoo SRms
'Bird Dancer' (Dw/St) ♀H1c CSpe EPPr EWoo MHer MNHC SIvy WBrk WFib
(Birdbush Series) 'Birdbush Bobby' (Sc) SRms
- 'Birdbush Bold and Beautiful' (Sc) SRms
- 'Birdbush Eleanor' (Z) WFib
- 'Birdbush Nutty' (Sc) SRms
'Birthday Girl' (R) ♀H1c ECtt WFib
'Bitter Lemon' (Sc) ECtt EWoo WFib
'Black Butterfly' see *P.* 'Brown's Butterfly'
'Black Country Bugle' (Z/d) WFib
'Black Knight' (R) ECtt MHer
'Black Knight' (A) SPet
'Black Prince' (R/Dec) CSpe EWoo WFib
'Black Velvet' (R) EWoo
'Black Vesuvius' see *P.* 'Red Black Vesuvius'
'Blackman Beauty' **new** NWsh
BLANCHE ROCHE ('Guitoblanc') (I/d) MBros MHer SCoo
§ 'Blandfordianum' (Sc) EWoo MHer NWsh
I 'Blandfordianum Album' (Sc) WFib
'Blandfordianum Roseum' (Sc) EWoo MHer WFib
'Blazonry' (Z/v) WFib
(Blizzard Series) BLIZZARD BLUE ('Fisrain'PBR) (I) SCoo
- BLIZZARD DARK RED ('Fisblizdark') (I) EWoo
- BLIZZARD RED ('Fizzard') (I) SCoo
- BLIZZARD WHITE ('Fisbliz'PBR) (I) SCoo
'Blue Beard' see *P.* 'Barbe Bleu'
BLUE WONDER ('Pacbla'PBR) (Z/d) SSea
'Bob Newing' (Min/St) WFib
'Bobberstone' (Z/St) WFib
'Bold Ann' (Dw/Z/d) WFib
'Bold Appleblossom' (Z) WFib
'Bold Bridesmaid' (Dw/d) WFib
'Bold Carousel' (Z/d) WFib
'Bold Cherie' (Dw/d) WFib
'Bold Cherub' (Z/d) WFib
'Bold Cyclamen' (Dw/d) WFib
'Bold Debonair' (Dw/d) WFib
'Bold Dove' (Dw) WFib
'Bold Flame' (Z/d) WFib
'Bold Gem' (Z/d) WFib
'Bold Limelight' (Z/d) WFib
'Bold Minstrel' (Z/d) WFib
'Bold Moonlight' (Dw) WFib
'Bold Pixie' (Dw/d) WFib
'Bold Princess' (Z/d) WFib
'Bold Special' (Z) WFib
'Bold Spirit' (Z) WFib
'Bold Sunset' (Z/d) ♀H1c WFib
'Bolero' (U) ♀H1c WFib
'Bon Bon' (Min/St) WFib
'Bontrosai'PBR (Sc) MCot MHer
'Bosham' (R) WFib

'Both's Snowflake' (Sc/v)	WFib
'Bourbon Rose' (Sc)	MHer
bowkeri	WFib
BRAVO ('Fisbravo') (Z/d)	WFib
'Brenda' (Min/d)	WFib
'Brenda Hyatt' (Dw/d)	WFib
'Brian West' (Min/St/C)	WFib
'Brian West Butterfly' (Z/St) ♀H1c	WFib
'Bright Eyes' ambig. (Dw)	WFib
'Brightstone' (Z/d)	ECtt WFib
'Brilliant' (Dec)	ENfk SPet WFib
'Brilliantine' (Sc)	ENfk EPri EWoo MHer NWsh SRms WFib
'Britannia' (R)	WFib
'Brixworth Pearl' (Z)	WFib
'Broadway Scarlet' **new**	CWCL
'Brook's Purple'	see *P.* 'Royal Purple'
'Brookside Flamenco' (Dw/d)	WFib
'Brookside Primrose' (Min/C/d)	WFib
'Brookside Serenade' (Dw)	WFib
§ 'Brown's Butterfly' (R)	EWoo WFib
'Brunswick' (Sc)	EWoo MHer SMrm WFib
'Bushfire' (R) ♀H1c	EWoo WFib
BUTTERFLY ('Fisam'^{PBR}) (I)	SCoo
caespitosum	MHer
caffrum	EWoo WFib
- 'Diana'	MHer
'Cal'	see *P.* 'Salmon Irene'
'California Brilliant' (U)	MHer
'Calignon' (Z/St)	WFib
'Cameo' (Dw/d)	WFib
'Camphor Rose' (Sc) ♀H1c	SRms
'Can-can' (I/d)	WFib
CANDY FLOWERS VIOLET ('Camvio'^{PBR}) (Candy Flowers Series) (R) **new**	EWoo
canescens	see *P.* 'Blandfordianum'
'Cape Town' (Dw/Z/v)	WFib
capitatum	ENfk EWoo WFib
'Capri' (Sc)	SMHy WFib
'Captain Starlight' (A) ♀H1c	EShb EWoo MHer SPet WFib
'Carefree' (U) ♀H1c	ECtt WFib
§ 'Carisbrooke' (R) ♀H1c	WFib
'Carmel' (Z)	WFib
carnosum	MHer
'Carole Munroe' (Z/d)	WFib
'Caroline' (Dec)	WFib
'Caroline Schmidt' (Z/d/v)	ECtt MCot WBrk WFib
'Carolyn Hardy' (Z/d)	WFib
'Catford Belle' (A)	MHer
caucalifolium subsp. ***caucalifolium***	EWoo MHer
- subsp. ***convolvulifolium***	WFib
'Cedric Morris Corvette' (Z)	WFib
'Celebration' (Z/d)	WFib
'Celestial Rose' (Z/d)	WFib
'Cézanne' (R)	MCot
'Charity' (Sc) ♀H1c	ENfk MCot MHer MNHC NWsh SPet SRms WFib
'Charlotte Bronte' (Dw/v)	WFib
'Charmay Cocky' (Z/d)	WFib
'Charmay Hampshire' (Z/d)	WFib
'Charmay Snowflake' (Sc/v)	SRms
'Charmay Snowflurry' (Sc/v)	WFib
'Chavarri Hermanos' (Z/d)	WFib
'Chelsea Gem' (Z/d/v) ♀H1c	WFib
'Chelsea Morning' (Z/d)	WFib
'Cherry' (Min)	WFib
'Cherry Baby' (Dec) ♀H1c	ECtt WFib
'Cherry Orchard' (R)	WFib
'Chew Magna' (R)	WFib
'Chieko' (Min/d)	WFib
'Chinese Cactus' (Z/St)	WFib
§ 'Chocolate Peppermint' (Sc)	ECtt ELan ENfk EWoo MCot MHer NWsh SPet SRms SSal WFib
'Chocolate Tomentosum'	see *P.* 'Chocolate Peppermint'
'Choun Cho' (I)	LCro LOPS WFib
'Chrissie' (R)	WFib
'Cindy' (Dw/d)	WFib
'Citriodorum' (Sc) ♀H1c	ELan MCot MHer WFib
'Citronella' (Sc)	SRms WFib
'Claret Rock Unique' (U)	EWoo WFib
'Clorinda' (U/Sc)	ENfk EShb EWoo MCot MHer MNHC NWad SPet SRms WFib
'Clown' (R)	WFib
'Coddenham' (Dw/d)	WFib
'Cola Bottles'	CCht CDow ELan NPer NWsh SPet SPoG WABo WFib
§ 'Colonel Baden-Powell' (I/d)	WFib
COLUMBIA (St)	WFib
'Colwell' (Min/d)	WFib
'Concolor Lace'	see *P.* 'Shottesham Pet'
'Conron' (Sc)	NWsh
'Contrast' (Z/C/v)	SCoo SPoG WFib
'Cook's Peachblossom' (Z/d)	WFib
'Copthorne' (U/Sc) ♀H1c	CDow EWoo MCot MHer NWsh SPet SRms WFib
cordifolium	EPPr WFib
- var. ***rubrocinctum***	EWoo MHer NWsh
coriandrifolium	see *P. myrrhifolium* var. *coriandrifolium*
'Cornell' (I/d)	WFib
cortusifolium	MHer
'Costanza da Schio'	SAll
'Cotta Lilac Queen' (I/d)	ECtt
'Cottenham Bliss' (A)	WFib
'Cottenham Cynthia Haird' (A)	SPet WFib
'Cottenham Delight' (A)	WFib
'Cottenham Glamour' (A) ♀H1c	MHer
'Cottenham Harmony' (A)	SPet WFib
'Cottenham Jubilee' (A)	MHer
'Cottenham Surprise' (A) ♀H1c	SPet
'Cottenham Wonder' (A) ♀H1c	MHer SPet WFib
cotyledonis	EWoo WFib
'Countess of Scarborough'	see *P.* 'Lady Scarborough'
'Cover Girl' (Z/d)	WFib
'Covina' (R)	WFib
'Cramdon Red' (Dw)	WFib
'Crampel's Master' (Z)	WFib
'Creamery' (d)	WFib
'Creamy Nutmeg' (Sc/v)	ENfk EShb EWoo MHer NWad SRms
'Credo' (Z)	WFib
'Crimson Unique' (U) ♀H1c	CSpe ELan ENfk EWoo MCot MHer WFib
§ ***crispum*** (Sc)	GPoy
- 'Cy's Sunburst' (v) ♀H1c	CLau ECtt MHer NWsh SPet WFib
§ - 'Golden Well Sweep' (Sc/v)	WFib
- 'Major' (Sc)	WFib
- 'Peach Cream' (Sc/v)	ENfk WFib
- 'Prince Rupert' (Sc)	NWsh
- 'Variegatum' (Sc/v) ♀H1c	ECtt ENfk GPoy MHer SPet SRms WCot WFib

crithmifolium	EWoo MHer
'Crock O Day' (I/d)	ECtt
'Crocodile' (I/C/d) ♀^{H1c}	CDow ECtt ELan EWoo MHer MNHC NWad WCot WFib
'Crowfoot Rose' (Sc)	WFib
'Crystal Palace Gem' (Z/v)	CDow ECtt WFib
cucullatum	WFib
- 'Flore Pleno' (d)	WFib
- subsp. ***strigifolium***	EWoo
'Cupid' (Min/Dw/d)	WFib
'Cynthia'^{PBR} (R)	LCro LOPS
§ 'Czar' (Z/C)	SCoo
'Dainty Maid' (Sc)	ECtt ENfk SPet
'Dale Queen' (Z)	WFib
'Dark Delight' (I)	SAll
'Dark Red Irene' (Z/d)	WFib
'Dark Secret' (R)	CSpe SMrm WFib
'Dark Venus' (R)	WFib
'Davina' (Min/d)	WFib
'Deacon Avalon' (Dw/d)	WFib
'Deacon Barbecue' (Z/d)	WFib
'Deacon Bonanza' (Z/d)	WFib
'Deacon Clarion' (Z/d)	WFib
'Deacon Coral Reef' (Z/d)	WFib
'Deacon Fireball' (Z/d)	WFib
'Deacon Gala' (Z/d)	WFib
'Deacon Golden Bonanza' (Z/C/d)	WFib
'Deacon Golden Lilac Mist' (Z/C/d)	WFib
'Deacon Lilac Mist' (Z/d)	WFib
'Deacon Mandarin' (Z/d)	WFib
'Deacon Minuet' (Z/d)	WFib
'Deacon Peacock' (Z/C/d)	WFib
'Deacon Picotee' (Z/d)	WFib
§ 'Deacon Summertime' (Z/d)	WFib
'Deborah Miliken' (Z/d) ♀^{H1c}	WFib
'Decora Lavender'	see *P.* 'Decora Lilas'
§ 'Decora Lilas' (I)	ECtt
'Decora Mauve'	see *P.* 'Decora Lilas'
'Decora Pink'	see *P.* 'Decora Rouge'
'Decora Red'	see *P.* 'Decora Rouge'
§ 'Decora Rose' (I)	ECtt
§ 'Decora Rouge' (I)	ECtt
'Deerwood Angel Wings' (A)	EWoo WFib
'Deerwood Darling' (Min/d/v)	WFib
'Deerwood Lavender Lad' (Sc)	ENfk MHer SAng SPet WFib
'Deerwood Lavender Lass' (Sc)	EWoo MCot MHer SRms
'Deerwood Pink Puff' (St/d)	WFib
'Delightful' (R)	WFib
'Delli' (R) ♀^{H1c}	MHer NPer SMrm WFib
denticulatum	EWoo MHer
§ - 'Filicifolium' (Sc)	ELan ENfk EPPr EPri EWoo MCot MHer NWsh SPet WFib
'Diana Louise' (Z/d)	WFib
'Diana Palmer' (Z/d)	WFib
dichondrifolium (Sc)	EWoo MHer WFib
'Dick Key' (Z/d)	WFib
'Display' ambig. (Dw/v)	WFib
'Distinction' (Z)	CSpe EWoo SPoG WFib WMal
'Dodd's Super Double' (Z/d)	SMrm WFib
'Dolce Vita'	SSea
'Dolly' (R)	WFib
'Dolly Varden' (Z/v) ♀^{H1c}	ECtt WFib
'Don Franco'^{PBR} (R)	LCro LOPS
'Don Palido'^{PBR} (R)	LCro LOPS
'Don Valentino'^{PBR} (R)	LCro LOPS
'Don's Helen Bainbridge' (Z/C)	MHer WFib
'Don's Richard A. Costain' (Z/C)	WFib
'Don's Stokesley Gem' (Z/C)	WFib
'Doris Hancock' (R)	WFib
'Doris Shaw' (R)	ELan WFib
'Dorothy Baker' (R)	WFib
'Double New Life' (Z/d)	WFib
'Double Pink' (R/d)	WFib
'Dovedale' (Dw/C)	WFib
'Downlands' (Z/d)	WFib
'Dresden Pink' (Dw)	MHer
'Dresden White' (Dw)	MHer WFib
'Dubonnet' (R)	WFib
'Duchess of Devonshire' (U)	WFib WMal
'Duke of Buckingham' (Z/d)	WFib
'Duke of Edinburgh'	see *P.* 'Hederinum Variegatum'
'Dunkery Beacon' (R)	WFib
'E. Dabner' (Z/d)	WFib
§ 'Eastbourne Beauty' (I/d)	WFib
echinatum	MHer WFar
- 'Album'	EWoo NWsh SIvy WFib
'Eclipse' (Dw/d)	ECtt
'Eden Gem' (Min/d)	WFib
'Edmond Lachenal' (Z/d)	WFib
'Edward Hockey' (Z)	WFib
'Eileen Postle' (R) ♀^{H1c}	WFib
'Elaine Ward' (R)	WFib
'Elizabeth Taylor' (Z)	WFib
'Ella' (Sc) **new**	NWsh
'Ella Jane' (Z/d)	WFib
'Elmsett' (Dw/C/d)	ECtt WFib
'Els' (Dw/St)	WBrk
'Elsi' (I × Z/d/v)	WFib
'Elsie Gillam' (St)	WFib
'Elsie Taylor' (R)	WFib
'Embassy' (Min)	WFib
EMILIA ('Pactina'^{PBR}) (Z)	SSea
'Emma Hössle'	see *P.* 'Frau Emma Hössle'
'Emma Jane Read' (Dw/d)	WFib
'Emma Louise' (Z)	WFib
'Emperor Nicholas' (Z/d)	WFib
endlicherianum	MHer WAbe WCot
'Endsleigh' (Sc)	WFib
'Eros'	SAll
'Eskay Gold' (A)	WFib
'Eskay Jewel' (A)	WFib
'Eskay Sugar Candy' (A)	WFib
'Eskay Verglo' (A)	WFib
EVENING GLOW	see *P.* 'Bergpalais'
'Evka'^{PBR} (I/v)	ECtt SCoo
'Exotica'	SAll
exstipulatum	EPPr EWoo MHer SMHy
'Fair Ellen' (Sc)	MHer WFib
'Fairlee' (Dw)	WFib
'Fairy Orchid' (A)	SPet WFib
'Fallen Angel' (Z/St)	ECtt
'Fandango' (Z/St)	SMrm WFib
'Fanny Eden' (R)	EWoo WFib
'Fantasia' white-flowered (Dw/d) ♀^{H1c}	WFib
FANTASIA BRIGHT RED IMPROVED **new**	WHil
FANTASIA WHITE IMPROVED **new**	WHil
'Fareham' (R) ♀^{H1c}	WFib
'Femme Fatale'	SAll

'Fern Mint' (Sc)	MHer SRms
'Fiat Queen' (Z/d)	WFib
'Fieldings Unique' (U)	EWoo SPet
'Fiery Sunrise' (R)	WFib
'Fifth Avenue' (R)	SGro WFib
'Filicifolium'	see *P. denticulatum* 'Filicifolium'
'Fir Trees Catkins' (A)	MHer
'Fir Trees Echoes of Pink' (A)	EWoo
'Fir Trees Eileen' (St)	SMrm
'Fir Trees Fiesta' (R) 🏆H1c	ECtt
'Fir Trees Flamingo' (Dw)	EWoo
'Fir Trees Hayley' (R)	WFib
'Fir Trees Pearl Anniversary' (Z/C)	WFib
'Fir Trees Silver Wedding' (Z/C/d)	WFib
'First Blush' (R)	WFib
FIRST YELLOW ('Pacyell'[PBR]) (Z/d)	WFib
'Fleetlands' (St/v)	SAll
'Fleur d'Amour' (R)	WFib
'Fleurisse' (Z)	WFib
'Floria Moore' (Dec)	EWoo
(Flower Fairy Series) FLOWER FAIRY BERRY ('Sweberry'[PBR]) (Z)	SSea
- FLOWER FAIRY ROSE ('Swero'[PBR]) (Z)	SSea
- FLOWER FAIRY VELVET ('Swevel'[PBR]) (Z)	SSea
- FLOWER FAIRY WHITE SPLASH ('Swewhi'[PBR]) (Z)	SSea
fragrans	CDow ECtt ENfk EWoo MBow SPet SRms SSal
Fragrans Group (Sc)	CDow GPoy MCot MHer NWsh WFib WGwG
§ - 'Fragrans Variegatum' (Sc/v) 🏆H1c	MCot NWsh SPet SPoG WFib
- 'Snowy Nutmeg'	see *P.* (Fragrans Group) 'Fragrans Variegatum'
'Fragrant Frosty' (Sc/v)	CDow
'Fraiche Beauté' (Z/d)	WFib
'Francis Gibbon' (Z/d)	WFib
'Francis Parmenter' (Min/I/v)	CDow
'Francis Parrett' (Min/d) 🏆H1c	WFib
'Frank Bolton' (Z/d)	MHer
'Frank Headley' (Z/v) 🏆H1c	ECtt EShb MCot NPer SCoo SMrm SPoG WFib
§ 'Frau Emma Hössle' (Dw/d)	WFib
'Freak of Nature' (Z/v)	MHer WFib
'Frensham' (Sc)	ENfk MHer NWsh WFib
'Freshwater' (St/C)	WFib
'Friary Wood' (Z/C/d)	WFib
'Friesdorf' (Dw/Fr)	MCot MHer WBrk WFib WMal
'Fringed Apple' (Sc)	WFib
'Fringed Aztec' (R) 🏆H1c	WFib
'Frosty' misapplied	see *P.* 'Variegated Kleine Liebling'
'Frosty Petit Pierre'	see *P.* 'Variegated Kleine Liebling'
'Fruity' (Sc)	SRms
'Frumpy' (Z/Min)	SAll
fruticosum	CDow EPPr EWoo WFib
fulgidum	EWoo MCot MHer WFib
fumariifolium <u>**new**</u>	NWsh
'Gabriel' (A)	EWoo WFib
'Galway Star' (Sc/v) 🏆H1c	MHer WFib
'Ganther' (Dec)	WFib
'Gareth Mark Pratt' (Z/C)	WFib
'Garland' (R)	WFib
'Garnet Rosebud' (Min/d)	WFib
'Garnet Wings' (R)	WFib
'Gartendirektor Herman' (Dec) 🏆H1c	ELan EWoo MHer SSal WFib
'Gaudy' (Z)	WFib
'Gemini' (Z/St/d) 🏆H1c	WFib
'Gemstone' (Sc) 🏆H1c	ENfk MHer SPet WFib
'Genie' (Z/d)	WFib
'Gentle Georgia' (R)	WFib
'Georgia' (R)	WFib
'Georgia Peach' (R)	WFib
'Georgina Blythe' (R) 🏆H1c	WFib
'Georgina Forever' (A)	WFib
'Giant Butterfly' (R)	WFib
gibbosum	CSpe EWoo MHer SSal WFib
'Gillian Shaw' (R)	WFib
'Glacis' (Quality Series) (Z/d)	SSea
'Gladys Evelyn' (Z/d)	WFib
'Gladys Weller' (Z/d) 🏆H1c	WFib
§ ***glutinosum***	WFib
'Goblin' (Min/d)	MHer
'Goesta' (Z/d)	SSea
GOLDEN ANGEL	see *P.* 'Sarah Don'
'Golden Brilliantissimum' (Z/v)	WFib
'Golden Chalice' (Min/v)	WFib
'Golden Clorinda' (U/Sc/C)	NWsh SPet WFib
'Golden Ears' (Dw/St/C) 🏆H1c	NPer WFib
'Golden Edinburgh' (I/v)	WFib
'Golden Lilac Gem' (I/d)	WFib
'Golden Princess' (Min/C)	WFib
'Golden Square' (Dw/St)	WFib
'Golden Staphs' (Z/St/C)	MHer
'Golden Warwick' <u>**new**</u>	MHer
'Golden Well Sweep'	see *P. crispum* 'Golden Well Sweep'
'Gosport' (Z/v)	WFib
'Grace Thomas' (Sc) 🏆H1c	MHer WFib
'Grace Wells' (Min)	WFib
'Grainger's Antique Rose' (Z/d)	WFib
'Grand Slam' (R) 🏆H1c	WFib
GRANDEUR BUTTERFLY BICOLOUR RED (I)	LSou
GRANDEUR BUTTERFLY IVY WHITE (I)	LSou
GRANDEUR BUTTERFLY NEON (I)	LSou
GRANDEUR BUTTERFLY PINK (I)	LSou
GRANDEUR BUTTERFLY PURPLE (I)	LSou
grandiflorum	EShb EWoo MCot MHer WFib
'Granny Barter' (Z)	SAll
graveolens L'Hér.	see *P.* 'Graveolens'
graveolens ambig.	SEND SGro SMHy
graveolens *sensu* J.J.A. van der Walt	WFib
§ 'Graveolens' (Sc)	ENfk GPoy MHer SPet SVen WBrk WFib
'Graveolens Minor' (Sc)	EWoo
'Great Glemham Lemon' (Sc)	EWoo
'Green Eyes' (I/d)	MHer
'Greetings' (Min/v)	WFib
GRETA ('Pacgret') (Darkline Series) (Z)	SSea
'Grey Lady Plymouth' (Sc/v)	CPbh EWoo LCro LOPS MCot MHer NWsh WFib
'Grey Sprite' (Min/v)	WFib
§ ***grossularioides***	EWoo MHer
§ 'Hannaford Star' (Z/St)	WFib

	'Hansen's Pinkie' (Dec)	WFib
	'Hansen's Wild Spice' (Sc)	NWsh WFib
	'Happy Thought' (Z/v) ♀H1c	ECtt MCot SCoo WFib
	'Harbour Lights' (R)	WFib
	'Harewood Slam' (R)	WFib
	'Harlequin Pretty Girl' (I × Z/d)	WFib
	'Harlequin Rosie O'Day' (I)	ECtt WFib
	'Harvard' (I/d)	WFib
	'Hazel' (R)	WFib
	'Hazel Cherry' (R)	WFib
	'Hazel Dean' (R)	ECtt
	'Hazel Glory' (R)	WFib
	'Hazel Gypsy' (R)	WFib
	'Hazel Peach' (R)	WFib
	'Hazel Star' (R)	WFib
	'Hazel's Finale' (Dec)	WFib
§	'Hederinum' (I)	SAll
§	'Hederinum Variegatum' (I/v)	ECtt WFib
	'Helen Christine' (Z/St) ♀H1c	MHer WFib
	'Henry Weller' (A) ♀H1c	WFib
	'Hermanus Show' (Sc)	WFib
	'Hermione' (Z/d)	WFib
	'Highfields Attracta' (Z/d)	WFib
	'Highfield's Cameo' (Z)	SAll
	'Highfields Candy Floss' (Z/d)	ECtt WFib
	'Highfields Choice' (Z) ♀H1c	WFib
	'Highfields Delight' (Z)	WFib
	'Highfields Festival' (Z/d) ♀H1c	ECtt WFib
	'Highfields Flair' (Z/d)	WFib
	'Highfields Melody' (Z/d)	WFib
	'Highfields Pink' (Z)	WFib
	'Highfields Pride' (Z)	WFib
	'Highfields Snowdrift' (Z)	WFib
	'Highfields Symphony' (Z)	WFib
	'Highfields Vogue' (Z)	WFib
	'Hilda's Memory' (Dw/Z/d)	WFib
	'Hills of Snow' (Z/v)	MHer WFib
	'Hindoo' (R × U) ♀H1c	EWoo SAll WFib
	hispidum	MHer
	'Hit Parade' (I/d)	WFib
	'Hitcham' (Min/d)	WFib
	'Holbrook' (Dw/C/d)	WFib
	'Holt Beauty'	EWoo
	'Honeywood Lindy' (R)	WFib
	Horizon Series (Z)	MBros
	- 'Horizon Deep Salmon Improved' (Z)	MBros
	- 'Horizon Deep Scarlet' (Z)	MBros
	- 'Horizon Lilac Rose' (Z)	MBros
	'House and Garden' (R)	ECtt
	'Hula' (R × U)	EWoo WFib
	'Icing Sugar' (I/d)	WFib
	ignescens	EWoo WFib
	'Immaculatum' (Z)	WFib
	'Imperial Butterfly' (A/Sc) ♀H1c	ENfk MHer SPet SRms WFib
	iocastum	EWoo
	ionidiflorum	CSpe EShb EWoo MCot MHer MNHC SRms WAvo
	'Irene' (Z/d)	WFib
	'Irene Cal' (Z/d)	WFib
	'Irene Toyon' (Z)	WFib
	'Isabel Pearce' (Z)	SAll
	'Islington Peppermint' (Sc)	SPet SRms WFib
	'Italian Mystery'	SAll
	'Ivalo' (Z/d)	WFib
	'Ivory Snow' (Z/d/v)	WFib
	'Jack of Hearts' (I × Z/d)	WFib
	'Jack Phillips' (Z/d)	WFib
§	'Jackie' (I/d) ♀H1c	SAll WFib
	'Jackie Davies' (R)	EWoo
	'Jackie Gall'	see *P.* 'Jackie'
	'Jackie Totlis' (Z/St)	WFib
	'Jackpot Orchid Mist' (Z)	SAll
	'Jackpot Wild Rose' (Z/d)	WFib
	'Jane Chapman' (Z/d)	SAll
	'Jane Innes' (I/d)	WFib
	'Janet Hofman' (Z/d)	WFib
	'Janet Kerrigan' (Min/d)	WFib
	'Jayne Eyre' (Min/d)	WFib
§	'Jeanne d'Arc' (I/d)	WFib
	'Jer'Rey' (A)	EWoo WFib
	'Jip's Bishops Wood' (Dw/d)	WFib
	'Jip's Desert Poppy' (Z/Min)	WFib
	'Jip's Eleanor Renton' (Dw/d)	WFib
	'Jip's Little Lady' (Dw)	WFib
	'Jip's Megan' (Z/C/D)	ECtt
	'Jip's Pippin' (Dw)	WFib
	'Jip's Proud Sentinel' (Dw/d)	WFib
	'Jip's Sky Gipsy' (Dw)	WFib
	'Jip's Twilight' (Dw)	WFib
	'Joan Fontaine' (Z)	WFib
	'Joan Morf' (R) ♀H1c	EWoo WFib
	'Joan of Arc'	see *P.* 'Jeanne d'Arc'
	'Joy' (R) ♀H1c	CSpe ECtt WFib
	'Joy Lucille' (Sc)	NWsh
	'Julie Smith' (R)	WFib
	'Juniper' (Sc)	WFib
	'Just Beth' (Z/C/d)	WFib
	'Just Jip' (Dw/Z)	WFib
	'Just Joss' (Dw/d)	WFib
	'Just William' (Min/C/d)	WFib
	'Kamahl' (R)	WFib
	'Karl Hagele' (Z/d)	WFib
	'Karmin Ball'	WFib
	'Karrooense'	see *P. quercifolium*
	'Katie Hillier' (R)	WFib
	'Kaufman's Bonfire' (R)	WFib
	'Keepsake' (Min/d)	WFib
	'Kenny's Double' (Z/d)	ECtt WFib
	'Kerensa' (Min/d)	WFib
	'Kesgrave' (Min/d)	WFib
	'Kewense' (Z)	EShb WFib
	'Key's Unique' (U)	WFib
	'Kimono' (R) ♀H1c	ECtt
	'King Edmund' (R) ♀H1c	WFib
	'King of Denmark' (Z/d)	WFib
	'King Solomon' (R)	WFib
	'King's Ransom' (R)	WFib
§	'Kleine Liebling' (Min)	WFib
	'La France' (I/d) ♀H1c	ECtt LCro LOPS WFib
	'La Jolla' (Z/d)	WFib
	'La Paloma' (R)	WFib
§	'Lachskönigin' (I/d)	WFib
	'Lady Ilchester' (Z/d)	WFib
	'Lady Love Song' (R)	WFib
	'Lady Mary' (Sc)	MHer SRms WFib
	'Lady Mavis Pilkington' (Z/d)	WFib
	'Lady Plymouth' (Sc/v) ♀H1c	CPbh ECtt ELan ENfk EPPr EWoo GLog MCot MHer NWad NWsh SEND SPet SRms SSal WFib WGwG
§	'Lady Scarborough' (Sc)	ENfk MHer SPet SRms WFib

	laevigatum	MHer
	'Lancastrian' (Z/d)	ECtt WFib
§	***lanceolatum***	EWoo MHer
	'Land of Song' (A)	ENfk
	'Lara Ballerina' (Sc/d) 🏆H1c	SPet SRms
	'Lara Beacon'	CSpe EWoo
	'Lara Candy Dancer' (Sc) 🏆H1c	MAsh NWsh SPet WFib
	'Lara Dora Price' (Za)	WFib
	'Lara Jester' (Sc)	ECtt ENfk EWoo NWsh WFib
	'Lara Largo' (Za)	WFib
	'Lara Mandarin' (Za/d)	WFib
	'Lara Marjorie' (Za)	WFib
	'Lara Rajah' (R)	EWoo
	'Lara Starshine' (Sc) 🏆H1c	ENfk EPPr EWoo MHer SPet SRms WFib
	'Lara Susanne' (Za)	WFib
	'Lara Waltz' (R/d)	WFib
	'Laurel Hayward' (R)	WFib
	'Lauren Alexandra' (Z/d)	WFib
	'Lavender Grand Slam' (R) 🏆H1c	WFib
	'Lavender Lindy' (Sc)	CDow EWoo MHer NWsh SPet WFib
	'Lavender Mini Cascade'	see *P.* LILAC MINI CASCADE
	'Lavender Sensation' (R)	WFib
	'Lawrenceanum'	EWoo LCro LOPS WFib
	laxum	WFib
	'L'Élégante' (I/v) 🏆H1c	CDow MCot MHer WFib
	'Lemon Air' (Sc)	WFib
	'Lemon Crisp'	see *P. crispum*
	'Lemon Fancy' (Sc) 🏆H1c	MHer NWad NWsh SPet WFib
	'Lemon Kiss' (Sc)	CSpe EWoo NWsh SPet WFib
	'Lemon Meringue' (Sc)	WFib
	'Leslie William Burrows'	EWoo
	'Letitia' (A)	ENfk
	LILA COMPAKT-CASCADE	see *P.* 'Decora Lilas'
	LILAC ('Paclilac'[PBR]) (I)	SSea
	'Lilac Gem' (Min/I/d)	ENfk
§	LILAC MINI CASCADE ('Lilamica'[PBR]) (I) 🏆H1c	CDow
	'Lilian Pottinger' (Sc) 🏆H1c	ENfk EPPr EWoo MHer NWsh WFib
	'Lilian Woodberry' (Z)	WFib
	'Limoneum' (Sc)	ENfk EWoo MHer NWsh SPet WFib
	'Lincolnshire Lady' (R)	ECtt
	'Lipstick' (St)	WFib
	'Lisa' (Min/C)	WFib
	'Lisa Jo' (St/v/Dw/d)	WFib
	'Little Alice' (Dw/d) 🏆H1c	WFib
	'Little Gem' (Sc)	ENfk MHer WFib
	'Little Jip' (Z/d/v) 🏆H1c	WFib
	'Little Spikey' (St/Min/d)	MHer WFib
	'Lizzie Hillier' (R)	WFib
	'Lollipop' (Z/d)	WFib
	'Lord Baden-Powell'	see *P.* 'Colonel Baden-Powell'
	'Lord Bute' (R) 🏆H1c	CSpe ECtt ELan EWoo LCro LOPS MCot MHer NPer SMrm SPet SSal SVen WABo WFib WGwG
	'Lord de Ramsey'	see *P.* 'Tip Top Duet'
	'Lord Roberts' (Z)	WFib
	'Lottie Lungburgh' (Z/St)	WFib
	'Lotusland' (Dw/St/C) 🏆H1c	ECtt SPoG WFib
I	'Louise' (R) 🏆H1c	ECtt WFib
	'Love Song' (R/v)	WFib
	'Lovely Greta' (Za)	WFib
	'Lovely Wera' (Za/d)	WFib
	'Lucy Gunnett' (Z/d/v) 🏆H1c	ECtt WFib
	'Lyewood Bonanza' (R)	WFib
	'Lyric' (Min/d)	WFib
	'Mabel Grey' (Sc) 🏆H1c	CSpe ECtt ENfk EWoo MHer MNHC NPer NWsh SPet SSal WFib
§	'Madame Auguste Nonin' (U/Sc)	ENfk MHer NWsh SPet WFib
	'Madame Crousse' (I/d) 🏆H1c	EWoo WFib
	'Madame Layal' (A) 🏆H1c	WFib
	'Madame Margot'	see *P.* 'Hederinum Variegatum'
	'Madame Recamier' (Z/d)	ECtt
	'Madame Salleron' (Min/v)	EShb WFib
	magenteum	MHer
	'Magnum' (R)	WFib
	'Majestic' (Z/d)	WFib
	'Mandarin' (R)	ECtt
	'Mangles' Variegated' (Z/v)	WFib
	'Mani di Fata' (St)	SAll
	'Maple Leaf' (Sc)	EWoo NWsh
	'Maréchal MacMahon' (Z/C)	ENfk
	'Margaret Soley' (R) 🏆H1c	WFib
	'Margaret Waite' (R)	WFib
	'Margery Stimpson' (Min/d)	WFib
	'Marie Thomas' (Sc)	SGro
	MARIMBA ('Fisrimba'[PBR])	SCoo
	'Marion Saunders' (Dec)	WFib
	'Mariquita' (R)	WFib
	'Mark' (Dw/d)	WFib
	'Marmalade' (Min/d)	WFar
	'Marquis of Bute' (R/v)	MHer
	'Martin Parrett' (Min/d)	WFib
	'Mary Harrison' (Z/d)	WFib
I	'Maureen' Hoddinott (Z/d)	MHer
	'Mauve Beauty' (I/d)	WFib
	'Maxime Kovalevski' (Z)	WFib
	'May Day' (R)	WFib
	'May Magic' (R)	WFib
	'Meadowside Dark and Dainty' (St)	WFib
	'Meadowside Midnight' (St/C)	WFib
	'Medley' (Min/d)	WFib
	MELOCHERRY ('Pacmel'[PBR]) (Tempo Series) (Z/d)	SSea
	'Memento' (Min/d)	WFib
	'Mendip' (R)	WFib
	'Mendip Candy Floss' (R)	WFib
	'Mendip Royale' (R)	WFib
	'Meon Maid' (R)	SMrm WFib
	'Mere Casino' (Z)	WFib
	'Mexican Beauty' (I)	WFib
	'Mexicana'	see *P.* 'Rouletta'
	'Mexicanerin'	see *P.* 'Rouletta'
	'Michael' (A) 🏆H1c	EWoo MHer SPet
	'Michelle West' (Min)	WFib
	'Mike West' (St)	WFib
	'Millfield Gem' (I/d)	WFib
	'Millfield Rose' (I/d)	EWoo
	'Millmoor Clover'	SAll
	'Millmoor Porcelain'	SAll
	'Mimfy' (Z)	SAll
	'Mini Czech' (Cas/Min)	ECtt WBrk
	'Minnie' (Z/d/St)	WBrk WFib
	'Minstrel Boy' (R)	EWoo WFib
	'Minx' (Min/d)	WFib
	'Miss Burdett Coutts' (Z/v)	MHer WFib
	'Miss Muffett' (Min/d)	WFib
§	'Miss Stapleton'	LCro LOPS MHer WFib
	'Misterioso' (R)	WFib
	'Misty Morning' (R)	EWoo WFib
	'Modesty' (Z/d)	WFib
	'Mohawk' (R)	WFib
	'Mole'	see *P.* 'The Mole'
	'Molly' (A)	ENfk
	'Monique McEwan' (Z/St)	WFib

'Monsieur Ninon' misapplied	see *P.* 'Madame Auguste Nonin'
§ 'Monsieur Ninon' (U)	WFib
'Mont Blanc' (Z/v)	CDow WFib
'Montague Garabaldi Smith' (R)	WFib
'Monty's Magic' (R)	ECtt ELan
'Moon Maiden' (A)	WFib
'More's Victory' (U/Sc)	WFib
'Morval' (Dw/C/d) 🏆H1c	WFib
'Morwenna' (R)	MHer WCot WFib
'Mosaic Gay Baby' (I/d/v)	WFib
'Mr Henry Cox' (Z/v) 🏆H1c	MHer WFib
'Mr Wren' (Z)	ECtt ELan EPri EShb SIvy WFib
'Mrs Cannell' (Z)	WFib
'Mrs Farren' (Z/v)	MCot
'Mrs G.H. Smith' (A) 🏆H1c	ECtt SPet WFib
'Mrs J.C. Mappin' (Z/v) 🏆H1c	ECtt
'Mrs Kingsbury' (U)	WFib
'Mrs Martin' (I/d)	WFib
'Mrs McKenzie' (Z/St)	WFib
'Mrs Morf' (R)	ECtt
'Mrs Parker' (Z/d/v)	ECtt WFib
'Mrs Pollock' (Z/v)	ECtt ELan MBow MBros MCot SCoo WBrk WFib
'Mrs Quilter' (Z/C) 🏆H1c	ECtt SMrm WBrk WFib
'Mrs W.A.R. Clifton' (I/d)	WFib
multibracteatum	WFib
multiradiatum	WFib
mutans	WFib
'My Chance' (Dec)	WFib
myrrhifolium	EWoo
§ - var. ***coriandrifolium***	MHer WFib
'Mystery' (U) 🏆H1c	CWCL ECtt LCro LOPS WFib
'Narina' (I)	SCoo
'Needham Market' (A)	ENfk SPet
'Nellie Nuttall' (Z)	WFib
'Nervosum' (Sc)	ENfk
'Nervous Mabel' (Sc) 🏆H1c	MHer WFib
'New Gypsy' (R)	ELan
'Newchurch' (Z/St)	WFib
'Nicor Star' (Min)	WFib
'Night' (I)	EWoo
'Noche' (R)	SMrm
'Noele Gordon' (Z/d)	WFib
'Occold Shield' (Dw/C/d) 🏆H1c	ECtt SMrm WBrk WFib
'Occold Tangerine' (Z)	WFib
'Occold Volcano' (Dw/C/d)	WFib
odoratissimum (Sc) 🏆H1c	ENfk EWoo GPoy MHer SPet SRms WFib
'Odyssey' (Min)	WFib
'Old Spice' (Sc/v)	ENfk SPet WFib
'Oldbury Duet' (A/v) 🏆H1c	MHer SPet
'Olivia' (R)	WFib
'Opera House' (R)	WFib
'Orange Fizz' (Sc) 🏆H1c	CCht EWoo MHer NWsh SPet SRms WFib WGwG
'Orange Parfait' (R)	WFib
'Orangeade' (Dw/d)	WFib
'Orchid Clorinda' (Sc)	WFib
'Orchid Paloma' (Dw/d)	WFib
'Orion' (Min/d)	WFib
'Orsett' (Sc) 🏆H1c	GLog WFib
otaviense	WFib
'Our Flynn' (Z/St)	WFib
'Our Gynette' (Dec)	EWoo
'Our Henry' (Dw/d)	WFib
PAC cultivars	see under selling name
'Pagoda' (Z/St/d)	MHer WFib
'Paisley Red' (Z/d)	WFib
Palladium Series	MBros
'Pamela Vaughan' (Z/St)	WFib
'Pampered Lady' (A)	SPet
panduriforme	WFib
papilionaceum	ELan EPri EShb EWoo MCot MHer WFib
'Parisienne' (R) 🏆H1c	EWoo WFib
'Party Dress' (Z/d)	WFib
'Pat Hannam' (St)	WFib
'Paton's Unique' (U/Sc) 🏆H1c	CDow ECtt ELan ENfk EWoo MCot MHer SPet SVen WCot WFib
'Patricia Andrea' (Z/T) 🏆H1c	NPer WFib
patulum	WFib
'Paul Crampel' (Z) 🏆H1c	EShb EWoo MCot MHer WFib
'Paul West' (Min/d)	NWad SGro
'Pauline Harris' (R)	WFib
'Peace' (Min/C)	WFib
'Peach Princess' (R)	ECtt
PELFI cultivars	see under selling name
peltatum	EWoo SIvy WFib
'Penny' (Z/d)	WFib
'Penny Lane' (Z)	WFib
'Pensby' (Dw)	WFib
'Peppermint Lace' (Sc)	EWoo NWsh SPet
'Perfect' (Z)	WFib
'Pershore Princess'	SSal WAvo WBrk
'Petals' (Z/v)	SPoG
'Peter Godwin' (R)	WFib
'Peter's Choice' (R)	WFib
'Petit Pierre'	see *P.* 'Kleine Liebling'
'Phyllis Richardson' (R/d)	WFib
'Phyllis Variegated' (U/v)	ECtt ENfk EWoo MHer NWsh SPet WCot WFib
'Pink Aurore' (U)	WFib
'Pink Bonanza' (R)	WFib
'Pink Capitatum'	see *P.* 'Pink Capricorn'
§ 'Pink Capricorn' (Sc)	CCBP ENfk EPPr EPri EWoo LCro LOPS MBow NWsh SAng SRms SSal WFib
'Pink Champagne' (Sc)	MHer
'Pink Dolly Varden' (Z/v)	ECtt WFib
'Pink Fondant' (Min/d)	WFib
'Pink Gay Baby'	see *P.* 'Sugar Baby'
'Pink Happy Thought' (Z/v)	ECtt WFib
'Pink Hindoo' (Dec)	EWoo
'Pink Needles' (Min/St)	MHer WFib
'Pink Pandora' (T)	WFib
'Pink Pet' (U)	ECtt
'Pink Rambler' (Z/d)	WFib
'Pink Rosebud' (Z/d)	WFib
'Playboy Cherry'	SAll
'Playmate' (Min/St)	WFib
'Plum Rambler' (Z/d)	ECtt EShb WBrk WFib
'Polka' (U) 🏆H1c	EWoo SPet WFib
'Pompeii' (R)	WFib
'Poquita' (Sc)	SRms
'Porchfield' (Min/St)	WBrk
praemorsum	WFib
'Preseli Lottie' (Z/d)	WFib
'Preston Park' (Z/C)	WFib
'Pretty Polly' (Sc)	WFib
'Pride of Exmouth'	CWCL
'Prim' (Dw/St/d)	WFib
'Prince of Orange' (Sc) 🏆H1c	CCBP CCht ECtt ENfk EWoo GPoy MCot MHer NWsh SEND SPet SRms WFib
'Princeanum' (Sc) 🏆H1c	WFib
'Princess Abigail' (Dw/d)	ECtt WFib
'Princess Josephine' (R)	WFib

'Princess of Wales' (R)	WFib
'Princess Virginia' (R/v)	WFib
'Priory Beacon'	SAll
'Priory Salmon' (St/d)	EShb
'Priory Star' (St/Min/d)	WFib
pseudoglutinosum	EWoo WFib
'Pulsar Salmon Splash' (Pulsar Series) (Z)	EHyd
'Pungent Peppermint' (Sc)	SRms
'Purple Rogue' (R)	WFib
'Purple Unique' (U/Sc)	ECtt ENfk EShb EWoo MCot MHer SPet SVen WFib
'Pygmalion' (Z/d/v)	WFib
'Quantock' (R)	WFib
'Quantock Angelique' (A)	SPet
'Quantock Butterfly' (A)	SPet
'Quantock Candy' (A) ♀H1c	ELan SPet
'Quantock Clare' (A)	SPet
'Quantock Classic' (A)	EWoo
'Quantock Double Dymond' (A/d) ♀H1c	MHer WFib
'Quantock Kirsty' (A) ♀H1c	SPet
'Quantock Louise' (A)	SPet
'Quantock Marjorie' (A) ♀H1c	SPet
'Quantock May' (A)	SPet
'Quantock Perfection' (A) ♀H1c	MHer SPet WFib
'Quantock Sally' (A/d)	ENfk SPet
'Queen of Denmark' (Z/d)	WFib
'Queen of Hearts' (I × Z/d)	WFib
'Queen of the Lemons'	EWoo
quercifolium (Sc)	ECtt ELan EWoo GPoy SSal WFib WSMil
quinquelobatum	CSpe EWoo WFib
radens (Sc)	ENfk EWoo WFib
'Radula' (Sc) ♀H1c	CCBP ELan MHer SPet SRms WFib
'Radula Roseum' (Sc)	EWoo WFib
'Rager's Star' (Dw)	MHer
RAINBOW NEON ('Genraineon') (Rainbow Series) (I)	SSal
'Ray Bidwell' (Min)	WFib
§ 'Red Black Vesuvius' (Min/C)	MHer WFib WSMil
'Red Capri' (Sc)	EWoo
'Red Cascade' (I) ♀H1c	SAll WFib
'Red Gables'	WAvo WCot
'Red Pandora' (Z/T) ♀H1c	WFib
'Red Pimpernel' (Z/T)	WFib
'Red Rambler' (Z/d)	WBrk WFib
'Red Robin' (R)	ENfk EPPr WCot
'Red Spider' (Dw/Ca)	WFib
'Red Startel' (Z/St/d)	WFib
'Red Susan Pearce' (R)	WFib
'Red Victus Spider'	SAll
'Red Witch' (Dw/St/d)	EWoo MHer WBrk WFib
§ RED-MINI-CASCADE ('Rotemica') (I)	CDow
'Reflections' (Z/d)	WFib
'Regina' (Z/d) ♀H1c	WFib
'Rembrandt' (R)	WFib
'Renate Parsley' ♀H1c	EWoo LCro LOPS MHer WFib
reniforme	EWoo MHer WFib
'Reunion Rose' (Sc)	WFib
'Richard Gibbs' (Sc)	ENfk MHer SPet
'Richard Key' (Z/d/C)	WFib
'Rietje van der Lee' (A)	ENfk WFib
'Rimfire' (R) ♀H1c	ELan EWoo LCro LOPS MHer NWad WFib
'Rio Grande' (I/d)	MHer WFib
'Rober's Lemon Rose' (Sc)	ENfk EWoo MHer SPet SRms WBrk WFib
'Robert Fish' (Z/C)	SCoo
'Robert McElwain' (Z/d)	WFib
'Robin' (R)	ECtt
'Robin's Unique' (U)	MHer WFib
'Rogue' (R)	WFib
§ 'Roi des Balcons Lilas' (I)	SAll
'Roller's Echo' (A)	SPet WFib
'Roller's Pioneer' (I/v)	ENfk EWoo
'Roller's Satinique' (U)	MHer WFib
'Rollison's Unique' (U)	MHer WFib
'Romeo' (R)	EWoo
'Rose Bengal' (A)	ENfk
'Rose Eye' (Dw)	WFib
'Rose of Amsterdam' (Min/d)	WFib
'Rose Paton's Unique' (U/Sc)	SMrm
'Rose Silver Cascade' (I)	ECtt MCot MHer
'Rosebud Supreme' (Z/d)	WFib
'Rosmaroy' (R)	WFib
'Rosy Dawn' (Min/d)	WFib
'Rote Mini-cascade'	see *P.* RED-MINI-CASCADE
§ 'Rouletta' (I/d)	WFib
'Royal Ascot' (R)	EWoo SMrm SPet
ROYAL LAVENDER ('Klepp07196'PBR) (Royal Series) (I)	SSea
'Royal Oak' (Sc) ♀H1c	CPbh ECtt ENfk EPPr EWoo MCot MHer MNHC NWad NWsh SPet SPoG SRms SVen WFib
§ 'Royal Purple' (Z/d)	SAll WFib
'Royal Sovereign' (R)	WFib
'Royal Surprise' (R) ♀H1c	EWoo
'Ruby' (Min/d)	WFib
'Rushmere' (Dw/d)	WFib
'Rushmoor Golden Rosebud' (Za)	ECtt WFib
'Rushmoor Golden Ruffles' (Z/St/Min/C/d)	MHer
'Rushmoor Mrs Eve Scott' (Za/d)	ECtt WFib
(Rushmoor River Series) 'Rushmoor Amazon' (Za/d)	WFib
- 'Rushmoor Amur' (Za)	WFib
- 'Rushmoor Avon' (d/Za)	WFib
- 'Rushmoor Beautiful' (d/Za)	WFib
- 'Rushmoor Colorado' (d/Za)	WFib
- 'Rushmoor Congo' (Za/d)	WFib
- 'Rushmoor Danube' (Za)	WFib
- 'Rushmoor Euphrates' (Za)	WFib
- 'Rushmoor Ganges' (Za)	WFib
- 'Rushmoor Indus' (Za)	WFib
- 'Rushmoor Irtysh' (Za)	WFib
- 'Rushmoor Krishna' (Za)	WFib
- 'Rushmoor Main' (Za)	WFib
- 'Rushmoor Mekong' (Za/d)	WFib
- 'Rushmoor Mississippi' (Za)	WFib
- 'Rushmoor Missouri' (Za)	WFib
- 'Rushmoor Morava' (Za)	WFib
- 'Rushmoor Mosman' (Za)	WFib
- 'Rushmoor Murray' (Za)	WFib
- 'Rushmoor Niger' (Za)	WFib
- 'Rushmoor Nile' (Za/d)	WFib

- 'Rushmoor Orinoco' (Za/d) WFib
- 'Rushmoor Paraná' (Za) WFib
- 'Rushmoor Rhine' (Za/d) WFib
- 'Rushmoor Rhone' (Za/d) WFib
- 'Rushmoor Ribble' (Za/d) WFib
- 'Rushmoor Rio Grande' (Za) WFib
- 'Rushmoor Saint Lawrence' (Za/d) WFib
- 'Rushmoor Salween' (Za/d) WFib
- 'Rushmoor Sava' (Za) WFib
- 'Rushmoor Severn' (Za/d) WFib
- 'Rushmoor Thames' (Za/d) WFib
- 'Rushmoor Tiber' (Za/d) WFib
- 'Rushmoor Vistula' (Za/d) WFib
- 'Rushmoor Wheaton' (Za) WFib
- 'Rushmoor Yamuna' (Za/d) WFib
- 'Rushmoor Yangtze' (Za/d) WFib
- 'Rushmoor Yarra' (Za/d) WFib
- 'Rushmoor Yenisei' (Za/d) WFib
- 'Rushmoor Zambezi' (Za/d) WFib

'Saint Elmo's Fire' (St/Min/d) MHer WFar WFib
SAINT MALO ('Guisaint') (I) ECtt
'Salmon Angel' **new** CSpe
'Salmon Beauty' (Dw/d) WFib
§ 'Salmon Irene' (Z/d) WFib
'Salmon Queen' see *P.* 'Lachskönigin'
SALMON QUEEN ('Pacsalque'PBR) (Z) SSea
salmoneum WFib
'Samantha' (R) WFib
'Samantha Stamp' (Dw/C/d) WFib
SAMELIA ('Pensam'PBR) (Dark Line Series) (Z/d) SSea
'Sammi Brougham' (Dw/Z) WFib
'Sancho Panza' (Dec) CSpe WFib
'Sandra Lorraine' (I/d) WFib
'Sanguineum' CSpe
§ 'Sarah Don' (A/v) ECtt WFib
'Sarah Jane' (Sc) WFib
'Satsuki' (R) ♀H1c ECtt
'Saxifragoides' WFib
'Scarlet Gem' (Z/St) WBrk WFib
'Scarlet Pet' (U) ♀H1c CDow ECtt ENfk NWsh SMrm SPet
'Scarlet Rambler' (Z/d) ECtt EShb SMrm WFib
'Scarlet Unique' (U) CSpe EPri EWoo MCot MNHC WFib
schizopetalum MHer WFib
'Schottii' ♀H1c CPbh EWoo MHer WFib
'Scottow Star' (Z/C) WFib
'Seaview Silver' (Min/St) WFib
'Seaview Sparkler' (Z/St) WFib
'Secret Love' (Sc) SRms
'Seeley's Pansy' (A) EWoo MHer
'Sefton' (R) ♀H1c WFib
'Shannon' EWoo WFib
'Shelley' (Dw) WFar
§ 'Shottesham Pet' (Sc) CCBP CCht ENfk EWoo MHer NWad SPet SRms WGwG
sidoides ♀H1c CDow CPbh CSpe CTtf CWCL EAJP ECtt ELan ENfk EWoo LCro LOPS MCot MHer NWsh SGro SPhx SPlb SSal SVen WAvo WFib WHer WKif
'Silver Blazon' (Z/Dw/C/v) WFib
'Silver Dawn' (Min/St) MHer
'Silver Delight' (d/v) WFib
'Silver Kewense' (Dw/v) WFib
'Silver Snow' (Min/St/d) WFib
'Skelly's Pride' (Z) WFib
'Skies of Italy' (Z/C/d) WFib
'Snow Flurry' (Sc) WFib
'Snowbaby' (Min/d) WFib
'Snowdrift' (I/d) WFib
'Snowflake' (Min) see *P.* 'Atomic Snowflake'
'Snowstorm' (Z) WFib
'Sofie' see *P.* 'Decora Rose'
'Solferino' (A) ENfk
'Something Special' (Z/d) ♀H1c WFib
'Sophia' (Z) WGwG
SOPHIE CASADE see *P.* 'Decora Rose'
'Sophie Dumaresque' (Z/v) ♀H1c WFib
'Sophie Emma' (Z) WFib
'Sophie Marion' (Dw/Z) WFib
'South American Bronze' (R) ♀H1c SMrm WFib
'Southern Rosina' (Dw) WFib
'Southern Sundae' **new** MHer
'Souvenir de Prue' EWoo
'Spanish Angel' (A) ♀H1c MHer SPet WFib
'Spellbound' (R) WFib
'Spital Dam' (Dw/d) WFib
'Spitfire' (Z/Ca/d/v) CDow ECtt WFib
§ 'Splendide' ♀H1c CPbh CSpe CTtf EWoo MHer SWvt WFib
'Spot-on-bonanza' (R) ♀H1c ECtt WFib
'Springfield Black' (R) MCot
'Springtime' (Z/d) WFib
'Stadt Bern' (Z/C) ♀H1c CSpe
× ***stapletoniae*** see *P.* 'Miss Stapleton'
'Startel Salmon' (Z/St) MHer
'Stella Ballerina' SMrm
'Stellar Arctic Star' see *P.* 'Arctic Star'
'Stellar di Formosa' SAll
'Stellar Hannaford Star' see *P.* 'Hannaford Star'
'Stewart Meehan' (R) WFib
'Strawberry Fayre' (Dw/St) WFib
§ 'Sugar Baby' (DwI) MHer WFib
'Summer Cloud' (Z/d) WFib
SUMMER RAIN (mixed) (I) MBros
'Summertime' (Z/d) see *P.* 'Deacon Summertime'
'Sun Rocket' (Dw/d) WFib
'Sundridge Moonlight' (Z/C) WFib
'Sundridge Surprise' (Z) WFib
'Sunraysia' (Z/St) WFib
'Sunset Snow' (R) WFib
'Sunspot Petit Pierre' (Min/v) WFib
'Sunstar' (Min/d) WFib
'Supernova' (Z/St/d) WFib
'Surcouf' (I) WFib
'Susan Hillier' (R) WFib
'Susan Payne' (Dw/d) MHer
'Susie' (Z/C) WFib
'Sussex Gem' (Min/d) WFib
'Sussex Lace' see *P.* 'White Mesh'
'Swanland Lace' (I/d/v) WFib
'Swedish Angel' (A) WFib
'Sweet Annette' (Z) SAll
'Sweet Mimosa' (Sc) ♀H1c CCBP CCht CPbh ECtt ELan ENfk EWoo MCot MHer NWsh SEND SPet SRms WFib
'Sweet Sixteen' (R) WFib
'Sybil Holmes' (I/d) ECtt WFib
'Tammy' (Dw/d) WFib

TANGO NEON PURPLE ('Fistaneon'PBR) (Z/d)	SSea
'Tara Caws' (Z)	WFib
tetragonum	EShb EWoo MHer SIvy SSal WFib
'The Boar' (Fr) ♀H1c	EShb EWoo MCot WFib
'The Culm' (A)	MHer WFib
'The Czar'	see *P.* 'Czar'
'The Joker' (I/d)	WFib
'The Kenn-Lad' (A)	EWoo
'The Marchioness of Bute' (R)	MHer WFib
§ 'The Mole' (A)	WFib
'The Tamar' (A)	EWoo MHer
'The Yar' (Z/St)	WFib
'Thomas Earle' (Z)	WFib
'Tinker West' (Z/St/Dw)	WFib
§ 'Tip Top Duet' (A) ♀H1c	MHer SMrm SPet WFib
'Tirley Garth' (A)	WFib
tomentosum (Sc) ♀H1c	CPbh CSpe ENfk EPPr EShb EWoo GLog GPoy LCro LOPS MCot MHer NWad NWsh SEND SIvy SPet SSal WABo WFib
- 'Chocolate'	see *P.* 'Chocolate Peppermint'
TOMMY ('Pactommy') (I)	ELan SSea
tongaense	WFib
'Topscore' (Z/d)	WFib
'Tornado' (R) ♀H1c	LCro LOPS WFib
'Torrento' (Sc)	EWoo MHer NWsh SPet SRms WFib
'Tortoiseshell' (R)	WFib
transvaalense	CPbh EWoo
'Treasured Memories' (A)	SAll
tricolor misapplied	see *P.* 'Splendide'
tricolor Curt.	CPbh
tricuspidatum	EShb EWoo MHer WFib
trifidum	EWoo WFib
'Trino'	SAll
'Triomphe de Nancy' (Z/d)	WFib
triste	EWoo MHer WFib
'Trudie' (Dw/Fr)	MHer WFib
'Turkish Coffee' (R)	WFib
'Turkish Delight' (Dw/C)	WFib
'Turtle's Surprise' (Z/d/v)	WBrk
'Two Dees' (Dw/d)	WFib
'Tyabb Princess' (R)	EWoo
'Unicorn Bride' (Za/d)	WFib
'Unicorn Diva' (Za)	WFib
'Unicorn Frills' (Za)	WFib
'Unicorn Gold' (Za)	WFib
'Unicorn Hot Butter' (Za/d)	WFib
'Unicorn Hot Pepper' (Za/d)	WFib
'Unicorn Rose' (Za/d)	WFib
'Unique Aurore' (U)	CSpe MHer
'Unique Mons Ninon'	see *P.* 'Monsieur Ninon'
urbanum	EWoo
'Urchin' (Min/St)	WFib
'Ursula Key' (Z/c)	WFib
'Ursula's Choice' (A)	SPet WFib
'Val Merrick' (Dw/St)	WFib
'Valentine' (Z/C)	WFib
'Vancouver Centennial' (Dw/St/C) ♀H1c	ECtt MHer SCoo SPoG SSea WFib
'Vandersea' (Sc)	EWoo MCot MHer NWsh
'Variegated Clorinda' (Sc/v)	WFib
'Variegated Fragrans'	see *P.* (Fragrans Group) 'Fragrans Variegatum'
§ 'Variegated Kleine Liebling' (Min/v)	WFib
'Variegated Petit Pierre' (Min/v)	MHer WFib
'Vectis Cascade' (I)	EWoo
'Vectis Glitter' (Z/St) ♀H1c	WBrk WCot WFib

'Vectis Pink' (Dw/St)	WFib
'Vectis Purple' (Z/d)	WFib
'Vectis Starbright' (Dw/St)	WFib
'Vectis Volcano' (Z/St)	WFib
'Vicki' (R)	EWoo MHer
'Vicki Town' (R)	WFib
VICKY ('Pacvicky'PBR) (I)	SSea
'Vicky Claire' (R)	SMrm WFib
VILLE DE DRESDEN ('Pendresd') (I)	EWoo
'Vina' (Dw/C/d)	WFib
violareum misapplied	see *P.* 'Splendide'
'Viscossisimum' (Sc)	MHer
viscosum	see *P. glutinosum*
'Vivat Regina' (Z/d)	WFib
'Voodoo' (U) ♀H1c	CPbh CSpe ECtt ENfk EWoo MCot MHer SIvy SPet WCot WFib
'Wallis Friesdorf' (Dw/C/d)	WFib
'Wantirna' (Z/v) ♀H1c	ECtt
'Warrenorth Coral' (Z/C/d)	WFib
'Warrenorth Emerald' (Z) **new**	MHer
'Wayward Angel' (A)	ENfk SPet
'Wedding Royale' (Dw/d)	WFib
'Welling' (Sc)	ENfk SPet WFib
'Wendy Jane' (Dw/d)	WFib
'Wendy Read' (Dw/d)	WFib
'Westdale Appleblossom' (Z/C/d)	ECtt MHer WFib
'Westside' (Z/d)	MHer WFib
'Westwood' (Z/St)	WFib
'Whisper' (R)	EWoo WFib
'White Bird's Egg' (Z)	WFib
'White Boar' (Fr)	CSpe ECtt EShb WFib
'White Bonanza' (R)	WFib
'White Eggshell' (Min)	WFib
'White Feather' (Z/St)	MHer
§ 'White Mesh' (I/v)	CDow
'White Unique' (U)	SPet WFib
'Wilhelm Kolle' (Z)	WFib
'Wilhelm Langath' (Z/v)	ECtt EShb MBow SCoo WBrk WHil
'Willa' (Dec)	WFib
'Wirral Moonlight' (Z/C/d)	WFib
'Wolverton' (Z)	WFib
'Wootton's Unique' (U)	EWoo
'Wychwood' (A/Sc)	EWoo
'Yale' (I/d) ♀H1c	WFib
'Yan le Grounch' (Z/C)	WFib
'Yhu' (R)	SMrm WFib
'York Florist' (Z/d/v)	ECtt
'Yvonne' (Z)	WFib
'Zinc' (Z/d)	WFib
zonale	EWoo WFib
'Zulu King' (R)	WFib
'Zulu Warrior' (R)	WFib

Peliosanthes (*Asparagaceae*)

caesia B&SWJ 5183	WCru
macrostegia B&SWJ 3639 **new**	WCru
teta subsp. ***humilis*** RWJ 10044	WCru

Pellaea (*Pteridaceae*)

atropurpurea	GBin
falcata ♀H4	EShb
ovata	SPlb
rotundifolia ♀H2	CBdn CLAP CRos CTsd EHyd EShb LEdu LLWG LRHS MAsh NBro NRHS WCot
viridis	EShb LEdu WPGP

Pellionia see *Elatostema*

Peltandra (*Araceae*)

undulata	see *P. virginica* (L.) Schott
§ ***virginica*** (L.) Schott	LLWG NPer

Peltaria (*Brassicaceae*)

alliacea	CCBP CSpe LEdu WCot

Peltiphyllum see *Darmera*

Peltoboykinia (*Saxifragaceae*)

§ ***tellimoides***	LShi MPnt NBir WFar WPnP
watanabei	CElw CPla EBee EHed GEdr GPSL LEdu LShi MACG MBriF MMrt NFav NLar SBls SPad WCru WPnP

Pennellianthus see *Penstemon*

Pennisetum ✿ (*Poaceae*)

advena 'Fireworks'PBR (v)	CBcs CBod CKel EBee EHyd EPfP LPar LRHS MAsh MCot NRHS SWvt
§ - 'Rubrum' ♀H3	CBcs CBct CExl CKno EBee EHyd EShb EWoo LCro LOPS LRHS MAsh MBros NRHS NWsh SCoo SMad SWvt
§ ***alopecuroides***	CBcs CBod CWCL ECha EHyd EPfP EWhm LRHS NGdn NRHS SCob SMrm SPer SPlb SWvt XLum XSen
- AUTUMN WIZARD	see *P. alopecuroides* 'Herbstzauber'
- 'Black Beauty'	CKno EBlo ECha ETod IPot LShi SMHy SMea SSut WHoo
- 'Cassian's Choice' ♀H3	CKno EWes GWyn ILea SHar
- 'Caudatum'	CKno
- 'Dark Desire'	CKno CRos CSde EHyd EPfP LEdu LRHS NRHS
- 'Foxtrot'	EPPr
- 'Gelbstiel'	CKno EBee EHyd ELon EPfP LRHS NRHS
- 'Goldstrich'	ELon SAko XSen
- 'Hameln' ♀H3	Widely available
- 'Hameln Gold'PBR	CBod CKel CKno ELon EWes LRHS NLar SPeP XSen
§ - 'Herbstzauber'	CBod CKno EBee ELon NLar XLum XSen
- 'JS Jommenik'PBR	EBee ELon
- 'Little Bunny'	CBod CKel CMac CSde EBee EHyd ELan ELon EPfP LRHS LSRN MACG MAsh MHol NGdn NLar NRHS SCob SMea SWvt XSen
- 'Little Honey' (v)	ELan ELon WPnP XLum XSen
- 'Magic'	CBod EBee ELon SMea
- 'Moudry'	CBod CExl CSde EBee ELon EPPr EPfP EShb IPot LRHS MACG NLar XLum
- 'Red Head' ♀H3	CKno CMac CMea CRos EBee EBlo EHyd ELan ELon EPfP EWes LEdu LRHS LSou LSun MACG MAvo MBel MHol NLar NRHS NSti SEdd SMad SMea SPeP SPoG WChS WCot XSen
- f. ***viridescens***	CBod EAJP EHyd ELon EPPr EShb LEdu LRHS NRHS SBls SCob SMad SPtp XLum XSen
- 'Weserbergland'	CKno EBee EBlo ELon EPPr SAko
- 'Woodside'	CKno XLum
clandestinum	EShb
compressum	see *P. alopecuroides*
'Fairy Tails' ♀H3	CKno CRos ECha EHyd ELon EPPr EPfP LCro LOPS LPla LRHS MAsh MAvo MBel NDov NRHS NWsh SEdd SMHy SMea SPoG WCot WHoo
flaccidum	EPPr
glaucum 'Purple Baron'	MPri
- 'Purple Majesty'	CSpe SWvt
incomptum	XLum
longistylum misapplied	see *P. villosum*
macrourum	CBod CKno CSde CSpe EAJP EBlo ECha EHyd EPPr EPfP EShb LEdu LRHS MACG MAvo MNrw NDov NRHS NWsh SDix SMHy SMad SPlb SPtp WABo WPGP XSte
- 'Short Stuff'	CKno
- 'Tail Feathers'	CGrG SBls
massaicum 'Red Bunny Tails'	CChe NRHS SRms
- 'Red Buttons'	see *P. thunbergii* 'Red Buttons'
orientale ♀H3	CBod CKno CRos CSde CSpe EBlo ECha EGrI EHyd EPfP LRHS LSun MRav NBir NRHS SEND SPer SRkn SWvt WABo WKif XLum XSen
- 'Flamingo'	EHyd IPot NRHS SMea
- 'Karley Rose'PBR	CKno CPar CSpe EWes EWoo LRHS MAvo NDov NRHS SCob SIvy SMad SWvt WPGP
I - 'Robustum'	EPPr WPGP
- 'Shogun'	CKno CRos ECha EHyd EPPr EPfP LRHS NRHS SMHy SMea
- 'Tall Tails'	EBee EHyd EPPr EShb EWes GMaP LRHS NDov SMea XLum
'Paul's Giant'	EBee ELon XLum
PRINCESS CAROLINE ('Tift-17') <u>new</u>	SPeP
purpureum	SRms
setaceum 'Rubrum'	see *P.* × *advena* 'Rubrum'
thunbergii	CBod EHyd
§ - 'Red Buttons'	CKno CRos CSde EHyd ELon EPPr EPfP EShb LEdu LRHS MACG MAsh MAvo MGos MNrw NRHS SBls SCob SMHy SMea SPoG SSut WAvo WHoo WPGP
VERTIGO ('Tift-8'PBR)	WCot
§ ***villosum*** ♀H3	Widely available
- 'Cream Falls'	SBls

pennyroyal see *Mentha pulegium*

Penstemon ✿ (*Plantaginaceae*)

'Abbotsmerry'	EGrI ELon MBNS MCot MGil SGBe SIvy SLon
§ 'Alice Hindley'	Widely available
alpinus	GWyn
'Amy Gray'	WAvo WBrk
§ 'Andenken an Friedrich Hahn' ♀H5	Widely available
§ ***angustifolius***	CSpe SBls
'Apple Blossom' misapplied	see *P.* 'Thorn'
'Apple Blossom'	Widely available
'Arabesque Appleblossom'	CBod EHyd LRHS NRHS
'Arabesque Orchid'	CBod LRHS SCoo
'Arabesque Pink'	EHyd LRHS MHol NRHS
'Arabesque Red'	CBod EHyd LRHS NRHS SCoo
'Arabesque Violet'	EHyd LRHS MHol NRHS SCoo
arizonicus	see *P. whippleanus*
'Ashton'	WAvo
attenuatus var. ***attenuatus***	GKev
- subsp. ***militaris***	SPlb
'Audrey Cooper'	CMac WAvo
azureus	GKev
'Barbara Barker'	see *P.* 'Beech Park'
§ ***barbatus***	ECha SPer SRms SSut XSen

- 'Coccineus'	CSde CSpe GBin SBut XLum
- 'Iron Maiden'	LRHS
- 'Jingle Bells'	EPfP GArf MACG SBls SPeP
- orange-flowered	SPlb
- Pinacolada Series	EHyd LRHS NRHS
- - 'Pinacolada Blue'	CRos LRHS
- - 'Pinacolada Dark Rose'	EHyd LRHS NRHS
- - 'Pinacolada Rosy Red'	EHyd LRHS NRHS
- - 'Pinacolada White'	EHyd LRHS NRHS SRms
- var. ***praecox*** f. ***nanus*** 'Rondo'	EAJP
- - 'Pristine Lila Purple' new	CBod
- 'Roseus'	SHar
'Beckford'	CWCL EWes LRHS MBNS MGil SGBe
§ 'Beech Park' ♀H4	EBee EHyd ELan EPfP LRHS SRms WAvo
'Bisham Seedling'	see *P.* 'White Bedder'
'Blackbird' (Bird Series)	Widely available
'Blue Riding Hood'PBR (Riding Hood Series)	SPoG
'Blue Spring' misapplied	see *P. heterophyllus* 'Blue Spring'
'Blueberry Taffy'PBR	ECtt EHyd LRHS NRHS
'Bodnant' ♀H4	WAvo WBrk WHoo WMal
'Boysenberry Taffy'PBR	EHyd LRHS NRHS
'Bredon'	WAvo
brevisepalus	LPla
'Bubblegum' (Ice Cream Series)	SCoo
'Burford Purple'	see *P.* 'Burgundy'
'Burford Seedling'	see *P.* 'Burgundy'
'Burford White'	see *P.* 'White Bedder'
§ 'Burgundy'	CMac ECtt GMaP NBir NPer SMrm SRms WAvo XLum
caeruleus	see *P. angustifolius*
§ ***campanulatus***	CRos EHyd EPot EWes GKev LRHS NRHS SHar SRms
- 'Roseus' misapplied	see *P. kunthii*
cardinalis subsp. ***regalis***	GKev
cardwellii	EWes
'Castle Forbes'	EBee GMaP MBNS SRms WAvo
'Cathedral Rose'	EBee EHyd ELan EPfP LRHS
'Catherine de la Mare'	see *P. heterophyllus* 'Catherine de la Mare'
'Centra'	WAvo
'Charles Rudd'	ECtt ELan ELon EPfP LSRN MBNS MGil MHer NLar SGBe SRms SWvt WAvo
§ 'Cherry'	ECtt MBNS SHar SMrm WAvo
'Cherry Ripe' misapplied	see *P.* 'Cherry'
§ 'Chester Scarlet'	ECtt EGrI MBNS WAvo WCFE WKif
'Choirboy'	EWes
cinicola	GArf
cobaea	CSpe
'Comberton'	WAvo
confertus	CTri EBee EPot GKev
- RCB/MO A-7	WCot
'Connie's Pink' ♀H4	SRms WAvo
'Coral Sea'	LSou WFar
'Cottage Garden Red'	see *P.* 'Windsor Red'
§ 'Countess of Dalkeith'	ECtt GBin MCot MRav SHar SRms SWvt WAvo WCFE
'Craigieburn Taffeta'	WAvo
cristatus	see *P. eriantherus*
* ***cyananthus*** var. ***utahensis***	WCot
'Dark Towers'PBR	CAbb CBod CWGN EBee ECtt EHyd EMor EPfP EWTr LRHS MBNS MBel MBow MHol MNrw MPie MSCN NCou NHpl NRHS SCoo SEdd SGBe SLon SMad SPad SPoG WBrk WCot WHoo
davidsonii	EPot EWes GEdr
- var. ***davidsonii***	WAbe
- var. ***menziesii*** 'Microphyllus'	GEdr GKev NWad WAbe
- var. ***praeteritus***	GEdr
- 'Silverwells'	EPot
'Dazzler'	SWvt WAvo
'Delfts Blue Riding Hood'PBR (Riding Hood Series)	LCro LOPS
'Devonshire Cream'	WAvo
diffusus	see *P. serrulatus*
digitalis	EGrI SRms
- 'Gold Foil' new	LShi
- 'Goldfinger'	LRHS
§ - 'Husker Red'	Widely available
- 'Isa'	WCot
- 'Mystica'	EBee EHyd EPfP LRHS NRHS SPeP SRms
- 'Purpureus'	see *P. digitalis* 'Husker Red'
§ 'Drinkstone Red'	SDix SRms WAvo
eatonii	GKev
(Elgar Series) 'Elgar Crown of India'	WCot
- 'Elgar Firefly'	WCot
- 'Elgar Light of Life'	WCot
- 'Elgar Nimrod'	WCot
'Ellenbank Amethyst'	SDys
'Ellenbank Cardinal'	WKif
'Ellwood Red Phoenix'	WAvo
'Elmley'	WAvo
§ ***eriantherus***	GKev SPlb
ETNA ('Yatna') (Volcano Series)	ECtt EPfP LRHS NRHS SCoo SPad SRms
euglaucus	GKev
§ 'Evelyn' ♀H4	CMac ECha ELan ELon EPfP LRHS LSRN MBNS MCot MGil MHer MRav SPer SPoG SRms SWvt WAvo WBrk WHoo WKif WSHC XLum
'Fanny's Blush'	SWvt
'Firebird'	see *P.* 'Schoenholzeri'
'Flame'	WAvo
'Flamingo'	EBee ECtt ELon EPfP EWes GBin MBNS NLar SCoo SGbt SHar SRms SWvt WAvo
§ ***fruticosus*** var. ***scouleri*** ♀H4	MAsh
- - 'Albus' ♀H4	WAbe
- - 'Amethyst'	WAbe
FUJIYAMA ('Yayama'PBR)	CBod CPla ECtt EPfP LRHS MBow SCoo SLon SPad SRms SWvt
'Garden Red'	see *P.* 'Windsor Red'
'Garnet'	see *P.* 'Andenken an Friedrich Hahn'
gentianoides B&SWJ 10271	WCru
'Geoff Hamilton'	CElw ECtt MBNS MGil SGBe SLon SPoG WAvo
§ 'George Home' ♀H3	EWes GBin MBNS SMrm SRms WAvo
'George Moon'	SPad
'Gilchrist'	SAng
glaber	CMea EWld MBow SPlb
- 'Roundway Snowflake'	SHar SRms
'Gloire des Quatre Rues'	XLum
'Grape Taffy'PBR	EHyd LRHS NRHS
hallii	EPot EWes GEdr SPlb
hartwegii 'Albus'	SHar SRms
- 'Picotee Red'	EHyd NRHS
§ ***heterophyllus***	LRHS NBir SIvy SRkn SRms
- 'Blue Gem'	CElw
§ - 'Blue Spring'	CFis CSpe EHyd EPfP MRav
§ - 'Catherine de la Mare'	EBee EGrI EHyd EPPr EWTr GBin LSRN MGil NLar NRHS SCob SHar SIvy SWvt WKif WSMil WSpi XLum

	– 'Electric Blue'	CBod CRos EHyd LRHS LSou MBNS NRHS SCoo SLon WFar
	– 'Heavenly Blue'	Widely available
	– 'Jeanette'	CMea
	– 'True Blue'	see *P. heterophyllus*
	– 'Züriblau'	SPlb WHil
§	'Hewell Pink Bedder' ♀H4	CBar CBod CMea CRos EHyd EPfP GBin LRHS MBNS MRav NCou NRHS SCoo SHar SIvy SRms SWvt WAvo WHil
	'Hidcote Pink' ♀H3	Widely available
	'Hidcote Purple'	SHar WHoo XLum
	'Hidcote White'	MHer SWvt WBrk
	'Hillview Pink'	SLon XLum
§	***hirsutus***	EBee SBut XLum
	– 'Blue Foam'	GWyn
	– var. ***pygmaeus***	CMea EDAr EPfP EPot EWTr GKev NHpl NRya SBut SPlb SRms WHoo
*	– – f. ***albus***	GArf WHoo
	– – 'Purpureus'	WAbe
	'Hopleys Variegated' (v)	SWvt
	'Hot Pink Riding Hood' PBR (Riding Hood Series)	EHyd LCro LOPS LRHS NRHS
	JEAN GRACE ('Penbow')	ECtt
	'John Nash' misapplied	see *P.* 'Alice Hindley'
	'John Nash'	SRms
	'Juicy Grape' (Ice Cream Series)	WCot
	'June'	see *P.* 'Pennington Gem'
	'Jupiter'	XLum
	KILIMANJARO ('Yajaro') (Volcano Series)	EPfP LRHS SCoo SLon SRms WFar
	'King George V'	Widely available
§	***kunthii***	MAsh
§	***laetus*** subsp. ***roezlii***	MAsh
§	'Le Phare'	WAvo XLum
	'Lilac and Burgundy'	SHar SRms SWvt WAvo
	'Lilac Frost'	EPfP
	linarioides 'Marilyn Ross'	ECtt
	'Lord Home'	see *P.* 'George Home'
	lyallii	GAbr GWyn SRms
	'Lynette'	WAvo
	'Macpenny's Pink'	CMac MBNS WAvo XLum
	'Madame Golding'	XLum
	'Margery Fish' ♀H3	CFis ECtt EWes
	'Maurice Gibbs' ♀H3	CBcs CMac CWCL EGrI ELon EPfP EWes LSRN MBNS MGil NGBl SRms WHil
	'Melting Candy' (Ice Cream Series)	WCot
	mensarum	CPla EPfP GLog MACG SBls WKif
	Mexicali hybrids	SBut
	– (Carillo Series) 'Carillo Purple'	CRos CSpe EHyd LRHS NRHS
	– – 'Carillo Red'	CRos EHyd LRHS NRHS
	– PIKE'S PEAK PURPLE ('P007s') **new**	GArf
	× ***mexicanus*** 'Sunburst Amethyst'	ELan SRms XLum
	– 'Sunburst Ruby'	EBou ELan
	'Midnight'	EAJP ECtt EGrI ELan LRHS MGil MRav MSwo SEND SHar SIvy SWvt WAvo XLum
	'Miniature Bells'	EPfP
	'Modesty'	SRms
	'Mother of Pearl'	CBcs CTri EHyd ELan EMor EPfP GMaP LRHS LSRN MCot MSwo SHar SRms SWvt WAvo
	'Mrs Morse'	see *P.* 'Chester Scarlet'
	'Mrs Oliver'	EWes
	multiflorus	EBee
§	'Myddelton Gem'	SRms
	newberryi ♀H5	GKev
	– f. ***humilior***	EPot LShi
§	– subsp. ***sonomensis***	SRms WAbe
	'Newbury Gem'	SHar SWvt
	'Oaklea Red'	WAvo
§	'Old Candy Pink'	LRHS SWvt WAvo
	'Osprey' (Bird Series) ♀H3	CWGN EAJP EBee ECtt EHyd EMor EPfP EWes LRHS NBir SGBe SHar SRms SWvt WAvo WMal
	ovatus	CMac SPhx SRms WKif
	'Overbury'	SRms WAvo WBrk
	'Papal Purple'	MBNS SBut SHar SRms WAvo XLum
	'Patio Wine'	WAvo
	'Peace'	GBin
§	'Pennington Gem'	CTri MHer NBir SHar SRms SWvt WAvo
	(Pensham Series) 'Pensham Amelia Jane'	CRos CWGN ECtt EGrI EHyd ELon EPau EPfP GWyn LRHS NLar NRHS SCoo SLon SPer SRms SWvt WCav
	– 'Pensham Arctic Fox'	CSpe ECtt ELon EPfP LRHS MGil SBut SLon SPoG WSpi
	– 'Pensham Avonbelle' ♀H4	SRms
	– 'Pensham Bilberry Ice'	EGrI SWvt
	– 'Pensham Blackberry Ice'	ECtt SLon SRms
	– 'Pensham Blueberry Ice'	ECtt SWvt
	– 'Pensham Charlotte Louise'	ECtt SRms
	– 'Pensham Czar'	CDor CRos ECtt EHyd ELon EPPr EPfP GWyn LRHS MBNS MCot MGos NLar NRHS SCoo SEdd SGbt SLon SPer SPoG SRkn SRms SWvt WBor WFar WHoo
	– 'Pensham Dorothy Wilson'	EGrI
	– 'Pensham Eleanor Young'	CRos ECtt EPfP SEdd SLon SWvt
	– 'Pensham Freshwater Pearl'	SRms WHoo
	– 'Pensham Jessica Mai'	ECtt SCob SPer SRms SWvt
	– 'Pensham Just Jayne' ♀H4	ECtt EGrI ELon EPfP SLon SRms SWvt WBrk WHoo WSpi XLum
	– 'Pensham Laura'	CDor CRos CWGN ECtt EGrI EHyd EPPr EPfP LCro LOPS LRHS MBNS NRHS SCob SCoo SEdd SLon SPer SRms SWvt WBor WBrk WCav WFar WHoo
	– 'Pensham Loganberry Ice'	SLon
	– 'Pensham Miss Wilson'	SRms
	– 'Pensham Plum Jerkum'	CDor CRos CWGN EBee ECtt EGrI EHyd ELon EPPr EPfP LCro LOPS LRHS MBNS MBel MHer MPie NLar NRHS SCob SEdd SLon SPer SRms SWvt WCav WFar
	– 'Pensham Raspberry Ice'	SLon
	– 'Pensham Skies'	SRms
	– 'Pensham Son of Raven'	WAvo WBrk
	– 'Pensham Tayberry Ice'	ECtt SLon SRms
	– 'Pensham Victoria Plum' ♀H4	CElw SGro SHar SRms WHoo
	– 'Pensham Wedding Bells'	ELon SRms
	– 'Pensham Wedding Day'	EBee EHyd EPfP LSRN NLar NRHS SCoo SEdd SLon SPer SPoG WFar WMal
	– 'Pensham Westminster Belle'	ECtt LBuc SCob SRms WHil
	(Pentastic Series) PENTASTIC PINK ('Yapmine')	LCro LOPS LSou MHol
	– PENTASTIC RED ('Yapruby')	CWGN LCro LOPS LSou MHol
	– PENTASTIC ROSE ('Yaprose')	CWGN LCro LOPS LSou MHol
	'Pershore Anniversary'	WAvo
	'Pershore Carnival'	SRms WAvo

'Pershore Fanfare' WAvo
'Pershore Festival' WAvo
'Pershore Pink Necklace' EGrI SRms SWvt WAvo
'Phare' see *P.* 'Le Phare'
(Phoenix Series) PHOENIX APPLEBLOSSOM 09 ('Peni Ablos09') CRos EHyd LRHS NRHS
- PHOENIX LAVENDER ('Peni Laver') EHyd
- PHOENIX MAGENTA 09 ('Peni Mag09') CRos EHyd LRHS NRHS
- PHOENIX MAGENTA ('Pheni Magna') EPfP
- PHOENIX PINK ('Pheni Pinka') EHyd LRHS NRHS
- PHOENIX RED ('Pheni Reeda'PBR) CRos EHyd EPfP LRHS NRHS SRms
- PHOENIX VIOLET 09 ('Peni Vio09'PBR) CRos EHyd EPfP LRHS NRHS
- PHOENIX VIOLET ('Pheni Vio') SRms
'Phyllis' see *P.* 'Evelyn'
pinifolius ♀H4 CMea CRos CTri EHyd EPot GArf GKev LRHS LShi MAsh NRHS NSla SRms WFar WHoo XSen
- 'Compactum' GKev
- 'Mersea Yellow' CMea EBee EHyd ELan EPfP EPot GKev LRHS LShi MAsh MHer NRHS SLee SPlb SRms WIce XLum
- 'Wisley Flame' ♀H4 EPfP EPot EWes GEdr GKev MBNS MHer NHpl NSla
'Pink Bedder' see *P.* 'Hewell Pink Bedder', 'Sutton's Pink Bedder'
'Pocahontas' **new** LRHS
'Port Wine' ♀H3 CTri ELon EPfP GMaP LRHS MGil NBir SEND SPoG SWvt WAvo WKif
'Powis Castle' ECtt WAvo WBrk
'Prairie Twilight'PBR CBod
procerus GKev
var. ***brachyanthus***
§ - var. ***formosus*** SRms WAbe
§ - 'Roy Davidson' ♀H5 CMea EPot MHol MMrt WAbe
- var. ***tolmiei*** CPla EPot GEdr GKev WAbe
pseudospectabilis XSen
pubescens see *P. hirsutus*
pulchellus Greene see *P. procerus* var. *formosus*
pulchellus Lindl. see *P. campanulatus*
'Purple and White' see *P.* 'Countess of Dalkeith'
'Purple Bedder' CMac CRos EGrI EHyd ELan EPfP GBin LRHS LSRN NBir NRHS SCoo SGBe SPoG SRkn SRms SWvt XLum
'Purple Passion' CRos EBee EBlo EHyd ELan ELon EPfP LRHS NRHS SCob
'Purple Riding Hood'PBR (Riding Hood Series) EHyd LCro LOPS LRHS NRHS
'Purple Sea' WFar
'Purpureus Albus' see *P.* 'Countess of Dalkeith'
'Raven' (Bird Series) ♀H3 Widely available
'Razzle Dazzle' SPlb SRms WAvo WCot
'Red Emperor' WAvo
'Red Knight' WAvo
'Red Riding Hood'PBR (Riding Hood Series) EHyd EPfP LCro LOPS LRHS NRHS SPoG
RED ROCKS ('P008s') EWTr WCot
'Red Sea' WFar
'Rich Purple' MBNS SPlb XLum
'Rich Ruby' ♀H3 CFis CRos EHyd ELan EPfP EWes GBin LRHS MBel NBir NRHS SBut SHar SPlb SWvt WAvo XLum
'Ridgeway Red' WAvo
(Rock Candy Series) ROCK CANDY LIGHT PINK ('Novapenlig') **new** LRHS
- ROCK CANDY RUBY ('Novapenrub') **new** LRHS
roezlii Regel see *P. laetus* subsp. *roezlii*
'Roger Skipper' ECtt
'Ron Sidwell' WAvo WBrk
'Rosy Blush' MBNS SPlb WAvo
'Roy Davidson' see *P. procerus* 'Roy Davidson'
'Royal White' see *P.* 'White Bedder'
'Rubicundus' ♀H4 CRos CWCL EHyd ELan ELon EPfP LRHS LSRN MGil NRHS SRms SWvt WBor
'Ruby' misapplied see *P.* 'Schoenholzeri'
'Ruby Candle' ECtt
rupicola ♀H5 GArf GKev NSla
- 'Conwy Lilac' WAbe
- 'Conwy Rose' EPot WAbe
'Russian River' ECtt EPfP LRHS SPlb SWvt XLum
rydbergii SPlb
§ 'Schoenholzeri' ♀H4 Widely available
scouleri see *P. fruticosus* var. *scouleri*
§ ***serrulatus*** EWes GKev XLum
'Sherbourne Blue' WAvo
'Sissinghurst Pink' see *P.* 'Evelyn'
'Six Hills' GBin SDys WAbe
smallii EBee EHyd EMor EPPr EPfP EWes LSRN MHer SPhx
'Snow Storm' see *P.* 'White Bedder'
'Snowflake' see *P.* 'White Bedder'
sonomensis see *P. newberryi* subsp. *sonomensis*
'Sour Grapes' misapplied see *P.* 'Stapleford Gem'
'Sour Grapes' ambig. CBcs CDor CTri LShi MBow MSCN NGdn SCob SGBe SPoG WCAu
§ 'Sour Grapes' M. Fish ♀H4 Widely available
'Southcombe Pink' WAvo
'Southgate Gem' GWyn MHCG SRms SWvt WAvo
'Souvenir d'Adrian Regnier' MHCG
'Souvenir d'André Torres' misapplied see *P.* 'Chester Scarlet'
spatulatus EPot
'Species RLB' **new** EGrI
spectabilis CSpe
§ 'Stapleford Gem' ♀H4 CFis CMac EPPr LRHS MRav SBut SHar SRms SWvt WAvo WBrk WFar WHoo WMal
'Strawberries and Cream' (Ice Cream Series) EPPr EPfP NLar WCot
'Strawberry Fancy' SRms
'Strawberry Fizz' SRms
'Strawberry Taffy'PBR (Taffy Series) LRHS
strictus EBee EPfP GKev SPhx XSen
STROMBOLI ('Yaboli') (Volcano Series) CTri WHoo
superbus GKev
§ 'Sutton's Pink Bedder' WAvo
'Sweet Cherry' (Ice Cream Series) SCob WCot
tall, pink-flowered see *P.* 'Welsh Dawn'
'The Juggler' ECtt SWvt
§ 'Thorn' ECtt LRHS SRms SWvt WAvo
'Threave Pink' ECtt SHar SMrm SRms SWvt WAvo
'Thundercloud' WAvo WBrk
'Tiger Bell Coral' NChi
'Torquay Gem' WAvo
'True Sour Grapes' see *P.* 'Sour Grapes' M. Fish
tubaeflorus CPla
'Vanilla Plum' (Ice Cream Series) EGrI SCob

	venustus purple-flowered	SBrt
	VESUVIUS ('Yasius') (Volcano Series)	CRos EPfP LRHS NRHS SCoo SLon SRms WFar
	virgatus 'Blue Buckle'	EPfP SPlb WFar
	'Watermelon Taffy'PBR (Taffy Series)	ECtt EHyd LRHS NRHS
§	'Welsh Dawn'	MBNS
§	***whippleanus***	LRHS MHer MMuc SBut SPlb
	- 'Chocolate Drop'	SBls
§	'White Bedder'	Widely available
	'Whitethroat' Sidwell	MBNS WHoo
	'Willy's Purple'	ECtt
§	'Windsor Red'	CTri ECtt EPfP LRHS SGBe SLon SRms SWvt WAvo WBrk WCot
	'Woodpecker'	ECtt ELon IPot LPla SRms WAvo WHoo

Pentadenia see *Columnea*

Pentaglottis (*Boraginaceae*)

§	***sempervirens***	EPfP SRms WSFF

Pentapanax see *Aralia*

Pentapterygium see *Agapetes*

Pentas (*Rubiaceae*)

	lanceolata	CCCN EShb

Peperomia ✿ (*Piperaceae*)

§	***argyreia*** ♀H1b	CDoC
	ferreyrae	CDoC EShb
	graveolens	EShb
	polybotrya 'Raindrop'	CDoC LCro LOPS
	prostrata new	EShb
	quadrangularis new	CDoC
	sandersii	see *P. argyreia*
§	***verticillata***	EShb

pepino see *Solanum muricatum*

peppermint see *Mentha* × *piperita*

Perezia (*Asteraceae*)

	recurvata	EPot

Pericallis (*Asteraceae*)

§	× ***hybrida*** Senetti Series	MPri NPer SPoG
	- - SENETTI BLUE ('Sunsenebu'PBR)	SPoG
	- - SENETTI BLUE BICOLOR ('Sunseneribuba'PBR)	MGos SPoG
	- - SENETTI MAGENTA ('Sunsenere'PBR)	SPoG
	- - SENETTI MAGENTA BICOLOR ('Sunsenereba'PBR)	MGos SPoG
§	***lanata*** (L'Hér.) B. Nord.	EShb
	- Kew form	CSpe

Perilla (*Lamiaceae*)

	frutescens	WJek
§	- var. ***crispa*** ♀H3	CLau CSpe
	- var. ***nankinensis***	see *P. frutescens* var. *crispa*
	- var. ***purpurascens***	CLau WJek

Periploca (*Apocynaceae*)

	graeca	CBcs CBod CCCN EBee MGil WHil
	sepium	CExl GEdr
	- W/O 7191 new	GGro

Pernettya see *Gaultheria*

Perovskia (*Lamiaceae*)

	abrotanoides	XLum
	atriplicifolia	CMea MGil MHer MNHC WChS WKif
	- 'Blue Shadow'	EHyd NLar
	- BLUE SPRITZER ('Balperobritz') new	LRHS
	- 'Blue Steel' new	SBls
	- 'Rocket Man' new	LRHS
	'Blue Spire' ♀H5	Widely available
	'Filigran'	CBod EHyd EPfP GBin LRHS LSou MBel NLar NRHS SBrt SPoG WSpi XSen
	'Hybrida'	WMal
	LACEY BLUE ('Lisslitt'PBR)	CBod CRos EBee EHyd EPfP LRHS MAsh NLar NRHS SCob SWvt XSen
	LITTLE LACE ('Novaperlac') new	LRHS
	'Little Spire'PBR	Widely available
	'Longin'	XLum
	SILVERY BLUE ('Lissvery'PBR)	CBcs CBod CMac EHyd LRHS MMrt NLar NRHS SNig WNPC XSen

Persea (*Lauraceae*)

	americana	CCCN SVic
	indica	CCCN
	- B&SWJ 12535	WCru
	japonica B&SWJ 12789	WCru
	thunbergii B&SWJ 12747	WCru

Persicaria (*Polygonaceae*)

	B&SWJ 11268 from Sumatra	WCru
§	***affinis***	CBcs CSBt GAbr MSCN NBro SCob WFar
	- 'Darjeeling Red' ♀H7	Widely available
	- 'Dimity'	see *P. affinis* 'Superba'
	- 'Donald Lowndes' ♀H7	Widely available
	- 'Kabouter'	EBee GBin GWyn NLar WBor
§	- 'Superba' ♀H7	Widely available
	alata	see *P. nepalensis*
	alpina ♀H6	CBcs CBct CBod EBee ECha ELan EPPr EPfP EWhm GBin GGro GMaP GQue IPot LEdu LRHS MAvo MRav NDov SCob SDix SMad SPlb SPoG WCot WPnP WSpi
	amphibia	CPud EWat LLWG XLum
§	***amplexicaulis***	CCBP CKno ELan EWes GMaP GWyn MBel MCot NChi WBor WBrk WFar WWtn XLum
	- 'Alba'	Widely available
	- 'Amethyst'	CKno
	- 'Ample Pink'	MAvo
	- 'Arends Pride'	SDix
	- 'Arends Stolz' new	ECha
	- 'Atrosanguinea'	CBod CMac CTri EBlo ECha EHyd ELan ELon EPfP GLog GQue LRHS MMuc MRav MSpe NBir NLar NRHS SEND SPer SRms SWvt WFar XLum
	- 'Betty Brandt'	GWyn
	- 'Black Adder'	ELon
	- 'Blackfield'PBR	Widely available
	- 'Blush Clent'	WBor
	- 'Clent Charm'	MBriF MHCG MSpe NChi
	- 'Cottesbrooke Gold'	ECtt EWhm MAvo
	- 'Dikke Floskes'	CBct CBod CKno EBee ECtt ELon EPPr GBin LEdu LRHS MHol MSpe SRms WBrk WCot WHoo
	- 'Early Pink Lady'	ELon EPPr
	- 'Fascination'	ELon WCot

- 'Fat Domino'PBR	CBct CKno CRos EBee ECtt EHyd EPfP EWoo GQue ILea IPot LPla LRHS LSun MBel MCot MHol MNrw MSCN NCou NDov NLar NRHS SEdd SHeu SPoG WCAu WCot WNPC
- 'Fat White'	ELon GBin
- 'Firedance'	CKno ECtt ELon EPPr GQue IPot MSpe NDov SPhx SRms WCot WFar
- 'Firetail'	Widely available
- 'Golden Arrow' (v)	CBct CBod CTtf EBee ECtt EHyd ELon EMor GBin MBros MSCN NEoE NSti SCob SPeP SPoG SRms WCAu WFar WHil WPnP WTor
- 'High Society'	CKno SPoG SRms WCAu
- 'Inverleith'	CBct CBod CKno EBee ECha ECtt EHyd ELon GBin GMaP GQue LRHS MAvo MMuc MSpe NBid NBir NGrd NRHS SGbt SPoG WBor WCAu WPnP
I - 'Jo and Guido's Form'	ELon EPPr MSpe NLar WCAu WFar
- 'JS Caliente'PBR	CBod ECtt ELon EMor GQue LRHS LSun MHol MNrw NBir SAko SCob SHar SHeu SRms WCot WPnP WSpi
- 'JS Calor'PBR	EBee GQue GWyn
- 'JS Delgado Macho'PBR	CKno EBee ELon MNrw SHeu SRms
- 'Lisan'	CBod EPPr MNrw WCAu
- 'Marchant's Red Devil' **new**	SMHy
- 'October Pink'	EPPr SMHy
- ORANGE FIELD ('Orangofield'PBR)	CBct CBod CKno CMea CRos EBee ECtt EHyd ELan ELon EMor EPfP EShb EWoo GMaP GQue LRHS MCot MHol MNrw NLar NRHS SAko SCob SGbt SPeP WBor WCAu WHoo WWtn
- var. ***pendula***	ELon GBin GGro MBel NBir SMHy WFar
- - HWJK 2255	WCru
- 'Pink Elephant'	see *P.* 'Pink Elephant'
- 'Pink Knot'	CRos EBlo EHyd LRHS NRHS
- 'Pink Lady'	MPie
- 'Pink Mist'	WGoo
- 'Red Baron'	CBod ECtt ELon EPPr WFar
- 'Rosea'	Widely available
- 'Rowden Gem'	EBee ELon GBin IPot MSpe WCAu
- 'Rubie's Pink'	ECha
- 'September Spires'	CKno NDov WGoo
- 'Seven Oaks Village'	EBee
- 'Spotted Eastfield' (v)	EPPr WCot WFar
- 'Summer Dance'	CKno EBee ECtt ELon EPPr
- TAURUS ('Blotau')	CDor CElw CRos EBlo ECha ECtt EHyd ELon EPPr EWTr EWoo GBin GKev IPot LRHS MCot NLar NRHS NSti SMHy SRkn SRms WCAu WFar
- 'White Eastfield'	CBod CDor CKno ECha ELan GPSL MACG NDov NLar SAko WCAu
§ ***bistorta***	GPoy MHer MMuc NBir NGrd NLar SRms WFar WSFF WShi
- subsp. ***carnea***	CBod CRos CTtf EBee ECha EHyd ELon EPPr EWhm GPSL LRHS MBNS MMuc MPie NBir NBro NRHS WCot
- 'Hohe Tatra'	CBod CRos ECtt EHyd EPPr GMaP LRHS LSun MBel MCot MHol NCou NDov NRHS SDix SPoG WBrk WCot WFar
- 'Superba' ♀H7	Widely available
campanulata	CBod CElw EBee ECha ECtt EGrI GAbr LShi MACG MMuc MRav NSti SMad SPer WFar
- Alba Group	CElw MPie
- 'Madame Jigard'	ECha GBin GGro WFar WMal
- 'Rosenrot'	ILea
- 'Southcombe White'	ECha
§ ***capitata***	XLum
- 'Pink Bubbles'	CExl LPot NBir SWvt
chinensis B&SWJ 11268	WCru
dshawachischwilii	MAvo SMHy
× ***fennica*** 'Johanniswolke'	IPot
* ***hydropiper*** var. ***rubra***	WJek
'Indian Summer'	EBee EPPr GGro LPla SBrt WCot WFar WMal
* ***kahil***	GBin NLar WCot
§ ***macrophylla***	GArf WCot
- 'Ellie's Pink' **new**	WCot
microcephala	MHer MPie
- 'Dragon's Eye'PBR	EBee
- 'Red Dragon'PBR	Widely available
- 'Silver Brown' **new**	GBin
milletii	EBee EHyd LRHS MAvo NDov NRHS NSti WCru
nakaii	WCot
neofiliformis	EShb GGro MSpe
§ ***nepalensis***	CExl EPPr EShb GGro
§ ***odorata***	CLau ENfk GPoy LLWG MHer MNHC NGrd SEdi SPre SRms WHer WJek XAbr
orientalis	CSpe SMrm SPhx SSal
§ 'Pink Elephant'	CDor ECha ELon EPPr GBin ILea MNrw NDov NLar SAko SCob SEdd SHeu SIvy SRms WCAu WFar WHoo WMal WNPC WSpi
polystachya	see *P. wallichii*
regeliana	EBlo
§ ***runcinata***	EBee WFar
- Needham's form	GGro
- 'Purple Fantasy'	CBod CDTJ CPla CSde CSpe ECtt ELan EMor EPPr EShb GGro LPla LRHS MBel MBriF MNrw MSpe NSti SCob SDix SEdd SPtp WFar WMal WNPC
scoparia	see *Polygonum scoparium*
'Silver Dragon'PBR	CBct CWit EMor LPla LSun NSti SPeP SPoG WCot
sphaerostachya Meisn.	see *P. macrophylla*
tenuicaulis	GBin MAvo SBrt SGro WCru
§ ***tinctoria***	WSFF
§ ***vacciniifolia*** ♀H5	CBcs CSBt CTri EBou ECha ECtt GAbr GEdr GKev GMaP MCot MHer NBid NBir NFav NLar SCob SDix SLee SPlb SRms SWvt WAbe WBor WFar WHoo WIce WSpi
- 'Harran' **new**	GArf
§ ***virginiana***	LEdu LSun WWtn
- 'Alba'	EPPr LPla
- 'Brushstrokes'	EShb SDix WCot
- var. ***filiformis***	CBod CSpe ELan LEdu MBel MPie NChi SBrt SPoG SPtp SRkn SWvt WCot
- - 'Ballet'	WCot
- - 'Batwings'	SPtp
- - 'Compton's Red'	CBod ECha ECtt EMor EPPr EShb MAvo WCot WFar
- - 'Guizhou Bronze'	LEdu LPla SBrt
- - 'Lance Corporal'	CMac CMea EPPr EShb GBin LPot MAvo MHol NLar
- Variegated Group (v)	ECha EShb MBNS WCot WFar
- - 'Painter's Palette' (v)	CBod CDTJ CMac EBee ECha ECtt ELan EMor EPPr EShb GWyn LRHS LShi MHol MPie MRav NRHS NSti SPer SRms SWvt WCot WFar WMal XLum

§ ***wallichii***	CSpe MMuc NLar SDix SEND WCot XLum
§ ***weyrichii***	NBir NBro NLar WFar XLum

persimmon see *Diospyros virginiana*

persimmon, Japanese see *Diospyros kaki*

Petalostemon see *Dalea*

Petamenes see *Gladiolus*

Petasites (*Asteraceae*)

albus	GPoy MHer NSti
fragrans	ELan SRms WHer XLum
§ ***frigidus*** var. ***palmatus***	NLar WCot
- var. ***palmatus*** 'Golden Palms'	MHer WBor
hybridus	SPhx
- 'Variegatus' (v)	XLum
japonicus	CAgr CBcs GPoy
- var. ***giganteus***	ECha EPfP GGro LEdu MBel WCru
§ - - 'Nishiki-buki' (v)	CMac EBee ECha EWld GGro GQue LEdu MHer NBir NSti SMad WBor WFar XLum
- - 'Variegatus'	see *P. japonicus* var. *giganteus* 'Nishiki-buki'
palmatus	see *P. frigidus* var. *palmatus*
paradoxus	EWld LEdu LPot MBel SBrt WCot WFar

Petrea (*Verbenaceae*)

volubilis	CCCN

Petrocallis (*Brassicaceae*)

lagascae	see *P. pyrenaica*
§ ***pyrenaica***	WAbe
- white-flowered	WAbe

Petrocoptis (*Caryophyllaceae*)

pyrenaica	EWes SRms

Petrocosmea ✿ (*Gesneriaceae*)

barbata	WDib
begoniifolia	SPlb WAbe WDib
coerulea	WDib
§ ***cryptica***	WAbe WDib
- 'Yumebutai'	WDib
flaccida	WDib
'Fluffer Nutter'	WDib
forrestii	WAbe WDib
grandiflora	WAbe WDib
- 'Crème de Crûg'	WCru
'Ht-2'	WDib
iodioides ♀H1c	WDib
kerrii	WDib
'Keystone's Angora'	WDib
'Keystone's Bantam'	WDib
'Keystone's Barnswallow'	WDib
'Keystone's Belmont'	WDib
'Keystone's Blue Jay'	WDib
'Keystone's Lafayette'	WDib
'Keystone's Magic'	WDib
minor	WDib
parryorum	WDib
'Paul Kroll'	WDib
'Rosemary Platz'	WDib
rosettifolia misapplied	see *P. cryptica*
sericea	WDib
'Yuki-no-sei'	WDib

Petrophytum (*Rosaceae*)

caespitosum	CMea GKev WAbe
cinerascens	WFar
§ ***hendersonii***	GArf WAbe

Petrorhagia (*Caryophyllaceae*)

saxifraga ♀H4	CSpe EPPr GLog MACG MBel NLar NSla SBls SBut SRms XLum

Petroselinum (*Apiaceae*)

§ ***crispum***	CArg CLau ENfk GPoy LCro LOPS MNHC MPri NPol SPhx SPoG SRms XAbr
- 'Bravour' ♀H6	MHer
- 'Champion Moss Curled'	MBros SVic
- 'Curlina' ♀H4	LCro LOPS
- 'Extra Moss Curled'	LCro LOPS
- French	CCBP CLau ENfk LCro LOPS LRHS MBros MHer MNHC MPri SPoG SRms
- 'Italian'	see *P. crispum* var. *neapolitanum*
- 'Laura'PBR	CLau
- 'Moss Curled' ♀H6	CHby EHyd EKin LRHS MCtn NRHS NRob SRms
§ - var. ***neapolitanum***	CLau ENfk LCro LOPS SPoG SRms SVic
§ - var. ***tuberosum***	CLau SRms SVic
hortense	see *P. crispum*
tuberosum	see *P. crispum* var. *tuberosum*

Petteria (*Fabaceae*)

ramentacea	EBtc

Petunia (*Solanaceae*)

AMORE QUEEN OF HEARTS (Amore Series)	MBros MPri
× ***atkinsiana*** 'Storm Lavender' ♀H2	LCro LOPS
BABYDOLL ('Kleph17342')	SCob
BALCONY MIX	LCro LOPS
BEDDING STRIPED MIX	LCro LOPS
BLACK VELVET ('Balpevac'PBR)	MBros
BOLERO (mixed) (d) **new**	MPri
CASCADIAS RIM MAGENTA ('Dcas298'PBR) (Cascadias Series) ♀H2	LSou MPri
CRAZYTUNIA MANDEVILLE ('Wespecramand') (Crazytunia Series)	MBros
DESIGNER BUZZ PURPLE ('Kerbuzzby') (Designer Series) ♀H2	LSou MBros MPri
Double Pirouette Series (d)	LCro LOPS
- 'Double Pirouette Rose' (d)	LCro LOPS
Duo Series	MBros
EASY WAVE BERRY VELOUR ('Pas982903') (Easy Wave Series)	MBros
exserta	CSpe WCot
FANTASIA MIX	LCro LOPS
Frenzy Series	MBros
- FRENZY REFLECTION MIX	LCro LOPS
'Lightning Sky' **new**	LSou
NIGHTSKY ('Kleph15313') ♀H2	LSou MBros MPri SCob
OVATION DARK HEART (Ovation Series)	MPri
patagonica	SPlb WAbe

'Pegasus Purple Vein' (Pegasus Series) **new** — LSou
PHANTOM ('Balpephan'PBR) — MBros
PINSTRIPE ('Balpepin'PBR) — MBros
'Prism Sunshine' (Prism Series) — MBros
(Surfinia Series) SURFINIA BLUE ('Sunblu') — LSou MPri
- SURFINIA BLUE TOPAZ ('Sunsurfbupa') — MBros
- SURFINIA BLUE VEIN ('Sunsolos'PBR) — MBros
- SURFINIA BURGUNDY ('Keiburtel'PBR) — MBros
- SURFINIA GIANT PURPLE ('Sunlapur'PBR) — MBros
- SURFINIA HEAVENLY BLUE ('Sunsurf Skytatsu'PBR) — LSou
- SURFINIA HOT PINK ('Sunrovein'PBR) ♀H2 — LSou MBros MPri
- SURFINIA HOT RED ('Sunhore'PBR) — LSou MBros
- SURFINIA IMPULZ SNOW ('Sunsurfkuri'PBR) ♀H2 — MBros MPri
- SURFINIA LIME ('Keiyeul'PBR) — MBros
- SURFINIA PINK VEIN ('Suntosol') ♀H2 — MBros
- SURFINIA PURPLE ('Sunpurple'PBR) ♀H2 — LSou MPri
- SURFINIA ROSE VEIN ('Sunrove'PBR) — MBros
- SURFINIA VARIEGATED PURPLE MINI ('Sunpapuhu'PBR) (v) — LSou
- SURFINIA WHITE ('Kesupite') — LSou
- SURFINIA YELLOW DREAM — MBros
(Tumbelina Series) TUMBELINA BELINDA (d) — MBros
- TUMBELINA BELLA (d) **new** — MBros
- TUMBELINA CANDYFLOSS ('Kercan'PBR) (d) — MBros
- TUMBELINA CHERRY RIPPLE ('Kerripcherry'PBR) (d) — LSou
- TUMBELINA CRAZY RIPPLE **new** — LSou
- TUMBELINA INGA (d) — MBros
- TUMBELINA MARGARITA ('Kermar') — MBros
- TUMBELINA MARIA (d) — MBros
- TUMBELINA PRISCILLA ('Kerpril'PBR) (d) ♀H1c — LSou MBros

Peucedanum (*Apiaceae*)

officinale — CSpe EHyd GBin LRHS SPhx SPlb
ostruthium — GPoy LEdu
- 'Daphnis' (v) — EBee ECha EWhm GGro LEdu MBriF MNrw NChi NGrd NLar SPtp WAvo WCot WHil WHrl WSHC XLum
rablense — EPPr GBin LEdu NDov SPhx
verticillare — CRos CSpe EBee EHyd GBin GGro GWyn LEdu LPla LRHS MAvo MBel MBriF NDov NRHS SBrt SDix SPhx WCot

Phacelia (*Boraginaceae*)

bolanderi — CPla GEdr
sericea — LShi
tanacetifolia — LCro SVic WSFF

Phaedranassa (*Amaryllidaceae*)

viridiflora — WCot

Phaenocoma (*Asteraceae*)

prolifera — SPlb

Phaenosperma (*Poaceae*)

globosa — CBod CSpe ECha EPPr EShb GBin GQue LRHS MACG SPlb WCot WPGP WSMil WWtn XLum

Phaiophleps see *Olsynium*

nigricans — see *Sisyrinchium striatum*

Phalaris (*Poaceae*)

arundinacea — CPud MBNS SPlb SVic
- 'Elegantissima' — see *P. arundinacea* var. *picta* 'Picta'
- var. ***picta*** — CBen CTri MHol NBir NPer WFar XLum
- - 'Arctic Sun' (v) — CKno EBee EShb GBin LBuc LLWG MAsh MHol MMuc NEoE SEND SPoG
- - 'Aureovariegata' (v) — MRav NPer XLum
- - 'Feesey' (v) — CMac CRos CSBt EBou ECha ECtt EHyd EPfP EShb EWes GQue LRHS MAsh MGos MMuc NBid NBro NRHS NWsh SCob SCoo SDix SEND SGbt SIvy SMad SPoG SRms WPnP XLum
- - 'Luteopicta' (v) — EPPr MMuc XLum
§ - - 'Picta' (v) — CBod EHyd ELan EPfP LRHS MMuc NRHS SCob SEND SPer
- - 'Streamlined' (v) — EPPr NWsh

Phanerophlebia (*Dryopteridaceae*)

caryotidea — see *Cyrtomium caryotideum*
falcata — see *Cyrtomium falcatum*
fortunei — see *Cyrtomium fortunei*

Pharbitis see *Ipomoea*

Phedimus see *Sedum*

Phegopteris (*Thelypteridaceae*)

§ ***connectilis*** — CLAP EFer LEdu NHar
decursive-pinnata — CBdn CBod CRos EHyd LEdu LRHS MMuc NRHS SEND WFib WPnP
hexagonoptera — CBdn LEdu
levingei — LEdu

Phellodendron (*Rutaceae*)

amurense — CBcs CCCN CMCN EBee EPfP GBin IPap LMaj LRHS MBlu SEND WBor
- B&SWJ 11000 — WCru
japonicum B&SWJ 11175 — WCru

Phemeranthus (*Portulacaceae*)

sediformis — GKev

Pherosphaera (*Podocarpaceae*)

fitzgeraldii — CKen WPav WThu

Philadelphus ✿ (*Hydrangeaceae*)

SDR 2823 — CExl
SDR 4946 — CExl
'Atlas' (v) — NLar
'Avalanche' — CExl MMuc NLar SPer SRms

'Beauclerk' 𝕐H6	CBod CBrac CCCN CDoC CEme CKel CTri EBee EPfP LRHS MGos MMuc MRav NLar NWea SCob SPer SRms SWvt WLov WSpi
'Belle Étoile' 𝕐H6	Widely available
'Bialy Sopel'	CCCN WAvo
'Bicolore'	NLar WAvo WSpi
'Bouquet Blanc'	MRav NLar SGol SRms WLov
brachybotrys	MRav
'Buckley's Quill' (d)	EBee EPfP MRav SWvt
'Burfordensis'	MMuc MRav SEND WSpi
'Casa Azul'	EBee WPGP
coronarius	CBcs EPfP LBuc LPar LRHS MRav SPer WSpi
- 'Aureus' 𝕐H6	Widely available
- 'Bowles's Variety'	see *P. coronarius* 'Variegatus'
§ - 'Variegatus' (v) 𝕐H6	CMac CRos ELan ELon EPfP EWTr GBin LPot LRHS MGil MGos MMuc MRav MSwo NLar SCob SPer SPoG SRms WAvo WCFE WCot WFar WKif WLov WSpi
coulteri	EBee EPfP SBrt WPGP
'Coupe d'Argent'	MRav
'Dainty Lady'[PBR]	GBin LCro LOPS LRHS SGBe SLon
'Dame Blanche' (d)	EPfP MRav NLar WFar
delavayi	EPPr EPfP GBin LEdu NLar SPer WLov WPGP WSpi
- var. ***calvescens***	MRav SPtp
- - BWJ 8005	WCru
- f. ***melanocalyx***	EPfP MRav SChF WPGP
- - B&L 12168	EBee WPGP
- - 'Nyman's Variety' 𝕐H6	CExl WKif WLov WPGP
aff. ***delavayi***	SBrt
'Enchantement' (d)	MRav SDix
'Erectus'	CBod CKel CSBt EBee ELan ELon EPfP LRHS MRav NLar SBrt SPer SPoG WAvo WLov WSpi
'Étoile Rose'	WAvo
'Falconeri'	MRav
'Frosty Morn' (d)	CBcs EShb EWTr LEdu MBlu MRav SPer SPoG
incanus B&SWJ 8616	WCru
§ 'Innocence' (v) 𝕐H6	CAgr CExl CMac CRos CTsd CWGN EHyd ELan EPfP EWTr LRHS MAsh MGos MMuc MRav MSwo NEoE NLar NRHS SPad SPer SPoG SRms WFar WLov
'Innocence Variegatus'	see *P.* 'Innocence'
§ ***insignis***	MRav NLar
'Karolinka'	NLar
karwinskianus F&M 152	WPGP
'Lemoinei'	CBcs CTri GDam LPar NLar NWea SCob WSpi
lewisii	CExl SPhx
- L 1896	CExl
- 'Snow Velvet'	EPfP
- 'Waterton'	ELon WAvo WSpi
'Limestone'	MRav
'Little White Love'	SGol
maculatus 'Mexican Jewel'	CBcs CBod CExl CKel EBee EHed ELan ELon EMil EPfP GBin LEdu LRHS MNHC NLar SChF SMad SPad WGob WKif WLov WPGP
- 'Scented Storm'	EBee WPGP
- 'Sweet Clare' 𝕐H5	CRos EHyd EPfP LCro LOPS LRHS NRHS SPoG WSpi
madrensis	EBee MRav
- F&M 326	WPGP
'Manteau d'Hermine' (d) 𝕐H6	Widely available
'Marjorie'	NLar

mexicanus B&SWJ 10253	WCru
- 'Rose Syringa'	CExl SBrt WLov WPGP
mexicanus* × *palmeri	EBee
microphyllus	CBrac CKel CMCN CTri EBee ELan ELon EPfP GBin LRHS MGos MRav NLar SLon SMad SPer SPoG WFar WKif
'Minnesota Snowflake' (d)	CBcs EHed EHyd ELon EPfP EWes LRHS LSRN MMuc MRav NLar NRHS SGol WFar
'Mont Blanc'	CBcs GKin MRav NLar
'Mrs E.L. Robinson' (d)	CMac CRos EHyd ELon EPfP GLog LRHS MGos NRHS WAvo WCFE WLov
myrtoides B&SWJ 10436	WCru
'Natchez' (d)	CBod CMac LEdu NLar WLov
'Norma'	WLov
palmeri	EBee LRHS WPGP
'Patricia'	WAvo WLov
pekinensis	CExl NLar
'Perryhill'	MRav
'Polar Star'	NLar
purpurascens	CExl CJun EBee EPfP ESwi EWes GLog LEdu MBlu MGos MRav NLar SChF WCFE WLov WPGP
- BWJ 7540	WCru
'Purpureomaculatus'	ELon MRav NLar WPGP
'Pyramidal' (d)	CBrac
'Rachel' **new**	CMac
satsumi	NLar
- B&SWJ 10811	WCru
- B&SWJ 11004	WCru
schrenkii	EHed NLar
- B&SWJ 8465	ESwi WCru
sericanthus	NLar
§ 'Silberregen' 𝕐H6	CKel CMac EBee EHed ELan ELon EPfP LEdu LRHS MAsh MGos MMuc MRav NEoE NLar SCob SMad SPoG SRms SWvt
SILVER SHOWERS	see *P.* 'Silberregen'
'Snowbelle' (d)	CCCN CDoC CEnd CKel EBee EHyd EPfP EWTr LCro LOPS LRHS MAsh MPri NLar SCob SPoG SRms SWvt SavN WLov
'Snowgoose'	SGol
'Souvenir de Billiard'	see *P. insignis*
'Starbright'[PBR]	CBcs CBod CCCN EBee EHyd EPfP LRHS MAsh NLar SCob SPoG
subcanus	CExl SPtp
- L 524	CExl
'Sybille' 𝕐H6	CMac EHyd EPfP LRHS MRav MSwo SDix SPer SRms WAvo WKif WLov WSpi
tomentosus	CExl
- B&SWJ 2707	WCru
- GWJ 9215	WCru
'Velléda'	WAvo
'Virginal' (d)	Widely available
'Voie Lactée'	MRav NLar WSpi
WHITE ROCK ('Pekphil') 𝕐H6	CMac LSRN MRav NLar SPer
'Yellow Hill'	CKel CMac EPfP LRHS MMrt

Philesia (*Philesiaceae*)

buxifolia	see *P. magellanica*
§ ***magellanica***	CExl CRHN GEdr GGGa MGil WCru
- 'Rosea'	CRHN

Phillyrea (*Oleaceae*)

angustifolia	CBcs CBod CMCN EBee EHyd ELan EPfP ERom EShb LPar LRHS LTop

	MGos MRav NLar SArc SEND SPer SWeb WLov WPGP XSen
- f. ***rosmarinifolia***	CCCN CCoa CExl
- - 'French Fries'	EBee EPfP WPGP
decora	see *Osmanthus decorus*
§ ***latifolia***	CBcs CBod CCCN CDoC CKel EBee EHyd ELan EPfP LRHS LTop SArc SEND WPGP XSen
media	see *P. latifolia*

Philodendron (*Araceae*)

bipennifolium	SPlb
bipinnatifidum ♀H2	SEND
scandens ♀H1b	LCro LOPS
xanadu	LCro LOPS NGBl SPlb

Philotheca (*Rutaceae*)

§ ***myoporoides***	ILea LRHS XSte

Phlebodium (*Polypodiaceae*)

§ ***aureum*** ♀H1b	CSpe SPlb WCot
- var. ***areolatum***	EShb
- 'Glaucum'	CSpe WCot
pseudoaureum ♀H3	LEdu MAsh SEND WCot
- 'Virginia Blue'	LEdu

Phleum (*Poaceae*)

phleoides	EHyd LRHS NRHS
pratense	WSFF

Phlomis ✿ (*Lamiaceae*)

alpina	SPlb
* ***anatolica***	EHyd LRHS
- 'Lloyd's Variety'	see *P. grandiflora* 'Lloyd's Silver'
anisodonta white-flowered	XSen
armeniaca	XSen
atropurpurea	GGro SBrt
- BWJ 7922	WCru
bourgaei	XSen
- NJM 12.008	WPGP
bovei subsp. ***maroccana***	SEND WHal XLum
capitata	XSen
cashmeriana	CBod CPla CRos EBee ECha EHyd EPfP ILea LRHS MCot NQui NRHS SBls WAvo WCFE WSpi XSen
chrysophylla ♀H5	ECha EHyd ELan EPfP LRHS MAsh MRav NLar WCFE WSpi XSen
cretica	SVen WMal
× ***cytherea***	XSen
'Edward Bowles'	CKel EBee ECha EHyd EPfP GBin LRHS MRav NLar SEND SMad SWvt WAvo WCFE WSpi XSen
* 'Elliot's Variety'	CExl
fruticosa ♀H5	Widely available
- white-flowered	CBcs
aff. ***fruticosa***	WSpi
grandiflora	EBee EPfP MNrw SEND XSen
- NJM 10.014	WPGP
§ - 'Lloyd's Silver' ♀H5	CRos EHyd ELan LRHS MAsh NLar
herba-venti	XSen
italica	Widely available
lanata	CRos CSde EBee EHyd EPfP LRHS SBrt SPer XSen
- 'Pygmy'	XSen
'Le Chat'	XSen
'Le Sud'	LRHS WCot XSen
leucophracta	SVen
* ***libanotica***	EBee
longifolia	CBod CDoC CKel EBee EHyd EPfP LRHS MNrw SEND SPer WPGP XSen
- var. ***bailanica*** ♀H4	CRos EHyd EPfP LRHS NRHS XLum
- var. ***longifolia***	WSpi
lychnitis	XSen
lycia	LRHS XSen
- NJM 10.016	WPGP
macrophylla	LPla SPhx
× ***margaritae***	XSen
'Marina'	XSen
monocephala	XSen
purpurea	CBod CExl CRos EHyd ELan EPfP LRHS MAsh NBir NRHS SEND WCot XSen
I - 'Alba'	CBod ELan EWTr GBin LRHS MMrt SMad
- subsp. ***almeriensis***	XSen
§ ***russeliana*** ♀H6	Widely available
- PAB 7444	LEdu
- 'Dappled Shade' (v)	WCot
samia Boiss.	see *P. russeliana*
samia L.	CMac EHyd EWoo LRHS MNrw NBir NGdn NLar NRHS SBrt SEND SPtp WMal XSen
- JMT	EPPr
- 'Green Glory'	WCot
× ***termessi***	XSen
'Toob'	SBrt WPGP
'Tramuntana'	XSen
tuberosa	CBcs CBod EHyd ELan EPfP EWTr ILea LEdu LRHS LSRN MACG MPnt SPhx WCAu WMal XLum XSen
- 'Amazone' ♀H5	Widely available
- 'Bronze Flamingo'	CMac CRos EPfP GBin ILea LRHS MHol MNrw MPnt MRav NLar SBls SPoG SPtp WSpi
viscosa misapplied	see *P. russeliana*

Phlox ✿ (*Polemoniaceae*)

adsurgens 'Alba'	WFar
- 'Wagon Wheel'	CBor ECtt EHyd EPot EWes LRHS NHpl NRHS SPlb SRms WFar
amplifolia	WCot XLum
- 'Apanatschi' **new**	WCot
- 'Augenstern'	WFar
- 'Minnehaha' **new**	NDov
- 'Winnetou'	IPot NDov
× ***arendsii*** 'Andrew'	WCot
- 'Autumn's Pink Explosion'	WCot
- 'Babyface'	ELon NGdn
- 'Casablanca'	NDov
- 'Dylan'	WCot
- 'Eyecatcher'	NBro
- 'Gary'	WCot
- 'Hesperis'	CMiW ECha ELon GBee GWyn LRHS MAvo MNrw NDov SPhx WBor WHil WSHC
- 'Luc's Lilac' ♀H7	ECtt EPPr LPla LRHS NBro NDov NSti SGbt SPhx WCot
§ - 'Miss Jill' (Spring Pearl Series)	ELan EPfP WCot
§ - 'Miss Karen' (Spring Pearl Series)	EBee NBro
§ - 'Miss Margie' (Spring Pearl Series)	EGrI
§ - 'Miss Mary' (Spring Pearl Series) ♀H7	EBee EHyd ELan EPfP ILea NLar SRkn
§ - 'Miss Wilma' (Spring Pearl Series)	EBee ELan EPfP
- 'Paul'	MNrw WCot WSHC
- 'Ping Pong'	SGbt
- 'Pink Attraction'	LRHS NBro
- 'Utopia' ♀H7	CSpe EBee ELon GBin LPla MAvo NDov SPhx WCAu WCot

	austromontana	EPot NWad
	bifida 'Ralph Haywood'	ECtt EPot
	- 'Thefi'	ECtt
	borealis	see *P. sibirica* subsp. *borealis*
	caespitosa	CMea EWes
	- subsp. ***pulvinata***	see *P. pulvinata*
	- 'Zigeunerblut'	CMea ECtt EPot NWad WAbe WHal
	canadensis	see *P. divaricata*
	carolina subsp. ***angusta***	LPla
	- 'Bill Baker'	see *P. glaberrima* 'Bill Baker'
	- 'Magnificence'	EBee EWes GWyn SMad SPlb WCot
	- 'Miss Lingard' ♀H6	CBod CDor CKel ECtt EHyd GBee LRHS LSou MRav NBir NGdn NLar NRHS NSti SGbt WCAu WCot
	'Chattahoochee'	see *P. divaricata* subsp. *laphamii* 'Chattahoochee'
	'Daniel's Cushion'	see *P. subulata* 'McDaniel's Cushion'
	diffusa	EPot WAbe
§	***divaricata*** ♀H5	SPlb
	- 'Blue Dreams'	ECtt LSou MNrw WFar
	- 'Blue Moon'	CWCL
	- 'Blue Perfume'	EBee ECtt GWyn LCro LOPS
	- 'Charles'	XLum
	- 'Clouds of Perfume'	Widely available
	- 'Dirigo Ice'	EHyd LRHS NRHS WSHC
	- 'Fuller's White'	CWCL
	- subsp. ***laphamii***	CWCL EBee EWes MACG WFar
§	- - 'Chattahoochee' ♀H5	CBcs CBod CPla CWCL EAJP ECtt EHyd ELan EMor EPfP EShb EWes EWld GBin GKev GWyn LCro LOPS MBow MCot MNrw MSCN NDov NHpl NLar NRHS NSla SPoG SWvt WSpi
	- 'May Breeze'	CWCL EAJP ECtt EHyd GMaP LRHS MNrw MPnt NRHS WAvo
	- 'Plum Perfect'	ECtt
	- 'White Perfume'	CWCL EBee EHyd EPfP EWes LRHS MACG MBel MMrt MSpe NDov NLar SBut SPoG WFar XLum
	douglasii	SRms
	- 'Apollo'	CBor CTri ECtt
	- 'Boothman's Variety' ♀H6	ECha ECtt ELan SRms
	- 'Crackerjack' ♀H6	CBod CMea CTri EBou ECtt EHyd ELan ELon EPot GKev GMaP LRHS MAsh MBow NBir NHol NHpl NRHS NSla SLee SPoG SRot WIce
	- 'Eva'	CBor EBou ECtt EHyd ELon EPot GArf GMaP GQue LRHS LSRN MAsh NBir NHpl NLar NRHS NWad SLee WFar WIce
	- 'Georg Arends'	CBor ECtt WFar
	- 'Ice Mountain'	CBor CMea ECtt ELan EPot NHol NWad SPoG SRot WCav WFar
	- 'J.A. Hibberson'	EPot EWes NWad
	- 'Lilac Cloud'	ECtt EWTr
	- LILAC QUEEN	see *P. douglasii* 'Lilakönigin'
§	- 'Lilakönigin'	CTri
	- 'Napoleon'	ECtt EPot GArf NWad
	- 'Ochsenblut'	CBor CSma ECtt EHyd EPot GArf LRHS NLar NRHS NSla NWad WIce
	- 'Red Admiral' ♀H5	ECtt ELan EPfP EWes GMaP LRHS NWad WFar
	- 'Rose Cushion'	EWes
	- 'Rosea'	ECha EGrI ELan MAsh MMuc NHpl SLee SRot WIce
	- 'Sprite'	SRms
	- 'Tycoon'	see *P. subulata* 'Tamaongalei'
	- 'Violet Queen'	GArf
	- 'Waterloo'	CBor EBou ECtt EHyd EPot LRHS NRHS

I	- 'White Admiral'	CRos CTri ECtt EHyd ELan EPfP GBin LRHS LSRN NRHS
	drummondii 'Crème Brûlée' **new**	CKel
	- POPSTARS MIXED	LSou MBros
	(Fashionably Early Series) 'Fashionably Early Crystal'	LCro LOPS WHil
	- 'Fashionably Early Flamingo' **new**	WHil
	- 'Fashionably Early Princess'	LCro LOPS WHil
	- 'Fashionably Lavender Ice'	LCro LOPS WHil
	'Flare'	see *P. paniculata* 'Neon Flare'
§	***glaberrima***	CKel EAJP ECha ECtt EGrI ELon
	'Bill Baker' ♀H6	EPfP GMaP LEdu MAsh MBow MNrw NBir NGdn NSti SBut SWvt WCAu WFar WMal XLum
	- 'Morris Berd'	WFar WSHC
	- var. ***triflora*** 'Triple Play' (v)	SPtp
	'Goliath'	CBod
	hendersonii	WAbe
	hoodii	WAbe
	'Jeff's Pink'	ECtt NLar
	'Kelly's Eye' ♀H5	CBor EBou ECtt EHyd EPot LRHS NBir NRHS SPoG
	kelseyi 'Lemhi Purple'	EPot WAbe
	- 'Rosette'	NWad
	LIGHT PINK FLAME ('Bareleven'PBR)	CBod ECtt EHyd SPoG
	LILAC FLAME ('Barten'PBR)	EHyd LRHS NRHS SCob WHil
	maculata	EGrI
	- 'Alba'	EGrI SAko
	- 'Alpha' ♀H6	CWCL EBee ECha ECtt EHyd EMor EPfP EWoo GMaP ILea LEdu LRHS NLar NRHS SGbt SPer SWvt WCAu WFar WSHC WTyc XLum
	- AVALANCHE	see *P. maculata* 'Schneelawine'
	- 'Delta'	EHyd EMor LRHS NLar SAko SGbt SPer SRkn SWvt
	- 'Natascha' ♀H6	CMac CWCL EAJP EBee ECtt EHyd ELon EMor EPfP EWes EWoo GMaP LRHS LSRN NGdn NHol NLar NRHS NWad SAko SGbt SMad SPer SRkn SWvt WCAu WFar WHil WTyc
	- 'Omega' ♀H6	CBod CExl CMac ECha ECtt EWoo GBee ILea LEdu LRHS MPie NGdn NLar SGbt SPer SWvt WCAu WFar WSpi WTyc
	- 'Princess Sturdza' ♀H6	NDov SDix
	- 'Reine du Jour'	LPla MAvo MHol NDov SPhx WSHC
	- 'Rosalinde'	CBod ECtt EMor LRHS LSou MCot NLar SAko SWvt WSHC
§	- 'Schneelawine'	EHyd SPer SPlb WSpi
	'Millstream'	see *P.* × *procumbens* 'Millstream'
	'Minnie Pearl'	EWes LPla NDov WCot
	nivalis 'Nivea'	EPot WAbe
	paniculata	EPPr LEdu NBid NDov SDix WCot
	- 'A.E.Amos'	ELon
	- (Adessa Series) ADESSA ORANGE	NLar WHil
	- - ADESSA PINK STAR	LRHS NLar NRHS WHil
	- - ADESSA RED	NLar
	- - ADESSA ROSE EYE	NLar WHil
	- - ADESSA SPECIAL DEEP PURPLE	WHil
	- - ADESSA SPECIAL FIRE	NLar WHil
	- - ADESSA SPECIAL LILAC TWIST	WHil

- - ADESSA SPECIAL PURPLE STAR NRHS WHil
- - ADESSA WHITE NLar
- var. ***alba*** ECha MAvo SDix WCot
- 'Alba Grandiflora' ♀H7 MAvo MNrw NChi WCot WHoo
- 'Alexandra'PBR LCro LOPS
- 'Aljonuschka' **new** GBin
- 'All in One' MAvo
- 'Amethyst' ambig. EGrI
- 'Amethyst' misapplied see *P. paniculata* 'Lilac Time'
- 'Amethyst' Foerster ELon GWyn LRHS MRav MSpe NBir NLar WBor WCAu
- 'Anne' ELon MSpe
- 'Argus' ECtt
- 'Balmoral' CMac ECtt ELon NCou NSti SWvt
- BAMBINI CANDY CRUSH ('Verscan'PBR) CWGN WHil
- BAMBINI DESIRE ('Versde'PBR) CWGN
- BARPHLEARPIDEYE ('Barphlearpideye'PBR) (Early Series) WHil
- 'Becky Towe'PBR (v) ♀H7 ECtt MHol MNrw NHol NSti SPoG WCot
- 'Blauer Morgen' XLum
- 'Blue Boy' CRos EBee ECtt EHyd ELan ELon EMor EPfP GMaP GWyn LRHS MSpe NBir NRHS SWvt WBor WCAu WFar
- 'Blue Evening' EBee ELon LCro LOPS MSpe NLar
- 'Blue Ice' CBod
- 'Blue Moon' ELon
- 'Blue Paradise' Widely available
- 'Blushing Bride' SRms
- 'Bold and Beautiful' (Neon Series) **new** SPad
- 'Bonny Maid' MAvo
- 'Border Gem' CBcs CBod CMac ECtt ELon EShb LRHS MRav MSpe SDix SPeP SWvt WBrk WCot
- 'Bosvigo Pink' ELon MAvo SAko SHar
- 'Brigadier' CBod CTri EBee ECtt ELan LRHS MNrw MSpe SPer SRms
- 'Bright Eyes' Widely available
- 'Burgi' SDix
- 'Butonik' ELon
- 'Cardinal' NDov
- 'Caroline van den Berg' SAko SRms
- 'Charlotte' MSpe WGoo
- 'Cheriton' EBlo EHyd LRHS NRHS
- 'Chintz' EHyd LRHS MRav NRHS SRms
- 'Cinderella' ECtt
- 'Cleopatra'PBR NLar SPad
- COMPACT LILAC see *P. paniculata* SWEET SUMMER FAVOURITE
- COMPACT ROSE WHITE see *P. paniculata* SWEET SUMMER CANDY
- 'Cool Best' NDov
- 'Cool Water' NLar
- CORAL FLAME ('Barsixtytwo'PBR) (Flame Series) CBod CMac LSou NLar SCob SRkn WHil
- 'Coral Queen' SRms
- 'Cosmopolitan'PBR EPfP MHol MNrw NLar
- COUNT ZEPPELIN see *P. paniculata* 'Graf Zeppelin'
- 'Crème de Menthe' (v) EMor
- 'Danielle' ♀H7 LRHS NRHS SHar
- 'Darwin's Choice' see *P. paniculata* 'Norah Leigh'
- 'David' ♀H7 Widely available
- 'David's Lavender' ♀H7 EBlo EHyd ELon IPot LRHS NLar NRHS WSpi
- 'Delilah'PBR CWGN ECtt NHpl
- 'Discovery' EShb EWes LCro LOPS LPla MRav MSpe SHar
- 'Dodo Hanbury-Forbes' MNrw
- 'Doghouse Pink' SAko SDix
- 'Drakon' ELon
- 'Dresden China' SHar
- 'Duchess of York' MAvo MNrw MSpe SDix

§ - 'Düsterlohe' EBee ECtt EHyd ELon GBin GQue GWyn ILea IPot LRHS MHer MRav NBir NDov NLar NRHS NSti SPer SRkn SRms WCAu WCot WSpi XLum

- (Early Series) EARLY CERISE WHil
- - EARLY LIGHT PINK IPot
- - EARLY PINK CANDY WHil
- - EARLY RED WHil
- - EARLY WHITE **new** WHil
- 'Eclaireur' misapplied see *P. paniculata* 'Düsterlohe'
- 'Eclaireur' Lemoine MAvo
- 'Eden's Flash' CElw ECtt MPie
- 'Edentuin' IPot
- 'Elisabeth' (v) LSRN MAvo NWad
- 'Elizabeth Arden' ECtt ELon LPla
- 'Elizabeth Campbell' EHyd EPPr
- 'Ending Blue' MAvo
- 'Etoile de Paris' see *P. paniculata* 'Toits de Paris' Symons-Jeune
- 'Europa' EBee ECtt ELan ELon EWoo IPot LRHS NBir NGdn NLar SPer WBor WCAu WSHC
- 'Eva Cullum' ♀H7 CBod CRos EBee ECtt EHyd ELan ELon EPfP EWoo GBee GMaP GWyn LRHS MHer NHpl NRHS SAko SDix SPer WCAu WCot WFar
- 'Eva Foerster' ♀H7 EHyd GWyn LRHS NRHS XLum
- 'Eventide' CMac EBee ECtt EHyd EPfP LRHS MArl MAvo MNrw MRav NRHS SPer WFar
- 'Fairytale of the Ural' see *P. paniculata* 'Uralskie Skazy'
- (Famous Series) FAMOUS CERISE **new** EPfP LRHS
- - FAMOUS LIGHT PURPLE **new** LRHS MPri
- - FAMOUS PINK DARK EYE **new** LRHS MPri
- - FAMOUS PURPLE **new** EPfP LRHS MPri
- - FAMOUS WHITE EYE **new** LRHS MPri
- - FAMOUS WHITE **new** LRHS
- - FLAME LIGHT BLUE CBod WHil
- 'Flamingo' ♀H7 EBee ECtt ELon MSpe NLar SWvt XLum
- 'Fondant Fancy'PBR SMrm
- 'Franz Schubert' ♀H7 CDor CRos ECtt EHyd ELan EPfP EWTr EWoo GBin GWyn ILea LCro LRHS MAvo MCot MSpe NBir NChi NGdn NLar NRHS NSti SPer SWvt WCot WFar WHoo

§ - 'Frau Alfred von Mauthner' GKev

- 'Fujiyama' see *P. paniculata* 'Mount Fuji'
- 'Geisha's Blush' **new** SMHy
- 'Geisha's Glance' **new** SMHy
- 'Goldmine'PBR (v) EHyd MNrw SMad SPoG SRms WCot

§ - 'Graf Zeppelin' ECtt ELon MSpe NHol NLar SRms XLum

- 'Green Lady'PBR **new** EMor
- 'Grenadine Dream'PBR ♀H7 CWGN EHyd MNrw
- 'Grey Lady' ♀H7 EBlo EHyd LRHS MNrw NRHS WGoo

- 'Harlequin' (v) CMac CWGN ECha ECtt GBee WCot
- 'Herbstwalzer' ELon IPot WCot
- 'Ice Cream' CWGN ELon
- 'Iris' MNrw SRms WCot
- 'Jade' (Neon Series) ECtt ELon EMor EWoo GQue LEdu LRHS MBros MNrw NLar NSti WCot WHil
- 'Jeana' MNrw
- 'Jeff's Blue' NLar WCot
- 'Judy' MAvo
- 'Jules Sandeau' LRHS
- § - 'Juliglut' EHyd ELon LRHS NRHS WCot
- JULY GLOW see *P. paniculata* 'Juliglut'
- 'Junior Dance' GBee
- 'Katherine' EHyd EMor IPot LRHS MSpe NRHS
- 'Katja' EGrl IPot NLar
- 'Kirchenfürst' CElw CRos EHyd ELon LCro LOPS LRHS MACG NBir NLar NRHS SAko WBor WCAu WFar
- 'Kirmesländler' ECtt IPot MSpe NLar SAko
- 'Königin der Nacht' (Zauberflöte Series) 𝕐H7 **new** SMHy
- 'Ksenija' ELon
- 'Lads Pink' SDix
- 'Lady Clare' SRms
- 'Landhochzeit' WFar
- 'Larissa'PBR LCro LOPS MNrw
- 'Laura' see *P. paniculata* 'Uspekh'
- § - 'Lavendelwolke' EPPr LRHS MSpe NBir NLar WCot
- LAVENDER CLOUD see *P. paniculata* 'Lavendelwolke'
- 'Le Mahdi' 𝕐H7 NLar SRms WBor
- 'Lichtspel' LPla NDov SPhx
- § - 'Lilac Time' CElw CRos ECtt EHyd EPfP GKev GMaP LRHS NLar NRHS SCob SWvt WSpi
- 'Little Boy' CElw ELon LRHS MNrw NLar SGbt WHil
- 'Little Laura' ECtt LRHS LSRN MNrw MSpe NLar WCot WHoo
- 'Little Princess' ELon NLar
- 'Little Sara' NDov
- 'Logan Black' SHar WSHC
- MAGICAL DREAM see *P. paniculata* SWEET SUMMER DREAM
- MAGICAL FAVORITE see *P. paniculata* SWEET SUMMER FAVOURITE
- MAGICAL SURPRISE see *P. paniculata* SWEET SUMMER SURPRISE
- 'Manoir d'Hézèques' WCot
- 'Marchant's Darkest' **new** SMHy
- 'Mardi Gras' EPfP
- 'Mary Christine' (v) LRHS NBid NRHS
- 'Maude Stella Dagley' ELon MSpe
- 'Mia Ruys' MArl
- 'Mies Copijn' ELon
- 'Mike's Favourite' EBee MBros
- 'Milly van Hoboken' WKif
- 'Miss Holland' NGdn SGbt XLum
- 'Miss Jill' see *P.* × *arendsii* 'Miss Jill'
- 'Miss Karen' see *P.* × *arendsii* 'Miss Karen'
- 'Miss Kelly' EShb NLar
- 'Miss Margie' see *P.* × *arendsii* 'Miss Margie'
- 'Miss Mary' see *P.* × *arendsii* 'Miss Mary'
- 'Miss Pepper' 𝕐H7 ECtt EHyd ELon EWoo LRHS MBel MMuc MSpe NGdn NLar NRHS
- 'Miss Universe' ELon
- 'Miss Wilma' see *P.* × *arendsii* 'Miss Wilma'
- 'Modern Art' MNrw
- 'Monica Lynden-Bell' 𝕐H7 CCBP CDor CWGN EBee ELon EWTr EWoo GMaP GWyn LRHS LSun MBriF MNrw MPie MRav NBid NChi NDov NLar NSti SGbt WCot WKif WSHC
- 'Monte Cristallo' GWyn MSpe
- 'Mother of Pearl' 𝕐H7 GWyn IPot LRHS WSpi
- § - 'Mount Fuji' Widely available
- 'Mount Fujiyama' see *P. paniculata* 'Mount Fuji'
- 'Mrs A.E. Jeans' SRms
- 'Natural Feelings'PBR (Feelings Series) NLar
- § - 'Neon Flare' (Neon Series) CWGN MHol WHil
- 'Newbird' EBee ECtt MSpe SRms
- 'Nicky' see *P. paniculata* 'Düsterlohe'
- § - 'Norah Leigh' (v) 𝕐H7 CElw CMac CWGN EBee ECha ECtt ELan EMor EPfP EWes GWyn LRHS MBel MHer MPie NPer NRHS NSti NWad SDix SPer SPoG SRms SWvt WCAu WCFE WCot WFar
- 'Oljenka' ELon
- 'Orange Perfection' see *P. paniculata* 'Prince of Orange'
- 'Othello' CBod ECtt ELon LRHS MSpe NGdn SMrm WHoo
- 'Otley Choice' ECtt EGrI GWyn MRav NCou NLar NSti
- 'Otley Purple' MAvo MHer NCou
- 'P.D. Williams' WCot
- 'Pallas Athene' IPot
- 'Pastorale' WCot
- (Peacock Series) PEACOCK CHERRY RED 𝕐H7 CRos EHyd LRHS NRHS WCFE WTor
- - PEACOCK LILAC 𝕐H7 CRos EHyd LRHS NRHS
- - PEACOCK NEON PURPLE 𝕐H7 CRos EHyd LRHS NRHS
- - PEACOCK PURPLE BICOLOR CRos EHyd LRHS NRHS
- - PEACOCK WHITE 𝕐H7 CRos EHyd GDam LRHS NRHS WTor
- 'Peppermint Twist' CWGN EHyd ELon GKev GWyn MNrw NLar SWvt WFar
- 'Picasso' CWGN ECtt IPot NLar WHil WTyc
- 'Pina Colada'PBR CWGN ECtt LRHS MPri SMrm WCAu WFar WHil
- PINK EYE FLAME ('Barthirtyfive'PBR) 𝕐H7 EHyd EPfP LRHS NRHS SPoG SRkn SRms
- 'Pink Lady'PBR EBee WFar
- 'Pink Posie' (v) WCot
- PINK RED EYE FLAME ('Barthirtyfour') SPoG
- 'Popeye' IPot LPla WCot
- 'Prime Minister' ELon
- § - 'Prince of Orange' 𝕐H7 CBcs CBod CMac CRos CSBt EBee ECtt EHyd EPfP LRHS MACG MAvo MHol MRav MSCN NLar NRHS SCob SGbt SPer SRms SWvt WCot XLum
- 'Prospero' 𝕐H7 CElw CSpe EBee EBlo GWyn LRHS MRav NBid
- PURPLE EYE FLAME ('Barthirtythree'PBR) 𝕐H7 EHyd LRHS NRHS SPad SRkn SWvt WCAu WFar
- 'Purple Kiss'PBR CWGN ECtt LRHS MHol MPri SMrm WFar WHil
- 'Purple Paradise' LRHS
- 'Rainbow' ELon NLar
- 'Raving Beauty' LRHS
- 'Red Caribbean' ECtt LRHS MPri NLar
- 'Red Feelings' (Feelings Series) CBod LRHS SGbt
- 'Red Flame' CWGN ECtt EHyd EPfP MNrw SAko SRkn WFar
- 'Red Riding Hood' see *P.* × *arendsii* 'Miss Mary'
- I - 'Reddish Hesperis' MAvo

	– 'Rembrandt'	CExl EHyd ELon EPfP LCro LOPS LRHS NRHS WCAu XLum
	– 'Rijnstroom'	CBcs ECha ECtt ELon MArl NLar SCob WBrk WCAu
	– 'Robert Poore'	ECtt ELon
	– 'Roberta'	LCro LOPS WTyc
	– 'Rosa Pastell' ♀H7	CDor CSpe ECtt ELon EWoo GBin IPot LRHS MAvo MPie NLar SPtp WCot
	– 'Rowie'	NBid
	– 'Sandringham'	ECtt LRHS MArl MRav NBir NCou NRHS SMrm SPer SWvt
§	– 'Schneerausch'	LPla SPhx
	– 'Septemberglut'	CRos EBee EHyd ELon EPfP LRHS NRHS
	– 'Shockwave' (v)	WCot
	– 'Spätsommer'	IPot
	– 'Speed Limit 45'	WCot
	– 'Spitfire'	see *P. paniculata* 'Frau Alfred von Mauthner'
	– 'Starfire' ♀H7	Widely available
I	– 'Stars and Stripes'	LRHS
	– 'Steeple Bumpstead'	WCot
I	– 'Stellata'	EHyd
	– 'Sterling Brocade' (v)	WCot
	– 'Sternhimmel'	LPla MSpe
	– 'Strawberry Daiquiri'PBR	WFar
	– SWEET MELODY	see *P. paniculata* (Sweet Summer Series) SWEET SUMMER MELODY
§	– (Sweet Summer Series) SWEET SUMMER CANDY ('Ditosdre'PBR)	WHil
§	– – SWEET SUMMER DREAM ('Ditomdre'PBR)	MAvo MPri NLar WCAu
	– – SWEET SUMMER FANTASY ('Ditopur'PBR)	MAvo MPri WCAu WTor
§	– – SWEET SUMMER FAVOURITE ('Ditomfav'PBR) ♀H7	NLar WCAu WHil
	– – SWEET SUMMER FESTIVAL ('Ditoros'PBR)	WHil
	– – SWEET SUMMER FIREBALL **new**	MPri
	– – SWEET SUMMER FRAGRANCE ('Ditomfra'PBR)	WHil
§	– – SWEET SUMMER MELODY ('Ditosmel'PBR)	WHil
	– – SWEET SUMMER PURPLE WHITE	see *P. paniculata* (Sweet Summer Series) SWEET SUMMER TEMPTATION
	– – SWEET SUMMER QUEEN ('Ditoran'PBR)	MPri NLar WHil
	– – SWEET SUMMER SENSATION ('Ditosse'PBR)	MPri WCAu WHil
§	– – SWEET SUMMER SURPRISE ('Ditomsur'PBR)	ECtt MPri WCAu
§	– – SWEET SUMMER TEMPTATION ('Ditostem'PBR)	WHil
	– – SWEET SUMMER WINE ('Ditowine'PBR)	ECtt IPot MAvo NLar WHil
	– 'Swizzle'	CBod CWGN ECtt WBor WFar
	– 'Tatjana'	EBee IPot
	– 'Tenor'	CTri ECtt ELon EPfP LEdu LRHS NLar NRHS SGbt SRms SWvt WCAu WSHC
	– 'Tequila Sunrise'PBR	ECtt LRHS MNrw
	– 'The King' ♀H7	EBee ECtt MACG MAvo MSpe NLar WSHC WSpi
	– 'Tiara'PBR (d)	ECtt LRHS MPie NGdn SWvt WCot
	– 'Toits de Paris' ambig.	MAvo
§	– 'Toits de Paris' Symons-Jeune	WSHC
	– 'Twister'	EBee MBros MNrw WFar
§	– 'Uralskie Skazy'	IPot
§	– 'Uspekh' ♀H7	Widely available
	– 'Valentina'	EBee
	– 'Veg Plot Pink'	SMHy
	– 'Veg Plot White'	SMHy
	– 'Velvet Flame' ♀H7	EHyd LRHS NRHS
	– 'Vintage Wine'	MNrw
	– 'Violetta Gloriosa'	ELon SAko WFar
	– 'Visions' ♀H7	EBlo EHyd
	– 'Volcano Betty'	MNrw
	– 'Watermelon Punch'	ECtt LRHS NLar WFar
	– 'Wendy House'	LEdu MAvo MNrw NHol
	– 'White Admiral' ♀H7	CBcs CElw CRos EBee ECtt EHyd ELan ELon EPfP EWoo GArf GKev GMaP LRHS MNrw MSpe NGrd NLar NRHS SCob SCoo SGbt SPer SPhx SRms SWvt WCAu WFar XLum
	– WHITE FLAME ('Bartwentynine'PBR) ♀H7	CDor CWGN EHyd EPfP IPot LBuc LRHS LSou NLar NRHS SCob SWvt WCot
	– 'White Pepper'	MAvo
	– 'Wilhelm Kesselring'	ECtt EHyd ELon NChi WBor
	– 'Willow Lodge'	SHar
	– 'Windsor'	EBee ECtt ELon EMor EPfP LRHS NCou NHol SRms SWvt WCAu
	– (Younique Series) YOUNIQUE BICOLOR ('Versbicolor')	WFar
	– – YOUNIQUE MAUVE ('Versmauve')	LCro LOPS
	– – YOUNIQUE OLD BLUE ('Versoldblue')	CDor LRHS MBros WFar
	– – YOUNIQUE OLD CERISE ('Verscerise')	MBros WFar
	– – YOUNIQUE OLD PINK ('Versoldpink')	MBros WFar
	– – YOUNIQUE OLD PURPLE	WFar
	– – YOUNIQUE WHITE ('Verswhite')	LEdu MBros MNrw WFar
	'Peppermint Candy'	WFar
	'Petticoat'	CSma ECtt WIce
	PINK FLAME ('Bartwelve'PBR)	EHyd EPfP LSou NLar SCob SRkn SRms
	'Pride of Rochester'	CBor EBou ECtt EHyd LRHS NRHS
§	× ***procumbens*** 'Millstream' ♀H5	ECtt
	– 'Variegata' (v)	EBou ECha ECtt SLee SRot WCav
§	***pulvinata***	SPlb WAbe
	PURPLE FLAME ('Barfourteen'PBR)	EHyd EPfP GWyn LRHS LSou NRHS SCob SRkn SRms WFar
	'Sherbet Cocktail'PBR	CWGN MSCN NHol
§	***sibirica*** subsp. ***borealis***	WAbe
	'Sileniflora'	WAbe
	'Spätsommer' **new**	NDov
	stolonifera	MNrw
I	– 'Alba'	EPfP NLar WFar WKif
	– 'Ariane'	ECha ECtt MNrw
I	– 'Atropurpurea'	CBod
	– 'Blue Ridge' ♀H6	CExl EAJP EBee ECha ECtt EPfP EWld LSRN MRav SRms WFar
	– 'Fran's Purple'	ECtt EWld MNrw WAvo WBrk WFar WKif WMal
	– 'Home Fires'	EAJP ECtt EPfP LEdu SPlb
	– 'Janusz'	NWad
	– 'Pink Ridge'	WFar XLum

	- 'Purpurea'	EPfP
	- 'Violet Vere'	EAJP
	subulata	LPar
	- 'Alexander's Surprise'	CMea ECtt EHyd EPfP EPot LRHS MAsh NBir NRHS
	- 'Amazing Grace'	CBor CTri CWCL ECtt EHyd EPfP EPot EWes IPot LRHS NBir NDov NRHS NSla NWad SPoG WCav WFar WHoo WIce
	- 'Apple Blossom'	CBod GKev NHol SCoo SPoG SRms
	- 'Atropurpurea'	EPfP SPoG XLum
	- 'Bavaria'	CBod CBor CMea CRos ECtt EHyd EPfP EPot LCro LOPS LRHS NRHS WFar
	- BEAUTY OF RONSDORF	see *P. subulata* 'Ronsdorfer Schöne'
	- 'Blue Eyes'	see *P. subulata* 'Oakington Blue Eyes'
	- 'Bonita'	ECtt EHyd EPot GWyn MAsh NRHS WIce
	- 'Bressingham Blue Eyes'	see *P. subulata* 'Oakington Blue Eyes'
	- 'Candy Stripe'	see *P. subulata* 'Tamaongalei'
	- 'Cavaldes White'	ECtt
	- 'Coral Eye'	ECtt
	- 'Daisy Hill'	XLum
	- 'Drumm'	see *P. subulata* 'Tamaongalei'
	- (Early Spring Series) EARLY SPRING LIGHT PINK ('Barsixtyfour'PBR)	CBod
	- - EARLY SPRING PURPLE ('Barseventyfour'PBR)	CBod CRos EHyd EPfP LRHS NRHS
	- - EARLY SPRING WHITE ('Barseventythree'PBR)	CBod SGBe
	- 'Emerald Cushion'	CBod CBor CTri EBou ECtt EGrI ELon EPfP LRHS NHol NHpl NSla SGBe SGbt WCFE WTor XLum
	- 'Emerald Cushion Blue'	CExl CTri EBou ECtt EHyd ELan EPfP LRHS MAsh MHCG MHol NBir NRHS SEdd SPlb SPoG SRot WCAu WCav WFar
	- 'Fabulous Blue Violet'	CBod EPfP LRHS
	- 'Fort Hill'	ECtt
	- 'G.F.Wilson'	see *P. subulata* 'Lilacina'
	- 'Holly'	EPot NHol NWad
	- 'Kimono'	see *P. subulata* 'Tamaongalei'
§	- 'Lilacina'	CMea ECha EPfP MAsh MBel
§	- 'Maischnee'	CTri ECtt MAsh SPlb
	- 'Marjorie'	EBou ECtt EGrI GArf GKev MBow MHer NBir SPoG
	- MAY SNOW	see *P. subulata* 'Maischnee'
§	- 'McDaniel's Cushion' 🏆^{H6}	CBod CExl CPla CRos CTri EBou ECha ECtt EDAr EHyd ELan ELon EPfP EPot LRHS MAsh MHol MMuc NRHS SGBe SLee SPlb SPoG WCAu WCav WFar WHil WHoo WIce
	- 'Mikado'	see *P. subulata* 'Tamaongalei'
	- 'Millstream Daphne'	IPot
	- 'Moerheimii'	IPot
	- 'Nettleton Variation' (v)	CRos EHyd EPot EWes LRHS MMuc NRHS SPoG SRms SRot WFar WHoo
§	- 'Oakington Blue Eyes'	CTri GWyn SRms
	- 'Purple Beauty'	CMea ECtt EHyd EPfP GMaP LRHS NRHS NWad SPoG WCFE WFar WHoo XLum
	- 'Red Wings' 🏆^{H6}	CBod ECtt EPfP MACG SRms
§	- 'Ronsdorfer Schöne'	EPfP NBir
	- 'Samson'	EPot SRot
	- 'Scarlet Flame'	CBod CMea EBou ECtt EGrI EPfP MACG MAsh NHol NHpl SLee WCAu
	- 'Snow Queen'	see *P. subulata* 'Maischnee'
	- 'Snowflake'	NSla
§	- 'Tamaongalei'	CBod CPla CRos CTri EBou ECtt EHyd ELan ELon EWes GKev LRHS MAsh MMuc NRHS NWad SLee SRot WCFE WCav WFar WHil WIce XLum
	- 'Temiskaming'	CTri ECtt EHyd EWes LRHS NRHS NSla SRms WSHC
	- 'White Delight'	CBod CMea ECtt EHyd ELan ELon EPfP MACG SPoG WCAu
	- white-flowered **new**	NSla
	VIOLET FLAME ('Barsixtyone'PBR)	CBod CDor EPfP LSun MHol NLar SPoG WCot WHil
	'Violet Pinwheels'	CBor WFar
	WHITE EYE FLAME ('Barsixty'PBR)	CBod CDor CWGN EPfP IPot LSou NLar WHil
	'White Kimono'	CRos EHyd LRHS NRHS
	'Zwergenteppich'	CBor CRos EHyd EPfP LRHS NRHS SPoG WFar

Phoenix (*Arecaceae*)

	canariensis 🏆^{H2}	CBod CDoC CExl EBee EPfP LPar SArc SChr SEND SPalm SPlb SPoG SWeb WSMil
	dactylifera (F)	SPalm
	roebelenii 🏆^{H1b}	CDTJ CTsd LCro LOPS
	theophrasti	CPHo SPalm

Phormium ✿ (*Hemerocallidaceae*)

§	'Alison Blackman'PBR	CBcs CBod EBee EHyd EPfP LSRN MAsh MGos SCob SCoo SEND SPoG SWvt XSte
	'Amazing Red'	SPer
	'Apricot Queen' (v)	CAbb CBcs CBrac CCCN CDoC CSBt EBee EHyd EPfP LCro LOPS LRHS LSRN MGos NLar NRHS SCob SEND SGbt SPer SPoG
	BACK IN BLACK ('Seilack'PBR)	CBcs CCht CMac EHyd SCob SPeP SPer SWvt WFar XSte
	'Black Adder'PBR	CMac EBee EHyd EPfP ILea LRHS LSRN MAsh NRHS SCob SEND SGbt SPoG
	'Black Rage'	CBcs EPfP
	BLACK VELVET ('Seivel'PBR)	CBcs CCht CTsd EHyd ELan EPfP LRHS MSwo WCot
	'Blondie'PBR (v) **new**	LRHS
	'Bronze Baby'	CBcs CCCN CDoC CSBt EBee EHyd ELan EPfP LRHS LSRN MGos MSwo NRHS SCob SPoG SWvt
	'Brown Sugar' **new**	CTsd
	'Buckland Ruby'	EBee
	'Chocomint'PBR	CBod CDoC ELan SCob SPeP XSte
	colensoi	see *P. cookianum*
§	***cookianum***	GAbr SArc
	- 'Alpinum Purpureum'	see *P. tenax* 'Nanum Purpureum'
	- subsp. ***hookeri*** 'Cream Delight' (v) 🏆^{H4}	CAbb CBcs CCCN CCht CDoC CEnd CMac CSBt EBee EGrI EHyd EPfP LRHS LSRN MAsh MGos MSwo NRHS SCob SCoo SPeP SPer SWvt WFar
	- - 'Tricolor' (v) 🏆^{H4}	CBcs CBrac CChe CDTJ CDoC CMac CRos CSBt EBee EHyd ELan EPfP LCro LOPS LRHS MGos NRHS SArc SCob SEND SPalm SPer SPoG SRms SWvt WFar XSte
	'Crimson Devil'	CBcs EHyd EPfP LRHS NRHS
	'Dark Delight'	CBcs XSte
	'Duet' (v) 🏆^{H3}	CBcs CCCN SEND SWvt
	'Dusky Chief'	CSBt EBee
	'Evening Glow' (v)	CBcs CCCN CDoC EHyd EPfP LRHS LSRN MGos NRHS SPalm SPoG SRms SWvt

'Firebird'	LSRN SWvt
'Flamingo' (v)	CBcs CCCN CDTJ CDoC EPfP MGos SCob SGbt SPer SPoG
'Gold Ray' (v)	CBcs CBod CBrac CTsd EHyd EPfP LRHS NRHS SCoo SWvt WLov
'Gold Sword' (v)	CBcs CCCN CMac CSBt EHyd EPfP SCob SGbt
'Golden Alison'	see *P.* 'Alison Blackman'
'Green Sword'	CCCN
'Jack Spratt' (v)	SWvt
'Jester' (v)	CBcs CBod CBrac CCCN CChe CCht CDoC CEme CKel CMac CSBt EHyd ELan EPfP GDam LRHS LSRN MAsh MGos MSwo NRHS SCob SCoo SGbt SPalm SPoG SRkn SRms WSMil XSte
'Limelight'	SEND SWvt
§ 'Maori Chief' (v)	CSBt EPfP SWvt WFar
§ 'Maori Maiden' (v)	CCCN CDoC CTri EBee EHyd EPfP MSwo SRms SWvt
§ 'Maori Queen' (v)	CBcs CBod CBrac CCCN CDTJ CDoC CMac EBee EHyd EPfP LCro LOPS LRHS MGos MSwo NRHS SCoo SEND SGbt SPer SWvt WFar XSte
§ 'Maori Sunrise' (v)	CBcs CCCN CDoC CMac EGrI EHyd IArd LCro LOPS LSRN MGos SCoo SRms SWvt
'Margaret Jones' PBR	CCCN LSRN XSte
'Moonraker' PBR	CBcs SCob
'Pink Panther' (v)	CAbb CBcs CBod CCCN EHyd EPfP LSRN MGos SPoG SRms XSte
'Pink Stripe' (v)	CBcs CSBt EGrI EHyd EPfP LRHS MAsh MGos NRHS SCob SGbt SGsty SPalm SPoG SWvt XSte
'Platt's Black'	CBod CCCN EBee EHyd EPfP LCro LOPS LSRN MGos MSwo NBir SCob SPer SPoG SWvt WFar WLov
'Rainbow Chief'	see *P.* 'Maori Chief'
'Rainbow Maiden'	see *P.* 'Maori Maiden'
'Rainbow Queen'	see *P.* 'Maori Queen'
'Rainbow Sunrise'	see *P.* 'Maori Sunrise'
'Red Sensation'	CDoC CEme LSRN SPeP
'Sundowner' (v) ♀H3	CBcs CCCN CMac CRos CSBt CTsd EBee EGrI EHyd EPfP LCro LOPS LRHS MAsh MGos NBir NRHS SCob SCoo SEND SGsty SPoG SWvt WLov XSte
'Sunset' (v)	CBcs CCCN CSBt SWvt
'Surfer' (v)	CDoC
'Surfer Bronze'	CCCN
'Surfer Green'	CCCN
'Sussex Velvet'	SCoo
tenax	CAgr CBcs CBrac CMac EHyd EPfP GArf GDam LCro LOPS LPar MGos MPri MSwo NGdn SArc SCob SEND SGsty SPer SPlb SPoG SWeb SWvt
- 'All Black'	MGos SCoo XSte
- 'Bronze'	SWvt
- 'Co-ordination' (v)	CCCN
- 'Croce di Malta'	SArc
- 'Joker' (v)	CBcs CDoC EBee NLar SCob XSte
* - ***lineatum***	SEND
§ - 'Nanum Purpureum'	SArc
- Purpureum Group ♀H5	CBod CBrac CDoC CMac EBee EGrI EHyd ELan EPfP GAbr GArf GDam LPar MPri MSwo NLar SCob SEND SGsty SLon SPlb SWeb WFar XLum
- 'Thumbelina'	CCCN
- 'Tiny Tiger' (v)	EPfP
- 'Tom Thumb'	LRHS
- 'Variegatum' (v) ♀H5	CDTJ CDoC EBee EPfP LPar MGos MPri SArc SCob SEND SGsty SRms SWeb
- 'Veneer' PBR (v)	XSte
- 'Yellow Queen' (v)	WFar
'Yellow Wave' (v) ♀H4	Widely available

Photinia ✿ (*Rosaceae*)

arbutifolia	see *Heteromeles salicifolia*
arguta var. ***arguta***	SMad
- - KR 10738	WPGP
beauverdiana var. ***notabilis***	IDee
CORALLINA ('Bourfrits' PBR)	CBod
davidiana	CMac CTri ELan EPfP IDee MGil MRav NLar SPer SPtp SRms SVen WPav
- PAB 8097	LEdu
- 'Dwarf Ness' **new**	GKev
- 'Palette' (v)	CBcs CBod CBrac CMac ELan ELon EPfP MAsh MGos MSwo NLar SGol SPer SPoG SRms SWvt WFar WMat
- Salicifolia Group	WPav
- var. ***undulata*** 'Fructu Luteo'	CMac MRav NLar
- - 'Prostrata'	CMac CTri MRav NLar WCFE
'Diamond Red'	CDoC
× ***fraseri***	LPar WTSh
I - 'Atropurpurea Nana'	CBcs CDoC MGos
- 'Birmingham'	CMac SRms
- 'Canivily' ♀H5	CEnd CRos EHyd EShb LRHS MGos NLar NRHS SGol SWvt
- 'Carré Rouge' **new**	SGsty
- CHICO ('Br2011') **new**	LRHS
- CRACKLIN' RED ('Parred' PBR)	LPar
- 'Devil's Dream' **new**	LRHS
- 'Dicker Tony' **new**	NLar
* - 'Ilexifolium'	ESwi
- 'Little Red Robin'	Widely available
- 'Louise' (v)	CBod CRos CSBt EBee EHyd LBuc LPar LRHS MAsh MGos MHed NLar NOrn NRHS SCob SGBe SWvt WFar
- MAGICAL VOLCANO ('Kolmavoca' PBR)	LRHS MAsh NLar SGol SGsty SMad SPoG
- PINK MARBLE ('Cassini') (v) ♀H5	Widely available
- 'Red Robin' ♀H5	Widely available
- 'Red Robin Variegated' (v)	SavN
- 'Red Select'	WFar
- 'Robusta'	CMac EPfP LRHS SRms SWvt
I - 'Robusta Compacta'	LSRN SGsty
glabra	GKev SArc
§ - 'Parfait' (v)	CMac MAsh
- 'Pink Lady'	see *P. glabra* 'Parfait'
- 'Rubens'	EHyd EPfP LRHS MAsh MRav
- 'Variegata'	see *P. glabra* 'Parfait'
lasiogyna	CMCN
lucida	WCru
microphylla B&SWJ 11837	WCru
- HWJ 564	WCru
niitakayamensis	MVil SPtp
- CWJ 12435	WCru
cf. ***prionophylla*** 'Bodnant'	SBrt
'Redstart'	CMac ELan EPfP LRHS MMuc NLar SLon SPer SWvt WFar
§ ***serratifolia***	CBcs CMCN EPfP NLar SArc SEND SPer WFar WPGP
- var. ***ardisiifolia*** NMWJ 14513	WCru
I - 'Compacta'	LPar
- CRUNCHY ('Rev100' PBR)	EPfP LBuc LRHS MMrt NOrn SCob

- CURLY FANTASY ('Kolcurl'PBR)	LRHS MAsh MRav NLar SavN
- 'Jenny'	NLar SavN WFar
- PINK CRISPY ('Oploo5'PBR)	ELan LPar LRHS NLar SPoG SavN
serrulata	see *P. serratifolia*
SUPER HEDGE ('Branpara'PBR)	MSwo WFar
'Super Red'	CSBt NLar
villosa	EPfP WPav
- B&SWJ 8665	WCru
- var. ***coreana*** B&SWJ 8789	WCru
- var. ***laevis***	CExl EBee EPfP WPGP
- - B&SWJ 8877	WCru
- f. ***maximowicziana***	CDoC NLar
* - var. ***zollingeri*** B&SWJ 8903	WCru

Phragmites (*Poaceae*)

sp.	CHab
from Sichuan, China	EPPr
§ ***australis***	CBen CHab CPud CWat NMir NWea SVic WMAq XLum
- subsp. ***australis*** var. ***striatopictus***	EPPr
- - 'Variegatus' (v)	CBen CNat CWat EPPr LLWG MMuc NBir SEND XLum
- subsp. ***humilis***	CHab
- subsp. ***pseudodonax***	EPPr
communis	see *P. australis*

Phuopsis (*Rubiaceae*)

§ ***stylosa***	Widely available
- 'Purpurea'	EBee ECha MNrw MRav NChi

Phygelius (*Scrophulariaceae*)

aequalis	MRav
- ***albus***	see *P. aequalis* 'Yellow Trumpet'
- 'Aureus'	see *P. aequalis* 'Yellow Trumpet'
- 'Cream Trumpet'	see *P. aequalis* 'Yellow Trumpet'
- 'Indian Chief'	see *P.* × *rectus* 'African Queen'
- 'Sani Pass'	MHer SIvy SPlb
- 'Trewidden Pink' ♀H4	EHyd ELan GBin LRHS MHer MSCN NLar NRHS SWvt XLum
§ - 'Yellow Trumpet' ♀H4	CSBt ELan GMaP LSRN MAsh MGil SDix SEND SGbt SWvt WAvo
CANDY DROPS SALMON ORANGE ('Kerphysalm'PBR) (Candy Drops Series)	SRms
capensis	CTri MHer SRms
'Golden Gate'	see *P. aequalis* 'Yellow Trumpet'
Logan form	GBin
NEW SENSATION ('Blaphy'PBR)	EPfP MRav SRms SWvt
'Passionate'PBR	NLar
§ × ***rectus*** 'African Queen' ♀H5	CTri EBee EHyd ELan EPfP LRHS MGil MRav MSwo NBir NGdn SCob SDix SEND SPlb SWvt WAvo WGwG WKif WLov XLum
- 'Devil's Tears' ♀H4	CBcs CPla GArf SCob SEND SWvt
- 'Ivory Twist'	NLar SPer
- 'Jodie Southon'	LSou SDys WCot
- 'Moonraker'	CBcs CTri EBee ELan EPfP GBin GWyn MAsh MGil MHer MRav NGdn NLar SCob SEND SPer SPlb SRms WKif XLum
- 'Salmon Leap' ♀H5	CBcs CTri EHyd ELan EPfP LRHS LSRN MGos MRav NLar NRHS SBut SCob SPlb SRms SWvt
- (Somerford Funfair Series) SOMERFORD FUNFAIR APRICOT ('Yapapr')	SWvt
- - SOMERFORD FUNFAIR CORAL ('Yapcor'PBR)	EGrI EHyd EPfP MAsh NLar SRkn SWvt
- - SOMERFORD FUNFAIR CREAM ('Yapcre'PBR)	CBod EHyd EPfP MBros SPoG SWvt
- - SOMERFORD FUNFAIR ORANGE ('Yapor'PBR)	CBod CPla EBou EHyd EPfP MAsh SCob SRms SWvt
- - SOMERFORD FUNFAIR WINE ('Yapwin')	CBod CChe EGrI EHyd ELan EPfP LRHS MAsh NRHS SCob SPoG SWvt
- - SOMERFORD FUNFAIR YELLOW ('Yapyel'PBR)	EHyd EPfP MAsh SWvt
§ - 'Winchester Fanfare'	CSBt GWyn MGos MRav NLar SPer SWvt
- 'Winton Fanfare'	see *P.* × *rectus* 'Winchester Fanfare'
'Rory'PBR	SRms
YELLOW SOVEREIGN ('Croyelsov'PBR) (Croftway Series) new	LRHS

Phyla (*Verbenaceae*)

lanceolata	LLWG
§ ***nodiflora***	ECha MBow MHer SLee SRms WJek XSen
- 'Alba'	SEND
§ - var. ***canescens***	CKel XLum

Phylica (*Rhamnaceae*)

arborea	LRHS
pubescens	CPbh

× *Phylliopsis* (*Ericaceae*)

'Coppelia' ♀H5	EPot GKev ITim
hillieri 'Askival'	EPot GKev WThu
- 'Pinocchio'	EPot GKev WThu
- 'Sugar Plum'	CCCN SWvt
'Hobgoblin'	ITim
'Mermaid'	EPot GRum ITim
'Puck'	EPot
'Sprite'	EPot ITim
'Swanhilde'	WThu

Phyllitis see *Asplenium*

scolopendrium	see *Asplenium scolopendrium*

Phyllocladus (*Podocarpaceae*)

aspleniifolius	WPav
trichomanoides new	IDee
- var. ***alpinus*** 'Blue Blades'	MGil SLim
- - 'Highland Lass'	MGil SLim
- - 'Highlander'	MGil SLim

Phyllodoce (*Ericaceae*)

aleutica	GKev WThu
§ - subsp. ***glanduliflora***	EPot
§ - - 'Flora Slack'	WThu
- - white-flowered	see *P. aleutica* subsp. *glanduliflora* 'Flora Slack'
× ***alpina***	GRum
caerulea ♀H6	GArf
- ***japonica***	see *P. nipponica*
- 'Murray Lyon'	GArf
- 'W.M. Buchanan's Peach Seedling'	GRum
empetriformis	GRum WThu
glanduliflora	see *P. aleutica* subsp. *glanduliflora*
× ***intermedia*** 'Drummondii'	GArf
- 'Fred Stoker'	GRum
§ ***nipponica***	GKev WThu

× *Phyllosasa* ✿ (*Poaceae*)

tranquillans	MMuc MWht SEND
- 'Shiroshima'	CAbb CDTJ CDoC EPfP LPar MBrN MMuc MWht SEND

Phyllostachys ✿ (*Poaceae*)

angusta	MWht
arcana 'Luteosulcata'	MMuc MWht
§ ***atrovaginata***	CBdn LPar MWht SGol
aurea ♀H6	Widely available
- 'Albovariegata' (v)	EPfP MWht SPoG
- 'Holochrysa'	CDTJ CJun LPar MWht NLar
- 'Koi'	CDTJ LPar MWht SGol
aureocaulis	see *P. aureosulcata* f. *aureocaulis*, *P. vivax* f. *aureocaulis*
aureosulcata	LPar
§ - f. ***aureocaulis***	CAbb CBcs CBdn CBod CJun CKel ELon EPfP LCro LOPS LRHS LSRN MGos MSwo MWht NRHS SArc SCob SCoo SEWo SEdd SGol SGsty SPoG SWvt
- 'Lama Tempel'	CDTJ CJun
- f. ***spectabilis*** ♀H5	Widely available
bambusoides	CDTJ
- 'Allgold'	see *P. bambusoides* 'Holochrysa'
- 'Castillonii' ♀H5	CBct EWes LEdu LPar MWht
- 'Castillonii Inversa'	LEdu MWht
§ - 'Holochrysa' ♀H5	CDTJ MMuc MWht SEND WPGP
- f. ***lacrima-deae***	CDTJ
- 'Marliacea'	CBdn
- 'Sulphurea'	see *P. bambusoides* 'Holochrysa'
- 'Tanakae'	CDTJ
bissetii ♀H5	CAbb CAgr CBcs CBdn CBod CCVT CDoC EPfP GDam LCro LOPS LPar LRHS MAvo MBrN MGos MMuc MSwo MWht NLar NRHS SCoo SEND SEdd SGol SGsty SPlb SWeb WPGP WSMil
congesta misapplied	see *P. atrovaginata*
decora	MMuc MWht
dulcis	CBdn EPfP MWht
§ ***edulis***	CAgr SPlb
- 'Bicolor'	LPar
- f. ***pubescens***	see *P. edulis*
flexuosa	CBcs MWht SGol
glauca	EPfP LPar MWht
- f. ***yunzhu***	MWht
heteroclada 'Solid Stem' misapplied	see *P. purpurata* 'Straight Stem'
heterocycla var. ***pubescens***	see *P. edulis*
humilis	CBdn LPar MMuc MWht SEND
iridescens ♀H5	MWht
mannii	MWht
nigra ♀H5	Widely available
- 'Boryana'	CBdn CCVT CEnd EPfP MGos MMuc MWht NLar SEND SWvt
- 'Hale'	CBct MWht
- f. ***henonis*** ♀H5	CBdn MMuc MWht NLar SEND SGol WPGP
- 'Megurochiku'	MWht
- f. ***punctata***	MAvo MMuc SEND
nuda	MWht
- f. ***localis***	MWht
parvifolia	MWht
propinqua	MWht
§ ***purpurata*** 'Straight Stem'	MWht
rubromarginata	MWht
stimulosa	MWht
sulphurea 'Houzeau'	MMuc SEND
§ - f. ***viridis***	LPar
violascens	CAgr MWht
viridiglaucescens	CAgr CDTJ LPar MMuc MWht SEND WCot
viridis	see *P. sulphurea* f. *viridis*
vivax	EPfP MWht NLar
§ - f. ***aureocaulis*** ♀H5	CAbb CAgr CBcs CCVT CDoC CEnd EPfP LEdu LMaj LPar LSRN MGos MMuc MWht NLar SCob SEND SGol SWeb WPGP
- - 'Huangwenzhu'	CDTJ MWht
- 'Katrin'	LEdu

Phymatosorus (*Polypodiaceae*)

diversifolius	see *Microsorum diversifolium*

Phymosia (*Malvaceae*)

§ ***umbellata***	LEdu LRHS MPkF WPGP XSte

Phyodina see *Callisia*

Physalis (*Solanaceae*)

alkekengi ♀H7	CTri EPfP LPot NBir NLar SBls SWvt WMal
- var. ***franchetii***	CBcs CMac CSBt CTri EBee ECha EHyd ELan EPfP GQue LCro LOPS LRHS MBel MNrw NBir NBro NRHS SCob SPer SPoG SRms WFar
- - dwarf	EHyd NLar
- - 'Gigantea'	CBct CBod CRos EHyd LRHS MBros NLar NRHS SPlb WFar
- - 'Gnome'	see *P. alkekengi* var. *franchetii* 'Zwerg'
- - 'Variegata' (v)	EWes LEdu SEND WPGP
§ - - 'Zwerg'	CDor EBou EHyd LSun SEdi
- 'Halloween King'	EBee NLar
- 'Halloween Queen'	NLar
edulis	see *P. peruviana*
§ ***peruviana*** (F)	CCCN CSpe SPlb SVic XAbr

Physaria (*Brassicaceae*)

alpina	SPlb

Physocarpus (*Rosaceae*)

'Brown Sugar'	CBod WNPC
capitatus 'Tilden Park'	EBee
LITTLE DEVIL	see *P. opulifolius* 'Donna May'
'Midnight'	MAsh SGBe WFar
opulifolius	MTrO
- ALL BLACK ('Minall2'PBR) **new**	LRHS MPkF WCot XSte
- ALL RED ('Minalco') **new**	WNPC
- AMBER JUBILEE ('Jefam'PBR)	CDoC LCro LOPS LPar LRHS NEoE SCob SRms
- 'Angel Gold'	CCCN CDoC CRos EHyd LRHS MAsh NRHS SPoG XSte
- 'Anny's Gold'PBR	EBee NLar SRms
- 'Burning Embers'	CBod CDoC EGrI SRms
- 'Chameleon'	CKel EBee NEoE SCob SGol
- COPPERTINA	see *P. opulifolius* DIABLE D'OR
- 'Dart's Gold' ♀H7	Widely available
§ - DIABLE D'OR ('Mindia'PBR)	CBar CBod CCCN CDoC CEnd CKel CRos EBee EHed EHyd EPfP ILea LCro LOPS LRHS LSRN MAsh MBlu MGos NLar NOra NRHS SGbt SGol WLov
- 'Diabolo'PBR ♀H7	Widely available
§ - 'Donna May'PBR	EPfP EShb LPar LSou MAsh MGos NEoE SCob WFar
- 'Firebrand'	NEoE

§ - LADY IN RED ('Tuilad'PBR) ♀H7 — Widely available
- LITTLE ANGEL ('Hoogi016'PBR) — CBod CKel CWGN EMil EPfP LCro LOPS MThu SCob SPad SPoG
- MIDNIGHT ('Jonight'PBR) — CBcs MGil SCob XSte
- 'Red Baron' — WFar
- RUBY SPICE — see *P. opulifolius* LADY IN RED
- SUMMER MOON ('Tuimon') — CBcs NEoE SGol WFar
- SUMMER WINE ('Seward'PBR) — CDoC CKel EBee EPfP EWTr EWes MAsh NLar WSpi
- TINY WINE ('Smpotw'PBR) — EPfP LPar MAsh NLar SGsty

Physochlaina (*Solanaceae*)

orientalis — CSpe GEdr WCot

Physoplexis (*Campanulaceae*)

§ ***comosa*** ♀H6 — EPot

Physostegia (*Lamiaceae*)

I 'Aquatica' — LLWG
§ ***virginiana*** — CBod CSBt CTri GMaP ILea LShi MBel SBut SRms
- 'Alba' — CBod CMac CSBt CTri EBee ELon EMor EPfP GAbr GMaP LEdu MBros SPlb WCav XLum
- 'Autumn Carnival' **new** — NLar
§ - 'Crown of Snow' — EHyd EPfP GWyn LRHS MHer MRav NRHS SBea SPeP SWvt WTre
- 'Crystal Peak White' — LRHS NLar WFar
- 'Grandiflora' — WTre
- 'Miss Manners' — CBod EBee ECtt EHyd LRHS MCot MPie NGdn NLar NRHS SCoo SGbt
- 'Pink Manners' — NLar
- 'Red Beauty' — NLar
- 'Rose Crown' — SPer
- 'Rose Queen' — CTri EMor SBls WFar
- 'Rosea' — EHyd EPfP GJos GPSL GWyn LPot LRHS NChi NCou NGdn NRHS SHar SPoG SWvt WFar WHrl
- SCHNEEKRONE — see *P. virginiana* 'Crown of Snow'
- 'Snow Queen' — see *P. virginiana* 'Summer Snow'
§ - var. ***speciosa*** 'Bouquet Rose' — CBod CRos EBee ECha EPfP EWTr EWoo LEdu LRHS MHol MRav NBir NLar NRHS SGbt SPeP SPer SRms SWvt WCAu WFar XLum
- - ROSE BOUQUET — see *P. virginiana* var. *speciosa* 'Bouquet Rose'
- - 'Variegata' (v) — CMac EBee ECtt ELan ELon EPfP GLog LRHS MRav NBir NGdn NHol SBea SPeP SPer SPoG SRms WCAu WCot WFar XLum
§ - 'Summer Snow' ♀H7 — CBcs CCBP ECha ELan EPfP EWTr EWoo LRHS MHol NGBl NLar SBls SPer SRms WCAu WCot
- 'Summer Spire' — LRHS
- 'Vivid' ♀H7 — CBod CCBP CMac EBee ECha EHyd ELan ELon EMor EPfP LRHS MHer MNrw MPie MRav NGBl NHol NLar NRHS SDix SGbt SPer SPlb SRms WCAu WCav WHil WWtn XLum
- 'Wassenhove' — SMrm

Phyteuma (*Campanulaceae*)

balbisii — see *P. cordatum*
betonicifolium — GJos
comosum — see *Physoplexis comosa*
confusum — GJos
§ ***cordatum*** — GJos
halleri — see *P. ovatum*
hemisphaericum — GKev NSla
humile — GArf WThu
nigrum — GEdr NBid SBrt WBor
orbiculare — GEdr GJos
§ ***ovatum*** — SPlb
scheuchzeri — EBee EBou EDAr ELan EPfP GEdr GJos GWyn MMrt MSCN SMad SPad SRms WCot WIce XLum
spicatum — GJos NBro
- subsp. ***coeruleum*** — GJos

Phytolacca (*Phytolaccaceae*)

acinosa — EWld WHil
- HWJ 647 — WCru
§ ***americana*** — CBcs CCBP EBee EGrI ELan EPfP ESwi EWld GPoy MBNS MHer MPie NChi SPlb SRms
- B&SWJ 12743 — ESwi
- B&SWJ 8817A — WCru
- 'Silberstein' (v) — EBee
bogotensis B&SWJ 14221 — ESwi WCru
clavigera — see *P. polyandra*
decandra — see *P. americana*
dioica — CExl SPlb
esculenta — LEdu SEND
icosandra — WHil
- Purpurascens Group — WFar
- - B&SWJ 11251 — WCru
japonica B&SWJ 3005 — NBid WCru
- B&SWJ 3522 — WCru
'Laka Boom' — SSal
§ ***polyandra*** — EGrI NBid NBro SRms
aff. ***polyandra*** **new** — GGro

Picea ✿ (*Pinaceae*)

§ ***abies*** — CAco CCVT CLnd CMac CSBt CTri EPfP GBin GQue IPap LBuc LMaj NWea SCoo SPoG WMou WTSh
- 'Aarburgh' **new** — CAco
- 'Acrocona' ♀H7 — CAco LPar NLar
- 'Archer' — CKen
- 'Archer's Pygmy' **new** — NLar
- 'Argenteospica' (v) — CAco
- 'Aurea' — CAco
- 'Aurea Magnifica' — CAco
- 'Bago' — CKen
- 'Bally' — CKen
- 'Capitata' — CKen LRHS MGil
- 'Clanbrassiliana' ♀H7 — ELan EPfP NWad
- 'Cobra' **new** — CAco
- Compacta Group — CAco
I - 'Congesta' — CKen
- 'Cranstonii' **new** — CAco
- 'Crippsii' — CKen
I - 'Cruenta' — CKen
- 'Cupressina' — CAco CKen
- 'Dáblice' **new** — CAco
- 'Diedorfiana' **new** — CAco
- 'Diffusa' — CKen MGil
- 'Dumpy' — CKen NHol
- 'Dundaga' **new** — CAco
- 'Echiniformis' — CKen
- 'Elegantissima' **new** — CAco
- 'Emsland' — LRHS
- 'Excelsa' — see *P. abies*
- 'Fahndrich' — CKen
- 'Finedonensis' — CAco
- 'Formanek' — CAco SAko
- 'Four Winds' — CKen
- 'Frohburg' — CAco CKen NLar
- 'Glimra' **new** — CAco

	- 'Globosa'	CAco
	- 'Gold Drift'	NLar
	- 'Gold Finch'	NLar
	- 'Gregoryana'	CKen
	- 'Hasin'	SAko
	- 'Heartland Gem'	CKen
	- 'Horace Wilson'	CKen
	- 'Humilis'	CKen
	- 'Humphrey's Gem'	CKen
	- 'Hystrix'	NWad
	- 'Inversa' ♀H7	CAco CKen MBlu SLim
	- 'J.W. Daisy's White'	see *P. glauca* var. *albertiana* 'J.W. Daisy's White'
	- 'Jana'	CKen NLar
	- 'Jermyns Broom No. 1'	CKen
	- 'Kámon' **new**	CAco
	- 'Kral'	CKen
	- 'Krenek'	NLar
	- 'Lemon Drop'	NLar
	- 'Lithuanian Snake' **new**	CAco
	- 'Little Gem' ♀H7	CKen CMen ELan EPfP LRHS MAsh MGil MGos NHol NLar NWad NWea SCoo
	- 'Little Santa' **new**	LRHS
	- 'Loreley' **new**	CKen
	- 'Lucky Strike'	CAco MAsh NLar
	- 'Marcel'	CKen
	- 'Maxwellii'	CAco
	- 'Mini Kalous'	CKen
	- 'Nana Compacta'	CKen CMen MAsh SCoo
	- 'Nidiformis' ♀H7	CKen CMac CMen CSBt LPar LRHS MGos SRms
	- 'Norrköping'	CKen
	- 'Ohlendorffii'	CKen
	- 'Pachyphylla'	CKen
	- 'Parsonsii'	SAko
	- 'Parviformis' **new**	CAco
	- 'Pendula' **new**	CAco
	- 'Perry's Gold' **new**	LRHS
	- 'Pumila'	WCFE
	- 'Pusch'	CAco CKen CMen NLar
	- 'Pygmaea'	CKen LPar
	- 'Reflexa'	CAco
	- 'Remontii'	NLar
	- 'Ripley Broom'	CKen
	- 'Roseospicata'	CAco NLar
	- 'Rothenhausii' **new**	CAco
	- 'Rubra Spicata' **new**	CAco
	- 'Rydal' ♀H7	CAco CBcs CKen MAsh NLar
	- 'Sargentii' **new**	MGil
	- 'Spring Fire'	CKen
	- 'Tuka Puka' **new**	CAco
	- 'Typner'	CKen NLar
	- 'Vermont Gold'	CKen LRHS NLar
	- 'Virgata' **new**	CAco
	- subsp. ***virgata*** 'Aurea' **new**	CAco
	- 'Wagner'	NLar
	- 'Weeping Blue' **new**	CAco
	- 'Wichtel'	CKen
	- WILL'S DWARF	see *P. abies* 'Wills Zwerg'
§	- 'Wills Zwerg'	LRHS NLar
	- 'Ylivska Snake' **new**	CAco
	alcoquiana	CAco
§	- var. ***alcoquiana***	SLim
	asperata	CAco
	- glaucous-leaved **new**	CAco
	- 'Mongolei'	NLar
	bicolor	see *P. alcoquiana* var. *alcoquiana*
	brachytyla	CAco
	- var. ***brachytyla***	CAco
	breweriana ♀H7	CAco CBcs CMac EPfP GKin IDee IPap LEdu MBlu MGos NLar NWea SLim SSta WCFE WTSh
	- 'Frühlingsgold'	CKen NLar
	- 'Kohout's Dwarf'	CKen NLar
	chihuahuana	CAco
	crassifolia **new**	CAco
	engelmannii	CAco LMaj NWea
	- 'Blue Magoo' **new**	CAco
	- 'Bush's Lace'	CAco
	- 'Cienega'	CKen
	- 'Compact'	SLim
	- subsp. ***engelmannii***	CKen
	- Glauca Group	CAco LMaj
	- 'Jasper'	CAco CKen NLar
	- 'Lace'	NLar
	- subsp. ***mexicana*** **new**	CAco
	- - 'Pervana' **new**	CAco
	farreri	CAco
	glauca	CAco SWvt
	- var. ***albertiana***	CAco
	- - ALBERTA BLUE ('Haal'^{PBR})	CAco CKen LRHS
	- - 'Alberta Globe' ♀H7	CAco CBrac ELan GKin LRHS MAsh MGos NHol NWad SCoo SPoG
	- - 'Conica' ♀H7	CAco CBcs CBrac CMac CSBt ELan EPfP LCro LOPS LPar LRHS MAsh MGil MGos MMuc NHol NOrn NWea SCob SCoo SEND SLim SPoG SRms SVic SWvt WCFE
	- - 'Gnome'	CKen
§	- - 'J.W. Daisy's White' ♀H7	CBcs CBrac CKen ELan EPfP GKin LRHS MAsh MGos NHol NLar NOrn NWea SCoo SLim SMad SPoG
	- - 'Laurin' ♀H7	CKen NWad SCoo SLim
	- - 'Lilliput'	CKen EPfP NWad NWea SPoG
	- - 'Piccolo'	CKen NWad
	- - 'Sander's Blue'	CAco CKen EPfP GKin LRHS SAko SCoo SPoG SVic
	- - 'Tiny'	CKen MGil NWad
	- 'Arneson's Blue Variegated' (v)	CKen MAsh
	- 'Baby'	NWea
	- 'Biesenthaler Frühling'	CKen SLim
	- 'Blue Planet'	CKen
	- 'Cy's Wonder'	CKen
	- 'Dendroforma Gold'	CKen
	- 'Eagle Rock'	NLar
	- 'Echiniformis' ♀H7	CKen LRHS MGil
	- 'Goldilocks'	CAco CKen
	- 'Jalako Gold'	NLar NWea
I	- 'Julian Potts Monstrosa'	NLar
	- 'Milford'	CKen
§	- 'Nana'	CKen
	- 'Pendula'	CAco CKen
	- 'Pixie'	CKen
	- 'Pixie Dust'	CKen
	- 'Rainbow's End' (v)	CKen LRHS SCoo
	- 'Spring Surprise'	CKen NLar
	- 'Zuckerhut'	LRHS
	glehnii	CAco
	- 'Shimezusei'	CKen
	jezoensis	CAco CKen CMen NWea
	- subsp. ***hondoensis***	CMen
	- 'Landis' **new**	CAco
	- 'Marianbad'	CKen
	- 'Mariánské Làzně'	NLar
	- 'Pygmy'	CKen
	- 'Yatsabusa'	CKen CMen
	koraiensis	CAco
	kosteri 'Glauca'	see *P. pungens* 'Koster'

	koyamae	CAco
	- 'Bedgebury Cascade'	CAco SLim
	likiangensis	CAco EPfP NLar
	- var. ***balfouriana***	see *P. likiangensis* var. *rubescens*
§	- var. ***rubescens***	CAco SLim
	× ***lutzii*** **new**	LPar
	mariana	EPfP MAsh
	- 'Austria Broom'	CKen
	- 'Bill Archer'	NWad
	- 'Blue Teardrop'	CKen
	- 'Fastigiata'	CKen
	- 'Nana' Υ^{H7}	CAco CKen CMac CMen EPfP MGos MMuc NHol NWad NWea SCoo SLim SPoG
I	- 'Pygmaea'	CKen NWad SLim
	× ***mariorika*** 'Machala'	CAco
	meyeri	EPfP
	morrisonicola	CKen
	obovata	CAco
	omorika Υ^{H7}	CAco CBcs CBrac CCVT CJun CMCN EPfP EWTr EWhm IPap LBuc LPar MMuc NWea SCob SEND SEWo WCFE WMou
	- 'Berliner's Weeper' witches' broom	NLar
	- 'Cinderella'	NLar
	- 'Elegance'	SAko
	- 'Frohnleiten'	CKen
	- 'Frondenberg'	CKen
	- 'Karel'	CKen LRHS SLim
	- 'Linda' **new**	NLar
	- 'Minimax'	CKen
	- 'Nana' Υ^{H7}	CAco LPar SLim WCFE
	- 'Pendula' Υ^{H7}	CAco LRHS MBlu SSta
	- 'Pendula Bruns'	CAco MBlu NLar SAko SLim
	- 'Pévé Tijn'	NLar SLim
	- 'Pimoko'	CKen NLar SLim
	- 'Pygmy'	CKen
	- 'Schneverdingen'	CKen SAko
	- 'Tijn'	CKen SLim
	- 'Treblitsch'	CKen NLar SAko SLim
	- 'Virgata' **new**	CAco
	orientalis Υ^{H7}	NWea WThu
	- 'Aurea' (v) Υ^{H7}	CAco
	- 'Aureospicata'	CAco LRHS MAsh MBlu SLim
	- 'Bergman's Gem'	CKen
	- 'Early Gold' (v)	SMad
	- 'Golden Start'	SLim
	- 'Gowdy Gold'	NLar
	- 'Horstmann' **new**	CAco
	- 'Juwel'	CKen NLar
	- 'Kenwith'	CKen
	- 'Little Kya' **new**	NLar
	- 'Mount Vernon'	CKen NLar
	- Nana Group	CAco GKin
	- 'Pévé Tiny Gold'	CKen NLar
	- 'Professor Langner'	CKen NLar
	- 'Shadow's Broom'	CKen CMen
§	- 'Silver Seedling'	NLar
	- 'Skylands' Υ^{H7}	CAco MAsh NLar SLim
	- 'Sulphur Flush'	see *P. orientalis* 'Silver Seedling'
	- 'Tom Thumb'	CKen
	- 'Wittboldt'	CKen LRHS NLar
	pungens	CAco CCVT EWhm LMaj
	- 'Anton'	NLar
	- 'Baby Blueeyes'	NLar
	- 'Blaukissen'	CKen NLar
	- 'Blue Diamond'	LPar LRHS SPoG
	- 'Blue Pearl'	CKen NLar
	- 'Blue Waters' **new**	CKen
	- 'Donna's Rainbow'	NLar
	- 'Edith' Υ^{H7}	CAco CKen LRHS NLar NOrn SCoo SGsty WMat
	- 'Erich Frahm'	CAco CCVT MAsh MTrO NLar SCoo SPoG WMat
	- 'Fat Albert' Υ^{H7}	CAco CCVT LPar LRHS MAsh NLar NWea SGsty SPoG
	- Glauca Group	CAco CBrac CCVT CMac EWTr IPap NWea SCoo SPoG WMou WTSh
	- - 'Barabits' Blue' **new**	CAco
	- - 'Bizon Blue' **new**	CAco
	- - 'Blue Totem' **new**	CAco
	- - 'Glauca Pendula'	CAco
	- - 'Glauca Procumbens'	CKen
§	- - 'Glauca Prostrata'	SLim
I	- - 'Globosa' Υ^{H7}	CBcs CCVT CKen CSBt EPfP LPar LRHS MAsh NHol NLar SCoo SGsty SLim SPoG SWeb
	- - 'Hoopsii' Υ^{H7}	CAco EPfP GKin LMaj MAsh MGos NLar NOrn NWea SCoo SPoG SWvt WMat
	- - 'Iseli Fastigiate'	CAco CCVT GKin LRHS MAsh SCoo SLim SPoG
	- - 'Khaibab' **new**	CAco
§	- - 'Koster'	EPfP NWea SPoG
	- - 'Misty Blue' **new**	CAco
	- - 'Oldenburg'	NWea SLim
	- - 'Thomsen'	CAco
	- - 'Virgata' **new**	CAco
	- 'Glauca Globosa'	see *P. pungens* (Glauca Group) 'Globosa'
	- 'Globe'	CKen CMen
	- 'Gloria'	CKen SLim
	- 'Hermann Naue'	CKen
	- 'Horizontalis Glauca' **new**	CAco
	- 'Iseli Foxtail'	CAco
	- 'Koster Fastigiata'	LPar
	- 'Maigold' (v)	CAco CKen NLar SLim
	- 'Montgomery'	CKen
	- 'Mrs Cesarini'	CKen
	- 'Niemitz'	NLar
	- 'Nimetz'	CKen
	- 'Novák' **new**	CAco
	- 'Ökrös' **new**	CAco
	- 'Omega'	CAco
	- 'Pali' **new**	CAco
	- 'Porcupine'	NLar
	- 'Prostrata'	see *P. pungens* 'Glauca Prostrata'
	- 'Saint Mary's Broom'	CKen
	- 'Silvanus Conica' **new**	CAco
	- 'The Blues'	CKen NLar
	- 'Thuem'	SCoo
	- 'Waldbrunn'	CAco CKen
	- 'Waterfall' **new**	CAco
	- 'Yvette'	NLar
	purpurea	EPfP
	retroflexa	CAco
	rubens	NWea
	× ***saaghii*** **new**	CAco
	schrenkiana	CAco CMCN
	sitchensis	IPap MAsh NWea WTSh
	- 'Foxtail' **new**	CAco
	- 'Foxy Lady' **new**	CAco
	- 'Nana'	NLar
	- 'Papoose'	CAco EPfP SLim
	- 'Pévé Wiesje'	NLar
	- 'Silberzwerg'	CAco CKen SAko SLim
	- 'Strypemonde'	CKen
	- 'Tenas'	CAco CKen SLim SPoG
	smithiana	CAco EPfP
I	- 'Aurea'	CAco

	- 'Sunray'	NLar SLim
	torano new	CAco
	wilsonii	CAco CKen
	'Wodan' new	NLar

Picrasma (*Simaroubaceae*)

	ailanthoides	see *P. quassioides*
§	***quassioides***	CMCN EBee EPfP WPGP

Picris (*Asteraceae*)

	echioides	see *Helminthotheca echioides*

Picrorhiza (*Plantaginaceae*)

	kurrooa	GPoy LEdu

Pieris (*Ericaceae*)

	'Balls of Fire'	CMac
	'Bert Chandler'	CBod CMac WSpi
	'Brouwer's Beauty'	LRHS NLar SPoG
	'Firecrest' 🏆H5	SCob
	'Flaming Silver' (v) 🏆H5	Widely available
	floribunda	CBrac
	'Forest Flame' 🏆H5	Widely available
	formosa	GKev
	- B&SWJ 2257	WCru
	- var. ***forrestii***	CDoC NWea SCob XSte
	- - 'Charles Michael'	CExl
	- - 'Jermyns'	CMac MRav
	- - 'Wakehurst' 🏆H5	CBod CCCN CExl CMac CTri EHyd ELon EPfP GKin LMil LRHS MAsh MGos MRav NWea SAko SCob SPer WSpi
	HAVILA ('Mouwsvila') (v)	CCCN CMac MAsh SCob
	japonica	CMac SavN
	- 'Bonfire' 🏆H5	CBod CBrac CCCN CRos EHyd ELan EPfP ILea LRHS MAsh MGos NRHS SCob SGbt SGsty SPer SPoG XSte
	- 'Carnaval' (v) 🏆H5	CCCN CDoC CMac CRos CSBt CTsd EHyd ELan ELon EPfP EShb LBuc LRHS LSRN MAsh MGos MPri NLar NRHS SCoo SPoG SWvt WFar
§	- 'Christmas Cheer'	CMac EPfP LSRN SCob SNig
	- 'Cupido'	MAsh SLim WFar WGwG
	- 'Debutante' 🏆H5	CDoC GKin MAsh MGos NLar SCob SCoo SGsty SWvt WFar
	- 'Don'	see *P. japonica* 'Pygmaea'
	- 'Dorothy Wyckoff'	CMCN NLar SCob SGbt SSta
	- 'Erik'	GKev SAko
	- 'Flaming Star'	SGbt SWvt
	- 'Flamingo'	CMac
	- 'Hino Crimson'	SWeb
I	- 'Katsura' PBR	CBcs CBod CDoC CMac CRos EHyd ELan EPfP GKin LBuc LMil LPar LRHS LSRN MAsh MBlu MGos NHol NLar NRHS SCoo SPer SPoG SWvt WFar
	- 'Little Heath' (v)	Widely available
	- 'Little Heath Green'	CBrac CCCN CMac ELon GKin LPar MAsh MGos SCob SPer SPoG SWvt WFar XSte
	- 'Minor'	GKev NWad WFar WThu
	- 'Mountain Fire' 🏆H5	Widely available
	- 'Passion' PBR	CBcs CBod CDoC CEnd CKel CRos CSBt EBee EGrI EHyd EPfP LCro LMil LOPS LRHS LSRN MAsh MMrt NLar NRHS SPer XSte
	- 'Pink Delight' 🏆H5	CDoC CRos LMil LRHS LSRN MAsh MGos MRav SCob SRms
	- 'Prelude' 🏆H5	CRos CSBt EHyd EPfP LMil LRHS MAsh WAbe
	- 'Purity' 🏆H5	CBcs CBod CCCN CMac MAsh MGos SArc SCob SWvt WFar
§	- 'Pygmaea'	EGrI NWad
	- 'Ralto' PBR	CRos EHyd LCro LMil LOPS LRHS MAsh MGos MRav NLar NRHS SCob SPoG XSte
	- RALTO ROSE ('Opstal10')	XSte
	- RED MILL ('Zebris')	CEnd SPer
	- 'Sarabande' 🏆H5	ILea MAsh SCob SPer XSte
	- 'Scarlett O'Hara'	CSBt
	- 'Snowdrift'	LRHS
	- Taiwanensis Group	CMac GKin NLar SRms WFar
	- 'Temple Bells'	CSBt
	- 'Valley Rose'	CSBt GKin MAsh NLar
	- 'Valley Valentine' 🏆H5	CBcs CDoC CMac CRos CSBt EGrI EHyd EPfP LCro LMil LOPS LRHS LSRN MAsh MGos NHpl NLar NRHS SCob SCoo SNig SPer SPoG SRkn SWvt WFar XSte
	- 'Variegata' misapplied	see *P. japonica* 'White Rim'
	- 'Variegata' ambig.	CBcs CBrac LMil SPer
	- 'Variegata' (Carrière) Bean (v)	CRos EHyd LRHS NRHS
	- 'Wada's Pink'	see *P. japonica* 'Christmas Cheer'
	- 'White Cascade'	SCob
	- 'White Pearl'	CMac SCob
§	- 'White Rim' (v)	CMac EPfP MAsh SCob SPlb
	- 'William Buchanan'	NWad WThu
	- var. ***yakushimensis***	NLar
	nana	WThu
	'Tilford'	CMac

Pilea (*Urticaceae*)

	sp. new	SBrt
	angulata subsp. ***petiolaris*** PB 96-1074 new	GGro
	cadierei 🏆H1c	EShb
	insolens new	GGro
	kiotensis PB 08-880 new	GGro
	libanensis	EShb
	matsudai 'Taiwan Silver' new	GGro
	peperomioides 🏆H1c	CCBP CDoC EShb LCro LOPS
	plataniflora 'Glossy' new	GGro
	- 'Pelling'	GGro MHid SBrt
	scripta PB 02-520 new	GGro

Pileostegia (*Hydrangeaceae*)

	viburnoides	Widely available
	- B&SWJ 3565	WCru
	- B&SWJ 3570 from Taiwan	WCru
	- B&SWJ 7132	WCru
	- from Taiwan	CDoC SMad WSHC XSte

Pilgerodendron (*Cupressaceae*)

	uviferum	CAco LRHS

Pilosella (*Asteraceae*)

§	***aurantiaca***	CBor CWCL EBou ELan EPfP GJos IRos LCro LEdu LOPS LPot LRHS MBow MHer MNHC NBid NBir SPhx SRms WCot WHer WSFF WShi
§	- subsp. ***carpathicola***	MMuc SEND
§	***officinarum***	NRya SPhx XSen
	rubra	CSpe

Pilularia (*Marsileaceae*)

	globulifera	CPud

Pimelea (*Thymelaeaceae*)

	coarctata	see *P. prostrata*

	drupacea	IDee
	ferruginea	SVen
	oreophila	GArf WThu
§	***prostrata***	EPot EWes GEdr GRum

Pimpinella (*Apiaceae*)

	anisum	SPhx SVic XAbr
	major	LEdu
	- 'Rosea'	Widely available
	saxifraga	CHab EBou SPhx WSFF
	siifolia	WHil
	tripartita	ECha SPhx
	- PAB 6112	LEdu

pineapple see *Ananas comosus*

pineapple guava see *Acca sellowiana*

Pinellia (*Araceae*)

	cordata	LEdu WCru XLum
	pedatisecta	GKev MRav
	peltata	GKev
	pinnatisecta	see *P. tripartita*
	ternata	EBee GEdr GKev NLar
§	***tripartita***	CExl GKev WCot

Pinguicula (*Lentibulariaceae*)

	grandiflora 🏆H4	EPot EWld GKev NRya WAbe

pinkcurrant see *Ribes rubrum* (P)

Pinus ✿ (*Pinaceae*)

	albicaulis 'Falling Rock' **new**	CAco
	- 'Flinck'	CKen
	- 'Lake Sabrina' **new**	CAco
	- 'Nana'	see *P. albicaulis* 'Noble's Dwarf'
	- 'No 3'	CKen
§	- 'Noble's Dwarf'	CAco CKen
	aristata ambig.	CAco SAko WHwl
	aristata Engelm.	CMCN CMen
	- 'Bashful'	CKen
	- 'Cecilia'	CKen
	- 'Kohout's Mini'	CKen
	- 'Lemon Frost' **new**	CAco
	- 'Sherwood Compact'	CKen MAsh NLar SLim
	- 'Silver Day' **new**	CAco
	- 'Silver Doll' **new**	CAco
	arizonica	CAco
	var. ***ornelasii*** **new**	CAco
	armandi	CAco CMCN EPfP MGil SPtp WHwl
	attenuata	CAco
	austriaca	see *P. nigra* subsp. *nigra*
	ayacahuite	CAco CKen
	- 'Maya' **new**	CAco
	balfouriana	CAco
	- dwarf	CKen
	banksiana	CAco LPar
	- 'Chippewa'	CKen
I	- 'Compacta'	CKen
	- 'Manomet'	CAco
	- 'Neponset'	CKen
	- 'Schneverdingen'	NLar
	- 'Schoodic'	NLar SLim
	'Bayo' **new**	CAco
	bhutanica	CAco WPGP
	- KR 10358	WPGP
	brutia	CAco
	- var. ***brutia***	CAco
	- var. ***eldarica***	CAco
	- var. ***pityusa***	CAco
	bungeana	CAco CTsd EPfP MBlu MGil SPtp
	- 'Diamant'	CKen
	- 'June's Broom'	CKen
	- white bark **new**	CAco
	canariensis	CAco
	cembra	CAgr EPfP LRHS MCoo WHwl
	- 'Aurea'	see *P. cembra* 'Aureovariegata'
§	- 'Aureovariegata' (v)	CAco
	- 'Barnhourie'	CKen
	- 'Blue Mound'	CKen
	- 'Compacta Glauca'	CAco
	- Glauca Group	CAco
	- 'Inverleith'	CKen
	- 'Jermyns'	CKen
	- 'King's Dwarf'	CKen
	- 'Ortler'	CKen
	- 'Stricta'	CAco CKen LRHS NLar
	- witches' broom	CKen
	cembroides	CAco
	- 'Fancy Nancy'	CKen
	- subsp. ***orizabensis*** **new**	CAco
	clausa	CAco
	contorta	CAco CBcs GJos IPap SPlb WHwl
	- 'Anna' **new**	CAco
	- 'Asher'	CAco CKen NLar
	- 'Chief Joseph' 🏆H6	CAco CKen MAsh NLar SLim
	- var. ***contorta***	CAco
	- 'Fordham's Dwarf Rug'	CKen
	- 'Frisian Gold'	CAco
	- var. ***latifolia***	CAco
	- var. ***murrayana***	CAco
	- 'Spaan's Dwarf'	CAco CKen NLar SLim
	- 'Taylor's Sunburst'	CAco CKen NLar
	coulteri	CAco EPfP WPGP
	densata	CAco
	densiflora	CAco EBtc WHwl
	- 'Alice Verkade' 🏆H7	CAco CMen LPar MAsh WFar
	- 'Aurea'	CAco
I	- 'Bedgebury Sport Broom'	CKen
	- 'Burke's Red Variegated' (v) **new**	CAco
	- 'Glitzer's Weeping' **new**	CAco
	- 'Golden Ghost'	CAco NLar
	- 'Haybud'	CAco MMrt
	- 'Jim Cross'	CKen
	- 'Kim'	NLar
	- 'Low Glow'	CAco CKen LRHS NLar SCoo SLim SPoG
	- 'Oculus-draconis' (v)	CAco SLim
	- 'Pendula'	CAco CKen MBlu MGil SLim
	- 'Rata'	CAco
	- 'Umbraculifera'	CAco CMen MAsh WHwl
	× ***densithunbergii***	CAco CMen LPar NLar SLim SPoG
	'Jane Kluis' 🏆H7	WLea
§	***devoniana***	CAco
	durangensis	CAco
	echinata	CAco
	edulis	CAco CMCN
	- 'Juno'	CKen
	elliottii	CAco
	- var. ***densa***	CKen
	engelmannii	CAco
	fenzeliana	CAco CKen
	flexilis	CAco
	- 'Blackfoot'	CAco
	- 'Cesarini Blue'	NLar
	- 'Cow Creek'	NLar
	- 'Damfino'	CAco
	- 'Extra Blue'	CAco
	- 'Firmament'	SLim WMat
	- 'Glenmore Dwarf'	CKen

- 'Lil Wolf'	NLar
- 'Nana'	CKen
- 'Navajo' new	CAco
I - 'Pygmaea'	CAco
- var. ***reflexa***	CAco
- 'Ririe'	CKen
- 'Tarryall'	CKen
- 'Tiny Temple'	CAco MGil
- 'Vanderwolf's Pyramid'	CAco CCVT LPar MGos MTrO NLar SLim WLea WMat
- WB No 1	CKen
- WB No 2	CKen
'Fulda' new	CAco
gerardiana	CAco
glabra	CAco
greggii	CAco EBtc
griffithii McClell.	see *P. wallichiana*
× ***hakkodensis*** new	CAco
halepensis	CAco SEND
§ ***heldreichii***	CAco EPfP LPar LRHS SLim WMat
- 'Atze Saule'	NLar
- 'Aureospicata'	NLar
- 'Barabits' Compact' new	CAco
- 'Beran Conical' new	CAco
- 'Compact Gem' ♀H6	CAco CKen LRHS NLar SEWo SLim
- 'Dolce Dorme'	CKen
- 'Emerald Arrow'	CAco NLar
- 'Green Bun' new	CAco
- 'Green Giant'	NLar WLea
- 'Green Pyramid'	NLar WLea
- 'Groen'	CKen
- 'Indigo Eyes' new	CAco
- 'Irish Bell'	CAco CKen NLar
- var. ***leucodermis***	see *P. heldreichii*
- 'Little Dracula'	LRHS NLar SCoo
- 'Malink'	CAco CKen
- 'Mint Truffle' new	CAco
- 'Pirin No 3'	CAco SAko
- 'Pygmy'	CKen
- 'Satellit' ♀H6	CAco CKen MAsh SLim
- 'Schmidtii'	see *P. heldreichii* 'Smidtii'
§ - 'Smidtii' ♀H6	CAco CKen CMen MAsh NLar NPoe SCoo SLim SPoG
- 'Zwerg Schneverdingen'	CKen SLim
× ***holfordiana***	CAco EPfP WPGP
jeffreyi	CAco CMCN EBtc
- 'Joppi'	CAco CKen SLim
- 'Misty Lemon'	CAco
kesiya	CAco
koraiensis	CAco
- 'Anna' new	NLar
- 'Baishan'	NLar
- 'Bergman'	CKen NLar
- 'Blue Ball'	CAco CKen NLar
- 'China Boy'	NLar
- 'Dongling'	NLar
- 'Dragon Eye'	CKen SLim
- 'Jack Corbit'	CAco CKen NLar WFar
- 'Shibamichi' (v)	CAco CKen
- 'Silver Lining'	CAco
- 'Silveray'	CAco CKen NLar
- 'Silvergrey'	CKen
- 'Spring Grove'	CKen NLar
- 'Tong Hua'	NLar
- 'Tsingtao'	NLar
- 'Winton'	CKen NLar
lambertiana	CAco
latteri	CAco
lawsonii	CAco
leiophylla	CAco
leucodermis	see *P. heldreichii*
longaeva	CAco
luchuensis new	CAco
magnifica	see *P. devoniana*
'Marie Bregéon' PBR	LRHS
massoniana	CAco
maximartinezii	CAco
maximinoi	CAco
monophylla	CAco
- 'Oregon' new	CAco
- 'Wrinkle'	NLar
montezumae ambig.	CAco
montezumae Lamb.	CAco SArc WPGP
- NJM 09.016	WPGP
- 'Forde Abbey' new	CAco
- glaucous-leaved, from Mexico new	CAco
- 'Grahame Oakey Pendula' new	CAco
- var. ***montezumae***	CAco
- 'Nymans' new	CAco
- 'Sheffield Park'	CAco SLim
monticola	CAco
- 'Ammerland' new	CAco
- 'Crawford'	NLar
- 'Ondulata'	CAco NLar
- 'Pendula'	CAco CKen
- 'Pygmy'	see *P. monticola* 'Raraflora'
§ - 'Raraflora'	CKen
- 'Strobicola'	CAco EPfP
- 'Windsor Dwarf'	CKen
mugo	CAco CBcs CTsd EPfP GDam MGos SCob SGsty SWeb WHwl
- 'Agnieszka' new	CAco
- 'Allgäu'	CKen NLar
- 'Alpen Hexe'	NLar
- 'Benjamin'	CKen LPar NLar WLea
- 'Big Tuna' new	CAco
- 'Bisley Green'	NLar
- 'Boži Dar' new	CAco
- 'Brownie'	CKen
- 'Carsten' ♀H7	CAco CKen EPfP LRHS MAsh NLar SCoo SJap SLim SPoG
- 'Columbo'	WHwl
- 'Corley's Mat'	CKen LRHS NLar SLim
- 'Cristata Contorta' new	CAco
- 'Dezember Gold'	SLim
- 'Elemér' new	CAco
- 'Filigran' new	CAco
- 'Fischleinboden' new	CAco
- 'Flanders Belle'	SLim
- 'Fructata' new	CAco
- 'Gnom'	CAco EPfP GKin LRHS MAsh MGos SCoo SJap SLim
- 'Gold Star'	NLar
- 'Golden Glow'	CAco LRHS NLar SLim SPoG
- 'Grüne Kugel'	NLar
- 'Hesse'	SCoo
- 'Hoersholm'	CKen
- 'Hulk'	CKen
- 'Humpy' ♀H7	CAco CKen CRos LPar LRHS MAsh SCoo SLim
- 'Ironsides'	CKen
- 'Jacobsen'	CAco CKen NLar SLim
- 'Jalubi' new	CKen
- 'Janovsky'	CKen
- 'Kissen' ♀H7	EPfP NHol SLim
- KLOSTERGRUN	see *P. mugo* 'Klosterkötter'
§ - 'Klosterkötter'	SCoo
- 'Kobold'	LPar
- 'Krauskopf'	CKen
- 'Laarheide'	CAco LRHS SPoG

	- 'Laurin'	CKen LPar
	- 'Lemon'	CAco NLar
	- 'Little Gold Star'	CKen
	- 'March'	CKen NLar
	- 'Mini Mini'	CKen
	- 'Mini Mops'	CKen SLim
	- 'Minikin'	CKen
	- 'Minima Kalous' **new**	CAco
	- 'Misty Lemon' **new**	CAco
	- 'Mitsch Mini'	CKen
	- 'Mops' ♀H7	CMen EPfP IPap LPar LRHS MAsh MBlu MGos SCob SCoo SGsty SJap SLim SPoG WHwl
	- 'Mops Gold'	NLar
	- 'Mops Midget'	CMen MAsh
§	- subsp. ***mugo***	CSBt SCob SGol
	- - 'Milky Way'	CAco CKen NLar
	- 'Mumpitz'	CKen LRHS
	- 'Northern Lights'	CKen
	- 'Ophir' ♀H7	CAco CBcs EPfP LRHS MAsh MGos SCoo SLim SPoG WLea
	- 'Pal Maleter' (v)	CAco SCoo SLim SPoG
	- 'Pici' **new**	CAco
	- 'Picobello'	CAco LRHS MAsh NHol NLar SLim
	- 'Piggelmee'	CKen
	- Pumilio Group	CAco ELan EPfP IPap LPar LRHS MGos MMuc NLar SCob SEND SJap SPad
	- - 'David Compressa'	SAko
	- - 'Emerald Dwarf'	NLar
	- 'Rigi'	NLar
	- 'Rock Garden'	NLar
	- var. ***rostrata***	see *P. mugo* subsp. *uncinata*
	- subsp. ***rotundata*** 'Ježek'	CKen MAsh NLar
	- 'Sandy'	NLar
	- 'Sherwood Compact'	LRHS NLar SLim WLea
	- 'Spaan'	CKen
	- 'Starkl' **new**	CAco
	- 'Sunshine' (v)	CAco NLar
	- 'Suzi'	CKen NLar
	- 'Tuffet'	CAco CKen NHol SLim
	- 'Uelzen'	CKen
§	- subsp. ***uncinata***	CAco IDee
	- - 'Etschtal'	CKen
	- - 'Grüne Welle'	CAco CKen NLar SLim
	- - 'Heideperle'	NLar
	- - 'Kostelnicek'	CAco CKen NLar
	- - 'Leuco-like'	CKen
	- - 'Litomysl'	NLar
	- - 'Offenpass'	CKen
	- - 'Paradekissen'	CAco CKen NLar
	- - 'Süsse Perle'	CKen
	- 'Varella'	CAco LPar LRHS NLar SCoo SLim
	- 'White Tip'	CKen
	- 'Winter Gold'	EPfP LPar LRHS MGos NHol
	- 'Winter Sun'	LRHS MAsh NLar
	- 'Winzig'	CKen
	- 'Yellow Marble' **new**	CAco
	- 'Yellow Tip' (v)	CAco NHol SLim
	- 'Zundert'	CKen SPoG
	- 'Zwergkugel'	CKen NLar SAko
	muricata	CAco
	× ***murraybanksiana*** **new**	CAco
	nigra	CAco CBcs CLnd CMac CTri EPfP MGos NOrn SArc
	- var. ***austriaca***	see *P. nigra* subsp. *nigra*
	- 'Bambino'	CKen
	- 'Black Prince' ♀H7	CAco CKen SLim WMat
	- 'Bobo'	CAco CKen
	- 'Brepo'	LRHS
	- var. ***calabrica***	see *P. nigra* subsp. *laricio*

	- 'Caperci's Golden Cream' **new**	CAco
	- var. ***caramanica***	see *P. nigra* subsp. *pallasiana*
	- var. ***cebennensis***	see *P. nigra* subsp. *salzmannii*
	- 'Cebennensis Nana'	CKen
	- 'Cobra' **new**	CAco
	- var. ***corsicana***	see *P. nigra* subsp. *laricio*
	- subsp. ***dalmatica***	CAco
*	- 'Fastigiata'	CAco
	- 'Frank'	CKen
	- 'Globosa'	CAco
	- 'Green Tower'	CAco LPar LRHS NLar SLim WHwl
	- 'Helga'	CAco LPar NLar
	- 'Hornibrookiana'	CAco CKen LPar
	- 'Hubert' **new**	CAco
	- 'Karaca Ball'	CAco
	- 'Keightley Broom'	SLim
	- 'Komet'	NLar SAko SLim
§	- subsp. ***laricio***	CAco CBod CCVT CMac MMuc SArc SCob SEND SLim
	- - 'Aurea'	CAco MBlu
	- - 'Bobby McGregor'	CKen
	- - 'Globosa Viridis'	LPar
	- - 'Goldfinger'	NLar
	- - 'Pygmaea'	CKen
	- - 'Wurstle'	CAco CKen LPar
	- subsp. ***maritima***	see *P. nigra* subsp. *laricio*
	- 'Molette'	CAco
	- 'Moran'	NLar
	- 'Moseri'	CAco CKen NLar
	- 'Nana'	LPar LRHS
§	- subsp. ***nigra***	CAco CBrac CCVT CLnd CMac EWTr IPap LMaj LPar LRHS MMuc SCob SEND SEWo SGsty WHwl
	- - 'Birte'	CKen
	- - 'Helga'	NLar
	- - 'Schovenhorst'	CKen
	- - 'Skyborn'	CKen
	- - 'Strypemonde'	CKen
	- - 'Yaffle Hill'	CKen
	- 'Obelisk'	CKen NLar
	- 'Ola'	CKen
	- 'Oregon Green'	CAco CKen NLar WHwl
§	- subsp. ***pallasiana***	CAco
	- 'Pierrick Bregéon' PBR	LPar LRHS
	- 'Pirin' **new**	CAco
	- 'Richard'	CAco CKen NLar SLim
	- 'Rondello'	CAco
§	- subsp. ***salzmannii***	CAco
	- 'Smaragd' **new**	CAco
	- 'Spielberg'	LPar LRHS NLar
	oocarpa	CAco
	palustris	CAco
	parviflora	CAco SPlb WHwl
	- 'Aaba-jo'	CKen
	- 'Adcock's Dwarf' ♀H7	CAco CKen SLim
	- 'Al Fordham'	CAco CKen
	- 'Ama-no-gawa' **new**	CAco
	- 'Aoi'	CAco CKen
	- 'Ara-kawa'	CKen CMen
	- 'Atco-goyo'	CKen
	- Azuma-goyo Group	CKen CMen
I	- 'Baasch's Form'	CAco CKen LRHS MGil
	- 'Beran'	SLim
	- 'Bergman'	CAco MAsh NLar SLim
	- 'Blue Angel'	CAco MBlu
	- 'Blue Giant'	CAco IArd MBlu WLea
	- 'Blue Lou'	CAco NLar
	- 'Bonnie Bergman' ♀H7	CAco CKen EPfP LRHS NHol NLar
	- 'Brevifolia'	CAco SEWo
	- 'Bunty'	CKen LRHS MGil

	– 'Catherine Elizabeth'	CKen NLar
	– 'Chikusa Goten'	CAco
	– 'Cuddles' **new**	CKen
	– 'Dai-ho'	CKen
	– 'Daisetsusan'	CKen
	– 'Daisy Sunset' **new**	NLar
	– 'Debbie'	NLar
	– 'Dougal'	CKen
	– 'Fatsumo'	CAco
	– 'Frick Estate' **new**	LRHS
	– 'Fukai' (v)	CAco CKen NHol SLim
	– 'Fukiju'	CKen
	– Fukushima-goyo Group	CKen CMen
	– 'Fuku-zu-mi'	CAco CKen
	– 'Fu-shiro'	CAco CKen
	– 'Gemstar'	CKen
	– 'Gin-sho-chuba'	CKen
	– Glauca Group	CAco LMaj LRHS MAsh MBlu
	– – 'Glauca' ♀^{H7}	CAco
I	– – 'Glauca Nana'	CKen
	– 'Goykuri'	CAco CKen
	– 'Green Monkey' **new**	CAco
	– 'Gyok-kan'	LRHS
	– 'Gyok-kasen'	CKen
	– 'Gyo-ko-haku'	CKen
	– 'Gyokusen Sämling'	CKen
	– 'Gyo-ku-sui'	CKen CMen
	– 'Hagaromo Seedling'	CAco CKen CMen
	– 'Hakko'	CKen
	– 'Hatchichi'	CKen
	– 'Ha-tzumari'	CAco MGil NLar SLim
	– 'Hobbit'	CKen
	– 'Ibo-can'	CKen CMen
	– 'Ichi-no-se'	CAco CKen
	– 'Iona'	CKen
	– 'Iri-fune'	CKen
	– Ishizuchi-goyo Group	CKen
	– 'Jim's Mini Curls'	CKen NLar
	– 'Ka-ho'	CKen
	– 'Kanrico'	CKen
	– 'Kanzan'	CKen
	– 'Kenwith'	NLar
	– 'Kin-po'	CKen NLar
	– 'Kiyomatsu'	CAco CKen
	– 'Kobe'	CAco CKen
	– 'Kokonoe'	CKen CMen
	– 'Kokuho'	CAco CKen
	– 'Kusu-dama'	CKen
	– 'Little Hedgehog'	CKen
	– 'Lorraine'	CKen
	– 'Mai-tsuzumi' **new**	CAco
	– 'Mano-jama' **new**	CAco
	– 'Masami'	CKen
	– 'Meiko'	CKen
	– 'Michinoku'	CKen
	– 'Momo-yama'	CKen NLar
	– 'Myo-jo'	CKen
	– Nasu-goyo Group	CKen
	– 'Negishi' ♀^{H7}	CAco CKen CMen LRHS MAsh MTrO NLar SLim WMat
	– 'Nellie D.'	CAco
	– 'Ōgon-goyo'	CKen
	– 'Ōgon-janome'	CAco CKen MAsh SLim
	– 'Ooh la la' **new**	CAco NLar
	– 'Ossorio Dwarf'	CKen
I	– var. ***pentaphylla*** 'Glauca'	NLar
	– 'Perido'	NLar
	– 'Primorge' **new**	CKen
	– 'Regenhold Broom'	CKen
	– 'Richard Lee'	CKen MAsh NLar
	– 'Ryo-ku-ho'	CKen
	– 'Ryu-ju'	CKen
	– 'Sa-dai-jin'	CKen
	– 'San-bo'	CKen
§	– 'Saphir'	CAco CKen NLar
	– 'Schoon's Bonsai'	CAco LRHS NHol NLar
	– 'Setsugekka'	CKen NLar SAko
	– 'Shika-shima'	CKen
	– Shikoku-goyo Group	CAco
	– 'Shimada'	CKen
	– Shiobara-goyo Group	CKen
	– 'Shiro-Janome' (v)	CKen
	– 'Shizukagoten'	CKen SLim
	– 'Shu-re'	CKen NLar
	– 'Sieryoden'	CKen
	– 'Smout'	CKen
	– 'Tani-mano-uki'	CAco CKen
	– 'Tayo-nishiki'	CAco
	– 'Tempelhof'	CAco LPar NLar NOrn
	– 'Tenysu-kazu'	CAco CKen EPfP LRHS SLim
	– 'Tokyo Dwarf'	CKen
	– 'Walker's Dwarf'	CKen
	– 'Watnong'	CKen
	– 'Zelkova'	CMen
	– 'Zui-sho'	CAco CKen
	patula ♀^{H4}	CAco CBcs CBod CCCN CMCN ECre EPfP IDee SArc SCoo SIvy SLim SMad SPlb SPoG WMat WPGP
	peuce	CAco EPfP MMuc SEND
	– 'Arnold Dwarf'	CAco CKen
	– 'Cesarini'	CKen NLar
	– 'Daniel'	CKen NLar
	– 'Harlekin'	NLar
	– 'Thessaloniki Broom'	CKen
	– 'Wageningen' **new**	CAco
	'Pichounet'	NLar
	pinaster	CAco CBcs CBod EPfP IPap MMuc SEND
	pinea ♀^{H4}	CAco CAgr CCVT CLnd EPfP IPap LPar MGil MGos MMuc SArc SCob SCoo SEND SEWo SGsty SPlb SWeb WPGP
	– 'Queensway'	CKen
	ponderosa	CAco EPfP IPap MMuc NLar
	– 'Penaz' **new**	CAco
	– var. ***ponderosa*** **new**	CAco
	– – SDL2	NLar
	pseudostrobus	CAco
	– var. ***apulcensis*** **new**	CAco
	pumila	CAco
	– 'Blue Mops'	NLar
	– 'Blue Note'	NLar
	– 'Buchanan'	CKen
	– 'Draijer's Dwarf'	NLar SLim
	– 'Dwarf Blue'	CAco NHol
	– 'Glauca' ♀^{H7}	CAco CKen MAsh
	– 'Globe'	CAco MAsh NLar SLim
	– 'Jeddeloh'	CAco CKen
	– 'Pinocchio'	CKen
	– 'Säntis'	CAco CKen MAsh NLar
	– 'Saphir'	see *P. parviflora* 'Saphir'
	pungens	CAco
	radiata	CAco CBcs CBod CBrac CCVT CCoa CDoC CMCN CMac CSBt CSde ELan EPfP IPap LMaj LRHS MMuc NOrn SArc SCoo SPtp WHwl WMat
	– Aurea Group	SCoo SLim SPoG WMat
	– – 'Aurea' ♀^{H5}	CAco CKen
	– 'Bodnant'	CKen
	– 'Marshwood' (v)	CKen SLim

	resinosa	CAco
	- 'Don Smith'	CAco CKen
	- 'Joel's Broom'	CKen
	- 'Nana'	CAco LPar
	- 'Pillnitz' **new**	CAco LRHS
	- 'Quinobequin'	CKen
	- 'State Trooper' **new**	CAco
	rigida	CAco
	roxburghii	EBtc
	sabineana	CAco CMCN
	× ***schwerinii***	CAco CKen
	- 'Wiethorst' ♀H7	CAco CKen LRHS NLar SLim WMat
	serotina **new**	CAco
	sibirica 'Blue Smoke'	CKen
	- 'Mariko'	CKen
	strobiformis	CAco
	- 'Coronado'	CKen
	- 'Fox Tail'	CAco
	- 'Loma Linda'	SLim
	strobus	CAco CBcs CCVT CMen EPfP IPap LPar MGos MMuc SCob SEND WHwl
§	- 'Alba'	SLim
	- 'Angel Falls'	CAco CKen NLar
	- 'Anna Fiele'	CAco CKen
	- 'Aurea'	CAco
	- 'Bergman's Mini'	CKen LRHS NLar SLim
	- 'Bergman's Pendula Broom'	CKen
I	- 'Bergman's Sport of Prostrata'	CKen
	- 'Beth'	CKen
	- 'Bloomer's Dark Globe'	CKen
	- 'Blue Shag' ♀H7	CAco ELan LPar LRHS NLar SCoo SLim
	- 'Bob's Wishes'	NLar
	- 'Brevifolia'	CKen SArc
	- 'Cedar Ridge Broom'	SLim
	- 'Cesarini'	CAco CKen
	- var. ***chiapensis*** **new**	CAco
	- 'Contorta'	CAco
	- 'Densa'	CKen LRHS
	- 'Densa Hill'	CAco SLim
	- 'Diggy'	NLar
	- 'Ed's Broom'	CKen
	- 'Elf'	NLar
	- 'Elkins Dwarf'	CKen NLar
	- 'Fastigiata'	CAco CKen MBlu WLea
	- 'Fastigiata Devine' **new**	NLar
	- 'Golden Candles'	NLar
	- 'Green Curls'	CKen
	- 'Green Twist'	CAco CKen NLar SLim
	- 'Greg'	CKen LRHS NLar
	- 'Ground Hugger'	CAco NLar
	- 'Hershey'	CKen
	- 'Hillside Gem'	CKen NLar
	- 'Horsford'	CKen SLim
	- 'Horsford Sister'	CKen
	- 'Jamaican Curls'	CKen
	- 'Joe's Best Blue'	NLar
	- 'Julian Pott'	CKen
	- 'Julian's Dwarf'	CKen
	- 'Krügers Lilliput'	CAco NLar SLim
	- 'Louie'	CAco CKen MAsh NLar SLim
	- 'Macopin'	CAco WFar
	- 'Mary Butler'	CKen NLar
	- 'Mary Sweeny'	NLar
	- 'Merrimack'	CAco CKen
	- 'Minima' ♀H7	CKen LSRN MBlu SLim SPoG
	- 'Minuta'	CKen LRHS SLim
	- 'Nana'	see *P. strobus* Nana Group
§	- Nana Group	SEWo
	- 'Niagara Falls'	CAco CKen NLar
	- 'Nivea'	see *P. strobus* 'Alba'
	- 'North Star Gold' **new**	NLar
	- 'Northway Broom'	CKen
	- 'Pacific Sunrise'	NLar
	- 'Paul Waxman'	NLar
	- 'Pendula'	CAco CKen ELan MBlu MGil
I	- 'Pendula Broom'	CKen
	- 'Pygmaea'	MGil
	- 'Radiata'	CAco NLar
	- 'Sayville'	CKen
	- 'Sea Urchin'	CAco CKen MAsh SLim
	- 'Secrest'	LRHS
	- 'Smokey Hollow'	NLar
	- 'Soft Touch'	SLim
	- 'Squiggles'	LRHS
	- 'Stowe Pillar'	CAco NLar SLim
	- 'Tiny Kurls'	CAco CKen LRHS MAsh MGos MTrO NLar SLim
	- 'Torulosa'	CAco MBlu
	- 'Uncatena'	CKen
	- 'Verkade's Broom'	CKen
	- 'White Mountain'	CAco MBlu MGil NLar
	sylvestris	Widely available
	- from the Casadéen Massif, Auvergne **new**	CAco
	- 'Abergeldie'	CKen
	- 'Andorra'	CKen
	- 'Anny's Wintersun'	NLar
	- Aurea Group	CKen LRHS MBlu SLim WMat
	- - 'Aurea' ♀H7	CAco MAsh
	- 'Avondene'	CKen
	- 'Beuvronensis' ♀H7	CAco CMen LPar MGil NLar SLim
	- 'Bialogon' **new**	CAco
	- 'Blue Sky'	NLar
	- 'Brentmoor Blonde' **new**	CAco
	- 'Buchanan's Gold'	CKen
	- 'Burghfield'	CMen
	- 'Candlelight'	CAco NLar
	- 'Chantry Blue'	CAco CCVT EPfP LPar LRHS MAsh MGos NLar SCoo SLim SPoG WMat
	- 'Clumber Blue'	CKen
	- 'Denny Boy'	NLar
	- 'Dereham'	CKen
	- 'Doone Valley'	CKen
	- 'Edwin Hillier'	SLim WMat WPGP
	- Fastigiata Group	CAco CEnd CKen CLnd CMen NLar SCoo SLim WHwl
	- 'Filip's Silver Surprise' **new**	CAco
	- 'Frensham' ♀H7	CAco CKen MAsh NLar
	- 'Globosa'	CAco
	- 'Gold Coin' ♀H7	CAco CKen EPfP SPoG
	- 'Gold Medal'	CAco CKen LRHS
	- 'Grand Rapids'	CKen
	- 'Green Penguin'	NLar
	- 'Greg's Variegated' (v) **new**	CAco
	- 'Gwydyr Castle'	CKen
	- var. ***hamata*** **new**	CAco
	- 'Hillside Creeper'	CAco CKen SLim
	- 'Humble Pie'	CKen
	- 'Irchester Park' **new**	CKen
	- 'Isaszeg'	CAco
	- 'Jeremy'	CKen
	- 'John Boy'	CKen CMen
	- 'Kelpie'	CAco SLim
	- 'Kenwith'	CKen
	- 'Lodge Hill'	CMen MAsh SLim
	- 'Longmoor'	CKen
	- 'Martham'	CKen
	- 'Meffen Gold'	CAco NLar

	- 'Mitsch Weeping'	CKen
	- var. ***mongolica***	CAco
	- 'Mosaic' new	CAco
	- 'Nana' misapplied	see *P. sylvestris* 'Watereri'
	- Nana Group	CAco SWeb WLea
	- - 'Nana Compacta'	CMen
§	- 'Nisbet's Gem'	CKen
	- 'Ødegård' new	CAco
	- 'Padworth'	CMen
	- 'Piskowitz'	CKen
	- 'Pixie'	CKen MAsh
I	- 'Prostrata'	SLim
	- 'Pulham'	CKen
	- 'Repens'	CAco CKen
	- 'Rita' new	CAco
	- 'Saint George'	CKen
	- 'Sandringham'	NLar
	- 'Saxatilis'	CAco CKen CMen NLar
	- subsp. ***scotica***	CAco
	- 'Scott's Dwarf'	see *P. sylvestris* 'Nisbet's Gem'
	- 'Sé' new	CAco
	- 'Sentinel'	CKen
	- 'Skjak I'	CKen
	- 'Skjak II'	CKen SLim
	- 'Spaan's Slow Column'	CKen SLim
	- 'Tabuliformis'	CAco
	- 'Tage'	CKen
	- 'Tanya'	CKen
	- 'Tilhead'	CKen
	- 'Treasure'	CKen MAsh
	- 'Trefrew Quarry'	CKen
	- 'Trollguld'	CAco CKen NLar
§	- 'Watereri'	CAco CCVT LMaj LPar NLar SCoo SLim WHwl
	- 'Westonbirt'	CKen CMen MAsh
	- 'Wintergold'	CAco
	- 'Wittichenau'	CKen
	- 'Xavery'	NLar
	tabuliformis	CAco SLim
	- 'Jiuzhaigou Valley' new	CAco
	- var. ***mukdensis*** new	CAco
	- 'Shenyang' new	NLar
	taeda	CAco
	taiwanensis	CAco EPfP NLar
	- var. ***taiwanensis*** new	CAco
	tecunumanii	CAco SLim
	teocote	CAco
	thunbergii	CAco CBod CMen ELan MMuc SEND
	- 'Akame'	CKen CMen
	- 'Akame Yatsabusa'	CMen
	- 'Aocha-matsu' (v)	CKen CMen
	- 'Arakawa-sho'	CKen CMen
	- 'Banshosho'	CAco CKen CMen NLar SLim
	- 'Beni-kujaku'	CKen CMen
	- 'Compacta'	CKen CMen
	- var. ***corticosa*** 'Fuji'	CMen
	- - 'Iihara'	CMen
	- 'Dainagon'	CKen CMen
	- 'Hayabusa'	CMen
	- 'Iwai'	CMen
	- 'Janome' (v)	CMen
	- 'Katsuga'	CMen
	- 'Kotobuki'	CAco CKen CMen NLar
	- 'Koyosho'	CMen
	- 'Kyokko'	CKen CMen
	- 'Kyushu'	CKen CMen
	- 'Maijima'	CAco
	- 'Mikawa'	CMen MBlu
	- 'Miyajuna'	CKen CMen
	- 'Nishiki-ne'	CKen CMen
	- 'Nishiki-tsusaka'	CMen
	- 'Ogi-matsu'	CKen
	- 'Ōgon'	CAco CMen NLar SLim
	- 'Porky'	CKen CMen
§	- 'Sayonara' ♀H7	CMen MAsh SLim
	- 'Senryu'	CKen CMen
	- 'Shinsho'	CKen CMen
	- 'Shio-guro'	CKen CMen
	- 'Suchiro'	CAco
	- 'Suchiro Yatabusa'	CKen CMen
	- 'Sunsho'	CKen CMen
	- 'Taihei'	CMen
I	- 'Thunderhead' ♀H7	CAco CKen CMen NLar SLim
	- 'Torafu' new	CAco
	- witches' broom	CKen
	- 'Yatsubusa'	see *P. thunbergii* 'Sayonara'
	- 'Ye-i-kan'	CKen
	- 'Yoshimura'	CMen
	- 'Yumaki'	CAco CKen
	torreyana	CAco CBcs
	uncinata	see *P. mugo* subsp. *uncinata*
	virginiana 'Wate's Golden'	CKen
§	***wallichiana*** ♀H6	CAco CBcs CCVT CLnd CMCN EPfP IDee IPap LMaj LRHS MAsh MBlu MGil MGos MHid MMuc NHol NLar NOrn SCob SEND SEWo SGol SGsty SLim SMad WHwl WMat WPGP
	- 'Densa Hill'	CAco LRHS
	- 'Frosty'	CAco CKen
	- 'Glauca' new	CAco
	- 'Kenwith Cascade'	CKen
	- 'Nana' ♀H6	CAco CKen LRHS MBlu MGil NLar SCoo SLim
	- 'Winter Light'	CAco NLar
	- 'Zebrina' (v)	CAco LRHS MBlu NHol NLar
	yunnanensis	CAco
	- var. ***yunnanensis***	SLim

Piper (*Piperaceae*)

	auritum	GPoy LEdu
	betle	GPoy
	excelsum	see *Macropiper excelsum*
	heydei B&SWJ 10445	WCru

Piptanthus (*Fabaceae*)

	forrestii	see *P. nepalensis*
	laburnifolius	see *P. nepalensis*
§	***nepalensis***	CBcs CSpe EBee EHed EHyd EPfP GKev IDee LRHS MGil MGos MMrt NBid NLar SBrt SPer SRms SSal WAvo
	aff. ***nepalensis***	SWvt

Pistacia (*Anacardiaceae*)

	chinensis	CBcs CMCN EBee EPfP IDee XSen
	lentiscus	CBcs CCCN CKel SEND SVen XSen
	terebinthus	XSen
	- NJM 11.004	WPGP
	vera	EBee

Pistia (*Araceae*)

	stratiotes	LCro LLWG LOPS NPer SCoo SVic

Pitavia (*Rutaceae*)

	punctata	IArd

Pitcairnia (*Bromeliaceae*)

	heterophylla	WCot
	pungens	WCot
	punicea	WCot
	ringens	WCot

Pittosporum (*Pittosporaceae*)

adaphniphylloides	CBcs
anomalum	CCCN CTrC CTsd GBin SEle SIvy
'Arundel Green' (f) ♀H4	CBrac CDoC CRos EHyd ELon EPfP LRHS MAsh NRHS SCob SLim SPer SWvt
bicolor	CTsd WPGP
'Bicton Silver' (m/v)	CCCN
buchananii	SVen
'Collaig Silver'	EHyd EPfP LRHS MAsh MHed NRHS SLim SWvt
crassifolium	CBcs CCCN CCoa CSde CTsd IDee SPlb
- 'Variegatum' (v)	CBcs CCCN CKel MGil WAvo
'Crinkles' (f)	SPer SVen
dallii	CCCN SPlb
daphniphylloides	EBee ELan WPGP
- B&SWJ 6789	WCru
- CWJ 12404	WCru
- RWJ 9913	WCru
eugenioides	CCht CMCN CSde ELon SEND
- 'Platinum' (v)	CCCN
- 'Variegatum' (v) ♀H3	CBcs CCCN CCoa CDoC CKel CMac CSde EBee EHyd ELan EPfP LRHS MGos NLar NRHS SAko SNig SVen WAvo
'Garnettii' (v) ♀H3	Widely available
glabratum	EBee WPGP
- var. ***neriifolium*** B&SWJ 11685	WCru
heterophyllum	CKel EHed EPfP EWes LRHS MMrt SEND SMad
- variegated (v)	CCCN CKel EBee EHyd EPfP LRHS
illicioides	WPGP
var. ***angustifolium***	
- - B&SWJ 14560	WCru
- - RWJ 9846	WCru
- var. ***illicioides*** B&SWJ 6712	WCru
- - PAB 9004	LEdu WPGP
× ***intermedium***	SWvt
- 'Craxten' (f)	CCCN
'Nanum Variegatum'	see *P. tobira* 'Variegatum'
napaulense	WCru
oblongilimbum DJHV 06137	WCru
omeiense	EWes
- VdL 80626	WPGP
parvilimbum	WPGP
patulum	WPGP
phillyreoides	CTsd
ralphii	CCCN CTsd
- 'Green Globe'	CBod
- 'Variegatum' (v)	CCCN WPGP
'Saundersii' (v)	SCoo
tenuifolium	Widely available
- 'Abbotsbury Gold' (f/v)	Widely available
- 'Atropurpureum'	CBcs ELan
- 'Brockhill Compact'	CCCN LRHS SAko SWvt
- 'County Park'	CBrac CCCN SRms
- 'County Park Dwarf'	MAsh
- 'County Park Green'	ELon
- 'Cratus'	SArc
- 'Elizabeth' (m/v)	Widely available
- EMERALD DOME ('Minpitto'PBR)	EWTr SGsty
- 'French Lace'	CBcs CCCN CCoa CDoC CSde ELan NLar SCob WFar WHwl
- 'Gold Star'	CBcs CBrac CCoa CKel CRos CSde EHyd ELan EPfP LPar LRHS MAsh MGil MGos NRHS SCob SCoo SEle SGBe SGbt SLim SPer SPoG SRms SWvt SavN WFar WHwl WLov
- 'Golden Ball'	LRHS SGsty SNig
- 'Golden King'	CBrac CCCN CKel CMac CSBt EPfP LRHS MAsh MGos NRHS SLim SRms
- 'Golf Ball'PBR	CBcs CBod CBrac CDoC CEme CKel CRos EHyd ELan EPfP LCro LOPS LPar LRHS LSRN MGil MGos NRHS SArc SCob SEWo SGbt SGsty SPer SPoG SWvt WFar XSte
- 'Green Elf'	XSte
- 'Green Thumb'	CCCN CMac EBee EPfP
- 'Irene Paterson' (m/v) ♀H4	Widely available
- 'James Stirling'	CCCN
- 'John Flanagan'	see *P. tenuifolium* 'Margaret Turnbull'
- 'Limelight' (v)	CBcs CBod CBrac CCCN CKel CSBt EBee EPfP LRHS LSRN SPoG
- 'Loxhill Gold'	CCCN CCoa EHyd EPfP SGol SGsty
§ - 'Margaret Turnbull' (v)	CTrC EWes MGos SGsty
- 'Marjory Channon' (v)	CKel EHyd LRHS NRHS
- 'Moonlight' (v)	CBod MRav
- 'Mountain Green'	CMac
- 'Nutty's Leprechaun'	CBod CCCN CTrC
- 'Oliver Twist'	CTrC EHyd EPfP LRHS LSRN MAsh NRHS SCoo SSta
- 'Pompom'	CCCN EHyd LRHS LSRN NRHS
- 'Purpureum' (m)	CBrac CCCN CDoC CMac CSBt CTri EHyd ELon EPfP GBin LRHS LSRN MAsh MGil NRHS SAko SCob SEND SPer SPoG SRms WAvo WCot WFar
- 'Silver Ball' (v)	CBcs CBod CDoC LRHS LSRN SGsty SNig SPer XSte
- 'Silver Magic' (v)	CBcs CBod EPfP SEle SRkn
- 'Silver Queen' (f/v) ♀H4	Widely available
- 'Silver Sheen' (m)	CBcs CBod CMac EBee EHyd LRHS NRHS SCob SWvt
- 'Stevens Island'	CBod CCoa CDoC CTrC LRHS
- 'Tandara Gold' (v)	CBcs CBod CCCN CCoa CDoC CKel CMac CSBt CTrC EHyd ELan ELon EPfP LRHS MAsh MGil MGos NRHS SCoo SGBe SRms WAvo WHwl
- 'Tiki' (m)	CCCN
- 'Tom Thumb' ♀H4	Widely available
- 'Tresederi' (f/m)	CCCN
- 'Variegatum' (m/v)	CBcs CBod CKel CSBt EBee EHyd ELon EPfP EWTr LCro LOPS LPar LRHS LSRN MGos MHed MSwo NRHS SArc SCob SEND SGbt SGsty SLim SWeb SWvt WFar
- 'Victoria' (v)	CBcs CBod CCCN EBee LSRN SPer WFar XSte
- 'Warnham Gold' (m) ♀H4	CBcs CBod CBrac CCCN CDoC CKel CMac CRos EBee EHyd ELan EPfP LRHS MAsh MGos NLar NRHS SCob SLim SNig SPoG SRms SVen WHwl
- 'Wendle Channon' (m/v)	CCCN CMac CSBt EPfP LRHS MAsh WHwl
- 'Wrinkled Blue'	CBcs CBod CBrac CDoC CRos EBee EHyd EPfP LRHS MAsh MRav MSwo NRHS SPoG SWvt XSte
tobira ♀H3	Widely available
* - 'Nanum'	CBcs CCCN CCoa CMac CSde EGrl EHyd ELan EPfP ETod LCro LOPS LPar LRHS LSRN MGos SCob SGsty SPer SPoG SWeb WHwl XSen

- 'Tall 'n' Tough'	SMad
§ - 'Variegatum' (v) 🏆H3	CBcs CCCN CCoa CKel CMac CSde EHyd ELan EPfP LRHS LSRN MGos SArc SCob SEND SLon SPer SPoG
- 'West Acre Gold'	CBod LRHS
'Trim's Hedger'	CBod ELan
truncatum	CCCN CExl
undulatum	WAvo WHwl WLov
viridiflorum	EShb

Plagianthus (*Malvaceae*)

betulinus	see *P. regius*
lyallii	see *Hoberia lyallii*
§ ***regius***	CBcs

Plagiorhegma see *Jeffersonia*

Planera (*Ulmaceae*)

aquatica	IDee

Plantago (*Plantaginaceae*)

coronopus	CAgr GGro
holosteum	GKev
lanceolata	CAgr CHab SPhx SVic WSFF
major	GPoy SPhx WSFF
- 'Atropurpurea'	see *P. major* 'Rubrifolia'
- 'Bowles's Variety'	see *P. major* 'Rosularis'
- 'Frills'	GGro NPoe
- 'Purple Perversion'	CSpe GGro
- 'Rosenstolz'	CTtf NChi
§ - 'Rosularis'	CSpe CTtf GGro LEdu NBro NPoe SRms WHer
§ - 'Rubrifolia'	CBod CSpe EShb GGro NBid NPoe SHar SRms XLum
- 'Tony Lewis'	CNat
- 'Variegata' (v)	GGro
media	CHab MHer NMir
nivalis	EDAr GEdr
rosea	see *P. major* 'Rosularis'
subulata	EDAr

Platanthera (*Orchidaceae*)

bifolia	NLAp
chlorantha	NLAp

Platanus ✿ (*Platanaceae*)

× ***acerifolia***	see *P.* × *hispanica*
§ × ***hispanica*** 🏆H6	CAco CCVT CDoC CLnd CMCN ELan EPfP IPap LMaj LPar MGos MMuc NRog NWea SArc SCob SEND SEWo SGol SPer WMat WMou WTSh
- 'Alphen's Globe'	LPar
- 'Malburg' **new**	LMaj
- 'Pyramidalis'	IPap LMaj
orientalis	CAco CCVT CMCN EBee EPfP ESwi IPap WPGP
- PAB 346	LEdu
§ - f. ***digitata*** 🏆H6	CCVT CLnd CMCN EPfP WMou
- var. ***insularis***	WPGP
- 'Laciniata'	see *P. orientalis* f. *digitata*
- 'Mirkovec'	EPfP IArd

Platycarya (*Juglandaceae*)

strobilacea	SPtp

Platycerium (*Polypodiaceae*)

alcicorne misapplied	see *P. bifurcatum*
§ ***bifurcatum*** 🏆H1b	CCCN CDoC NCft SPlb
§ ***superbum*** 🏆H1a	CCCN EShb NCft

Platycladus (*Cupressaceae*)

§ ***orientalis***	CAco LEdu MAsh
§ - 'Aurea Nana' 🏆H7	CBod CBrac CMac CSBt EPfP LBee LPar LRHS MAsh MGos SCoo SGol SGsty SLim SPoG
- 'Autumn Glow'	CKen
- 'Conspicua'	CKen CSBt
- 'Franky Boy' 🏆H7	SPoG
- 'Golden Pygmy'	CKen
- 'Kenwith'	CKen
- 'Little Susie'	LRHS
- 'Meldensis'	CTri
- 'Miller's Gold'	see *P. orientalis* 'Aurea Nana'
- 'Minima Glauca'	CKen
I - 'Pyramidalis Aurea'	LBee SCoo
- 'Rosedalis'	CSBt EPfP LBee MAsh SCoo SLim
- 'Sanderi'	WCFE
- 'Shirley Chilcott'	MAsh
- 'Southport'	LBee LRHS
- 'Summer Cream'	CKen

Platycodon (*Campanulaceae*)

grandiflorus 🏆H5	CTri ECha EPfP GKev MHer SRms XAbr
- W/O 7195 **new**	GGro
- 'Albus'	EPfP GKev SPer SWvt
- Apoyama Group 🏆H5	WThu
- - 'Fairy Snow'	EBou
- (Astra Series) 'Astra Blue'	CRos EHyd EPfP LRHS NRHS SPoG
- - 'Astra Pink'	CRos LRHS SPoG
- - 'Astra White'	CRos SPoG
- 'Fuji Blue'	SBls SPeP WHoo XLum
- 'Fuji Pink'	MRav SPeP SPer SWvt WHoo XLum
- 'Hakone'	MRav
- 'Hakone Blue'	CPla EPfP
- 'Hakone Double Blue' (d)	SRms
- 'Hakone White'	EPfP GGro LSun MRav
- 'Mariesii' 🏆H5	CSBt EBee EPfP MRav NBir SPer SPlb SRms SWvt WHoo WSHC
§ - 'Perlmutterschale'	MRav
- pink-flowered	GKev
- 'Sentimental Blue'	XLum
- 'Willy'	XLum
- 'Zwerg'	CSpe

Platycrater (*Hydrangeaceae*)

arguta	EBee SHor WCru WPGP
- B&SWJ 6266	WCru

Plecostachys (*Asteraceae*)

§ ***serpyllifolia***	LSou

Plectranthus ✿ (*Lamiaceae*)

from Angola No 5 **new**	SSal
ambiguus 'Manguzuku' 🏆H1c	SSal
- 'Nico'	CBct SDix
amboinicus	CCBP MNHC
argentatus 🏆H1c	CBct CDTJ CSpe IDee MCot SEND SRkn WKif
- 'Hill House' (v)	EShb MPie SSal
- 'Silver Shield'	EShb MCot MPie SSal
australis misapplied	see *P. verticillatus*
behrii	see *P. fruticosus*
BLUE ANGEL ('Edelblau') (Cape Angels Series)	SSal
bojeri **new**	SSal
'Brusendorf' **new**	SSal
caninus	CRos SPoG
'Cara's Blush' **new**	SSal

chiridensis **new**	SSal
ciliatus	CPbh EShb SRkn
- 'Easy Gold' (v) 𝕐H1c	MPie WDib
- 'Nico' **new**	SSal
- 'Richard'	SSal
- 'Sasha' (v)	CCCN ECtt EShb MPie SSal
'Cloud Nine'	SSal
coleoides 'Marginatus'	see *P. forsteri* 'Marginatus'
- 'Variegatus'	see *P. madagascariensis* 'Variegated Mintleaf'
Cuban oregano	ENfk SSal
aff. ***cyaneus*** **new**	SSal
ecklonii	SSal
- 'Erma' **new**	SSal
- 'Medley Wood'	SSal
ernstii	SSal WCot
- blue-flowered	WCot
forskohlii	SSal
§ ***forsteri*** 'Marginatus'	SSal
'Franklin's Limelight' **new**	SSal
'Franklin's Olive' **new**	SSal
'Frills'	SSal
§ ***fruticosus***	CPbh SSal
- 'Behr's Pride'	SSal
- 'James' 𝕐H2	SSal WKif
grandidentatus	SSal
variegated (v) **new**	
hadiensis var. ***tomentosus*** 'Carnegie'	SSal
madagascariensis	EShb WKif
- 'Lothlorien' (v)	SSal
- 'Lynne' (v) **new**	WDib
§ - 'Variegated Mintleaf' (v) 𝕐H1c	MNHC SRms
aff. ***madagascariensis*** variegated (v) **new**	SSal
'Marble Ruffles'	SSal
MONA LAVENDER ('Plepalila'PBR) 𝕐H1b	CCht CPla MHol SSal WKif WWFP
mutabilis	SSal
neochilus	CCBP CSpe SSal
'Nicoletta' **new**	SSal
§ ***oertendahlii*** 𝕐H1c	CPbh EBak SSal WDib
ornatus	SSal
- variegated (v)	SSal
parviflorus BLUE SPIRES ('Limplep1') (v)	SSal
purpuratus 𝕐H1c	SSal
- subsp. ***purpuratus*** **new**	SSal
saccatus	SSal WKif
subsp. ***pondoensis***	
sinensis	EHyd
spicatus	SSal
Swedish ivy	see *P. oertendahlii*, *P. verticillatus*
§ ***thyrsoideus***	SSal
venteri	SSal
§ ***verticillatus***	EPri EShb SSal
- 'Barberton'	SSal
- 'Pink Surprise'	SSal
zuluensis	CPbh CWCL EPri SDix SRkn SSal WBor
- 'Sky'	SSal

Pleioblastus (*Poaceae*)

§ ***argenteostriatus***	CBod GMaP MWht NLar NWad
f. ***pumilus***	SCob SPlb
auricomus	see *P. viridistriatus*
- 'Vagans'	see *Sasaella ramosa*
chino f. ***elegantissimus***	CBcs EPfP EShb MMuc SEND
- var. ***hisauchii***	MWht
- 'Kimmei'	SEND
'Gauntlettii'	see *P. argenteostriatus* f. *pumilus*
glaber 'Albostriatus'	see *Sasaella masamuneana* 'Albostriata'
humilis var. ***pumilus***	see *P. argenteostriatus* f. *pumilus*
kongosanensis 'Aureostriatus' (v)	MWht
linearis	EShb MWht
§ ***pygmaeus***	CTri ELan GMaP MBrN SCob SGol SPer SRms
§ - 'Mirrezuzume'	CExl
* - var. ***pygmaeus*** 'Mini'	MMuc WCot
§ ***simonii***	CAgr CRos EHyd LRHS MMuc MWht NRHS SEND SPoG
- 'Variegatus' (v)	CBcs CRos EHyd LRHS NRHS SPer SPoG
§ ***variegatus*** (v) 𝕐H5	CBcs CBod ELan EPfP GMaP MBrN MWht SCob SDix SPlb SWvt WFar
§ - 'Fortunei' (v)	MMuc SEND SGol
- 'Tsuboii' (v)	CAbb CDTJ MBrN SGol
§ ***viridistriatus*** 𝕐H5	CBod CExl CKel ECha ELon EPfP GMaP LRHS MMuc MRav MWht NWsh SCob SDix SEND SGol SPer SRms WFar WSMil
- f. ***variegatus*** (v)	SWvt

Pleione (*Orchidaceae*)

Alishan gx 'Mother's Day'	GEdr
Asama gx 'Red Grouse'	GEdr
Askia gx	GEdr
aurita	GEdr GKev SDir
Berapi gx 'Purple Sandpiper'	LEdu WPGP
Brigadoon gx 'Stonechat'	LEdu WPGP
Britannia gx 'Doreen'	GEdr LEdu WPGP
§ ***bulbocodioides***	CExl GEdr GKev
- 'New Forest'	GEdr
§ - 'Yunnan'	GEdr
Burnsall gx	GEdr
chunii	GEdr
Eiger gx	GEdr
Erebus gx 'Redpoll'	GEdr
formosana 𝕐H3	EPot GKev LCro LEdu LOPS MHer NHpl SDeJ SDir WFar WPGP
- Alba Group	GKev WFar
- - 'Claire'	WPGP
- - 'Snow Bunting'	LEdu WPGP
- 'Blush of Dawn'	NHpl
- 'Snow White'	CExl LEdu WPGP
forrestii	EPot GKev NHpl SDir
Gerry Mundey gx	GEdr
§ ***grandiflora***	GKev
Hekla gx 'Locking Stumps'	GEdr
- 'Partridge'	GEdr
- 'Partridge' × **Zeus Weinstein gx**	GEdr
hookeriana	GKev
humilis orange-red-flowered	GKev
Irazu gx 'Cheryl'	GEdr
Jorullo gx 'Long-tailed Tit'	GEdr
limprichtii 𝕐H2	GKev LEdu
maculata	GKev
Myojin gx	GEdr
Orinoco gx 'Gemini'	GEdr
Orizaba gx	GEdr
pinkepankii	see *P. grandiflora*
Piton gx	EPot
pogonioides (Rolfe) Rolfe	see *P. bulbocodioides*
praecox	GKev
Rakata gx 'Blackbird'	MHer
- 'Locking Stumps'	GEdr
- 'Shot Silk'	GEdr
- 'Skylark'	LEdu WPGP

'Rossini'	GEdr GKev SDir
Shantung gx	NHpl
- 'Muriel Harberd' ♀H2	GEdr
Sorea gx	GEdr
Soufrière gx	GEdr
Stromboli gx 'Fireball'	CExl EPot LEdu WPGP
- 'Robin'	GEdr
Tolima gx 'Moorhen'	LEdu WPGP
Tongariro gx	EPot GEdr GKev LCro LEdu LOPS LRHS MHer MNrw WPGP
'Verdi'	GEdr GKev
Versailles gx	NHpl
- 'Bucklebury'	GEdr LEdu WPGP
- 'Muriel Turner'	GEdr
Vesuvius gx	GEdr
- 'Tawny Owl'	GEdr
Volcanello gx 'Honey Buzzard'	GEdr
yunnanensis ambig.	GEdr SDir

Pleomele see *Dracaena*

Pleurospermum (*Apiaceae*)

SDR 7941	GKev
SDR 7985	GKev
benthamii B&SWJ 2988	WCru
brunonis	GKev
camtschaticum B&SWJ 12627	WCru

plum see *Prunus domestica*

Plumbago (*Plumbaginaceae*)

§ ***auriculata*** ♀H2	CBcs CCCN CSBt CSpe CTri CWCL EBak ELan EPfP EPri EShb LRHS MGil MRav SEND SPer SPoG SRms WAvo WFib
- f. ***alba*** ♀H2	CBcs CCCN CRHN ELan EPfP EShb IDee SEND WFib
- 'Crystal Waters'	CCCN EShb
- dark blue-flowered	CRHN WFib
- (Escapade Series) 'Escapade Blue'	CWGN EShb SPre
- - 'Escapade White'	EShb
capensis	see *P. auriculata*
larpentiae	see *Ceratostigma plumbaginoides*

Plumeria (*Apocynaceae*)

'Divine' **new**	CCCN
rubra ♀H1b	CCCN WSFF
'Thumbelina' **new**	CCCN

Poa (*Poaceae*)

alpina	XLum
chaixii	EPPr
cita	SBls SPlb
glauca 'Blue Hills'	CBod LPla
labillardierei	CKno CWCL EBee ECha EHyd ELan ELon EPPr EPfP EShb LRHS MBel SEND XLum
pratensis	CHab SPhx SVic

Podalyria (*Fabaceae*)

calyptrata	SPlb
sericea	SPlb

Podanthus (*Asteraceae*)

ovatifolius	SVen

Podocarpus ✿ (*Podocarpaceae*)

andinus	see *Prumnopitys andina*
'Autumn Shades' (m)	NLar
'Blaze' (f)	LEdu
chilinus	see *P. salignus*
'Chocolate Box' (f)	ELan LRHS MAsh NLar SLim
'County Park Fire' PBR (f) ♀H6	CBcs EPfP LRHS MAsh MGos NHol NLar SCoo SLim SRms SWvt WFar
cunninghamii	see *P. laetus*
dacrydioides	see *Dacrycarpus dacrydioides*
elongatus	CTrC
- 'Blue Chip'	CBcs
'Flame' (m)	GKev NFav NLar SLim
'Guardsman'	LRHS SLim
hallii	see *P. laetus*
henkelii	CBcs CTrC
§ ***laetus*** 'Roro' (m)	CBcs
lawrencei	CBcs
- 'Blue Gem' (f)	CBod CJun GKev LRHS MAsh MMuc NFav SCoo SLim WAbe WFar
- 'Red Tip'	CBod GKev SCoo SPad
macrophyllus	CAco SArc WPGP
- (m)	CMCN
'Maori Prince' (m)	NFav
matudae	WPGP
nivalis	CBcs CTrC NGKo SRms WThu
- 'Jack's Pass' (m)	LRHS
- 'Kilworth Cream' (m/v) ♀H6	CBcs LRHS NFav NHol SCoo SLim SWvt WCot
- 'Livingstone' (f)	CBcs
- 'Otari' (m)	MAsh
- 'Ruapehu' (m)	MGil
'Red Embers' (f)	LRHS SCoo SLim
§ ***salignus*** ♀H4	CBcs CExl EPfP IDee LRHS MGil SArc SLim WPGP WPav WThu
'Spring Sunshine' (f)	CBcs
totara	CBrP CTrC LEdu
- 'Albany Gold'	CTrC LRHS
- 'Aureus'	CBcs
- 'Pendulus'	LRHS MGil SMad WFar
'Young Rusty' (f)	CBcs LRHS MAsh SLim WFar

Podophyllum (*Berberidaceae*)

aurantiocaule	CExl GGGa GKev
- subsp. ***aurantiocaule***	GEdr
§ ***delavayi***	CDTJ CExl EBlo WCot WSHC
difforme	LEdu
- 'Hunan'	WFar
emodi	see *Sinopodophyllum hexandrum* var. *emodi*
- var. ***chinense***	see *Sinopodophyllum hexandrum* var. *chinense*
guangxiensis **new**	WFar
hexandrum	see *Sinopodophyllum hexandrum*
- var. ***chinense***	see *Sinopodophyllum hexandrum* var. *chinense*
'Kaleidoscope' (v)	CBcs CBct CBod CMiW EBee ECtt ELan EMor GBin GKev IPot LEdu MAvo MBNS MPnt NHpl NLar SEdd WCot WFar WSHC
peltatum	CBct CBro CMiW CTtf CWCL EBee EGrI EMor EPfP EWld GBin GGro GKev GPoy ILea LEdu MBel NLar NSti SPhx SPtp WCru WPGP WPnP
pleianthum ♀H4	CMiW GEdr LEdu WCot WCru WPGP
- B&SWJ 282 from Taiwan	WCru
- var. ***album***	GEdr
- short	WCru
veitchii	see *P. delavayi*
versipelle	LEdu WCru WSHC
- 'Spotty Dotty' PBR (v) ♀H4	Widely available

Podranea (*Bignoniaceae*)

brycei	SPlb
§ ***ricasoliana*** ^{H1c}	EShb SPoG WBor

Pogonia (*Orchidaceae*)

sp.	NDav
ophioglossoides	GArf NLAp

Pogostemon (*Lamiaceae*)

§ ***cablin***	EOHP GPoy
patchouly	see *P. cablin*

Polemonium ✿ (*Polemoniaceae*)

ambervicsii	see *P. pauciflorum* subsp. *hinckleyi*
'Apricot Beauty'	see *P. carneum* 'Apricot Delight'
archibaldiae ^{H5}	NBir SRms WSHC
'Blue Pearl'	EHyd ELan EPfP GJos LRHS MBel NBro NGdn NLar SPer WFar WSpi
§ ***boreale***	CPla GJos NPol SWvt
- 'Heavenly Habit'	EHyd GJos
brandegeei misapplied	see *P. pauciflorum*
§ ***brandegeei*** Greene	GJos GKev
- subsp. ***mellitum***	see *P. brandegeei* Greene
§ ***caeruleum***	CBod CTri ECha EHyd ELan ENfk EPfP GKev GMaP GPoy LCro LOPS LRHS MBow MHer MNHC NBro NGrd NLar NPol NRHS SPer SPlb SPoG SRms SSal SWvt WCAu WSpi
- subsp. ***amygdalinum***	see *P. occidentale*
- - 'Album'	see *P. caeruleum* subsp. *caeruleum* f. *album*
- 'Bambino Blue'	EPfP SRms SWvt
- BRISE D'ANJOU ('Blanjou'^{PBR}) (v)	CMac CMea CRos ECtt EHyd ELan EPfP EShb EWes LRHS MAsh MBel MHol MPri NBir NRHS SCob SPeP SPer SPoG SWvt
- subsp. ***caeruleum***	GKev
§ - - f. ***album***	CRos CWCL EBee ECha EHyd ELan EPfP EWoo GQue LRHS MBNS MBel MHer MRav NBro NRHS SCob SGbt SPer SPoG SRms WBrk WCAu WSpi
- - - 'White Pearl'	GWyn
- 'Days of Thunder'	EBee
I - f. ***dissectum***	NPol
- 'Filigree Skies'	NGdn
§ - subsp. ***himalayanum***	GGro
- 'Humile'	see *P.* 'Northern Lights'
- 'Snow and Sapphires' (v)	CWGN MPnt NPer SWvt
- 'Southern Skies'	NPol
- subsp. ***vulgare***	NPol
- white-flowered	GJos
carneum	CElw CTri ECha EHyd EWTr NPol
§ - 'Apricot Delight'	CTtf EMor GJos GMaP LShi MNHC MNrw NGdn NPol NQui SBut SGbt SIvy SRms WSpi
cashmerianum	see *P. caeruleum* subsp. *himalayanum*
'Churchills'	NPol WSHC
'Dawn Flight'	NPol
'Eastbury Purple'	CElw NPol
'Elworthy Amethyst'	CElw EBee NPol
flavum	see *P. foliosissimum* var. *flavum*
foliosissimum misapplied	see *P. archibaldiae*
foliosissimum A. Gray	NPol
- var. ***albiflorum***	see *P. foliosissimum* var. *alpinum*
§ - var. ***alpinum***	NPol
- 'Bressingham'	SCoo
- 'Cottage Cream'	LEdu NPol WFar
§ - var. ***flavum***	NPol
- var. ***foliosissimum***	NPol WSpi
- 'Scottish Garden'	NPol
- 'White Spirit'	NPol
'Glebe Cottage Lilac'	CDor EBee NBir NPol
'Glebe Cottage Violet'	NPol
'Hannah Billcliffe'	ECtt LPla MBrN NChi NPol SWvt WFar
'Heaven Scent'^{PBR}	CRos EBee ECtt EHyd EMor LRHS LSou MBNS MPnt MPri NDov NLar NRHS SCoo SGBe WCAu WCav WGrn
§ 'Hopleys'	EBee MNrw NChi
× ***jacobaea***	EPPr WCot
'Katie Daley'	see *P.* 'Hopleys'
'Lambrook Mauve'	Widely available
'Mary Mottram'	NPol
mellitum	see *P. brandegeei* Greene
'North Tyne'	NChi NPol NWad
§ 'Northern Lights' ^{H7}	Widely available
'Norwell Mauve'	MNrw NPol WFar
§ ***occidentale***	NPol
§ ***pauciflorum***	CTtf ELan GJos NBir
§ - subsp. ***hinckleyi***	GKev NPol
§ - subsp. ***pauciflorum***	NPol
- silver-leaved	see *P. pauciflorum* subsp. *pauciflorum*
- 'Sulphur Trumpets'	GBin GJos SWvt
- subsp. ***typicum***	see *P. pauciflorum* subsp. *pauciflorum*
'Pink Beauty'	EBee ECtt EHyd ELan EPfP NGdn NPol
pulchellum Salisb.	see *P. reptans*
pulchellum Turcz.	see *P. caeruleum*
pulcherrimum misapplied	see *P. boreale*
- 'Tricolor'	see *P. boreale*
§ ***reptans***	GPoy MHer NBro NPol SRms
- 'Album'	see *P. reptans* 'Virginia White'
- 'Blue Ice'	NPol
- 'Jacob's Gold' (v)	EBee EHyd ELan EPfP LRHS NPol NRHS SCob
* - 'Sky Blue'	NBro
- 'Stairway to Heaven'^{PBR} (v)	Widely available
- 'Touch of Class'^{PBR} (v)	CBod CWGN EMor MBel MPri NLar SCob SPoG
§ - 'Virginia White'	EWes NChi NPol NQui
'Ribby'	NPol
× ***richardsonii*** misapplied	see *P.* 'Northern Lights'
× ***richardsonii*** Graham	see *P. boreale*
'Sapphire'	EHyd
'Sonia's Bluebell'	CWCL ECtt EPPr EWes EWld GBin LSou MNrw NDov NPol NSti SGro WFar
'Sunnyside Storm'	NPol
'Theddingworth'	NPol
'Triffids' Lilac' **new**	CTtf
viscosum	NPol SPlb
- f. ***leucanthum***	NPol
yezoense	NPol WFar
- var. ***hidakanum***	GAbr NPol
- - BRESSINGHAM PURPLE ('Polbress')	Widely available
- - 'Halfway to Paradise'	SCob WGrn WNPC
- - 'Purple Rain'	CDor CGrG CMac CSpe EAJP EHyd ELan ELon EPfP EWes GJos GMaP GWyn LEdu LRHS LSun MAsh MRav NLar NPol NRHS SBls SCob SRkn SRms WCot WFar WKif WTre
- 'Kaleidoscope' (v)	LRHS NPol SCoo SHar WNPC

Polianthes (*Asparagaceae*)

elongata	WCot

tuberosa	CBcs CCCN GKev LCro LOPS XLum
- 'Cinderella'	GKev
- 'Golden Harvest'	GKev
- 'Pink Sapphire'	GKev WCot
- 'Sensation'	EShb GKev SDeJ
- 'Super Gold'	GKev SDeJ
- 'The Pearl' (d)	CBor EShb GKev LCro LOPS SDeJ XLum
- 'Yellow Baby'	GKev WCot

Poliomintha (*Lamiaceae*)

bustamanta	NBir SPhx WSHC

Poliothyrsis (*Salicaceae*)

sinensis	CBcs CMCN EBtc EPfP

Pollia (*Commelinaceae*)

japonica	ESwi WCot

Polygala (*Polygalaceae*)

'Africana'[PBR]	CPbh
africana 'Nana'	SGBe
arillata	LEdu
calcarea	WAbe
- Bulley's form	EPot WFar
- 'Lillet' ♀H7	EHyd EPot GEdr LRHS NRHS SChF WAbe
chamaebuxus	see *Polygaloides chamaebuxus*
§ × ***dalmaisiana*** ♀H1c	CAbb CBod CCCN CDoC CKel CSde CSpe CTsd CWit ECre EGrI EHed ELan SEND SIvy WCFE
'Dolomite'	GEdr
microphylla new	GKev
myrtifolia ♀H1c	CCCN CPbh CTrC SAdn SGBe SPlb WSMil
- BIBI PINK ('Polylap')	CTrC
- 'Grandiflora'	see *P.* × *dalmaisiana*
'Purple Passion'	CCCN SRms WFar
virgata	CCCN ELan SIvy

Polygaloides (*Polygalaceae*)

§ ***chamaebuxus*** ♀H7	GKev MAsh MGos NLar NSla NWad SRms WThu
I - ***alba***	WAbe
§ - 'Grandiflora' ♀H7	CBcs EPfP EPot GAbr GEdr GKev MAsh MGos NBir NHpl NSla SPlb SPoG WAbe WFar
- 'Kamniski'	EPot
- 'Loibl'	EPot WFar
- 'Purpurea'	see *P. chamaebuxus* 'Grandiflora'
- 'Rhodoptera'	see *P. chamaebuxus* 'Grandiflora'

Polygonatum ✿ (*Asparagaceae*)

SBQE 310	LEdu MAvo
altelobatum B&SWJ 286	WCru
- B&SWJ 1886	WCru
annamense B&SWJ 9752	WCru
arisanense B&SWJ 271	WCru
- B&SWJ 3839	WCru
§ ***biflorum***	CBod CRos CWCL EBee ECtt EHyd ELan EMor EPfP GBin GKev GMaP ILea LRHS MACG MAvo NLar NRHS SPoG SWvt WCru WFar WPnP WSMil XLum
- dwarf	EHyd
brevistylum B&SWJ 2421	WCru
canaliculatum	see *P. biflorum*
cathcartii B&SWJ 2429	WCru
- yellow-flowered B&SWJ 2412	WCru
cirrhifolium	CBor EBee EPot GAbr GEdr LEdu MAvo MNrw NHpl SBut WCru WPGP
- ARGS 320	EPPr
- from China	WCru
- red-flowered	NLar
commutatum	see *P. biflorum*
costatum B&SWJ 6599	WCru
cryptanthum	WCru
curvistylum	CAvo CBct CDor EPPr ESwi EWld GEdr GKev ILea LEdu NLar NRya WCru WFar WSHC
cyrtonema misapplied	see *Disporopsis pernyi*
cyrtonema Hua	GKev WCru
- B&SWJ 271	LEdu MAvo
* ***desoulavyi*** var. ***yezoense*** B&SWJ 764	WCru
falcatum misapplied	see *P. humile*
falcatum A. Gray	EBee GEdr NHpl NRya
- B&SWJ 1077	CBct WCru
- B&SWJ 5054	WCru
- NJM 11.012	WPGP
- 'Shikoku Silver'	CBct EPPr GKev LEdu SMHy WCru
- 'Silver Mist'	LEdu
- 'Variegatum'	see *P. odoratum* var. *pluriflorum* 'Variegatum'
'Falcon'	see *P. humile*
filipes	EBee EPPr LEdu WCru
fuscum	WCru
geminiflorum	CBct LEdu LPla WCru WFar
giganteum	see *P. biflorum*
glaberrimum	WCot WPGP
'Golden Gift'	CBct LPla
§ ***graminifolium***	CBct EBlo EGdr GKev WCru WThu
§ ***hirtum***	CBct ECha EHyd EPPr LEdu WCru
- W&B BG C-2	WCot
- 'Robustum'	WCru
hookeri	CBct CBor CExl CSpe CTtf EBee EHyd EPPr EPot EWld GBin GEdr GKev GQue LEdu NBid NHpl NLar NRya NSla SPhx SPtp WCru WFar
§ ***humile***	CBct CWCL EBee ELan EMor EPPr EPfP EPot EWTr GKev ILea ITim LEdu LRHS MAvo NGdn NLar SPtp SWvt WCav WCru WHil WPGP WTor XLum
- 'Shiro-shima-fu' (v)	WFar
I - 'Variegatum' (v)	CMac WCot
§ × ***hybridum*** ♀H7	Widely available
- 'Bere'	LEdu WPGP
- 'Betberg'	CTtf ECha EHed ELon EPPr GKev IPot LEdu LPla MAvo MBriF NBir WCot WFar
- 'Flore Pleno' (d)	WHer
- 'Nanum'	CBct MRav WCot
- 'Purple Katie'	ESwi MAvo MMrt
§ - 'Striatum' (v)	Widely available
- 'Variegatum'	see *P.* × *hybridum* 'Striatum'
- 'Wakehurst'	LEdu
- 'Weihenstephan'	EPPr GKev LEdu MAvo
- 'Welsh Gold' (v)	CAvo EBee ESwi
inflatum	WCru
- B&SWJ 922	WCru
involucratum	WCru
- B&SWJ 4285	WCru
japonicum	see *P. odoratum*
kingianum	GGro LEdu WMal
- red-flowered	GKev
- yellow-flowered B&SWJ 6545	WCru
- - B&SWJ 6562	WCru

'Langthorn's Variegated' (v)	ELan
lasianthum	MAvo SMHy WCru
- B&SWJ 671	WCru
latifolium	see *P. hirtum*
macranthum new	GGro
maximowiczii	EPPr LEdu LPla WCru WPGP
mengtzense f. ***mengtzense*** HWJ 588	WCru
- - HWJ 861	LEdu WCru
- f. ***tonkinense*** B&SWJ 8246	LEdu WCru
- - HWJ 551	WCru
- - HWJ 567	WCru
- - HWJ 573	CBct EPot WCru
- - HWJ 861	LEdu
'Multifide'	EBee GKev
multiflorum misapplied	see *P.* × *hybridum*
multiflorum L.	CAgr CBcs CDoC CHab CMac CSBt CWCL EBee ECha EGrI EMor EPfP EWoo GAbr LSou LSun MHol MRav NGdn NLar SEdd SPlb SRms SWvt WCAu WCru WFar WHer XLum
- CC 4572	WCot
- 'Flore Pleno' (d)	WFar
- ***giganteum*** hort.	see *P. biflorum*
- 'Ramosissima'	LEdu MAvo WCru
- var. ***ramosum***	LEdu
* ***nanum*** 'Variegatum' (v)	CBcs
nodosum	GKev WCru
§ ***odoratum***	CAvo CBct CBro EBee ECha EPfP GKev GMaP LEdu MBriF MPnt NBid NLar NRya WCru
- 'Byakko' (v)	GKev
- 'Dai Koga' (v)	WFar
- 'Dusky Bere'	ESwi WPGP
§ - dwarf	LEdu
- 'Flatmate'	ESwi LEdu MAvo WCru
- 'Flore Pleno' (d)	CAvo CDor GKev LEdu MBriF MHer WCot WHoo
- 'Georgia'	WPGP
- 'Goldilocks' (v)	WCot
- 'Grace Barker'	see *P.* × *hybridum* 'Striatum'
- Kew form	EPot
- var. ***odoratum***	GKev
§ - var. ***pluriflorum*** 'Variegatum' (v)	Widely available
- 'Pruhonice'	ECha
- 'Red Stem'	CMea ECha LEdu MAvo SMHy WCru
- 'Silver Wings' (v)	CBct ECha IPot LEdu NBir NLar WFar WSHC
- var. ***thunbergii***	WCru
- 'Triglav'	MAvo
- 'Ussuriland'	EPPr LEdu LPla MAvo
- 'Ussuriland Roundleaf'	ESwi LEdu MAvo
officinale	see *P. odoratum*
oppositifolium B&SWJ 2537	WCru
§ ***orientale***	CAvo EBee EPfP ESwi GKev
- S&F 364	WCot
pluriflorum	see *P. graminifolium*
polyanthemum	see *P. orientale*
prattii	EBee EPot GKev ILea WCru
- CLD 325	GEdr LEdu
pubescens	CBct WCru WThu
pumilum	see *P. odoratum* dwarf
punctatum ambig.	LEdu NBid WPGP
punctatum Royle ex Kunth	WCot
- B&SWJ 2395	CBct WCru
racemosum	CBct
roseum	EBee EPPr ESwi GKev MAvo SMHy WCru
sewerzowii	EMor EPPr
sibiricum	CAvo CBct ESwi GKev WCru WFar
- DJHC 600	EBee LEdu MAvo WPGP
singalilense	LEdu WCru
stenanthum B&SWJ 11425	WCru
- B&SWJ 5727	LEdu WCru
stenophyllum	WCru
stewartianum	EBee EPPr EPri ESwi ILea MAvo NRya
tessellatum	WPGP
- PAB 8336	LEdu
verticillatum	CBct CBro EBee ECha EHed EHyd EPPr EPfP ESwi GEdr GKev LEdu LRHS MACG MBriF MNrw MRav SMad WCru WFar WPGP WSMil WWtn
- B&SWJ 2147	WCru
- CLD 1308	EPPr
- PAB 2455	LEdu
- 'Himalayan Giant'	CSpe EBlo EMor EPPr GKev MAvo WPnP
- 'Krynica'	LEdu WPGP
* - 'Roseum'	CAvo EBlo EPri LRHS
- 'Rubrum'	CBct EHed EHyd EMor EPPr GEdr GGro ILea LEdu MAvo MBel MHid NBid NChi NLar WCot WCru WFar WHoo
- 'Serbian Dwarf'	CBct ESwi GKev WPGP
aff. ***verticillatum***	CSpe CTtf
yunnanense	CBct EBee ESwi LEdu WPGP
zanlanscianense	EBee ESwi EWld LEdu MAvo MVil WCru
aff. ***zanlanscianense*** new	SPlb

Polygonum (*Polygonaceae*)

affine	see *Persicaria affinis*
amplexicaule	see *Persicaria amplexicaulis*
aubertii	see *Fallopia baldschuanica*
baldschuanicum	see *Fallopia baldschuanica*
bistorta	see *Persicaria bistorta*
capitatum	see *Persicaria capitata*
equisetiforme misapplied	see *P. scoparium*
filiforme	see *Persicaria virginiana*
forrestii	EBee GKev
multiflorum	see *Fallopia multiflora*
odoratum	see *Persicaria odorata*
polystachyum	see *Persicaria wallichii*
§ ***scoparium***	EPPr ESwi EWes LRHS SDys SVen WFar XLum XSte
vacciniifolium	see *Persicaria vacciniifolia*
weyrichii	see *Persicaria weyrichii*

Polylepis (*Rosaceae*)

australis	CBcs IDee SMad
- tall	WPGP

Polymnia (*Asteraceae*)

sonchifolia 'Red China'	WPGP

Polypodiodes (*Polypodiaceae*)

formosana ♀H3	GBin IKel SPlb WCot

Polypodium ✿ (*Polypodiaceae*)

aureum	see *Phlebodium aureum*
australe	see *P. cambricum*
- Pat's form	EBee
azoricum	WCot
californicum	EBee LEdu
§ ***cambricum***	CLAP EFer WCot WFib
- GG 20131	SMHy
- 'Barrowii'	CLAP WFib WGwG

	- 'Bob's Choice'	WCot
I	- 'Cambricum' ♀H7	WAbe
	- 'Conwy'	EBee WFib
	- 'Cristatum'	EBee WCot WFib WHoo
	- Cristatum Group old form **new**	SMHy
	- - 'Grandiceps Fox' ♀H7	MRav WFib
	- - 'Herbert Whitley' **new**	LEdu
	- 'Hornet'	WFib
	- 'Macrostachyon'	LEdu NBid WFib
	- 'Oakleyae'	CDor EBee EWld LEdu SMHy WCot
	- 'Omnilacerum Oxford'	LEdu
	- 'Prestonii'	CDor CLAP WCot WFib
	- Pulcherrimum Group	SDys WAbe
	- - bifid	EBee
	- - 'Pulcherrimum Addison'	EBee LEdu WCot WFib
	- - 'Pulchritudine'	LLWG WCot
	- 'Richard Kayse' ♀H7	CLAP EShb EWes MPie SMHy WAbe WBrk WCot WFib WPGP
	- Semilacerum Group	EFer
	- - 'Carew Lane'	LEdu WFib
	- - 'Falcatum O'Kelly'	WCot
	- - 'Robustum'	EBee WFib
	- 'Whilharris' ♀H7	CDor SMHy WCot
I	× ***coughlinii*** bifid	WFib
	× ***font-queri*** **new**	CNat
	glycyrrhiza	GPoy LEdu NBro SMHy WFib
	- bifid	see *P.* × *coughlinii* bifid
	- 'Lawrence Crocker'	LEdu WCot
	- 'Longicaudatum' ♀H7	EFer EShb SMHy WBrk WCot WFib
	- 'Malahatense'	CLAP GBin SMHy
	- 'Malahatense' (sterile)	EBee WCot
	glycyrrhiza × ***scouleri***	EBee
	guttatum	SPlb
	interjectum	EFer EShb MRav WCot
	- 'Glomeratum Mullins'	WFib
	macaronesicum	LEdu WCot
	× ***mantoniae***	CLAP LEdu WFib
	- 'Bifidograndiceps'	NBid WFib
	- 'Cornubiense' ♀H7	CDor CLAP EShb EWld LEdu MHost NBid NBir NHar SMHy
	pseudoaureum 'Virginia Blue'	EHyd LRHS NRHS
	scouleri	CBdn CLAP EBee EFer EHyd EShb ESwi LEdu LRHS MAsh MRav NBro NRHS WCot WPGP
	vulgare	Widely available
	- 'Bifidocristatum'	CBdn CLAP CTsd CWCL ELon EPfP GBin GEdr LEdu LLWG MAsh MGos MRav NLar WBrk
	- 'Bifidomulticeps'	WCot
*	- 'Congestum Cristatum'	SRms
	- 'Cornubiense Grandiceps'	SRms
*	- 'Cornubiense Multifidum'	WCot
	- 'Elegantissimum'	NBid WFib
	- 'Parsley'	LEdu WCot
	- 'Ramosum Hillman'	GBin WCot
	- 'Trichomanoides Backhouse'	CLAP WAbe WFib
	'Whitley Giant'	CBdn CTsd EBee ECtt EMor EShb ESwi GBin GEdr ITim LEdu LLWG LPla LSun MHol MPie NBid NLar WCot

Polypompholyx see *Utricularia*

Polyspora (*Theaceae*)

§	***axillaris***	CCCN CTsd EBee LRHS XSte
	longicarpa B&SWJ 11704	WCru
	- WWJ 11604	WCru
	- WWJ 11894	WCru
	speciosa B&SWJ 11708 from Vietnam	WCru
	- B&SWJ 11750	WCru
	- WWJ 11934	WCru

Polystichum ✿ (*Dryopteridaceae*)

	acrostichoides	CDTJ CLAP EHed EHyd EMor LEdu LRHS NBro NLar NRHS SPlb WCot WPGP XLum
	aculeatum ♀H7	CKel CLAP CRos ECha EFer EHyd ELan EMor EShb GMaP LCro LEdu LRHS MGos MMuc NBid NLar NRHS SCob SCoo SPoG SRms SWvt WBrk WFib XLum
I	- Densum Group	EFer
	- 'Portia'	WFib
	andersonii	CLAP NBro
	biaristatum	WPGP
	bissectum	CExl
	braunii	CBcs CBdn CDoC CDor CLAP CMac CRos CWCL EHyd EMor EPfP GMaP LRHS MAsh NBid NBro NLar NRHS SPoG WFib WPnP XLum
	caryotideum	see *Cyrtomium caryotideum*
	× ***dycei*** ♀H5	CLAP EHyd LEdu LRHS MAsh NRHS WCot WPGP
	falcatum	see *Cyrtomium falcatum*
	falcinellum	EBee
	fortunei	see *Cyrtomium fortunei*
	imbricans	CLAP
	interjectum	MRav
	makinoi	CBdn CCCN CLAP CRos EHyd LLWG LRHS MAsh NBid NBro NRHS SPlb SRot WCot WFib
	mayebarae	CLAP EBee
	munitum ♀H7	Widely available
	neolobatum	CLAP EBee EHed NBro WCot WFib WPGP
	- BWJ 8182	WCru
	polyblepharum ♀H7	Widely available
	- 'Jade'	EBee
	proliferum misapplied	see *P. setiferum* Acutilobum Group
	proliferum (R. Br.) C. Presl	CLAP LBuc WAbe WFib WPGP
*	- ***plumosum***	SWvt
	rigens	CBod CLAP CSta CWCL EFer EHyd ELon EPau LEdu LRHS NBro NLar NRHS SEdd SRms SRot WFib
	setiferum ♀H7	Widely available
§	- Acutilobum Group	CBod ECha EHyd EMor GMaP LLWG LRHS NHar NRHS SCob SDix SPad SRms WBor WPGP XLum
	- Congestum Group	CDor CLAP ELon EMor EShb NBro NHol NLar SRms SRot WBrk WFib
	- - 'Congestum'	CSta CWCL EHyd ELan EPfP LEdu LRHS MAsh MCot MRav NBir NGdn NHol NRHS SCoo SMHy SPad SPoG XLum
	- 'Cristatopinnulum'	CLAP LEdu NHar WPGP
	- Cristatum Group	CLAP SRms
	- - 'Multifidum Polydactylum'	LEdu
	- (Decompositum Group) 'Proliferum'	CWCL
	- Divisilobum Group ♀H7	CLAP EBee EFer ELan MCot MGos SRms WAbe WFar WFib WHoo WPGP
	- - 'Dahlem'	CBdn CKel CMac CRos EBee ECha ECtt EFer EHyd ELan ELon EMor EPfP GMaP LRHS LSRN NBid NLar NRHS SPer WBrk WFib XLum
	- - 'Divisilobum Densum' ♀H7	CMac EPfP MRav NBir

- - 'Divisilobum Grandiceps'	CLAP
- - 'Divisilobum Iveryanum' ♀H7	CLAP EFer SRms WFib
- - 'Divisilobum Laxum'	EBee
§ - - 'Divisilobum Wollaston'	CDTJ CLAP CRos CSta CWCL ECtt EHyd EMor GBin LEdu LRHS MAsh MGos MRav NBid NLar NRHS SCob WCot
- - 'Herrenhausen'	Widely available
- - 'Proliferum'	NLar
- Foliosum Group	EFer
- 'Gracile'	MRav NBir
§ - 'Gracillimum'	CLAP
- 'Grandiceps'	EFer
- GREEN LACE	see *P. setiferum* 'Gracillimum'
- 'Hamlet'	WFib
- 'Helena'	WFib
- 'Hirondelle'	SRms
- Lineare Group	WFib
- Multilobum Group	SRms WFib
- 'Nantes'	WCot
- 'Othello'	WFib
- Perserratum Group	NBid WFib
- 'Plumo-Densum'	see *P. setiferum* Plumosomultilobum Group
- 'Plumosodensum'	see *P. setiferum* Plumosomultilobum Group
- Plumosodivisilobum Group	EBee ECha EHed EWoo MPnt NBid NBro WAbe WFib
- - 'Baldwinii'	WFib
- - 'Bland'	WFib
§ - Plumosomultilobum Group	CDor CWCL EMor EPfP GBin GQue LCro LOPS LRHS MCot MGos NBir NLar SEdd WCot WFib WHoo WPnP
I - - 'Plumosomultilobum Densum'	CLAP CRos CSta ECtt EHyd LLWG LRHS LSun MBel MSCN NRHS SEdd SMad WBrk WCot WFar
- Plumosum Group	CMac CSpe EFer EHyd ELon EMor EPfP LLWG LRHS MAsh NHar NRHS SArc
- - dwarf	CSBt
* - ***plumosum grande*** 'Moly'	SRms
- Proliferum Group	see *P. setiferum* Acutilobum Group
- 'Proliferum Wollaston'	see *P. setiferum* (Divisilobum Group) 'Divisilobum Wollaston'
- 'Pulcherrimum Bevis' ♀H7	CBdn CLAP EFer EHed EHyd ELon EShb ESwi LEdu LRHS MPie NLar NRHS SArc SMHy SWvt WFib WLov WPGP
- (Rotundatum Group) 'Cristatum'	CLAP
- 'Smith's Cruciate'	MRav WFib
- 'Wakeleyanum'	EFer SRms
'Spiny Holly'	CLAP
tsussimense ♀H6	Widely available
- 'K Rex'	CRos EHyd LRHS NRHS
wawranum	LEdu WPGP
xiphophyllum	CLAP EBee NBro WPGP
yunnanense	CTsd

Polytaenia (*Apiaceae*)

nuttallii	SPhx

Pomaderris (*Rhamnaceae*)

apetala	CExl
elliptica	CExl

pomegranate see *Punica granatum*

Poncirus see *Citrus*

Ponerorchis see *Hemipilia*

Pontederia (*Pontederiaceae*)

cordata ♀H5	CBen CPud CWat EPfP EWat LCro LLWG LOPS MWts NPer SPlb WMAq WPnP WWtn XLum
- f. ***albiflora***	CPud CWat EPfP EWat LLWG WPnP XLum
§ - var. ***lancifolia***	CBen CWat LLWG MNrw MWts NPer WWtn
- pink-flowered	LLWG
- 'Sunsplash' (v)	LLWG
dilatata	see *Monochoria hastata*
lanceolata	see *P. cordata* var. *lancifolia*

Populus ✿ (*Salicaceae*)

× ***acuminata***	WMou
alba	CBcs CCVT CLnd CMac CTri EPfP IPap LBuc LPar MMuc NRog NWea SCob SEWo SGol SPer WMou WTSh
- 'Bolleana'	see *P. alba* 'Pyramidalis'
§ - 'Pyramidalis'	WMou
§ - 'Raket'	CCVT ELan NRog SPer
- 'Richardii'	EBtc SDix WCot WMou
- ROCKET	see *P. alba* 'Raket'
§ 'Balsam Spire' (f)	NWea WMou
§ ***balsamifera***	CCVT CLnd CSBt CTri GAbr SPer WCot
- 'Vita Sackville West'	MBlu
§ × ***canadensis*** 'Aurea' ♀H7	SPer WMat WMou
- 'Aurea' × ***jackii*** 'Aurora'	CCCN ELan WFar
- 'Columbia'	WMou
- 'Eugenei' (m)	WMou
- 'Robusta' (m)	CCVT CLnd LBuc NRog NWea WMou
- 'Serotina' (m)	NRog WMou
× ***canescens***	CLnd NWea WMou
- 'Tower'	WMat
ciliata new	WPGP
deltoides 'Fuego'	SGol
- 'Purple Tower'PBR	CBcs EBee ELan EPfP IArd MBlu MMuc MTrO NOra SLim WMat
× ***generosa*** 'Beaupré'	WMou
glauca	SPtp WPGP
× ***jackii*** 'Aurora' (f/v)	CBcs CCVT CLnd CMac CSBt CTsd IPap NOrn NRog NWea SPer WFar WMou
lasiocarpa	CBcs CExl CMCN EPfP IArd IDee MBlu SPtp WMou WPGP
- (m/f)	WPGP
maximowiczii	SPtp WMou
nigra	CHab CLnd CTri NOrn NWea
- (f)	MMuc
- (m)	MMuc
- subsp. ***betulifolia***	CCVT CHab CLnd NWea WMou
- - (f)	EBtc WMou
- - (m)	EBtc WMou
- 'Hanging Tree' new	MTrO
§ - 'Italica' (m) ♀H7	CBod CCVT CLnd CMac CSBt ELan IPap LBuc LPar MGos MMuc NRog NWea SCob SEWo SPer WMou
§ - 'Lombardy Gold' (m)	SMad
- 'Pyramidalis'	see *P. nigra* 'Italica'
purdomii	SPtp WPGP
'Serotina Aurea'	see *P.* × *canadensis* 'Aurea'
simonii 'Fastigiata'	WMou
- 'Obtusata'	NRog
szechuanica	WMou
§ - var. ***tibetica***	WMou WPGP
tacamahaca	see *P. balsamifera*

'Tacatricho 32'	see *P.* 'Balsam Spire'
tomentosa	WMou
tremula	CCVT CHab CLnd CMac CTri ELan GAbr IPap LBuc LPar NRog NWea SCob SEWo WMou WSFF WTSh
§ - 'Erecta' 🏆H7	CEnd LPar LRHS MBlu MMuc NOrn WMat WMou
- 'Fastigiata'	see *P. tremula* 'Erecta'
- 'Pendula' (m)	CEnd WMou
- 'Tapiau' **new**	LMaj
trichocarpa	NRog SPer
- 'Fritzi Pauley' (f)	WMou
violascens	see *P. szechuanica* var. *tibetica*
× ***wilsocarpa*** 'Beloni'	WPGP
wilsonii	WPGP
- KR 3993 **new**	WPGP
- MF 20088 **new**	WPGP
yunnanensis	WMou

Porophyllum (*Asteraceae*)

ruderale	WJek

Portulaca (*Portulacaceae*)

sp. **new**	MBros
gilliesii **new**	NFav
grandiflora	SVic
oleracea	ENfk SSim SVic
- var. ***aurea***	MNHC

Portulacaria (*Didiereaceae*)

afra	CDoC EShb NCft
- 'Variegata' (v)	CDoC EShb NCft SIvy SSim

Potamogeton (*Potamogetonaceae*)

crispus	CBen CWat LLWG MWts WMAq
lucens	LLWG
malainus	LLWG
natans	LLWG WSFF XLum
perfoliatus	LLWG

potato see AGM Vegetables Section

Potentilla ✿ (*Rosaceae*)

alba	CTri ECha ELan GKev LPot LShi MRav NChi NWad SPer WSHC
alchemilloides	CMac
ambigua	see *P. cuneata*
ancistrifolia var. ***dickinsii***	GEdr GKev
anserina	CAgr MHer SPhx WHer XLum
- 'Golden Treasure' (v)	NSti
arbuscula misapplied	see *P. fruticosa* 'Elizabeth'
arbuscula 'Beesii'	see *P. fruticosa* 'Beesii'
'Arc-en-ciel'	Widely available
argentea	SPlb WFar XLum
argyrophylla	see *P. atrosanguinea* var. *argyrophylla*
atrosanguinea	Widely available
- CC 7167 **new**	GGro
§ - var. ***argyrophylla***	CDor CWCL EBee EBou ECha ELan EPfP GKev GPSL LPot MRav NBir NBro NChi NLar SRms XLum
- - 'Golden Starlit'	CBod CChe EDAr MACG SVic
- - 'Orange Starlit' **new**	SBls
§ - - 'Scarlet Starlit'	CBod CChe CDor EBou EDAr EHyd ELon EPfP GJos LLWG MACG NCou NEoE SVic
- 'Chadwell's Tibetan Velvet' **new**	GGro
- var. ***leucochroa***	see *P. atrosanguinea* var. *argyrophylla*
* - 'Sundermannii'	NWad SBrt
aurea	ECtt GArf GBin
- 'Plena' (d)	NRya
'Blazeaway'	CBod EBee ECtt EHyd EPfP LRHS MArl MBel NEoE NGdn NRHS SRms
calabra	ECha EWes MMuc SPhx
§ ***cinerea***	CTri
'Congo' **new**	EBlo LRHS
§ ***crantzii***	CMea EBou SRms
- 'Nana'	see *P. crantzii* 'Pygmaea'
§ - 'Pygmaea'	ECtt
§ ***cuneata*** 🏆H7	GKev
davurica 'Abbotswood'	see *P. fruticosa* 'Abbotswood'
'Emilie' (d)	CWCL ECtt GWyn LRHS MBNS MBel MNrw NLar SWvt WFar
§ ***erecta***	GPoy MBow MNHC SPhx SRms
eriocarpa	EPot GArf GEdr NSla WAbe WIce
'Esta Ann'	CBod CMac ECtt LRHS LShi MArl MBel MNrw MSCN MTin NLar NRHS NSti WCAu
'Etna'	CWCL ECtt EHyd ELan GArf GJos LRHS MACG MNrw MPie MTin NBir NLar NRHS WCAu WFar WHrl
'Everest'	see *P. fruticosa* 'Mount Everest'
'Fireflame'	EBee NLar
fissa	MNrw NBir NLar SPhx
'Flambeau' (d)	EBee ECtt EHyd EPfP EShb MArl MRav MSpe NChi NGdn NLar NRHS NSti WCAu
'Flamboyant' (d)	MSCN
'Flamenco'	CRos CTri ECtt EHyd LRHS MArl MBNS MMrt MRav NBir NRHS WFar
fragariiformis	see *P. megalantha*
fruticosa	LBuc NWea
§ - 'Abbotswood' 🏆H7	Widely available
- 'Annette'	NLar
- var. ***arbuscula*** hort.	see *P. fruticosa* 'Elizabeth'
- 'Argentea Nana'	see *P. fruticosa* 'Beesii'
§ - 'Beesii'	CRos EHyd EPfP LRHS MAsh NRHS
- BELLA BIANCA ('Hachbianca'PBR) **new**	CBod LRHS
- BELLA SOL ('Hachdon')	CBod EBee LRHS SPad
- BELLISSIMA ('Hachliss'PBR)	CBod CKel EMil LRHS SEdd
- 'Bewerley Surprise'	WFar
- 'Bo-Peep'	CEnd EHyd LSRN WFar
- 'Chelsea Star' 🏆H7	CDoC CKel CMac CRos EBee EHyd EPfP LRHS LSRN MAsh NRHS SPoG SRGP
- 'Clotted Cream'	SGbt
- var. ***dahurica*** 'Hersii'	see *P. fruticosa* 'Snowflake'
- 'Dakota Sunrise'	WFar
- DANNY BOY ('Lissdan'PBR)	CBod CKel CRos EBee EHyd EMil EPfP LCro LOPS LRHS MAsh NEoE NRHS SCob SLon SPad SPoG
- 'Daphne'	NWad
- 'Dart's Golddigger'	CTri
- 'Daydawn'	CBcs CBrac CMac CTri EHyd ELan EPfP LRHS MAsh MGil MMuc MRav MSwo NLar NRHS NWad SCob SGol SPer SRms SWvt WFar
- 'Farreri'	see *P. fruticosa* 'Gold Drop'
- 'Friedrichsenii'	CBrac
- 'Glenroy Pinkie'	MRav
§ - 'Gold Drop'	CMac NHol
- 'Goldfinger'	CAgr CBod CBrac CChe CDoC CKel CRos CSBt EHyd EPfP LRHS MAsh MGos MMuc MRav MSwo NRHS SCob SCoo SPer SPlb SPoG WFar XSen
- GOLDKUGEL	see *P. fruticosa* 'Gold Drop'
- 'Goldstar'	EHyd IArd MMuc SCob SEND SLon SRms WFar

- 'Goldteppich'	LBuc
- 'Grace Darling'	EPfP SRGP SWvt
- 'Groneland' 🏆H7	CRos EHyd ELan EPfP LRHS MAsh NRHS SCoo SPoG
- 'Hopleys Orange' 🏆H7	CBrac CDoC CKel CRos EHyd EPfP EWes LRHS NHol NRHS SEdd SGbt SGol SNig SRms WFar
- 'Jackman's Variety' 🏆H7	EHyd EPfP LRHS MAsh SRms
- 'Katherine Dykes'	CTri EBee EHyd EPfP GDam GKin LRHS LSRN MAsh NRHS NWea SCob SCoo SGbt SPer SRms WFar
- 'King Cup' 🏆H7	CRos EHyd EPfP LRHS MAsh
§ - 'Klondike'	CBcs CBrac GAbr NWea
- 'Kobold'	CDoC NLar
- 'Lemon and Lime'	see *P. fruticosa* 'Limelight'
§ - 'Limelight' 🏆H7	CBod CKel CRos CSBt EBee EHyd EPfP GKin LRHS MAsh MMuc MRav MSwo NEoE NRHS NWad SRms WFar WLov
- 'Lovely Pink'	see *P. fruticosa* 'Pink Beauty'
§ - 'Maanelys'	CBrac CSBt NLar NWea SPer
- 'Macpenny's Cream'	CMac SRms
§ - 'Manchu'	CKel CMac MRav SPer SRms WCFE
- MANGO TANGO ('Uman'PBR)	CBod CKel CRos CSBt EHyd EPfP LRHS LSRN MAsh NEoE NLar NRHS SCob SPoG WFar
§ - MARIAN RED ROBIN ('Marrob'PBR) 🏆H7	CBod CDoC CRos EHyd ELan EPfP GKin LCro LOPS LRHS MAsh MRav MSwo NRHS NWea SCoo SLon SNig SPer SRms SWvt WFar WLov
- 'McKay's White'	NLar
- 'Medicine Wheel Mountain' 🏆H7	CBod CKel CRos EBee EHyd ELan EMil EWes IArd LRHS MAsh MRav NEoE NLar NRHS SCoo SPer SPoG WFar
- MOONLIGHT	see *P. fruticosa* 'Maanelys'
§ - 'Mount Everest'	CMac CTri MMuc NWea SLon
- 'Nana Argentea'	see *P. fruticosa* 'Beesii'
- 'New Dawn'	CBcs GKin MAsh
- 'Orangeade'	CRos EHyd EPfP LRHS MAsh SCoo SPoG
§ - 'Pink Beauty'PBR 🏆H7	CBar CDoC CKel CRos CSBt EBee EHyd ELan EPau EPfP GKin LCro LOPS LRHS LSRN MAsh MRav NHol NRHS SCob SCoo SPer SPoG SRkn SRms SWvt WFar
- PINK PARADISE ('Kupinpa'PBR)	SCob
- 'Pink Pearl'	WFar
- 'Pink Queen'	SRGP
- 'Pink Whisper'	SRms
- 'Pretty Polly'	CRos EHyd ELan EPfP LRHS MSwo NHol NLar NWad WFar
- 'Primrose Beauty' 🏆H7	Widely available
§ - PRINCESS ('Blink')	CBcs CDoC CKel EBee EHyd ELan EPfP LRHS MAsh MRav NLar NRHS SCob SCoo SRms WFar
- var. ***pumila***	WAbe
- 'Red Ace'	Widely available
- 'Red Joker' **new**	LRHS NLar
- 'Red Lady'PBR	CRos EBee EHyd ELan EPfP LRHS MAsh NEoE NHol NRHS SPoG
- RED ROBIN	see *P. fruticosa* MARIAN RED ROBIN
- 'Red Surprise'	WFar
- 'Royal Flush'	NWad
- SILVER 'N' GOLD ('Lisstreas') **new**	LRHS
- 'Snowbird'	NEoE WFar
§ - 'Snowflake'	CBcs
- 'Sommerflor' 🏆H7	CRos EHyd EPfP LRHS MAsh NRHS
- 'Sophie's Blush'	MGil MRav NWea
§ - (Sulphurascens Group) 'Elizabeth'	CBcs CBod CMac EPfP LSRN MGos MMuc MSwo NHol SCob SGbt SGol SPer SRms SWvt WFar
- - 'Longacre Variety'	CMac CTri IArd MSwo NLar NWea
- 'Sunset'	CBcs CBrac CMac GKin LSRN NLar NWea SCoo SPer SRms WFar
- 'Tangerine'	CBcs CBod CBrac CDoC CMac CTri EHyd EPfP GBin LRHS MAsh MGos MRav MSwo NHol NLar NRHS NWea SCob SEdd SNig SPer SPlb SRms SWvt WFar
- 'Tilford Cream'	CDoC CRos CSBt CTri EBee EHyd ELan EPfP GKin LRHS LSRN MRav MSwo NHol NRHS SCob SGbt SNig SPer SRms WCFE WFar
- 'Tom Conway'	CMac SRms
- var. ***veitchii***	CSBt
- 'Vilmoriniana'	CKel CMac CTri EHyd ELan EPfP GBin LRHS MAsh MRav NWea SPer SPoG SWvt WSpi
- 'Whirligig'	CMac
- 'White Lady'PBR	CBod NEoE
- 'Yellow Bird' 🏆H7	CRos EHyd LRHS MAsh
'Gibson's Scarlet' 🏆H7	Widely available
§ ***glandulosa*** subsp. ***nevadensis***	CTri MAsh
'Gloire de Nancy' (d)	EBee LRHS MRav NBir NChi NLar
'Herzblut'	NLar
hippiana	EBee
× ***hopwoodiana***	CMea CSpe CTtf CWCL EAJP EBee ECha ECtt ELan EPPr GMaP ILea LEdu MCot MNrw MRav NBir NChi NDov NLar SPer WCAu WFar
× ***hybrida*** 'Jean Jabber'	GLog MBow MRav NEoE NLar WFar
hyparctica	CPla GJos
kurdica	XLum
'Light My Fire'	ECtt MAsh MHol MNrw
'Mandshurica'	see *P. fruticosa* 'Manchu'
§ ***megalantha***	CBod CBro CRos EBou ECtt EDAr EHyd ELan EPfP EPri GGro GQue LRHS MBNS MPie MRav NBir NBro NRHS NSti SCoo SGbt SPer SRms XLum
- 'Gold Sovereign'	WMal
'Melton Fire'	EPfP GKin GPSL MNrw NBir
micrantha 'Purple Haze'	LEdu
- 'Purple Heart'	WPGP
'Monarch's Velvet'	see *P. thurberi* 'Monarch's Velvet'
'Monsieur Rouillard' (d)	CBod CElw CMac CRos EBee ECtt EHyd GPSL LRHS MACG MArl MNrw MRav NGdn NLar NRHS WHoo
'Mont d'Or'	EBee MRav NLar
montenegrina **new**	GJos
nepalensis	CPla EHyd LRHS NBro NChi NRHS XLum
- 'Craigieburn'	NChi
- 'Helen Jane'	CDor EBee EWld GBin GJos GQue LEdu NBir NHol NLar NWad WFar WHrl
§ - 'Miss Willmott'	Widely available
- 'Ron McBeath'	CDor CRos CWCL ECtt EHyd ELan EPfP EWld EWoo GAbr GBin ILea LRHS MAvo MRav NDov NFav NHol NLar NRHS NSti SRkn SRms SWvt WGwG WHoo
- 'Roxana'	EBee ELan EWTr MRav NBro SBut
- 'Shogran'	CRos EBee EBlo EBou EHyd GJos GQue LRHS NChi NHol NLar NRHS
§ ***neumanniana***	MAsh NBir NPoe WCav
- 'Goldrausch'	XLum

§	- 'Nana'	EBou EPot GArf MAsh NRya NWad SLee SPlb SRms WFar WHoo WIce XLum
	nevadensis	see *P. glandulosa* subsp. *nevadensis*
	nitida	EPot MAsh WAbe
	- 'Alba'	EPot GArf
	- 'Rubra'	EDAr GEdr NBir WAbe
	ovina var. ***ovina***	GKev
	palustris	CPud CWat EWat LLWG MWts NAts NLar NMir XLum
	parvifolia 'Klondike'	see *P. fruticosa* 'Klondike'
	pedata	NChi XLum
	peduncularis	GKev
	'Pink Panther'	see *P. fruticosa* PRINCESS
	aff. ***polyphylla***	GKev
	porphyrantha	GEdr GJos
	recta	SRms XLum
	- 'Alba'	GMaP
	- 'Citrina'	see *P. recta* var. *sulphurea*
	- 'Macrantha'	see *P. recta* 'Warrenii'
§	- var. ***sulphurea***	CFoA CMea EAJP EGrI EPPr EWTr GWyn LSun MNrw NBir NLar NSti NWad SPhx SRkn WBrk WCAu WHal WHoo WHrl WMal XLum
§	- 'Warrenii'	CSBt EHyd EPfP GMaP MRav NBir SHar SRms WHal WHrl XLum
	'Red Giant' new	CBod
	reptans 'Pleniflora' (d)	WCot
I	× ***rosea*** 'Pleniflora' (d) new	LRHS
	'Roxanne' (d)	MHer
	rupestris	CFoA CMea CNat ECha EPPr EWTr GJos GQue LSun MACG MHer NSti SBut WCAu WFar WHal
	× ***russelliana***	EHyd
	salesovianum new	GKev
	'Scarlet Starlet'	see *P. atrosanguinea* var. *argyrophylla* 'Scarlet Starlit'
	speciosa	EWes
	sterilis	WHer WSFF
*	***sundermanii***	WHrl
	tabernaemontani	see *P. neumanniana*
	thurberi	LRHS NLar NRHS SPhx XLum
§	- 'Monarch's Velvet'	Widely available
	tommasiniana	see *P. cinerea*
	× ***tonguei*** ♀H5	Widely available
	tormentilla	see *P. erecta*
	tridentata	see *Sibbaldiopsis tridentata*
	'Twinkling Star'	MHol NEoE
	verna misapplied	see *P. neumanniana*
	- 'Pygmaea'	see *P. neumanniana* 'Nana'
	'Versicolor Plena' (d)	NLar
	villosa	see *P. crantzii*
	'Vogue'	EBee
	'Volcan'	CWCL EWes NChi WCAu WFar WHal
	'White Queen'	GLog MRav SBut SHar SRms
	'William Rollisson' ♀H7	Widely available
	willmottiae	see *P. nepalensis* 'Miss Willmott'
	'Yellow Queen'	CMac CTri EHyd GKin GMaP LRHS MRav NLar NRHS SPer SRms WCAu

Poterium see *Sanguisorba*

	sanguisorba	see *Sanguisorba minor*

Prangos (*Apiaceae*)

	ferulacea	WCot

Pratia (*Campanulaceae*)

§	***angulata***	GArf
§	- 'Treadwellii'	ECha ECtt ELan NBro SPlb SRms WFar WHal
	montana	see *Lobelia montana*
§	***pedunculata***	CTri EBou ECha ECtt EDAr EPfP GQue LLWG LRHS LSun MAsh NFav NHpl SLee SPlb SRms SRot WFar WIce
I	- 'Alba'	EWes LRHS NHpl SLee SRms WFar WIce
	- 'County Park'	CBod CExl CMea CTri EBou ECha ECtt EDAr ELan EPfP EWTr EWoo GWyn LLWG LRHS MAsh NHpl SLee SPlb SPoG SRms SRot WCav WFar WIce XLum
	- 'White Stars'	LLWG

Prenanthes (*Asteraceae*)

§	***alba***	GGro

Preslia see *Mentha*

Primula ✿ (*Primulaceae*)

	(Si)	MAsh
	acaulis	see *P. vulgaris*
	'Adrian Jones' (Au)	NSum
	'Alan Robb' (Pr/Prim/d)	ECtt
	'Alexina' (*allionii* hybrid) (Au)	NHar
	'Alice Collins'	NSum
§	***allionii*** (Au)	GKev WAbe
	- 'Aire Waves'	see *P.* × *loiseleurii* 'Aire Waves'
	- 'Allen Charm' (Au)	ITim
	- 'Allen Moonbeam' (Au)	GAbr ITim NHar
	- 'Anna Griffith' (Au)	WAbe
	- 'Anne' (Au)	NSum
	- 'Apple Blossom' (Au)	NHpl
	- 'Archer' (Au)	ITim
	- 'Ares' (Au)	NHar
	- 'Aries Violet' (Au)	ITim NHar
	- 'Bill Martin' (Au)	ITim NSum NWad
	- 'Cherry' (Au)	WAbe
	- 'Chivalry' (Au)	WAbe
	- 'Circe's Flute' (Au)	NHar
	- 'Cissie' (Au)	ITim NHar
	- 'Crystal' (Au)	NSum
	- 'Edrom' (Au)	NSum
	- 'Elizabeth Burrow' (Au)	WAbe
	- 'Eureka' (Au)	NSum WAbe
	- 'Eveline Burrow' (Au)	WAbe
	- 'Fanfare' (Au)	MAsh NHar
I	- 'Forma' (Au)	XBar
	- 'Frank Barker' (Au)	NWad
	- 'Gilderdale Glow' (Au)	NHar
	- 'Hartside 6' (Au)	ITim
	- 'Hemswell' (Au)	NHpl
	- 'Henry Burrow' (Au)	WAbe
	- 'Herald' (Au)	ITim
	- 'Horwood' (Au)	ITim
	- 'Jenny' (Au)	GKev
§	- 'Joan Elliott' (Au)	EWoo
	- 'Lee Mayers' (Au)	WFar
	- 'Lepus' (Au)	WAbe
	- 'Lucy' (Au)	NHar
	- 'Malcolm' (Au)	ITim
	- 'Marion' (Au)	XBar
	- 'Marjorie Wooster' (Au)	XBar
	- 'Neptune's Wave' (Au)	NHar
	- 'New Dawn' (Au)	ITim
	- 'Peace' (Au)	NHar
	- 'Peggy Wilson' (Au)	EWld GKev WThu
	- 'Pennine Pink' (Au)	GArf
	- 'Phoebe's Moon' (Au)	NHar
	- 'Pinkie' (Au)	WAbe
	- 'Raymond Wooster' (Au)	GKev

- 'Snowflake' (Au)	GKev
- 'Tranquility' (Au)	ITim
- 'William Earle' (Au)	XBar
***allionii* × *allionii* 'Apple Blossom' (Au)**	GArf
allionii* × *auricula	NWad WFar
misapplied 'Old Red Dusty Miller' (Au)	
allionii* × *auricula 'Blairside Yellow' (Au)	GArf NSum
allionii* × *hirsuta (Au)	GArf
allionii × 'Lismore Treasure' (Au)	ITim NHpl
allionii* × *pubescens (Au)	NHpl
allionii* × *pubescens 'Harlow Car' (Au)	WFar
allionii × 'White Linda Pope' (Au)	NHpl
alpicola (Si) 🏆^{H6}	CWCL GAbr GKev GQue LShi MMuc NBid NGdn NWad WTyc XBar
- var. ***alba*** (Si)	CPla GAbr GRum NBid NChi
§ - var. ***alpicola*** (Si)	GRum
- hybrids (Si)	GEdr MACG NHpl
- var. ***luna***	see *P. alpicola* var. *alpicola*
- var. ***violacea*** (Si)	CPla EBee GAbr GGro GRum MNrw NBid NWad
- - 'Royal Blue' (Si)	GKev
'Altaica'	see *P. elatior* subsp. *meyeri*
altaica grandiflora	see *P. elatior* subsp. *meyeri*
amoena	see *P. elatior* subsp. *meyeri*
'Amy Smith' (Pr/Prim)	GAbr
anisodora	see *P. wilsonii* var. *anisodora*
× ***anisodoxa*** 'Kevock Surprise' (Pf)	CWCL GKev
'Annemijne' (Pr/Poly)	WCot
apoclita (Mu)	GKev XBar
I 'Appleblossom' (Pr/Prim/d)	GEdr
× ***arctotis***	see *P.* × *pubescens*
aurantiaca (Pf)	GAbr GKev GRum NHpl XBar
- 'Harperley Pink' (Pf)	GBin MPnt NHpl
aurantiaca* × *pulverulenta (Pf)	GRum NFav
aureata (Pe)	NHar
auricula L. (Au) 🏆^{H5}	CRos EDAr EHyd EWld GKev GRum LRHS MAsh NRHS NSla SPer SPlb SPoG
- subsp. ***bauhinii*** (Au)	CWCL GKev
- - var. ***albocincta*** (Au)	GKev
auricula misapplied (Au)	EBou ECha EHyd LRHS MBow NRHS WCav
- A74 (Au)	MMuc SEND
- 'Abdor' (Au/St)	EWoo NDro
- 'Abundance' (Au/A)	EWoo NDro
- 'Achates' (Au/A)	EWoo WAln
- 'Admiral' (Au/A)	NDro WAln
- 'Adrian' (Au/A)	GAbr ITim NDro NSum XBar
- 'Adrienne' (Au/A)	EGrI EWoo GKev
- 'Adrienne Ruan' (Au/A)	NDro NSum WAln
- 'Aga Khan' (Au/A)	NDro WAln
- 'Agamemnon' (Au/A)	EWoo NDro NSum XBar
- 'Airy Fairy' (Au/S)	NDro
- 'Alamo' (Au/A)	NDro
- 'Albert Bailey' (Au/d)	GAbr NDro WFar WHil XBar
- 'Alexandra Georgina' (Au/A)	WAln
- 'Alf' (Au/A)	NDro NSum WHil XBar
- 'Alfred Charles' (Au/A)	WAln
- 'Alice' (Au/d)	NDro
- 'Alice Haysom' (Au/S)	ELan GAbr ITim NDro WHil XBar
- 'Alicia' (Au/A)	GAbr NDro NSum XBar
- 'Alien' (Au/S)	NDro
- 'Alison' (Au/S)	NDro
- 'Alison Jane' (Au/A)	NDro NSum WHil XBar
- 'Alison Rose' (Au/B)	NDro
- 'Alison Telford' (Au/A)	NWad WHil
- 'Allard' (Au/A)	WAln
- 'Alloway' (Au/d)	WAln
- 'Amicable' (Au/A)	NDro NSum WHil XBar
- 'Amie Rosalind' (Au/B)	NDro
- 'Amore' (Au/St)	NDro
- 'Ancient Order' (Au/A)	WAln
- 'Ancient Society' (Au/A)	EWoo NDro NSum NWad XBar
- 'Andrea Julie' (Au/A)	NDro WHil XBar
- 'Andrew Hunter' (Au/A)	NDro NSum XBar
- 'Andy Cole' (Au/A)	NDro WAln
- 'Angel Eyes' (Au/St)	EWoo NDro
- 'Angel Islington' (Au/S)	EGrI NDro
- 'Angela Gould' (Au/B)	EWoo NDro XBar
- 'Angela Grace' (Au/d)	XBar
- 'Angostura' (Au/d)	EBee EWoo WHil
- 'Ann Brookes' (Au/d)	WAln
- 'Ann Taylor' (Au/A)	WAln
- 'Anna' (Au/B)	NDro
- 'Anne Hyatt' (Au/d)	NDro
- 'Annette' (Au/B)	NDro
- 'Ansells' (Au/S)	EGrI WAln
- 'Anwar Sadat' (Au/A)	EWoo NDro NSum WHil XBar
- 'Apple Blossom' (Au/B)	NDro WHil
- 'Applecross' (Au/A)	NDro NHpl NSum WHil XBar
- 'April Moon' (Au/S)	NDro WHil
- 'Arab Prince' (Au/A)	WAln
- 'Arab Queen' (Au/A)	WAln
- 'Arabian Night' (Au/A)	NDro WAln
- 'Arctic Fox' (Au/A)	WAln WHil XBar
- 'Argentine' (Au/S)	XBar
- 'Argus' (Au/A)	EGrI ITim LSun NDro NWad WHil XBar
- 'Arlene' (Au/A)	WAln
- 'Armorique' (Au/d)	XBar
- 'Art Deco' (Au/B)	NDro
- 'Arthur Delbridge' (Au/A)	NDro NSum WHil XBar
- 'Artwork' (Au/S)	NDro
- 'Arundell' (Au/S/St)	EBee ITim NDro NSum WFar WHil XBar
- 'Ascot Gavotte' (Au/S)	NDro
- 'Ashcliffe Gem' (Au/A)	NDro WAln
- Ashwood strain (Au)	MAsh
- 'Astolat' (Au/S)	EBee NDro NHpl WHil XBar
- 'Athene' (Au/S)	ITim NDro
- 'Atlantic' (Au/S)	NDro
- 'Aubergine' (Au/B)	NDro
- 'Audacity' (Au/d)	NDro WAln
- 'Audrey' (Au/S)	NDro
- 'Aurora' (Au/A)	EDAr NSum WAln
- 'Austin' (Au/A)	NSum WAln
- 'Autumn Fire' (Au/A)	EWoo
- 'Autumn Glow' (Au/d)	NDro
- 'Autumn Jewels' (Au/d)	XBar
- 'Avon Citronella' (Au/d)	XBar
- 'Avon Tan' (Au/d)	GAbr
- 'Avon Twist' (Au/d)	EWoo
- 'Avondale' (Au/B)	LRHS
- 'Avonwick' (Au/B)	NDro
- 'Avril' (Au/A)	NDro WAln WHil XBar
- 'Avril Hunter' (Au/A)	EWoo ITim NDro NSum WHil XBar
- 'Aztec' (Au/d)	WAln
- 'Baby Blue' (Au)	LRHS WHil
- 'Bacchante' (Au/d)	WAln
- 'Bacchus' (Au/A)	NDro WHil XBar
- 'Baggage' (Au/St)	ITim NDro WHil
- 'Bailey Boy' (Au/B)	NDro

- 'Bakerloo Line' (Au/S) NDro
- 'Balbithan' (Au/B) NDro
- 'Ballynahinch' (Au) ITim
- 'Baltic Amber' (Au/d) GAbr NDro WAln WHil XBar
- 'Bank Error' (Au/S) NDro WAln
- 'Barbara Mason' (Au) NDro WAln
- 'Barbarella' (Au/S) NDro XBar
- 'Barbe à Papa' (Au/B) **new** XBar
- 'Barber's Pole' (Au/St) NDro
- Barnhaven Border hybrids (Au/B) XBar
- - doubles (Au/d) GAbr XBar
- 'Barr Beacon' (Au/A) ITim NDro NSum
- 'Bartl' (Au/A) EBee
- 'Basilio' (Au/S) NDro
- 'Basuto' (Au/A) EWoo ITim NSum WHil XBar
- 'Beatrice' (Au/A) CTri EWoo NDro NHpl WFar WHil XBar
- 'Beauty of Bath' (Au/S) WAln
- 'Beckminster' (Au/A) WAln
- 'Bedford Lad' (Au/A) NDro
- 'Beechen Green' (Au/S) ITim
- 'Beeches Variegated' (Au/A/v) EBee WFar
- 'Beervelde' (Au/B) WHil
- 'Belgravia Gold' (Au/B) NDro
- 'Bellamy Pride' (Au/B) NDro NSum
- 'Belle Zana' (Au/S) NDro
- 'Bellini' (Au/d) XBar
- 'Ben Wyves' (Au/S) NDro
- 'Bendigo' (Au/S) NDro WAln
- 'Benny Green' (Au/S) NDro XBar
- 'Beppi' (Au/B) NDro WHil
- 'Bessie' (Au/d) XBar
- 'Best Wishes' (Au/F) NDro
- 'Bethan McSparron' (Au/B) NDro
- 'Betty Sherriff' (Au/B) GAbr
- 'Betty Stewart' (Au/A) WAln
- 'Betty Wilson' (Au/St) NDro
- 'Bewitched' (Au/A) NDro WAln XBar
- 'Bielfeld' (Au/B) NDro
- 'Big Thrill' (Au) WFar
- 'Bilbao' (Au/A) WAln
- 'Bilbo Baggins' (Au/A) NDro WAln
- 'Bill Bailey' (Au/d) GAbr NDro
- 'Bingley Folk' (Au/B) NDro
- 'Bingley Snowflake' (Au/B) NDro
- 'Bisto' (Au/S) WAln
- 'Bitterne Primrose' (Au/d) EWoo
- 'Bizarre' (Au) NDro
- 'Black Diamond' (Au/d) WHil XBar
- 'Black Jack'PBR (Au/d) CBod CWCL ECtt NHpl NLar SEdd
- 'Blackhill' (Au/S) EWoo ITim NHpl
- 'Blackpool Rock' (Au/St) NDro XBar
- 'Blairside Yellow' (Au/B) NDro NSla WAbe
- 'Blakeney' (Au/d) NDro
- 'Blossom' (Au/A) EWoo XBar
- 'Blue Bella' (Au/B) NDro
- 'Blue Belle' (Au/B) NDro
- 'Blue Bonnet' (Au/A/d) EWoo GAbr NDro XBar
- 'Blue Boy' (Au/S) WHil
- 'Blue Chip' (Au/S) NDro NSum WHil XBar
- 'Blue Cliff' (Au/S) NDro WAln
- 'Blue Frills' (Au/d) NDro WAln
- 'Blue Heaven' (Au/A) EWoo NDro XBar
- 'Blue Jay' (Au/A) **new** WHil
- 'Blue Lace' (Au/A) WAln
- 'Blue Merle' (Au/B) NDro
- 'Blue Mist' (Au/B) NDro
- 'Blue Night' (Au/B) ITim NDro
- 'Blue Ridge' (Au/A) NDro
- 'Blue Skies' (Au/St) NDro
- 'Blue Velvet' (Au/B) EWoo GAbr GQue NDro NHpl NSum WHil XBar
- 'Blue Wave' (Au/d) CBor
- 'Blue Waves' (Au/B) EGrl NDro
- 'Blue Yodeler' (Au/A) EGrl NDro NSum WFar WHil XBar
- 'Blue Yonder' (Au/S) ITim
- 'Blush Baby' (Au/St) EBee EWoo NDro NSum NWad WHil XBar
- 'Blyth Spirit' (Au/A) NDro WAln XBar
- 'Bob Lancashire' (Au/S) GAbr ITim NDro WHil XBar
- 'Bokay' (Au/d) WAln
- 'Bold Tartan' (Au/St) NDro
- 'Bolero' (Au/A) NDro WAln
- 'Bonafide' (Au/d) EWoo WAln
- 'Bonanza' (Au/S) WAln
- 'Bonnie the Cat' (Au) WHil
- 'Bookham Firefly' (Au/A) NDro WHil XBar
- 'Border Bandit' (Au/B) EWoo GAbr NDro WHil XBar
- 'Border Beauty' (Au/St) NDro
- 'Border Blue' (Au/B) NDro
- 'Border Patrol' (Au/B) ITim NDro
- 'Border Tawny' (Au/B) NDro
- 'Boromir' (Au/A) EWoo NDro NSum WAln
- 'Bournebrook' (Au/A) WAln
- 'Bowen's Blue' (Au/B) EWoo NDro
- 'Bradford City' (Au/A) CFis EBee NDro WFar WHil XBar
- 'Bradmore Bluebell' (Au/B) NDro
- 'Bramshill' (Au/S) NDro
- 'Bran' (Au/B) NDro
- 'Brandaris' (Au/A) WAln
- 'Branston' (Au/d) XBar
- 'Brasso' (Au/S) NDro WAln XBar
- 'Brazen Hussy' (Au/d) CRos WAln
- 'Brazil' (Au/S) EBee GAbr NDro WHil
- 'Brazos River' (Au/A) NDro
- 'Breckland Joy' (Au/A) NDro WAln
- 'Brenda's Choice' (Au/A) EWoo NDro NSum XBar
- 'Brenda's Dilemma' (Au/S) NDro
- 'Brick Lane' (Au/S) NDro
- 'Bright Eyes' (Au/A) XBar
- 'Bright Ginger' (Au/S) NDro WAln
- 'Brigitte' (Au/A) XBar
- 'Brimstone and Treacle' (Au/d) WAln
- 'Brixton' (Au/S) NDro
- 'Broad Gold' (Au/A) NDro NSum XBar
- 'Broadwell Gold' (Au/B) GAbr NDro NSum
- 'Brocade' (Au/St) NDro
- 'Brookfield' (Au/S) GAbr NDro NHpl XBar
- 'Broughton' (Au/S) NDro
- 'Brown Ben' (Au/A) EWoo WFar WHil
- 'Brown Bess' (Au/A) GAbr ITim WHil
- 'Brownie' (Au/B) GAbr NBir NDro NSum WHil XBar
- 'Brownie Point' (Au/B) NDro
- 'Brunhilde' (Au/B) NDro
- 'Bucks Green' (Au/S) NDro
- 'Buffy' (Au/St) NDro
- 'Bunny Black' (Au) GKev
- 'Bunty' (Au/A) XBar
- 'Buoyance' (Au/A) WAln
- 'Burnished Gold' (Au/d) WAln
- 'Bush Baby' (Au/B) NDro
- 'Buttermere' (Au/d) WAln
- 'Butterwick' (Au/A) GAbr ITim NDro NSum XBar
- 'C.G. Haysom' (Au/S) NDro
- 'C.W. Needham' (Au/A) ITim NDro XBar
- 'Cadiz Bay' (Au/d) EWoo WAln
- 'Café au Lait' (Au/A) XBar
- 'Calico' (Au/d) XBar
- 'Calypso' (Au/d) EWoo NDro WAln

- 'Cambodunum' (Au/A) NSum WHil
- 'Cambodunum' (Au/A) NDro WFar WHil XBar
- 'Cambrai' (Au/d) WHil
- 'Camelot' (Au/d) EWoo NDro WFar XBar
- 'Cameo' (Au/A) NHpl
- 'Cameo Beauty' (Au/d) NDro
- 'Candy Stripe' (Au/St) NDro
- 'Cannelle' (Au/d) XBar
- 'Caramel' (Au/A) GAbr WAln
- 'Cardinal Red' (Au/d) NDro
- 'Cardington' (Au/A) WAln
- 'Carioca' (Au/A) WAln
- 'Carmel' (Au/d) EWoo NDro WAln XBar
- 'Carnaval' (Au/B) WHil XBar
- 'Carne' (Au/d) NDro
- 'Carnival' (Au/A) WAln
- 'Carole' (Au/A) NSum WHil
- 'Carousel' (Au/B) EWoo NDro NSum WHil
- 'Carreras' (Au) NDro
- 'Carsa Wakes' (Au/d) NDro WAln
- 'Carzon' (Au/A) NDro
- 'Catherine Wheel' (Au/St) NDro
- 'Catta Ha' (Au/d) NDro
- 'Celtic One' (Au/St) NDro
- 'Ceri Nicolle' (Au/B) NDro
- 'Chaffinch' (Au/S) EGrI GAbr NDro NSum
- 'Chamois' (Au/B) NDro NSum NWad WHil
- 'Chamomile' (Au/B) new NDro
- 'Chanel' (Au/S) WAln
- 'Charisma' (Au/St) NDro
- 'Charles Bronson' (Au/d) GAbr NDro XBar
- Charles Rennie' (Au/B) EWoo NDro NSum WHil XBar
- 'Charlie's Aunt' (Au/A) NDro WAln
- 'Charlotte' (Au/B) NDro
- 'Charlotte Brookes' (Au/d) WAln
- 'Checkmate' (Au/d) EWoo WAln XBar
- 'Cheeky' (Au/d) EWoo
- 'Chelsea Bridge' (Au/A) EGrI EWoo NDro WHil
- 'Chelsea Girl' (Au/d) NDro
- 'Cheops' (Au/A) EGrI NDro NSum
- 'Cherille' (Au/S) NDro
- 'Cherry' (Au/S) GAbr NDro
- 'Cherry Picker' (Au/A) EGrI NDro NSum
- 'Chestnut' (Au/B) NDro
- 'Cheyenne' (Au/S) GAbr NDro
- 'Chiffon' (Au/S) NDro NSum XBar
- 'Chiquita' (Au/d) EWoo NDro
- 'Chirichua' (Au/S) WAln
- 'Chloë' (Au/S) GRum NDro NHpl
- 'Choir Boy' (Au/A) WAln
- 'Chorister' (Au/S) EBee ITim NDro NSum WHil
- 'Chyne' (Au) NDro
- 'Cicero' (Au/A) WAln
- 'Cinders' (Au/St) NDro
- 'Cindy' (Au/A) NDro
- 'Cinnamon' (Au/d) GAbr NDro WFar WHil XBar
- 'Ciribiribin' (Au/A) WAln
- 'Clara' (Au/d) WFar
- 'Clare' (Au/S) NDro
- 'Classy Stripe' (Au/St) ITim
- 'Clatter-Ha' (Au/d) NSum WHil
- 'Claud Wilson' (Au/St) NDro
- 'Claudia Taylor' (Au) NSum
- 'Cleft Stick' (Au) NDro
- 'Cloth of Gold' (Au/A) NDro
- 'Clotted Cream' (Au/B) NDro
- 'Clouded Yellow' (Au/S) NDro
- 'Cloudscape' (Au/S) NDro
- 'Cloudy Bay' (Au/B) GAbr NDro WCot
- 'Cloverdale' (Au/d) WAln
- 'Clunie' (Au/S) NDro XBar
- 'Cobbydale Orange' (Au/B) NDro
- 'Cobden Meadows' (Au/A) WAln
- 'Cocoa' (Au/d) XBar
- 'Coffee' (Au/S) NDro WFar
- 'Colbury' (Au/S) NDro
- 'Colonel Champney' (Au/S) NDro
- 'Colonel Mustard' (Au/d) XBar
- 'Comet' (Au/S) NDro
- 'Connaught Court' (Au/A) CBor EWoo NDro NSum
- 'Conquistador' (Au/A) NDro WAln
- 'Conservative' (Au/S) NDro
- 'Consett' (Au/S) WHil
- 'Cooper's Gold' (Au/B) NDro
- 'Coppi' (Au/A) EWoo NDro
- 'Cornish Cream' (Au/B) NDro
- 'Cornmeal' (Au/S) NDro WHil XBar
- 'Corntime' (Au/S) WAln
- 'Corrie Files' (Au/d) WAln
- 'Cortina' (Au/S) EGrI EWoo ITim NDro WHil
- 'County Park Red' (Au/B) NDro
- 'Coventry Street' (Au/S) NDro NSum
- 'Crackling Rosie' (Au/A/d) WAln
- 'Craig Nordie' (Au/B) NDro
- 'Craig Vaughan' (Au/A) NDro NSum
- 'Cranborne' (Au/A) WAln
- 'Crimple' (Au/S) NDro WHil
- 'Crimson Glow' (Au/d) EWTr GAbr ITim LCro LOPS NDro NSum WHil XBar
- 'Crinoline' (Au/S) NDro
- 'Cuckoo Fair' (Au/S) ECtt NDro NSum WFar
- 'Cuddles' (Au/A) EWoo NDro WAln
- 'Curry Blend' (Au/B) NDro NWad WHil
- 'D.S.J.' (Au/S) NDro
- 'Daftie Green' (Au/S) NDro
- 'Dales Red' (Au/B) EWoo NDro NHpl NSum WHil
- 'Dan Tiger' (Au/St) EWoo NDro WHil

I - 'Daniel' (Au/d) XBar
- 'Daniel' (Au/A) NDro WAln
- 'Daniel T. Taylor' (Au/A) NDro WAln
- 'Darent Tiger' (Au/St) NDro XBar
- 'Dark Eyes' (Au/d) EWoo NDro NSum WHil
- 'Dark Lady' (Au/A) WAln
- 'D'Artagnan' (Au/B) NDro
- 'Darth Vader' (Au/d) XBar
- 'David Beckham' (Au/d) WAln
- 'David McSparron' (Au/B) NDro
- 'Day by Day' (Au/St) NDro
- 'Deal' (Au/S) NDro
- 'Deckchair' (Au/St) NDro
- 'Dedham' (Au/d) WAln
- 'Del Boy' (Au/A) WAln
- 'Delilah' (Au/d) NDro NSum WFar WHil
- 'Denise' (Au/S) WAln
- 'Denna Snuffer' (Au/d) EWoo GAbr NDro
- 'Derrill' (Au/B) NDro
- 'Derwent Water' (Au/S) NDro
- 'Deuce of Hearts' (Au/St) NDro
- 'Devon Cream' (Au/d) NDro XBar
- 'Devon's Road' (Au/S) NDro
- 'Diamond Dust' (Au/B) NDro
- 'Diane' (Au/A) NDro
- 'Dick Rogers' (Au/B) NDro
- 'Dido' (Au/B) XBar
- 'Digby' (Au/d) NDro WAln
- 'Digit' (Au/d) NDro WAln
- 'Dill' (Au/A) NDro NSum WHil
- 'Dilly Dilly' (Au/A) NDro XBar
- 'Divint Dunch' (Au/A) NDro WHil XBar

- 'Doctor Lennon's White' (Au/B) EWoo GAbr NDro NWad WHil XBar
- 'Dolly' (Au/B) NDro
I – 'Dolly Mixture' (Au/B) XBar
- 'Don Carlos' (Au/d) XBar
- 'Donhead' (Au/A) ITim NDro WHil
- 'Donn' (Au/d) WAln
- 'Donna Clancy' (Au/S) NDro XBar
- 'Doreen Stephens' (Au/A) NDro
- 'Doris Jean' (Au/A) NDro
- 'Doublet' (Au/d) EGrI NDro NSum WHil
- 'Doubloon' (Au/d) XBar
- 'Doublure' (Au/d) EWoo NDro WHil
- 'Douglas Bader' (Au/A) ITim NDro NSum WHil
- 'Douglas Black' (Au/S) EGrI EWoo GAbr NDro WHil
- 'Douglas Green' (Au/S) EWoo NDro
- 'Dovedale' (Au/S) NDro
- 'Doyen' (Au/d) EWoo ITim NDro NHpl WAln WHil
- 'Dragon's Hoard' (Au/A) WAln
- 'Drax' (Au/A) WAln
- 'Dubarii' (Au/A) NDro WAln
- 'Duke of Edinburgh' (Au/B) NDro
- 'Dusky Girl' (Au/A) NDro WAln
- 'Dusky Maiden' (Au/A) EWoo GAbr NDro NSum WHil
- 'Dusky Yellow' (Au/B) NDro
- 'Dusty Miller' (Au/B) NBir
- 'Eastern Promise' (Au/A) EWoo NDro NSum WHil
- 'Eaton Dawn' (Au/S) XBar
- 'Ed Spivey' (Au/A) NDro
- 'Eddy Gordon' (Au/A) WAln
- 'Eden Alexander' (Au/B) EWoo NDro XBar
- 'Eden Amethyst' (Au/B) NDro
- 'Eden Aramis' (Au/B) NDro
- 'Eden Blue Star' (Au/B) EWoo GAbr NDro NSum WFar WHil
- 'Eden Bramley' (Au/B) NDro
- 'Eden Carmine' (Au/B) EWoo NDro NWad WHil XBar
- 'Eden Dark Eyes' (Au/B) NDro
- 'Eden David' (Au/B) NDro WFar WHil
- 'Eden Elegance' (Au/B) **new** WHil
- 'Eden Ensign' (Au/B) NDro WFar WHil
- 'Eden Fanfare' (Au/B) NDro WFar
- 'Eden Glow' (Au/B) NDro
- 'Eden Goldfinch' (Au/B) EWoo NDro WFar
- 'Eden Greenfinch' (Au/B) EWoo NDro NSum WHil XBar
- 'Eden Lilactime' (Au/B) NDro WFar
- 'Eden Moonlight' (Au/B) NDro WHil XBar
- 'Eden Porthos' (Au/B) NDro
- 'Eden Rhiann' (Au/B) NDro
- 'Eden Royalty' (Au/B) WFar WHil
- 'Eden Ruby Star' (Au/B) NDro
- 'Eden Simon' (Au/B) NDro
- 'Eden Sunrise' (Au/B) NDro NSum
- 'Eden Surprise' (Au/B) NDro
- 'Eden Wendy' (Au/B) NDro
- 'Edinburgh' (Au/A) WAln
- 'Edith Major' (Au/d) NSum
- 'Eglinton' (Au) NDro NSum
- 'Eileen K' (Au/S) NDro
- 'Elegance' (Au/S) WFar
- 'Elf Star' (Au/A) NSum
- 'Eli Jenkins' (Au) WAln
- 'Elizabeth Ann' (Au/A) NDro
- 'Ellen Thompson' (Au/A) EGrI NDro WHil XBar
- 'Ellie May' (Au/S) XBar
- 'Eloise' (Au/d) **new** XBar
- 'Elsie May' (Au/A) EWoo ITim NDro
- 'Embley' (Au/S) NDro NHpl
- 'Emery Down' (Au/S) NDro
- 'Emily Mary' (Au/B) NDro
- 'Emmett Smith' (Au/A) NDro NSum WAln
- 'Ems Blue' (Au/B) NDro
- 'Ems Funny Face' (Au/B) NDro
- 'Enlightened' (Au/A) NDro
- 'Erica' (Au/A) EWoo NDro NSum WHil XBar
- 'Erjon' (Au/S) NDro
- 'Error' (Au/S) NDro
- 'Eschman Starflower' (Au/S) WHil
- 'Ethel' (Au) CBor NDro
- 'Ethel Wilkes' (Au/d) WAln
- 'Etna' (Au/S) NDro
- 'Euston Road' (Au/S) NDro
- 'Eve Guest' (Au/A) NDro NSum WAln
- 'Everest Blue' (Au/S) NDro XBar
- 'Everso Lovely Blue' (Au/B) NDro
- 'Excalibur' (Au/d) NDro NSum
- 'Exhibition Blau' (Exhibition Series) (Au/B) WHil
- 'Eye Candy' (Au/St) NDro
- 'Eyeopener' (Au/A) NDro NSum WHil XBar
- 'Fabuloso' (Au/St) EWoo NDro
- 'Fairy' (Au/A) WAln
- 'Fairy Dust' (Au/D) XBar
- 'Fairy Light' (Au/S) NDro
- 'Fairy Moon' (Au/S) NDro
- 'Fairy Queen' (Au/S) NDro
- 'Faliraki Fanciful' (Au) NDro
- 'Falstaff' (Au/d) WAln
- 'Fanciful' (Au/S) NDro WHil XBar
- 'Fancy Free' (Au) EWoo
- 'Fancy Pants' (Au/S) NDro
- 'Fandancer' (Au/A) WAln
- 'Fandango' (Au/St) NDro
- 'Fanfare' (Au/S) NDro
- 'Fanny Meerbeck' (Au/S) GAbr NDro WHil
- 'Fantasia' (Au/d) NDro
- 'Faro' (Au/S) NDro
- 'Favourite' (Au/S) ITim NDro NSum WHil XBar
- 'Femme Fatale' (Au/St) NDro
- 'Fennay' (Au/S) EWoo NSum
- 'Ferrybridge' (Au/A) NDro WAln
- 'Festubert' (Au/d) WHil
- 'Fiddler's Green' (Au/d) GAbr NDro WCot XBar
- 'Figaro' (Au/S) NDro XBar
- 'Figurine' (Au/d) WAln
- 'Finchfield' (Au/A) EWoo NDro WAln
- 'Fine Art' (Au/S) NDro
- 'Finley' (Au/B) NDro
- 'Firecracker' (Au) NSum WAln
- 'Firsby' (Au/d) NDro WHil
- 'First Lady' (Au/A) WAln WFar
- 'First Light' (Au/B) NDro NSum
- 'Fleet Street' (Au/S) NDro NSum WFar WHil XBar
- 'Fleminghouse' (Au/S) NDro
- 'Flemington' (Au) **new** GAbr
- 'Flirty' (Au/St) NDro
- 'Florence Brown' (Au/S) NDro
- 'Fluffy Duckling' (Au/S) NDro
- 'For You' (Au/St) NDro
- 'Forest Autumn Glow' (Au/d) WHil
- 'Forest Beech' (Au/d) WHil
- 'Forest Blush' (Au/d) WHil
- 'Forest Bordeaux' (Au/d) WHil
- 'Forest Bracken' (Au/d) EWoo WHil
- 'Forest Brown Sugar' (Au/d) WHil
- 'Forest Burgundy' (Au/d) WHil
- 'Forest Burnt Gold' (Au/d) WHil
- 'Forest Buttercup' (Au/d) WHil

- 'Forest Canary' (Au/d) **new** WHil
- 'Forest Cappuccino' (Au/d) EWoo WHil
- 'Forest Chocolate Teapot' (Au/d) **new** WHil
- 'Forest Coffee' (Au/d) NDro WHil
- 'Forest Dawn' (Au/d) WHil
- 'Forest Delight' (Au/d) WHil
- 'Forest Diamond' (Au/d) WHil
- 'Forest Disco Dancer' (Au/d) WHil
- 'Forest Dream' (Au/d) WHil
- 'Forest Duet' (Au/d) EWoo NDro WFar WHil
- 'Forest Dusk' (Au/d) WHil
- 'Forest Emperor' (Au/d) WHil
- 'Forest Evermore' (Au/d) **new** WHil
- 'Forest Fall' (Au/d) WHil
- 'Forest Fancy That' (Au/d) WHil
- 'Forest Fire' (Au/d) EWoo GAbr NSum WHil
- 'Forest Foxy Girl' (Au/d) WHil
- 'Forest Frost' (Au/d) WHil
- 'Forest Garnet' (Au/d) WHil
- 'Forest Glade' (Au/d) WHil
- 'Forest Golden Crown' (Au/d) WHil
- 'Forest Gorse' (Au/d) WHil
- 'Forest Greenfinch' (Au/d) WHil
- 'Forest Heartbreaker' (Au) WHil
- 'Forest Hint of Pink' (Au/d) WHil
- 'Forest Hot Stuff' (Au/d) WHil
- 'Forest Kingcup' (Au/d) WHil
- 'Forest Lemon' (Au/d) EWoo WHil
- 'Forest Lemon Sorbet' (Au/d) WHil
- 'Forest Lime' (Au/d) WHil
- 'Forest Love' (Au/d) WHil
- 'Forest Mayday' (Au/d) WHil
- 'Forest Old Thumper' (Au/d) WHil
- 'Forest Peach' (Au/d) WHil
- 'Forest Pecan' (Au/d) WHil
- 'Forest Pink Lustre' (Au/d) WHil
- 'Forest Pink Sensation' (Au/d) WHil
- 'Forest Pink Surprise' (Au/d) WHil
- 'Forest Plum' (Au/d) WHil
- 'Forest Prince' (Au/d) WHil
- 'Forest Purple Penny' (Au/d) WHil
- 'Forest Raspberry Delight' (Au) **new** WHil
- 'Forest Red Beret' (Au/d) WHil
- 'Forest Red Mist' (Au/d) WHil
- 'Forest Red 'n' Fred' (Au/d) WHil
- 'Forest Redstart' (Au) WHil
- 'Forest Rocket' (Au/d) WHil
- 'Forest Rose' (Au/d) EWoo
- 'Forest Scarlet Woman' (Au/d) WHil
- 'Forest Shade' (Au/d) WHil
- 'Forest Smokey' (Au/d) WHil
- 'Forest Sorcerer' (Au/d) WHil
- 'Forest Splendid' (Au/d) **new** WHil
- 'Forest Starlet' (Au/d) WHil
- 'Forest Sunbeam' (Au/d) WHil
- 'Forest Sunburst' (Au/d) WHil
- 'Forest Sunfire' (Au/d) WHil
- 'Forest Sunlight' (Au/d) WHil
- 'Forest Sunshade' (Au/d) WHil
- 'Forest Sunshine' (Au/d) WHil
- 'Forest Thatch' (Au/d) WHil
- 'Forest Twilight' (Au/d) EWoo WHil
- 'Forest Way' (Au/d) WHil
- 'Forest Zest' (Au/d) WHil
- 'Foundling' (Au) ITim
- 'Foxfire' (Au/A) WAln
- 'Foxy' (Au/B) NDro
- 'Fradley' (Au/A) NDro WAln WFar WHil
- 'Françoise' (Au/d) XBar
- 'Frank Bailey' (Au/d) EWoo WAln
- 'Frank Crosland' (Au/A) NDro NSum WHil
- 'Frank Faulkner' (Au/A) WAln
- 'Frank Hemmingway' (Au/B) NDro
- 'Frank Jenning' (Au/A) NDro WAln
- 'Fred Booley' (Au/d) EWoo NDro NSum WFar WHil XBar
- 'Fred Livesley' (Au/A) WAln
- 'Fresco' (Au/A) WAln
- 'Freya' (Au/S) NDro XBar
- 'Fridl' (Au) EBee
- 'Friends of Ashwood' (Au/S) NDro
- 'Friskney' (Au/d) EWoo WAln
- 'Frittenden Yellow' (Au/B) NDro
- 'Fromelles' (Au/d) WHil
- 'Frosty' (Au/S) NDro
- 'Fuller's Red' (Au/S) NDro WHil XBar
- 'Funny Valentine' (Au/d) EWoo NDro NSum WHil
- 'G.L.Taylor' (Au/A) NDro
- 'Gaia' (Au/d) WHil
- 'Gail Atkinson' (Au/A) NSum WAln
- 'Galator' (Au/A) WAln
- 'Ganymede' (Au/d) WAln
- 'Gary Pallister' (Au/A) WAln
- 'Gay Crusader' (Au/A) NDro WFar WHil
- 'Gazza' (Au/A) WAln
- 'Gee Cross' (Au/A) NDro NSum
- 'Geldersome Green' (Au/S) GRum NDro
- 'Geldersome Green No. 2' (Au/S) ITim
- 'Gemini' (Au/S) NDro
- 'Generosity' (Au/A) NDro NSum WHil
- 'Geordie' (Au/A) WAln
- 'George Edge' (Au/B) NDro
- 'George Jennings' (Au/A) NDro
- 'George Swinford's Leathercoat' (Au/B) NDro
- 'Geronimo' (Au/S) NDro
- 'Gerry Thompson' (Au/A) **new** WAln
- 'Ghost Ridge' (Au/B) NDro
- 'Gild Green' (Au/S) NDro
- 'Gimli' (Au/A) WAln
- 'Ginger Spice' (Au/B) NDro WHil
- 'Girl Guide' (Au/S) WHil
- 'Gizabroon' (Au/S) CBor CFis EBee GAbr NDro NLar WHil XBar
- 'Gleam' (Au/S) EDAr NDro NSum WHil XBar
- 'Gleneagles' (Au/S) GRum NDro
- 'Glenelg' (Au/S) GAbr ITim NDro WHil XBar
- 'Glenluce' (Au/S) EWoo NDro
- 'Gloire de Dijon' (Au/S) XBar
- 'Gnome' (Au/B) GAbr GArf NDro WHil
- 'Goeblii' (Au/B) NDro WHil XBar
- 'Gold Seam' (Au/A) WAln WHil
- 'Gold Star' (Au/St) NDro

- 'Golden Boy' (Au/A) NDro NSum WAln
- 'Golden Chartreuse' (Au/d) EWoo NDro
- 'Golden Fleece' (Au/S) GAbr NDro
- 'Golden Galator' (Au/A) **new** WAln
- 'Golden Girl' (Au/A) WAln
- 'Golden Glory' (Au/A) NDro WAln
- 'Golden Hind' (Au/d) EWoo NDro NSum WHil
- 'Golden Splendour' (Au/d) EWoo NDro NSum WFar WHil
- 'Golden Wedding' (Au/A) NDro WAln WHil XBar
- 'Goldie' (Au/S) NDro
- 'Goldwin' (Au/A) NDro NSum
- 'Gollum' (Au/A) NDro WAln WFar
- 'Good Report' (Au/A) NDro NSum WFar WHil
- 'Goody Goody' (Au/St) NDro
- 'Googie' (Au/d) NDro WHil
- 'Gordon Files' (Au/S) WAln
- 'Gorey' (Au/A) EWoo NDro WHil
- 'Grabley' (Au/S) NDro
- 'Grace Ellen' (Au/S) NDro
- 'Gracie Lou' (Au/B) NDro
- 'Grandad's Favourite' (Au/B) EWoo NDro WHil
- 'Grasmere' (Au/d) NDro
- 'Green Abundance' (Au/B) EWoo
- 'Green Finger' (Au/S) EWoo
- 'Green Frill' (Au) NSum
- 'Green Goddess' (Au/St) EWoo NDro
- 'Green Isle' (Au/S) NDro XBar
- 'Green Jacket' (Au/S) NDro
- 'Green Lane' (Au/S) XBar
- 'Green Parrot' (Au/S) GAbr NDro WHil
- 'Green Shank' (Au/S) NDro WHil XBar
- 'Greenfinger' (Au/S) NSum
- 'Greenpeace' (Au/S) GAbr NDro XBar
- 'Grenache' (Au/B) XBar
- 'Grenville' (Au) **new** EGrI
- 'Greswolde' (Au/d) EWoo
- 'Greta' (Au/S) GAbr NDro WHil XBar
- 'Grey Cloud' (Au/B) NDro
- 'Grey Day' (Au/S) NDro
- 'Grey Hawk' (Au/S) NDro
- 'Grey Lag' (Au/S) NSum XBar
- 'Grey Monarch' (Au/S) EWoo GAbr WHil XBar
- 'Grey Owl' (Au/S) NDro
- 'Grey Shrike' (Au/S) NDro
- 'Grüner Veltliner' (Au/S) NDro
- 'Guinea' (Au/S) GAbr NDro
- 'Gwai Loh' (Au/B) NDro
- 'Gwen' (Au/A) NDro WAln XBar
- 'Gwen Baker' (Au/d) NDro
- 'Gwenda' (Au/A) NDro WAln WHil
- 'Gypsy Boy' (Au/A) WAln
- 'H Old Gold' (Au/S) NDro
- 'Habanera' (Au/A) NDro NSum WFar
- 'Hallmark' (Au/A) NDro NSum WAln
- 'Handsome Lass' (Au/St) EWoo NDro XBar
- 'Hannah' (Au/A) WAln
- 'Harlequin' (Au/B) NDro
- 'Harmony' (Au/B) EWoo NDro NSum XBar
- 'Harry Armitage' (Au/B) NDro WHil
- 'Harry Hotspur' (Au/A) NDro NSum WFar WHil XBar
- 'Harry 'O'' (Au/S) NDro
- 'Harthorpeburn' (Au/B) NDro
- 'Harvest Glow' (Au/S) NDro WFar WHil
- 'Hawkwood' (Au/S) EBee GAbr NDro WHil XBar
- 'Hazel' (Au/B) NDro XBar
- 'Hazel' (Au/A) NDro WHil
- 'Headdress' (Au/S) GAbr
- 'Heady' (Au/A) EWoo NDro WHil XBar
- 'Heart of Gold' (Au/A) NDro NSum WAln
- 'Hearts of Oak' (Au/A) WAln
- 'Heaven Scent' (Au) NDro
- 'Hebers' (Au) NDro WAln
- 'Helen' (Au/S) GAbr NDro WHil
- 'Helen Barter' (Au/S) NDro NSum WHil
- 'Helen Ruan' (Au) **new** NSum
- 'Helen Ruane' (Au/d) GQue NDro WFar
- 'Helena' (Au/S) NDro WAln WHil
- 'Helena Dean' (Au/d) WAln
- 'Henry's Bane' (Au/St) NDro
- 'Her Nibs' (Au/St) NDro
- 'Hermes the Cat' (Au) WHil
- 'Hermia' (Au/A) WHil
- 'Hetty Woolf' (Au/S) GAbr NDro
- 'Hew Dalrymple' (Au/S) NDro
- 'Highland Park' (Au/A) NDro NSum WHil XBar
- 'Hillhook' (Au/A) NSum WAln
- 'Hillview Hermes' (Au/S) NDro
- 'Hinton Admiral' (Au/S) GAbr NDro NSum WHil XBar
- 'Hinton Fields' (Au/S) NDro WFar WHil
- 'Hit Parade' (Au) **new** WAln
- 'Hobby Horse' (Au/St) ITim NSum
- 'Holyrood' (Au/S) ITim NDro NHpl XBar
- 'Honey' (Au/d) EWoo GAbr NDro NSum
- 'Honeydawn' (Au/B) NDro
- 'Hopleys Coffee' (Au/d) EWoo GAbr NDro WAln
- 'Hopton Gem' (Au/B) NDro
- 'Hortense' (Au/d) **new** XBar
- 'Hughie' (Au/A) WAln
- 'Hurstwood Midnight' (Au) XBar

* - 'Hyacinth' (Au/S) EBee NDro WCAu
- 'Iago' (Au/S) NDro
- 'Ian Greville' (Au/A) NDro NSum XBar
- 'Ibis' (Au/A) WAln
- 'Ice Cap' (Au/d) XBar
- 'Ice Maiden' (Au/A) GAbr NDro NSum WHil XBar
- 'Idgy' (Au/d) WHil
- 'Idmiston' (Au/S) GAbr NDro WHil XBar
- 'Imari Stripe' (Au/St) WHil
- 'Immaculate' (Au/A) NDro NSum WHil
- 'Impassioned' (Au/A) XBar
- 'Imperturbable' (Au/A) NDro
- 'Indian Love Call' (Au/A) EGrI GAbr ITim NDro NSum WHil

I - 'Innominata' (Au/S) NDro
- 'Innsworth' (Au/A) WAln
- 'Iris Scott' (Au/A) ITim NDro
- 'Isabel' (Au/S) WAln
- 'Isabella' (Au/A) NDro
- 'Jack Dean' (Au/A) WFar WHil XBar
- 'Jack Horner' (Au) NDro
- 'Jack Redfern' (Au/A) NDro
- 'Jaffa' (Au/A) NDro NSum WAln
- 'James Arnot' (Au/S) GAbr NDro XBar
- 'James Wattam' (Au/S) NDro
- 'Jane' (Au/S) WAln
- 'Jane Myers' (Au/d) WAln WHil
- 'Janet Watts' (Au/B) NDro
- 'Janie Hill' (Au/A) XBar
- 'Jb' (Au) GAbr
- 'Je t'Adore' (Au/St) NDro
- 'Jean Fielder' (Au/A) NDro WAln
- 'Jean Jacques' (Au/A) NDro WAln

I - 'Jean Jacques' (Au/d) XBar
- 'Jean-Claude' (Au/d) XBar
- 'Jeanne' (Au/A) EWoo
- 'Jeannie Jingles II' (Au/St) NDro
- 'Jeannie Telford' (Au/A) NDro XBar
- 'Jeff Scruton' (Au/A) WAln
- 'Jenny' (Au/A) EWoo NDro NSum WFar XBar
- 'Jersey Bounce' (Au/A) EWoo ITim NDro WHil

- 'Jessie' (Au/d) NDro
- 'Jilting Jessie' (Au/St) NDro NSum
- 'Joanne' (Au/d) NDro
- 'Joanne' (Au/A) EWoo GAbr NDro
- 'Joe Perks' (Au/A) EWoo ITim NDro WHil XBar
- 'Joel' (Au/S) EGrl EWoo ITim NDro NSum XBar
- 'Johann Bach' (Au/B) NDro NSum
- 'John Hart' (Au/A) NDro WHil
- 'John Wayne' (Au/A) EWoo NDro WHil XBar
- 'John Woolf' (Au/S) NDro
- 'Jonathon' (Au/A) NDro WAln
- 'Joy' (Au/A) EWoo NDro NSum NWad WHil XBar
- 'Joyce' (Au/A) GAbr NDro NSum WFar WHil XBar
- 'Judith Borman' (Au/d) GAbr NDro
- 'Julia Jane' (Au/B) NDro
- 'Julie Nuttall' (Au/B) GAbr NDro NSum NWad WHil
- 'June' (Au/A) NDro NSum
- 'Jungfrau' (Au/d) EWoo NDro WAln
- 'Jupp' (Au/d) EBee
- 'Jura' (Au/A) WAln
- 'Just Steven' (Au/A) WAln
- 'Justin Case' (Au/B) NDro
- 'K S' (Au/S) NDro
- KALEIDOSCOPE (mixed) (Au) EDAr ELan
- 'Karen Cordrey' (Au/S) EBee EWoo GKev NDro NSum WHil
- 'Karen McDonald' (Au/A) NDro NSum
- 'Kate Haywood' (Au/B) NDro WHil
- 'Ken Chilton' (Au/A) EWoo NDro WHil XBar
- 'Kenco' (Au/d) GAbr
- 'Kentucky Blues' (Au/d) EWoo NDro WAln
- 'Kercup' (Au/A) EWoo
- 'Kersey' (Au/S) NDro
- 'Kevin' (Au/A) WAln
- 'Kevin Keegan' (Au/A) NDro NSum WHil XBar
- 'Key West' (Au/A) NDro WAln
- 'Khachaturian' (Au/A) NDro WAln
- 'Khaki' (Au) WHil
- 'Kilby' (Au/A) NDro NSum
- 'Kim' (Au/A) NDro WHil
- 'Kimberworth Boy' (Au/A) NDro WAln
- 'Kingcup' (Au/A) GAbr NDro XBar
- 'Kingfisher' (Au/A) EWoo NDro NSum WHil
- 'Kingpin' (Au/St) NDro
- 'Kirklands' (Au/d) ITim NDro WHil
- 'Kitterford Cross' (Au/B) NDro
- 'Kiwi' (Au/B) NDro
- 'Kohinoor' (Au/A) NSum WHil
- 'Königin der Nacht' (Au/St) NDro WHil
- 'Krithia' (Au/d) WHil
- 'Lady Daresbury' (Au/A) NDro WHil XBar
- 'Lady Day' (Au/d) EWoo WAln
- 'Lady Diana' (Au/S) EWoo NDro
- 'Lady Emma Monson' (Au/S) NDro
- 'Lady Joyful' (Au/S) NDro
- 'Lady of the Vale' (Au/A) NDro WAln
- 'Lady Penelope Sitwell' (Au/St) NDro
- 'Lady Zoë' (Au/S) NDro
- 'Lambert's Gold' (Au/B) GAbr WHil
- 'Lambrook Gold' (Au/B) NDro
- 'Lamplugh' (Au/d) EWoo NSum WHil
- 'Lancelot' (Au/d) EWoo
- 'Landy' (Au/A) NDro
- 'Langley Park' (Au/A) NDro WHil XBar
- 'Laphroaigh' (Au/S) WAln
- 'Lara' (Au/A) NDro NSum XBar
- 'Laredo' (Au/A) EWoo WAln
- 'Larry' (Au/A) EWoo NDro WFar XBar
- 'Late Romantic' (Au/d) CDor ECtt GAbr GRum MHol NHpl NLar WHil
- 'Lavender Hill' (Au/St) NDro
- 'Lavender Lady' (Au/B) NDro
- 'Lavender Ridge' (Au/B) NDro
- 'Laverock' (Au/S) NBir WHil
- 'Laverock Fancy' (Au/S) GAbr NDro XBar
- 'Lazy River' (Au/A) EWoo NDro WAln
- 'Le Cateau' (Au/d) WHil
- 'Leather Jacket' (Au/B) GAbr WHil
- 'Leathercoat' (Au/B) EWoo
- 'Lechistan' (Au/S) NDro NSum WHil
- 'Lee' (Au/A) NDro WAln
- 'Lee Clark' (Au/A) NDro NSum WAln
- 'Lee Paul' (Au/A) EWoo GAbr NDro NSum WHil XBar
- 'Lee Sharpe' (Au/A) EWoo NDro NSum WAln
- 'Legolas' (Au/A) WAln
- 'Leicester Square' (Au/S) NDro
- 'Lemon Drop' (Au/S) ITim NDro
- 'Lemon Sherbet' (Au/B) EWoo GAbr GRum NDro WHil
- 'Lemon Sorbet' (Au) NDro
- 'Lepton Jubilee' (Au/S) GAbr NDro
- 'Leroy Brown' (Au/A) WAln
- 'Lester' (Au/d) WAln WHil
- 'Leverton' (Au/d) NSum
- 'Light Fantastic' (Au/S) NDro
- 'Light Hearted' (Au/A) NDro XBar
- 'Light Music' (Au/d) WAln
- 'Likely Lad' (Au/St) EWoo
- 'Lila' (Au/S) NDro WAln
- 'Lilac Domino' (Au/S) GAbr NDro WHil
- 'Lilac Ladywood' (Au/d) EWoo WFar
- 'Lilac Mist' (Au/d) XBar
- 'Lilian Hill' (Au/A) EWoo WAln XBar
- 'Lillibet' (Au/A) NDro
- 'Lima' (Au/d) WAln
- 'Lime 'n' Lemon' (Au) ITim NDro
- 'Lime Ridge' (Au) NDro WAln
- 'Limelight' (Au/A) NDro
- 'Limelight' (Au/S) NDro
- 'Lincoln Bullion' (Au/d) EWoo NDro WHil XBar
- 'Lincoln Chestnut' (Au/d) EWoo NDro XBar
- 'Lincoln Cuckoo' (Au/d) NDro XBar
- 'Lincoln Imp' (Au/d) NDro
- 'Lincoln Imperial' (Au/d) GAbr NDro
- 'Lincoln Melody' (Au/St/d) NDro XBar
- 'Lincoln Poacher' (Au/d) NDro
- 'Lincoln Whisper' (Au/d) NDro
- 'Linda' (Au/A) WAln WHil
- 'Lindley' (Au/S) NDro
- 'Ling' (Au/A) GAbr NDro XBar
- 'Linnet' (Au/B) NDro
- 'Lintz' (Au/B) EWoo NDro WHil XBar
- 'Linze 2' (Au/S) NDro
- 'Lisa' (Au/A) EWoo NDro WFar WHil XBar
- 'Lisa Clara' (Au/S) EWoo NDro NHpl WFar XBar
- 'Lisa's Smile' (Au/S) NDro WHil
- 'Little Bo Peep' (Au) NDro
- 'Little Rosetta' (Au/d) GAbr NDro NSum WHil
- 'Lizzie Files' (Au/A) WAln
- 'Lockyer's Gem' (Au/B/St) NDro
- 'Lockyer's Green' (Au) EWoo WHil
- 'Lofty' (Au/St) NDro
- 'Lolita' (Au/St) EWoo NDro NSum XBar
- 'Lord Saye and Sele' (Au/St) EWoo GAbr NDro NSum NWad WHil XBar
- 'Loudhailer' (Au/B) NDro
- 'Louis' (Au/d) XBar
- 'Louise Jordan' (Au/A) NDro

- 'Lovebird' (Au/S) GAbr NDro NHpl XBar
- 'Lowther Show' (Au/St) NDro
- 'Luca' (Au/d) WHil
- 'Lucia' (Au/B) XBar
- 'Lucy Locket' (Au/B) EWTr GAbr LCro LRHS MPnt NDro
- 'Ludlow' (Au/S) NDro
- 'Lunar Eclipse' (Au/d) CWCL GRum MHol NLar WTor
- 'Lupy Minstrel' (Au/S) NDro
- 'Lynn' (Au/A) WAln
- 'Lynn Cooper' (Au/S) EWoo
- 'MacWatt's Blue' (Au/B) GAbr GArf NDro NWad WHil XBar
- 'Maggie' (Au/S) GAbr
- 'Mametz' (Au/d) WHil
- 'Mamm-Gozh' (Au/d) XBar
- 'Mandarin' (Au/A) GAbr NDro NSum WFar WHil XBar
- 'Mandy' (Au/S) NDro
- 'Marble Arch' (Au/S) NDro
- 'Mardi Gras' (Au/d) WAln
- 'Margaret' (Au/S) GAbr NDro NSum
- 'Margaret Faulkner' (Au/A) GAbr XBar
- 'Margaret Martin' (Au/S) NDro
- 'Margaret Merril' (Au) GAbr
- 'Margot' (Au/S) WAln
- 'Margot Fonteyn' (Au/A) EWoo GAbr WHil XBar
- 'Marie Crousse' (Au/d) CMea ITim NDro WCot WFar WHil
- 'Marie Pierre' (Au/d) XBar
- 'Marion Tiger' (Au/St) NDro
- 'Mark' (Au/A) GAbr NDro XBar
- 'Marmion' (Au/S) NDro WHil XBar
- 'Mars Bars' (Au/St) NDro
- 'Martha's Choice' (Au/A) WAln
- 'Martin Luther King' (Au/S) EWoo NDro WHil XBar
- 'Mary' (Au/d) GAbr NDro NSum
- 'Mary Poppins' (Au/S) NDro
- 'Mary Taylor' (Au/S) NDro
- 'Mary Zach' (Au/S) NDro WHil
- 'Matthew' (Au) GKev
- 'Matthew Yates' (Au/d) GAbr ITim NDro NHpl WCot
- 'Maureen Millward' (Au/A) NDro
- 'May' (Au/A) EWoo NDro NSum
- 'Mazetta Stripe' (Au/S/St) GAbr NDro WHil
- 'Meadowlark' (Au/A) EWoo ITim NDro NSum WHil XBar
- 'Mehta' (Au/A) NDro WAln
- 'Mellifluous' (Au/A) WHil
- 'Melody' (Au/S) NDro
- 'Merlin' (Au/S) NSum WFar
- 'Merlin Stripe' (Au/St) NDro WHil XBar
- 'Mermaid' (Au/d) GAbr
- 'Merridale' (Au/A) GAbr WHil
- 'Mersey Tiger' (Au/S) GAbr ITim NDro NSum WHil XBar
- 'Mexicano' (Au/A) NDro WAln
- 'Michael Wattam' (Au/S) NDro
- 'Mick' (Au/A) WHil
- 'Midland Marvel' (Au/St) NDro
- 'Midnight' (Au/A) WAln
- 'Mikado' (Au/S) NSum XBar
- 'Milkmaid' (Au/A) WMAq
- 'Millicent' (Au/A) NDro NSum WHil
- 'Millwood's Lemon and Lime' (Au/d) **new** CBor
- 'Mink' (Au/A) NDro
- 'Minley' (Au/S) GAbr NBir NDro XBar
- 'Minstrel' (Au/S) ITim NDro
- 'Minty' (Au/St) NDro
- 'Mipsie Miranda' (Au/d) EWoo
- 'Mirabella Bay' (Au/A) WAln
- 'Mirandinha' (Au/A) NDro
- 'Mish Mish' (Au/d) NDro WHil
- 'Miss Bluey' (Au/d) EWoo NDro WAln XBar
- 'Miss Jones' (Au/St) NDro
- 'Miss Muffet' (Au/S) NDro
- 'Miss Newman' (Au/A) NDro NSum
- 'Miss Pinky' (Au/d) EWoo NDro
- 'Miss Teak' (Au/S) NDro
- 'Misty' (Au/d) NDro
- 'Mojave' (Au/S) GAbr GArf GEdr GKev GRum ITim NDro NHpl NSum XBar
- 'Mollie Langford' (Au/A) NDro WHil XBar
- 'Mondeo' (Au/A) WAln
- 'Monet' (Au/S) NDro
- 'Moneymoon' (Au/S) EWoo NDro WHil
- 'Monk' (Au/S) NDro WHil XBar
- 'Monmouth Star' (Au/St) WHil
- 'Mons' (Au/d) WHil
- 'Moon Fairy' (Au/S) NDro WHil XBar
- 'Moondance' (Au/d) WAln
- 'Moonlight' (Au/S) EWoo WAln
- 'Moonrise' (Au/S) EWoo NDro
- 'Moonriver' (Au/A) EWoo WHil
- 'Moonshine' (Au/d) WAln
- 'Moonshot' (Au/d) NDro
- 'Moonstone' (Au/d) WAln WHil
- 'Moorcroft' (Au/S) NDro
- 'Morello' (Au/d) XBar
- 'Morning Glory' (Au/B) NDro
- 'Morven' (Au) GAbr
- 'Moselle' (Au/S) NDro
- 'Mr A' (Au/S) NDro WHil
- 'Mr Bojangles' (Au/d) WAln
- 'Mr Hollis' (Au/St) NDro
- 'Mrs Cairn's Blue' (Au/B) NDro
- 'Mrs Dargan' (Au/d) NDro
- 'Mrs Harris' (Au/B) NDro
- 'Mrs L. Hearn' (Au/A) EWoo GAbr ITim NDro NSum WHil XBar
- 'Mrs Lowry' (Au/B) NDro
- 'Mrs R. Bolton' (Au/A) WHil
- 'Mrs Wilson' (Au) GAbr
- 'Murray Lakes' (Au/A) EGrI EWoo NDro NSum WAln
- 'Mustard Sauce' (Au/B) NDro
- 'My Fair Lady' (Au/A) NDro
- 'My Friend' (Au/B) GAbr NDro
- 'Mystery' (Au) GAbr
- 'Nancy Dalgetty' (Au/B) NDro
- 'Nantenan' (Au/S) GAbr NDro NSum
- 'Neat and Tidy' (Au/S) EWoo GAbr ITim NDro NWad XBar
- 'Nefertiti' (Au/A) EWoo NDro NSum WHil
- 'Nessun Dorma' (Au/A) EWoo NDro WAln
- 'Neville Telford' (Au/S) EWoo NDro WFar
- 'Newsboy' (Au/A) WAln
- 'Newton Harcourt' (Au/A) NDro WHil
- 'Nicholas van Zanten' (Au/B) NDro
- 'Nick Drake' (Au/d) NDro
- 'Nickity' (Au/A) EWoo GAbr ITim NDro NSum WHil XBar
- 'Nicola Jane' (Au/A) EWoo MAvo WAln
- 'Nigel' (Au/d) GAbr NDro
- 'Nightwink' (Au/S) WAln
- 'Nina' (Au/A) NDro WAln
- 'Nita' (Au/d) WAln
- 'No 21' (Au/S) NDro
- 'Nocturne' (Au/S) NDro NSum
- 'Noelle' (Au/S) NDro NSum
- 'Nona' (Au/d) EWoo NDro NSum WHil
- 'Nonchalance' (Au/A) NDro NSum WHil
- 'Norma' (Au/A) EWoo NDro
- 'Northern Blue' (Au/S) **new** NDro
- 'Northern Lights' (Au/S) GAbr NDro
- 'Nymph' (Au/d) EWoo GAbr GRum NDro WHil
- 'Oakie Dokie' (Au/St) NDro

– 'Oban' (Au/S)	NDro XBar
– 'Odette' (Au/d)	WHil
– 'O'er the Moon' (Au/S)	WAln
– 'Oikos' (Au/B)	NDro
– 'Old Black Isle Dusty Miller' (Au/B)	NDro WHil
– 'Old Buffer' (Au/St)	NDro
– 'Old Clove Red' (Au/B)	GAbr NDro NSum NWad WHil
– 'Old Cottage Blue' (Au/B)	EWoo GAbr NDro WFar WHil
– 'Old Dublin Blue' (Au/B)	NDro
– 'Old England' (Au/S)	GAbr NDro
– 'Old Fashioned Sally' (Au/B)	NDro
– 'Old Gold' (Au/S)	EGrI GAbr NDro WFar
– 'Old Gold Double' (Au/d)	EWoo
– 'Old Gold Dusty Miller' (Au/B)	NDro
– 'Old Irish Blue' (Au/B)	NDro WCot
– 'Old Irish Green' (Au/B)	GAbr NDro NSum
– 'Old Irish Scented' (Au/B)	EWoo GAbr NDro NWad WHil XBar
– 'Old Irish Yellow' (Au/B)	NDro NHpl
– 'Old Kent Road' (Au/S)	NDro
– 'Old Mustard' (Au/B)	EGrI GAbr NDro SMHy
– 'Old Pink Dusty Miller' (Au/B)	EWoo GAbr
§ – 'Old Purple Dusty Miller' (Au/B)	GAbr
– 'Old Red' (Au)	GArf
– 'Old Red Dusty Miller' (Au/B)	EWoo GAbr NDro NSum WFar WHil
– 'Old Red Elvet' (Au/S)	GAbr
– 'Old Smokey' (Au/A)	EWoo NDro WHil XBar
– 'Old Suffolk Bronze' (Au/B)	EWoo GAbr NDro WHil
– 'Old Yellow Dusty Miller' (Au/B)	EWes EWoo GAbr NDro NLar NWad WHil
– 'Old-Fashioned' (Au/B)	NDro
– 'Olton' (Au/A)	NDro WFar XBar
– 'Optimist' (Au/St)	EWoo GAbr NDro
– 'Opus One' (Au/A)	EWoo WAln
– 'Orb' (Au/S)	GRum WHil XBar
– 'Ordvic' (Au/S)	NDro
– 'Orlando' (Au/S)	NDro
– 'Orwell Tiger' (Au/St)	EWoo NDro NSum XBar
– 'Osborne Green' (Au/B)	EWoo GAbr GArf GQue WHil
– 'Ossett Sapphire' (Au/A)	NDro XBar
– 'Otto Dix' (Au/A)	WAln
– 'Our Sophie' (Au/B)	NDro
– 'Overdale' (Au/A)	NDro NSum WAln
– 'Oyster' (Au/B)	NDro
– 'Paddlin' Madeleine' (Au/A)	EWoo NDro WAln XBar
– 'Pageboy' (Au/A)	WAln
– 'Pale Blue' (Au/B)	WHil
– 'Paleface' (Au/A)	NDro NSum
– 'Pall Mall' (Au/St)	NDro WHil
– 'Palpatine' (Au/D)	XBar
– 'Panache' (Au/S)	WAln
– 'Pang Tiger' (Au/St)	EWoo NDro
– 'Paradise Yellow' (Au/B)	EWoo GAbr GEdr NDro
– 'Paragon' (Au/A)	WHil
– 'Parakeet' (Au/S)	EWoo NDro
– 'Party Animal' (Au/St)	NDro XBar
– 'Passchendaele' (Au/d)	EWoo WHil
– 'Pastures New' (Au)	NDro
– 'Pat Barnard' (Au)	NSum
– 'Pat Mooney' (Au/d)	NDro
– 'Patience' (Au/S)	WHil
– 'Pauline' (Au/A)	NDro
– 'Pavarotti' (Au/A)	ITim NDro NSum
– 'Paxton's Blue Eden' (Au/B)	NDro
– 'Pearl the Cat' (Au)	WHil
– 'Pegasus' (Au/d)	EWoo NDro
– 'Peggy' (Au/A)	GAbr ITim WHil
– 'Pen Pink Stripe' (Au/St)	WHil
– 'Pendeford Yellow' (Au/B)	NDro
– 'Pendle Promise' (Au/A)	NDro
– 'Penelope' (Au/d)	WHil
– 'Pequod' (Au/A)	NDro NSum
– 'Perirot' (Au)	ITim
– 'Persephone' (Au/B)	NDro
– 'Phantom' (Au/d)	NSum WAln
– 'Pharaoh' (Au/A)	EGrI EWoo GAbr NDro XBar
– 'Phoenix' (Au/A)	WAln
– 'Phyllis Douglas' (Au/A)	NDro WHil
– 'Piccadilly' (Au/S)	NDro
– 'Piccalilli' (Au/d)	XBar
– 'Pierot' (Au/A)	EGrI NDro NSum WHil XBar
– 'Piers Telford' (Au/A)	GAbr MAvo NDro NSum WFar WHil XBar
– 'Piglet' (Au/d)	EWoo GAbr NDro NSum XBar
– 'Pikey' (Au/S)	NDro
– 'Pimroagh' (Au/A)	GAbr
– 'Pink Floyd' (Au/A)	XBar
– 'Pink Fondant' (Au/d)	GAbr NDro
– 'Pink Hint' (Au/B)	EWoo NDro
– 'Pink Lady' (Au/A)	GAbr NSum WHil
– 'Pink Lilac' (Au/A/S)	NDro
– 'Pink Triumph' (Au/B)	NDro WHil
– 'Pinkerton' (Au/d)	EWoo
– 'Pinkie Dawn' (Au/B)	EWoo NDro NWad
– 'Pinstripe' (Au)	GAbr NDro NSum
– 'Pioneer Stripe' (Au/S)	EWoo GAbr
– 'Pippin' (Au/A)	EGrI EWoo GAbr NDro XBar
– 'Pixie' (Au/A)	EWoo NDro
– 'Playboy' (Au/A)	NDro WAln
– 'Plum Pudding' (Au/d)	EWoo WAln
– 'Plums and Custard' (Au/B)	XBar
– 'Poacher's Lady' (Au/d)	NDro
– 'Poacher's Sky' (Au/d)	XBar
– 'Poacher's Starlight' (Au/d)	NDro XBar
– 'Polar Sight' (Au/B)	NDro
– 'Polestar' (Au/A)	NDro NSum WHil XBar
– 'Polly' (Au/B)	GKev NDro NSum WHil
– 'Pop's Blue' (Au/S/d)	EWoo
– 'Portree' (Au/S)	GAbr
– 'Pot o' Gold' (Au/S)	EBee NDro WHil XBar
– 'Powder Puff' (Au/B)	EWoo NDro
– 'Powys' (Au/St)	NDro
– 'Prague' (Au/S)	GAbr NBir NDro
– 'Pretty Prop' (Au/St)	NDro
– 'Pretty Purple' (Au/d)	NDro WAln
– 'Pride of Poland' (Au/S)	EWoo
– 'Prima' (Au/d)	NDro
– 'Prince Bishops' (Au/S)	WAln
– 'Prince Charming' (Au/S)	NDro
– 'Prince John' (Au/A)	EWoo NDro WHil
– 'Proctor's Yellow' (Au/B)	GAbr NDro NWad WHil
– 'Prometheus' (Au/d)	EWoo GAbr ITim NDro NSum WHil
– 'Prosperine' (Au/S)	NDro
– 'Psyche' (Au/S)	NDro
– 'Pumpkin' (Au)	NHpl
– 'Purple Dusty Miller'	see *P. auricula* 'Old Purple Dusty Miller'
– 'Purple Glow' (Au/d)	WAln
– 'Purple Pip' (Au/d)	CBod CWCL EWTr GRum NLar SEdd
– 'Purple Profusion' (Au/B) **new**	NDro
– 'Purple Prolific' (Au/B)	NDro
– 'Purple Promise' (Au/B)	GAbr ITim NDro
– 'Purple Prose' (Au/St)	WHil
– 'Purple Rose' (Au/d)	ITim WAln

- 'Purple Royale' (Au/B) GAbr NDro
- 'Purple Sage' (Au/S) ITim NDro NSum WHil
- 'Purple Velvet' (Au/S) NDro
- 'Quality Street' (Au/d) XBar
- 'Quatro' (Au/d) EWoo
- 'Queen Alexandra' (Au/B) EWoo GAbr NDro WHil
- 'Queen Bee' (Au/S) EWoo GAbr NDro
- 'Quintessence' (Au/A) EWoo NDro WHil
- 'R.L. Bowes' (Au/A) NDro
- 'Rab C. Nesbitt' (Au/A) WAln
- 'Rabley Heath' (Au/A) GAbr ITim NDro NSum WHil
- 'Rachel' (Au/A) NDro WAln
- I 'Rachel' (Au/d) XBar
- 'Radiant' (Au/A) NDro
- 'Rag Doll' (Au/S) NDro
- 'Ragnald the Magnificent' (Au/S) WAln
- 'Rainy Days' (Au/B) NDro
- 'Rajah' (Au/S) EWoo GAbr NHpl WHil XBar
- 'Raleigh Stripe' (Au/St) EWoo GAbr NWad
- 'Rameses' (Au/A) NDro NSum
- 'Randall's White' (Au/B) NDro
- 'Rebecca Baker' (Au/d) WHil
- 'Red Admiral' (Au/S) NDro WAln
- 'Red Arrows' (Au/S) NDro WAln
- 'Red Bordeaux' (Au/S) NDro
- 'Red Embers' (Au/S) WAln
- 'Red Ensign' (Au/B) NDro
- 'Red Gauntlet' (Au/S) EGrI GAbr NDro NSum
- 'Red King' (Au/S) WAln
- 'Red Mark' (Au/A) WHil XBar
- 'Red Rum' (Au/S) GAbr
- 'Red Wire' (Au/St) NDro NSum
- 'Red Wrekin' (Au/S) NDro
- 'Redcar' (Au/A) GAbr NDro XBar
- 'Reddown Apricot' (Au/B) NDro
- 'Reddown Barley Meal' (Au/B) NDro
- 'Reddown Bat' (Au/d) NDro
- 'Reddown Brownie' (Au/B) NDro
- 'Reddown Dark Pink' (Au/B) NDro
- 'Reddown First Swallow' (Au/B) NDro NSum
- 'Reddown Rainman' (Au/B) NDro
- 'Reddown Tickled Pink' (Au/B) NDro
- 'Redstart' (Au/S) EWoo GKev NDro WHil
- 'Regency' (Au/A) NDro
- 'Regency Carousel' (Au/St) NDro
- 'Regency Emperor' (Au/St) EWoo NDro WHil XBar
- 'Regency Paperchase' (Au/St) NDro
- 'Regency Saint Clements' (Au/St) NDro
- 'Reilly' (Au) **new** WAln
- 'Remus' (Au/S) ITim NDro WHil XBar
- 'Rene' (Au/A) ELan GAbr NDro WHil XBar
- 'Renown' (Au/A) NDro WAln
- 'Requiem' (Au/d) WAln
- 'Resi' (Au/A) WHil
- 'Respectable' (Au/A) WAln
- 'Reverie' (Au/d) WAln
- 'Reynardine' (Au/d) WAln
- 'Rhinegold' (Au/d) XBar
- 'Rhubarb Rock' (Au/B) WHil
- 'Riatty' (Au/d) EWoo GAbr NDro
- 'Richard Shaw' (Au/A) EWoo NDro
- 'Ring of Fire' (Au/A) WAln
- 'Rintein' (Au/B) NDro
- 'Risdene' (Au/A) WAln
- 'Rivendell' (Au/A) WAln
- 'Robbo' (Au/B) GAbr NDro
- 'Robert Green' (Au/S) NDro
- 'Robert Lee' (Au/A) WAln
- 'Roberto' (Au/S) NDro
- 'Robin Hood Stripe' (Au/St) EWoo NDro NSum
- 'Robinette' (Au/d) EWoo GAbr
- 'Rock Sand' (Au/S) GAbr ITim NDro WHil
- 'Rodeo' (Au/A) EWoo GAbr
- 'Rolts' (Au/S) GAbr NDro WHil XBar
- 'Rondy' (Au/S) ITim WHil
- 'Ronnie Johnson' (Au) WAln
- 'Rosalie Edwards' (Au/S) NDro
- 'Rose Conjou' (Au/d) EWoo GAbr NDro WHil XBar
- 'Rose Kaye' (Au/A) GAbr
- 'Rose Petal' (Au/d) XBar
- 'Rosebud' (Au/S) GAbr NDro
- 'Rosemarket Rackler' (Au/B) NDro
- 'Rosemary' (Au/S) EWoo GAbr NDro
- 'Rosewood' (Au/d) EWoo WAln
- 'Rosie' (Au/S) NDro
- 'Rostock' (Au/B) NDro
- 'Rouge Gorge' (Au/B) XBar
- 'Rowena' (Au/A) NDro NSum WHil
- 'Roxborough' (Au/A) EWoo
- 'Roxburgh' (Au/A) NDro
- 'Roy Keane' (Au/A) NSum WAln
- 'Royal Mail' (Au/S) EGrI EWoo NDro NSum XBar
- 'Royal Velvet' (Au/S) GAbr NDro WFar WHil
- 'Ruby Hyde' (Au/B) EWoo GAbr NDro NSum WHil
- 'Ruddy Duck' (Au/S) EWoo NDro
- 'Runwell' (Au/B) NDro
- 'Rusty Dusty' (Au) EWoo GAbr NDro
- 'Rusty Red' (Au/B) NDro
- 'Ryecroft' (Au/A) WAln
- 'Sabrina' (Au/A) WAln
- 'Saginaw' (Au/A) WAln
- 'Sailor Boy' (Au/S) NDro
- 'Saint Boswells' (Au/S) GAbr
- 'Saint Elmo' (Au/A) GAbr
- 'Saint-Émilion' (Au/d) XBar
- 'Salad' (Au/S) GAbr
- 'Sale Green' (Au/S) EWoo NDro
- 'Sally' (Au/A) NDro NSum
- 'Sam Brown' (Au/S) WAln
- 'Sam Gamgee' (Au/A) NDro WAln
- 'Sam Hunter' (Au/A) NDro
- 'Samantha' (Au/A) NDro WAln
- 'Samantha' (Au/d) NDro WFar XBar
- 'San Antonio' (Au/A) NDro
- 'San Gabriel' (Au/A) WAln
- 'Sanctuary Wood' (Au/d) WHil
- 'Sandhills' (Au/A) WHil
- 'Sandra' (Au/A) GAbr NDro WHil XBar
- 'Sandra's Lass' (Au/A) EWoo
- 'Sandwood Bay' (Au/A) EWoo GAbr NDro WHil
- 'Sappho' (Au/S) NDro
- 'Sarah Gisby' (Au/d) NDro
- 'Sarah Humphries' (Au/d) WAln
- 'Sarah Lodge' (Au/d) GAbr NDro WHil
- 'Sarah Suzanne' (Au/B) NDro
- 'Saruman' (Au/A) WAln
- 'Sasha Files' (Au/A) WAln
- 'Satsuma' (Au/d) WAln
- 'Scaraben' (Au) GAbr
- 'Schaumburg' (Au/B) NDro
- 'Schicchi' (Au/d) XBar

- 'Scipio' (Au/S) NDro
- 'Scorcher' (Au/S) GAbr NSum XBar
- 'Scrumpy' (Au/St) NDro
- 'Second Victory' (Au/S) NDro WHil XBar
- 'Seen-a-Ghost' (Au/S) NDro
- 'Serenity' (Au/S) WHil XBar
- 'Sergeant Wilson' (Au/S) NDro
- 'Shadow Boxer' (Au/St) NDro
- 'Shalford' (Au/d) GAbr WCot WHil
- 'Shaun' (Au/d) ECtt GAbr NHpl NLar
- 'Sheila' (Au/S) GAbr NDro WHil
- 'Shere' (Au/S) EWoo NDro NSum
- 'Sherwood' (Au/S) GAbr NDro NHpl XBar
- 'Shirley' (Au/S) NDro
- 'Show Bandit' (Au/St) NDro
- 'Showtime' (Au/S) NDro
- 'Sibsey' (Au/d) EWoo NDro WFar
- 'Silas' (Au/B) NDro
- 'Silbermond' (Au/B) NDro
- 'Silmaril' (Au/d) WAln
- 'Silverway' (Au/S) GKev NDro WHil
- 'Simply Red' (Au/S) EWoo NDro NSum XBar
- 'Sir John' (Au/A) NDro WHil
- 'Sir John Hall' (Au) NDro
- 'Sir Robert' (Au/d) GAbr WAln
- 'Sirbol' (Au/A) EWoo GAbr NDro
- 'Sirius' (Au/A) EWoo GAbr NDro NSum WHil XBar
- 'Skylark' (Au/A) GAbr ITim NDro WHil XBar
- 'Skyliner' (Au/A) NDro
- 'Slack Top Red' (Au) NDro NSla WHil
- 'Slim Whitman' (Au/A) NDro NSum WHil
- 'Slioch' (Au/S) EWoo GAbr NSum WFar XBar
- 'Slip Anchor' (Au/A) WAln
- 'Smoothy' (Au/St) NDro
- 'Snips' (Au/St) NDro
- 'Snooty Fox' (Au/A) GAbr
- 'Snooty Fox II' (Au/A) NDro
- 'Snowstorm' (Au/S) NDro
- 'Snowy Owl' (Au/S) NDro XBar
- 'Snowy Ridge' (Au/B) NDro
- 'Soliloquy' (Au/B) NDro
- 'Soncy Face' (Au/A) WHil
- 'Sonia Nicolle' (Au/B) NDro
- 'Sonja' (Au/S) NDro
- 'Sonny Boy' (Au/A) NDro WAln
- 'Sooty' (Au/d) EWoo NDro XBar
- 'Sophie' (Au/d) WAln
- 'Sophie' (Au/A) NDro
- 'South Barrow' (Au/d) GAbr WHil
- 'Southport' (Au/B) EWoo GAbr NDro
- 'Sparky' (Au/A) NDro
- 'Spider' (Au/S) NDro
- 'Splendide' (Au/d) XBar
- 'Split Ends' (Au/St) NDro
- 'Spring Meadows' (Au/S) GAbr GKev NDro NSum
- 'Stafford Blue' (Au/B) NDro
- 'Standish' (Au/d) GAbr
- 'Stant's Blue' (Au/S) NDro NSum
- 'Star Spangle' (Au/St) NDro
- 'Star Wars' (Au/S) GAbr NDro XBar
- 'Starling' (Au/B) EWoo GAbr NDro NSum
- 'Steiff' (Au/S) NDro
- 'Stella Coop' (Au/d) NDro
- 'Stella North' (Au/A) NDro WAln
- 'Stella South' (Au/A) NDro WFar
- 'Stepney Green' (Au/S) NDro
- 'Stetson' (Au/A) WAln
- 'Stirling Castle' (Au/St) NDro
- 'Stoke Poges' (Au/A) NDro
- 'Stoney Cross' (Au/S) WAln
- 'Stonnal' (Au/A) NDro WHil
- 'Stormin' Norman' (Au/A) NDro
- 'Stowe Pool' (Au) **new** WAln
- 'Strand' (Au/St) NDro
- 'Strawberry Fields' (Au/S) EGrl NDro
- 'Stripe Tease' (Au/St) EWoo
- 'Stripe U Like' (Au/St) NDro
- 'Striped Ace' (Au/St) EWoo NDro WHil
- 'Stripey' (Au/d) NDro
- 'Stromboli' (Au/d) EGrl EWoo GAbr ITim NDro NSum WCot XBar
- 'Subliminal' (Au/A) NDro
- 'Sue Ritchie' (Au/d) NSum
- 'Sugar Plum Fairy' (Au/S) GAbr NDro NSum
- 'Summer Sky' (Au/A) NDro
- 'Summer Wine' (Au/A) EWoo NDro XBar
- 'Sumo' (Au/A) EWoo GAbr NDro NSum XBar
- 'Sunflower' (Au/A/S) EWoo GAbr ITim NDro WHil
- 'Sunlight' (Au/A) WAln
- 'Sunlit Tiger' (Au/S) EWoo GAbr NDro
- 'Sunshine' (Au/d) **new** XBar
- 'Sunspot' (Au/A) WAln
- 'Sunstar' (Au/S) NDro NSum
- 'Super Para' (Au/S) GAbr WHil
- 'Superb' (Au/S) XBar
- 'Surething' (Au/A) WAln
- 'Susan' (Au/A) GAbr NDro NSum
- 'Susannah' (Au/d) EWoo GAbr NDro NSum WFar WHil XBar
- 'Sweet Caramel' (Au/d) **new** XBar
- 'Sweet Chestnut' (Au/S) CArg
- 'Sweet Georgia Brown' (Au/A) NDro WAln
- 'Sweet Lorraine' (Au/S) NDro
- 'Sweet Pastures' (Au/S) GAbr NDro
- 'Swiss Royal Velvet' (Au/B) NDro
- 'Sword' (Au/d) EWoo GAbr NDro NSum WFar XBar
- 'Symphony' (Au/A) ITim NDro WHil XBar
- 'T.A. Hadfield' (Au/A) EWoo NDro NSum WHil
- 'Taffeta' (Au/S) GAbr LCro LOPS MAvo NDro NSum WFar WHil
- 'Tally-ho' (Au/A) WAln
- 'Tamar Mist' (Au/d) WHil
- 'Tamino' (Au/S) NDro
- 'Tango' (Au/d) NDro WAln
- 'Tarantella' (Au/A) GAbr NDro NSum
- 'Tawny Owl' (Au/B) GAbr
- 'Tay Tiger' (Au/St) EWoo GAbr NDro WHil XBar
- 'Taylor's Grey' (Au/S) NDro
- 'Teawell Pride' (Au/d) EWoo ITim NHpl WHil
- 'Ted Gibbs' (Au/A) NDro NSum WHil
- 'Ted Roberts' (Au/A) CBor ITim NDro WHil XBar
- 'Teem' (Au/S) GAbr NDro XBar
- 'Telford's Surprise' (Au/A) WAln
- 'Tenderly' (Au/St) NDro
- 'Terpo' (Au/A) NDro WAln WHil
- 'Tess' (Au/A) XBar
- 'The Argylls' (Au/St) NDro
- 'The Baron' (Au/S) EWoo GAbr GKev WHil XBar
- 'The Bishop' (Au/S) ITim WAln WHil XBar
- 'The Bride' (Au/S) NDro
- 'The Cardinal' (Au/d) EWoo WAln
- 'The Czar' (Au/A) GAbr NDro
- 'The Egyptian' (Au/A) EWoo NDro WHil XBar
- 'The Hobbit' (Au/A) WAln
- 'The Lady Galadriel' (Au/A) NDro
- 'The Raven' (Au/S) GAbr ITim WHil
- 'The Sneep' (Au/A) EWoo GAbr NDro NSum XBar
- 'The Snods' (Au/S) EWoo NDro
- 'Thea' (Au/B) XBar
- 'Theodora' (Au/S) XBar

- 'Thetis' (Au/A) XBar
- 'Thisbe' (Au/A) NDro
- 'Three Way Stripe' (St) EWoo GAbr WHil
- 'Thutmoses' (Au/A) NDro WAln
- 'Tiana' (Au/B) XBar
- 'Tim' (Au/d) GAbr ITim NDro NSum
- 'Timpany Blues' (Au/B) ITim NDro
- 'Timpany Dawn' (Au/B) NDro
- 'Tim's Fancy' (Au/S) NDro
- 'Tinker' (Au/S) NDro
- 'Tinkerbell' (Au/S) NDro
- 'Tiptoe' (Au/St) EWoo NDro
- 'Toffee Apple' (Au/d) NDro
- 'Toffee Crisp' (Au/A) EWoo GAbr NDro NSum XBar
- 'Tomboy' (Au/S) NDro XBar
- 'Toolyn' (Au/S) EWoo NDro
- 'Topaz' (Au/B) NDro
- 'Tosca' (Au/S) GAbr NDro NSum WHil XBar
- 'Trafalgar' (Au/S) NDro
- 'Trafalgar Square' (Au/S) EWoo GAbr NDro XBar
- 'Tregor Orange' (Au/d) WCot
- 'Tregor Stripe' (Au/St) XBar
- 'Trish' (Au) GAbr
- 'Trouble' (Au/d) EWoo GAbr GQue NDro NSum WHil
- 'Troy Aykman' (Au/A) NDro NSum WAln WHil XBar
- 'Trudy' (Au/S) EWoo GAbr ITim NDro WHil
- 'True Briton' (Au/S) NDro
- 'Truman' (Au/B) NDro
- 'Trumpet Blue' (Au/S) NDro
- 'Tudor Rose' (Au/S) XBar
- 'Tumbledown' (Au/A) EWoo NDro
- 'Tummel' (Au/A) EWoo GAbr NDro WHil
- 'Tupelo Honey' (Au/d) WAln
- 'Twiggy' (Au/S) GAbr NDro NSum WFar XBar
- 'Typhoon' (Au/A) EWoo WHil
- 'Uncle Arthur' (Au/A) WAln WHil
- 'Upperfields' (Au/B) NDro
- 'Ursula' (Au/d) WAln
- 'Valerie' (Au/A) ITim
- 'Valerie Clare' (Au/S) WAln WHil
- 'Vee Too' (Au/A) GAbr NDro WHil
- 'Vega' (Au/A) WAln
- 'Velvet Moon' (Au/A) NSum WAln
- 'Venetian' (Au/A) EWoo ITim NDro WHil
- 'Venus' (Au/A) WAln
- 'Vera' (Au/A) NDro WAln
- 'Vera Eden' (Au) WAln
- 'Vera Hill' (Au/A) NSum WAln
- 'Verdi' (Au/A) WAln
- 'Veronique' (Au/A) **new** XBar
- 'Vesuvius' (Au/d) EGrl EWoo GAbr NDro NSum
- 'Victoria de Wemyss' (Au/A) NDro WHil XBar
- 'Victoria Jane' (Au/A) WAln
- 'Victoria Park' (Au/A) WAln XBar
- 'Vienna' (Au/B) NDro
- 'Violet Surprise' (Au/St) EWoo NDro
- 'Voodoo Mama' (Au/St) NDro
- 'Vulcan' (Au/A) NDro XBar
- 'Walhampton' (Au/S) NDro
- 'Walton' (Au/A) EWoo GAbr NDro WHil XBar
- 'Walton Heath' (Au/d) EWoo GAbr NDro NWad WCot WFar WHil
- 'Wanda's Moonlight' (Au/d) WAln
- 'Warpaint' (Au/St) EWoo NDro NSum
- 'Warwick' (Au/S) NDro
- 'Watchett' (Au/S) NDro
- 'Wedding Day' (Au/S) EWoo
- 'Weirdo' (Au) NDro
- 'Wentworth' (Au/A) WAln
- 'Werner Müller' (Au/B) NDro
- 'West Harrow' (Au/S) NDro
- 'Westbourne Park' (Au/S) NDro
- 'Wheal' (Au/S) NDro
- 'Whistlejacket' (Au/S) NDro
- 'White Ensign' (Au/S) GAbr NDro NWad
- 'White Pyne' (Au/B) NDro
- 'White Satin' (Au/S) NDro
- 'White Water' (Au/A) EWoo NDro WHil
- 'White Wings' (Au/S) ITim NDro NHpl NSum
- 'Whoopee' (Au/A) EWoo NDro WAln
- 'Wichita Falls' (Au/A) NDro WAln
- 'Wide Awake' (Au/A) NDro
- 'Wild and Grey' (Au/S) NDro
- 'Wilf Booth' (Au/A) XBar
- 'William Gunn' (Au/d) EWoo NDro NSum WAln
- 'Wincha' (Au/S) ITim NDro NSum
- 'Windward Blue' (Au) NDro
- 'Windways Mystery' (Au/B) GAbr NDro NSum
- 'Windy Border' (Au/B) NDro
- 'Windy Goldtop' (Au/A) WAln
- 'Winifred' (Au/B) see *P.* × *pubescens* 'Winnifred'
- 'Winifrid' (Au/A) NDro NWad WHil
- 'Wonderous One' (Au/St) NDro
- 'Wong' (Au) **new** WAln
- 'Woodlands Lilac' (Au/B) NDro
- 'Woodmill' (Au/A) EWoo NDro NSum WHil XBar
- 'Wookey Hole' (Au/A) NDro
- 'Woottens Glory' (Au/S) **new** EWoo
- 'Wycliffe Harmony' (Au/B) NDro
- 'Wycliffe Midnight' (Au/B) EWoo GAbr ITim NDro WHil
- 'X2' (Au/S) WHil
- 'Xavier' (Au/d) EBee
- 'Yellow Ace' (Au) GAbr
- 'Yellow Isle' (Au/S) WAln
- 'Yellow Muff' (Au/S) NDro
- 'Yellow Ribbon' (Au) WAln
- 'Yitzhak Rabin' (Au/A) NDro WHil
- 'Yorkshire Grey' (Au/S) GAbr NDro
- 'Young Ian' (Au/B) NDro
- 'Young Love' (Au/B) NDro
- 'Zambia' (Au/d) GAbr ITim
- 'Zephyr' (Au/St) NDro
- 'Ziggy' (Au/St) NDro
- 'Zircon' (Au/S) NDro
- 'Zoe' (Au/A) WAln
- 'Zoe Ann' (Au/S) WAln

I - 'Zona' (Au/A) NDro
- 'Zorro' (Au/St) NDro

auriculata (Or) CTsd GKev SVic
- subsp. ***olgae*** (Or) GKev

balbisii (Au) CWCL GKev

'Balmoral' (Royal Oakleaf Series) (Pr/Poly) MMrt

'Barbara Barker' (Au) NWad

'Barbara Midwinter' (Pr) EBee GAbr NSum SHar WCot

Barnhaven Blues Group (Pr/Prim) XBar

Barnhaven doubles (Pr/Prim/d) XBar

Barnhaven Gold Group (Pr/Prim) XBar

Barnhaven Gold-laced Group see *P.* Gold-laced Group Barnhaven

Barnhaven Pixies Group (Pr/Prim) XBar

'Beamish Foam' (Pr/Poly) GAbr

'Beatrice Wooster' (Au) EHyd GAbr GArf NRHS NWad WFar XBar

'Beeches' Pink' (Prim/Poly)	GAbr LShi
beesiana (Pf) ♀H6	Widely available
Belarina Series	LRHS
- Belarina Amethyst Ice ('Kerbelpicotee'PBR) (Pr/Prim/d)	CDor LRHS LSou WHil WTor
- Belarina Butter Yellow ('Kerbelbut'PBR) (Pr/Prim/d)	CDor CExl EPfP LRHS LSou WHil
- Belarina Buttermilk ('Kerbelmilk'PBR) (Pr/Prim/d)	LSou NLar
- Belarina Cobalt Blue ('Kerbelcob'PBR) (Pr/Prim/d)	CExl CWCL LRHS LSou NHpl WHil
- Belarina Cream ('Kerbelcrem'PBR) (Pr/Prim/d)	CDor CExl LRHS NHpl WHil
- Belarina Goldie (Pr/Prim/d) **new**	LRHS WHil
- Belarina Lively Lilac (Pr/Prim/d) **new**	LRHS
- Belarina Pink Champagne ('Kerbelchamp'PBR) (Pr/Prim/d)	CWCL LRHS LSou WHil
- Belarina Pink Ice ('Kerbelpice'PBR) (Pr/Prim/d)	CDor CWCL LSou MAvo MHol NHpl NLar WTor
- Belarina Rosette Nectarine ('Kerbelnec'PBR) (Pr/Prim/d)	CDor CExl CWCL ECtt LRHS SPad WHil
- Belarina Rosette Valentine ('Kerbelred'PBR) (Pr/Prim/d)	CDor CWCL LRHS LSou NLar WHil WTor
- Belarina Vanilla (Pr/Prim/d) **new**	LRHS
- Belarina Yellow Ruffles (Pr/Prim/d) **new**	LRHS
bellidifolia (Mu)	GKev NGdn
beluensis	see *P.* × *pubescens* 'Freedom'
× ***berninae*** (Au)	GArf GKev
'Berries and Cream Shades' (Pr/Prim/d) **new**	LRHS
'Bewerley White'	see *P.* × *pubescens* 'Bewerley White'
bhutanica	see *P. whitei* 'Sherriff's Variety'
× ***biflora*** (Au)	GArf GRum
bileckii	see *P.* × *forsteri* 'Bileckii'
'Blindsee' (Au)	NHar NSum
blinii (Y)	GKev
'Blue Ice' (Pr/Prim/d)	XBar
Blue Julians Group (Pr/Prim)	XBar
'Blue Riband' (Pr/Prim)	WFar
'Blue Sapphire' (Pr/Prim/d)	CMiW MBel XBar
'Bon Accord Cerise' (Pr/Poly/d)	GAbr LShi
'Bon Accord Purple' (Pr/Poly/d)	CMiW
'Bonheur' (Pr/Prim/d)	XBar
boothii subsp. ***repens*** (Pe)	GKev
'Boothman's Ruby'	see *P.* × *pubescens* 'Boothman's Variety'
boveana (Sp)	GKev
bracteata (Bu)	GKev WAbe
§ - subsp. ***dubernardiana*** (Bu)	WAbe
brevicula SDR 4452 (Cy)	GKev
'Brittany Blue' (Pr/Prim/d)	XBar
'Broadwell Chameleon' (Au)	ITim NHar NRya
'Broadwell Milkmaid' (Au) ♀H5	ITim NSum NWad WAbe
'Broadwell Ruby' (Au)	ITim WAbe
'Broadwell Snowstorm' (Au)	ITim NSum
'Broxbourne' (Au) ♀H5	EPot ITim XBar
'Buckland Wine' (Pr/Prim)	CElw EBee ECtt EPfP GEdr XBar
bullata (Bu)	GKev
× ***bulleesiana*** (Pf)	CBod CDor CTsd EHyd EPfP EShb EWTr GAbr GKev GMaP GWyn LRHS MCot NChi NGdn NHol NRHS SAko SCob WFar WPnP XBar
bulleyana (Pf) ♀H7	Widely available
- hybrids (Pf)	CWat GKev
'Burgundy Ice' (Pr/Prim/d)	XBar
burmanica (Pf)	CWCL GKev MMuc WHoo XBar
Butterscotch Group (Pr/Prim)	XBar
'Caerulea Plena' (Pr/Prim)	NBid
calderiana subsp. ***calderiana*** (Pe)	GKev
- purple-flowered (Pe)	GKev
- subsp. ***strumosa*** (Pe)	GKev
calliantha (Cy)	GKev
'Camaieu' (Pr/Prim/d)	XBar
Candelabra hybrids (Pf)	EGrl GAbr ITim MBriF NBir NGdn NHpl SMrm WCav
Candy Pinks Group (Pr/Prim)	XBar
capitata (Ca)	CBcs CPla EPfP EPot GArf GKev GRum NGBl NHpl SPer SRot WCAu WCot
- CC 3843	SRms
- subsp. ***crispata*** (Ca)	GKev
- subsp. ***mooreana*** (Ca)	CAvo CExl CSpe CTsd EDAr EPfP GKev LRHS NChi NGdn NHpl NLar SPlb XBar
- 'Noverna Deep Blue' (Ca)	LRHS SRms WCav
- 'Salvana' (Ca)	MACG
- subsp. ***sphaerocephala*** (Ca) ♀H7	GKev
'Captain Blood' (Pr/Prim/d)	CMiW NHpl
Carnation Victorians Group (Pr/Poly)	XBar
carniolica (Au)	GKev WCot
cawdoriana (So)	GKev
cernua (Mu)	XBar
Chartreuse Group (Pr/Poly)	XBar
'Cherry' (Pr/Prim)	GAbr
'Cherry Ripple' (Pr/Prim/d) **new**	XBar
§ ***chionantha*** (Cy) ♀H6	CPla GAbr GArf GEdr GKev GRum NBir NGdn WFar XBar
- subsp. ***chionantha*** (Cy)	GKev
- subsp. ***melanops***	see *P. melanops*
§ - subsp. ***sinopurpurea*** (Cy)	GKev NBir
chungensis (Pf)	CBod CDor CTsd ELan EPfP GAbr GArf GBin GKev GLog GQue GWyn NGdn NHol NLar SPtp SWvt WFar WMAq XBar
§ ***chungensis*** × ***pulverulenta*** (Pf)	GBin GKev MPnt SAko WSpi
× ***chunglenta***	see *P. chungensis* × *pulverulenta*
'Cisca' (Pr)	WCot
'Clarence Elliott' (Au) ♀H5	GArf GKev MPnt NRya NSum NWad WFar WIce
'Clarissa White' (Pr/Poly)	XBar

	clarkei (Or)	GKev
	clusiana (Au)	GKev WAbe
	- 'Murray-Lyon' (Au)	NDro NHar
	cockburniana (Pf) 𝕐H6	CSpe CTsd GAbr NWad XBar
	- SDR 1967	EBee GKev
	- 'Kevock Sunshine' (Pf)	GKev NWad XBar
	- orange-flowered (Pf)	GKev
	concholoba (Mu)	GKev XBar
	'Corporal Baxter' (Pr/Prim/d)	CMiW ECtt EShb GMaP MBel XBar
	cortusoides (Co)	EBee GKev GRum XBar
	'Cottage Cream' (Pr)	LSou MBros SVic
	Cowichan Amethyst Group (Pr/Poly)	XBar
	Cowichan Blue Group (Pr/Poly)	XBar
	Cowichan Garnet Group (Pr/Poly)	MBriF XBar
	Cowichan strain (Pr/Poly)	CElw
	Cowichan Venetian Group (Pr/Poly)	XBar
	Cowichan Yellow Group (Pr/Poly)	XBar
	'Craddock White' (Pr/Prim)	CFis CMiW
	'Crème du Tregor' (Pr/Prim/d)	XBar
	Crescendo Series (Pr/Poly)	WHil
	'Crimson Velvet' (Au)	NSum WThu XBar
	crispa	see *P. glomerata*
	cuneifolia (Cu)	GKev
	- subsp. ***heterodonta*** (Cu)	GKev
	'Custard the Cat'	WHil
	daonensis (Au)	GKev
	darialica (Al)	GKev
	'Dark Rosaleen' (Pr/Poly)	CExl CRos ECtt EHyd EMor EPfP GAbr LRHS LShi MBNS MBriF MMuc MNrw MPie NHpl NLar NRHS NWad SAko SPoG WBrk WCot WFar
	'David Green' (Pr/Prim)	CMiW
	'David Valentine' (Pr/Poly)	CFis NSum WCot XBar
	'Dawn Ansell' (Pr/Prim/d)	CDor CMiW ECtt EPfP MBNS MBow NBir NHpl WCAu WHer XBar
	Daybreak Group (Pr/Poly)	XBar
	'Dentelle' (Pr/Prim/d)	XBar
	denticulata (De) 𝕐H6	Widely available
	- var. ***alba*** (De)	Widely available
	- blue-flowered (De)	EPfP GAbr GBin GWyn MPri NLar
	- 'Bressingham Beauty' (De)	EBee EBlo EHyd
	- var. ***cachemiriana*** hort. (De)	EWTr GRum NWad
	- hybrids (De)	EGrl WFar XBar
	- 'Karryann' (De/v)	WCot
	- lilac-flowered (De)	CRos EHyd EPfP EShb LRHS NHol NRHS SCob WTor
	- 'Miss Esther' (De)	NSum
	- red-flowered (De)	CAvo EPfP NBir SCob
	- 'Rubin' (De)	CRos CTsd CWCL CWat EBee EBou EHyd EPfP GAbr GMaP LRHS MBel NChi NLar NRHS SPer SPoG SRms XLum
	- 'Rubinball' (De)	GRum NHol
	deorum (Au)	GKev
	Desert Sunset Group (Pr/Poly)	XBar
	deuteronana (Pe)	GKev
	dickieana (Am)	GKev
	× ***digenea*** (Pr)	XBar
	'Don Keefe' (Pr/Poly)	CBcs ECtt MBNS MBel MBriF MNrw MPie NGBl NHpl NLar WCot WFar
	'Double Lilac'	see *P. vulgaris* 'Lilacina Plena'
	dubernardiana	see *P. bracteata* subsp. *dubernardiana*
	'Duchess of York' (Pr/Poly)	CMiW ECtt LShi MHCG NLar
	'Duckyls Red' (Pr/Prim)	NBir
	'Easter Bonnet' (Pr/Prim)	LRHS MMuc SEND
	edgeworthii	see *P. nana*
§	***elatior*** (Pr) 𝕐H6	CBod CDor CMac EPfP EWTr EWoo GAbr GJos GKev GMaP LCro LOPS LRHS MBow MHer MNHC MNrw MPri NAts NChi NLar SPer SPoG SRms SWvt WBrk WCav WHoo XBar
	- hose-in-hose (Pr/d)	NBid
	- hybrids (Pr)	SPlb
	- 'Magnifica' (Pr)	GKev
§	- subsp. ***meyeri*** (Pr)	GKev SBrt
I	- - 'Alba' (Pr)	GRum
	- subsp. ***pallasii*** (Pr)	GKev SPhx
	- subsp. ***pseudoelatior*** (Pr)	GKev WAbe
	'Elizabeth Browning' (Pr/Poly)	ECtt GAbr WCot
	'Elizabeth Killelay' PBR (Pr/Poly/d)	CDor CExl CMiW ECtt ELan MNrw NBir NHpl NLar SPer WCot WFar
	'Ellen Page' (Au)	XBar
	'Ethel Barker' (Au)	NWad
	'Eugénie' (Pr/Prim/d)	ECtt MRav
	euprepes	see *P. melanantha*
	'Fairy Rose' (Au)	NWad
	fangii (Pu)	GKev
	- BO 16-118 **new**	GGro
	farinosa (Al)	GArf GKev NGdn XBar
	- var. ***denudata*** (Al)	GKev
	fasciculata (Ar)	SPlb
	- CLD 345	GEdr WAbe
	'Feuerkönig' (Au)	NDro
	'Fire Opal' (Pr/Poly)	CRos EBlo EHyd LRHS NRHS
	Firefly Group (Pr/Poly)	WCot XBar
§	***firmipes*** (Si)	GArf LPot
§	***flaccida*** (Mu)	GEdr GKev GRum NHpl
	Flamingo Group (Pr/Poly)	XBar
	× ***floerkeana*** f. ***biflora*** 'Alba' (Au)	GRum
	florindae (Si) 𝕐H7	Widely available
	- bronze-flowered (Si)	NBir
	- 'Dave's Red' (Si)	LEdu
	- hybrids (Si)	CMac EShb WFar WWtn XBar
	- Keillour hybrids (Si)	NGdn SBls SWvt
	- orange-flowered (Si)	GArf GPSL LLWG MNrw SRms WPnP
	- peach-flowered (Si)	CSpe
	- 'Ray's Ruby' (Si)	CTsd MNrw NBir NChi WCot
	- red and copper hybrids (Si)	MWts SWvt WHoo
	- 'Red Shades' (Si)	GRum NWad
	- red-flowered (Si)	CSpe GKev GPSL LLWG NBid NLar WFar
	- terracotta-flowered (Si)	NGdn
	Footlight Parade Group (Pr/Prim)	XBar
	forbesii (Mo)	WCot
	- CC 4084	CExl
	forrestii (Bu)	GKev XBar
	- SDR 4304	CExl
§	× ***forsteri*** (Au)	NHpl NLar
§	- 'Bileckii' (Au)	GMaP NBir NHar NSla NSum
	- 'Dianne' (Au)	GAbr GKev NRya NSum WAbe
	'Francisca' (Pr/Poly) 𝕐H7	CBod CExl CMac CWCL CWGN EBee ECtt EMor EPfP GBin LPot MBNS MBel MCot NChi NHpl NLar SPad WBrk WCAu WCFE WCot WFar XLum

'Fred Salter' (Au)	NRya
frondosa (Al) 🏆H5	EWTr MPnt WAbe
'Frou-frou' (Pr/Prim/d)	XBar
Fuchsia Victorians Group (Pr/Poly)	XBar
'Garnet' (*allionii* hybrid) (Au)	XBar
'Garryarde Guinevere'	see *P.* 'Guinevere'
geraniifolia (Co)	GKev
'Gigha' (Pr/Prim)	EBee GKev MNrw WFar
'Gilded Garnet' (Pr/Poly/d)	LRHS NHpl
Gilded Ginger Group (Pr/Poly)	XBar
'Ginger Spice' (Au)	NDro
§ ***glomerata*** (Ca)	GKev XBar
'Glowing Embers' (Pf)	GKev NBir
glutinosa All.	see *P. allionii*
Gold-laced Group (Pr/Poly)	CDor CTsd ECtt EHyd ELan EMor EPfP GQue LRHS LSRN LShi MAsh MMuc MNHC NGdn NHpl NLar NRHS SEND SPer SPlb SPoG WCAu WFar WHil
§ - Barnhaven (Pr/Poly)	MAsh NBir XBar
- - 'Gold-laced Jack in the Green' (Pr/Poly)	XBar
- Beeches strain (Pr/Poly)	XBar
- hose-in-hose (Pr/Poly)	XBar
- 'Lightly Laced' (Pr/Poly)	NWad
- red-flowered (Pr/Poly)	CRos ELan
gracilipes (Pe)	GKev NHar WFar
- 'Minor'	see *P. petiolaris* Wall.
graminifolia	see *P. chionantha*
Grand Canyon Group (Pr/Poly)	XBar
grandis (Sr)	GKev XBar
'Green Lace' (Pr/Poly)	ECtt
'Groenekan's Glorie' (Pr/Prim)	CFis EBee ECtt NBir NSum WFar WHil
'Guernsey Cream' (Pr/Prim/d)	XBar
§ 'Guinevere' (Pr/Poly) 🏆H6	CExl CMiW CRos CSpe EBee ECtt EHyd EWTr GAbr GArf GMaP LRHS LShi MBow MBriF MMuc MNrw NBid NBir NGrd NHpl NRHS NRya SEND SEdd SPlb WCot WFar WHil XBar
'Hall Barn Blue' (Pr/Prim)	CSpe EBee ELan EPfP EWhm GAbr GArf GEdr GMaP GRum MHCG MMuc NSum SEND WCot
§ ***halleri*** (Al)	GAbr GKev XBar
- 'Longiflora'	see *P. halleri*
- subsp. ***platyphylla*** (Al)	GKev
handeliana × ***maximowiczii*** (Cy)	GKev
Harbinger Group (Pr/Prim)	XBar
Harbour Lights Group (Pr/Poly)	XBar
Harlow Car hybrids (Pf)	CRos EHyd EPfP LRHS NRHS NSla NWad WHil XBar
Harvest Yellows Group (Pr/Poly)	XBar
helodoxa	see *P. prolifera*
'Hemswell Blush' (Au)	NHpl NSum WFar
'Hemswell Ember' (Au)	ECtt
heucherifolia (Co)	CPla
- SDR 3224	GKev
hidakana (R)	GEdr
hirsuta (Au)	GKev MMuc SEND
- 'Lismore Snow' (Au)	NWad
- red-flowered (Au)	GKev
- white-flowered (Au)	NRya
hirsuta × ***minima***	see *P.* × *forsteri*
hoffmanniana	GKev NHar SPlb
hose-in-hose (Pr/Poly/d)	EWes MNrw
- Barnhaven (Pr/Poly/d)	XBar
ianthina	see *P. prolifera*
Indian Reds Group (Pr/Poly)	XBar
'Ingram's Blue' (Pr/Poly)	CFis CMiW EBee EPfP
'Innisfree Pink' (Pr/Prim)	CBod
Inshriach hybrids (Pf)	GBin SPer
integrifolia (Au)	GKev
§ 'Inverewe' (Pf)	EBee GBin GEdr GKev MPnt NBir NFav NHar NHpl XBar
involucrata	see *P. munroi*
'Iris Mainwaring' (Pr/Prim)	CFis EBee ECtt ELan GKev
irregularis hybrid (Pe) **new**	NHar
'Jackie Richards' (Au)	NWad
Jack-in-the-Green Group (Pr/Poly)	GAbr MNrw NWad
- Barnhaven (Pr/Poly)	XBar
- red-flowered (Pr/Poly)	MMuc WHil
'Jack-the-Lad' (Pr/Prim/d)	XBar
japonica (Pf)	ECha GAbr MSCN MWts NBro NGdn
- 'Alba' (Pf)	CBod CTri CTsd EHyd EPfP EShb EWoo LLWG MBel MCot MHol NChi NGdn NLar SPer WCAu WFar WHil
- 'Apple Blossom' (Pf)	Widely available
* - 'Carminea' (Pf)	CDor GKev LShi MSCN NBro NGdn SPer WFar
- 'Fuji' (Pf)	GAbr NBro
- hybrids (Pf)	CMac WFar
- 'Jim Saunders' (Pf)	SLon
- 'Miller's Crimson' (Pf) 🏆H6	Widely available
- 'Oriental Sunrise' (Pf)	GKev XBar
- pale pink-flowered (Pf)	ITim
- 'Postford White' (Pf) 🏆H6	CBcs CCBP CDor CPla CRos EBee EHyd ELan EPfP GAbr GKev GMaP ITim LRHS LSRN LShi NBir NRHS SCob SPer SPoG SRms SWvt WBor WBrk XBar
- 'Valley Red' (Pf)	GKev
- Violet Oriental Group (Pf)	XBar
- violet-flowered (Pf)	GKev
'Jay-Jay' (Pr)	XBar
'Jenny' ambig.	GArf
jesoana (Co)	GKev
- var. ***pubescens*** (Co)	GKev
'Jewel' (Pr)	GAbr
'Joan Hughes' (*allionii* hybrid) (Au)	WAbe
'Joanna' (Pr/Poly)	ECtt MPnt
'Johanna' (Pu)	GArf GKev LEdu NGdn NSum WAbe
'John Fielding' (Pr)	CBro CElw GAbr
'Jo-Jo' (Au)	ITim NSum WAbe XBar
'Jubilee' (Pr/Prim/d)	XBar
juliae (Pr)	CBor EHyd EWld GKev GRum LRHS NBid NHpl NRHS SPlb WAbe
'Ken Dearman' (Pr/Prim/d)	CMiW ECtt EShb EWTr NBir NHpl WHil XBar
× ***kewensis*** (Sp) 🏆H3	GKev XBar
'Kingscote' (Au)	NDro
'Kinlough Beauty' (Pr/Poly)	EBee ECtt GKev GMaP SRot XBar
§ ***kisoana*** (Co)	CExl GKev
- var. ***alba*** (Co)	NHar XBar
- 'Barnhaven Blush' (Co)	XBar
- 'Iyo-beni' (Co)	NHar XBar
- 'Noushoku' (Co)	XBar
- var. ***shikokiana***	see *P. kisoana*

	kitaibeliana (Au)	GKev
	'Koblenz' (Au)	NSum
	komarovii (Pr)	SPlb
	'Kusum Krishna' (Au)	GEdr GRum MBNS MHol MPie NHpl NLar NRya WCot WFar
	'Lady Greer' (Pr/Poly) ♀H5	CMac CMea CMiW EBee ECtt ELan EPPr EPfP GAbr GKev GMaP GWyn LShi MTin NChi NGdn NHar NLar NSum WCAu WFar XBar
	'Lambrook Mauve' (Pr/Poly)	CElw CFis GAbr
§	***latifolia*** (Au)	GArf GKev
	latisecta (Co)	GEdr GKev
§	***laurentiana*** (Al)	EWes GKev
	'Lee Myers' (*allionii* hybrid) (Au)	WFar XBar
	'Lemon and Lime'	CMea WHil
	leucophylla	see *P. elatior*
	'Lilac Lace' (Pr/Poly) **new**	CRos WHil
	lilacina (Mu)	GKev
	'Lilian Foster' (Pr/Prim)	WCot
	'Lilian Harvey' (Pr/Prim/d)	CMiW
	limbata (Cy)	GKev
	'Lindum Angelic' (Au)	NHar
	'Lindum Aria' (Au)	NHar
	'Lindum Celebration' (Au)	NHar
	'Lindum Countess' (Au) **new**	NHar
	'Lindum Crepes Suzette' (Au)	ITim NHar
	'Lindum Dove' (Au)	NHar
	'Lindum Finale' (Au)	NHar
	'Lindum First Kiss' (Au)	ITim
	'Lindum Flirtatious' (Au) **new**	NHar
	'Lindum Frosty Moon' (Au)	ITim
	'Lindum Gecko' (Au)	NHar
	'Lindum Golden Orb' (Au)	NHar
	'Lindum Heavenly' (Au)	XBar
	'Lindum Lancelot' (Au)	WMal
	'Lindum Lavender Mist' (Au)	NSum XBar
	'Lindum Limelight' (Au)	ITim
	'Lindum Lyric' (Au)	NHar
	'Lindum Memories' (Au) **new**	NHar
	'Lindum Moonlight' (Au)	WMal XBar
	'Lindum Morning Flight' (Au)	NHar
	'Lindum Rapture' (Au)	NHar
	'Lindum Storm Cloud' (Au)	NHar
	'Lindum Wedgwood' (Au)	GEdr ITim NHar NSum XBar
	'Lingwood Beauty' (Pr/Prim)	CElw CFis
	'Linn's Red' **new**	GKev
	'Lismore' (Au)	NWad
	'Lismore Peardrop' (Au)	NSum
	'Lismore Pink Ice' (Au)	NWad
	Lissadel hybrids (Pf)	CBod
	Little Egypt Group (Pr/Poly)	XBar
	littoniana	see *P. vialii*
	'Lizzie Green' (Pr/Prim)	NLar
	× ***loiseleurii*** 'Aire Mist' (Au) ♀H5	ITim NHpl NRya NSla NSum NWad WFar XBar
§	– 'Aire Waves' (Au)	ITim NHar NRya
	– 'Lismore Yellow' (Au)	XBar
	longiflora	see *P. halleri*
	longipes (Cy)	GKev
	'Lopen Red' (Pr/Prim)	CMiW GKev WSHC XBar
	lutea (Au)	GKev
	luteola (Or)	GKev NGdn NHpl XBar
	macrocalyx	see *P. veris*
	macrophylla (Cy)	EWes GKev
	– var. ***moorcroftiana*** (Cy)	GKev
	'MacWatt's Claret' (Pr/Poly)	ECtt GAbr
	'MacWatt's Cream' (Pr/Poly)	CTtf EBee EHyd GAbr LEdu LRHS NLar NRHS NSum WHil
	'Mademoiselle Zia' (Pr/Poly)	XBar
	magellanica (Al)	GKev SPlb WAbe
	mairei (Al)	GKev
	'Maisie Michael' (Pr/Prim)	GEdr NHpl WAbe
	malacoides (Mo) ♀H2	XBar
	malvacea (Ma)	GKev
	marginata (Au) ♀H5	EHyd EWoo LRHS MMuc NRHS NSla SEND WAbe
	– 'Adrian Evans' (Au)	GEdr WIce
	– 'Adrian Jones' (Au)	XBar
	– 'Alba' (Au)	EHyd GEdr GKev NBro NRHS NRya NWad XBar
	– 'Ardfearn' (Au)	GEdr
	– 'Baldock's Purple' (Au)	NRya XBar
	– 'Barbara Clough' (Au)	GEdr NRya NSum NWad XBar
	– 'Beamish' (Au) ♀H5	GEdr NBro NRya NSla NWad
	– 'Beatrice Lascaris' (Au)	EHyd GEdr NRHS NRya WAbe
	– 'Bill Crow' (Au)	GEdr NRya
	– 'Caerulea' (Au)	GArf GEdr NRya NWad XBar
	– 'Casterino' (Au)	NRya WAbe
	– 'Clear's Variety' (Au)	GKev XBar
	– 'Crookes Variety' (Au)	NRya
	– 'Doctor Jenkins' (Au)	NRya NWad
	– 'Dolomites' (Au)	NWad
	– 'Drake's Form' (Au)	NRya XBar
	– dwarf (Au)	EHyd LRHS NRHS NRya
	– 'Earl L. Bolton'	see *P. marginata* 'El Bolton'
§	– 'El Bolton' (Au)	NRya NSum NWad
	– 'Elizabeth Fry' (Au)	GEdr
	– 'Grandiflora' (Au)	NWad
	– 'Highland Twilight' (Au)	NSla
	– 'Holden Variety' (Au)	NRya NWad XBar
	– 'Holly Leaf' (Au)	GEdr
	– 'Ivy Agee' (Au)	NRya
	– 'Janet' (Au)	GEdr NWad
	– 'Johannes Holler' (Au)	NRya
	– 'Kesselring's Variety' (Au)	CMea GEdr NSum NWad WAbe WFar WIce XBar
	– 'Laciniata' (Au)	EHyd GKev GRum LRHS NRHS XBar
	– 'Lemon Sorbet' (Au)	NSum
	– 'Linda Pope' (Au) ♀H5	GArf GEdr NBir WThu XBar
	– 'Manfield' (Au)	NRya
	– maritime form (Au)	GArf NSum XBar
	– 'Millard's Variety' (Au)	NWad
	– 'Mrs Carter Walmsley' (Au)	NRya NWad
	– 'Mylene' (Au)	NRya NSum
	– 'Napoleon' (Au)	GEdr NRya NWad
	– 'Peggy Fell' (Au)	NWad WHil
	– 'Prichard's Variety' (Au) ♀H5	GEdr GPSL NRya WAbe
	– 'Sheila Denby' (Au)	NRya NWad
	– 'The President' (Au)	NWad
	– 'Waithman's Variety' (Au)	NRya NSum NWad
	– wild-collected (Au)	GArf
	'Maria Talbot' (*allionii* hybrid) (Au)	NSum
	Marine Blues Group (Pr/Poly)	XBar
	MARLI ROSE SHADES (Marli Series) **new**	LRHS
	'Mars' (*allionii* hybrid) (Au)	XBar
	'Marven' (Au)	GEdr
	'Mary Anne' (Pr)	GAbr LShi
	matthioli	see *Cortusa matthioli*
	'Mauve Mist' (Au)	WCot
	Mauve Victorians Group (Pr/Poly)	XBar

maximowiczii (Cy)	EDAr GEdr NGdn
§ - var. ***maximowiczii*** (Cy)	GKev NHpl
- Red-flowered Group	see *P. maximowiczii* var. *maximowiczii*
maximowiczii* × *tangutica (Cy)	GKev
megaseifolia (Pr)	GKev
melanantha (Cy)	GKev
- 'Moonshine' (Cy)	GKev
§ ***melanops*** (Cy)	GKev
'Melenoc'h' (Pr/Prim/d)	MBow XBar
Midnight Group (Pr/Prim)	XBar
'Miel' (Pr/Prim/d)	XBar
'Millstream Cream' (Au)	NLar
'Millwood Blush' (Pr/Prim)	CMiW WMal
'Millwood Double' (Pr/Prim/d)	CMiW
'Millwood Lemon' (Pr/Prim)	CMiW
minima (Au)	GKev NBro
minor (Cy)	GKev
'Miss Doris' (Pr/Prim/d)	XBar
'Miss Indigo' (Pr/Prim/d)	CMiW CTsd ECtt EPfP MBNS MBow NHpl WCAu XBar
mistassinica (Al)	XBar
- var. ***macropoda***	see *P. laurentiana*
miyabeana (Pf)	GKev
modesta (Al)	XBar
- var. ***faurieae*** (Al)	GKev
- - f. ***leucantha*** (Al)	GKev
- var. ***samanimontana*** (Al)	GKev
'Moerheimii' (Pr/Prim)	GAbr GEdr
moupinensis (Pe)	CExl NHar
- subsp. ***barkamensis*** (Pe)	GKev
'Mrs Eagland' (Pr/Prim)	GAbr
'Mrs Frank Neave' (Pr/Prim)	GAbr WFar
'Mrs Marjorie Banks' (Pr)	GKev
'Mrs McGillivray' (Pr/Prim)	GAbr
§ ***munroi*** (Ar)	GKev WAbe XBar
- subsp. ***munroi*** (Ar) CC 5311	GKev
- white-flowered (Ar)	WAbe
§ - subsp. ***yargongensis*** (Ar)	GArf GKev XBar
muscarioides (Mu)	GKev
Muted Victorians Group (Pr/Poly)	XBar
'Myline'	WThu
§ ***nana*** (Pe)	GEdr NHar
- 'Alba' (Pe)	GEdr NHar
'Netta Dennis' (Pe)	NHar
New Pinks Group (Pr/Poly)	XBar
'Nightingale' (Au)	ITim XBar
nivalis Pallas	see *P. chionantha*
nutans Delavay ex Franch.	see *P. flaccida*
'Oak Leaf Yellow Picotee' (Pr) **new**	LRHS MPri
obconica subsp. ***werringtonensis*** (Ob)	GKev
obtusifolia (Cy)	GKev
odontocalyx (Da) **new**	GKev
'Old Port' (Pr/Poly)	GKev GQue LShi NSum
Old Rose Victorians Group (Pr/Poly)	XBar
'Ooh La La Pastel Pink' (Ooh La La Series) (Pi × Sp)	LCro LRHS
optata (Cy)	GKev
'Orange Flame' (Pf)	GKev
orbicularis (Cy)	GKev NHpl
Osiered Amber Group (Pr/Prim)	XBar
'Our Pat' (Pr/Poly/d)	CMiW
ovalifolia (Da) **new**	GKev
palinuri (Au)	WMal
palmata (Co)	GEdr GKev
Paris '90 Group (Pr/Poly)	XBar
parryi (Pa)	GEdr GKev
pedemontana 'Alba' (Au)	GEdr WThu XBar
'Perle von Bottrop' (Pr/Prim)	ECtt GBin NSum WCot
petelotii (Ch)	GEdr
'Peter Klein' (Or)	ECtt EPot GKev
petiolaris misapplied	see *P.* 'Redpoll'
§ ***petiolaris*** Wall. (Pe)	NHar
- Sherriff's form	see *P.* 'Redpoll'
'Petticoat' (Pr/Prim/d)	CMiW ECtt NWad WCot XBar
'Pink Aire' (Au)	NSum NWad XBar
'Pink Fairy' (Au)	ITim
'Pink Grapefruit' (Pr/Prim/d)	XBar
'Pink Ice' (*allionii* hybrid) (Au)	GKev LRHS NSum NWad XBar
'Pink' (Primlet Series) (Pr/Prim)	EHyd LRHS NRHS
'Pink Star' (Pr/Prim/d)	XBar
poissonii (Pf)	CDoC CDor CFis CTri EDAr EHyd EPfP EPot GAbr GKev GRum LRHS NGdn NHpl NRHS WShi WWtn
polyanthus (Pr/Poly)	MMuc SVic
polyneura (Co)	CTsd EBee EGrI GAbr GArf GKev GRum MACG MHol NGdn WCot
'Port Wine' (Pr)	GAbr
'Powdery Pink' (Pf)	EHyd LRHS NRHS
prenantha SDR 3909 (Pf)	GKev
'Primadiente Rose' (Co)	WHil
§ ***prolifera*** (Pf) ♀H4	EHyd ELan EPfP GKev LRHS MNrw NGdn NHpl NWad SPtp XBar
§ × ***pubescens*** (Au) ♀H5	CDor EHyd LRHS MHer NGdn NRHS
- 'Balfouriana' (Au)	NWad
§ - 'Bewerley White' (Au)	EBee EPfP EWoo NDro
§ - 'Boothman's Variety' (Au)	CTri EPfP EWoo GKev NSla WBrk WHoo
- 'Carmen'	see *P. × pubescens* 'Boothman's Variety'
- 'Christine' (Au)	CMea GKev NBir NSum WCot
- 'Cream Viscosa' (Au)	EWoo NSum SPlb WFar
- 'Faldonside' (Au)	NSla NSum
§ - 'Freedom' (Au)	CTri EWoo GKev NBir NSla NSum XBar
- 'George Harrison' (Au)	GArf NDro
- 'Harlow Car' (Au)	CMea MPnt NSum NWad
- 'Hazel's White' (Au)	GAbr
- 'Henry Hall' (Au)	NSum
- 'Joan Danger' (Au)	NDro
- 'Joan Gibbs' (Au)	NHpl XBar
- 'Lilac Fairy' (Au)	GKev ITim NWad WThu
- 'Moonlight' (Au)	NDro
- 'Mrs J.H. Wilson' (Au)	NRya XBar
- 'Pat Barwick' (Au)	NDro NSum
- 'Rufus' (Au) ♀H5	GAbr GEdr NDro NHar XBar
- 'Rumbling Bridge' (Au)	GRum
- 'Sid Skelton' (Au)	NRya
- 'Slack Top Violet' (Au)	NSla
- 'Snowcap' (Au)	ITim XBar
- 'Sonya' (Au)	NSum
- 'The General' (Au)	CTri GEdr NSum
§ - 'Wedgwood' (Au)	GAbr NDro NSum WHil XBar
§ - 'Winnifred' (Au)	EGrI GAbr NDro
× ***pubescens*** × 'White Linda Pope' (Au)	GArf
pulchella (Pu)	GKev
pulchra (Pe)	GKev
pulverulenta (Pf) ♀H6	Widely available
- Bartley hybrids (Pf) ♀H6	GEdr GKev GRum GWyn NHpl NWad

'Purple' (Primlet Series) (Pr/Prim) EHyd LRHS NRHS
'Purple Storm' (Pr/Prim/d) WFar XBar
'Quaker's Bonnet' see *P. vulgaris* 'Lilacina Plena'
'Rachel Kinnen' (Au) GAbr WFar XBar
Ramona Group (Pr/Poly) XBar
'Raspberry Ripple' (Pr/Prim/d) EHyd MBow XBar
'Ravenglass Vermilion' see *P.* 'Inverewe'
'Red Hugh' (Pf) **new** NHpl
'Red' (Primlet Series) (Pr/Prim) CRos EHyd LRHS NRHS
'Red Ruffles' (Pr/Poly/d) ECtt
§ 'Redpoll' (Pe) GArf GEdr NHar
reidii (So) GEdr GKev
– var. ***williamsii*** (So) GEdr GKev
* – – ***alba*** (So) GEdr
reticulata (Si) GKev
Reverie Group (Pr/Poly) XBar
'Rheniana' (Au) NRya
'Romance' (Pr/Prim/d) CWCL LRHS
'Romeo' (Pr/Prim) NSum NWad WCot
'Rose' (Primlet Series) (Pr/Prim) CRos EHyd LRHS NRHS
rosea (Or) ♀H5 EPfP GKev GLog GMaP MMuc NBid NBir NRya SCob WPnP XBar
– CC 5260 MAsh
– 'Gigas' (Or) GAbr WMAq
– 'Grandiflora' (Or) CMac EPfP GKev GPSL LRHS MBel SPoG SRms XLum
'Rosemary Cottage' (Pr/Poly) GAbr WCot
§ ***rotundifolia*** (Cf) GKev
I 'Rowena' (Pr/Prim) CFis GAbr WCot
roxburghii see *P. rotundifolia*
'Roy Cope' (Pr/Prim/d) NBir
rubra see *P. firmipes*
'Ruby Tuesday' (Au) NDro
rupicola (Y) GKev
rusbyi (Pa) GKev
– subsp. ***ellisiae*** (Pa) GKev
'Sapphire' (Au) XBar
scandinavica (Al) GKev
scapigera (Pe) WFar
§ 'Schneekissen' (Pr/Prim) CMiW CRos CWCL EBee EHyd LRHS NBro NChi NRHS NSum SRot WFar WTor
'Scirocco Neon Violet' **new** CRos
'Scirocco Red' **new** CRos
scotica (Al) GKev GPoy GRum NSla SPlb WAbe
secundiflora (Pf) CTsd ELan EWes GArf GKev LLWG NBir NChi NWad SPlb XBar
serratifolia (Pf) GKev
sharmae (Al) GKev
'Sheryl Louise' (Pr/Prim) NHar
sibthorpii see *P. vulgaris* subsp. *sibthorpii*
sieboldii (Co) ♀H5 EHyd EWld GKev MACG MAsh MNrw NHpl NRHS NSla SGro SRms
– 'Aiaigasa' (Co) CSta
– 'Aka Tonbo' (Co) CSta WFar
– 'Aki-no-yosooi' (Co) CSta
– 'Alba' (Co) **new** CSta EBlo WHil
– 'Amaendo' (Co) **new** CSta
– 'Andromeda' (Co) EBee
– 'Aoba-no-fue' (Co) CSta WFar
– 'Aoi-no-ue' (Co) CSta
– 'Aoyagi-zome' (Co) CSta XBar
– 'Appare' (Co) CSta
– 'Apple Blossom' (Co) XBar
– 'Ariake' (Co) CSta
– 'Arimayama' (Co) CSta WFar
– 'Asahi' (Co) CSta WFar
– 'Asahigata' (Co) CSta WFar
– 'Ayanami' (Co) WFar
– 'Ayasegawa' (Co) CSta WFar WHil
– 'Beeches Star' (Co) EBee
– 'Benjamin' (Co) CSta WFar WHil
– 'Bide-a-Wee Blue' (Co) NBid
– 'Bide-a-Wee Lace' (Co) NBid
– 'Bijyonomai' (Co) GWyn WFar
I – 'Blue Lagoon' (Co) CBor CRos CSta EBee EHyd EPfP LRHS NLar NRHS WFar WHil
– 'Blue Shades' (Co) CWCL
– blue-flowered (Co) CSta WHil
– 'Blush' (Co) CSta WFar WHil
– 'Bonbori' (Co) CSta WFar
– 'Bureikou' (Co) CSta WFar
– 'Carefree' (Co) CSta ECtt NBro NLar WFar WHil XBar
– 'Carmine Pink' (Co) WHil
– 'Cherubim' (Co) CSta EBee EBlo EHyd LRHS WFar WHil
– 'Chidoriasobi' (Co) CSta
– 'Daikoshi' (Co) CSta WFar
– 'Daiminnishiki' (Co) CSta WFar
– 'Dancing Ladies' (Co) ECtt GWyn NBro WFar XBar
– 'Dart Rapids' (Co) CSta WFar WHil
– 'Duane's Choice' (Co) CSta
– 'Edasango' (Co) GWyn WFar
– 'Edomurasaki' (Co) CSta GWyn NPnk WFar WHil
– 'Ekiro-no-suzu' (Co) **new** CSta
– 'Elegance' (Co) CSta WFar
– 'Emerald Sun' (Co) WFar
– 'Essie' (Co) CSta WFar
– 'Flamenco' (Co/d) WFar XBar
– 'Frilly Blue' (Co) CBor CRos CSta EBee EHyd GWyn LRHS NRHS WFar
– 'Frilly White' (Co) WFar
– 'Fuji Shishi' (Co/d) WFar XBar
– 'Fuji-no-mai' (Co) **new** CSta
– 'Fukiagezakura' (Co) CSta
– 'Fukuju' (Co) CSta
– 'Galactic' (Co) CSta WFar
– 'Galaxy' (Co) NBro
– 'Geisha Girl' (Co) CDor CRos CSpe CSta EBee ECtt EHyd GWyn LRHS NLar NRHS WFar
– 'George' (Co) CSta
– 'Ginfukurin' (Co) CSta WFar
– 'Gin-kaji-oku' (Co) WFar
– 'Gin-pukurin' (Co) CSta WFar
– 'Girl of the Limberlost' (Co) CSta WFar XBar
– 'Gloaming' (Co) WFar XBar
– 'Gunma' (Co) WFar
– 'Gunma Niizatia' (Co) CSta
– 'Gyokk-bai' (Co) CSta
– 'Hakutaka' (Co) CSta
– 'Hana-angya' (Co/d) CSta WFar XBar
– 'Hanaguruma' (Co) CSta WFar
– 'Hana-monyo' (Co) CSta
– 'Hana-nishiki' (Co) CSta
– 'Haru-no-yoi' (Co) CSta WFar
– 'Harutugedoric' (Co) GWyn WFar
– 'Hatu-garasu' (Co) CSta WFar
– 'Hatu-goromo' (Co) CSta WFar
– 'Heart's Desire' (Co) EBee WFar
– 'Hidamari' (Co) CSta
– 'Higurasi' (Co) WFar
– 'Hinomaru' (Co) CSta
– 'Hokutosei' (Co) CSta
– 'Ikoko-no-e-beni' (Co) WFar
– 'Inukima Mincura' (Co) CSta GWyn WFar
– 'Inukine White' (Co) CSta

- 'Irino-no-miyako' (Co) **new** CSta
- 'Isamijishi' (Co) CSta
- 'Iso-botan' (Co) CSta WFar XBar
- 'Izutu' (Co) CSta
- 'Janomegasa' (Co) CSta
- 'Jessica' (Co) CSta WFar
- 'Jintsūriki' (Co) CSta
- 'Jisshū-no-sora' (Co) CSta
- 'Kafajin' (Co) CSta
- 'Kafka on the Shore' (Co) **new** CSta
- 'Kakuremino' (Co) CSta
- 'Kamiyo-no-kanmuri' (Co) CSta
- 'Kansenden' (Co) WFar
- 'Kara-chirimen' (Co) **new** CSta
- 'Karafune' (Co) CSta
- 'Karakoromo' (Co) CSta
- 'Kashima' (Co) CSta WFar
- 'Kassai' (Co) WFar
- 'Keepsake' (Co) CSta
- 'Kenkou' (Co) CSta
- 'Kihi-no-yume' (Co) CSta
- 'Kiraboshi' (Co) WFar XBar
- 'Koenji' (Co) CSta
- 'Kohara-biyori' (Co) CSta
- 'Kokonoe-beni' (Co/d) **new** WFar
- 'Kokoroiki' (Co) CSta GWyn WFar
- 'Komodo-ne' (Co) WFar
- 'Kotobuki' (Co) CSta WFar
- 'Kotonoshirabe' (Co) CSta WFar
- 'Kotyou-no-mail' (Co) CSta
- 'Kourohou' (Co) GWyn WFar
- 'Kozakura-genji' (Co) CSta
- 'Kumoizuru' (Co) CSta
- 'Kurama' (Co) GWyn WFar
- 'Ky-kanoko' (Co) CSta
- 'Laced Lady' (Co) WFar
- 'Lacewing' (Co) CSta WHil
- f. ***lactiflora*** (Co) CSta EHyd GWyn LRHS NBro
- 'Lilac Blue' (Co) CSta
- 'Lilac Crinoline' (Co) WFar XBar
- 'Lilac Sunbonnet' (Co) MACG WFar
- 'Mai-momiji' (Co/d) CSta WFar
- 'Mai-ōgi' (Co) CSta WFar
- 'Makazebeni' (Co) GWyn WFar
- 'Maki-no-o' (Co) CSta
- 'Managuruma' (Co) WFar
- 'Manakoora' (Co) ECtt EGrI NBro WFar XBar
- 'Mangeto' (Co) CSta WFar
- 'Martin Nest Blue' (Co) CSta WFar WHil
- 'Martin Nest Pink' (Co) CSta WFar
- 'Matu-no-yuki' (Co) CSta WFar WHil
- 'Mejirodai' (Co) CSta
- 'Miho-no-koji' (Co) CSta WFar
- 'Mikado' (Co) CSta EBee ECtt EHyd WFar
- 'Mikini-no-mare' (Co) CSta GWyn WFar
- 'Mikuni-beni' (Co) CSta
- Minuet Group (Co) XBar
- 'Mitajiman' (Co) CSta WFar
- 'Miyakowakare' (Co) WFar
- 'Miyuki' (Co) GWyn WFar
- 'Molly' (Co) CSta
- 'Momijbashi' (Co) CSta
- 'Momo-kagari' (Co) WFar
- 'Mukashi-no-ume' (Co) WFar
- 'Musashino' (Co) CSta WFar
- 'Musasi' (Co) CSta
- 'Naka-fu' (Co) WFar
- 'Nami-no-ue' (Co) CSta
- 'Nankin-kozakura' (Co) CSta WFar XBar
- 'Nirvana' (Co) WFar XBar
- 'Noboruko' (Co) CSta WFar WHil
- 'Nuretubame' (Co) CSta WFar XBar
- 'Ochibagoromo' (Co) CSta
- 'Okinanotomo' (Co) WFar
- 'Okinosabi' (Co) WFar
- 'Old Vienna' (Co) WFar XBar
- 'Oni-gokko' (Co) CSta WFar XBar
- 'Oriental Beauty' (Co) EBee
- 'Oshibori' (Co) CSta GKev GWyn MNrw WFar WHil
- 'Our White' (Co) WFar WHil
- 'Pago-Pago' (Co) CSta ECtt NBro WFar XBar
- 'Pale Moon' (Co) WFar XBar
- 'Pink Laced' (Co) GWyn WFar
- pink-flowered (Co) NBir NRya
- 'Purity' (Co) WFar
- 'Purple Dusk' (Co) WFar XBar
- 'Raspberry Buttons' (Co) WFar
- 'Rasyoumon' (Co) WFar
- 'Rock Candy' (Co) CSta WFar
- 'Romance' (Co) XBar
- 'Ryokuryū' (Co) CSta
- 'Saiun' (Co) CSta WFar WHil
- 'Sakuragawa' (Co) CSta GWyn WFar
- 'Sakura-no-miya' (Co) WFar
- 'Sangoguko' (Co) GBin GKev GWyn MNrw
- 'Sato-zakura' (Co) CSta WFar XBar
- 'Sekidaiko' (Co) CSta
- 'Senshō' (Co) CSta GWyn WFar
- 'Sen-yū' (Co) CSta
- 'Seraphim' (Co) CRos CSta EBee EBlo EHyd LRHS NLar NRHS WFar
- 'Seto-no-ume' (Co) CSta WHil
- 'Shibori Gasane' (Co/d) XBar
- 'Shibori-tatuta' (Co) CSta
- 'Shiokemuri' (Co) CSta WHil
- 'Shira-tonbo' (Co) CSta
- 'Shira-washi' (Co) CSta WFar
- 'Shiro-tombo' (Co) XBar
- 'Shirousagi' (Co) WFar
- 'Shishi-funjin' (Co) CSta WFar
- 'Sikoubai' (Co) WFar
- 'Sinakatonba' (Co) GWyn WFar
- 'Sinipukurn' (Co) CSta GWyn WFar
- 'Sinnkirou' (Co) WFar
- 'Sinseto' (Co) CSta WFar
- 'Siritonbo' (Co) GWyn WFar
- 'Sitikenjin' (Co) WFar
- 'Snow Flakes' (Co) CSta
- 'Snowbird' (Co) CSta XBar
- 'Snowdrop' (Co) CDor CSta ECtt GBin GKev GWyn LSou MACG MBel MNrw MPie SEdd WCot WFar
- 'Snowflake' (Co) CSta EBee EHyd EPfP GKev GWyn LRHS NLar SBut WFar
- 'Sorcha's Pink' (Co) CSta WFar
- 'Sōshiari' (Co) CSta WFar
- 'Sotodorihime' (Co) WFar
- 'Spring Blush' (Co) CSta WFar
- 'Spring Song' (Co) CSta WFar
- 'Suibijin' (Co) WFar
- 'Suiloijiw' (Co) GWyn
- 'Sumida-no-hatu' (Co) GWyn WFar
- 'Sumisonegawa' (Co) WFar
- 'Sumizomegenji' (Co) CSta WFar WHil XBar
- 'Sweetie' (Co) CSta WFar
- 'Syosin' (Co) CSta
- 'Syutyuka' (Co) CSta
- 'Tagonoura' (Co) CSta GWyn WFar WHil
- 'Tah-ni' (Co) NBro XBar
- 'Tairou-no-tsuki' (Co) CSta
- 'Takane-no-yuki' (Co) CSta

- 'Tamagawa-zome' (Co)	CSta
- 'Tamashiki-no-miya' (Co)	CSta
- 'Tanuki-bayashi' (Co) **new**	CSta
- 'Taoyami' (Co)	CSta
- 'Tatsuta-no-yū' (Co)	CSta
- 'Tatuta-no-yūbe' (Co)	CSta WFar
- 'Tobitake' (Co)	CSta
- 'Tokasamesi' (Co)	WFar
- 'Tokimeki' (Co/d)	CSta WFar XBar
- 'Toyonoharu' (Co)	GWyn WFar
- 'Trade Winds' (Co)	CSta WFar XBar
- 'Tsuki-no-miyake' (Co)	CSta
- 'Tsukumo-jishi' (Co)	CSta
- 'Tukasamesi' (Co)	CSta
- 'Turu-no-kegoromo' (Co)	CSta
- 'Ue-no-ume' (Co)	CSta
- 'Ukima Aka' (Co)	CSta
- 'Ukimashiro' (Co)	CSta
- 'Usujanome' (Co)	CSta
- 'Utyū' (Co) **new**	CSta
- 'Vilia' (Co)	XBar
- 'Vivid Pink' (Co)	CSta WFar WHil
- 'White Buttons' (Co)	WFar
- 'Winter Dreams' (Co)	CWCL ECtt GKev GWyn MBel NBid NBro WFar
- 'Yousei' (Co) **new**	CSta
- 'Yugeshiki' (Co)	WFar
- 'Yūhi-beni' (Co)	CSta WFar
- 'Yukiguruma' (Co)	GWyn WFar
- 'Yukizakura' (Co)	CSta
sikkimensis (Si) ♀H6	EBee EHyd EPfP GAbr GKev MBel NGdn SPoG
- CC	GGro
- var. ***pseudosikkimensis*** (Si)	GKev
- var. ***pudibunda*** (Si)	GArf GKev NWad
- red-flowered (Si)	GKev
aff. ***sikkimensis*** (Si)	NGdn XBar
Silver-laced Group (Pr/Poly)	EPfP SEND SPoG SWvt WFar XBar
- black-flowered (Pr/Poly)	EMor WCAu
simensis (Sp)	GKev XBar
sinopurpurea	see *P. chionantha* subsp. *sinopurpurea*
'Sir Bedivere' (Pr/Prim)	WCot
smithiana	see *P. prolifera*
'Snow Carpet'	see *P.* 'Schneekissen'
'Snow Ruffles' (Au)	ITim NSum XBar
'Snow White' (Pr/Poly)	GBin MRav
SNOWCUSHION	see *P.* 'Schneekissen'
'Snowgoose' (Pr/Prim/d)	XBar
sonchifolia (Pe)	GKev
- subsp. ***emeiensis*** (Pe)	GKev
sorachiana	see *P. yuparensis*
Sorbet Group (Pr/Poly)	XBar
'Soup Plate' (Pe) **new**	NHar
spectabilis (Au)	GKev
Spice Shades Group (Pr/Poly)	XBar
× ***steinii***	see *P.* × *forsteri*
'Stella Scarlet Pimpernell' (Pr/Poly) **new**	WHil
Stella Series (Pr/Poly)	LCro LOPS
stenocalyx (Pu)	GAbr GKev
stenodonta (Pf)	GKev
'Stradbrook Charm' (Au)	NRya XBar
'Stradbrook Dainty' (Au)	NWad WFar XBar
'Stradbrook Dream' (Au)	ITim WFar XBar
'Stradbrook Lucy' (Au)	GEdr ITim NWad
'Strawberries and Cream' (Pr/Prim)	XBar
stricta (Al)	GKev
Striped Victorians Group (Pr/Poly)	XBar
'Strong Beer' (Pr/Prim/d)	CBod CMiW EBee ECtt EPfP GEdr GWyn NHpl SAko WBrk WCot WFar WHil WKif XBar
'Sue Jervis' (Pr/Prim/d)	CMiW EShb EWTr NBir NGrd NHpl WHil XBar
suffrutescens (Su)	WAbe
'Sundae' (Pr/Prim/d)	MBow XBar
'Sunrise' (Au)	CRos EHyd LRHS NRHS
'Sunshine Susie' (Pr/Prim/d)	CMiW EPfP GArf GMaP XBar
SWEETHEART (mixed) (Pr/Prim)	LCro LOPS LRHS
takedana (Bu)	GEdr
Tango Group (Pr/Poly)	XBar
tangutica (Cy)	GKev
- BO 16-123 **new**	GGro
'Tantallon' (Pe)	NHar WMal
Tartan Reds Group (Pr/Prim)	XBar
'Tawny Port' (Pr/Poly)	CElw CFis ELan
'Theodora' (Pr)	EBee ELan GAbr WFar
'Tie Dye' (Pr/Prim)	MMrt MNrw NLar SAko WCot WFar
'Tinney's Moonlight' (Pe)	NHar NSum SGro
'Tipperary Purple' (Pr/Prim)	ECtt NHpl NWad
'Tomato Red' (Pr/Prim)	CMil NHpl WCAu WCot WFar
'Tony' (Au) ♀H5	XBar
'Tortoiseshell' (Pr/d)	ECtt
tosaensis (R)	GArf
Traditional Yellows Group (Pr/Prim)	CWCL XBar
'Tregor Truffle' (Pr/Prim/d) **new**	XBar
tschuktschorum (Cy)	GAbr
- var. ***pumila*** **new**	GKev
tyrolensis (Au)	GKev
'Val Horncastle' (Pr/Prim/d)	CMiW ECtt EPfP EShb EWTr GMaP NHpl WHil XBar
Valentine Victorians Group (Pr/Poly)	XBar
× ***venusta*** (Au)	GKev
'Vera Maud' (Pr)	MBriF XBar
§ ***veris*** (Pr) ♀H5	Widely available
- PAB 3777	LEdu NRHS
- subsp. ***columnae*** (Pr)	GKev
- Coronation Cowslips Group (Pr/Poly)	XBar
- hose-in-hose (Pr/d)	CElw EWes WHoo
- hybrids (Pr)	GDam
- 'Katy McSparron' (Pr/d)	CDor CExl CMiW ECtt GBin LRHS MNrw MPie NHpl NLar SPer WCot WFar
- 'Lady Agatha' (Pr)	XBar
- 'Lime with Orange' (Pr) **new**	LRHS
- Lord Alfred Group hose-in-hose (Pr)	XBar
- subsp. ***macrocalyx*** (Pr)	CPla NWad
- red-flowered (Pr)	NBid NGdn
- 'Sunset Shades' (Pr)	CDor EAJP EMor EPfP LShi NGdn NLar SWvt WCAu
- subsp. ***veris*** (Pr)	CPla LSou
'Veristar Yellow' (Pr) **new**	CRos
vernalis	see *P. vulgaris*
verticillata (Sp)	CPla GKev
§ ***vialii*** (So) ♀H5	Widely available
- 'Alison Holland' (So)	CBod GBin GEdr LRHS MPnt NHpl SPad WTyc
§ ***villosa*** (Au)	GKev
- var. ***commutata*** (Au)	GKev
- var. ***cottia***	see *P. villosa*
'Vintage' (Pr/Prim/d)	XBar

violacea (Mu)	GKev
Violet Victorians Group (Pr/Poly)	XBar
viscosa All.	see *P. latifolia*
§ × ***vochinensis*** (Au)	GEdr
§ ***vulgaris*** (Pr/Prim) ♀H7	Widely available
- var. ***alba*** (Pr/Prim)	WBrk
- 'Alba Plena' (Pr/Prim/d)	CMiW GAbr LShi
- 'Avoca' (Pr/Prim)	NHar WFar
- 'Avondale' (Kennedy Irish Series) (Pr/Prim)	CBod CDor CElw EBee GJos MAvo MBriF MNrw NHar WCot
- 'Blarney Castle Blush' (Pr/Prim)	NHar WFar
- 'Blarney Castle Pink' (Pr/Prim)	NHar NHpl
- 'Blarney Castle Red' (Pr/Prim)	GAbr NHar NHpl XBar
- 'Carrigdale' (Pr/Prim)	CBod CDor MBriF NHar WCot WFar XBar
- 'Catherine Thompson' (Pr/Prim)	NBir
- 'Claddagh' (Pr/Prim)	CBod MBriF NHar NHpl WCot
- Cornish pink (Pr/Prim)	GKev
- DRUMCLIFFE ('K74'PBR) (Pr/Prim)	CBod ECtt EMor EWTr GBin LRHS MBel MNrw NHpl NLar SEdd WCot WFar XBar
- 'Dunbeg' (Kennedy Irish Series) (Pr/Prim)	CBod CDor ELan EPfP GAbr GBin LRHS MBriF NLar WCot XBar
- 'Glengarriff' (Kennedy Irish Series) (Pr/Prim)	CBod LRHS MBriF NHar NHpl WCot
- 'Golden Gem' (Pr/Prim/d)	WCot
- green-flowered	see *P. vulgaris* 'Viridis'
- hybrids (Pr/Prim)	CTsd
- INNISFREE ('K72'PBR) (Pr/Prim)	CBod CDor CMil ECtt EMor EPfP GAbr GBin GWyn LRHS MBel MMuc MNrw NHpl WCot WFar
§ - 'Lilacina Plena' (Pr/Prim/d)	CMiW GArf NHpl XBar
- 'Moneygall' (Kennedy Irish Series) (Pr/Poly/d)	LRHS NHar NHpl WFar XBar
- 'Mount Juliet' (Pr/Prim)	NHar
- PRIMA BELARINA CARMEN ('Kerbelcarmen') (Prima Belarina Series) (Pr/Prim/d) **new**	LRHS
§ - subsp. ***sibthorpii*** (Pr/Prim) ♀H5	CDor CMiW CRos EBee EHyd ELan EMor EPfP GAbr GBin GKev LRHS MBriF MCot MNrw NBro NChi NRHS NWad SPtp SRms WFar
- 'Taigetos' (Pr/Prim) ♀H7	CBro CExl
- 'Tara' (Pr/Prim)	NHar NHpl XBar
- 'Tarragem Sparkling Ruby' (Pr/Prim/d)	CWCL LRHS MBriF NHpl WCot XBar
- 'Vanilla Cream' (Pr/Prim)	MBriF WCot
§ - 'Viridis' (Pr/Prim/d)	MNrw
- subsp. ***vulgaris*** (Pr/Prim) ♀H7	MBriF WCav WMAq
waltonii (Si)	EPfP GAbr GJos GKev GRum MNrw
- butter-yellow-flowered (Si) **new**	GRum
'Wanda' (Pr/Prim) ♀H7	CBcs CRos CTri EHyd ELan GBin GKev GQue GWyn LRHS LShi MBel MHer MMuc NBid NRya SRms WBrk WCFE WCot WGwG XBar
Wanda Group (Pr/Prim)	NBro
- 'Wanda Hose-in-hose' (Pr/Prim/d)	CMiW NBir
- 'Wanda Jack-in-the-Green' (Pr/Prim)	WCot
- 'Wanda Tomato Red' (Pr/Prim)	CMiW MBriF NHpl
wardii	see *P. munroi*
warsheneuwskiana (Or)	EPot EWes GKev NRya NSum WAbe WGwG
watsonii (Mu)	GKev XBar
- maroon-flowered (Mu)	GKev
'Wedgwood'	see *P.* × *pubescens* 'Wedgwood'
Westonbury Mill hybrids	WWtn
'Wharfedale Bluebell' (Au)	NBir NHar NSum
'Wharfedale Buttercup' (Au)	ITim NSum
'Wharfedale Gem' (*allionii* hybrid) (Au)	NSum NWad WIce XBar
'Wharfedale Ling' (*allionii* hybrid) (Au)	XBar
'Wharfedale Sunshine' (Au)	GKev WFar
'Wharfedale Superb' (*allionii* hybrid) (Au)	CBor XBar
'Wharfedale Village' (Au)	MPnt NHar NWad
'White Linda Pope' (Au)	GArf GEdr NSum
'White Valentine' **new**	GAbr
'White Wanda' (Pr/Prim)	XBar
'White Waves' (*allionii* hybrid) (Au)	ITim
§ ***whitei*** 'Sherriff's Variety' (Pe)	NHar
wilsonii (Pf)	CTri GAbr LLWG NBir NGdn WTyc WWtn XBar
- SDR 7824	GKev
§ - var. ***anisodora*** (Pf)	GKev GLog GRum NGdn NHpl XBar
- var. ***wilsonii*** (Pf)	GKev
Winter White Group (Pr/Prim)	CWCL XBar
§ 'Wisley Red' (Pr/Prim)	CElw CMiW
'Woodland Walk' (Pr/Prim)	EPfP SRms
wulfeniana (Au)	CWCL GKev
yargongensis	see *P. munroi* subsp. *yargongensis*
'Yellow' (Primlet Series) (Pr/Prim)	CRos EHyd LRHS NRHS
yunnanensis (Y)	GKev
§ ***yuparensis*** (Al)	GArf GKev
zambalensis (Ar)	GKev
'Zebra Blue' (Pr/Prim)	MBel WHil

Primulina (*Gesneriaceae*)

'Aiko'	WDib
'Candy'	WDib
'Chastity'	WDib
'Diane Marie'	WDib
§ ***dryas*** ♀H1c	WDib
- 'Hisako'	WCot WDib
dryas × ***linearifolia***	WDib
'Erika'	WDib
flavimaculata	WDib
heterotricha	WDib
'Keiko'	WDib
linearifolia	WDib
longgangensis	WDib
'New York'	WDib
'Periwinkle' **new**	WDib
'Stardust'	WDib
'Sweet Dreams'	WDib
tabacum 'Deco'	WDib

Prinsepia (*Rosaceae*)

sinensis	MBlu NLar SLon

Prionosciadium (*Apiaceae*)

thapsoides	SDix

Pritzelago see *Hornungia*

Prosartes (*Liliaceae*)

§	***hookeri***	CMiW EBee MNrw
§	- var. ***oregana***	EBee WCru
§	***lanuginosa***	EHed EHyd EPPr ESwi LEdu WCru WFar WPGP
§	***maculata***	LEdu MNrw NLar WCru
§	***smithii***	EBee EWld GAbr GKev GLog LEdu LRHS MNrw NHar NLar WCru WPGP WSHC
§	***trachycarpa*** SDR 8177	GKev

Prostanthera (*Lamiaceae*)

	aspalathoides	CCCN
	'Badja Peak'	CCCN CTrC CTsd MAsh
	baxteri	CTrC
	- 'Silver Ghost'	SGBe
	calycinia **new**	CTsd
	cuneata ♀H4	Widely available
	- 'Alpine Gold' (v)	MAsh
	- 'Blushing Bride'	CMac CTrC LBuc MHtn
*	***digitiformis***	CTsd
	incana	CTsd
	incisa	EGrI
	lasianthos	CBcs CCCN CTsd SPlb SVen
	- var. ***subcoriacea***	CExl
	latifolia	CTsd
	melissifolia	CTsd
§	- var. ***parvifolia***	CCCN
	'Mint Royale'	CCCN LEdu SGBe
	'Mint-Ice'	SGBe
	ovalifolia ♀H3	CCCN SEle WAvo
I	- 'Variegata' (v)	CBcs CBod CCCN CExl CKel CMac CTrC CTsd ELan LRHS LSou MAsh MGil SEle SIvy SNig WAvo WGrn XSte
	phylicifolia	CBcs CTrC CTsd MGil
	'Poorinda Ballerina'	CBod CCCN CKel ELan LRHS MAsh SEle SGBe SPer SRkn
	'Poorinda Petite'	CBod CCCN CKel CTsd ELan LRHS
	rotundifolia ♀H2	CAbb CBod CCCN CCht CTri CTsd EBee EGrI EHed EPfP EWTr IDee MGil SEle SIvy SNig SPer SVen WCFE WGrn WKif
	- 'Chelsea Girl'	see *P. rotundifolia* 'Rosea'
§	- 'Rosea' ♀H2	CCCN CTrC CTsd EPfP
	rugosa	CTsd
	sieberi Benth.	CTsd
	spinosa	CTrC CTsd
	'Starlight' (v)	CTsd
	walteri	CBcs CCCN EGrI EHed MGil SIvy SPhx

Protea (*Proteaceae*)

aurea	CTrC SPlb
- subsp. ***aurea***	CPbh
burchellii	SPlb
'Clark's Red'	LRHS XSte
coronata	CPbh SPlb
cryophila **new**	SPlb
cynaroides	CCCN CPbh CTrC SPlb XSte
- 'King Pine'	CCCN
- 'King White'	CCCN
- 'Little Prince'PBR	CBcs CCCN
- 'Madiba'	CCCN
- 'Mini King'	CCCN
- 'White Crown'PBR	CCCN
effusa	SPlb
eximia	CCCN CPbh SPlb
grandiceps	CCCN CPbh SPlb
'Juliet'	CCCN
lacticolor	CPbh SPlb
laurifolia	SPlb
lepidocarpodendron	CPbh
longifolia	CPbh
nana	SPlb
neriifolia	CCCN CPbh CTrC SPlb
- 'Snowcrest'	CPbh
obtusifolia	SPlb
'Pink Crown'	XSte
'Pink Ice'	LRHS
repens	CPbh LRHS SPlb
- 'Ruby Blush'	CCCN
scolymocephala	LRHS SPlb
'Southern Cross'	CCCN
'Special Pink Ice'	CCCN
subvestita	CPbh SPlb
susannae	CPbh CTrC SPlb
'Susara'	CCCN LRHS
'Sylvia'	CCCN

Prumnopitys (*Podocarpaceae*)

§	***andina***	CBcs IDee LRHS WFar
	elegans	see *P. andina*

Prunella (*Lamiaceae*)

§	***grandiflora***	CBod CHby ECha NFav SCob SPhx SRms
	- 'Alba'	CBod EBee ECha ELan EPfP GMaP NBid NLar SPer SRms WCAu
	- 'Altenberg Rosa'	WCAu
	- 'Bella Blue' **new**	LRHS MACG
	- 'Blue Loveliness'	EBee SWvt
	- 'Blue Pearl'	MHol
	- 'Carminea'	EBee MRav SPer
	- 'Gruss aus Isernhagen'	GBee
	- 'Loveliness'	CMac ECha ELan GMaP MACG MRav NBro NGdn NSti SPer SPlb WCAu WFar
	- 'Pagoda'	CSpe NLar
	- 'Pink Loveliness'	CRos EBee SRms WFar
	- 'Rosea'	SBut WFar
	- 'Rubra'	NLar
	- violet-flowered	NSti
	- 'White Loveliness'	CMac SRms
	'Icing Sugar'	WFar
	incisa	see *P. vulgaris*
	SUMMER DAZE ('Binsumdaz'PBR)	LSou STPC
§	***vulgaris***	CBod CCBP CHab CTri ENfk GPoy MBow MNHC NMir SPhx SRms SVic WHer WWild XAbr
	- f. ***leucantha***	WHer
	- 'Rose Pearl'	CBod EBou LSRN MHol NHpl SRms WCav
	× ***webbiana***	see *P. grandiflora*

Prunus ✿ (*Rosaceae*)

	'Accolade' (d) ♀H6	Widely available
§	'Amanogawa' ♀H6	Widely available
	amygdalus	see *P. dulcis*
	angustifolia	MNic
	'Aprimira' (miracot) (F)	MTrO
	APRISALI (aprium)	NOra
	armeniaca	MPri SGsty
	- 'Alfred' (F)	CBod CMac NRog SKee SPer
	- 'Bergecot' (F) **new**	SKee
	- 'Bergeron' (F)	MTrO NOra SKee WMat
	- 'Bergeval' (F) **new**	CAgr MTrO
	- COMPACTA (F)	MTrO NOra SCoo
	- 'Delicot'PBR (F)	SSFr

- 'Early Moorpark' (F)	CAgr CBod CMac EPfP LEdu NOra NRog SEND SLon SSFr SWeb WMat
- FLAVORCOT ('Bayoto'PBR) (F)	CAgr EPfP EPom MCoo NOra SKee SPer SSFr SWeb WMat
- 'Garden Aprigold' (F)	EPom MTrO SSFr WMat
- 'Goldcot' (F)	CAgr LRHS MTrO NOra SKee SPoG SSFr WMat
- 'Golden Glow' (F)	CAgr CBod CTri EPfP EPom LRHS MGos MTrO NOra SGbt SKee SSFT WMat
- 'Goldrich' (F)	CAgr
- 'Hargrand' (F)	CAgr SVic
- 'Harogem' (F)	CAgr
- 'Helena de Roussilon' (F)	CAgr CMac MTrO NOra
- 'Hemskirke' (F)	NRog SKee
- 'Hungarian Best' (F) **new**	SVic
- 'Isabella' (F)	NRog
- 'Kioto'PBR (F)	CAgr LRHS MTrO NOra
- 'Luizet' (F) **new**	SGsty
- 'Moorpark' (F)	CHab CMac CSBt CTri ELan EWTr LBuc MPri MRav NRog SBdl SEdi SKee
- 'New Large Early' (F)	CBod NRog SBdl SEND SEdi
- ORANGE SUMMER ('Zaitorde'PBR) (F)	EPom
- 'Petit Muscat' (F)	EPom SKee
- 'Robada'PBR (F)	CAgr ELan MTrO NOra
- 'Tomcot' (F)	CAgr CTri EPfP EPom LBuc LSRN MTrO NOra SKee SPer SPoG SSFr WMat
- 'Tross Orange' (F)	NRog
- 'Vigama' (F)	NOra WMat
'Asano'	CLnd
avium	Widely available
- 'Alfheim' (F)	SBdl
- 'Amber Heart' (F)	CArg MTrO NOra NRog SKee WMat
- 'Archduke' (F)	SBdl
- 'Belgian Rivers' (F)	SBdl
- 'Bigarreau Burlat' (D) **new**	CBod LMaj
- 'Bigarreau de Schrecken' (F)	SBdl SKee
- 'Bigarreau Gaucher' (F)	NRog SBdl SKee WMat
§ - 'Bigarreau Napoléon' (F)	CArg EPom LPar MTrO NOra NRog SBdl SEdi SGsty SKee SSFr SVic WMat
- 'Birchenhayes'	see *P. avium* 'Early Birchenhayes'
- 'Black Eagle' (F)	SBdl
- 'Black Elton' (F)	SBdl SKee
- 'Black Glory' (F)	SBdl
- 'Black Oliver' (F) **new**	CTsd MTrO NOra NRog SBdl WWct
- 'Black Tartarian' (F)	SBdl SKee
- 'Black Varik' (F)	SBdl
- 'Bradbourne Black' (F)	SBdl SKee
- 'Bullion' (F)	CEnd SBdl
- 'Burcombe' (F)	CEnd SBdl
- 'Cariad' (F)	WGwG
- CELESTE ('Sumpaca'PBR) (D)	CAgr CArg CMac CTri MTrO NLar NOra NWea SCoo SGbt SLim SPoG SSFT WMat
- 'Cherokee'	see *P. avium* 'Lapins'
- 'Circassian' (F)	SBdl
- 'Colney' (F)	CArg EPom NOra NRog SBdl SKee SSFr WMat
- 'Cooper's Black' (F)	SBdl
- 'Coroon' (F)	SBdl SKee
- CRISTALINA ('Sumnue'PBR) (F) **new**	SBdl
- 'Crown Morello' (F)	SBdl
- 'Danelia' (D)	WMat
- 'Dun' (F)	CBod CHab NRog WMat
§ - 'Early Birchenhayes' (F)	CEnd SBdl
- 'Early Rivers' (F)	CSBt IArd LPar LSRN MTrO NOra NRog SBdl SEdi SKee SSFr SVic WMat
- 'Elton Heart' (F)	SBdl
- 'Emperor Francis' (F)	SBdl SKee
- 'Erianne' (F)	SBdl
- 'Fice' (F)	CEnd SBdl
- 'Florence' (F)	SBdl SKee
- 'Frogmore Early' (F)	SBdl
- 'Früheste der Mark' (D)	SBdl
- 'Garden Bing' (F)	EPom
- 'Giorgia' (D)	WMat
- 'Goodnestone Black' (D)	SBdl SKee
- 'Governor Wood' (F)	SBdl SKee
- 'Grandiflora'	see *P. avium* 'Plena'
- 'Guigne d'Annonay' (D)	SBdl
- 'Hannaford' (D/C)	CHab NRog
- 'Hertford' (F)	LPar MTrO NOra SBdl SEdi SKee SSFr WMat
- 'Inga' (F)	SBdl SKee
- 'Karina' (D)	WMat
- 'Kent Bigarreau' (F)	SBdl
- 'Kentish Red' (F)	SBdl SKee
- 'Knauff's Riesen' (F)	SBdl
- 'Knauff's Schwarze' (F)	SBdl
- 'Knight's Early Black' (D)	CArg MTrO NOra NRog SBdl WMat
- 'Kordia' (D) 🏆H6	CArg EPom LMaj LPar MTrO NOra SBdl SKee SSFr WMat WWct
- 'Kozerska' (F)	WMat
§ - 'Lapins' (F) 🏆H6	CAgr CArg CBod CLnd EPfP EPom LMaj LPar MRav NLar NOra NWea SEdi SGsty SKee SSFT SSFr WJas WMat WWct
- 'Mansfield Black' (F)	SBdl SKee
- 'May Duke'	see *P.* × *gondouinii* 'May Duke'
- 'Merchant' (F) 🏆H6	MTrO NOra NRog SBdl SEdi SKee SSFT SSFr WMat WWct
- 'Mermat' (F)	SBdl
- 'Merpet' (F)	SBdl
- 'Merton Bigarreau' (F)	CArg CTsd NOra NRog SBdl SKee SSFr WMat
- 'Merton Crane' (F)	SBdl SKee
- 'Merton Favourite' (F)	SBdl SKee
- 'Merton Glory' (F)	CAgr CArg CSBt EPfP MTrO NOra NRog SBdl SEWo SEdi SKee SLim SSFr WMat WWct
- 'Merton Late' (F)	SBdl
- 'Merton Marvel' (F)	SBdl
- 'Merton Premier' (F)	LPar NRog SBdl SVic
- 'Merton Reward'	see *P.* × *gondouinii* 'Merton Reward'
- 'Mizia' (D)	WMat
- 'Moserkirsche' (F)	SBdl
- 'Nabella' (F)	MAsh SBdl
- 'Napoléon'	see *P. avium* 'Bigarreau Napoléon'
- 'Newstar' (F)	SBdl
- 'Noble' (F)	SBdl SKee
- 'Noir Boccard' (F)	SBdl
- 'Noir de Guben' (F)	NRog SBdl SKee WMat
- 'Noir de Meched' (D)	SKee
- 'Nutberry Black' (F)	SBdl
- 'Octavia' (D)	WMat
- 'Old Black Heart' (F)	SKee
- 'Penny'PBR (F) 🏆H6	CAgr CArg CTri EPom MTrO NOra NRog SKee WMat WWct
- 'Petit Noir' (F)	CArg MTrO NOra WMat
§ - 'Plena' (d) 🏆H6	Widely available
- 'Polstead Black' (F) **new**	SKee
- 'Regina' (F)	EPom LPar MTrO NLar NOra SBdl SKee WMat
- 'Ronald's Heart' (F)	SBdl SKee
- 'Roundel Heart' (F)	NRog SKee WMat

- 'Sandra Rose' (F) **new**	SBdl
- 'Santina'PBR (F) **new**	SBdl
- 'Sasha' (F)	CBod SBdl
- 'Schauenburger' (F)	SBdl
- 'Schneiders Späte Knorpel' (D)	SBdl
- 'Skeena'PBR (F)	CArg MTrO NOra WMat
- 'Small Black' (F)	CHab NRog
- 'Smoky Dun' (F)	SBdl
- STARBLUSH ('Spc 207'PBR) (F) **new**	NOra
- STARDUST ('13-7-70') (F)	LCro LOPS MTrO NOra SCoo
- 'Starkrimson' (F)	SBdl
- 'Stella' (F) ♀H6	Widely available
- 'Stella Compact' (F)	LSRN SBdl SEdi
- 'Strawberry Heart' (F)	SBdl
- 'Summer Sun' (D) ♀H6	CAgr CArg CLnd CMac CTri EPom LBuc MAsh MGos MTrO NLar NOra NRog SBdl SCoo SKee SLim SPoG SSFT SSFr WMat WWct
- 'Summit' (F)	CLnd SBdl SEdi SKee SSFr WMat
- 'Sunburst' (D)	Widely available
- 'Sweetheart' (F) ♀H6	CAgr CArg CLnd CTri EPom LCro LMaj LOPS LPar LRHS LSRN MAsh MTrO NOra NRHS NRog NWea SCoo SEWo SKee SLim SPoG SVic WMat
- 'Sylvia' (F)	CAgr CBod NOra WMat
- 'Turkish Black' (F)	SBdl
- 'Van' (F)	CAgr CArg CSBt EPom LMaj NLar NOra NRog SBdl SEdi SKee WMat
- 'Vanda'PBR (F)	NOra WMat
- 'Vega' (F)	CAgr CArg NOra NRog SBdl SEdi SKee SSFr WMat
- 'Vera'PBR (F) **new**	SBdl
- 'Vroege van Werder' (F)	SBdl
- 'Waterloo' (F)	MTrO NOra NRog SBdl SKee WWct
- 'Wellington A' (F)	SBdl
- 'Werder's Early Black' (F)	SBdl
- 'Werdersche Braune' (F)	SBdl
- 'White Heart' (F)	CHab NRog SBdl SKee
- 'Zoe' (F) **new**	NRog
- 'Zweitfrühe' (F)	SBdl
§ 'Beni-tamanishiki' ♀H6	CBcs MTrO NOra WMat
'Beni-yutaka' ♀H6	CBcs CCVT EPfP MAsh MRav MSwo MTrO NOra NOrn NRHS SCoo SLim WHwl WMat
besseyi	WKor
'Blaze'	see *P. cerasifera* 'Nigra'
× ***blireana*** (d) ♀H5	CAco CBod CEnd CLnd CTri EPfP LCro LOPS LRHS MGos MRav MSwo SCob SCoo SPer SPoG WMou
- 'Moseri' (d)	WTSh
BLUSHING BRIDE	see *P.* 'Shōgetsu'
campanulata 'Felix Jury'	EBee NOra WMat
canadensis **new**	MTrO
CANDY FLOSS	see *P.* 'Matsumae-beni-murasaki'
'Carmine Jewel' (F) **new**	CAgr
caroliniana	SArc
'Catherine' **new**	MTrO
cerasifera (F)	CAco CAgr CBrac CHab CTri EPfP EPom LBuc MNic NRog NWea SCob SKee SPer WKor
- 'Countess' (F)	EPom NOra
- CRIMSON POINTE ('Cripoizam')	EBee MTrO NOra SGsty SPoG
- 'Golden Sphere' (F)	CAgr CArg CTri EPom MTrO NOra SKee SSFr WMat
- 'Gypsy' (F)	CAgr MTrO NOra SKee SSFr WMat
- 'Hessei' (v)	MRav NOrn SEle
§ - Myrobalan Group (F)	MRav SPre SVic WMat
§ - 'Nigra' ♀H6	Widely available
- 'Pendula'	SWvt
§ - 'Pissardii'	CDoC EPfP LCro LMaj LSRN NOrn NRog NWea SCoo SGsty SLon SWvt WFar WJas
- 'Ruby' (F)	CAgr EPom MTrO SKee
- 'Woodii'	CSBt
cerasus 'Maynard'	SSFr
- 'Meteor Korai'	CAgr NOra NRHS WMat
- 'Montmorency' (F)	NOra SBdl SKee
- 'Morello' (C) ♀H6	Widely available
- 'Nabella' (F)	SKee
- 'Semperflorens'	CLnd
'Cheal's Weeping'	EBar SBdl
CHOCOLATE ICE	see *P.* 'Matsumae-fuki'
§ × ***cistena*** ♀H6	CBcs CDoC CRos EBee EHyd ELan EPfP LRHS MAsh MGos MSwo NRHS SCob SCoo SGol SPoG SWvt WFar
- 'Crimson Dwarf'	see *P.* × *cistena*
'Collingwood Ingram' ♀H6	EPfP LRHS MBlu MTrO NOra NOrn SLim WHwl WMat
'Cot-N-Candy' (Aprium Series)	CAgr EPom
'Daikoku'	CBcs EBee LRHS MTrO NOra WMat
davidiana	SPlb
'Delma'PBR (F)	CSBt NOra WMat
domestica (D/C)	SPre
- 'Angelina Burdett' (D)	CHab NRog SKee
- 'Anna Späth' (C/D)	NRog SKee
- 'Ariel' (C/D)	SKee
- 'Avalon' (D)	CAgr CCVT CLnd LBuc MTrO NOra SBdl SEdi SKee SSFr WMat
- 'Belgian Greengage' (F)	CHab SKee
- 'Belgian Purple' (C)	NRog
- 'Belle de Louvain' (C)	CArg CHab CLnd CTri MTrO NOra NRog SBdl SEdi SKee WMat WWct
- 'Birchenhayes' (F)	CEnd
- 'Blaisdon Red' (C)	NOra SKee WMat
- 'Blaisdon Red' misapplied (C) **new**	MTrO
- 'Blue Rock' (C/D) ♀H5	SKee
- 'Blue Tit' (C/D) ♀H5	CAgr CBod EPom MMuc NOra NRog SEND SKee SSFr WMat WWct
- 'Bohemian' (C)	SKee
- 'Bonne de Bry' (D)	SKee
§ - 'Bountiful' (C)	SEdi
- 'Brandy Gage' (C/D)	SKee
- 'Bryanston Gage' (D)	SKee WMat
- 'Bühler Frühzwetschge' (C) **new**	NRog
- 'Burbank's Giant'	see *P. domestica* 'Giant Prune'
- 'Burcombe' (F)	CBod CEnd MTrO
- 'Cambridge Gage' (D) ♀H5	Widely available
- 'Coe's Golden Drop' (D)	CAgr CArg CHab CLnd EPom MGos MRav MTrO NOra NRog NWea SBdl SEdi SKee SPer WMat WWct
- 'Conwy Castle' (F)	WMat
- 'Count Althann's Gage' (D)	CHab NOra NRog SSFr WWct
- 'Cropper'	see *P. domestica* 'Laxton's Cropper'
- 'Czar' (C) ♀H6	Widely available
- 'Delicious'	see *P. domestica* 'Laxton's Delicious'
- 'Denbigh' (C)	CHab WGwG
- 'Denniston's Superb'	see *P. domestica* 'Imperial Gage'
- 'Des Bejonnieres' (D)	SKee
- 'Dittisham Ploughman' (C)	CBod SKee WMat
- 'Dunster Plum' (F)	CBod CTri WMat
- 'Early Green Gage' (D)	MTrO
- 'Early Laxton' (C/D)	CHab LPar MMuc NRog SBdl SEND SEdi SKee

	- 'Early Orleans'	see *P. domestica* 'Monsieur Hâtiff'
	- 'Early Prolific'	see *P. domestica* 'Early Rivers'
§	- 'Early Rivers' (C)	CAgr CArg CHab CSBt CTri EBee EPom EWTr LPar LSRN MTrO NOra NRog SBdl SCoo SEdi SKee SPer SSFr WMat WWct
	- 'Early Transparent Gage' (C/D)	CAgr CBod CEnd CMac CSBt LBuc LRHS MTrO NOra NRog SBdl SCoo SKee SPer SSFr WMat
	- 'Early Victoria' (C/D)	SGbt
	- 'Edda' (D)	NOra WMat
	- 'Edwards' (C/D)	CTri NRog SBdl SEdi SKee SSFr
	- 'Excalibur' (D)	CAgr EPom IArd LBuc LPar LSRN NOra SBdl SEdi SKee WMat
	- 'Finger Plum' (F)	WMat
§	- German Prune Group (C)	NLar NOra NRog SKee WMat WWct
§	- 'Giant Prune' (C)	MMuc NRog SEND SEdi SKee SSFr
	- 'Gold Dust' (F)	WMat
	- 'Golden Transparent' (D)	NRog SKee
	- 'Goldfinch' (D)	NRog SEND SKee
	- 'Gordon Castle' (D)	MTrO NLar SKee WMat
	- Green Gage Group	see *P. domestica* Reine-Claude Group
	- 'Grove's Late Victoria' (D)	WWct
	- 'Guinevere' (C)	CAgr CBod CEnd EPom LRHS MAsh MTrO NOra SKee SSFT WMat
	- 'Guthrie's Late Green' (D)	SKee
	- 'Haganta'PBR (F) ♀H5	CAgr MTrO NOra WMat
	- 'Hauszwetsche' (C/D) **new**	LMaj
	- 'Herman' (D)	CAgr CEnd CMac EPom LRHS MAsh MTrO NOra NRog SKee WMat
	- 'Heron' (C)	NOra SKee WMat WWct
§	- 'Imperial Gage' (D) ♀H5	CAgr CArg CLnd CMac CSBt CTri EPom EWTr LRHS MMuc MTrO NOra NRog SEND SKee SPer SSFT SSFr WMat
	- 'Italian Prune' (F)	NRog
	- 'Jan James' (F)	CEnd
	- 'Jefferson' (D) ♀H5	CAgr CArg CHab CLnd MTrO NOra NRog SKee SSFr SVic WMat
*	- 'Jubilaeum' (D)	CAgr CLnd CMac EPom LBuc MTrO NOra SCoo SEWo SKee SSFr
	- 'Kea' (C)	CBod CLnd SKee WMat
	- 'Kirke's' (D)	CHab ELan NOra NRog SKee SSFr WMat
	- 'Kulinaria' (D)	LRHS MTrO SPoG
	- 'Lancelot' (F) **new**	MTrO
	- 'Landkey Yellow' (F)	WMat
	- 'Langley Gage' (D)	CAgr
	- 'Late Muscatelle' (D)	SKee
	- 'Late Transparent Gage' (D)	SKee
§	- 'Laxton's Cropper' (C)	CHab NRog SEdi SKee
§	- 'Laxton's Delicious' (D)	CHab NRog
	- 'Laxton's Jubilee' (C/D)	CSBt MTrO NRog SGbt SSFr WMat
	- 'Mallard' (D) ♀H6	NOra SKee WMat
	- 'Manaccan' (C)	CBod WMat
	- 'Manns No. 1' (C/D)	SKee WMat
	- 'Marjorie's Seedling' (C) ♀H5	Widely available
	- 'Meritare' (F)	MTrO NOra WMat
	- 'Merton Gage' (D)	SKee
	- 'Merton Gem' (D)	SKee
	- 'Miraclaude' (F)	EPom
	- 'Monarch' (C)	SKee
§	- 'Monsieur Hâtiff' (D)	NRog
	- (Myrobalan Group) 'Myrobalan B' (F)	WTSh
	- Old English gage	CLnd EBee EPom SBdl SEdi
	- 'Ontario' (D)	LPar NRog
	- 'Opal' (D) ♀H6	Widely available
	- 'Oullins Gage' (C/D) ♀H5	Widely available
	- 'Pershore' (C)	CAgr CHab MTrO NOra NRog SBdl SEdi SKee WMat WWct
	- 'Pershore Emblem' (F)	WWct
	- 'Pozegaca' (D)	SKee
	- 'President' (C)	CHab MMuc NOra NRog SEND SSFr
	- 'Purple Pershore' (C) ♀H5	CAgr CHab CTri IArd NOra NRog SKee WMat WWct
	- 'Queen's Crown' (C/D)	MTrO WMat
	- 'Quetsche d'Alsace'	see *P. domestica* German Prune Group
	- 'Red Magnum Bonum' (C) **new**	NRog
	- 'Reeves' (C)	NLar NOra NRog SKee
	- 'Regina Claudia' (D) **new**	LMaj
	- 'Reine-Claude Noire' (F) **new**	NRog
	- 'Reine-Claude Dorée'	see *P. domestica* Reine-Claude Group
§	- Reine-Claude Group (D)	CAgr ELan LRHS MTrO NOra NRog NWea SEND SKee SLim SPer WMat
	- - 'Ingall's Grimoldby Green Gage' (D)	SKee
	- - 'Lindsey Gage' (F)	MTrO NOra SKee
	- - 'Old Green Gage'	see *P. domestica* (Reine-Claude Group) 'Reine-Claude Vraie'
	- - 'Reine-Claude de Bavais' (D)	CArg CLnd CTri NOra NRog WMat
	- - 'Reine-Claude de Vars' (D)	SVic
	- - 'Reine-Claude van Schouwen' (F) **new**	NRog
	- - 'Reine-Claude Violette' (D)	CAgr NOra NRog SKee
§	- - 'Reine-Claude Vraie' (C/D)	CAgr CArg CDoC CRos CSBt EPom LBuc LCro LOPS LPar LRHS LSRN MPri MTrO NOra NRog SEWo SGbt SSFr WMat
§	- - 'Willingham Gage' (C/D)	EBee LSRN MTrO NOra NRog SKee WMat
	- 'Sanctus Hubertus' (D)	CTri NRog SKee WWct
	- 'Seneca' (D)	EPom NOra SKee SSFr WMat
	- 'Severn Cross' (D)	SSFr
	- 'Stanley' (C/D)	LMaj SGsty SVic
	- 'Stella' (F)	CCVT GDam LOPS LSRN MPri MTrO SLim
	- 'Stella's Star' (D)	CAgr MTrO NOra WMat
	- 'Swan' (C)	NOra SKee WMat WWct
	- 'Syston White' (F)	MGos
	- 'Thames Cross' (D)	NOra
	- 'Transparent Gage' (D)	SKee
	- 'Valor' (D) ♀H5	LPar NOra NRog SKee
	- 'Verity' (C/D)	SKee WMat
	- 'Victoria' (D) ♀H5	Widely available
	- 'Victory' (D) **new**	NOra SBdl
	- 'Violet'	MTrO
	- 'Violetta'PBR (D)	CAgr MTrO
	- 'Voyageur' (F) **new**	NRog
	- 'Warwickshire Drooper' (C)	CAgr CHab MAsh MTrO NOra NRog SKee SLon SSFr WMat WWct
	- 'Wheat Plum' (F) **new**	NRog
	- 'Willingham'	see *P. domestica* (Reine-Claude Group) 'Willingham Gage'
§	***dulcis***	CAco CHab CLnd CTri EPfP EPom LMaj LRHS MGos MMuc NWea SCob SCoo SEND SWvt WMou
	- 'Ai' (F)	CAgr
	- 'Ardéchoise' (F)	CAgr
	- 'Ferraduel' (F)	CAgr

- 'Ferragnès' (F) CAgr
- 'Genko' (F) **new** LMaj
* - 'Phoebe' (F) CAgr
- 'Praecox' (F) **new** MTrO
- 'Princesse' (F) SKee
- 'Sultane' (F) SKee
- 'Supernova' (F) CCCN
- 'Sweetheart' (F) SBdl
- 'Tuono' (F) CCCN

EASTER BONNET ('Comet'[PBR]) CTri EPfP NLar
× ***eminens*** 'Umbraculifera' LPar SGsty
'Flavor King' (Pluot Series) (D) CAgr LCro LOPS MTrO WMat
'Flavour Supreme' (F) EPom
FRAGRANT CLOUD see *P.* 'Shizuka'
FRILLY FROCK ('Fpmspl') (v) EBee LRHS MTrO NLar NOra SGbt SGsty SPoG WMat
fruticosa WFar
- 'Globosa' SGsty
§ 'Fugenzō' 🏆H6 CArg CCVT CLnd CMCN CMac CSBt EBar EPfP GKin IPap LCro LOPS LRHS LSRN MAsh MMuc MRav MTrO NOra NOrn SBdl SCob SEND SGol SGsty SPer SWeb WHwl WMat WMou
'Fugenzō' misapplied see *P.* 'Kofugen'
glandulosa 'Alba Plena' (d) CEnd CMac CSBt SDix SGol SPlb SRms SWvt WCFE
- 'Rosea Plena' see *P. glandulosa* 'Sinensis'
§ - 'Sinensis' (d) CEnd CExl CMac CSBt SGol SRms
§ × ***gondouinii*** 'May Duke' (F) CBod NRog SKee
§ - 'Merton Reward' (F) SBdl SEdi SKee
GORIS GOLD ('Goris11'[PBR]) CBod
grayana B&SWJ 10903 WCru
'Gyoikō' CBcs CEnd CLnd EBee LRHS MTrO NOra WMat
'Hally Jolivette' CEnd EBee LRHS MAsh MTrO NOra NOrn SPoG WHwl WMat
§ 'Hanagasa' 🏆H6 CBcs CEnd EPfP MTrO NOra NWea SGbt WMat WMou
'Hillieri Spire' see *P.* 'Spire'
'Hilling's Weeping' LCro LOPS SLon
himalaica CJun NOra WMat WPGP
'Hokusai' 🏆H6 CBcs CBrac EBee EPfP LRHS MTrO NOra SGol WMat
HOLLYWOOD see *P.* 'Trailblazer'
'Horinji' CBcs LRHS MTrO NLar NOra SCoo WMat
'Howard No. 3' WMat
'Ichiyo' (d) 🏆H6 CBcs CLnd EPfP MTrO NOra SBdl SCoo SPer WMat
ilicifolia subsp. ***lyonii*** WPGP
× ***incam*** 'Okamé' 🏆H6 Widely available
- 'Shosar' see *P.* 'Shosar'
incisa CTri NRog
- 'Beniomi' MRav
- 'February Pink' CJun SGol
- 'Fujimae' 🏆H6 NLar
- 'Kojo-no-mai' 🏆H6 Widely available
- 'Mikinori' CEnd CJun CMac CSBt ELon EPfP EWTr MAsh MBlu MTrO NLar NOra NOrn SCoo SEWo WMat
- 'Oshidori' (d) 🏆H6 CMac CSBt EHed ELon EPfP LRHS MMrt MRav MTrO NLar NOra NQui SRms WMat WSpi
- 'Paean' ELon WFar
- 'Pendula' 🏆H6 ELan EWTr LRHS MTrO NOra SCoo WMat
- 'Praecox' CSBt EPfP NOra SCoo WMat

§ - f. ***yamadei*** 🏆H6 CJun MAsh MTrO NOra WSpi
insititia (F) MWht
- 'Abergwyngregin' (C) WMat
- 'Aylesbury Prune' (C) CAgr MTrO NOra SKee WMat
- 'Blue Violet Damson' (C) CAgr MTrO NOra NWea SKee WMat
§ - 'Bradley's King Damson' (C) CArg CLnd NOra SKee WMat
- bullace (C) LEdu SEdi
- 'Countess' (C) CTri
- 'Dittisham Damson' (C) WMat
- 'Farleigh Damson' (C) 🏆H6 CAgr CArg CDoC CHab EPfP EPom EWTr LBuc LEdu MTrO NLar NOra NRog NWea SEdi SKee SPer SVic WJas WMat WWct
- 'King of Damsons' see *P. insititia* 'Bradley's King Damson'
- 'Langley Bullace' (C) CAgr CTri LEdu NOra NRog SKee SSFr WMat
- 'Lisna' (C) CTri WMat
- 'Merryweather Damson' (C) Widely available
- 'Michaelmas Damson' (C) **new** WWct
- 'Mirabelle Countess' (C) EPom LRHS MTrO WMat
- 'Mirabelle de Metz' (C) SKee
- 'Mirabelle de Nancy' (C) CAgr EPom LMaj MTrO NOra NRog SEWo SKee WMat
- 'Mirabelle Ruby' (C) CArg LRHS NOra SPoG WMat
§ - 'Prune Damson' (C) 🏆H6 CAgr CArg CHab CLnd CMac CTri EBee EPfP EPom LBuc LCro LRHS MMuc MTrO NLar NOra NRog NWea SEND SEWo SGbt SKee SPer SSFr WJas WMat WWct
- 'Shepherd's Bullace' (C) MCoo MTrO NLar SKee
- 'Shropshire Damson' see *P. insititia* 'Prune Damson'
- 'Small Bullace' (C) SKee
- 'Westmorland Prune' (C) CHab NLar NRog NWea
- 'Yellow Apricot' (C) SKee
'Jacqueline' 🏆H6 EBee LRHS MTrO NLar NOra WMou
§ ***jamasakura*** LRHS
'Jō-nioi' CEnd LRHS
kansuensis IArd
§ 'Kanzan' (d) 🏆H6 Widely available
§ 'Kiku-shidare-zakura' Widely available
'Kobuku-zakura' EWTr NOra WMat
§ 'Kofugen' NOra WMat
Korean hill cherry see *P. verecunda*
'Kursar' CDoC CLnd CSBt CTri EPfP GKin LRHS LSRN MTrO NOrn NRog NWea SBdl SCoo SGbt SLim SLon SPer SSFr SWvt WHwl WMat WSpi
laurocerasus CAco CBcs CBrac CCVT CDoC CMac EBee ELan EPfP EShb GDam GKin LMaj LPar MGos MHed MPri MRav NWea SArc SCob SGbt SGol SGsty SPer WMat WMou WTSh
- 'Angustifolia' CDoC SCob
- 'Camelliifolia' CMac CTri MBlu WCFE
- 'Castlewellan' (v) CBrac CDoC CMCN CTri ELon EPfP EShb LPar LRHS MGos MRav MSwo NLar NWad SCob SDix SPer SPoG WFar
- 'Caucasica' CEnd LMaj MNic NLar SEND SGol SGsty
- ETNA ('Anbri'[PBR]) 🏆H5 CBod CMac EHyd LBuc LPar MAsh SCob SWvt
- 'Gajo'[PBR] CBod
- GENOLIA ('Mariblon'[PBR]) LPar SGol
- 'Green Marble' (v) CTri EBee

- 'Ivory'PBR	CBod
§ - 'Latifolia'	LRHS WCFE WMou
- 'Magnoliifolia'	see *P. laurocerasus* 'Latifolia'
- 'Mano'	LMaj
- 'Marbled White'	see *P. laurocerasus* 'Castlewellan'
- 'Mount Vernon'	CTri LBuc LPar MBlu
- 'Novita'	CBod CBrac CDoC EPfP GDam LMaj LSRN MNic MPri NLar NOrn SCob SGsty SWeb
- 'Otto Luyken' ♀H5	CBcs CBod CBrac CCVT CMCN CMac CTri EBee ELan EPfP LBuc LPar MAsh MGos MSwo NBir NWea SArc SCob SPer SPlb WCFE WFar
- 'Piranha'PBR	NEoE
- 'Rotundifolia' ♀H5	Widely available
- 'Variegata' misapplied	see *P. laurocerasus* 'Castlewellan'
- 'Variegata' ambig. (v)	SRms
- 'Zabeliana'	CMac CTri GDam LPar MSwo NWea SCob SRms WCFE
litigiosa	EBee MTrO NLar NOra WMat
'Little Pink Perfection'	EPom LCro LOPS MTrO NLar NOra NOrn SCoo SPoG WMat
* ***longipedunculata***	LRHS WHwl
lusitanica ♀H5	Widely available
- subsp. ***azorica***	CExl EBee WMou WPGP
- 'Brenelia'PBR	CBod
- 'Myrtifolia' ♀H5	CBar CDoC CRos CTri EHyd EPfP EShb LMaj LPar LRHS MRav MTrO NLar NOra SArc SCob SGol SGsty SLon SPoG SWvt WCFE WMat
- 'Variegata' (v)	CBar CBod CBrac CMac ELan ELon LPar MGos MRav MSwo SCob SGol SGsty SPer SPoG SSta SWvt WFar
maackii	LMaj NOrn
- 'Amber Beauty'	CBcs EBee EPfP EWTr IPap LMaj LPar MMuc MRav MTrO NOra SEND SGol SLon WMat WMou
maritima	WKor
§ 'Matsumae-beni-murasaki'	CBcs LRHS MTrO NLar NOra WMat
'Matsumae-beni-tamanishiki'	see *P.* 'Beni-tamanishiki'
§ 'Matsumae-fuki' ♀H6	CBcs EBee LRHS LSRN MTrO NLar NOra NOrn NRHS NWea SLim WHwl WMat
'Matsumae-hanagasa'	see *P.* 'Hanagasa'
maximowiczii B&SWJ 10967	WCru
Miracot Series **new**	MTrO
'Mount Fuji'	see *P.* 'Shirotae'
mume	CMen ELon LPar MMrt
- 'Beni-chidori' ♀H5	CBcs CEnd CMac CSBt EHed ELon EPfP LCro LOPS LRHS MBlu MTrO NLar NOra NOrn SCoo SPoG WCot WJas WMat
§ - 'Omoi-no-mama' (d)	CEnd CMen NOrn SAko
- 'Omoi-no-wac'	see *P. mume* 'Omoi-no-mama'
myrobalana	see *P. cerasifera* Myrobalan Group
nigra	WMat
nipponica var. ***kurilensis*** 'Brillant'	CBcs CBod CDoC CRos CSBt EHyd ELon EPfP LRHS MHtn NHol NLar NOrn NRHS SPoG
- - 'Ruby'	EWTr LSRN
'Oku-miyako' misapplied	see *P.* 'Shōgetsu'
padus	CArg CCVT CHab CLnd CMac CSBt LBuc LPar MGos MSwo NLar NRog NWea SavN SCob SEND SEWo SGsty WKor WMou WTSh
- 'Albertii'	CCVT LPar MMuc NOra WMat
- 'Colorata' ♀H6	CArg CEnd CMac ELan EWTr IPap LPar MGos MMrt MMuc MRav NLar SBdl SEND SGol SPer SWvt
- 'Grandiflora'	see *P. padus* 'Watereri'
- 'Le Thoureil'	LRHS MMrt MTrO NOra
- 'Purple Queen'	SGol
§ - 'Watereri' ♀H6	CArg CBod CCVT CEnd CLnd CMCN CMac ELan EPfP LMaj LPar SCob SEND SEWo SGol SPer WMat WMou
'Pandora' ♀H6	Widely available
pendula	MTrO
§ - f. ***ascendens*** 'Rosea' ♀H6	LRHS MRav MTrO NOra WMat
- 'Pendula Plena Rosea' (d)	MTrO NOra WHwl WMat
§ - 'Pendula Rosea'	CAco CEnd CLnd CTri EPfP LPar MTrO NRog NWea SGsty SPer
§ - 'Pendula Rubra' ♀H6	CCVT CLnd CMac CSBt ELan EPfP EPom LRHS MSwo MTrO NOra NOrn SBdl SCob SCoo SGbt SLim SPer SPoG WMat
§ - 'Stellata' ♀H6	EPfP MTrO NOra SGbt SPer WMat
persica	SGsty SPre
- 'Advance' (F)	NRog
- 'Amber' (F)	SBdl
- 'Amsden June' (F)	CLnd MTrO NOra NRog SEdi SKee WMat
- 'Avalon Pride' (F)	CAgr CBod EPom MTrO NOra SCoo SKee SPoG SSFr
- 'Bellegarde' (F)	LRHS MTrO NOra SKee WMat
- 'Bonanza' (F)	EPom LSRN SSFr
- 'Cal Red' (F) **new**	SGsty
- 'Carman' (F)	WMat
- 'Champion' (F)	CLnd
- 'Crimson Bonfire' (F)	EPom SGsty
- 'Crimson Cascade' (F)	ELan
- 'Darling' (F)	SVic
- 'Diamond' (F)	EPom
- 'Dixi Red' (F)	CAgr SGsty
- 'Doctor Hogg' (F)	NRog
- 'Duke of York' (F)	CBod SBdl SKee SSFr
- 'Early Alexander' (F)	NRog
- 'Fayette' (F) **new**	SGsty
- 'Francis' (F)	SKee
- 'Frost' (F)	WMat
- 'Garden Lady' (F)	EPom MTrO NOra SEWo SLim WMat
- 'Gorgeous' (F)	MTrO NOra SKee WMat
- 'Hale's Early' (F)	CAgr MMuc MRav MTrO NOra SEdi SKee SLim WMat
- 'Hylands' (F)	NRog
- 'Jalousia' (F)	EPom NRog SVic
- 'Kestrel' (F)	SKee
- 'Lacrima' (F)	EPom
- 'Madison' (F)	NRog
- 'Melred' (F)	LRHS WMou
- 'Mesembrine'PBR (F)	EPom LRHS MTrO NOra
- var. ***nectarina*** 'Earliglo' (F)	NOra WMat
- - 'Early Gem' (F)	NRog
- - 'Early Rivers' (F)	LSRN MTrO NRog WMat
- - 'Fantasia' (F)	NRog SSFr
- - 'Fire Gold' (F)	NRog
- - 'Flavortop' (F)	SSFr
- - 'Garden Beauty' (F/d)	MTrO WMat
- - 'Honey Kist'PBR (F)	EPom
- - 'Humboldt' (F)	CAgr SBdl SEdi SKee WMat
- - 'Lord Napier' (F)	CAgr CBod CSBt CTri EPfP EPom EWTr IPap LRHS MGos MTrO NOra SBdl SEND SEdi SGbt SKee SLim SPer SSFT SSFr SVic WMat
- - 'Madame Blanchet' (F)	CBod NRog SVic
- - 'Nana Red Prolific' (F) **new**	SGsty
- - 'Nectared' (F)	SGsty

- - 'Nectarella' (F)	EPom LSRN MTrO NOra NRog SLim WMat
- - 'Pineapple' (F)	CAgr CTri LRHS MTrO NOra SKee WMat
- - RUBIS ('Necta Zee'PBR) (F)	EPom
- - 'Sauzee Bel' (F)	EPom
- - 'Sauzee King' (F)	EPom
- - 'Snow Baby' (F)	EPom
- - 'Snow Queen' (F)	SSFr
- - 'Terrace Ruby' (F)	MGos WMat
- 'Peregrine' (F)	Widely available
- 'Redhaven' (F)	CAgr NOra NRog SKee SVic WMat
- 'Redlate Necta'PBR (F)	SEdi
- 'Redwing' (F)	CAgr NRog
- 'Robin Redbreast' (F)	CAgr NRog
- 'Rochester' (F)	CAgr CBod CLnd CMac CSBt ELan EPom LRHS LSRN MGos MTrO NLar NOra NRog SBdl SEdi SKee SLim SSFT SSFr SWeb WMat
- 'Royal George' (F)	NRog
- 'Sanguine de Savoie' (F)	EPom NOra WMat
- 'Saturne' (F)	CAgr CLnd CMac EPom LRHS MAsh NOra SKee SSFr WMat
§ - 'Spring Snow'PBR	NLar
- 'Springtime' (F)	NRog
- 'Terrace Amber' (F)	SEWo SSFr WMat
- 'Terrace Diamond' (F)	WMat
- 'Terrace Garnet' (F)	MGos WMat
- 'Victor' (F) **new**	SBdl
× ***persicoides***	NWea SBdl
- 'Ingrid' (F)	CAgr CEnd LRHS MGos NOra SCoo SKee SSFr WMat
- 'Pollardii'	WJas
- 'Robijn' (F)	CAgr CBod ELan EPom LEdu NOra SKee SVic
- 'Spring Glow'	CBod CCVT CEnd CLnd EMil EPfP LRHS MSwo MTrO NOra NRog SCoo SEND SLim SLon WJas WMat
phaeosticta NJM 10.072	WPGP
'Pink Ballerina' **new**	EWTr
'Pink Candy' (F)	EPom
PINK PARASOL	see *P.* 'Hanagasa'
'Pink Perfection' ♀H6	CAco CBcs CBod CBrac CLnd CSBt ELan ELon EPfP EPom GQue LRHS MGos MSwo MTrO NOra NOrn NRog SBdl SCob SGbt SGsty SPer SSFr WJas WMat
'Pink Shell'	CLnd EPfP EPom EWTr MTrO NOra NRog SBdl SPer SSFr WMat
PINK SNOW SHOWERS ('Pisnshzam')	EPom
pissardii	see *P. cerasifera* 'Pissardii'
'Pissardii Nigra'	see *P. cerasifera* 'Nigra'
prostrata	WCot
pumila var. ***depressa***	MRav SAko
'Royal Burgundy' (d) ♀H6	Widely available
ROYAL FLAME ('Mieke') **new**	EWTr MTrO
rufa	CBcs CJun CLnd CRos MAsh MTrO NOra SLon WMat
salicina 'Lizzie' (F)	EPom
- 'Methley' (D)	CAgr NOra WMat
sargentii	Widely available
- 'Charles Sargent' ♀H6	CMCN LMaj LPar LSRN MBlu MTrO
- 'Columnaris'	EBee LRHS MTrO NOra WMat
- 'Rancho'	CLnd LMaj LPar MAsh NOrn SCoo SLim SPer SPoG WMat
× ***schmittii***	CBcs CCVT EBee LMaj LPar NOra SBdl SCob WMat
'Sekiyama'	see *P.* 'Kanzan'
§ ***serrula***	Widely available
- 'Branklyn' ♀H6	CJun EBee EPfP LRHS MGos NOra
- 'Dorothy Clive' ♀H6	EBee
- 'Princesse Sturdza'	MBlu
- var. ***tibetica***	see *P. serrula*
- 'Vario' **new**	CJun
serrula × ***serrulata***	WPGP
serrulata (d)	NRog
- 'Erecta'	see *P.* 'Amanogawa'
- 'Grandiflora'	see *P.* 'Ukon'
- 'Longipes'	see *P.* 'Shogetsu'
- 'Miyako' misapplied	see *P.* 'Shogetsu'
- var. ***pubescens***	see *P. verecunda*
- 'Rosea'	see *P.* 'Kiku-shidare-zakura'
'Shidare-zakura'	see *P.* 'Kiku-shidare-zakura'
'Shimizu-zakura'	see *P.* 'Shogetsu'
'Shirofugen'	see *P.* 'Fugenzo'
§ 'Shirotae' ♀H6	Widely available
§ 'Shizuka' ♀H6	CAco CBcs ELon IPap LBuc LRHS MSwo MTrO NLar NOra NOrn SCob SCoo SGbt SLim SPer WHwl WMat WMou
§ 'Shōgetsu' ♀H6	CAco CBcs CDoC CEnd CLnd CMCN CMac CSBt ELan EPfP EPom LMaj LRHS LSRN MAsh MMuc MTrO NLar NOra NOrn NRog SBdl SCob SEWo SLim SPer WHwl WMat
'Shogun' **new**	MTrO
§ 'Shosar' ♀H6	CEnd SCoo SPer
simonii	SPre
'Slocot' **new**	MCoo
SNOW FOUNTAINS ('Snofozam')	LRHS SGsty SPer
'Snow Goose'	CMac EBee ELan EPfP EPom EWTr LCro LOPS LRHS MBlu MMuc MTrO NLar NOra NOrn SCoo SGol SPoG WMat
'Snow Showers'	CBod CCVT CDoC CEnd CMac EBee ELan EPfP EPom LCro LRHS LSRN MAsh MGos MPri MTrO NLar NOra NOrn NWea SEND SLim SPer SPoG WHwl WMat
spinosa	Widely available
- 'Plena' (d)	CEnd MBlu
- 'Purpurea'	MBlu WMou
§ 'Spire' ♀H6	Widely available
SPRING SNOW	see *P.* 'Beni-tamanishiki'
'Spring Snow'	see *P. persica* 'Spring Snow'
'Stefania'	WMat
× ***subhirtella*** var. ***ascendens***	see *P. pendula* f. *ascendens*
- 'Autumnalis'	Widely available
- 'Autumnalis Rosea'	Widely available
§ - 'Dahlem'	MTrO
- 'Falling Stars'	SLon
- 'Fukubana'	CLnd CMac ELon EPfP NLar SGsty WHwl WMat WMou
- 'Pendula' misapplied	see *P. pendula* 'Pendula Rosea'
- 'Pendula Rosea'	see *P. pendula* 'Pendula Rosea'
- 'Pendula Rubra'	see *P. pendula* 'Pendula Rubra'
- 'Plena'	see *P.* × *subhirtella* 'Dahlem'
- 'Rosea'	see *P. pendula* f. *ascendens* 'Rosea'
- 'Stellata'	see *P. pendula* 'Stellata'
'Sunset Boulevard' ♀H6	CCVT CDoC CLnd EBee ELan EPfP LMaj LRHS LSRN MGos MTrO NLar NOra SCob WMat
'Tai-haku' ♀H6	Widely available
TAOFLORA RED ('Mintao13') **new**	LRHS
'Taoyame' ♀H6	CLnd
tenella	WCot
- 'Alba'	WFar

	- 'Fire Hill'	CBcs ELan EPfP MGos MMrt NLar SPer WCot WJas WSpi
	'The Bride' ♀H6	CAco CBcs CBrac CEnd CJun EBee EPfP EPom EWTr LCro LOPS LRHS MAsh MTrO NOra NOrn SChF SCoo SEWo SGbt SPer WMat WMou
	tibetica	see *P. serrula*
	'Tiltstone Hellfire'	CBod EBee EWTr GBin LRHS MTrO NLar NOra WMat
	tomentosa	CAgr WKor
§	'Trailblazer' (C/D)	CEnd CLnd CMac EMil EPfP MRav MSwo MTrO SCob SKee SLon
	triloba	CBcs LCro LOPS MBlu MGos
	- 'Multiplex' (d)	SRms WAvo WJas
§	'Ukon' ♀H6	CBcs CLnd CMCN CMac CTri EBee ELan EPfP EWTr LCro LOPS LRHS MAsh MGos MRav MTrO NLar NOra NOrn NRog NWea SBdl SCob SGol SLim SPer WFar WMat
	'Umineko'	CCVT CLnd LMaj LPar MGos MMuc SCob SEND SEWo SPer
§	***verecunda***	CLnd NRog SBdl WJas
	'Victoria Willis'	WMat
	virginiana	WKor
	- 'Canada Red' **new**	LMaj
	- 'Schubert'	CBod ELan LPar NWea
	'White Cloud'	CAco
	'Woodfield Cluster'	IArd
	yamadae	see *P. incisa* f. *yamadei*
	× ***yedoensis***	CCVT CLnd CSBt ELan LMaj LPar MRav MTrO NOra NWea SCob SEWo SGsty SLon SPer WMat WMou
	- 'Ivensii'	CAco CSBt EPom NRog NWea SCoo SPer
	- 'Pendula'	see *P.* × *yedoensis* 'Shidare-Yoshino'
	- 'Perpendens'	see *P.* × *yedoensis* 'Shidare-Yoshino'
§	- 'Shidare-Yoshino'	CAco CCVT CMac CSBt IPap LBuc LRHS MGos MRav MSwo MTrO NOrn NWea SGsty SLim SLon SPer WMat
§	- 'Somei-Yoshino' ♀H6	CCVT CMCN CTri MTrO SBdl SLim SSFr WJas
	'Yoshino'	see *P.* × *yedoensis* 'Somei-Yoshino'
	'Yoshino Pendula'	see *P.* × *yedoensis* 'Shidare-Yoshino'

Pseuderanthemum (*Acanthaceae*)

	laxiflorum	EShb

Pseudocydonia (*Rosaceae*)

§	***sinensis***	CBcs CHab CMen LPar NRog SEND WKor

Pseudofumaria see *Corydalis*

	alba	see *Corydalis ochroleuca*

Pseudogynoxys (*Asteraceae*)

§	***chenopodioides***	CCCN CSpe ECre EShb SVen

Pseudolarix (*Pinaceae*)

	amabilis ♀H7	CAco CMen EPfP LPar MBlu MPkF SLim
	kaempferi (Lamb.) Gordon	see *Larix kaempferi*

Pseudomuscari see *Muscari*

Pseudopanax ✿ (*Araliaceae*)

	(Adiantifolius Group)	CAbb CBcs CCCN CTrC CWit EBee
	'Adiantifolius'	SVen
	- 'Cyril Watson' ♀H3	CBcs CWit EBee EPfP SEND SVen WPGP
	arboreus	see *Neopanax arboreus*
	'Bronze Eagle'	LRHS XSte
	'Chainsaw'	CBct
	chathamicus	SArc
	crassifolius	CBrP CCCN CDTJ CWit ELon GBin SArc WPGP XSte
	- var. ***trifoliolatus***	CBcs CDTJ WPGP
	'Dark Star'	CBcs CTrC LRHS XSte
	discolor	LEdu
	ferox	CBrP CDTJ CTrC CTsd GBin LCro LOPS LRHS SVen XSte
	'Gecko Gold' (v)	LRHS XSte
	laetus	see *Neopanax laetus*
	lessonii	CBcs CBrP
	- 'Gold Splash' (v) ♀H3	CBcs CBod CCCN CTrC EBee ELon EPfP SEND SVen XSte
	- 'Goldfinger'	LRHS XSte
	- 'Nigra'	CTrC
	- 'Rangitira'	CTrC LRHS XSte
	'Linearifolius'	CTrC IDee LEdu
	'Moa's Toes'	CBcs CBct CCht CTrC CTsd MHtn SCob SEND WCot
	'Purpureus' ♀H3	CBod CCCN CDTJ CTrC CTsd CWit ELon EPfP IDee SEND SVen
	'Sabre'	CAbb CBcs CCCN CDTJ CTrC EBee ELon EPfP IDee LRHS SEND SEdd XSte
	'Trident' ♀H3	CTrC SEND SVen
	'Tuatara'	CAbb CBcs CCht CTrC GBin LRHS MHtn SCob

Pseudosasa (*Poaceae*)

	sp.	CAco
	amabilis misapplied	see *Arundinaria gigantea*
§	***japonica*** ♀H5	CAbb CAco CAgr CBcs CBod CSBt EHyd EPfP GArf GBin LCro LOPS LPar LRHS MMuc MWht NLar NRHS SArc SCob SEND SGsty SPoG SWeb WFar
§	- 'Akebonosuji' (v)	SWeb WPGP
I	- var. ***pleioblastoides***	MWht
	- 'Tsutsumiana'	ELon MWht NLar
	viridula	MWht

Pseudotaxus (*Taxaceae*)

	chienii	CBcs LRHS SPtp WPGP

Pseudotsuga (*Pinaceae*)

§	***menziesii***	CAco CBcs CLnd EPfP LPar MBlu MMuc NWea SCob WTSh
	- 'Bhiela Lhota'	CAco CKen
	- 'Blue Wonder'	CKen
	- 'Densa'	CKen
	- 'Fastigiata'	CAco CKen
	- 'Fletcheri'	CAco CKen SLim
	- 'Foxy Fir'	SLim
	- var. ***glauca***	CAco
	- 'Glauca Pendula'	CAco LRHS MBlu
	- 'Gollen'	SLim
I	- 'Gotelli's Pendula'	CKen
	- 'Graceful Grace'	CKen
	- 'Hillside Pride'	NLar
	- 'Holata' **new**	CAco
	- 'Holmstrup' **new**	CAco
	- 'Idaho Gem'	NLar
	- 'Julie'	CKen
	- 'Les Barres'	SLim
	- 'Little Jamie'	CKen
	- 'Little Jon'	CAco
	- 'Lohbrunner'	CKen SLim
	- 'Maruška' **new**	CAco
	- 'Misty First' **new**	CAco

- 'Moerheimii' CAco NLar
- 'Nana' CKen
- 'Nýřany' SLim
- 'Pannenhoef' SLim
- 'Pannonia' **new** CAco
- 'Seattle Mountain' SLim
- 'Serpentine' CAco MBlu NLar SLim
- 'Skryje' **new** CAco
- 'Stairii' CKen
- 'Tidal Wave' **new** CAco
- 'Uwes Golden' SLim

taxifolia see *P. menziesii*

Pseudowintera (*Winteraceae*)

§ ***colorata*** CBcs CCCN CDoC CExl CMac CPla CTrC EBee GAbr GKin MRav NLar SBrt SEle WFar WSHC XSte
- 'Marjorie Congreve' CBcs CDoC GKin IArd
- 'Moulin Rouge' CBcs CTrC SEle
- 'Red Glow' CBcs
- 'Red Leopard' CBcs CTrC LRHS SEle WFar

Psidium (*Myrtaceae*)

cattleyanum see *P. littorale* var. *longipes*
guajava (F) CCCN CMCN SPlb SVic
littorale var. ***littorale*** (F) WKor
§ - var. ***longipes*** (F) CCCN WKor

Psophocarpus (*Fabaceae*)

tetragonolobus LOPS SPhx

Psoralea (*Fabaceae*)

aphylla SVen
* ***fleta*** SPlb
glabra SPlb
glandulosa SPlb
oligophylla SPlb
pinnata CExl IArd

Psychotria (*Rubiaceae*)

capensis CExl

Psylliostachys (*Plumbaginaceae*)

suworowii LRHS SPhx

Ptelea (*Rutaceae*)

trifoliata CBcs CLnd ELan EPfP MBlu MVil SPer SRms WPGP
- 'Aurea' ♀H6 CExl CJun CLnd ELan EPfP EWTr MBlu MMuc SPer WBor

Pteracanthus see *Strobilanthes*

Pteridium (*Dennstaedtiaceae*)

aquilinum XLum

Pteridophyllum (*Papaveraceae*)

racemosum CMiW EWld GEdr GGro LEdu NHpl WCru WFar

Pteris (*Pteridaceae*)

cretica var. ***albolineata*** see *P. nipponica*
- 'Mayi' (v) CRos EHyd LRHS NRHS WCot
- 'Ouvradii' SPlb
- 'Parkeri' CBdn EHyd
- 'Rivertoniana' EHyd LRHS NRHS
- 'Rowei' CRos EHyd LRHS NRHS
- 'Wimsettii' ♀H4 CBdn CRos EHyd LEdu LRHS MAsh NRHS WCot

ensiformis 'Evergemiensis' (v) CTsd EShb
incompleta LEdu WPGP
§ ***nipponica*** ♀H1c EHed EHyd EShb GGro LLWG LRHS NRHS SEND WCot
tremula EShb NBro WCot
tricolor EShb
umbrosa CBdn CCht CLAP CRos CTsd EHed EHyd LLWG LRHS MAsh MHol NBro NRHS SEND SPlb WCot WPGP WSMil
wallichiana SMad WCot WPGP

Pterocactus (*Cactaceae*)

hickenii F&W 10240 WCot

Pterocarya ✿ (*Juglandaceae*)

fraxinifolia CBcs CCVT CLnd CMCN EBee EPfP IArd IDee IPap LMaj LRHS MBlu MCoo MMuc MRav SChF WTSh
- NJM 13.007 WPGP
- PAB 13.052 LEdu
- 'Abbotsbury Giant' WPGP

macroptera var. ***insignis*** CExl EBee SMad WPGP
× ***rehderiana*** MBlu WMou
rhoifolia CMCN EPfP IArd
stenoptera CBcs CDTJ CDoC NLar WMou
- 'Fern Leaf' ♀H6 CDoC CExl EBee MBlu WPGP

tonkinensis WPGP

Pterocephalus (*Caprifoliaceae*)

parnassi see *P. perennis*
§ ***perennis*** CMea MHer SRms WHoo
spathulatus WAbe

Pterostylis (*Orchidaceae*)

curta ♀H2 CBro SGro

Pterostyrax ✿ (*Styracaceae*)

corymbosa CBcs CMCN GBin LPar LRHS MBlu MVil XSte
- CWJ 12838 WCru

hispida ♀H5 CBcs CMCN EPfP ESwi MBlu MRav MVil NLar SAko WFar
psilophyllus CMCN MBlu SPtp
- var. ***leveillei*** EBee MBlu WPGP
- trilobed EBee WPGP

Ptilostemon (*Asteraceae*)

§ ***diacantha*** CBod EBee EHyd
echinocephalus CBod

Ptilotrichum see *Alyssum*

Ptilotus (*Amaranthaceae*)

exaltatus SPlb

Pulicaria (*Asteraceae*)

§ ***dysenterica*** CHab NGrd NMir WHer WSFF

Pulmonaria (*Boraginaceae*)

angustifolia CTri EPfP GKev GMaP MNrw NWad SHeu SRms
- 'Azurea' CElw EBee EGrI ELan EPPr EPfP GAbr GMaP MCot MMuc MRav NBro NGrd NLar SRms WCAu WSpi
- 'Blaues Meer' EBee ECtt EHyd LRHS MNrw NRHS NSti SGbt SHeu WSpi
- 'Munstead Blue' MCot MRav NRya SRms

'Apple Frost' SHeu
'Ballyrogan Blue' ♀H6 EBlo EHyd LRHS
'Barfield Regalia' NChi NSti
'Benediction' MBriF MNrw NSti WBrk WCot WMal

	'Beth Chatto'	CElw
	'Beth's Pink'	GAbr
	'Blake's Silver'	CDor CWCL LPla MHol MNrw NSti SCob SMrm WBrk WCot WHoo
	'Blauer Hügel'	NSti
	'Blue Crown'	CElw WBrk
	'Blue Ensign' ♀H6	Widely available
	'Blue Moon'	see *P. officinalis* 'Blue Mist'
	'Blue Pearl'	EHyd LRHS NRHS
	'Bonnie'	CMea
	'Bubble Gum'PBR	EHyd EMor SCob SHeu
	'Cleeton Red'	MNrw WMal
	'Coral Springs'	NLar
	'Cotton Cool' ♀H6	EBee ECha ECtt EHyd EShb EWoo GBin GQue LRHS MBNS MBel MBriF MCot MRav MTin NHol NRHS NSti NWad SGbt SHeu SPer SSut WCAu WGwG WSMil WWtn
	'Dark Vader'	ECtt EHyd SHeu SPoG
	'Diana Clare' ♀H6	Widely available
	'Elworth Sentinel'	MBriF
	'Excalibur'	ECtt NLar SHeu SRms
	'Fiona'	MNrw
	'Gavin Compton' (v)	MNrw
	'Glacier'	NChi WCot
	'High Contrast'	ECtt SHeu
	'Highdown'	see *P.* 'Lewis Palmer'
	'Ice Ballet' (Classic Series)	CDor EBee ECtt EPfP LRHS MAsh MBriF MNrw SCob SHar SHeu WCAu
	'Joan Curtis'	MNrw
§	'Lewis Palmer' ♀H6	CBro CDor CWCL GMaP LRHS MNrw NBir SRms WAvo WBrk WHoo
	'Little Star' ♀H6	CElw CRos EBee EBlo ECha EHyd LRHS MAvo NRHS NSti SHeu WFar
	longifolia	ECha ECtt EHyd ELan EPfP GBin GKev LRHS LSou NBir NLar NRHS NSti SBls SRms WWtn
§	- 'Ankum'	CElw NBir WCot
	- 'Bertram Anderson'	EBee ECtt GMaP NBir NLar NRHS SHeu SPer SRms SWvt
	- subsp. ***cevennensis***	EHyd EMor LRHS NLar NRHS SHeu WBrk WFar WSpi
	- 'Coen Jansen'	see *P. longifolia* 'Ankum'
	- 'Dordogne'	NBir NLar
	- 'Howard Eggins'	WAvo WBrk
	'Mado'	ECha
	'Majesté'	CDor CMiW CRos EAJP EBee ECha EHyd ELan EMor EPfP EWes GMaP LRHS MBel MRav NBir NLar NRHS NSti SCob SHeu SPer SPoG SRms WCAu WCot WFar
	'Marchant's Spotted Dick'	SMHy
	'Margery Fish'	CDor LRHS NChi SHeu WBrk
	'Mary Mottram'	NBir NSti SHeu WCot
	'Mawson's Blue'	NBir NChi SWvt
	'Milky Way'	CWCL ECtt EPfP SHeu SPoG
	'Miss Elly'	MAvo NSti
	mollis	CBod EHyd GBin MNrw NSti WCAu
	- 'Royal Blue'	MRav
	'Monksilver'	CElw
	'Moonshine'PBR	CMil CRos ECtt EHyd EPfP GKev LRHS MAsh MBel NRHS NSti SHeu
	'Moonstone'	CElw
	'Mrs Kittle'	CWCL EHyd GPSL LRHS MBel MBriF MRav NBir NHol NLar NRHS NSti SHeu SSut WSMil WWtn
	'Netta Statham'	MAvo
	'Nürnberg'	CDor
	officinalis	CHby MHer NChi NGrd WBrk WCFE XAbr
	- 'Alba'	WBrk
§	- 'Blue Mist'	GMaP NBir WAvo WCot
	- 'Bowles's Blue'	see *P. officinalis* 'Blue Mist'
	- Cambridge Blue Group	MRav NBir NGdn WCot WWtn
	- 'White Wings'	NLar
	OPAL ('Ocupol') ♀H6	Widely available
	'Patric's Early Dawn' **new**	ECha
	'Pierre's Pure Pink'	EBee EHyd SHeu
	'Pink Haze'PBR	ECtt NLar SWvt
	'Purple Haze'	NSti SCob
	'Raspberry Splash'PBR	CBod CRos CWCL ECtt ECul EHed EMor EPfP GKev LCro LOPS LPla LRHS MNrw NBir NLar NSti SCob SHeu SWvt WCAu WCot WPnP
	'Richard Nutt'	WCot
*	'Rowlatt Choules'	MNrw
	'Roy Davidson'	CDor ECtt EHyd EPPr EPfP MBow NBir NChi NHol NRHS SRms SWvt WWtn
	rubra	CBcs CElw ECha ELan GAbr LCro LOPS LShi MMuc MNrw NBid NChi NLar NSti SHeu SRms WCAu
	- var. ***alba***	see *P. rubra* var. *albocorollata*
§	- var. ***albocorollata***	EBee EBlo ECha EHyd EPfP GBin LRHS NBid
	- 'Ann'	GBin GQue
	- 'Barfield Pink'	MNrw NBir NLar SHeu
	- 'Bowles's Red'	CBod GPSL MAsh MNrw MRav NBir WFar WGwG WWtn
	- 'David Ward' (v)	ECha ECtt EHyd ELan EMor LRHS MRav NBir NSti SCob SHeu SPoG SRms WCAu WCFE WCot
	- 'Rachel Vernie' (v)	NQui WAvo
	- 'Redstart'	CBod CCBP CDor ECtt GKev GMaP LRHS MNrw MRav NBir NGrd NLar SCob SHeu SPer SRms SWvt WBrk WCAu WFar
§	***saccharata***	ECha GMaP MMuc SRms
	- 'Alba'	CElw SRms
	- Argentea Group ♀H6	CTri EPfP GMaP MRav NGdn
	- 'Clent Skysilver'	WAvo WBrk
	- 'Dora Bielefeld'	CBod ECha EGrI EPfP EWTr EWes GMaP MBriF MNrw MRav NBir NChi NGdn NHol NRHS NSti SHeu SPer SWvt WCav WFar
	- 'Frühlingshimmel'	CDor ECha LPla MRav
	- 'Glebe Cottage Blue'	CElw
	- 'Leopard'	CDor CMea CRos CWCL ECtt EHyd EMor EPfP LRHS MNrw NBir NGdn NLar NRHS NSti SHeu SWvt WCAu WCot WGwG WHoo WSpi
	- 'Mrs Moon'	CBod CTri EBee EBlo ECtt EHyd EPfP GMaP LCro LOPS LRHS MBriF MNHC NLar SCob SHeu SPer SWvt WCAu WCav
	- 'Old Rectory Silver'	NBir
	- 'Picta'	see *P. saccharata*
	- 'Pink Dawn'	EBee
	- 'Reginald Kaye'	ECha
	- 'Silverado'PBR	ECtt NGdn NLar SCob SHeu SWvt
	- 'Stanhoe'	EWes
	'Saint Ann's'	EBee EHyd LRHS NRHS NSti
	'Samurai' ♀H6	CWCL EMor LRHS MAvo MNrw NLar NSti SHeu WFar WGrn
	'Shrimps on the Barbie' **new**	CBod
	'Silver Bouquet'PBR	ECtt ECul EPfP LCro LOPS LPla LRHS LSou MBros NHpl NSti SHeu
	'Silver Lance'	SHeu
	'Silver Shimmers'PBR	SHeu

'Sissinghurst White' $\mathbb{Y}^{H6}$	Widely available
'Smoky Blue'	MRav SCob SHeu
'Spilled Milk'	SHeu
'Stillingfleet Meg'	CDor CRos ECtt EHyd EPfP LRHS MBNS MBriF NGdn NRHS NSti NWad SCoo SHeu WCAu WGwG WWtn
'Trevi Fountain' $\mathbb{Y}^{H6}$	Widely available
'Vera May' $\mathbb{Y}^{H6}$	MBriF MNrw
'Victorian Brooch'PBR	CBod CRos CWCL ECtt EHed EHyd EPfP GKev GMaP LPla LRHS MHol MNrw NCou NRHS SHeu SPoG WCAu WSpi
'Weetwood Blue'	EBee EBlo EHyd LRHS MNrw NRHS WMal
'Wendy Perry'	EBee EBlo EHyd LRHS

Pulsatilla (*Ranunculaceae*)

albana	EHyd GKev LRHS NRHS
- 'Lutea'	GKev NSla
alpina	SPlb SRms
- subsp. ***alpina***	GKev
§ - subsp. ***apiifolia***	GKev
- subsp. ***austriaca*** **new**	GKev
- subsp. ***sulphurea*** misapplied	see *P. alpina* subsp. *apiifolia*
ambigua	GEdr
bungeana	GKev SBrt
campanella	EBee GArf GEdr GKev
- W/O 7223 **new**	GGro
caucasica	EHyd LRHS NRHS
halleri $\mathbb{Y}^{H5}$	EBee GBin GKev WSHC
- subsp. ***slavica*** $\mathbb{Y}^{H5}$	EPot GJos GKev
- subsp. ***taurica***	GEdr
lutea	see *P. alpina* subsp. *apiifolia*
montana	SPlb
occidentalis	GEdr
§ ***patens***	NGdn
- subsp. ***flavescens***	GEdr
pratensis	GPoy SRms
- subsp. ***nigricans***	GEdr MHer WAbe
red-flowered	CTri
rubra	CAvo CMea CRos EAJP EBou EGrI EHyd ELan EMor EPfP GJos GKev GMaP LPot LRHS MHer NBir NGdn NLar NRHS SPeP SPer SPoG SRms SRot WAbe WHoo WIce
* ***serotina***	EBee GKev
subslavica	GKev WAbe
sugawarae	GEdr
tatewakii	GEdr NSla
turczaninovii	EBee GEdr GJos NSla WFar
§ ***vernalis***	GEdr GJos NLar NSla WAbe
violacea	CBcs
§ ***vulgaris*** $\mathbb{Y}^{H5}$	Widely available
- 'Alba'	CRos EBee ECha EGrI EHyd ELan EPfP EShb EWTr EWoo GJos GKev LPot LRHS LSun MBel MHer NBir NGdn NRHS NSla SPeP SPer SPoG SWvt WFar WGwG WIce XLum
- 'Barton's Pink'	CRos EHyd LRHS NRHS
- 'Blaue Glocke'	CRos EHyd GEdr GJos LRHS NRHS SHar SWvt
- blue-flowered	CTri
- 'Eva Constance'	CRos EHyd LRHS NRHS
- subsp. ***grandis***	CFis EHyd GEdr LRHS NLar NRHS NSla
- - 'Papageno'	CDor CSpe EAJP EBee ELon GAbr GEdr LRHS LSou MAvo MBel MHol NHol NHpl NLar NSla
- Heiler hybrids	EShb LRHS LSou MArl MPie MRav NDov NGdn NSla SGbt SVic WGwG
- 'Perlen Glocke'	EDAr EHyd EWTr GEdr LRHS NLar NRHS SEdd WIce
- pink-flowered	EAJP GKev WFar
- (Pinwheel Series) PINWHEEL BLUE VIOLET SHADES	EHyd LRHS MACG MHol NRHS
- - PINWHEEL DARK RED SHADES	CBod LRHS MACG MHol
- - PINWHEEL WHITE	LRHS MHol WFar
- RED CLOCK	see *P. vulgaris* 'Röde Klokke'
- red-flowered	CTsd EBee GAbr SGbt WFar
§ - 'Röde Klokke'	CRos ECtt EHyd EPfP GEdr GWyn LRHS LSun MBel NRHS NSla SEdd SHar SWvt XLum
- ROTE GLOCKE	see *P. vulgaris* 'Röde Klokke'
- 'Violet Bells'	EBou NSla
- violet-blue-flowered	EBee EHyd EPfP LRHS NRHS
§ - 'Weisse Schwan'	EPfP GEdr GMaP
- 'White Bells'	NHol WFar
- WHITE SWAN	see *P. vulgaris* 'Weisse Schwan'
zimmermannii	GJos

Pultenaea (*Fabaceae*)

daphnoides	SVen
juniperina	SPlb SVen

pummelo see *Citrus maxima*

Punica (*Lythraceae*)

granatum	CBcs CCCN CMCN CMen ELan EPfP ETod LPar MGil SEND SGsty SIvy SPre SVic SWeb SWvt WLov
- 'Chico' (d)	CBcs SEND
- 'Fina Tendral' (F)	CCCN EShb XSen
- 'Flore Pleno'	see *P. granatum* f. *plena* 'Albescens Flore Pleno'
- 'Legrelleae' (F/d)	SEND
- 'Maxima Rubra' (d)	EShb
- 'Mollar de Elche'	XSen
- var. ***nana*** $\mathbb{Y}^{H3}$	CCCN CMen CTsd EHyd EPfP EShb LEdu MHer SPad SPre SRms SVen SVic SWeb WKor WLov WPGP
- f. ***plena*** (d)	CBcs EPfP LRHS MRav SPer WCFE
§ - - 'Albescens Flore Pleno' (d)	EHed ETod
- 'Provence' (F)	EPom XSen
- 'Wonderful' (F)	CAgr LRHS XSen

Puschkinia (*Asparagaceae*)

peshmenii white-flowered **new**	NRog
scilloides	NBir NRog
- 'Alaverdi' **new**	NRog
- 'Aragat's Gem'	GKev NRog
- blue-flowered	GKev
- large-flowered clone	GKev
- var. ***libanotica*** $\mathbb{Y}^{H6}$	CRos EHyd EPot ERCP GKev LCro LOPS LRHS MPie NRHS SDeJ SEND SPer WShi
- - 'Alba'	EPot GKev NRog SDeJ
- 'Piatigorsk' **new**	NRog
- 'Sky Vision' **new**	NRog
- 'Snowdrift'	NRog
- 'Zanzegur' **new**	NRog

Puya ✿ (*Bromeliaceae*)

RH 1809	WCot
RH 2910A	WCot
RH 2961C	WCot
RH 3425B	WCot
alpestris	CCCN CPla EShb SPlb

- subsp. ***zoellneri***	CCCN CDTJ EShb SPlb SVen WCot
assurgens	LRHS XSte
bicolor B&SWJ 14869	WCru
boliviensis	WCot
castellanosii	SPlb WCot
chilensis	CAbb CBod CCCN CDTJ CPla SPlb SVen WCot
coerulea	CCCN CDTJ CPla CTsd SPlb WSMil
§ - var. ***violacea***	LRHS XSte
dyckioides	LRHS WCot
- red-bracted	WCot
ferruginea	LRHS SPlb WCot
grantii B&SWJ 14819	WCru
hromadnikii	SPlb
humilis	WCot
killipii B&SWJ 14801	WCru
laxa	SPlb WCot
lineata B&SWJ 14878	WCru
mirabilis	CAbb CDTJ GBin SPlb WSMil
- B&SWJ 14825	WCru
- B&SWJ 14827	WCru
aff. ***nitida*** B&SWJ 14396	WCru
- B&SWJ 14887	WCru
ochroleuca B&SWJ 14716	WCru
santosii B&SWJ 14783	WCru
trianae B&SWJ 14818	WCru
- B&SWJ 14921	WCru
venusta	CBcs CCCN CDTJ CPla LRHS SPlb SVen WCot
violacea	see *P. coerulea* var. *violacea*
yakespala	LRHS WCot

Pycnanthemum (*Lamiaceae*)

albescens	ECha
curvipes	EBee LEdu
muticum	CSpe EBee LEdu MHol SPhx WPGP
pilosum	CLau EBee EBou MHer SPhx WFar WJek XLum
tenuifolium	NLar SPhx
virginianum	EBee SPhx

Pycnostachys (*Lamiaceae*)

urticifolia	EWes

Pygmea see *Chionohebe*

Pyracantha (*Rosaceae*)

ALEXANDER PENDULA ('Renolex')	MRav MSwo SRms
angustifolia	WCFE
- KR 2481	WPGP
§ ***atalantioides***	SPlb WCFE
coccinea 'Lalandei'	CMac
- 'Red Column'	Widely available
- 'Red Cushion'	ELan GDam SArc SRms
crenulata	WCFE
DART'S RED ('Interrada')	CSBt
'Fiery Cascade'	EHyd LRHS NRHS SPoG WFar
'Firelight' **new**	CBod
gibbsii	see *P. atalantioides*
'Golden Charmer'	CDoC CMac EHyd EPfP LBuc LRHS MGos MSwo NLar NWea SCoo SGol SNig SPer SPoG SRms SWvt WFar
'Golden Glow'	LPar LRHS SGol
'Golden Paradise'PBR	CBod EBee NEoE
'Golden Sun'	see *P.* 'Soleil d'Or'
'Harlequin' (v)	CMac SGol WFar
'Knap Hill Lemon'	MBlu
koidzumii 'Victory'	WAvo
'Mohave'	CRos CTri EHyd ELan LRHS MAsh NRHS SCob SRms SWvt WFar
'Mohave Silver' (v)	CMac EHyd ELan EShb LRHS NHol NRHS
'Navaho'	LMaj SGsty
'Orange Charmer'	CBrac CMac CTri ELan LPar MGos NHol NWea SCob SCoo SGol SPer SPlb WFar
'Orange Glow' ♀H6	CArg CBod CBrac CRos CSBt CTri EHyd EPfP EShb GDam LBuc LRHS MAsh MGos MSwo NLar NRHS NWea SArc SCob SCoo SEND SEWo SGol SPer SRms SWvt WAvo WFar
'Red Charmer'	NHol
* 'Red Pillar'	GDam SGbt
'Red Star'	LRHS NRHS
rogersiana 'Flava' ♀H5	CRos CSBt EHyd EPfP LRHS NRHS SPoG SWvt WAvo
'Rosedale'	EHyd WAvo
SAPHYR JAUNE ('Cadaune'PBR)	CBcs CBod CCVT CDoC CEnd EBee EPfP ILea LCro LOPS LPar LRHS MAsh MGos MRav NHol NLar SCob SGbt SGol SGsty SPer SWeb
SAPHYR ORANGE ('Cadange') ♀H6	CBcs CBod CCVT CDoC CEnd CMac CSBt EBee EHyd EPfP ILea LCro LOPS LPar LRHS MGos MRav NLar NRHS SCob SCoo SGbt SGol SGsty SPer SWeb
SAPHYR ROUGE ('Cadrou') ♀H6	Widely available
'Shawnee'	CMac MSwo
§ 'Soleil d'Or'	CBod CTri EBee EHyd ELan EPfP GDam MAsh MRav NLar NWea SCob SCoo SEND SEWo SGol SLon SPer SPlb SRms SWvt WAvo WFar
'Sparkler' (v)	CMac EBee MHtn SMad SPoG
'Teton' ♀H6	CMac EHyd ELan EPfP LRHS MAsh MGos MSwo NRHS SCoo SGol SPoG SRms WFar
'Watereri'	WSpi
'Yellow Sun'	see *P.* 'Soleil d'Or'

× *Pyracomeles* (*Rosaceae*)

vilmorinii	IDee SAko

Pyrethropsis see *Rhodanthemum*

Pyrethrum see *Tanacetum*

Pyrola (*Ericaceae*)

rotundifolia	LEdu WHer

Pyrrocoma (*Asteraceae*)

clementis	EBee

Pyrrosia (*Polypodiaceae*)

hastata	CMen WCot
- 'Harima Jishi'	CMen
- 'Ryujin'	CMen
- 'Sekaiichi' **new**	CMen
- 'Shikoku Jishi'	CMen
- 'World Champion'	CMen
linearifolia 'Urakoryu Jishi'	CMen
lingua	CMen LEdu
- 'Hiryu'	CMen
- 'Ōgon Nishiki' (v)	GGro WCot
- 'Tachiba Koryu'	CMen
polydactyla	CMen WCot
sheareri	EHyd WCot

Pyrus ✿ (*Rosaceae*)

amygdaliformis	CMCN

– W&B B-10	WCot
betulifolia	SBdl
calleryana 'Bradford'	CLnd
– 'Capital'	LPar
– 'Chanticleer'	Widely available
– 'Chanticleer' variegated (v)	MAsh
– 'Redspire'	CBod CCVT ELan NWea SCob SPer
caucasica	WMat
communis (F)	CCVT CTri LBuc NRog NWea SPer SPlb SPre WMou WTSh
– 'Admiral Gervais' (D)	SBdl
– 'Alexandrina Bivort' (D)	SBdl
– 'André Desportes' (D) **new**	SBdl
– 'Autumn Bergamot' (D)	SBdl
– 'Ayrshire Lass' (D)	SBdl
– 'Bambinella' (D)	SBdl SKee
– 'Barland' (Perry)	CHab NRog SBdl SKee
– 'Barnet' (Perry)	CHab NRog SBdl
– 'Baronne de Mello' (D)	NOra SBdl SKee WMat
– 'Beech Hill' (F)	CBod EBee LMaj LPar SCob SPer
– 'Belle de Jumet' (D) **new**	SBdl
– 'Belle de Soignies' (D) **new**	SBdl
– 'Belle Guérandaise' (D)	SBdl SKee
– 'Belle Julie' (D)	SBdl SKee
– 'Bellissime d'Hiver' (C)	SBdl
– BENITA ('Rafzas') (F)	LCro LOPS LRHS MTrO WMat
– 'Bergamotte Esperen' (D)	SBdl SKee
– 'Beth' (D) ♀H6	Widely available
– 'Beurré Alexandre Lucas' (D)	NRog SBdl SKee
– 'Beurré Bedford' (D)	SBdl SKee
– 'Beurré Brown' (F) **new**	SBdl
– 'Beurré Clairgeau' (C)	SBdl SKee
– 'Beurré d'Amanlis' (D)	SBdl SKee
– 'Beurré d'Anjou' (F)	SBdl
– 'Beurré d'Arenberg' (D) **new**	SBdl
– 'Beurré d'Avalon' (D)	SBdl SKee
– 'Beurré de Beugny' (D)	SBdl SKee
– 'Beurré de Jonghe' (D)	SBdl
– 'Beurré de l'Assomption' (D)	SBdl
– 'Beurré de Naghin' (C/D)	SBdl
– 'Beurré Diel' (D)	SBdl
– 'Beurré Dubuisson' (D)	SBdl
– 'Beurré Dumont' (D)	CAgr SBdl
– 'Beurré Fouqueray' (D) **new**	SBdl
– 'Beurré Giffard' (D)	CAgr SBdl
– 'Beurré Hardy' (D) ♀H6	CAgr CArg CCVT CMac CSBt CTri ELan EPfP EPom IArd IPap LMaj MCoo MTrO NOra NRog NWea SBdl SEND SEdi SGsty SKee SPer SSFT SSFr WMat WWct
– 'Beurré Henri Courcelle' (D) **new**	SBdl
– 'Beurré Jean van Geert' (D)	SBdl
– 'Beurré Mortillet' (D)	SBdl
§ – 'Beurré Précoce Morettini' (D)	SBdl WWct
– 'Beurré Rance' (C/D)	SBdl SKee
– 'Beurré Six' (D)	SBdl
– 'Beurré Sterckmans' (D)	SBdl
– 'Beurré Superfin' (D) ♀H6	MTrO SBdl SKee SSFr
– 'Bianchettone' (D)	SBdl
– 'Bishop's Thumb' (D)	SBdl SKee
– 'Black Worcester' (C)	CHab MTrO NOra NRog SBdl SKee WJas WMat WWct
– 'Blakeney Red' (Perry)	CHab MTrO NOra NRog SBdl SKee WMat
– 'Blickling' (D)	SBdl SKee

– 'Bon Chrétien d'Hiver' (D)	SBdl
– 'Brandy' (Perry)	CAgr CArg CHab MTrO NOra NRog SBdl SKee SVic WMat
– 'Bristol Cross' (D)	CAgr CHab NRog NWea SBdl
– 'Brown Bess' (Perry)	NRog
– 'Butt' (Perry)	CHab NRog SBdl
– 'Calebasse Bosc' (D)	NOra SBdl SKee
– 'Canal Red' (D)	SBdl
– 'Cannock' (F)	CArg WMat
– 'Cascade' (D) **new**	SBdl
– 'Catillac' (C)	CAgr CHab LMaj MTrO NOra NRog SBdl SKee WMat
– 'Chalk'	see *P. communis* 'Crawford'
– 'Charles Ernest' (D)	SBdl
– 'Charneaux' (F)	LMaj
– 'Chaumontel' (D)	SBdl SKee
– 'Citron des Carmes' (C)	SBdl SKee
– 'Citron des Carmes Panaché' (D) **new**	SBdl
– 'Clapp's Favourite' (D)	CHab NOra NRog SBdl SEdi SKee SVic WMat
– 'Colette' (D) **new**	SBdl
– 'Colmar d'Eté' (D)	SBdl
– 'Comte de Lamy' (D)	SBdl
– 'Comte de Paris' (F) **new**	SBdl
– 'Concorde' (D) ♀H6	Widely available
– 'Conference' (D) ♀H6	Widely available
– 'Constance Mary' PBR (F) **new**	SBdl
– 'Coscia' (C/D)	SBdl
– 'Craig's Favourite' (D)	SBdl
– 'Crassane' (D)	SBdl
§ – 'Crawford' (D)	SBdl
– 'Dana's Hovey' (F)	SBdl
– 'Docteur Jules Guyot' (D)	CAgr NRog SBdl
– 'Double de Guerre' (C/D)	SBdl
– 'Doyenné Blanc' (F)	SBdl
– 'Doyenné Boussoch' (D)	SBdl SKee
– 'Doyenné d'Alençon' (D) **new**	SBdl
– 'Doyenné d'Été' (D)	MCoo SBdl SKee
– 'Doyenné du Comice' (D) ♀H6	Widely available
– 'Doyenné Georges Boucher' (D)	SBdl
– 'Duchesse d'Angoulême' (D)	SBdl
– 'Duchesse de Bordeaux' (D)	SBdl
– 'Durondeau' (D)	NOra NRog SBdl SKee WMat WWct
– 'Easter Beurré' (D)	SBdl
– 'Emile d'Heyst' (D)	SBdl SKee WMat
– 'Enfant Nantais' (D) **new**	SBdl
– 'English Caillot Rosat' (D)	SBdl
– 'Eva Baltet' (D)	SBdl
– 'Fair Maid' (D)	SBdl
– 'Fertility' (D)	SBdl
– 'Fertility Improved'	see *P. communis* 'Improved Fertility'
– 'Flemish Beauty' (F) **new**	NOra
– 'Fondante d'Automne' (D)	CAgr MTrO NOra SBdl SKee WMat
– 'Fondante de Bailly Maître' (D) **new**	SBdl
– 'Forelle' (D)	SBdl SKee
– 'Gansel's Bergamot' (D)	SBdl SKee
– 'Garden Gem' (F)	SGsty WMat
– 'General Leclerc' (D) **new**	SBdl
– 'General Tottleben' (C/D) **new**	SBdl
– 'Gieser Wildeman' (F)	NRog SBdl
– 'Gin' (Perry)	CHab MTrO NRog SBdl WMat

– 'Glou Morceau' (D)	CAgr CArg MTrO NOra NRog SBdl SKee SSFT SSFr WMat WWct
– 'Gorham' (D) ♀H6	CAgr MTrO NOra SBdl SKee SSFT SSFr WMat
– 'Green Horse' (Perry)	CHab MTrO NRog SBdl WMat
– 'Green Pear of Yair' (D)	SBdl SKee
– 'Gregoire Bordillon' (D)	SBdl
– 'Gros Blanquet' (D) **new**	SBdl
– 'Hacon's Incomparable' (D)	SBdl SKee
– 'Harvest Queen' (D/C)	CAgr SBdl
– 'Harvester' (C)	SBdl
– 'Hellen's Early' (Perry)	CArg CHab NRog SBdl SKee WMat
– 'Hendre Huffcap' (Perry)	CAgr CHab EPom MTrO NOra NRog SBdl SKee WMat
– 'Hessle' (D)	CAgr CHab NRog NWea SBdl SEdi SKee
– 'Highland' (D)	SBdl
– HUMBUG ('Pysanka') (D)	CArg EPom MTrO NOra SKee SSFT WMat
– 'Huyshe's Victoria' (C/D) **new**	SBdl
§ – 'Improved Fertility' (D)	CAgr SBdl SKee
– INVINCIBLE ('Delwinor') (D/C)	CAgr CArg CDoC EPom LBuc MNHC MTrO NOra NRog SLim SSFT SSFr WMat
– 'Jargonelle' (D)	CAgr CHab MTrO NRog SBdl SKee WMat
– 'Jeanne d'Arc' (D)	SBdl
– 'Joséphine de Malines' (D) ♀H6	CAgr IArd MTrO NOra SBdl SKee
– 'Judge Amphlett' (Perry)	EPom MTrO NOra NRog SBdl WMat
– 'Jules d'Airolles' (D) **new**	SBdl
– 'Kieffer' (C)	SBdl
– 'Lady Naomi' (F) **new**	LPar
– 'Laird Lang' (D)	SBdl
– 'Laxton's Early Market' (C/D)	SBdl
– 'Laxton's Foremost' (D)	CAgr SBdl
– 'Laxton's Satisfaction' (D)	SBdl
– 'Le Brun' (D) **new**	SBdl
– 'Le Lectier' (D)	SBdl SKee
– 'Légipont' (D)	CAgr NRog SBdl
– 'Louise Bonne of Jersey' (D)	CAgr CArg CBod CLnd CMac CTri EPfP EPom IArd MGos MTrO NOra NRog SBdl SEdi SKee SSFr WMat WWct
– 'Luisa' (D) **new**	LRHS
– 'Madame Treyve' (D)	SBdl
– 'Madernassa' (D) **new**	SBdl
– 'Maggie' (D)	SBdl
– 'Magnate' (D) **new**	SBdl
– 'Magness' (D) **new**	SBdl
– 'Magyar Kobak' (C)	SBdl SKee
– 'Maréchal de Cour' (D)	SBdl
– 'Marguérite Marillat' (D)	SBdl
– 'Marie Benoist' (D) **new**	SBdl
– 'Marie-Louise' (D)	SBdl SKee
– 'Marquise' (D)	SBdl
– 'Martin Sec' (C/D)	SBdl SKee
– 'Max Red Bartlett'	SBdl
– 'Merrylegs' (Perry)	CHab
– 'Merton Pride' (D)	CAgr CArg CLnd EPom NOra SBdl SKee SSFr WMat WWct
– 'Merton Star' (D)	SBdl SKee
– 'Messire Jean' (D) **new**	SBdl
– 'Michaelmas Nelis' (D) **new**	SBdl
– 'Monarch' (D)	SBdl
– 'Monsieur le Curé'	see *P. communis* 'Vicar of Winkfield'
– 'Moonglow' (F)	CAgr NOra SBdl SKee WMat

– 'Moorcroft' (Perry)	NRog SBdl SKee
– 'Morettini'	see *P. communis* 'Beurré Précoce Morettini'
– 'Mrs Seden' (D)	SBdl
– 'Nec Plus Meuris' (F)	SBdl
– 'Nouveau Poiteau' (C/D)	CAgr SBdl SKee
– 'Nouvelle Fulvie' (D)	SBdl
– 'Nuvar Anniversary' (D)	SKee
– 'Nuvar Celebration' (F)	MTrO SKee WMat
– 'Nye Russet Bartlett' (F)	CAgr SBdl
– 'Obelisk' (D)	EPom LCro LOPS LRHS MTrO NOra SPoG
– 'Old Home' (Perry)	SBdl WMat
– 'Oldfield' (Perry)	CHab NRog SBdl
– 'Olivier de Serres' (D)	SBdl
– 'Onward' (D)	CAgr CArg CBod CHab CTri EBee EPom IArd MTrO NOra NRog NWea SBdl SKee SSFT SSFr WMat WWct
– 'Ovid' (D)	CAgr SBdl
§ – 'Packham's Triumph' (D)	CAgr CTri EPom MTrO NOra NRog SBdl SEdi SKee SSFr WMat
– 'Parsonage' (Perry)	CHab SBdl
– 'Passe Colmar' (D)	SBdl
– 'Passe Crassane' (D)	SBdl SKee
– 'Pear Apple' (D)	CHab
– 'Penrhyn' (D)	WGwG WMat
– 'Pero Nobile' (D)	SBdl
– 'Petit Muscat'	SBdl
I – 'Petite Poire' (D)	EPom
– 'Pierre Corneille' (D) **new**	SBdl WWct
– 'Pitmaston Duchess' (C/D)	NRog NWea SBdl SKee WMat WWct
– 'Précoce de Trévoux' (D)	SBdl SKee
– 'Président Barabé' (D)	SBdl
– 'Président Héron' (D) **new**	SBdl
– 'Red Comice' (D/C)	SBdl SKee
– 'Red Pear' (Perry)	CHab NRog WMat
– 'Red Sensation Bartlett' (D/C)	CArg EPom LBuc LRHS MTrO NOra NRog NWea SKee SSFT SSFr WMat
– 'Redbald' (D)	SBdl SKee
– 'Reimer Red' (C)	SBdl
– 'Robin' (C/D)	SBdl SEdi SKee WMat
– 'Rogue Red' (D) **new**	SBdl
– 'Roosevelt' (D)	SBdl
– 'Saels' PBR (F) **new**	SBdl
– 'Saint-Rémy' (D) **new**	NRog
– 'Santa Claus' (D)	SBdl SKee
– 'Seckel' (D)	NOra SBdl SKee
– 'Shipova'	see × *Sorbopyrus auricularis* 'Shipova'
– 'Sierra' (D)	CAgr SBdl
– 'Sirrine' (C)	SBdl
– 'Snowdon Queen' (D)	CHab WGwG
– 'Souvenir du Congrès' (D)	SBdl
– 'Starkrimson' (D)	SBdl
– 'Sucrée de Montluçon' (D)	SBdl
– 'Summer Bergamot' (F)	SBdl
– 'Swan's Egg' (D)	SBdl SKee
– 'Taynton Squash' (Perry)	NOra SBdl WMat
– 'Terrace Pearl' (D)	WMat
– 'Tettenhall Dick' (C/D)	NRog SBdl
– 'Thompson's' (D)	SBdl
– 'Thorn' (Perry)	CAgr CHab EPom MTrO SBdl SKee WMat
– 'Triomphe de Jodoigne' (D) **new**	SBdl
– 'Triomphe de Vienne' (D)	NRog SBdl
– 'Triumph'	see *P. communis* 'Packham's Triumph'
– 'Turners Barn' (Perry) **new**	NRog

- 'Uvedale's St Germain' (C) SBdl SKee
- 'Van Mons Léon Leclerc' (D) new SBdl
- 'Verbelu' (C) SBdl SKee
- 'Verdi' (F) EPom
§ - 'Vicar of Winkfield' (C) SBdl SKee
- 'Virgouleuse' (D) SBdl
- 'Williams' Bon Chrétien' (D/C) Widely available
- 'Williams' Red' (D/C) NRog SBdl SEdi SGsty SKee
- 'Williams' Rouge Delbard' (F) EPom
- 'Windsor' (D) SBdl SKee
- 'Winnal's Longdon' (Perry) EPom MTrO NRog WMat
- 'Winter Christie' (F) MTrO
- 'Winter Nelis' (D) CAgr CArg CHab CTri MTrO NLar NOra NRog SBdl SKee WMat WWct
- 'Winter Orange' (D) SBdl
- 'Woodhall' (F) WMat
- 'Zéphirin Grégoire' (D) SBdl

cordata NWea
elaeagrifolia LMaj MAsh
- var. ***kotschyana*** NOrn SLim WHwl
- 'Silver Sails' CBod CLnd CMac EBee EMil LRHS MTrO NOra NOrn SCoo WMat WPGP

× ***michauxii*** SVen
nivalis CLnd EBee EPfP LEdu LMaj NWea SPer WHwl
- 'Catalia' CLnd MAsh WMat

pashia EBee LEdu LRHS NLar WMat
pyraster CHab SBdl
pyrifolia '20th Century' see *P. pyrifolia* 'Nijisseiki'
- 'Chojuro' (F) CAgr NRog
- 'Hayatama' (D) new NRog
- 'Hosui' (F) CAgr NRog SVic
- 'Kosui' (F) NRog SVic
- 'Kumoi' (F) CAgr EPom LRHS MAsh MGos MTrO NOra NRog SKee SSFr WMat
- 'Niitaka' (D) new NRog
§ - 'Nijisseiki' (F) CBod NRog SKee SVic
- 'Olympic' (D) new NRog
- 'Shinko' (F) CAgr NRog SVic
- 'Shinseiki' (F) CAgr CTri MGos MTrO NOra NRog SKee SVic WMat
- 'Shinsui' (F) NRog SKee
- 'Tama' (D) new NRog

salicifolia 'Pendula' ♀H6 Widely available

Pyrus × *Sorbus* see × *Sorbopyrus*

Q

Qiongzhuea see *Chimonobambusa*

Quercus ✿ (*Fagaceae*)

acerifolia CMCN EPfP
§ ***acuta*** CMCN
acutissima CAco CBcs CLnd CMCN EPfP IPap LMaj NLar
- subsp. ***kingii*** NJM 13.077 WPGP

aegilops see *Q. ithaburensis* subsp. *macrolepis*
affinis ♀H5 CMCN EPfP
agrifolia CMCN EBtc LMaj
ajudaghiensis see *Q. hartwissiana*
alba CMCN EBtc IPap WPGP
× ***alentejana*** CMCN
aliena CMCN
alnifolia CBrP CMCN SBrt
austrina CMCN
× ***beadlei*** see *Q.* × *saulii*
'Bear Creek Ranch' MBlu
benthamii CMCN
berberidifolia CMCN
bicolor CLnd CMCN EPfP IArd IDee IPap LMaj MBlu
§ × ***bimundorum*** 'Crimschmidt' CLnd EPfP EWTr MBlu SGol
borealis see *Q. rubra*
brantii CMCN
breweri see *Q. garryana* var. *breweri*
buckleyi CBcs CMCN EPfP IPap
- 'Dazzling Red' EPfP MBlu

× ***bushii*** CMCN EPfP MBlu
- 'Seattle Trident' EPfP MBlu SAko WPGP

calophylla CMCN
canariensis ♀H5 CLnd CMCN EPfP IPap SPtp WPGP
canbyi CMCN
castaneifolia CMCN EBtc
- 'Green Spire' ♀H6 CLnd CMCN EBee EPfP MBlu MMuc SEND

cerris CArg CBcs CCVT CMCN EPfP IPap LMaj LPar MGos NRog NWea SCob SEND SPer
- 'Afyon Lace' MBlu
§ - 'Argenteovariegata' (v) CEnd CMCN ELan EPfP MBlu NWea
- 'Athena' MBlu
- 'Bolte's Obelisk' MBlu
- 'Variegata' see *Q. cerris* 'Argenteovariegata'
- 'Wodan' MBlu

chenii CMCN
chrysolepis CMCN
coccifera CMCN EPfP SVen WPGP XSen
- NJM 12.006 WPGP
- subsp. ***calliprinos*** CMCN

coccinea CAco CBcs CLnd CMCN EBee EPfP IArd IPap LMaj LPar MBlu MMuc MWht NRog SCob SEWo WTSh
- 'Splendens' ♀H6 CEnd CMCN EBee ELan EPfP MBlu SGol SPer SPoG

crassifolia CMCN WPGP
§ × ***crenata*** 'Ambrozyana' NLar
- 'Diversifolia' CMCN MBlu
- 'Fulhamensis' CMCN MBlu MMuc SEND SGol
§ - 'Lucombeana' ♀H6 CMCN CSBt EPfP MBlu MMuc
- 'Waasland Select' LPar MMuc NLar NOrn SEND SGol WMou
- 'Wageningen' CMCN IPap MMuc SEND

CRIMSON SPIRE see *Q.* × *bimundorum* 'Crimschmidt'
dentata CMCN EWTr IArd
- 'Carl Ferris Miller' CBcs CMCN EPfP MBlu MMuc WLov WPGP
- 'Pinnatifida' CMCN EPfP MBlu MPkF NLar WCot WLov
- 'Sir Harold Hillier' CMCN MBlu
- subsp. ***yunnanensis*** CMCN MBlu

douglasii CMCN EBtc
durata CMCN
× ***egglestonii*** CMCN
ellipsoidalis CMCN MMuc NLar SGol
- 'Hemelrijk' ♀H6 CMCN EPfP EWTr MBlu

engleriana CMCN
fabrei CMCN
faginea WPGP
falcata CMCN EBtc WPGP
- var. ***pagodifolia*** see *Q. pagoda*

× ***fernaldii*** CMCN EPfP MBlu
'Fire Water' MBlu

frainetto	CLnd CMCN EPfP IPap LMaj LPar NWea SGol SPer WMou
- 'Hungarian Crown' ♀H6	CMCN EPfP MBlu MMuc
- 'Tortworth'	SEdd
- 'Trump'	CMCN MMuc SEND
franchetii	WPGP
gambelii	CMCN EBtc
garryana	CMCN EPfP
§ - var. ***breweri***	CMCN
- var. ***fruticosa***	see *Q. garryana* var. *breweri*
georgiana	CMCN
germana	WPGP
gilva	CMCN
glabrescens	CMCN WPGP
glandulifera	see *Q. serrata* Thunb.
glauca	CMCN IPap MMuc NLar
- from Korea	WPGP
gravesii	CMCN EPfP
greggii	WPGP
grisea	CMCN
§ ***hartwissiana***	CMCN EPfP
× ***hastingsii***	CMCN
hemisphaerica	CMCN EPfP
× ***heterophylla***	CLnd CMCN
× ***hickelii***	CMCN EPfP
× ***hispanica*** misapplied	see *Q.* × *crenata*
× ***humidicola***	CMCN
hypoleucoides	CMCN EPfP
ilex	Widely available
ilicifolia	CMCN EPfP
imbricaria	CAco CBcs CLnd CMCN EPfP IArd WPGP
incana Roxb.	see *Q. leucotrichophora*
§ ***incana*** Bartram	CMCN
insignis	CBcs
§ ***ithaburensis*** subsp. ***macrolepis***	CMCN LEdu
- - 'Hemelrijk Silver'	EPfP MBlu WCot WPGP
kelloggii	CMCN EPfP
× ***kewensis*** ♀H6	CMCN SEND WMou
laevigata	see *Q. acuta*
laevis	CMCN EPfP
§ ***laurifolia***	CMCN EPfP
laurina	CMCN WPGP
- NJM 05.013A	WPGP
× ***leana***	CMCN
§ ***leucotrichophora***	LEdu
liaotungensis	see *Q. wutaishanica*
× ***libanerris***	IPap
- 'Rotterdam'	CMCN
libani	CMCN EPfP
lobata	CMCN
× ***lucombeana***	see *Q.* × *crenata* 'Lucombeana'
- 'William Lucombe'	see *Q.* × *crenata* 'Lucombeana'
× ***ludoviciana***	EPfP
lyrata	CMCN
- 'Arnold'	MBlu
macranthera	CMCN EPfP WMou
- PAB 13.002	LEdu
macrocarpa	CMCN EPfP IPap WPGP
macrolepis	see *Q. ithaburensis* subsp. *macrolepis*
marilandica	CMCN EPfP MBlu
'Mauri'	LMaj MBlu
'Maya' ♀H5	CBcs EPfP LPar NLar SGol SLim WHwl WMat WMou WPGP
× ***megaleia***	CMCN
mexicana	CMCN
§ ***michauxii***	CMCN EPfP MBlu
mongolica	EPfP MBlu
- subsp. ***crispula***	CMCN
'Monument'	WCot
muehlenbergii	CMCN MBlu WPGP
- 'Dallas'	EPfP
myrsinifolia	CBcs CMCN ELan IArd IPap LMaj MMuc NLar SArc
myrtifolia	WPGP
nigra	CAco CMCN EBtc EPfP IPap WMou
- 'Beethoven'	MBlu
- 'Thierry'	MBlu
nuttallii	see *Q. texana*
obtusa	see *Q. laurifolia*
oglethorpensis	CMCN
§ ***pagoda***	CMCN IPap WPGP
palustris ♀H6	CArg CCVT CDoC CLnd CMCN ELan EPfP IArd IPap LMaj LPar MBlu MMuc NLar NOrn NRog NWea SCob SEWo SGol SPer WMou WTSh
- 'Flaming Suzy'	MBlu
- 'Green Dwarf'	CMCN LCro LMaj LOPS MBlu NLar
- GREEN PILLAR ('Pringreen')	CDoC EBee EPfP IArd LMaj MBlu MTrO NLar NOra NOrn SEdd SGol SGsty WMat
- 'Isabel'	CDoC EPfP MPkF NLar WMat
- 'Pendula'	CEnd CMCN
- 'Swamp Pygmy'	CMCN EPfP MBlu
- 'Windischleuba'	MBlu
pedunculata	see *Q. robur*
pedunculiflora	see *Q. robur* subsp. *pedunculiflora*
§ ***petraea***	CArg CDoC CHab CLnd CTri EPfP GAbr IPap LMaj MBlu MMuc NRog NWea SCob SPer WFar WMou WTSh
- 'Laciniata'	see *Q. petraea* 'Laciniata Crispa'
§ - 'Laciniata Crispa'	CEnd CMCN EPfP MBlu
- subsp. ***polycarpa*** NJM 13.025	WPGP
§ - 'Purpurea'	CMCN EPfP MBlu
- 'Rubicunda'	see *Q. petraea* 'Purpurea'
§ ***phellos***	CAco CLnd CMCN EPfP IArd IPap LMaj MBlu NLar
- HIGHTOWER ('Qpsta')	SGol
- var. ***latifolia***	see *Q. incana* Bartram
phillyreoides	CBcs CLnd CMCN EPfP IPap MMuc
polymorpha	CMCN WPGP
Pondaim Group	CMCN NOra NWea
- 'Pondaim Giant'	MBlu
pontica	CMCN EPfP EWTr LMaj MBlu SEND
prinoides	CMCN
prinus misapplied	see *Q. michauxii*
§ ***prinus*** L.	CMCN
pubescens	CMCN IPap LMaj MMuc SEND
§ - subsp. ***crispata*** NJM 12.016	WPGP
- - NJM 12.017	WPGP
pumila Michx.	see *Q. prinus* L.
pungens	CMCN
pyrenaica	CMCN MMuc SEND
- 'Pendula' ♀H6	CMCN EPfP
rhysophylla	see *Q. rysophylla*
§ ***robur***	Widely available
- 'Argenteomarginata' (v)	CMCN MBlu
- 'Atropurpurea'	EBtc NWea
- 'Blue Gnome'	MBlu
- 'Compacta'	MBlu
- 'Concordia'	CEnd CMCN ELan EPfP MBlu
- Cristata Group	CMCN
- 'Dissecta'	CMCN
- Fastigiata Group	CLnd EBee IArd LPar MGos NWea SGol SLim SPer

	- - 'Koster' ♀H6	CMCN CMac EPfP IPap LMaj MBlu MRav NRog NWea SCob SGsty WMat
§	- - 'Salfast'	MBlu
	- 'Filicifolia' misapplied	see *Q. robur* 'Pectinata'
	- 'Filicifolia' Hort. ex Loud.	CEnd
	- var. ***haas***	CAco
	- 'Irtha'	EPfP MBlu
	- 'Menhir'	MBlu WLov
§	- 'Pectinata'	EPfP MBlu
§	- subsp. ***pedunculiflora***	CMCN
	- 'Pendula'	CEnd CMCN MBlu
	- 'Purpurascens'	CEnd CMCN
	- 'Purpurea'	MBlu
	- 'Raba'	CMCN
	- 'Salicifolia Fastigiata'	see *Q. robur* 'Salfast'
	- 'Strypemonde'	CMCN
	- 'Timuki'	LPar MBlu
	- 'Tromp Dwarf'	MBlu
	- (Variegata Group) 'Fürst Schwarzenburg' (v)	MBlu
	rotundifolia	CAgr CMCN EPfP WPGP
§	***rubra***	Widely available
	- 'Aurea'	CEnd CMCN EPfP MBlu
	- 'Bolte's Gold'	MBlu NOra WHwl WMat
	- 'Haaren' **new**	NLar
	- 'Magic Fire' ♀H6	CMCN EPfP MBlu
	- 'Red Queen'	EPfP MBlu
*	- 'Sunshine'	CMCN MBlu WCot
	× ***runcinata***	CMCN
§	***rysophylla***	CMCN EPfP IArd MBlu WPGP
	sadleriana	CMCN WPGP
	salicina	WPGP
	× ***sargentii*** 'Thomas'	EPfP MBlu
	sartorii	CMCN
§	× ***saulii***	CMCN
	× ***schochiana***	EPfP MBlu
	schottkyana	WPGP
	seemanii	CMCN
	semecarpifolia	CBcs CMCN MBlu WPGP
§	***serrata*** Thunb.	CAco CMCN EPfP
	- 'Herkenrode'	MBlu
	sessiliflora	see *Q. petraea*
	shumardii	CMCN EPfP EWTr IPap LMaj MBlu NLar
	- 'Del Rio'	MBlu
	stellata	CMCN EPfP
	suber	CAgr CBcs CMCN CTsd EBee ELan EPfP IArd IPap LEdu LMaj LPar MBlu MGos SArc SCob SEND SPer SWeb WCot WHwl WMou WPGP
	- 'Sopron'	CAco EPfP MBlu
	× ***substellata***	CMCN
§	***texana***	CMCN EPfP IPap NOra
	- 'New Madrid'	EPfP ESwi MBlu WMat WMou WPGP
	trojana	CMCN WPGP
	turbinella	CMCN
	× ***turneri***	CLnd CMCN EPfP WSpi
	- 'Pseudoturneri' ♀H5	EBee ELan LPar MBlu MMuc SEND SGol WMou
	vacciniifolia	CMCN
	variabilis	CMCN EPfP
	velutina	CBcs CMCN EPfP NLar NWea
	- 'Albertsii'	MBlu
	- 'Golden Dragon' **new**	MBlu
	- 'Oakridge Walker'	MBlu
	- 'Rubrifolia'	CMCN EPfP
	'Vilmoriana'	CMCN
	virginiana	CBcs CMCN
	× ***warburgii***	EBee EPfP
	× ***warei***	CMCN
	- 'Chimney Fire'	EPfP MBlu
	- KINDRED SPIRIT	see *Q.* × *warei* 'Nadler'
§	- 'Long'	EBee ELan EPfP EWTr MBlu MTrO NOra WMat
§	- 'Nadler'	SEdd SGol
	- REGAL PRINCE	see *Q.* × *warei* 'Long'
	- 'Windcandle'	CDoC LMaj MBlu
	wislizeni	CMCN NLar
§	***wutaishanica***	CMCN

Quillaja (*Quillajaceae*)

	saponaria	CCCN CWit EBee GBin SPlb

quince see *Cydonia oblonga*

Quisqualis see *Combretum*

R

Racosperma see *Acacia*

Radermachera (*Bignoniaceae*)

	sinica ♀H1b	EShb

radish see AGM Vegetables Section

Raffenaldia (*Brassicaceae*)

	primuloides **new**	GKev

Ramonda (*Gesneriaceae*)

§	***myconi*** ♀H5	EMor EWes GEdr NSla SRms
	- var. ***alba***	WThu
	nathaliae ♀H5	WAbe WThu
	- 'Alba'	NSla
	pyrenaica	see *R. myconi*
	serbica	WThu

Ranunculus (*Ranunculaceae*)

	aconitifolius	CMiW CTtf EBee ECha GJos GMaP NLar SHar WFar WHal WSHC
	- Cally form	MNrw
	- 'Flore Pleno' (d) ♀H7	Widely available
	acris	CHab NBir NMir NPer SPhx SRms SVic WSFF
	- subsp. ***acris***	SBut
	- - 'Stevenii'	LPla SDix WHal
	- 'Citrinus'	CElw CMiW CTtf ECha EMor GQue LLWG LSun SRot WChS WCot WHal WHrl WMal
	- 'Flore Pleno' (d) ♀H7	CDor CWCL EBee ECha ELan EPfP GMaP LEdu LLWG MACG MCot MRav NBid NBro NDov NGdn NRya NSti SPoG SRms WCAu WFar WSHC XLum
	- 'Hedgehog'	MMrt MNrw
	- 'Sulphureus'	EBee WCAu WHal
	alpestris	GEdr NSla SBrt WFar
	- 'Flore Pleno' (d)	GEdr
	amplexicaulis	EBee GEdr GJos GKev GMaP NSla WCot
	aquatilis	CPud CWat EWat LLWG MWts WMAq WSFF
	asiaticus	ERCP
	- 'Aviv Orange'	SDeJ
	- 'Aviv Red'	LCro LOPS
	- 'Aviv Rose'	LCro LOPS
	- 'Aviv White'	LCro LOPS

- 'Bloomingdale Pink Shades' (Bloomingdale Series)	SDeJ
bilobus	GArf
bulbosus	SPhx SVic
§ - 'F.M. Burton'	CElw NRya WCot
- ***farreri***	see *R. bulbosus* 'F.M. Burton'
- 'Speciosus Plenus'	see *R. constantinopolitanus* 'Plenus'
bullatus	GJos
calandrinioides 🏆^{H5}	GKev NBir SBrt SGro WAbe
circinatus	LLWG
§ ***constantinopolitanus*** 'Plenus' (d)	CMiW EBee GAbr GMaP MNrw MRav NBid NBro NLar WCot WMal WSHC
cortusifolius	CPla ECre SBrt
crenatus	GEdr
crithmifolius	GKev
ficaria	see *Ficaria verna* subsp. *verna*
× ***flahaultii***	GArf
flammula	CBen CHab CPud CWat LLWG MWts
- subsp. ***minimus***	EWat
gouanii	NRya
'Gowrie'	GEdr
gramineus 🏆^{H7}	EBee EHyd GEdr GMaP LRHS NFav NRHS NRya SRms
- 'Pardal'	SMHy WCot WSHC
hederaceus	CPud
illyricus	WHal
lanuginosus	EPPr NGrd
lingua	CPud SPlb WSFF
- 'Grandiflorus'	LLWG NPer WHal WMAq
lyallii	GKev
millefoliatus	WAbe
montanus double-flowered (d)	SHar WCot WSHC
- 'Miss Austria' (d)	NHpl
- 'Molten Gold' 🏆^{H5}	GEdr GMaP MMrt MRav WFar
nivicola	WCot
parnassiifolius	GAbr GEdr GKev MNrw WAbe WCot
platanifolius	EHyd LRHS NRHS SBrt
× ***prietoi*** 'Moonlight'	LEdu MMrt WCot
'Purple Heart' (d)	EPfP LCro LOPS SDeJ
repens 'Buttered Popcorn' (v)	EBee
- var. ***pleniflorus*** (d)	EWoo LLWG MSCN NGrd
- 'Timothy Clark' (d)	WMal
seguieri	EHyd GEdr NRHS WAbe
speciosus 'Flore Pleno'	see *R. constantinopolitanus* 'Plenus'
traunfellneri	WAbe
uniflorus	GKev

Ranzania (*Berberidaceae*)

japonica	GEdr GKev WCru WFar

Raoulia (*Asteraceae*)

australis misapplied	see *R. hookeri*
australis ambig.	EPot GAbr GKev GMaP GQue NHpl WCot WTor
australis Hook.f. ex Raoul	ITim MAsh
§ - Lutescens Group	ECha SPlb WIce
§ ***hookeri***	CMea ECha EPot EWes MAsh SPlb SRms SRot WAbe XSte
× ***loganii***	see × *Leucoraoulia loganii*
lutescens	see *R. australis* Lutescens Group
petriensis	EPot SPlb WAbe
× ***petrimia*** 'Margaret Pringle'	WAbe
subsericea	ECha
tenuicaulis	ECha GArf SPlb

raspberry see *Rubus idaeus*; see also AGM Fruit Section

Ratibida (*Asteraceae*)

columnifera	CBod CRos EHyd EPfP LRHS LShi MACG NRHS SBut
- f. ***pulcherrima***	EHyd EPfP LRHS NRHS SBut XLum
- - 'Red Midget'	CSpe EHyd MACG NGBl
mexicana	EBee EHyd ELan LRHS NRHS SPhx
pinnata	CDor CSpe EPfP NBir NGBl SIvy SPhx SPlb WCot

Raukaua (*Araliaceae*)

laetevirens	WPGP

Ravenala (*Strelitziaceae*)

madagascariensis	SPlb

Ravenea (*Arecaceae*)

rivularis	CCCN

Rechsteineria see *Sinningia*

redcurrant see *Ribes rubrum* (R); see also AGM Fruit Section

Regelia (*Myrtaceae*)

velutina	SPlb

Rehderodendron (*Styracaceae*)

indochinense B&SWJ 12115	WCru
- NJM 09.116	WPGP
- WWJ 11869	WCru
kwangtungense WWJ 11940	WCru
kweichowense WWJ 12019	WCru
macrocarpum	CBcs CJun EBee LEdu WPGP
- B&SWJ 11841	WCru
- KWJ 12310	WCru
- WWJ 11952	WCru

Rehmannia (*Plantaginaceae*)

angulata misapplied	see *R. elata*
§ ***elata*** 🏆^{H3}	CBcs CBod CDor CPla CSpe CTsd EBee EHyd ELan EPfP EShb GGro LRHS LShi LSun MHol MNHC MPie SAdn SBls SDys SRms WGwG WHil WKif XLum
- white-flowered **new**	WHil
henryi	CSpe EBee XSte
piasezkii	LShi
'Polina'^{PBR}	XSte
WALBERTON'S MAGIC DRAGON ('Walremadra'^{PBR})	CRos EHyd EPfP LBuc LRHS LSRN NRHS SCoo SHar SPad SPoG SRms

Reineckea (*Asparagaceae*)

§ ***carnea***	CDor CExl EBee ECha ELan EPPr GEdr GKev LEdu MPie NSti SBls SDys SEND SPlb WCot WPGP XLum
- B&SWJ 4808	WCru
- 'Baoxing Booty'	WCru
- 'Crûg's Broadleaf'	WCru
- 'Crûg's Linearleaf'	LEdu
- 'Jinfo Jewel'	WCru

- RBGE form GGro
- 'Variegata' (v) WCot
aff. ***carnea*** from Sichuan WCot
incurva RKN 3605 **new** EBee
- 'Crug's Linearleaf' ESwi WCru
yunnanense see *R. carnea*

Reinwardtia (*Linaceae*)

§ ***indica*** CCCN CExl SAdn SEle

Remusatia (*Araceae*)

hookeriana B&SWJ 2529 WCru
vivipara SPlb

Reseda (*Resedaceae*)

alba SPhx
lutea SPhx SRms
luteola CBod CHab CHby GPoy MHer MNHC WSFF
odorata SVic
- 'Ameliorata' **new** SSal

Restio (*Restionaceae*)

festuciformis CPbh LRHS
multiflorus LRHS XSte
paniculatus CBod CCCN CDTJ CPbh CTrC LRHS XSte
similis CPbh XSte
subverticillatus CPbh LRHS XSte
tetraphyllus see *Baloskion tetraphyllum*
- 'Cornish Gold' see *Baloskion tetraphyllum* 'Cornish Gold'

Retama (*Fabaceae*)

sphaerocarpa SBrt

Reynoutria see *Fallopia*

Rhamnus (*Rhamnaceae*)

alaternus XSen
§ - 'Argenteovariegata' (v) 🏆^{H5} Widely available
- 'Variegata' see *R. alaternus* 'Argenteovariegata'
cathartica CCVT CHab CLnd CTri EPfP LBuc MCoo NLar NWea SCob SEWo WMou WSFF WTSh
frangula see *Frangula alnus*
grandifolia SPtp
imeretina WCot WPGP
ludovici-salvatoris SBrt
lycioides SBrt
- subsp. ***oleoides*** XSen
microcarpa GKev
taquetii NLar

× *Rhaphiobotrya* (*Rosaceae*)

§ 'Coppertone' CBcs CDoC ELan IPap LPar SArc SEND SGsty WPGP XSte

Rhaphiolepis (*Rosaceae*)

× ***delacourii*** EBee EPfP SEND
- 'Coates' Crimson' CDoC EBee ELan EPfP LRHS MAsh MGil WLov
- ENCHANTRESS ('Moness') CCCN ELan EPfP LRHS MAsh MRav SLon
- 'Pink Cloud' EPfP
indica SEND
- B&SWJ 8405 WCru
- 'Coppertone' see × *Rhaphiobotrya* 'Coppertone'
- SPRINGTIME ('Monme') CBcs EGrl EPfP LCro LOPS LPar WSMil
integerrima CMCN
minor B&SWJ 14669 WCru
umbellata CBcs CBod CTri CTsd EBee EGrl ELan EPfP GBin LEdu MAsh MGil MRav SEND SLon SVen SavN WLov WPGP
- f. ***ovata*** B&SWJ 4706 WCru

Rhaphithamnus (*Verbenaceae*)

cyanocarpus see *R. spinosus*
§ ***spinosus*** CBcs EBee EPfP LEdu MGil SMad SPoG WPGP WPav

Rhapidophyllum (*Arecaceae*)

hystrix CBrP CPHo SPalm WSMil

Rhapis ✿ (*Arecaceae*)

§ ***excelsa*** 🏆^{H1b} CCCN LCro LOPS SEND SPalm SPlb WSMil

Rhaponticum (*Compositae*)

carthamoides GGro
§ ***centaureoides*** CBod CCBP CDor ECha EWTr MAvo MSpe NBid NSti SPeP WCot WMal WSpi
coniferum GGro
§ ***exaltatum*** SPhx

Rhazya (*Apocynaceae*)

orientalis see *Amsonia orientalis*

Rheum ✿ (*Polygonaceae*)

CC GGro
Chen Yi WCot
GWJ 9329 from Sikkim WCru
§ 'Ace of Hearts' 🏆^{H6} Widely available
'Ace of Spades' see *R.* 'Ace of Hearts'
acuminatum HWJCM 252 WCru
- HWJK 2354 WCru
- PAB 2487 LEdu
alexandrae CBct EWes GBin GEdr GGro GKev MMrt NLar SBls SGBe SPlb WFar WHil
- SDR 2924 EBee
§ ***australe*** CRos EBee EHyd GEdr LRHS NLar NRHS WCot WFar
- CC 7492 **new** GKev
- 'Pink Marble' (v) WCot
aff. ***australe*** HPA 1385 **new** GGro
'Cally Giant' EWes GBin
cordatum **new** GGro
delavayi NLar
- BWJ 7592 WFar
emodi see *R. australe*
'Great Bere' LEdu WPGP
× ***hybridum*** from Isle of Ely Horticultural Institute NRog
- 'Amerikiane Kampfe' **new** NRog
- 'Apple Delight' LCro LOPS
- 'Brandy Carr Scarlet' CTri LEdu MRav
- 'Champagne' CAgr CDoC EPfP EPom LCro LEdu LOPS LRHS NLar NRHS SCoo SGbt SKee SPer SPoG SRms SVic WMat
* - 'Champagne Rood' NRHS
- 'Collis's Ruby' NRog
- 'Donkere Bloedrede Zoet' NRog
- 'Early Red Victoria' **new** NRog
- 'Early Victoria' SRms
- 'Exhibition Red' NRog
- 'Fenton's Special' CTri MRav
- 'Fulton's Strawberry Surprise' 🏆^{H5} CDoC

– 'Glaskin's Perpetual'	CAgr CRos CTsd EHyd LBuc LRHS NRHS SCoo SRms SVic
– 'Goliath'	EBee NRog
– 'Grandad's Favorite' ♀H5	CRos EBlo EHyd LRHS NRHS
– 'Hawke's Champagne' ♀H5	WCot
– 'Holsteiner Blut'	EBee NLar SPoG
– 'Livingstone'PBR	CDoC EPom LCro LOPS LRHS
– 'Merton's Broadleaf'	NRog
– 'Pink Champagne'	EBee EPfP
– 'Raspberry Red' ♀H5	CDoC CMac CRos EPfP EPom LCro LOPS NRHS SPoG
– 'Red Champagne'	ELan EMor EPfP LBuc WSpi
– 'Red Prolific'	NRog
– 'Royal Albert' new	NRog
– 'Seedling Piggot'	NRog
– 'Seedling Streeter' new	NRog
– 'Stein's Champagne'	NRob
– 'Stockbridge Arrow'	CArg CTri NRog
– 'Stockbridge Cropper'	NRog
– 'Stockbridge Harbinger'	NRog
– 'Strawberry'	LCro LOPS NBir NRog
– 'Thompson's Terrifically Tasty'	EPom
– 'Timperley Early' ♀H5	Widely available
– 'Timperley Early 1'	SRms
– 'Victoria'	Widely available
– 'Vinrabarber Svenborg'	NRog
– 'Vroege Engelse'	LEdu
kialense	EBee GGro LEdu NBid NSti
moorcroftianum	GEdr
nobile	GJos GKev
officinale	CBct
palmatum	CBcs CRos CWat EBee ECha ELan EPfP GKev LRHS MGos MRav NGdn NRHS SCob SHar SRms
– 'Atropurpureum'	see *R. palmatum* 'Atrosanguineum'
§ – 'Atrosanguineum'	CBct CDor CRos ECha EHyd ELan EPfP EShb EWoo LEdu LRHS MBel MGos MRav NBid NBro NRHS NWad SCob SPer SPlb SPoG WCru WFar WSMil WSpi
– 'Bowles's Crimson' ♀H7	MRav NBid WCot
– 'Ferguson's Red'	CBct WCot
– 'Hadspen Crimson' ♀H6	CBct CBod ECtt LSun MNrw NBid WCot
– 'Red Herald'	CBct WCot
– 'Rubrum'	CBct EHyd LRHS NBir NRHS
– 'Savill' ♀H7	CBct MRav
– var. ***tanguticum***	CAgr CBct CBod CDoC EBee ECha ELan ELon EPfP EWoo GMaP LSun MACG MRav NBid NLar NRHS NWad SBls SCob SPalm SPeP SPoG SRms SWvt WFar WPnP WWtn
rhaponticum	NLar
ribes	WCot WCru
tanguticum	SGBe
tataricum	LEdu

Rhinanthus (*Orobanchaceae*)

alectorolophus new	WSFF
minor	CHab LCro LOPS SVic WSFF

Rhodanthe (*Asteraceae*)

chlorocephala subsp. ***rosea*** 'Pierrot'	CSpe

Rhodanthemum (*Asteraceae*)

'African Eyes'	ELan EPfP MBrN MGos SCoo SVen WMal
'African Rose' new	MHol
'African Spring'	CDoC SIvy
§ ***atlanticum***	EWes
'Casablanca'PBR (Atlas Daisy Series)	CBod CDoC CRos EPfP LRHS NRHS SCoo SIvy SPoG
§ ***catananche***	CCCN EWes WMal
§ – 'Tizi-n-Test'	WAbe
– 'Tizi-n-Tichka'	CRos EHyd EPot EWes LRHS NRHS WAbe
§ ***gayanum***	CCCN
– 'Pretty in Pink'	CBcs MHol SPoG
§ ***hosmariense*** ♀H4	CCCN CRos EBou ECha EHyd ELan ELon EPfP GMaP LRHS MCot MHol NRHS SEND SGBe SPer SPhx SRms WCav WIce WMal
'Marrakech' (Atlas Daisy Series)	CDoC SCoo SPoG
§ MOONDANCE ('Usrhod0701')	LRHS
'Tangier' (Atlas Daisy Series)	LRHS

Rhodiola (*Crassulaceae*)

SSSE 10	NWad
chrysanthemifolia WJC 13669	WCru
crassipes	see *R. wallichiana*
cretinii	NRya
– HWJK 2283	WCru
§ ***fastigiata***	CSpe GGro WThu
– BWJ 7544	WCru
§ ***heterodonta***	MRav WCot
himalensis misapplied	see *R.* 'Keston'
himalensis (D. Don) Fu	CTri
– WJC 13723	WCru
§ ***integrifolia***	SPlb
§ 'Keston'	CTri
§ ***kirilowii***	EHyd
– var. ***rubra***	EBee EGrI EHyd EPfP LRHS NRHS
§ ***pachyclados***	CPla CRos ECtt EGrI EHyd EPPr EPot GBin GKev GMaP GWyn LRHS MHer MMuc NBir NHpl NRHS NRya NSla NWad SEND SLee SPlb SRot SSim SWvt WAbe WCot WFar XLum
rhodantha	NLar
§ ***rosea***	Widely available
§ ***saxifragoides***	EHyd LRHS NRHS SLee SPlb
semenovii	GKev NLar
sinuata HWJK 2318	WCru
– HWJK 2326	WCru
tibetica	GKev
trollii	see *R. saxifragoides*
§ ***wallichiana***	NBid
– GWJ 9263	WCru
– HWJK 2352	WCru
§ ***yunnanensis*** BWJ 7941	WCru

Rhodochiton (*Plantaginaceae*)

§ ***atrosanguineus*** ♀H2	CBcs CCCN CPla CRos CSpe EPfP GBee IDee LBuc LCro LOPS MBow MPri SPoG
volubilis	see *R. atrosanguineus*

Rhodocoma (*Restionaceae*)

arida	CCCN
capensis	CAbb CBod CCCN CPbh CTrC
foliosa	LRHS
gigantea	CCCN CPbh CTrC LRHS SPlb XSte

Rhododendron ✿ (*Ericaceae*)

aberconwayi	LMil MHid SLdr
– 'His Lordship'	GGGa LMil LRHS
'Abigale' (A)	SLdr
'Addy Wery' (EA)	SPer
adenogynum	GKev LMil

	adenosum	GGGa LMil
	'Admiral Piet Hein'	SSta
	'Adonis' (EA/d) ♀H5	CBcs CMac
	'Advance' (EA)	SLdr
	aeruginosum	see *R. campanulatum* subsp. *aeruginosum*
	aganniphum var. ***aganniphum***	MHid
	'Agayon' **new**	LRHS XSte
	'Airy Fairy'	LMil
	'Aksel Olsen'	CTri EGrI
	'Aladdin' (EA)	SLdr
	'Aladdin' (*auriculatum* hybrid)	SSta
	(Aladdin Group) 'Aladdin'	XSte
	(Albatross Group) 'Albatross'	SSta
	- 'Albatross Townhill Pink'	LMil
	'Albert Schweitzer' ♀H5	CDoC IDee LMil LPar LRHS LSRN NLar SCob SLdr SLim SPer XSte
	albrechtii (A)	GGGa GKev LMil
	- Whitney form (A)	LMil
	'Album Grandiflorum' (G)	LRHS XSte
	'Alexander' (EA) ♀H4	LMil LSRN
	'Alice' ♀H5	LMil SLdr
	Alison Johnstone Group	SLdr
	- 'Alison Johnstone'	CAco LMil WThu
	'All Gold'	GGGa
	'Al's Picotee' (EA/d)	MPkF XSte
	alutaceum var. ***iodes*** 'White Plains'	MHid
	amagianum (A)	LMil
	ambiguum	LMil MHid
	- 'Golden Summit'	GGGa
	- 'Jane Banks'	LMil
	'Ambrosia' (EA)	CSBt
	'Amity'	LMil
	Amor Group	SLdr
	'Anah Kruschke'	LCro MAsh SGsty SPoG
	'Analin'	see *R.* 'Anuschka'
	'Anchorite' (EA)	SLdr
	Angelo Group	GGGa LMil
	- 'Angelo'	CBcs LMil SLdr SSta
	'Ann Lindsay'	SLdr
	'Anna Baldsiefen'	SPoG
	'Anna Rose Whitney'	CBcs CTri EPfP LRHS LSRN MAsh MPri SLim WFar XSte
	'Annabella' (K)	SSta
	annae	IDee LMil LRHS
	'Anne Frank' (EA)	CDoC WFar
	'Anne Teese'	IDee LMil
	'Anneke' (A)	CDoC EGrI LMil LRHS MGos MMuc MPkF NHol NLar SCob SPer SSta XSte
	'Anouk' (EA)	CDoC CEnd
	anthopogon	LMil
	- 'Betty Graham'	GGGa
	- subsp. ***hypenanthum***	LRHS
	- - 'Annapurna'	GGGa IDee LMil WAbe WThu
	'Antilope' (Vs) ♀H6	LMil MMuc SLdr SSta
§	'Anuschka'	LMil MAsh
	anwheiense	GGGa LMil
	apodectum	see *R. dichroanthum* subsp. *apodectum*
	'Apotrophia'	SLdr
	'Apple Blossom' ambig.	CMac GKin
	'Appleblossom' (EA)	see *R.* 'Ho-o'
	'Apricot Blaze' (A)	SSta
	'Apricot Fantasy'	LMil LRHS SSta
	'Apricot Surprise'	CTri EGrI MAsh
	'April Showers' (A)	LMil

	'Aquamarin'	NLar
	'Arabesk' (EA)	CDoC GKin ILea MAsh MGos MPkF NLar SGsty SWeb XSte
	arborescens (A) ♀H6	GGGa LMil
	arboreum	GGGa GKev IKel LMil LRHS NLar SLdr
	- B&SWJ 2244	WCru
	- subsp. ***albotomentosum*** KW 21976 **new**	LMil
	- subsp. ***arboreum***	MHid
	- subsp. ***cinnamomeum*** ♀H4	GGGa LMil
	- - Sch 2049	LMil
	- - WJC 13821	WCru
	- - var. ***album***	GGGa GKev
	- - 'Everest Reunion'	LMil
	- - var. ***roseum***	GGGa
	- - - SDR 749	GKev
	- - - 'Tony Schilling'	GKin LMil SSta
	- subsp. ***delavayi***	GGGa LMil SLdr
§	- subsp. ***nilagiricum***	MHid
	- 'Rubaiyat'	GKin LMil
§	- subsp. ***zeylanicum***	GGGa
	'Arctic Fox' (EA)	LMil
	'Arctic Tern' ♀H5	CDoC CSBt CTri LCro LMil LOPS MGos NLar NWad WThu
	'Ardeur' (EA)	NLar
§	***argipeplum***	GGGa LMil MHid
	- 'Fleurie'	LMil
	(Argosy Group) 'Argosy'	LMil
	argyrophyllum subsp. ***argyrophyllum***	GGGa
	- subsp. ***nankingense***	GGGa
	- - 'Chinese Silver' ♀H5	LMil MHid
	arizelum	GGGa LMil MHid WPGP
	aff. ***arizelum*** KR 10420	WPGP
	'Arneson Gem' (A) ♀H6	CBcs CDoC GGGa GKin LMil LRHS MPkF NLar XSte
§	(Aronense Group) 'Fumiko' (EA)	CBcs CDoC CSBt LCro LMil NLar SCob SLdr WFar
§	- 'Hanako' (EA)	WFar
§	- 'Haruko' (EA) **new**	LMil
§	- 'Kazuko' (EA)	CDoC NLar SCoo
§	- 'Michiko' (EA)	SAko
§	- 'Momoko' (EA)	EGrI LRHS WFar
§	- 'Noriko' (EA)	SLdr
§	- 'Satschiko' (EA) ♀H5	CBcs CDoC GGGa LMil LRHS MPri NLar NRHS
	'Arpège' (Vs)	LMil NLar
§	'Arthur J. Ivens'	SLdr
	'Arthur Stevens'	SLdr
	asterochnoum	GGGa MHid
	atlanticum (A)	GGGa LMil WFar XSte
	- 'Seaboard' (A)	LMil
	'August Rose' (A) **new**	LRHS
	augustinii	CBcs GGGa LMil NLar SLdr SSta
	- subsp. ***augustinii***	MHid
	- 'Bowood Blue'	IDee LMil
	- 'Carolles'	XSte
§	- subsp. ***chasmanthum***	GGGa
	- Electra Group	LMil LRHS SLdr
§	- - 'Electra' ♀H4	GGGa XSte
	- Exbury form	GGGa LMil
§	- subsp. ***hardyi***	GGGa
§	- subsp. ***rubrum***	MHid
*	- 'Trewithen'	LMil
I	- 'Werrington'	CExl SSta
	auriculatum	GGGa LMil MHid SLdr SSta
	austrinum (A)	IDee LMil NLar
	AUTUMN EMPRESS ('Conles'PBR) (Encore Series) (EA) **new**	EGrI

'Autumn Gold'	SLdr
AUTUMN SUNSET ('Roblen') (Encore Series) (EA) **new**	EGrI
(Avalanche Group) 'Avalanche'	LMil
Avocet Group	LMil SLdr
'Award'	LMil
(Azor Group) 'Azor' **new**	XSte
Azrie Group	SLdr
§ 'Azuma-kagami' (Kurume) (EA)	CAco LMil SCob SLdr
'Azurika'	NLar XSte
'Azurro'	LMil NLar SLdr
'Babuschka'	LMil
'Baden-Baden' ♀H6	CMac CTri EGrI GKin LCro LMil MAsh SLdr WFar
balangense	LMil
balfourianum	MHid
'Baltic Amber' (A)	CDoC
'Balzac' (K)	GKin MAsh
'Barbara Reuthe'	SSta
'Barbarella'	IDee LMil LRHS
barbatum	GGGa GKev LMil MHid
- WJC 13686	WCru
'Barbecue' (K)	EGrI LMil
'Barmstedt'	MAsh
'Barnaby Sunset'	LRHS MAsh
§ ***basilicum***	LMil MHid
'Bastion'	LMil
bauhiniiflorum	see *R. triflorum* var. *bauhiniiflorum*
beanianum	LMil
- compact	see *R. piercei*
'Beatrice Keir'	LMil SSta
(Beau Brummell Group) 'Beau Brummell'	LMil
beesianum	MHid
'Beethoven' (Vuykiana) (EA)	SLdr XSte
BELAMI ('Hachbela')	LMil
'Belkanto'	CAco GKin NLar
'Bellini'	LMil
'Ben Cruachan' (K)	GGGa
'Ben Lawers' (K)	GGGa
'Ben Lomond' (K)	GGGa
'Ben Morrison' (EA)	LMil XSte
'Bengal'	CDoC CRos EGrI LRHS LSRN MAsh NLar SLdr SLim
'Bengal Beauty' (EA)	SLdr
'Bengal Fire' (EA)	CMac SLdr
benhallii 'Honshu Blue'	GGGa
- 'Plum Drops'	GGGa
- 'Slieve Donard'	CMac
- 'Ylva'	GGGa
'Beni-giri' (Kurume) (EA)	CMac SLdr
'Beni-kirishima' (A)	SWeb
'Benny Gery' (EA)	NLar
'Bergensiana'	SSta
'Bergie Larson' ♀H4	LMil
'Berg's Queen Bee' **new**	LMil
'Bernard Shaw'	SSta
'Bernstein'	CAco MAsh
'Berryrose' (K) ♀H6	CBcs CDoC CMac CSBt CTri EGrI EPfP GKin LMil LRHS MAsh MGos SCob WFar XSte
'Bert's Own'	CBcs
'Betty' (Kaempferi) (EA)	SLdr
'Betty Anne Voss' (EA)	CEnd LMil MAsh SCoo SLdr
bhutanense	GGGa
Bibiani Group	LMil
'Big Point' (EA) **new**	LMil
'Bijou de Ledeberg' (Indian) (EA/v)	CMac
'Birthday Girl'	LMil LSRN MAsh
(Biskra Group) 'Biskra'	GGGa LMil
'Blaauw's Pink' (Kurume) (EA) ♀H4	CMac CSBt EGrI EPfP GKin LCro LMil LOPS SCob SGsty SLdr SPer SPlb SPoG XSte
'Black Knight' (EA)	SLdr
'Black Magic'	CAco CBcs GKin LMil WTyc
'Black Widow'	SSta
'Blaney's Blue'	XSte
'Blattgold' (v)	LMil LRHS
BLAUE DONAU	see *R.* 'Blue Danube'
'Blaue Jungs'	GGGa
'Blewbury' ♀H5	LMil
BLOOMBUX ('Microhirs3'PBR)	LCro LMil LOPS SJap XSte
BLOOMCHAMPION PINK (EA) **new**	LMil
BLOOMCHAMPION PURPLE (EA) **new**	LMil
BLOOMCHAMPION WHITE (EA) **new**	LMil
'Blue Boy'	LMil
§ 'Blue Danube' (EA) ♀H3	CBcs CDoC CMac CRos CSBt CTri CTsd EGrI EPfP GKin LCro LMil LOPS LRHS MAsh MGos MPri NLar SCob SCoo SGsty SLdr SLim SPer SPoG SSta WFar
Blue Diamond Group	CBcs EPfP
- 'Blue Diamond'	CSBt EGrI LRHS LSRN MAsh NRHS SLdr
'Blue Jay'	XSte
'Blue Monday' (EA)	SLdr
'Blue Peter' ♀H6	CAco CBcs CSBt LCro LMil LOPS MAsh NHol SCob SSta
'Blue Pool'	LMil
Blue Ribbon Group	SLdr
'Blue Silver'	GGGa LMil MAsh XSte
'Blue Star'	EGrI GEdr
'Blue Steel'	see *R. fastigiatum* 'Blue Steel'
Blue Tit Group	CBcs CDoC CMac EPfP GGGa LRHS MAsh MGos NLar NRHS SLdr SLim SPer
Bluebird Group	SLdr
'Blueshine Girl'	SLdr
'Blutopia'	LMil
'Boddaertianum'	LMil LRHS XSte
BOHLKEN'S LUPINENBERG	LMil
BOHLKEN'S LUPINENBERG LAGUNA	IDee LMil LRHS
BOHLKEN'S SNOW FIRE	LMil
(Bo-peep Group) 'Bo-peep'	LMil SLdr
'Boskoop Ostara'	LMil
'Bouquet de Flore' (G) ♀H6	LMil XSte
Bow Bells Group	SCob
- 'Bow Bells' ♀H4	EGrI EPfP GEdr LMil LRHS MAsh MGos NHol SLdr
brachycarpum	GKev
§ - subsp. ***fauriei*** B&SWJ 4326	WCru
'Brazier' (EA)	SLdr
'Bremen'	LMil
'Bright Forecast' (K)	MPkF
'Brigitte'	MAsh
'Brilliant Blue' (EA)	MAsh
'Britannia'	CSBt NHol SCob SSta
'Bronze Fire' (A)	NHol SSta
'Broughtonii'	XSte
'Brown Eyes'	CAco MAsh
'Bruce Brechtbill'	GKin MAsh NLar
§ 'Bruns Gloria'	LMil NLar
'Bruns Schneewitchen'	SSta

'Buccaneer' (Glenn Dale) (EA) SLdr
bullatum see *R. edgeworthii*
'Bungo-nishiki' (Wada) (EA/d) CMac
bureavii ♀H6 GGGa IDee LMil LRHS MHid SSta
bureavioides MHid
'Burletta' LRHS
burmanicum CBcs
Bustard Group LMil
'C.B. van Nes' SLdr
calendulaceum (A) GGGa IDee LMil
- red-flowered (A) LMil
- yellow-flowered (A) LMil
(Calfort Group) 'Calfort' GGGa
callimorphum GKev
calophytum ♀H5 GGGa LMil SLdr
calostrotum 'Gigha' ♀H6 CBcs GGGa LMil
§ - subsp. ***keleticum*** ♀H6 GEdr LCro LOPS WThu
- - R 58 GGGa LMil
§ - - Radicans Group GEdr GGGa NWad WAbe WThu
- subsp. ***riparioides*** LMil
§ - subsp. ***riparium*** Nitens Group CBcs GGGa WThu XSte
'Calsap' XSte
Calstocker Group LMil
camelliiflorum MHid
campanulatum GKev LMil
- B&SWJ 13934 WCru
- HWJCM 195 WCru
- HWJCM 409 WCru
§ - subsp. ***aeruginosum*** LMil MHid
- subsp. ***campanulatum*** MHid
- 'Topper' **new** LMil
'Campfire' J.B. Gable (EA) SLdr
campylocarpum CBcs LMil LRHS
- subsp. ***campylocarpum*** MHid
campylogynum GKev LCro LMil LOPS
- SBEC 0519 GGGa
- 'Album' see *R.* 'Leucanthum'
- Charopoeum Group WThu
- - 'Patricia' EGrI GEdr
- Myrtilloides Group ♀H5 GGGa LMil WAbe WThu
camtschaticum GGGa GKev LMil LRHS WAbe
- 'Glendoick Lilac' GKev
- red-flowered GGGa
canadense (A) GGGa GKev
- f. ***albiflorum*** (A) GGGa LMil
- dark-flowered (A) LMil
CANDY LIGHTS ('UMinn's Candy Lights') (A) LRHS XSte
§ ***canescens*** (A) LMil LRHS MPkF
'Cannon's Double' (K/d) ♀H6 CBcs CDoC GKin LMil LRHS MGos NLar SPer
'Canzonetta' (EA/d) ♀H5 CEnd CRos EPfP GGGa LMil LRHS MAsh NLar NRHS SAko SLdr SPer
'Captain Jack' GGGa
'Carat' (A) NLar
(Carita Group) 'Golden Dream' LMil
Carmen Group GKev
- 'Carmen' ♀H6 CRos EGrI GEdr GGGa GKin LMil MAsh SLdr
'Caroline Allbrook' MAsh NLar WFar
'Cary Ann' CAco CTri LRHS MAsh
'Casablanca' (EA) SLdr
catawbiense CMCN SLdr
'Catawbiense Album' CAco CTri MAsh
'Catawbiense Grandiflorum' CAco LMil MAsh
'Catharine van Tol' LMaj
'Caucasicum Pictum' LMil LRHS SLdr
'Cavalier' **new** XSte
'Cayenne' (EA) SLdr
'Cecile' (K) CBcs CMac CTri EGrI GKin LMil LSRN MMuc MPkF
'Celestial' (EA) CMac
cephalanthum LMil
- subsp. ***cephalanthum*** SBEC 0751 WThu
- - Crebreflorum Group GGGa LMil WAbe WThu
cerasinum LMil MHid
- COALS OF FIRE GGGa
chaetomallum see *R. haematodes* subsp. *chaetomallum*
'Chanel' (Vs) NLar SSta
Chanticleer Group **new** NRog
'Chanticleer' (Glenn Dale) (EA) SLdr
chapaense see *R. maddenii* subsp. *crassum*
'Chariots of Fire' (EA) IDee LMil
charitopes LMil
- F 25570 LMil
- subsp. ***charitopes*** MHid
* 'Charlotte de Rothschild' (EA) SLdr
'Charlotte Megan' (A) LMil
chasmanthum see *R. augustinii* subsp. *chasmanthum*
'Cheer' MAsh
'Chelsea Reach' (K/d) ♀H6 LMil
'Chelsea Seventy' SLdr
'Cherokee' (EA) SLdr
'Cherries and Merlot' **new** LRHS
'Cherry Cheesecake' LRHS
'Cherry Drops' (EA) EPfP LRHS MAsh SPoG
CHERRY KISS ('Hachcher'PBR) GGGa IDee LMil LRHS SAko
'Chetco' (A) LMil MGos
'Chikor' CDoC EGrI GKin MGos
'Chionoides' SLdr
'Chipmunk' (EA/d) LRHS MAsh NRHS
'Chippewa' (Indian) (EA) CTri LMil SAko
'Chocolate Dane' LMil
Choptank River Group (A) GKev
(Choremia Group) 'Choremia' ♀H5 LMil
'Christina' (Vuykiana) (EA/d) SLdr
'Christmas Cheer' (EA/d) see *R.* 'Ima-shojo'
'Christmas Cheer' (*caucasicum* hybrid) ♀H5 CBcs CDoC CRos EPfP GGGa GKin LCro LMil LOPS MAsh MGos MPri NLar SLdr
'Christopher Loder' SLdr
chryseum see *R. rupicola* var. *chryseum*
ciliatum CBcs SLdr
- deep rose-flowered SLdr
- white-flowered SLdr
Cilpinense Group CBcs
- 'Cilpinense' ♀H5 CMac CSBt EPfP LMil LRHS MAsh MMuc MPri SLdr XSte
cinnabarinum GKev LMil LRHS SLdr XSte
- subsp. ***cinnabarinum*** MHid
- - BL&M 234 LMil
- - 'Nepal' LMil
- - Roylei Group GGGa LMil
- - - B&SWJ 13972 WCru
- - - 'Vin Rosé' LMil
- Cinzan Group LMil
§ - (Conroy Group) 'Conroy' LMil
§ - subsp. ***xanthocodon*** GGGa GKev LMil WPGP
- - 'Apricot Belle' LMil
§ - - Concatenans Group GGGa LMil
- - - KW 5874 LMil
- - Purpurellum Group GGGa

	citriniflorum	LMil
	- R 108	LMil
	- var. ***citriniflorum***	LMil
	- var. ***horaeum*** F21850 **new**	LMil
	clementinae F 25705	LMil
	'Cliff Garland'	LMil
	'Coccineum Speciosum' (G) 🏆H6	CMac LMil LRHS SSta XSte
	'Cockatoo' (K)	LMil
	coeloneurum	LMil MHid
	- EGM 334	LMil
	'Colin Kenrick' (K/d)	LMil
	Colonel Rogers Group	SLdr
	columbianum	SLdr
	'Colyer' (EA)	SLdr
	Comely Group	SLdr
	concatenans	see *R. cinnabarinum* subsp. *xanthocodon* Concatenans Group
	concinnum	MHid
	- Pseudoyanthinum Group 🏆H5	GGGa
	'Concorde'	CMac
	'Connie' (Kaempferi) (EA)	SSta
	'Conroy'	see *R. cinnabarinum* 'Conroy'
	'Contina'	LMil
	'Conversation Piece' (EA)	CEnd SLdr
	'Coral Seas' (V)	GGGa
	'Corany' (A)	CDoC LMil NLar SCoo
	coriaceum	LMil
	'Corneille' (G/d)	LMil LRHS XSte
	Cornish Early Red Group	see *R.* Smithii Group
	'Cornish Red'	see *R.* Smithii Group
	'Coronation Day'	LMil
	'Cosmopolitan'	CDoC LCro LOPS MGos NLar SCob SPer SPoG XSte
	'Cotton Candy'	LMil
	'Countess of Athlone'	CMac
	'Countess of Haddington'	CBcs LMil LRHS
	Cowslip Group	CTri LMil MAsh MGos
	- 'Cowslip' 🏆H4	CDoC CRos EGrl EPfP IDee LRHS NLar
	'Crane' 🏆H5	EPfP GGGa GKev LMil LRHS MAsh
	crassum	see *R. maddenii* subsp. *crassum*
	'Cream Crest'	CDoC CRos GKin NLar SLim XSte
	'Creamy Chiffon'	CAco NLar
	crinigerum	GKev LMil
	'Crinoline' (EA)	SLdr
	'Croceum Tricolor' (G)	LMil
	Crossbill Group	SLdr
	'Crosswater Belle'	LMil
	'Crosswater Red' (A) 🏆H6	LMil
	cubittii	see *R. veitchianum* Cubittii Group
	cucullatum	see *R. roxieanum* var. *cucullatum*
	cumberlandense (A)	LMil
	- 'Sunlight'	LMil
	cuneatum	LRHS
	'Cunningham's White'	CAco CBcs CDoC CTri ELan EPfP GGGa LCro LMaj LMil LOPS LPar LRHS MAsh MGos MPri NHol NLar NWea SArc SCob SGsty SLdr SLim SPer SPoG SSta XSte
	'Curlew' 🏆H5	CMac GEdr GKev GKin MAsh NHol SCob SLdr
	cyanocarpum	GKev
	'Cynthia' 🏆H6	CBcs CMac GGGa LMil LSRN SCob SLdr SSta
	'Daisetsuzan' (EA)	MPkF XSte
	dalhousieae	LRHS
	(Damozel Group) 'Damozel'	LMil
	'Darkness' (EA)	SWeb

	'Dartmoor Shepherd's Delight'	SSta
	dauricum 'Album'	see *R. dauricum* 'Hokkaido'
§	- 'Hokkaido'	LMil
	- 'Mid-winter' 🏆H6	GGGa LMil
	davidii	LMil
	davidsonianum 🏆H5	CMac LMil MHid
	- Bodnant form	LMil
	- 'Caerhays Blotched'	GGGa
	- 'Ruth Lyons'	LMil
	'Daviesii' (G) 🏆H6	CBcs CDoC CEnd CRos CSBt CTri ELan EPfP GKin LCro LMil LOPS LRHS MAsh MMuc MPkF MPri NLar SCob SPer SPoG SSta XSte
	'Daybreak' (EA/d)	see *R.* 'Kirin'
	'Dear Barbara'	LSRN
	'Dear Grandad' (EA)	CTri LMil LSRN
	'Dear Grandma' (EA)	LMil LSRN
	'Dearest' (EA)	LMil LRHS MAsh MPri NRHS SCoo
	'Debutante'	SSta
	decorum 🏆H6	CBcs GGGa IDee LMil LRHS SLdr
	- subsp. ***cordatum***	MHid
	- - C&H 7132	GGGa
	- subsp. ***decorum***	MHid
§	- subsp. ***diaprepes***	MHid
	- pink-flowered	GGGa
§	***degronianum*** subsp. ***degronianum***	LMil
	- subsp. ***heptamerum*** 'Ho Emma'	LMil
	- - 'Oki Koki'	LMil
	- 'Rae's Delight'	LMil
	'Delicatissimum' (O) 🏆H5	CTsd GGGa GKin LRHS MPkF XSte
	'Delta'	CDoC MGos NLar SLdr SLim WFar
	dendrocharis	LMil
	- GLENDOICK GEM ('Gle002')	GGGa
*	'Denny's Rose' (A)	SSta
	'Denny's Scarlet'	NHol SSta
	'Denny's White' (A)	LMil NHol SSta
	denudatum	LMil MHid
	- EGM 294	LMil
	'Devisiperbile' (EA)	SLdr
	Diamant Group lilac-flowered (EA)	LMil
§	- red-flowered (EA)	EGrl SLdr
	'Diamant Rot'	see *R.* Diamant Group red-flowered
I	'Diana'	SLdr SWeb
	dichroanthum	LMil
§	- subsp. ***apodectum***	LMil
§	- subsp. ***scyphocalyx***	LMil
	didymum	see *R. sanguineum* subsp. *didymum*
	'Diorama' (Vs)	SSta
	discolor	see *R. fortunei* subsp. *discolor*
	'Doc'	CBcs SLdr SSta XSte
	'Doctor Arnold W. Endtz'	SSta
	'Doctor M. Oosthoek' (M)	GKin
	'Doctor Reiger'	CDoC NLar
	'Dolores' (EA) **new**	NLar
	'Dopey' 🏆H5	CAco CBcs CDoC CRos ELan EPfP GGGa LMil LPar LRHS MAsh MGos NHol NLar SCob SGsty SLdr SLim SSta
	'Dora Amateis' 🏆H6	CBcs GGGa GKev LMil LRHS MAsh MGos MPri NRHS SCob SLdr SLim XSte
	Dormouse Group	LMil MAsh
	'Dorothy Hayden' (EA)	SGsty SLdr SWeb
	'Dotella'	SSta
	'Double Beauty' (Vuykiana) (EA/d)	SSta

'Dracula' (K)	LMil
Dragonfly Group	SSta
'Dreamland' ♀H5	CBcs CDoC CRos EPfP LCro LMil LOPS LPar LRHS MAsh MGos NLar NRHS SCob SLdr SLim SPoG SSta WFar XSte
'Driven Snow' (EA)	SLdr
'Dusty Miller'	MAsh SLdr WFar
'E.J.P. Magor' **new**	LMil
'Earl of Donoughmore'	SSta
'Easter Parade' (EA)	SLdr
eclecteum	GGGa LMil MHid
§ ***edgeworthii*** ♀H3	CBcs GGGa LMil LRHS MPkF
'Edith Bosley'	CDoC LMil LRHS NLar SLdr
'Edna Bee' (EA)	LMil SLdr
'Egret' ♀H4	GEdr GGGa LMil SLdr
'El Camino'	SLdr
(Eleanore Group) 'Eleanore'	SLdr
'Electra'	see *R. augustinii* 'Electra'
elegantulum	LMil MHid
'Elfin Gold'	LMil
(Elisabeth Hobbie Group) 'Elisabeth Hobbie' ♀H5	CDoC LMil NLar SLdr
'Elizabeth' (EA)	CMac EPfP SCob SLdr
Elizabeth Group	CBcs LMil MAsh SLdr
§ - 'Creeping Jenny'	GGGa SLdr
- 'Elizabeth'	CTri LRHS LSRN NHol NRHS XSte
'Elizabeth Jenny'	see *R.* (Elizabeth Group) 'Creeping Jenny'
'Elizabeth Red Foliage'	CTri LMil MAsh MPkF SLdr XSte
'Elsie Lee' (EA/d) ♀H5	CEnd CSBt EPfP LMil MAsh SCob SLdr WFar
'Emasculum'	SLdr
'Endsleigh Pink'	LMil
eriocarpum 'Gumpō' (EA)	CMac SLdr
eriogynum	see *R. facetum*
'Esmeralda'	CMac
'Esther May' (A)	SSta
'Etna' (EA)	SLdr
'Etoile de Sleidinge'	CRos NLar SPer
'Etta Burrows'	GGGa SLdr
'Eucharis' (Glenn Dale) (EA)	MPkF
'Eucharitis' **new**	XSte
'Eunice Ann' (A)	SSta
'Europa'	LMil SSta
'Eurydice'	LMil
'Evelyn Hyde' (EA)	SLdr
'Everbloom' (EA)	SLdr
'Everitt Hershey' (A)	SLdr
EVERRED ('851C' PBR)	GGGa
exasperatum KW 6855	LMil
Exburiense Group	MMuc
'Exbury Calstocker'	LMil
excellens	LMil
eximium	see *R. falconeri* subsp. *eximium*
'Exquisitum' (O) ♀H5	CBcs EGrI GGGa GKin LMil
'Extraordinaire'	CBcs LMil MPkF SSta XSte
(Fabia Group) 'Fabia' ♀H4	CMac GGGa GKin LMil SLdr
§ - 'Fabia Tangerine'	CMac
- 'Fabia Waterer'	LMil
§ ***facetum***	GGGa LMil
'Faggetter's Favourite' ♀H5	LMil LRHS SSta
Fairy Light Group	LMil SLdr
faithae CGG 14142	GGGa
falconeri ♀H4	CBcs GGGa IKel LMil LRHS SLdr
- KR 10420	WPGP
- WJC 13825	WCru
§ - subsp. ***eximium***	GGGa GKev LMil MHid
- subsp. ***falconeri***	MHid
'Falling Snow'	SAko
'Fanal' (K)	NLar
'Fanny'	see *R.* 'Pucella'
'Fantasia' **new**	LRHS
'Fantastica' ♀H6	CAco CDoC CRos ELan GGGa LMil MAsh MGos MPri NLar SCob SGsty SLim SPoG XSte
fargesii	see *R. oreodoxa* var. *fargesii*
farinosum	LMil
fastigiatum	EGrI GEdr LMil SLdr WAbe
- SBEC 0804	WThu
- SDR 7990	GKev
§ - 'Blue Steel' ♀H6	CTri GKin LMil LRHS MAsh MPri NRHS SLdr SPlb WAbe
- 'Indigo Steel'	GGGa
'Fastuosum Flore Pleno' (d) ♀H6	CBcs CMac CSBt GGGa IDee LMil SCob SLdr SSta
fauriei	see *R. brachycarpum* subsp. *fauriei*
'Favorite' ambig. (EA)	SLdr
'Fawley' (K)	SLdr
'Fay Norman'	LMil
ferrugineum	GKev LMil LRHS
'Feuerwerk' (K)	NLar
fictolacteum	see *R. rex* subsp. *fictolacteum*
Fine Feathers Group	CMac
'Fire Bird'	SLdr
'Fire Rim'	LRHS MAsh
'Fireball' (K) ♀H6	CBcs CDoC CTri EGrI EPfP GBin GGGa GKin IDee LMil LRHS MAsh MGos MMuc MPri NLar SCob SPer SPoG XSte
'Fireball' (hybrid)	MPkF
'Firecracker' (A)	LRHS MAsh
'Fireglow' (EA)	GKin LMil
'Firelight' (EA)	CDoC CRos LPar
'Firelight' (hybrid)	GKin LMil NLar SPer
§ 'Firestorm'	MPri
'First Light' (V)	LRHS XSte
'Flaming Gold'	LMil LRHS LSRN MAsh SLdr
§ ***flammeum*** (A)	IDee LMil LRHS
'Flanagan's Daughter'	LMil MAsh
Flava Group	see *R.* Volker Group
fletcherianum 'Yellow Bunting'	GGGa
floccigerum	LMil
floribundum	LMil
'Florida' (EA/d) ♀H4	CDoC CMac LMil SCob SCoo SLdr
'Florida Ogada' **new**	SPer
'Flower Arranger' (EA)	LMil MAsh SCoo
formosum	CBcs
§ - var. ***formosum*** Iteaphyllum Group	GGGa
forrestii subsp. ***forrestii***	LMil
- - Repens Group	LMil
- - - 'Seinghku'	GGGa
Fortune Group	SLdr
fortunei ♀H5	GGGa LMil
§ - subsp. ***discolor*** ♀H5	CBcs LMil MHid
- - (Houlstonii Group) 'John R. Elcock'	LMil
- - var. ***kwangfuense*** AC 5208	LMil
- subsp. ***discolor*** × 'Lodauric Iceberg'	GKin
- subsp. ***fortunei***	MHid
- 'Mrs Butler'	see *R.* 'Sir Charles Butler'
fragariiflorum	GGGa
'Fragrant Memories'	LMil
'Fragrant Star' (A)	LRHS MPkF XSte
'Fragrantissimum' ♀H3	CBcs CDoC CEnd CSBt CTsd GGGa LMil LRHS MPkF MRav NLar SLdr XSte
'Frank Galsworthy'	SCob

(Fraseri Group) 'Fraseri' (M)	LMil
'Fred Peste' ♀H4	LMil MGos SCob SLdr SLim
(Fred Wynniatt Group) 'Fred Wynniatt'	LMil
'Fred Wynniatt Stanway'	see *R.* 'Stanway'
'Freya' (R/d)	LMil LSRN
'Fridoline' (EA)	SAko
'Frigate' (EA)	SLdr
'Frilly Lemon' (Ad)	ELan EPfP LRHS MPkF XSte
'Frosted Orange' (EA)	LMil MAsh
'Frosthexe'	WAbe
'Fulbrook'	LMil
fulgens	LMil MHid
fulvum ♀H5	GGGa IDee LMil SSta
'Furious Fujiori'PBR (EA)	NLar
'Furnivall's Daughter' ♀H5	CAco CBcs CMac CSBt IDee LMaj LMil NHol SLdr SPer SSta
fuyuanense	GGGa
'Gabrielle Hill' (EA)	MAsh SLdr
'Gaiety' (Glenn Dale) (EA)	LMil SLdr
galactinum	GGGa LMil
'Gandy Dancer'	CAco SLdr
'Garden State Glow' (EA/d)	SLdr
'Gartendirektor Glocker'	CDoC CMac EGrI LMil MGos SCob SLim
'Gartendirektor Rieger' ♀H5	CBcs GGGa IDee LMil XSte
'Geisha Dunkellachsrot'	see *R.* (Aronense Group) 'Michiko'
'Geisha Dunkellila'	see *R.* (Aronense Group) 'Haruko'
'Geisha Karmin'	see *R.* (Aronense Group) 'Noriko'
'Geisha Orange'	see *R.* (Aronense Group) 'Satschiko'
'Geisha Pink'	see *R.* (Aronense Group) 'Momoko'
'Geisha Purple'	see *R.* (Aronense Group) 'Fumiko'
'Geisha Red'	see *R.* (Aronense Group) 'Kazuko'
GELB DUFTHECKE ('Rhodunter 150') (Inkarho)	LMil
'Gena Mae' (A/d) ♀H6	SLdr
'General Practitioner'	SLdr
'General Wavell' (EA)	CMac
'Gene's Favourite'	SSta
'Geoffroy Millais'	LMil
'Georg Arends' (A)	CDoC CRos EPfP LMil LRHS MAsh
'George Hyde' (EA)	EPfP LRHS LSRN MAsh SCoo
'Germania'	CBcs CDoC CRos LPar LRHS MAsh MGos MPri NLar SCob SGsty SPoG SSta
Gertrud Schäle Group	CDoC CTri EGrI NLar
'Gibraltar' (K) ♀H6	CBcs CDoC CSBt CTri EGrI EPfP GGGa GKin LMil LRHS MAsh MGos MPkF MPri NHol NLar SCob SLim SPer SSta XSte
Gibraltar Group	LMil WFar
'Gilbert Mullie' (EA)	CDoC LMil NLar SLim SSta
'Gillian Bramley'	SLdr
'Ginger' (K)	LMil
'Ginny Gee' ♀H5	CBcs CDoC EGrI EPfP GEdr GGGa GKin LMil LRHS MAsh MGos NLar NRHS NWad SSta WFar XSte
§ 'Girard's Hot Shot' (EA)	LRHS MPkF NRHS SCoo SSta
§ 'Girard's Variegated Hot Shot' (EA/v) ♀H4	GGGa MAsh SLdr SPoG XSte
'Gislinde' (A)	SAko
'Glacier' (EA)	SLdr
glanduliferum	GGGa MHid
- 'Peter the Great'	LMil
glaucophyllum	GGGa LMil MHid
- Borde Hill form	LMil
- 'Deer Dell'	LMil
GLENDOICK CANDYFLOSS ('Gle033') (EA/d) **new**	GGGa

GLENDOICK CHIFFON ('Gle034') (EA/d) **new**	GGGa
GLENDOICK FLAMINGO ('Gle026')	GGGa
GLENDOICK FRANGIPANI ('Gle035') (EA/d) **new**	GGGa
GLENDOICK GARDENIA ('Gle036') (EA/d) **new**	GGGa
GLENDOICK GEORGETTE ('Gle037') (EA/d) **new**	GGGa
GLENDOICK GLACIER ('Gle009') (EA)	GGGa
GLENDOICK GLAMOUR ('Gle039') (EA) **new**	GGGa
GLENDOICK GOBLIN ('Gle010') (EA)	GGGa
GLENDOICK GOLD ('Gle011')	GGGa
GLENDOICK MYSTIQUE ('Gle014')	GGGa
GLENDOICK PETTICOATS ('Gle015')	GGGa
GLENDOICK PRINCESS ('Gle040') (EA/d) **new**	GGGa
GLENDOICK ROSEBUD ('Gle022') (EA)	GGGa
GLENDOICK SHERBET ('Gle029')	GGGa
GLENDOICK SNOWFLAKES ('Gle001') (EA)	GGGa
GLENDOICK SORBET ('Gle028')	GGGa
GLENDOICK VANILLA ('Gle017')	GGGa
GLENDOICK VELVET ('Gle018')	GGGa
'Gletschernacht'	SAko
glischrum	GGGa
- subsp. ***glischroides***	LMil
§ - subsp. ***rude***	LMil MHid
'Gloria'	see *R.* 'Bruns Gloria'
'Gloria Mundi' (G)	XSte
'Glory of Littleworth' (Ad)	LMil
'Glory of Penjerrick'	XSte
'Glowing Embers' (K)	CDoC CTri EGrI GKin LMil LRHS MAsh MGos MMuc NHol NLar SCob SGsty SLim SPer SSta
'Goblin'	SLdr
'Gog' (K)	CSBt
'Golden Coach'	CAco
'Golden Eagle' (K) ♀H6	CBcs CDoC CRos EGrI GKin LMil LRHS MGos NLar SLdr SPer WFar
GOLDEN EVEREST ('Hachgold'PBR)	GGGa LMil LRHS
'Golden Flame' (A) **new**	EGrI
'Golden Flare' (A)	CBcs EGrI GKin
'Golden Fleece'	LMil
'Golden Gate'	CDoC CRos MGos NLar SCob SLdr SPer
'Golden Lights' (A)	EGrI GKin NLar
'Golden Princess'	LMil
'Golden Splendour'	LMil
'Golden Sunset' (K) ♀H6	EPfP LMil LRHS MAsh MPkF WFar XSte
'Golden Torch' ♀H5	CBcs CDoC CRos CSBt ELan EPfP LCro LMil LOPS LPar LRHS MAsh MGos MPri NLar SCob SLdr SLim SPer SPoG
'Golden Wedding'	CBcs LMil LSRN MAsh SLdr
'Golden Wit'	MAsh
'Golden Wonder'	MAsh

	'Goldflimmer' (v)	CDoC EPfP LPar LRHS MAsh MGos MPri NLar SCob SLim SPer SPoG WFar
	'Goldika'	LMil
	GOLDINETTA ('Hachinetta')	IDee LMil
	'Goldkrone' ♀H5	MAsh SCob SPoG
	'Goldsworth Orange'	CAco CMac SLdr
	'Goldsworth Yellow'	CSBt
	'Goldtopas' (K)	CTri EPfP GGGa GKin LMil LRHS
	'Gomer Waterer' ♀H6	CBcs CMac CSBt ELan EPfP GGGa IDee LCro LMil LOPS LRHS MAsh MGos NLar SCob SLdr SPoG SSta
	'Gorbella'	CDoC NLar
	Gowenianum Group (Ad)	LMil LRHS MGos SPer
	'Grace Seabrook' ♀H5	CBcs CSBt CTri GGGa SLdr SPer
	GRAFFITO ('Hachgraf')	CBcs GGGa IDee LMil LRHS
	'Graham Thomas'	LMil
	grande	CBcs IDee LMil MHid NLar
	- WJC 13804	WCru
	'Grandeur Triomphante' (G)	XSte
	gratum	see *R. basilicum*
	'Graziella'	GGGa LCro LOPS LRHS MGos MPkF SArc SPoG SSta WFar XSte
	'Greensleeves'	LMil
	'Greenway' (Kurume) (EA)	CBcs MPkF SLdr XSte
	griersonianum	GGGa LMil
	- F 30392	LMil
	griffithianum	MHid
	- B&SWJ 2425	WCru
	'Gristede' ♀H5	CDoC CRos LMil LRHS NLar SSta
	groenlandicum	LMil NLar SPer WAbe
	- 'Compactum'	LRHS NLar
	- 'Helma'	LMil NLar
	- 'Lenie'	NLar
	(Grosclaude Group) 'Grosclaude'	LMil
	'Grumpy'	EPfP LMil LRHS MAsh XSte
	'Gwenda' (EA)	CTri SLdr
	habrotrichum	LMil
	'Hachmann's Brasilia'	SSta
	'Hachmann's Charmant'	CBcs GGGa SAko XSte
	'Hachmann's Constanze'	LMil
	'Hachmann's Eskimo'	CAco CRos IDee LMil LRHS NLar SLdr
	'Hachmann's Feuerschein'	SAko
	'Hachmann's Juanita' (K)	CRos CSBt LMil
	'Hachmann's Junifeuer'	SSta
	HACHMANN'S KABARETT ('Hachkaba')	CDoC IDee LMil LPar LRHS NLar SPer XSte
	'Hachmann's Mamamia'	SAko
	'Hachmann's Marlis' ♀H6	LMil LRHS
§	'Hachmann's Metallica'	IDee LMil LRHS
§	'Hachmann's Orakel'	IDee LMil LRHS SSta
	'Hachmann's Pinguin'	CBcs SSta XSte
§	'Hachmann's Polaris' ♀H7	CDoC LMil
	'Hachmann's Porzellan' ♀H6	LMil LRHS SGsty XSte
§	'Hachmann's Rokoko' (EA)	CEnd LMil SSta
	'Hachmann's Sunny Boy'	LMil
	haematodes	GGGa LMil
§	- subsp. ***chaetomallum***	LMil
	- subsp. ***haematodes***	LMil
	'Halfdan Lem' ♀H5	CBcs CDoC GKin LMil LPar LRHS MGos NLar SLim SPer SPoG SSta XSte
	'Hallelujah'	CBcs
	'Halopeanum'	GGGa LMil XSte
	'Hamlet' (M)	LMil
	'Hammondii'	LMil
	'Hampshire Belle'	LMil LRHS SSta
	hanceanum Nanum Group ♀H5	CBcs

	'Hanger's Flame' (A)	LMil
	'Hansel'	MAsh
	'Hardijzer Beauty' (Ad)	SLdr
	'Hardy Gardenia' (EA/d)	SSta
	hardyi	see *R. augustinii* subsp. *hardyi*
	'Harkwood Red' (EA)	SLdr
	Harmony Group	SLdr
	'Haru-no-sono' (EA)	MPkF SWeb XSte
	'Harvest Moon' (K)	LMil NLar SSta
	'Hatsu-giri' (EA)	CMac LCro LMil LOPS SLdr SSta
	(Hawk Group) 'Crest' ♀H4	CBcs LMil SSta
	'Heather Macleod' (EA)	SLdr
	'Heidi'PBR (EA)	SLdr
	'Helen Close' (Glenn Dale) (EA)	SLdr
	'Helen Curtis' (EA)	SLdr
	'Helena Evelyn' (A)	LMil
	'Helene Schiffner'	SSta
	heliolepis	LMil
	- var. ***fumidum***	see *R. heliolepis* var. *heliolepis*
§	- var. ***heliolepis***	GKev
	hemsleyanum	LMil MHid
	'Hendrik's Kers' (V) **new**	LRHS XSte
	'Herbert' (EA)	CDoC CMac CRos MGos NLar SCoo SLdr SLim
§	'Hexe de Saffelaere' (EA)	NLar
	'High Summer'	LMil LRHS
	'Hilda Margaret'	SSta
	'Himalayan Child' **new**	IDee
	'Hinamayo'	see *R.* (Obtusum Group) 'Hinomayo'
	'Hino-crimson' (Kurume) (EA) ♀H5	CBcs CDoC CMac CSBt CTri EGrI GKin LMil MAsh MGos MPkF NHol NLar SCob SLdr SPer SPoG SSta XSte
	'Hinode-giri' (EA)	CBcs CMac CSBt SLdr
	'Hino-scarlet' (EA)	CBcs
	hippophaeoides	CBcs GKev LMil WFar
	- 'Bei-ma-shan'	see *R. hippophaeoides* 'Haba Shan'
§	- 'Haba Shan' ♀H6	LMil LRHS WThu
	hirsutum	LMil WAbe
	hirtipes	GGGa MHid
	hodgsonii	LMil MHid
	- B&SWJ 2195A	WCru
	'Holden'	MAsh NLar
	'Homebush' (K/d) ♀H6	CBcs CDoC CMac CTri EGrI EPfP LMil LRHS MAsh MGos MMuc NLar SCob SPer SPoG SSta XSte
	'Honey Butter'	MGos
	'Honeysuckle' (K)	NHol SSta
§	'Ho-o' (Kurume) (EA)	EGrI SLdr
	'Ho-oden' (EA)	XSte
	hookeri	LMil
	'Hoppy'	CBcs CDoC CRos LMil MAsh MGos NLar SCob SLdr SLim
	'Horizon Lakeside'	GGGa
	'Horizon Monarch' ♀H4	CAco CBcs CDoC CRos EGrI ELan GGGa GKin LMil LPar LRHS MGos NLar SCob SGsty SLdr SLim SPer SSta WFar XSte
	'Hortulanus H. Witte' (M)	SSta XSte
	'Hot Flush'	LMil LRHS
	'Hot Shot'	see *R.* 'Girard's Hot Shot'
	'Hot Shot Variegated'	see *R.* 'Girard's Variegated Hot Shot' (EA/v)
	'Hotei'	CAco CSBt EGrI EPfP GKin LMil MAsh NHol SSta
	(Hotspur Group) 'Hotspur' (K)	MMuc
	- 'Hotspur Red' (K) ♀H6	EGrI EPfP GKin LMil MAsh MMuc MPkF XSte
	huanum	LMil

	– EGM 316	LMil
	'Hugh Koster'	SLdr
	'Huisman's Sun Star' (A/d)	LMil LRHS
	Humming Bird Group	EGrI GEdr IDee LMil LRHS SLdr
	hunnewellianum	MHid
	'Hussar'	IDee LMil LRHS
	'Hydon Dawn' ♀H5	CBcs LMil LRHS NLar SLdr SSta
	'Hydon Hunter' ♀H5	SSta
	'Hydon Velvet'	CBcs CTsd LMil LRHS NLar SLdr XSte
	hyperythrum	GGGa LMil
	– 'Ariel' **new**	LMil
	'Ice Cube'	MMuc SLdr
	'Iceberg'	see *R.* 'Lodauric Iceberg'
	(Idealist Group) 'Idealist'	LMil
§	'Ilam Melford Lemon' (A)	LMil
§	'Ilam Ming' (A)	LMil
	'Ilam Violet'	CMac LMil
	'Imago' (K/d)	LMil
§	'Ima-shojo' (Kurume) (EA/d)	CMac LRHS SLdr
	impeditum	CBcs CSBt EGrI GEdr LCro LOPS MGos SLdr SSta
	– 'Blue Steel'	see *R. fastigiatum* 'Blue Steel'
	– 'Indigo'	GKin
	– 'Pygmaeum'	WAbe WThu
	– 'Select'	XSte
	(Impi Group) 'Impi'	LMil
§	***indicum*** 'Macranthum' (EA)	SLdr SRms
	insigne ♀H6	GGGa LMil MHid
	– 'Annie Darling'	LMil
	Intrifast Group	GGGa
	'Irene Koster' (O) ♀H5	CBcs CDoC EGrI ELan GGGa GKin LMil MGos MPkF NLar SCob SLim SPer XSte
	'Irohayama' (Kurume) (EA) ♀H5	CBcs CEnd CMac EPfP LMil LRHS MAsh MPri NRHS SCoo XSte
	irroratum	LMil SLdr
	– subsp. ***irroratum***	MHid
	– 'Polka Dot'	GGGa LMil
	– subsp. ***yiliangense***	MHid
	– – EGM 339	LMil
	'Isabel' (EA)	MAsh
	'Isabel' (hybrid)	MPri
	iteaphyllum	see *R. formosum* var. *formosum* Iteaphyllum Group
	'Ivette' (Kaempferi) (EA)	CMac
	'Izumi-no-mai' (EA)	SLdr
	'J.C. Williams'	CBcs
	'J.M. de Montague'	see *R.* 'The Honourable Jean Marie de Montague'
	'Jackwill'	SAko
	(Jalisco Group) 'Jalisco Janet'	SLdr
	– 'Jubilant'	LMil
	'James Barto'	LMil
	'James Burchett' ♀H6	LMil LRHS SSta
	'James Gable' (EA)	MAsh SLdr
	Janet Group	LMil
	'Janet Rhea' (EA)	SLdr
	japonicum (A. Gray) J.V. Suringar	see *R. molle* subsp. *japonicum*
	– var. ***pentamerum***	see *R. degronianum* subsp. *degronianum*
	'Jason'	LMil
	'Jean Marie Montague'	see *R.* 'The Honourable Jean Marie de Montague'
	'Jeff Hill' (EA)	SLdr
	'Jenny'	see *R.* 'Creeping Jenny'
	'Jeritsa'	LMil
	'Jessica Rose' (A)	LMil
	'Jessica de Rothschild' **new**	LMil
	'Jingle Bells'	XSte
	'Joanna'	CBcs
	'Jock'	SLdr
	'Jock Brydon' (O) ♀H6	GGGa LMil LRHS
	'Johann Sebastian Bach' (EA)	SLdr
	'Johanna' (EA) ♀H5	CDoC CEnd CTri EGrI EPfP LMil LRHS MAsh MGos MPkF MPri NHol NLar NRHS SCob SGsty SLdr SPer SWeb XSte
	'John Cairns' (Kaempferi) (EA)	CMac SLdr
	johnstoneanum	CBcs GGGa SLdr
	– NJM 12.068	WPGP
	– 'Double Diamond' (d)	LMil
	'Jolie Madame' (Vs) ♀H6	CDoC CRos EGrI ELan EPfP GKin LMil LRHS MAsh MGos MPkF MPri NLar SGsty SPer WFar XSte
	'Joseph Hill' (EA)	CEnd NLar
	'Jubilee'	SLdr
	'June Fire' (A)	SSta
	'Juniduft' (A)	GGGa
	kaempferi (EA)	LMil SLdr
§	– 'Mikado' (EA)	LMil SLdr
	– orange-flowered (EA)	CMac
	'Kalinka'	CDoC CRos LMil MAsh MGos MHtn SPoG WFar
	'Karen Triplett'	LMil
	'Karl Naue'	GGGa SSta
	KARMINKISSEN ('Hachkarmin')	LMil LRHS
	'Kasane-kagaribi' (EA)	SLdr
	'Kathleen' van Nes (EA)	SLdr
	'Katisha' (EA)	SLdr
	'Katy Watson'	SSta
	'Keija' (EA)	SLdr
	keiskei var. ***ozawae*** 'Yaku Fairy' ♀H5	LMil
	keleticum	see *R. calostrotum* subsp. *keleticum*
	'Kentucky Minstrel' (K)	MPkF
	'Kermesinum' (EA)	CDoC CTri MAsh MGos NWad SCob SLdr SLim
I	'Kermesinum Rosé' (EA) ♀H5	CDoC CRos CSBt LMil NLar SLdr SLim
	kesangiae	GGGa LMil
	– var. ***album***	GGGa
	keysii	LMil
	'Kilian' (A)	XSte
	(Kilimanjaro Group) 'Kilimanjaro'	LMil
	'Kimbeth'	GGGa
	'King George' Loder	see *R.* 'Loderi King George'
	kingianum	see *R. arboreum* subsp. *zeylanicum*
	'Kings Ride'	LMil
§	'Kirin' (Kurume) (EA/d)	CBcs LMil SLdr SRms XSte
	'Kirin' (Tsutsuji) (EA)	MPkF
	kiusianum (EA)	LMil WAbe
I	– 'Album' (EA)	LMil WAbe
	– 'Hillier's Pink' (EA)	LMil
	– var. ***kiusianum*** (EA)	SLdr
	'Kleiner Prinz' (EA)	SAko
	'Klondyke' (K) ♀H6	CBcs CDoC CRos CSBt CTri EGrI EPfP GGGa GKin LCro LMil LOPS LRHS MAsh MGos MPkF MPri NLar SCob SLdr SPer XSte
	'Kluis Sensation' ♀H5	CAco CBcs CMac LMil SLdr SSta
	'Kluis Triumph'	SSta
	'Knap Hill Apricot' (K)	LMil
	'Knap Hill Red' (K)	LMil
	'Knap Hill Salmon' (K) **new**	EGrI

	'Koichiro Wada'	see *R. yakushimanum* 'Koichiro Wada'
	'Kokardia'	LMil SAko
	'Königstein' (EA)	LMil MGos SSta
§	'Koningin Emma' (M)	LMil
	'Koningin Wilhelmina' (Vuykiana) (EA)	SLdr
	'Koran-yuki' (EA)	SRms
	'Koromo-shikibu' (EA)	MPkF XSte
	'Koster's Brilliant Red' (M)	SSta
	'Kromlauer Parkperle'	SAko
§	'Kure-no-yuki' (Kurume) (EA/d)	CEnd LMil
	(Lactcombei Group) 'Robert Keir'	SLdr
	lacteum	GGGa LMil
	'Lady Alice Fitzwilliam' ♀H3	CBcs CTsd GKin IDee LMil
	(Lady Chamberlain Group) 'Salmon Trout'	LMil LSRN
	'Lady Clementine Mitford' ♀H6	CBcs LMil LRHS SLdr SPer
	'Lady Dark' (EA)	LMil SAko
	'Lady Eleanor Cathcart'	SLdr
	'Lady Elphinstone' (Kurume) (EA)	SLdr
	'Lady Louise' (EA)	SLdr
	Lamellen Group	LMil
	lanatoides	GGGa
	lanatum	LMil
	lanigerum	LMil
	lapponicum	GKev
	- Parviflorum Group	GGGa
	'Lapwing' (K)	SLdr
	'Laramie'	LMil
	'Lavender Brilliant' (EA)	SLdr
	'Lavender Girl' ♀H6	LMil SLdr SSta
	'Lavendula'	LMil
	'Lee's Dark Purple'	CAco SCob
	'Lee's Scarlet'	LMil
	'Lemon Dream'	CDoC EPfP LRHS MAsh MGos MPri NRHS SLim
*	'Lemon Drop' (A)	GGGa
	'Lemonora' (M)	CBcs GKin
	'Lem's 45'	SLdr
	'Lem's Cameo' ♀H5	GGGa LMil SSta
	'Lem's Monarch' ♀H4	CBcs GGGa IDee LMil LRHS SLdr SSta XSte
	'Lem's Tangerine'	LMil
	'Lemur' (EA)	EGrI GGGa LMil
	'Leni'	LRHS MAsh NRHS
	'Leo' (EA)	SLdr
	'Leonore'	LMil
	lepidostylum	CMac GGGa LMil MHid WFar
	lepidotum yellow-flowered McB 110	WThu
§	'Leucanthum'	WThu
	leucaspis	SLdr
	'Libretto'	CRos
	'Lila Pedigo'	SLdr
	LILAC DUFTHECKE ('Rhodunter 149'PBR)	LMaj LMil
	'Lilac Time' (EA)	SLdr
	'Lilactina'	SLdr
	'Lily Marleen' (EA)	CTri
	'Linda' ♀H5	CBcs CMac EPfP GGGa LMil LSRN MAsh SLdr
	lindleyi	CBcs LRHS MPkF XSte
	'Linearifolium'	see *R. stenopetalum* 'Linearifolium'
	'Lingot d'Or' (A)	MPkF SGsty XSte
	Lionel's Triumph Group	LMil
	'Little Beauty' (EA)	SLdr
	'Little Ben'	EGrI
	'Little Favourite' (EA) **new**	EGrI
	'Loch Awe'	GGGa LMil
	'Loch Earn'	GGGa
	'Loch Faskally'	GGGa
	Lodauric Group	SLdr
§	- 'Lodauric Iceberg'	LMil
	Loderi Group	SLdr
	- 'Loderi Fairy Queen'	SLdr
	- 'Loderi Game Chick'	LMil SLdr
	- 'Loderi Georgette'	SLdr
	- 'Loderi Helen'	LMil SLdr
§	- 'Loderi King George' ♀H5	CAco CBcs GGGa GKin LMil LRHS SLdr SSta XSte
	- 'Loderi Patience'	SLdr
	- 'Loderi Pink Coral'	LMil SLdr
	- 'Loderi Pink Diamond' ♀H5	CBcs LMil SLdr XSte
	- 'Loderi Pink Topaz'	SLdr
	- 'Loderi Pretty Polly'	SLdr
	- 'Loderi Princess Marina'	SLdr
	- 'Loderi Sir Edmund'	LMil SLdr
	- 'Loderi Sir Joseph Hooker'	SLdr
	- 'Loderi Titan'	SLdr SSta
	- 'Loderi Venus' ♀H5	LMil SLdr SSta
	- 'Loderi White Diamond'	SLdr
	'Loder's White' ♀H5	CMac LMil SSta
	longesquamatum	GGGa
	longipes	LMil MHid
	- EGM 336	LMil
	- var. ***chienianum***	LMil MHid
	'Lord Roberts' ♀H6	CAco CBcs CDoC CMac CTri EGrI ELan LCro LMil LOPS MAsh MGos NHol SCob SLdr SLim SPer SSta
	'Louisa' (EA)	MAsh NLar
	'Louise Dowdle' (Glenn Dale) (EA)	LMil SLdr
	'Lovely William'	CMac IDee LMil LRHS SLdr
	'Lucy Lou'	GGGa
	ludlowii	GGGa
	'Lullaby' (EA)	SLdr
	'Lumina'	CRos NLar
	luteiflorum	MHid
	lutescens	CBcs CMac LMil SLdr
	- 'Bagshot Sands' ♀H3	GGGa LMil SLdr
	- 'Exbury'	CExl
	luteum (A)	Widely available
	- 'Golden Comet' (A)	GGGa
*	'Mac Ovata'	CMac
	macabeanum ♀H4	CBcs GGGa GKev GKin IDee IKel LMil LRHS MHid NLar SSta
	- NAPE 052	GGGa
	macabeanum × wardii	GGGa
	macrophyllum B&SWJ 9561	WCru
	macrosmithii	see *R. argipeplum*
	'Macrostemon' (EA)	XSte
	'Madame Ad. van Hecke' (EA)	CTri GKin LMil MAsh SLim
	'Madame Albert van Hecke' (EA)	CDoC LCro NLar SLdr
	'Madame de Bruin'	SLdr
	'Madame Galle'	CDoC NLar SLdr
	'Madame Masson' ♀H6	CAco CDoC CTri ELan EPfP LMil LRHS LSRN MAsh MGos MPri NLar SCob SGsty SPer SSta WFar XSte
	maddenii	CBcs LMil SAko
§	- subsp. ***crassum***	CBcs CExl GGGa LRHS WPGP
§	- subsp. ***maddenii*** Polyandrum Group	CBcs
	'Magic Flute' (EA)	LRHS MAsh NRHS SCoo

I	'Magic Flute' (V)	LMil SCoo
	magnificum	GKev
	'Mai-ogi' (EA)	SAko
	'Maischnee' (EA)	GGGa
	'Maja' (G)	SSta
§	***makinoi*** ♀H5	LMil MPkF SSta XSte
	mallotum	GGGa LMil
	'Manda Sue'	NLar
	'Mandarin Lights' (A)	NLar
	'Manderley'	LMil
	'Maraschino' (EA)	SAko
	'Mardi Gras'	MGos NLar SPer
	'Maria Elena' (EA/d)	CDoC CRos MGos NLar SLdr
	'Marie Fortie'	CDoC LRHS MGos NLar
	'Marie Hoffman'	LMil
	'Marilee' (EA)	EPfP LRHS MAsh NLar SLdr
	'Marinja' (EA)	LMil
	'Marinus Koster'	SSta
	'Markeeta's Prize' ♀H4	CAco CDoC CTsd ELan EPfP GGGa LMil LRHS MAsh MGos MPri NLar SGsty SLdr SLim XSte
	'Marlies' (A)	NLar
	'Marsalla'	SAko
	'Martha Isaacson' (Ad)	LMil SLdr
	'Martha Wright'	CDoC EPfP GGGa MAsh MPri NLar XSte
	'Maruschka' (EA) ♀H5	CDoC EPfP GGGa LMil LRHS MAsh NLar SAko SCoo
	'Mary Desby' (EA)	CEnd
	'Mary Helen' (Glenn Dale) (EA)	CDoC LMil LRHS MAsh MGos NRHS SCoo SLdr SLim
	'Mary Poppins' (A)	CSBt EGrl GKin LMil LSRN MGos MPkF SCoo SLdr SLim XSte
	(Matador Group) 'Matador'	LMil SLdr XSte
	'Mathie' (A)	SSta
	maximum	GKev MHid
	'Maxine Childers'	LRHS
§	'Maxwellii' (EA)	CMac SLdr
	May Day Group	CBcs MGos
	- 'May Day' ♀H5	CMac SLdr
	'Mayor Johnstone'	CTri EPfP MAsh MPri
	'Mécène' (R) **new**	XSte
	meddianum	LMil
	var. ***atrokermesinum*** F 2649	
	Medusa Group	SLdr
	'Megan' (EA)	LSRN MAsh SLdr
	megaphyllum	see *R. basilicum*
	megeratum KR 9426	LMil
	- 'Bodnant'	NWad WAbe
	'Melford Lemon'	see *R.* 'Ilam Melford Lemon'
	'Melle'PBR	MPkF
	'Melrose Flash'	XSte
	'Melville'	XSte
	'Merganser' ♀H4	GGGa LMil SLdr
	'Merlin' (Glenn Dale) (EA)	LMil
	METALLICA	see *R.* 'Hachmann's Metallica'
	metternichii var. ***pentamerum***	see *R. degronianum* subsp. *degronianum*
	'Mi Amor'	LMil
	'Michael Hill' (EA)	MAsh
	micranthum	LMil LRHS
	microgynum	GGGa MHid
	'Midnight Beauty'	CBcs EPfP LMil LRHS SAko
	'Midnight Mystique'	SSta
	'Midsummer'	SLdr
	'Midsummer Coral' (A)	IDee LMil LRHS
	'Midsummer Girl' (A)	LMil
	'Midsummer Mermaid' (A)	LMil
	'Midsummer Moon' (A)	IDee LMil LRHS
	'Midsummer Rose' (A)	LMil
	'Midsummer Star' (A)	LMil
	'Midsummer Wedding' (A)	LMil
	'Mikado' (EA)	see *R. kaempferi* 'Mikado'
	'Millennium' (A)	LRHS
	'Millennium Gold'PBR	IDee LMil
	'Milton' (R)	LMil LRHS
	'Mimi' (Kaempferi) (EA)	CMac
	'Ming'	see *R.* 'Ilam Ming'
	'Minnetonka'	CDoC
	minus	CBcs GKev
	- var. ***minus*** (Carolinianum Group) 'Epoch'	LMil
	'Moerheim' ♀H5	CBcs EPfP LRHS MAsh MPri SLim
§	'Moerheim's Pink'	SLdr
	(Mohamet Group) 'Mohamet'	LMil
	'Moidart' (Vs)	LMil
	'Moira Salmon' (EA)	SLdr
	molle 'Arctic Flush'PBR (A) **new**	EGrl
§	- subsp. ***japonicum*** (A)	LMil
	Mollis, orange-flowered (M)	GKin SGsty SRms
	- pink-flowered (M)	GKin SGsty SRms
	- red-flowered (M)	GKin SGsty
	- yellow-flowered (M)	GKin SRms
	'Molly Ann'	EGrl LSRN
	'Molten Gold' (v)	GGGa LMil LRHS MAsh
	'Monsieur Marcel Ménard' ♀H6	CBcs CDoC EPfP IDee LMil LRHS MAsh MGos MPri NLar SCob SLdr SPer SSta WFar XSte
	montroseanum	GGGa LMil MHid
	Moonstone Group	CMac
	- 'Moonstone Pink'	SLdr
	- 'Moonstone Yellow'	SLdr
	'Moonwood Ivory' (V) **new**	LRHS XSte
§	'Morgenrot'	CDoC WFar
	morii	GGGa MHid
	'Morning Cloud'	CDoC EPfP LPar LRHS MAsh MGos NHol NLar SCob SLim SSta
	MORNING RED	see *R.* 'Morgenrot'
	'Moser's Maroon'	CBcs CDoC GGGa LSRN NLar SGsty SLdr WFar XSte
	'Mother of Pearl'	SLdr
	'Mother's Day' (Kurume) (EA) ♀H4	CDoC CMac CRos CSBt CTri EGrl EPfP GKin LCro LMil LOPS LRHS LSRN MAsh MGos MPri NHol NLar NRHS SCob SLdr SLim SPer SPoG SRms SSta WFar
§	***moulmainense***	CMCN
	'Mount Everest'	LMil SSta
	'Mount Rainier' (A)	LRHS MPkF XSte
	'Mount Saint Helens' (A)	CDoC LMil NLar SLim SPer
	'Mount Seven Star'	see *R. nakaharae* 'Mount Seven Star'
	moupinense	GGGa SLdr
	'Mrs A.T. de la Mare' ♀H6	LMil SSta
	'Mrs Betty Robertson'	CMac GBin SLdr
	'Mrs Charles E. Pearson' ♀H6	CBcs CSBt LMil SLdr SSta XSte
	'Mrs Davies Evans'	SSta
	'Mrs Emil Hager' (EA)	SLdr
	'Mrs G.W. Leak'	XSte
	'Mrs J.G. Millais'	LMil
	'Mrs James Horlick'	CAco
	'Mrs T.H. Lowinsky' ♀H6	CBcs CDoC CMac GGGa GKin LMil LRHS MAsh MGos NLar SCob SLdr SLim SPer
§	× ***mucronatum*** (EA)	LRHS SLdr
	mucronulatum	CBcs XSte
	- B&SWJ 786	WCru
	- B&SWJ 8657	WCru
	- var. ***albiflorum***	LMil SLdr

	'Muffet' (EA)	SLdr
	'Mulroy Cream'	LMil
	'Mum'	LMil
	'Nabucco' (A)	CRos EGrI LRHS MGos MMuc MPkF NLar SLdr
	nakaharae (EA) ♀H5	SLdr
	- 'Mariko' (EA)	EPot WThu
§	- 'Mount Seven Star' (EA) ♀H5	LMil SLdr WThu
§	- orange-flowered (EA)	LMil LRHS MAsh NRHS SLdr XSte
	- pink-flowered (EA)	SLdr XSte
	'Nakahari Orange'	see *R. nakaharae* orange-flowered
	nakotiltum	MHid
	'Nancy Evans' ♀H5	CDoC CRos EPfP GGGa GKin LMil LPar LRHS LSRN MAsh MGos MPri NLar SCob SLdr SLim SSta
	'Nani-wagata' (EA) **new**	CSBt CTsd EGrI
	'Nanki Poo' (EA)	SLdr
	'Naomi' (EA)	SLdr
	(Naomi Group) 'Exbury Naomi'	LMil
	- 'Naomi Nautilus'	LMil
	- 'Naomi Pink Beauty'	LMil
	- 'Naomi Stella Maris'	LMil
	'Narcissiflorum' (G/d) ♀H6	CBcs EGrI GKin IDee LMil LRHS MPkF NLar XSte
	'Naselle'	LMil
	NEGLIGÉ ('Hachneg'PBR) (EA)	MPkF
	neoglandulosum	NLar
	neriiflorum	GGGa GKev LMil
	- CN&W 906	LMil
	- subsp. ***neriiflorum***	MHid
§	- subsp. ***phaedropum***	LMil MHid
	- - KR 9308	LMil
	'Newcomb's Sweetheart'	LMil
	'Niagara' (Glenn Dale) (EA) ♀H5	CMac LMil SLdr
	'Niamh' (A) **new**	LMil
	'Nicholas de Rothschild' (A/d)	LMil
	'Nico' (EA)	CMac LMil LRHS MAsh SCoo
	'Night Sky' ♀H5	CDoC CRos EPfP GGGa GKev LMil LRHS MGos NLar SLdr
	'Nimrod' **new**	XSte
	'Nishiki' (EA)	CMac
	nitens	see *R. calostrotum* subsp. *riparium* Nitens Group
	nitidulum	GKev
	- var. ***omeiense***	WThu
	nivale	GKev
	- subsp. ***boreale***	GKev
§	- subsp. ***nivale***	ITim NWad
	niveum ♀H5	GGGa LMil LRHS MHid
	- B&SWJ 2611	WCru
	- B&SWJ 2659	WCru
	- B&SWJ 2675	WCru
	Nobleanum Group	GGGa LMil SLdr SSta
	- 'Nobleanum Coccineum'	CMac LMil SLdr
	- 'Nobleanum Venustum'	LMil SSta
	- 'Oudijk's Sensation'	MAsh SLdr
	Nobleanum Album Group	CMac GGGa LMil SLdr
	'Nordlicht' (EA)	SLdr
	'Northern Hi-Lights' (A)	CDoC CRos GKin LMil LRHS MGos MPkF NLar SCob SLim SPer XSte
	'Nova Zembla'	CAco CBcs CDoC CTri EGrI EPfP IDee LCro LMil LOPS LPar LRHS MAsh MGos MPkF SCob SGsty SLim SPer SSta XSte
	'Nuccio's Blue Moon' (EA)	LMil MPkF SLdr
	'Nuccio's Wild Cherry' (EA)	SWeb

	nudiflorum	see *R. periclymenoides*
	nuttallii	LMil
	'Oban'	EPot GEdr ITim
	Obtusum Group (EA)	SLdr
	- 'Amoenum' (EA/d)	CBcs CMac CSBt EGrI LMil SLdr SPer XSte
	- 'Amoenum Coccineum' (EA/d)	SLdr SSta
§	- 'Hinomayo' (EA) ♀H5	CBcs CMac CTri EPfP GKin LMil SCob SLdr XSte
	occidentale (A)	GKev GKin LMil LRHS SLdr
	- SIN 1830	GGGa
	ochraceum ♀H5	GGGa LMil
	- C&H 7042	LMil
	'Odee Wright'	CAco MAsh
	'Oi-no-mezame' (Kurume) (EA)	SLdr
	'Old Port'	LMaj LMil SCob
	oldhamii (EA) B&SWJ 3742	WCru
	'Olga' ♀H5	LMil SSta XSte
	'Olive'	LMil
	'Olivia' **new**	LMil
	'Opossum' (EA)	GGGa
	ORAKEL	see *R.* 'Hachmann's Orakel'
	'Orange Beauty' (Kaempferi) (EA)	CBcs EGrI ILea MAsh SLdr SRms
	'Orange King' (EA) ♀H5	CDoC LMil LRHS MGos NLar SLdr SPoG
	'Orangeade' (K)	LRHS MPkF XSte
	orbiculare ♀H5	GGGa LMil
	- subsp. ***orbiculare***	MHid
	'Orchid Lights'	MAsh
	'Oregon' (EA)	SLdr
	Oregonia Group	LMil
	oreodoxa	LMil
§	- var. ***fargesii*** ♀H5	GGGa LMil MHid
	- var. ***oreodoxa***	LMil MHid
	oreotrephes ♀H5	LMil MHid
§	- Exquisitum Group	SLdr
	- 'Pentland'	GGGa LMil
	'Orion' ambig.	NLar
	'Orpheus' (EA) **new**	XSte
	'Osaraku Seedling' (EA)	LRHS
	'Osmar' ♀H5	GGGa
	'Ostara'	CBcs
	'Oudijk's Favorite'	SLdr
	'P. den Ouden' × ***williamsianum***	LMaj
	pachysanthum ♀H5	GGGa GKin LMil SLdr
	- 'Crosswater'	IDee LMil LRHS
	- 'Little White Dane'	LMil
	pachytrichum	GGGa
	- var. ***pachytrichum***	MHid
	- - 'Sesame'	LMil
	'Palestrina' (Vuykiana) (EA) ♀H5	CBcs CMac CSBt EPfP GKin MAsh MPkF SCob SGsty SLdr SPer SSta
	paludosum	see *R. nivale* subsp. *nivale*
	'Pancake'	CMac
	'Panda' (EA) ♀H5	CSBt EPfP GGGa LMil LRHS MAsh SLdr SSta
	'Parfait' (EA)	LMil
	'Parkfeuer' (A) ♀H6	GGGa SGsty
	parmulatum	LMil
	- KW 5876	LMil
	- 'Ocelot'	GGGa
	'Patricia's Day'	LMil
	'Patty Bee' ♀H5	CBcs CDoC CTri EGrI EPfP GEdr GGGa GKev LMil LRHS MAsh MGos MPri NLar SCob SLim SSta XSte
	'Pavlova' (A)	LMil
	'Pearce's American Beauty'	LMaj NLar

	'Pearl Betteridge'	LMil
	'Peep-bo' (EA)	SLdr
	'Peeping Tom'	NHol SSta
	'Peggy'	LMil
	'Pemakofairy'	WThu
	pendulum	GGGa MHid
	'Penheale Blue' 🏆H5	GKev GKin LMil
	'Penjerrick'	GGGa
	'Pennsylvania' (Vs) **new**	LRHS
	'Penny Tomlin'	SSta
	'Peppermint Candy'	LMil
	'Peppina'	LMil
	'Percy Wiseman' 🏆H5	CBcs CDoC CSBt EPfP GGGa GKin LCro LMil LOPS LPar LRHS MAsh MGos NLar SCob SGsty SLdr SLim SPer SSta WFar XSte
§	***periclymenoides*** (A)	GKev LMil
	'Persil' (K) 🏆H6	CBcs CSBt CTri EGrI ELan EPfP GGGa GKin IDee LMil LRHS MAsh MPri NHol NLar SCob SCoo SLdr SSta WFar
	'Peter Bee'	LMil LRHS
	'Peter Gable' (EA)	SLdr
	'Peter John Mezitt'	see *R.* (PJM Group) 'Peter John Mezitt'
	'Peter Koster' (M)	MPkF XSte
	'Peter Koster' (hybrid)	GKin
	petrocharis	GGGa
	PETTICOAT ('Hachpett') (EA)	LMil
	'Pfauenauge'	GGGa LMil
	phaedropum	see *R. neriiflorum* subsp. *phaedropum*
	phaeochrysum	GKev
	- var. ***agglutinatum***	GKev
	- 'Glossy Dane'	LMil
	- var. ***phaeochrysum***	MHid
	'Phalarope'	EGrI GEdr
	'Phyllis Korn'	LMil LRHS NLar
§	***piercei***	GGGa LMil
	pingianum	EPfP GGGa
	- EGM 304	LMil
	'Pink and Sweet' (A)	LRHS MGos
	'Pink Bride'	SLdr
	'Pink Cameo'	CAco
	'Pink Cherub' 🏆H6	LMil MAsh
I	'Pink Delight' (K)	GKin
	'Pink Drift'	CSBt GEdr LMil
	'Pink Gin'	LMil
	'Pink Mimosa' (Vs)	SLdr
	'Pink Pancake' (EA) 🏆H4	EPfP LMil LRHS MAsh MPkF MPri SLdr
	'Pink Pearl' (EA)	see *R.* 'Azuma-kagami'
	'Pink Pearl' (hybrid) 🏆H4	CBcs CSBt CTri GGGa LMil MAsh SLdr SSta
	'Pink Pebble' 🏆H5	CExl MAsh
	'Pink Perfection'	CMac SLdr
	'Pink Polar Bear'	LMil
	'Pink Purple Dream' **new**	LRHS
	'Pink Spider'PBR (EA)	LMil LRHS SCoo
	'Pintail'	LMil LRHS MAsh
	'Pippa' (EA)	CMac
§	(PJM Group) 'Peter John Mezitt'	NLar
	platypodum	LMil
	- CGG 14005	GGGa
	'Pleasant White' (EA)	CDoC LCro LMil LOPS NLar SCob
	'Plover'	LRHS XSte
	pocophorum var. ***pocophorum***	MHid
	'Polar Bear' (EA)	CAco SLdr
	Polar Bear Group	LMil
	- 'Polar Bear'	GKin LMil
	'Polaris' (EA)	LRHS
	'Polaris'	see *R.* 'Hachmann's Polaris'
	'Polarnacht'	CBcs CRos LMil NLar SLdr SPer XSte
	poluninii KR 8231	LMil
	polyandrum	see *R. maddenii* subsp. *maddenii* Polyandrum Group
	polylepis	MHid
	'Polyroy'	GGGa
	ponticum	CAco CMac CTri NHol WFar XSte
	- 'Filigran'	LMil
§	- 'Variegatum' (v)	CAco CMac EPfP IDee MAsh MGos MPri NLar SLdr SPer SPoG SRms XSte
	'Praecox' 🏆H6	CBcs CDoC GBin GGGa GKin LCro LMil LOPS LRHS MAsh MGos MPri NLar SLdr SLim SPer SPoG
	praestans	GKin LMil
	prattii	GGGa MHid
	'President Roosevelt' (v)	CMac EPfP GKin MAsh MPri SCob SLdr SPoG SSta XSte
	'Pridenjoy'	LMil
	primuliflorum 'Doker-La'	GGGa LMil WAbe
	'Princess Alice'	CBcs IDee SLdr
	'Princess Anne' 🏆H6	CBcs CDoC CMac CRos IDee LCro LMil LOPS MGos NHpl NLar SCob SLdr SLim SPer SPoG SSta
	'Princess Margaret of Windsor' (K)	LMil
	principis	LMil
	- 'Lost Horizon'	LMil
§	- Vellereum Group	MHid
	prinophyllum (A)	GGGa LMil
	- 'Philip Holmes'	LMil
	'Prins Bernhard' (EA)	MAsh SLdr
	'Prinses Juliana' (Vuykiana) (EA)	SLdr
	'Prinses Máxima'	IDee LMil
	'Professor Hugo de Vries'	SLdr
	pronum R.B. Cooke form	GGGa
	- Towercourt form	GGGa
	proteoides	GGGa
	prunifolium (A)	LMil
	- 'August Fire' (A) **new**	LMil
	- 'Ted's Red' (A) **new**	LMil
	pseudochrysanthum 🏆H6	GGGa LMil
	- dwarf RWJ 9807	WCru
	'Ptarmigan' 🏆H6	GGGa GKev LMil WThu
§	'Pucella' (G)	MPkF XSte
	'Pulchrum Maxwellii'	see *R.* 'Maxwellii'
	pumilum	WAbe WThu
	'Purple Cushion' (EA)	EPfP LMil LRHS MAsh MPri NRHS
	'Purple Gem'	CDoC CRos MGos NLar SCob
	'Purple Passion'PBR	CDoC LMil LRHS LSRN NLar SLdr SPer
	'Purple Queen' (EA/d)	MAsh
	'Purple Splendor' (Gable) (EA)	CMac SGsty SLdr
	'Purple Splendour'	CBcs LMil MGos SCob SPer SSta
	'Purple Triumph' (Vuykiana) (EA) 🏆H5	LMil SLdr
	'Purpurtraum' (EA) 🏆H5	LMil
	qiaojiaense NN 0903	LMil
	'Quail'	GGGa
	'Queen Alice'	CDoC NLar
	'Queen Elizabeth II'	LRHS
	QUEEN EMMA	see *R.* 'Koningin Emma'
	'Queen Mary'	SSta
	'Quiet Thoughts' **new**	LRHS
	quinquefolium (A)	IDee LMil LRHS MHid SLdr
	RABATZ ('Hachraba')	GGGa LMil SAko

racemosum 𝕐^{H6}	GKev LMil MHid
- BWJ 7811	WCru
- 'Rock Rose' 𝕐^{H5}	LMil SLdr
'Racoon' (EA)	GGGa LMil
radicans	see *R. calostrotum* subsp. *keleticum* Radicans Group
'Ramapo' 𝕐^{H6}	CDoC GGGa IDee LMil LRHS MAsh MGos NLar NRHS SCob SLdr SLim
ramsdenianum	MHid
'Rasputin'	LMil NLar
'Razorbill' 𝕐^{H5}	CDoC GGGa GKin LMil NLar SLim
recurvoides	IDee LMil LRHS SLdr
'Red and Gold'	EPfP GGGa LMil LRHS MPri
'Red Dawn'	LRHS NRHS
'Red Delicious'	LMil SLdr
'Red Diamond'	see *R.* Diamant Group red-flowered
'Red Heart'	LMil
'Red Jack'	MGos SPoG SSta
'Red Pimpernel' (EA)	SLdr
'Red Wing'	see *R.* 'Hexe de Saffelaere'
'Red Wood'	GGGa
'Redwings' (EA)	SLdr
'Reich's Signifikant'	SAko
Remo Group	CMac
'Rennie' (A)	MMuc
'Renoir' 𝕐^{H5}	LMil
reticulatum (A)	CBcs LMil LRHS
'Reuthe's Purple'	WThu
'Rêve d'Amour' (Vs)	SSta
'Rex' (EA)	MAsh SGsty
rex 𝕐^{H5}	GGGa GKev GKin IDee LMil SLdr
- EGM 295	LMil
§ - subsp. ***fictolacteum*** 𝕐^{H5}	GGGa GKin LMil LRHS MHid SLdr
- subsp. ***rex*** 𝕐^{H5}	MHid
'Rexima'	LMil
'Ria Hardijzer' (Ad)	LMil
'Ribbon Candy' (A)	LRHS MPkF
rigidum	GGGa
- 'Album'	LMil
'Ring of Fire'	LMil LRHS MPkF XSte
ririei	GGGa
'Robert Croux'	SLdr
'Robert Seleger'	GKin LMil MAsh NLar
'Robin Hill Frosty' (EA)	SLdr
'Robin Hill Gillie' (EA)	SLdr
'Robinette'	MAsh
'Rocket'	CAco CDoC LPar LRHS MAsh MGos SLim SPer SPoG
'Roehr's Peggy Ann' (EA)	MPkF XSte
'Rokoko'	see *R.* 'Hachmann's Rokoko'
(Romany Chai Group) 'Romany Chai'	XSte
'Rosa' (EA)	CDoC
Rosalind Group	CMac
- 'Rosalind'	WFar
'Rosalinda' (EA)	SLdr
'Rosata' (Vs) 𝕐^{H5}	SSta
'Rose Bud'	CBcs CSBt CTri WThu
'Rose Glow' (A)	SSta
'Rose Greely' (Gable) (EA) 𝕐^{H5}	CRos NLar SCoo SLim SPer
'Rose Haze' (Vs)	SSta
'Rose Marie' **new**	XSte
'Rosebud' (EA/d)	CMac SLdr SSta SWeb
'Rosemary Hyde' (EA)	SLdr
roseum	see *R. canescens*
'Roseum Elegans'	CAco CDoC LCro LMaj LOPS LPar LRHS MAsh SCob SGsty SLim
'Rosevallon'	MHid
ROSINETTA ('Hachrosi') (EA)	LMil

'Rosy Dream'	MAsh
'Rosy Fire' (A)	LMil
rothschildii	GGGa LMil MHid SLdr
roxieanum	GGGa LMil
§ - var. ***cucullatum***	GKev
- var. ***oreonastes*** 𝕐^{H5}	GGGa LMil
§ - var. ***roxieanum***	MHid
'Royal Command' (K)	CBcs CTri EPfP GKin LMil LRHS
'Royal Lodge' (K)	LRHS MPkF XSte
'Royal Windsor'	LMil
'Roza Stevenson'	SLdr
'Rubicon'	SLdr
rubiginosum 𝕐^{H6}	GGGa GKev LMil
- var. ***rubiginosum***	MHid
RUBY WEDDING	see *R.* 'Firestorm'
rude	see *R. glischrum* subsp. *rude*
§ ***rupicola*** var. ***chryseum***	GKev
russatum 𝕐^{H6}	CBcs LMil SLdr
- blue-black-flowered	LMil
- 'Purple Pillow'	SCob
Russautinii Group	SLdr
'Rusty Dane'	LMil
'Rwain'	NLar XSte
'Ryde Heron' (EA)	SLdr
'Sabina' (EA)	SLdr
'Sacko'	CDoC LMil NLar SLim
'Saffron Queen'	CBcs CTsd LMil LRHS MPkF XSte
'Sahara' (K)	SLdr
'Saint Kew'	SLdr
'Saint Merryn' 𝕐^{H5}	CBcs EGrI
'Saint Minver'	LMil
'Saint Tudy'	SLdr
'Sakata Red' (EA)	SLdr
'Salmon Sander' (EA)	SLdr
'Salmon's Leap' (EA/v)	CMac CSBt LMil LRHS MAsh SCoo SSta
saluenense	LMil SLdr WThu
'Samuel Taylor Coleridge' (M)	GKin
sanguineum	LMil
§ - subsp. ***didymum***	GGGa SLdr
- subsp. ***sanguineum*** var. ***haemaleum***	GGGa LMil
- - var. ***sanguineum*** F 25521	LMil
'Santa Maria' (EA) 𝕐^{H5}	CDoC CRos LMil LSRN NLar SCob SSta
§ 'Saotome' (EA)	SLdr
'Sappho'	CAco CMac GGGa GKin LMil SCob SLdr SSta
sargentianum	WAbe WThu
(Sarled Group) 'Sarled' 𝕐^{H5}	LMil
'Sasonade' **new**	LMil
'Satan' (K) 𝕐^{H6}	IDee LMil LRHS MGos MPri NLar SCob SSta
Satsuki Group (EA)	SLdr SRms SWeb
- 'Gumpo Pink' (EA)	SLdr
- 'Gumpo Pink & White' (EA)	SLdr
- 'Gumpo White' (EA)	LRHS MAsh NRHS SPoG
'Saturnus' (M)	EGrI GKin
saxifragoides (V)	LRHS
'Saxon Blush'^{PBR} (v) **new**	LRHS XSte
§ ***scabrifolium*** var. ***spiciferum***	CMac SLdr
'Scarlet Wonder' 𝕐^{H6}	CBcs CDoC CRos EGrI EPfP GKev GKin LMil LRHS MAsh MGos MPri NHpl NLar SCob SPer WFar
schlippenbachii (A) 𝕐^{H6}	CBcs CMCN GGGa IDee LMil LRHS SLdr
'Schneebukett' (Inkarho)	NLar
'Schneekrone' 𝕐^{H6}	LMil

SCHNEEPERLE ('Hachschnee') (EA) ♀H5	LMil LRHS NRHS
'Scintillation' ♀H6	CDoC CRos ELan LMil LPar MAsh MGos MMuc NLar SCob SLdr SPer
scopulorum	SLdr
'Scout' (EA)	LMil MAsh SLdr
scyphocalyx	see *R. dichroanthum* subsp. *scyphocalyx*
'Seaview Sunset'	GGGa MGos
seinghkuense	GGGa LMil
- CCH&H 8106	LMil
§ ***selense*** subsp. ***dasycladum***	MHid
semnoides	LMil
'Sennocke'	LMil LRHS
'September Red'	LMil LRHS
'September Song' ♀H4	GGGa LMil MAsh NHol
serotinum	GGGa LMil MHid
'Shamrock' ♀H6	CDoC CTsd EGrI EPfP GEdr LRHS MAsh MGos NLar SCob SLim SPoG WFar
'Sheila' (EA)	CSBt MAsh MPri
'Shelley' (EA)	LMil LSRN
'Shiko' (EA)	MAsh
'Shiko Lavender' (A)	LMil SPoG
Shilsonii Group	LMil
'Shin-sekai' (Kurume) (EA/d)	SLdr
sikangense var. ***exquisitum***	MHid
- var. ***sikangense***	MHid
'Silbervelours'	LMil
§ 'Silberwolke' ♀H6	EPfP LMil LRHS MAsh WFar XSte
SILVER CLOUD	see *R.* 'Silberwolke'
'Silver Edge'	see *R. ponticum* 'Variegatum'
'Silver Glow' (EA)	CMac
'Silver Jubilee' ♀H4	IDee LMil
'Silver Moon' (Glenn Dale) (EA)	SLdr
'Silver Queen' (EA)	MPkF SPoG XSte
'Silver Sixpence'	EPfP LRHS LSRN SLdr
'Silver Skies'	LMil
'Silver Slipper' (K) ♀H5	CBcs GKin LCro LMil LOPS NHol SSta WFar
'Silver Sword' (EA/v)	SPoG
'Silvester' (Kurume) (EA)	CTri LMil LRHS MAsh SCoo SLdr
simsii (EA)	CMac SLdr
sinofalconeri	GGGa GKev LMil MHid
- KR 7342	LMil
- SEH 229	LMil
sinogrande ♀H4	CBcs ELon GGGa GKin IDee LMil LRHS MPkF NLar
- KR 4027	LMil
§ 'Sir Charles Butler'	LMil
'Sir Charles Lemon' ♀H4	CBcs GGGa LMil LRHS MAsh XSte
'Sir Robert' (EA)	LRHS MAsh
'Sleeping Beauty'	WAbe
'Sleepy'	CBcs MAsh NHol
smirnowii	LMil LRHS MHid
§ Smithii Group	CBcs XSte
smithii	see *R. argipeplum*
'Sneezy' ♀H5	CBcs CRos EPfP LMaj LMil LRHS MAsh MGos SGsty SLdr SLim SSta XSte
'Snipe'	CDoC CTri CTsd LMil LRHS MAsh MGos NLar NRHS SLdr SLim SPer WThu
'Snow Crown' (*lindleyi* hybrid)	MAsh
'Snow Hill' (EA) ♀H5	CEnd LMil
'Snow Lady'	CBcs CDoC EGrI EPfP GEdr GKin MAsh SLdr
'Snow Pearl'	CRos EPfP MAsh MPri NLar SCoo
Snow Queen Group	LMil
- 'Snow Queen'	LMil
'Snowbird' (A)	CBcs ELan
'Snowflake' (EA/d)	see *R.* 'Kure-no-yuki'
'Snowwhite' (EA)	CDoC MGos NLar SLdr
'Soft Lights' (A/d)	LMil
'Soir de Paris' (Vs) ♀H6	CBcs CEnd CSBt GGGa GKin LMil NHol SSta WFar
(Solent Group) 'Drury Lane' (K)	LMil
'Solidarity'	CAco CBcs SLdr SSta
'Sonata'	GGGa
'Sonatine'	LMil
'Songbird'	LMil SLdr
sororium (V)	LMil
- KR 3085	LMil
souliei	GKev LMil LRHS
'Souvenir de D.A. Koster'	SLdr
'Souvenir of Anthony Waterer'	SSta
'Souvenir of W.C. Slocock'	NLar
'Special Dane' **new**	LRHS
speciosum	see *R. flammeum*
'Spek's Orange' (M)	GKin SPer
sphaeranthum	see *R. trichostomum*
sphaeroblastum	MHid
- 'Super Dane'	LMil
spiciferum	see *R. scabrifolium* var. *spiciferum*
spilotum	MHid
'Spinner's Glory'	MAsh
'Spitfire'	NHol SSta
'Spring Rose'	SLdr
'Spring Sunshine'	LMil
'Squirrel' (EA) ♀H5	CDoC GGGa GKin LMil MAsh NLar SLdr SLim
'Stadt Essen'	LMil SLdr
§ 'Stanway'	LMil
'Starbright Champagne'	MAsh SSta
'Statuette'	SAko
stenaulum	see *R. moulmainense*
§ ***stenopetalum*** 'Linearifolium' (EA)	CBcs CMac LMil LRHS SLdr XSte
stenophyllum	see *R. makinoi*
stewartianum	MHid
'Stewartstonian' (EA)	CMac LCro LOPS
'Stoat' (EA)	NLar
'Stopham Girl' (A)	LMil
'Stopham Joy' (A)	IDee LMil LRHS
'Stopham Lad' (A)	LMil
'Strategist'	SLdr
'Strawberry Cream'	EPfP LMil LRHS
'Strawberry Ice' (K) ♀H6	CBcs CSBt EGrI ELan GGGa GKin MMrt SCob SPer
'Strawberry Sundae'	SLdr
strigillosum	GGGa
'Suga-no-ito' (Kurume) (EA)	SLdr
sulfureum	MHid
'Summer Blaze' (A)	SLdr
'Summer Dawn'	LMil
'Summer Fragrance' (A) ♀H6	LMil MPkF SSta
'Summer Snow'	SAko
'Summer Sorbet'	LMil
'Summer Sunshine' (A)	LMil
'Sun Chariot' (K)	CBcs
'Sun Fire'	EGrI LMil LRHS
'Sun Star' (EA)	GGGa LMil
'Sunte Nectarine' (K) ♀H6	CRos GKin MPkF NLar
suoilenhense	CMCN GGGa MHid

- NVD 18	GGGa
'Surprise' ambig. (EA)	CTri EGrI SLdr
'Surrey Heath'	CBcs CDoC EPfP LMil LPar LRHS MGos SCob SLdr SLim SPer
'Susan' (EA)	IDee NLar SSta
'Susan' J.C. Williams	LMil
'Susannah Hill' (EA)	SLdr
sutchuenense	GGGa LMil
'Swansong' (EA)	CMac
'Swift' 𝕐H4	EPfP GEdr GGGa IDee LMil LRHS MAsh NRHS SLdr
'T.S. Black' (EA)	SLdr
'Tahitian Dawn' **new**	LRHS XSte
'Talavera'	LMil
taliense	LMil
- SBEC 0350	GGGa
- 'Honigduft'	LMil LRHS
- 'Woolly Dane'	LMil
Tally Ho Group	LMil
'Tamanini' (EA)	MPkF XSte
'Tama-no-utena' (EA)	SLdr
'Tangerine'	see *R.* (Fabia Group) 'Fabia Tangerine'
'Tapestry' PBR	LMil NLar
'Taragona' **new**	SPer XSte
tatsienense	GKev
'Taurus' 𝕐H5	CBcs EPfP GKin IDee LMaj LMil LRHS MAsh SAko SLdr
'Ted Millais'	LMil
'Teddy Bear'	EPfP LMil SSta
Temple Belle Group	EGrI SLdr
'Tequila Sunrise'	LRHS
'Terracotta'	LMil LRHS NLar
'Terra-cotta Beauty' (EA)	WThu
(Tessa Group) 'Tessa'	CMac
'Thai Gold' (V)	LRHS
§ 'The Honourable Jean Marie de Montague' 𝕐H4	CDoC GGGa GKin LMil MAsh MGos NLar SPer SSta
'The Marquis of Lansdowne'	LMil LRHS
'Thomas David' (A)	LMil
thomsonii	GGGa LMil MHid
- B&SWJ 2638	WCru
- WJC 13737	WCru
'Thor'	GGGa
'Tibet'	LMil LRHS
'Tidbit' 𝕐H3	CMac IDee LMil SLdr
'Tina' (EA)	MPkF
'Tinkerbird'	CDoC EPfP GGGa LMil LRHS MAsh MGos MPri XSte
titapuriense	GGGa
'Titian Beauty'	CBcs CDoC CRos EPfP GGGa LMil LRHS MAsh MGos NRHS SLdr SLim SPer SPoG
'Titness Park'	LMil
'Tit-Willow' (EA)	LRHS MAsh NRHS SCoo SLdr
tomentosum	MGil WThu
'Too Bee'	EGrI GEdr
'Torchlight' (EA) 𝕐H5	CDoC CRos LMil MGos NLar
'Toreador' (EA)	SLdr
'Tornado'	EGrI
(Tortoiseshell Group) 'Champagne' 𝕐H3	CBcs CDoC LMil MAsh MPri NLar SPer
- 'Tortoiseshell Orange' 𝕐H3	CBcs IDee LMil LRHS MGos NLar SCob SGsty SLim SPer SSta XSte
- 'Tortoiseshell Wonder' 𝕐H3	EPfP LRHS MAsh
'Toucan' (K)	CSBt LMil LRHS MPkF XSte
'Tower Beauty' (A)	LMil
'Tower Dainty' (A)	LMil
'Tower Daring' (A)	LMil
'Tower Dexter' (A)	LMil
'Tower Dragon' (A)	LMil

traillianum	GKev LMil
- var. ***dictyotum*** 'Kathmandu'	LMil
- var. ***traillianum***	MHid
'Treasure' (AE)	SGsty
'Tree Creeper'	GGGa GKev LMil
'Trewithen Orange'	SLdr
trichanthum 'Honey Wood'	LMil SLdr
trichocladum	GKev
§ ***trichostomum***	GGGa WAbe
- Ledoides Group	LMil
triflorum	LMil
§ - var. ***bauhiniiflorum***	CMac
- var. ***triflorum***	MHid
'Tri-Lights' (A)	MPkF
'Tromba'	IDee LMil LRHS
'Tropic Glow' (V)	LRHS
'Tropical Salad' (A) **new**	LRHS
'True Blue' **new**	XSte
tsariense	LMil XSte
- var. ***trimoense***	LMil
- - KW 8288	LMil
- var. ***tsariense***	MHid
'Tuffet' (EA)	LMil SLdr
'Tunis' (K)	EGrI EPfP MAsh MPri
'Turnstone'	GGGa
'Umpqua Queen' (K)	MPkF XSte
'Unique' (G)	CBcs EPfP
'Unique' (*campylocarpum* hybrid)	MAsh SLdr
uvariifolium var. ***griseum***	MHid
- 'Reginald Childs'	LMil
valentinianum	SLdr
'Van'	CDoC IDee LMil LPar LRHS MGos NLar SLim SPer
'Van Nes Sensation'	LMil
Vanessa Group	LMil
- 'Vanessa Pastel' 𝕐H4	CMac GGGa LMil SLdr SSta
vaseyi (A) 𝕐H5	GGGa LMil
- 'White Find'	GGGa
- white-flowered (A)	LMil
'Vayo' (EA)	SLdr
§ ***veitchianum*** Cubittii Group	CBcs
'Velasquez' (R) **new**	MPkF
venator	GGGa
'Venetia' (K)	SSta
vernicosum × ***wardii*** SDR 5026	GKev
'Vernum' **new**	LRHS
'Veryan Bay'	LMil
'Vida Brown' (Kurume) (EA/d)	CMac SLdr
'Vinecourt Dream' (M)	GKin NLar SLdr
'Vinecourt Duke' (A/d)	GKin MMuc
'Vineland Dream' (K/d)	GKin
'Vintage Rosé' 𝕐H5	LMil MMuc SSta
'Violetta' (Glenn Dale) (EA)	SLdr
'Violette Funken'	LMil
'Virgile' (R)	MPkF
'Virginia Richards'	LPar LRHS MAsh SLdr
§ ***viridescens***	MHid
- 'Doshong La'	LMil
§ - Rubroluteum Group	SLdr
viscosum (Vs) 𝕐H6	CBcs CDoC CMac CRos GGGa LMil LRHS MGos MMrt NLar SLdr SPer
- 'Framingham' (A) **new**	LRHS
- 'Grey Leaf' (Vs)	LMil
- f. ***rhodanthum*** (Vs)	LMil
- 'Roseum' (Vs)	LMil

	- 'Sea of Stars' (A) **new**	LMil
	- 'Sparkler' (A) **new**	LRHS
	- 'Weston's Lemon Drop' (A) **new**	LRHS
	- 'White Ness' (Vs)	LMil
	'Viscount Powerscourt'	SLdr
	'Viscy' ♀H5	GKin LMil SLdr
	'Viscy' (Inkarho)	NLar
	'Vladimir Bukovski' (V) **new**	LRHS XSte
§	Volker Group	LMil LRHS NRHS SGsty
	'Vollblut'	SSta
	'Vulcan' ♀H4	EPfP IDee LMil LRHS
	'Vuyk's Rosyred' (Vuykiana) (EA) ♀H6	CBcs CMac CTri EGrI GKin LMil MAsh NHol NWad SLdr SPer SPoG SRms SWeb WFar
	'Vuyk's Scarlet' (Vuykiana) (EA) ♀H6	CBcs CMac CSBt CTri EGrI GKin LRHS MAsh MPri NHol NRHS NWad SCob SGsty SLdr SPer SPlb SSta
	W.F.H. Group ♀H3	LMil SLdr
§	WALBERTON'S MAUVE RUFFLES ('Walmauvruf'PBR) (EA/d)	ILea
§	WALBERTON'S SNOW RUFFLES ('Walsnowruf'PBR) (EA/d)	ILea
	WALKÜRE ('Hachwalk')	LMil LRHS
	wallichii	GKev LMil MHid
	'Wallowa Red' (A)	EGrI MMuc MPkF XSte
	'Wally Miller'	MAsh
	'Wanna Bee'	LMil LRHS
	wardii	LMil
	- L&S 5679	GGGa
	- var. ***wardii***	MHid
	'Ward's Ruby' (EA)	SLdr
	wasonii	LMil LRHS
	- f. ***rhododactylum***	LMil
	- yellow-flowered	GGGa
	'Water Baby' (A)	LMil
	'Water Girl' (A)	LMil LRHS
	'Water Pixie'	LMil
	'Waterfall'	SLdr
	'Wee Bee' ♀H5	CBcs CDoC CRos EGrI GEdr GKin LMil MAsh MGos NLar SLim SSta WThu
	'Weinlese'	SAko
	'Wendy'	MAsh
	'Western Lights' (A)	LRHS MPkF
	'Westminster' (O)	LMil
	'Weston's Innocence' (A)	MPkF
	'Weston's Lollipop' (A)	LRHS MPkF
	'What a Dane'	GGGa
	'Whidbey Island'	LMil
	'Whisperingrose'	EGrI LMil
	'White Brocade'	SSta
§	WHITE DUFTHECKE ('Rhodunter 48'PBR)	LMil
	'White Frills' (EA)	LRHS MPkF SLdr
	'White Gold'	GGGa
	'White Jade' (EA)	SLdr
	'White Lady' (Kaempferi) (EA)	SLdr
	'White Lights' (A) ♀H7	CTri
	'White Moon' (EA)	XSte
	'White Perfume' (A)	SSta
	'White Prince' (EA/d)	MPkF XSte
	'White Rosebud' (EA)	MHtn
	'White Swan' (K)	LRHS
	'White Swan' (hybrid)	LMil
	'White Wings'	SLdr
	'Whitestone'	SSta
	'Whitethroat' (K/d) ♀H6	CBcs EPfP IDee LMil LRHS SSta
	'Whitney's Orange'	SLdr
	'Wigeon'	LMil
	wightii	CPla MHid
	'Wilgen's Ruby'	CDoC CRos CSBt MGos SCob SLdr SLim SPer XSte
	'Willbrit'	CBcs MAsh SLdr
	williamsianum ♀H5	CBcs EGrI GGGa IDee LMil SLdr
	- Caerhays form	CExl
	'Willy' (Kaempferi) (EA)	LMil SLdr
	wiltonii ♀H5	GGGa LMil
	'Wine and Roses'PBR	CBcs GGGa IDee LMil LPar LRHS MPkF XSte
	Winsome Group	CMac MAsh
	- 'Winsome' ♀H5	CBcs CDoC EPfP GKin MGos MPri NLar SLdr SSta XSte
	'Witchery'	GGGa
	'Wombat' (EA) ♀H5	CDoC CTri EPfP GGGa LMil LRHS MAsh MGos MPri NLar SLdr
	wongii	CMac
	'Woodcock'	SLdr
	'Wren' ♀H5	EGrI GEdr GGGa LMil MAsh WThu
	xanthocodon	see *R. cinnabarinum* subsp. *xanthocodon*
	'XXL'	LRHS MGos SPer SSta
	'Yaku Angel'	LMil SAko
	'Yaku Incense'	LMil MAsh
	'Yaku Prince'	MAsh SLdr
	yakushimanum ♀H5	GKin LMil MAsh NHol SCob SSta
	- from Exbury	CMac
	- FCC form	see *R. yakushimanum* 'Koichiro Wada'
§	- 'Koichiro Wada' ♀H6	CBcs CExl CMac GGGa IDee LMil LRHS SAko SLdr
	- 'Schneekissen'	SAko
	Yellow Hammer Group	SPer SSta
	- 'Yellow Hammer' ♀H5	CAco CBcs CMac GGGa GKin SLdr
	'Yellow Petticoats'	SSta
	'Yellow Rolls Royce'	LMil
	yuefengense	GGGa LMil
	yunnanense	GGGa GKev LMil MHid
	- 'Openwood' ♀H3	LMil
	- pink-flowered	GGGa
	- 'Red Throat'	SLdr
	- red-blotched	LMil
§	- Suberosum Group	SLdr
	- white-flowered	GGGa
	zaleucum	LMil SLdr
	zeylanicum	see *R. arboreum* subsp. *zeylanicum*

Rhodohypoxis ✿ (*Hypoxidaceae*)

'1000 Cranes'	IBal WPGP
'Alice'	WFar
'Andromeda'	EWes IBal
'Ann Brazier'	NWad
baurii ♀H3	CAvo CCCN IBal LRHS MAsh NSla SEdd SPoG WAbe WAvo WCav WIce
- 'Alba'	CRos EHyd EWes IBal LRHS NRHS SEdd WFar
- 'Albrighton'	CTri EWes GEdr NHol NHpl NWad WAbe
- 'Apple Blossom'	EWes GKev IBal ITim LBee LEdu NHol NWad WFar WPGP
- 'Badger'	ITim NWad WAbe
- var. ***baurii***	CBor EWes
- 'Bridal Bouquet' (d)	EWes GEdr IBal NHol WFar
- 'Caro'	EWes
- 'Charlotte'	EWes
- 'Coconut Ice'	EWes LEdu WPGP

- var. ***confecta***	CBor CElw EWes GEdr IBal NHol NWad WFar WTyc
- 'Daphne Mary'	EWes
- 'David Scott'	EWes
- 'Dawn'	CPla EWes GEdr GKev IBal WAbe
- 'Douglas'	EWes GEdr GKev IBal LEdu NHol NHpl NWad SEdd WAvo WPGP
- 'Dulcie'	EWes GEdr IBal WAbe
- 'Emily Peel'	EWes GKev IBal
- 'Eva-Kate'	EWes IBal
- 'Fred Broome'	CRos EWes GEdr IBal LEdu LRHS NHol NWad WFar
- 'Goliath'	EWes GEdr IBal MNrw
- 'Harlequin'	EWes GEdr IBal NHol NWad
§ - 'Helen'	CBor EPot EWes GEdr GKev IBal LEdu NHol NHpl NWad WAbe WPGP
- 'Jeanette'	EWes IBal
- 'Kitty'	EWes IBal WFar
- 'Lily Jean' (d)	CPla CTri EWes GEdr GKev IBal ITim NHpl NWad SEdd WFar WIce WTyc
- 'Luna'	EWes
- 'Margaret Rose'	EWes IBal NHol
- 'Mars'	CBor CRos EHyd EWes IBal LEdu LRHS NHol NRHS WFar WPGP
- 'Monique'	EWes
- 'Perle'	CBor EWes GEdr IBal LRHS NHol NWad
- 'Picta' (v)	EWes GKev IBal LEdu NHol NHpl NWad WAbe
- 'Pink Pearl'	EWes IBal NHol
- pink-flowered	WLov
- var. ***platypetala***	EWes GEdr GKev IBal NHol NHpl NWad WAvo
- var. ***platypetala* × *milloides***	IBal NHol NWad
- - Burtt 6981	EWes
- 'Rebecca'	EWes
- 'Red King'	EWes IBal
- red-flowered	LRHS SPlb WLov
- 'Ruth'	EWes GEdr GKev IBal NHol SDeJ WFar
- 'Susan Garnett-Botfield'	EWes GEdr IBal NHpl
- 'Tetra Pink'	EWes GEdr IBal LRHS NHol NWad WTyc
- 'Tetra Red'	EGrI EWes GEdr GKev IBal NHol NWad SDeJ WFar
- 'The Bride'	EWes GEdr
- white-flowered	WLov
'Betsy Carmine'	CCCN GEdr IBal NWad WFar
'Beverly'[PBR]	LCro LOPS
'Bright Eyes' (d)	EWes
'Burgundy'	IBal
'Butterfly Wings'	NWad
'Candy Stripe'	EWes GEdr NWad
'Carina'	EWes
'Caroline'	EWes IBal WFar
'Cathy'	EWes IBal
'Confusion'	EWes LEdu NHol NHpl NWad
'Dainty Dee' (d)	EWes
'Damson'	CBor
deflexa	CBor CRos EWes GKev IBal ITim LEdu LRHS MNrw NHol NHpl NRHS NWad SIvy WAbe WFar WPGP
'Donald Mann'	EWes GEdr IBal LRHS NHol
'Dusky'	EWes GEdr IBal NWad
'E.A. Bowles'	EWes IBal NHpl NSla WFar
'Ellicks'	IBal
'Flashing Ruby'	GEdr WFar
'Forge Robies'	EWes

'Garnett'	EWes NWad WFar
'Gemma'	EWes
'Giant Pink'	CBor
'Goya' (d)	NHpl
'Great Scot'	EWes GEdr IBal NHpl NWad WAbe
'Hebron Farm Biscuit'	see *Hypoxis parvula* var. *albiflora* 'Hebron Farm Biscuit'
'Hebron Farm Cerise'	see × *Rhodoxis* 'Hebron Farm Cerise'
'Hebron Farm Pink'	see × *Rhodoxis hybrida* 'Hebron Farm Pink'
'Hinky Pinky'	GEdr NWad
'Holden Rose' (d)	IBal NHol NWad WFar
'Hope' (d)	IBal
'Indy'	IBal
'Jap Double'	CBor
'Jupiter'	CBor GEdr NWad WFar
'Kiwi Joy' (d)	EGrI EWes GEdr GKev IBal NHol NHpl NWad SDeJ WTyc
'Knockdolian Red'	GEdr IBal NHol NWad WFar
'Lisette'	EWes
'Louise'	IBal
'Midori'	EPfP EWes GEdr IBal NWad SDys WFar
milloides	CBor CPla CRos EWes GEdr IBal ITim LBee LEdu LRHS NHol NHpl NRHS NWad WAbe WFar WPGP
- 'Claret'	CBod CElw CRos ELon EPot EWes GEdr IBal ITim LRHS NHol SDys SEdd SIvy WAbe WFar WTyc
- 'Claudia'	CRos EHyd EPfP GWyn LRHS NRHS WFar
- 'Damask'	CRos EWes GKev IBal LRHS SDys
- 'Drakensberg Snow'	EWes
- giant	WFar
- 'Susan'	EWes
'Monty'	EWes GEdr IBal NWad WAbe WFar
'Mystery'	CBor EWes IBal NHol
'Naomi'	EWes
'New Look'	EWes GEdr IBal NHpl NWad SEdd
'Ori Zuru'	GEdr NWad
'Origami'	IBal LEdu
'Pat Lacey'	EWes IBal
'Paula'	IBal
'Pink Ice'	GEdr IBal NWad
'Pink Star'	LRHS
'Pinkeen'	CBor EWes WFar
'Pinkie'	IBal SDys WFar
'Pintado'	CBor CRos EHyd EWes GEdr IBal LEdu LRHS NRHS NWad SDys WFar WPGP WTyc
'Raspberry Ice'	IBal NHol NWad WFar
'Rosalie'	IBal
'Rosie Lee'	CBor EWes
'Ruby Giant'	GEdr LRHS WFar
'Shell Pink'	EWes IBal NHol NWad
'Shirazz'	CBor
Slack Top hybrids	NSla
'Snow'	EWes
'Snow White'	EWes NHol
'Starlett'	EWes NHol
'Starry Eyes' (d)	EWes IBal WFar
'Stella'	CCCN EPot EWes GEdr GKev IBal NHol NHpl NWad SDys WFar
'Sunburst'	GEdr NWad
'Telios'	IBal
'Tetra Rose'	GEdr
'Tetra White'	see *R. baurii* 'Helen'
thodiana	CBor EWes GEdr IBal NHol NHpl NWad WAbe WFar
TWINKLE STAR (mixed)	LRHS
'Two Tone'	EWes

'Venetian' CBor CMea IBal NHol NWad WFar
'Westacre Picotee' EWes
'White Prince' WFar
'Wild Cherry Blossom' EWes IBal

Rhodoleia (*Hamamelidaceae*)

championii B&SWJ 11603 WCru
- FMWJ 13155 WCru
- WWJ 11858 WCru
aff. ***henryi*** B&SWJ 11782 WCru
- DJHV 0640 WCru
parvipetala FMWJ 13422 WCru
- WWJ 11866 WCru
- WWJ 11943 WCru

Rhodophiala (*Amaryllidaceae*)

rosea GKev

Rhodora see *Rhododendron*

Rhodotypos (*Rosaceae*)

kerrioides see *R. scandens*
§ ***scandens*** CBcs CBod CEme CExl EBee EHyd ELan EPfP GBin GKev LEdu LRHS MGil MMrt MMuc MNrw NHol NLar NQui SBrt SEND SLon SPoG WAvo WCru

× *Rhodoxis* ✿ (*Hypoxidaceae*)

'Abigail' EWes IBal WFar
'Anne Crock' EWes IBal
'Aurora' EWes IBal LRHS WFar
'Betsy' EWes GKev NWad
'Bloodstone' EWes IBal NHol NWad
FAIRYTALE ('Hil200802'[PBR]) MPkF WTyc XSte
'Fanny' EWes
'Hebron Farm Biscuit' see *Hypoxis parvula* var. *albiflora* 'Hebron Farm Biscuit'
§ 'Hebron Farm Cerise' CBor CCCN CElw CRos EHyd EWes GEdr GKev IBal LEdu LRHS NRHS SDys WFar
'Hebron Farm Rose' IBal
§ ***hybrida*** EWes
- 'Aya San' EWes GKev IBal LRHS WFar
- FAIRY KISSES ('Im201208'[PBR]) MPkF XSte
§ - 'Hebron Farm Pink' CBor CElw CPla CRos EWes GEdr GKev IBal LRHS NHol WFar WIce
- 'Hebron Farm Red Eye' CCCN EWes GKev IBal NHpl WFar
- 'Pink Stars' IBal
- 'Ruby Giant' EWes GEdr IBal
- 'White Stars' EWes
'Jenny' EWes
'Little Pink Pet' EWes IBal WFar
'Otterlo Ruby' CBor EWes GKev WFar
'Pink Glow' IBal
'Pink Tips' IBal
'Red Flyer' EWes IBal
'Ria' EWes
'Sandra' EWes
'Sandy' CBor EWes GKev
'Sonja' CBor GKev
'Sue' EWes WFar
'Summer Pink' IBal
(Summer Stars Series) 'Summer Stars Candy' IBal
- 'Summer Stars Peppermint' IBal WFar
- 'Summer Stars Pink Blush' IBal WFar
- 'Summer Stars Pinky' CDoC IBal WFar
- 'Summer Stars Ruby' IBal

Rhoeo see *Tradescantia*

Rhoicissus (*Vitaceae*)

digitata EShb

Rhombophyllum (*Aizoaceae*)

dolabriforme SSim

Rhopalostylis (*Arecaceae*)

sapida CBrP LRHS

rhubarb see *Rheum* × *hybridum*; also AGM Vegetables Section

Rhus (*Anacardiaceae*)

ambigua see *Toxicodendron orientale*
aromatica CAgr MMrt NLar WKor
chinensis CMCN IDee
copallinum EBtc SBrt
cotinus see *Cotinus coggygria*
glabra CBcs EPfP SPer
- 'Laciniata' ambig. EGrI WFar
hirta see *R. typhina*
incisa SPlb
potaninii EBee EPfP NLar WPGP
× ***pulvinata*** (Autumn Lace Group) 'Red Autumn Lace' ♀H5 MBlu SPer
radicans see *Toxicodendron radicans*
succedanea see *Toxicodendron succedaneum*
toxicodendron see *Toxicodendron radicans*
trilobata WKor
typhina CAgr CBcs CBrac CDoC CMac ELan EPfP GDam GKin IPap LCro LMaj LOPS LPar MAsh MGos NHol NLar NWea SCob SEND SGol SLim SPer SSta WFar
§ - 'Dissecta' ♀H6 CBar CBcs CBod CDoC ELan EPfP LMaj LPar MGos MRav NLar SArc SCob SEND SGol SGsty SLim SPer WFar
- 'Laciniata' hort. see *R. typhina* 'Dissecta'
- RADIANCE ('Sinrus') ♀H6 EHyd LRHS MAsh MBlu NLar SPoG
- TIGER EYES ('Bailtiger'[PBR]) ♀H6 ELan EPfP MAsh MGos SCob SEWo SGol SWvt
verniciflua see *Toxicodendron vernicifluum*

Rhynchelytrum see *Melinis*

Rhynchospora (*Cyperaceae*)

colorata LLWG LRHS MPkF NPer SBrt XSte
latifolia SDix SMad

Ribes ✿ (*Grossulariaceae*)

alpinum CExl LPar MRav NWea SPer SRms WKor WSpi
americanum 'Variegatum' (v) NLar NWad
aureum misapplied see *R. odoratum*
aureum ambig. CAgr NWea WKor
aureum Pursh. subsp. ***gracillimum*** SBrt
§ × ***beatonii*** CExl CKel CSBt CSde CWit EBee EGrI EHed EHyd EPfP EShb GBin IDee LEdu LRHS MMuc NLar SGol SPer SPoG SRms WAvo WCot WFar WMal WSpi
'Ben Hope'[PBR] (B) CAgr CDoC CSBt EPom MPri SCoo SWvt
'Black Velvet' (D) CAgr MCoo

bracteosum B&SWJ 14159	WCru
californicum	SBrt
cereum	SBrt
× ***culverwellii*** (F)	CAgr CCCN CTri EPom LBuc LCro LEdu LOPS NLar SVic SWvt WMat
divaricatum	CAgr LEdu WKor
gayanum	LEdu NLar WKor
glaciale PAB 3004	LEdu
× ***gordonianum***	see *R.* × *beatonii*
griffithii	WCot
- GWJ 9331	WCru
- PAB 4871	LEdu
jostaberry	see *R.* × *nidigrolaria*
laurifolium	CBcs CBod CEnd CExl CTri EBee EHyd ELan EWes LRHS MRav NLar SCob SGBe SMad SPer WCFE WFar WSpi
- (f)	EPfP SRms
- (m)	EPfP
- 'Mrs Amy Doncaster'	CBcs CRos EBee EHed EHyd EPfP LEdu LRHS NRHS SEle SPoG SRms WBor WCot WGob WLov WMal WPGP WSpi
- Rosemoor form	CDoC CKel CRos EBee EPfP LRHS NLar SPoG WCot
longeracemosum	GGGa
menziesii	EWes NQui WCot
nevadense	SBrt
§ × ***nidigrolaria*** (F)	CDoC CMac GDam NWea SCoo SEdi
nigrum (B) PAB 3755	LEdu
- 'Baldwin' (B)	CTri EPfP LBuc MTrO NLar SCoo SEdi SPer SSFr WMat
- 'Barchatnaja' (B)	CAgr
- 'Ben Alder' (B)	CAgr EPom GDam SCoo
- 'Ben Connan' (B) ♀^{H6}	Widely available
- 'Ben Gairn'^{PBR} (B)	CAgr MCoo MMuc
- 'Ben Lomond'^{PBR} (B)	CAgr CDoC CSBt CTri EPfP LBuc LSRN MAsh MGos MNHC MPri MRav MTrO NLar NRog NWea SBdl SCoo SEdi SKee SPer SPoG SRms SSFr SVic WMat
- 'Ben More' (B)	CAgr MPri
- 'Ben Nevis' (B)	CAgr EBee SEdi SKee SPer
- 'Ben Sarek' (B)	Widely available
- 'Ben Tirran' (B)	CAgr CDoC CSBt EHyd EPom LBuc LRHS LSRN MAsh MGos NLar SBdl SCoo SRms SWvt WMat
- 'Ben Tron' (B)	CRos LRHS
- 'Big Ben'^{PBR} (B) ♀^{H6}	CArg CRos EBee EHyd EPfP EPom LBuc LCro LOPS LRHS LSRN MTrO NRHS SBdl SGbt SKee SPer SPoG WMat
- 'Black Reward' (B)	CAgr
- 'Boskoop Giant' (B)	CAgr ELan NRog
- 'Byelorussian Sweet' (B)	CAgr
- 'Cassis Blanc' (B)	CAgr
- CASSISSIMA NOIROMA (B) **new**	LRHS
- 'Ebony' (B)	CArg CMac EPom NRog SVic
- 'Hystawneznaya' (B)	CAgr LEdu
- 'Jet' (B)	CAgr NRog
- 'Kosmicheskaya' (B)	CAgr
- 'Pilot Alexander Mamkin' (B)	CAgr
- 'Polar' (B)	CAgr
- 'Seabrook's' (B)	CAgr
- 'Titania' (B)	LRHS MCoo MTrO NLar SEdi WMat
- 'Vertti' (B)	CAgr
- 'Wellington XXX' (B)	CAgr LBuc LEdu NRog NWea SEdi SSFr
§ ***odoratum***	CBcs CKel CMac CSBt EBee EHed EHyd ELan ELon EPfP EWTr LRHS MGos MMuc MNrw MRav NLar NWea SCob SPer SPoG SRms WCot WLov WSpi
- 'Crandall'	CAgr LEdu
orientale PAB 7066	LEdu
'Pink Perfection'	CMCN
praecox	MMuc SEND
rubrum 'Bar-le-Duc'	NRog
- 'Blanka' (W)	CAgr CArg CMac EHyd LRHS NRog SVic
- 'Cascade' (R)	CAgr
- 'Cherry' (R)	CAgr
- 'Fay's New Prolific' (R)	NRog
- 'Gloire de Sablons' (P)	EPom SPer SRms
- 'Jonkheer van Tets' (R) ♀^{H6}	CAgr CDoC CRos CSBt EHyd EPfP EPom IArd LRHS LSRN MAsh MCoo MPri NLar NRHS NWea SBdl SCoo SEND SEdi SGbt SKee SPer SRms SSFr WMat
- 'Junifer' (R)	CAgr CRos EHyd EPom LEdu LRHS NRHS NRog SKee
- 'Laxton's Number One' (R)	CAgr CDoC CTri EPfP EPom LCro LEdu LOPS LRHS LSRN NLar NRog NWea SCoo SGbt SPer SPoG SRms SSFr WMat
- 'Lisette' (R)	LRHS
- 'Red Lake' (R) ♀^{H6}	CAgr CTri ELan EPfP EPom LBuc LEdu MGos MPri NLar NRog SEdi SKee SPer SPoG SRms SSFr WMat
- 'Redstart' (R)	CAgr CTri LBuc MAsh MMuc SKee WMat
- RIBEST SONETTE (R) **new**	LRHS
- 'Rolan' (R)	CAgr NRog
- 'Rondom' (R)	CAgr NRog SVic
- ROSA SPORT (P)	LRHS
- 'Rosetta' (R)	CAgr CDoC NRog SBdl SCoo SRms
- 'Rotet' (R)	LEdu NRog
- 'Rovada' (R)	CAgr CArg CMac CRos CSBt EHyd EPfP EPom LBuc LEdu LRHS LSRN MAsh MPri NLar NRHS SBdl SCoo SEdi SKee SPoG SRms SVic WMat
- 'Roxby Red' (R)	LEdu NRog
- 'Stanza' (R) ♀^{H6}	CAgr NRog SEND
- 'Versailles' (R) **new**	MAsh
§ - 'Versailles Blanche' (W/C)	CAgr CRos CSBt CTri EHyd EPfP EPom GQue LBuc LCro LOPS LRHS LSRN MGos MMuc MPri NRHS NRog SBdl SCoo SEdi SKee SPer SRms SSFr WMat
- 'Weisse Langtraubige' (W)	CAgr
- 'White Dutch' (W)	NRog
- 'White Grape' (W) ♀^{H6}	CTri LEdu NRog
- 'White Pearl' (W)	ELan NRog SEdi SVic
- WHITE VERSAILLES	see *R. rubrum* 'Versailles Blanche'
sachalinense	WKor
sanguineum	GDam LPar SavN
- AMORE ('Annys2003'^{PBR})	LRHS
- 'Brianjou'	SRms
- 'Brocklebankii'	CExl CMac EPfP LRHS MRav NLar SChF SPer SRms WCFE WSHC
- 'Carneum'	EHyd LRHS NRHS
- 'Elkington's White'	CRos EHed EHyd EPfP EWTr LBuc LCro LOPS LRHS LSRN MAsh MGos NLar NRHS NSti SCoo SLon SRms WBor WCot WSpi
- 'King Edward VII'	Widely available
- 'Koja' ♀^{H6}	CBod CRos EHyd EPfP GBin LEdu LRHS LSRN MAsh MGos MMuc

	NLar NRHS SCoo SEle SGol SPoG SRms WCot WFar WLov WSpi
- 'Lombartsii' ♀H6	CRos EHyd EPfP LRHS MRav NRHS
- 'Poky's Pink' ♀H6	CRos EHyd LRHS MAsh MRav SPoG SRms
- 'Pulborough Scarlet'	Widely available
- 'Red Bross'	CRos EPfP LRHS MAsh SWvt
- 'Red Pimpernel'	CSBt EHyd EPfP LRHS MAsh NRHS SRms SWvt WFar
- 'Somerset White'	LRHS MAsh
- 'Tydeman's White'	CExl CSBt EPfP NLar NWea WSpi
- var. ***variegata***	CMac
- WHITE ICICLE ('Ubric') ♀H6	CBcs CBod CDoC CTri EBee EHyd ELan EPfP EShb GBin LRHS MAsh MBlu MHer MRav MSwo NBir NLar NRHS SCob SPer SPoG SRms SWvt WCot WFar WLov
speciosum ♀H4	Widely available
uva-crispa 'Admiral Beattie' (F)	NRog
- 'Alma'	NRog
- 'Annelii' (F)	CAgr
- 'Australia' (D)	NRog
- 'Bellona' (D)	NRog
- 'Broom Girl' (D)	NRog
- 'Captivator' (C)	CDoC CMac CRos CSBt EPom LBuc LRHS MAsh MCoo MNHC MTrO NLar NRHS SBdl SCoo SKee SPoG SRms WMat
- 'Careless' (C/D) ♀H6	CSBt CTri EPom LSRN MAsh MGos NRog SCoo SEdi SPer WMat
- 'Cousen's Seedling' (D)	NRog
- CRISPA FLAVIA (D) **new**	LRHS
- 'Criterion' (D)	NRog
- 'Early Sulphur' (D)	CTri ELan NRog NWea
- EASYCRISP LADY SUN (D)	LRHS
- 'Freedom' (C)	NRog
- 'Green Gem' (C/D)	NRog
- 'Greenfinch' (C) ♀H6	CAgr
- 'Heart of Oak' (D)	NRog
- 'Hero of the Nile' (D)	NRog
- 'Hinnonmäki' (D)	CAgr LBuc SPer
- 'Hinnonmäki Grön' (D)	CAgr CDoC CMac CSBt EBee EPom LRHS LSRN MAsh MRav MTrO NRog SBdl SCoo SEdi SKee SRms
- 'Hinnonmäki Gul' (D)	CAgr CDoC CMac EBee EPfP EPom LBuc LRHS MAsh MGos MTrO NRHS SEdi SKee SPer SRms SSFr SVic WMat
- 'Hinnonmäki Röd' (C/D)	Widely available
- 'Invicta' (C/D) ♀H6	Widely available
- 'Ironmonger' (D)	NRog
- 'Jubilee' (C/D)	LBuc NRog
- 'Jubilee Careless' (C/D)	EPom
- 'King of Trumps' (D)	NRog
- 'Lancashire Lad' (C/D)	NRog
- 'Langley Gage' (D)	MCoo NRog
- 'Larell' (C/D)	CAgr
- 'Leveller' (D) ♀H6	MCoo NRog NWea SEdi SPer
- 'London' (C/D)	CTri NRog NWea
- 'Lord Derby' (C/D)	NRog
- 'Lord Kitchener' (D)	NRog
- 'Marigold' (F)	NRog
- 'Martlet' (D)	NRog
- 'Matchless' (D)	NRog
- 'Mucurines' (D)	CAgr
- 'Pax' PBR (D)	CAgr SSFr SVic
- 'Peru' (D)	NRog
- 'Pitmaston Green Gage' (D)	NRog
- 'Redeva' PBR (D)	CAgr
- 'Rokula' (C/D)	ELan MCoo WMat
- 'Speedwell' (F)	NRog
- 'Spinefree' (C)	CAgr
- 'Talfourd' (D) **new**	NRog
- 'Trumpeter' (D)	NRog
- 'Victoria' (C/D)	NRog
- 'Whinham's Industry' (C/D) ♀H6	ELan LBuc LSRN MGos MMuc MPri NRog SEND SEdi SPer SRms
- 'White Eagle' (C/D)	NRog
- 'Whitesmith' (C/D)	CTri LSRN MCoo NRog
- 'Woodpecker' (D)	NRog
- 'Xenia' (D)	CArg CRos EHyd EPfP EPom LCro LEdu LOPS MCoo NRHS NRog SPoG WMat
- 'Yellow Champagne' (D)	NRog
valdivianum	WCot WFar
viburnifolium	NLar SBrt SEND
'Worcesterberry' (C)	CHab IDee NRog

Richteria (*Asteraceae*)

leontopodium **new**	GKev

Ricinus (*Euphorbiaceae*)

communis	CBod CDTJ SPlb WSMil
- 'Carmencita' ♀H2	NGBl
- 'Carmencita Pink'	CDTJ
- 'Carmencita Red'	CDTJ
- 'Dominican Republic'	CDTJ
- 'Gibsonii'	CDTJ
- 'Impala'	CDTJ
- 'New Zealand Black'	CDTJ CSpe EShb SBls SSal
- 'Zanzibariensis' ♀H2	CDTJ

Ridolfia (*Apiaceae*)

segetum	CKel LCro LOPS SPhx

Rigidella see *Tigridia*

Riocreuxia (*Apocynaceae*)

torulosa	CCCN SPlb

Robinia (*Fabaceae*)

§ ***hispida***	CEnd CLnd EPfP MBlu SPer
- var. ***fertilis***	SBrt
- var. ***kelseyi***	WSpi
- 'Macrophylla'	CEnd
§ - var. ***rosea***	LSRN
- 'Rosea' misapplied	see *R. hispida*, *R. hispida* var. *rosea*
- 'Rosea' ambig.	CBcs
× ***margaretta*** CASQUE ROUGE	see *R.* × *margaretta* 'Pink Cascade'
§ - 'Pink Cascade'	CBod CEnd EBee ELan EPfP IPap LRHS MAsh MGos MTrO NOrn SCob SCoo SEND SGbt SGol WMat
pseudoacacia	CAgr CCVT ELan IPap LBuc MCoo MMuc NRog SEND SGol SPlb
- 'Bessoniana'	ELan EPfP LPar
- 'Frisia'	CBcs CBod CTri EBee ELan EPfP IPap LPar LRHS LSRN MGos MRav MSwo MTrO NLar NOrn NRog SCob SEND SGbt SGol SLim SPer WMat WTSh
- 'Inermis' hort.	see *R. pseudoacacia* 'Umbraculifera'
§ - 'Lace Lady' PBR	CSBt ELan EPfP LBuc LRHS MAsh MGos MTrO NLar SCoo SPer SPoG WMat
- 'Myrtifolia'	SMad
- 'Tortuosa'	CEnd SPer
- 'Twisty Baby'	see *R. pseudoacacia* 'Lace Lady'
§ - 'Umbraculifera'	CLnd LMaj LPar LSRN SArc SCob SGsty

× ***slavinii*** 'Hillieri' Υ^{H6}	CBcs CEnd ELan EPfP LRHS LSRN MAsh MBlu NLar NOrn SLon WSpi

Rochea see *Crassula*

Rodgersia ✿ (*Saxifragaceae*)

CLD 1432	CExl
from Castlewellan	EBlo
from Tibet	EBlo
aesculifolia Υ^{H6}	Widely available
- SSSE 36	SMHy
- var. ***henrici***	CRos EHyd EPfP GLog LRHS MRav NBro NRHS SGbt WBor WHoo
- - KW 21015	WCru
- - 'Cherry Blush'	CBod EPfP GWyn ILea NLar SPad WFar
- - hybrid	NLar XLum
- large-leaved **new**	LRHS
- 'Red Dawn'	IBlr
- 'Red Leaf'	EWTr EWoo
'Badenweiler'	EBlo ECha EHyd LRHS NRHS
'Blickfang' Υ^{H6}	EBlo EHyd LRHS MMrt NRHS
'Bloody Mary'	ECtt SCob WFar
'Borodin'	EBee
'Bronze Peacock'	CBod CPla CRos CTsd EBee ECtt EHed ELan EMor GBin LCro LOPS LPar LRHS LSou MHol MPie NDov NEoE NLar SCob SEdd SEle SHeu SMad SPad SPeP SPoG WTor XSte
'Dark Pokers'	ECtt LRHS MCot MHol NLar SRms WFar
'Die Schöne'	NLar
'Die Stolze'	EBee GBin LEdu
'Fascination'	IBlr
'Grande Blanche'	EBlo EHyd
'Herkules'	ECha ECtt EHyd ELon GDam GMaP GWyn LEdu MBNS MMuc NLar NQui WCot WPnP WSMil
'Irish Bronze' Υ^{H6}	CRos ECtt EHed EHyd EMor EPfP EShb GPSL GQue LEdu LRHS LSRN MBel NRHS NSti SMad WFar WPnP
'Koriata'	IBlr
'Kupfermond'	NBir
'La Blanche'	ECtt EHed EHyd ELon LEdu LRHS MHol NLar SEdd
nepalensis	EHyd LEdu LRHS WPGP
- EMAK 713	IBlr
- HWJK 2140	WCru
- 'High Flier'	WCru
new hybrids	SBls
'Parasol'	CBro CDor CMac EHyd IBlr NBir NHol NWad
pinnata	CTri EPau EPfP EWTr GMaP LEdu LRHS LSRN MBel MGos MRav NHol NRHS SCob SMad SPeP SRms WPnP WWtn XLum
- B&SWJ 7741A	CBcs WCru
- L 1670	CExl ELan
- 'Alba'	EHyd EMor
- 'Buckland Beauty' Υ^{H6}	CDor CRos EBlo EHyd EPfP IBlr LRHS NRHS WFar
- 'Cally Salmon'	EWes IBlr SMHy
- 'Candy Clouds' (d)	EBee NLar
- 'Chocolate Wing'	Widely available
- 'Crûg Cardinal'	CRos EBee EHyd EPfP GBin LRHS NLar NRHS SHeu WCru WPnP
- 'Elegans' Υ^{H7}	CBod CDor CRos EBee EPfP GKev GMaP LEdu LRHS MRav NHol NRHS NWad SCob SPoG SRms SWvt WCAu WCFE
- 'Fireworks'^{PBR}	EBee ECtt EPfP NLar
- 'Hanna'	GBin SHeu
- hybrids	EHyd LRHS
- 'Jade Dragon Mountain'	IBlr LEdu
- 'Maurice Mason' Υ^{H6}	CExl EBlo GKev IBlr LRHS NLar SDix SMHy
- 'Panache'	IBlr
- 'Pink Beauty'	EBee
- pink-flowered	WCru
- 'Shangri-La'	WCru
- 'Snow Clouds'	EBee
- 'Superba' Υ^{H6}	Widely available
- white-flowered	WCru
pinnata* × *sambucifolia	IBlr
podophylla	Widely available
- B&SWJ 10818	WCru
- B&SWJ 10823	WCru
- 'Braunlaub'	EWoo ILea LCro LOPS MCot NBro SMad WPnP
- 'Crûg's Colossus'	WCru
- Donard selection	IBlr
- 'Rotlaub' Υ^{H6}	EBee
- 'Saarbrücken' **new**	MBNS
- 'Smaragd'	CRos EBee EHyd EShb LRHS MRav NBir NLar NRHS
purdomii hort.	CMac EHyd LRHS NRHS WCot WPGP
'Rosenlicht'	EHyd
sambucifolia	CBcs CMac CRos EHyd EWTr LEdu LRHS MMuc NBir NLar NRHS SCob SEND WCAu WFar WPnP XLum
- B&SWJ 7899	WCru
- large, red-stemmed	NBir
- 'Mountain Select'	EBee
'Stoke Gabriel'	EBee
tabularis	see *Astilboides tabularis*

Rohdea (*Asparagaceae*)

delavayi	WCot
japonica	CMac WCot WPGP
- B&SWJ 4853	WCru
- B&SWJ 5091	WCru
- 'Godaishu' (v)	WCot
- 'Gunjaku' (v)	WCot
- 'Lance Leaf'	LEdu WPGP
- long-leaved	WCot
- 'Miyakonojo' (v)	WCot
- 'Talbot Manor' (v)	CBct WCot WPGP
- 'Tama-jishi' (v)	WCot
- 'Tuneshige Rokujo' (v)	WCot
tonkinensis HWJ 562	WCru
watanabei B&SWJ 1911	WCru
wattii	WCot

Roldana (*Asteraceae*)

§ ***cristobalensis***	WCot
§ ***petasitis***	CAbb WCot

Romanzoffia (*Boraginaceae*)

californica	EBee
§ ***sitchensis***	CTri
suksdorfii Greene	see *R. sitchensis*
unalaschcensis	SRms

Romneya (*Papaveraceae*)

coulteri Υ^{H5}	Widely available
§ - 'White Cloud' Υ^{H5}	CBct CExl EBee EPfP MGil MRav SChF WPGP WSpi
× ***hybrida***	see *R. coulteri* 'White Cloud'

Romulea (*Iridaceae*)

bulbocodium var. ***clusiana***	GKev NRog

- var. ***crocea*** GKev
- var. ***leichtliniana*** GKev
columnae subsp. ***columnae*** NRog
- subsp. ***grandiscapa*** **new** NRog
hallii **new** NRog
komsbergensis **new** NRog
ligustica var. ***rouyana*** GKev
linaresii NRog
- subsp. ***graeca*** GKev
longituba see *R. macowanii*
§ ***macowanii*** GKev
- var. ***alticola*** GArf
ramiflora CExl GKev
rosea NRog
sabulosa WHil
tempskyana GKev

Rosa ✿ (*Rosaceae*)

NJM 11.048 from Guizhou, China WPGP
90TH CELEBRATION ('Tan10558') (HT) MFry
'À Longs Pédoncules' (Ce) EBls
'A. Mackenzie' (S) EBls
A ROSE FOR RYEDALE ('Websunshine') (F) **new** NRog
A ROSE OF DISTINCTION ('Tan98130') (F) ESty
A SHROPSHIRE LAD ('Ausled'PBR) (S) 🏆H6 CArg CRos EBee EPfP LBuc LRHS MAsh MSwo NLar NRHS SCob SPer SPoG SSea
A WHITER SHADE OF PALE ('Peafanfare'PBR) (HT) 🏆H6 CDoC CSBt EBls ECnt ESty LCro LOPS LSRN MFry MGos MRav SApu SLon SPer SSea
ABBIE'S ROSE (F) LSRN
ABIGAILE ('Tanelaigib') (F) LSRN
ABRACADABRA ('Korhocsel') (HT) ESty
ABRAHAM DARBY ('Auscot') (S) EPfP MRav NLar
ABSENT FRIENDS ('Dicemblem'PBR) (F) ESty WBor
ABSOLUTELY FABULOUS ('Wekvossutono'PBR) (F) 🏆H6 CArg CBod CDoC CGro CSBt EBls ECnt ELon EPfP ESty LBuc LRHS LSRN MAsh MFry MGos MPri MRav NRog SApu SCoo SPad SPer SPoG SRGP
abyssinica EBtc LEdu
ACAPULCO ('Dicblender') (HT) NRog
acicularis var. ***nipponensis*** EBls
'Adam' (ClT) EBls LSRN
'Adam Messerich' (Bb) EBls ETWh NLar
ADAM'S ROSE ('Wekromico') (F) LSRN
'Adélaïde d'Orléans' (Ra) 🏆H6 CArg CRHN EBls ETWh NLar SEND SPer
'Admiral Rodney' (HT) NRog
'Agatha' (G) EBls
AGATHA CHRISTIE ('Kormeita') (ClF) EBls EPfP LRHS LSRN MAsh
'Agathe Incarnata' (D × G) EBls
'Aglaia' (Ra) EBls ETWh
'Agnes' (Ru) CBcs CDoC EBls EPfP ETWh IArd MRav NLar NRog SPer
'Aimée Vibert' (N) EBee EBls ELon ETWh NLar SPer
'Alain Blanchard' (G) EBls ETWh
ALAN TITCHMARSH ('Ausjive'PBR) (S) LCro LOPS LSRN SPer
ALASKA ('Korjoslio'PBR) (ClHT) ESty
× ***alba*** (A) EBls NRog
§ - 'Alba Maxima' (A) 🏆H6 EBls ETWh GBin NLar NRog SEND SPer WFar WHer
§ - 'Alba Semiplena' (A) 🏆H6 EBls ETWh GBin LRHS NLar SPer WHer
- CELESTIAL see *R.* 'Céleste'
- 'Maxima' see *R.* × *alba* 'Alba Maxima'
'Albéric Barbier' (Ra) 🏆H5 CArg CDoC CEnd CRHN CSBt CTri EBee EBls ECnt ELan EPfP ETWh LCro LOPS MFry MRav MSwo NLar NRog NWea SApu SCob SCoo SEND SPer SSea WHer
'Albertine' (Ra) 🏆H6 Widely available
'Alchymist' (ClS) CRHN EBls EPfP ESty ETWh LRHS MRav NLar SPer
ALDEN BIESEN ('Lengrati') (HM) WKif
ALDERLEY PARK ('Frygladiator') (F) MFry
ALEC'S RED ('Cored') (HT) CArg CBcs CTri EBls LSRN MFry MRav NRog SCob SPer SPoG SRGP
ALEXANDER ('Harlex') (HT) 🏆H6 EBls LHkn LSRN MRav SApu SPer
'Alexander Hill Gray' (T) EBls
'Alexandre Girault' (Ra) 🏆H6 CRHN EBee EBls ETWh LRHS NRHS SPer WHer
'Alfred Colomb' (HP) EBls
'Alfred de Dalmas' misapplied see *R.* 'Mousseline'
ALFRED SISLEY ('Delstrijor'PBR) (S) ESty ETWh LRHS
'Alfresco'PBR (ClHT) MSwo
§ 'Alibaba'PBR (ClHT) 🏆H6 CBod CDoC CGro CSBt ECnt ELon EPfP ESty LBuc LRHS LSRN MAsh MFry MPri MRav SApu SPer SPoG SSea
'Alice Bracegirdle' (HT) **new** NRog
'Alida Lovett' (Ra) CRHN
ALISON ('Coclibee'PBR) (F) LSRN
ALISSAR, PRINCESS OF PHOENICIA ('Harsidon'PBR) (S) ETWh LHkn NLar
'Alister Clark' (F) EBls
§ 'Alister Stella Gray' (N) 🏆H5 EBls EPfP ESty ETWh MMuc NLar NRog SEND SPer SSea
ALL AMERICAN MAGIC ('Meiroylear'PBR) (HT) ESty
ALL MY LOVING ('Fryrisky') (HT) LRHS MAsh MFry
'Allen Chandler' (ClHT) EBls
ALNWICK CASTLE see *R.* THE ALNWICK ROSE
'Aloha' (ClHT) 🏆H6 CArg CBcs CGro CTri EBee EBls ELon EPfP ESty ETWh EWTr LPar LRHS MAsh MRav NLar NRog SPer SPoG SRGP WSpi
alpina see *R. pendulina*
'Alpine Sunset' (HT) CTri EBls ELon MGos MRav SCob SPer SPoG
altaica misapplied see *R. spinosissima* 'Grandiflora'
altaica Willd. see *R. spinosissima*
ALTISSIMO ('Delmur') (Cl) CEnd EBls ETWh NLar SPer SSea
ALWAYS REMEMBER ME ('Macpadspo') (HT) LSRN
ALWAYS YOU ('Webalways') (HT) ESty
'Amadis' (Bs) ETWh
AMANDA ('Beesian') (F) EBls ESty LSRN
'Amanda Paternotte' (D) ETWh
AMAZING DAY ('Raw1113') (S) ESty

'Ambassador Nogami' (S)	EBls
AMBER ABUNDANCE ('Harfizz'PBR) (Abundance Series) (F)	LHkn
AMBER QUEEN ('Harroony') (F) ♀H6	CArg CDoC CSBt CTri EBls ELan IArd LCro LHkn LOPS MFry MRav NRog SApu SPer
AMBER STAR ('Manstar') (Min)	NRog
AMBER SUNSET ('Manamsun') (Min)	NRog
AMBER SWEET DREAM ('Fryritz') (Patio)	CDoC CSBt MFry MRav
AMBIANCE ('Bensiete') (Patio)	NRog
amblyotis RBS 0262	NLar
'Amélia'	see *R.* 'Celsiana'
AMELIA ('Poulen011'PBR) (Renaissance Series) (S)	ECnt ETWh LSRN
AMÉLIE NOTHOMB ('Delathom') (HT) **new**	EBls
'American Pillar' (Ra)	CArg CBcs CDoC CEnd CGro CRHN CRos CSBt CTri EBls ECnt ELan EPfP ETWh LPar LRHS MAsh MGos MRav MSwo NLar NRog SApu SCob SPer SPoG SSea WBor
AMETHYST QUEEN ('Raw1074') (F)	ESty
AMNESTY INTERNATIONAL ('Delcreja') (Cl)	ESty SSea
AMPLEFORTH ('Rawforth') (F) **new**	NRog
'Amy Robsart' (RH)	EBls
ANABELL ('Korbell') (F)	LSRN NRog
ANDREA STELZER ('Korfachrit') (HT) **new**	NRog
§ 'Anemone' (Cl)	EBls ETWh
anemonoides	see *R.* 'Anemone'
ANGEL EYES ('Albravo') (HT)	LRHS MAsh
ANGELA ('Grifgela') (S)	LSRN NRog
ANGELA RIPPON ('Ocaru') (Min)	CSBt
'Angela's Choice' (F)	LSRN
ANISLEY DICKSON ('Dickimono') (F)	NRog SPer
ANN ('Ausfete'PBR) (S)	LSRN
ANN HENDERSON ('Fryhoncho') (F)	LSRN MFry
ANNA FORD ('Harpiccolo') (Min/Patio) ♀H5	SCob
'Anna Olivier' (T)	EBls
'Anna Pavlova' (HT)	EBls
ANNAKARINA! ('Scherendee'PBR) (HT) **new**	CPla
ANNE BOLEYN ('Ausecret'PBR) (S)	EHyd EPfP LRHS NRHS SCoo
ANNE HARKNESS ('Harkaramel') (F)	LHkn
'Anne of Geierstein' (RH)	EBls
'Anne Watkins' (HT)	EBls
ANNE'S ROSE ('Frynippy'PBR) (F)	LSRN
ANNIVERSARY WALTZ ('Raw237') (HT)	ESty
ANNIVERSARY WISHES ('Noa140721') (F)	MAsh
'Anthony' (S)	EBls
ANTIQUE '89 ('Kordalen') (ClF)	EBls ETWh

APHRODITE ('Tan00847'PBR) (S) ♀H6	CDoC CEnd ESty ETWh LSRN MRav SApu
APHRODITE ('Tanetidor') (HT)	CArg
apothecary's rose	see *R. gallica* var. *officinalis*
'Apple Blossom' (Ra)	CBod EBls SHar
'Applejack' (S)	EBls
'Apricot Ingrid' (Patio) **new**	NRog
'Apricot Silk' (HT)	CTri SPer
APRICOT SUNBLAZE ('Savamark') (Min)	CSBt
ARC ANGEL ('Fryorst') (HT)	MFry
ARCANUM ('Tuckarc') (Min) **new**	NRog
'Archduke Charles' (Ch)	EBls
'Archiduc Joseph' misapplied	see *R.* 'Général Schablikine'
'Archiduchesse Elisabeth d'Autriche' (HP)	EBls
ARCHIE MOSS ('Dickumon') (S)	IDic
'Arctic Circle' (HT)	ESty NRog
'Ardoisée de Lyon' (HP)	EBls
'Ards Rover' (ClHP)	EBls
'Arethusa' (Ch)	EBls ETWh
'Arizona Sunset' (Min)	NRog
§ ***arkansana*** var. ***suffulta***	EBls ETWh
ARMADA ('Haruseful') (S)	EBls
'Arthur Bell' (F) ♀H6	Widely available
'Arthur de Sansal' (DPo)	ETWh
arvensis	CCVT CHab CLnd EBls ETWh LBuc NWea WTSh
§ 'Aschermittwoch' (ClHR)	EBls
ASCOT ('Tan01757'PBR) (HT)	ESty MFry
ASH WEDNESDAY	see *R.* 'Aschermittwoch'
'Astra Desmond' (Ra)	EBls ETWh MNrw
I 'At Peace Rose' (HT)	LSRN
ATLANTIC STAR ('Fryworld'PBR) (F)	MFry
ATTLEBOROUGH ('Beaat') (ClHT)	EBls
AUDIENZ	see *R.* TIMELESS CREAM
AUDREY WILCOX ('Frywilrey') (HT)	ELon ESty MFry
'Auguste Gervais' (Ra)	EBls
Austrian copper rose	see *R. foetida* 'Bicolor'
Austrian yellow	see *R. foetida*
'Autumn' (HT)	LSRN NRog
'Autumn Delight' (HM)	EBls ETWh NRog
AUTUMN FIRE	see *R.* 'Herbstfeuer'
AUTUMN SONG	see *R.* PURE POETRY ('Jacment') (F)
'Autumn Sunset' (ClS)	EBls MCot
'Autumnalis'	see *R.* 'Princesse de Nassau'
AVEC AMOUR ('Tan04341'PBR) (HT)	ESty
'Aviateur Blériot' (Ra)	CRHN EBls
'Avon' (HT)	CBod
AVON ('Poulmulti'PBR) (GC)	EBls ETWh MRav SApu SPer
AWAKENING ('Probuzení') (ClHT)	CEnd CRos EBee EBls EPfP ETWh LRHS MAsh MSwo NLar
'Ayrshire Splendens'	see *R.* 'Splendens'
BABE ('Raw1090') (F)	ESty
'Baby Bio' (F/Patio)	NRog
'Baby Faurax' (Poly)	EBls
'Baby Katie' (Min)	NRog
BABY MASQUERADE ('Tanba') (Min)	CGro MRav NRog SPer
BABYFACE ('Rawril'PBR) (Min)	ESty
BADMINTON GIRL ('Dicfiesta') (F)	IDic

'Bajazzo' (HT) **new**	SSea
'Ballerina' (HM/Poly) ♀H6	Widely available
BALMORAL ('Poulcas027'PBR') (Palace Series) (Patio)	EBls MAsh
'Baltimore Belle' (Ra)	CRHN EBee EBls ETWh NLar
banksiae (Ra)	SNig SRms SWeb
- ***alba***	see *R. banksiae* var. *banksiae*
§ - var. ***banksiae*** (Ra/d)	CBcs CBod CRHN CSBt CTri CTsd EBls EHyd ELan EPfP ETWh LCro LOPS LPar LRHS SGsty SLon WCot WLov XSen
- 'Lutea' (Ra/d) ♀H5	Widely available
- 'Lutescens' (Ra)	EBls WPGP
- var. ***normalis*** (Ra)	CSBt EBls EPfP SLon WCot WHer WPGP
I - 'Rosea' (Ra)	EWTr LPar NLar SGsty
'Bantry Bay' (ClHT)	CArg EBls ELan LSRN SLon SPer
BARAKURA ('Beajap') (GC/S)	EBls
BARBARA ('Raw1050')	LSRN
BARBARA ANN	see *R.* SCENT FROM HEAVEN
BARBRA STREISAND ('Wekquaneze') (HT)	LSRN
BARKAROLE ('Tanelorak') (HT)	SApu
'Baron Girod de l'Ain' (HP)	EBee EBls ELon ETWh LSRN NLar NRog SPer
'Baroness Rothschild' ambig.	see *R.* Climbing Baronne Edmond de Rothschild
BARONESSE ('Tan97094'PBR') (F)	MFry
§ 'Baronne Adolph de Rothschild' (HP)	EBls ETWh
'Baronne Prévost' (HP)	EBls
BAROQUE FLOORSHOW ('Harbaroque'PBR') (S)	CDoC MRav
BARRY STEPHENS ('Horcabellero') (HT)	LSRN
'Basye's Purple' (Ru) **new**	ETWh
BATHSHEBA ('Auschimbley') (Cl)	CRos CSBt ESty LRHS MAsh SPer
BEATRIX POTTER ('Beafolly') (S)	EBls
BEAUTY STAR	see *R.* LIVERPOOL REMEMBERS
BEHOLD ('Savahold') (Min)	NRog
'Belinda' (HM)	EBls LSRN
§ BELLA ('Pouljill'PBR') (Renaissance Series) (S)	LSRN
BELLA CHRISTINA ('Mandella') (F)	LSRN NRog
BELLA DIANA ('Mandiana') (F)	LSRN NRog
'Bellard' (G)	ETWh
'Belle Amour' (A × D)	EBls ETWh
'Belle de Crécy' (G)	CGro CTri EBls ETWh LRHS MAsh MNrw MPri NLar SPer
'Belle des Jardins' misapplied	see *R.* × *centifolia* 'Unique Panachée'
BELLE EPOQUE ('Fryyaboo'PBR') (HT)	ESty LRHS MFry
BELLE HAPPINESS ('Meileodevin'PBR') (Cl)	NRog
'Belle Isis' (G)	EBls ETWh NRog SPer
'Belle Lyonnaise' (ClT)	EBls
'Belle Poitevine' (Ru)	NRog
'Belle Vichyssoise' (N)	EBls
BELMONTE ('Harpearl'PBR') (F)	LHkn
§ 'Belvedere' (Ra) ♀H6	ETWh NLar SPer
BENITA ('Dicquarrel') (HT)	IDic
BENJAMIN BRITTEN ('Ausencart'PBR') (S)	CDoC EHyd EPfP ESty LBuc LRHS MAsh NRHS SPer
§ 'Bennett's Seedling' (Ra)	ETWh
'Bérénice' Vibert (G)	NRog
BERKSHIRE ('Korpinka'PBR') (GC) ♀H6	EBls SApu SCob SSea
BERYL JOYCE ('Tan96145'PBR') (HT)	ESty LSRN MRav
BEST IMPRESSION ('Tan04247'PBR') (HT)	ECnt ESty
BEST OF FRIENDS ('Pouldunk'PBR') (HT)	LSRN
BEST WISHES ('Chessnut'PBR') (ClHT/v)	LSRN
'Betty Curry' (HT) **new**	NRog
BETTY HARKNESS ('Harette'PBR') (F)	LHkn
'Betty Sherriff' (Ra)	ETWh GBin
'Betty Uprichard' (HT)	EBls
BETTY'S SMILE ('Websmile') (HT)	LSRN NRog
'Bewitched' (HT)	LSRN
BIANCO ('Cocblanco') (Patio/Min)	CDoC
BIDDULPH GRANGE ('Frydarkeye') (S)	MFry
BIENVENUE ('Delrochipar') (Cl)	EBls ESty
§ 'Big Chief' (HT)	NRog
BIG PURPLE ('Stebigpu') (HT)	ECnt NRog SApu
BILLET DOUX ('Delrosar') (S)	ESty
BIRTHDAY BOY ('Tan97607'PBR') (HT)	CBod CDoC ESty LSRN MRav NRog SApu SPoG
BIRTHDAY GIRL ('Meilasso') (F)	CBod CDoC CGro CSBt EPfP ESty LRHS LSRN MAsh MFry MRav NRog SApu SCob SCoo SPoG
BIRTHDAY SURPRISE ('Guesyoga') (F)	ESty
BIRTHDAY WISHES (Patio)	see *R.* SHRIMP HIT (Patio)
BIRTHDAY WISHES ('Guesdelay') (HT)	LSRN SSea
'Bishop Darlington' (HM)	EBls
BLACK BACCARA ('Meidebenne'PBR') (HT)	NRog
BLACK GOLD ('Cleblack') (Min)	NRog
'Black Jack' (Ce)	see *R.* 'Tour de Malakoff'
BLACK JACK ('Minkco') (Min/Patio)	NRog
'Black Prince' (HP)	EBls
BLACKBERRY NIP ('Somnip'PBR') (HT)	ELon
'Blairii Number Two' (ClBb)	CArg EBls ETWh NLar NRog
'Blanche de Belgique' (A)	NRog
'Blanche Double de Coubert' (Ru) ♀H7	CArg CBcs CBod CDoC CTri EBee EBls ECnt ELan EPfP ETWh LBuc LCro LOPS LRHS LSRN MFry MSwo NLar SApu SCob SEND SPer WKif
'Blanche Moreau' (CeMo)	EBls ETWh SPer
'Blanchefleur' (Ce × G)	EBls ETWh NRog
BLENHEIM ('Tanmurse') (GC)	SApu
'Blessings' (HT)	CArg CBcs CSBt CTri EBls LBuc LSRN MAsh MGos MRav NRog SApu SCob SPer
'Bleu Magenta' (Ra) ♀H6	CRHN EBls ELan ETWh GBin IArd NLar NRog SSea
BLISS ('Kormarzau'PBR') (F)	EBls
BLOOM OF RUTH ('Harmedley'PBR') (HT)	ECnt ESty LHkn LSRN
'Bloomfield Abundance' (Poly)	EBls ETWh MMuc NLar
'Bloomfield Courage' (Ra)	ETWh

'Bloomfield Dainty' (HM)	EBls
'Blossomtime' (ClHT)	NRog SPer
BLUE DIAMOND ('Athysumo'^{PBR}) (HT) **new**	ESty MFry
BLUE FOR YOU ('Pejamblu'^{PBR}) (F) $\mathbb{Y}^{H6}$	CDoC CEnd CGro CRos EBls ECnt ELan ELon EPfP ESty LBuc LCro LRHS MAsh MFry MGos MPri NRHS SApu SCoo SMad SPoG SSea
BLUE MOON ('Tannacht') (HT)	CDoC CTri EBls ELan MGos MRav NRog SApu SCob SPer SPoG SRGP
BLUEBERRY HILL ('Wekcryplag') (F)	EBls
'Blush Boursault' (Bs)	MMuc
'Blush Damask' (D)	EBls
'Blush Noisette'	see *R.* 'Noisette Carnée'
'Blush Rambler' (Ra)	CRHN CSBt EBls ELan EPfP ETWh LBuc MMuc SPer
'Blushing Lucy' (Ra) $\mathbb{Y}^{H6}$	CRHN ETWh MNrw NLar SMrm SPer
'Bobbie James' (Ra) $\mathbb{Y}^{H6}$	CArg CRHN CTri EBee EBls EHyd EPfP ETWh LPar LRHS MNrw MRav MSwo NLar NRHS SApu SCob SPer SSea WFar
'Bobby Charlton' (HT)	LSRN NRog
BOBBY DAZZLER ('Smi133-02'^{PBR}) (F)	CDoC ESty MRav
BOLLYWOOD ('Poulbt010') (HT)	MFry
'Bon Silène' (T)	EBls
BONFIRE ('Bencincuenta') (Min) **new**	NRog
BONICA ('Meidomonac') (GC) $\mathbb{Y}^{H6}$	Widely available
§ BONITA ('Poulen009'^{PBR}) (Renaissance Series) (S)	ECnt
'Bonn' (HM/S)	NRog
BOOGIE-WOOGIE ('Poulyc006'^{PBR}) (Courtyard Series) (ClHT)	ECnt MAsh
BORDURE ABRICOT ('Delbora') (F) **new**	EBls
BORDURE CAMAIEU ('Delcapo') (S) **new**	EBls
BORN AGAIN	see *R.* RENAISSANCE
BOSCOBEL ('Auscousin'^{PBR}) (S)	CRos CSBt ECnt EHyd EPfP ESty LBuc LRHS NRHS
'Botzaris' (D)	EBls ETWh
'Bougainville' (N/T) **new**	ETWh
'Boule de Neige' (Bb)	CBcs CBod CTri EBls ECnt ELan EPfP ETWh LCro LOPS LRHS LSRN MRav NLar NRHS SApu SCob SPer
'Bouquet de Marie' (HP/N) **new**	ETWh
'Bouquet d'Or' (N)	EBls ETWh NLar
'Bouquet Tout Fait' misapplied	see *R.* 'Nastarana'
'Bouquet Tout Fait' (N)	EBee ETWh
BOWLED OVER ('Tandolgnil'^{PBR}) (F) $\mathbb{Y}^{H6}$	ESty
§ ***bracteata*** (S)	CRHN EBls ECre ETWh EWes SSea
BRAVE HEART ('Horbondsmile') (F)	CSBt MRav
BREATH OF LIFE ('Harquanne'^{PBR}) (ClHT)	CDoC EBls ELan LHkn MFry MRav SApu SPer
BREATHTAKING ('Hargalore'^{PBR}) (HT)	ESty LHkn
'Bride and Groom'^{PBR} (HT)	CBod CDoC ESty LSRN MFry MRav SApu SCoo
BRIDE ('Fryyearn'^{PBR}) (HT)	LSRN MFry MRav
BRIDGE OF SIGHS ('Harglowing'^{PBR}) (Cl)	ECnt ESty LBuc LHkn LRHS MAsh MFry SPoG
BRIGHT AND BREEZY ('Dicjive') (F)	ECnt
BRIGHT AS A BUTTON ('Chewsumsigns'^{PBR}) (S) $\mathbb{Y}^{H5}$	EBee EBls ETWh LRHS MAsh MFry NLar SApu SLon SPer
BRIGHT FIRE ('Peaxi'^{PBR}) (ClHT)	MSwo SPer
BRIGHT FUTURE ('Kirora'^{PBR}) (Cl)	CBod ELon ESty SApu
BRIGHT IDEAS ('Horcoffdrop') (ClHT)	CGro EBls EPfP LRHS MAsh MPri
BRIGHT SMILE ('Dicdance') (F/Patio)	NRog
BRILLIANT SWEET DREAM ('Frysassy') (Patio)	CSBt ECnt
BROADLANDS ('Tanmirsch'^{PBR}) (GC)	NLar SApu
BROTHER CADFAEL ('Ausglobe'^{PBR}) (S)	CArg CDoC EHyd EPfP LRHS MAsh NRHS SCoo SPer
BROWN VELVET ('Maccultra') (F)	SPer
§ ***brunonii*** (Ra)	CExl EBls EWes WFar
- HPA 1386 **new**	GGro
- KR 10350	WPGP
- PAB 3083	LEdu
§ - 'La Mortola' (Ra)	ETWh NLar SPer
BRUSH-STROKES ('Guescolour') (F)	ESty
BUCKLEBURY BOY ('Webspell') (Patio) **new**	NRog
'Buff Beauty' (HM) $\mathbb{Y}^{H6}$	CArg CEnd CGro CSBt CTri EBee EBls ECnt EPfP ETWh EWTr LCro LOPS MAsh MCot MFry MRav MSwo NLar NRog SApu SCob SEND SPer WCFE WFar
BUKAVU ('Lenbrirus'^{PBR}) (HM) **new**	NRog
'Bullata'	see *R.* × *centifolia* 'Bullata'
§ 'Burgundiaca' (G)	EBls ETWh
Burgundian rose	see *R.* 'Burgundiaca'
§ BURGUNDY ICE ('Prose'^{PBR}) (F)	CArg CBod EBee EBls EPfP ESty LBuc LCro LOPS LRHS MAsh MFry MRav MSwo NRHS SApu SCob SCoo SMad SPoG SSea
'Burgundy Iceberg'	see *R.* BURGUNDY ICE
'Burgundy Rose'	see *R.* 'Burgundiaca'
burnet, double pink	see *R. spinosissima* double, pink-flowered
- - white	see *R. spinosissima* double, white-flowered
BURNING DESIRE ('Frysizzle') (F)	MFry
BUTTER CREAM ('Marbutter') (Patio) **new**	NRog
BUTTERCUP ('Ausband'^{PBR}) (S)	LRHS
BUXOM BEAUTY ('Korbilant'^{PBR}) (HT) $\mathbb{Y}^{H6}$	CArg EBls ELon EPfP LRHS LSRN MGos NRog SSea
'C.F. Meyer'	see *R.* 'Conrad Ferdinand Meyer'
CAFÉ AU LAIT ('Simgrey') (F)	ESty
CAJUN MOON ('Wekonine') (HT) **new**	NRog
'Cajun Signature' (HT) **new**	NRog
'Cajun Sunrise' (HT) **new**	NRog
'Caledonian' (HT)	NRog
CALENDAR GIRL ('Rawcalendar') (F) **new**	NRog

	californica 'Plena'	see *R. nutkana* 'Plena'
	'Callisto' (HM)	ETWh
§	CALYPSO ('Poulclimb'PBR) (ClHT)	SApu
	'Camayeux' (G)	EBls ECnt ETWh NLar NRog
	CAMBRIDGESHIRE ('Korhaugen'PBR) (GC)	CTri EBls ETWh SApu SCob SPer SSea
	CAMELOT ('Tan05372'PBR) (ClF)	ESty
	CAMILLE PISARRO ('Destricol') (F)	EBls ESty
	CANADIAN NORTHLIGHT ('Man-cl') (HT) **new**	NRog
	'Canary Bird'	see *R.xanthina* 'Canary Bird'
	CANDY FLOSS ('Natucandy') (HT) **new**	MAsh
	CANDY KISSES ('Simwatu') (HT)	ESty
	CANDY LAND ('Wekrosopela'PBR) (ClHT)	ECnt ESty
	canina (S)	CArg CCVT CGro CHab CLnd CTri EPfP EPom GDam LBuc LCro LOPS MRav NLar NWea SCob SEWo SPer WKor WMat WMou WTSh
	'Cantabrigiensis' (S) ♀H6	EBls ETWh NRog SPer SSea
	CANZONETTA ('Noa84497d') (F)	MAsh
	CAPEL MANOR HOUSE ('Beajammie') (ClS)	EBls
	'Capitaine John Ingram' (CeMo)	CArg EBls ETWh NLar
	'Captain Christy'	see *R.* 'Climbing Captain Christy'
	'Captain Hayward' (HP)	ETWh
	'Captain Scarlet' (ClMin)	ESty
	'Cardinal de Richelieu' (G)	CArg CBcs CTri EBls EPfP ETWh EWTr LCro LOPS LRHS MAsh MRav MSwo NLar NRog SCob SPer SPoG
	CARDINAL HUME ('Harregale') (S)	LHkn
	CAREFREE DAYS ('Meirivoui'PBR) (Patio) ♀H6	CBod EBls EPfP LBuc LRHS MFry MPri NRHS SApu SPoG SSea
	CARING FOR YOU ambig.	LSRN
	'Carmen' (Ru)	EBls
	'Carmenetta' (S)	EBls
	'Carol' (F)	see *R.* 'Carol Amling'
§	'Carol Amling' (F)	LSRN
	CAROL ANN ('Peapost') (F)	LSRN
	'Caroline Testout'	see *R.* 'Madame Caroline Testout'
	CAROLINE VICTORIA ('Harprior'PBR) (HT)	LHkn LSRN SApu
	CAROLYN KNIGHT ('Austurner'PBR) (S)	CRos EHyd EPfP LCro LOPS LRHS LSRN NRHS
	CARON KEATING ROSE ('Harkoral'PBR) (F)	LHkn
	CARRIS ('Harmanna'PBR) (HT)	LHkn MAsh MFry MGos NRHS
§	CASINO ('Macca') (ClHT)	CTri EBls ETWh MRav SPer
	'Castle Apricot'	see *R.* LAZY DAYS
	'Castle Cream'	see *R.* PERFECT DAY
	CASTLE OF MEY ('Coclucid') (F)	NRog
	'Castle Shrimp Pink'	see *R.* FASCINATION ('Poulmax')
	'Castle Yellow'	see *R.* SUMMER GOLD
	CATHERINE COOKSON ('Noscook') (HT)	NRog
§	'Cécile Brünner' (Poly) ♀H5	CBod CTri EBee EBls ELan ETWh LRHS LSRN MMuc NLar NRog NWea SPer
	CELEBRATING LIFE ('Harvixon') (F) **new**	LHkn
	CELEBRATION TIME	see *R.* CINCO DE MAYO
§	'Céleste' (A) ♀H6	CTri EBls EPfP ETWh GBin NLar SEND SPer
	'Célina' (CeMo)	GBin LSRN
	'Céline Forestier' (N)	CArg EBee EBls ETWh SPer
§	'Celsiana' (D) ♀H7	EBls ETWh LRHS LSRN NLar NRog SPer
	CENTENAIRE DE LOURDES ('Delge') (F)	EBls
§	× ***centifolia*** (Ce)	EBls ETWh NRog SPer
§	- 'Bullata' (Ce)	EBls
§	- 'Cristata' (Ce) ♀H6	CArg EBls ETWh LEdu NRog SPer WBor
§	- 'De Meaux' (Ce)	EBls ETWh NLar SPer
§	- 'Muscosa' (CeMo)	EBls ETWh GBin LEdu NRog SCob
	- 'Parvifolia'	see *R.* 'Burgundiaca'
§	- 'Shailer's White Moss' (CeMo)	EBls ETWh NRog
	- 'Spong' (Ce)	EBls ETWh
§	- 'Unique' (Ce)	EBls ETWh
§	- 'Unique Panachée' (Ce)	EBls ETWh
	'Centifolia Variegata'	see *R.* × *centifolia* 'Unique Panachée'
	CENTRE STAGE ('Chewcreepy'PBR) (S/GC) ♀H6	LRHS MAsh
	'Cerise Bouquet' (S) ♀H6	EBls ETWh NLar WSpi
	CHAMPAGNE CELEBRATION ('Frylimbo') (HT)	MFry
	CHAMPAGNE CELEBRATION ('Simluck') (F)	ESty
	CHAMPAGNE COCKTAIL ('Horflash') (F)	NRog
§	CHAMPAGNE MOMENT ('Korvanaber'PBR) (F) ♀H6	CArg CBcs CDoC CEnd CGro CRos CSBt EBls ECnt ELan EPfP ESty LBuc LRHS LSRN MAsh MFry MGos MPri MRav NRHS SApu SCob SMad SPer SPoG SSea
	'Champion of the World' (Bb)	EBls
	CHANDOS BEAUTY ('Harmisty'PBR) (HT) ♀H6	CDoC CGro CRos ECnt ELon EPfP ESty ETWh LBuc LHkn LRHS LSRN MAsh MFry MGos MRav NLar SApu SPer SPoG SSea
	'Chanelle' (F)	EBls NRog SDix SPer
	CHANNABELLE ('Hartempter') (F) **new**	LHkn
	Chapeau de Napoléon	see *R.* × *centifolia* 'Cristata'
	'Chaplin's Pink Climber' (Cl)	ETWh
	CHARDONNAY ('Simtely') (F)	ESty
	CHARISMA ('Jelroganor') (F)	MPri
	CHARISMA ('Noa16071'PBR) (HT)	EBls EPfP LBuc LRHS MFry SPoG
	CHARISMATIC ('Decmatic') (Patio) **new**	NRog
	'Charles Albanel' (Ru/GC)	CDoC
	CHARLES AUSTIN ('Ausles') (S)	CDoC MGos MRav
	CHARLES DARWIN ('Auspeet'PBR) (S)	CDoC EHyd EPfP LBuc LRHS MAsh NLar NRHS SCoo SPer
	'Charles de Mills' (G) ♀H6	CDoC CTri EBls ECnt ELan EPfP ETWh EWTr LCro LOPS LRHS LSRN MRav MSwo NLar NRog SPer WHer
	CHARLES DICKENS ('Raw1064') (HT)	ESty
	'Charles Mallerin' (HT)	EBls

CHARLIE'S ROSE ('Tanellepa') (HT) 𝕐H6	ESty LSRN SApu
CHARLOTTE ('Auspoly'PBR) (S) 𝕐H6	CRos EHyd ELan EPfP ESty LBuc LCro LOPS LRHS LSRN MBNS MSwo NRHS SCoo SPer
CHARLOTTE VIELI ('Diclooker') (F)	IDic
CHARTERED ('Diclingo') (F)	IDic
CHARTREUSE DE PARME ('Delviola') (S)	EBls ESty ETWh MRav NLar
CHATSWORTH ('Tanotax') (Patio/F) 𝕐H6	SPer
CHAWTON HOUSE ('Harxcel') **new**	LHkn
CHECKMATE ('Diclanky') (ClF)	IDic MRav SApu
§ CHEEK TO CHEEK ('Poulslas'PBR) (Courtyard Series) (ClMin)	EBls LRHS MAsh SApu
CHEERFUL CHARLIE ('Cocquimmer'PBR) (F)	LSRN MRav
CHELSEA BELLE ('Talchelsea') (Min)	NRog
CHERIE	see *R.* RED ABUNDANCE
CHERRY BONICA ('Meipeporia'PBR) (S)	CRos ECnt
CHERRY BRANDY '85 ('Tanryrandy'PBR) (HT)	CSBt
CHERRY HINTON ('Dicprolong') (S)	IDic
CHESHIRE ('Fryelise'PBR) (HT)	MFry
'Chevy Chase' (Ra)	EBls LRHS MAsh SApu
'Chewton Rose' (S)	EBls
CHIANTI ('Auswine') (S)	EBls ETWh NLar
CHICAGO PEACE ('Johnago') (HT)	CArg EBls NRog SCob
CHILD OF ACHIEVEMENT	see *R.* BELLA
CHILD OF MY HEART ('Beapeace') (HT)	EBls
CHILD'S PLAY ('Savachild') (Min)	NRog
CHILTERNS ('Kortemma') (GC)	SCob
'Chinatown' (ClF) 𝕐H6	CArg CTri LRHS MAsh MPri MRav NRog SApu SCob SCoo SPer
chinensis Jacq. (S)	EBls
- 'Minima' *sensu stricto* hort.	see *R.* 'Rouletii'
- 'Mutabilis'	see *R.* × *odorata* 'Mutabilis'
- 'Old Blush'	see *R.* × *odorata* 'Pallida'
- 'Semperflorens' (S)	EBls WCot
- var. ***spontanea*** (S)	WPGP
- 'White Beauty' (S)	WCot
CHLOE ('Poulen003'PBR) (Renaissance Series) (S)	ECnt ESty ETWh LSRN NLar
CHLOE'S STAR ('Pazstar') (Min) **new**	NRog
'Chloris' (A)	EBee ETWh NRog
§ CHOCOLATE RIPPLES ('Simstripe') (Cl)	ESty
CHOIR OF ANGELS	see *R.* OUR JANE
CHRIS ('Kirsan'PBR) (ClHT)	CArg ESty LSRN SApu
CHRISTIAN DIOR ('Meilie') (HT)	EBls
CHRISTOPHER ('Cocopher') (HT)	LSRN
CHRISTOPHER COLUMBUS ('Poulbico'PBR) (F)	SApu
'Chrysler Imperial' (HT)	EBls
'Chuckles' (F)	ESty
CIDER CUP ('Dicladida') (Min/Patio)	NRog
§ CINCO DE MAYO ('Wekcobeju'PBR) (F) 𝕐H6	MRav NRog
'Cinderella' (Min)	CSBt NLar
'Cinderella' (Ra)	EBee
'Cinderella' ambig.	CDoC
CINDERELLA ('Korfobalt') (ClS)	ETWh
CITY LIVERY ('Harhero 2000') (F)	LBuc LHkn
CITY OF CARLSBAD	see *R.* HANKY PANKY
'City of Leeds' (F)	MGos SPer
CITY OF LONDON ('Harukfore') (F)	CSBt EBls LRHS
CITY OF YORK	see *R.* 'Direktör Benschop'
CLAIR MATIN ('Meimont') (ClS)	EBls ETWh
CLAIRE AUSTIN ('Ausprior'PBR) (S)	CRos EHyd EPfP ESty LRHS MAsh MSwo NRHS SCob SCoo SPer SPoG
CLAIRE BEAR ('Webwelcome') (F) **new**	NRog
'Claire Jacquier' (N)	EBls ETWh
CLAIRE MARSHALL ('Harunite'PBR) (F)	ECnt ELon EPfP ESty LHkn LRHS SApu SRGP
CLAIRE ROSE ('Auslight'PBR) (S)	LSRN
'Clarence House' (Cl)	CGro EBls EPfP LRHS MAsh
CLARET ('Frykristal'PBR) (HT) 𝕐H6	EPfP ESty MFry MRav SApu
CLAUDE MONET ('Delstrirocrem') (Cl)	EBls ESty
CLAUDE MONET ('Jacdesa') (HT)	EBls ESty
CLEAR COVER ('Poultc013') (Towne & Country Series) (GC/S)	ETWh
'Clementina Carbonieri' (T)	EBls ETWh NLar
CLEO ('Beebop') (HT)	LSRN
'Cliff Richard' (F)	ESty LSRN NRog
'Climbing Alec's Red' (ClHT)	SPer
'Climbing Arthur Bell' (ClF)	CGro CSBt CTri ELon ESty ETWh MAsh MPri MSwo NRog SApu SCob SCoo SPer SPoG SRGP SSea
'Climbing Ballerina' (Ra)	CSBt
§ CLIMBING BARONNE EDMOND DE ROTHSCHILD ('Meigrisosar') (ClHT)	CSBt
CLIMBING BETTINA ('Mepalsar') (ClHT)	EBls
'Climbing Blue Moon' (ClHT)	ELan ELon ESty SApu SSea
§ 'Climbing Captain Christy' (ClHT)	EBls
'Climbing Cécile Brünner' (ClPoly) 𝕐H5	CArg CEnd CSBt CTri EBls ECnt EPfP ETWh LCro LOPS LSRN MCot MRav NLar NRog SApu SCob SEND SPer SSea
'Climbing Château de Clos-Vougeot' (ClHT)	EBls
§ 'Climbing Columbia' (ClHT)	EShb ETWh NRog SPer
'Climbing Crimson Glory' (ClHT)	EBls EPfP ETWh NLar NRog SSea
§ 'Climbing Devoniensis' (ClT)	EBls ETWh
'Climbing Ena Harkness' (ClHT)	CRos EBls LHkn MRav NRog SPer SPoG

'Climbing Étoile de Hollande' (ClHT) ♀H5	CSBt CTri EBee EBls ELon EPfP ETWh LBuc LCro LOPS MPri MRav NRog SApu SMad SPer SPoG SSea WBor
'Climbing General MacArthur' (ClHT)	EBls
§ 'Climbing Golden Dawn' (ClHT)	EBls
'Climbing Home Sweet Home' (ClHT)	LSRN
'Climbing Iceberg' (ClF) ♀H5	Widely available
'Climbing Jazz'	see *R.* THAT'S JAZZ
'Climbing Josephine Bruce' (ClHT)	EBls ETWh
§ 'Climbing Lady Hillingdon' (ClT) ♀H4	CArg EBls ELan EPfP ETWh LBuc LRHS LSRN MCot MRav NLar SPer SSea
'Climbing Lady Sylvia' (ClHT)	CSBt EBls ETWh LRHS LSRN NRHS NRog SPer
'Climbing Little White Pet'	see *R.* 'Félicité Perpétue'
'Climbing Madame Butterfly' (ClHT) ♀H6	EBls
'Climbing Madame Caroline Testout' (ClHT)	EBls ETWh NRog SPer
'Climbing Masquerade' (ClF)	CGro CTri EBls ELan ETWh MRav NRog SApu SCob SPer SSea
'Climbing Mrs Aaron Ward' (ClHT)	EBls
'Climbing Mrs Herbert Stevens' (ClHT)	EBls EPfP ETWh MRav NRog SPer
'Climbing Mrs Sam McGredy' (ClHT)	CArg CSBt EBls ETWh NLar NRog
'Climbing Niphetos' (ClT)	EBls
'Climbing Ophelia' (ClHT)	EBls ETWh
CLIMBING ORANGE SUNBLAZE ('Meiji Katarsar') (ClMin)	SPer
§ 'Climbing Paul Lédé' (ClT)	CEnd EBls ETWh
'Climbing Peace' (ClHT)	ETWh
§ 'Climbing Pompon de Paris' (ClMinCh)	CTri EBls MNrw MRav SEND SMrm SPer
'Climbing Roundelay' (Cl)	EBls
'Climbing Ruby Wedding' (ClHT)	LSRN
'Climbing Shot Silk' (ClHT) ♀H6	ETWh SPer
§ 'Climbing Souvenir de la Malmaison' (ClBb)	EBls ETWh SPer
'Climbing The Queen Elizabeth' (ClF)	CDoC
'Climbing White Cloud'	see *R.* WHITE CLOUD ('Korstacha')
CLOUD NINE ('Fryextra'PBR) (HT)	CDoC MFry
'Clytemnestra' (HM)	EBls
COACHELLA ('Jackhill') (F) **new**	NRog
COCO ('Korferse') (F)	LSRN
'Coconut Ice' (HT)	SCoo
COLCHESTER BEAUTY ('Cansend') (F)	ECnt
§ 'Colonel Fabvier' (Ch)	EBls ETWh NLar
colonial white	see *R.* 'Sombreuil'
'Columbian'	see *R.* 'Climbing Columbia'
COMEBACK	see *R.* TIMELESS PINK
'Commandant Beaurepaire' (Bb)	EBls ETWh NRog
common moss	see *R.* × *centifolia* 'Muscosa'
COMMONWEALTH GLORY ('Harclue'PBR) (HT)	LHkn
'Compassion' (ClHT) ♀H6	Widely available
'Complicata' (G)	CTri EBls EPfP ETWh MRav NLar NRog SApu SEND SMad SPer
'Comte de Chambord' misapplied	see *R.* 'Madame Boll'
'Comtesse Cécile de Chabrillant' (HP)	EBls ETWh
'Comtesse de Lacépède' misapplied	see *R.* 'Du Maître d'Ecole'
§ 'Comtesse de Murinais' (DMo)	EBls
'Comtesse d'Oxford' (HP)	EBls
§ 'Comtesse du Caÿla' (Ch)	EBls
'Comtesse O'Gorman' (HP)	EBls
'Comtesse Vandal' (HT)	EBls
CONCERT	see *R.* CALYPSO
'Conchita' (Poly) **new**	MBros
'Conditorum' (G)	EBls ETWh NRog
CONGRATULATIONS ('Korlift') (HT)	CBcs CSBt ECnt IArd LCro LOPS LSRN MGos MRav NRog SApu SCob SCoo SPer
§ 'Conrad Ferdinand Meyer' (Ru)	EBee EBls NRog SPer
CONSERVATION ('Cocdimple') (Min/Patio)	SCoo
CONSTANCE FINN ('Hareden'PBR) (F)	LHkn
'Constance Spry' (ClS) ♀H6	CArg CDoC CTri EBee EBls EHyd EPfP ETWh LCro LOPS LRHS MAsh MGos MMuc MRav MSwo NLar NRHS NRog SCob SCoo SEND SPer
§ 'Cooperi' (Ra)	CRHN EBls EPfP ETWh SPer SSea WKif WPGP
Cooper's Burmese	see *R.* 'Cooperi'
'Copenhagen' (ClHT)	EBls
'Copper Delight' (F)	NRog
COPPER LIGHTS ('Simhigh') (HT)	ESty
'Coral Creeper' (ClHT)	CRHN
'Coral Dawn' (ClHT)	EBls
CORAL GEM ('Simplan') (HT)	ESty
CORAL SWEET DREAM ('Fryrader') (Patio)	MFry
'Coralie' (D)	EBls
'Cornelia' (HM) ♀H6	CArg CBcs CTri EBee EBls EPfP ETWh IArd LCro LOPS LRHS LSRN MAsh MCot MRav NLar NRog SCob SPer
CORONATION STREET ('Wekswetrup') (F)	LSRN
'Coryana' (S)	EBls ETWh
corymbifera (S)	EBls
COSMOPOLITAN ('Simgrid') (HT)	ESty
cottage maid	see *R.* × *centifolia* 'Unique Panachée'
COTTAGE ROSE ('Ausglisten') (S)	LSRN
COUNTESS OF WESSEX ('Beacream') (S)	EBls LRHS MAsh NRHS
COUNTRY MUSIC ('Harcheer') (S)	LSRN NRog
COUNTY OF YORKSHIRE ('Korstarnow'PBR) (GC) ♀H6	EBls ESty
COURAGE ('Poulduf'PBR) (HT)	ECnt
'Cramoisi Supérieur' (Ch)	EBls ETWh
CRAZY FOR YOU ('Wekroalt'PBR) (F) ♀H6	EBls ESty LBuc LSRN

CREAM ABUNDANCE ('Harflax'^{PBR}) (Abundance Series) (F)	LHkn SApu SSea
CREAM DREAM ('Koromtar') (HT)	CTri NRog
CREAMCRACKER ('Dicorigin') (F)	IDic
CREAMSICLE (Min) **new**	NRog
CRÈME DE LA CRÈME ('Gancre'^{PBR}) (ClHT)	CDoC CRos CSBt EBee EBls ECnt ELan ESty ETWh LRHS MRav SApu SPer SPoG SSea
'Crépuscule' (N)	EBee EBls ETWh EWTr NLar
crested moss	see *R.* × *centifolia* 'Cristata'
CRIMSON BLUSH ('Sieson') (A) **new**	NRog
CRIMSON CASCADE ('Fryclimbdown') (ClHT) Υ^{H6}	CDoC EBls ESty LBuc LRHS MAsh MFry MGos MRav MSwo SApu SPer SPoG
crimson damask	see *R. gallica* var. *officinalis*
'Crimson Descant' (ClHT)	ECnt
'Crimson Glory' (HT)	CArg CTri EBls SSea
'Crimson Shower' (Ra)	CArg CBod CTri ELan ETWh LPar LRHS MBNS MMuc MRav MSwo NLar NRog SApu SPer WHer
CRIMSON SWEET DREAM ('Frynogo') (Patio)	CSBt ECnt ESty MFry SCoo
'Cristata'	see *R.* × *centifolia* 'Cristata'
CROCUS ROSE ('Ausquest'^{PBR}) (S) Υ^{H6}	EHyd EPfP LCro LOPS LRHS NLar NRHS SCob SPer
CROWN PRINCESS MARGARETA ('Auswinter'^{PBR}) (S) Υ^{H6}	CDoC CRos EHyd ELan EPfP ESty LBuc LCro LOPS LRHS MAsh NLar NRHS SCob SCoo SPer SPoG
cuisse de nymphe	see *R.* 'Great Maiden's Blush'
CUMBERLAND ('Harnext'^{PBR}) (ClF)	ETWh LHkn NLar
'Cupid' (ClHT)	EBls ETWh SPer
I 'Cutie' (Patio)	ESty
cymosa	EBls
- 'Rebecca Rushforth' (Cl)	EBee WPGP
'Cynthia Brooke' (HT)	EBls
DACAPO ('Poulcy012'^{PBR}) (Courtyard Series) (ClPatio)	ECnt
'D'Aguesseau' (G)	ETWh
DAILY SKETCH ('Macai') (F)	ESty
'Dainty Bess' (HT)	EBls ETWh NLar
'Dale Farm' (F/Patio)	NRog
× ***damascena*** var. ***bifera***	see *R.* × *damascena* var. *semperflorens*
- 'Kazanlik' (D)	EBls ETWh NRog
§ - 'Professeur Émile Perrot' (D)	WFar
§ - var. ***semperflorens*** (D) Υ^{H6}	EBls ETWh NLar NRog
§ - 'Versicolor' (D)	EBls SPer SSea
DAME JUDI DENCH ('Ausquaker') (HM)	CRos CSBt EPfP ESty LRHS MBNS MSwo SCoo
'Danaë' (HM)	EBls ETWh NRog
DANCING FLAME ('Tucflame') (Min) **new**	NRog
DANCING PINK ('Hendan') (F)	NRog
DANCING QUEEN ('Fryfestoon') (ClHT) Υ^{H6}	CArg CDoC CGro EBls ECnt LBuc LRHS LSRN MAsh MFry MRav SApu SSea
DANCING SUNSET ('Guesunusal') (ClHT)	ESty
DANIEL ('Webwhite') (HT)	ESty
DANNY BOY ('Dicxcon'^{PBR}) (Patio)	IDic LSRN
'Danse du Feu' (ClF)	CArg CBcs CBod CSBt CTri EBls ELan ETWh LRHS MAsh MGos MRav NRog SApu SCob SPer
'Daphne' ambig.	EBls LSRN
DARCEY BUSSELL ('Ausdecorum'^{PBR}) (S) Υ^{H6}	CGro CRos CSBt EBee ECnt EHyd ELan EPfP ESty LBuc LCro LOPS LRHS LSRN MAsh MGos MSwo NLar NRHS SCoo SPer SPoG
'Darius' (G) **new**	NRog
'Darling Jenny' (HT)	LSRN NRog
DAVID WHITFIELD ('Gana') (F)	LSRN
davidii (S)	EBls WPav
DAVID'S STAR ('Hordadstar') (HT)	LSRN NRog
DAWN CHORUS ('Dicquasar') (HT) Υ^{H6}	CSBt EPfP ESty LRHS MRav SApu SCob SPer SPoG SSea
'Daybreak' (HM)	CTri EBls ETWh NLar NRog
'De Meaux'	see *R.* × *centifolia* 'De Meaux'
'De Meaux, White'	see *R.* 'White de Meaux'
§ 'De Resht' (DPo) Υ^{H7}	CArg CDoC CTri EBls ECnt EPfP ETWh LBuc LRHS MAsh MCot MPri MRav NLar SPer
DEAR BARBARA ('Rawbar') (HT)	LSRN
DEAR DAD ('Smi87-02') (HT)	ESty
'Dear Daughter' (F)	ESty
DEAR JOAN ('Rawjo') (F)	LSRN
§ DEAR MARGARET ('Raw293') (HT)	LSRN
DEAR MICHAEL ('Raw1065') (F)	LSRN
'Dearest' (F)	CArg CTri NRog SCob SPer
'Debbie Thomas' (HT)	LSRN NRog
DEB'S DELIGHT ('Legsweet'^{PBR}) (F)	LSRN
'Debutante' (Ra) Υ^{H7}	CRHN EBls ETWh EWTr
DEEP IMPRESSION ('Tan03162') (F)	MFry
'Deep Secret' (HT)	CArg CBcs CBod CSBt CTri EBls ECnt ELan ELon EPfP ESty LBuc LRHS MAsh MCot MFry MPri MRav NRog SApu SCoo SPer SSea
'Deidre Hall' (HT)	LSRN NRog
DELIGHTFUL ('Curspoglo') (ClMin)	ECnt ESty
DELLA BALFOUR ('Harblend'^{PBR}) (ClHT)	EBls LHkn SApu
DESDEMONA ('Auskindling'^{PBR}) (HM)	CGro CRos ECnt EHyd EPfP LRHS MBNS NLar NRHS
'Designer Sunset' (Patio)	CDoC MAsh
'Desperado' (HT) **new**	NRog
§ 'Desprez à Fleur Jaune' (N)	EBls ETWh IArd
'Devoniensis' (ClT)	see *R.* 'Climbing Devoniensis'
DIAMOND ('Korgazell'^{PBR}) (Patio) Υ^{H6}	LSRN SApu
DIAMOND ANNIVERSARY ('Morsixty') (Min)	LSRN
'Diamond Celebration' (HT)	LSRN
DIAMOND DAYS ('Hartribe'^{PBR}) (HT)	ESty LHkn LSRN MRav SPoG
DIAMOND DAYS FOREVER ('Fryjess'^{PBR}) (F)	ECnt LSRN MFry SApu
DIAMOND EYES ('Wekwibypur') (Min)	CBod ECnt ELon ESty
'Diamond Jubilee' (HT)	CEnd CSBt EBls LRHS MAsh
DIAMOND JUBILEE ('Tan022260') (HT)	CArg ELan MFry NRog SPer
DIAMOND WEDDING ('Raw1150') (F)	ESty

'Diamond Wishes' see *R.* MISTY HIT
DIANA ('Tananaid'PBR) (HT) LSRN
DICK'S DELIGHT ('Dicwhistle') (GC) LSRN
DIE WELT ('Diekor') (HT) NRog
DIENIE STEWART ('Dicpraise') (F) IDic
DIORESSENCE ('Deldiore') (F) ESty
§ 'Direktör Benschop' (ClF) EBls EPfP
DIXIELAND LINDA ('Beadix') (ClHT) EBls LRHS MAsh
DIZZY HEIGHTS ('Fryblissful'PBR) (ClHT) ♀H6 CDoC ELon LBuc MAsh MFry MRav SApu SGsty SPer SSea
'Docteur Grill' (T) EBls
DOCTOR DICK ('Cocbaden') (HT) NRog
'Doctor Huey' (Cl) CRHN EBls
DOCTOR JO ('Fryatlanta'PBR) (F) MFry
DOCTOR JOHN DICKMAN ('Briman') (Min) **new** NRog
DOCTOR MICHAEL NOBLE ('Manmichael') (Min) **new** NRog
DOCTOR TOMMY CAIRNS ('Benwales') (Min) **new** NRog
DOCTOR TROY GARRET ('Weltroy') (Patio) **new** NRog
'Doctor W. Van Fleet' (Ra) EBls
'Dogwood' (S) **new** NRog
DOLCE VITA ('Delcentoran') (F) ESty
DOLLY ('Poulvision') (F) LSRN
DOMAINE DE CHANTILLY ('Delagak') (HT) **new** ESty
DONA MARTIN ('Mardona') (HT) **new** NRog
'Donald Prior' (F) EBls
'Doncasteri' EBls
DONNA ('Pekcoupamaple') (HT) LSRN
'Doreen' (HT) LSRN NRog
DORIS MORGAN ('Brimorgan') (Min) NRog
'Doris Tysterman' (HT) CTri EBls NRog SCob
DOROTHY ('Cocrocket'PBR) (F) LSRN MRav
DOROTHY HOUSE ('Fryniffi') (F) MFry
'Dorothy Perkins' (Ra) CArg CRHN CTri EBls ETWh MAsh MFry MRav NPer NRog SApu SCob SPer WHer
'Dortmund' (S) ♀H7 EBls ETWh SPer
DOUBLE DELIGHT ('Andeli') (HT) EBls ELan ELon ESty LSRN NRog SCob SPer SSea
DOUBLE GOLD ('Savadouble') (Patio) NRog
DOUGLAS ('Cocfresco') (F) LSRN
DREAM LOVER ('Peayetti'PBR) (Patio) ESty
'Dreaming Spires' (ClHT) MSwo SApu SPer
'Dresden Doll' (MinMo) EBls
§ 'Du Maître d'Ecole' (G) EBls WHer
DUBLIN BAY ('Macdub') (ClF) ♀H6 CArg CBod CDoC CEnd CRos CSBt CTri EBls ECnt ELan ELon EPfP ETWh IArd LRHS LSRN MAsh MCot MFry MPri MRav MSwo NLar NRog SApu SCob SPer SPoG SSea WBor
'Duc de Guiche' (G) ♀H7 EBls EPfP ETWh MMuc NLar WHer
'Ducher' (Ch/T) **new** ETWh
DUCHESS OF CORNWALL ('Tan97157') (HT) ♀H6 CDoC CSBt EBee EBls ECnt ESty ETWh MFry MGos MRav SApu SCoo SMad SPer
DUCHESS OF DEVONSHIRE ('Stortebekerkal 2017') (HT) MFry
'Duchess of Portland' see *R.* 'Portlandica'
DUCHESS OF YORK see *R.* SUNSEEKER
'Duchesse d'Angoulême' (Ce × G) ♀H7 EBls ETWh NRog
'Duchesse d'Auerstädt' (N) EBls
'Duchesse de Berry' (G) NRog
'Duchesse de Brabant' (HT) EBls
'Duchesse de Buccleugh' (G) EBls ETWh
§ 'Duchesse de Montebello' (G) ♀H7 EBls ETWh EWTr NLar SPer
'Duke of Edinburgh' (HP) EBls
DUKE OF EDINBURGH (Patio) see *R.* THE GOLD AWARD ROSE
'Duke of Wellington' (HP) EBls ETWh
'Duke of Windsor' (HT) SPer
DUNHAM MASSEY ('Beajelly') (S) EBee EBls LRHS MAsh
'Dunwich Rose' (SpH) EBls EPfP ETWh NLar NRog SPer WCot
§ 'Duplex' (S) EBls ETWh
'Dupontii' (S) ♀H6 EBls ETWh NLar
'Dupuy Jamain' (HP) EBls
'Dusky Maiden' (F) EBls ELon ETWh
'Dutch Gold' (HT) CArg MGos NRog SPer
DWARF FAIRY ('Korweenu') (Min) MAsh
DYNAMIC DUO ('Fryvogue') (F) ECnt
DYNAMITE see *R.* HIGH FLYER
'E.H. Morse' see *R.* 'Ernest H. Morse'
'Earl of Eldon' (N) **new** ETWh
'Easlea's Golden Rambler' (Ra) ♀H5 CArg EBls ETWh MRav NLar
EAST PARK ('Harjope'PBR) (HT) LHkn
§ EASY DOES IT ('Harpageant'PBR) (F) ♀H6 CBod CDoC ECnt ESty ETWh LHkn MRav NLar
EASY GOING ('Harflow'PBR) (F) ♀H6 IArd LHkn
§ EBB TIDE ('Weksmopur'PBR) (F) CBod CGro CSBt EBls ECnt EPfP ESty LRHS MAsh SApu SPoG
ecae (S) ETWh
'Éclair' (HP) EBls
'Eddie Bailey' (Cl) **new** NRog
'Eddie's Crimson' (*moyesii* hybrid) LSRN
'Eddie's Jewel' (*moyesii* hybrid) EBls LSRN
'Eden Rose' (HT) NLar
EDEN ROSE '88 ('Meiviolin') (ClHT) EBls ETWh MAsh SApu SGsty SPer
EDITH HOLDEN ('Chewlegacy') (F) EBls
EDWARD'S ROSE ('Smi73/7/97') (F) ESty LSRN MRav
eglanteria see *R.* ***rubiginosa***
EGLANTYNE ('Ausmak'PBR) (S) CDoC CRos EHyd ELan EPfP LCro LOPS LRHS NRHS SCob SPer
'Eileen' (F) **new** NRog
EIRENE ('Tan10696') (F) **new** MFry
'Eleanor' (Patio) LSRN
ELEANOR ('Poulberin'PBR) (S) ECnt ETWh LSRN

§ ***elegantula*** 'Persetosa' (S)	EBls ETWh
'Elias' (S) **new**	NRog
§ ELINA ('Dicjana') (HT) 🏆H6	EBls ECnt LSRN MRav NRog SPer
ELIZABETH ASHBROOK ('Athybonper') (S) **new**	MFry
ELIZABETH CASSON ('Harkish'^{PBR}) (F) **new**	LHkn
'Elizabeth Harkness' (HT)	LHkn SPer
'Elizabeth Harwood' (Cl)	EBls
ELIZABETH OF GLAMIS ('Macel') (F)	CTri EBls NRog SPer
ELIZABETH STUART ('Maselstu') (Generosa Series) (S)	LSRN
ELLE ('Meibderos'^{PBR}) (HT)	LSRN
ELLEN ('Auscup') (S)	LSRN
'Ellen Willmott' (HT)	EBls ETWh
'Elmshorn' (S)	EBls
ELOISE ('Kirsandra'^{PBR}) (HT)	LSRN
ELVIS ('Adablarop'^{PBR}) (HT)	LSRN
ELY CATHEDRAL ('Beajolly') (S) **new**	EBls
EMILIA MARIA	see *R.* LA ROSE DE MOLINARD
EMILY ('Ausburton') (S)	LSRN
EMILY BRONTË ('Ausearnshaw') (S) **new**	CRos ESty LRHS MAsh
EMILY DAVIES ('Dicmars') (F) **new**	IDic
'Emily Gray' (Ra)	CRHN EBee EBls ETWh LBuc LRHS LSRN MAsh MPri NLar NRog SCob SPer
EMILY VICTORIA ('Boshipeacon') (F)	LSRN
EMMA CLARE ('Sheriscarlet') (Patio) **new**	NRog
EMMA MAY ('Sherisilver') (HT)	NRog
'Empereur du Maroc' (HP)	EBls ETWh
'Ena Harkness' (HT)	CDoC CTri EBls ELan LBuc LHkn LRHS NRHS NRog SCob
ENCHANTRESS ('Tan97281'^{PBR}) (HT)	EBee EBls SSea
§ 'Enfant de France' (HP)	EBls LSRN
ENGLAND'S HEROES ('Webjack') (F) **new**	NRog
ENGLISH GARDEN ('Ausbuff') (S)	CArg ETWh LSRN SPer
'English Miss' (F)	CArg CBod CDoC EBls ECnt EWTr LRHS MAsh MFry MGos MRav SApu SCob SPer SPoG
ENGLISH SONNET	see *R.* SAMARITAN
EQUITY ('Harplayer') (F) **new**	LHkn
'Erfurt' (HM)	EBee EBls ETWh
§ 'Ernest H. Morse' (HT)	CSBt CTri EBls NRog SPer
ESCAPADE ('Harpade') (F) 🏆H6	EBls NRog
'Esmé' (HT)	ETWh
ESPECIALLY FOR YOU ('Fryworthy'^{PBR}) (HT) 🏆H6	CSBt ESty LSRN MFry SApu SSea
ESPERANZA ('Harquark'^{PBR}) (S) **new**	LHkn
ESSEX ('Poulnoz') (GC)	EBls SApu SCob SPer
'Etain' (Ra)	ECnt
§ 'Étendard' (ClHT)	CDoC EBls ETWh MRav NLar SPer SPoG
ETERNALLY YOURS ('Macspeego'^{PBR}) (HT)	ESty
ETERNITY ('Moai150097') (F)	MAsh
ETERNITY ('Ricity') (Min)	LRHS
'Ethel' (Ra)	EBls ETWh LSRN NLar SApu
'Étoile de Hollande' (HT)	CArg CDoC CTri EBee EBls EHyd ELan LBuc LRHS LSRN MAsh MGos NLar SCob WSpi
'Etoile de Lyon' (T)	EBls
'Eugénie Guinoisseau' (Mo)	ETWh
EUPHORIA ('Intereup'^{PBR}) (GC/S)	SApu
EUREKA ('Meizambaizt'^{PBR}) (HT)	CEnd LRHS MAsh
'European Touch' (HT) **new**	NRog
'Eva' (HM)	EBls
'Evangeline' (Ra)	EBls NRog
EVE RUGGIEN ('Adarylop') (HT)	LSRN
EVELYN ('Aussaucer') (S)	CArg CSBt EPfP ESty ETWh LSRN SApu SLon
§ EVELYN FISON ('Macev') (F)	CSBt CTri EBls LSRN NRog SCob SPer
'Evelyn May' (HT)	EBls LRHS LSRN MAsh NRHS
'Everest Double Fragrance' (F)	EBls
'Excelsa' (Ra)	CSBt CTri EBls EGrI EPfP ETWh IArd LBuc MAsh NRog SCob SGsty SPoG
EYE OF THE STORM ('Wekeots') (F) **new**	ETWh SApu
EYE OF THE TIGER ('Chewbullseye'^{PBR}) (S)	CDoC CEnd CGro CRos EBls EHyd ELan EPfP ESty ETWh LRHS MAsh MFry MPri NLar NRHS SApu SLon SMad SPoG SSea
EYEOPENER ('Interop') (S/GC)	EBls
EYES FOR YOU ('Pejbigeye') (F) 🏆H6	CDoC CEnd CGro CRos CSBt EBee EBls EPfP ESty ETWh LBuc LRHS MAsh MFry MPri NLar NRHS SApu SLon SMad SPer SPoG SSea WCot WKif
'F.E. Lester'	see *R.* 'Francis E. Lester'
§ 'F.J. Grootendorst' (Ru)	EBls ETWh NRog SPer WHer
FAB AT 50 ('Woraunt') (F)	LSRN
FABULOUS AT 40 ('Webcountry') (F)	LSRN
FABULOUS AT 50 ('Rawfabsal') (F)	LSRN
FABULOUS AT 65 ('Raw1041') (F)	LSRN
FABULOUS AT 70	LSRN
FABULOUS AT 80 ('Rawcox') (F)	LSRN
FAB-U-LOUS! ('Forfab') (HT)	ESty
'Fabvier'	see *R.* 'Colonel Fabvier'
FAIR EVA ('Seaeva') (Ra/GC)	ESty
FAIRHOPE ('Talfairhope') (Min)	NRog
'Fairy Rose'	see *R.* 'The Fairy'
FAITH ('Horfaiwil') (HT) **new**	NRog
FAITHFUL FRIEND ('Beachallenge') (S)	EBls LSRN
FAITHFUL ('Haressay'^{PBR}) (F)	LHkn
FALSTAFF ('Ausverse'^{PBR}) (S)	CArg CRos CSBt EBee EHyd EPfP LCro LOPS LRHS LSRN MAsh MRav MSwo NLar NRHS SCob SCoo SPer
FAMILY LIFE ('Hargladly') (F) **new**	LHkn
FANCY PANTS ('Kinfancy') (Min)	NRog

'Fantin-Latour' (Ce) ♀H6 — CArg CTri EBls ECnt EHyd ELan ETWh LEdu LRHS MCot MMuc NLar NRog SEND SMad SPer
fargesii hort. — see *R. moyesii* var. *fargesii*
farreri f. ***persetosa*** — see *R. elegantula* 'Persetosa'
§ FASCINATION ('Poulmax'PBR) (F) ♀H6 — CArg EWTr MAsh SApu SCob SPer
FATHER'S FAVOURITE ('Gandoug'PBR) (F) — LSRN
fedtschenkoana Regel — EBls
aff. ***fedtschenkoana*** — ETWh
FÉE DES NEIGES — see *R.* ICEBERG
'Felicia' (HM) ♀H6 — CArg CSBt CTri EBee EBls ECnt ETWh EWTr LRHS MAsh MCot MRav MSwo NLar NRog SApu SCob SEND SPer SSea WKif
FELICITAS ('Korberis'PBR) (S) **new** — NRog
'Félicité Parmentier' (A × D) ♀H6 — CArg EBls EPfP ETWh NLar NRog SPer
§ 'Félicité Perpétue' (Ra) ♀H6 — CArg CBcs CBod CTri EBee EBls EHyd EPfP ETWh LRHS MRav MSwo NLar NRog SApu SCob SEND SPer SSea WFar
FELINE PARADE ('Poulpar095'PBR) (Patio) **new** — CBod
'Fellemberg' (ClCh) — ETWh
FELLOWSHIP ('Harwelcome') (F) ♀H6 — CBod EBls LCro LHkn LOPS SCob SSea
'Ferdinand Pichard' (Bb) ♀H6 — CArg CRos CSBt CTri EBls ECnt EHyd ELon EPfP ESty ETWh LCro LOPS LRHS MAsh MCot MPri MRav NLar NRHS NRog SApu SMad SPer SSea WFar WKif
FERDY ('Keitoli'PBR) (GC) — EBls SApu SPer
I 'Fern's Rose' (F) — LSRN
ferruginea — see *R. glauca* Pourr.
FESTIVAL ('Kordialo'PBR) (Patio) — CDoC MRav SPer
FESTIVE JEWEL ('Beacost') (S) — EBls EPfP LRHS
FETZER SYRAH ROSÉ ('Harextra'PBR) (S) — LHkn LRHS
§ 'Feuermeer' (F) — NRog
'Ffion' (Patio) **new** — NRog
FIGHTING TEMERAIRE ('Austrava'PBR) (S) — CRos EHyd EPfP LBuc LRHS NLar NRHS
FIGURINE ('Benfig') (Min) — NRog
§ ***filipes*** 'Kiftsgate' (Ra) ♀H6 — CArg CBcs CDoC CGro CSBt CTri EBee EBls ECnt ELan EPfP ETWh GKin LEdu LRHS MAsh MFry MRav NLar NRHS NRog NWea SApu SCob SPer SSea WBor
§ 'Fimbriata' (Ru) — EBls ETWh LEdu NLar SPer
FIONA ('Meibeluxen') (S/GC) — EBls LSRN MSwo
FIREBIRD ('Kortragoso'PBR) (F) **new** — SApu
'Firecracker' (F) — NRog
FIRESTAR — see *R.* EASY DOES IT
FIRST GREAT WESTERN ('Oracharpam'PBR) (HT) — CSBt ELon ESty
'Fisher and Holmes' (HP) — EBls
FLAME ('Frymatcho') (F) **new** — MAsh
FLAMING STAR ('Kortaltal') (HT) **new** — EBls
FLANDERS FIELD ('Horflan') (F) **new** — NRog
FLANDERS ROSE ('Beaknight') (F) **new** — EBls
FLIRT ('Korkopapp'PBR) (F) — MAsh
'Flora' (Ra) — EBls ETWh
'Flora McIvor' (RH) — EBls
'Florence Mary Morse' (S) — SDix
FLORENTINA ('Kortrameilo'PBR) (Cl) **new** — EBls
FLOWER CARPET AMBER ('Noa97400a'PBR) (GC) ♀H6 — CDoC CGro CRos CSBt EBls EHyd EPfP LBuc LCro LOPS LRHS MAsh MPri NRHS NRog SPoG SSea
'Flower Carpet Coral'PBR (GC) ♀H6 — CBod CGro CRos EBls EHyd EPfP LBuc LRHS LSRN MAsh MPri NRHS NRog SApu SPer SSea
FLOWER CARPET GOLD ('Noalesa'PBR) (GC) — CBod CDoC CGro CRos EBls ECnt EHyd LBuc LRHS MAsh MPri NRHS NRog SApu SPoG SSea
FLOWER CARPET PINK — see *R.* PINK FLOWER CARPET
FLOWER CARPET PINK SUPREME ('Noa168098f') (GC) — EBls LRHS MAsh
FLOWER CARPET RED VELVET ('Noare'PBR) (GC/S) ♀H6 — CBod CGro CRos EBls EHyd ELan EPfP LBuc LCro LOPS LRHS MAsh MPri NRHS NRog SCoo SPer
FLOWER CARPET RUBY (GC) — CDoC CRos EBls EHyd LBuc LRHS LSRN MAsh MPri NRHS NRog SApu SPoG
FLOWER CARPET SCARLET ('Noa83100b'PBR) (GC) ♀H6 — CDoC CRos EBls LBuc LCro LOPS LRHS MAsh NRHS NRog SSea
FLOWER CARPET SUNSET ('Deseo') (S) — CDoC CGro CRos LRHS MAsh MPri
§ FLOWER CARPET SUNSHINE ('Noason'PBR) (GC) ♀H6 — CDoC CRos EBls EHyd LCro LOPS LRHS MAsh MPri NRHS NRog SCoo SPer
FLOWER CARPET WHITE ('Noaschnee') (GC) ♀H6 — CBod CDoC CGro CRos EBee EBls ECnt EHyd EPfP LCro LOPS LRHS LSRN MAsh MPri NRHS NRog SApu SCoo SPer SPoG SSea
FLOWER POWER ('Frycassia'PBR) (Patio) ♀H6 — CDoC CSBt EBls ECnt ESty LCro LOPS LRHS MAsh MFry MGos MPri MRav SApu SPoG
FLOWER POWER GOLD ('Fryneon') (Patio) — CDoC CSBt EBls ECnt ESty LRHS MAsh MFry MPri NRHS SApu SPoG
§ ***foetida*** (S) — ETWh SPer
§ - 'Bicolor' (S) — EBls ETWh NLar NRog SPer
§ - 'Persiana' (S) — EBls
foliolosa — EBls
FOLKLORE ('Korlore') (HT) **new** — NRog
'Follette' (Cl) — EBls
FOND MEMORIES ('Kirfelix'PBR) (Patio) — EBls ESty LSRN SCoo
FOOLISH PLEASURE ('Decsure') (Patio) **new** — NRog
FOR LOVE ('Webforlove') (F) **new** — NRog
FOR YOU WITH LOVE ('Fryjangle') (Patio) — LBuc LSRN MAsh MFry
FOR YOUR EYES ONLY ('Cheweyesup'PBR) (S) — Widely available
FOREVER ROYAL ('Franmite') (F) — NRog
FORGET ME NOT ('Coccharm'PBR) (HT) — ESty
forrestiana (S) — EBls ETWh WPav
× ***fortuneana*** (Ra) — EBls
Fortune's double yellow — see *R.* × *odorata* 'Pseudindica'
FOSTER'S RUBY GLOW ('Webdesire') (HT) **new** — NRog

FOXY LADY ('Simmem') (HT)	ESty
FRAGONARD ('Delparviro'PBR) (HT)	EBls ESty
FRAGRANT BEAUTY ('Smi152-1-4') (HT)	ESty
FRAGRANT CELEBRATION ('Beamerry') (Cl) **new**	EBls
FRAGRANT CLOUD ('Tanellis') (HT)	CArg CBcs CEnd CRos CTri EBls ELan ELon EPfP ETWh LBuc LRHS LSRN MAsh MGos MRav NRog SCob SPer SPoG
'Fragrant Delight' (F) ♀H6	CArg CDoC CSBt EBls ELan MRav SCob SPer
FRAGRANT DREAM ('Dicodour') (HT)	ESty SCob
FRAGRANT MEMORIES ('Korpastato'PBR) (HT)	CSBt
FRAGRANT PLUM ('Aroplumi') (HT)	ESty NRog
'Francesca' (HM)	EBls ETWh LSRN NLar NRog SPer
'Francis Copple' (S)	EBls
'Francis Dubreuil' (T)	EBls
§ 'Francis E. Lester' (HM/Ra) ♀H6	CEnd CRHN CRos EBee EBls EHyd ELan EPfP ETWh LCro LOPS LRHS NLar NRHS SApu SPer SSea
× ***francofurtana*** misapplied	see *R.* 'Impératrice Joséphine'
- 'Empress Josephine'	see *R.* 'Impératrice Joséphine'
'François Juranville' (Ra) ♀H6	CArg CRHN EBee EBls EPfP ETWh LRHS MMuc MRav NLar NRog SApu SEND SLon SPer WFar WHer
'Frau Astrid Späth' (F)	NRog
§ 'Frau Karl Druschki' (HP)	ETWh
'Fred Loads' (F) ♀H7	EBls NRog
FREDDIE MERCURY ('Batmercury') (HT)	ESty LSRN NRog
FREE SPIRIT ('Fryjeru'PBR) (F) ♀H6	ECnt MFry
FREEDOM ('Dicjem') (HT) ♀H6	CArg CDoC CTri EBls ECnt MFry MRav NRog SApu SCob SPer
'Frensham' (F)	EBls SSea
FRIEND FOR LIFE ('Cocnanne'PBR) (F) ♀H6	CDoC LSRN MRav
FRIENDS FOREVER ('Korapriber') (F) ♀H6	CSBt EBls EPfP LRHS LSRN MAsh SLon
FRIENDSHIP OF STRANGERS ('633D9') (Cl)	EBls
FRILLY CUFF ('Beajingle') (S)	EBee EBls LRHS MAsh
'Fritz Nobis' (S) ♀H7	CArg ETWh NLar SPer
FROTHY ('Macfrothy') (Patio)	ECnt ESty
'Frozen' (Min) **new**	NRog
'Fru Dagmar Hastrup' (Ru) ♀H7	CArg CBcs CDoC CSBt CTri EBee EBls ECnt ELan EPfP ETWh EWTr LBuc LRHS MAsh MFry MSwo NLar SApu SCob SEND SPer
'Frühlingsduft' (SpH)	ETWh NRog
'Frühlingsgold' (SpH) ♀H7	CArg EBls ELan ETWh EWTr NLar NRog SCob SPer
'Frühlingsmorgen' (SpH) ♀H7	EBls ETWh NRog SCob SPer
'Fryvanity' (HT) **new**	ECnt
'Fulgens'	see *R.* 'Malton'
'Fyfield Princess' (F) **new**	NRog
GAIANA (PatioHit Series)	MBros SPad
§ ***gallica*** (G)	EBls ETWh
§ - var. ***officinalis*** (G) ♀H7	CRos CTri EBls EPfP ETWh GPoy LRHS MAsh MHer MNHC MRav NLar NRog SApu SPer SRms WFar WHer
- 'Velutiniflora' (G)	EBls
§ - 'Versicolor' (G) ♀H7	CArg CDoC CEnd CSBt CTri EBee EBls ECnt EHyd EPfP ETWh EWTr GPoy LRHS LSRN MAsh MCot MHer MRav NLar NRHS NRog NSti SApu SCob SPer SSea WBor WKif
GALWAY BAY ('Macba') (ClHT)	CArg ETWh LRHS MAsh NLar SPer
GARDEN FUN	see *R.* GARTENSPAß
GARDEN OF ROSES	see *R.* JOIE DE VIVRE
'Gardeners' Glory'PBR (ClHT) ♀H6	CArg CDoC CSBt ECnt ESty LBuc LRHS MAsh MFry MGos MPri MRav SApu SPoG SSea
GARDENERS' GOLD ('Harzoltan') (ClS) **new**	LHkn
GARDENERS' JOY ('Beadrum') (S)	EBls
'Gardenia' (Ra)	EBls ETWh MMuc MSwo NLar SPer
'Gareth Davies' (HT) **new**	NRog
'Garnette Carol'	see *R.* 'Carol Amling'
'Garnette Pink'	see *R.* 'Carol Amling'
§ GARTENSPAß ('Korgohowa'PBR) (F)	ETWh
'Gary Player' (HT)	NRog
'Gaujard'	see *R.* ROSE GAUJARD
'Gelbe Dagmar Hastrup'	see *R.* YELLOW DAGMAR HASTRUP
GEMINI ('Jacnepal') (HT)	ESty NRog
GEMMA ('Harlagoon'PBR) (F) **new**	LHkn
'Général Kléber' (CeMo) ♀H7	EBls
§ 'Général Schablikine' (T)	EBls ETWh NLar
GENESIS ('Fryjuicy'PBR) (Patio)	CDoC CGro MFry MRav
gentiliana misapplied	see *R.* 'Polyantha Grandiflora'
gentiliana H. Lév. & Variot	see *R. multiflora* var. *cathayensis*
GENTLE HERMIONE ('Ausrumba'PBR) (S)	CDoC CGro CRos EHyd ELan EPfP LBuc LCro LOPS LRHS MSwo NRHS SCob SPer SPoG
GENTLE TOUCH ('Diclulu') (Min/Patio)	CSBt MRav NRog SPer
GEOFF HAMILTON ('Ausham'PBR) (S)	LSRN MBNS SCob
'Geoffrey Smith' (Cl)	LSRN NDal NRog
GEORGE ('Simetna') (F)	ESty
GEORGE BEST ('Dichimanher'PBR) (Patio) ♀H6	IDic LSRN NRog
'George Dickson' (HT)	EBls
GEORGE'S PRIDE ('Manpride') (Min)	LSRN
'Georges Vibert' (G)	EBls ETWh
'Geranium' (*moyesii* hybrid) ♀H6	CArg CBcs CDoC CTri EBls ELan EPfP ETWh IArd MRav NLar SApu SPer
GERBE D'OR	see *R.* CASINO
GERTRUDE JEKYLL ('Ausbord'PBR) (S) ♀H6	CArg CDoC CGro CRos CSBt EBee ECnt EHyd ELan EPfP ESty GBin LCro LOPS LRHS LSRN MAsh MBNS MCot MGos MRav MSwo NLar NRHS SCob SCoo SPer SPoG SSea WKif
GETTYSBURG ('Poulen001'PBR) (F)	ETWh
'Ghislaine de Féligonde' (HM) ♀H5	EBee EBls EPfP ESty ETWh LRHS MAsh MCot NLar SApu SEND SMad SPer WBor WMal
GHITA	see *R.* MILLIE
§ GIARDINA ('Tan97289'PBR) (Cl)	ESty
gigantea	WPGP

gigantea* × *longicuspis	WPGP
GIGGLES ('Frynoodle'[PBR]) (Patio)	MFry SCoo
GIGGLES ('Kingig') (Min)	NRog
GINGER SYLLABUB ('Harjolina'[PBR]) (ClHT)	ECnt ESty LHkn MGos MRav SPer SPoG
GIPSY BOY	see *R.*'Zigeunerknabe'
GIRLGUIDING UK CENTENARY ROSE ('Harnova') (F) **new**	LHkn
GISELA'S DELIGHT ('Horpink') (S)	EBls
GLAD TIDINGS ('Tantide') (F)	CTri EBls MRav NRog SPer
GLAMIS CASTLE ('Auslevel'[PBR]) (S)	CArg CTri SCob SCoo
glauca ambig.	EGrI MHer MSwo SCob
§ ***glauca*** Pourr. (S) ♀H7	CBcs CDoC CKel CSBt CTri EBee EBls ECha ECnt ELan ELon EPfP ETWh EWTr LEdu LRHS MMuc MRav NLar NRog NWea SApu SEND SPer SPoG SSea WCot
'Glenfiddich' (F)	CArg CTri LSRN NRog SPer
'Glenn Dale' (Cl)	ETWh
GLOBAL BEAUTY ('Tan 94448') (HT)	EBee ECnt ETWh MFry MRav NLar SMad SSea
'Gloire de Bruxelles' (HP)	EBls
'Gloire de Dijon' (ClT)	CArg CEnd EBee EBls ECnt ELan ETWh LSRN MRav NLar NRog NWea SCob SPer
'Gloire de Ducher' (HP)	EBls
'Gloire de France' (G) ♀H7	CArg EBls ETWh NLar WHer
'Gloire de Guilan' (D)	ETWh
'Gloire des Mousseuses' (CeMo)	EBls ETWh
'Gloire Lyonnaise' (HP)	EBls ETWh
glomerata (Cl)	WFar
- NJM 11.048 **new**	WPGP
'Gloria Mundi' (Poly)	EBls ETWh
GLORIANA ('Chewpope'[PBR]) (ClMin)	CArg CBod CDoC ECnt ESty LBuc MAsh MRav SPer SPoG SSea
'Glory of Seale' (S)	SSea
GLOWING AMBER ('Manglow') (Min)	ESty NRog
GLYNDEBOURNE ('Harpulse'[PBR]) (S) **new**	LHkn
GODSTOWE GIRL ('Harfurore') (HT) **new**	LHkn
GOLD CHARM ('Chewalbygold') (Cl)	MAsh
'Goldbusch' (RH)	EBls
'Golden Angel' (Min)	LRHS MAsh
'Golden Anniversary' (Patio)	SPer SSea
'Golden Anniversary' (HT)	MGos
'Golden Autumn' (HT)	LSRN
'Golden Beauty' van Rossem (HT) **new**	MAsh
GOLDEN BEAUTY ('Clebeau') (Min)	LRHS
GOLDEN BEAUTY ('Korberbeni'[PBR]) (F) ♀H6	CArg CEnd CGro EBee EBls ETWh MAsh MFry
GOLDEN BERYL ('Manberyl') (Min)	LSRN NRog
GOLDEN CELEBRATION ('Ausgold'[PBR]) (S) ♀H6	CArg CDoC CGro CRos CSBt ECnt EHyd EPfP ESty LCro LOPS LRHS LSRN MAsh MSwo NLar NRHS SCoo SLon SPer SPoG
'Golden Chersonese' (S)	NRog
'Golden Dawn' (ClHT)	see *R.* 'Climbing Golden Dawn'
GOLDEN DELICIOUS ('Wekgobafa') (HT) **new**	ECnt ESty
GOLDEN EUREKA ('Meikanaro'[PBR]) (F)	NRog
'Golden Gate' (Cl/T) **new**	LPar
GOLDEN GATE ('Korgolgat'[PBR]) (ClHT) ♀H6	EBls ECnt EPfP LBuc LRHS MAsh NRHS SApu SSea
GOLDEN JEWEL ('Tanledolg'[PBR]) (F/Patio)	ESty
GOLDEN JUBILEE ('Cocagold') (HT)	CArg
GOLDEN MELODY ('Irene Churruca') (HT)	EBls
GOLDEN MEMORIES ('Korholesea'[PBR]) (F) ♀H6	CArg CSBt EBls EHyd LBuc LRHS MAsh MGos MPri MRav SCoo SPer
'Golden Moment'[PBR] (HT)	ESty MRav
GOLDEN OLDIE ('Fryescape'[PBR]) (HT)	MFry
'Golden Rambler'	see *R.*'Alister Stella Gray'
'Golden Showers' (Cl)	CArg CBcs CBod CEnd CGro CRos CSBt CTri EBee EBls ELan EPfP ETWh LCro LOPS LRHS LSRN MAsh MFry MMuc MRav NLar NRog SCob SPer SPoG SSea WBor
§ GOLDEN SMILES ('Frykeyno'[PBR]) (F) ♀H6	CArg EBls ECnt ESty LRHS LSRN MFry MPri
'Golden Unicorn' (S) **new**	NRog
GOLDEN WEDDING ('Arokris') (F)	CBod CDoC CGro CRos CSBt CTri EBls ECnt ELan EPfP IArd LCro LOPS LRHS LSRN MAsh MFry MGos MRav NRHS NRog SApu SCob SPer SPoG SSea
GOLDEN WEDDING ANNIVERSARY (F)	LSRN
'Golden Wedding Celebration' (F)	CEnd LSRN
'Golden Wings' (S)	CArg CTri EBls ELan ETWh GBin MCot MRav MSwo NLar SPer
GOLDEN YEARS ('Harween') (F)	CBod
'Goldfinch' (Ra)	CArg EBls ELan EPfP ETWh EWTr LCro LOPS MAsh NLar NRog SApu SEND SPer WFar
'Goldilocks' (F)	NRog
GOLDSTAR ('Candide') (HT)	ECnt
GOOD AS GOLD ('Chewsunbeam'[PBR]) (ClMin)	ECnt ESty MFry SPer
GORDON SNELL ('Dicwriter') (F)	IDic
GORGEOUS ('Poulpmt009'[PBR]) (HT)	CEnd CGro EPfP LBuc LRHS MAsh MPri
GORGEOUS GIRL ('Forshow') (HT)	ESty
GRACE ('Auskeppy'[PBR]) (S) ♀H6	CDoC CRos CSBt EHyd EPfP ESty LBuc LRHS LSRN NLar NRHS SCoo SPer
'Grace Abounding' (F)	LSRN NRog
'Grace Darling' (T)	EBls
GRACE DE MONACO ('Meimit') (HT)	EBls
GRACE DONNELLY ('Horlexstrip') (HT/F)	NRog
GRACE SHARINGTON ('Mangrace') (Patio)	NRog
'Graciously Pink' (Min)	LRHS
GRAHAM THOMAS ('Ausmas') (S) ♀H6	CArg CDoC CRos CSBt EBee ECnt EHyd EPfP EShb ESty LCro LOPS LRHS LSRN MAsh MCot MSwo

	NLar NRHS SCob SEND SLon SPer SPoG SSea WKif
GRAND AWARD ('Poulcy014'PBR) (Courtyard Series) (ClF)	ETWh NLar
GRANDE AMORE	see *R.* MY VALENTINE ('Korcoluma')
GRANDE AMORE ('Korliegra') (HT) **new**	LRHS
'Grandma' (F)	LSRN
GRAND-MÈRE JENNY ('Grem') (HT)	EBls
'Grandpa Dickson' (HT)	CArg EBls MAsh MGos SPer
GRANNY'S FAVOURITE (Patio/F)	LSRN
GREAT EXPECTATIONS ambig.	CDoC SSea
GREAT EXPECTATIONS ('Lanican') (HT)	CBcs
GREAT EXPECTATIONS ('Mackalves'PBR) (F)	EPfP IArd MGos MRav SPer
§ 'Great Maiden's Blush' (A) ♀H7	EBls ETWh NLar NRog
GREAT NORTH EASTERN ROSE	see *R.* SIR GALAHAD
'Great Ormond Street' (F)	EBls
'Great Western' (Bb)	EBls
GREENALL'S GLORY ('Kirmac') (F/Patio)	MRav
GREETINGS ('Jacdreco'PBR) (F)	CArg LBuc MAsh
GRETA HIT ('Poulpah076') (Patio)	EPfP
'Grimpant Cramoisi Supérieur' (ClCh)	EBls
'Grootendorst'	see *R.* 'F.J. Grootendorst'
'Grootendorst Supreme' (Ru)	NRog
'Gros Chou de Hollande' (Bb)	EBls
GROSVENOR HOUSE (HT)	LRHS MAsh
'Grosvenor House Rose' (S)	MAsh
GROUSE ('Korimro') (S/GC)	EBls ETWh NLar SEND SPer
GROUSE 2000 ('Korteilhab') (GC) ♀H6	SApu
'Gruss an Aachen' (Poly) ♀H6	EBls EPfP ETWh NLar NRog SPer
'Gruss an Teplitz' (China hybrid)	EBls ETWh NLar
GUIDING SPIRIT ('Harwolave') (Min/Patio) **new**	LHkn
'Guinée' (ClHT)	CArg CDoC CRos CTri EBls EHyd ELan EPfP ESty ETWh LCro LOPS MRav MSwo NLar SApu SPer WCot WKif
GUIRLANDE ROSE ('Velwichba') (Ra)	EBls
'Gustav Grünerwald' (HT)	EBls
GUY SAVOY ('Delstrimen'PBR) (F)	EBls ESty ETWh LRHS MRav
GUY'S GOLD ('Harmatch'PBR) (HT)	LHkn LRHS MAsh SPoG
GWENT ('Poulurt') (GC)	CSBt SCob SEND SPer
gymnocarpa	EBls
GYPSY BOY	see *R.* 'Zigeunerknabe'
HAKA ('Poulcy023'PBR) (Cl) **new**	MBros
HALLÉ ('Fryelectric'PBR) (HT)	MFry
'Hamburger Phönix' (Ra)	EBls
HAMILTON PRINCESS ('Harzinc') (HT) **new**	LHkn SApu
HAMPSHIRE ('Korhamp') (GC)	SCob
HÄNDEL ('Macha') (ClHT)	CBcs CBod CDoC CSBt CTri EBls ELan ELon EPfP ETWh LBuc LRHS MAsh MFry MGos MPri MRav NLar NRog SApu SCob SCoo SPer SPlb SSea
§ HANKY PANKY ('Wektorcent'PBR) (F)	CDoC CGro EBls ESty MAsh MRav SApu SLon
HANNAH GORDON ('Korweiso') (F)	EBls NRog SPer
'Hannah Hauxwell' (Patio/F)	NRog
HANNAH LUCY COCKROFT ('Rawgold') (HT) **new**	NRog
'Hanne' (HT)	NRog
'Hansa' (Ru)	EBls ETWh LBuc NLar NRog SPer
HAPPY 60TH BIRTHDAY	LSRN
HAPPY 70TH BIRTHDAY ('Rawday') (F)	LSRN
HAPPY 80TH BIRTHDAY	LSRN
HAPPY ANNIVERSARY ambig.	EPfP
HAPPY ANNIVERSARY ('Bedfranc'PBR) (F)	LSRN MPri SCoo
HAPPY ANNIVERSARY ('Delpre') (F)	CRos CTri EHyd LRHS MAsh MRav NRHS SPoG
'Happy Birthday' (Min/Patio)	ESty LCro LOPS LSRN SSea
HAPPY COUPLE ('Simreg') (F)	ESty
HAPPY DAYS ('Harquad'PBR) (S)	CDoC MRav
HAPPY GARDENING ('Smi89-2-04') (HT)	ESty
HAPPY GOLDEN WEDDING	see *R.* GOLDEN SMILES
'Happy Memories' (F)	EBls LRHS MAsh
HAPPY PEARL WEDDING (HT)	MFry
HAPPY RETIREMENT ('Tantoras'PBR) (F) ♀H6	CBcs EBls EPfP ESty LBuc LCro LOPS LSRN MAsh MFry MPri MRav SApu SCoo SPoG SSea
HAPPY RUBY WEDDING ('Frynoble'PBR) (HT)	CBcs CDoC ECnt MAsh MFry MPri
HAPPY SILVER WEDDING ('Frysilva') (F)	CRos LRHS LSRN MAsh MFry
HAPPY TIMES ('Bedone'PBR) (Patio/Min)	NRog
× ***harisonii*** (SpH)	EBls
§ - 'Williams' Double Yellow' (SpH)	EBls ETWh
HARLOW CARR ambig.	CDoC EHyd LRHS NRHS SCob
HARLOW CARR ('Aushouse'PBR) (S)	CRos EPfP LBuc LSRN MSwo SCob SCoo SPer
HARPER ADAMS ('Fryflash'PBR) (F)	MFry
'Harpippin' (ClHT)	LRHS
'Harry Edland' (F)	LCro LOPS LRHS
'Harry Wheatcroft' (HT)	CArg NRog SPer
HARVEST FAYRE ('Dicnorth') (F)	SPer
HAVANA HIT ('Poulpah032'PBR) (Patio)	EBls EPfP MPri
'Havering Rambler' (Ra)	ELon
'Hazel Le Rougetel' (Ru)	EBls WFar
HAZEL MCCALLION ('Manhazel') (Patio)	NRog
'Headleyensis' (S)	EBls
HEART OF GOLD ('Coctarlotte'PBR) (HT) ♀H6	ECnt ESty MRav
HEART'S DELIGHT ('Webhawk') (F) **new**	NRog

HEART'S DESIRE ('Raw1063') (F)	ESty
HEATHCLIFF ('Ausnipper'PBR) (S)	CSBt EPfP ESty LBuc NLar
HEATHER ('Poulcot007'PBR)	LSRN
'Heather Muir' (*sericea* hybrid) (S)	EBls
HEATHER SPROUL ('Sproheather') (Min) **new**	NRog
'Heaven Scent' (F)	LRHS NRog
§ 'Hebe's Lip' (D × RH)	ETWh
'Helen Knight' (*ecae* hybrid) (S)	EBls ESty
HELENA ('Poulna'PBR) (Renaissance Series) (S)	LSRN
helenae	CTri EBee EBls ETWh GLog NLar WPGP
- hybrid	ETWh
HELEN'S TRUST ('Taytrust') (HT)	LSRN NRog
hemisphaerica (S)	EBls
§ 'Henri Martin' (CeMo) ΨH7	CTri EBls ETWh LEdu NLar NRog SPer
HENRI MATISSE ('Delstrobla') (F)	ESty ETWh LRHS MRav SPoG
'Henry Kelsey' (Cl/S)	EBls
§ 'Herbstfeuer' (RH)	EBls ETWh NLar SPer
'Here's Sam' (HT)	LSRN NRog
HERITAGE ('Ausblush') (S)	CTri ELan EPfP ETWh SCob
'Hermosa' (Ch)	EBls ETWh NLar NRog
HERTFORDSHIRE ('Kortenay') (GC) ΨH6	CBod SCob SEND SPer
HERZOGIN CHRISTIANA ('Korgeowim'PBR) (F) **new**	EBls
'Hiawatha' (Ra)	EBls
× ***hibernica***	EBls
§ 'Hidcote Yellow' (Cl)	EBls ETWh SPer
HIDDEN GEM ('Gues11-50') (F)	ESty
HIGH FLIER ('Fryfandango'PBR) (ClHT)	EBls MFry
§ HIGH FLYER ('Jacsat') (ClHT)	MAsh SSea
HIGH HOPES ('Haryup'PBR) (ClHT)	EPfP LBuc MAsh NRog SApu SCob SPer SSea
'Highdownensis' (*moyesii* hybrid) (S)	EBls ELan
HIGHGROVE ('Hornightshade') (Cl)	EBls EPfP LBuc LRHS MAsh MPri NRog
HILDE ('Benhile') (Min)	NRog
'Hillieri' (*moyesii* hybrid)	EBls
'Hippolyte' (G)	NRog
hirtula (S)	EBls
HOLLYWOOD STAR ('Reshollywood') (HT) **new**	NRog
holodonta	see *R. moyesii* f. *rosea*
holy rose	see *R.* × *richardii*
'Home Sweet Home' (HT)	EBls
HOME SWEET HOME ('Sim2008/10') (HT)	ESty
HOME SWEET REDROW ('Dicprotector') (F) **new**	IDic
HOMMAGE À BARBARA ('Delchifrou'PBR) (HT)	CBod EBls ESty ETWh MGos MRav NLar WKif
HONEY BUNCH ('Cocglen') (F)	CBod MGos MRav SPer
HONEY DIJON ('Weksproulses'PBR) (F)	ESty
HONEYBUN ('Tan98264'PBR) (Patio)	ESty
HONEYMOON	see *R.* 'Honigmond'
§ 'Honigmond' (F)	CBcs CDoC
'Honorine de Brabant' (Bb) ΨH6	EBls ETWh LEdu NLar NRog SPer
HOPE FOR JUSTICE ('P48b') (F)	MFry
HORATIO NELSON ('Beahor') (S)	EBls
horrida	EBls
HOT CHOCOLATE ('Wekpaltlez') (F) ΨH6	CArg CBod CDoC CEnd CGro CRos CSBt EBls ECnt ELan ELon EPfP ESty LBuc LRHS MAsh MFry MGos MRav NRog SApu SCob SMad SPad SPer SPoG SSea
HOT PRINCESS ('Tantocnirp') (HT)	ESty NRog
HOT TAMALE ('Jacpoy') (Min)	NRog
HOUSE BEAUTIFUL ('Harbingo') (Patio)	MRav
HUDDERSFIELD CHORAL SOCIETY ('Rawchor') (F) **new**	NRog
'Hugh Dickson' (HP)	EBls ETWh LSRN NLar
hugonis	see *R.xanthina* f. *hugonis*
- 'Plenissima'	see *R.xanthina* f. *hugonis*
HUMANITY ('Harcross'PBR) (F)	MRav
Hume's blush	see *R.* × *odorata* 'Odorata'
HUMMINGBIRD ('Tynpam') (F)	ESty
'Hunter' (Ru)	EBls
'Hurdalsrosa' (A) **new**	NRog
HYDE HALL ('Ausbosky'PBR) (S)	EHyd LRHS MAsh
ICE CREAM ('Korzuri') (HT) ΨH6	CArg CDoC ECnt ESty MRav SApu SCob SCoo SPer SPoG
§ ICEBERG ('Korbin') (F) ΨH6	Widely available
'Ilse Krohn Superior' (ClHT)	EBls
IMOGEN ('Austritch'PBR) (S)	CRos EHyd EPfP ESty LRHS NLar NRHS
IMPÉRATRICE FARAH ('Delivour') (HT)	ESty
§ 'Impératrice Joséphine' (Gn) ΨH7	EBls ETWh NLar
'Impulse' (Patio)	NRog
IN MEMORY OF	LSRN
IN MEMORY OF MY CAT ('Webyum') (HT)	LSRN
IN MEMORY OF MY DOG ('Rawbark') (F)	LSRN
INCOGNITO ('Briincog') (Min)	NRog
INDIAN SUMMER ('Harwigwam') (ClMin)	ELon
INDIAN SUMMER ('Peaperfume') (HT) ΨH6	CSBt MGos MRav SApu
INDIANNA MAE ('Beacrunch') (S)	EBls
'Indigo' (DPo)	EBls ETWh
INFINITY ('Frytropic') (HT)	CArg EPfP LRHS
INGRID ('Maning')	LSRN NRog
INGRID BERGMAN ('Poulman'PBR) (HT) ΨH6	CBod CDoC CTri EBls ECnt ELon EPfP ETWh LRHS LSRN MFry MGos MRav NRog SApu SPer SSea
'Inspiration' (ClHT)	MAsh
INSPIRE ('Frytempo') (HT)	CSBt ECnt MFry

	'Intermezzo' (HT)	EBls
	INVINCIBLE ('Runatru') (F)	MFry
	'Ipsilanté' (G)	EBls
	'Irène Watts' (Ch)	CArg EBls LSRN NLar
	'Irene's Delight' (HT)	ESty LSRN NRog
	'Iridescent Pink' (S) **new**	NRog
	IRIS ('Coczero') (HT)	LSRN
	IRIS ('Ferecha') (HT)	LSRN
	IRISH EYES ('Dicwitness'[PBR]) (F) ♀[H6]	CArg CGro ESty IArd MAsh MGos MRav SApu SCob SCoo SPer
	IRISH HOPE ('Harexclaim'[PBR]) (F)	LRHS
	IRISH WONDER	see *R.* EVELYN FISON
	IRRESISTIBLE ('Tinresist') (Min/Patio)	NRog
	'Isabel'	ETWh LSRN
	ISABELLA ('Poulisab'[PBR]) (Renaissance Series) (S)	ECnt NLar
	'Isabella Sprunt' (HT)	EBls
	ISIS (HT)	see *R.* SILVER ANNIVERSARY ('Poulari')
	ISN'T SHE LOVELY ('Diciluvit'[PBR]) (HT) ♀[H6]	CArg EBls ELan ESty IDic LSRN NRog SApu
	'Ispahan' (D) ♀[H6]	CArg EBls EPfP ETWh LRHS MCot NLar NRog SApu SPer WFar
	IVOR'S ROSE ('Beadonald') (S)	EBls EPfP LRHS MAsh
	IVORY ROMANTICA ('Meisabeyla'[PBR]) (HT)	LSRN
	'Ivory Silk' (Min)	LSRN NRog
	'Jack Hume' (ClHT)	ESty
	JACK WOOD ('Frydabble'[PBR]) (F)	MFry
	JACK'S WISH ('Kirsil') (HT)	LSRN
§	× *jacksonii* 'Max Graf' (GC/Ru)	CBod ETWh EWTr NLar NRog SCob
	- RED MAX GRAF	see *R.* ROTE MAX GRAF
	'Jacky's Favorite' (F)	LSRN
	Jacobite rose	see *R.* × *alba* 'Alba Maxima'
	JACQUELINE DU PRÉ ('Harwanna') (S) ♀[H6]	CArg EBls ECnt ESty ETWh LCro LHkn LOPS LRHS LSRN MCot MRav NLar SApu SLon SPer
	JACQUELINE REDMILL ('Dicnuance') (F)	IDic
	'Jacques Cartier' misapplied	see *R.* 'Marchesa Boccella'
	JAM AND JERUSALEM ('Frymojo'[PBR]) (F)	CDoC CGro LRHS MAsh MFry MGos MRav
	JAMES GALWAY ('Auscrystal'[PBR]) (S)	CSBt EHyd EPfP ESty LBuc LRHS LSRN MAsh NRHS SCoo
	JAMES L. AUSTIN ('Auspike') (S)	CRos ECnt ESty LRHS
	'James Mason' (G)	EBls NRog
	'James Mitchell' (CeMo)	EBls
	'Jan Guest' (HT)	NRog
	JANE AUSTEN ('Harzircon') (F) **new**	LHkn
	JANEEN ('Harultra') (F) **new**	LHkn
	JANE'S ROSE ('Webloxley') (F)	NRog
	JANET ('Auspishus'[PBR]) (S)	LSRN
	'Janet's Pride' (RH)	EBls
§	'Japonica' (CeMo)	ETWh
§	JARDINS DE BAGATELLE ('Meimafris') (HT)	LSRN MRav SApu
	JASMINA ('Korcentex'[PBR]) (ClHT)	EBls ESty ETWh NLar
	'Jaune Desprez'	see *R.* 'Desprez à Fleur Jaune'
	'Jazz' (F)	LSRN
	JAZZ (ClF)	see *R.* THAT'S JAZZ
	JEAN ('Cocupland'[PBR]) (Patio)	LSRN
	JEAN KENNEALLY ('Tineally') (Min)	NRog
	'Jean Mermoz' (Poly)	NRog
	'Jean Rosenkrantz' (HP)	EBls NRog
	'Jeanne de Montfort' (CeMo)	ETWh
	JEANNE MOREAU ('Meidiaphaz') (HT)	ESty
	'Jenny Duval' misapplied	see *R.* 'Président de Sèze'
	'Jenny Wren' (F)	EBls
	JENNY'S ROSE ('Cansit') (F)	ECnt LSRN
	'Jens Munk' (Ru)	EBls ETWh
	JILL'S ROSE ('Ganjil'[PBR]) (F)	LSRN
	JILLY JEWEL ('Benmfig') (Min)	LSRN NRog
	JIVE ('Poulyc009'[PBR]) (Cl)	LSRN
	JOAN BEALES ('Beaagile') (S)	EBls
	'Jocelyn' (F)	LSRN
	JOHANN WOLFGANG VON GOETHE ROSE	see *R.* PURE POETRY ('Tan04179') (HT)
	'John Cabot' (S)	EBls
	'John Gwilliam'	MAvo MHCG
	'John Hopper' (HP)	EBls ETWh
	'John McCarthy' (Min) **new**	NRog
	JOHN WILLAN ('Fryeager') (HT)	MFry
	JOHNNY PLUNKETT ('Dicgolf') (F) **new**	IDic
§	JOIE DE VIVRE ('Korfloci 01'[PBR]) (Patio/S) ♀[H6]	CArg CDoC CEnd CGro CSBt EBls ELan EPfP ESty ETWh LRHS MFry MPri MRav NLar SApu SPer SPoG SSea
	JOLEEN ('Poulren032') (S) **new**	ETWh
§	JOSEPHINE ('Weksiamia') (HT)	LSRN
	'Josephine Bruce' (HT)	CBcs CTri EBls LSRN NRog SSea
	'Joseph's Coat' (ClS)	EBls ETWh IArd SCoo
	JOSIE WHITNEY ('Harfacey') (F) **new**	LHkn
	'Journey's End' (HT)	NRog
I	'Joy' (F)	NRog
	JOY VIELI ('Dickaramel') (F)	IDic
	JUBILÉ PAPA MEILLAND ('Meiceazar'[PBR]) (HT)	CSBt ESty SSea
	'Jubilee Celebration' (F)	CDoC EHyd EPfP LRHS NRHS
	JUBILEE CELEBRATION ('Aushunter'[PBR]) (S)	CRos CSBt EHyd LBuc LRHS NRHS SPer SPoG
	JUDE THE OBSCURE ('Ausjo'[PBR]) (S)	CDoC EHyd EPfP ESty LBuc LRHS MGos NRHS SCoo SPer
	'Julia's Kiss' (HT) **new**	NRog
	'Julia's Rose' (HT)	EBls LSRN SPer
	JULIE Y ('Harbinger') (HT) **new**	LHkn
	JULIET JACKSON-BONNER ('Rawjonber') (F) **new**	NRog
	JULIO IGLESIAS ('Meistemon'[PBR]) (F)	LSRN
	'Juno' (Ce)	EBls ETWh NLar
	JUST FOR YOU ('Moryou') (Min)	LSRN
	JUST JANE ('Raw1046') (F)	LSRN
	'Just Jenny' (Min)	LSRN NRog
	'Just Joey' (HT) ♀[H6]	CArg CBcs CBod CSBt CTri EBls ECnt ELan ELon ETWh IArd LCro LOPS LSRN MFry MGos MRav NRog SApu SCob SPer SPoG SRGP SSea
	JUST ROBERT ('Raw1075') (F)	LSRN

JUST STEVE ('Raw890') (F)	LSRN
'Karlsruhe' (ClF)	EBls
'Kasteel Hex' (S)	EBls
'Katharina Zeimet' (Poly)	CTri EBls ETWh NRog
'Kathleen' (HM)	EBls LSRN
'Kathleen Ferrier' (F)	EBls
'Kathleen Harrop' (Bb)	EBee EBls ETWh MMuc MSwo NLar NRog SEND SPer
KATHLEEN JANE ('Horcoed') (S)	LSRN
KATHLEEN'S ROSE ('Kirkitt') (F)	LSRN
KATHRYN ('Rawkat') (F)	LSRN NRog
'Katie' (ClF)	LSRN
KATIE'S ROSE ('Horrapture') (F)	LSRN
KEEP IN TOUCH ('Hardrama'PBR) (F)	LHkn
KEEP SMILING ('Fryflorida') (HT) ♀H6	CDoC CGro EBls LRHS MAsh MFry MRav SPoG
KEEPSAKE ('Kormalda') (HT)	ESty
'Keith Maughan' (Cl)	EBls LRHS MAsh
§ KENT ('Poulcov') (Towne & Country Series) (S/GC) ♀H6	CDoC CSBt EBls ECnt ELan EPfP ESty ETWh LCro LOPS LSRN MFry MMuc MRav MSwo NLar SApu SCob SEND SPer SPoG SSea
KEROS ('Harpacific'PBR) (S) **new**	LHkn
KEW GARDENS ('Ausfence'PBR) (S) ♀H6	EPfP LBuc LCro LOPS LRHS NRHS SCoo SPer
'Kew Rambler' (Ra)	CRHN EBee EBls ETWh NLar SApu SLon
'Kiftsgate'	see *R. filipes* 'Kiftsgate'
'Kiftsgate Superior' (S)	EBls
'Kim' (Patio/F)	LSRN NRog
KIND REGARDS ('Peatiger') (F)	CBod LSRN
'King's Ransom' (HT)	CSBt EBls MRav SCob SPer
KISS ME KATE ('Kornagelio') (ClS) **new**	EBls SApu SSea
KISSES OF FIRE ('Chewmultiseek') (ClMin)	CDoC ETWh MRav SSea
KITTY ('Beaarty') (S)	EBls
'Kitty Hawk' (Min)	NRog
× ***kochiana***	EBls
kokanica	WPGP
KOLO ('Poulcy033'PBR) (Courtyard Series) (Cl)	ECnt
§ 'Königin von Dänemark' (A) ♀H7	CArg EBls EPfP ETWh GBin LCro LOPS LRHS LSRN MRav NLar SPer
§ 'Kordes' Magenta' (S/F)	EBls
'Kordes' Robusta'	see *R.* ROBUSTA
KORONA ('Kornita') (F)	NRog SPer
'Korresia' (F) ♀H7	CArg CDoC CSBt CTri EBee EBls ECnt ELon EPfP LRHS MAsh MRav NRog SApu SCob SPer SPoG
KRISTIN ('Benmagic') (Min)	NRog
KRONENBOURG ('Macbo') (HT)	EBls
KRONPRINSESSE MARY ('Poulcas018') (F)	ETWh
'Kronprinzessin Viktoria von Preussen' (Bb)	ETWh
KYRA'S KISSES ('Horripple') (F) **new**	NRog
L.D. BRAITHWAITE ('Auscrim') (S)	CArg CTri ELan EPfP LRHS MBNS NLar SCob SPer
'La Belle Distinguée' (RH)	ETWh
'La Belle Sultane'	see *R.* 'Violacea'
'La France' (HT)	EBls
'La Mortola'	see *R. brunonii* 'La Mortola'
'La Perle' (Ra)	CRHN
'La Reine Victoria'	see *R.* 'Reine Victoria'
§ LA ROSE DE MOLINARD ('Delgrarose'PBR) (S) ♀H6	CArg CBod ESty ETWh MGos MRav NLar SApu
LA ROSE DE PETIT PRINCE ('Delgramau') (F)	EBls ESty ETWh
'La Rubanée'	see *R.* × *centifolia* 'Unique Panachée'
LA SÉVILLANA ('Meigekanu') (F/GC)	EBls MSwo SApu SPer WCot
LA VILLA COTTA ('Korbamflu'PBR) (S) **new**	EBls
'La Ville de Bruxelles' (D) ♀H7	EBls ETWh NLar
LACE ('Frymoody') (HT)	LSRN
'Lady Alice Stanley' (HT)	EBls
'Lady Anne' (F)	LSRN NRog
'Lady Barnby' (HT)	EBls
'Lady Curzon' (Ru)	EBls
'Lady Elgin'	see *R.* THAÏS
LADY EMMA HAMILTON ('Ausbrother'PBR) (S) ♀H6	CDoC CGro CRos EHyd EPfP ESty GBin LBuc LCro LOPS LRHS MAsh MBNS MCot NRHS SCoo SPer
'Lady Gay' (Ra)	ETWh WBor
'Lady Hillingdon' (T)	EBls MAsh SRGP
'Lady Hillingdon' (ClT)	see *R.* 'Climbing Lady Hillingdon'
LADY MARMALADE ('Hartiger'PBR) (F)	CArg CDoC CSBt ESty LBuc LHkn LRHS MAsh MFry MPri MRav SCoo SMad SPer SPoG
'Lady Mary Fitzwilliam' (HT)	EBls ETWh
LADY MITCHELL ('Haryearn') (HT)	ECnt LHkn
LADY OF MEGGINCH ('Ausvolume'PBR) (S)	LRHS
LADY OF SHALOTT ('Ausnyson'PBR) (S) ♀H6	CRos ECnt EHyd ELan EPfP LBuc LCro LOPS LRHS MAsh MCot NLar NRHS SCob SCoo SSea
LADY PENELOPE ('Chewdor'PBR) (ClHT)	MFry
§ 'Lady Penzance' (RH)	EBls
LADY ROSE ('Korlady') (HT)	MAsh
LADY RYDER OF WARSAW ('Harrelief') (S) **new**	LHkn
LADY SALISBURY ('Auscezed'PBR) (S)	EHyd EPfP LBuc LRHS MAsh NRHS SCoo
'Lady Sylvia' (HT)	EBls LSRN NRog SPer
'Lady Waterlow' (ClHT)	EBee EBls ETWh SPer WSpi
laevigata (Ra)	EBls MMuc WPGP
- 'Anemonoides'	see *R.* 'Anemone'
L'AIMANT ('Harzola'PBR) (F) ♀H5	LHkn LRHS MAsh MRav SApu
'Lamarque' (N)	EBls ETWh
LAMBADA ('Korapfhecki'PBR) (S) **new**	EBls
LANCASHIRE ('Korstesgli'PBR) (GC) ♀H6	CDoC ECnt ELan ESty ETWh LSRN MRav MSwo NLar SApu SCob SSea
LANCELOT ('Tan03542'PBR) (Cl)	ESty
§ 'Lanei' (CeMo)	EBls ETWh
latibracteata	EBls
LAUDATIO	see *R.* TIMELESS PURPLE
LAURA FORD ('Chewarvel') (ClMin) ♀H5	CDoC EBls ELan LRHS MAsh MFry MGos MRav NRog SCoo SPer SPoG
'Laura Louisa' (Cl)	EBls ETWh LRHS MAsh NLar
'Laure Davoust' (Ra)	EBls ETWh MMuc NLar

LAVENDER DREAM ('Interlav') (S) **new**	NRog
LAVENDER ICE ('Tan04249'^{PBR}) (F)	EBee LCro LOPS SMad SPoG WSpi
'Lavender Lassie' (HM)	EBls ETWh NLar SPer
'Lavender Pinocchio' (F)	EBls WKif
LAVENDER SYMPHONIE ('Meiptima') (Patio)	EBls NLar
LAVINIA	see *R.* LAWINIA
§ LAWINIA ('Tanklewi') (ClHT) 🏆^{H6}	SApu
'Lawrence Johnston'	see *R.* 'Hidcote Yellow'
laxa	EBls
§ LAZY DAYS ('Poulkalm'^{PBR}) (F)	ECnt
LE ROUGE ET LE NOIR ('Delcart') (HT)	ELon ESty
'Le Vésuve' (Ch)	EBls ETWh
LEADING LADY ('Benuno') (Patio) **new**	NRog
LEAH TUTU ('Hornavel') (S)	EBee EBls EPfP ESty LRHS MAsh
LEAPING SALMON ('Peamight'^{PBR}) (ClHT) 🏆^{H6}	CArg CBod CGro CSBt ELon ESty ETWh LSRN MGos MRav NLar SApu SCob SPer WSpi
'Leda' (D)	CArg EBls ETWh
LEGENDS	see *R.* JOSEPHINE
'Lemon Pillar'	see *R.* 'Paul's Lemon Pillar'
LEMON TWIST ('Harquiz'^{PBR}) (Patio) **new**	LHkn
LÉONARDO DE VINCI ('Meideauri'^{PBR}) (F)	CSBt
'Léonie Lamesch' (Poly)	EBls
'Léontine Gervais' (Ra)	CRHN EBls
'Leo's Eye' (Ra)	EPfP ETWh NLar WFar
LESLIE'S DREAM ('Dicjoon') (HT)	IDic
LET FREEDOM RING ('Wekearman') (HT)	ESty NRog
LET THERE BE LOVE ('Frysoda') (F)	CGro EBls LBuc LRHS MAsh MFry
LETCHWORTH CENTENARY ('Harjojo'^{PBR}) (Patio) **new**	LHkn
LET'S CELEBRATE ('Fryraffles'^{PBR}) (F) 🏆^{H5}	CBod CDoC EBls EPfP ESty LBuc LRHS MAsh MFry MPri MRav NRHS SPoG
LET'S DANCE ('Rawlik') (F) **new**	NRog
'Leverkusen' (ClF) 🏆^{H6}	CArg EBls ETWh NLar SCob SPer
'Ley's Perpetual' (ClT)	CArg EBls ETWh
× ***lheritieriana*** (Bs)	EBls
'Liberty Bell' (HT) **new**	NRog
LICHFIELD ANGEL ('Ausrelate'^{PBR}) (S) 🏆^{H6}	CRos EHyd EPfP LBuc LRHS NLar NRHS SCoo
LICHTKÖNIGIN LUCIA ('Korlillub') (S)	EBls
LIFE BEGINS AT 40! ('Horhohoho') (F)	LSRN
LIFELONG FRIEND ('Raw1168') (HT) **new**	ESty
LIGHT FANTASTIC ('Dicgottago') (F) 🏆^{H6}	CArg EPfP MFry NRog
LIGHTNING STRIKE ('Raw967') (F)	ESty
LILAC BOUQUET ('Chewlilacdays') (Cl)	EBls ECnt ELon ESty LRHS SSea
'Lilac Domino' (Ra) **new**	ETWh
LILAC WINE ('Dicmulti') (F) 🏆^{H5}	CDoC IDic MRav SApu
LILIANA ('Poulsyng'^{PBR}) (S)	EBee ECnt ETWh LSRN SLon
LILLI MARLENE ('Korlima') (F)	CTri EBee EBls NRog SCob SPer

LINCOLN CATHEDRAL ('Glanlin'^{PBR}) (HT)	SPer
LINCOLNSHIRE POACHER ('Glareabit') (HT)	ESty NRog
'Lincolnshire Yellow Belly' (F)	ESty
'Linville' (Min) **new**	NRog
LION'S FAIRY TALE	see *R.* CHAMPAGNE MOMENT
LIONS INTERNATIONAL ('Frycharm'^{PBR}) (HT)	MFry
LISA ('Kirdisco') (F)	LSRN
LITTLE AMY ('Battamy') (Min)	LSRN NRog
'Little Buckaroo' (Min)	SPer
'Little Dorrit' (Poly)	NRog
LITTLE DUET ('Guesbliss') (F)	ESty
'Little Emily' (Patio)	LSRN NRog
'Little Fin' (Min)	LSRN NRog
'Little Gem' (DPMo)	EBls ETWh
LITTLE JACKIE ('Savor') (Min)	LSRN NRog
LITTLE MUFF ('Horluisbond') (Min)	NRog
LITTLE RAMBLER ('Chewramb'^{PBR}) (MinRa) 🏆^{H6}	CArg CDoC EBls ECnt ELan ESty LCro LOPS LRHS MFry MGos MRav NRHS SApu SCoo SPer SSea
'Little White Pet'	see *R.* 'White Pet'
LIVERPOOL HOPE ('Beapike') **new**	EBls
§ LIVERPOOL REMEMBERS ('Frystar') (HT)	MFry
LIVING DAYLIGHTS ('Fryradical') (F)	MFry
'Living Fire' (F)	NRog
LIZZY ('Tan99552') **new**	SSea
LOADS OF PINK ('Fialopi') (F) **new**	NRog
LOCHINVAR ('Ausbilda'^{PBR}) (S)	LRHS
'Lolabelle' (S)	ETWh SPer
'Long John Silver' (Cl)	EBls ELan SApu
longicuspis misapplied	see *R.* 'Mulliganii'
longicuspis Bertol. (Ra)	NLar
§ - var. ***sinowilsonii*** (Ra)	ETWh
LORD BYRON ('Meitosier') (ClHT)	ESty
'Lord Penzance' (RH)	EBls ETWh EWTr NLar NRog SPer
LORNA ('Cocringer') (F)	LSRN
LOTS OF LOVE ('Forchriso') (F)	ESty
'L'Ouche' misapplied	see *R.* 'Louise Odier'
'Louis XIV' (Ch)	EBls ETWh MCot
LOUISA STONE ('Harbadge') (S)	LHkn
LOUISE CLEMENTS ('Clelou') (S)	EBls
'Louise d'Arzens' (N)	EBls
'Louise Estes' (HT) **new**	NRog
§ 'Louise Odier' (Bb)	CTri EBls ECnt EPfP ETWh IArd LCro LOPS LRHS LSRN MCot MRav NLar NRog SApu SPer SRGP
LOVE & PEACE ('Baipeace'^{PBR}) (HT) 🏆^{H7}	ESty NRog SApu
LOVE EVERLASTING ('Horfrancis') (F) **new**	NRog
LOVE KNOT ('Chewglorious'^{PBR}) (ClMin) 🏆^{H6}	CArg CBod CDoC CSBt ECnt EHyd EPfP ESty LRHS MAsh MRav
LOVELY BOY ('Simjas') (HT)	ESty

§	LOVELY BRIDE ('Meiratcan'^{PBR}) (Patio)	CRos EBls EHyd EPfP LRHS MAsh NRHS SApu SPoG
	LOVELY DAY ('Webpink') (Cl) **new**	NRog
	LOVELY LADY ('Dicjubell'^{PBR}) (HT) 🏆^{H6}	CBod CSBt EBls ECnt ESty LSRN MRav SApu SPer SSea
	LOVELY MEIDILAND	see *R.* LOVELY BRIDE
	LOVELY PARFUMA ('Kortekcho') (F) **new**	EBls
	LOVELY PINK ('Meinoplius'^{PBR}) (F)	NRog
	'Lovers' Meeting' (HT)	MRav SPer
	LOVESTRUCK ('Dicommatac') (F)	CArg CBod CDoC CGro CSBt EBls ECnt ESty ETWh IDic LBuc LCro LOPS LRHS MAsh MFry NLar SApu SCoo SPer
	LOVING MEMORY ('Korgund81') (HT)	CArg CBod CGro CSBt EBls ECnt ESty IArd LCro LOPS LSRN MFry MGos MPri MRav NRog SApu SCob SPer SPoG SSea
§	'Loving Mum'^{PBR} (HT)	CSBt ESty
	'Lowri' (HT) **new**	NRog
	LOWTHORPE DELIGHT ('Dicgoofy') (F)	IDic
§	***lucieae***	EGrI ETWh
	'Lucky' (F)	CBod CDoC EHyd LRHS NRog
	LUCKY! ('Frylucy') (F) 🏆^{H6}	CArg EBls EPfP ESty LBuc LSRN MAsh MFry MGos MPri MRav SApu SCoo SPer SPoG
	LUCKY STAR ('Raw1142') (F)	ESty
	LUCY ('Kirlis') (F)	LSRN
	LUIS DESAMERO ('Tinluis') (Min)	NRog
	LULLABY ('Kenfrilpin') (ClF)	ESty
	LUSCIOUS LUCY ('Tucklucy') (Patio)	LSRN
	LYDA ROSE ('Letlyda') (S)	EBls
	'Lykkefund' (Ra)	EBls ETWh
	LYNDA BELLINGHAM ('Harwise') (HT) **new**	LHkn
	'Mabel Morrison' (HP)	EBls
	Macartney rose	see *R. bracteata*, *R.* THE MCCARTNEY ROSE
	MACMILLAN NURSE ('Beamac') (S)	CEnd EBls ELan EPfP ESty ETWh LRHS MAsh MCot NLar NRHS SCoo
	'Macrantha' (Gallica hybrid)	EBls
	macrophylla (S)	WPav
	- B&SWJ 2603	WCru
	- GWJ 9306	WCru
	'Madame Abel Chatenay' (HT)	EBls
	'Madame Alfred Carrière' (N) 🏆^{H5}	Widely available
	'Madame Alice Garnier' (Ra)	CRHN EBls ETWh NLar SPer
	'Madame Antoine Mari' (T)	ETWh
§	'Madame Boll' (DPo)	CArg CDoC EBls ETWh MSwo NLar NRog SApu
	'Madame Butterfly' (HT)	EBls
§	'Madame Caroline Testout' (HT)	CTri EBls
	'Madame d'Arblay' (Ra)	ETWh
	'Madame de la Roche-Lambert' (DPMo)	EBls ETWh
	'Madame de Sancy de Parabère' (Bs)	EBls ETWh
	'Madame Driout' (ClT)	ETWh
	'Madame Ernest Calvat' (Bb)	EBls ETWh
	'Madame Eugène Résal' misapplied	see *R.* 'Comtesse du Cayla'
§	'Madame Grégoire Staechelin' (ClHT) 🏆^{H6}	CArg CBod CTri EBls ECnt EHyd ELan EPfP ETWh LCro LOPS LRHS MSwo NLar NRHS NRog SApu SCob SPer SPlb
	'Madame Hardy' (D) 🏆^{H7}	CBod CDoC CSBt EBls EHyd EPfP ETWh LCro LOPS LRHS LSRN MRav MSwo NLar NRog SApu SPer WFar
	'Madame Isaac Péreire' (ClBb)	CArg CDoC CSBt CTri EBls ECnt EPfP ETWh GBin LCro LOPS MCot MRav MSwo NLar NRog SApu SCob SMad SPer WFar
	'Madame Jules Gravereaux' (ClT)	EBls
	'Madame Knorr' (DPo) 🏆^{H7}	ECnt EPfP LRHS SPer
	'Madame Knorr' misapplied	see *R.* 'Madame Boll'
	'Madame Laurette Messimy' (Ch)	ETWh
	'Madame Lauriol de Barny' (Bb)	EBls ETWh MRav NLar
	'Madame Legras de Saint Germain' (A × N)	EBls ETWh NLar NRog SPer
	'Madame Louis Laperrière' (HT)	EBls
	'Madame Louis Lévêque' (DPMo)	EBls ETWh NLar
	'Madame Pierre Oger' (Bb)	CArg CTri EBls ECnt ETWh NLar SPer
	'Madame Plantier' (A × N)	CArg NLar NRog SPer WFar
	'Madame Victor Verdier' (HP)	EBls
	'Madame Zöetmans' (D)	ETWh
	'Madeleine Seltzer' (Ra)	EBls ETWh
	'Madge' (HM)	SDix
	'Magenta' (S/F)	see *R.* 'Kordes' Magenta' (S/F)
	MAGIC CARPET ('Jaclover'^{PBR}) (S/GC) 🏆^{H6}	CDoC EBls ELan MRav MSwo SApu SPer
	MAGIC MOMENT ('Forrusty') (HT)	ESty
	MAGIC SHOW ('Benjets') (Min) **new**	NRog
	'Magna Charta' (HP)	EBls
	MAGNETIC EYES ('Dicmimic') (S)	IDic
	'Maid Marion' (Ra)	LSRN
	MAID MARION ('Austobias'^{PBR}) (HM)	LSRN SCoo
	'Maid of Kent'^{PBR} (Cl)	CBod LSRN NLar SCob SCoo SPer
	'Maiden's Blush' (A)	CArg CTri ELan EWTr LEdu LRHS MAsh NRog SCob SPer WHer
	'Maiden's Blush, Great'	see *R.* 'Great Maiden's Blush'
	'Maigold' (ClPiH) 🏆^{H6}	CArg CBcs CGro CTri EBls ELan EPfP ETWh LCro LOPS LRHS MAsh MGos MRav MSwo NLar NRog SCob SMad SPer SRGP WBor
	Maltese rose	see *R.* 'Cécile Brünner'
§	'Malton' (China hybrid)	EBls
	MALVERN HILLS ('Auscanary'^{PBR}) (Ra) 🏆^{H5}	CRos CSBt EBee EPfP ESty LRHS MCot NLar SCoo SPer
	'Maman Cochet' (T)	EBls
	MAMMA MIA ('Poulcy013'^{PBR}) (Courtyard Series) (Ra)	MBros
	MAMMA MIA! ('Fryjolly'^{PBR}) (HT) 🏆^{H6}	CDoC EBls ECnt EPfP ESty LRHS MAsh MFry MRav SApu SPoG
	'Mandarin' (F)	SCob
	MANDARIN ('Korcelin') (Min)	EBls ESty MRav
	MANHATTAN BLUE ('Tanettahn') (F)	MFry
	'Manning's Blush' (RH)	EBls

'Mannington Cascade' (Ra)	EBls
'Mannington Mauve Rambler' (Ra)	EBls ESty
MANY CONGRATULATIONS ('Forshelly') (F)	ESty
MANY HAPPY RETURNS ('Harwanted') (F) ♀H6	CBcs CBod CDoC CGro CRos CSBt EBls ECnt ELan EPfP LHkn LRHS LSRN MAsh MFry MGos MPri MRav NRHS NRog SApu SCob SPer
§ 'Marchesa Boccella' (DPo) ♀H7	CArg CTri EPfP ETWh LRHS MPri NRog SApu SPer WHer
'Marchioness of Salisbury' (HT)	EBls
'Maréchal Davoust' (CeMo)	LEdu NRog
'Maréchal Niel' (N)	EBls EShb ETWh NLar NRog SPer SSea
MARGARET (HT)	see *R.* DEAR MARGARET
'Margaret' (HT)	LSRN
MARGARET GREVILLE ('Beajoker') (S)	EBls
MARGARET MERRIL ('Harkuly') (F)	CArg CBcs CDoC CGro CSBt CTri EBee EBls ELan EPfP ESty IArd LCro LHkn LOPS LRHS LSRN MAsh MFry MPri MRav NRog SApu SCob SPer SPoG SRGP SSea
MARGARET'S SMILE ('Dewlp1') (HT) **new**	NRog
'Margo Koster' (Poly)	NRog
'Marguerite Hilling' (S)	CTri EBls ETWh MSwo NRog SPer
MARIANA LILY ('Rawaninly') **new**	NRog
'Marie Bugnet' (Ru)	EBls
'Marie Louise' (D)	EBls ETWh
'Marie Pavič' (Poly)	ETWh NLar
'Marie van Houtte' (T)	EBls
'Marie-Jeanne' (Poly)	EBls
MARIGOLD SWEET DREAM ('Fryprospa') (Patio)	ECnt MFry
MARJORIE FAIR ('Harhero') (Poly/S) ♀H6	EBls ELan EPfP NRog SCob SRGP
MARLON'S DAY ('Wrimarlon') (HT) **new**	NRog
'Martha' (Bb)	EBls LSRN
'Martha's Choice' (HT)	NRog
'Martin Frobisher' (Ru)	EBls
I 'Mary' (Poly)	LSRN
'Mary B' (F) **new**	NRog
MARY BERRY ('Harupon') (HT)	ESty LHkn LRHS SApu
MARY JEAN ('Haryen') (HT)	ECnt LHkn
'Mary Manners' (Ru)	EBls
MARY ROSE ('Ausmary') (S)	CRos CSBt EHyd ELan EPfP LRHS LSRN NRHS SCob SLon SPer SPoG WKif
'Masquerade' (F)	CDoC CGro CTri EBls ELan NLar NRog SPer
MATANGI ('Macman') (F) ♀H6	NRog
MATAWHERO MAGIC	see *R.* SIMPLY THE BEST
MATCHMAKER ('Dicnarrow') (F)	CSBt IDic SApu
'Maurice Bernardin' (HP)	EBls
MAURICE UTRILLO ('Delstavo') (HT)	ESty
MAVERICK ('Mavrik') (HT) **new**	NRog
'Max Graf'	see *R.* × *jacksonii* 'Max Graf'
'Maxima'	see *R.* × *alba* 'Alba Maxima'
MAXIMA ROMANTICA ('Meikerira'PBR) (HT)	EBls ELon
'Maxime Corbon' (Ra) **new**	ETWh
'May Queen' (Ra)	CRHN EBls ETWh NLar SEND SPer
'McCartney Rose'	see *R.* THE MCCARTNEY ROSE
'McGredy's Sunset' (HT)	EBls NRog
'McGredy's Yellow' (HT)	NRog
'McMillan's Pink' (HT) **new**	NRog
§ MEDLEY RUBY ('Noa140715'PBR) (Min)	SPoG
'Meg' (ClHT)	CArg EBls ETWh EWTr LSRN NLar
'Meg Merrilies' (RH)	EBls
MELODY MAKER ('Dicqueen') (F)	NRog
MEMORY LANE ('Peavoodoo'PBR) (F)	LSRN
MERCY ROSE ('Harport') (F) **new**	LHkn
'Merlot' (Min)	LSRN
'Mermaid' (Cl) ♀H5	CArg CBcs CRos CSBt CTri EBls EHyd EPfP ETWh LRHS NLar NRHS NRog SApu SCob SEND SMad SNig SPer SSea
§ 'Mevrouw Nathalie Nypels' (Poly)	CArg EBls ETWh MRav NLar
MICHAELA'S ROSE ('Rawpurpink') (HT) **new**	NRog
'Michelle Cholet' (Min)	NRog
× ***micrugosa***	EBls
- 'Alba'	EBls
MIDDLESBOROUGH FOOTBALL CLUB ('Horflame') (HT)	LSRN NRog
MIDNIGHT BLUE ('Wekfabpur') (S)	CDoC EBls ECnt ESty MGos
MIDSUMMER ('Tan02280'PBR) (F)	MFry
MIDSUMMER NIGHT'S DREAM ('Rawroyal') (F)	ESty
MIKE THOMPSON ('Sherired') (HT)	NRog
§ MILLIE ('Poulren013'PBR) (Renaissance Series) (S) ♀H6	CArg CBcs CBod CDoC CEnd EBls ECnt ELan ESty ETWh LBuc LCro LOPS LRHS LSRN MFry MGos MPri NLar NRHS SApu SCoo SLon SPoG SRGP
MILLIE ROSE ('Wekblunez'PBR) (HT)	SApu
MILLIONAIRE ('Peazara') (F)	LSRN
MINERVA ('Visancar') (F)	CSBt ESty
'Minnehaha' (Ra)	EBls NRog SSea
MINNIE PEARL ('Savahowdy') (Min)	NRog
MINNIE THE MOOCHER ('Webriva') (Min) **new**	NRog
MIRANDA ('Ausimmon'PBR) (S) **new**	ETWh
mirifica stellata	see *R. stellata* var. *mirifica*
MISCHIEF ('Macmi') (HT)	LSRN NRog SPer
MISS ALICE ('Ausjake'PBR) (S)	LSRN
MISS DIOR ('Harencens'PBR) (S)	LHkn
'Miss Edith Cavell' (Poly)	EBls ETWh
MISS FLIPPINS ('Tuckflip') (Min)	NRog
MISS HARP ('Tanolg') (HT)	NRog
MISS KATE ('Dicpredict') (F)	IDic
'Miss Lakeland' (Min) **new**	NRog
MISS SCARLET ('Forbright') (Cl)	ESty
§ 'Mister Lincoln' (HT)	EBls SPer

	Name	Suppliers
§	MISTY HIT ('Poulhi011'[PBR]) (PatioHit Series) (Patio)	CDoC EBls ECnt LRHS LSRN NRHS
	'Misty Moon' (F)	ESty
	MITSOUKO ('Delnat') (HT)	ESty
	MODERN SLAVERY ('Dicpowwow') (F)	IDic
	MOLINEUX ('Ausmol'[PBR]) (S) 🏆H6	CRos EHyd LRHS LSRN MAsh NLar NRHS SPer
	'Molly Sharman-Crawford' (HT)	EBls
	MOM ('Rawtoks') (F)	LSRN NRog
	MOMENT IN TIME ('Korcastrav'[PBR]) (F) 🏆H6	CArg CBod CDoC CSBt EBee ECnt MAsh MPri MRav SPer SPoG
	MONICA BELLUCCI ('Meimonkeur'[PBR]) (HT)	ELon ESty NRog
	'Monique' (HT)	EBls
	MONSIEUR PÉLISSON	see *R.* 'Pélisson'
	MOODY BLUE ('Fryniche') (HT)	CDoC ECnt LBuc LRHS MAsh MFry MRav
	'Moonlight' (HM)	CArg CTri EBls ETWh EWTr MRav MSwo NRog SCob SPer
	MOONSTONE ('Wekcryland') (HT) **new**	NRog
	MOORCROFT ('Guesyearn') (F)	ESty
	'Morletii' (Bs)	EBls ETWh MMuc SEND
	MORNING BLUSH ('Siemorn') (A) **new**	NRog
	'Morning Jewel' (ClF) 🏆H7	LHkn NRog SPer
	MORNING MIST ('Ausfire') (S)	EPfP LRHS SPer
§	'Morsdag' (Poly/F)	LSRN
	MORTIMER SACKLER ('Ausorts'[PBR]) (S) 🏆H6	EHyd EPfP LBuc LRHS MAsh MCot NRHS SCoo SPer
	moschata (Ra)	EBls ETWh SSea
	- 'Autumnalis'	see *R.* 'Princesse de Nassau'
	- var. ***nepalensis***	see *R. brunonii*
	MOTHER'S DAY	see *R.* 'Morsdag'
I	'Mother's Day'	SPer
	MOTHER'S JOY ('Horsiltrop') (F)	LSRN
	MOTHER'S LOVE ('Tinlove') (Min)	NRog
	MOULIN ROUGE ('Simmarg') (HT)	ESty
	MOUNT AORANGI ('Sanaran') (HT)	ESty
	MOUNTAIN SNOW ('Aussnow') (Ra)	LRHS
	MOUNTBATTEN ('Harmantelle') (F) 🏆H6	EBls ELan LHkn MRav SCob SPer SPoG
§	'Mousseline' (DPoMo)	CArg EBls ETWh NRog
	'Mousseuse du Japon'	see *R.* 'Japonica'
	moyesii (S)	CTri EBls ELan ETWh GGro NRog NWea
§	- var. ***fargesii*** (S)	EBls ETWh
	- ***holodonta***	see *R. moyesii* f. *rosea*
§	- f. ***rosea*** (S)	EBls
	'Mr Lincoln'	see *R.* 'Mister Lincoln'
	'Mrs Anthony Waterer' (Ru)	ETWh
	'Mrs Foley Hobbs' (T)	ETWh
	'Mrs Honey Dyson' (Ra)	ETWh EWTr
	'Mrs John Laing' (HP)	EBls ETWh NLar
	'Mrs Oakley Fisher' (HT)	EBls ETWh MCot SMad SPer
	'Mrs Paul' (Bb)	ETWh
	'Mrs Reynolds Hole' (T) **new**	ETWh
	'Mrs Sam McGredy' (HT)	EBls
	'Mrs Yamada' (Bb)	EBls
	'Muff's Pet' (Min)	NRog
	'Mulliganii'	EBls EPfP ETWh GKin SPer
	multibracteata (S)	EBls ETWh GLog

	Name	Suppliers
	multiflora (Ra)	EBls ETWh LBuc
	- 'Carnea' (Ra)	EBls
§	- var. ***cathayensis*** (Ra)	EBls
§	- 'Grevillei' (Ra)	EBls ETWh MCot MMuc WFar
	- 'Platyphylla'	see *R. multiflora* 'Grevillei'
	- var. ***watsoniana***	see *R. watsoniana*
	MUM IN A MILLION	see *R.* MILLIE
	MUMMY	see *R.* NEWLY WED
	mundi	see *R. gallica* 'Versicolor'
	MUNSTEAD WOOD ('Ausbernard'[PBR]) (S) 🏆H6	CDoC CGro CRos EBee ECnt EHyd ELan EPfP EShb ESty LBuc LCro LOPS LRHS LSRN MBNS MCot MSwo NLar NRHS SCob SCoo SPer SPoG WSpi
	murielae	EBls
	'Murjami'	EBls
	'Muscosa Alba'	see *R.* × *centifolia* 'Shailer's White Moss'
	'Mutabilis'	see *R.* × *odorata* 'Mutabilis'
	MY BROTHER ('Raw1056') (F)	ESty
	MY DAD ('Boselftay'[PBR]) (F)	CBcs CBod EBls LSRN SApu
	'My Darling Husband' (F)	LSRN
	'My Darling Wife' (F)	LSRN
	MY GIRL ('Tan00798'[PBR]) (HT)	CDoC EBee
	'My Joy' (HT)	LSRN NRog
	'My Lovely Mum' (F)	MFry
	MY MUM ('Webmorrow'[PBR]) (F)	CBcs CBod ESty LSRN SApu SCoo
	MY NAN ('Fornan') (HT)	ESty
	MY SISTER ('Raw1052') (F)	ESty
§	MY VALENTINE ('Korcoluma'[PBR]) (HT) 🏆H6	CSBt LBuc LSRN
	MY VALENTINE ('Mormyval') (Min)	EBls LSRN MAsh
	MYRIAM ('Cocgrand') (HT)	LSRN
	MYSTERY GIRL ('Dicdothis'[PBR]) (HT)	NRog
	MYSTIC GLOW ('Raw1101') (F)	ESty
	NAHÉMA ('Deléri') (ClHT)	EBls
	NANCY JEAN ('Ricnancy') (Patio)	LSRN NRog
	NANCY ('Poulninga') (Renaissance Series) (S)	ETWh LSRN
	nanothamnus	SPtp
	'Naomi' (HT)	LBuc LRHS LSRN MAsh
	'Narrow Water' (Ra) 🏆H6	CArg EBls ETWh NLar
§	'Nastarana' (N)	EBls ETWh NLar
	NATALIE ('Poulren014'[PBR]) (Renaissance Series) (S)	ETWh LSRN
	NATANIA ('Dicseduce') (F)	IDic
	NATASHA RICHARDSON ('Harpacket'[PBR]) (F)	ELon LHkn LRHS MRav
	'Nathalie Nypels'	see *R.* 'Mevrouw Nathalie Nypels'
	'National Trust' (HT)	CArg CTri IArd MFry NRog SCob SCoo SPer
	NELSON'S JOURNEY ('Beaflirt') (S)	EBls
	'Nelson's Pride' (F)	EBls
	'Nestor' (G)	ETWh
	'Nevada' (S)	CArg CTri EBls EPfP ETWh IArd LEdu MRav NLar NRog SCob SPer
	NEVER FORGOTTEN ('Gregart') (HT)	LSRN
	NEW ARRIVAL	see *R.* 'Red Patio'
	NEW BEGINNINGS ('Korprofko'[PBR]) (F) 🏆H5	EBls ELan LSRN MAsh

§	'New Dawn' (Cl) 🏆H7	Widely available
	'New Home'	LSRN
§	NEWLY WED ('Dicwhynot'[PBR]) (Patio) 🏆H6	LSRN SSea
	NEWSFLASH ('Kendutch'[PBR]) (F) 🏆H5	ESty ETWh
	NICE DAY ('Chewsea'[PBR]) (ClMin)	CBod CDoC CTri EPfP ESty LRHS MAsh MFry MRav SApu SCoo SPer SPoG
	'Nicola' (F)	LSRN
	NIGHT LIGHT ('Poullight'[PBR]) (Courtyard Series) (ClHT)	ECnt SApu
	NIGHT OWL ('Wekpurosot') (Cl)	CDoC CEnd CGro ELon ESty ETWh GBin LRHS MRav NLar NPoe NRog SPer SPoG SSea
	NINA ('Mehnina'[PBR]) (S)	LSRN
	NINA ('Poulren018'[PBR]) (Renaissance Series) (S)	ECnt ETWh
	NIPPER ('Hareco'[PBR]) (GC) **new**	LHkn
	nitida	EBls NWea SCob SPer
	NOBLE ANTONY ('Ausway'[PBR]) (S)	EPfP
§	'Noisette Carnée' (N) 🏆H7	CArg CTri EBee EBls EPfP ETWh GBin LEdu LRHS MAsh MBNS MCot MRav NLar NRHS NRog SApu SCob SPer SSea WBor
	NORFOLK ('Poulfolk') (GC)	CTri EBls MSwo NLar SApu SCob SPer
	'Norma Major' (HT)	NRog
	NORTHAMPTONSHIRE ('Mattdor') (GC)	SCob
	'Northwest' (HT) **new**	NRog
	'Norwell' (Ra)	MNrw WFar
	'Norwich Castle' (F)	EBls
	NORWICH CATHEDRAL ('Beacath') (HT)	EBls
	'Norwich Union' (F)	EBls
	NOSTALGIA ('Savarita') (Min)	CGro EPfP LBuc LRHS MAsh
§	NOSTALGIA ('Taneiglat'[PBR]) (HT) 🏆H6	CEnd CSBt EBls ECnt ELon ESty MFry MGos MRav SApu SCoo SMad SPer SPoG SSea
	NOSTALGIE	see *R.* NOSTALGIA
	'Notre-Dame de Calais' (Cl)	EBee EBls EPfP LRHS MAsh
	NOVALIS ('Korfriedhar'[PBR]) (F) **new**	EBls
	'Nozomi' (ClMin/GC)	CBod CTri EBls ELan ESty ETWh NLar NRog SApu SPer
	'Nuits de Young' (CeMo) 🏆H7	CArg EBls EPfP ETWh NLar SApu
	'Nur Mahal' (HM)	CArg EBls ETWh
	NURSE TRACEY DAVIES ('Frykookie'[PBR]) (F) 🏆H6	MAsh MFry
	nutkana (S)	EBls
§	- var. ***hispida*** (S)	EBls
§	- 'Plena' (S/D) 🏆H7	EBls ETWh GKin NLar WHer
	'Nymphenburg' (HM)	ETWh SPer
	'Nyveldt's White' (Ru)	EBls
	OCTAVIA HILL ('Harzeal'[PBR]) (F)	ETWh LHkn MRav NLar SPer
	× ***odorata*** 'Fortune's Double Yellow'	see *R.* × *odorata* 'Pseudindica'
	- 'Hume's Blush Tea-scented China' (ClCh)	ETWh
§	- 'Mutabilis' (Ch) 🏆H5	Widely available
I	- 'Odorata' (Ch)	EBls
	- old crimson China (Ch)	EBls
§	- 'Pallida' (Ch)	EBls EPfP ETWh LRHS MCot NLar SCob WCot
§	- 'Pseudindica' (ClCh)	EBls IArd
§	- Sanguinea Group (Ch)	EBls ILea LRHS XSen
	- - 'Bengal Crimson' (Ch) 🏆H5	CRHN CRos ECre EHyd ELan EPfP ETWh EWTr LRHS NRHS SDix SLon SPoG WAvo WCFE WCot WKif
	- - 'Bob's Beauty' (Ch)	WCot
§	- 'Viridiflora' (Ch)	EBee EBls ETWh LEdu NRog SCob SLon SMad SPer SSea WCot WHer
	ODYSSEY ('Franski'[PBR]) (F)	ESty NRog
	officinalis	see *R. gallica* var. *officinalis*
	OH WOW! ('Wekspitrib'[PBR]) (ClHT)	ECnt ESty SSea
	old blush China	see *R.* × *odorata* 'Pallida'
	old cabbage	see *R.* × *centifolia*
	OLD GLORY ('Benday') (Min/Patio)	NRog
	OLD JOHN ('Dicwillynilly') (F)	LSRN
	old pink moss rose	see *R.* × *centifolia* 'Muscosa'
	OLD PORT ('Mackati') (F)	ELon ESty IArd SApu
	old red moss	see *R.* 'Henri Martin', *R.* 'Lanei'
	old velvet moss	see *R.* 'William Lobb'
	'Old Velvet Rose'	see *R.* 'Tuscany'
	old yellow Scotch (SpH)	see *R.* × *harisonii* 'Williams' Double Yellow'
	OLIVIA ('Wekquahofa') (HT)	LSRN
	OLIVIA ROSE ('Wisnut') (Min)	NRog
	OLIVIA ROSE AUSTIN ('Ausmixture'[PBR]) (S)	CGro CRos CSBt EHyd ELan EPfP ESty GBin LCro LOPS LRHS MAsh MCot NRHS SCoo SPoG
	'Olympic Flame' (F)	EPfP MAsh
	'Omar Khayyám' (D)	EBls ETWh NLar NRog
§	'Ombrée Parfaite' (G)	NRog
	omeiensis	see *R. sericea* subsp. *omeiensis*
	ONE IN A MILLION ('Poulren024'[PBR]) (S)	ETWh MAsh NLar
	OOH LA LA ('Gues05-64') (F)	ESty
	OPEN ARMS ('Chewpixcel'[PBR]) (ClMin) 🏆H6	CRos EBls EPfP ESty LCro LOPS MFry SApu SMad SPer SSea
	'Ophelia' (HT)	EBls
	ORANGE BLOSSOM SPECIAL ('Smi52/02') (ClMin)	ESty SSea
	'Orange Sensation' (F)	CTri NRog
§	ORANGE SUNBLAZE ('Meijikatar'[PBR]) (Min)	CSBt SCob SCoo SPer
	'Orange Triumph' (Poly)	EBls
	ORANGES AND LEMONS ('Macoranlem') (F)	CArg EBls ESty SApu SCob SSea WBor
	'Orpheline de Juillet'	see *R.* 'Ombrée Parfaite'
	OTHELLO ('Auslo'[PBR]) (S)	SPer
	OUR BETH ('Beacarol') (S)	CEnd EBls EPfP LRHS LSRN MAsh
	'Our Dream' (Patio)	EBls MAsh
	OUR ENDEAVOUR ('Bra063') (F) **new**	NRog
	OUR GEORGE ('Kirrush') (Patio)	LSRN
	OUR HILDA ('Lancoro') (F)	LSRN
§	OUR JANE ('Horengland') (F)	LSRN NRog
	OUR JUBILEE ('Coccages') (HT)	ESty
	'Our Millie' (HT)	LSRN NRog
	OUR MOLLY ('Dicreason') (GC/S)	IDic LSRN SPer
	OUT OF THE BLUE ('Simblue') (F)	ESty
	OVER THE MOON ('Oraclelon') (HT)	ESty NRog
	OXANA ('Dicovadatop') (F)	IDic SApu

OXFORDSHIRE ('Korfullwind'PBR) (GC) ♀H6 — SCob
'Ozena' **new** — SSea
PADDY MCGREDY ('Macpa') (F) — NRog
PAISLEY ABBEY ('Harrestore'PBR) (S) **new** — LHkn
PANACHE ('Poultop'PBR) (Patio/Min) — ECnt LRHS MPri
PAPA MEILLAND ('Meisar') (HT) — CSBt CTri EBls NRog SPer SSea
PAPER ANNIVERSARY (Patio) — LSRN
PAPI DELBARD ('Delaby') (ClHT) — CArg EBee EBls ETWh LSRN MGos MRav NLar SSea
'Papillon' (Ch) — EBls
I 'Parade' (Cl) ♀H6 — CArg EBls ETWh LSRN MFry NLar
'Parkdirektor Riggers' (Cl) — EBls ETWh LCro LOPS NLar SCob SPer
PARKY ('Harpresto'PBR) (S) — LHkn
Parson's pink China — see *R.* × *odorata* 'Pallida'
PARTRIDGE ('Korweirim') (GC) — EBls SPer
'Party Girl' (Min) — NRog
parvifolia — see *R.* 'Burgundiaca'
PAS DE DEUX ('Poulhult'PBR) (Courtyard Series) (ClF) — MAsh
PASCALI ('Lenip') (HT) — CArg CBcs CTri EBls NRog SCob SPer
PAT AUSTIN ('Ausmum'PBR) (S) — CArg CTri EPfP ETWh LSRN MBNS SCob
PATRICIA KENT ('Harmerry'PBR) (S) — LHkn
PATRICIA MAY ('Dicscenic') (F) — IDic
'Paul Crampel' (Poly) — NRog
'Paul Dauvesse' (Ra) **new** — ETWh
'Paul Lédé' (ClT) — see *R.* 'Climbing Paul Lédé'
PAUL MCCARTNEY (HT) — see *R.* THE MCCARTNEY ROSE
'Paul Neyron' (HP) — EBls ETWh
'Paul Noël' (Ra) — CRos LSRN
'Paul Ricault' (Ce × HP) — EBls ETWh
PAUL SHIRVILLE ('Harqueterwife'PBR) (HT) — EBls
'Paul Transon' (Ra) ♀H6 — CRHN CRos EBls EPfP ETWh LRHS MMuc NLar SEND WHer
'Paul Verdier' (Bb) — EBls
'Paula's Rose' (Patio) — LSRN NRog
§ 'Paulii' (Ru/GC) — EBls WSpi
'Paulii Alba' — see *R.* 'Paulii'
'Paul's Early Blush' (HP) — EBls
'Paul's Himalayan Musk' (Ra) ♀H6 — Widely available
§ 'Paul's Lemon Pillar' (ClHT) — CArg EPfP ETWh NLar NRog SPer
'Paul's Scarlet Climber' (Cl/Ra) — CArg CBod CDoC EBls ETWh LBuc LCro LOPS LRHS MAsh MPri MRav MSwo SCob SCoo SPer
'Paul's Single White Perpetual' (Ra) — CTri EBls ETWh NLar
PAWS ('Beapaw') (S) — EBls
'Pax' (HM) — EBls ETWh NRog WKif
PEACE ('Madame A. Meilland') (HT) ♀H6 — CArg CBcs CBod CEnd CSBt CTri EBls ECnt ELan EPfP LCro LOPS LRHS LSRN MAsh MFry MPri MRav NRHS NRog SApu SCob SPer SPoG SSea
PEACEKEEPER ('Harbella'PBR) (F) — LHkn
'Peach Grootendorst' (Ru) — ETWh
PEACHY ('Macrelea') (HT) — EBls EPfP MAsh SPoG
PEARL ('Korterschi'PBR) (F) ♀H6 — EBls LRHS MAsh MRav
PEARL ('Wekpearl') (HT) — CSBt
§ PEARL ABUNDANCE ('Harfrisky'PBR) (F) — CBod LHkn SApu
PEARL ANNIVERSARY ('Whitston'PBR) (Min/Patio) — CDoC ESty LCro LOPS LSRN MRav SApu SSea
PEARL DRIFT ('Leggab') (S) — CEnd EBls ETWh MCot MSwo NRog SPer
PEAUDOUCE — see *R.* ELINA
PEEL BROW GOLD ('Braapple') (HT) **new** — NRog
§ 'Pélisson' (CeMo) — EBls
§ ***pendulina*** — EBls ETWh
– 'Nana' — NWad
'Penelope' (HM) ♀H5 — CArg CSBt CTri EBee EBls ECnt ELan EPfP ETWh LCro LOPS LRHS LSRN MAsh MCot MFry MNrw MRav NLar NRog SCob SPer SSea
'Penelope Hobhouse' (HM) — EBls
PENNI OUR SPECIAL GIRL ('Raw1130') (F) **new** — ESty
PENNY LANE ('Hardwell'PBR) (ClHT) ♀H6 — CArg CBod CSBt EBee EBls ECnt EPfP ETWh LBuc LCro LHkn LOPS LRHS MAsh MFry MGos MRav NLar SApu SCob SCoo SPer SPoG SSea
PENNY LANE ('Talpen') (Min) — MSwo
× ***penzanceana*** — see *R.* 'Lady Penzance'
PERCEPTION ('Harzippee'PBR) (HT) — LHkn NRog
PERENNIAL BLUE ('Mehv9601') (Ra) ♀H6 — CBod CDoC CNat EBls ESty MRav SApu SCoo SSea
PERENNIAL BLUSH ('Mehbarbie'PBR) (Ra) ♀H6 — CArg CDoC ELan ESty MRav SApu
§ PERFECT DAY ('Poulcrem') (F) — ECnt
PERFECT GENTLEMAN ('Raw1059') (F) — ESty
PERFECT HARMONY ('Tangustedv') (HT) — EBls ESty SSea
PERFECT MATCH ('Hartie') (F) — LHkn
PERFECT PET ('Smi 122204'PBR) (F) — ESty
'Pergolèse' (DPo) — EBls ETWh
§ 'Perle d'Or' (Poly) ♀H6 — EBls ETWh NLar NRog SDix SPer
PERPETUALLY YOURS ('Harfable'PBR) (Cl) — CDoC CGro LHkn MRav NRog SSea
PERSIAN MYSTERY ('Hartroy') (*persica* hybrid) **new** — LHkn
Persian yellow — see *R. foetida* 'Persiana'
persica — SBrt
PETER BEALES ('Cleexpert') (S) — EBls
PETER COTTONTAIL ('Marpeter') (Patio) **new** — NRog
§ PETER COTTRELL ('Harentente'PBR) (F) — LHkn
PETER PAN ('Chewpan'PBR) (Min) ♀H6 — CDoC
PETER PAN ('Sunpete') (Patio) — MAsh
'Petite de Hollande' (Ce) — EBls ETWh NLar SPer
'Petite Lisette' (Ce × D) — NLar
'Petite Orléannaise' (Ce) — EBls
PHAB GOLD ('Frybountiful'PBR) (F) — MFry
PHEASANT ('Kordapt') (GC) — EBls SApu SPer
PHILLIPA ('Poulheart'PBR) (S) — ETWh LSRN SApu

PHOEBE (Ru)	see *R.* 'Fimbriata'
phoenicea	EBls
'Phyllis Bide' (Ra) ♀^{H6}	CArg EBee EBls EHyd ELan EPfP ETWh IArd LCro LOPS LRHS MBNS MCot MSwo NLar NRog SApu SPer SSea WKif
PICCADILLY ('Macar') (HT)	CSBt CTri NRog SCob SPer
PICCOLO ('Tanolokip') (F/Patio)	SApu
'Piccolo Pete' (S) **new**	NRog
'Picture' (HT)	NRog SPer
PIERRE CARDIN ('Meilolipo'^{PBR}) (HT)	ESty
PIERRINE ('Micpie') (Min)	NRog
PIGALLE '84 ('Meicloux') (F)	SCoo
'Pilgrim'	see *R.* THE PILGRIM
pimpinellifolia	see *R. spinosissima*
- 'Altaica'	see *R. spinosissima* 'Grandiflora'
- double yellow-flowered	see *R.* × *harisonii* 'Williams' Double Yellow'
PINK ABUNDANCE ('Harfrothy'^{PBR}) (Abundance Series) (F)	CArg LHkn SApu
PINK BELLS ('Poulbells') (GC)	CGro EBls SApu SPer
'Pink Bouquet' (Ra)	CRHN MAsh
PINK CHAMPAGNE ('Forchamp') (Cl)	ESty
'Pink Cloud' (ClHT)	ELan
'Pink Favorite' (HT)	NRog SCob SPer
PINK FIZZ ('Poulycool') (ClPatio)	ECnt
§ PINK FLOWER CARPET ('Noatraum') (GC) ♀^{H6}	CBod CDoC CGro CRos CSBt CTri EBee EBls ECnt EHyd ELan LCro LOPS LRHS LSRN MAsh MPri NRHS NRog SApu SCoo SEND SPer SPoG SSea
'Pink Garnette'	see *R.* 'Carol Amling'
'Pink Grootendorst' (Ru)	EBls EPfP ETWh LEdu NLar NRog SCob SPer
'Pink Gruss an Aachen' (F)	EBls ETWh
§ PINK HIT ('Poultipe'^{PBR}) (Min/Patio)	CGro EBls ECnt LRHS LSRN NRHS
'Pink Leda' (D)	ETWh
PINK MARTINI ('Tan04608'^{PBR}) (HT)	CDoC EBee EBls MFry MRav SSea
pink moss	see *R.* × *centifolia* 'Muscosa'
PINK PARADISE ('Delfluoros'^{PBR}) (HT)	CBod EBls ETWh
'Pink Parfait' (F)	NRog SPer
PINK PERFECTION ('Korpauvio'^{PBR}) (HT) ♀^{H5}	CEnd CSBt ECnt EPfP LRHS MAsh SSea
'Pink Perpétué' (Cl)	CArg CSBt CTri EBls ECnt EHyd ELan EPfP ETWh MRav NLar SCob SCoo SPer SPoG SRGP SSea
PINK PIROUETTE ('Harboul'^{PBR}) (Patio)	LHkn
'Pink Prosperity' (HM)	EBls NRog
'Pink Showers' (ClHT)	MSwo
PINK TOPAZ ('Manpaz') (Min) **new**	NRog
PINNACLE ('Beniowa') (F) **new**	NRog
PIPPIN ('Beajaffa') (S)	EBls MAsh
PIROUETTE ('Poulyc003'^{PBR}) (ClS)	EBls ECnt MAsh
PLAYGROUP ROSE ('Horsun') (F)	NRog
PLEINE DE GRÂCE ('Lengra') (S)	LEdu NRog
'Plentiful' (F)	EBls
POETRY IN MOTION ('Harelan'^{PBR}) (HT)	CArg EBls LHkn NRog
POLAR STAR ('Tanlarpost') (HT)	CArg CSBt EBls ECnt MFry NRog SCob SPer
'Polly' (HT)	LSRN NRog
'Polonaise' (S) **new**	NRog
§ 'Polyantha Grandiflora' (Ra)	EBls ETWh SVic WBor
pomifera	see *R. villosa* L.
POMPADOUR ('Deldour') (F)	ESty
'Pompon Blanc Parfait' (A)	EBls ETWh NRog
'Pompon de Bourgogne'	see *R.* 'Burgundiaca'
'Pompon de Paris' (ClMinCh)	see *R.* 'Climbing Pompon de Paris'
'Pompon de Paris' (MinCh)	WAbe WKif
PORT SUNLIGHT ('Auslofty'^{PBR}) (HM) ♀^{H6}	CRos EHyd EPfP ESty LRHS MAsh NRHS
Portland rose	see *R.* 'Portlandica'
'Portland Trailblazer'	see *R.* 'Big Chief'
§ 'Portlandica' (Po)	EBls ETWh LRHS MAsh SPer
'Poulpal038'^{PBR} (F)	LRHS MAsh MFry
POWER POINT ('Bennovecientos') (Patio)	NRog
'Prairie Clogger' (S) **new**	NRog
prairie rose	see *R. setigera*
'Prairie Star' (S) **new**	NRog
prattii	EBls
'Precious Amber' (F)	EBls LBuc LRHS MAsh
PRECIOUS GOLD ('Noa55504') (F)	EBls LRHS MAsh MFry
PRECIOUS GRANDDAUGHTER ('Raw1193') (F)	ESty
PRECIOUS GRANDSON ('Raw1088') (F)	ESty
PRECIOUS LOVE ('Kirlowo'^{PBR}) (F)	EBls LBuc LRHS MAsh
'Precious Memories' (Min)	LSRN
PRECIOUS MEMORIES ('Dichello'^{PBR}) (F)	CBod ESty
'Precious Platinum' (HT)	SPer
PRECIOUS TIME ('Oramarpa'^{PBR}) (HT)	ESty
PRESIDENT ARMAND ZINSCH ('Delzinsch') (HT) **new**	EBls
§ 'Président de Sèze' (G) ♀^{H6}	CArg EBls ETWh NLar SPer
'President Herbert Hoover' (HT)	EBls
'Prestige' (S)	NRog
PRETTY IN PINK ('Dicumpteen'^{PBR}) (GC) ♀^{H6}	ECnt
PRETTY JESSICA ('Ausjess') (S)	CDoC CGro LSRN MGos MRav SPer
PRETTY POLLY ('Meitonje') (Min) ♀^{H6}	CDoC EHyd EPfP ESty LCro LOPS LRHS MAsh MFry MRav SCob SCoo SPoG SSea
PRIDE & PREJUDICE ('Harwindow'^{PBR}) (F) **new**	LHkn
PRIDE OF ENGLAND ('Harencore'^{PBR}) (HT)	LHkn
'Pride of Lakeland' (HT) **new**	NRog
'Prima Ballerina' (HT)	CArg CTri EBls EPfP LRHS NRog SPer
primula	ETWh NLar NRog SPer
'Prince Charles' (Bb)	EBls ETWh NLar WKif
PRINCE JARDINIER ('Meitroni'^{PBR}) (HT) ♀^{H6}	CArg ESty

PRINCESS ('Korspobux'PBR) (HT)	ECnt NRog
PRINCESS ALEXANDRA ('Pouldra'PBR) (Renaissance Series) (S) H6	ECnt ETWh NLar
PRINCESS ALEXANDRA OF KENT ('Ausmerchant'PBR) (S)	CDoC CRos CSBt EHyd EPfP ESty LRHS NRHS SPer
PRINCESS ALICE ('Hartanna') (F)	LSRN NRog
PRINCESS ANNE ('Auskitchen'PBR) (S) H6	CSBt ECnt EHyd EPfP LBuc LRHS MAsh MSwo NRHS
'Princess Louise' (Ra)	EBls ETWh
PRINCESS NOBUKO ('Coclistine'PBR) (HT)	NRog
PRINCESS OF WALES ('Hardinkum'PBR) (F) H6	CDoC EBls LHkn MRav SApu SPer
§ 'Princesse de Nassau' (Ra)	EBls ETWh
'Princesse Louise' (Ra)	EBls
'Princesse Marie' misapplied	see *R.* 'Belvedere'
'Princesse Marie' Jacques (Ra)	EBls
'Prolifera de Redouté' misapplied	see *R.* 'Duchesse de Montebello'
PROPER JOB ('Tan02733'PBR) (HT)	CDoC EBee EBls ECnt ESty ETWh MFry NLar SLon SSea
'Prosperity' (HM) H6	CTri EBls ETWh MCot NLar NRog SPer
PROSPERO ('Auspero') (S)	ETWh
PURE GOLD ('Harhappen'PBR) (S)	LHkn
§ PURE POETRY ('Jacment') (F)	CBod LRHS
§ PURE POETRY ('Tan04179') (HT)	EBee EBls ELon ESty ETWh MFry SApu SPer SSea
'Purezza' (Ra)	EBls NLar SMad
'Purity' (ClHT)	ETWh
PURPLE EDEN	see *R.* EBB TIDE
PURPLE MOON ('Dicmover') (F)	SApu
PURPLE PRINCE ('Simpurple') (HT)	ESty
PURPLE SKYLINER ('Franwekpurp'PBR) (ClS)	CBod EBls LRHS MAsh MPri SApu SPer SPoG
PURPLE TIGER ('Jacpurr'PBR) (F)	CDoC ESty SApu SCob
'Purpurtraum' (Ru)	SApu
quatre saisons	see *R.* × *damascena* var. *semperflorens*
'Quatre Saisons Blanche Mousseuse' (DMo)	EBls ETWh NLar
QUEEN ANNE ('Austruck'PBR) (S)	ESty LSRN
QUEEN BEE (F)	MAsh MFry
QUEEN ELIZABETH	see *R.* 'The Queen Elizabeth'
QUEEN MOTHER ('Korquemu') (Patio) H6	CDoC CSBt ELan EPfP MRav SPer
QUEEN OF BHUTAN ('Harworld') (F) **new**	LHkn
'Queen of Bourbons' (Bb)	EBls ETWh LEdu NLar NRog
QUEEN OF DENMARK	see *R.* 'Königin von Dänemark'
QUEEN OF SWEDEN ('Austiger'PBR) (S)	CGro CRos ECnt EHyd EPfP LBuc LRHS MAsh MSwo NLar NRHS SCoo SPer
QUEEN'S LONDON CHILD ('Harlisted') (Patio) **new**	LHkn
'Quietness' (S) **new**	NRog

'Rachel' (HT)	CArg CDoC EWTr LBuc LRHS LSRN MAsh MPri NLar SLon
RACHEL ('Booyol') (S)	EBee
RACHEL ('Tangust'PBR) (HT) H6	CEnd CSBt EBls EPfP ESty ETWh MFry MRav SApu SPoG SSea
'Rachel Kathleen' (F) **new**	NRog
§ RACHEL LOUISE MORAN ('Jacdrama'PBR) (HT)	ESty
RACQUEL ('Poulren023'PBR) (S)	ETWh
RACY LADY ('Dicwaffle'PBR) (HT)	NRog
RADIANT ('Benrad') (Min)	NRog
'Rambling Rector' (Ra) H6	Widely available
RAMBLING ROSIE ('Horjasper'PBR) (Ra) H6	CArg CBod CRos CSBt EBee EBls ECnt EPfP ESty ETWh LSRN MSwo NLar NRog SApu SSea
'Ramona' (Ra)	EBls ETWh
RANDY SCOTT ('Siljonscott') (HT) **new**	NRog
RASPBERRY CREAM TWIRL ('Meiteratol'PBR) (ClHT)	LRHS MAsh
RASPBERRY QUEEN ('Tanneidol')	MFry
'Raspberry Royale' (F/Patio) H6	CDoC EBls EPfP MAsh SPoG
'Raubritter' ('Macrantha' hybrid)	EBls ETWh SPer
RAYMOND BLANC ('Delnado') (HT)	ETWh LSRN MRav NLar
'Raymond Carver' (S)	EBee EBls LRHS MAsh
REBECCA (Patio)	ESty LSRN
'Rebecca Claire' (HT)	LSRN
REBECCA MARY ('Dicjury'PBR) (F)	IDic
RECONCILIATION ('Hartillery'PBR) (HT)	LHkn
RED 4 ('Rawarrow') (HT) **new**	NRog
RED ABUNDANCE ('Harkimono'PBR) (Abundance Series)	EBls LHkn SApu
RED BELLS ('Poulred') (Min/GC)	SApu
RED BLANKET ('Intercell') (S/GC)	EBls SPer
RED COAT ('Auscoat') (F)	NRog
RED DEVIL ('Dicam') (HT)	CArg NRog
RED EDEN ROSE ('Meidrason'PBR) (Cl)	ESty SSea
RED FINESSE ('Korvillade'PBR) (F) H6	CArg ETWh NRog
RED FLAME ('Adabaring'PBR) (ClHT)	CGro MAsh
'Red Grootendorst'	see *R.* 'F.J. Grootendorst'
RED HAT LADY ('Harpeep'PBR) (F)	LHkn
RED LETTER DAY ('Beajackdaw') (S)	EBls LRHS MAsh NRHS
'Red Max Graf'	see *R.* ROTE MAX GRAF
red moss	see *R.* 'Henri Martin'
RED NEW DAWN	see *R.* 'Étendard'
§ 'Red Patio' (F/Patio)	LSRN
RED PERFUMELLA ('Meikeneza'PBR) (HT)	NRog
RED RASCAL ('Jacbed') (S/Patio)	CSBt MFry SApu
red rose of Lancaster	see *R. gallica* var. *officinalis*
RED SPLENDOUR ('Davona') (F)	NRog
'Red Wing' (S)	EBls

REDOVA ('Poulcy030'PBR) (Courtyard Series) (Cl) CBod CGro ECnt MAsh MBros
REGENSBERG ('Macyoumis'PBR) (F/Patio) CBod LEdu SPer
'Reine des Violettes' (HP) ♀H6 EBls ELon EPfP ETWh IArd LCro LOPS LSRN MCot MPri NLar SPer
§ 'Reine Victoria' (Bb) CDoC EBls ETWh LCro LOPS NLar NRog SPer
§ REMEMBER ('Poulht001'PBR) (HT) ♀H6 EBls ECnt EPfP LBuc LRHS MAsh NRHS NRog SPoG
REMEMBER ME ('Cocdestin') (HT) ♀H6 CArg CBod CGro CSBt EBls ECnt EPfP ESty IArd LCro LOPS LRHS LSRN MAsh MFry MGos MRav NRog SApu SCob SCoo SPoG
REMEMBRANCE ('Harxampton') (F) CArg CBod CRos EBls EPfP ESty LBuc LHkn LRHS LSRN MAsh MFry MPri MRav SApu SCob SCoo SPer SPoG
§ RENAISSANCE ('Harzart'PBR) (HT) CArg LHkn
'René André' (Ra) CRHN EBee ETWh NLar
RÉPUBLIQUE DE MONTMARTRE ('Delparfrou') (F) CBod
'Rescht' see *R.* 'De Resht'
'Rêve d'Or' (N) EBls ETWh
'Réveil Dijonnais' (ClHT) EBls
RHAPSODY IN BLUE ('Frantasia'PBR) (S) ♀H6 Widely available
RHUBARB AND CUSTARD ('Raw1138') (F) **new** ESty
RICHARD PORSON ('Beajuniper') (S) EBls
§ × ***richardii*** EBls ETWh
RICK STEIN ('Tan96205'PBR) (HT) LSRN
'Rita' ambig. WKif
'River Gardens' NPer
'Rivers's George IV' (Ch) ETWh
ROALD DAHL ('Ausowlish'PBR) (S) CRos CSBt EHyd ESty LRHS MSwo NRHS SCoo
ROB ROY ('Cocrob') (F) SPer
'Robert le Diable' (Ce × G) EBls ETWh SPer
ROBERT WINSTON ('Harsunup') (F) **new** LHkn
ROBIN ALONSO ('Alorobin') (Patio) **new** NRog
'Robin Hood' (HM) EBls ETWh
ROBIN REDBREAST ('Interrob') (Min/GC) EBls
§ ROBUSTA ('Korgosa') (Ru) EBls
ROCK & ROLL ('Wekgobnez') (HT) CSBt ELon ESty LSRN
'Roger Lambelin' (HP) EBls SPer
ROMANCE ('Tanezamor'PBR) (S) LSRN
ROMANZE ('Tan03434'PBR) (HT) CArg
'Rosa Mundi' see *R. gallica* 'Versicolor'
ROSARIUM UETERSEN ('Kortersen') (ClHT) EBls
'Rose à Parfum de l'Haÿ' (Ru) CTri
'Rose Ball' (S) EBls LRHS
§ 'Rose d'Amour' (S) ♀H6 EBls
'Rose de Meaux' see *R.* × *centifolia* 'De Meaux'
'Rose de Meaux White' see *R.* 'White de Meaux'
'Rose de Rescht' see *R.* 'De Resht'
ROSE DES CISTERCIENS ('Delarle') (HT) ESty ETWh LRHS
'Rose des Maures' misapplied see *R.* 'Sissinghurst Castle'
'Rose du Maître d'Ecole' see *R.* 'Du Maître d'Ecole'
'Rose du Roi' (HP/DPo) EBls ETWh NRog
ROSE FOR ELAINE ('Rawdenqueen') (HT) LSRN NRog
§ ROSE GAUJARD ('Gaumo') (HT) CArg CBod EBls LRHS MAsh
ROSÉE DE MATIN ('Evematch'PBR) (S) EBls
'Rose-Marie Viaud' (Ra) EBls ETWh MMuc
ROSEMARY HARKNESS ('Harrowbond') (HT) ESty LHkn SPer SRGP
'Rosemary Rose' (F) NRog SPer
ROSEMOOR ('Austough'PBR) (S) ♀H6 CRos EHyd LBuc LRHS MAsh NRHS SPer
'Roseraie de l'Haÿ' (Ru) ♀H7 Widely available
ROSEROMANTIC ('Korumneza'PBR) (F) **new** SApu
ROSIE ('Benros') (Min) LSRN
ROSSETTI ROSE ('Harjug'PBR) (F) **new** LHkn
'Rosy Cheeks' (HT) MAsh
ROSY CUSHION ('Interall') (S/GC) EBls ETWh EWTr MCot NLar NRog SApu SPer WKif
ROSY FUTURE ('Harwaderox') (F/Patio) LHkn
'Rosy Mantle' (ClHT) CSBt EBls
§ ROTARY SUNRISE ('Fryglitzy') (HT) LRHS MFry
§ ROTE MAX GRAF ('Kormax') (GC/Ru) EBls NLar
§ 'Rouletii' (Min) ITim
'Roundelay' (HT) EBls ETWh
roxburghii ETWh LEdu
- PAB 7331 LEdu
- f. ***normalis*** (S) EBls
§ ROYAL BROMPTON ROSE ('Meivildo') (HT) CBod ELon ESty
ROYAL COPENHAGEN see *R.* REMEMBER ('Poulht001')
'Royal Gold' (ClHT) EBls NRog
'Royal Highness' (HT) EBls NRog
ROYAL JUBILEE ('Auspaddle'PBR) (S) CSBt EPfP LCro LOPS SCoo SPer
'Royal Occasion' (F) SPer
ROYAL PARFUMA ('Kordiagraf'PBR) (HT) **new** EBls
ROYAL PARKS ('Harlyric'PBR) (HT) LHkn
ROYAL PHILHARMONIC ('Hardeed'PBR) (HT) LHkn
ROYAL SALUTE ('Macros') (Min) NRog
ROYAL WILLIAM ('Korzaun') (HT) ♀H6 CArg CDoC CSBt CTri EBls ELan LBuc LCro LOPS LRHS LSRN MAsh MFry MGos MPri MRav NRog SApu SCob SPer
§ ***rubiginosa*** CCVT EBls ETWh GPoy LBuc NWea SCob SPer WKor WMou WTSh
rubra see *R. gallica*
rubrifolia see *R. glauca* Pourr.
'Rubrotincta' see *R.* 'Hebe's Lip'
RUBY ANNIVERSARY ('Harbonny'PBR) (Patio) CDoC CGro CRos CSBt EBls EHyd ELan ELon EPfP ESty LBuc LCro LHkn LOPS LRHS LSRN MAsh MFry MRav MSwo NLar SApu SCob SCoo SPer SPoG SSea
'Ruby Baby' (Min) NRog
RUBY CELEBRATION ('Peawinner'PBR) (F) ♀H6 CBod EBls ELon ESty MRav SApu

'Ruby Pendant' (Min)	NRog
RUBY RIBBON ('Harruby'[PBR]) (Patio) **new**	LHkn
RUBY ROMANCE	see *R.* MEDLEY RUBY
RUBY RUBY	see *R.* RUBY SLIPPERS
§ RUBY SLIPPERS ('Weksactrumi') (Min)	LRHS NRHS SPoG
'Ruby Wedding' (HT)	CArg CBcs CDoC CEnd CRos CSBt CTri EBee ECnt ELan EPfP IArd LRHS LSRN MAsh MFry MGos MRav NRHS NRog SApu SCob SPer
'Ruby Wedding Anniversary' (F)	LSRN
rugosa (Ru)	CArg CBod CGro CLnd CTri EPfP EPom GAbr GArf LBuc MRav NWea SCob SPlb WMat WMou WTSh
- 'Alba' (Ru)	Widely available
- 'Rubra' (Ru)	CBcs CBod CCVT CGro CTri EBee ELan EPfP EPom GArf LBuc LCro LOPS LPar NWea SEWo SEdi SPer SPoG SSea SVic
- var. ***ventenatiana*** (Ru)	EBls
'Rugosa Atropurpurea' (Ru)	EPom NRog
'Rural England' (Ra)	EBee EBls LRHS MAsh
'Russelliana' (Ra)	ETWh NLar
'Sadler's Wells' (S)	EBls
'Safrano' (T)	EBls
SAINT BONIFACE ('Kormatt') (F/Patio)	CSBt
SAINT CHRISTOPHER ('Harcogent'[PBR]) (HT)	LHkn
SAINT EDMUNDS ROSE	see *R.* BONITA
SAINT ETHELBURGA ('Beabimbo') (S)	EBls EPfP LRHS MAsh MCot
SAINT JOHN ('Harbilbo') (F)	LHkn
Saint John's rose	see *R.* × *richardii*
Saint Mark's rose	see *R.* 'Rose d'Amour'
'Saint Nicholas' (D)	EBls
SAINT RICHARD OF CHICHESTER ('Harklement'[PBR]) (S)	LHkn
SAINT SWITHUN ('Auswith'[PBR]) (S)	EHyd EPfP ESty LRHS MAsh NRHS SCoo SPer
'Salet' (DPMo)	EBls ETWh
'Sally Holmes' (S) ♀H6	EBls ECnt ETWh LSRN MCot MRav NLar SApu SEND SLon SPer
SALLY KANE ('Frygroovy'[PBR]) (HT)	MRav
SALLY'S ROSE ('Canrem') (HT)	EBls ECnt LSRN
SALSA	see *R.* CHEEK TO CHEEK
SALVATION ('Harlark'[PBR]) (F)	ESty LHkn
§ SAMARITAN ('Harverag') (HT)	CSBt LHkn SApu
sancta	see *R.* × *richardii*
'Sander's White Rambler' (Ra) ♀H6	CEnd CRHN CTri EBee EBls EPfP ETWh MSwo NLar NRHS NRog SPer WFar
SANDRA ('Koreinek') (HT)	LSRN
SANDRA ('Poulen055'[PBR]) (Renaissance Series) (S)	ETWh LSRN NLar
SANDRA ('Sandkor') (HT) **new**	NRog
SANDRA LORRAINE ('Rawsand') (F) **new**	NRog
SANDRINGHAM ('Beamolly') (S)	EBee EBls EPfP LRHS MAsh
'Sandringham Centenary' (HT)	EBls
'Sanguinea'	see *R.* × *odorata* Sanguinea Group
SARAH (HT)	see *R.* JARDINS DE BAGATELLE
SARAH, DUCHESS OF YORK	see *R.* SUNSEEKER
SARAH ELIZABETH ('Athygrafos') (F) **new**	MFry
'Sarah van Fleet' (Ru)	CDoC CTri EBls ETWh IArd MRav MSwo NLar NRog SApu SCob SPer
'Satchmo' (F)	NRog
SAVOY HOTEL ('Harvintage') (HT)	CArg EBls LHkn MFry SApu SCob SPer
'Saxilby Belle' (Min) **new**	NRog
'Scabrosa' (Ru) ♀H7	EBls ECnt EPfP ETWh LBuc LRHS MAsh NLar NRog NWea SPer
SCARLET FIRE	see *R.* 'Scharlachglut'
SCARLET GLOW	see *R.* 'Scharlachglut'
SCARLET HIT ('Poulmo'[PBR]) (PatioHit Series) (Min/Patio)	EBls ECnt LRHS LSRN NRHS
SCARLET PATIO ('Kortingle') (Patio)	CRos MAsh SPoG
§ SCENT FROM HEAVEN ('Chewbabaluv') (ClHT)	CDoC CEnd CGro CRos CSBt EBls ECnt ELon EPfP ESty ETWh LBuc LCro LOPS LSRN MAsh MFry MGos SApu SCoo SMad SPer SPoG SSea
SCENTED CARPET ('Chewground'[PBR]) (GC) ♀H6	ECnt ELan ETWh NLar SApu
SCENTED GARDEN ('Chewscentity') (S)	CSBt ESty
SCENTED MEMORY ('Poulht002'[PBR]) (HT)	ECnt
SCENTIMENTAL ('Wekplapep'[PBR]) (F)	EBls EPfP ESty LRHS MAsh MGos MRav SApu SMad
SCENT-SATION ('Fryromeo'[PBR]) (HT)	CDoC MRav SPoG
SCENTSATIONAL ('Savamor') (Min) **new**	NRog
SCEPTER'D ISLE ('Ausland'[PBR]) (S)	CRos CSBt EHyd EPfP LBuc LRHS LSRN MCot NRHS SCoo SPer
§ 'Scharlachglut' (ClS)	EBls ETWh EWTr SPer
SCHLOSS BAD HOMBURG	see *R.* 'Alibaba'
'Schneelicht' (Ru)	NRog
SCHNEEWITTCHEN	see *R.* ICEBERG
§ 'Schneezwerg' (Ru) ♀H7	EBls ETWh NLar NRog SPer
'Schoolgirl' (ClHT)	CArg CBcs CDoC CTri EBls ELan EPfP ETWh LBuc LCro LOPS LRHS MAsh MFry MMrt MPri MRav MSwo NRog SApu SCob SPer SRGP
Scotch rose	see *R. spinosissima*
Scotch yellow (SpH)	see *R.* × *harisonii* 'Williams' Double Yellow'
SEA OF FIRE	see *R.* 'Feuermeer'
'Seagull' (Ra) ♀H6	CArg CTri EBls ECnt EPPr EPfP ETWh LCro LEdu LOPS LRHS LSRN MAsh MRav NLar NRog SApu SCob SLon SPer WHer
'Seale Pink Diamond' (S)	SSea
'Seale White Rambler' (Ra)	SSea
SEALED WITH A KISS ('Simwhat') (HT)	ESty
'Sealing Wax' (*moyesii* hybrid)	ETWh NLar
SECRET SMILE ('Dicswifty') (F) **new**	IDic
SELFRIDGES ('Korpriwa') (HT)	ESty NRog
'Semiplena'	see *R.* × *alba* 'Alba Semiplena'
sempervirens (Ra)	EBls

SERENITY ('Poulht009'[PBR]) (HT) **new**	ESty
sericea var. ***morrisonensis*** B&SWJ 7139	WCru
§ - subsp. ***omeiensis***	LEdu WPGP
- - BWJ 7550	WCru
- - PAB 2883	LEdu
- - f. ***pteracantha*** (S)	CTri EBee EBls ELan EPfP ETWh GKev IDee NLar NRog SApu SPer SSea
§ ***setigera***	EBls
setipoda	EBls
seven sisters rose	see *R. multiflora* 'Grevillei'
SEXY REXY ('Macrexy') (F)	CArg CBcs EBls LSRN MAsh MGos MRav NRog SCob SPer SPoG
'Shailer's White Moss'	see *R.* × *centifolia* 'Shailer's White Moss'
SHANTY ('Tan96191') (F)	ESty MFry
SHEER SILK ('Harpatter'[PBR]) (Patio) **new**	LHkn
SHEILA'S PERFUME ('Harsherry') (F) ♀H6	CArg CBod CDoC CEnd EBls ECnt EPfP ESty LRHS LSRN MAsh MFry MGos MRav SApu SPer SPoG
SHINE ON ('Dictalent'[PBR]) (Patio) ♀H6	ECnt MFry
SHIRYNNE COWAN ('Manian') (Patio) **new**	NRog
'Shot Silk' (HT)	SCob
SHOW STOPPER ('Benseah') (Patio) **new**	NRog
'Showtime' Lindquist (HT)	EBls MAsh
SHOWTIME ('Baitime') (ClS)	MAsh SPoG
§ SHRIMP HIT ('Poulshrimp'[PBR]) (Patio)	EBls ECnt MFry SPoG
SHROPSHIRE STAR ('Chewsummit') (ClS)	ELon ESty SSea
SIGHTSAVER ('Fryaffair'[PBR]) (HT)	MFry
SIGNATURE ('Jacnor') (HT) **new**	NRog
'Silver 25th Anniversary' (F)	LPar MGos
SILVER ANNIVERSARY ambig.	CArg CGro LSRN
SILVER ANNIVERSARY ('Meiborfil') (HT)	ELon
§ SILVER ANNIVERSARY ('Poulari'[PBR]) (HT) ♀H6	CBod CDoC CEnd CRos CSBt EBls ECnt EHyd ELan LRHS LSRN MAsh MFry MGos MPri MRav NRHS NRog SApu SCoo SPer SPoG SSea
SILVER CELEBRATION ('Guescloud') (F)	ESty
'Silver Jubilee' (HT)	CArg CBcs CTri EBls IArd LRHS MAsh MRav NRHS NRog SCob SPer
SILVER SHADOW ('Frystereo'[PBR]) (HT)	ECnt ESty SApu
'Silver Wedding' (HT)	CBcs CDoC CTri EBls ELan IArd MRav MSwo NRog SCob SPer
'Silver Wedding Celebration' (F)	ESty LSRN
SILVER WISHES	see *R.* PINK HIT
SIMBA ('Korbelma') (HT)	LSRN
'Simone' (HT)	EBee ETWh
SIMPLE GOLD ('Harsymbol') (S) **new**	LHkn
SIMPLE PEACH ('Harwarmth') (S) **new**	LHkn
SIMPLE YELLOW ('Harsonnet') (S) **new**	LHkn
SIMPLY GORGEOUS ('Formaui') (HT)	ESty
SIMPLY SALLY ('Harpaint'[PBR]) (Patio)	LHkn LSRN
§ SIMPLY THE BEST ('Macamster'[PBR]) (HT) ♀H6	CArg CDoC CEnd CGro CSBt EBls ELan EPfP ESty LRHS LSRN MAsh MFry MGos MPri MRav NRHS SApu SCob SCoo SPer SPoG
sinowilsonii	see *R. longicuspis* var. *sinowilsonii*
'Sir Cedric Morris' (Ra)	EBls ETWh NLar SSea
SIR DAVID MICHELS ('Dewraw4') (S) **new**	NRog
'Sir Frederick Ashton' (HT)	EBls
§ SIR GALAHAD ('Hareasy') (F)	LHkn MRav
'Sir Galahad' white-flowered	see *R.* SIR GALAHAD
SIR HENRY CECIL ('Webpegasus') (F)	LSRN
SIR JOHN BETJEMAN ('Ausvivid'[PBR]) (S)	EHyd EPfP LBuc LRHS MAsh MSwo NRHS
SIR JOHN MILLS ('Beadaffy') (Cl)	EBls
'Sir Joseph Paxton' (Bb)	ETWh EWTr
SIR PAUL SMITH ('Beapaul') (ClHT)	EBls EPfP LRHS MAsh
SIR WALTER RALEIGH ('Ausspry') (S)	CDoC MGos MRav
§ 'Sissinghurst Castle' (G)	EBls
SISTER ELIZABETH ('Auspalette'[PBR]) (S)	LSRN
SKYLARK ('Ausimple'[PBR]) (S) ♀H6	MAsh
'Skyrocket'	see *R.* 'Wilhelm'
SMARTY ('Intersmart') (S/GC)	EBls SPer
SMILING EYES ('Chewrocko'[PBR]) (S/GC)	EBls EPfP ETWh LRHS NLar
SNAZZEE ('Wekzazette'[PBR]) (F)	CBod ECnt ESty
SNOW BUNNY ('Korsnokinu'[PBR]) (Min) **new**	EBls SApu
'Snow Dwarf'	see *R.* 'Schneezwerg'
SNOW GOOSE ('Auspom'[PBR]) (ClS)	EBee EPfP LRHS NLar SPer
SNOW HIT ('Poulsnows'[PBR]) (Min/Patio)	ECnt
'Snow Queen'	see *R.* 'Frau Karl Druschki'
SNOW QUEEN ('Simseen') (HT)	ESty
SNOWBALL ('Macangeli') (Min/GC)	LSRN
SNOWCAP ('Harfleet'[PBR]) (Patio)	CBod CGro ESty LHkn SPer
'Snowdon' (Ru)	EBls
SOEUR EMMANUELLE ('Delamo'[PBR]) (S)	ESty ETWh LSRN MRav
SOLAR FLAIR ('Benbaas') (Patio) **new**	NRog
'Soldier Boy' (Cl)	EBls ETWh NLar
'Soleil d'Or' (S)	EBls
SOLEIL VERTICAL ('Delsov') (Cl)	CBod EBls ESty
§ SOLO MIO ('Poulen002'[PBR]) (Renaissance Series) (S)	ECnt ETWh NLar
§ 'Sombreuil' (ClT)	CArg EBls EPfP ETWh IArd MAsh MRav NLar SApu SPer
SOME LIKE IT HOT ('Gueschorus') (F)	ESty
SOMEDAY SOON ('Seasoon') (Min)	NRog
SOMETHING SPECIAL ('Macwyo'[PBR]) (HT)	ESty
SOMMERGOLD ('Noa51071'[PBR]) (Cl) **new**	LRHS

SONGBIRD ('Raw1151') (F)	ESty
'Sophia'	see *R.* SOLO MIO ('Poulen002')
'Sophie's Perpetual' (ClCh)	CTri EBls ETWh SLon
SOPHY'S ROSE ('Auslot'[PBR]) (S)	LSRN
SORBET FRUITÉ ('Meihestries'[PBR]) (ClF)	SSea
soulieana (Ra/S)	ETWh
'Soupert et Notting' (DPoMo)	ETWh NLar SPer
'Southampton' (F) 🏆[H6]	CArg EBls LSRN NRog SPer SSea
SOUTHERN BELLE ('Wekspococ') (HT)	ESty
'Souvenir d'Alphonse Lavallée' (ClHP)	EBls
SOUVENIR DE BADEN-BADEN ('Korsouba'[PBR]) (HT) **new**	EBls
'Souvenir de Claudius Denoyel' (ClHT)	CArg EBls ETWh NRog SPer
'Souvenir de Jeanne Balandreau' (HP)	EBls ETWh
'Souvenir de la Malmaison' (ClBb)	see *R.*'Climbing Souvenir de la Malmaison'
'Souvenir de la Malmaison' (Bb)	CArg EBls ETWh MRav NLar NRog SPer
SOUVENIR DE LOUIS AMADE ('Delilac') (S)	EBls
'Souvenir de Madame Auguste Charles' (Bb)	ETWh
'Souvenir de Madame Léonie Viennot' (ClT)	EBls ETWh MRav NLar
'Souvenir de Pierre Vibert' (DPMo)	ETWh
'Souvenir de Saint Anne's' (Bb)	EBls ETWh NLar
'Souvenir d'Elise Vardon' (T)	EBls
'Souvenir du Docteur Jamain' (ClHP)	CSBt EBee EBls ELan ELon EPfP ESty ETWh LCro LOPS LSRN MGos MRav NLar SApu SCob SPoG SSea WFar WKif
'Souvenir d'un Ami' (T)	EBls
spaldingii	see *R. **nutkana*** var. ***hispida***
'Spanish Beauty'	see *R.*'Madame Grégoire Staechelin'
SPARKLE ('Frymerlin'[PBR]) (HT)	ECnt ESty LBuc MAsh MFry
SPARKLER	see *R.* KENT
SPARKLING BURGUNDY ('Raw1007') (F)	ESty
SPARKLING SCARLET ('Meihati') (ClF)	MAsh
SPECIAL ANNIVERSARY ('Whastiluc'[PBR]) (HT) 🏆[H6]	CBcs CBod CDoC CGro CRos CSBt EBls ECnt ELan ELon EPfP ESty ETWh LCro LOPS LRHS LSRN MAsh MFry MPri MRav NLar NRHS SCoo SPoG SSea
SPECIAL CHILD ('Taniripsa'[PBR]) (F/Patio) 🏆[H6]	CDoC MRav SApu SSea
'Special Dad' (HT)	CGro LCro LOPS
'Special Daughter' (F)	LSRN
SPECIAL EVENT ('Meibrelon') (HT)	ESty
SPECIAL FRIEND ('Kirspec'[PBR]) (Patio)	EBls ESty LSRN SApu SCoo
'Special Grandad' (Patio)	LSRN
SPECIAL GRANDCHILD ('Flimika') (F)	ESty
SPECIAL GRANDMA (F)	ESty LSRN
SPECIAL GRANDPA (F)	ESty
SPECIAL MEMORIES ('Fortop') (F)	ESty
'Special Mum' (F)	LCro LOPS LSRN
SPECIAL OCCASION ('Fryyoung'[PBR]) (HT)	MFry MGos MRav SCoo
SPECIAL SON (F)	ESty
'Spectabilis' (Ra)	EBls ETWh
'Spencer' misapplied	see *R.*'Enfant de France'
SPICE OF LIFE ('Diccheeky'[PBR]) (F/Patio)	EBls
§ ***spinosissima***	CArg CCCN CSde EBls ELan ETWh LBuc NRog NWea SCob SPer WKor WTSh
- 'Andrewsii' 🏆[H7]	MRav
- 'Cedric Morris'	WCot
§ - double, pink-flowered	WBor
§ - - white-flowered 🏆[H7]	EBls ECha ETWh LEdu
- 'Falkland'	ECha
§ - 'Grandiflora'	EBls ETWh
- 'Marbled Pink'	ETWh
- 'Mary, Queen of Scots'	EBls ETWh GBin NLar SRms
- 'Merthyr Mawr'	WCot
- 'Mrs Colville'	EBls
- 'Single Cherry'	EBls
- 'William III'	EBls EWes WCot WMal
SPIRIT OF FREEDOM ('Ausbite'[PBR]) (S)	EHyd EPfP LRHS MAsh NRHS SCoo
§ 'Splendens' (Ra)	EBls ETWh
SPLISH SPLASH ('Raw1020') (F)	ESty
ST CLARE ('Horbamber') (F)	EBls
ST HELENA ('Canlish') (F)	ECnt
STAMFORD'S SANCTUARY ('Beajealous') (Cl)	EBls
'Stanwell Perpetual' (SpH) 🏆[H7]	CArg CTri EBls ETWh NLar SPer
STAR DUST ('Morstar') (Min)	ELon
'Star of Waltham' (HP)	ETWh
'Star Performer'[PBR] (ClPatio)	CDoC CSBt ECnt EPfP ESty LRHS MAsh SApu SPoG SSea
STARDUST ('Peavandyke'[PBR]) (Patio/F)	ESty
STARLIGHT EXPRESS ('Trobstar'[PBR]) (Cl)	CDoC ELon LBuc LRHS MAsh MFry MGos MPri SPer
STARLIGHT SYMPHONY ('Harwisdom') (ClS)	CArg CDoC CEnd CGro ECnt ELon ESty EWTr LBuc LHkn LRHS MAsh MFry MGos SPer SSea
STARRY EYED ('Horcoexist') (Patio)	NRog
STARSHIP ('Bristar') (Patio) **new**	NRog
STELLA (HT)	LSRN
§ ***stellata*** var. ***mirifica***	ETWh
'Stephen'	LSRN
STEPHEN RULO ('Wecrulo') (F) **new**	NRog
STOP STREET ('Kordorsten') **new**	NRog
STORYTELLER ('Diccayman') (F)	IDic
STRAWBERRIES AND CREAM ('Geestraw') (Min/Patio)	ESty
STRAWBERRY FAYRE ('Arowillip') (Min/Patio)	ESty MRav SPoG
STRAWBERRY HILL ('Ausrimini'[PBR]) (S) 🏆[H6]	CSBt EHyd ESty LCro LOPS LRHS NLar NRHS SCoo
STRIKE IT RICH ('Wekbepmey'[PBR]) (HT) 🏆[H6]	CDoC CGro ESty MGos MRav SApu

§ SUE HIPKIN ('Harzazz'PBR) (HT)	ESty MRav
'Suffolk' (HT)	SCob
SUFFOLK ('Kormixal') (S/GC) 🏆H6	CSBt EBls MRav SCob
suffulta	see *R. arkansana* var. *suffulta*
SUGAR AND SPICE ('Peaallure'PBR) (Patio)	SPoG
SUGAR 'N' SPICE ('Tinspice') (Min)	CDoC MRav
SUMA ('Harsuma') (GC)	ESty
SUMMER BEAUTY ('Kororbe'PBR) (F) 🏆H6	CArg EBls
SUMMER FRAGRANCE ('Tanfudermos') (Castle Series) (HT)	EBls
§ SUMMER GOLD ('Poulreb'PBR) (F)	MAsh
'Summer Holiday' (HT)	SPer
SUMMER LOVE ('Franluv') (F)	CBcs
SUMMER LOVING ('Raw1152') (Cl)	ESty
SUMMER MAGIC ('Websplash') (F) **new**	NRog
SUMMER MEMORIES ('Koruteli'PBR) (Palace Series) (F)	EBls ETWh NLar
SUMMER SONG ('Austango'PBR) (S)	EHyd EPfP ESty LRHS LSRN
'Summer Sunrise' (GC)	EBls
'Summer Sunset' (GC)	EBls
SUMMER SWEETHEART ('Harquasar'PBR) (ClMin) **new**	LHkn
SUMMER WINE ('Korizont'PBR) (ClHT) 🏆H6	CGro CSBt EBls ECnt EPfP ESty ETWh LRHS MAsh SApu SPer SPoG
SUMMERTIME ('Chewlarmoll'PBR) (ClPatio) 🏆H6	CArg CBod CDoC CSBt EBls ECnt ELan EPfP MFry MGos MPri MRav SApu SPer SPoG
SUN HIT ('Poulsun'PBR) (PatioHit Series) (Min/Patio)	ECnt MRav SPoG
'Sunblaze'	see *R.* ORANGE SUNBLAZE
SUNBLEST ('Landora') (HT)	MRav NRog SCob
SUNCHARM ('Harfab'PBR) (Patio)	LHkn
SUNDERLAND SUPREME ('Nossun') (HT)	NRog
'Sunfire' Barni (F)	ECnt
SUNNY ABUNDANCE	see *R.* PETER COTTRELL
SUNNY DAY ('Savasun') (S)	ETWh
SUNNY SKY ('Koraruli'PBR) (HT)	CRos CSBt ECnt EHyd EPfP ESty LBuc LRHS MAsh MFry MGos MPri NRHS SCoo SPer SPoG
SUNNY SKY ('Korvestavi') (HT)	CDoC
SUNRISE ('Kormarter') (S)	EPfP ESty NRog SApu SPoG
§ SUNSEEKER ('Dicracer') (F/Patio) 🏆H6	CGro MAsh MFry MRav SPoG
SUNSET BOULEVARD ('Harbabble'PBR) (F)	SPer
SUNSET CELEBRATION	see *R.* WARM WISHES
SUNSET GLOW	see *R.* 'Alibaba'
SUNSET STRIP ('Arocore') (Min)	NRog
SUNSHINE BABYLON EYES ('Intereybabnus') (Babylon Eyes Series) (*persica* hybrid) **new**	SGsty
SUNSWEPT ('Benbrett') (Min) **new**	NRog
SUPER DOROTHY ('Heldoro') (Ra) 🏆H6	LSRN
SUPER ELFIN ('Helkleger'PBR) (Ra)	CDoC CRos LRHS MFry MRav NLar SApu
SUPER EXCELSA ('Helexa') (Ra) 🏆H6	EBls ELan SApu
SUPER FAIRY ('Helsufair'PBR) (Ra) 🏆H6	CDoC EBee EBls ECnt LSRN MFry MGos MRav NLar SApu SPer SSea
§ SUPER STAR ('Tanorstar') (HT)	CArg CDoC EBls MRav
SUPER TROUPER ('Fryleyeca'PBR) (F) 🏆H6	CArg CBod CDoC CGro CSBt EBls ECnt ELan ESty LRHS LSRN MAsh MFry MRav SApu SCoo SPer SSea WBor WCot
'Surpasse Tout' (G)	EBls ETWh
§ 'Surpassing Beauty of Woolverstone' (ClHP)	EBls
SURREY ('Korlanum') (GC) 🏆H6	CBod CDoC CSBt CTri EBls ELan ESty ETWh LCro LOPS LSRN MRav MSwo NLar SApu SCob SPer SSea
SUSAN ('Poulsue') (S)	ECnt LSRN NLar SLon
SUSAN DANIEL ('Harlady') (F) **new**	LHkn
SUSAN HAMPSHIRE) ('Meinatac') (HT	EBls
SUSAN WILLIAMS-ELLIS ('Ausquirk'PBR) (S)	CRos EHyd EPfP LRHS MAsh NLar NRHS SPoG
SUSIE ('Harwhistle') (ClPatio)	CGro ECnt ESty LHkn LSRN
SUSSEX ('Poulave') (GC)	CSBt EBls MSwo SCob SMad SPer
'Sutter's Gold' (HT)	EBls
SWAN LAKE ('Macmed') (Cl)	CArg CEnd EBls ECnt EPfP ETWh MFry NLar SCob SPer
SWANY ('Meiburenac') (Min/GC)	EBls ESty MSwo SApu SPer
SWEET CAROLINE ('Micaroline') (Min)	LSRN NRog
SWEET CHILD OF MINE (HT)	ELon ESty SSea
SWEET DREAM ('Fryminicot') (Patio) 🏆H6	CArg CDoC CGro CSBt CTri EBls ELan EPfP LCro LOPS LRHS LSRN MAsh MFry MGos MRav NRog SApu SCob SMad SPer SPoG SSea
'Sweet Fairy' (Min)	CSBt
SWEET HAZE ('Tan97274'PBR) (F) 🏆H6	MRav SPer
SWEET HONEY ('Korkularis') (HT) **new**	EBls
SWEET HONEY ('Kormecaso'PBR) (F) **new**	ECnt ESty ETWh
SWEET JESSICA ('Wekneflocjuc') (F)	ESty
SWEET JULIET ('Ausleap') (S)	MSwo
SWEET LIZZIE ('Webevening') (HT) **new**	NRog
SWEET MAGIC ('Dicmagic'PBR) (Min/Patio) 🏆H6	MRav SCob SCoo SPoG
SWEET MEMORIES ('Whamemo') (Patio)	CDoC EBls ECnt ELan EPfP ESty LRHS MPri MRav NRHS SCob SCoo SPer SPoG
§ SWEET PARFUM DE PROVENCE ('Meiclusif'PBR) (HT) 🏆H6	CArg CBod EBls ELan ELon EPfP ESty LBuc LRHS LSRN NRHS
SWEET REMEMBRANCE ('Kirr') (HT)	SCoo

	Name	Suppliers
	SWEET SYRIE ('Harwilling') (Cl)	ESty LHkn LRHS
	'Sweet Wonder' (Patio)	EPfP MAsh
	sweginzowii	EWld GLog
	'Sydonie' (HP)	ETWh
	'Sylvia Dot' (F)	LSRN
	'Sympathie' (ClHT)	EBls SPer
	TALL STORY ('Dickooky') (F) 🏆H6	EBee EBls ETWh NLar SApu
	TAM O'SHANTER ('Auscerise'[PBR]) (S)	EPfP
	TAMMY CLEMONS ('Declemons') (Patio) **new**	NRog
	TANGERINE TANGO ('Cheworangemane') (Cl)	SSea
	TANGO SHOWGROUND ('Chewpattens'[PBR]) (GC)	ESty
	TATTON ('Fryentice'[PBR]) (F)	EBls MRav
§	'Tausendschön' (Ra)	EBls
	TEAR DROP ('Dicomo') (Min/Patio)	MFry SApu SCob
	TEASING GEORGIA ('Ausbaker'[PBR]) (S) 🏆H6	CRos ECnt EHyd EPfP ESty LBuc LRHS LSRN MAsh MSwo NLar NRHS SCob SCoo SPer
	'Temple Bells' (ClMin/GC)	NRog
	TEMPTRESS ('Korramal') (ClS) 🏆H6	EPfP LRHS
	TENACIOUS ('Macblackpo'[PBR]) (F)	ESty
	TEQUILA SUNRISE ('Dicobey') (HT) 🏆H6	CArg CGro CTri EBls ELan EPfP ESty LBuc MFry MGos MRav NRog SApu SPer SSea
	TESS OF THE D'URBERVILLES ('Ausmove'[PBR]) (S)	CRos EHyd ELan EPfP ESty LRHS LSRN MAsh MCot MSwo NLar NRHS SCoo
	'Tessa' (F)	LSRN
§	THAÏS ('Memaj') (HT)	EBls
	'Thalia' (Ra)	EBls
	THANK YOU ('Chesdeep'[PBR]) (Patio)	ESty LCro LOPS LSRN
§	THAT'S JAZZ ('Poulnorm'[PBR]) (Courtyard Series) (ClF)	CArg ECnt LSRN MFry
	THE ALBRIGHTON RAMBLER ('Ausmobile'[PBR]) (Ra)	CRos EBee EHyd EPfP LRHS MSwo NLar NRHS SCoo
	THE ALEXANDRA ROSE ('Ausday') (S)	EPfP
§	THE ALNWICK ROSE ('Ausgrab'[PBR]) (S)	CRos EHyd EPfP LBuc LRHS MAsh MGos MSwo NLar NRHS SCob SCoo SPer
	THE ANCIENT MARINER ('Ausoutcry') (S)	EHyd LCro LOPS LRHS NRHS SCoo
	THE ANNIVERSARY ROSE	see *R.* SWEET PARFUM DE PROVENCE
	THE BEE'S KNEES ('Guesbehold') (F)	ESty
	THE BOSWORTH ROSE ('Raw1014') (F)	ESty
	'The Boy's' (F) **new**	NRog
	'The Bride' (T)	ETWh
	THE BROWNIE ROSE ('Harlassie'[PBR]) (F)	LHkn
	THE CHESHIRE REGIMENT ('Fryzebedee') (HT)	MFry
	THE CHURCHILL ROSE ('Horoften') (S)	EBee EBls LRHS MAsh
	THE COMPASSIONATE FRIENDS ('Harzodiac'[PBR]) (F)	CDoC
	THE COVENTRY CATHEDRAL ROSE ('Smi72-02') (F)	ESty
	THE DEBBIE PHILLIPS ROSE ('Harverve') (HT) **new**	LHkn
	THE DIAMOND WEDDING ROSE (HT)	EBls LSRN MAsh
	'The Doctor' (HT)	EBls
	THE EVE ROSE ('Harwinsome') (F) **new**	LHkn
§	'The Fairy' (Poly) 🏆H6	CArg CBod CDoC CSBt CTri EBee EBls ECnt ELan ETWh EWTr LRHS MAsh MCot MFry MRav NLar NRog SApu SCob SDix SMad SPer SRGP SSea WCFE WCot WHer XSen
	THE FEMININE TOUCH ('Wekmootono'[PBR]) (F) **new**	SApu
	'The Garland' (Ra) 🏆H6	CArg EBee EBls EPfP ETWh GBin MMuc NLar SApu SPer
	THE GENEROUS GARDENER ('Ausdrawn'[PBR]) (S) 🏆H6	CRos CSBt EBee EHyd ELan EPfP ESty LBuc LRHS LSRN MAsh MCot MGos MSwo NLar NRHS SCob SCoo SPer SSea
§	THE GOLD AWARD ROSE ('Poulac008'[PBR]) (Palace Series) (Patio)	ECnt
	THE HILDA OGDEN ROSE ('Korchakon') (Patio)	MAsh
	THE INGENIOUS MR FAIRCHILD ('Austijus'[PBR]) (S)	EPfP SCoo
	THE JUBILEE ROSE ('Poulbrido'[PBR]) (F)	ECnt
	THE LADY ('Fryjingo'[PBR]) (S)	ESty
	THE LADY GARDENER ('Ausbrass'[PBR]) (S)	CRos EHyd ELan EPfP LRHS NRHS SCoo
	THE LADY OF THE LAKE ('Ausherbert'[PBR]) (Ra)	CRos EHyd EPfP LRHS NLar NRHS SCob SCoo
	THE LADY'S BLUSH ('Ausoscar'[PBR]) (S)	EHyd EPfP LRHS
	THE LAKELAND ROSE ('Harspiral') (Cl)	LHkn SApu
	THE LARK ASCENDING ('Ausursula'[PBR]) (S)	EHyd LBuc LCro LOPS LRHS MAsh NRHS SCoo
	THE MAYFLOWER ('Austilly'[PBR]) (S) 🏆H6	CRos CSBt LBuc LRHS MAsh MSwo NRHS
	THE MAYOR ('P48a') (F)	MFry
§	THE MCCARTNEY ROSE ('Meizeli') (HT)	LSRN SApu
	THE MILL ON THE FLOSS ('Austulliver') (S) **new**	CRos ESty LRHS MAsh
	'The New Dawn'	see *R.* 'New Dawn'
	'The One and Only' (HT)	LRHS MAsh
	THE PAINTER ('Mactemaik'[PBR]) (F)	LSRN
	THE PERSE ROSE ('Beajargon') (S)	EBls
§	THE PILGRIM ('Auswalker') (S) 🏆H6	CRos CSBt EHyd EPfP LBuc LRHS MAsh NLar NRHS SCoo SPer SPoG
	THE POET'S WIFE ('Auswhirl'[PBR]) (S)	CDoC CRos CSBt ECnt EHyd EPfP ESty LRHS NRHS SCoo SPoG
	THE PRINCE'S TRUST ('Harholding'[PBR]) (Cl)	LHkn LRHS MAsh
§	'The Queen Elizabeth' (F)	CArg CBod CDoC CSBt CTri EBls ELan LCro LHkn LOPS LRHS LSRN MFry MGos MRav NRog SApu SCob SPer SSea
	THE QUEEN'S JUBILEE ROSE ('Beajubilee') (S)	CEnd EBls LRHS MAsh
	THE ROTARIAN	see *R.* ROTARY SUNRISE
	'The Royal Brompton Rose'	see *R.* ROYAL BROMPTON ROSE
I	'The Rugby Rose' (HT)	LSRN

	Name	Suppliers
	THE SHEIKH KHALIFA ROSE ('Dickoolkid') (Patio)	IDic
	THE SIMPLE LIFE ('Hartrifle'PBR) (Cl)	LHkn MRav SApu SSea
	THE SOHAM ROSE	see *R.* PEARL ABUNDANCE
	THE SOROPTIMIST ROSE ('Benstar') (Patio)	NRog
	THE SUN AND THE HEART ('Hartyre') (S) **new**	LHkn
	THE TIMES ROSE ('Korpeahn') (F) ♀H6	ECnt SCob SPer
	THE WAINWRIGHT ROSE ('Frylovely') (HT)	NRog
	THE WEDGWOOD ROSE ('Ausjosiah'PBR) (ClS)	EHyd EPfP LRHS MAsh NRHS
	THE WREN ('Kormamtiza'PBR) (F/Patio)	EBls EPfP MAsh
	THE YORKSHIRE REGIMENT ('Webterrific') (F) **new**	NRog
	'Thelma' (Ra)	EBls
	'Thérèse Bugnet' (Ru) ♀H7	EBls NRog
	THINKING OF YOU ('Frydandy'PBR) (HT) ♀H6	EBls ELon EPfP ESty LRHS LSRN MAsh MFry SApu SCoo SPer SSea
	THIS IS THE DAY ('Sproday') (Min) **new**	NRog
	THIS MORNING ('Harzephyr') (S) **new**	LHkn
	'Thisbe' (HM)	EBls ETWh
	THOMAS À BECKET ('Auswinston'PBR) (S)	CRos ECnt EHyd EPfP ESty LCro LOPS LRHS MSwo NRHS SPer
	'Thoresbyana'	see *R.* 'Bennett's Seedling'
	THOUSAND BEAUTIES	see *R.* 'Tausendschön'
	threepenny bit rose	see *R. elegantula* 'Persetosa'
	THUMBS UP ('Hornothing') (S)	EBls
	TICKLED PINK ('Fryhunky'PBR) (F) ♀H6	CArg CBod CDoC CTri EBls LCro LOPS LRHS LSRN MAsh MFry MRav NRog SApu SPer SPoG SSea
§	TIMELESS CREAM ('Noa112130'PBR) (HT) **new**	CRos LBuc
§	TIMELESS PINK ('Noa1811108'PBR) (HT) **new**	CRos LBuc
§	TIMELESS PURPLE ('Noa38121'PBR) (HT) **new**	CRos LBuc
	TIMES PAST ('Harhilt'PBR) (ClHT)	ELon ETWh LHkn MRav SApu SPoG
	'Tina Turner' (HT)	LSRN NRog
	TIP TOP ('Tanope') (F/Patio)	NRog
	'Tipo Ideale'	see *R.* × *odorata* 'Mutabilis'
	TITANIC ('Macdako'PBR) (F)	ESty
	TOGETHER FOREVER ('Dicecho'PBR) (F)	EBls LSRN MAsh MFry
	TOGMEISTER ('Beahappy') (F)	CEnd EBee EBls LRHS MAsh NRHS
	'Tom Marshall' (Ra)	ETWh LSRN
	'Tom Wood' (HP)	ETWh
	'Tony Bracegirdle' (HT) **new**	NRog
	'Tony Jacklin' (F)	LSRN NRog
	TOOTS ('Braable') (Patio) **new**	NRog
	TOP MARKS ('Fryministar') (Min/Patio)	MFry MRav SApu SCob SCoo SPer
	TOPAZ JEWEL	see *R.* YELLOW DAGMAR HASTRUP
	'Topsi' (F/Patio)	NRog SPer
	TOTTERING-BY-GENTLY ('Auscartoon') (S) **new**	CRos ESty LRHS
§	'Tour de Malakoff' (Ce)	EBls NLar SPer
	TOWER BRIDGE ('Haravis') (HT)	LHkn
	TOYNBEE HALL ('Korwonder') (F)	EBls LRHS
	TRADITION (ClHT)	see *R.* TRADITION '95
§	TRADITION '95 ('Korkeltin'PBR) (ClHT)	ETWh NLar
	TRANQUILITY ('Barout') (HT)	EHyd EPfP LRHS MAsh MSwo NRHS SCoo
	TRANQUILLITY ('Ausnoble'PBR) (S)	CRos CSBt ECnt ESty LBuc SCoo SPer
	'Treasure Trove' (Ra)	CRHN EBls
	'Tricolore de Flandre' (G)	EBls ETWh
	'Trier' (Ra)	EBls ETWh NLar WMal
	'Triomphe de Laffay' (Ch)	EBls
	'Triomphe des Noisettes' ambig. (N) **new**	ETWh
	'Triple Delight' (S)	LSRN NRog
I	'Trish's Rose' (Ru)	LSRN
	TROIKA ('Poumidor') (HT)	CBod ELon LRHS MAsh SPer
	TROPICAL TWIST ('Jacorca') (Min) **new**	NRog
	'Tropicana'	see *R.* SUPER STAR
	TRUE FRIEND ('Smi35-2-02') (F)	ESty
	'Truly Loved' (F)	LSRN MAsh
	'Truly Scrumptious'PBR (HT)	ESty MRav
	TRUMPETER ('Mactru') (F) ♀H6	CArg CBod CGro CTri EBee ECnt IArd LBuc MAsh MFry MRav NRog SPer SPoG
§	'Tuscany' (G)	EBls
	'Tuscany Superb' (G) ♀H7	CArg CBcs CDoC CRos CSBt CTri EBee EBls EHyd ELan EPfP ETWh LCro LEdu LOPS LRHS MCot MGos MRav NLar NRog SCob SPer SSea WBor WFar WHer WKif
	TWENTY-ONE AGAIN! ('Meinimo') (HT)	LSRN
	TWICE IN A BLUE MOON ('Tan96138'PBR) (HT) ♀H6	CArg CDoC CGro CSBt EBls ECnt ELon ESty LRHS MFry MRav SApu SCob SCoo SPoG SSea
	TWIGGY'S ROSE ('Harteam'PBR) (F)	LHkn
	TWILIGHT ZONE ('Wekebtidere') (HT) **new**	ECnt ESty
	TWIST ('Poulstri'PBR) (Courtyard Series) (ClPatio)	CArg ECnt LSRN SApu
	TYNWALD ('Mattwyt') (HT)	SPer
	'Ulrich Brünner'	see *R.* 'Ulrich Brünner Fils'
§	'Ulrich Brünner Fils' (HP)	EBls
	UNBRIDLED ('Decbridled') (Patio) **new**	NRog
	'Uncle Bill' (HT)	EBls
	UNCLE WALTER ('Macon') (HT)	EBls
	'Unique Blanche'	see *R.* × *centifolia* 'Unique'
	VALENTINE HEART ('Dicogle') (F) ♀H6	CArg CSBt ESty IArd LSRN MRav SApu SPoG
	VANESSA BELL ('Auseasel') (S)	CRos ESty LRHS MAsh MSwo SCoo
	'Vanity' (HM)	EBls
	VARENNA ALLEN ('Harmode'PBR) (F)	LHkn
	'Variegata di Bologna' (Bb)	EBls EPfP ETWh NRog
	'Vatertag' (Min)	LSRN
	'Veilchenblau' (Ra) ♀H7	Widely available

	VELVET FRAGRANCE ('Fryperdee') (HT)	CArg CBod CSBt ECnt ESty MFry MGos MRav SApu SCob SPoG
	'Vera Parker' (Min) **new**	NRog
	VERONICA ARNOTT ('Harjob') (S) **new**	LHkn
	VERONICA MARGARET ('Dicpursue') (F)	IDic
	'Verschuren' (HT/v)	ESty
	'Versharben' **new**	SSea
	versicolor	see *R. gallica* 'Versicolor'
	VETERANS' HONOR ('Jacopper') (HT) **new**	NRog
	'Vick's Caprice' (HP)	EBls ETWh NLar
	'Vicomtesse Pierre du Fou' (ClHT)	EBls
	VICTORIA ('Simlast') (HT)	ESty
	VICTORIA JOY ('Diciwill') (F)	IDic
	VICTORIA PENDLETON ('Harpace'^{PBR}) (F) **new**	LHkn
	'Village Maid'	see *R.* × *centifolia* 'Unique Panachée'
§	***villosa*** L.	EBls ETWh WKor
§	'Violacea' (G)	EBls ETWh
	VIOLET CLOUD ('Harquick'^{PBR}) (Min)	CDoC ESty LHkn MGos MRav
	'Violette' (Ra)	EBls ESty ETWh SPer WFar WHer
	'Violinista Costa' (HT)	EBls
	VIRGINIA MCKENNA OBE ('Harsong') (S)	LHkn LSRN
	virginiana Υ^{H7}	EBls NWea SCob SDix
	- 'Plena'	see *R.* 'Rose d'Amour'
	'Viridiflora'	see *R.* × *odorata* 'Viridiflora'
	VISION OF HOPE ('Webjuly') (F) **new**	NRog
	'Vivid' (Bourbon hybrid)	EBls
	VOICE OF THOUSANDS ('Horsunsmile') (F)	NRog
	WALLACE HARTLEY ('Horlazarus') (F) **new**	NRog
	WALTZ ('Poulkrid'^{PBR}) (Courtyard Series) (ClPatio)	ECnt LSRN
	WARM WELCOME ('Chewizz') (ClMin) Υ^{H6}	CBcs CBod CDoC CEnd CGro CRos EBls ECnt ELan EPfP ESty LCro LOPS LSRN MAsh MFry MRav NPoe NRog SApu SCoo SMad SPer SPoG SSea
§	WARM WISHES ('Fryxotic'^{PBR}) (HT) Υ^{H6}	CEnd CSBt EBls ECnt EPfP LBuc LRHS LSRN MAsh MFry MGos MRav NRHS SCob SSea
	WARWICKSHIRE ('Korkandel') (GC)	EBls SCob
§	***watsoniana*** (Ra)	EBls EBtc
	WB YEATS ('Dicoodles') (F)	IDic SApu
	webbiana	ETWh
	WEDDING BELLS ('Korsteflali'^{PBR}) (HT)	CBod EPfP LSRN NRog
	WEDDING CELEBRATION ('Poulht006'^{PBR}) (HT)	EBls ECnt
	'Wedding Day' (Ra)	Widely available
	'Weetwood' (Ra)	CRHN
	WEISSE WOLCKE	see *R.* WHITE CLOUD ('Korstacha')
	WELL-BEING ('Harjangle'^{PBR}) (S)	CArg ELon LHkn
	'Welsh Gold' (Patio) **new**	NRog
	WELWYN GARDEN GLORY ('Harzumber'^{PBR}) (HT)	LHkn
	'Wendy Cussons' (HT)	CTri EBls MRav NRog SApu SCob SPer SSea
	WESTERLAND ('Korwest') (S) Υ^{H6}	CDoC EBls ETWh LRHS MRav NLar NRog
	WHERE THE HEART IS ('Cocoplan'^{PBR}) (HT)	ESty
	WHIRLAWAY ('Decwhirl') (Patio) **new**	NRog
	WHISKY MAC ('Tanky') (HT)	CBcs CGro CSBt CTri EBee EBls ELan ELon LSRN MFry MGos MRav NRog SApu SCob SPer
	'White Bath'	see *R.* × *centifolia* 'Shailer's White Moss'
	'White Cécile Brünner' (Poly)	EBls
§	WHITE CLOUD ('Korstacha'^{PBR}) (ClHT)	ESty LRHS SApu SSea
	'White Cockade' (ClHT)	EBls ETWh MSwo SPer
	WHITE COVER	see *R.* KENT
§	'White de Meaux' (Ce)	EBls
	WHITE DIAMOND ('Interamon'^{PBR}) (S)	ECnt
	WHITE FOX ROSE ('Harzebek') (F)	ESty LHkn LRHS
§	WHITE GOLD ('Cocquiriam'^{PBR}) (F) Υ^{H6}	CSBt
	'White Grootendorst' (Ru)	EBls ETWh
	'White Maman Couchet' (HT)	EBls
	WHITE MEIDILAND ('Meicoublan') (S/GC)	LRHS LSRN MAsh
	white moss	see *R.* × *centifolia* 'Shailer's White Moss', *R.* 'Comtesse de Murinais'
	'White New Dawn' (Cl)	EBls
	'White Patio' (Min/Patio)	CRos EBls LRHS MAsh SPoG
	WHITE PERFUMELLA ('Meicalanq'^{PBR}) (HT)	CBod ELan ESty LSRN NRog
§	'White Pet' (Poly) Υ^{H6}	CArg CTri EBee EBls ECnt ELan EPfP ETWh LCro LOPS LRHS LSRN MCot MFry MRav NLar NPoe NRog SApu SCob SEND SPer WKif
	white Provence	see *R.* × *centifolia* 'Unique'
	white rose of York	see *R.* × *alba* 'Alba Semiplena'
	WHITE STAR ('Harquill') (ClHT) Υ^{H5}	ECnt LHkn MAsh MRav SSea
	'White Wings' (HT)	CArg EBls ETWh SPer WKif
	wichurana	see *R. lucieae*
	'Wickwar' (Ra) Υ^{H6}	EBls ETWh NLar
	WILD EDRIC ('Aushedge'^{PBR}) (Ru) Υ^{H6}	ECnt MAsh MMuc SCoo
	WILD ROVER ('Dichirap') (F) Υ^{H6}	EBls ELon ESty MFry SApu
	WILDEVE ('Ausbonny'^{PBR}) (S) Υ^{H6}	EHyd LRHS NRHS
	WILDFIRE ('Fryessex') (Patio)	CArg CGro EBls ECnt ESty LRHS MAsh MFry MGos MRav SApu SPoG
§	'Wilhelm' (HM)	EBls ETWh SPer
	WILLIAM AND CATHERINE ('Ausrapper'^{PBR}) (S)	EPfP LCro LOPS
	'William Cobbett' (F)	SSea
§	'William Lobb' (CeMo) Υ^{H7}	CArg CDoC EBls EHyd EPfP ETWh LRHS MCot MNrw MRav NLar NRHS NRog SCob WHer WKif
	WILLIAM MORRIS ('Auswill'^{PBR}) (S)	CSBt
	WILLIAM SHAKESPEARE 2000 ('Ausromeo'^{PBR}) (S)	CArg CSBt ESty NLar SCob
	WILLIAM SHAKESPEARE ('Ausroyal') (S)	SCob
	'William Tyndale' (Ra)	ETWh
	'Williams' Double Yellow'	see *R.* × *harisonii* 'Williams' Double Yellow'
	willmottiae	ETWh
	WILTSHIRE ('Kormuse') (S/GC) Υ^{H6}	CSBt CTri EBls ETWh MRav SApu SCob SEND SLon SSea

WIMI ('Tanrowisa') (HT)	NRog
WINCHESTER CATHEDRAL ('Auscat') (S)	CArg CGro CRos CTri EHyd EPfP LCro LOPS LRHS LSRN MAsh MSwo NLar NRHS SCob SCoo SLon SPer SPoG
WINDRUSH ('Ausrush') (S)	ETWh
WINE AND DINE ('Dicuncle') (GC)	EBls
WINTER SUN ('Korbatam'[PBR]) (HT) **new**	EBls
WISLEY 2008 ('Ausbreeze'[PBR]) (S)	CSBt EHyd EPfP LBuc LRHS NRHS SCoo
WIZARD (HT)	NRog
'Woburn Abbey' (F)	EBls
WOLLERTON OLD HALL ('Ausblanket'[PBR]) (S)	CRos CSBt EBee EHyd EPfP ESty LBuc LRHS MAsh MSwo NLar NRHS SCoo SPer
'Wolley-Dod'	see *R.* 'Duplex'
WONDERFUL HUSBAND ('Raw982') (F)	ESty
WONDERFUL NEWS ('Jonone'[PBR]) (Patio)	ESty
WONDERFUL WIFE ('Raw1025') (HT)	ESty
WONDERFUL YOU ('Smi 170-2-4') (HT)	ESty
woodsii (S)	EBls
- var. ***fendleri***	EBls ETWh
- var. ***ultramontana***	EBls
'Woolverstone Church Rose'	see *R.* 'Surpassing Beauty of Woolverstone'
WORCESTERSHIRE ('Korlalon'[PBR]) (GC) ♀H6	CDoC MRav SApu SPer
WYMONDHAM ABBEY ('Beadevil') (ClHT)	EBls LRHS MAsh
xanthina Lindl. **new**	LShi
§ - 'Canary Bird' (S) ♀H6	CArg CBcs CDoC CSBt EBee EBls ECnt ELan EPfP ESty ETWh LRHS LSRN MAsh MFry MGos MRav NLar SApu SCob SPer SPoG SSea SWvt
§ - f. ***hugonis***	EBls ELan ETWh NLar NRog SPer
X-RATED ('Tinx') (Min)	NRog
YARDLEY BAROQUE ('Beayar') (HT)	EBls
'Yellow Cécile Brünner'	see *R.* 'Perle d'Or'
§ YELLOW DAGMAR HASTRUP ('Moryelrug') (Ru)	ETWh NLar NRog SApu SPer
YELLOW FLOWER CARPET	see *R.* FLOWER CARPET SUNSHINE
'Yellow Mutabilis' (Ch)	EBls
'Yellow Patio' (Min/Patio)	CRos MAsh SCob SPoG
yellow Scotch	see *R.* × *harisonii* 'Williams' Double Yellow'
YELLOW SUNBLAZE ('Meitrisical') (Min)	CSBt
'Yesterday' (Poly/FCl) ♀H6	EBls ETWh SCob
'Yolande d'Aragon' (HP)	EBls ETWh
York and Lancaster	see *R.* × *damascena* 'Versicolor'
YORK MINSTER ('Harquest') (F)	LHkn MRav
YORKSHIRE BANK ('Rutrulo') (HT)	MFry
YORKSHIRE ('Korbarkeit'[PBR]) (GC)	EBls MRav
'Yorkshire Lady' (HT)	LSRN NRog
YORKSHIRE PRINCESS ('Dicmouse') (Patio)	IDic MRav
'You Only Live Once' (F)	LSRN
YOUNG AT HEART ('Raw922') (F)	ESty
YOUNG LYCIDAS ('Ausvibrant'[PBR]) (S)	CSBt EPfP LBuc LRHS LSRN NRHS
'Your Wedding Day' (F)	CGro
YOU'RE BEAUTIFUL ('Fryracy'[PBR]) (F) ♀H6	CDoC CSBt EBee EBls ECnt ELan LBuc LCro LOPS LRHS MAsh MFry MRav NRHS SApu SLon SPer SPoG
YOURS IN CONTINUED FRIENDSHIP ('Harpal') (F) **new**	LHkn
YVES PIAGET	see *R.* ROYAL BROMPTON ROSE
'Yvonne Rabier' (Poly) ♀H6	EBls ETWh NLar SPer
'Zéphirine Drouhin' (Bb)	Widely available
§ 'Zigeunerknabe' (S)	EBls ETWh NLar SPer WFar
'Zoe'	LSRN

Roscoea ✿ (*Zingiberaceae*)

alpina	CBro CExl CMiW EPot GEdr GKev NHar WCru WFar XLum
- CC 1820	IBlr
- pink-flowered	IBlr
- purple-flowered	IBlr
- short	WCru
§ ***auriculata*** ♀H5	CAvo CBct CBro CLAP CTsd EPfP EPot GEdr GKev IBlr ITim LEdu MAsh NChi NWad SChF SDeJ SDir SPer WCru WHil
- B&SWJ 2594	WCru
- B&SWJ 2687	WCru
- GWJ 9230	WCru
- 'Anorexia'	IBlr
- brown-stemmed × ***purpurea***	CJun IBlr
- early-flowering	IBlr WCru
- 'Floriade'	CAvo CJun SDir SPVi WFar WPGP WSHC
- green-stemmed × ***purpurea***	CJun IBlr
- late-flowering	WCru
- 'White Cap'	CJun EBee
auriculata* × *cangshanensis	WCru
auriculata* × *purpurea	WCru
australis	EBee ELon GEdr GGro MAsh MNrw WCru WThu
australis* × *humeana	MAsh
'Ballyrogan Lavender'	IBlr
'Ballyrogan White'	IBlr NHar
× ***beesiana*** ♀H5	CBcs CDTJ EPfP MAsh NHar SMHy
- 'Ballyrogan Purple'	CJun IBlr
- Cream Group	CJun EBee IBlr LEdu NBir SDeJ SDir WCru
- Dark Group	IBlr
- Gestreept Group	CBro CLAP CMea ECha EHed EHyd EPot EWoo GEdr GKev LRHS MHol NRHS SDir SPer WCru
- - white-flowered	GKev
- 'Lemon and Lavender'	CJun IBlr NHar
- 'Monique'	CDTJ CJun EBee EPfP IBlr NHar WFar
- 'Moonlight'	CJun IBlr NHar
- 'Petite Purple'	IBlr
bhutanica PAB 3826	LEdu
Blackthorn strain	IBlr WCru
cangshanensis	CMiW GKev MAsh SPVi WFar
- BWJ 7848	WCru
capitata	IBlr
cautleyoides	CAvo CBro CMiW CRos CWCL ECha EGrI EHyd EMor EPot GKev IBlr LRHS MHid MNrw NGdn NHar NLar NRHS WCot WCru
- blue-leaved	NHar

– var. ***cautleyoides*** f. ***atropurpurea***	IBlr
– 'Crûg's Late Lemon'	WCru WFar
– 'Doge Purple'	IBlr
– 'Early Purple'	CJun
– early-flowering	EHyd NRHS
– 'Himalaya' ♀H5	WHil
– 'Ice Age' **new**	CMiW
– 'Jeffrey Thomas' ♀H5	CBro CJun EHyd ELan LRHS NRHS WHil
– 'Last Emperor'	CLAP
– late, lavender-flowered	IBlr
– 'Lemon Giraffe'	CJun IBlr
– mauve-flowered	WHil
– 'Nguluko Village'	WFar
– 'Pennine Purple'	NHar
– plum-flowered	IBlr
– var. ***pubescens***	CJun
– 'Purple Giant'	CJun
– 'Purple Queen' ♀H5	WFar
– purple-flowered	CMiW IBlr
– 'Reinier'	CJun
– f. ***sinopurpurea***	GKev IBlr
– 'Vanilla'	CJun LEdu
– 'Vien Beauty'	NHar
– 'Washfield Purple'	IBlr
– 'Wine Red'	WHil
– 'Yeti'	CJun WHil
aff. ***cautleyoides***	MAsh SPlb
cautleyoides* × *humeana	IBlr NHar
debilis var. ***debilis***	IBlr
forrestii f. ***forrestii***	IBlr NHar
– – pubescent	IBlr
– 'Ice Maiden'	IBlr
– f. ***purpurea***	IBlr
'Harvington Evening Star'	CJun CKel CLAP ECha EHyd LRHS MAsh NHar NRHS WFar
Harvington hybrids	NHar
'Harvington Imperial'	NHar
'Harvington Raw Silk' ♀H5	CBro CJun CLAP ECha EHyd LEdu LRHS NHar NRHS WFar WHil
'Harvington Royale'	CJun EHyd LRHS NHar NRHS WFar
humeana	CBro CMiW CRos EHyd EPot GEdr GKev LRHS NHar NRHS WThu
– from Cruickshank Botanic Garden	IBlr NHar
– f. ***alba***	CJun EWld IBlr MAsh NHar
– 'Guincho White Stripe'	IBlr
– 'Long Acre Sunrise'	CJun
– f. ***lutea*** ♀H5	CJun GEdr IBlr NHar WFar
– 'Purple Streaker'	CJun
– purple-flowered	ECha
– 'Rosemoor Plum'	CJun CMiW
– 'Snowy Owl'	CJun GEdr MHid WFar
– 'Stephanie Bloom' ♀H5	EBee EBlo EHed LBuc NHar
– 'Two Tone'	CJun IBlr
– f. ***tyria*** ♀H5	CJun WHil
– – Inkling Group	NHar
'Ice Maiden'	CJun IBlr
'Kew Beauty' ♀H5	CBcs CBro CExl CJun CLAP CMea CMiW EBee ECha EHed EHyd EMor EPfP LRHS MPie NFav NHar NRHS SPoG WFar
'McBeath's Pink'	EHyd NHar NRHS SPVi WFar
nepalensis	CJun
'Pallid Sun'	IBlr
'Pinky'	CMea
praecox	GEdr IBlr
procera misapplied	see *R. auriculata*
procera Wall.	see *R. purpurea*
'Purple King'	CJun
§ ***purpurea***	Widely available
– CC 1757	IBlr
– CC 3628	CExl IBlr
– HWJK 2020	WCru
– HWJK 2169	WCru
– HWJK 2175	WCru
– HWJK 2400	WCru WFar
– HWJK 2407	WCru
– KW 13755	IBlr
– MECC 2	CJun
– MECC 10	CJun
– 'Ant Marian'	GKev
– Blackthorn hybrids	CLAP NHar
– bronze-leaved	CMiW
– 'Brown Peach'	EMor
– 'Brown Peacock'	CAvo CJun GKev IBlr NHar SDir SPVi WCot WCru WFar
– 'Cinnamon Stick'	CJun CLAP CWGN ECtt EHed EMor EWld GBin GKev MAsh NHar SPVi WCot
– Emperor Group	NHar
– var. ***gigantea***	WHil
– – CC 1757	IBlr
– 'Harvington Imperial' **new**	SPVi
– 'Julie's Glory'	WFar
– 'Nico'	CJun ELan
– pale-flowered	WFar
– 'Peacock'	CJun EMor GKev WHil
– 'Peacock Eye'	CJun GEdr WFar
– var. ***procera***	see *R. purpurea*
– 'Purple Dwarf'	IBlr
– 'Purple Tower'	IBlr
– 'Red Foot'	WFar
– 'Red Gurkha'	see *R. purpurea* f. *rubra*
– 'Red Riding Hood'	WFar
– red-stemmed	NHar
– Royal Purple hybrids	CJun MAsh NHar SPVi WPGP
§ – f. ***rubra*** ♀H5	Widely available
– – 'Gurkha Redstem'	CJun CLAP SPVi SPoG WCru
– 'Salt 'n' Pepper'	EMor GKev
– short	IBlr
– 'Slender Wisp'	IBlr
– 'Snow Goose'	WCru
– 'Spice Island'	CJun CLAP CSpe CWGN ECtt EHed GEdr GPSL IPot MMrt MPkF SEdd SMad SPVi SPoG WCot WFar XSte
– Sultan Group	NHar SPVi WHoo
– tall	WCru
– 'Twin Towers'	EMor GKev
– 'Typico'	IBlr
– 'Vannin'	CJun LEdu SPVi WCru
– 'Vincent'	CJun EMor EPot GKev WFar
– 'Wisley Amethyst'	CBro CJun EBee EHyd IBlr MAsh MNrw NHar NRHS WFar
schneideriana	CJun GKev IBlr WFar WThu
– robust form	IBlr
scillifolia	CBro CRos EHyd GEdr LRHS NBir NRHS SDeJ SPlb
– f. ***atropurpurea***	CMiW EPot EWld GKev IBlr MAsh WCru WThu
– black-flowered	NHpl
– f. ***scillifolia***	EWld GGro IBlr MPie NHpl WCru WFar WHil WThu
aff. ***scillifolia*** purple-flowered	GEdr
'Snow Queen'	NHar
'Summer Deep Purple' ♀H5	CJun EHyd LRHS NHar NRHS WFar
tibetica	GArf GEdr GKev IBlr SPlb WCru WFar WSHC WThu
– ACE 2538	IBlr WCru
– BWJ 7878	WCru

- f. ***atropurpurea*** BWJ 7640	WCru
- narrow-leaved **new**	GGro
- f. ***rosea***	WCru
I - white-flowered	GRum
'Two Tone'	CJun NHar
wardii ♀H5	CExl GKev IBlr

rosemary see *Rosmarinus officinalis*

Rosmarinus ✿ (*Lamiaceae*)

'Barwinnock Dwarf Blue'	WHer
'Blue Cascade' **new**	SGBe
corsicus 'Prostratus'	see *R. officinalis* Prostratus Group
× ***lavandulaceus*** misapplied	see *R. officinalis* Prostratus Group
× ***noeanus***	XSen
officinalis	Widely available
- 'Abraxas'	WFar
- f. ***albiflorus***	CBcs CBod CLau EHyd ENfk EPfP EWhm LRHS MMrt MNHC NPol SCob SDow SPlb SPoG SRms WGwG WJek XSen
- - 'Lady in White'	CRos CSBt EHyd ELan EPfP LRHS MAsh NRHS SPer SPoG SRms WGwG WJek
- 'Alderney'	WGwG WJek
- 'Amethyst Beauty'	SDow
§ - var. ***angustissimus*** 'Benenden Blue' ♀H4	CBod CSBt ELan GPoy LRHS MBNS SPer SPlb SPoG SRms WGwG WJek WSpi XSen
- - 'Corsican Blue'	GPoy MHer SDow SPer SRms WGwG
- 'Arp'	CBod ENfk EWes SEdi WGwG XSen
- 'Aureovariegatus'	see *R. officinalis* 'Aureus'
§ - 'Aureus' (v)	SRms WHer WJek
- 'Barbecue'PBR	CLau ECul ENfk EWhm SRms XSen
- 'Blue Lagoon'	CBod CBrac CDoC CLau ECul ENfk EWhm MHer MNHC SGBe SRms WGwG WHer WJek
- 'Blue Rain'	CBod EWhm MHer MSwo NQui WFar WGwG WHer
- 'Blue Winter'	CBod
- 'Bolham Blue' **new**	CRos
- 'Britannia'	CBod
- 'Capercaillie'	SDow WGwG
- 'Cascade' **new**	LRHS
- 'Collingwood Ingram'	see *R. officinalis* var. *angustissimus* 'Benenden Blue'
- 'Cottage White'	WHer
- 'Farinole'	MNHC SRms WGwG
- 'Fota Blue'	CLau CTsd EHyd IArd LRHS MHer NPol NRHS SAko SDow SRms SVen SWvt WGwG WJek
- 'Foxtail'	CDoC CLau ENfk SGBe SRms WJek XSen
- 'Frimley Blue'	see *R. officinalis* 'Primley Blue'
- 'Golden Rain'	see *R. officinalis* 'Joyce DeBaggio'
- 'Gorizia'	CBod LRHS SDow SRms
- 'Green Ginger' ♀H4	CBod CLau CMea EBee ELan EPfP GBin LRHS MGos MHer MNHC MRav MSCN NPer SCob SDow SPoG SRms SVen WGwG WJek
- 'Guilded'	see *R. officinalis* 'Aureus'
- 'Haifa'	CCBP CLau CSde ENfk SEdi SRms WGwG XSen
- 'Heavenly Blue'	WGwG WHer
- Israeli	XAbr
- 'Jekka Blue'	WJek
§ - 'Joyce DeBaggio' (v)	MHer SDow WGwG WHer
- 'Knightshayes Blue'	CRos EHyd LRHS NRHS
- ***lavandulaceus***	see *R. officinalis* Prostratus Group
- 'Lilies Blue'	GPoy WGwG
- 'Lockwood Variety'	see *R. officinalis* (Prostratus Group) 'Lockwood de Forest'
- 'Majorca Pink'	CBcs CBrac CLau CSBt CSpe ENfk LRHS MHer MNHC SDow SGBe SPer SRms WGwG WHer WJek XLum XSen
- 'Marenca'	MNHC SRms WGwG
- 'McConnell's Blue' ♀H4	EHyd EPfP LRHS MGos MNHC NRHS SDow SRms WGwG WHer WJek
* - 'Miss Jessopp's Prostrate'	SEdi
- 'Miss Jessopp's Upright' ♀H4	Widely available
- 'Pointe du Raz'	CDoC EPfP MAsh SRms WGwG WSpi XSen
§ - 'Primley Blue'	CBod CLau EBou ECtt MNHC MRav SRms SVic WGwG WJek
§ - Prostratus Group	Widely available
- - 'Capri'	CBod EPfP SCob SRms WFar WJek
- - 'Jackman's Prostrate'	GBin SDix
§ - - 'Lockwood de Forest'	WGwG WHer
- - 'Rampant Boule'	CBod CLau EWhm MHer SDow SMad SRms WGwG WJek XLum XSen
- - 'Sea Level'	MHer WGwG
- - 'Sheila Dore'	SPlb SVen
- - white-flowered	GPoy
- - 'Whitewater Silver'	ELan LRHS MBros SPad WJek
- 'Punta di Canelle'	XSen
§ - 'Pyramidalis'	XSen
- ***repens***	see *R. officinalis* Prostratus Group
- 'Rex'	WGwG XSen
- 'Roman Beauty'PBR	CBcs CBod CRos CSBt EBee EHyd EPfP EWoo LRHS LSRN NRHS SGBe SRms SWvt WFar WHer WSpi
- 'Roseus'	CCBP CRos ELan ENfk EPfP GPoy LRHS MAsh MHer MNHC NRHS SCob SDow SEND SPoG SRms SVen WAvo WGwG WJek XAbr
- 'Salem'	CBod MHer
- 'Severn Sea' ♀H4	CBcs CBod CLau CRos CSBt CSde CTri ECtt ELan EPfP EWhm GPoy LRHS MGos MNHC MRav MSwo NRHS SEdi SLon SPer SRms SSut SVen SVic WAvo WGwG WJek WSpi
- 'Shimmering Stars'	SDow WGwG
- 'Silver Sparkler'	WFar WHer
- 'Sissinghurst Blue' ♀H4	CBod CDoC CKel CRos CSde EBee ECha ELan EPfP LRHS MAsh MHer MNHC MRav NRHS SDow SPer SPlb SRms SWvt WGwG XAbr
- 'Sorcerer's Apprentice'	SDow
- 'Spice Island'	CBod SPer XSen
- 'Sudbury Blue'	CLau CTsd EWhm SAko SDow SRms SVic WGwG
- 'Sunkissed'PBR	SGBe SRms
- 'Tuscan Blue'	CBcs CBod CExl CKel CLau ECha ECtt EHyd EPfP LRHS MBow MHer MSwo NRHS SMad SPer SRms WGwG XSen
- 'Variegatus'	see *R. officinalis* 'Aureus'
- 'Vatican Blue'	WJek
- WILMA'S GOLD ('Wimtim01'PBR)	CLau
repens	see *R. officinalis* Prostratus Group

Rostrinucula (*Lamiaceae*)

dependens	CBcs CMCN CTsd EBee EPfP ESwi EWes IDee LCro LOPS LPar LRHS NLar SBrt SPad WCFE
sinensis	CExl

Rosularia (Crassulaceae)

§ ***aizoon***	CRos EDAr EHyd LRHS NRHS SRms WFar
alba	see *Sedum sedoides* var. *album*
§ ***chrysantha***	CRos EDAr EHyd LRHS NHpl NRHS SPlb SRms WAbe WFar
crassipes	see *Rhodiola wallichiana*
hirsuta	NHpl
libanotica RCB RL 20	WCot
§ ***muratdaghensis***	SPlb
pallida A. Berger	see *R. chrysantha*
pallida Stapf	see *R. aizoon*
pallida ambig.	EPot
platyphylla misapplied	see *R. muratdaghensis*
rechingeri	EDAr GArf SRms
sempervivum	EWes WThu
§ - subsp. ***glaucophylla***	CRos EHyd LRHS NRHS SPlb SRms WFar WHal WThu
serpentinica	EWes WAbe
spatulata hort.	see *R. sempervivum* subsp. *glaucophylla*

Rotheca (Lamiaceae)

§ ***myricoides*** 'Ugandense' ♀H1b	CCCN ELan EShb WSFF

Rubia (Rubiaceae)

peregrina	GPoy
tinctorum	CHab CHby GJos GPoy MNHC SRms WSFF

Rubus ✿ (Rosaceae)

RCB/Eq C-1	WCot
acuminatus	ESwi LEdu SBrt
alceifolius Poir.	SDys
- B&SWJ 1833	WCru
arcticus	EBee LEdu NHar SHar WKor WPGP XLum
bambusarum	EBee EShb ESwi GGro IDee MRav WCFE WCru
'Benenden' ♀H5	CBcs CExl CKel CTri EBee EHyd ELan EPfP GKin LRHS LSRN MBNS MMuc MRav NBid NLar SPer SPhx WCFE WLov WSpi
'Betty Ashburner'	CAgr CBcs CDoC EPPr GLog MCoo MGos MRav NLar SCob SPer SPoG XLum
biflorus ♀H6	LEdu LRHS MBlu MMuc SEND WKor WPGP
'Boysenberry' (F)	CArg EHyd LEdu LRHS
boysenberry, thornless (F)	CDoC CMac LBuc LSRN NRog SPer WLea
buergeri B&SWJ 5555	WCru
caesius	NRog WCot WKor
calophyllus	CBcs CKel EBee EPfP ESwi LRHS WPGP
- PAB 13.171	LEdu WPGP
calycinoides Hayata ex Koidz.	see *R. rolfei*
calycinoides Kuntze	GKev MGil SGol
chamaemorus	GPoy
cockburnianus (F)	CBcs ELan EPfP LBuc LCro LOPS LPar MMuc MRav MSwo NLar NSti NWea SCob SPer SPlb SRms WSpi
- 'Goldenvale' ♀H6	CBcs CDoC CKel EHyd ELon EPfP LRHS MBlu MGos MMuc MRav MSwo NBir NLar NSti SEND SLon SPer SPoG SRms WFar
crataegifolius	MRav
discolor	NWea
fockeanus misapplied	see *R. rolfei*
formosensis	CBod SBrt
- B&SWJ 1798	EBee ESwi WCru
fruticosus agg.	CArg NWea SCob WSFF
- 'Adrienne' (B)	CAgr CDoC CHab CSBt LEdu MTrO NRog SBdl SCoo SRms SSFr
- 'Apache' (B)	CHab CRos LCro LOPS LRHS MNHC MTrO SKee SPoG
- 'Ashton Cross' (B)	SSFr
- 'Asterina' (B)	CMac
- 'Bedford Giant' (B)	CHab CSBt LSRN MAsh MGos NRog NWea SCoo SSFr
- 'Black Butte' (B)	CHab EPom NRog SLon SVic
- 'Black Cascade'	see *R. fruticosus* 'Dart's Black Cascade'
- 'Black Satin' (B)	CAgr NLar NRog SEdi SVic
- 'Čačanska Bestrna' (B)	NRog
- 'Chester' (B)	CMac CRos EHyd EPom LEdu LRHS NRHS NRog SKee
§ - 'Dart's Black Cascade' (B)	EPom LCro LOPS SCoo
- 'Fantasia' (F)	NRog
- 'Helen' (B)	CAgr NRog SSFr
- 'Himalayan Giant' (B)	CHab NLar NRog
- 'Karaka Black'PBR (B)	CHab EHyd EPom LBuc NRog SPoG SSFr SVic
- 'Loch Maree'PBR (B/d)	CHab EPom LEdu MCoo NRog SLon
- 'Loch Ness'PBR (B) ♀H6	CAgr CArg CHab CMac CRos EHyd EPom IArd LCro LOPS LRHS LSRN NRHS NRog NWea SCoo SKee SPer SSFr SVic
- 'Loch Tay'PBR (B) ♀H6	CArg CHab CMac CRos EHyd EPom LRHS NRHS NRog SPoG
- LOWBERRY LITTLE BLACK PRINCE (B) **new**	SCoo
- 'Merton Thornless' (B)	CDoC CSBt CTri LBuc LEdu LSRN MAsh MGos NRog NWea SBdl SCoo SRms
- 'Navaho' (B)	CHab CRos EHyd NRHS NRog SPoG
- 'Navaho Big and Early' (B)	LRHS
- 'Obsidian' (B)	LEdu
- 'Oregon Thornless' (B)	CAgr CSBt EPfP LCro LOPS LRHS LSRN MAsh MRav MTrO NLar NRog NWea SCoo SEdi SGbt SPer SPoG SRms SSFr SVic WMat
- 'Ouachita'PBR (B)	CMac CRos EPfP LCro LOPS LRHS MTrO NRHS NRog SKee SPoG
- 'Purple Opal' (B)	LCro LOPS
- 'Reuben' (B)	CHab CRos EHyd EPfP EPom LBuc LCro LOPS LRHS MCoo MTrO NRHS NRog SKee SPoG SRms WMat
- 'Thornfree' (B)	CAgr CTri EPfP MTrO NLar NRog SGbt WMat
- 'Triple Crown' (B)	CHab CMac MCoo
- 'Variegatus' (v)	CMac MBlu WCot
- 'Waldo' (B)	CAgr CDoC LBuc LEdu LSRN MAsh MGos NRog SBdl SCoo SRms SSFr
'Glencoe' (B)	EPom MCoo SVic
henryi	CBcs EBee ESwi GBin NLar SPoG WBor
- var. ***henryi***	WCru
ichangensis	CBcs ESwi
idaeus	GPoy LRHS
- 'All Gold' (F) ♀H6	CDoC CMac EPfP EPom NLar NRog SCoo SPer SRms SVic WMat
- 'Alpengold'PBR (F)	CAgr CRos EBee LOPS LRHS MCoo SPoG
- 'Aureus' (F)	ECha MRav NBid WCot
- 'Autumn Amber' (F)	CMac LRHS NRog
- 'Autumn Bliss' (F) ♀H6	Widely available

- 'Autumn Treasure'PBR (F)	EPom SLon SVic
- 'Black Jewel' (F)	LOPS NRog
- 'Cascade Delight' (F)	CArg CRos CSBt EHyd EPom LBuc LOPS LRHS MAsh NRHS NRog
- 'Chemainus' (F)	EPom
- 'Erika'PBR (F)	CRos EBee EHyd EPom LCro LOPS LRHS MCoo NLar NRHS NRog SRms WMat
- 'Fallgold' (F)	LSRN SKee
- 'Glen Ample'PBR (F) 🏆H6	Widely available
- 'Glen Clova' (F)	CAgr CDoC CRos CSBt CTri EBee EHyd LRHS LSRN MAsh MGos MPri NLar NRHS NWea SEdi SGbt SKee SPoG SRms WMat
- 'Glen Dee' (F)	SRms
- 'Glen Doll'PBR (F)	CAgr MAsh NLar NRHS SCoo SRms WMat
- 'Glen Fyne'PBR (F)	CAgr NRog
- 'Glen Lyon' (F)	CArg CSBt EPfP LBuc MAsh MPri NRog SBdl SCoo SEdi
- 'Glen Magna'PBR (F) 🏆H6	CAgr CArg CSBt MAsh MPri SCoo SEdi SKee SRms
- 'Glen Moy'PBR (F)	CAgr CArg MAsh MGos NWea SCoo SKee SPer
- 'Glen Prosen'PBR (F)	CAgr CDoC CSBt MAsh MGos MPri NRog NWea SCoo SEdi SKee SPlb SPoG SRms SSFr WMat
- 'Heritage' (F)	LSRN MAsh SCoo SRms
- HIMBO TOP ('Rafzaqu'PBR) (F)	NRog
- 'Joan J'PBR (F) 🏆H6	CArg CMac EPom LBuc LSRN NRog SBdl SPer SRms SSFr
- 'Korpiko' (F) **new**	NRog
- 'Leo'PBR (F) 🏆H6	CSBt LCro LOPS MAsh NRog SCoo SKee SRms SSFr
- LOWBERRY LITTLE RED PRINCESS (F) **new**	SCoo
- 'Malling Admiral' (F) 🏆H6	CSBt CTri EPom LSRN MAsh NRog NWea SCoo SKee SPer
- 'Malling Delight' (F)	SCoo SEdi SPlb
- 'Malling Jewel' (F) 🏆H6	CAgr CArg CDoC CSBt CTri EPfP EPom LBuc LSRN MAsh MPri NRog NWea SEdi SKee SPer SRms
- 'Malling Juno'PBR (F) **new**	CMac SVic
- 'Malling Minerva' (F)	CAgr EPom NRog SRms SVic
- 'Octavia'PBR (F)	CAgr CArg CDoC CTri EPom LBuc MAsh MCoo NLar NRHS NRog NWea SBdl SEdi WMat
- 'Paris'PBR (F)	EPom
- 'Polka'PBR (F) 🏆H6	CArg CDoC CRos EHyd EPfP EPom LBuc LCro LOPS LRHS LSRN MAsh MCoo MRav NRHS NRog SBdl SCoo SKee SPer SRms SSFr WMat
- RUBY BEAUTY ('Nr7'PBR) (F)	CDoC CSBt EHyd EPom LBuc LCro LOPS LSRN MGos NRHS SCoo SPoG SRms
- 'Sanibelle' (F)	LRHS
- 'Sugana'PBR (F)	LCro LOPS LRHS MAsh NRog SKee
- 'Tadmor'PBR (F)	CArg CRos EHyd EPom LCro LOPS LRHS NRHS SKee SRms WMat
- 'Tulameen' (F) 🏆H6	CAgr CArg CDoC CSBt EBee EHyd ELan EPfP EPom LBuc LCro LOPS LPar LRHS LSRN MAsh NRHS NRog NWea SBdl SCoo SEWo SEdi SKee SPer SPoG SRms SSFr SVic WMat
- TWOTIMER SUGANA YELLOW (F)	LRHS SRms
- 'Zeva' (F)	SRms
illecebrosus (F)	CSpe LEdu WKor XLum
irenaeus	LEdu SEND WHal
Japanese wineberry	see *R. phoenicolasius*
'Jungle Karlostachys' **new**	WPGP
'Kenneth Ashburner'	NLar
laciniatus 'Thornless Evergreen'	NRog
lambertianus PAB 8931	LEdu
- var. ***glandulosus*** B&SWJ 14507	WCru
leucodermis	WKor
lineatus	CBcs CDTJ CKel CMCN EHyd EPfP EWes GBin LEdu LRHS MCot WCru WPGP
- B&SWJ 11261 from Sumatra	WCru
- PAB 13.163	LEdu
- HWJ 892 from Vietnam	WCru
- HWJK 2045 from Nepal	WCru
- from Vietnam	SBrt WPGP
× ***loganobaccus*** (F)	CMac
- 'Ly 59' (F)	EPfP MMuc SKee SRms
- 'Ly 654' (F) 🏆H5	CRos CSBt EHyd EPom LBuc LRHS NRHS NRog SPer SSFr SVic
- thornless (F)	CAgr CDoC CTri EPfP EPom LEdu SCoo SEdi SPoG WMat
malvaceus FMWJ 13324	WCru
'Margaret Gordon'	MRav
microphyllus 'Variegatus' (v)	MRav
§ ***nepalensis***	CAgr GKev LEdu WKor WPGP
- CC 7626 **new**	GGro
niveus	WKor
nutans	see *R. nepalensis*
occidentalis	WKor
odoratus	CAgr CExl ELan EPPr EPfP LEdu MBlu NBid NLar SPer WBor WKor
palmatus var. ***coptophyllus***	MMuc
paniculatus CC 7635 **new**	GGro
parkeri PAB 6891	LEdu
parviflorus	WKor
- 'Bill Baker'	LEdu
- double-flowered (d)	EPPr
- 'Sunshine Spreader'	LEdu
parvus	LEdu
pectinellus var. ***trilobus*** B&SWJ 1669B	WCru
peltatus	NLar
pentalobus	see *R. rolfei*
§ ***phoenicolasius***	CAgr CBcs CCCN CKel CMac ELan EPPr EPfP LCro LEdu LOPS LRHS MBlu MCoo MRav NRog SPer SPoG SVic WBor WFar WKor WPGP XAbr
PRIMEBERRY AUTUMN FIRST (F) **new**	LRHS
reflexus var. ***hui***	EShb
§ ***rolfei***	GGro MCoo NWad
- B&SWJ 3546 from Taiwan	WCru
- B&SWJ 3878 from the Philippines	WCru
- 'Emerald Carpet' 🏆H5	CAgr NLar
rosifolius NJM 10.142	WPGP
- 'Coronarius' (d)	CBcs EBee ESwi GBin MHol MNHC MNrw WCot WTyc
rubrisetulosus PAB 9532	LEdu
'Rushbrook Redleaf'	SBrt
saxatilis	WKor
setchuenensis	CMCN EPPr NLar
'Silvan' (F)	EBee SEND
spectabilis	EPPr LEdu MGil MRav WKor
- 'Flore Pleno'	see *R. spectabilis* 'Olympic Double'
§ - 'Olympic Double' (d)	Widely available
splendidissimus B&SWJ 2361	WCru

squarrosus	EShb SMad WFar
'Sunberry' (F)	CCCN LEdu NRog
swinhoei B&SWJ 1735	WCru
taiwanicola	EWes NWad
- B&SWJ 317	ESwi
Tayberry Group (F)	CRos CSBt CTri EHyd GDam LRHS LSRN MGos NLar NRHS SPer SRms SVic
- 'Buckingham' (F)	CArg EHyd EPom LBuc LCro LOPS LRHS NLar NPer NRog SEdi SVic WMat
- 'Medana Tayberry' (F)	CAgr CMac CTri EPfP LEdu LRHS MNHC NLar NRog NWea SEdi SKee SPoG WMat
- 'Tayberry' (F) ♀H5 **new**	CDoC SCoo
- thornless (F) **new**	WLea
§ ***thibetanus*** ♀H6	CBcs CBod CDoC CEme CKel CMac EBee EHyd ELan EPfP GBin LRHS MBriF MGos MMuc MRav MSwo NLar SCob SDix SEND SPer SPoG SWvt WSpi
- 'Silver Fern'	see *R. thibetanus*
treutleri B&SWJ 2139	WCru
tricolor	CAgr CBcs CBod CDoC CSBt CTri ELan GGro GKev MBlu MCoo MMuc MRav MSwo NLar SCob SDix SGol SPer
trilobus B&SWJ 9096	WCru
'Tummelberry' (F)	EHyd MCoo NRog SVic
ulmifolius 'Bellidiflorus' (d)	EPPr MRav NLar
ursinus	SVic WKor
xanthocarpus	LEdu NLar XLum

Rudbeckia (Asteraceae)

AUTUMN SUN	see *R. laciniata* 'Herbstsonne'
'Berlin'	EBee ECtt LRHS NRHS
californica	EHyd
- B&SWJ 14105	WCru
deamii	see *R. fulgida* var. *deamii*
'Dublin'	ECtt MBNS
fulgida	SWvt WFar
- 'City Garden'	ECtt GBin LRHS NLar SRms WFar
§ - var. ***deamii*** ♀H6	Widely available
- 'Early Bird Gold'	CWGN EBee ECtt EHyd EPfP GBin GMaP LCro LRHS MHol NLar NRHS SAko SCob WCAu WFar
- - 'Forever Gold' **new**	SEdd SMad
- var. ***fulgida***	CMea EBee EPfP LEdu SPhx SPoG
- 'Little Goldstar' PBR	CBod CKno CRos EBee ECtt EHyd ELan EPfP LCro LOPS LRHS MAsh MPri MTin NDov NLar NRHS SCob SCoo SLon SPoG SRms WFar WHil
§ - var. ***speciosa*** ♀H6	EBee ECha ECtt EHyd ELan ELon EPfP GAbr GBin GWyn LRHS MMuc NRHS SEND SEdd SHar SPlb SPtp SRms SWvt WFar XLum
- var. ***sullivantii***	CDoC
- - 'Goldsturm' ♀H6	Widely available
- - 'Pot of Gold'	NLar SCob
- VIETTE'S LITTLE SUZY ('Blovi')	CBod EHyd LRHS LSou NRHS SRms WFar
grandiflora	EHyd
- 'Sundance'	SPhx
§ ***hirta***	SIvy
- AUTUMN COLORS (mixed)	EHyd ELan LCro LOPS LRHS NRHS
- 'Cappuccino'	EHyd ELan EPfP LRHS NRHS
- CHEROKEE SUNSET (mixed) (d)	CSpe
- 'Cherry Brandy'	CSpe LRHS MNHC NGBl SPhx
- CHIM CHIMINEE (mixed)	NGBl SCoo
- 'Goldilocks'	SVic
- 'Indian Summer' ♀H3	CRos EHyd EPfP LRHS MNHC NRHS SPhx
- 'Irish Eyes'	SPhx SSal SVic
- 'Marmalade'	EHyd EPfP SPhx SVic
- 'Prairie Sun'	CRos EHyd EPfP LRHS MBros NGBl NRHS SPhx
- 'Sonora'	NGBl
- (Sunbeckia Series) SUNBECKIA ALICIA	LRHS
- - SUNBECKIA OLIVIA	LRHS
- (Toto Series) 'Toto Lemon'	LRHS
- - 'Toto Rustic'	LRHS
- - 'Toto' ♀H3	LCro LOPS LRHS SWvt
JULY GOLD	see *R. laciniata* 'Juligold'
laciniata	CKno CMac CSpe EBee EHyd ELan EPPr GQue LEdu MNrw NDov NGBl NLar SMHy SPeP SPhx SRms WChS WCot WWtn XLum
- 'Golden Glow'	see *R. laciniata* 'Hortensia'
- 'Goldquelle' (d)	CBod CEme CRos EBee ECha ECtt EHyd ELan ELon EPfP GMaP GWyn LRHS MACG MAsh NGBl NRHS SCob SPer SPoG SRms SWvt WCAu WFar XLum
§ - 'Herbstsonne' ♀H6	Widely available
§ - 'Hortensia' (d)	EBee LPot MAvo MRav NGBl WBrk WCot WFar WHoo
§ - 'Juligold'	CBod CRos EBee ECtt EHyd ELon EPfP EShb LRHS MBNS MPie NGdn NRHS SPoG WSpi
- 'Starcadia Razzle Dazzle' ♀H6	EWld MACG SAko WCot WFar
maxima	Widely available
missouriensis	CRos EAJP EHyd EPfP LPla LRHS MMuc MNrw NRHS SPhx
- 'Fairly Free' **new**	MNrw
mollis	CRos EHyd LRHS NRHS
newmannii	see *R. fulgida* var. *speciosa*
nitida	WSpi
occidentalis	EHyd LRHS NChi NRHS
- 'Black Beauty' PBR	NDov WSpi
- 'Green Wizard'	CBod CMac CRos EBee ECtt EHyd ELan EPfP EWoo GBin GQue GWyn LRHS LShi MCot NGBl NLar NRHS NSti SBls SCob SPeP SRms WSpi
* ***paniculata***	CDor ECha NGBl WCot
'Peking' PBR	ECtt EPfP MBNS MHol
purpurea	see *Echinacea purpurea*
speciosa	see *R. fulgida* var. *speciosa*
subtomentosa	CRos EHyd EPfP EWes LEdu LRHS MACG MMuc NDov NRHS NSti SDix SMHy WCot WSpi XLum
- 'Henry Eilers'	Widely available
- 'Little Henry' PBR	CBod CKno CSpe CTtf EAJP EBee ECtt EHyd ELon EPfP LRHS MAvo MBNS MBel MCot MHol MTin NFav NRHS NWsh SCob SPoG WFar
- 'Loofahsa Wheaten Gold'	GBin LEdu MAvo NDov WCot WGoo
- 'Poligny'	MNrw
Summerina Series	LRHS SCob
- SUMMERINA BROWN ('Et Rdb 03' PBR)	CKno CRos EHyd EPfP LRHS MBNS NGBl NRHS SCob SMad SPoG WCot
- SUMMERINA BUTTERSCOTCH BISCUIT ('Et Rdb 410')	CRos EPfP LRHS
- SUMMERINA ELECTRA SHOCK ('Et Rdb 404')	EPfP LRHS
- SUMMERINA ORANGE ('Et Rdb 01' PBR)	CRos EHyd EPfP LPla LRHS MBNS NRHS SCob SGBe SMad SPad SPoG SRkn XSte

- Summerina Pecan Pie ('Et Rdb 401')	EPfP LRHS SPad
- Summerina Pumpernickel ('Et Rdb 402')	EPfP LRHS XSte
- Summerina Yellow ('Et Rdb 02'PBR)	CRos EHyd EPfP LRHS MBNS NGBl NRHS SCob SGBe SPoG SRkn WCot
Tiger Eye Gold ('Syntigeygol')	SPoG
triloba ♀H6	CRos CSpe ECha EHyd EPfP GQue LRHS MNrw NGBl NGdn NRHS SCob SDix SPhx WCAu WSpi
- 'Blackjack Gold' **new**	EAJP EBlo
- 'Prairie Glow'	CBcs CBod CDor CSpe EBee ECha EHyd ILea LRHS MACG MAsh MHol NGBl SBls SCob SCoo SMad SPer SPhx SRkn SSal WHil

rue see *Ruta graveolens*

Ruellia (*Acanthaceae*)

amoena	see *R. brevifolia*
§ ***brevifolia***	ECre WFib
humilis	EBee GEdr MNrw
macrantha	CCCN EShb
strepens	EBee
tweediana	EShb WFib
- pink-flowered **new**	EShb

Rulingia (*Sterculiaceae*)

hermanniifolia	WAbe

Rumex (*Polygonaceae*)

acetosa	CAgr CCBP CHab CHby CLau CTsd ENfk GPoy MCoo MHer MNHC NBir SPhx SRms SVic WCot WHer WJek WSFF WWild XAbr
- 'Abundance'	CLau LEdu
- subsp. ***acetosa*** 'Saucy' (v)	LEdu MHol WCot
- broad-leaved	SVic
- 'De Belleville'	CLau
- 'Profusion'	GPoy
- red-veined	LCro LOPS
acetosella	CAgr CHab SRms WSFF
alpinus	LEdu WCot WPGP
flexuosus	CSpe GGro LPot
hydrolapathum	CBod CHab MMuc SEND SPlb WCot WSFF
patientia	CHab CLau
sanguineus	CLau CWat EGrI ENfk EShb LEdu LShi NLar NQui SRms XLum
- var. ***sanguineus***	CHby ELan GQue MHer MNHC NBro NGrd WFar WHer
scutatus	CBod CCBP CHby CLau ENfk GPoy MNHC NGrd SPlb SRms WJek
- 'Armenian Steel'	LEdu
- subsp. ***induratus***	SEND
- 'Silver Shield'	EPPr LEdu MHer NGrd SRms WFar

Rumohra (*Dryopteridaceae*)

adiantiformis ♀H3	CBdn CCCN CRos EHyd LEdu LRHS MAsh NRHS SEND WFib

Rungia (*Acanthaceae*)

klossii	WJek

Ruschia (*Aizoaceae*)

putterillii	SPlb
spinosa	SPlb
tumidula	SPlb

Ruschiella (*Aizoaceae*)

argentea **new**	SSim

Ruscus ✿ (*Asparagaceae*)

aculeatus	CBcs CMac ELan EPfP GPoy LEdu LPar LRHS MGil NFav NLar NWea SPlb SRms SWvt WMou
- hermaphrodite	EPfP MNrw SEND SMad WAvo
- (f)	NFav SCob WSpi
- var. ***angustifolius*** (f)	WCru
- - PAB 254	LEdu
- 'John Redmond'PBR (f/m) ♀H5	CBcs ELan EPfP EShb NHol NLar NWad SPer SWvt WBor WFar WSpi
* - 'Wheeler's Variety' (f/m)	CJun MRav
colchicus PAB 1753	LEdu
hypoglossum	CMac IArd SEND WCot WSpi
hypophyllum B&SWJ 15009	WCru
× ***microglossus*** (f) B&SWJ 14041	WCru
racemosus	see *Danae racemosa*

Ruspolia (*Acanthaceae*)

hypocrateriformis	CCCN

Ruspolia × *Ruttya* see × *Ruttyruspolia*

Russelia (*Plantaginaceae*)

§ ***equisetiformis*** ♀H1c	WFib
- 'Lemon Falls' ♀H1c	WFib
- 'Tangerine Falls'	WFib
juncea	see *R. equisetiformis*

Ruta (*Rutaceae*)

chalepensis	XLum
corsica	XLum
graveolens	CBod CCBP CHab ENfk GPoy GQue MNHC SVic WJek XAbr XLum XSen
- 'Alderley Blue'	WJek
- 'Jackman's Blue'	CBcs EGrI ELan EPfP GMaP GPoy MHer MNHC MRav MSwo SRms SWvt WFar WSMil WSpi XLum
- 'Variegata' (v)	LShi MNHC NPer SRms

Ruttya (*Acanthaceae*)

fruticosa	CCCN

× *Ruttyruspolia* (*Acanthaceae*)

lutea	CCCN
'Phyllis van Heerden'	CCCN

S

Sabal (*Arecaceae*)

§ ***mexicana***	SPalm
minor	CPHo SPalm SPlb
palmetto	SPalm
texana	see *S. mexicana*
uresana	LRHS

Saccharum (*Poaceae*)

arundinaceum	CKno
officinarum	SPlb
- purple-stemmed	SPlb WCot
- var. ***violaceum***	SDix SSal
ravennae	EBee SBls SMad SPlb

sage see *Salvia officinalis*

sage, annual clary see *Salvia viridis*

sage, biennial clary see *Salvia sclarea*

sage, pineapple see *Salvia elegans*

Sageretia (*Rhamnaceae*)

§	***thea***	CMen

Sagina (*Caryophyllaceae*)

	subulata	LRHS SVic XLum
	- var. ***glabrata***	MAsh
§	- - 'Aurea'	CMea EBou ECha ECtt EDAr ELan EPfP GMaP MAsh MHer NHpl SJap SPoG SRms SRot
	- 'Supreme' **new**	EPfP LRHS

Sagittaria (*Alismataceae*)

	graminea	LLWG SBrt
	- 'Crushed Ice' (v)	LLWG
	japonica	see *S. sagittifolia*
	lancifolia	LLWG
	latifolia	CAgr NPer
§	***sagittifolia***	CPud CWat EWat LLWG MWts WMAq WPnP XLum
	- var. ***leucopetala***	WMAq
	- - 'Flore Pleno' (d)	CWat EWat NPer XLum

Saintpaulia see *Streptocarpus*

Salicornia (*Amaranthaceae*)

	europaea	SVic

Salix ✿ (*Salicaceae*)

	acutifolia 'Blue Streak' (m) ♀H6	CEnd EPfP EWes MBlu NBir NLar WMou
	'Aegma Brno' (f)	WMou
	aegyptiaca	EBtc MBlu WMou
	alba	CCVT CHab CLnd LBuc LMaj LPar MAsh NRog NWea SCob SEWo SGol WMou WTSh XAbr
	- f. ***argentea***	see *S. alba* var. *sericea*
	- 'Aurea'	WCot WMou
	- var. ***caerulea***	CAco CLnd NRog NWea WMou
	- 'Chermesina' hort.	see *S. alba* var. *vitellina* 'Britzensis'
	- 'Golden Ness' ♀H6	CRos EBee EHyd EPfP GQue LRHS MAsh MBlu MTrO NLar NOra NRHS WFar WMat
	- 'Hutchinson's Yellow Bark'	MTrO NLar NWea
	- 'Liempde' (m)	SCob
§	- var. ***sericea*** ♀H6	CLnd EPfP MBlu MRav NLar NRog NWea SPer WCot WMou
	- 'Splendens'	see *S. alba* var. *sericea*
	- 'Tristis' misapplied	see *S.* × *sepulcralis* var. *chrysocoma*
§	- 'Tristis' ambig.	CBrac CLnd CTri ELan IPap LMaj LRHS MGos MRav MSwo MTrO NLar NOra SCob SEWo
	- var. ***vitellina***	EPfP LBuc MBNS MMuc NLar NRog NWea SGol SLon SRms
§	- - 'Britzensis' (m)	Widely available
	- - 'Nova'	ELan
§	- - 'Yelverton' ♀H6	CRos EBee EHyd EPfP LRHS MTrO NLar NOra NOrn NRHS SPoG WFar WMat
	- 'Vitellina Tristis'	see *S. alba* 'Tristis' ambig.
§	***alpina***	NHar
	'Americana' (m)	SWeb
§	***arbuscula***	ELan WAbe
	arenaria	see *S. repens* var. *argentea*
	aurita	MMuc NWea
	babylonica	CAco CEnd LPar WMou
	- 'Annularis'	see *S. babylonica* 'Crispa'
	- 'Bijdorp'	NLar
§	- 'Crispa'	CBod ELan GBin MMrt NQui NSti SMad SPoG WFar WGrn
	- 'Pan Chih-kang'	NLar
	- var. ***pekinensis*** 'Pendula'	IArd
§	- - 'Tortuosa' (f)	CAco CBcs CSBt ELan EPfP IPap LPar LRHS MGos MMuc NGrd NOrn NPer SEND SGol SGsty SLon SPer SPlb SRms WFar WSMil
*	- 'Tortuosa Aurea'	SGol SWvt
	bockii	EHyd EPfP ESwi LRHS SBrt SDys SPlb
§	'Bowles's Hybrid'	WMou
	'Boydii' (f) ♀H7	ELan EPfP EPot GAbr GEdr GJos GKev GMaP ITim LRHS MGos NBir NFav NPoe NRya NSla SAko WAbe WFar WLov
	candida	WFar
	caprea	CArg CBcs CCVT CHab CLnd CTri EPfP LBuc NRog NWea SCob SEWo SPer WMou WSFF WTSh
§	- 'Kilmarnock' (m)	CBcs CBod CCVT CDoC CMac CSBt CTri ELan EPfP IPap LPar LRHS MAsh MGos MMuc MTrO NLar NOrn NRHS NWea SCob SGol SGsty SLim SPer SPoG SWvt WFar
	- var. ***pendula*** (m)	see *S. caprea* 'Kilmarnock' (m)
	- - (f)	see *S. caprea* 'Weeping Sally'
	- 'Pendula'	see *S. caprea* 'Kilmarnock', *S. caprea* 'Weeping Sally'
§	- 'Weeping Sally' (f)	WMat
	capusii	LEdu WPGP
	cashmiriana	GEdr
	'Chrysocoma'	see *S.* × *sepulcralis* var. *chrysocoma*
	cinerea	CBcs CTri NWea SCob SEWo WMou WTSh
	'Coire Kander'	EBee GKev
	daphnoides	CBcs CCVT CLnd ELan EPfP LMaj MGos MMuc MSwo NLar NRog NWea SCob SEND SPer SRms WMou WSFF
	- 'Aglaia' (m) ♀H6	CTri
	- 'Oxford Violet' (m)	NWea
	× ***dasyclados*** 'Grandis'	NWea
	'E.A. Bowles'	see *S.* 'Bowles's Hybrid'
	× ***ehrhartiana***	CNat
§	***elaeagnos***	CCVT EPfP LShi MBrN MMuc NWea SCob SLon SMHy SPer WMou WSpi
§	- subsp. ***angustifolia*** ♀H6	ELan EPfP LShi MMuc MRav MSwo NLar SEND SRms
	exigua ♀H5	CBcs CEme CLnd ELan EPfP EWes IDee LEdu MBlu MBrN MGos MSwo NLar NWea SChF SCob SEdd SMad SPer WMou WPGP WSpi
	fargesii ♀H6	CBcs CBod CBrac CDoC CEnd CExl CKel CMac EBee EHed EHyd ELan EPfP GBin GGro LRHS MBlu MGos MMuc MRav NBid NFav NOra SBrt SCob WCru WFar WLov
	fargesii × ***magnifica***	EHed
	formosa	see *S. arbuscula*
§	× ***fragilis***	CCVT CHab CLnd NWea WMou WTSh
	- 'Basfordiana' (m)	CLnd MBNS WMou
	- 'Flanders Red' (f)	XAbr
§	- var. ***furcata***	GKev

	fruticulosa	see *S.* × *fragilis* var. *furcata*
	'Fuiri-koriyanagi'	see *S. integra* 'Hakuro-nishiki'
	furcata	see *S.* × *fragilis* var. *furcata*
	'Golden Curls'	see *S.* × *sepulcralis* 'Erythroflexuosa'
	gracilistyla	NWea WMou
§	- 'Melanostachys' (m) ♀H5	EHed ELan EPfP GBin GQue LRHS MAsh MBNS MBlu MBrN MGos MMuc MRav NBir NLar NWea SBrt SGol SRms WBor WFar WLov
	- 'Mount Aso'	CMCN EBee EHed ELon EPfP IDee LCro LEdu LOPS LPar LRHS MMrt NLar SBrt SEdd SMad WFar WLov WPGP XSte
	hastata 'Wehrhahnii' (m) ♀H6	CBcs EBee ELan EPfP GKev LRHS MAsh MBlu MMrt MMuc MRav MSwo NBir NLar NWea SCob
	helvetica ♀H7	CBcs CEme CKel CMac EBee ELan EPfP LPar LRHS MAsh MBlu MRav NBir NLar NWea WFar
	herbacea	GEdr WAbe
	hibernica	see *S. phylicifolia*
	hookeriana	CExl MBlu MBrN MCoo NLar WCFE WMou
	incana	see *S. elaeagnos*
	integra 'Albomaculata'	see *S. integra* 'Hakuro-nishiki'
	- 'Flamingo'PBR	ELan NLar SPoG WTSh
§	- 'Hakuro-nishiki' (v) ♀H5	Widely available
	- 'Pendula' (f)	CEnd MAsh NOrn
	irrorata ♀H5	CLnd EPfP MBlu MSwo MTrO NOra WMat
	'Jacquinii'	see *S. alpina*
§	***koriyanagi***	NLar
	'Kuro-me'	see *S. gracilistyla* 'Melanostachys'
	lanata ♀H7	CBcs CMac ELan ELon EPfP GKev LRHS MAsh MGos NBir NLar NWea SPer WCFE
	lapponum	LEdu MMuc NLar SRms
	- compact	GKev
	- 'Corrieshalloch'	GKev
	magnifica	CExl EPfP GBin IArd LEdu LRHS MMrt MMuc NLar SMad WCot WFar WHer WMou WPGP WSpi XSte
	'Mark Postill' (f)	EHyd GBin MBNS MMuc NLar SAko
	matsudana 'Tortuosa'	see *S. babylonica* var. *pekinensis* 'Tortuosa'
	- 'Tortuosa Aureopendula'	see *S.* × *sepulcralis* 'Erythroflexuosa'
	'Melanostachys'	see *S. gracilistyla* 'Melanostachys'
	moupinensis	CBcs EPfP
§	***myrsinifolia***	ELan MBlu MMuc NLar NWea WLov
	myrsinites var. ***jacquiniana***	see *S. alpina*
	myrtilloides 'Pink Tassels' (m)	NHar SBrt
	nakamurana var. ***yezoalpina***	CDoC CKel CRos EBee EHyd ELan EWes GEdr GKev LRHS MBlu MMuc MRav NFav NHar NLar SMad SSta WFar WLov
	nigra	XAbr
	nigricans	see *S. myrsinifolia*
	nivalis	see *S. reticulata* subsp. *nivalis*
	pentandra	CLnd LMaj NWea WMou
§	***phylicifolia***	NWea WMou
§	***purpurea***	CCVT MVil NWea SWeb WMou XAbr
	- 'Dark Dicks' (f)	NLar WSFF
	- 'Goldstones'	NLar
	- f. ***gracilis***	see *S. purpurea* 'Gracilis'
§	- 'Gracilis'	LPar MMuc NLar NWea SCob WCot
	- 'Helix'	see *S. purpurea*
	- 'Howki' (m)	WMou
	- var. ***japonica***	see *S. koriyanagi*
	- 'Nancy Saunders' (f) ♀H6	EShb EWld GLog LEdu MBNS MBlu MBow MBrN NBir NLar NOrn NSti SDix SMHy WCot WGrn
	- 'Pendula' ♀H6	CCVT CEnd CMac LRHS MAsh MSwo NOrn NRog NWea
	pyrenaica	EWes
	radinostachya KR 7622	WPGP
	repens	NWea SRms
§	- var. ***argentea***	EHyd ELan EWes MMuc MRav SCob SPer WFar
	- 'Armando'PBR	WFar
	reticulata ♀H7	EPot GKev NBir NSla WAbe WFar
§	- subsp. ***nivalis***	EPot LShi
	retusa	NBir
	rosmarinifolia misapplied	see *S. elaeagnos* subsp. *angustifolia*
	rosmarinifolia L.	EPfP NLar SCob
	× ***rubens***	see *S.* × *fragilis*
	× ***rubra*** 'Eugenei' (m)	MBlu
	× ***sepulcralis*** 'Caradoc'	LPar
§	- var. ***chrysocoma*** ♀H5	Widely available
	- 'Dart's Snake' (m)	ELan EShb MAsh MRav NLar WCot WFar
§	- 'Erythroflexuosa' (m) ♀H5	CBcs CBod CEnd EBee ELan EPfP LRHS MAsh MGos MMrt MMuc MTrO NOra NOrn NWea SCob SEND SGol SGsty SLim SPer SPoG WCFE WMat
	serpyllifolia	GKev
	- 'Chamonix'	NSla
	serpyllum	see *S.* × *fragilis* var. *furcata*
	'Setsuka'	see *S. udensis* 'Sekka'
	subopposita	ELan MGil MMuc SBrt
	× ***tetrapla*** 'Hutchinson's Nigricans'	CNat
	triandra	WMou
	- 'Black Hollander' (m)	NLar
	- 'Rouge d'Orléans'	EBtc
	udensis 'Golden Sunshine'PBR	CKel CMac CRos EBee EHyd EPfP LRHS MAsh MMrt MPkF NEoE NLar NRHS SEdd SPer SSta XSte
§	- 'Sekka' (m)	CBcs MBlu NBir NWea WMou
	viminalis	CCVT CDoC CLnd CMac EPfP LBuc MMuc NWea SCob SEWo SVic WMou WSFF
	vitellina 'Pendula'	see *S. alba* 'Tristis' ambig.
	'Yelverton'	see *S. alba* var. *vitellina* 'Yelverton'

Salpiglossis (*Solanaceae*)

sinuata Royale Series ♀H2	LCro LOPS

Salvia ✿ (*Lamiaceae*)

	CD&R 1162	SPhx
	from Catamarca, Argentina	CFoP SDys SEdd
	absconditiflora	XSen
	acerifolia	CFoP SDys
	acetabulosa	see *S. multicaulis*
	aethiopis	EWes SPhx
I	'African Sky'	CCBP CFoP ECre ECtt EHyd EPPr EWld MAvo MCot MHer MPie MIdl NRHS SBut SDys SEdd SIvy SPhx WAvo WBrk WGrn
§	***africana***	CFoP EBee
	africana-caerulea	see *S. africana*
	africana-lutea	see *S. aurea*
	agnes	SDys
	'Alegría'	CFoP SDys
	algeriensis	LRHS SPhx
	'Allen Chickering'	SDys
	'Amante' **new**	SIvy WNPC

amarissima	CFoP
'Amber'	LPla
ambigens	see *S. guaranitica*, *S. guaranitica* 'Blue Enigma'
'Amethyst Lips' **new**	CRos IPot MBel MPnt MPri MidI SDys WHil WNPC WTyc
'Aminia' **new**	CFoP
'Amistad'PBR ♀H3	Widely available
'Amparito'	XSen
ampelophylla	SDys
§ ***amplexicaulis***	CFoP MACG NLar SMrm SRms XSen
angustifolia Cav.	see *S. reptans*
angustifolia Mich.	see *S. azurea*
'Anna'	SDys
'Anthony Parker'	CFoP
apiana	EWld GJos SPhx SPlb SRms SVen XSen
(Arctic Blaze Series) ARCTIC BLAZE FUCHSIA ('Novasalfuc')	XSen
- ARCTIC BLAZE PURPLE ('Novasalpur')	XSen XSte
- ARCTIC BLAZE RED ('Novasalred')	XSen
argentea ♀H4	CBcs CBod CDor CFoP CKel CRos CSpe CTsd ECha EHyd ELan EPfP EWoo LRHS NRHS SMad SPer SPhx WKif WSMil XSen
arizonica	EWld MAsh SDys SIvy WSHC
atrocyanea	CFoP CSpe ECre EWes EWld MAsh MAvo MGil SDys SIvy SMHy WAvo WHal WKif WSHC
atropatana	WCot
aucheri	CFoP
§ ***aurea***	CBcs CFoP EPri SPlb XLum
- 'Kirstenbosch'	CFoP CTtf ECtt EWld SEdd WCot WKif
aurita	CFoP
'Azure Snow' (Color Spires Series) **new**	WTor
§ ***azurea***	SBrt SPhx XSen
- var. ***grandiflora***	SBls WCot
bacheriana	see *S. buchananii*
'Ballerina'	XSen
§ ***barrelieri***	ESwi
'Bee's Bliss'	XSen
'Belhaven'	EBee EPPr SRms
benthamiana	SDys
biserrata	CFoP
BLACK & BLOOM ('Balsaloom')	CDoC CFoP CRos ECtt LRHS MAsh
'Black Knight'	CFoP MAsh
blepharophylla	EPPr MSCN WAvo XSen
- 'Diablo'	ECtt
- 'Painted Lady'	MAsh SDys
'Bleu Armor'PBR	SPhx XSen
'Blue Chiquita' pale form **new**	CFoP
'Blue Merced'	SDys
'Blue Moon'	SDys
'Blue Note'PBR	Widely available
'Blue Sky'	EWld MidI
bogotensis	CFoP
bowleyana	CFoP
'Bright Eyes' (Suncrest Series)	CWGN IPot
broussonetii	CFoP
§ ***buchananii*** ♀H2	CFoP MAsh MRav SDys SRkn WKif
bulleyana misapplied	see *S. flava* var. *megalantha*
bulleyana Diels	CBcs CExl EWes GPSL NQui
- 'Blue Lips'	CBod EBee ECtt IPot MidI WHil
bullulata	CFoP
- pale blue-flowered	CFoP EWld SDys SIvy
cacaliifolia ♀H2	CExl CFoP CSde CWCL EBee ECtt EWld MAsh MHer MidI SDys SRkn WAvo
caerulea misapplied	see *S. guaranitica*, *S. guaranitica* 'Black and Blue'
caerulea L.	see *S. africana*
caespitosa	XSen
campanulata	CFoP
- B&SWJ 9232	WCru
- CC 21538 **new**	GGro
- GWJ 9294	WCru
- var. ***hirtella*** GWJ 9397	WCru
canariensis	CFoP WCot
- f. ***albiflora***	CFoP
- f. ***candidissima***	CFoP
candelabrum ♀H3	CFoP CKel ECre MHer SPhx WKif WSHC XSen
canescens	XSen
cardinalis	see *S. fulgens*
carnea	CFoP MAsh
- from Valle de Bravo, Mexico	SDys
'Cavalieri d'Alto'	MAvo MidI SPhx WHil
'Cavaliero Celeste'	SPhx
caymanensis	CFoP
§ ***chamaedryoides***	CFoP ELan MAsh SBrt SIvy SPhx XSen
- var. ***isochroma***	EPfP EWld MAsh SDys WPGP XSen
- 'Marine Blue'	MAsh MCot
- silver-leaved	CSpe SEdd SPhx XLum
chamelaeagnea	CFoP EPPr EWoo SDys SEdd XSen
'Cherbourg'	XSen
'Cherry Lips' **new**	MPnt WNPC
'Cherry Pie' **new**	ENfk MidI SIvy
'Cherry Queen'	CWGN MAsh
chiapensis	CFoP MAsh SDys
chionophylla	CFoP
'Christine Yeo'	CElw EBee ECtt ELon EPPr EPri EWld MAsh MidI SDys SEND SIvy WAvo WKif XSen
chrysophylla	CFoP SDys
'Château Cathare'	XSen
cleistogama misapplied	see *S. glutinosa*
clevelandii	CFoP MHer
- 'Winnifred Gilman'	SDys
clinopodioides	CFoP EBee SDys
'Clotted Cream'	CBcs CDoC CWGN EPfP LRHS MidI SIvy WFar WMal
coahuilensis misapplied	see *S. greggii* × *serpyllifolia*
coahuilensis ambig.	MAsh SIvy SLon SMrm SRkn WSHC XLum
coccinea 'Coral Nymph' (Nymph Series)	CFoP
- 'Forest Fire'	CFoP
- 'Lady in Red' (Nymph Series) ♀H3	EWld
cocuyana B&SWJ 14861	WCru
concolor misapplied	see *S. guaranitica*
concolor Lamb. ex Benth.	EPPr EWld SDys SIvy
confertiflora	CBcs CExl CFoP CSpe CWCL EBee ECre ECtt EGrI EPPr IPot MAsh MHer MHol SDix SDys SIvy SPlb SRkn SVen WAvo WFar WHer WKif WPGP
congestiflora	CFoP
corrugata	CElw CFoP CTsd EBee ECtt MAsh MCot MHer SDys SEdd SIvy SPhx WFar
'Crazy Dolls'	CFoP ECtt SDys SIvy
'Crème Caramel'	EBee ECtt MAsh MAvo MidI SDys
cuatrecasana	CFoP

curviflora	CElw CFoP EWld IPot MAsh SDys SEle SGro SIvy SRkn WAvo
- 'Tubular Bells'	WFar
cuspidata subsp. ***gilliesii***	CFoP
cyanescens	CFoP EPot XSen
cyanicalyx	CFoP SDys
cyclostegia	CExl
daghestanica	CSpe GKev SPhx
'Dancing Dolls'	CWGN IPot LRHS MidI XSen
I ***dangitalis*** SDR 4332	CExl
darcyi J. Compton	CExl CFoP EWes EWld SDys WSHC XLum
- peach-flowered **new**	CSpe
'Day Glow'	CChe ECtt MidI SAdn
deserta	GGro GQue LRHS SBrt SPhx WCot
- from Kazakhstan **new**	GGro
desoleana	CFoP
'Didi'	NDov
discolor	CFoP CSpe ECtt EPPr EWld MAsh MHer MidI SAng SDys WAvo WTyc
disermas	SPlb
disjuncta	SBrt
dolichantha	NLar
dolomitica	CFoP
dombeyi	CFoP ECre EWld SDys SIvy WAvo WPGP
dominica	CFoP
dorisiana	MAsh MHer SDys SVen
'Dorset Wonder'	NDov
'Dyson's Crimson'	CFoP CSde ECtt ELan ELon MCot SDys SPhx WTre
'Dyson's Gem'	CSpe ECtt SDys
'Dyson's Joy' ♀H3	CBcs CBod CDoC ECtt EPPr LRHS MAsh MAvo MCot MHer MidI SDys SEdd SIvy SRkn WKif
eigii	CFoP
eizi-matudae	CFoP SDys
§ ***elegans***	CBor CLau CPla EBee EWes EWhm IDee IPot NPol NWad SEdi WFar WHer WSHC XLum XSen
- 'Golden Delicious'	CBod CFoP EBee ENfk EPPr EWes EWld MBriF SRms WFar WSMil
- 'Honey Melon'	CFoP ENfk MAsh SDys
- 'Scarlet Pineapple'	CBod CExl ELan ENfk ETod EWld GPoy MBow MHer MNHC SDys SIvy SRms SVen WHer WJek
- 'Sonoran Red'	SDys
- 'Tangerine'	CBod CLau CTsd ENfk EWhm LCro LOPS MBow MHer MNHC NQui SRms WJek
EMBER'S WISH ('Sal 0101'PBR)	Widely available
'Endless Love'	EBee MidI NDov SIvy SRms
eremostachya	CFoP
'Eveline'	CFoP CKno CMac CWGN EBee ECtt EHyd EPfP MidI NLar SRms STPC
farinacea 'Fairy Queen'	SDys
- 'Midnight Candle'	CCht LRHS NRHS
- 'Rhea'	SPoG
- 'Strata'	MBros SPoG
'Fire Dancer' (Suncrest Series)	MidI XSen
'Flamenco Rose' (Suncrest Series)	ELan LRHS MidI XSen
§ ***flava*** var. ***megalantha***	CBod CFoP EHyd ESwi GGro LRHS LSRN LShi NRHS SIvy XSen
'Flower Child'	CSpe ECtt IPot SDys WFar
forreri	EBee MAsh NDov SDys SEdd SIvy
- 'Karen Dyson'	SDys
§ ***forsskaolii***	CBod CCBP CElw CExl CFoP EPfP EWoo GAbr GGro GKev MMuc MNrw MRav NChi NLar NQui NSti SAko SEND SPtp WCAu WCot WFar WTre XLum XSen
- white-flowered	CFoP EBee
§ ***fruticosa***	EHyd LRHS SLon SPhx SRms XAbr XSen
§ ***fulgens*** ♀H3	CFoP EWld MAsh SDys SRkn WFar WHer
- from Mount Popocatépetl, Mexico	CFoP
- green calyx	CFoP
gachantivana	CFoP SEdd
gesneriiflora	ECtt
- mountain form	ECre SDys SEdd
'Gigi'	WFar
glabrescens B&SWJ 11152	WCru
* - var. ***robusta*** B&SWJ 11147	WCru
§ ***glutinosa***	CBod CFoP CMac CSpe EBee EHyd EWld GGro GWyn MMuc NBro NLar NSti SEdd SIvy SPtp WCAu WHil XLum XSen
grahamii	see *S. microphylla* var. *microphylla*, *S. microphylla* var. *microphylla* 'Newby Hall'
'Great Comp'	NDov SDys
greggii	EHyd EPfP EWes LPot NRHS SPlb SRms WHil WKif XLum
- CD&R 1148	SDys
- 'Alba'	MidI XLum XSen
- 'Blush Pink'	see *S. microphylla* 'Blush Pink'
- 'Caramba' (v)	CDow
§ - 'Desert Blaze' (v)	CWGN EAJP EHyd ELan EPfP LRHS MRav MidI NRHS SDys SEdd SPoG WAvo WGrn XLum
- 'Devon Cream'	see *S. greggii* 'Sungold'
- 'Diane'	MAsh
- 'Emperor'	CFoP CWGN EBee EPri EWTr EWes IPot MAvo MBel MBrN MidI SEle SIvy WFar
- 'Flame'	CWGN EBee ELan LRHS MidI
- 'Icing Sugar'PBR	CBod CDoC CFoP CLau CRos CWGN EBee ECtt EHyd ELan ENfk EPfP EWoo LCro LOPS LRHS MAsh MAvo MCot MHol MidI NDov NRHS SCoo SDys SEle SIvy SRkn WCav
- 'Lara'	LEdu MAvo
- 'Lipstick'	CExl ECtt EHyd ETod GWyn LCro LOPS LRHS MAsh MidI NRHS
- 'Magenta'	CFoP WHil
- 'Peach' misapplied	see *S.* × *jamensis* 'Pat Vlasto'
- 'Peach'	CBod CFoP CWGN EPfP MAsh MidI SDys XLum
- 'Pink Preference'	CFoP MAsh SDys
- 'Purple Pastel'	LRHS MidI
- 'Raspberry Red'	XLum
- 'Rose Pink'	LRHS
- salmon-flowered	MidI
- 'Sierra San Antonio'	see *S.* × *jamensis* 'Sierra San Antonio'
- 'Sparkler'	see *S. greggii* 'Desert Blaze'
- 'Stormy Pink'	CSpe ECtt IPot MAsh MBriF MCot MNrw MPie MidI WFar WKif WTre
- 'Strawberries and Cream'	MidI
- 'Suncrest Fire Dancer' **new**	LRHS
§ - 'Sungold'	CWGN ECtt EHyd EPfP MAsh SDys SPhx WFar XSen
- variegated (v)	XSen
- yellow-flowered	XLum
greggii × ***lycioides***	see *S. greggii* × *serpyllifolia*
§ ***greggii*** × ***serpyllifolia***	CSpe MAsh MidI SDys

§ ***guaranitica***	ECtt MHer MidI WKif WPGP WTre XLum
- 'Argentina Skies'	CDow CFoP ECtt EGrI EPPr SDys SIvy SMrm
- 'Black and Blue'	Widely available
§ - 'Blue Enigma' ♀H3	CDor CDow CExl CFoP CSde CWGN EBee ECha ECtt EHyd ELan EPfP EWoo LRHS MAsh MGos MPie MRav MSpe MidI NRHS SDix SDys SGbt SIvy SPer WSHC WSpi XLum XSen
- 'Costa Rica Blue'	LPla SDys SIvy WKif
- 'Indigo Blue'	MAsh
- 'Midnight'	CFoP CSpe
- purple-flowered	CFoP EPPr SDys
- 'Rhythm and Blues' (Bodacious Series) new	LRHS
- small form	CBct
- 'Super Trouper'	ECtt EWld IPot MidI SDys
- violet-flowered	CFoP SDys
'Guarini'	SDys
haenkei	CElw
- 'Prawn Chorus'	CFoP MAsh
'Hannah'	MAvo
heldreichiana	XSen
hians	CBod CTsd EBee ESwi ILea LPot LShi SRms
- CC 1787	CExl
hierosolymitana	EBee EHyd LRHS NRHS SPhx WHil XSen
hispanica misapplied	see *S. lavandulifolia*
holwayi	SDys
horminum	see *S. viridis* var. *comata*
§ 'Hot Lips' ♀H5	Widely available
'I Cavalieri del Tau'	MidI SDys WFar
'Indiansummer'	SDys
indica	CFoP LRHS SPhx
'Indigo Spires'	CDow CExl CFoP CMea CSpe CWGN ECre ECtt MAsh MBrN MidI NDov SDix SDys SEle SPhx WAvo WBrk WFar WKif XLum
interrupta	EWld MCot SEdd SPhx XSen
involucrata ♀H3	MCot NBro SDys SMrm SVen WGrn WSHC
- 16339 new	EGrI
- 'Bethellii' ♀H3	CKel CSde CTsd CWCL EBee ECtt ELan EPfP EWes EWld EWoo LRHS MAsh MHer MNrw MPie SDys SEdd SRkn WFar WKif WSHC WSpi XLum
- 'Boutin' ♀H3	CFoP EBee EPPr MAsh MHol SDys SEle
§ - 'Hadspen'	CFoP CRHN CSpe EBee EPPr EWes SIvy WAvo
- 'Mrs Pope'	see *S. involucrata* 'Hadspen'
involucrata* × *wagneriana	SDys
iodantha	CFoP
× ***jamensis***	MAsh
- 'Amarillo'	SDys
- 'California Sunset'	IPot MAsh MidI SDys
- 'Dark Dancer'	MAsh SDys SEdd
- 'Devantville'	XLum
- 'Dysons' Orangy Pink'	NDov SDys
- 'El Durazno'	XSen
- 'Flammenn'PBR	CRos EHyd LRHS NRHS XSen
- 'Golden Girl'	CFoP CSpe CWGN EBee MidI WHil WSHC
- (Heatwave Series) 'Heatwave Blast'PBR	MidI XSen
- - HEATWAVE BLAZE ('Eggben005')	MidI XSen
- - 'Heatwave Glimmer'PBR	CSpe LRHS MCot MidI XSen
- - 'Heatwave Glitter'PBR	MidI XSen
- - HEATWAVE SCORCHER	CFoP
- - HEATWAVE SPARKLE ('Eggber004')	MidI XSen
- 'James Compton'	LPla SMrm XSen
- 'Javier' ♀H5	CFoP CSpe ECtt EPPr EWld GBin MAsh MidI SDys SIvy
- 'Kentish Pink'	SDys SEdd SIvy
- 'La Luna'	ECtt ELan EPPr MAsh MPie MRav MidI NDov WSHC XLum XSen
- 'La Siesta'	EBee IPot MAsh MPie XSen
- 'La Tarde'	MAsh
- 'Lemon Light'	ELan MidI SPer XSen XSte
- 'Lemon Sorbet'	WNPC
- 'Los Lirios'	CSpe MCot WAvo WHil
- 'Maraschino'	ECtt EHyd EPfP MAsh MBel MidI SDys SIvy SRms WHil XLum
- 'Melen'PBR	CRos EBee LRHS SPhx SRms XSen
- 'Moonlight Over Ashwood' (v)	MAsh WSHC
- 'Moonlight Serenade'	MAsh SDys
§ - 'Pat Vlasto'	CFoP
- 'Peter Vidgeon' ♀H5	CDow CFoP CWGN ECha EHyd EPPr EPfP EPri EWld GBin LRHS MAsh MBrN MBriF MCot MPri MidI NRHS SDys SEdd SGBe SIvy SPhx WAvo WMal WPGP WSHC WTyc
- pink-flowered	SBls
- 'Pleasant Pink'	MAsh
- 'Pluenn'PBR	CKel CRos EHyd LRHS LSRN NRHS XSen
- 'Raspberry Royale'	ECtt EHyd EPfP IPot MAsh MPie NRHS SDys SEdd XLum XSen
- 'Red Velvet'	ECtt EWld MAsh MCot SDys SEdd SPhx WAvo WBrk WHrl WSHC
- RÊVE ROUGE ('Fauresal02'PBR)	LRHS XSen XSte
- 'Señorita Leah'	CWGN ENfk MAsh MCot NDov SDys WFar WMal
- 'Shell Dancer'PBR	LRHS MidI XSen XSte
§ - 'Sierra San Antonio'	EHyd EPfP IPot LRHS MAsh MidI NRHS SDys SMrm WBrk XLum XSen
- 'Stormy Sunrise'	SDys
§ - 'Trebah'	CBod CDow ECre ENfk MAsh MCot MidI SDys WKif
- 'Trenance'	ECre ELon MHer WMal
- VIOLETTE DE LOIRE ('Barsal'PBR)	ECul LRHS LSRN SPhx SRms XSen
'James Curry'	CFoP
japonica* var. *formosana NMWJ 14469	WCru
'Jean's Jewel'	CFoP MidI SDys
'Jean's Purple Passion'	MAsh SDys
§ 'Jeremy'	ECtt LRHS MNrw MidI SDys SRms
'Jezebel' ♀H3	CFoP EHyd EPfP GBin MidI NRHS SDys
'Joan'	CFoP CWGN EPPr MAsh MAvo MBriF MCot MHol SDys
judaica	MSpe XSen
jurisicii	EHyd EPfP SAng XLum XSen
karwinskyi	ECre SDys SIvy
karwinskyi* × *univerticillata	SDys
keerlii	CFoP
'Kisses and Wishes' new	ECtt MidI SHar
koyamae	CFoP EBee GGro
- B&SWJ 10919	WCru
'Krystle Pink'	MidI
'La Mancha'	ECtt SDys WFar

	'Lalarsha'	CFoP ELan MAsh MAvo MCot NDov SDys
	lanceolata	CFoP CSpe EWld LRHS
§	***lavandulifolia***	CFoP CRos EBee EHyd ELan EPfP EWes GPoy LRHS MAsh MHer MNHC MRav SAng SBut SGro SRms WHoo WJek WKif XLum XSen
§	- subsp. ***blancoana***	ECha SPhx XSen
	- subsp. ***gallica***	XSen
	- 'Roquefure'	XSen
	- subsp. ***vellerea***	XSen
	lavanduloides	CFoP
	'Lavender Dilly Dilly'	ENfk MAvo SIvy WMal
	'Lemon Pie'	CFoP CSpe MidI SDys WNPC
	leptophylla	see *S. reptans*
	leucantha ♀H2	CCBP CMCN ECre ELan EPPr EWld MAsh MGil MNrw MPie MRav SPlb SRkn SVen WFar WHer WKif
	- 'Eder' (v)	MAsh SDys
	- 'Purple Velvet'	CFoP CSpe EBee ECtt MAsh MHer SDix SDys SEdd SIvy WAvo WTyc
	- 'Santa Barbara'	CFoP LRHS MAsh SDys WFar
	- 'White Mischief'	SEdd SIvy
	leucocephala	CFoP SDys
	libanensis	SDys
	littae	SDys
	'Little Azur'	ECtt EPPr SDys
	longistyla	SDys SVen
	LOVE AND WISHES ('Serendip6'[PBR])	Widely available
	lycioides misapplied	see *S. greggii* × *serpyllifolia*
	lycioides A. Gray	CFoP SDys WAvo
	lyrata 'Burgundy Bliss'	see *S. lyrata* 'Purple Knockout'
§	- 'Purple Knockout'	EHyd EPfP LPot LRHS NRHS SAng XSen
	- 'Purple Volcano'	see *S. lyrata* 'Purple Knockout'
	macellaria misapplied	see *S. microphylla*
	macrophylla	SDys WPGP
	- purple-leaved	CFoP SDys WPGP
	'Madeline'[PBR]	CBod CFoP CWGN EHyd EPfP EWTr GMaP LCro LOPS LRHS LSou MHol MNrw MidI NDov SPer WTyc
	madrensis	CFoP SDys
	'Magenta Magic'	CFoP EWld IPot SDys
	'Magic Potion'	CWGN
	'Mas de Lunès'	XSen
	melaleuca B&SWJ 14863	WCru
	mellifera	CFoP
	'Merlin's Magenta' <u>**new**</u>	ENfk
	MESA AZURE ('Mes Azur') <u>**new**</u>	CFoP
	mexicana 'Limelight'	CFoP
	- var. ***minor***	EWld SDys SIvy
§	***microphylla***	CBod CMac CTri EGrI EWes EWhm MBow SVen XLum
	- 'Albert'	LCro LOPS
	- 'Baby Doll' <u>**new**</u>	MidI
	- 'Belize'	CFoP MAsh
	- 'Blind Faith'	CSpe MAvo
	- 'Blue Monrovia'	IPot LRHS MRav SEdd
§	- 'Blush Pink'	CTtf MAvo SDys
	- 'Bordeaux'	CFoP CSpe ILea LRHS MidI SIvy SPhx XSte
	- 'Cerro Potosí' ♀H4	Widely available
	- 'Chalk White'	GBin SMHy SPhx
	- 'Hot Lips'	see *S.* 'Hot Lips'
	- 'Kew Red'	MNrw WAvo
I	- 'Lutea'	CDow ENfk MAsh SDys
	- 'Maroon'	CFoP EPfP EPri MAvo MCot MidI SDys SEdd
§	- var. ***microphylla***	CDow CFoP CRHN CTri ECtt ENfk EPPr LCro LOPS LSRN MCot MHer MNHC MRav SAng SEND SRkn SRms SVic XLum
	- - 'La Foux'	SMrm SPhx WAvo
§	- - 'Newby Hall'	CSde ECtt EWes LRHS MAvo NWad SPhx WSHC
	- var. ***neurepia***	see *S. microphylla* var. *microphylla*
	- 'Norwell'	MNrw
	- 'Orange Door'	SDys
	- orange-red-flowered	MRav
	- 'Oregon Peach'	EHyd EPfP NRHS
	- 'Oxford'	EGrI MidI
	- 'Pink Blush'	CWGN EAJP ECtt EHyd ELan ELon EPfP MAsh MCot MHer MNHC SEND SEdd SRkn WAvo WHil WHoo WKif WSHC XSen
	- 'Pleasant View'	WHil
	- 'Robin's Pride'	ECtt SDys WHil
	- 'Rodbaston Rosy Cheeks'	MSCN
	- 'Ruby Star'	ECtt IPot
	- 'San Carlos Festival'	MAsh MidI SDys
	- 'Trelawny Rose Pink'	see *S.* 'Trelawney'
	- 'Trelissick Creamy Yellow'	see *S.* 'Trelissick'
	- 'Trewithen Cerise'	see *S.* 'Trewithen'
	- 'Wendy's Surprise'	CWGN ECtt EWld MCot SDys SRkn
	- 'Wild Watermelon'	CWGN EBee ECtt EWes EWld GPSL IPot MAsh MAvo MHer MidI NQui SDys SIvy WGrn WHil
§	- var. ***wislizeni***	CElw SPhx
	- 'Wollerton White'	MCot MRav
	miltiorrhiza	CSpe GGro XLum XSen
	miniata	SIvy
	(Mirage Series) MIRAGE CHERRY RED ('Balmircher')	CBod LRHS WFar
	- MIRAGE CREAM ('Balmiream')	CBod WFar WHil
	- MIRAGE DEEP PURPLE ('Balmirdepur')	CBod LRHS WFar
	- MIRAGE NEON ROSE ('Balmirpink')	LRHS WHil
	- MIRAGE SOFT PINK ('Balmirsopin')	CBod WFar WHil
	muelleri misapplied	see *S. greggii* × *serpyllifolia*
	muelleri ambig.	CPla CSpe NDov
	'Mulberry Jam'	CCBP CDow CFoP EAJP EBee ECtt ELan EPfP EWoo MAsh MCot MidI SDys SEle SIvy SRkn WFar WKif
§	***multicaulis*** ♀H3	MAsh XSen
	munzii	CFoP SDys
	MYSTIC SPIRES BLUE ('Balsalmisp'[PBR])	CFoP CRos CSpe CWGN ECtt EPfP MBros MHer NRHS SPoG
	'Nachtvlinder' ♀H5	Widely available
	namaensis	CFoP EWld WKif
	nana 'Curling Waves'[PBR]	ECtt LSou
	napifolia	EWes LPot MNrw NLar
	'Nel'	EBee WMal
	nemorosa	LSRN LSun SPhx SRms XLum XSen
	- 'Amethyst' ♀H7	CRos CWGN EBee EBlo ECha EHyd ELon EPfP LCro LOPS LRHS MACG MBel MRav MSpe NDov NRHS SCob SPer SPhx SRms WCAu WCot XSen
	- 'Blaureiter'	EBee
	- BLUE BOUQUETTA ('Alkif')	CWGN LSou MHol MidI NLar SDys SPad WNPC
	- BLUE MARVEL ('Balsalarv'[PBR])	CBod LCro LOPS LRHS LSou MHol MidI SCob SPoG SRms
	- BLUE MOUND	see *S.* × *sylvestris* 'Blauhügel'
	- 'Bordeau Steel Blue'	EHyd ELon LRHS NRHS SRms

	- 'Caradonna' ♀H7	Widely available
	- 'Crystal Blue' (Color Spires Series)	CWGN IPot LCro LOPS LRHS Midl SEdd SHar
	- EAST FRIESLAND	see *S. nemorosa* 'Ostfriesland'
	- 'Giovanni' **new**	Midl
	- 'Jan Spruyt' **new**	NDov
	- 'Little Friesland'	EHyd LRHS NRHS
	- 'Lubecca' ♀H7	CBod CRos ECtt EHyd EPfP LRHS Midl NDov NGdn NLar SPer SPhx WCAu WFar XSen
	- LYRICAL SILVERTONE ('Balyricsil'PBR)	CBod WFar
	- LYRICAL WHITE	see *S. nemorosa* SENSATION WHITE
	- MARCUS ('Haeumanarc'PBR)	CBod CRos EBee ECtt EHyd ELan ELon EPfP LRHS LSRN MBNS MRav MTin NRHS SDys SPoG WFar
	- 'New Dimension Blue'	MACG Midl WCav WHil
	- 'New Dimension Rose'	CBod MACG Midl NLar WHil
§	- 'Ostfriesland' ♀H7	Widely available
	- 'Pink Beauty'	CRos EHyd EPfP LRHS NRHS
	- 'Pink Friesland'PBR	CBod CCht CDor ECtt EPfP GMaP LSou NGdn NRHS SCob WSpi
	- 'Plumosa'	see *S. nemorosa* 'Pusztaflamme'
§	- 'Pusztaflamme' ♀H7	EBee ECha EPfP MRav SEdd
	- 'Rose Marvel'	LRHS Midl
	- 'Rose Queen'	CBod ELon EShb EWTr GMaP GWyn NBir NLar SCob SPer SPhx WCot WFar XLum XSen
	- 'Rosenwein'	CDor CRos EHyd GWyn LRHS NRHS SGbt SPhx XSen
	- SALLYROSA JUMBO PINK (Sallyrosa Series) **new**	CFoP
	- 'Schwellenburg'	CKno CRos ECtt EWes LCro LRHS NLar NRHS SAko
	- (Sensation Series) SENSATION BLUE ('Florsalvioblu'PBR)	CRos EHyd LRHS NRHS WHil
	- - SENSATION BLUE IMPROVED	EHyd Midl
	- - SENSATION DEEP BLUE ('Florsaldblue')	CBod CRos EBee EHyd ELon LRHS LSou Midl NRHS
	- - SENSATION DEEP ROSE ('Flor Sal Roz')	CBod NRHS
	- - SENSATION DEEP ROSE IMPROVED	EHyd Midl SPoG
	- - SENSATION MEDIUM PINK ('Florsalpi')	CBod CRos
	- - SENSATION PINK	LRHS Midl NRHS
	- - SENSATION ROSE	CRos EGrI EHyd LCro LOPS LRHS LSRN LSou MAvo MHol MMrt Midl NRHS SCob SHar SRms
§	- - SENSATION WHITE ('Florsalwhite')	CBod CRos CWGN EHyd GKev LRHS MBel Midl NRHS SCob WHil
§	- subsp. ***tesquicola***	NLar SMrm SPhx WFar
	- 'Theodor'	ECtt
§	- 'Violet Queen' **new**	LSun SBls
	- 'West Friesland'	see *S. nemorosa* 'Violet Queen'
	- 'Wesuwe'	ECha ELon Midl NDov
	'Neon'	CFoP EBee Midl SEdd WAvo
	neurepia	see *S. microphylla* var. *microphylla*
	nipponica	CFoP EBee GGro SBrt
	- B&SWJ 5829	WCru
	nubicola	CExl ESwi GPoy
	- CC 6306	GGro
	aff. ***nubicola*** HPA 1355 **new**	GGro
	'Nuchi'	EHyd LRHS Midl NRHS SPoG
	nutans	GGro SAng SPhx XSen
	officinalis	Widely available
	- 'Albiflora'	CBcs ECha MBriF WJek XSen
	- 'Aurea' ambig.	GPoy SCob
	- 'Berggarten' ♀H5	CBod CCBP CLau ECha EWhm GBin LRHS MHer MRav SPhx WHer WHil XLum XSen
	- 'Blackcurrant'	CBod CLau WFar
§	- broad-leaved	CLau MHer SEdi WJek
	- 'Crispa'	XSen
	- 'Grete Stölzle'	LPla XSen
	- 'Grower's Friend'	CBod CTsd
§	- 'Icterina' (v) ♀H5	CBcs CBod CLau CTri EBee EBou ECha ELan ENfk EWhm GJos LRHS LShi MGos MHer MMuc MNHC MRav MSwo SCob SEND SPer SPoG SRms SVic WFar WJek WKif XLum XSen
	- ***latifolia***	see *S. officinalis* broad-leaved
	- narrow-leaved	see *S. lavandulifolia*
	- 'Nazareth'	XSen
	- ***prostrata***	see *S. lavandulifolia*
	- 'Purpurascens' ♀H5	Widely available
	- 'Robin Hill'	EHyd LRHS NRHS
	- 'Tricolor' (v)	CBcs CBod CTri EBee EHyd ELan ENfk EPfP EWhm GPoy LRHS LShi MAsh MHer MNHC SCob SEdi SPer SPoG SRms WCav WFar WJek
	- 'Variegata'	see *S. officinalis* 'Icterina'
	- variegated (v)	MHer
	- 'Würzburg'	XSen
	omeiana	CFoP
	- BWJ 8062	WCru
	- 'Crûg Thundercloud'	ESwi WCru
	oppositiflora misapplied	see *S. tubiflora*
	oppositiflora ambig.	CFoP SDys
	'Orchid Glow' (Suncrest Series)	CWGN ELan LRHS Midl XSen
	oxyphora	CFoP EWld MHer MPie Midl SDys SEdd SIvy SSal WFar
	pachyphylla	EHyd SBls XSen
	'Pakhuis Pass'	CFoP
	pallida	SEdd
	'Pam's Purple'	MAsh
	'Pasadena'	EWld SDys
§	***patens*** ♀H3	CFoP CSde CSpe EBee ECha ECtt EPfP LCro LOPS LRHS MAsh MHer MNHC MRav NGdn SDix SDys SRms WFar WKif WSHC WSpi WWFP
	- 'Alba' misapplied	see *S. patens* 'White Trophy'
	- 'Blue Angel'	CCht CWGN EHyd EPfP EWes LEdu LRHS SBls
*	- 'Blue Trophy'	Midl
	- 'Cambridge Blue' ♀H3	CExl CFoP CSpe CWGN EBee ECtt EHyd ELan EPfP EWoo LRHS MAsh MHer MRav Midl NLar NPer NRHS SAng SDys WFar WSHC
	- 'Chilcombe'	SDys
	- 'Dot's Delight'	CExl CSpe ECtt IPot LRHS SDys
	- 'Guanajuato'	CExl CSBt ECtt EWld EWoo IPot Midl NLar SAng SDys SEdd SHar WKif WSHC
	- large	CFoP CSpe
	- light blue-flowered	EHyd LRHS NRHS
	- OCEANA BLUE ('Salsyll')	EBee Midl
	- 'Oxford Blue'	see *S. patens*
	- (Patio Series) 'Patio Deep Blue'	CBod CWGN EPfP MBros SPoG WHil
	- - 'Patio Sky Blue'	CBod SCoo WCav WHil WSpi
	- 'Pink Ice'	ECtt EWld Midl SDys
	- 'Royal Blue'	see *S. patens*
§	- 'White Trophy'	CExl CFoP CSde ECtt EWes LRHS Midl SDys
	'Peach Cobbler'	CWGN EPPr MAvo Midl WNPC

'Peach Parfait'	CWGN EShb MAvo Midl SDys WAvo WNPC
'Peaches and Cream'	Midl
'Penny's Smile'	CElw CMac ELon IPot MAsh MCot MSCN Midl SDys SIvy SPhx WFar WGrn WHil WSHC
'Peru Blue'	CFoP SDys
'Phyllis' Fancy'	CFoP CSde CSpe CWGN EBee ECre EWes EWld LPla MAsh MBrN MCot MHer Midl NDov SAng SDys SEdd SIvy SPlb SRms WAvo WFar WKif
'Pink Lace'	ECtt SBut SDys
PINK LIPS	see *S.* 'Jeremy'
pisidica	XSen
polystachya	SEdd
pratensis	CBee CCBP EPfP GJos LCro LOPS MNHC MRav SPhx SRms WCot WWild XSen
- W&B BGH-3	WCot
- 'Dear Anja'	see *S.* × *sylvestris* 'Dear Anja'
§ - Haematodes Group ♀H7	MNrw SRms
- 'Indigo' ♀H7	CBod CRos ECtt EHyd ELon GMaP LCro LOPS LRHS MAsh MRav NLar NRHS SPhx SPoG WCot WGwG WPGP
- 'Lapis Lazuli'	EBee EWes LPla LRHS
- 'Pink Delight'PBR	EBee ECtt EHyd EPfP EWTr LRHS NRHS SRms
- 'Rose Rhapsody' (Ballet Series)	CDor EPPr EPfP MMrt NLar SBls SPhx XSen
- 'Rosea'	ECha
- 'Sky Dance' (Ballet Series)	CDor Midl SBut
- 'Swan Lake' (Ballet Series)	CDor EBee GWyn MACG NLar SBls SPhx SPlb XSen
- 'Sweet Esmeralda' (Ballet Series)	CDor EBee EGrl MACG NGdn SPhx XSen
- 'Twilight Serenade' (Ballet Series)	CDor EBee EBou ECtt ELan EPPr EPfP LRHS NLar SBls SPhx XSen
- 'White Swan'	LRHS
procurrens	CFoP EBee EWld XSen
przewalskii	CExl CFoP EHyd GGro LRHS NRHS SEdd XSen
- ACE 1157	WCru
- BWJ 7920	WCru XLum
'Purple Majesty'	ECtt SDys WKif WSpi XLum
'Purple Queen'	CBod CElw CFoP EBee EHyd ENfk EPfP EShb MCot NRHS SDys SEdd SEle SPhx WFar
'Purple Rhythm' (Bodacious Series) **new**	LRHS
purpurea	LSRN
'Radio Red'	CBod Midl WFar WGrn WHil
radula	EWld
'Raspberry Truffle'	SDys
raymondii subsp. ***raymondii***	CFoP
recognita	EHyd SPhx XSen
'Red Swing'PBR	EBee EHyd EWoo LRHS LShi Midl NRHS
regeliana misapplied	see *S. virgata* Jacq.
regla	CFoP MAsh SDys WPGP
§ ***reptans***	SBrt SIvy
- from western Texas	SAng SDys SEdd WCot WFar
- 'Summer Skies'	MSCN Midl
'Ribambelle' ♀H3	EAJP IPot MAsh MCot WHrl WMal XLum
ringens	XSen
ROCKIN' DEEP PURPLE ('Bbsal09001') **new**	CPla CRos ENfk LRHS Midl
ROCKIN' FUCHSIA ('Bbsal00301') **new**	CRos
§ ***roemeriana***	CSpe
- 'Hot Trumpets'	EHyd EPfP LBuc LRHS NRHS
'Rolando'	CFoP SDys
'Royal Bumble' ♀H4	Widely available
rubescens B&SWJ 14368	WCru
- subsp. ***dolichothrix***	CFoP
rutilans	see *S. elegans*, *S. elegans* 'Scarlet Pineapple'
sagittata	CFoP EBee EWld MHer SDix SPlb SSal
'Saint Jean de Beauregard'	WFar
'Sally Light Blue'	Midl
SALLYFUN BLUE ('Dansalfun1')	MPri
SALMIA DARK PURPLE **new**	LSou
SALMIA PINK **new**	LSou
'Salmon Dance'	CSpe CWGN ECtt EHyd EMor EPPr EWld IPot LCro LOPS LRHS MAvo NRHS WNPC
scabra	CFoP EBee XSen
schlechteri	CFoP
sclarea	CBod CHby EBou ENfk GPoy MNHC Midl NLar SEdi SRms SVic XAbr XLum XSen
- var. ***sclarea***	EPfP EWoo
- var. ***turkestanica*** hort.	see *S. sclarea* var. *turkestaniana* 'Vatican Pink'
- var. ***turkestaniana*** (Bruant Mottet) 'Vatican Pink'	CDor CSpe CTtf EAJP ECha EHyd EPfP EWTr LRHS LSRN LSun MRav NRHS SAng SMrm SPer SPhx SRkn WKif XAbr XSen
- - 'Vatican White'	CFoP CSpe EAJP EBee ECha EHyd LRHS NLar NRHS SPhx SWvt WLov XSen
- white-bracted	see *S. sclarea* var. *turkestaniana* 'Vatican White'
'Sebastian'	CFoP Midl
semiatrata misapplied	see *S. chamaedryoides*
semiatrata ambig.	CFoP EWld SPhx
- 510	SEdd
semiatrata Zucc.	CSpe EPPr
serboana	EBee EPfP EWld SAko WKif WPGP WSHC
- B&SWJ 10236	WCru
'Serenade'	CBod ELon Midl NDov SDys WCot WHoo
'Shame'	MAvo NDov
'Silas Dyson'	CDow CTtf EBee ECre ECtt EHyd ELan ELon EPfP EWld IPot MAsh MAvo MCot NDov NRHS SDys SIvy SPoG WAvo WBrk WFar WKif WMal WSHC
'Silke's Dream'	CFoP EBee ECtt EHyd EPfP MAsh MCot SDys WAvo WMal XSen
'Silke's Red'	SDys WFar
'Smoke'	SDys
'So Cool Pale Blue' **new**	SDys
'So Cool Purple' **new**	SDys
somalensis	CFoP EBee
'Southern Belle'	SDys
spathacea ♀H4	CFoP XSen
splendens	CFoP
- GO-GO PURPLE ('Insalgopur'PBR)	XSte
- 'Jimi's Good Red'	SDys
- 'Lighthouse Purple'	CSpe
- 'Red Indian'	SDys
- 'São Borja'	SDys
- 'Vanguard' ♀H3	MPri
§ - 'Van-Houttei' ♀H3	SDys
'Spring King'	SDys

	stachydifolia	CFoP SPhx WPGP
	- CDPR 3071	EBee WPGP
	'Stephanie'	SDys
	stepposa	GBin
	stolonifera	CFoP CSde CSpe ECre EPPr EWes EWld EWoo MAsh MAvo MHer SDys SIvy SMHy SPhx WAvo WPGP
	- 723	SEdd
	striata	SDys
	- pink-flowered	CFoP
	- red-flowered	CFoP
	styphelus	CFoP MIdl SDys SEdd
	- 619	SEdd
	subrotunda	CFoP SDys
	- 'Caitymary'	CFoP
	'Sue Templeton'	CFoP
	'Sunset Strip'	CDow SDys
	× ***superba***	CBod EBee ECha ECtt EHyd ELan EPfP LRHS LSRN LShi NRHS SDix SGbt SPer SRms WCAu WHoo
	- 'Adrian'	ECtt EHyd ELon EPfP LSRN SAng SPoG WCot
	- 'Lyon Rose'	EBee EPfP
§	- 'Merleau'	EHyd LRHS
	- 'Merleau Pink'	EHyd
	- 'Merleau Rose'	EBee MRav SBut SRms
*	- 'Rosea'	EBee
	- 'Rubin' ♀H7	ECtt
I	- 'Superba'	ECtt MRav SPhx SRkn
	× ***sylvestris***	LSRN
§	- 'Blauhügel' ♀H7	CBod CDoC CRos EAJP ECha ECtt EHyd ELan EPfP EShb GBin LCro LOPS LRHS MArl MPri MRav NDov NRHS SCob SCoo SPer SPhx SRms WCAu WHoo XSen
§	- 'Blaukönigin'	CDor CNor CRos CSBt EHyd ELon EPfP GMaP LBuc LRHS MIdl NLar NRHS SBls SPlb SPoG SRms SSut SWvt WCot WFar WHil XLum
	- BLUE QUEEN	see *S.* × *sylvestris* 'Blaukönigin'
§	- 'Dear Anja'	EBee ECtt LCro LOPS LRHS MIdl NDov SPhx WCot
	- 'Lye End'	MRav WCot
	- (Lyrical Series) LYRICAL BLUES ('Balyriclu'PBR)	WHil
	- - LYRICAL ROSE ('Balyricose'PBR)	SPoG WHil
§	- 'Mainacht' ♀H7	Widely available
	- MAY NIGHT	see *S.* × *sylvestris* 'Mainacht'
	- 'Negrito'	EBee ECtt MAvo NLar
	- 'Rhapsody in Blue'PBR	CBod EPfP MBNS MHol MIdl NLar WCot
	- 'Rose Queen'	CBod CMac CRos CSBt ECha EHyd ELan ELon EPfP EShb LCro LOPS LRHS MRav NRHS NSti SCoo SGbt SPer SPhx SPoG SRms SWvt WGwG XLum XSen
	- 'Rügen'	CBod CRos EHyd ELon GQue LRHS NDov NRHS SAko WCAu
	- 'Schneehügel'	CBcs CBod CCBP CMac CRos EAJP EBee ECha ECtt EHyd ELan ELon EPPr EPfP GMaP GWyn LCro LOPS LRHS MBNS MRav MIdl NLar NRHS SAng SCoo SPer WCAu XSen
	- 'Tänzerin' ♀H7	EBee ECtt GBin LRHS MIdl NDov NLar SAko SPhx
	- 'Viola Klose' ♀H7	CBod CRos EBee EBlo ECha ECtt EHyd ELan EPfP EShb IPot LCro LOPS LRHS LSRN LSou MCot MIdl NDov NGdn NLar NRHS SAko SRms
	tachiei hort.	see *S. forsskaolii*
	taraxacifolia	XSen
	tesquicola	see *S. nemorosa* subsp. *tesquicola*
	'The Infuddle's Shadow' **new**	CNat
	'Theresia'	EBee SDys
	tiliifolia	SRms
	tingitana	WHil
	tomentosa	XSen
	transsylvanica	SRms XSen
	- 'Blue Spire'	SPhx SRkn
	'Trebah Lilac White'	see *S.* × *jamensis* 'Trebah'
§	'Trelawney'	ECtt EHyd EPPr EWld LRHS MCot MHer MHol MPie MIdl NRHS SGbt
§	'Trelissick'	CBod EBee EHyd ENfk LRHS MAsh MCot MHer MIdl NRHS SDys SEND SEle SIvy SPhx SRkn
§	'Trewithen'	CBod CExl ECre EWoo MIdl SIvy XLum
	trijuga	CFoP
	triloba	see *S. fruticosa*
§	***tubiflora*** ♀H2	CFoP ECre MAsh
	'Tutti Frutti'	MAvo MIdl WHoo
	uliginosa ♀H4	Widely available
	- 'African Skies'	CChe CWGN EWTr EWoo NRHS SRkn WAvo
	- 'Ballon Azul'	CSde CSpe EBee ECha ECtt ELan EPPr EWes LRHS MAsh MIdl SDys SEdd SEle SMad SPoG SPtp WLov WPGP WSHC
	- 'Reach for the Skies'	SPtp
	'Ultra Violet'	CWGN LRHS
	urica short	SDys
	'Valerie'	MPie SDys
	'Van-Houttei'	see *S. splendens* 'Van-Houttei'
	'Vatican City'	see *S. sclarea* var. *turkestaniana* 'Vatican White'
	verbenaca	MHer SVic WWild XSen
	verticillata	CCBP EPfP LEdu NLar SPhx SRms WFar
§	- 'Alba'	CDor EBee EMor EPfP GQue LRHS MRav MIdl NGdn NLar NRHS SCob SPer XSen
	- 'Hannay's Blue'	CDor ECha EPPr GMaP LPla MAvo MIdl SMHy SPhx WCAu WFar WHrl XSen
	- 'Hannay's Purple'	ECtt EPPr EWld MIdl
	- 'Purple Rain'	Widely available
	- 'Smouldering Torches'	EBee MAvo NDov SCob SPhx
	- 'White Rain'	see *S. verticillata* 'Alba'
	villicaulis	see *S. amplexicaulis*
	'Violin Music'PBR	CBod EBee ECtt EHyd LRHS MHer MSCN MIdl NRHS SPhx SRkn
§	***virgata*** Jacq.	CFoP EBee XSen
	- 'Alba'	WHil
	viridis	CBod CHby MNHC SDys
	- 'Blue Denim'	LOPS
	- blue-flowered	LCro LOPS
	- Claryssa Series	SRms
§	- var. ***comata***	CFoP
	- (Marble Arch Series) 'Marble Arch Blue'	CSpe
	- - 'Marble Arch White'	WFar
	viscosa ambig.	CFoP SBut
	vitifolia	CFoP CSpe SAng SDys SEdd WAvo
	'Waverly'	CFoP EBee EPPr EWTr EWld MAsh MBriF MHer SDys SEdd SEle
	'Wendy's Wish'PBR	CDoC CRos EBee ECtt EGrI EHyd ELan EPfP EWoo IPot LCro LRHS LSou MAsh MHol MPri MRav MSpe MIdl NRHS SCob SCoo SDys SEdd SPoG SRkn SRms WNPC

	× ***westerae***	CFoP
	yunnanensis	CFoP
	aff. ***yunnanensis*** BWJ 7874 **new**	ESwi

Salvinia (*Salviniaceae*)

	natans	CBen LLWG

Sambucus ✿ (*Adoxaceae*)

	'14th December' **new**	WCot
	'Black Cherry'	WCot
	caerulea	see *S. nigra* subsp. *caerulea*
	'Chocolate Marzipan'	WCot
	coraensis	see *S. williamsii* subsp. *coreana*
	ebulus	EBee EPPr LEdu LShi NSti SMad WCot
	- B&SWJ 15307 **new**	WCru
	'Florence' **new**	WCot
	formosana	WCot
	'Gate into Field'	WCot
*	***himalayensis***	WCot
§	***javanica***	WCot
	mexicana B&SWJ 10349	WCot WCru
	'Milk Chocolate'	CBod CTsd EHed GBin MPie SEdd SPad WCot
	'Milk Chocolate Orange' **new**	WCot
	miquelii	WCot
	nigra	CArg CBcs CCVT EPom GDam GPoy LBuc NWea SCob SEWo SPer SVic WKor WMat WMou WSFF WTSh
	- 'Albomarginata'	see *S. nigra* 'Marginata'
	- 'Ardwall'	CAgr EPPr GBin WCot
	- 'Aurea'	CBcs CMac ELan EPom SCob SPer WCot
	- 'Aureomarginata' (v)	ELan EPPr MMuc MRav SEND WCot WFar
	- 'Beaujolais' **new**	NLar
	- 'Bont Oosterwoldë'	WCot
	- 'Bradet'	CAgr WCot WFar
	- 'Broadway' (v)	WCot
	- 'Cae Rhos Lligwy'	CAgr WCot WHer
§	- subsp. ***caerulea***	SMad WCot WKor WPGP
	- subsp. ***canadensis***	SPhx WKor
	- - 'Adams' (F)	WCot
	- - 'Aurea'	WCot
	- - 'Johns'	CAgr WCot
	- - 'Maxima'	SDix SMad WCot
	- - 'Rubra'	WCot
	- - 'York' (F)	CAgr WCot
	- 'Castledean'	WCot
	- 'Dart's Greenlace'	WCot
	- 'Dolomite' (v)	WCot
	- 'Donau'	CAgr WCot
	- 'Frances' (v)	EPPr WCot
	- 'Franzi'	CAgr WCot
	- 'Fructuluteo'	WCot
	- 'Godshill' (F)	CAgr WCot
	- GOLDEN SPARK (v) **new**	CBod NEoE
	- GOLDEN TOWER ('Jdeboer001'PBR)	CDoC LPar LRHS MMrt SPoG
	- 'Haidegg 17' (F)	CAgr
	- 'Haschberg'	CAgr SVic WCot
	- 'Heterophylla'	see *S. nigra* 'Linearis'
	- 'Hillier's Dwarf'	WCot
	- 'Ina'	CAgr WCot
	- 'Körsör' (F)	NLar WCot
	- f. ***laciniata*** ♀H6	CBcs EBee EHyd ELan EPfP LRHS MBlu MMuc MRav SCob SDix SLon SPer SPoG WCot WFar
§	- 'Linearis'	EHed MRav NLar WCot
	- 'Long Tooth'	WCot
	- 'Lutea Punctata'	WCot WFar
	- 'Madonna' (v)	LEdu MBlu MRav NPol NQui SPoG WAvo WCot
§	- 'Marginata' (v)	CMac GBin MHer MRav WCot WFar
	- 'Marion Bull' (v)	WCot
I	- 'Marmorata'	NLar WCot
	- 'Mint Julep'	WCot
I	- 'Monstrosa'	WCot
	- 'Nana'	WCot
	- 'Naomi'	WCot
	- 'Norfolk Speckled' (v)	WCot
	- 'Pingo Trail'	WCot
	- 'Plena' (d)	WCot
	- f. ***porphyrophylla*** 'Black Beauty'	see *S. nigra* f. *porphyrophylla* 'Gerda'
	- - 'Black Lace'	see *S. nigra* f. *porphyrophylla* 'Eva'
	- - BLACK TOWER ('Eiffel 1'PBR)	Widely available
	- - 'Blue Sheen'	CRos EHyd EPfP LRHS NRHS SCoo WCot
§	- - 'Eva'PBR ♀H6	Widely available
§	- - 'Gerda'PBR ♀H6	Widely available
§	- - 'Guincho Purple'	CBcs CBod CTri EGrI EPPr EPfP LRHS MRav NLar NWea SPlb WCot WFar
	- - 'Purple Pete'	WCot
	- - 'Thundercloud' ♀H6	ELon EWes MAsh MNrw NEoE NLar SPhx WCot WFar
	- 'Pulverulenta' (v)	MRav NQui SMad SPad SRms WCot WFar
	- 'Purpurea'	see *S. nigra* f. *porphyrophylla* 'Guincho Purple'
	- 'Pyramidalis'	MRav WCot
	- 'Riese aus Vossloch'	WCot
	- 'Robert Piggin' (v)	WCot
	- var. ***rotundifolia***	WCot
	- 'Sambu' (F)	CAgr WCot
	- 'Samdal' (F)	CAgr WCot WFar
	- 'Samidan' (F)	CAgr WCot
	- 'Samnor' (F)	CAgr WCot
	- 'Sampo' (F)	CAgr WCot
	- 'Samyl' (F)	CAgr WCot
	- 'Serenade'	CBcs CBod CPla CRos EBee EHyd GBin LRHS NEoE NLar NRHS SCob WCot WFar
	- 'Urban Lace'	CAgr WCot
	- 'Variegata'	see *S. nigra* 'Marginata'
	- f. ***viridis***	CAgr WCot
	'Ocean Depths'	GBin NEoE
	palmensis	WCot
	racemosa	EPfP NWea WCot WKor
	- 'Altamont'	WCot
	- 'Aurea'	EPfP WFar
	- var. ***callicarpa***	WCot WFar
	- subsp. ***kamtschatica***	WCot
	- LEMONY LACE ('Smnsrd4')	EHed LBuc LRHS
	- var. ***melanocarpa***	WCot
	- 'Plumosa Aurea'	EPfP LPar MGos MRav MSwo NLar NWea SCob SRms WAvo WCot
	- var. ***pubens***	WCot
§	- var. ***sieboldiana***	WCot
	- 'Sutherland Gold' ♀H7	Widely available
	- 'Tenuifolia'	WCot
	sieboldiana	see *S. racemosa* var. *sieboldiana*
	× ***strumpfii*** SERENADE ('Jonade')	LCro LOPS SGBe
	SUNNY DAYS ('Jonsun')	CBod LRHS WNPC
I	'The Sweet One' **new**	WCot
	tigranii	WCot WFar

'Vermilion Summers'	WCot
WELSH GOLD ('Walfinb'PBR)	CRos EHyd LRHS MAsh SPoG
wightiana	see *S. javanica*
§ ***williamsii*** subsp. ***coreana***	WCot

Sandersonia (*Colchicaceae*)

aurantiaca	CAvo EPot GKev SBrt SDeJ SDir

Sanguinaria (*Papaveraceae*)

canadensis	CAvo EGrI EHyd EPPr EPot GEdr GKev GPoy LEdu LRHS MMuc NHol NHpl NRHS NRya SMHy WFar WPnP
- f. ***multiplex*** (d)	EHyd NBir NRHS SPhx
- - 'Plena' (d) ♀H5	CMea CWCL EBee ECha EHyd EMor EPfP GEdr GKev GPoy LRHS MCor NFav NHar NHol NHpl NPoe NRHS NRya NSla NSti SDeJ WFar WPnP
- pink-flowered	GEdr
- 'Star'	GKev

Sanguisorba ✿ (*Rosaceae*)

from Japan	GGro LPla MAvo
§ ***albiflora***	CDoC CKno ECha EPfP EShb EWhm GBee GGro ILea LEdu LRHS LShi MMuc MNrw MRav MSpe MidI NDov NGdn SEND SPhx SRkn WCAu
- 'Cindy's Tall White'	SPVi
'All Time High'	GBin LEdu NDov
alpina	GLog MMuc SEND
'Ankum's Thums'	MAvo MHol
applanata	GGro SBrt WCot WFar WPGP
armena	EWes LEdu MNrw MPie SPhx WFar WWtn
'Autumn Bliss'	GMaP
'Autumn Red'	MAvo
'Beetlewings'	NDov
'Blacksmith's Burgundy'	LEdu
'Blackthorn'	CKno CMea ECtt GMaP LPla LRHS MAvo MBel NDov NLar SMHy SMad SPhx WCAu WCot WHoo
'Burr Blanc'	GMaP MSpe SMHy SPhx
canadensis	Widely available
- hybrid	MAvo
- 'Twisty'	LPla
'Candy Floss'	MAvo WHoo
'Cangshan Cranberry'	EBee ECtt GMaP LPla LRHS MAvo MBel NDov SMHy SMad SPhx WCot
'Ccc'	MAvo
'Chocolate Tip'	CDor EBee ECtt EPPr GPSL ILea MAvo NGrd SEdd SPVi SPhx
'Coen's Cranberry'	NDov
dodecandra	EBee MAvo
'Foxtail'	MAvo SPVi
hakusanensis	CBod CKno EBee ECha EHyd ELan EWhm GKev GMaP LEdu MAvo MBriF MNrw NBir NBro NChi NFav NGBl NLar SBls SBut SPVi SPeP SPhx WCAu WCot WFar
- B&SWJ 8709	WCru
- 'Alster Luft' **new**	SPVi
- 'Lilac Squirrel'	CKno ECtt EMor GBin GMaP ILea IPot LEdu LRHS LSou MAvo MBel MNrw MPie MSCN MSpe NDov NLar SMad SPVi SPad SRms WCAu WFar WTor
'Hendrickx' **new**	LEdu
'Ivory Towers'	MAvo SPhx WFar
'John Coke'	NLar
'Joni'	CKno MAvo
'Little Angel'	CBct CBod CKno CSpe CWGN EBee ECtt ELon EMor EPfP EShb EWhm GBee LSou MAvo MBNS MBel MHol MPie NEoE NLar SEdd SPad SPoG WCot WFar WMal WTor WTyc WWtn
'Maartjes Merlot' **new**	SPVi
magnifica	EWes LEdu
- ***alba***	see *S. albiflora*
menziesii ♀H7	Widely available
- 'Dali Marble' (v)	ECtt NLar
- 'Misbourne'	LPla
- 'Wake Up'	MBNS NDov
§ ***minor***	CAgr CBod CCBP CHby CLau GJos GPoy GQue LEdu MBow MHer MNHC NMir NPol SPhx SPlb SRms SVic WHer WWild XAbr XLum
- subsp. ***minor***	CHab
'Misbourne Pink'	LPla
'Miss Elly'	MAvo
'Nettlesworth Wand'	SMHy SPhx
obtusa	Widely available
- 'Chatto'	CTtf MAvo NLar WPGP
- silver-leaved	MNrw WFar
- white-flowered	EBee EWTr MBel WPGP
officinalis	CHab CSpe EGrI GJos GKev GQue LShi MACG MBow MHer NMir NPol SCob SPer SPhx SRms WCAu WFar
- CDC 262	EPPr LEdu SMHy SPhx
- CDC 282	CSpe SPhx
- CDC 292	MAvo WCot
- DJHC 535	LEdu NLar
- 'Arnhem'	CDor CKno EBee ECtt EPPr GPSL ILea LEdu LRHS NDov NLar SEdd SMHy SPhx WCot WTor
- 'Burgundy Buttons'	CRos LRHS NDov NSti
- 'Crimson Queen'	EBee ECtt GMaP GQue IPot MidI NLar
- dark-flowered	MAvo
- early-flowering	GMaP GWyn
- 'False Tanna'	WFar
- 'Lemon Splash' (v)	EBee ECtt LEdu WCot WFar WPGP
- 'Lum'	MAvo NDov
- 'Martin's Mulberry'	EBee EWes LEdu MAvo MNrw NDov
- 'Morning Select'	EBee ECtt EPPr GMaP NLar
- 'Red Buttons'	MAvo NDov WMal
- 'Red Thunder'	CSpe EBee ECtt EPPr EWhm EWoo GMaP GPSL ILea LCro LEdu LOPS LRHS MAvo MBel MHol NLar SEdd SPVi WCAu WCot WGwG WPGP
- 'Shiro-fukurin' (v)	EBee ECtt EShb EWes EWhm GMaP LEdu MBel MHol MNrw MSpe NLar WCot WFar WHer WSHC
- 'Tsetseguun'	LEdu LRHS MAvo SPhx WPGP
- 'White Tanna'	SCob
parviflora	see *S. tenuifolia* var. *parviflora*
pimpinella	see *S. minor*
'Pink Brushes'	CKno CTtf ECtt EMor GMaP GQue ILea IPot LRHS MAvo MBriF MNrw NDov NGrd NLar WCAu
'Pink September'	MAvo MHol
'Pink Tanna'	Widely available
'Prim and Proper'	MAvo MHol
'Proud Mary'	NDov
'Purple Tails'	MAvo
'Raspberry Coulis'	MAvo WMal
'Raspberry Mivvi'	MAvo SPhx WMal
'Red Busby'	MAvo SMHy
'Rock and Roll'	EBee ECtt EMor EPPr MSpe NLar

	'Ruby Velvet' **new**	IPot MNrw
	'Sangria'	MAvo MHol
	'Sanguine Dwarf'	MAvo
	'Scapino'	ESwi MAvo SMHy
	sitchensis	see *S. stipulata*
§	***stipulata***	CMac EBee EBlo EHyd LEdu LPla LRHS MHer MNrw NRHS
	- var. ***riishirensis***	EMor EPPr MNrw WFar
	'Sussex Prairies Cheyenne'	SPVi
	'Sussex Prairies Iroquois'	SPVi
	'Sussex Prairies Iroquois Alba'	SPVi
	'Sussex Prairies Navaho'	SPVi
	'Swarm'	MAvo
	'Tall Tanna'	MAvo
	'Tanna' ♀H7	Widely available
	tenuifolia	CBod ECha EHyd GKev LShi MACG NChi NGBl NGrd NLar SPhx WCot
	- from Ernst Pagels	MAvo
	- var. ***alba***	Widely available
	- - CDC	MRav
	- - 'Korean Snow'	EPPr GMaP LEdu LPla LRHS NDov SMHy SPhx SSut
	- 'Big Pink'	MAvo MNrw MidI WFar
	- 'Bordeaux'	CDor EBee ECtt MAvo
	- 'Henk Gerritsen'	MAvo NLar SEdd SPVi WCAu WFar
§	- var. ***parviflora***	EBee LEdu MAvo NLar SBut WHoo WPGP
	- 'Pieters'	ILea MAvo
	- 'Pink Elephant'	CKno EBee ECha ECtt EMor EPPr EWTr EWhm GJos GKev GMaP GQue ILea LRHS MAvo NLar SCob SEdd SPVi SPhx WCAu WFar
	- pink-flowered	SMHy
	- var. ***purpurea***	EBee GBin
	- 'Purpurea'	CKno EBee EPPr GPSL GQue ILea LPla MAvo NFav SPhx WCAu WCot WPGP
	- 'Stand Up Comedian'	LEdu MAvo MNrw NDov NLar SHar WPGP
	- 'Strawberry Frost'	MAvo MHol SMHy
	- 'Strawberry Fruli'	LEdu WPGP
	- 'Sturdy Guard'	LEdu
	- 'The Invisible'	MAvo WCAu
	- 'White Tanna'	EBee EPPr GQue LEdu MAvo SPVi
	'Tully' **new**	MAvo
	'Woottens' **new**	LPla

Sanicula (*Apiaceae*)

§	***epipactis*** ♀H7	Widely available
	- 'Harry Foley' (v)	NWad
	- 'Thor' (v)	ECha EWes GBin GEdr MNrw NBir NGrd SPVi WAbe
	- 'Variegata'	see *S. epipactis* 'Thor'
	europaea	CEls CTtf GPoy NGrd NMir

Sansevieria (*Asparagaceae*)

bacularis 'Mikado'	LCro LOPS
cylindrica	CDoC EShb SPlb
- 'Straight'	SPad
trifasciata	NGKo
- 'Golden Hahnii' (v) ♀H1b	EShb
- 'Hahnii' ♀H1b	EShb NGKo
- var. ***laurentii*** (v) ♀H1b	CDoC LCro LOPS
- 'Moonshine' ♀H1b	CDoC EShb
zeylanica	LCro LOPS

Santolina ✿ (*Asteraceae*)

	'Apple Court'	EHyd
	benthamiana	EBtc
§	***chamaecyparissus***	Widely available
	- var. ***corsica*** misapplied	see *S. chamaecyparissus* 'Nana'
	- subsp. ***insularis***	XSen
	- 'Lambrook Silver'	CBod CFis CKel CRos EBee EHyd ENfk EPfP LRHS MAsh NLar NRHS SCoo XSen
	- 'Lemon Queen'	CBod CCBP CRos EGrI ENfk EPfP EWhm LRHS MAsh MSwo NBir NLar NRHS SCob SRms XSen
	- subsp. ***magonica***	EBtc XSen
§	- 'Nana' ♀H5	CRos EHyd EPfP LRHS MAsh MHer MRav MSwo SCob SGBe SRGP SRms XSen
	- 'Pretty Carroll' ♀H5	CBod CDoC CKel CRos EBee EBtc ELan EPfP LRHS LSRN MAsh NLar SPoG WFar
	- 'Small-Ness'	ELan EPfP EWes LRHS MHer NLar SWvt WAbe WHer XSen
	etrusca	EAJP EBtc ECha LRHS XSen
	incana	see *S. chamaecyparissus*
*	***lindavica***	CKel EBtc XSen
	pectinata	see *S. rosmarinifolia* subsp. *canescens*
	pinnata	CTri EBtc
§	- subsp. ***neapolitana*** ♀H5	ECha ELan ENfk EPfP MRav SCob SDix SEND
	- - cream-flowered	see *S. pinnata* subsp. *neapolitana* 'Edward Bowles'
§	- - 'Edward Bowles'	CBod CKel EBee EGrI EPfP EWhm EWoo GMaP LRHS LSRN MAvo MHer MNHC MRav MSwo NBir NLar NPer SCob SEdd SPoG SRms SVen SWvt WCFE WFar WGwG WHer XSen
	- - 'Sulphurea'	CDoC CKel CMea CRos EGrI EHyd EPfP LRHS MAsh SPer SPhx WKif
	rosmarinifolia	CBod CCBP CRos EHyd GPoy GQue LRHS MRav NRHS SCob SLon SPlb SRms
§	- subsp. ***canescens***	EBtc EGrI
	- 'Green Fizz'	WFar
	- 'Lemon Fizz' ♀H5	Widely available
§	- subsp. ***rosmarinifolia***	CEme ECha ELan ENfk EPfP LShi MHer MRav SAng SCob SDix SPer SRms SWvt WFar XLum XSen
	- - 'Primrose Gem' ♀H5	CBcs CBod CDoC CKel CRos CTri ECha EGrI EPfP LRHS MAsh MAvo MNHC MSwo NRHS SCob SEND SGbt SPer SRms SWvt XSen
	- - white-flowered	WHer
	SHADES OF JADE ('Sant101')	EBtc SCob SRms
	tomentosa misapplied	see *S. pinnata* subsp. *neapolitana*
	virens	see *S. rosmarinifolia* subsp. *rosmarinifolia*
	viridis	see *S. rosmarinifolia* subsp. *rosmarinifolia*
	'Yellow Buttons' **new**	LRHS

Sanvitalia (*Asteraceae*)

AZTEKENGOLD	see *Melampodium montanum* AZTEC GOLD
procumbens misapplied	see *Melampodium montanum*

Sapindus (*Sapindaceae*)

mukorossi B&SWJ 14689	WCru

Saponaria (*Caryophyllaceae*)

	'Bressingham' ♀H5	CBod ECtt ELan EPfP EPot WAbe WFar WIce
	Bressingham hybrid	MAsh
	caespitosa	EWes
§	***intermedia***	NDov WCot

× ***lempergii*** 'Fritz Lemperg'	NDov WCot WMal
- 'Max Frei'	EBee ECtt ELon EPPr LCro LOPS LPla MCot MRav NDov SGro SPhx WCot WMal XLum
ocymoides ♀H5	CMea EBee ECha ECtt ELan EPfP LShi MAsh MHol MNHC NHpl SBls SPlb SPoG SRms XLum
- 'Alba'	ECha NSla WFar
- 'Snow Tip'	GRum NGdn
officinalis	CBod CCBP ENfk GBin GPoy GQue LShi MBow MHer MNHC SPlb SRms WCAu WHer WSFF XAbr
- 'Alba Plena' (d)	EBee NLar SEND WCAu WFar XLum
- 'Betty Arnold' (d)	ECtt EMor EPPr EWes LPla WCot WGob
- 'Flore Pleno' (d)	CBod GAbr WFar
- 'Red Splash'	WFar
- 'Rosea Plena' (d)	CMac EBee ELan EPfP LEdu LRHS MCot MHer MHol MMuc NBid NBir NGdn SEND SPer WFar WGwG
- 'Rubra Plena' (d)	CCBP EPPr EWes MMuc WGob
× ***olivana*** ♀H5	ECtt EPot GArf GMaP GRum MAsh NLar XLum
sicula subsp. ***intermedia***	see *S. intermedia*
zawadskii	see *Silene zawadskii*

Saposhnikovia (*Apiaceae*)

divaricata	SPhx

Saracha (*Solanaceae*)

punctata B&SWJ 14882	WCru
quitensis B&SWJ 14748	WCru

Sarcococca ✿ (*Buxaceae*)

confusa ♀H5	Widely available
hookeriana	ELon EPfP EWoo GDam GKin LSRN MBlu MSwo NFav NLar NWad SGbt SWvt SavN WFar WPGP WSpi
- B&SWJ 2585	WCru
- HWJK 2393	WCru
- HWJK 2428	WCru
- var. ***digyna***	Widely available
- - SDR 7816	GKev
- - 'Purple Stem' ♀H5	CBcs CBod CBrac CDoC CEnd CExl CJun CTri EBee ELan EPfP GKin LCro LEdu LOPS LRHS MGos MNrw NLar SCob SCoo SPer SPoG SWvt WCru WSMil WSpi
§ - - 'Tony Schilling'	CExl CJun WCru
- var. ***hookeriana***	CJun LSRN
- - GWJ 9222	WCru
- - GWJ 9344	WCru
- - GWJ 9369	WCru
- - HWJK 2102	WCru
- - HWJK 2366	WCru
- - HWJK 2393	WCru
- - 'Daman'	CExl
- - 'Ghorepani' ♀H5	CRos EHyd LCro LOPS LRHS NRHS
- var. ***humilis***	Widely available
- WINTER GEM ('Pmoore03'PBR)	CBod CDoC CRos CSBt EBee EHyd ELon EPfP LCro LOPS LRHS LSRN MAsh MGos MSwo NFav NHol NLar NRHS SCob SGBe SLon SPoG SRkn WFar WGrn
orientalis	CBct CExl CJun CKel CMCN CRos EBee EHyd ELon EPfP IDee LEdu LRHS MAsh NLar NRHS NWad SPoG WLov WPGP WSpi
'Roy Lancaster'	see *S. ruscifolia* var. *chinensis* 'Dragon Gate'
'Rudolph'	CJun CKel EPfP
ruscifolia	Widely available
- var. ***chinensis***	CJun NLar WCru WPGP
§ - - 'Dragon Gate' ♀H5	CDoC CExl CJun CKel CRos EBee EGrI EHed EHyd ELan ELon EPfP LRHS LSRN MAsh MGos NRHS SLon SPoG SWvt WCru WLov WPGP WSpi XSte
saligna	CBcs CJun EBee EPfP GKev MRav SLon WCru WLov
- HWJK 2428	WCru
- MF P2056	WCru
- NJM 12.043	WPGP
I ***taiwaniana*** RWJ 9999	WCru
trinervia B&SWJ 9500	WCru
vagans B&SWJ 7285	WCru
- B&SWJ 9760	WCru
- B&SWJ 9766 from Vietnam	WCru
aff. ***vagans*** B&SWJ 7265 from north Thailand	WCru
wallichii	CBcs CBod CExl EHed ELon EPfP IKel LEdu LRHS MBlu MGil SPoG WCot WLov WPGP
- B&SWJ 2291	CJun WCru
- GWJ 9427	WCru
- HWJK 2425	WCru
- HWJK 2428	WCru
- PAB 13.077	LEdu
aff. ***wallichii***	EBee
- NJM 12.043	WPGP
zeylanica B&SWJ 10199	WCru
- var. ***brevifolia*** GWJ 9480	WCru
- - GWJ 9483	WCru

Sarcopoterium (*Rosaceae*)

spinosum	CKel SVen

Sarmienta (*Gesneriaceae*)

repens	see *S. scandens*
§ ***scandens*** ♀H1c	CExl WAbe WPGP

Sarothamnus see *Cytisus*

Sarracenia ✿ (*Sarraceniaceae*)

× ***ahlesii***	CHew WFar
- (*S. alata* 'Red Throat' × (× *areolata*)) **new**	WFar
alata	SHmp WFar WSSs
- from George County, Mississippi **new**	WFar
- from Nicholson County, Mississippi **new**	WFar
- from Robertson County, Texas	WFar
- var. ***alata***	CHew
- all green	SHmp
- var. ***atrorubra***	CHew
- 'Black Tube' ♀H3	WFar WSSs
- 'Black Tube' × ***oreophila*** **new**	WFar
- 'Citronelle'	WFar
- heavily veined	SHmp WSSs
- - from East Texas **new**	WFar
- large lid, robust, from Texas **new**	WFar
- var. ***nigropurpurea***	CHew WSSs
- var. ***ornata***	CHew WSSs
- pubescent	SPlb WSSs
- - from Deer Park, Alabama	WFar
- 'Red Lid'	WFar WSSs
- 'Red Lid' × ***purpurea*** subsp. ***venosa*** **new**	WFar

- var. ***rubrioperculata***	CHew WSSs
- veined, from Angelina County, Texas **new**	WFar
- wavy lid	SHmp WSSs
- white-flowered	WSSs
alata* × *flava	see *S.* × *soperi*
alata* × *oreophila	WFar
***alata* × (× *willisii*) new**	WFar
× ***areolata***	CHew SHmp WFar WSSs
'Camisole' × 'Jenny Helen' **new**	WFar
× ***catesbaei***	CHew SHmp WFar WSSs
- (*S. flava* × *purpurea* subsp. *purpurea* f. *heterophylla*) **new**	WFar
- 'Heterophylla' **new**	WFar
- Melanorhoda Group **new**	WFar
- Melanorhoda Group × (× *moorei* 'Marston Clone') **new**	WFar
- snakeskin-veined **new**	WFar
× ***catesbaei*** × (× ***excellens***) **new**	WFar
× ***catesbaei*** × ***leucophylla*** **new**	WFar
× ***catesbaei*** × (× ***moorei***) **new**	WFar
× ***catesbaei*** × (× ***popei***) **new**	WFar
× ***catesbaei*** × ***rubra*** **new**	WFar
× ***chelsonii*** **new**	WFar
× ***chelsonii*** × ***flava*** var. ***ornata*** **new**	WFar
× ***courtii***	SHmp WFar
× ***courtii*** × ***purpurea*** subsp. ***venosa*** ruffled lid **new**	WFar
'Dainty Maid' **new**	WFar
'Daniel Rudd' **new**	WFar
'Decora' **new**	WFar
'Diane Whittaker'	WFar WSSs
'Dutch Stevens' ♀H3 **new**	SHmp
'Eva' ♀H3	SHmp WFar WSSs
'Evendine' **new**	WFar
× ***excellens***	CHew WFar WSSs
- 'Judy' **new**	WFar
- 'Loch Ness' **new**	WFar
× ***excellens*** × ***leucophylla*** × ***rubra*** subsp. ***gulfensis***	WFar
× ***excellens*** × (× ***readei***) **new**	WFar
× ***excellens*** × ***rubra*** **new**	WFar
× ***exornata***	SPlb SRms WFar
- 'Peaches'	WFar WSSs
'Fiona'	SHmp
flava	LCro LOPS WSSs WTyc
- all green giant	see *S. flava* var. *maxima*
- var. ***atropurpurea***	SHmp WFar WSSs
- - from Blackwater, Florida	WFar
- - from North Carolina **new**	WFar
- - from Wewahitchka, Florida **new**	WFar
- var. ***cuprea***	CHew SHmp WFar WSSs
- - from North Carolina **new**	WFar
- var. ***flava***	CHew WFar WSSs
- - from Prince George County, Virginia **new**	WFar
- - 'Bronze Blush' **new**	WFar
- - 'Marston Dwarf' **new**	WFar
- 'Goldie' **new**	WFar
§ - var. ***maxima***	CHew SHmp WFar WSSs
- var. ***maxima*** × ***oreophila*** heavily veined **new**	WFar
- var. ***maxima*** × (× ***moorei*** 'Brooks's hybrid')	SPlb
- var. ***ornata***	CHew SHmp WFar WSSs
- - from Apalachicola, Florida **new**	WFar
- - from Bay County, Florida **new**	WFar
- var. ***rubricorpora***	CHew SHmp SPlb WFar WSSs
- - from Apalachicola, Florida **new**	WFar
- - 'Burgundy'	WFar WSSs
- - 'Claret'	WFar WSSs
- - 'Claret' × ***oreophila*** × ***purpurea***	WFar
- var. ***rugelii***	CHew SHmp SPlb WSSs
- - from Milton County, Florida **new**	WFar
- - from N. Florida **new**	WFar
- - from Prince George County, Virginia **new**	WFar
- - from Telogia, Florida **new**	WFar
- - giant and robust **new**	WFar
- - wavy lid **new**	WFar
- f. ***viridescens***	CHew
× ***formosa*** **new**	WFar
'Frogita' **new**	WFar
'Ghost' **new**	WFar
'God's Gift' **new**	WFar
× ***harperi*** **new**	WFar
'Hugh Jampton' **new**	WFar
'Hummer's Hammerhead' **new**	WFar
'Jedi'	WTyc
'Johnny Marr'	SHmp
'Joyce Cooper'	CHew
'Judith Hindle' ♀H3	SHmp WFar WSSs
'Judith Hindle' × (× ***moorei*** 'Elizabeth') **new**	WFar
'Juthatip Soper' ♀H3	SHmp WFar WSSs
'Ladies in Waiting' ♀H3	WFar
leucophylla	CDoC SHmp SPlb SRms WFar WSSs WTyc
- from Okaloosa Co., Florida	SHmp
- from Perdido, Alabama **new**	WFar
- var. ***alba***	CHew WSSs
- 'Deer Park Alabama'	SHmp WSSs
- green	WSSs
- - from Milton, Florida **new**	WFar
- green and white	WSSs
- var. ***leucophylla***	CHew
- pubescent	WSSs
- - from Deer Park, Alabama	SHmp
- red and white **new**	WFar
- 'Schnell's Ghost' ♀H3	SHmp WFar WSSs
- 'Tarnok'	WFar WSSs
- f. ***viridescens***	CHew WSSs
- white-topped **new**	WFar
leucophylla × ***oreophila*** **new**	WFar
leucophylla × (× ***popei***) **new**	WFar
'Lynda Butt' ♀H3	SHmp WFar WSSs
× ***miniata***	SHmp WFar WSSs
minor	SHmp WFar WSSs
- from Pine Mountain, Georgia **new**	WFar

- from Waycross, Georgia **new**	WFar
- var. ***minor***	CHew
§ - 'Okee Giant'	WSSs
- 'Okefenokee Giant'	see *S. minor* 'Okee Giant'
- var. ***okefenokeensis***	CHew WFar WSSs
- - from Deeland County, Florida **new**	WFar
- - from Waycross, Georgia **new**	WFar
- var. ***okefenokeensis*** × (× ***willisii***) **new**	WFar
minor × ***oreophila*** **new**	WFar
minor × ***rubra*** **new**	WFar
× ***mitchelliana***	CHew SHmp WFar WSSs
- 'Bella' ♀H3	SHmp WSSs
- 'Mr Purplehaze' ♀H3	SHmp WSSs
- pale **new**	WFar
- 'Rita Soper' ♀H3	SHmp
× ***moorei***	CHew SHmp WFar WSSs
- (*S.* × *mitchelliana* 'Rita Soper') × (× *moorei* 'Leah Wilkerson') **new**	SHmp
- 'Adrian Slack'	CHew WFar WSSs
- 'Brooks's Hybrid' ♀H4	CHew SHmp WFar WSSs
- Gulf Coast form **new**	SHmp
- 'Leah Wilkerson'	CHew WFar WSSs
- Marston Clone **new**	WFar
- 'Marston Mill' **new**	WFar
- 'Peaches' **new**	WFar
- 'Welsh Dragon' **new**	WFar
× ***moorei*** × (× ***readei***) **new**	WFar
oreophila	SHmp SPlb WFar WSSs
- from Boaz, Alabama **new**	WFar
- from Boaz, Alabama × ***purpurea*** subsp. ***venosa*** **new**	WFar
- from Cherokee, Alabama **new**	WFar
- from Sand Mountain, Georgia **new**	WFar
- heavily veined **new**	WFar
- var. ***oreophila***	CHew
- var. ***ornata***	CHew
oreophila × ***purpurea*** subsp. ***venosa*** **new**	WFar
× ***popei***	WFar WSSs
- (*S. flava* var. *maxima* × (× *popei*)) **new**	WFar
× ***popei*** × ***purpurea*** subsp. ***venosa*** **new**	WFar
× ***popei*** × (× ***swaniana***) **new**	WFar
'Pretty 'n' Pink' **new**	WFar
psittacina	SHmp SRms WSSs
- var. ***okefenokeensis***	CHew
- var. ***psittacina*** ♀H3	CHew
purpurea	SPlb WCot WTyc
- subsp. ***purpurea*** ♀H6	CHew SHmp WFar WSSs
- - f. ***heterophylla*** ♀H6	WSSs
- - 'Lake Hiron' **new**	WFar
- subsp. ***venosa***	CHew SHmp SPlb WFar WSSs
- - var. ***burkii*** ♀H3	SHmp WSSs
× ***readei***	SHmp WFar WSSs
× ***rehderi***	SHmp WFar WSSs
rubra	WSSs
- subsp. ***alabamensis*** ♀H3	CHew SHmp WSSs
- subsp. ***gulfensis***	CHew SHmp WSSs
- - f. ***luteoviridis***	WSSs
- subsp. ***jonesii***	CHew SHmp WFar WSSs
- - from McClures Bog, North Carolina **new**	WFar
* - - f. ***heterophylla***	WFar
- - f. ***viridescens***	WSSs
- subsp. ***rubra***	CHew SHmp WSSs
- - long lid **new**	WFar
- subsp. ***wherryi***	CHew WSSs
- - 'Chatom Giant'	WFar
- - giant	WSSs
- - yellow-flowered	WSSs
'Scarlet Belle'	SHmp WFar
× ***soperi***	CHew SHmp WFar
- all red	SHmp WFar
- (*S. alata* × *S. flava* var. *maxima*)	WFar WSSs
- (*S. alata* 'Red Lid' × *flava* var. *rubricorpora* 'Burgundy') **new**	WFar
× ***swaniana***	SHmp SRms WFar
'Tara'	WTyc
'True Blood' **new**	WFar
'Tygo'PBR	SHmp
'Vogel' ♀H3	SHmp WSSs
× ***willisii*** **new**	WFar
× ***wrigleyana***	SRms WFar WTyc

Saruma (*Aristolochiaceae*)

henryi	EMor EPfP ESwi EWld GEdr GGro GKev GLog LEdu MAvo MPie NLar SBls SBrt SMad WCot WCru WFar WSHC

Sasa (*Poaceae*)

glabra f. ***albostriata***	see *Sasaella masamuneana* 'Albostriata'
kurilensis	MWht
§ - 'Shima-shimofuri' (v)	EShb
§ ***palmata***	LCro LOPS MMuc SArc
- f. ***nebulosa***	CBcs LPar MWht NLar SArc
tessellata	see *Indocalamus tessellatus*
tsuboiana	CBcs MWht NLar SGol
§ ***veitchii***	CBcs GArf GQue MMuc MRav MWht NLar SCob SGol WFar

Sasaella (*Poaceae*)

§ ***masamuneana*** 'Albostriata' (v)	MWht
§ ***ramosa***	CBcs GBin MWht

Sassafras (*Lauraceae*)

albidum	CBcs CMCN EHyd ELan EPfP LRHS MAsh MMrt NLar SLon SPoG WPGP

satsuma see *Citrus reticulata*

Satureja ✿ (*Lamiaceae*)

biflora	WJek
coerulea ♀H5	EWes XSen
douglasii	CBod WJek
- 'Indian Mint'PBR	ENfk MHer SRms
hortensis	CBod CLau ENfk LCro LOPS MHer MNHC SRms SVic WJek XAbr
intricata	XSen
montana	CCBP CHby CLau EBou ELan ENfk EWhm GJos GPoy GQue LCro LOPS MBros MHer MNHC NGrd SEND SPhx SRms SVic WJek XAbr XSen
* - ***citriodora***	GPoy MHer XAbr XSen
§ - subsp. ***illyrica***	SPhx WJek XLum XSen
- 'Purple Mountain'	GPoy MHer

	- *subspicata*	see *S. montana* subsp. *illyrica*
	repanda	see *S. spicigera*
§	***spicigera***	CBod EBou ENfk EPot EWhm LEdu MHer MMuc SPhx SRms WJek XLum XSen
*	- 'Prostrata'	CLau
	thymbra	SPhx SRms

Sauromatum (*Araceae*)

	gaoligongense	WCot
	giganteum	GKev
	guttatum	see *S. venosum*
§	***venosum***	CExl CPla CRos EBee EHyd EPfP EShb EWld GKev LEdu LRHS NGKo NRHS SPlb WCot WSMil WTyc XLum

Saururus (*Saururaceae*)

cernuus	CBen CBod CWat ELan LLWG WMAq WWtn XLum
- 'Hertford Streaker' (v)	WCot
chinensis	LLWG SBrt
- PB 95-85 **new**	GGro

Saussurea (*Asteraceae*)

centiloba	GGro
subsp. ***pachyneura*** W/O 7247 **new**	
costus	GPoy
pseudoalpina	WCot
stella	GKev

savory, summer see *Satureja hortensis*

savory, winter see *Satureja montana*

Saxegothaea (*Podocarpaceae*)

conspicua	CBcs IDee NLar
- 'Ray Wood' **new**	WPGP

Saxifraga ✿ (*Saxifragaceae*)

	JJH 9309174	NMen
	acerifolia (5)	GEdr
	'Ada' (× *petraschii*) (7)	WHoo
§	'Afrodite' (*sempervivum*) (7)	NMen
	aizoides (9)	GKev
	'Akibare' (*fortunei*) (5)	GEdr
	'Aladdin' (× *borisii*) (7)	NMen
	'Alan Hayhurst' (8)	EPot NSla NWad WAbe
	'Alan Martin' (× *boydilacina*) (7)	EPot EWes NMen
	'Alba' ambig.	CRos EHyd LRHS NRHS
	'Alba' (× *apiculata*) (7) 🏆H5	EPot MAsh NMen NRya SPlb SRms
	'Alba' (*dinnikii*) (7) **new**	EPot
	'Alba' (*oppositifolia*) (7)	ELan EWes NWad WAbe
	'Albert Einstein' (× *apiculata*) (7) 🏆H5	NMen
	'Albertii' (*callosa*)	see *S.* 'Albida'
§	'Albida' (*callosa*) (8)	NWad WAbe
	'Albrecht Dürer' (Lasciva Group) (7)	NMen
	'Aldo Bacci' (Milford Group) (7)	NMen NSla
	'Alexander Humboldt' (Expedition Group) (7)	NMen
	'Alfons Mucha' (7)	EPot NMen
	'Allendale Accord' (7)	NMen
	'Allendale Andante' (× *arco-valleyi*) (7)	NMen
	'Allendale Angel' (× *kepleri*) (7)	NMen
	'Allendale Argonaut' (7)	NMen
	'Allendale Ballad' (7)	NMen
	'Allendale Ballet' (7)	NMen
	'Allendale Bamby' (× *lismorensis*) (7)	EPot
	'Allendale Banshee' (7)	NMen
	'Allendale Beau' (× *lismorensis*) (7)	NMen
	'Allendale Beauty' (7)	WAbe
	'Allendale Betty' (× *lismorensis*) (7)	NMen
	'Allendale Billows' (7)	NMen NSla
	'Allendale Bonny' (7)	EPot NSla WAbe
	'Allendale Boon' (× *izari*) (7)	NMen
	'Allendale Bounty' (7)	NMen
	'Allendale Bravo' (× *lismorensis*) (7)	NMen WHoo
	'Allendale Cabal' (7)	NMen
	'Allendale Carol' (7)	NMen
	'Allendale Cavalier' (7)	NMen
	'Allendale Charm' (Swing Group) (7)	EPot GKev NMen WAbe WHoo
	'Allendale Chick' (7)	NMen
	'Allendale Citation' (7)	NMen
	'Allendale Delight' (7)	NMen
	'Allendale Desire' (7)	WAbe
	'Allendale Divine' (7)	NMen
	'Allendale Dream' (7)	NMen
	'Allendale Duo' (7)	NMen
	'Allendale Eden' (7)	NMen
	'Allendale Elegance' (7)	NMen WAbe
	'Allendale Elf' (7)	NMen WHoo
	'Allendale Elite' (7)	NMen WAbe
	'Allendale Enchantment' (7)	NMen
	'Allendale Epic' (7)	NMen
	'Allendale Fairy' (7)	WHoo
	'Allendale Fame' (7)	NMen
	'Allendale Frost' (7)	NMen WAbe
	'Allendale Ghost' (7)	NMen
	'Allendale Goblin' (7)	NMen
	'Allendale Grace' (7)	NMen WAbe
	'Allendale Gremlin' (7)	NMen
	'Allendale Harvest' (7)	NMen
	'Allendale Hobbit' (7)	NMen
	'Allendale Host' (7)	NMen
	'Allendale Ice' (7)	NMen
	'Allendale Icon' (× *polulacina*) (7)	NMen
	'Allendale Imp' (7)	NMen
	'Allendale Ina' (7)	NMen
	'Allendale Jinn' (7)	NMen NSla
	'Allendale Jo' (7)	NMen WAbe
	'Allendale Joy' (× *wendelacina*) (7)	NMen
	'Allendale Magic' (7)	NMen
	'Allendale News' (7)	NMen
	'Allendale Noon' (7)	NMen
	'Allendale Snow' (× *rayei*) (7)	EWes NMen
	'Allendale Tommy' (7)	NMen
	'Alpenglow' (7)	NMen
	alpigena (7)	NSla WAbe
	ALPINO EARLY LIME ('Sax20007') (15)	LRHS WFar
	ALPINO EARLY PICOTEE ('Saxz0010'[PBR]) (× *arendsii*) (15)	LRHS
	ALPINO EARLY PINK ('Saxz0009'[PBR]) (× *arendsii*) (15)	LRHS

	ALPINO EARLY PINK HEART ('Saxz0008'^{PBR}) (× *arendsii*) (15)	LRHS
	ALPINO EARLY WHITE ('Saxz0001') (× *arendsii*) (15)	LRHS MAvo
	'Amberglow' (× *anglica*) (7)	EPot NMen NSla
	'Amberine' (× *anglica*) (7)	NMen WHoo
	'Amedeo Modigliani' (7)	NMen
	'Amitie' (× *gloriana*) (7)	NMen
	× ***andrewsii*** (8 × 11)	XLum
	angustifolia Haw.	see *S. hypnoides*
	'Anna' (× *fontanae*) (7)	EPot NMen NSla
	'Anne Beddall' (× *goringiana*) (7)	NMen
	'Anneka Hope' (8)	GKev
	'Antonín Dvořák' (× *arco-valleyi*) (7)	NMen
	'Antonio' (× *bertolonii*) (7)	NMen
	'Antonio Vivaldi' (7)	NMen
	'Aphrodite' (*sempervivum*)	see *S.* 'Afrodite'
	× ***apiculata*** (7)	EBou GKev GMaP MAsh
	× ***apiculata*** *sensu stricto* hort.	see *S.* 'Gregor Mendel'
	'Apple Blossom' (Mossy Group) (15)	ECtt EPfP NEoE NRya
	'Aramis' (7)	NMen
§	'Arco' (× *arco-valleyi*) (7)	EPot
	× ***arco-valleyi*** *sensu stricto* hort.	see *S.* 'Arco'
	× ***arendsii*** purple-flowered (15)	CPla MMuc SCob SPlb
	- white-flowered	SCob
§	'Aretiastrum' (× *boydii*) (7)	NMen
	'Argia Romani' (7)	NMen
	'Arleta' (Southside Seedling Group) (8)	WIce
	'Arthur' (× *anglica*) (7)	NMen
	'Assimilis' (× *petraschii*) (7)	EPot NMen
	'Athena' (7)	NMen
	'Atropurpurea' (*paniculata* subsp. *cartilaginea*) (8)	GMaP NFav NHol NSla WFar WHoo WIce XLum
	'Audrey Lowe' (*oppositifolia*) (7)	WAbe
	'Auguste Renoir' (Decora Group) (7)	NSla
	'Aurea Maculata' (*cuneifolia*)	see *S.*'Aureopunctata'
	'Aurea' (*umbrosa*)	see *S.* 'Aureopunctata'
§	'Aureopunctata' (× *urbium*) (11/v)	CMac CTri CTtf ECha EHyd ELan EPfP GAbr GKev GMaP LEdu LRHS MHer MPie MPnt MRav NRHS SCoo SMad SPer SPlb SPoG SRms SRot WFar XLum
	'Autumn Tribute' (*fortunei*) (5)	GEdr WAbe WFar
	'Ayako' (*fortunei*) (5)	GEdr WFar
	'Ayer's Rock' (7)	NMen
	'Bacci Cf13' (7)	NMen
	'Balcana' (*paniculata*) (8)	WAbe
	'Baldensis'	see *S. paniculata* var. *minutifolia*
	'Ballawley Guardsman' (Mossy Group) (15)	NFav
	'Beatles' (Beat Group) (7)	NMen NSla
§	'Beatrix Stanley' (× *anglica*) (7)	CRos EHyd LRHS MHer NMen NRHS
	'Beautiful Girl' (*fortunei*) (5)	WFar
	'Becky Foster' (× *borisii*) (7)	EPot NMen
	'Bedřich Smetana' (*marginata*) (7)	NMen
	'Beinn Eighe' (× *concinna*) (7)	NMen
	'Beinne Alligin' (× *concinna*) (7)	NMen
	'Ben Loyal' (× *concinna*) (7)	NMen WAbe
	'Beni-karen' (*fortunei*) (5)	GEdr WFar
	'Beni-kirin' (*fortunei*) (5)	GEdr WFar
	'Benimine' (*fortunei*) (5)	GEdr WFar
	'Beni-tsukaji' (*fortunei*) (5)	NBro SHeu
	'Beni-tsukasa' (*fortunei*) (5)	ECtt GEdr GMaP NHar NHpl NLar WFar
	'Beni-zakura' (*fortunei*) (5)	GEdr WFar
	'Berenika' (× *bertolonii*) (7)	EPot NMen
	'Berounka' (Prominent Group) (7)	NMen
	'Bertramka' (Holenka's Miracle Group) (× *megaseiflora*) (7)	NMen NSla
	'Bettina' (× *paulinae*) (7)	NMen
	× ***biasolettoi*** *sensu stricto* hort.	see *S.* 'Phoenix'
	× ***biasolettoi*** Sünd. (7)	CRos EHyd LRHS NRHS
	'Bizourtouse' (× *luteopurpurea*) (7)	NMen NSla
	'Black Beauty' (15)	ECtt NWad
	BLACK RUBY (*fortunei*) (5)	CBcs CExl CSpe CTsd EBee ECha ECtt ELan GAbr GGro GMaP LEdu LRHS MNrw MPnt MSCN MThu NBro NHpl NLar SPlb SPoG SWvt WCot WFar WPnP WSpi WWtn
	'Blackberry and Apple Pie' (*fortunei*) (5) ♀^{H4}	CExl CRos ECtt EHyd EPfP LRHS NRHS SGro SMad SWvt WFar
	'Blaník' (7)	NMen
	'Blütenteppich' (Mossy Group) (15)	MAvo
	'Bob Hawkins' (Mossy Group) (15/v)	NHol NWad
	'Bohdalec' (× *megaseiflora*) (7)	NMen
	'Bohemia' (7)	NMen NSla WAbe
	'Bohemian Karst' (Prominent Group) (7)	NMen
	'Bohemian Paradise' (Region Group) (7)	NMen
	'Bohnice' (× *megaseiflora*) (7)	NMen
	'Bohunka' (7)	NMen
	'Boston Spa' (× *elisabethae*) (7)	CRos EHyd LRHS MAsh MHer NLar NRHS SPlb
	'Boží Dar' (Sessile Group) (7)	NMen
	'Brailes' (× *poluanglica*) (7)	NMen
	'Brian Arundel' (Magnus Group) (7)	NMen
	'Bridget' (× *edithae*) (7)	EHyd NMen NRHS
	'Brimstone' (7)	NMen
	'Brno' (× *elisabethae*) (7)	NMen
	'Brookside' (*burseriana*) (7)	EPot NMen
	brunoniana	see *S. brunonis*
§	***brunonis*** (1)	GKev
	'Bryn Llwyd' (Vanessa Group) (7)	NMen WAbe
	× ***burnatii*** (8)	CRos EHyd LRHS NRHS NSla WFar
	burseriana (7)	GKev NMen WAbe
	'Bychan' (*fortunei*) (5)	WAbe
	caesia L. (8)	SRms
§	***callosa*** (8) ♀^{H5}	CRos EDAr EHyd GKev LRHS MHer MMuc NRHS SEND WAbe
§	- subsp. ***catalaunica*** (8)	WAbe
	- ***lingulata***	see *S. callosa*
	'Candy Floss' (7)	NMen
	× ***canis-dalmatica***	see *S.*'Canis-dalmatica'

	Name	Suppliers
§	'Canis-dalmatica' (× *gaudinii*) (8)	CRos CTtf EBou ECtt EHyd GAbr GArf GJos GKev GQue LRHS NRHS NWad SIvy WFar
	'Carniolica' (× *engleri*) (8)	WAbe
§	'Carniolica' (*paniculata*) (8)	NBro NHol NWad
	carolinica	see *S.*'Carniolica' (*paniculata*)
	cartilaginea	see *S. paniculata* subsp. *cartilaginea*
	catalaunica	see *S. callosa* subsp. *catalaunica*
	'Cathy Read' (× *polulacina*) (7)	NMen
	cebennensis (15)	NMen NRya
	- dwarf (15)	NMen WAbe
	'Celebration'	WAbe
	cespitosa (15)	WAbe
	'Chambers' Pink Pride'	see *S.* 'Miss Chambers'
	'Charles Chaplin' (7)	NMen
	'Charles Darwin' (7)	NMen
	CHEAP CONFECTIONS (*fortunei*) (5)	ECtt EHed GEdr MMrt MPnt NLar SGro SPoG WFar
	CHERRY PIE (*fortunei*) (5)	GEdr NBir NHpl
	'Cherrytrees' (× *boydii*) (7)	NMen
	'Chodov' (Holenka's Miracle Group) (× *megaseiflora*) (7)	EPot NMen
	'Christine' (× *anglica*) (7)	NMen
	cinerea (7)	WAbe
	'Cio-Cio-San' (Vanessa Group) (7)	EPot NMen
	'Citronella' (7)	NMen
	'Claire Felstead' (7)	WAbe
	'Clare' (× *anglica*) (7)	NHol
	'Clare Island' (*rosacea*) (15)	SLee
§	'Clarence Elliott' (London Pride Group) (*umbrosa*) (11) 🏆H5	CTri EBou ECtt EWes GJos GKev GMaP LSun NDov NFav NLar NRya NWad WFar WIce
	'Claude Monet' (Impression Group) (7)	EPot NMen NSla
	'Claudia' (× *borisii*) (7)	NSla
	'Cleo' (× *boydii*) (7)	NMen
§	× ***clibranii*** hort. (15)	WIce
	'Cloth of Gold' (*exarata* subsp. *moschata*) (15)	CRos ECha ECtt EHyd ELan EPfP GKev GWyn LRHS MAsh NEoE NFav NHol NHpl NRHS NWad SPlb SPoG SRms SRot WAbe WIce
	cochlearis (8)	CRos CTri EHyd NBro NRHS NSla WAbe
	- hybrid (8)	MAsh
	'Cockscomb' (*paniculata*) (8)	ECtt ITim NLar NWad WAbe
	× ***concinna*** 'Helvellyn' (7)	WAbe
	'Conwy Snow' (*fortunei*) (5) 🏆H4	WAbe WFar
	'Conwy Star' (*fortunei*) (5)	GEdr WAbe WFar
	'Coolock Gem' (7)	WAbe WHoo
	'Coolock Kate' (7) 🏆H5	EPot NMen NSla WAbe WFar WHoo
	'Corennie Claret'	see *S.*'Glowing Ember'
	'Corona' (× *boydii*) (7)	NMen
*	× ***correvensis***	EBou GWyn
	'Correvoniana' misapplied	see *S.*'Lagraveana'
	'Correvoniana' Farrer (*paniculata*) (8)	EDAr MHer MMuc SEND WHoo XLum
	cortusifolia var. ***stolonifera*** (5)	CBct XLum
	COTTON CROCHET (*fortunei*) (5/d)	ECtt GEdr NBro SHeu WFar
	cotyledon (8)	CRos EHyd LEdu LRHS NRHS SGro WAbe WCFE
	COVENTRY TEARS	see *S.*'Slzy Coventry' (× *proximae*)
§	'Cranbourne' (× *anglica*) (7) 🏆H5	CRos EHyd EPot LRHS NMen NRHS NSla
	'Crenata' (*burseriana*) (7) 🏆H5	CRos EHyd NRHS
	'Crimscote-love' (*poluanglica*) (7)	NMen
	'Crimson Rose' (*paniculata*)	see *S.* 'Rosea' (*paniculata*)
	'Crinoline' (7)	NMen NSla WAbe
§	***crustata*** (8)	EPot GKev NMen WAbe WThu XLum
	- var. ***vochinensis***	see *S. crustata*
	CRYSTAL PINK (*fortunei*) (5/v)	CExl EBee ECtt MBNS NHpl WCot WFar
	'Crystalie' (× *biasolettoi*) (7)	EHyd NRHS
	'Cultrata' (*paniculata*) (8)	NBro
	'Cumulus' (7) 🏆H5	EPot GKev NMen SPlb
§	***cuneifolia*** (11)	MHer NWad XLum
	- var. ***capillipes***	see *S. cuneifolia* subsp. *cuneifolia*
§	- subsp. ***cuneifolia*** (11)	GJos
	'Cuscutiformis' (*stolonifera*) (5)	CElw CExl EWld GEdr MAvo MBel MSCN SGro SRms WBor WFar XLum
	dahurica	see *S. cuneifolia*
	'Dai Uchu' (*fortunei*) (5)	GEdr
	'Dainty Dame' (× *arco-valleyi*) (7)	EHyd NMen NRHS
	'Dana' (Prichard's Monument Group) (× *megaseiflora*) (7)	EPot NMen
	'Darcies Cross'	EDAr
	'David' (7)	NMen
	'Dawn Frost' (7)	EPot
	'Delia' (× *hornibrookii*) (7)	EPot
§	'Dentata' (London Pride Group) (× *polita*) (11)	CElw CMiW ECha LEdu LPla MPnt SMHy WBor
	'Dentata' (× *urbium*)	see *S.*'Dentata' (× *polita*)
I	'Diana' (× *lincolni-fosteri*) (7)	WIce
	diapensioides (7)	NSla WAbe
	dinnikii (7)	WAbe
	× ***dinninaris*** (7)	EPot NSla
	'Dobruška' (× *irvingii*) (7)	NMen
	'Doctor Clay' (*paniculata*) (8)	CRos ECtt EHyd EPot GKev LRHS NHol NRHS NRya NSla SPlb WAbe
	'Doctor Ramsey' (8)	CRos EHyd EWes GArf LRHS NRHS NWad WAbe
	'Doctor Watson' (7)	EPot
	'Dominika' (7)	NMen
	'Don Giovanni' (7)	NMen
	'Donald Mann' (15)	EWes
	'Donatello' (7)	NMen
	'Donnington Chalice' (7)	NMen
	'Donnington Gold' (7)	NMen
	'Donnington Rose' (7)	NMen
	'Donnington Veil' (7)	NSla
	'Dora Ross' (× *baccii*) (7)	NMen
	'Drakula' (*ferdinandi-coburgi*) (7)	CRos EHyd LRHS NMen NRHS NSla
	'Earl Grey' (8)	NSla
	'Edgar Irmscher' (7)	NMen
	'Edith' (× *edithae*) (7)	EHyd
	'Édouard Manet' (Impression Group) (7)	NMen
	'Eiga' (*fortunei*) (5)	GEdr WFar
	'Elegance'	WFar
	'Elf' (7)	see *S.* 'Beatrix Stanley'
	'Elf' (*exarata* subsp. *moschata*) (15)	MAsh SRms
	'Elf Rose' (15)	CRos EHyd EPfP LRHS NEoE NRHS
	'Eliot Hodgkin' (× *millstreamiana*) (7)	NMen
	'Elizabeth Sinclair' (× *elisabethae*) (7)	GKev
	'Elliott's Variety'	see *S.* 'Clarence Elliott' (*umbrosa*)

	'Emil Holub' (Ethography Group) (7)	NMen
	epiphylla (5) BWJ 8177	WCru
	erioblasta (15)	WAbe
§	'Ernst Heinrich' (× *heinrichii*) (7)	NMen
	'Esther' (× *burnatii*) (8)	CMea CRos EBou EHyd GMaP LRHS NRHS NSla SEdd SLee WAbe WHoo
§	'Eulenspiegel' (× *geuderi*) (7)	EPot
	'Eva Hanzliková' (× *izari*) (7)	EPot NMen NSla
	'Excellent' (Exclusive Group) (7)	NSla
	'Exee' (7)	NSla
	'Exhibit' (Exclusive Group) (7)	NMen
	fair maids of France	see *S.* 'Flore Pleno'
	'Fairy' (*exarata* subsp. *moschata*) (15)	NBir NEoE
	'Falstaff' (*burseriana*) (7)	NMen
	× ***farreri*** (15)	WFar WIce
	× ***farreri*** hort.	see *S.* 'Reginald Farrer' (Silver Farreri Group)
	'Fasolt Th98'	NMen
§	***federici-augusti*** (7)	WFar
§	- subsp. ***grisebachii*** (7) ♀H5	CRos EHyd GKev LRHS NRHS NSla WAbe WFar
	ferdinandi-coburgi (7)	NSla WAbe
§	- subsp. ***chrysosplenifolia*** var. ***rhodopea*** (7)	CRos EHyd LRHS NRHS
	'Findling' (Mossy Group) (15)	ECtt EPfP NWad SPoG WAbe WIce
	'Firebrand' (× *kochii*) (7)	WAbe
	'Flavescens' misapplied	see *S.* 'Lutea' (*paniculata*)
	'Fleece' (15)	CBod NHpl
§	'Flore Pleno' (*granulata*) (15/d)	CElw CMiW EBee EWes LEdu NBir
	'Florenc' (7) **new**	GKev
	'Flowers of Sulphur'	see *S.* 'Schwefelblüte'
	fortunei (5) ♀H4	CMac NBir SCob SRms WAbe WFar
	- f. ***alpina*** (5)	NBro
	- var. ***obtusocuneata*** (5)	GEdr GPSL WAbe
	- pink-flowered (5)	WAbe
	'Foster's Gold' (× *elisabethae*) (7)	NMen
	'Four Winds' (Mossy Group) (15)	EWes SPoG
	'Francis Cade' (8)	EPot GAbr NSla WAbe
	'Frank Sinatra' (× *poluanglica*) (7)	NMen
	'Franz Liszt' (7)	NMen
	'Franzii' (× *paulinae*) (7)	NMen
	'Freckles'	GKev NHpl SGro
	'Frederik Chopin' (7)	EPot NMen
	'Friar Tuck' (× *boydii*) (7)	NMen
	'Fumiko' (*fortunei*) (5)	SPlb WAbe
	'G.W. Gould No. 2'	EPot
	'Gaia' (fortunei) (5) **new**	LEdu
	'Gaiety' (15)	CRos EHyd LRHS NEoE NRHS SPoG
	'Galaxie' (Holenka's Miracle Group) (× *megaseiflora*) (7)	NMen
	'Ganymede' (*burseriana*) (7)	NMen
	× ***gaudinii*** (8)	XLum
	'Gelber Findling' (7)	EPot NMen
	'Gelbes Monster' (*fortunei*) (5)	EBee ECtt ELan GEdr GPSL NHar NHpl NLar SBls WCot WFar WSpi WWtn
	'Gem' (× *irvingii*) (7)	CRos EHyd LRHS NRHS
	'Gemma' (× *megaseiflora*) (7)	EHyd NRHS

	'Geoff Wilson' (× *biasolettoi*) (7)	NMen
	'Geoffrey Gould' (7)	NMen
	'George Gershwin' (Blues Group) (7)	NMen
	georgei (7)	WAbe
	× ***geuderi*** *sensu stricto* hort.	see *S.* 'Eulenspiegel'
§	× ***geum*** (11)	CTtf EPPr GBin MRav SDix WFar
	- Dixter form (11)	ECha EWes LEdu NDov NFav SMHy SPhx
	'Gina Lollobrigida' (Blues Group) (7)	EPot
	'Ginkgo 98' (*stolonifera*) (5)	GGro WFar
	'Gleborg' (Mossy Group) (15)	SPoG
	'Gloria' (*burseriana*) (7)	CRos EHyd EPot LRHS MAsh NMen NRHS NSla WIce
	'Gloriana'	see *S.* 'Godiva'
	× ***gloriana*** *sensu stricto* hort. (7)	see *S.* 'Godiva'
	'Gloriosa' (× *gloriana*) (7)	see *S.* 'Godiva'
§	'Glowing Ember' (Mossy Group) (15)	EWes
§	'Godiva' (× *gloriana*) (7)	NMen
	'Gokka' (*fortunei*) (5)	NHar NHpl SHeu XSte
	'Golden Eye' (× *poluanglica*) (7)	NMen
	'Golden Falls' (Mossy Group) (15/v)	SPlb SPoG
	GOLDEN PRAGUE (× *pragensis*)	see *S.* 'Zlatá Praha'
	'Golem' (7)	NMen
	'Goring White' (7)	NMen
	'Gothenburg' (7)	NMen
	'Grace Farwell' (× *anglica*) (7)	NLar
	granulata (15)	EWes GJos NAts
	'Gratoides' (× *grata*) (7)	EPot
	'Grébovka' (× *megaseiflora*) (7)	NMen
	'Gregor' (× *poluanglica*) (7)	NMen
§	'Gregor Mendel' (× *apiculata*) (7) ♀H5	CRos EHyd LRHS NLar NMen NRHS NSla SRms WAbe WHoo
	grisebachii	see *S. federici-augusti* subsp. *grisebachii*
	'Haagii' (× *eudoxiana*) (7)	CTri GKev
	'Hakubai' (*fortunei*) (5)	GEdr WFar
	'Halo' (Liberty Ships Group) (7)	NMen
	'Hardii' (Mossy Group) (15)	EBou
	'Hare Knoll Beauty' (8)	CRos EHyd EPot GKev LRHS NFav NHol NHpl NRHS NSla NWad WAbe WFar WIce
	'Harlow Car' (× *anglica*) (7)	EPot NSla
	'Harlow Car' (× *anglica* × ***poluniniana***) (7)	NMen
	'Harold Bevington' (*paniculata*) (8)	NSla
	'Harold Lloyd' (7)	NMen
	'Harvest Moon' (*stolonifera*) (5)	WFar WHer
	'Heda' (*marginata*) (7)	NMen
	× ***heinreichii*** *sensu stricto* hort.	see *S.* 'Ernst Heinrich'
	'Helga Hufflepuff' (*cortusifolia*) (5)	SGro
	'Henri Rousseau' (Conspecta Group) (7)	NMen
	'Herbert Cuerden' (× *elisabethae*) (7)	EPot

'Hi-Ace' (Mossy Group) (15/v)	NHpl SPlb
'Highlander Red' (Mossy Group) (15)	GWyn
'Highlander Rose Shades' (Mossy Group) (15) **new**	LRHS
'Highlander White' (Mossy Group) (15)	GWyn LRHS
'Hime' (*stolonifera*) (5)	GGro SRms
'Hindhead Seedling' (× *boydii*) (7)	CRos EHyd LRHS NMen NRHS WAbe
'Hi-no-mai' (*fortunei*) (5)	GEdr WFar
'Hiogi' (*fortunei*) (5)	GEdr WFar
hirsuta (11)	CMac ESwi EWTr EWld LEdu MMuc MNrw SSal WCot WCru
§ 'Hirsuta' (*paniculata*) (8)	WFar
'Hirsuta' (× *geum*)	see *S.* × *geum*
'Hirtella' Ingwersen (*paniculata*) (8)	EPot
'His Majesty' (× *irvingii*) (7)	EPot NMen
'Hiten' (*fortunei*) (5)	EBee GKev
'Hitomebore' (*fortunei*) (5)	WFar
'Hocker Edge' (× *arco-valleyi*) (7)	NMen WAbe
'Honeybunch' (Safran Group) (7)	NMen
'Honington' (× *poluanglica*) (7)	NMen
hostii (8)	GArf GKev NWad XLum
- subsp. ***hostii*** (8)	XLum
- - var. ***altissima*** (8)	XLum
- subsp. ***rhaetica*** (8)	NBro WThu XLum
'Hsitou Silver' (*stolonifera*) (5)	WCot
'Hyoseki' (*fortunei*) (5)	GEdr WFar
§ ***hypnoides*** (15)	WAbe
'Iceland' (*oppositifolia*) (7)	EWes WAbe
imparilis (5)	WCru
'Ingeborg' (Mossy Group) (15)	CElw SLee
iranica (7)	NMen
'Irena' (7)	NMen
'Irene Bacci' (× *baccii*) (7)	EPot
× ***irvingii*** *sensu stricto* hort.	see *S.* 'Walter Irving'
'Iyo Haksui' (*fortunei*) (5)	GEdr
× ***jacggiana***	NSla
'James' (7)	NMen NSla
'Jan Amos Kómenský' (× *anglica*) (7)	NMen
'Jan Neruda' (× *megaseiflora*) (7)	EPot NMen
'Jan Palach' (× *krausii*) (7)	NMen
'Jan Preisler' (Conspecta Group) (7)	EPot
'Jaromir' (8)	NMen NSla WAbe
'Jaroslav Horný' (*marginata*) (7)	NMen WAbe
'Jenkinsiae' (× *irvingii*) (7)	EHyd EPot MMuc NLar NMen NRHS NSla WAbe WIce
'Joachim Barrande' (× *siluris*) (7)	EPot
'Jocelynne Bacci' (7)	NMen
'Johanka' (7)	NMen
§ 'Johann Kellerer' (× *kellereri*) (7)	EPot
'John Byam-Grounds' (Honor Group) (7)	WAbe
'John Tomlinson' (*burseriana*) (7)	NMen NSla
'Jorg' (× *biasolettoi*) (7)	EPot

'Josef Čapek' (Holenka's Miracle Group) (× *megaseiflora*) (7)	EPot NMen
'Joy Bishop' (7)	NMen
'Juliet'	see *S.* 'Riverslea'
§ ***juniperifolia*** (7)	SRms XLum
'Jupiter' (Holenka's Miracle Group) (× *megaseiflora*) (7)	EPot NMen
'Kampa' (Holenka's Miracle Group) (7)	NMen
× ***karacardica*** (7)	NMen NSla
karadzicensis (7)	NMen
karadzicensis × ***scardica*** (7)	EPot
'Karasin' (7)	NMen
'Karel Čapek' (Prichard's Monument Group) (× *megaseiflora*) (7)	CRos EHyd EPot LRHS NMen NRHS
'Karlštejn' (× *borisii*) (7)	EPot NMen
§ 'Kaspar Maria Sternberg' (× *petraschii*) (7) ♀^{H5}	CRos EHyd LRHS NRHS
'Kath Dryden' (7)	NMen
'Kathleen Pinsent' (8)	WAbe
'Kathleen' (× *polulacina*) (7)	EPot NMen
'Kath's Delight' (8)	GKev
'Katrin' (× *borisii*) (7)	NSla
'Kawazu-beni' (*fortunei*) (5)	GEdr WFar
'Kbley'	NMen
× ***kellereri*** *sensu stricto* hort.	see *S.* 'Johann Kellerer'
'Ken McGregor' (7)	NMen
'Kestoniensis' (× *salmonica*) (7)	NMen
'Kineton' (× *poluanglica*) (7)	NMen
'King Lear' (× *bursiculata*) (7)	CRos EHyd EPot NRHS
'Kinki Purple' (*stolonifera*) (5)	CDTJ CDoC CSpe CTsd EPPr EPri EShb EWld GWyn WCru WFar WPnP
'Kirke' (7)	EPot
'Klondike' (× *boydii*) (7)	EPot NMen WAbe
'Klonk' (Stratotyp Group) (7)	NMen
'Knapton Pink' (Mossy Group) (15)	GBin NEoE SPoG WIce
'Koda' (Rezervace Group) (7)	NMen
'Kokoryu-nishiki' (*fortunei*) (5)	GEdr WFar
'Komochi-daimonji' (*fortunei*) (5)	GEdr WFar
'Kon Tiki' (7)	NMen
'Korin' (*fortunei*) (5)	WFar
'Krasava' (Prichard's Monument Group) (× *megaseiflora*) (7)	NMen
'Křivoklát' (7)	NMen
'Labe' (× *arco-valleyi*) (7)	EHyd LRHS NMen NRHS
§ 'Labradorica' (*paniculata*) (8)	NRya
'Lady Beatrix Stanley'	see *S.* 'Beatrix Stanley'
§ 'Lagraveana' (*paniculata*) (8) ♀^{H5}	CRos EHyd GKev LRHS NRHS WFar
'Laka' (7)	NMen NSla
'Lantoscana' (*callosa* subsp. *callosa* var. *australis*) (8)	GKev
'Lantoscana Superba' (*callosa* subsp. *callosa* var. *australis*) (8)	NWad

	Name	Suppliers
	'Laura Sinclair' (× *fallsvillagensis*) (7)	NMen
	'Lemon Puff'	NSla NWad WFar
	'Lenka' (× *byam-groundsii*) (7)	EPot NMen
	'Leo Gordon Godseff' (× *elisabethae*) (7)	EHyd LRHS NRHS NSla
	'Leonardo da Vinci' (7)	EPot NMen WAbe
§	'Leonore' (× *landaueri*) (7)	EHyd LRHS NRHS
	'Letchworth Gem' (London Pride Group) (× *urbium*) (11)	CRos EHyd GAbr LRHS NRHS WFar
	'Libuse' (7)	NMen
	'Lidice' (7)	NMen WHoo
	lilacina (7)	NMen NSla WAbe
	'Limelight' (*callosa* subsp. *callosa* var. *australis*) (8)	NWad
	'Lincoln Foster' (8)	NWad
	'Lindau' (7)	NMen
	lingulata	see *S. callosa*
	'Lismore Carmine' (× *lismorensis*) (7)	EPot NMen
	'Lismore Mist' (× *lismorensis*) (7)	EPot
	'Lissadell' (*callosa*) (8)	GKev
*	'Little Piggy' (*epiphylla*) (5)	WCru
	'Lizzy' (7)	NMen
	llonakhensis (1)	WAbe
	'Lohmuelleri' (× *biasolettoi*) (7)	GKev
	lolaensis (7)	WAbe
	London Pride Group	LPot WBrk
	longifolia (8)	EHyd GEdr GKev NHpl NRHS NSla
	- hybrids	GKev
	'Louis Armstrong' (Blues Group) (7)	NMen WAbe
	LOVE ME	see *S.* 'Miluj Mne'
	lowndesii (7)	WAbe
	'Loxley' (× *poluanglica*) (7)	NMen
	'Ludmila Šubrová' (× *bertolonii*) (7)	NMen
	'Lusanna' (× *irvingii*) (7)	GKev
	'Lutea' (*aizoon*)	see *S.* 'Lutea' (*paniculata*)
§	'Lutea' (*paniculata*) (8)	EBou GMaP NBro NHol NRya NSla NWad
§	'Luteola' (× *boydii*) (7)	NMen
	'Lydia' (× *hornibrookii*) (7)	WAbe
	macedonica	see *S. juniperifolia*
	'Maigrün' (*fortunei*) (5)	EBee
	'Mai-hime' (*fortunei*) (5)	GEdr
	'Major' (*cochlearis*) (8)	GKev
	'Major Lutea'	see *S.* 'Luteola'
	'Mangart' (*burseriana*) (7)	NMen
	'Marcela' (× *megaseiflora*) (7)	NMen
	marginata (7) ♀H5	GKev NMen NSla WAbe
	- var. ***bubakii*** (7)	NMen NSla
	- subsp. ***marginata*** var. ***boryi*** (7)	EHyd LRHS NRHS
	- - var. ***coriophylla*** (7)	WAbe
§	- - var. ***rocheliana*** (7)	EHyd LRHS NRHS
	'Marianna' (× *borisii*) (7)	EPot
	'Marie' (7)	NMen
	'Marilyn Monroe' (Vanessa Group) (7)	NMen
	'Maroon Beauty' (*stolonifera*) (5)	EBee ECtt EPPr LPot MCot NBid WCot WFar
	'Mars' (× *elisabethae*) (7)	NMen
	'Marsyandi' (*andersonii*) (7) **new**	WAbe

	Name	Suppliers
	'Marto Hot Rose' (× *arendsii*) (Marto Series) (15) **new**	CBod
	'Mary Golds' (Swing Group) (7)	GKev NLar NMen NSla
	'Masami' (*fortunei*) (5)	GEdr
	× ***megaseiflora*** *sensu stricto* hort.	see *S.* 'Robin Hood'
	mertensiana (6)	NBir WSHC
	'Meteor' (7)	NHol NMen NSla
	'Michelangelo' (Rutil Group) (7)	NMen
	'Mikawa-beni' (*fortunei*) (5)	GEdr WFar
	'Millstream Cream' (× *elisabethae*) (7)	NMen
§	'Miluj Mne' (× *poluanglica*) (7)	CSma NMen NSla SPlb WHoo
	'Minor' (*cochlearis*) (8) ♀H5	CRos EHyd GKev LRHS NRHS
	'Mirko Webr' (Harmonia Group) (7)	NMen
§	'Miss Chambers' (London Pride Group) (11)	CBod CMac EWes LPla SMHy WBrk WCot WFar WSHC
	'Moe' (*fortunei*) (5) ♀H4	GEdr WFar
	'Mollie Broom' (7)	NMen WAbe
	'Momo Tarou' (*fortunei*) (5)	GEdr
	'Mona Lisa' (× *borisii*) (7)	GKev
	'Monarch' (8) ♀H5	CRos EHyd EWes GAbr GKev ITim LRHS NFav NHpl NRHS NWad WAbe WFar WIce
§	'Mondscheinsonate' (× *boydii*) (7)	NMen
	'Monika' (*webrii*) (7)	NMen
	'Moon Beam' (× *boydilacina*) (7)	NMen
	'Moonlight Sonata' (× *boydii*)	see *S.* 'Mondscheinsonate'
	'Moonlight' (× *boydii*)	see *S.* 'Sulphurea'
	'Morava' (7)	NMen
	Mossy Group (15)	LRHS MBros MHol
	- pink-flowered (15)	GAbr MMuc SPoG
	- red-flowered (15)	SPoG
	- white-flowered (15)	MMuc
	'Mossy Triumph'	see *S.* 'Triumph'
	'Mother of Pearl' (× *irvingii*) (7)	GKev NMen
	'Mount Nachi' (*fortunei*) (5) ♀H4	EHyd EPfP EWes GAbr GEdr GMaP LRHS NBro NHar NHpl NRHS SPlb WAbe WFar WSpi
	'Mrs Helen Terry' (× *salmonica*) (7) ♀H5	CRos EHyd GArf LRHS NMen NRHS
	'Myra' (× *anglica*) (7)	NMen WHoo
	'Myra Cambria' (× *anglica*) (7)	NMen
	'Myriad' (7)	WAbe
	'Myriad Seedling' (7)	EPot NMen
	'Naarden' (7)	NMen
	'Namiyama' (*fortunei*) (5)	GEdr WFar
	'Nancye' (× *goringiana*) (7)	NSla
	'Neride' (7)	NMen
	'New Europe' (× *krausii*) (7)	NMen
	'Nicholas' (8)	GKev NHpl
	'Nimbus' (*iranica*) (7)	NMen
	'Nottingham Gold' (× *boydii*) (7)	EPot NMen
	'Nouhime' (*fortunei*) (5)	GEdr WFar
§	***obtusa*** (7)	MHer NMen
	'Ogon-no-mai' (*fortunei*) (5)	GEdr WFar
	'Oh Yes' (*cochlearis*) (8)	WAbe
	'Olsany' (× *megaseiflora*) (7)	NMen
	'Olympus' (× *boydilacina*) (7)	NMen
	'Omar Khayyám' (7)	NMen

'Opatov' (× *megaseiflora*) (7) NMen
oppositifolia (7) NHol NSla SPlb SRms WAbe WSHC
- subsp. ***oppositifolia*** var. ***latina*** (7) ELan GArf GKev
'Oradour' (× *lincolni-fosteri*) (7) new NMen
'Orava' (7) NMen
'Ottone Rosai' (Toscana Group) (7) NMen NSla
'Pablo Picasso' (Conspecta Group) (7) NMen
paniculata (8) EDAr GKev GMaP NSla SPlb SRms WAbe
- from Gorges du Verdon, France GKev
§ - subsp. ***cartilaginea*** (8) GKev
- 'Foster's Red' (8) new GKev
- subsp. ***kolenatiana*** see *S. paniculata* subsp. *cartilaginea*
§ - var. ***minutifolia*** (8) CRos EHyd GQue LRHS NBro NHpl NRHS NRya NSla SLee SPlb WAbe WHoo WIce
paradoxa (15) CRos EHyd EPot LRHS NHol NRHS NWad
'Parcevalis' (× *finnisiae*) (7 × 9) WAbe
'Parsee' (× *margoxiana*) (7) NMen
'Paul Cézanne' (Decor Group) (7) new NSla
'Paul Gauguin' (Conspecta Group) (7) EPot NMen
'Paul Rubens' (7) WAbe
'Peach Blossom' (7) NMen
'Peach Melba' (7) ♀^{H5} CRos CSma EHyd EPot LRHS NHpl NLar NMen NRHS NSla WHoo WIce
'Peachy Head' (7) NMen
'Pearl Rose' (× *anglica*) (7) EPot NMen
'Pearly Gates' (× *irvingii*) (7) NMen
'Pearly King' (Mossy Group) (15) ECtt GMaP WAbe
'Pearly King' variegated (15/v) GKev
'Penelope' (× *boydilacina*) (7) CRos EHyd EPot LRHS NLar NMen NRHS NSla WHoo
'Perikles' (7) NMen
'Perseus' (7) NMen
'Peter Burrow' (× *poluanglica*) (7) EPot NMen
'Peter Pan' (Mossy Group) (15) CRos ECtt EDAr EHyd EPfP EWoo GMaP LRHS MHer NHol NLar NRHS NWad SPoG WCav WFar
'Petra' (7) EPot NMen
§ 'Phoenix' (× *biasolettoi*) (7) EHyd NMen NRHS
'Pierantonio Micheli' (Renaissance Group) (7) NMen
'Pink Candy' (*fortunei*) (5) WFar
'Pink Cloud' (*fortunei*) (5) EPri GEdr NBro NHar WAbe WFar
'Pink Haze' (*fortunei*) (5) ♀^{H4} GEdr WAbe WFar
'Pink Melba' (7) CRos
'Pink Mist' (*fortunei*) (5) GEdr WAbe WFar
'Pink Pagoda' (*nipponica*) (5) EBee WCot WCru WFar
'Pink Star' (× *boydilacina*) (7) EPot GKev GMaP NLar NMen
'Pixie' (15) ECtt GKev MAsh NHol NRya NWad SLee SPoG SRms SRot WFar WIce
'Pixie Alba' see *S.* 'White Pixie'
'Plena' (*granulata*) see *S.* 'Flore Pleno'
'Poils Hirsutes' (*stolonifera*) (5) new GGro

'Polar Drift' CRos EHyd EPot LRHS NRHS NSla NWad WAbe WFar WIce
poluniniana × 'Winifred' (× *poluanglica*) (7) EPot
'Pomona Sprout' (*cortusifolia*) (5) SGro
'Pompadour' (15) NEoE
'Popelka' (*marginata* subsp. *marginata* var. *rocheliana*) (7) EHyd NRHS
porophylla (7) GKev
'Portae' (× *fritschiana*) (8) XLum
'Precious Piggy' (*epiphylla*) (5) WCru
'Primrose Bee' (× *apiculata*) (7) GKev
'Primrose Dame' (× *elisabethae*) (7) EPot NMen WIce
'Primulaize Salmon' (9 × 11) NHar WHoo
'Primuloides' (*umbrosa*) (11) EDAr MMuc SRms SRot SWvt
'Primuloides' variegated (*umbrosa*) (11/v) SRms
'Prince Hal' (*burseriana*) (7) CRos EHyd EPot LRHS NRHS
'Princess' (*burseriana*) (7) CRos EHyd EPot LRHS NMen NRHS NSla
'Probynii' (*cochlearis*) (8) EPot NSla WAbe WFar
'Prometheus' (× *prossenii*) (7) NMen
'Prosek' (× *megaseiflora*) (7) NMen
× ***prossenii*** *sensu stricto* hort. see *S.* 'Regina'
'Pseudo-paulinae' (× *paulinae*) (7) NMen
'Pseudo-valdensis' (*cochlearis*) (8) NMen WAbe
pubescens (15) WAbe
'Punctatissima' (*paniculata*) (8) NWad
'Purple Piggy' (*epiphylla*) (5) WCru
'Purpurea' (*fortunei*) see *S.* 'Rubrifolia'
'Pygmalion' (× *webrii*) (7) NMen
'Pyramidalis' (*cotyledon*) (8) GKev XLum
'Quarry Wood' (× *anglica*) (7) NMen
'Rachael Young' (× *borisii*) (7) NMen
'Rachel' (8) GKev
'Radka' (× *megaseiflora*) (7) NMen
'Rainsley Seedling' (8) EPot GKev NBro
'Ray Woodliffe' (× *dinninaris*) (7) WAbe
'Red Poll' (× *poluanglica*) (7) GAbr NHpl NMen WAbe
* 'Regent' WAbe
§ 'Regina' (× *prossenii*) (7) NMen
§ 'Reginald Farrer' (Silver Farreri Group) (8) ♀^{H5} WAbe
'Rembrandt van Rijn' (7) EPot NMen
retusa (7) WAbe
'Rex' (*paniculata*) (8) CMac NWad
'River Thame' (× *polulacina*) (7) NMen
§ 'Riverslea' (× *hornibrookii*) (7) NMen
§ 'Robin Hood' (× *megaseiflora*) (7) NMen WHoo
'Rocco Red' (× *arendsii*) (15) CBod LRHS MACG
'Rockies White' (× *arendsii*) (Rockies Series) (15) new LRHS
'Rockrose'[PBR] (× *arendsii*) (15) SPoG
§ 'Rockwhite' (× *arendsii*) (15) WIce

	'Roklan' (7) **new**	NMen
	'Rokujō' (*fortunei*) (5) ♀H4	EBee NBro NFav NLar SHeu
	'Romulus' (7)	NMen
	'Rosa Tubbs' (8)	EWes
	'Rosea' (× *arendsii*) (15)	SCob
§	'Rosea' (*paniculata*) (8) ♀H5	CBod GMaP GWyn MMuc NBro NRya NSla SEND SRms WFar
	'Rosemarie' (7)	NMen
	'Rosina Sündermann' (× *rosinae*) (7)	CRos EHyd LRHS NMen NRHS
	rotundifolia (12)	CElw EBee ECha MPnt WBor
	'Roztyly' (× *megaseiflora*) (7)	NMen
	'Rubella' (× *irvingii*) (7)	NMen
	'Rubin' (× *hornbrookii*) (7)	MHer
	'Rubra' (*aizoon*)	see *S.* 'Rosea' (*paniculata*)
§	'Rubrifolia' (*fortunei*) (5) ♀H4	CMac ECha ECtt GAbr GEdr LEdu LRHS NBro NHpl SMad SWvt WCot WCru WFar WPnP
*	'Ruby Wedding' (*cortusifolia*) (5)	WFar
	'Rufina' (7)	NMen
	'Rumba' (7)	NMen
	'Russell V. Prichard' (× *irvingii*) (7)	NMen
	'Ruth Draper' (*oppositifolia*) (7) ♀H5	WAbe
	'Ruth McConnell' (15)	CMea
	'Ruznyě' (× *megaseiflora*) (7)	NMen
	'Saint John's' (8)	GKev WAbe
	'Salome' (× *lincolni-fosteri*) (7)	NMen
§	'Salomonii' (× *salmonica*) (7)	SRms
	sancta (7)	CRos EHyd LRHS NRHS NSla SRms
	- subsp. ***pseudosancta***	see *S. juniperifolia*
	- - var. ***macedonica***	see *S. juniperifolia*
	'Sanne' (7) **new**	CMHG NMen
	'Saotome' (*fortunei*) (5)	GEdr
	'Šárka' (7)	NMen
	sarmentosa	see *S. stolonifera*
	'Satchmo' (Blues Group) (7)	NMen NSla
	'Saturn' (× *megaseiflora*) (7)	EPot NMen
	(Saxony Series) 'Saxony Red' (× *arendsii*) (15)	CBod
	- 'Saxony White' (× *arendsii*) (15) **new**	CBod
	'Sázava' (× *poluluteopurpurea*) (7)	NMen NSla
§	***scardica*** (7)	GArf GKev NBro NMen WAbe
	- var. ***dalmatica***	see *S. obtusa*
	- subsp. ***korabensis*** (7)	EPot
§	'Schelleri' (× *petraschii*) (7)	EPfP NMen
§	'Schwefelblüte' (15)	EHyd GMaP NRHS
	'Seissera' (*burseriana*) (7)	NMen
	sempervivum (7)	NGdn WFar
	'Seren y Gwanwyn' (*oppositifolia*) (7)	WAbe
	'Shaggy Hair' (*stolonifera*) (5)	WFar
	'Shanghai' (*stolonifera*) (5) **new**	GGro
	'Sherlock Holmes' (7)	ECha NMen WAbe
	'Shimanami' (*fortunei*) (5)	EMor MNrw NHar
	'Shimmy'	WAbe
	'Shiomoe' (*fortunei*) (5)	GEdr
	'Shiranami' (*fortunei*) (5) ♀H4	CBcs EBee ECtt EHed ELan EWes GEdr GGro GPSL LSun MMrt NHpl SPlb WCot WFar WSpi WWtn
	'Sibyll Trelawney JP' (*fortunei*) (5)	EBee EPfP GPSL MPie NHar WFar

§	'Silver Cushion' (15/v)	CRos CTri EHyd ELan LRHS NFav NHpl NRHS SPlb SPoG SRms SRot WAbe WIce
	'Silver Hill' (*paniculata*) (8)	NSla
	'Silver Maid' (× *engleri*) (8)	ITim NSla
	'Silver Mound'	see *S.* 'Silver Cushion'
	'Silver Velvet' (*fortunei*) (5/v)	EBee ECtt MBNS NHpl SHeu WCot
	'Sissi' (7)	ECha EPot NMen
	'Slack's Ruby Southside' (Southside Seedling Group) (8) ♀H5	ITim NSla NWad WCav WFar WIce
	'Slack's Supreme' (8)	NSla WFar
	'Slack's Vesuvius' (8) **new**	WFar
	'Slavia' (7)	NMen
§	'Slzy Coventry' (× *proximae*) (7)	EPot NMen
	'Sněhurka' (Fenomen Group) (7)	NMen
	'Snow White' (7)	NMen
	'Snowcap' (*pubescens*) (15)	NMen WAbe
	'Snowflake' (Silver Farreri Group) (8) ♀H5	CRos EHyd LRHS NRHS WAbe
	Southside Seedling Group (8)	Widely available
	- 'Southside Star' (8) ♀H5	LEdu NHpl WAbe
	spathularis (11)	MACG WCot
	'Splendens' (*oppositifolia*) (7) ♀H5	EBou EPfP GAbr GKev MMuc SRms WAbe
	'Spotted Dog'	see *S.* 'Canis-dalmatica'
	'Sprite' (15)	SPoG
	spruneri (7)	EHyd LRHS NRHS
	'Stansfieldii' (*rosacea*) (15)	EBou SPlb SPoG
	'Starfire' (8)	GKev NHar WThu
	'Starlight' (8)	GKev
	startorii	see *S. scardica*
	stolitzkae (7)	EPot
§	***stolonifera*** (5) ♀H2	CSpe ECha EShb GGro NBro SDix SWvt WCot WFar WWtn
	- large-flowered (5)	WCot WGrn
	'Strawberry Melba' (7)	NMen
	stribrnyi (7)	WHoo
*	- var. ***degenii*** (7)	NSla
	'Sturmiana' (*paniculata*) (8)	SRms
	'Sue Tubbs' (8)	GKev
	'Suendermannii Major' (× *kellereri*) (7)	EHyd LRHS NRHS
	'Suendermannii' (× *kellereri*) (7)	CRos EHyd LRHS NMen NRHS
	SUGAR PLUM FAIRY ('Toujya') (*fortunei*) (5) ♀H4	ECtt EShb SHeu WFar XSte
§	'Sulphurea' (× *boydii*) (7)	CRos EHyd LRHS NMen NRHS NSla WHoo
	'Sun Dance' (× *boydii*) (7)	NMen
	'Superba' (*callosa* subsp. *callosa* var. *australis*) (8)	NSla
	'Symons-Jeunei' (8)	NWad
	'Tamayura' (*fortunei*) (5)	GEdr
	'Tankei' (5)	SAko
	'Tenerife' (Swirly Group) (7)	EWes NMen WAbe
	'Tetín' (Teta Group) (7)	NMen
	'Thalia' (7)	NMen
	'Theoden' (*oppositifolia*) (7)	CMea EWes GArf WAbe
	'Theresa Cooper' (7)	EPot
	'Thór Heyerdahl' (Ocean Group) (7)	EPot NMen
	'Timmy Foster' (× *irvingii*) (7)	NMen

	tombeanensis (7)	EPot WAbe
	'Torrisholme Rose' (7)	NMen
	TOURAN DEEP RED ('Rockred') (Mossy Group) (15)	EHyd EPfP LBuc LRHS NRHS
	TOURAN LARGE WHITE ('Rocklarwhi'PBR) (Mossy Group) (15)	EHyd EPfP LBuc LRHS NRHS
	TOURAN PINK (× *arendsii*) (15)	LRHS
	TOURAN RED ('Saxz0006') (× *arendsii*) (15)	SPoG WIce
	TOURAN WHITE IMPROVED ('Saxz0004'PBR) (× *arendsii*) (15)	SPoG WIce
	'Tricolor' (*stolonifera*) (5) ♀H2	CDoC EBak EShb
§	'Triumph' (× *arendsii*) (15)	CPla EPfP GMaP MAsh SPoG WSMil
	'Tully' (× *elisabethae*) (7)	NMen
	'Tumbling Waters' (8) ♀H5	CRos EHyd EPot LEdu LRHS NFav NHol NHpl NRHS NSla NWad WAbe
§	'Tvoje Píseň' (× *poluanglica*) (7)	GKev WHoo
§	'Tvůj Polibek' (× *poluanglica*) (7)	NMen
§	'Tvůj Přítel' (× *poluanglica*) (7)	GArf GKev
§	'Tvůj Úsmev' (× *poluanglica*) (7) ♀H5	GKev NHpl
§	'Tvůj Úspěch' (× *poluanglica*) (7)	EPot NMen
	'Two Kings' (*fortunei*) (5)	WFar
	'Tycho Brahe' (× *doerfleri*) (7)	GKev WAbe
	'Tysoe' (7)	EPot
	'Tysoe Blush' (Blues Group) (7)	NSla WFar
	'Tysoe Burgundy' (Blues Group) (7)	NSla WFar
	'Tysoe Everest' (7)	EPot NMen
	'Tysoe Makalu' (7)	NSla
	'Tysoe Pink-Perfection' (Blues Group) (7)	NMen NSla
	'Tysoe Splendour' (Blues Group) (7)	NSla
	umbrosa (11)	CMac CRos EDAr EHyd EPfP GAbr LEdu LRHS MMuc MRav NRHS SEND SHar SPlb SPoG SRms SRot SWvt WFar XLum
*	**- *subinteger***	MMuc
	unguipetala (7)	NMen
	× *urbium* (11) ♀H5	CBod CCBP CKel CTri CTtf EGrI EHyd ELan EPfP EWTr EWoo GMaP GQue LEdu LRHS MBel MCot NSti SBut SCob SEdd SPer SRms WBor WCAu WHoo WSpi WTor
	'Vaccariana' (*oppositifolia*) (7)	EPot SHar
	'Václav Hollar' (× *gusmusii*) (7)	NMen
	'Valborg'	see *S.* 'Cranbourne'
	'Valentine'	see *S.* 'Cranbourne'
	'Valerie Finnis'	see *S.* 'Aretiastrum'
	'Valerie Keevil' (× *anglica*) (7)	NMen
I	'Variegata' (*cuneifolia*) (11/v)	CRos EBou ECtt EHyd EPfP LRHS NFav NHol NHpl NRHS NRya NWad SLee SPlb SPoG WBrk WHoo WIce
I	'Variegata' (*exarata* subsp. *moschata*) (15/v)	GMaP
	'Variegata' (*umbrosa*)	see *S.* 'Aureopunctata'
I	'Variegata' (× *urbium*) (11/v)	EBee EHyd EPfP GPSL MBel NDov NLar SCob SPtp SRms WFar WHoo WTor
	vayredana (15)	WAbe
	'Večerní Hvězda Hvezda' (7)	NMen WAbe
	veitchiana (5)	NBro WFar XLum
	'Verona' (× *caroli-langii*) (7)	WAbe
	'Vesna' (× *borisii*) (7)	NMen
	'Vikos Gold' (7)	EPot NMen
	'Vincent van Gogh' (× *borisii*) (7)	EPot NMen
	'Violeta' (7) new	NMen
	'Vítkov' (× *megaseiflora*) (7)	NMen
	'Vladana' (× *megaseiflora*) (7)	EHyd GArf NMen NRHS NSla
	'Vlasta Burian' (7)	NMen
	'Vreny' (8)	GKev
	'Wada' (*fortunei*) (5)	CMac CSpe ECtt EPri GArf GKev GMaP LRHS MNrw NBir NBro NHar NRHS SRms WCot WFar WSHC
	'Walpole's Variety' (8)	NWad
	'Walter Ingwersen' (*umbrosa*) (11)	SRms
§	'Walter Irving' (× *irvingii*) (7) ♀H5	NSla WAbe
	'Welsh Dragon' (15)	WAbe
	'Welsh Red' (15)	WAbe
	'Welsh Rose' (15)	WAbe
	wendelboi (7)	NMen
	'Wendrush' (× *wendelacina*) (7)	NMen
	'Wendy' (× *wendelacina*) (7)	NMen
	'Wheatley Lion' (× *borisii*) (7)	NMen
	'Wheatley Rose' (7)	CRos EHyd LRHS NMen NRHS
	'White Delight' (× *megaseiflora*) (7)	CRos EHyd LRHS NMen NRHS NSla
	'White Imp' (7)	NMen
§	'White Pixie' (15)	CPla EBou ECtt EDAr EPfP MHer NEoE NFav NHol NRya NWad SLee SPlb SPoG SRms SRot WCAu WFar WIce
	'White Star' (*fortunei*) (5)	EHyd LRHS NRHS
	'White Star' (× *petraschii*)	see *S.* 'Schelleri'
	'Whitehill' (8) ♀H5	CMea CRos EBou EHyd ELan EPot GEdr GMaP LRHS NFav NRHS NRya NSla NWad SEdd SGro SLee WHoo
	'William Shakespeare' (Blues Group) (7)	NMen WAbe
	'Winifred Bevington' (8 × 11)	CRos CSma CTtf EBou EDAr EHyd GBin GEdr GMaP LRHS MBel NBro NFav NHpl NLar NRHS NRya NWad SGro SIvy SLee SRms WAbe WCav WFar WHoo
	'Winifred' (× *anglica*) (7)	EPot NMen WAbe
	'Winston Churchill' (15)	CRos EHyd EPfP LRHS NEoE NHol NRHS NWad
I	'Winston Churchill Variegata' (15/v)	NHol WIce
	'Winton' (× *paulinae*) (7)	EPot NMen
	'Wisley' (*federici-augusti* subsp. *grisebachii*) (7) ♀H5	GKev
	'Yellow Rock' (7)	NMen
	YOUR FRIEND	see *S.* 'Tvůj Přítel'
	YOUR GOOD FORTUNE	see *S.* 'Tvůj Úspěch'
	YOUR KISS	see *S.* 'Tvůj Polibek'
	YOUR SMILE	see *S.* 'Tvůj Úsmev'

YOUR SONG see *S.*'Tvoje Píseň'
YOUR SUCCESS see *S.*'Tvůj Úspěch'
'Zbraslav' (× *megaseiflora*) (7) NMen
× ***zimmeteri*** (8 × 11) NSla
'Ziva' (7) NMen
§ 'Zlatá Praha' (× *pragensis*) (7) EPot NMen WAbe
'Zlatý Kůň' (× *laeviformis*) (7) EPot
'Zlin' (× *leyboldii*) (7) NMen

Scabiosa (*Caprifoliaceae*)

africana CElw
- 'Jocelyn' SHar
alpina L. see *Cephalaria alpina*
argentea EWes WPGP
- PAB 1229 LEdu
atropurpurea LCro LOPS
- 'Ace of Spades' EPfP LRHS SPhx
- 'Beaujolais Bonnets' CRos EHyd EPfP LRHS NGBl NRHS SBls
- 'Black Knight' CSpe CWCL LCro LOPS SMrm SPhx
§ - 'Chile Black' CBcs EAJP EHyd ELan EPfP ETod GWyn LShi NLar NRHS SCob SPer SPoG SRkn SWvt
§ - 'Chilli Pepper' LRHS
- 'Fata Morgana' CKel
- Kudos Series LSou SCoo
banatica see *S. columbaria*
'Barocca' CWGN EBee ELan EPfP ETod LRHS NLar SCob SRms
'Blackberry Fool' (Dessert Series) SCob
BLUE DIAMONDS ('Kiescalibu') GJos WFar
'Blue Mound' SPhx
'Blueberry Muffin' (Dessert Series) SCob
§ 'Butterfly Blue' Widely available
caucasica CMac EHyd EPfP GKev LRHS NRHS XSen
- var. ***alba*** CBcs EPfP NGBl
- 'Blausiegel' CBod EShb LRHS MRav SGbt WHoo
- 'Clive Greaves' ♀H4 EBee ECha EWTr GMaP MBNS MBel NDov NLar NRHS SGbt SPad SPer SRms SWvt WCAu WFar
- 'Deep Waters' LRHS SPtp
- 'Fama' CSpe NBir NGBl NLar SPlb SRms WFar WHoo
- 'Fama Deep Blue' CBod CDor LRHS MACG MHer MHol NRHS SHar WFar
- 'Fama White' EHyd LRHS MACG NRHS SHar
- 'Goldingensis' WHil
- House's hybrids NGdn SRms
- 'Isaac House' WFar XLum
- 'Kompliment' WFar
- 'Miss Willmott' ♀H4 EBee ECha ECtt EHyd EShb GBin LRHS MArl MHer MRav NDov NLar NRHS SGbt SPad SPer SWvt WCAu WGwG WHoo XSen
- Perfecta Series EHyd LRHS MACG NGdn NLar NRHS SCob SPoG
- - 'Perfecta Alba' CDor CRos EHyd EPfP ETod EWoo GMaP LRHS MBel NLar NRHS SBut SCob SPer SPoG SPtp WCAu XLum
- - 'Perfecta Blue' CBod CDor EPfP EWTr EWoo GMaP MBel NDov XLum
- - 'Perfecta Lilac Blue' SPer
- 'Stäfa' EBee ECha EHyd LRHS MBel MHer NLar NRHS SCob SGbt

'Cherry Pie' (Dessert Series) SCob
CHERRY VANILLA SCOOP ('Dchrunscop') (Scoop Series) **new** WHil
'Chile Black' see *S. atropurpurea* 'Chile Black'
§ ***columbaria*** CBod CCBP CFis CHab CRos EBee EHyd GBee GQue LCro LOPS LRHS MBow NGrd NMir NRHS SBut SPhx WHer WSFF WWild
* - ***alpina*** GKev
- 'Big Blue' LRHS
- 'Blue Note'^{PBR} LRHS MACG MPri
- blue-flowered NHpl
- FLUTTER DEEP BLUE ('Balfluttdelu'^{PBR}) CBod LRHS LSou MHol WHil
- FLUTTER PURE WHITE ('Bafflutturite') **new** CBod MPri WHil
- FLUTTER ROSE PINK ('Balfluttropi'^{PBR}) CBod LRHS LSou MHol SCoo WHil
- 'Mariposa Blue'^{PBR} CBod LRHS MACG MHol MPri NRHS WHil
- 'Mariposa Blush' LRHS WHil
- 'Misty Butterflies' ECtt EPfP GJos LRHS NCou NGdn NLar SBls SEdd SGBe SRms WFar
- 'Nana' EHyd EPfP GArf GQue GWyn LRHS NBir NGdn NRHS WCFE XLum
§ - subsp. ***ochroleuca*** CCBP CDor CElw CKno CSpe CTtf ECha EHyd EPfP EWTr EWoo LRHS NBir NGBl SBut SEdd SHar SPhx SPoG SRms SSut WBrk WCAu
- - 'Moon Dance' CDor CMea CRos CSpe CWGN EAJP EHyd EShb LRHS LSun MACG NRHS SAko SCob SEdd SGBe SGbt SPoG WCot WHoo
- 'Pincushion Blue' EHyd LRHS MACG NRHS
- 'Pincushion Pink' EBou EHyd GJos GWyn LRHS MACG NGdn NRHS
cretica XLum
drakensbergensis GBin GKev LRHS SLon SPtp WCot
gigantea see *Cephalaria gigantea*
graminifolia EBee EHyd LRHS NBir NRHS SGro SRms XLum XSen
- 'Green Dome' GKev
- ***rosea*** EWes
'Helen Dillon' EWes
incisa 'Kudo' CBod CNor CRos CWGN EBee ECtt EHyd ELan EPfP LCro LOPS LRHS LSou MHol NRHS NSti SHar SMrm SPad SPoG SWvt WHil WNPC XSte
- 'Kudo White' CRos CWGN ECtt ELan LCro LOPS LRHS LSou MBros MHol NSti SGBe WHil WNPC XSte
'Irish Perpetual Flowering' see *S.*'Butterfly Blue'
japonica var. ***alpina*** EBee EPfP GGro GKev NGdn SPhx SPtp WFar WHoo XLum XSen
- - 'Blue Star' EBee SGbt
- - pink-flowered NBir
- - 'Ritz Blue' CMea GRum LRHS MACG MHer WCav WHil
- - 'Ritz Rose' CMea MACG
lachnophylla SPhx WCot
LAVENDER SCOOP ('Dlvndrscop') (Scoop Series) WHil
'Little Cracker' GBin LRHS SLon
'Little Emily' ELon
lucida CBod EHyd EPfP LRHS MMuc MRav NRHS SEND SGbt WCAu XLum
MARSHMALLOW SCOOP ('Dmarshscop') (Scoop Series) WHil

'Midnight'	CMea
'Miss Havisham'	CElw EWes MNrw
montana Mill.	see *Knautia arvensis*
ochroleuca	see *S. columbaria* subsp. *ochroleuca*
parnassi	see *Pterocephalus perennis*
'Perpetual Flowering'	see *S.* 'Butterfly Blue'
PINK BUTTONS ('Walminipink')	LRHS
'Pink Diamonds'	CBod EBee ELan EPfP LRHS WFar
'Pink Mist'	CBod CRos EBee ECtt EHyd ELan EPfP GBin LCro LOPS LRHS MAsh MPie NBir NDov NHpl NLar NRHS SCob SCoo SPer SPoG SRms WTor
pterocephala	see *Pterocephalus perennis*
RASPBERRY SCOOP ('Draspscop') (Scoop Series)	WHil
'Raspberry Sorbet' (Dessert Series)	SCob
RED VELVET SCOOP ('Drevelscop') **new**	WHil
rhodopensis	EBee
'Rosie's Pink'	ECtt
rumelica	see *Knautia macedonica*
'Satchmo'	see *S. atropurpurea* 'Chile Black'
stellata	SPhx
STRAWBERRY SCOOP ('Dstrawscop') **new**	WHil
succisa	see *Succisa pratensis*
tatarica	see *Cephalaria gigantea*
'Vivid Vi'PBR	CAbb CBod CDor CRos EBee ECtt EHyd ELan EPfP LBuc LRHS LSRN MMuc MNrw NHpl NLar NRHS SAko WBrk

Scadoxus ✿ (*Amaryllidaceae*)

membranaceus	WCot
multiflorus	CCCN EShb GKev SDeJ SDir
§ - subsp. ***katherinae*** ♀H1b	WCot
§ - subsp. ***multiflorus***	WCot
natalensis	see *S. puniceus*
§ ***puniceus***	GKev WCot

Scaevola (*Goodeniaceae*)

aemula 'Abanico Blue' **new**	LSou
- 'Abanico Rose' **new**	LSou
- 'Abanico White' **new**	LSou
- 'Blue Fan'	see *S. aemula* 'Blue Wonder'
- BLUE PRINT ('Kingscablin')	LSou
§ - 'Blue Wonder'	NPer SWvt
- 'Fancy'	LSou
- 'Zig Zag'PBR	CCCN
BLAUER FACHER ('Saphira'PBR)	CCCN
'Mini Blue'	CCCN
'Topaz Pink'	LSou

Sceletium (*Aizoaceae*)

tortuosum	SPlb

Schefflera (*Araliaceae*)

NJM 13.128	WPGP
alpina B&SWJ 8247	WCru
- B&SWJ 11827	WCru
- HWJ 936	WCru
- NJM 09.140	WPGP
- NJM 09.157	WPGP
- large-leaved WWJ 11999	WCru
arboricola ♀H1c	SEND
- 'Gold Capella' ♀H1c	SEND
- variegated (v) **new**	SEND
brevipedicellata	CDTJ
- HWJ 870	WCru
- KWJ 12224	WCru
aff. ***brevipedicellata***	IKel
- NJM 10.102	WPGP
§ ***chapana*** B&SWJ 11833	WCru
- B&SWJ 11848	WCru
- HWJ 983	WCru
delavayi	CDTJ IKel WCru WPGP
digitata	CTrC IKel
enneaphylla HWJ 1018	WCru
fantsipanensis B&SWJ 11666	WCru
- B&SWJ 11671	WCru
gracilis	EBee
- HWJ 622	WCru
- HWJ 878	WCru
gracilis × ***taiwaniana***	WCru
hoi B&SWJ 11747	WCru
kornasii B&SWJ 11830	WCru
- HWJ 918	WCru
macrophylla B&SWJ 8210	WCru
- B&SWJ 9788	WCru
- B&SWJ 11842	WCru
- WWJ 11681	WCru
microphylla B&SWJ 3872	WCru
multinervia B&SWJ 11727	WCru
aff. ***myriocarpa*** B&SWJ 11828	WCru
pauciflora WWJ 11986	WCru
rhododendrifolia	CBcs CBct CDTJ CDoC CExl EBee IKel WPGP
- GWJ 9375	WCru
shweliensis NJM 13.130	WPGP
- PAB 13.216	LEdu
taiwaniana ♀H4	CBct CTsd EBee IKel WCot WPGP
- B&SWJ 3575	WCru
- B&SWJ 3788	WCru
- B&SWJ 7096	WCru
- RWJ 10000	WCru
- RWJ 10016	WCru
trevesioides BWJ 15158 **new**	WCru
trianae B&SWJ 14313 **new**	WCru
vietnamensis	see *S. chapana*

Schima (*Theaceae*)

argentea	CBcs CCCN CExl CTsd EBee WPGP
aff. ***argentea*** NJM 13.042	WPGP
khasiana	CBcs WPGP
- PAB 3447	EBee LEdu
wallichii	CExl

Schinus (*Anacardiaceae*)

latifolius	ESwi
lentiscifolius	SPlb SVen
molle	CKel SPlb
montanus	SPlb
patagonicus	MGil
polygama	MGil SPlb

Schisandra (*Schisandraceae*)

arisanensis	CRHN MBlu NLar WPGP
- B&SWJ 3050	WCru
arisanensis × ***sphaerandra*** **new**	CRHN
chinensis	CAgr CBcs CRHN GKev GPoy LEdu MGil MSwo NLar SBrt WPGP
- B&SWJ 4204	WCru

- B&SWJ 4611A	WCru
- B&SWJ 4611B	WCru
- 'Bere'	LEdu WPGP
- 'Sadova No.1'	CAgr
grandiflora ♀H4	CBcs CBod CRos EHyd ELan EPfP ESwi GBin LRHS MBlu SBrt WPGP
- B&SWJ 2245	WCru WSHC
- PAB 3673	LEdu
- WJC 13666	WCru
- var. ***cathayensis***	see *S. sphaerandra*
- 'Jamu' (m)	CRHN WCru
- 'Lahlu' (f/F)	CRHN WCru
aff. ***grandiflora***	CRHN IDee
- WJC 13817	WCru
grandiflora × rubriflora	MMuc WCru
henryi subsp. ***yunnanensis*** B&SWJ 6546	WCru
incarnata BWJ 7898	WCru
incarnata × rubriflora	WCru
lancifolia	MBlu
nigra	see *S. repanda*
perulata FMWJ 13100	WCru
aff. ***plena*** HWJ 664	WCru
propinqua	CMac CRHN LEdu NLar WPGP
subsp. ***sinensis***	
- - BWJ 8148	WCru
§ ***repanda*** B&SWJ 5897	WCru
- B&SWJ 11455	WCru
rubriflora ♀H5	CBcs CRos CTri EPfP LRHS MBlu MGos NLar SBrt SDix SLon WCFE WPGP
- BWJ 7557	WCru
- (f)	IDee WSHC WSpi
- 'Bodnant Redberry' (f)	WCru
§ ***sphaerandra***	CBcs CRHN MBlu
- BWJ 7739	WCru
- BWJ 8082	WCru
sphenanthera	CKel EBee MBlu NLar WSHC
- BWJ 8151	WCru

Schizachyrium (*Poaceae*)

§ ***scoparium***	CBod CKno EPfP LRHS NRHS SBls SCob SPeP XLum
- 'Blaze'	NDov SBls
- 'Blue Heaven'	ELon IPot LEdu MAvo NDov SAko SCoo SEdd SMHy WPGP WSpi
- 'Cairo'	EBee IPot
- 'Prairie Blues'	CSpe EBou EHyd EPfP LSun MACG NDov SBls SEdd SMea WCot
- 'Standing Ovation'	CBod CSpe LCro LOPS NDov SCoo

Schizocarphus (*Asparagaceae*)

nervosus	WCot

Schizocodon see *Shortia*

Schizophragma (*Hydrangeaceae*)

fauriei	NLar
- B&SWJ 1701	WCru
- B&SWJ 6831	WCru
- B&SWJ 7052	WCru
- CWJ 12405	WCru
- CWJ 12433	WCru
- WINDMILLS ('Plooster')	CKel CMil LRHS
hydrangeoides	CBcs CBct CCCN CKel CWit EBee EHyd ELan EPfP EWTr IDee LCro LOPS LRHS MBlu MGos NRHS SCob SGol SLon SPer SPoG SWvt WSpi
- 'Brookside Littleleaf'	see *Hydrangea anomala* subsp. *petiolaris* var. *cordifolia* 'Brookside Littleleaf'
- BURST OF LIGHT (v)	ETho
- var. ***concolor*** B&SWJ 5954	WCru
- - 'Moonlight' ♀H5	CBcs CDoC CKel CMac CRos CWGN EHyd ELan EPfP LRHS MBlu MGil MGos MMuc NRHS SGol SLon SPoG SWvt WCot WCru WPGP
- var. ***hydrangeoides*** B&SWJ 5489	WCru
- - B&SWJ 5732	WCru
- - 'Iwa Garami'	NLar
- - 'Roseum' ♀H5	CArg CBcs CCCN CDoC CMac CMil ELan EPfP EWes IArd MBlu MGil MGos SCob SGol SLon SNig SPer SWvt WCot WCru WPGP
- 'Rose Sensation'	CCCN CKel CRos EBee EHyd EPfP LRHS NRHS SGol SLon SPoG
- SNOW SENSATION ('Minsnow3') **new**	SNig
- var. ***taquetii*** B&SWJ 8771	WCru
- - 'Cheju's Early'	WCru
- var. ***ullungdoense*** B&SWJ 8505	WCru
- - B&SWJ 8522	WCru
- var. ***yakushimense*** B&SWJ 6119	WCru
integrifolium ♀H5	CBcs CCCN CKel CRHN EBee EHyd ELan EPfP LRHS MBlu NLar SPer WKif WPGP
- BWJ 8150	WCru
molle HWJ 1011	WCru
- WWJ 11905	WCru

Schizostylis see *Hesperantha*

Schoenoplectus (*Cyperaceae*)

§ ***lacustris***	CPud CWat LLWG
§ - subsp. ***tabernaemontani***	CSpe LLWG
- - 'Albescens' (v)	CBen CWat MMuc MNrw WHal WWtn XLum
- - 'Zebrinus' (v)	CBen CPud CWat ELan MNrw SPlb WMAq WWtn XLum

Schoenus (*Cyperaceae*)

pauciflorus	LLWG

Sciadopitys (*Sciadopityaceae*)

verticillata ♀H6	CAco CBcs CKen CMCN CMac CSBt EPfP GKin LMaj LPar LRHS MAsh MBlu MGil MGos MMuc NHol NWea SAko SCoo SEND SLim SPoG SWvt WHwl XSte
- 'Firework'	CKen
- 'Globe'	CKen
- 'Gold Star'	CKen
- 'Goldammer'	CAco
- 'Golden Rush'	CKen MAsh
- 'Goldmahne'	CKen
- 'Grüne Kugel'	CKen MAsh
- 'Jeddeloh Compact'	CKen
- 'Koja Maki'	NLar
- 'Kupferschirm'	CKen
- 'Mecki'	CKen
- 'Megaschirm'	CAco CKen
- 'Mr Happy'	NLar
- 'Ossorio Gold'	CAco CKen
- 'Perlenglanz'	CAco CKen
- 'Picola'	CKen MAsh WHwl
- 'Pygmy'	CKen
- 'Richie's Cream'	CKen
- 'Richie's Cushion'	CKen
- 'Shorty'	CKen

– 'Speerspitze'	CKen
– 'Star Wars'	CKen
– 'Starburst'	CKen
– 'Sternschnuppe'	CKen NLar
– 'Tsai Cheng'	NLar
– variegated (v) **new**	CAco
– 'Wintergreen'	CKen

Scilla (*Asparagaceae*)

adlamii	see *Ledebouria cooperi*
'Aigeus' **new**	GKev
× ***allenii***	NRog
– 'Frà Angelico' 🏆H6	NDry
amethystina	see *S. litardierei*
amoena	GKev NRog WCot
autumnalis	CAvo EHyd EPot GKev NRHS NRog SChr WShi WThu
– subsp. ***fallax***	NRog
– white-flowered	NRog
bifolia 🏆H6	CAvo EPot GKev LRHS NRog SDeJ SPhx WCot WShi
– 'Alba'	NRog SDeJ SPhx
– 'Norman Stevens'	NDry NRog
– 'Rosea'	CRos EHyd ERCP GKev LRHS NRHS NRog SDeJ
bithynica 🏆H6	GKev NRog WCot WShi
'Blue Giant'	CAvo ELan EPot ERCP LRHS NRog WCot
campanulata	see *Hyacinthoides hispanica*
chinensis	see *S. scilloides*
cilicica	GKev NRog
§ ***forbesii***	EHyd EPot LCro LOPS LRHS NBir NHpl NRHS NRog SDeJ SRms WShi
– 'Violet Beauty'	SDeJ
– 'Zwanenburg'	NRog
greilhuberi	EPPr EPri GKev NDry NRog SGro WCot
hohenackeri	GKev NRog WCot WThu
– BSBE 811	WCot
§ ***hughii***	CBro NRog
hyacinthoides	ERCP GKev NRog SDir WCot
– 'Blue Arrow'	CAvo EPfP GKev LHWs SDir SPer WFar
ingridiae	GKev NRog WCot
italica	see *Hyacinthoides italica*
japonica	see *S. scilloides*
liliohyacinthus	CAvo CBro GKev IBlr NRog NWad WCot WShi
– 'Alba'	CAvo
§ ***litardierei*** 🏆H6	EPPr EPot EPri ERCP GKev NRog SDeJ SPhx WShi
lucilae misapplied	see *S. forbesii*
lucilae ambig.	CAvo EHyd GWyn LCro LOPS LRHS NRHS NRog
luciliae (Boiss.) Speta 🏆H6	LCro SDeJ SPer
– 'Alba'	EHyd LHWs LRHS MBros NHpl NRHS NRog SDeJ SPer
– Gigantea Group	GKev NRog
– – 'Alba'	EPot GKev NRog
– 'Rosy Queen'	GKev
lutea hort.	see *Ledebouria socialis*
madeirensis	WCot
'Medea' **new**	GKev
melaina	GKev NRog WCot
– 'Vaclav' **new**	NRog
mesopotamica	GKev NRog
messeniaca	GKev NRog
– from Greece MS 38	WCot
mischtschenkoana 🏆H6	CAvo CRos EHyd EPot EWld LCro LOPS LRHS NRHS SDeJ WShi
§ – 'Tubergeniana' 🏆H6	CMea GKev NRog SPhx WCot
monanthos	GKev
monophyllos	GKev NRog WCot
morrisii	GKev NRog
natalensis	see *Merwilla plumbea*
non-scripta	see *Hyacinthoides non-scripta*
nutans	see *Hyacinthoides non-scripta*
obtusifolia subsp. ***intermedia***	WCot
persica 🏆H4	GKev NRog WCot
peruviana	Widely available
– SB&L 20/1	WCot
– 'Alba'	CBro CWCL ECha EPri EWes MPtr NHpl WCot XLum
– 'Blue Moon'	CDoC CRos LRHS
– Carribean Jewels Series	CBod MHol
– 'Hughii'	see *S. hughii*
– 'Sapphire Blue' (Carribean Jewels Series)	WFar
– var. ***venusta*** S&L 311/2	WCot
– 'White Moon'	EBee EHed ERCP GKev
'Pink Giant'	CAvo EHyd ELan EPot ERCP GKev LCro LOPS LRHS NRHS NRog SDeJ XLum
pratensis	see *S. litardierei*
puschkinioides	GKev NRog
ramburei	GKev
rosenii	CWCL NRog
– 'Alba' **new**	NRog
– 'Bakuriani'	NRog
– 'Caucasian Giant' **new**	NRog
– 'Cloudy Sky'	WCot
'Rosiba' **new**	NRog
sardensis 🏆H6	EHyd EPot ERCP LRHS NRHS NRog SDeJ SPhx SRms WCot WShi
§ ***scilloides***	EPot GKev
* – 'Alba'	SDeJ
siberica 🏆H6	CRos EHyd ELan EShb GKev LCro LOPS LRHS NRHS NRog SPer SPhx WShi
– 'Alba'	EHyd EPot EShb GKev NRog SDeJ WShi
– subsp. ***armena***	GKev NRog
– 'Enem'	GKev
– 'Spring Beauty'	CAvo CMea CRos EHyd EPot ERCP GKev LRHS NRHS NRog SDeJ SRms
siehei 'Rosea'	GKev NHpl NRog
'Tubergeniana'	see *S. mischtschenkoana* 'Tubergeniana'
'Valentine Day'	EPot
verna	GKev WShi WThu
vicentina	see *Hyacinthoides vincentina*
violacea	see *Ledebouria socialis*
vvedenskyi	NRog

Scindapsus (*Araceae*)

pictus 'Argyraeus' 🏆H1a **new**	EShb

Scirpus (*Cyperaceae*)

cernuus	see *Isolepis cernua*
'Green Mist'	WCot
lacustris	see *Schoenoplectus lacustris*
– 'Spiralis'	see *Juncus effusus* f. *spiralis*
tabernaemontani	see *Schoenoplectus lacustris* subsp. *tabernaemontani*

Scleranthus (*Caryophyllaceae*)

biflorus	CBor CPla CSma CTrC EDAr EPot EWes GBin GQue LEdu MAsh SPlb WFar XLum
uniflorus	CPla CTrC EPot GArf LEdu NHpl SMad SPlb SRot XLum XSte

Sclerochiton (*Acanthaceae*)

harveyanus EShb

Scoliopus (*Liliaceae*)

hallii GBin GKev MNrw NHar

Scolopendrium see *Asplenium*

Scopolia (*Solanaceae*)

anomala HWJK 2252 WCru
- PAB 4925 LEdu

carniolica CTtf ECha EPPr EWld GBin GPoy ILea LEdu NChi NLar NSti SBls SPlb WCru WPav WSHC XLum
- from Poland LEdu

§ - var. ***brevifolia*** CTtf EBee EBlo EHed EHyd EPPr EPfP EWld LEdu LRHS MPie NRHS SPhx WCot WPGP WPav
- 'Zwanenburg' CBor EPPr EWes LEdu NLar SPhx WFar XLum

hladnikiana see *S. carniolica* var. *brevifolia*

stramoniifolia WPav

Scorzonera (*Asteraceae*)

hispanica 'Long Black Maxima' SVic

Scorzoneroides (*Asteraceae*)

autumnalis CHab NMir

Scrophularia (*Scrophulariaceae*)

aquatica misapplied see *S. auriculata*

§ ***auriculata*** CHab CPud NPer WHer

§ - 'Variegata' (v) CBct ECha EHyd EPfP GLog LRHS MHer NRHS NSti SGbt SHar SPer WSMil

buergeriana 'Lemon and Lime' misapplied see *Teucrium viscidum* 'Lemon and Lime'

calliantha SBrt SPtp WMal

macrantha SPhx

nodosa GPoy NMir WHer
- ***variegata*** see *S. auriculata* 'Variegata'

vernalis CBgR

Scutellaria (*Lamiaceae*)

§ ***alpina*** GJos SPlb SRms
- 'Arcobaleno' GEdr
- 'Sapphire' **new** LRHS

altissima CFis ECha GJos GPSL NBro NGrd SBut SPlb WFar WWtn XSen

baicalensis CSpe GJos GPoy MGil MNHC

canescens see *S. incana*

costaricana CCCN EShb

galericulata CBod CHab ENfk GPoy LEdu LLWG MBow MHer NAts SPhx WHer

hastata see *S. hastifolia*

§ ***hastifolia*** CTri EBou GJos

havanensis **new** GJos

§ ***incana*** CFis CFoA CMea CSpe EHyd MAvo NDov SMrm SPhx WCot WSHC WTor

indica GEdr
- var. ***japonica*** see *S. indica* var. *parvifolia*

§ - var. ***parvifolia*** CSpe EBou EWes GEdr GMaP ITim NBir SLee WFar
- - 'Alba' SLee WAbe

integrifolia SPhx

laeteviolacea **new** WAbe

lateriflora GJos GPoy MGil SRms
- PAB 3921 LEdu

maekawae EBee
- B&SWJ 557A WCru

orientalis WAbe

pontica EBou SPhx XSen

red-flowered CCCN

scordiifolia CFis CMea CSpe ECha MACG NRya SBut SHar SRms WCav WFar
- 'Seoul Sapphire' GBin LEdu SPtp

serrata LPla

'Sherbert Lemon' CMea

suffrutescens XSen
- 'Texas Rose' CMea CSpe EBou EDAr EPfP NHpl SEdd SLee SRot WAbe WHil WHoo WIce WTor

supina see *S. alpina*

tournefortii ECtt EHyd GJos LPla LRHS NRHS

* ***zhongdianensis*** EPPr MSpe

seakale see *Crambe maritima*

Sebaea (*Gentianaceae*)

rehmanii SPlb

thomasii GEdr WAbe
- 'Bychan' WAbe

Securigera (*Fabaceae*)

§ ***varia*** CDor EWld GJos LEdu LRHS MMuc SEND SIvy SRms XLum

Sedastrum see *Sedum*

× *Sedeveria* (*Crassulaceae*)

'Harry Butterfield' WCot

'Letizia' SChr

'Starburst' SAll

Sedum ✿ (*Crassulaceae*)

'Abbey Dore' see *Hylotelephium* 'Abbey Dore'

acre CRos CTri EHyd EPfP GPoy GQue LRHS MNHC NMir NRHS SPlb XLum
- 'Aureum' EDAr ELan EPfP NHpl NLar NRya SLee SPoG SRms SSim WCav WCot WIce WSMil XLum
- 'Elegans' ECtt
- 'Golden Queen' CRos EBou EHyd LRHS NHpl NRHS SPlb SPoG SRms
- 'Minus' CRos EHyd LRHS NFav NRHS SRms

§ - subsp. ***neglectum*** var. ***majus*** NLar
- 'Oktoberfest' GJos

aizoon MAsh SPlb WFar XLum
- 'Aurantiacum' see *S. aizoon* 'Euphorbioides'

§ - 'Euphorbioides' ECha ECtt LPot LShi MHer MMuc MRav NLar SEND SPlb XSen

§ - subsp. ***maximowiczii*** NWad

alatum WFar

alboroseum see *Hylotelephium erythrostictum*

§ ***album*** CRos EHyd GJos LRHS MMuc NBro NMir NRHS SEND SRms XLum
- chocolate-leaved **new** GRum
- 'Coral Carpet' CKel EBou ECtt ELan EPPr EPfP GFgr GKev GWyn MRav NHpl NLar NRya SCoo SLee SPoG WFar WSMil XLum
- subsp. ***teretifolium*** var. ***micranthum*** 'Chloroticum' NFav XLum

§ - - var. ***murale*** CTri EHyd LRHS NHpl NRHS WFar XLum

alpestre XLum

	altissimum	see *S. sediforme*
	anacampseros	see *Hylotelephium anacampseros*
	anglicum	SSut
	athoum	see *S. album*
	AUTUMN JOY	see *Hylotelephium* (Herbstfreude Group) 'Herbstfreude'
	batallae ISI 1496	NWad
	beauverdii	WCru
	subsp. ***vietnamense*** HWJ 824	
	'Bertram Anderson'	see *Hylotelephium* 'Bertram Anderson'
	beyrichianum misapplied	see *S. glaucophyllum*
	brevifolium	EWes NHpl
§	- var. ***quinquefarium***	WIce
	burrito	CDoC CPla EShb SIvy
	'Carl'	see *Hylotelephium* 'Carl'
	cauticola	see *Hylotelephium cauticola*
	chrysicaulum	EPot
	clavatum ISI 1161	NWad
	confusum Hemsl.	SEND SIvy WMal
	crassipes	see *Rhodiola wallichiana*
	crassularia	see *Crassula setulosa* 'Milfordiae'
	cryptomerioides B&SWJ 054	WCru
	dasyphyllum	NBir NHpl NRya SLee SPlb SRms WCot
	- subsp. ***dasyphyllum*** 'Lilac Mound'	NFav
	dendroideum	NWad SChr SEND
	subsp. ***praealtum***	
	divergens	GKev XLum
	'Dudley Field'	EPot MHer
	'Eleanor Fisher'	see *Hylotelephium telephium* subsp. *ruprechtii*
	ellacombeanum	see *S. kamtschaticum* var. *ellacombeanum*
	'Elworthy Rose'	CElw
	erythrostictum	see *Hylotelephium erythrostictum*
	ewersii	see *Hylotelephium ewersii*
	fabaria	see *Hylotelephium telephium* subsp. *fabaria*
	fastigiatum	see *Rhodiola fastigiata*
	forsterianum	SEND SPlb XLum
	subsp. ***elegans***	
	- - 'Silver Stone'	GJos MMuc
§	- f. ***purpureum***	NRya
	furfuraceum	CBod NHpl NWad SPlb WAbe
§	***glaucophyllum***	EDAr GJos XLum
	'Gold Mound'	GWyn NHpl SEdd
	Herbstfreude Group	see *Hylotelephium* Herbstfreude Group
	hernandezii	SSim
	- FO 199	NWad
	heterodontum	see *Rhodiola heterodonta*
	hidakanum	see *Hylotelephium pluricaule*
	himalense misapplied	see *Rhodiola* 'Keston'
	hispanicum	SPlb
	- 'Blue Carpet'	EPPr LRHS NHpl SSim WFar WGrn
	- ***glaucum***	see *S. hispanicum* var. *minus*
§	- var. ***minus***	ECtt MMuc NHpl SEND SPlb WCot
	'Honey Gold' new	NLar
	humifusum	EPot NHpl SPlb WAbe WFar
§	***hybridum***	XLum
	- 'Czar's Gold'	GJos NGdn
	'Indian Chief'	see *Hylotelephium* (Herbstfreude Group) 'Herbstfreude'
	indicum var. ***yunnanense***	see *Sinocrassula yunnanensis*
	integrifolium	see *Rhodiola integrifolia*
	'Joyce Henderson'	see *Hylotelephium* 'Joyce Henderson'
	kamtschaticum ♀H5	EDAr GJos MBel
	- B&SWJ 10870	WCru
§	- var. ***ellacombeanum*** ♀H5	CRos EHyd LRHS MAsh MMuc NRHS SEND WCot XLum
	- - B&SWJ 8853	WCru
§	- var. ***floriferum***	XSen
§	- - 'Weihenstephaner Gold'	CTri EBou ECtt ELan EPfP GJos GKev GMaP LPot MHer MMuc MRav NBir NSla SLee SPlb SPoG SRms SRot WCav WFar WSMil XLum XSen
	- var. ***kamtschaticum*** 'Variegatum' (v) ♀H5	CMea CRos EBou EHyd ELan EPfP LRHS MHer MMuc MSCN NHpl NRHS SLee SPoG SRms SRot SSim SWvt WIce XLum
	'Katharine's Gold'	MNrw
	lineare	CDoC
	- 'Variegatum' (v)	LRHS XLum
	'Little Dove'	SGro
	'Little Missy'	see *Crassula pellucida* subsp. *marginalis* 'Variegata'
	× ***luteoviride***	NWad
§	***lydium***	CTri EGrI GFgr NHpl SLee SPlb
	- 'Bronze Queen'	see *S. lydium*
	makinoi	SEdd SSim
	'Manoir de Gaudon'	WCot
	'Matrona'	see *Hylotelephium* 'Matrona'
	maweanum	see *S. acre* subsp. *neglectum* var. *majus*
	mendozae new	SSim
	middendorffianum	MBrN MHer MMuc SRms SRot XLum
§	***montanum***	MMuc
	moranense	MMuc XLum
	morganianum ♀H2	EBak EShb NCft NWad SIvy
	morrisonense B&SWJ 7078	WCru
	'Mr Goodbud'	see *Hylotelephium* 'Mr Goodbud'
	'Munstead Red'	see *Hylotelephium* 'Munstead Red'
	murale	see *S. album* subsp. *teretifolium* var. *murale*
	nevii misapplied	see *S. glaucophyllum*
	nevii ambig.	SPlb
	nicaeense	see *S. sediforme*
	niveum	EPot
	nussbaumerianum ♀H2	CBod NWad SEdd SIvy
	obtusatum misapplied	see *S. oreganum*
§	***obtusatum*** A. Gray	NBro NSla
	obtusifolium	SGro
	- var. ***listoniae***	EDAr MHer
	ochroleucum	NWad WCot WFar
	oppositifolium	see *S. spurium* 'Album'
§	***oreganum***	ECha GAbr GKev GMaP LPot MHer NBir NFav SLee SMad SPlb SRms SRot XLum
	- 'Procumbens'	see *S. oreganum* subsp. *tenue*
§	- subsp. ***tenue***	NHol NRya NWad
§	***oregonense***	CRos EHyd LRHS MHer NRHS WFar
	'Oriental Dancer'	see *Hylotelephium* 'Oriental Dancer'
	pachyclados	see *Rhodiola pachyclados*
	palmeri	MRav NBir SChr WSMil XLum
§	- subsp. ***palmeri*** tetraploid	SEND SIvy
	pilosum	GKev WAbe
	'Pink Dove'	SGro
	pluricaule	see *Hylotelephium pluricaule*
	polytrichoides 'Chocolate Ball'	CPla NHpl SEdd SLee SSim WSMil
	populifolium	see *Hylotelephium populifolium*
	pulchellum	SLee WFar
	'Red Cauli'	see *Hylotelephium* 'Red Cauli'
	'Red Star'	MAvo
	reflexum L.	see *S. rupestre* L.
	- 'Cristatum'	NHpl

	- red-leaved	GRum NHpl
	rhodiola	see *Rhodiola rosea*
	rosea	see *Rhodiola rosea*
	rubroglaucum Praeger	see *S. obtusatum* A. Gray
	× ***rubrotinctum*** ♀H3	CBod SEND SEdd SIvy SSim
	- 'Aurora' ♀H2	CDoC SAll SIvy
	'Ruby Glow'	see *Hylotelephium* 'Ruby Glow'
§	***rupestre*** L.	CPla EGrI ELan GJos GQue MMuc SEND SPhx SPlb SRot WFar XLum
	- 'Angelina'	CBod CKno EBou ECtt EPPr EWes LPot LRHS MHer NBir NDov NHol NWad SLee SPoG SSim WCot WFar WGrn WIce WSMil XLum
	- 'Aureum'	WFar
	- 'Blue Cushion'	LShi
	- 'Blue Spruce'	IPot
	- 'Monstrosum Cristatum'	NBir WCot WFar XLum
	- 'Yellow Cushion'	XSte
	ruprechtii	see *Hylotelephium telephium* subsp. *ruprechtii*
	'Sandra Mottram'	NWad
	sarcocaule hort.	see *Crassula sarcocaulis*
	sarmentosum	XLum
§	***sediforme***	CKel MMuc SEND SRms SSim XSen
	- ***nicaeense***	see *S. sediforme*
§	***sedoides*** var. ***album***	EBou EDAr NHpl SRms XLum
	selskianum	GJos NLar XLum
	- 'Goldilocks'	GJos
	sexangulare	CKel EBou ELon EPfP GJos MHer MMuc NFav NRya SPlb SRms XLum
	- f. ***elatum***	WFar
	- 'Weisse Tatra'	WFar
	sibiricum	see *S. hybridum*
	spathulifolium	CTri ECha EPot
	- Atropurpureum Group	GQue SRot
	- 'Aureum'	ECtt
	- 'Cape Blanco' ♀H5	Widely available
	- 'Purpureum' ♀H5	CRos CTri CWCL EBou ECtt EDAr EHyd ELan EPfP EPot GAbr GArf GJos GKev GMaP GWyn LRHS MBel MHer NHol NHpl NRHS NRya NWad SLee SPlb SPoG SSim WAbe XLum
	- 'William Pascoe'	EPot
	spectabile	see *Hylotelephium spectabile*
	spinosum	see *Orostachys spinosa*
	spurium	GJos GKev MAsh MMuc SEND SRms WFar XSen
§	- 'Album'	NRya XLum
	- 'Atropurpureum'	ECha XLum
	- 'Coccineum'	GJos GQue MMuc SEND
	- DRAGON'S BLOOD	see *S. spurium* 'Schorbuser Blut'
	- 'Erdblut'	CTri
	- 'Fuldaglut'	CRos CTri EBou ECtt EGrI EHyd EPPr LRHS MNrw NRHS NRya SRms
	- 'Green Mantle'	ECha EHyd EPfP
	- 'John Creech'	ECtt
	- PURPLE CARPET	see *S. spurium* 'Purpurteppich'
	- 'Purpureum'	SLee SRms
§	- 'Purpurteppich'	ECtt GJos MRav NBro NLar NWad SRms SVen
	- 'Roseum'	SRms WHil
	- 'Ruby Mantle'	GKev NBro NEoE SPoG SRms SWvt XLum
§	- 'Schorbuser Blut' ♀H5	CMea CRos ECtt EHyd ELan EPfP GKev LPot LRHS MAsh MBow MCot NBir NDov NRHS NRya NSla SEdd SLee SPlb SRms SRot SSim WFar WHoo WIce XLum
I	- 'Splendens Roseum'	XLum
	- 'Summer Glory'	NLar
§	- 'Tricolor' (v)	CTri EBou ECha EPfP GEdr GKev LShi MAsh MHer MRav NHol NRya NWad SIvy SLee SPlb SPoG SRot SSim XLum
	- 'Variegatum'	see *S. spurium* 'Tricolor'
	- 'Voodoo'	CBod CPla CWCL EBou ECtt EDAr EPfP EWes LPot LShi MBel MHer NBro NDov NGdn XLum
	stahlii	SIvy
	stefco	XLum
	stenopetalum	SPlb
§	- 'Douglasii'	MHer SRms
	'Stewed Rhubarb Mountain'	see *Hylotelephium* 'Stewed Rhubarb Mountain'
	stribrnyi	see *S. urvillei* Stribrnyi Group
	subtile PB 08-639 **new**	GGro
	takesimense	XLum
	- B&SWJ 8493	WCru
	- B&SWJ 8518	WCru
	tatarinowii	see *Hylotelephium tatarinowii*
	telephium	see *Hylotelephium telephium*
	ternatum	MHer
	tetractinum 'Coral Reef'	NBir SRms XLum
	trollii	see *Rhodiola saxifragoides*
	urvillei Sartorianum Group	XLum
§	- Stribrnyi Group	XLum
	ussuriense	see *Hylotelephium ussuriense*
	valens	SPlb
	'Vera Jameson'	see *Hylotelephium* 'Vera Jameson'
	verticillatum	see *Hylotelephium verticillatum*
	viviparum	see *Hylotelephium viviparum*
	'Washfield Purple'	see *Hylotelephium telephium* (Atropurpureum Group) 'Purple Emperor'
	'Weihenstephaner Gold'	see *S. kamtschaticum* var. *floriferum* 'Weihenstephaner Gold'
	weinbergii	see *Graptopetalum paraguayense*
	yezoense	see *Hylotelephium pluricaule*
	yunnanense	see *Rhodiola yunnanensis*

Seemannia (*Gesneriaceae*)

§	***nematanthodes***	SBrt
	- 'Evita'	EShb WCot WFar
§	***sylvatica***	EShb
	- 'Bolivian Sunset'	WDib

Selaginella (*Selaginellaceae*)

braunii	WCot
helvetica	EBee WSHC XLum
kraussiana ♀H2	CBrP CKel CTsd ESwi GArf
- 'Aurea'	CBdn CCCN EHed EHyd LRHS MAsh NRHS
- 'Brownii' ♀H2	CCCN
- 'Gold Tips'	CCCN EHed EHyd ESwi GGro LRHS MAsh NRHS
lepidophylla	GKev SVic
martensii 'Jori' (v)	WCot
moellendorfii	EHyd LRHS NRHS
uncinata ♀H1b	EHyd NRHS

Selinum (*Apiaceae*)

CC 6869	MSpe
KWJ 12281 from northern Vietnam	WCru
alatum **new**	WCru
candollei HWJK 2329	WCru
carvifolium	CCBP CExl CMac ELan EMor LEdu LLWG MHol MNrw NLar SPtp WCot

– HWJK 2347	ESwi WCru
– PAB 2676	LEdu
cryptotaenium	SPtp
– FMWJ 13250	WCru
– PAB 8948	LEdu
filicifolium	CBod LLWG MBel MHol MNrw SMad WCot
tenuifolium	see *S. wallichianum*
§ ***wallichianum*** ♀H6	Widely available
– CC 6869	GKev
– EMAK 886	EBee
– HPA 1389 new	GGro
– HWJK 2347	WCru
– PAB 3579	LEdu WPGP
– PAB 8969	LEdu WPGP
– WJC 13656 from Sikkim	WCru
– from Bhutan	WPGP
– from Manipur	WPGP
– from Nagaland, India	WPGP

Selliera (*Goodeniaceae*)

radicans	GAbr LShi

Semele (*Asparagaceae*)

androgyna	CRHN EShb WCot

Semiaquilegia (*Ranunculaceae*)

§ ***adoxoides***	GGro GKev
– double-flowered (d)	GKev
§ ***ecalcarata*** ♀H5	CDor CSpe CWCL EBee GArf GKev MNrw NGdn NHpl SBut SRms WHal
'Moody Blues'	CBor WFar
simulatrix	see *S. ecalcarata*
'Sugar Plum Fairy'	CBor CRos CSma EHyd EPfP LBuc LRHS NRHS SPoG WFar
'Tinkerbell'	CBor WFar

Semiarundinaria (*Poaceae*)

§ ***fastuosa*** ♀H6	CBcs CJun EPfP LPar MMuc MWht SArc SEND SPlb
– var. ***viridis***	MWht WCru
kagamiana	EPfP MMuc MWht
§ ***lubrica***	MWht
makinoi	MWht
nitida	see *Fargesia nitida*
§ ***okuboi***	CBdn MWht
villosa	see *S. okuboi*
yamadorii	MWht
yashadake	MWht
– f. ***kimmei***	CBod CRos EHyd EPfP LRHS MMuc MWht NLar NRHS SPoG

Semnanthe see *Erepsia*

Sempervivella see *Rosularia*

Sempervivum ✿ (*Crassulaceae*)

'Aaroundina'	NMen
'Abba'	CMea NMen WHal
'Abbe' new	NMen
'Achalm'	GFgr NMen
acuminatum	see *S. tectorum* var. *glaucum*
'Adamina'	NMen SSem
'Adelaar'	NMen
'Adelmoed'	NMen
'Ageet'	NMen
'Aida'	NMen
'Aladdin'	MSCN NMen SRms
'Alchimist'	NMen SSim XLum
'Aldo Moro'	EDAr NMen WIce XLum
'Alenco'	NMen
'Alesia'	NMen
'Alfons-Roelands'	NMen
'Aline' new	SSem
allionii	see *Jovibarba allionii*
'Allison'	GFgr
'Alluring'	NMen
'Alpha'	CMea NMen SRms WHal XLum
'Alsem' new	CMHG
altum	CRos EHyd LRHS NRHS SPlb SRms XLum
'Amanda'	MBrN NMen SRms WHoo
'Ambergreen'	NMen
'Andinn Tunrida'	NMen
andreanum	see *S. tectorum* var. *alpinum*
'Andrenor'	NMen
'Andrenor' sport	NMen
'Antiquity'	WFar
'Apache' Haberer	NMen
'Apanatschi'	NMen
'Apollo'	XLum
'Apollo's Frog'	NMen
'Apple Blossom'	CMea NMen
'Apricot'	NMen
'Aqua'	NMen
arachnoideum ♀H7	Widely available
– from the Abruzzi, Italy	NMen SLee
– from Zermatt, Switzerland	XLum
– 'Ararat'	SDys
– var. ***bryoides***	CRos EHyd LRHS NRHS SRms SSem WFar
– 'Clärchen'	MSCN NMen WAbe XLum
– cristate	XLum
* – ***densum***	EDAr EPPr GAbr SSem WAbe
– subsp. ***doellianum***	see *S. arachnoideum* subsp. *tomentosum* var. *glabrescens*
– giant	WFar
– 'Laggeri'	see *S. arachnoideum* subsp. *tomentosum* (C.B. Lehm. & Schnittsp.) Schinz & Thell.
– 'Opitz'	SRms
– 'Peña Prieta'	XLum
– 'Piletina'	WFar
– 'Red Papaver'	LRHS
– 'Red Wings'	NMen XLum
– 'Rheinkiesel'	XLum
– 'Rubin'	MCot NHpl SSim WFar
– 'Rubrum'	CDoC CRos EBou GMaP LRHS NRHS SPlb SSem WFar XLum
– 'Spider's Nest'	WFar
– 'Spider's Web'	WFar
– subsp. ***tomentosum*** misapplied	see *S.* × *barbulatum* 'Hookeri'
– subsp. ***tomentosum*** ambig.	EBou XLum
§ – subsp. ***tomentosum*** (C.B. Lehm. & Schnittsp.) Schinz & Thell. ♀H7	CRos EHyd NFav NPer NRHS NWad SPlb SRms SSem WAbe
§ – – var. ***glabrescens***	SDys XLum
– – 'Minor'	SSim WFar
– – 'Minus'	EHyd EPfP LRHS
§ – – 'Stansfieldii'	CRos EHyd EPPr LRHS NRHS SLee SRms WFar WHal
– 'Web Cluster'	WFar
§ – 'White Christmas'	MHer NMen
arachnoideum* × *montanum	see *S.* × *barbulatum*
arachnoideum* × *nevadense	SDys
arachnoideum* × *pittonii	NMen SRms WAbe
arenarium	see *Jovibarba arenaria*
'Argus Eye'	NMen

	'Arondina'	NMen
	'Aross'	CMea
	'Arrowheads Red'	NMen
	'Artist'	NMen
	'Ashes of Roses'	EGrI MSCN NHol NMen XLum
	'Athen' **new**	NMen
	'Atlantic'	SRms
	atlanticum	MMuc NMen SLee SSem
	– from Oukaïmeden, Morocco	GAbr NMen SRms
	– 'Edward Balls'	NMen SDys SRms WFar
	'Atlantis' ambig.	NFav NMen SRms
	'Atropurpureum' ambig.	EGrI EPot GAbr MBrN NMen WFar
	'Attraction'	NMen
	'Aureum'	see *Greenovia aurea*
	'Averil'	NMen
	'Babette'	NMen
	'Baby Skrocki'	NMen
	balcanicum	NMen SRms XLum
	ballsii	CRos EHyd LRHS NMen NRHS SRms
	– from Smólikas, Greece	NMen
	– from Tschumba Petzi, Greece	SDys XLum
	'Banderi'	NMen
	'Bandi' **new**	NMen
	'Banjo'	NMen
	'Banyan'	CRos EHyd LRHS NRHS SRms SSem
§	× ***barbulatum***	GAbr SDys SSem
§	– 'Hookeri'	CTri GKev NMen SSim WAbe WHoo XLum
	'Baronesse'	NMen
	'Bascour Zilver'	CMea MSCN SRms WHal
	'Be Mine'	MSCN
I	'Beate' G. Dillmann	NMen
	'Beatles Memory'	NMen
	'Beaute'	NMen
	'Beautiful'	NMen
	'Bedazzled'	NMen
	'Bedivere'	NMen SRms
	'Bedivere Crested'	NMen
*	'Bedley Hi'	NMen
	'Bella Donna'	NMen
	'Bella Meade'	NMen SRms
	'Bellotts Pourpre'	NMen
	'Benala'	NMen
	'Bennerbroek'	NMen
	'Bernstein'	EDAr EPPr GFgr GKev MHer MSCN NMen NWad SLee WHal WIce XLum
	'Beta'	NMen WAbe XLum
	'Bethany'	CMea NWad WHal
	'Bianca'	NMen
	'Big Blue' **new**	SSem
	'Bijou'	NMen
	'Birchmaier'	NMen
	'Bitter Chocolate'	GFgr
	'Björn'	NMen
	'Black Beauty'	EBou NMen
	'Black Cap'	NMen
	'Black Knight'	CMea CRos EHyd LRHS MHer NRHS SPlb SRms SSem WHal WHoo
	'Black Mini'	GKev NBir NMen SLee SRms
	'Black Mountain'	GKev NMen
	'Black Rose'	NMen
	'Black Velvet'	NMen
	'Black Widow'	NMen
	'Blackcurrant Ice'	GFgr
	'Blade of Steel'	NMen
	'Blauer Ritter'	NMen
	'Blood Tip'	CMea CRos EHyd GAbr LRHS LSun MHer NHol NMen NRHS NRya NWad SEND SPlb SPoG SRms WFar WHal WHoo

	'Bloody Goose'	NMen
	'Blue Angel' **new**	NMen
	'Blue Bird'	NMen
	'Blue Boy'	CRos EBou EHyd EPPr GAbr GFgr LRHS MSCN NMen NRHS SPlb SRms SSem WFar
	'Blue Knight'	NMen
	'Blue Lady' **new**	NMen
	'Blue Moon'	NMen SSem
	'Blue Time'	WFar WHoo XLum
	'Blush'	NMen
	'Blushes' **new**	SSem
	'Boissieri'	see *S. tectorum* subsp. *tectorum* 'Boissieri'
	'Bokkenrijders'	NMen
	'Bold Chick'	NMen
	'Bombardier'	EDAr
	'Booth's Red'	NMen
	borisii	see *S. ciliosum* var. *borisii*
	borissovae	EPot NMen SDys
	'Boromir'	NMen XLum
	'Boule de Neige'	NMen NRya WFar
	'Bowles's Variety'	NMen
	'Braune Maus'	GFgr
I	'Braunella'	NMen
	'Brilland Red Brun'	NMen
	'Britta'	NMen SDys
	'Brock'	CRos EHyd LRHS NRHS SRms SSem
	'Bronco' ♀H5	CRos EBou EGrI EHyd EPfP GAbr GBin LRHS MMuc NHol NMen NRHS NRya NWad SEND SLee SRms SRot SSem SSim WBrk WCot WFar WPGP XLum
	'Bronze Pastel'	EDAr MSCN NHpl NMen NSla SRms SSem
	'Brown Owl'	EBou NMen SRms SSem
	'Brown Web'	NMen
	'Brownii'	NMen
	'Brunette'	GAbr
	'Brunhilde'	NMen
	bungeanum hort.	NMen
	'Burgundy'	NMen
	'Burning Bush'	WFar
	'Burnished Bronze'	NMen
	'Burnt Embers'	NMen
	'Butterbur'	NMen
	'Butterfly'	NMen
	'Café'	MSCN NHol NMen SRms
*	***calabricum***	NHol
	calcareum	CMea CRos EBou EHyd GKev GQue LRHS MCot MMuc NBro NHol NHpl NMen NRHS SArc SEND SEdd SPlb SPoG SRms SSem SSim WFar XLum
	– GDJ 92.16 from Petite Ceüse, France	SRms
	– from Cleizé, France	see *S. calcareum* 'Limelight'
	– from Col Bayard, France	GAbr NMen
	– from Colle St Michel, France	SRms
	– from Queyras, France	NMen
	– from Triora, Italy	NMen
	– 'Atropurpureum'	CCal
	– 'Benz'	SDys
	– 'Button'	WFar
	– 'Extra' ♀H5	CCal EWes GAbr MSCN NMen SRms SSem WFar
	– 'Greenii'	CRos EHyd LRHS MSCN NMen NRHS SPlb SRms
§	– 'Grigg's Surprise'	NMen SPlb
	– 'Guillaumes' ♀H5	CRos EHyd GFgr LRHS NMen NRHS SRms SSem SSim WHoo

§ - 'Limelight'	CMea CRos EHyd LRHS NMen NRHS SLee SSem WHal WHoo
- 'Monstrosum'	see *S. calcareum* 'Grigg's Surprise'
- 'Mrs Giuseppi'	EGrI EWoo GAbr LSun NHpl NMen SEdd SRms SSem WAbe WFar WIce XLum
- 'Nigricans'	NMen
- 'Pink Pearl'	MSCN NMen SDys SPlb XLum
- 'Sir William Lawrence' 🏆H5	CCal CMea CRos EBou EDAr EGrI EHyd GFgr LRHS NMen NRHS SGro SLee SRms SRot SSem WAbe WHal XLum
'Cameo'	see *Jovibarba heuffelii* var. *glabra* 'Cameo'
'Campagha'	NMen
'Canada Kate'	NMen
'Cancer'	XLum
'Candy Floss'	NMen
cantabricum	MMuc NMen WFar XLum
- from Navafria, Spain	NMen
- from Ticeros	XLum
- from Valvanera, Spain	NMen
- subsp. ***cantabricum*** from Leitariegos, Spain	GAbr
- subsp. ***guadarramense***	see *S. vicentei* subsp. *paui*
- - from Pico del Lobo, Spain, No 1	SRms
- subsp. ***urbionense***	SRms
- - from El Gatón, Spain	GFgr
'Caramel'	NMen
'Carlo's II'	NMen
'Carmen'	GAbr NMen
'Carneum'	NMen
'Carnival'	NMen
'Casablanca'	NMen
'Caspara'	NMen
'Cassiopeia' **new**	CBod
caucasicum	CRos EHyd LRHS NMen NRHS SRms XLum
'Cavo Doro'	NMen
'Celon'	NMen
'Centaurus' **new**	CBod
'Centennial'	NMen SSem
charadzeae	XLum
'Cherry Dream' **new**	SSem
'Cherry Frost'	NHol NMen XLum
'Cherry Glow'	see *Jovibarba heuffelii* 'Cherry Glow'
'Cherry Tart'	NMen SPlb SSem
'Chilli Pepper'	MSCN
'Chivalry'	NMen
'Cho' **new**	NMen
'Chocolate'	NHpl WAbe
'Choctaw'	NMen
'Cholie'	GKev NMen
'Christmas Time'	NMen
chrysanthum	SSim
ciliosum 🏆H7	CMea NRya SPlb SRms
- from Alí Butús, Bulgaria	SDys
§ - var. ***borisii***	EPPr GKev NRya SSem WAbe WFar WHal
- var. ***borisii*** × ***ciliosum*** var. ***ciliosum***	CTri
- var. ***galicicum*** 'Mali Hat'	NMen
- subsp. ***octopodes*** **new**	NMen
'Cindy'	SRms
'Claey's Fluweel'	NMen
'Clara Noyes'	NMen
'Clare'	MHer NMen
'Classic Rock'	NMen
'Clemanum'	NMen
'Cleveland Morgan'	XLum

'Climax' ambig.	WFar
'Climax' Ford	NMen
'Cobweb Capers'	NMen
'Cobweb Centres'	EWes NMen
'Colchicum'	SRms
'Collecteur Anchisi'	SDys
'Commander Hay'	CTri EBou EWes GKev GMaP MSCN NHpl NMen NPer NRya SRms WHal XLum
'Comte de Congae'	NMen
'Concorde'	SSem
'Congo'	NMen XLum
'Corio'	NMen
'Corona'	NMen
'Coronet'	NMen
'Corsair'	EPPr GFgr GKev MBrN MMuc NMen SRms SSem WBrk WFar
'Cream Tea'	GFgr
'Crimson Velvet'	CMea XLum
'Crimson Webb'	WFar
'Cripello'	NMen
§ 'Crispyn' 🏆H5	CCal CMea CRos EHyd EPot LRHS MMuc MSCN NMen NRHS SEND SRms SSem WFar
'Crows'	NMen
'Crucify'	NMen
'Cupream'	NMen SRms
'Cyclops'	NMen
'Dakota'	EDAr NMen
'Dallas'	NMen SRms
'Damask'	MSCN NMen
'Dancer's Veil'	NMen
'Danji'	NMen
'Darjeeling'	NMen
'Dark Beauty'	CMea CRos EHyd LRHS NHol NRHS SRms SSem WAbe WCot WHal
'Dark Cloud'	CMea NMen WHoo XLum
'Dark Point'	NMen
'Dark Velvet'	CMea
'De Kardijk'	NMen
'Deep Fire'	NMen SRms SSem
× ***degenianum***	GAbr NMen XLum
'Delta' 🏆H5	NMen WHoo
densum	see *S. tectorum*
'Desert Dream'	WFar
'Devil's Teeth'	MSCN
'Devil's Touch' **new**	SSem
'Devon Glow'	MSCN
'Dippy Dame' **new**	NMen
'Director Jacobs'	EDAr NHpl NMen
'Direktor General'	NMen
'Ditto'	GFgr
'Doeskin' **new**	SSem
'Dolfien' **new**	NMen
'Dolle Dina's'	NMen
dolomiticum	NMen XLum
dolomiticum × ***montanum***	NBro NMen
'Donarrose'	NMen
'Donnerlüttchen' **new**	SSem
'Dornröschen'	NMen
'Downland Queen'	NMen
'Dr Fritz Köhlein'	NMen SSem
'Dragoness'	NMen SSem
'Dream Catcher'	NMen
'Dune' **new**	NMen
'Dyke'	CTri NMen WHal
dzhavachischvilii	NMen XLum
'Edge of Night'	SRms
'Edwardine'	NMen
'Edwina' **new**	SSem

'Eefje'	NMen
'Eisbär' **new**	SSem
'El Greco'	NMen
'El Toro'	NHpl NMen SSem
'Electra'	SSem
'Elgar'	NMen
'Elva'	NMen
'Elvis'	NMen SLee
'Emerald Empress' **new**	NMen
'Emerald Giant'	SRms
'Emerald Haze'	WFar
'Emerald Lustre'	WFar
'Emerson's Giant'	NMen SRms
'Emmchen'	NMen
'Engle's'	CMea CRos CTri EHyd GKev LRHS MMuc NMen NRHS SEND SPlb SRms SSem WFar WHal
'Engle's 13-2'	NMen
'Engle's Rubrum'	NMen
'Eos'	NMen
'Erdbeermond' **new**	NMen
erythraeum	CRos EHyd LRHS NHpl NMen NRHS SPlb SRms SSem WHal
- from Mesta Valley, Bulgaria	NMen
'Essence of Lime'	GFgr
'Euphemia'	NMen
'Evening Glow'	NMen
'Excalibur'	NMen
'Exhibita'	SDys SRms
'Exorna'	EDAr NMen SSem
'Eyjafjalla' **new**	SSem
'Fair Lady'	NMen
'Fairy'	NMen
'Fame'	NMen SPlb
'Famke' **new**	SSem
'Faramir'	NMen
'Farida'	NMen
'Fat Jack'	NMen
× ***fauconnetii***	LRHS
- 'Rubellum'	NMen
- 'Thompsonii'	SRms
'Feldmaier'	NMen WFar
'Fernanda' **new**	NMen
'Fernwood'	NMen
'Fernzünder' **new**	SSem
'Festival'	NMen
'Fiery Furness'	NMen
'Fiesta' ambig.	NMen WHal
'Fifty One Shades'	WFar
× ***fimbriatum***	see *S.* × ***barbulatum***
- 'Joy of Life' **new**	SSim
'Finerpointe'	NMen
'Fire Flies'	NMen
'Fire Glint'	NMen SRms WFar
'Firebird'	NMen
'Firgrove Early Riser'	NMen
'Firgrove Silver'	GFgr
'Firlefanz' **new**	SSem
'First Try'	NMen
flagelliforme	XLum
'Flaming Heart'	EDAr MBrN NMen
'Flaming Sword'	NMen
'Flaming Web'	WFar
'Flamingo'	NMen
'Flanders Passion'	EWes NMen SRms SSem
'Flasher'	NMen SSem SSim
'Fluweel'	MSCN NMen
'Forden'	GFgr NMen
'Ford's Amiability'	SDys
'Ford's Giant'	XLum
'Ford's Shadows'	SDys
'Ford's Spring'	NMen SRms SSem
'Freckles'	NMen
'Fronika'	NMen
'Frosty'	GFgr NMen SRms
'Fuego' ♀H5	CCal CRos EHyd GFgr LRHS NMen NRHS SRms SSem
'Fuji'	NMen
× ***funckii***	EGrI MBrN NMen XLum
'Fuzzy Wuzzy'	NMen
'Gabrielle'	SSem
'Galadriel' **new**	SSem
'Galahad'	NMen
'Galaxis' **new**	NMen
'Galifa' **new**	SSem
'Gallivarda' ♀H5	CRos EHyd GFgr LRHS NMen NRHS
'Gambol'	NWad
'Gamma'	NMen SRms
'Gargamel' **new**	SSem
'Garnet'	NMen
'Gay Jester'	CTri NMen SLee WHoo
'Gazelle'	XLum
'Georgette'	NMen XLum
'Georgia Rowan'	NMen
'Gilosum'	EDAr
'Ginger Nut'	NMen
'Ginnie's Delight'	NMen
'Gipsy'	NMen
giuseppii ♀H7	CRos EHyd GKev LRHS NRHS SRms
- from Peña Espigüete, Spain	SDys SRms
'Gizmo'	NMen
'Glaucum'	see *S. tectorum* var. *glaucum*
'Glaucum Minor'	NMen
globiferum	XLum
subsp. ***globiferum***	
'Minor'	
'Gloriosum' ambig.	NMen
'Glowing Embers'	NMen WHal XLum
'Glückskinder' **new**	NMen
'Godaert'	MMuc SEND XLum
'Gog'	NMen
'Goldie'	NMen
'Goldmarie'	NMen SSem
'Goldschatz'	NMen
'Goovy'	NMen
'Granada'	EDAr NMen
'Granat'	GWyn MHer NMen SRms XLum
'Granby'	SDys
'Grand Mère'	NMen
grandiflorum	NMen WThu XLum
- 'Fasciatum'	NMen
'Grannie's Favourite'	NMen
'Grapetone'	NMen SDys WHal
'Gratiana'	NMen
'Graupurpur'	XLum
'Green Apple'	GAbr NMen SDys
'Green Caro'	NMen
'Green Disk'	SRms
'Green Dragon'	CRos EGrI EHyd LRHS MSCN NMen NRHS SRms
'Green Gables'	EDAr
'Green Ice'	GFgr NMen SLee SSem
'Green Wheel'	NMen
'Greenwich Time'	EDAr NMen
* ***greigii***	MSCN
'Grey Dawn'	CRos EHyd LRHS NMen NRHS SRms XLum
'Grey Ghost'	NMen SSem SSim
'Grey Lady'	NMen
'Grey Owl'	CRos EHyd GFgr LRHS MSCN NMen NRHS SRms WFar

	'Grey Velvet'	NMen
	'Greyfriars'	CMea CRos EDAr EHyd LRHS MSCN NMen NRHS SRms SSem
	'Greyolla'	NMen
	'Grünschnabel'	XLum
	'Grunspur'	NMen
	'Gulle Dame'	CMea NMen SRms
	'Gummibärchen' **new**	NMen
	'Gwiazda'	GBin WFar
	'Halley' **new**	NMen
I	'Hall's Hybrid'	MSCN NBro NMen SRms
	'Happy'	NMen SLee SRms SSem
	'Harriet'	NMen
	'Hart'	GFgr NMen SSem
	'Havana'	NMen
	'Havendijker Splitt'	NMen
	'Havendijker Teufel' **new**	SSem
	'Havendijks Millenium'	NMen
	'Havendijks Pride'	NMen
	'Hayling'	EHyd EWes GAbr NMen NRHS NWad SRms SSem SSim WFar XLum
	'Haynaldii' **new**	NMen
	'Heigham Red'	CRos EBou EHyd GKev LRHS NMen NRHS SRms SSem WFar WIce
	'Heike'	NMen
	'Heiko' **new**	NMen
	'Helen'	EDAr NMen WFar
	'Heliotroop'	NMen SDys
	helveticum	see *S. montanum*
	'Hermann Näpfel'	NMen
	'Hermine'	NMen
	'Hester'	MBrN NBro NMen
	'Hey-hey'	CRos EGrI EHyd LRHS MBrN NMen NRHS SEdd SPlb SSem WCot XLum
	'Hidde'	EGrI NMen SPlb
	'Highland Mist'	NMen
	'Hirsutum'	see *Jovibarba allionii*
	hirtum	see *Jovibarba hirta*
	'Honigmond' **new**	SSem SSim
	'Honymoon'	NMen
	'Hookeri'	see *S.* × *barbulatum* 'Hookeri'
	'Hopi'	NMen
	'Hortulanus Smit'	XLum
	'Hot Boyz'	NMen
	'Hot Peppermint'	NMen
	'Hualalai' **new**	NMen
	'Hullabaloo'	EDAr GAbr NMen
	'Hunlaf's Strange' **new**	CNat
	'Hurricane'	NMen
	'Icicle'	CMea CRos EHyd LRHS MSCN NBro NHol NMen NRHS SRms
	imbricatum	see *S.* × *barbulatum*
	'Impact'	NMen
	'Imperial'	NMen SPlb
	'Infinity'	GFgr
	'Ingemarie' **new**	NMen
	ingwersenii	NMen XLum
	ingwersenii* × *pumilum	GFgr NMen SRms
	'Irazu'	CMea CRos EHyd EPot LRHS MSCN NMen NRHS SDys SRms SSem WHoo
	'Isaac Dyson'	SDys SLee SRot SSem
	'Isabelle'	NMen
	italicum	XLum
	'Itchen'	NMen
	'Ivonne'	NMen
	'Iwo'	NMen
	'Jack Frost'	NBro NMen XLum
	'Jacquette'	NMen
	'Jade' ambig.	NMen
	'Jadestern'	NMen
I	'Janus'	NMen
	'Jelly Bean'	GFgr NMen
	'Jet Stream' ♀H5	CRos EHyd LRHS MSCN NMen NRHS SDys SPlb SRms SSem WFar
	'Jewel Case'	CRos EHyd LRHS NRHS SRms
	'Jim Knopf'	NMen
I	'John Hobbs seedling No. 2'	NMen
	'John T' × 'Saffron'	NMen
	'Joke'	NMen
	'Jolly Green Giant'	NMen
	'Jo's Spark'	NMen
	'Jubilee'	CMea EDAr ELan MAsh MHer NMen SRms XLum
	'Jubilee Tricolor'	NHol NMen SPlb SSim WAbe
	'Jungle Fires'	CCal CMea SDys SRms WHoo
	'Jungle Shadows'	EDAr NMen NWad XLum
	'Jupiter'	GKev XLum
	'Jurrina'	NMen
	'Just Peachy'	EPot
	'Justine's Choice'	NMen SRms
	'Kai'	NMen
	'Kappa'	NBro NMen SDys
	'Karin'	NMen SSem
	'Katmai'	GFgr NMen
	'Keder' **new**	NMen
	'Keiko'	NMen
	'Kelly Jo'	EWoo WBrk
	'Kermit'	NMen
	'Khaleesi'	WFar
	'Kiara'	NMen
	'Kibo'	NMen
	'Kidlington'	NMen
	'Kildare'	NMen
	'Kim'	NMen
	'Kimba'	NMen
	'Kimble'	NMen
	'Kimono'	NMen NWad
	kindingeri	NMen SRms XLum
	'King George'	CTri EBou GKev MMuc NMen SEND SRms WHal WHoo XLum
	'Kip'	CMea NMen
	'Kismet'	NMen
	'Kohala' **new**	SSem
	'Koko Flanel'	CCal GFgr GKev NMen SRms SSem
	'Korspel Beauty'	NMen
	'Korspel Cherry' **new**	NMen
	'Korspel Prince'	NMen
	'Korspel Sport'	NMen
	'Korspelsegietje'	GAbr NMen SRms
	kosaninii	NMen
	- from Koprivnik, Slovenia	MSCN WAbe XLum
	- 'Hepworth'	SPlb
	'Kramer's Spinrad'	CMea EPPr GAbr GFgr GKev NMen SPlb SRms WFar WHoo WThu
	'Krankii'	XLum
	'Krater'	NMen
	'Lady Di'	NMen
	'Lady Kelly'	CMea
	'Lamia'	NMen
	'Lancer'	NMen
	'Landemine' **new**	NMen SSem
	'Larissa'	GFgr
	'Latex' **new**	SSem
	'Laura Lee'	MMuc NMen SEND
	'Lavender and Old Lace'	CRos EHyd LRHS MSCN NMen NRHS SPlb SRms SSem WFar WIce XLum
	'Lavenderspross'	NMen
	'Le Congai'	NMen
	'Legolas'	NMen
	'Leneca'	NMen

	'Lennik's Glory'	see *S.* 'Crispyn'
	'Lennik's Sport'	XLum
	'Lentezon'	GFgr NMen
	'Leocadia's Nephew'	NMen
	'Leopold' **new**	SSem
	leucanthum	XLum
	'Lilac Queen'	NMen
	'Lilac Time' ♀H5	CCal CMea CRos EHyd EPPr GFgr LRHS MBrN MHer MSCN NMen NRHS SPlb SRms SSem WFar WHal XLum
	'Lilehammer' **new**	NMen
	'Limbo'	NMen
	'Limburg' **new**	NMen
	'Lion King'	CCal GFgr MSCN NMen
	'Lioness'	NMen
	'Lipari'	LRHS SRms WCot XLum
	'Lipstick'	GQue NMen
	'Little Coffee Cup'	GFgr
	'Little Flirt'	MSCN
	'Little Rock'	NMen
	'Lively Bug'	CRos EHyd EPPr EPot LRHS MSCN NMen NRHS SDys SLee SRms SSem XLum
	'Lloyd Praeger'	see *S. montanum* subsp. *stiriacum* 'Lloyd Praeger'
	'Long Shanks'	MSCN
	'Lonzo'	NMen SRms
	'Lord Alan'	GKev NMen
	'Lord Morton'	NMen
	'Lovely Roset'	NMen
	'Lucy Liu'	SSem
	'Ludmila'	NMen
	'Luftsprung' **new**	NMen
	'Lumeseen'	NMen
	'Lynn's Choice'	NMen NWad WHal
	'Lyra'	NMen
	macedonicum	NMen SPlb SRms XLum
	'Magic Morning' **new**	SSem
	'Magic Spell'	NMen
	'Magical'	NMen
	'Magnificum'	GFgr NMen XLum
	'Mahogany'	CTri EDAr EGrI GKev MHer MSCN NHol NMen NRya SRms WHal XLum
	'Mai Appel' **new**	NMen
	'Maia'	SSim
	'Maigret'	NMen SSem
	'Majanka'	NMen
	'Majestic'	NMen
	'Malby's Hybrid'	see *S.* 'Reginald Malby'
	'Maria Laach'	NMen
	'Marijntje'	NMen
	'Mariska'	NMen
	'Marjory'	NMen
	'Marland Ruby'	NMen WCot
	'Marmalade'	NMen
§	***marmoreum***	EHyd EPot NMen NRHS SRms WHal
	– from Börzöny, Hungary	XLum
	– from Kanzan Gorge, Bulgaria	XLum
	– from Okol, Albania	NMen
	– 'Brunneifolium'	GAbr XLum
	– subsp. ***marmoreum*** var. ***dinaricum***	MHer NMen
§	– – 'Rubrifolium'	XLum
	'Marshall'	NMen
	'Marsupilami' **new**	NMen
	'Mary-Beth'	NMen
	'Matthew's Day Dream'	GKev NMen SSim
	'Mauvine'	NMen NWad XLum
	'May Red' **new**	NMen
	'Mayfair'	EDAr NMen
	'Maytime'	NMen SSem
	'Meadow Blaze'	WFar
	'Melanie'	CMea MBrN NMen SSem
	'Mercury'	CRos EHyd LRHS NBro NMen NRHS SRms
	'Merlin'	MSCN
	mettenianum	NMen
	'Michael' **new**	SSem
	'Mickey Mouse'	NMen
	'Midas'	CRos EHyd LRHS NRHS SRms
	'Mini Frost'	NMen
	'Minuet'	NMen
	'Mira'	MHol
	'Mixed Spice'	CMea
	'Moerkerk's Merit'	EHyd NMen XLum
	'Mona Lisa'	NMen
	'Mondstein'	MSCN NMen SRms
	'Monseigneur Desmet'	GQue
§	***montanum***	XLum
	– from Haute-Loire, France	XLum
	– from Mont Aigoual, France	XLum
	– from the Pyrenees	XLum
	– from Vallée d'Estaing, France	XLum
	– 'Caesar'	MSCN
	– subsp. ***carpaticum*** 'Cmiral's Yellow'	GKev WAbe WFar
	– subsp. ***montanum*** var. ***braunii***	LRHS
	– 'Rubrum'	see *S.* 'Red Mountain'
	– subsp. ***stiriacum***	SRms XLum
§	– – 'Lloyd Praeger'	NMen SDys
	'More Honey'	NMen
	'Morning Glow'	NMen WHal
	'Moss Rose'	NMen SSem
	'Mount Hood'	CRos EHyd LRHS NMen NRHS SRms WHal
	'Mount Skippet'	NMen
	'Mount Usher'	NMen
	'Mulberry Wine'	SRms SSem WHoo
	'Mystic'	MBrN NMen SSem
	'Naemi'	NMen
	'Neon'	NMen
	'Neptune'	WFar
*	***netaginatum***	XLum
	nevadense	GArf NMen NRya SRms
	– 'Hirtellum'	SRms
	'New Rose'	WFar XLum
	'Nico'	NMen NWad SRms
	'Night Detector'	NMen
	'Nigrum'	see *S. tectorum* 'Nigrum'
	'Niobe'	NMen WHal
	'Nocturno'	NMen XLum
	'Noellie'	NMen
	'Noir'	EHyd EPfP GKev LRHS NBro NMen NRHS SSem WFar XLum
	'Norbert'	NMen SRms XLum
	'Nörtofts Beauty'	NMen
	'Nouveau Pastel'	CMea NMen WHal XLum
	'Nova'	NMen
	'Novalis'	NMen
	'Obaldina' **new**	NMen
	'Oberon'	NMen
	'Obsession'	WFar
	'Ockerwurz'	WFar
	'Octet'	NMen
	octopodes	NBir NRya XLum
	– var. ***apetalum***	EPPr GAbr MSCN NMen WHoo
	'Oddity'	LRHS MBrN MHer NMen NWad WFar WHal

'Oh My'	NMen
'Ohio Burgundy'	CRos EHyd LRHS MSCN NMen NRHS SRms SSem WAbe WFar
'Olcina'	NMen
'Old Man Sage'	SPlb
'Olivia'	NMen
'Olivine'	GFgr
'Omega'	NMen
'Orange Glow' **new**	SSem
'Orestes' **new**	NMen
'Ornatum'	MHer WAbe WHal
ossetiense	GAbr NMen XLum
'Othello' ♀H5	CTri NBir NMen SRms SSem WCot WPGP XLum
'Ottelein'	NMen
'Pachamama'	NMen
'Pacific Blazing Star' **new**	SSem
'Pacific Blue Ice'	SSem
'Pacific Charm'	NMen
'Pacific Devils Food'	NMen
'Pacific Hazy Embers'	NMen
'Pacific Opal'	NMen
'Pacific Purple Shadows'	NMen WFar
'Pacific Second Try'	NMen
'Pacific Sexy'	NMen SSem
'Pacific Sunset'	NMen
'Packardian'	NMen NWad
'Painted Lady'	NMen
'Palissander'	EDAr GAbr NMen XLum
'Pallas'	XLum
'Pandaros' **new**	SSem
'Papucchini'	NMen
'Passionata'	NMen SSem
'Pastel'	CTri GFgr MHer SLee
patens	see *Jovibarba heuffelii*
'Patrician'	NMen SRms
'Pavilion'	NMen
'Peggy'	CCal NMen
'Pekinese'	CRos EBou EHyd LRHS MBrN NBro NMen NRHS SRms SSim WBrk XLum
'Peridot'	GFgr
'Persephone' **new**	NMen
'Peterson's Ornatum'	SDys
'Petsy'	NMen SRms
'Phoebe'	NMen
'Picasso' **new**	NMen SSem
'Pilatus'	EHyd EPfP SRms WFar XLum
'Pine Cone'	GFgr NMen
'Pineapple Punch'	GFgr
'Pink Astrid'	NMen
'Pink Cloud'	NMen SSem
'Pink Delight'	MSCN
'Pink Flamingoes'	NMen SSem
'Pink Grapefruit'	NMen
'Pink Lemonade'	NMen SSem
'Pink Mist'	SRms
'Pink Puff'	NMen
'Pinkerton' **new**	SSem
'Pinochio' **new**	NMen
'Pippin'	CMea NMen SRms SSem
pittonii ♀H5	CMea NMen WHal XLum
'Pixie'	GFgr NMen
'Plum Frosting'	GFgr MSCN
'Plum Mist'	NWad
'Plumb Rose'	NMen
'Plush' **new**	NMen
'Pluto'	NMen XLum
'Polaris'	NMen SSem
'Poldark'	NMen
'Pompeja' **new**	NMen
'Poollicht' **new**	SSem
'Popocatepetl' **new**	SSem
I 'Powellii'	NMen SLee
'Prairie Sunset'	NMen
'President Arsac'	XLum
'Princess Little'	NMen
'Probus'	NMen
'Procton'	NMen
'Proud Zelda'	EDAr GAbr MSCN NMen SSem
'Pseudo-ornatum'	SRms
pulchellum	XLum
'Pumaros'	SDys
pumilum	CRos EHyd LRHS NMen NRHS SRms
- from Techensis, Caucasus Mountains	SRms
- 'Sopa'	MSCN
'Purdy'	NHpl NMen WAbe
'Purdy's 50-6'	NMen
'Purdy's 70-40'	NMen
'Purdy's 90-1'	NMen
'Purdy's Big Red'	NMen
'Purple Beauty'	NMen
'Purple Dazzler'	NMen
'Purple Haze'	NMen
'Purple King'	CMea NMen SDys
'Purple Queen'	CRos EDAr EHyd EPPr LRHS NMen NRHS NRya SRms SSem WFar
'Purple Shadows'	NMen
'Purple Violet'	NMen
'Purpurkranz' **new**	NMen
'Pygmalion'	NMen
'Queen Amalia'	see *S. reginae-amaliae*
'Queen Elizabeth' **new**	SSem
'Quintessence'	MSCN NMen SRms
'Racey'	GFgr
'Ramses'	SDys
'Raspberry Ice'	CMea GKev MSCN NBro NHpl NMen
'Rauer Kulm'	NMen
'Rauhreif'	XLum
'Ravenheart'	MSCN
'Rebecca'	GKev
'Red Ace'	NBro NEoE WFar
'Red Beam'	EHyd NMen NRHS
'Red Chief'	EPfP GKev LRHS XLum
'Red Delta'	NBir NMen WCot WPGP WSMil
'Red Devil'	CMea CRos EGrl EHyd EWoo LRHS NMen NRHS SPlb SRms SSem WHoo
'Red Heart'	CCal
'Red King'	NMen
'Red Lion'	NMen
§ 'Red Mountain'	EWoo LSun NMen NRya SLee SRms
'Red Pink'	CMea GFgr NMen
'Red Pluche'	NMen
'Red Robin'	NMen
'Red Shine' **new**	NMen
'Red Spider'	NBro NMen
'Red West'	NMen
'Regal'	NMen
'Regenbogen' **new**	SSem
'Regensburger Knirps'	NMen
'Regensburger Kokon' **new**	NMen
reginae	see *S. reginae-amaliae*
§ ***reginae-amaliae***	CRos EHyd GKev LRHS NMen NRHS SRms XLum
- from Kambeecho, Greece, No 2	SDys
- from Sarpun, Turkey	SDys
§ 'Reginald Malby'	CRos EHyd LRHS NMen NRHS SRms

	'Reinhard' ♀H5	CCal CMea CRos EDAr EHyd EPot GKev GMaP LRHS MAsh MBrN MHer MSCN NHpl NMen NRHS NRya SLee SPlb SRms SRot SSem SSim WBrk WFar WHal WHoo WIce
	'Remus'	ELan NMen SRms
	'Rex'	NMen
	'Rhône'	NMen
	'Rhubarb Crumble'	GFgr
	'Rio de Janeiro'	NMen
	'Rita Jane'	NMen SSem
	'Robin'	NBro NHol NMen SRms XLum
	'Rococo' **new**	NMen
	'Romantic Knights' **new**	NMen
	'Romantik Ritter'	NMen
I	'Ronsdorfer Hybride'	NMen
	'Roosemaryn'	EDAr
	'Rosa Mädchen'	NMen SSem
	'Rosenherz' **new**	SSem
	'Rosenhügel' **new**	SSem
	× ***roseum***	NMen
	'Rosie'	CCal CMea CRos EHyd GMaP LRHS MAsh MMuc MSCN NHol NMen NRHS SLee SRms SSim WBrk WFar WHal WHoo WIce
	'Rotkopf' ♀H5	CCal CRos EHyd GFgr LRHS MSCN NMen NRHS NWad SSem XLum
	'Rotmantel'	NMen
	'Rotund'	MSCN
	'Royal Opera'	EDAr GKev NMen
	'Royal Ruby'	SLee
	'Rubellum Mahogany'	GFgr
	'Rubikon Improved'	NMen
	'Rubin'	CBod CMea CTri EBou EPfP LRHS MAsh MHol NBir NHpl NMen SPoG SRms SSem SSim WAbe WIce WSMil XLum
I	'Rubra Ash'	NMen
I	'Rubra Ray'	CCal NMen
	'Rubrifolium'	see *S. marmoreum* subsp. *marmoreum* 'Rubrifolium'
*	'Ruby Glow'	EDAr
	'Ruby Heart'	CBod MCot SSim
	'Ruby Meadows'	WFar
	'Russian River'	WHoo
	'Rusty'	NMen
	ruthenicum	CRos EHyd EPPr LRHS NMen NRHS NRya SRms XLum
	- 'Regis-Fernandii'	XLum
	'Ruth's Choice'	WFar
	'Saffron'	NMen
	'Saga'	NMen
	'Samwise'	NMen
	'Sanford's Hybrid'	NMen
	'Sanne'	NMen
	'Santis'	GKev NMen
	'Sarah'	EDAr NMen
	'Sarotte'	NMen
	'Sassy Frass'	NMen
	'Saturn'	MSCN NMen SRms WFar
	schlehanii	see *S. marmoreum*
	schnittspahnii	XLum
	'Schwarze Rose' **new**	NMen SSem
	'Scooby'	WFar
	'Sea Breeze'	GFgr
	'Sea Urchin'	GFgr
	'Seerose' **new**	SSem
	seguieri	XLum
	'Seneca' **new**	NMen
	'Sephora' **new**	NMen
	'Seren'	GBin
	'Serendipity'	EDAr
	'Sharon's Pencil'	NMen
	'Sha'uri'	NMen
	'Sheila'	GAbr
	'Shepherd's Warning'	WFar
	'Shirley Moore'	NMen
	'Shirley's Joy'	NMen XLum
	'Show Baby'	NMen
	'Sideshow'	NMen
	'Sigma'	NMen
	'Silberand' **new**	LRHS
	'Silberkarneol' misapplied	see *S.* 'Silver Jubilee'
	'Silberkarneol' ambig.	EGrI GFgr SEdd
	'Silberspitz'	CRos EHyd LRHS MHer NBro NMen NRHS SPlb SRms
	'Silver Andre'	NMen
§	'Silver Jubilee'	CMea CRos EDAr EHyd GQue LRHS NBro NMen NRHS NRya SPlb SRms WFar WHoo XLum
	'Silver Sixpence'	GFgr
	'Silver Thaw'	EHyd NRHS
	'Silverine'	EDAr NMen
	'Silvertone'	NMen
	'Simonkaianum'	see *Jovibarba hirta*
	'Simply Nightfall'	SSim
	'Sioux'	MBrN NMen SSem WHal
	'Sirius'	CBod GBin MHol NMen
	'Skrocki's Beauty'	GAbr NMen SRms
	'Skrocki's Bronze'	CRos EHyd LRHS NRHS
	'Smaragd'	EHyd NMen XLum
	'Smit's Seedling'	NMen
	'Smokey Jet'	GFgr NMen
	'Snowberger'	CMea EBou NMen SRms WHal
	soboliferum	see *Jovibarba sobolifera*
	'Solamith'	NMen
	'Solar Meadows'	WFar
	'Sombrero'	NMen
	'Sonnenkuss' **new**	SSem
	'Soothsayer'	NMen
	sosnowskyi	NMen XLum
	'Soul'	CCal NMen
	'Space Dog'	NMen
	'Spangle'	NMen
	'Spangle' sport	NMen
	'Spanish Dancer'	NMen
	'Spartan's Sunrise'	WFar
	'Spherette'	EDAr MBrN NMen WAbe
	'Spice'	NMen
	'Spider's Lair' ♀H5	SLee SRms
	'Spinellii'	WThu
	'Spiver's Velvet'	NMen
	'Sponnier'	XLum
	'Spring Beauty'	NMen
	'Springmist'	CRos EHyd GFgr LRHS NRHS SRms SSem
	'Sprite'	CRos EHyd LRHS NMen NRHS SDys SRms SSem SSim
	'Squib'	CCal MSCN NMen
	'Standard Green'	CCal
	stansfieldii	see *S. arachnoideum* subsp. *tomentosum* 'Stansfieldii'
	'Starburst'	CRos EHyd LRHS NMen NRHS
	'Starion'	NMen
	'State Fair'	EDAr NMen SSem
	'Steerosentern'	NMen
	'Storm Chaser'	GFgr
	'Strawberry Sundae'	NFav
	'Strider'	NMen
	'Stuffed Olive'	NMen SDys SLee SRms
	'Sugary'	NMen
	'Suite Minuet' **new**	SSem

	'Sun Kiss' **new**	NMen
	'Sun Waves'	SDys
	'Sunburst' **new**	SSim
	'Sunrise'	NMen
	'Super Dome'	GFgr NMen
	'Superama'	NMen
	'Svava'	NMen
	'Sweet Brown Sugar' **new**	NMen
	'Sweetheart'	NMen
	'Syston Flame'	NMen
	'Tamberlane'	EDAr
	'Tarita'	NMen
	'T'Boz'	NMen
§	***tectorum*** ♀H7	CHby CTri ELan GPoy MNHC SPlb SSem XAbr XLum
§	– var. ***alpinum***	CRos EHyd LRHS NBro NRHS SRms
	– var. ***andreanum***	XLum
	– 'Atropurpureum'	ELan SRms
	– 'Atroviolaceum'	NMen SPlb XLum
*	– 'Aureum'	GFgr NMen
	– var. ***boutignyanum*** GDJ 94.04 from Route de Tuixén, Spain	SRms
§	– var. ***glaucum***	NMen XLum
	– 'Mettenianum'	XLum
	– monstrose	SPlb SRms
	– 'Murale'	GFgr XLum
§	– 'Nigrum'	EGrI MHer NBro SDys XLum
	– 'Red Flush'	MBrN NMen
	– 'Royanum' ♀H7	MSCN NMen SRms
*	– subsp. ***sanguineum***	EDAr SSim
	– 'Sunset'	CMea EDAr EWes GAbr NMen SDys SSim WHal
§	– subsp. ***tectorum*** 'Boissieri'	NMen
	– – 'Triste'	NHpl NMen SSim XLum
	– 'Violaceum'	EBou NMen SPlb SRms
	'Teddy Bear'	MSCN NMen
	'Tederheid'	NMen
	'Teide' **new**	SSem
	'Telfan'	NMen
	'Terlamen'	NMen
	'Terracotta Baby'	CCal CMea GFgr NMen SLee SSim WFar
	'Tesoro' **new**	SSem
	'Thayne'	NMen
	'The Flintstones' **new**	SSim
	'The Platters'	NMen
	'The Rocket'	GFgr
	'Thistle Hill'	NMen
	'Thunder'	NMen
	'Tiger Bay'	NMen
	'Timmy'	NMen
	'Tinner Bell'	NMen
	'Tintenblut'	NMen SSem
	'Tintinabulum'	NMen
	'Tip Top'	EPot GFgr NMen WFar
	'Tipsy'	NMen
	tissieri	XLum
	'Titania'	NMen WHal
	'Tjabine'	NMen
	'Tommella'	XLum
	'Topaz'	NMen SRms XLum
	'Tordeur's Memory'	NMen SEND SRms
	'Tormulin' **new**	LRHS
I	'Tourmalyi'	NMen
	'T'Pol'	NMen
	'Tracy Sue'	XLum
	'Traffic Lights'	GFgr SSem
	'Trail Walker'	NMen SRms
	transcaucasicum	XLum
	'Tree Beard'	NMen
	'Trine'	NMen
	'Tristesse' ♀H5	EDAr NMen SSem
	'Troika'	NMen
	'Trude'	NMen
	'Truva'	GFgr NMen
	'Twilight Blues'	CCal CRos EHyd LRHS NRHS SRms
	'Twist'	NMen
	'Twizzler'	MSCN
	'U4'	NMen
	'Udine'	NMen
	'Uralturmalin'	NMen
	'Uranus'	XLum
	'Urmel' **new**	NMen
	'Urmina'	NMen
	'Utopian'	EGrI LRHS
	× ***vaccarii***	XLum
	'Van der Steen'	NMen
	'Vanbaelen'	NMen SDys
	'Vasi Petru'	NMen
	'Vega'	MHol
	'Venus'	NMen XLum
	'Veughelen'	NMen SSem
	vicentei	NMen WFar
	– from Gaton, Spain	EHyd NMen
§	– subsp. ***paui***	NSla
	'Video'	NMen
	'Viking'	NMen
	'Violet Queen'	CMea GFgr NMen
	'Virgil'	EDAr MBrN MSCN NMen NWad SDys SPlb SSem WAbe WCot WFar WIce
I	'Virginius'	GAbr NMen
	'Vulcano'	NMen
	'Wasti'	NMen
	'Waterlily'	GFgr NWad
	'Watermelon Rind'	NMen
	webbianum	see *S. arachnoideum* subsp. ***tomentosum*** (C.B. Lehm. & Schnittsp.) Schinz & Thell.
	'Webbyola'	NMen
	'Weitblick' **new**	SSem
	'Wendy'	NMen
	'Westerlin'	NMen
	'Wheel of Fire'	NMen
	'Whirlpool'	GFgr
	'White Christmas'	see *S. arachnoideum* 'White Christmas'
	'White Ladies'	NMen
	'Whitening'	WFar
	× ***widderi***	NMen
	'Wilhelm Tell'	NMen
	'Wine Queen'	NMen
	'Winsome'	NFav NWad
	'Wok'	NMen
I	'Woolcott's Variety'	GFgr NBir NMen SRms
	wulfenii	XLum
	– subsp. ***juvanii***	XLum
	'Yanisha'	NMen
	'Yolanda'	NMen
	'Yvette'	NMen
	'Zaccour'	NMen
	'Zackenkrone'	NMen
	'Zannalee'	NMen
	'Zeeuwse Winner' **new**	NMen
	'Zelca'	NMen
	zeleborii	NMen WHal
	'Zenith'	NMen SRms
	'Zenocrate'	NHol WHal
	'Zilver Moon'	NMen
	'Zilver Snowflake'	NMen

'Zilver Suzanna' NMen
'Zilverprinsesje' NMen
'Zircon' EDAr NMen
'Zone' NMen
'Zorba' NMen
'Zulu' NMen

Senecio (*Asteraceae*)

§ ***barbertonicus*** EShb
bidwillii see *Brachyglottis bidwillii*
candicans misapplied see *Jacobaea maritima*
candidans ANGEL WINGS ('Senaw'[PBR]) CBcs LCro LOPS LRHS MBros MPnt NHpl NSti SIvy SPeP SRkn WCot XSte
chrysanthemoides misapplied see *Euryops chrysanthemoides*
cinerascens SVen
coccinilifera hort. see *Kleinia grantii*
compactus see *Brachyglottis compacta*
confusus see *Pseudogynoxys chenopodioides*
crassissimus EShb
cristobalensis see *Roldana cristobalensis*
doria EPfP EShb MMuc SAko SDix WHrl
elegans SVen
gerberifolius B&SWJ 10357 WCru
- B&SWJ 10361 MHol WCru
'Gregynog Gold' see *Ligularia* 'Gregynog Gold'
greyi misapplied see *Brachyglottis compacta* 'Sunshine'
greyi Hook. f. see *Brachyglottis greyi* (Hook. f.) B. Nord.
haworthii see *Caputia tomentosa*
herreianus Dinter SIvy
hoffmannii EShb
kleiniiformis EShb WSMil
laxifolius hort. see *Brachyglottis compacta* 'Sunshine'
leucostachys misapplied see *S. viravira*
macroglossus EShb
- 'Variegatus' (v) ♀H1c EShb
monroi see *Brachyglottis monroi*
petasitis see *Roldana petasitis*
polyodon 'Joe's Old Rose' **new** EPPr
- 'Joe's White' **new** EPPr
- var. ***polyodon*** CFoA CKel EPfP GBee GBin LRHS MMuc NFav SBut SWvt WCAu WCot WWFP
- var. ***subglaber*** CCCN CSpe EAJP EWes GLog MHol MNrw MPie WCFE WPGP
przewalskii see *Ligularia przewalskii*
pulcher CDTJ MHol SHar SMrm
reinoldii see *Brachyglottis rotundifolia*
rowleyanus see *Curio rowleyanus*
seminiveus EBee
serpens see *Curio repens*
§ ***smithii*** ELan NBid WWtn
squalidus subsp. ***aethnensis*** WCot
'Sunshine' see *Brachyglottis* (Dunedin Group) 'Sunshine'
tamoides SPlb
tanguticus see *Sinacalia tangutica*
§ ***viravira*** EPri EShb MCot SMrm SPhx WSHC

Senna (*Fabaceae*)

alexandrina CCCN EShb
artemisioides ♀H1b WCot
§ ***candolleana*** CCCN
§ ***corymbosa*** CBcs CCCN CRHN CTri ECre SMrm
× ***floribunda*** SBrt
hebecarpa SBls SBrt
§ ***marilandica*** CSpe EBee LRHS MGil
septemtrionalis CCCN EHyd LRHS

Sequoia (*Cupressaceae*)

sempervirens ♀H6 CAco CBcs CCVT CLnd CMCN CMen CTsd EPfP IPap LMaj MBlu MGil MMuc NOra NWea SCob SEND SGol WMat WMou WTSh
- 'Adpressa' CAco LRHS MAsh MGos SCoo
- 'Cantab' WMou WPav
- 'Filoli' CAco
- 'Glauca' MAsh
- 'Henderson Blue' SLim
- 'Korbel KT' **new** SMad
- 'Prostrata' EWhm WPav

Sequoiadendron (*Cupressaceae*)

giganteum ♀H6 Widely available
- 'Barabits Requiem' CAco MBlu
- 'Bultinck Yellow' MBlu
- 'Chief' NLar
- 'French Beauty' NLar
- 'Glaucum' CAco LPar LRHS MBlu SGsty SLim WPGP
* - 'Glaucum Compactum' MBlu
- 'Greenpeace' MBlu
- 'Kaatje' SLim
- 'Little Stan' NLar SLim
- 'Pendulum' CAco CCVT ELan ESwi LPar MBlu SLim WLea
- 'Pierie' NLar
- 'Powdered Blue' NLar

Serapias (*Orchidaceae*)

lingua peach-flowered WMal

Sericocarpus (*Asteraceae*)

asteroides GArf GKev

Seriphidium see *Artemisia*

Serratula (*Asteraceae*)

bulgarica see *Klasea bulgarica*
coronata subsp. ***insularis*** see *Klasea coronata* subsp. *insularis*
gmelinii see *Klasea radiata* subsp. *gmelinii*
lycopifolia see *Klasea lycopifolia*
shawii see *S. tinctoria* var. *seoanei*
tinctoria NLar SBut SPhx
§ - var. ***seoanei*** Widely available

Serruria (*Proteaceae*)

florida SPlb
phylicoides SPlb

Sesbania (*Fabaceae*)

punicea CCCN

Seseli (*Apiaceae*)

elatum PAB 9228 SPhx
- subsp. ***osseum*** LRHS SPhx SPtp
globiferum SPhx
gracile SPhx
gummiferum CSpe EAJP SMad SPhx SPtp WHil
hippomarathrum CElw CSpe ECha EPPr MNrw NGrd SBrt SPhx WCot WFar WHal WHrl WWtn
lehmannii WCot
§ ***libanotis*** EBee ECha EPPr GBin LEdu LRHS NAts NLar SPhx WFar

montanum	CMiW CSpe EBee LPla NDov SBut SHar WCot
petraeum	WHil
transcaucasicum B&SWJ 15352 **new**	WCru

Sesleria (*Poaceae*)

§ ***albicans***	CBod EPPr
§ ***argentea***	CKno
autumnalis ♀H7	CKno EBee ELon EPPr EShb EWes EWoo GBin GMaP LCro LOPS SCob SPhx WSpi XLum
caerulea	CBod CKno CSde EGrI ELan ELon EPfP GMaP GQue LCro LEdu LOPS LRHS SCob SPhx SPoG XLum
- subsp. ***calcarea***	see *S. albicans*
- 'Malvern Mop'	EBee WCot WHrl
* ***candida***	EPPr
cylindrica	see *S. argentea*
'Greenlee'	CKno LPla
heufleriana	CBod EPPr GBin LCro LOPS LPla NRya SMea SPhx SPlb SPtp WCot WSpi
insularis	EPPr EShb
nitida	CBod CKno LEdu SPhx WChS XLum
sadleriana	CBod EBee EPPr EWes

Setaria (*Poaceae*)

italica 'Red Jewel'	CSpe
macrostachya	SPhx
palmifolia ♀H2	CBod EShb MPie SBrt SDix SIvy SPlb WSMil
viridis	WCot

Setcreasea see *Tradescantia*

shaddock see *Citrus maxima*

Sharon fruit see *Diospyros kaki*

Shepherdia (*Elaeagnaceae*)

argentea	NLar WKor

Shibataea (*Poaceae*)

kumasaca ♀H6	CAbb CBcs LEdu MWht SCob SGol

Shortia (*Diapensiaceae*)

soldanelloides	GEdr

Sibbaldia (*Rosaceae*)

cuneata HPA 1390 **new**	GGro
procumbens	GKev

Sibbaldiopsis (*Rosaceae*)

§ ***tridentata***	GArf GKev SBrt

Sibthorpia (*Plantaginaceae*)

europaea	CExl

Sida (*Malvaceae*)

hermaphrodita	EBee SBls SBrt SMad

Sidalcea (*Malvaceae*)

'Brilliant'	CBcs CBod CNor GBin ILea MNrw NBir SPer WCAu WFar
campestris from Oregon, USA	NFav
candida	CBod CRos EBee ECtt EHyd ELan GMaP GWyn MBNS MMuc MRav NChi NGBl NGdn NLar NRHS NSti SGbt SPer WCAu WCot WGwG
- 'Bianca'	ELan EMor EPfP LSun NFav NLar SBut WFar
'Candy Girl'	CBod EBee NLar SGBe WCot WFar
'Crimson King'	WFar
'Croftway Red'	CBod CBor CRos EBee ELan LRHS MAvo MBel NBro NGdn NHol NHsp NRHS NWad SPer SWvt WFar
'Elsie Heugh' ♀H7	Widely available
LILAC CANDICE ('Midawioha')	WFar
'Little Princess'PBR	CBod CBor EBee EHyd EPfP EWes LRHS MNrw NGdn NHsp NLar NRHS SPoG WFar
'Loveliness'	CBod EBee ECtt EHyd ELan EShb LRHS LSou MAsh MAvo MBel MHer MRav NBro NHsp NRHS NWad SPoG WFar
malviflora	SRms
- subsp. ***purpurea***	EHyd LRHS NRHS
'Monarch'	WFar
'Moorland Rose Coronet'	WFar
'Mr Lindbergh'	MACG NHsp NLar SPer WCFE
'Mrs Borrodaile'	CMac MBel MRav NBro NEoE NGdn NLar WFar
'Mrs Galloway'	EHyd NHsp
'My Love'	ECha NDov NHsp
'Nimmerdor' **new**	EBlo
'Oberon' ♀H7	CRos EBee EBlo EHyd LRHS MRav NRHS
oregana	NGdn
- subsp. ***spicata***	WFar
'Party Girl'	CMac CRos CSBt EBee EHyd ELan EMor EPfP LRHS LSun MNHC MRav NBro NFav NGdn NLar NRHS SBut SCob SCoo SGBe SPlb SPoG WBor WFar XLum
'Purpetta'	EPfP NEoE NGBl NHsp NLar
'Reverend Page Roberts'	MRav WCot
'Rosaly'	CSpe EAJP EBlo EHyd ELan MACG NFav NHsp NLar WFar
'Rosanna'	CRos EBou EHyd EPfP GMaP LRHS NHsp NLar NRHS
'Rose Bud'	NHsp WFar
'Rose Queen'	CRos EBee ECha EHyd GKev LRHS MAvo MRav NBro NHol NRHS SGbt SHar SPer SRms WFar
'Rosy Gem'	SCob
Stark's hybrids	EHyd LRHS NFav NRHS SRms
'Sussex Beauty'	CBor EBee EHyd LSou MBel MHol MRav NDov NGdn SMad SPer SPoG WCot WFar
'Wensleydale'	CRos EBlo EHyd LRHS NRHS WFar
'William Smith' ♀H7	CRos EBee ECha ECtt EHyd EPfP EWes GBin LRHS MArl MMuc MRav NBir NGdn NHsp NLar NRHS SEND SGbt SPer WFar
'Wine Red'	CBod EBee EHyd EPfP EShb LRHS LSou MAsh MNrw NFav NGdn NRHS SPoG SWvt

Sideritis (*Lamiaceae*)

syriaca	MHer SBls XSen
- RCB UA 2	WCot

Sieversia (*Rosaceae*)

§ ***pentapetala***	WAbe
- 'Flore Pleno' (d)	WAbe

Silaum (*Apiaceae*)

silaus	SPhx

Silene (*Caryophyllaceae*)

RBS	EPPr

	acaulis	EDAr EPot GJos GKev SLee SRms WAbe WIce
§	- subsp. ***acaulis***	SPlb SRms WIce
	- 'Alba'	EPot WAbe
	- 'Blush'	EDAr NSla WAbe
	- 'Correvoniana'	NLar
	- subsp. ***elongata***	see *S. acaulis* subsp. *acaulis*
	- 'Frances'	EDAr ITim NLar NRya NSla SLee SRot WAbe
	- 'Helen's Double' (d)	GArf
	- 'Mount Snowdon'	EBou ELan EWes GArf NHpl NLar SLee SPlb SPoG SRms WHoo
	- 'Pedunculata'	see *S. acaulis* subsp. *acaulis*
	aegyptiaca	SPhx
	alba	see *S. latifolia* subsp. *alba*
§	***alpestris***	SBut SRms WThu
	- 'Flore Pleno' (d) 🏆H7	EBou EWes NSla WIce
	- 'Starry Dreams'	CBod CRos CSpe EHyd LRHS NRHS
	aomorensis	GGro
	armeria	GJos SDys
	- 'Electra'	CSpe CTtf MNHC
	asterias	CPla ECha EPPr EWld GGro GJos MNrw SBrt
	atropurpurea	see *Lychnis viscaria* subsp. *atropurpurea*
	caroliniana subsp. ***pensylvanica***	GJos
	- subsp. ***wherryi*** 'Short and Sweet'	CBor
	coeli-rosa 'Blue Angel'	SPhx
	'Confetti'	CPla CSpe EAJP ECha EDAr EShb GJos
	'Country Comet'	NChi
	delavayi	EDAr GJos
	dinarica	GKev
§	***dioica***	CCBP CHab CTtf EBee EBou EMor GJos GQue LCro LOPS MBow MHer MNHC NAts NGrd NLar NMir SBut SPhx SPoG SRms SVic WSFF WShi WWild
	- 'Clifford Moor' (v)	ECtt MHer NSti SCoo
	- 'Firefly'[PBR] (d)	CDor CMac ECtt NSti SWvt WSHC
§	- 'Flore Pleno' (d)	CBor EGrI MHol MRav NBid NBro NGdn WHoo
§	- 'Graham's Delight' (v)	NFav
	- 'Inane'	WMal WSHC
	- 'Innocence'	NGrd
§	- 'Minikin'	NGdn
	- 'Purple Prince'	MMuc SEND
I	- 'Ray's Golden Campion'	EMor EPPr NWad
	- 'Rollie's Favorite'[PBR]	CRos EBee ECtt EHyd EMor EPfP LRHS LSou MHol MNrw MPri MSCN NDov NRHS NSti SPeP SPoG WBor WCAu
	- 'Rosea Plena' (d)	MHer WSHC
	- 'Rubra Plena'	see *S. dioica* 'Flore Pleno'
	- 'Stella'	NGrd
	- 'Thelma Kay' (d/v)	NGdn
	- 'Valley High' (v)	EBee ECtt EWes WCot
	- 'Variegata'	see *S. dioica* 'Graham's Delight'
§	***fimbriata***	CSpe CTtf EBee ECha ELan EMor EPPr EShb GWyn ILea LPla MCot MMrt MNrw MRav NLar NSti SBut SDix WCAu WCot WFar WKif WWtn
	frivaldskyana	SPhx
	'Frivola Rose'	LPla MHol
	hookeri	GBin GKev SPlb
	- subsp. ***hookeri***	GKev
	- Ingramii Group	WAbe
	'Jiggy Pink'	LRHS
	'Jiggy White'	LRHS
	keiskei	GJos
	- var. ***akaisialpina***	NSla
	- - f. ***leucantha***	NSla
	- var. ***minor***	EHyd EWes LRHS NRHS
	laciniata 'Starburst'	CSpe
	latifolia	CHab GJos MHer MNHC NGrd NMir SVic WSFF
§	- subsp. ***alba***	GJos LRHS SPhx
	maritima	see *S. uniflora*
	multifida	see *S. fimbriata*
	multiflora	EPPr
	noctiflora	CHab WSFF
	nutans	NAts SBut SPhx SRms WSFF
	pusilla	CSpe GJos NHpl NLar
	quadridentata	see *S. alpestris*
	regia	SPhx WKif
	rubra	see *S. dioica*
	sachalinense new	GGro
	schafta 🏆H5	CTri ECha EGrI EPfP GJos GKev LRHS MAsh MMuc MPie MRav NBid SBls SEND SLee SRms WHoo XLum
	- 'Persian Carpet'	EBou
	- 'Shell Pink'	CRos ECha EHyd EPfP EWes GJos LRHS MMuc NBid NRHS NSla SEND WHoo
	sieboldii	see *Lychnis coronata* var. *sieboldii*
	SPARKLING ROSE ('Insilsparo'[PBR]) new	CRos LRHS MHol
	stellata	SPhx
	tatarica new	GGro
§	***uniflora***	CHab GJos LRHS MMuc NAts NBro SBut SPlb SRms SSut
	- 'Alba Plena'	see *S. uniflora* 'Robin Whitebreast'
I	- 'Compacta'	SPhx
§	- 'Druett's Variegated' (v)	CBod CRos CTri EBou ECtt EHyd ELan ELon EPot EWes LLWG LRHS MAsh NFav NHpl NRHS SPlb SPoG SRms SRot WCav WIce XLum
	- 'Flore Pleno'	see *S. uniflora* 'Robin Whitebreast'
	- pink-flowered	SBut
§	- 'Robin Whitebreast' (d)	ECha EPfP GBin LRHS NBid NBro NWad SPhx SRms WSHC XLum
	- 'Rosea'	ECtt GJos MHol MMuc NHpl SLee SPlb
	- 'Variegata'	see *S. uniflora* 'Druett's Variegated'
	- WEISSKEHLCHEN	see *S. uniflora* 'Robin Whitebreast'
	- 'White Bells'	CTri WKif
	viridiflora	SPhx
§	***vulgaris***	CAgr CCBP CHab GJos MMuc MNHC NMir SBut SPhx SRms WHer
	- subsp. ***maritima***	see *S. uniflora*
	wallichiana	see *S. vulgaris*
	'Wisley Pink'	ECtt
	yunnanensis	SPhx WSHC
§	***zawadskii***	GGro GJos GKev LSun MMuc SBrt SEND SPhx WTor

Siler (*Umbelliferae*)

montanum	see *Laserpitium siler*

Silphium (*Asteraceae*)

albiflorum new	SBrt
integrifolium	LPla SPhx WCot XLum
laciniatum	CMac CSpe LEdu LShi SBrt SPhx WHal XLum
mohrii	LPla SPhx
perfoliatum 🏆H7	CBod CSpe EBee EHyd GPoy LEdu LRHS MMuc NDov NLar NRHS SBls SDix SEND SPhx WCAu WCot XLum
- var. ***connatum***	SPhx

simpsonii SBrt
terebinthinaceum CSpe SPhx WCot XLum
trifoliatum EPPr SPhx WCot

Silybum (*Asteraceae*)
marianum CCBP EHyd ELan GPoy LRHS MNHC NBir SPhx SRms XAbr
- white SPhx

Sinacalia (*Asteraceae*)
§ ***tangutica*** ECha GGro GQue NBid NLar NSti SDix WCot WWtn

Sinapis (*Brassicaceae*)
alba SVic

Sinarundinaria (*Poaceae*)
anceps see *Yushania anceps*
jaunsarensis see *Yushania anceps*
murielae see *Fargesia murielae*
nitida see *Fargesia nitida*

Sinningia (*Gesneriaceae*)
calcaria WDib
canescens ♀H1a WDib
§ ***cardinalis*** EBak WDib
conspicua WDib
iarae new WDib
nivalis WDib
speciosa 'Blanche de Méru' SDeJ
- 'Hollywood' SDeJ
- 'Kaiser Friedrich' SDeJ
- 'Kaiser Wilhelm' SDeJ
- 'Mont Blanc' SDeJ
tuberosa MCot
tubiflora EAJP EShb EWld LEdu NSti SBrt WCot WFar WKif XLum

× *Sinocalycalycanthus* see *Calycanthus*

Sinocalycanthus see *Calycanthus*

Sinocrassula (*Crassulaceae*)
§ ***yunnanensis*** CBod CCht CDoC EShb GKev NHpl SEdd SPlb SSim

Sinofranchetia (*Lardizabalaceae*)
chinensis CRHN SAko WPGP
- DJHS 4117 WCru

Sinojackia ✿ (*Styracaceae*)
rehderiana IArd WPGP
xylocarpa CBcs CMCN

Sinopodophyllum (*Berberidaceae*)
§ ***hexandrum*** CWCL EBee ELan EMor EPot EWTr GBin GGro GKev GMaP GPoy GQue ILea LPla MNrw MPnt MRav NBid NBir NChi NLar SPlb WAvo WCot WKor WPnP WSHC WTyc
- from Kangding, Mugecuo Lake, Sichuan, China SBrt
§ - var. ***chinense*** GEdr GKev LEdu WCru
- - BWJ 7908 WCru
- - SDR 4409 CExl
- 'Chinese White' CExl
§ - var. ***emodi*** ECha EPfP ITim
- - 'Majus' CMiW GBin MCot

Siphocranion (*Lamiaceae*)
§ ***macranthum*** EBee EWes WPGP WSHC

Sisyrinchium (*Iridaceae*)
× ***anceps*** see *S. angustifolium*
§ ***angustifolium*** CWCL ECha EGrI NBir NChi SPlb SRms WBrk WCav
- f. ***album*** MCot NChi NLar
§ ***arenarium*** CWCL GArf
bellum hort. see *S. idahoense* var. *bellum*
bermudiana see *S. angustifolium*
'Biscutella' CBod CKno EPfP EWoo GMaP LEdu MACG NFav SLee SPlb SRot WCav WFar WHal WHoo WKif
'Blue France' EPot
'Blue Ice' GPSL LRHS NLar WAbe
'Blue Skies' WCav
boreale see *S. californicum*
brachypus see *S. californicum* Brachypus Group
'Californian Skies' CElw CExl CKno CRos EAJP ECha ECtt EHyd EPot EWoo GMaP LRHS NBir NDov NRHS NSla SRms SWvt WAvo WKif
§ ***californicum*** CBen CDoC EWoo GQue GWyn LLWG WMAq WSMil XLum
§ - Brachypus Group CTri EBou EMor EPfP GAbr LPot NBir NFav NLar SPlb SWvt WKif
- 'Yellowstone' CSBt EPfP SRms
* ***capsicum*** CExl
convolutum B&SWJ 9117 WCru
cuspidatum see *S. arenarium*
depauperatum NFav
'Devon Skies' CElw CMea CRos CWCL ECtt EDAr EHyd EPot GArf LRHS MACG MEch MNrw NLar NRHS SRms SWvt WAbe WIce
douglasii see *Olsynium douglasii*
'Dragon's Eye' CElw CKno CMea CPla EDAr EWes LPot MBrN MHer SRot WAbe WFar WHoo WIce
'E.K. Balls' Widely available
graminoides GWyn NWad
grandiflorum see *Olsynium douglasii*
'Hemswell Sky' ECtt GAbr NLar NRya
'Iceberg' CElw ECha EWTr EWes
idahoense ECha ECtt GAbr NDov NHpl SPlb SRms
§ - var. ***bellum*** EBou EPfP NFav SRms XLum
- - pale-flowered CKno SMHy
- - 'Rocky Point' CKno CRos EHyd EPfP EWes LRHS NRHS SPoG WFar
- var. ***macounii*** ELan GPSL SPlb
§ - - 'Album' ♀H4 CElw CMea ECtt ELan EWes LPot MMrt NFav WAbe WFar WIce
'Janet Denman' (v) CBor ECha EDAr EShb EWes SEdd SRot WFar
junceum see *Olsynium junceum*
littorale CExl
macrocarpon misapplied see *S. macrocarpum*
§ ***macrocarpum*** CMea EWld
'Marchants Seedling' SMHy
'Marion' CMea ECtt MBrN WHoo
'May Snow' see *S. idahoense* var. *macounii* 'Album'
'Miami' EWoo
montanum NHpl
montanum* × *nudicaule GAbr
narcissiflorum GArf
'North Star' see *S.* 'Pole Star'
nudicaule CBor NWad
palmifolium GKev LEdu LPla MHer MNrw NWad SMad WFar WSHC XLum
patagonicum CExl GKev

§ 'Pole Star' NLar
'Quaint and Queer' CCCN CExl EAJP ECha EShb EWoo LPot MBrN MNrw NBir SAng SEdd WAvo WSHC
'Raspberry' CKno CMea ECha EWoo WFar
'Sapphire' CBen CBor CCCN CKno ECtt EDAr ELan EWoo LPot MBow MHol NHpl NLar NWad SEdd SPoG WGrn WSMil
§ ***striatum*** Widely available
§ - 'Aunt May' (v) CBod CCCN CMac ECha EPfP EWoo GMaP LRHS LSRN MGos MRav MSpe NHpl NRHS NSti SCob SIvy SPoG SRms SWvt WCot WHil WPGP WSMil
- 'Variegatum' see *S. striatum* 'Aunt May'
aff. ***unispathaceum*** B&SWJ 10683 WCru

Sium (*Apiaceae*)

sisarum CLau LEdu MBriF NDov SDix SPhx WKor WSFF

Skimmia ✿ (*Rutaceae*)

anquetilia CMac
- (m) WCru
- (f) WCru
arborescens B&SWJ 11799 WCru
- B&SWJ 13902 WCru
- PAB 8774 LEdu
- subsp. ***nitida*** B&SWJ 8239 WCru
arisanensis B&SWJ 7114 WCru
- CWJ 12417 WCru
black-fruited B&SWJ 8259 from northern Vietnam (f/m) WCru
× ***confusa*** 'Kew Green' (m) ♀H5 Widely available
japonica CBod CDoC CMac EGrI MGos NWea SCob SGsty SSta SavN WFar
- (f) CMac CTri EPfP SRms
- B&SWJ 5053 (f) WCru
- B&SWJ 5053 (m) WCru
- 'Alba' see *S. japonica* 'Wakehurst White'
- 'Attraction' EBee MGos
- 'Bowles's Dwarf' LRHS
- 'Bowles's Dwarf Female' (f) CEnd MRav MWht
- 'Bowles's Dwarf Male' (m) NWad
- 'Bronze Knight' (m) CBod CMac MAsh MRav NLar NWad SRms
- 'Carberry' (f) CMac
- 'Dad's Red Dragon' (f) CDoC CMac MAsh SRms
- DELIGHT ('Delibolwi'^{PBR}) CDoC
- 'Emanuella' SGsty
- 'Finchy'^{PBR} (m) CRos EHyd EPfP LRHS MAsh NLar NRHS
- 'Foremanii' see *S. japonica* 'Veitchii'
§ - 'Fragrans' (m) ♀H5 CDoC CMac CRos CSBt CTri EBee EHyd EPfP LCro LOPS LRHS LSRN MAsh MGos MRav NLar NRHS SCob SPer SPoG SRms SWvt WFar
- 'Fragrant Cloud' see *S. japonica* 'Fragrans'
- 'Fructu Albo' see *S. japonica* 'Wakehurst White'
- 'Godrie's Dwarf' (m) CRos EHyd EPfP LPar LRHS MAsh NLar NRHS WFar
- 'Humpty Dumpty' (f) WFar
- var. ***intermedia*** f. ***repens*** see *S. japonica* subsp. *japonica* var. *intermedia*
§ - subsp. ***japonica*** var. ***intermedia*** B&SWJ 11165 WCru
- - B&SWJ 5560 WCru
- 'John Turner' (f) GBin
- 'Kew White' (f) CBcs CBrac CDoC CRos EHyd ELan ELon EPfP IArd LCro LOPS LPar LRHS MAsh MGos MRav NHol NRHS NWad SLon SPer SSta SWvt WLov
- LUWIAN ('Wanto') (m) EHyd LRHS NRHS
- 'Macpenny Dwarf' (m) CMac SRms
- 'Magic Marlot'^{PBR} (m/v) CRos EBee EHyd EPfP LRHS MAsh MGos MRav NHpl SPoG SWvt
- 'Marlot' (m) CDoC CRos EHyd EPfP LRHS NLar NRHS SPoG WLea
- 'Mystic Marlot'^{PBR} LRHS
- 'Nymans' (f) ♀H5 CBod CDoC CEnd CRos CTsd EHyd ELan EPfP GBin LCro LOPS LRHS MAsh MGos MRav NRHS SCob SPoG SRms SWvt
- OBSESSION ('Obsbolwi'^{PBR}) (m/f) LCro LOPS LPar LSRN MAsh MGos WLea
- 'Olympic Flame' (f) CDoC CRos EHyd EPfP IArd LRHS MAsh MBlu NLar NRHS SPoG
- 'Pabella'^{PBR} (f) CDoC ELan LPar LRHS MAsh SPoG
- PASSION ('Pasbolwi'^{PBR}) (f) **new** MPri
- 'Pigmy' (f) CExl
- PINK DWARF ('Moerings 47'^{PBR}) CDoC
- 'Red Diamonds' NRHS
- 'Red Princess' (f) CDoC MAsh
- 'Red Riding Hood' (f) CBod CRos EHyd ELon LRHS MAsh MMrt NLar NRHS NWad SLon SPer
- 'Redruth' (f) CBcs CMac CSBt ELon MAsh SEND WAvo WLov
§ - subsp. ***reevesiana*** CBcs CBod CBrac CMac CRos CSBt CTri EGrI EHyd ELan EPfP GBin LCro LOPS LRHS MGos MRav MSwo NLar SCob SPoG SRms SWvt
- - B&SWJ 3763 MAsh WCru
- - 'Chilan Choice' (f/m) WPGP
- - var. ***reevesiana*** B&SWJ 354 4 WCru
§ - Rogersii Group CMac CTri
- - 'Nana Mascula' (m) CTri
- - 'Rockyfield Green' MAsh
- - 'Rogersii' (f) CMac
- 'Rubella' (m) ♀H5 Widely available
- RUBESTA ('Moerings3'^{PBR}) CDoC
- RUBESTA OPTIMA ('Moeropti'^{PBR}) **new** LRHS NLar
- 'Rubinetta' (m) CBar EPfP IArd MAsh
- 'Ruby Dome' (m) CDoC LRHS NWad
- 'Ruby King' (m) IArd LSRN
- 'Scarlet Dwarf' (f) NHol WAvo
- SEDUCTION ('Redbolwi'^{PBR}) MGos
- 'Snow White'^{PBR} (m) LRHS WAvo
- 'Tansley Gem' (f) EHyd LRHS MAsh MWht SPoG
- 'Temptation'^{PBR} (f) CRos EHyd EPfP LCro LOPS LRHS NRHS
- 'Thereza'^{PBR} (m) EBee
§ - 'Veitchii' (f) CBar CBcs CBrac CDoC CKel CMac CSBt CTri EHyd EPfP LRHS LSRN MAsh MGos MRav NLar NRHS SEND SLim SPer SPoG SRms SWvt
§ - 'Wakehurst White' (f) CBcs CMac CSBt CTri EBee EPfP LRHS MAsh MRav NWad SPoG SRms
- 'White Bella' (m) EHyd LRHS NRHS

- WHITE DWARF ('Moerings 1'PBR) new	LRHS
- 'Winifred Crook' (f)	EHyd
- 'Winnie's Dwarf'	MAsh
- 'Wisley Female' (f)	CTri
laureola	CExl MRav SRms
- GWJ 9364	WCru
- 'Kew Green' new	EGrI
- subsp. ***laureola*** HWJK 2095	WCru
- subsp. ***multinervia*** GWJ 9374	WCru
reevesiana	see *S. japonica* subsp. *reevesiana*
rogersii	see *S. japonica* Rogersii Group
'Snowman'	WCFE

Smallanthus (*Asteraceae*)

sonchifolius	LEdu
- 'Morado'	WPGP

Smilacina see *Maianthemum*

Smilax (*Smilacaceae*)

sp. B&SWJ 6628 from Thailand	WBor
	WCru
aspera	CMac EShb ESwi LEdu WCru WPGP
china B&SWJ 4427	WCru
discotis	SEND
glaucophylla B&SWJ 2971	WCru
nipponica B&SWJ 4331	WCru
rotundifolia	LEdu
sieboldii	LEdu MRav
- B&SWJ 744	WCru

Smyrnium (*Apiaceae*)

olusatrum	CCBP CHab CSpe GJos LEdu LRHS SPhx SPtp SRms WHer WHil WSFF
- Cretan giant new	WPGP
perfoliatum	CBod CSpe EBee ELan EPfP EWes GBin LCro LEdu LOPS NAts NBir SAng SDix SPhx WBor WCot WHal WMal WSHC
rotundifolium	WCot
- PAB 6714	LEdu WPGP

Solandra (*Solanaceae*)

§ ***maxima***	CCCN

Solanum (*Solanaceae*)

aerial-rooting climbing species B&SWJ 14398	WCru
atropurpureum	CDTJ SPlb WCot
betaceum (F)	CCCN CDTJ EShb SVic
- yellow-fruited (F)	SPlb
burchellii	SPlb
crispum 'Autumnale'	see *S. crispum* 'Glasnevin'
§ - 'Glasnevin' ♀H4	Widely available
dulcamara	GPoy
- 'Lucia' (v)	CNat
- 'Variegatum' (v)	CMac MAsh
jasminoides	see *S. laxum*
laciniatum	CCCN CDTJ CExl SArc SEND SPlb SVen WSMil
§ ***laxum***	CKel CMac EBee EHyd LRHS MRav NRHS SGsty SPer SRms SWvt
- 'Album' ♀H4	Widely available
- 'Album Variegatum' (v)	SCob
* - 'Aureovariegatum' (v)	CMac EBee ELon SPlb
- 'Coldham'	EPPr MNrw SDix SMad
- 'Crèche du Pape'	ECha LRHS SRms
§ ***linearifolium***	CSpe
lycopersicum	SVic
mammosum	CDTJ
muricatum (F)	CCCN SPlb
- 'Pepino Gold' (F)	EShb
pinnatum	SPlb
pseudocapsicum	SPlb
- 'Thurino'	LSou
- variegated (v)	WCot
pyracanthum	CDTJ CTtf ECre SArc SPlb WCot
quitoense (F)	CDTJ SPlb
rantonnetii	see *Lycianthes rantonnetii*
rigescentoides	SPlb
sisymbriifolium	SPlb
aff. ***stenophyllum*** B&SWJ 10744	WCru
umbelliferum var. ***incanum***	SBrt
villosum	SVen
wendlandii	CCCN

Soldanella (*Primulaceae*)

alpina	CTsd EBee GKev NSla SRms WAbe
I - 'Alba'	CTtf GEdr NSla WAbe
carpatica	CBor CTtf GEdr GKev LEdu SPlb WAbe WPGP
- 'Alba'	CTtf LEdu
carpatica* × *pusilla	CTtf MNrw NRya SBut WAbe WSHC
carpatica* × *villosa	LEdu
cyanaster	CTtf GAbr GBin GJos GKev GLog LEdu NHpl NQui
dimoniei	CTtf GArf GKev LEdu WFar
hungarica	GEdr
minima	GEdr GJos LEdu WAbe
montana	CPla CTtf EMor EWld GBin GJos GKev LEdu MBel NLar WBor WTyc XBar
- hybrid	NSla
pindicola	GEdr LEdu
'Spring Symphony'	CElw CWCL ELan EPot GArf GBin GEdr GMaP GPSL LEdu MNrw NBro NHar NWad SAko SPoG WFar WPnP
'Sudden Spring'	CElw GBin LEdu NWad WAbe
villosa ♀H6	CElw CTtf GAbr GBin GEdr GKev GLog GPSL LEdu NHar NRya NWad SBrt WSHC

Soleirolia (*Urticaceae*)

soleirolii	CDoC CKel CTri ELan EPot LCro LLWG LOPS SEND SMad SPer SPtp SVic SWvt WHer XLum
- 'Argentea'	see *S. soleirolii* 'Variegata'
§ - 'Aurea'	EPot NHpl SIvy SVic SWvt
- 'Golden Queen'	see *S. soleirolii* 'Aurea'
- 'Silver Queen'	see *S. soleirolii* 'Variegata'
§ - 'Variegata' (v)	LLWG SVic

Solenopsis (*Campanulaceae*)

axillaris	see *Isotoma axillaris*

Solenostemon ✿ (*Lamiaceae*)

scutellarioides 'Angel of the North'	WDib
- 'Autumn Rainbow'	WDib
- 'Beauty of Lyons'	WDib
- 'Brilliant' (v)	WDib
- 'Bronze Pagoda'	WDib
- BURGUNDY WEDDING TRAIN ('Kakegawa Ce10')	WDib
- CAMPFIRE ('Uf12823')	WHil
- 'Chamaeleon' (v)	WDib
- 'City of Sunderland'	WDib

- 'Combat' (v) 🏆H1c	WDib
- 'Crimson Ruffles' (v) 🏆H1c	WDib
- 'Dazzler' (v)	WDib
- 'Durham Gala' 🏆H1c	WDib
- 'Firelight' (v)	WDib
- HENNA ('Balcenna'PBR) (v) 🏆H1c	ECtt MPri
- 'Illumination'	WDib
- 'Inky Fingers' (v)	WDib
- 'Juliet Quartermain' 🏆H1c	WDib
- 'Jupiter'	WDib
- 'Kentish Fire' (v)	WDib
- 'Kiwi Fern' (Stained Glassworks Series) (v)	WDib
- 'Lemon Chiffon'	WDib
- 'Lord Falmouth' (v) 🏆H1c	WDib
- 'Mrs Pilkington' (v)	WDib
- 'Muriel Pedley' (v)	WDib
- 'Paisley Shawl' (v)	WDib
- 'Peter Wonder' (v)	WDib
- 'Pineapple Beauty' (v) 🏆H1c	WDib
- 'Pineapplette' (v) 🏆H1c	WDib
- 'Pink Chaos' (v) 🏆H1c	WDib
- 'Red Angel' (v)	WDib
- 'Red Velvet' (v)	WDib
- 'Rose Blush' (v)	WDib
- 'Roy Pedley' (v) 🏆H1c	WDib
- 'Royal Scot' (v) 🏆H1c	WDib
- 'Saturn' (v)	WDib
- 'The Flume'	WDib
- 'Timotei'	WDib
- TRUSTY RUSTY ('Uf06419'PBR) (v) 🏆H1c	MPri
- 'Walter Turner' (v) 🏆H1c	WDib
- 'Winsome' (v) 🏆H1c	WDib
- 'Winter Sun' (v)	WDib
- 'Wisley Tapestry' (v) 🏆H1c	WDib
thyrsoideus	see *Plectranthus thyrsoideus*

Solidago (*Asteraceae*)

'Autumn Blaze'	WFar
BABYGOLD	see *S.* 'Goldkind'
'Ballardii'	SRms
brachystachys	see *S. cutleri*
caesia	CTtf EBee EHyd EWes NBir SAko SMHy WFar
canadensis	CTri SEND SPlb WBrk WFar WHer XAbr XLum
- var. ***salebrosa***	EHyd
- var. ***scabra***	NFav
'Citronella'	ECtt GQue
'Cloth of Gold'	CBod CMac ECtt EPfP LRHS NHol SGbt SPoG SWvt
§ 'Crown of Rays'	CRos ECtt ELan EPfP GBin LRHS MRav NRHS SAko SCob WFar
§ ***cutleri***	EBou EDAr NLar SPlb SRms WFar
'Dennis Strange'	MAvo MHol WCot
'Ducky'	SCob
'Early Bird'	NLar WFar
flabelliformis	WCot
§ ***flexicaulis***	GMaP SPhx WCot XLum
- 'Variegata' (v)	CBod EBee EHyd EShb GMaP LRHS NLar NRHS WFar XLum
'Foxbrook Fountain'	MAvo
'Foxbrook Gold'	ECha MAvo MHol WFar
'Gardone' 🏆H7	WFar
gigantea	WFar
glomerata	MMuc NLar SEND SMrm
GOLDEN BABY	see *S.* 'Goldkind'
§ 'Golden Dwarf'	CWCL SPoG SRms XLum
'Golden Fleece'	see *S. sphacelata* 'Golden Fleece'
'Goldenmosa' 🏆H7	CMac CSBt EWes GMaP SPer WFar
'Goldilocks'	SRms
§ 'Goldkind'	CSBt CTri EBee EBou ECtt EHyd ELan EPfP LPot LRHS NRHS SCob SRms SWvt WBrk WCav WFar
GOLDZWERG	see *S.* 'Golden Dwarf'
'Hiddigeigei' (v)	SPtp WCot WFar
hybrida	see *S.* × ***luteus***
latifolia	see *S. flexicaulis*
'Laurin'	NLar XLum
'Ledsham'	CBod CRos ECtt EHyd GBin LRHS NRHS SPoG
'Lena'	SRms
'Little Gem' **new**	LRHS
'Little Lemon'PBR	CBct EBee LRHS MTin NEoE
§ × ***luteus***	EBee SRms WFar XLum
- 'Lemore' 🏆H7	CBod CDor CKno CMea CMiW CTtf EBee ECha EPPr EPfP EShb GMaP LRHS LSou MSpe NSti NWsh SAko SBut SPer SPhx SPoG SRms WCot WFar WHoo XLum
ohioensis	XLum
- 'Four Seasons'	GBin
§ ***ptarmicoides***	EBee XLum
§ 'Queenie'	MHer
riddellii	XLum
rigida	SMrm
- subsp. ***humilis*** 'Golden Rockets'	SPhx
rugosa	ECha MBNS MBriF MMuc SEND SPhx WCot
- 'Fireworks' 🏆H7	CBod CCBP CMac CMea CTtf ECha ECtt EHyd ELon EShb GBin GQue LShi MAvo MBriF MSpe NLar SAko SDys SPhx SRms WBrk WCAu WCot WFar WHoo WSMil XLum
- 'Loydser Crown'	ELon MAvo NDov WCot
sempervirens	EHyd WFar
speciosa	SPhx WCot
spectabilis var. ***confinis*** KM 27-01	EBee
§ ***sphacelata*** 'Golden Fleece'	CBcs EHyd ELan EPfP SRms
STRAHLENKRONE	see *S.* 'Crown of Rays'
'Super'	WCot
SWEETY ('Barseven'PBR)	EHyd LRHS NRHS WHil
'Tom Thumb'	MRav NBir SRms
uliginosa	EShb
virgaurea	CBee GPoy MHer MMuc MNHC NAts NLar SMrm SRms WHer
- var. ***cambrica***	see *S. virgaurea* subsp. *minuta*
- subsp. ***leiocarpa*** **new**	WFar
§ - subsp. ***minuta***	GArf GBin GRum
'Yellow Springs'	GJos
'Yellow Stone'	EBee EHyd ELan LRHS

× *Solidaster* see *Solidago*

hybridus	see *Solidago* × *luteus*

Sollya (*Pittosporaceae*)

fusiformis	see *S. heterophylla*
§ ***heterophylla*** 🏆H3	Widely available
- 'Alba'	CBcs CCCN CRos EHyd ELan EPfP LRHS NRHS SCoo SEle SLon SPer SPoG SWvt
- 'Pink Charmer'	CBcs CKel EHyd ELan EPfP LRHS SEle SPer SPoG
- pink-flowered	CCCN CSBt CTsd SCoo SWvt

Solms-laubachia (*Brassicaceae*)

eurycarpa **new**	GKev

Sonchus (Asteraceae)

sp. new	SIvy
arboreus	SIvy
pinnatus	SPlb
tenerrimus	SPlb
subsp. ***tenerrimus*** new	

Sophora (Fabaceae)

cassioides	MGil
- NJM 08.008	WPGP
§ ***davidii***	CBcs CExl CWit EBee ELon EPfP ESwi LEdu LRHS MBlu SBrt SEND SIvy SNig SPoG WCot WGrn
flavescens	SBrt
fulvida	WPGP
howinsula	SNig WCot
japonica	see *Styphnolobium japonicum*
§ 'Little Baby'	CDoC ELan EPfP MGil MGos SEle SIvy SPoG SWvt WGrn WLov
macrocarpa	SWvt
microphylla	CTri
molloyi 'Dragon's Gold'	CBcs CKel EBee ELan ELon EPfP LRHS MAsh SCoo SEND SEle SPoG SWvt XSte
prostrata misapplied	see *S.* 'Little Baby'
prostrata ambig.	SavN
prostrata Buchanan	CMac
SUN KING ('Hilsop'[PBR]) ♀H4	CBcs CDoC CRos CWGN EHyd ELan EPfP EWes LRHS LSRN MGos MPkF NRHS SCoo SLon SPoG SWvt WCot
tetraptera	CBcs CTsd EHyd EPfP LRHS SEND SWvt
viciifolia	see *S. davidii*

Sorbaria (Rosaceae)

aitchisonii	see *S. tomentosa* var. *angustifolia*
arborea	see *S. kirilowii*
§ ***kirilowii***	CExl CMac MRav NLar SMad
sorbifolia	CBcs CMCN ELan IDee MGil MMuc SCob SEND SPer SPlb WFar WSpi
- PINK HOPI ('Cousorb05') new	SGol
- 'Sem'[PBR] ♀H5	Widely available
§ ***tomentosa***	GBin
§ - var. ***angustifolia*** ♀H5	CEme CTri EHyd ELan EPfP LRHS MMuc MRav NBid SEND SLon

× *Sorbaronia* (Rosaceae)

fallax	EPfP NLar

× *Sorbopyrus* (Rosaceae)

§ ***auricularis*** 'Shipova' (F)	CAgr MAsh WMat

Sorbus ✿ (Rosaceae)

KR 100 new	MVil
NJM 09.203	WPGP
adamii	CMCN
alnifolia	CMCN EPfP MBlu
- B&SWJ 8461	WCru
- B&SWJ 10948	WCru
- 'Red Bird'	EPfP LRHS MBlu MTrO NOra
'Amber Light'	EBee MTrO NLar NOra SGbt WMat
americana	CLnd NRog NWea
- 'Lafayette'	GKev
amoena	EGrI SPtp
'Apricot'	CEnd
'Apricot Queen'	CLnd NRog SGol WFar
aria	CCVT CHab CLnd CTri IPap LBuc LPar MGos MMuc NRog NWea SCob SEND SGol WKor WMou WTSh
- 'Aurea'	CLnd SPer
- 'Chrysophylla'	CSBt NRog
- 'Decaisneana'	see *S. aria* 'Majestica'
- 'Lutescens' ♀H6	Widely available
- 'Magnifica'	CLnd ELan ESwi LPar NLar NWea SEWo
§ - 'Majestica' ♀H6	CCVT CLnd CMac EBee MRav NRog NWea SCob WFar
- 'Mitchellii'	see *S. thibetica* 'John Mitchell'
aria × ***pseudovilmorinii***	EBee MTrO WPGP
aronioides misapplied	see *S. caloneura*
aronioides Rehder	GKev
§ ***aucuparia***	Widely available
- 'Aspleniifolia'	CCVT CMCN CMac CSBt EBee EWTr IPap LRHS MGos MNic MRav MTrO NLar NOra NOrn NRHS NRog NWea SCob SLim WFar WMat WMou
- subsp. ***aucuparia***	CDoC
§ - 'Beissneri'	CAgr MRav NRog NWea
- CARDINAL ROYAL ('Michred')	CCVT CDoC CLnd IPap LMaj LRHS MMuc SCob SCoo SEWo SLon
- 'Dirkenii'	WMat
§ - var. ***edulis*** (F)	CArg LBuc MMuc SPer
- - 'Rossica' misapplied	see *S. aucuparia* var. ***edulis*** 'Rossica Major'
§ - - 'Rossica Major'	SEWo
§ - 'Fastigiata'	CEnd CTri ELan EPfP GKin LPar
- 'Fingerprint'[PBR]	EBee MTrO NOra
- subsp. ***maderensis***	MBlu WLov
- ***pluripinnata***	see *S. scalaris* Koehne
- var. ***rossica*** Koehne	see *S. aucuparia* var. ***edulis***
- 'Sheerwater Seedling' ♀H6	CBcs CCVT CDoC CMCN CSBt EBee ELan EPfP GKin IPap LMaj LRHS MGos MMuc MRav MSwo NOrn NRog NWea SCob SEND SGol SPer WFar
- 'Wettra'	SGsty
- var. ***xanthocarpa***	NRog
aucuparia × ***scalaris***	NOrn
AUTUMN SPIRE ('Flanrock') ♀H6	CBcs CBod CDoC CEnd CLnd EBee ELan EPfP EWTr LRHS LSRN MAsh MGos MTrO NLar NOra NWea SCoo SGol SGsty SLim SLon SPer SPoG SWvt WMat
bissetii	WLov
- Yu 14299	WCru
- 'Pearls' new	LRHS MTrO NOra
brevipetiolata B&SWJ 11771	WCru
bulleyana	MVil
- KR 2809	WCru
- MF 96170	GKev
§ ***caloneura***	EBee EPfP LEdu MBlu SPtp WLov WPGP
- Guiz 80	WCru
carmesina	SPtp
- B&L 12545	EBee EPfP GKev WCru
- 'Emberglow'	EPfP MTrO NLar NOra WMat
cashmiriana misapplied pink-fruited	see *S. rosea*
cashmiriana Hedl. ♀H6	CBcs CCVT CLnd CMCN CMac CTri EHyd ELan EPfP GKev IPap LRHS MBlu MGos MMuc MRav MSwo MTrO NLar NOrn NWea SCob SGol SPer SPoG WMat
aff. ***cashmiriana*** ambig.	GKev LCro LOPS MAsh NHol NOra WFar WTSh
- B 751	WCru
chamaemespilus	GKev WThu
'Chinese Lace'	Widely available

§ ***commixta***	CEnd CLnd CMCN EWTr LCro LMaj LOPS MBlu MGos MMuc MSwo MTrO NLar NOrn NRog SGol SLim SPer
- B&SWJ 10839	WCru
- B&SWJ 11043	WCru
- B&SWJ 12640 from Ulleungdo, South Korea	WCru
- 'Carmencita'	EWTr MBlu
- 'Embley' 🏆H6	CBcs CCVT CLnd CMCN CSBt CTri ELan EPfP EWTr LCro LOPS MBlu MGos MMuc MRav NOrn NWea SCob SEND SGol SPer
- OLYMPIC FLAME	see *S. ulleungensis* 'Olympic Flame'
- 'Ravensbill'	EBee EPfP MTrO NLar NOra NWea SCoo SGbt SGol WHCr WMat
- var. ***rufoferruginea*** B&SWJ 11486	WCru
aff. ***commixta***	CBod WTSh
conradinae Koehne	see *S. esserteauana*
'Copper Kettle' 🏆H6	CBod EBee EPfP MAsh MBlu MTrO NLar NOra SCoo SGol WHCr WMat WMou
'Coral Beauty'	CLnd
corymbifera	GKev
- WWJ 11860	WCru
'Covert Gold'	CEnd
'Croft Coral'	MTrO NLar NOra
cuspidata	see *S. vestita*
decipentiformis	GKev
decora 'Gaspé'	GKev
- var. ***nana***	see *S. aucuparia* 'Fastigiata'
devoniensis 'Devon Beauty'	CAgr
discolor misapplied	see *S. commixta*
discolor (Maxim.) Maxim.	IPap MBlu MTrO NWea
- MF 96172	MAsh
- MF 97103	WCru
domestica	CLnd MMuc NRog NWea SEND
- 'Maliformis'	see *S. domestica* f. *pomifera*
§ - f. ***pomifera***	LEdu
§ - f. ***pyrifera***	LEdu
- 'Pyriformis'	see *S. domestica* f. *pyrifera*
- 'Rosie'	CAgr
dunnii	WPGP
'Eastern Promise' 🏆H6	CBod EPfP LCro MAsh MBlu MSwo MTrO NLar NOra NOrn NRog NWea SCob SCoo SGbt SLim WHCr WMat WMou
§ ***eburnea***	GKev NHar
- Harry Smith 12799	WPGP
eleonorae	SPtp
ellipsoidalis C 288	GKev
epidendron	WPGP
§ ***esserteauana***	CLnd
'Ethel's Gold'	MBlu
fansipanensis NJM 09.176	WPGP
'Fastigiata'	see *S. aucuparia* 'Fastigiata', *S.* × *thuringiaca* 'Fastigiata'
aff. ***filipes***	GKev
folgneri 'Emiel' 🏆H6	CBcs EPfP IArd MBlu NOra WMat
- 'Lemon Drop'	CEnd CLnd EBee MAsh MBlu NOra SCoo WMat
foliolosa	CLnd
forrestii 🏆H6	CBcs EBee EPfP GKev MVil NLar SPtp
§ ***frutescens*** 🏆H6	ELan NWad
fruticosa Crantz	GKev
- 'Koehneana'	see *S. koehneana* C.K. Schneid.
'Ghose'	CEnd EBee WMat
glabrescens	LEdu
'Glendoick Spire'	EBee LRHS MTrO NLar NOra WHCr WMat
'Glendoick White Baby'	MTrO NOra WMat
globosa HWJ 537 **new**	WCru
gonggashanica	EPfP GEdr LRHS SPtp WPGP
§ ***graeca***	WCot
'Granatnaja'	see × *Crataegosorbus* 'Granatnaja'
granulosa HWJ 1041	WCru
harrowiana	LEdu LRHS MTrO NLar WLov WMat WPGP
- KW 21009	WPGP
- from Burma	WPGP
- from Yunnan	WPGP
hedlundii	CExl EPfP LRHS MTrO NLar WMat WPGP
- GWJ 9363	WCru WPGP
- KR 1687	WPGP
- KR 1810	WPGP
- WJC 13806	WCru
helenae	MTrO NLar NOra WPGP
- EN 3088	GKev WPGP
hemsleyi	CBcs CExl CLnd SPtp WPGP
- 'John Bond' 🏆H6	LRHS MTrO NLar NOra WMat
henryi **new**	MTrO
× ***hostii***	CLnd
hugh-mcallisteri	MVil
- CLD 310	GKev
hupehensis misapplied	see *S. pseudohupehensis*
- 'November Pink'	see *S. pseudohupehensis* 'Pink Pagoda'
- var. ***obtusa*** misapplied	see *S. pseudohupehensis* 'Pink Pagoda'
- 'Rosea'	see *S. pseudohupehensis* 'Pink Pagoda'
aff. ***hupehensis***	CSBt EWTr NOra NOrn NRog SGol WFar WTSh
hybrida L. 'Gibbsii' 🏆H6	CDoC EPfP MAsh MTrO NOra NOrn WMat
incana **new**	LMaj
insignis	WLov WPGP
- from Arunachal Pradesh, India **new**	WPGP
- from Nepal **new**	WPGP
intermedia	CAco CBcs CCVT CDoC CLnd CSBt CTri IPap LMaj LPar NRog NWea SCob SGol WMou
- 'Brouwers'	CDoC CLnd IArd WMou
japonica	EBee NOra WMat
- B&SWJ 10813	WCru
- B&SWJ 11048	WCru
'Joseph Rock'	Widely available
aff. ***karchungii***	EBee
- AGS/ES 347	WPGP
I ***keenanii*** NJM 13.050	WPGP
keissleri	EBee WLov
- NJM 11.004	WPGP
- PAB 7916	LEdu
'Keith Rushforth'	WCru
§ × ***kewensis***	CLnd SPlb
khumbuensis	GKev SPtp
'Kirsten Pink'	CCVT SPer
koehneana misapplied	see *S. frutescens*
§ ***koehneana*** C.K. Schneid.	CLnd CMCN GKev WCru
aff. ***koehneana*** C.K. Schneid.	see *S. eburnea*, *S. tenuis*
lanata misapplied	see *S. vestita*
latifolia	NWea
'Leonard Messel' 🏆H6	EPfP MAsh MTrO NOra SGbt WMat
'Likjornaja'	EPfP LRHS
§ 'Lombarts Golden Wonder'	MMuc NWea
* ***maculata*** KR 5334	GKev
matsumurana misapplied	see *S. commixta*
matsumurana (Makino) Koehne	IArd WPGP
'Matthew Ridley'	EBee ELan

	megalocarpa	CJun CMCN WPGP
	- var. ***cuneata***	WPGP
	meliosmifolia	SPtp
	- B&SWJ 11709	WCru
	microphylla agg.	CMCN EPfP GKev
	- GWJ 9252	WCru
	- SICH 1009	EBee
	monbeigii (Cardot.) N.P. Balakr.	MGil
	moravica 'Laciniata'	see *S. aucuparia* 'Beissneri'
	muliensis F 22177	EBee GKev
§	***munda***	WCFE
	needhamii NJM 11.005	EBee WPGP
	'Nevezhinskaja'	MBlu
	olivacea	GKev SPtp
	aff. ***ovalis*** H 1948	EBee
	pallescens 'White House Farm'	WPGP
	paniculata NJM 13.067	WPGP
	- NJM 13.092	WPGP
	- PAB 9831	LEdu
	parvifructa	GKev WPGP
	'Peaches and Cream'	LCro LOPS
	'Pearly King'	MAsh
§	'Pink Pearl'	EPfP NOra
	'Pink-Ness'	EPfP MBlu MTrO NLar NOra SCoo WLov WMat
	pohuashanensis misapplied	see *S.* × *kewensis*
	pohuashanensis ambig.	CMCN
	poteriifolia ♀H5	GEdr GKev NHar
	- upright	GKev
	prattii misapplied	see *S. munda*
	prattii Koehne var. ***subarachnoidea***	see *S. munda*
§	***pseudohupehensis*** ♀H6	CBcs CLnd CMCN CMac CTri EPfP MMuc MTrO NWea SEND SGol
§	- 'Pink Pagoda' ♀H6	Widely available
	× ***pseudovertesensis*** new	GKev
	pseudovilmorinii	CBcs EBee GKev LRHS MGil MNic MTrO NOra WCru WMat
	- SBEC 974	WPGP
	randaiensis	EBee SPlb WPGP
	- B&SWJ 156	WPGP
	- B&SWJ 3202	WCru
	reducta ♀H5	GBin GEdr GKev MMuc MVil NFav NHar NHol NLar NSla WLov
	aff. ***reducta***	SRms
	reflexipetala misapplied	see *S. commixta*
	rehderiana misapplied	see *S. aucuparia*
	rehderiana Koehne	GKev MVil NOrn
	'Rose Queen'	MBlu MTrO NOra
§	***rosea***	GKev SPtp
	- SEP 492	WCru WPGP
	- 'Rosiness' ♀H6	CLnd EBee ELan EPfP LRHS MTrO NOra WMat
	'Rowancroft Coral Pink'	EBee
	rubescens	GKev
	rufopilosa	MVil
	rupicola	NWea
	rushforthii KR 5789	EBee GKev
	sambucifolia	GKev
	sargentiana ♀H6	CBcs CCVT CEnd CLnd CMCN CMac CTri EBee ELan EPfP MBlu MGos MRav MSwo MTrO NLar NOra NOrn NRog NWea SLim SPoG WMat
	'Savill Orange'	MMuc
	scalaris ambig.	CBcs CBod CMCN ELan GKev MAsh MSwo MTrO NOra NRog SPoG
§	***scalaris*** Koehne	CEnd CTri MBlu WMat
	'Schouten'	MMuc
	scopulina misapplied	see *S. aucuparia* 'Fastigiata'
	section *Discolores*	GKev MTrO
	- KR 5585	MVil WCru WPGP
	- KR 6308	WCru
	setschwanensis	CMCN
	'Showa'	GKev
	- KR 5585	WPGP
	subulata HWJ 925	WCru
	- KWJ 12272	WCru
	'Sunshine'	CCVT LRHS MAsh MGos MMuc MTrO NOra SEND SGol
§	***tenuis***	GKev
§	***thibetica*** 'John Mitchell' ♀H6	CAgr CBcs CEnd CLnd CMCN CRos EBee EPfP MBlu MGos MTrO NLar NOra SLim SPoG WMat
	aff. ***thibetica*** BWJ 7757a	WCru
	thomsonii GWJ 9363	WCru
	- WWJ 12004	WCru
§	× ***thuringiaca*** 'Fastigiata'	EBar SCoo WMat
	tianschanica	WCru
	'Titan'	EPfP MBlu
	torminalis	CAgr CBcs CBrac CCVT CHab CLnd CMCN CMac CTri EBee ELan EPfP MGos MMuc MRav MTrO NRog NWea SCob SEND SEWo SPer SPoG WKor WMou WSpi WTSh
	ulleungensis	WPGP
	- B&SWJ 12640	WCru
	- 'Dodong'	CSBt LRHS MNic SGsty
§	- 'Olympic Flame' ♀H6	CBod CEnd EBee EPfP GBin IArd LBuc LSRN MBlu MGos MNic MTrO NLar NOra NOrn NWea SCob SCoo SEWo SEdd SLim SPer SPoG WHCr WLov WMat WMou WPGP
	umbellata var. ***cretica***	see *S. graeca*
	ursina (Wall. ex G. Don) S. Schauer	see *S. foliolosa*
	× ***vertesensis*** new	GKev
§	***vestita***	EPfP WCru
	vexans	GBin
	vilmorinii ♀H6	Widely available
	- 'Pink Charm'	EPfP EWTr LRHS MAsh MNic MTrO NOra SGol WMat
	- 'Robusta'	see *S.* 'Pink Pearl'
	aff. ***vilmorinii***	GKin MTrO
	- KR 5095	GKev
	- KR 6453	WCru WPGP
	wallichii NJM 13.127	WPGP
	wardii	CBcs CLnd EPfP LRHS MBlu
	- KR 21127	EBee WPGP
	'White Wax'	CCVT EWTr MGos NWea SPer
	'Wilfrid Fox'	CCVT MGos
	wilsoniana	CLnd LRHS WLov
	'Wisley Gold' ♀H6	CBod LRHS MTrO NOra NWea SCoo SGbt SLim WMat WMou
	yuana	EBee WPGP
	zahlbruckneri C.K. Schneid.	WPGP

Sorghastrum (*Poaceae*)

	avenaceum	see *S. nutans*
§	***nutans***	CBod EBou EPPr SBls
	- 'Indian Steel'	CBod ECha NDov XLum
	- 'Sioux Blue'	NDov

Sorghum (*Poaceae*)

	nigrum	SSal

sorrel, common see *Rumex acetosa*

sorrel, French see *Rumex scutatus*

Souliea see *Actaea*

Sparaxis (*Iridaceae*)

'Bright Star'	GKev
bulbifera	WHil
elegans	SPlb WHil
- white-flowered **new**	WHil
grandiflora 🏆H2	WHil
- subsp. ***acutiloba***	CPbh NRog
- subsp. ***fimbriata***	NRog
- subsp. ***grandiflora***	CPbh
'Moonlight'	GKev
'Red Reflex'	GKev
'Skyline'	GKev
'Sunshine'	GKev NRog
tricolor	CPla GKev SDeJ
villosa	NRog

Sparganium (*Sparganiaceae*)

§ ***erectum***	CPud CWat NMir NPer WMAq WSFF XLum
ramosum	see *S. erectum*

Sparrmannia (*Malvaceae*)

africana 🏆H1c	CCCN ELan EShb SEND SPlb SSal SVen WCot
- 'Flore Pleno' (d)	CBcs

Spartina (*Poaceae*)

pectinata	XLum
- 'Aureomarginata' (v)	CBod CWCL EHyd ELan EPfP GMaP MACG MMuc NFav NWsh SEND SPer WWtn XLum

Spartium (*Fabaceae*)

junceum 🏆H5	CBcs CBod CCCN CDoC CEnd CMac EBee ELan ELon EPfP LRHS NFav NSti SEND SPer SRms WAvo XSen
- 'Brockhill Compact'	CDoC CKel EHyd EPfP

Spartocytisus see *Cytisus*

Spathantheum (*Araceae*)

orbignyanum	GKev WCot

Spathipappus see *Tanacetum*

Spathiphyllum (*Araceae*)

wallisii	SPre
- 'Bellini'	LCro LOPS

Spathodea (*Bignoniaceae*)

campanulata	SPlb

spearmint see *Mentha spicata*

Speirantha (*Asparagaceae*)

convallarioides	see *S. gardenii*
§ ***gardenii***	CBct CDTJ EPPr EPfP LEdu MHol MNrw WCru WHil WPGP

Sphacele see *Lepechinia*

Sphaeralcea (*Malvaceae*)

ambigua	SPlb
'Childerley'	CDor CMea CSpe ECtt MBNS MHol SMad SPad SPoG WCot WMal
coccinea	SPlb
fendleri	CCCN CSde
'Hopleys Lavender'	CCCN SWvt
incana	CBod CCCN CSde CSpe LPla MGil SIvy WMal
- 'Sourup'	ECtt SMHy WCot
malviflora	CDTJ
miniata	CCCN
munroana	CCCN ECtt ELan SMad SRkn
- pale pink-flowered	WABo
'Newleaze Coral'	CCCN EWld MAsh MGil MNrw SIvy SMad SPad SPoG SRkn SWvt WBor WCot WFar WLov WMal
'Newleaze Pink'	SRkn
remota	CExl SPlb
umbellata	see *Phymosia umbellata*

Sphagneticola (*Asteraceae*)

§ ***trilobata***	LLWG

Sphenomeris (*Dennstaedtiaceae*)

chinensis B&SWJ 6108	WCru

Spigelia (*Loganiaceae*)

marilandica	CBor EBee GKev ILea WCot WHil WSHC

Spilanthes (*Asteraceae*)

acmella misapplied	see *Acmella oleracea*
oleracea	see *Acmella oleracea*

Spiloxene see *Pauridia*

spinach see AGM Vegetables Section

Spiraea (*Rosaceae*)

alba var. ***latifolia***	MMuc
albiflora	see *S. japonica* 'Albiflora'
arborea	see *Sorbaria kirilowii*
§ 'Arguta' 🏆H6	Widely available
× ***arguta*** 'Bridal Wreath'	see *S.* 'Arguta'
aff. 'Arguta'	WLov
betulifolia	MRav WFar
- var. ***aemiliana***	MMuc
- 'Tor'	EPPr LPar
- 'Tor Gold'PBR	CBcs ELan LRHS MRav SPoG
× ***billardii*** misapplied	see *S.* × *pseudosalicifolia*
blumei CWJ 12829	WCru
× ***bumalda*** 'Wulfenii'	see *S. japonica* 'Walluf'
callosa 'Alba'	see *S. japonica* 'Albiflora'
canescens	CExl GKin
× ***cinerea*** 'Grefsheim' 🏆H6	CBcs CSBt ELan LBuc LPar NLar SCob SGol SPer SPlb
crispifolia misapplied	see *S. japonica* 'Bullata'
densiflora	GKev
- var. ***splendens***	SBrt
DOUBLE PLAY BIG BANG	see *S.* 'Tracy'
douglasii	CMac
formosana B&SWJ 1597	CExl WCru
fritschiana	CMac
hayatana	GKev SBrt
- RWJ 10014	WCru
hendersonii	see *Petrophytum hendersonii*
henryi	GKev
japonica	MVil
var. ***acuminata*** **new**	
§ - 'Albiflora'	CBod CBrac CEme CKel CMac CSBt CTri EHyd ELan ELon LRHS MRav MSwo NRHS NWad NWea SGbt SRms SWvt WFar
- 'Alpina'	see *S. japonica* 'Nana'
- 'Alpine Gold'	NEoE
- 'Anthony Waterer' (v)	CBcs CBod CBrac CCVT CDoC CMac EBee ELan EPfP EShb MAsh

		MGos MRav MSwo NLar NWea SCob SCoo SGbt SGol SGsty SNig SPer SPoG SRms WFar
§	– 'Bullata'	CMac NLar WAbe
	– 'Candlelight' ♀H6	CSBt ELan EPfP GBin GKin LRHS MAsh SCob SCoo SGol SPoG SWvt
	– 'Crispa'	EPfP NEoE NWad WFar WGrn
	– 'Dart's Red' ♀H6	ELan EPfP GKin
	– DOUBLE PLAY ARTISAN ('Galen')	SPoG
	– DOUBLE PLAY GOLD ('Yan')	SPoG
	– 'Firelight'	CBod CDoC CRos CSBt CTsd EBee ELan ELon EPfP EShb GKin LRHS MAsh MGos MSwo NHol NLar NRHS NWad SCob SCoo SGol SPer SRms SWvt WBor
§	– var. ***fortunei*** 'Macrophylla'	WLov
	– 'Froebelii'	EBee
§	– 'Genpei'	CChe CMac MAsh SGol SPer SPoG SRms
	– 'Gold Mound'	CBar CBrac CExl CMac EBee ELan EPfP MAsh MGos MRav MSwo NLar SCob SCoo SGol SPer SPlb SRms WFar
	– GOLDEN PRINCESS ('Lisp') ♀H6	CDoC CMac CRos CTri EHyd ELan EPfP LBuc LRHS MAsh MGos SCoo SGol SPer SRms WFar
	– 'Goldflame'	Widely available
	– 'Little Princess'	CBcs CBod CDoC CMac CRos EBee EHyd ELan EShb LRHS MAsh MRav MSwo NRHS NWea SCob SCoo SGol SGsty SPer SRms SWvt WFar
	– MAGIC CARPET ('Walbuma'PBR) (v) ♀H6	CBcs EHyd EPfP LBuc LRHS MAsh MMuc NLar NRHS SCoo SPoG SRms
	– 'Magnifica'	see *S. japonica* var. *fortunei* 'Macrophylla'
§	– 'Nana' ♀H6	CSBt MAsh SRms
	– 'Nyewoods'	see *S. japonica* 'Nana'
	– 'Nyewoods Gold'	CMac
	– 'Odessa'PBR **new**	GKev
	– 'Shiburi'	see *S. japonica* 'Albiflora'
	– 'Shirobana' misapplied	see *S. japonica* 'Genpei'
	– 'Shirobana'	see *S. japonica* 'Albiflora'
	– 'Stanton Gold'	WCFE
§	– 'Walluf'	CMac CTri GBin
	– 'White Cloud'	CDoC
	– 'White Gold'PBR	CBod CKel CMac CRos CSBt EHyd ELan EPfP LRHS LSou MAsh NEoE NHol NRHS NWad SCoo SPer SPoG SRms SWvt
	× ***margaritae***	SWvt
	micrantha	CExl
	nipponica 'Halward's Silver'	MRav NEoE
§	– 'Snowmound' ♀H6	Widely available
	– var. ***tosaensis*** misapplied	see *S. nipponica* 'Snowmound'
	palmata 'Elegans'	see *Filipendula purpurea* 'Elegans'
	prunifolia (d)	CBod CMac EPfP LRHS MRav SPer WAvo WCFE WFar WLov
§	× ***pseudosalicifolia*** 'Triumphans'	MMuc SPer
	salicifolia	GKev WFar
	sargentiana	GKev
	schneideriana	GKev
	SPARKLING CHAMPAGNE ('Lonspi'PBR)	CSBt LRHS LSRN NEoE NWad SCob SGBe SLon
	SUNDROP ('Bailcarol')	CBod LSou
	tarokoensis	CMCN
	thunbergii ♀H6	CBcs CBrac CMac CTri EPfP MMuc MRav NWea SBrt SCob SGol SPer SRms
	– 'Fujino Pink'	CRos LRHS
	– 'Golden Times'	EHyd SPoG
	– 'Mellow Yellow'	see *S. thunbergii* 'Ōgon'
	– 'Mount Fuji'	CMac MRav WFar
§	– 'Ōgon'	EPfP WFar
*	– 'Variegata' (v)	SRms
§	'Tracy'PBR	LRHS NEoE SCob
	ulmaria	see *Filipendula ulmaria*
	× ***vanhouttei***	CMac CTri ELan EPfP LPar MMuc MRav MSwo SEND SGsty SRms SavN WFar
	– 'Gold Fountain'	CMac ELan EPfP EShb GKev LPar LSRN MMuc NHol NLar SCoo SEND SPer WFar
	– 'Pink Ice' (v)	CBod CMac CRos EHyd EPfP LRHS MAsh MRav NLar SPer SPlb SPoG SWvt WFar
	veitchii	GLog MRav
	venusta 'Magnifica'	see *Filipendula rubra* 'Venusta'

Spiranthes (*Orchidaceae*)

	aestivalis	NLAp
	cernua	NGdn NLAp
	ochroleuca	NLAp
	odorata 'Chadd's Ford' ♀H4	CBod CExl EGrI MHer SBls WTor
	sinensis **new**	NLAp
	spiralis	NLAp

Spodiopogon (*Poaceae*)

	sibiricus	CBod CKno EPPr GBin NDov SPtp XLum
	– 'West Lake'	MAvo NDov

Sporobolus (*Poaceae*)

	airoides	CBod CKno EPPr EShb
	heterolepis	CKno CMea CSpe EBee ECha EPfP GBin GMaP LEdu LRHS MBel NDov SMHy SMea SPtp SSal WCot WPGP
I	– 'Wisconsin Strain'	EBee SBls
	'J.S. Delicatesse'	EPfP LRHS WTor
	wrightii	CKno EPPr SBls WAvo

Sprekelia (*Amaryllidaceae*)

	formosissima	EShb GKev LEdu SDeJ SDir

squashes see AGM Vegetables Section

Stachys (*Lamiaceae*)

	aethiopica 'Danielle'	see *S. thunbergii* 'Danielle'
§	***affinis***	GPoy LEdu SPlb SVic
	'Bello Grigio'	CBod MHol XSte
	betonica	see *Betonica officinalis*
§	***byzantina***	Widely available
§	– 'Big Ears'	Widely available
§	– 'Cotton Boll'	CBod CRos ECha EGrI LRHS SRms WFar XSen
	– 'Countess Helen von Stein'	see *S. byzantina* 'Big Ears'
	– 'Fuzzy Wuzzy'	WFar
	– gold-leaved	see *S. byzantina* 'Primrose Heron'
	– large-leaved	see *S. byzantina* 'Big Ears'
	– 'Limelight'	SAng WCot XLum
§	– 'Primrose Heron'	ECha EGrI GBin GKev GMaP MAsh MRav NLar NRHS SMrm SPer SWvt WCAu WFar WMal XLum
	– 'Pure Cotton' **new**	SBls

- 'Sheila McQueen'	see *S. byzantina* 'Cotton Boll'
- 'Silky Fleece'	EBou ECha ELan EPfP GWyn LRHS SPeP SRms XSen
- 'Silver Carpet'	Widely available
chamissonis var. ***cooleyae***	GBin
citrina	CMea LPla XSen
coccinea	GEdr
cretica	XSen
densiflora	see *S. monieri* (Gouan) P.W. Ball
discolor	see *Betonica nivea*
germanica	CNat NAts
grandiflora	see *Betonica macrantha*
'Hidalgo'	CSpe SRms
lanata Jacq.	see *S. byzantina*
lavandulifolia	WAbe
macrantha	see *Betonica macrantha*
- 'Hummelo'	see *Betonica officinalis* 'Hummelo'
mexicana misapplied	see *S. thunbergii*
monieri misapplied	see *Betonica officinalis*
monieri ambig.	CBor NLar NSti
- white-flowered	EBee
§ ***monieri*** (Gouan) P.W. Ball	LEdu
* - 'Rosea'	EBee LEdu NDov NLar SRms
- white-flowered	GKev
nivea	see *Betonica nivea*
officinalis	see *Betonica officinalis*
olympica	see *S. byzantina*
ossetica	see *Betonica nivea* subsp. *ossetica*
palustris	CHab CPud EWat GQue LLWG MCoo MMuc NLar NMir SEND SRms
- from Islay, Hebrides	MMuc SEND
§ ***recta***	CBee SBut
setifera	MHol XLum
spicata	see *Betonica macrantha*
sylvatica	CHab NMir WHer WSFF WWild
'The Bride'	NDov
thirkei	SAng WCot
§ ***thunbergii***	MBrN MBriF MNHC WKif
§ - 'Danielle'	CBod ECtt EGrI EPfP NLar SBut SDys SRkn SRms WMal
tuberifera	see *S. affinis*

Stachyurus (*Stachyuraceae*)

chinensis	CBcs CJun CMCN CTri EBee MVil NLar
- 'Celina' ♀H5	CJun CRos EHed EHyd ELon EPfP ESwi GKev GKin LRHS MBNS MGos NLar NRHS SPoG WPGP
- 'Goldbeater'	NLar
- 'Joy Forever' (v) ♀H5	CBcs CDoC CEnd CKel CMac EHyd EPfP ESwi LRHS MGos NLar NRHS SPer SPoG SSta SWvt WKif
- 'Senna'	NLar
- 'Wonderful Image'	ESwi
himalaicus	CBcs NLar
- HWJK 2035	WCru
- pink-flowered	see *S. himalaicus* subsp. *purpureus*
§ - subsp. ***purpureus*** HWJK 2052	WCru
aff. ***macrocarpus*** B&SWJ 14678	WCru
praecox ♀H5	Widely available
- B&SWJ 8898	WCru
- B&SWJ 10899	IDee LCro WCru
- var. ***leucotrichus***	CJun NLar
- var. ***matsuzakii***	CJun NLar
- - B&SWJ 11229	WCru
- 'Petra'	CJun
retusus	CExl
'Rubriflorus'	CJun EBee EPfP MAsh WPGP
salicifolius	CBcs CExl CJun EBee EPfP IArd IDee LRHS SPoG SSta WPGP XSte
sigeyosii	CBcs CExl EBee SSta
- B&SWJ 6915	WCru
- CWJ 12420	WCru
aff. ***szechuanensis***	CExl
- BWJ 8153	WCru
yunnanensis	CJun NLar WPGP

Stapelia (*Apocynaceae*)

grandiflora	SSim
marmoratum	see *Orbea variegata*
variegata	see *Orbea variegata*

Staphylea ✿ (*Staphyleaceae*)

bumalda	CBcs CJun LEdu NLar
- B&SWJ 11053	WCru
- B&SWJ 12744 from Korea	WCru
colchica	CBcs CMCN CRos EHyd ELan EPfP EWTr EWes LEdu LMaj LRHS MGos MMrt MRav SPer WKif XSte
holocarpa	CBcs CJun
- 'Innocence'	CBcs
- var. ***rosea***	CBcs CJun CMCN EPfP MBlu SMad SWvt
pinnata	CAgr CBcs CJun EPfP IDee MCoo MPkF NLar SEND XSte
- PAB 8427	LEdu
trifolia	CAgr EBee EHed EPfP

Statice see *Limonium*

sinuata	see *Limonium sinuatum*

Stauntonia (*Lardizabalaceae*)

from northern Vietnam	WCru
aff. ***chinensis*** DJHV 06175	WCru
hexaphylla	CBcs CCCN CKel CRHN CTri CWGN EBee EGrI EHyd EPfP ESwi LRHS MAsh MGil NLar SAdn SNig SPer SPoG SSta
- B&SWJ 4858	WCru
- B&SWJ 14655	ESwi WCru
libera KWJ 12218	WCru
obovata CWJ 12353	WCru
obovatifoliola B&SWJ 3685	WCru
purpurea	WPGP
- B&SWJ 3690	WCru
yaoshanensis B&SWJ 8223	WCru
- FMWJ 13171	WCru
- HWJ 1024	WCru

Stegnogramma (*Thelypteridaceae*)

pozoi	EFer

Stellaria (*Caryophyllaceae*)

graminea	CHab
holostea	CHab MBow NBir NMir WShi

Stemmacantha see *Rhaponticum*

Stenanthium (*Melanthiaceae*)

gramineum	EBee EWes

Stenomesson (*Amaryllidaceae*)

pearcei	CBor GKev

Stenotaphrum (*Poaceae*)

secundatum	EShb
- 'Variegatum' (v)	EShb XLum

Stephanandra (*Rosaceae*)

	incisa	CExl
§	- 'Crispa'	CBcs CDoC CMac CTri EBee EGrl ELan EPfP GArf GKin LPar LRHS MBlu MRav NHol SCob SGbt SPer SRms
	- 'Prostrata'	see *S. incisa* 'Crispa'
	tanakae	CBcs CExl CMac EBee ELan EPfP MBlu MGil MRav SLon SPer SRms

Stephania (*Menispermaceae*)

	aff. ***hernandiifolia*** B&SWJ 14950	WCru
	japonica CWJ 12823	WCru
	aff. ***tetrandra*** WWJ 11896	WCru

Stephanotis (*Apocynaceae*)

	floribunda ♀H1a	CBcs CCCN CDoC LCro LOPS

Sternbergia (*Amaryllidaceae*)

	candida	CBro NRog
§	***clusiana***	NRog
	colchiciflora	GKev NRog
	fischeriana	CBro
	greuteriana	EPot GKev NRog
	lutea ♀H4	CBro CTri ECha EHyd ELan EPot ERCP EWes GKev LCro LOPS LRHS NRHS NRog SDeJ SGro WHoo WIce XLum
	- from Bisceglie, Italy **new**	NRog
	- from Iran **new**	NRog
	- Angustifolia Group	CBro CMea WCot
	- var. ***graeca*** **new**	NRog
	macrantha	see *S. clusiana*
	sicula	CBro EPot NRog
	- 'Arcadian Sun'	EPot NRog
	- 'Dodona Gold'	GKev NRog
	- 'John Marr'	WCot WThu
	vernalis **new**	NRog

Stevia (*Asteraceae*)

	rebaudiana	CBod CGro ENfk GPoy LCro LOPS LShi MNHC SPre SRms SVic WCot WJek

Stewartia ✿ (*Theaceae*)

	gemmata	see *S. sinensis*
	'Korean Splendor'	see *S. pseudocamellia* Koreana Group
	koreana	see *S. pseudocamellia* Koreana Group
	monadelpha	CBcs CJun CMen EHed IDee LMaj LRHS MBlu MPkF NLar
	ovata	CJun
	pseudocamellia ♀H5	Widely available
	- B&SWJ 11044 from North Japan	WCru
§	- Koreana Group ♀H5	CBct CEnd CJun CMCN EHyd EPfP GKin LRHS MPkF NLar SChF SLim
	- 'Ogisu'	NLar
	pteropetiolata B&SWJ 11726	WCru
	- NJM 10.107	WPGP
	- WWJ 11939	WCru
	rostrata	CBcs CJun CLnd CMCN EGrl LMaj LRHS MBlu MPkF NLar SPtp WPGP XSte
	- 'Hulsdonk Pink'	CJun
	serrata	CJun CMCN MPkF WCru
§	***sinensis*** ♀H5	CBcs CCCN CDoC CJun EPfP IArd IDee LMaj MBlu MPkF NLar SAko SPtp WPGP

Stigmaphyllon (*Malpighiaceae*)

	ciliatum	CCCN
	littorale	CCCN

Stipa (*Poaceae*)

	arundinacea	see *Anemanthele lessoniana*
	barbata	CSpe ECha EPPr ETod XSen
	brachytricha	see *Calamagrostis brachytricha*
§	***calamagrostis*** ♀H4	CBod CElw CWCL EAJP EBee ECha EHyd ELan EMor EPPr EPfP EShb GDam GMaP LCro LOPS LRHS MRav NBro NDov NRHS SBls SCob SDix SEND SMea SRms WHal XSen
	- 'Allgäu' ♀H4	ECha WCot
	- 'Lemperg' ♀H4	EHyd NDov
	capillata	CBod CSpe EHyd EPPr EWhm GBin LRHS XSen
	- 'Brautschleier'	CBod
*	- 'Lace Veil'	WAvo
	elegantissima	CDoC
	extremiorientalis	EPPr
	gigantea ♀H4	Widely available
	- 'Alberich' **new**	ECha
	- 'Gold Fontaene' ♀H4	CKno EPPr EPfP EWes GBee LRHS MAvo MNrw NDov SMHy SMad WChS WCot
	- 'Goldilocks'	CKno CRos ECha EHyd LEdu LRHS NRHS
	- 'Pixie'	CRos EBee EHyd EPPr EPfP LRHS NRHS
	ichu ♀H4	CKno CRos CSpe EAJP ECha EHyd LRHS LSun MAvo NDov NRHS SDix SMea SPhx
	joannis	CBod
	lasiagrostis	see *S. calamagrostis*
	lessingiana ♀H5	CExl EPPr LRHS SBls SEND SPhx
	pennata	CKel CPla LRHS MACG XSen
	pseudoichu ♀H5	CBod CCht ECha ELan EPPr LPla LRHS MAvo MBNS NWsh SPeP SPtp WCot WHoo WPGP
	- RCB/Arg Y-1	ELon
	pulcherrima	EPPr
	robusta	EPPr
	splendens misapplied	see *S. calamagrostis*
	splendens Trin.	ECha SAko
	tenacissima	CDoC
	tenuifolia misapplied	see *S. tenuissima*
	tenuifolia Steud.	CMea LRHS MRav NBir NBro NSti WHal XLum XSen
§	***tenuissima*** ♀H4	Widely available
	- 'Wind Whispers'	CExl LEdu LRHS MBel SIvy SPtp

Stoebe (*Asteraceae*)

	alopecuroides	SPlb

Stokesia ✿ (*Asteraceae*)

	cyanea	see *S. laevis*
§	***laevis***	ECha EGrl EHyd EPfP LRHS NLar NRHS SGBe SPlb SRms WCAu
	- 'Alba'	ECha EGrl EHyd ELan EPfP EPri GPSL LEdu LRHS MRav NLar NRHS SGBe WCAu
	- 'Blue Frills'	ECtt EPfP
	- 'Blue Star'	CBcs CBod CDor CRos CWGN EBee ELan ELon EMor EPfP EWoo LRHS LSou LSun MACG MBel MHer MRav NRHS SGbt SPer SPhx SPoG SRkn SWvt WCav WSHC
	- 'Color Wheel'	ECtt EHyd
	- 'Divinity'	CRos ECtt LRHS SCob

- 'Klaus Jelitto'	ECtt EHyd EMor LEdu LRHS SCob SGbt SHar SPoG
- 'Mary Gregory'	CMac CNor CRos EBee EBlo ECtt ELan EMor EPfP EWTr LRHS MACG MBel MPie MRav NLar NRHS SCob SGbt SPhx SWvt WSHC
§ - 'Mel's'PBR	CRos ECtt EHyd LRHS NRHS
- MEL'S BLUE	see *S. laevis* 'Mel's'
- 'Omega Skyrocket'	SRms
- 'Peach Melba'	ECtt
- 'Peachie's Pick'	CBod ECtt EMor MACG SPad
- 'Purple Parasols'	CBod CDor CMac CRos CWGN EBee ECtt EPfP LEdu LRHS LSou MBel MPie NLar NRHS SGbt SPoG SWvt
- 'Purple Pixie'PBR	ECtt
- 'Silver Moon'	CBod ECtt EMor EPfP GBin LRHS NRHS SGbt SPer
§ - 'Träumerei'	CBod CWGN EBee ECtt EPfP LRHS MPie NRHS SGbt XLum
- 'White Star'	see *S. laevis* 'Träumerei'

Stranvaesia see *Photinia*

× *Stranvinia* see *Photinia*

Stratiotes (*Hydrocharitaceae*)

aloides	CBen CPud CWat EWat LCro LLWG LOPS MWts NPer SVic WMAq WPnP

strawberry see *Fragaria*; see also AGM Fruit Section

Strelitzia (*Strelitziaceae*)

alba	CCCN WSMil
nicolai	CCCN NPer SPlb
reginae ♀H1b	CAbb CCCN CDoC CPla CTsd ELan EShb ETod LCro LOPS NPer SPalm SPlb WSMil

Streptanthus (*Brassicaceae*)

farnsworthianus **new**	CSpe

Streptocarpella see *Streptocarpus*

Streptocarpus ✿ (*Gesneriaceae*)

'8e-Ajisai' (AV)	WDib
'Adele'	WDib
'Ae-Amur Elit' (AV)	WDib
'Ajohn's Fruit Cocktail' (AV)	WDib
'Ajohn's Yellow Submarine' (AV)	WDib
'Alamo Quest' (AV)	WDib
'Alana'	WDib
'Alan's Fallen Angel' (AV/d)	WDib
'Alan's White Feather' (AV)	WDib
'Albatross'	WDib
'Alchemy Yellow Star' (AV)	WDib
'Alissa'	WDib
'Allegro Appalachian Trail' (AV)	WDib
'Always Pink' (AV)	WDib
'Aly's Rosy Baby' (AV)	WDib
'Amanda' Dibley	WDib
'Amazing Grace' (AV)	WDib
'Ambiente' ♀H1c	WDib
'Amethyst' (AV)	WDib
'Amy'	WDib
'Anne' (d)	WDib
'Anouk' (AV)	WDib
'An-Rio Rita' (AV)	WDib
'Anthoflores Edith' (AV)	WDib
'Anwen'	WDib
'Apache Magic' (AV) **new**	WDib
'Apache Maiden' (AV/v)	WDib
'Apache Thunderbolt' (AV)	WDib
'Aussie Magic' (AV)	WDib
'Austin's Smile' (AV) **new**	WDib
'Awena'	WDib
'Baby Brian' (AV)	WDib
baudertii	WDib
'Beacon Trail' (AV)	WDib
'Beatrice Trail' (AV)	WDib
'Bella'	WDib
'Berry Splash' (AV/v)	WDib
'Bethan' ♀H1c	WDib
'Betty Stoehr' (AV)	WDib
'Bianca'	WDib
'Black Panther'	WDib
'Bliznecy' (AV)	WDib
'Bloomlover's Cat' (AV/d)	WDib
'Blue Dragon' (AV/d)	WDib
'Blue Frills' ♀H1c	WDib
'Blue Gem'	WDib
'Blue Leyla'	see *S.* 'Leyla'
'Blue Moon'	WDib
'Blue Nymph'	WDib
'Blue Tail Fly' (AV)	WDib
'Blushing Ivory' (AV)	WDib
'Bob Serbin' (AV/d)	WDib
'Bob's Omega' (AV)	WDib
'Bourane' (AV/v)	WDib
'Boysenberry Delight'	WDib
'Branwen'	WDib
brevipilosus (AV)	WDib
'Bristol's Black Bird'	WDib
'Bristol's Very Best'	WDib
'Buffalo Hunt' (AV/d)	WDib
caeruleus	WDib
'Caitlin'	WDib
'Calico Beauty' (AV)	WDib
candidus	WDib
'Candy Fountain' (AV)	WDib
'Candy Swirls' (AV)	WDib
'Cappuccino'	WDib
'Cariad'	WDib
'Carol'	WDib
'Carys' ♀H1c	WDib
'Cathedral' (AV)	WDib
caulescens	WDib
- var. ***pallescens***	see *S. pallidiflorus*
'Cedar Creek Stormy' (AV)	WDib
'Cedar Creek Trail of Hope' (AV)	WDib
'Celebration'	WDib
'Chantaspring' (AV)	WDib
'Chanticleer' (AV/d) **new**	WDib
'Charlotte' ♀H1c	WDib
'Cherokee Trail' (AV/v)	WDib
'Cherries 'n' Cream' (AV)	WDib
'Chiffon Fiesta' (AV)	WDib
'Chiffon Pageant' (AV)	WDib
'Chiffon Vesper' (AV)	WDib
'Chloe'	WDib
'Chorus Line'	WDib
'Cirelda' (AV)	WDib
'Constant Nymph'	WDib
'Country Romance' (AV/d)	WDib
'Crimson Ice' (AV)	WDib
'Crowning Glory' (AV)	WDib
'Crystal Beauty'	WDib
'Crystal Blush'	WDib

'Crystal Charm'	WDib
'Crystal Dawn'	WDib
'Crystal Ice'PBR ♀H1c	LCro LOPS WDib
'Crystal Snow'	WDib
'Crystal Wonder'	WDib
'Cupid's Jewel' (AV)	WDib
'Cupie Doll' (AV)	WDib
cyaneus	WDib
– subsp. ***polackii***	WDib
'Cynthia'	WDib
'Daphne'	WDib
'Dawn Michelle' (AV)	WDib
'Dee'	WDib
'Deep Sky' (AV)	WDib
'Definitely Darryl' (AV)	WDib
'Delft' (AV/d)	WDib
'Delia'	CSpe WDib
'Denim'	WDib
denticulatus	WDib
'Diana'	WDib
'Dibley's Beate' (AV)	WDib
'Dibleys Kaarina' (AV)	WDib
'Dibley's Leopold' (AV) **new**	WDib
'Dibleys Marion' (AV)	WDib
'Dibleys Mercedes' (AV)	WDib
'Dibley's Pat' (AV)	WDib
'Dinas'	WDib
'Ds-Horus'	WDib
dunnii	WDib
'Dwynwen'	WDib
'Edee's Rosebud Trail' (AV/d)	WDib
'Ek-Afrodita' (AV/v) **new**	WDib
'Ek-Gost'ya iz Budushchego' (AV)	WDib
'Ek-Sady Semiramidi' (AV)	WDib
'Ek-Shedevr Khudozhnika' (AV)	WDib
'Ek-Snezhnyi Bars' (AV)	WDib
'Ek-Vrata Raia' (AV)	WDib
'Elin'	WDib
'Elsi'	WDib
'Emerald Love' (AV)	WDib
'Emily'	WDib
'Ethel's Wild Side' (AV)	WDib
'Eve'	NWad WDib
'Falling Stars' ♀H1c	CSpe WDib
'Favorite Child' (AV)	WDib
'Festival Wales'	WDib
'Fiesta'	WDib
'Fiona'	WDib
'Fire Mountain' (AV)	WDib
'Flashy Angel' (AV/v)	WDib
'Flashy Trail' (AV)	WDib
floribundus	WDib
'Flower Drum' (AV)	WDib
formosus	WDib
'Franken Alayana'	WDib
'Franken Isabella'	WDib
'Franken Skye'	WDib
'Franken Strawberry Fondant'	WDib
'Freya'	WDib
'Frosty Diamond' ♀H1c	WDib
'Frozen in Time' (AV/v)	WDib
'Full Moon'	WDib
gardenii	WDib
'Gecko's Vespa Vino' (AV)	WDib
'Gillian' (AV/d)	WDib
glandulosissimus ♀H1c	WDib
'Gloria' ♀H1c	WDib
'Gold Dust'	WDib

'Gold Rose'	WDib
'Golden Dawn' (AV)	WDib
'Golden Eye' (AV)	WDib
'Golden Threads' (AV/d)	WDib
'Goluboi Tuman' (AV)	WDib
'Grandmother's Halo' (AV)	WDib
'Granger's Heart's Desire' (AV/d) **new**	WDib
'Green Dragon' (AV)	WDib
'Green Lace' (AV/d)	WDib
'Gwen'	WDib
'Halo's Aglitter' (AV)	WDib
'Hand-picked' (AV/v)	WDib
'Hannah' ♀H1c	CSpe WDib
'Happy Cricket' (AV)	WDib
'Harlequin Blue'PBR ♀H1c	LCro LOPS WDib
'Harlequin Damsel'	WDib
'Harlequin Dawn'	WDib
'Harlequin Delft'	WDib
'Harlequin Lace'PBR ♀H1c	WDib
'Harlequin Purple'	WDib
'Harlequin Rose'	WDib
'Harriet'	WDib
'Hayley'	WDib
'Heaven's A-calling' (AV)	WDib
'Heidi'	WDib
'Helen'	WDib
'Hope'	WDib
'Hot Summer Day' (AV)	WDib
'Ian-Minuet' (AV/d)	WDib
'In the Pink' (AV)	WDib
'Indian Trail' (AV)	WDib
'Indigo Ruffles' (AV)	WDib
'Iona'	WDib
ionanthus	WDib
subsp. ***grotei*** (AV)	
– subsp. ***ionanthus*** (AV)	WDib
– subsp. ***rupicola*** (AV)	WDib
– subsp. ***velutinus*** (AV)	WDib
'Isabella'	WDib
'Island Breezes' (AV)	WDib
'Jacquie'	WDib
'Jennifer' ♀H1c	WDib
'Jenny Lilac' (AV/d)	WDib
'Jessica' ♀H1c	WDib
'Joanna'	WDib
johannis	WDib
'Joli Concerto' (AV)	WDib
'Jolly Champ' (AV)	WDib
'Jolly Gala' (AV) **new**	WDib
'Jolly Gold' (AV)	WDib
'Jolly Orchid' (AV/d)	WDib
'Jolly Prize' (AV/d)	WDib
'Jolly Sun Chaser' (AV/d)	WDib
'Jolly Texan' (AV/d)	WDib
'Joy'	WDib
'Karen'	WDib
'Katie'PBR ♀H1c	WDib
kentaniensis	WDib
'Kim' ♀H1c	CSpe WDib
kirkii	WDib
'Kosmicheskaia Legenda 2' (AV)	WDib
'Kostina Fantaziia' (AV)	WDib
'Laura' ♀H1c	WDib
'Leah' **new**	WDib
'LE-Karusel' (AV/v)	WDib
'LE-Macho' (AV)	WDib
'Lemon Sorbet' **new**	WDib
'Lemon Whip' (AV/d)	WDib
'Letnaya Noch' (AV)	WDib

	'Letnie Sumerki' (AV)	WDib
§	'Leyla'PBR	WDib
	'Lil Bit O'Irish' (AV)	WDib
	'Lilla Blaklockan' (AV)	WDib
	'Little Axel' (AV)	WDib
	'Little Bo Peep' (AV)	WDib
	'Little Chatterbox' (AV) **new**	WDib
	'Little Seagull' (AV)	WDib
	'Lollipop' (AV)	WDib
	'Looking Glass' (AV)	WDib
	'Louise'	CSpe WDib
	'Louisiana Lullaby' (AV/d)	WDib
	'Love Spots' (AV)	WDib
	'Lubimaia Dochka' (AV)	WDib
	'Lucky Ladybug' (AV)	WDib
	'Lucy'	WDib
	'Luminescence' (AV)	WDib
	'Lyndee'	WDib
	'Lynne'	WDib
	'Lyon's Minnie-HaHa' (AV)	WDib
	'Lyon's Plum Pudding' (AV)	WDib
	'Maassen's White'	WDib
	'Mac's Black Jack' (AV)	WDib
	'Mac's Blowing Bubbles' (AV)	WDib
	'Mac's Carnival Clown' (AV)	WDib
	'Mac's Glacial Grape' (AV)	WDib
	'Mac's Just Jeff' (AV/d)	WDib
	'Mac's Nocturne' (AV/d)	WDib
	'Mac's Rouge Rogue' (AV)	WDib
	'Mac's Southern Springtime' (AV/d)	WDib
	'Mac's Tiamat' (AV/v)	WDib
	'Manon'	WDib
	'Margaret' Gavin Brown	WDib
	'Marie'	WDib
	'Marion'	CSpe WDib
	'Ma's Ching Dynasty' (AV/d)	WDib
	'Ma's Easter Parade' (AV)	WDib
	'Matilda'	WDib
	'Megan'	WDib
	'Melanie' Dibley	WDib
	'Menai'	WDib
	meyeri	WDib
	'Midget Silver Fox' (AV/v)	WDib
	'Midnight Flame' (AV/d)	WDib
	'Mikinda Girl' (AV/v)	WDib
	'Mindi Brooke' (AV)	WDib
	'Minnie'	WDib
	modestus	WDib
	'Myfanwy'	WDib
	'MyJoy' (MyViolet Series) (AV)	WDib
	'Nadine'	WDib
	'Natalie'	WDib
	'Nerys'	WDib
	'Ness' Antique Red' (AV)	WDib
	'Ness' Cherry Smoke' (AV)	WDib
	'Ness' Crinkle Blue' (AV/d)	WDib
	'Ness' Midnight Fantasy' (AV)	WDib
	'Ness' Orange Pekoe' (AV)	WDib
	'Ness' Satin Rose' (AV)	WDib
	'Ness' Sheer Peach' (AV)	WDib
	'Neverfloris' (AV)	WDib
	'Newtown Ohio' (AV)	WDib
	'Nia'	WDib
	'Nicola'	WDib
	nitidus (AV)	WDib
	'Norseman' (AV)	WDib
	'Number 32' (AV)	WDib
	'Ode to Beauty' (AV)	WDib
	'Ode to Grace' (AV) **new**	WDib
	'Okie Easter Bunny' (AV)	WDib
	'Oksana' (AV)	WDib
	'Olivia'	WDib
	'Optimara Little Moonstone' (AV)	WDib
	'Otoe' (AV/d)	WDib
	'Padarn'	WDib
§	***pallidiflorus***	WDib
	'Parnikovyi Effekt' (AV)	WDib
	'Pat Champagne' (AV/v)	WDib
	'Pat Tracey' (AV)	WDib
	'Paula'	WDib
	'Pearl' ♀H1c	CSpe WDib
	pentherianus	WDib
	'Pink Leyla' ♀H1c	WDib
	'Pink Mint' (AV/d)	WDib
	'Pink Souffle'	WDib
	'Pixie Blue' (AV)	WDib
	'Pixie Pink' (AV)	WDib
	'Podvenechnaia' (AV/d)	WDib
	'Polka-Dot Purple' ♀H1c	WDib
	'Polka-Dot Red'	WDib
	polyanthus subsp. ***dracomontanus***	WDib
	'Powder Keg' (AV/d)	WDib
	'Powwow' (AV/d)	WDib
	'Prancing Pony' (AV)	WDib
	primulifolius	WDib
	prolixus	WDib
	'Purple Passion' (AV)	WDib
	'Purple Velvet'	CSpe WDib
	'Rainbow's Limelight' (AV/d)	WDib
	'Rainbow's Quiet Riot' (AV)	WDib
	'Ramblin' Amethyst' (AV)	WDib
	'Ramblin' Lassie' (AV)	WDib
	'Ramblin' Sunshine' (AV)	WDib
	'Rare Tapestry' (AV)	WDib
	'Raspberry Crisp' (AV)	WDib
	'Rebel's Amy' (AV)	WDib
	'Rebel's Splatter Kake' (AV)	WDib
	'Rebel's Strawberry Bites' (AV)	WDib
	'Red Lantern' (AV/d)	WDib
	'Reflections of Spring' (AV/d)	WDib
	rexii	WDib
	'Rhapsodie Clementine' (AV)	WDib
	'Rhiannon'	WDib
	'Rob's Argyle Socks' (AV/d)	WDib
	'Rob's Bed Bug' (AV/v) **new**	WDib
	'Rob's Chilly Willy' (AV/d)	WDib
	'Rob's Dandy Lion' (AV/d/v)	WDib
	'Rob's Dust Storm' (AV/d)	WDib
	'Rob's Flim Flam' (AV)	WDib
	'Rob's Hot Tamale' (AV)	WDib
	'Rob's Ice Ripples' (AV/d)	WDib
	'Rob's Jitterbug' (AV)	WDib
	'Rob's Love Bite' (AV/d)	WDib
	'Rob's Mad Cat' (AV/d)	WDib
	'Rob's Melon Wedges' (AV)	WDib
	'Rob's Peedletuck' (AV)	WDib
	'Rob's Pewter Bells' (AV)	WDib
	'Rob's Sarsparilla' (AV/d)	WDib
	'Rob's Scrumptious' (AV)	WDib
	'Rob's Shadow Magic' (AV/d/v)	WDib
	'Rob's Smarty Pants' (AV/d)	WDib
	'Rob's Vanilla Trail' (AV/d)	WDib
	'Rob's Wooloomooloo' (AV/d)	WDib

	'Rose Halo'	WDib
	'Rosebud'	WDib
	(Roulette Series) 'Roulette Azur'PBR ♀H1c	WDib
	- 'Roulette Cherry'	WDib
	'Rs-Barbie' (AV) **new**	WDib
	'Rs-Bog Solntsa' (AV/d)	WDib
	'Rs-Boyarinya' (AV)	WDib
	'Rs-Gertsogninea' (AV)	WDib
	'Rs-Iolanta' (AV/v)	WDib
	'Rs-Kabaret' (AV)	WDib
	'Rs-Korrida' (AV)	WDib
	'Rs-Romantika' (AV)	WDib
	'Rs-Strast' (AV)	WDib
	'Rs-Utonchennyy-vkus' (AV)	WDib
	'Rs-Vodevil' (AV/v)	WDib
	'Rubina'PBR	WDib
	'Rubina Pink' ♀H1c	WDib
	'Ruby'	WDib
	'Ruffled Skies' (AV)	WDib
	'Ruth'	WDib
	'Sadie'	WDib
	'Sally'	WDib
	'Sandra'	WDib
	'Santa Anita' (AV)	WDib
	'Sapphire Halo' (AV)	WDib
	'Sarah'	WDib
	saxorum	CCCN LSou WDib
	- compact ♀H1c	CCCN WDib
	'Scarlett'	WDib
	'Senk's Arctic Fox' (AV)	WDib
	'Seren'	WDib
	shumensis (AV)	WDib
	'Shy Blue' (AV)	WDib
	'Sian'	WDib
	silvaticus	WDib
	'Silverglade Beads' (AV)	WDib
	'Sioned' ♀H1c	WDib
	'Sky Bells' (AV/v)	WDib
	'Sky Trail' (AV)	WDib
	'Snow Leopard' (AV)	WDib
	'Snow White' ♀H1c	CSpe WDib
	'Sparkleberry' (AV)	WDib
	'Special Treat' (AV)	WDib
I	'Stella'PBR Dibleys ♀H1c	WDib
§	'Stella' Fleischle (Marleen Series) ♀H1c	WDib
	'Stephanie'	WDib
	stomandrus	WDib
	'Sun Sizzle' (AV)	WDib
	'Sunkissed Rose' (AV)	WDib
	'Susan' ♀H1c	WDib
	'Sweet Melys'	WDib
	'Sweet Rosy'	WDib
	'Taffeta Blue' (AV/d)	WDib
	'Tanga'	see *S.* 'Stella' Fleischle
	'Tanya'	WDib
	'Teleri'	WDib
	'Texas Hot Chili'	CSpe WDib
	'The King' (AV)	WDib
	'The Madam' (AV)	WDib
	thompsonii	WDib
	THREE SISTERS (mixed) **new**	WDib
	'Tiger' (AV/v)	WDib
	'Tina' ♀H1c	WDib
	'Tina's April Fantasy' (AV)	WDib
	'Titania'	WDib
	'Top Dark Blue' (AV)	LCro LOPS
	'Toy Castle' (AV)	WDib
	'Tracey'	WDib
	'Tula' (AV)	WDib
	'Two-w Miss Sophie' (AV/d)	WDib
	'Vallartas Campanas Moradas' (AV)	WDib
	'Valor'	WDib
	vandeleurii	WDib
	variabilis	WDib
	'Warm Sunshine' (AV)	WDib
	'Wawel'	WDib
	wendlandii	WDib
	'Wendy'	WDib
	'Whirligig Star' (AV)	WDib
	'White Butterfly' ♀H1c	WDib
	'Wiesmoor Red'	WDib
	'Wild Irish Rose' (AV)	WDib
	'Winifred'	WDib
	'Wisteria' (AV/d)	WDib
	'Wrangler's Jealous Heart' (AV)	WDib
	'Wrangler's Snowfield's' (AV/v)	WDib
	'Yesterday's Child' (AV)	WDib
	'Zivai' (AV/d)	WDib
	'Zoe' **new**	WDib

Streptopus (*Liliaceae*)

amplexifolius	EBee ESwi GBin MNrw WCru WSHC
- var. ***papillatus***	GEdr
roseus	WCru
streptopoides	EBee EHed EHyd EPPr EPfP LEdu LRHS NBro SLon

Streptosolen (*Solanaceae*)

jamesonii ♀H1c	CCCN EBak EShb SWvt

Strobilanthes (*Acanthaceae*)

	CC 4071	CExl
	CC 4573	CExl
	angustifrons	SBrt
	anisophylla	EShb WSpi
	atropurpurea misapplied	see *S. attenuata*
	atropurpurea Nees	see *S. wallichii*
§	***attenuata***	CBod CRos EBee ECtt EGrI EHyd GGro ILea LEdu LRHS MBel MHer MPie MRav MSCN NChi NRHS NSti SBut SDix SPoG WCot WCru WSpi
	- 'Blue and White'	EBee
	- 'Blue Carpet'	NDov
	- 'Latham's Form'	WHil
	- subsp. ***nepalensis***	XLum
	dyeriana ♀H1b	EBak EShb SPlb SSal WCot
	flexicaulis B&SWJ 354	ESwi WCru
	aff. ***inflata*** B&SWJ 7754	WCru
*	***lactea***	EShb
	nutans	EBee EWld GGro NSti SBrt WBor XLum
	pentstemonoides	EPPr
	rankanensis	EPPr GPSL ILea SDys XLum
	- B&SWJ 1771	WCru
	violacea misapplied	EShb
§	***wallichii***	CMac EBee EPfP EWes EWld ILea MMuc NSti SEND WCAu WCru WMal
	- from Picton	WFar

Strophanthus (*Apocynaceae*)

speciosus	CCCN EShb

Strumaria (*Amaryllidaceae*)

aestivalis	NRog
discifera subsp. ***bulbifera***	WCot
gemmata	NRog

salteri	NRog
tenella subsp. ***tenella*** new	NRog
truncata	NRog
watermeyeri	NRog
subsp. ***watermeyeri***	

Stuartia see *Stewartia*

Stylidium (*Stylidiaceae*)

graminifolium	CTsd SPlb

Stylophorum (*Papaveraceae*)

diphyllum	CFis LEdu MAvo MPie WCru WPGP WPnP WWtn
lasiocarpum	CExl CSpe EMor EPPr EWld GEdr GGro MAvo MMrt NBid NSti SBls WCru WPnP
sutchuenense new	GGro

Styphelia (*Ericaceae*)

colensoi	see *Leucopogon colensoi*

Styphnolobium (*Fabaceae*)

§ ***japonicum***	CAco CBcs CHab CMCN CMac EPfP IPap LPar SPer SPlb WTSh
- 'China Gold'	EBee SPoG
- 'Flavirameum'	SMad
- 'Gold Standard' new	MTrO
- 'Pendulum'	LPar MPri
- 'Regent'	LPar

Styrax ✿ (*Styracaceae*)

NJM 11.013 from Guizhou, China	WPGP
NJM 11.085 from Guizhou, China	WPGP
americanus	EPfP
- Kankakee form	WPGP
confusus	CExl
dasyanthus	CExl
faberi	CExl
formosanus	CBcs CExl CJun EPfP MBlu SChF
var. ***formosanus***	WPGP
- - B&SWJ 3803	WCru
- - B&SWJ 6786	WCru
- var. ***hayatiana*** B&SWJ 6823	WCru
grandiflorus	CExl
hemsleyanus 🏆H5	CBcs CExl EGrI EPfP IDee LEdu MBlu NLar SPtp
hookeri	CExl
japonicus	CBcs CDoC CExl CLnd CMCN CRos CTri EHyd ELan ELon EPfP GKin IPap LEdu LMaj LRHS LSRN MAsh MBlu MGos MRav MVil NLar SGol SPer SPoG WHwl WPGP
- B&SWJ 4405	WCru
- B&SWJ 8770	WCru
- B&SWJ 11078	WCru
- Guiz 216	CExl WPGP
§ - Benibana Group	SChF WPGP
- - 'Pink Chimes'	CBcs CExl CJun CMCN EHed ELan GKin LMaj LRHS MBlu MPkF MTrO NLar NOra SAko WHwl WMat XSte
- 'Carillon'	CJun
- 'Evening Light'PBR	CBcs
- 'Fargesii' 🏆H5	CBcs CDoC CExl CJun LRHS SEdd XSte
- 'Fragrant Fountain'	LPar LRHS MBlu MPkF NLar SGsty XSte
- 'June Snow'PBR	LPar NLar WHwl
- 'Pendulus'	CBcs EPfP NLar WPGP
I - 'Pink Snowbell'	LRHS
- 'Purple Dress' 🏆H5	CJun MBlu NLar
- 'Roseus'	see *S. japonicus* Benibana Group
- SNOWCONEX ('Jfs-D')	LMaj SGsty
- 'Snowfall'	CJun EHed NLar
- 'Sohuksan' 🏆H5	CBcs CExl CJun MBlu WPGP
aff. ***japonicus*** B&SWJ 14182 from Heuksando, South Korea	WCru
limprichtii	CExl
obassia	CBcs CLnd CMCN EPfP LRHS MBlu NLar SPtp WGob WPGP
- B&SWJ 6023	WCru
- B&SWJ 10890	WCru
odoratissimus	CExl WPGP
officinalis	CJun WPGP
redivivus	CJun
serrulatus	CExl
shiraianus	CExl MBlu NLar WPGP
tonkinensis FMWJ 13134	WCru
wilsonii	CExl EBee
wuyuanensis	WPGP

Succisa (*Caprifoliaceae*)

§ ***pratensis***	Widely available
- 'Alba'	EWes
- 'Buttermilk'	CDor EWes LEdu
- 'Cassop'	GEdr GKev
- 'Derby Purple'	CSpe SPhx WHoo
- early-flowering	LEdu SPhx
- 'Peddar's Pink'	EWes LLWG LRHS MACG SPhx

Succisella (*Caprifoliaceae*)

inflexa	CSpe MSpe NFav SPhx WCAu
I - 'Alba' new	MSpe
- 'Frosted Pearls'	CDor CElw CFis CFoA EBee GBin LEdu LSun MACG MAvo NLar SBut SHar

sunberry see *Rubus* 'Sunberry'

Sutera (*Scrophulariaceae*)

cordata	see *Chaenostoma cordatum*

Sutherlandia ✿ (*Fabaceae*)

frutescens	CBod CSpe SPlb
montana	CSpe SBrt

swede see AGM Vegetables Section

sweet cicely see *Myrrhis odorata*

sweet corn see AGM Vegetables Section

sweet pepper see *Capsicum*; also AGM Vegetables Section

Swertia (*Gentianaceae*)

bimaculata	ECha
- PAB 8845	LEdu
perennis	GEdr

Syagrus (*Arecaceae*)

§ ***romanzoffiana***	LRHS SPalm

× *Sycoparrotia* (*Hamamelidaceae*)

semidecidua	CBcs CBct CCCN CJun EBee EPfP LMaj MBlu NLar NOrn
- 'Purple Haze'	CJun IArd IDee NLar
- 'Variegata' (v)	CJun

Sycopsis (*Hamamelidaceae*)

sinensis	CBcs CCCN CExl CJun CKel EBee EHyd EPfP GBin LEdu LMaj MGil MMuc NLar SSta SWvt WPGP

Symphoricarpos (*Caprifoliaceae*)

albus	CAco CBee CMac ELan MSwo NWea SCob WTSh
- 'Constance Spry'	SRms
§ - var. ***laevigatus***	LBuc
× ***chenaultii***	SRms
- 'Hancock'	CMac EBee ELan EPfP MRav MSwo SCob SPer
× ***doorenbosii*** 'Magic Berry'	CBrac EBee MRav NWea SCob SGbt
- 'Mother of Pearl'	EPfP LCro LOPS LPar MRav NWea SCob SPer SRms
- 'White Hedge'	LBuc LPar NWea SGbt SPer SPlb
guatemalensis B&SWJ 1016	WCru
MAGICAL CANDY ('Kolmcan'PBR)	CRos EHyd ELan LRHS LSRN NEoE NRHS SPoG
MAGICAL GALAXY ('Kolmgala'PBR)	CRos EHyd ELan EPfP LRHS NRHS SPoG
MAGICAL SWEET ('Kolmaswet'PBR)	CRos EHyd LRHS NRHS SPoG
orbiculatus	SLon
- 'Bowles's Golden Variegated'	see *S. orbiculatus* 'Foliis Variegatis'
§ - 'Foliis Variegatis' (v)	CMac CTri MRav
- 'George Gardiner'	CMac
- 'Variegatus'	see *S. orbiculatus* 'Foliis Variegatis'
rivularis	see *S. albus* var. *laevigatus*

Symphyandra see *Campanula*

Symphyotrichum (*Asteraceae*)

§ × ***amethystinum***	MNrw WCot
- 'Freiburg'	ELon EPPr MNrw NDov
'Anja's Choice'	EBee EPPr
'Ann Leys'PBR	EBee MNrw SMad WCot
'Aqua Compact' (Autumn Jewels Series)	CBod EHyd LRHS NRHS SGBe
'Beauté du Nord'	WCot
'Bee Lee Elliott' **new**	SPhx
'Blue Butterfly'	SPhx XLum
'Blütenregen'	MNrw WCot WFar
chilense 'Purple Haze'	EPPr
§ ***ciliolatum***	EBlo LRHS SPhx
'Climax' Vicary Gibbs	MNrw WFar
'Coombe Fishacre' 𝕐H7	CDor EBee ECtt ELan ELon EWTr GQue ILea LEdu LRHS MNrw NDov NLar SPhx SRms SWvt WCAu WCot WHoo WSpi
§ ***cordifolium***	SPhx
- from Piney Fork	EPPr
- 'Aldebaran'	LEdu
- 'Blue Heaven'	MNrw SAko
- 'Chieftain' 𝕐H7	LEdu MHCG SPhx
- 'Elegans'	EBee SDix
- 'Ideal'	ILea NLar SPhx XLum
- 'Silver Spray'	CKno ECtt ELon GMaP ILea XLum
- 'Sweet Lavender' 𝕐H7	EHyd
'Diamond Jubilee'	MAvo
drummondii	SPhx
§ ***dumosum***	CExl
- 'Beryll'	WFar
- 'Biteliness'	NLar
- 'Blue Lapis'	WFar
- 'Early Blue'	ILea
- SAPPHIRE ('Kiesapphire'PBR) (Autumn Jewels Series)	CChe ELon EWTr LRHS LSRN NCou SRkn SWvt XLum
ericoides 'Blue Star' 𝕐H7	CDor CTtf EHyd ELon LRHS NFav NLar NRHS SPer
- 'Blue Wonder'	EAJP ELon XLum
- 'Brimstone' 𝕐H7	MRav
- 'Cinderella'	EBee EHyd ELon NSti
- 'Constance'	MCot
- 'Deep Danziger'	SPhx XLum
- 'Erlkönig'	EBee ELon EPri EShb GQue LEdu NGdn NLar SDix SWvt WCAu WCot
- 'Esther'	ECha ECtt MMrt MNrw XLum
- 'First Snow'	WCot WFar
- 'Golden Spray' 𝕐H7	EBee ECtt ELan ELon EPfP EWes GMaP GQue NLar SPer
- 'Herbstmyrte'	EHyd LRHS NRHS
- 'Monte Cassino'	see *S. pilosum* var. *pringlei* 'Monte Cassino'
- 'Pink Cloud' 𝕐H7	CBod ECtt EHyd ELan ELon EPfP EPri EShb GQue LEdu LRHS MBel NLar NRHS NWad SAko SDix SHar SPer SPhx WCAu WMal WTre WWtn XLum
- var. ***prostratum***	EPot MRav SAko XSen
- - 'Snow Flurry' 𝕐H7	CMea CSpe ECha ECtt ELon EShb GBin GQue LEdu LPla MAvo MNrw NLar SAko SMrm SPhx SWvt WCot WHoo WPGP XLum
- 'Rosy Veil'	NBir NGdn
- 'Schneegitter'	EHyd SAko SPhx XLum XSen
- 'Schneetanne'	SAko
- 'Vimmer's Delight'	ECtt LPla WCot WFar
- 'White Heather'	ECtt NLar
- 'Yvette Richardson'	ECtt SMHy
'Ethereal'	WHoo
§ ***falcatum***	WCot
- var. ***commutatum***	WCot XLum
foliaceum from Montana	EPPr
- var. ***parryi***	ECha
'Foxbrook Fairy' (*ericoides*)	MAvo
GRANAT ('Kiastgranat') (Autumn Jewels Series)	SGBe
§ ***greatae***	EBee
'Herfstweelde'	LEdu MNrw SPhx
'Hill Close Blue'	MAvo MHCG
§ ***laeve***	CDor LEdu NLar SPhx
- 'Anneke Van der Jeugd'	MNrw WFar
§ - 'Arcturus'	CDor CElw LEdu MAvo MBel MNrw NBir SDix WCot WFar XLum
- 'Black Ice' **new**	MAvo
§ - 'Calliope'	CElw CKno CMea EBee ECtt EShb GBin GMaP ILea LEdu MCot MHol MMuc MNrw MSpe NBid NLar NWsh SBut SEND SMad SPhx SWvt WBor WFar WKif WPGP WSpi WWtn
- 'Cally Compact'	GQue MHol NLar WFar
- 'Climax'	CElw EBee ELan MMuc MRav NBid NSti SDix SEND WBrk XLum
- var. ***geyeri***	MNrw
- 'Glow in the Dark'	ECha EPPr LEdu MAvo MSpe NLar WBrk WCot WHoo WMal
- 'Jane Ward'	MNrw
- 'Les Moutiers'	CDor CMea CTtf EPPr LEdu MAvo MNrw SDix WBrk WFar WMal
- 'Nightshade'	EPPr MAvo MNrw WFar
- 'Orpheus'	ECha GBin LEdu MAvo MNrw WBrk WFar WMal
- 'Sharon' **new**	MNrw
- 'Vesta'	ECtt
§ - 'White Climax'	CDor MNrw WCot

- white-flowered WBrk
lanceolatum 'Edwin Beckett' MNrw SWvt WFar
§ ***lateriflorum*** SWvt
- 'Bleke Bet' WCot WFar
- 'Chloe' CDor MNrw NLar SPhx WCot WFar
- var. ***horizontale*** ♀H7 CBod CRos EBee ECha ECtt ELan ELon EPPr EPfP GKev GQue LRHS LShi MRav NBro NGdn NRHS NWad SCob SDix SGbt SPer SPlb SRms SWvt WCAu WSpi WWtn
- 'Lady in Black' CBcs CMea CSpe EAJP ECtt EHyd ELan ELon EPfP EWoo GMaP ILea LEdu LPot LRHS MNrw MRav NBir NLar NRHS NSti NWsh SCob SPhx SRms SSut SWvt WFar WWtn XLum
- 'Lovely' WCot
- 'Prince' CDor CMac CSBt ECha ECtt ELan ELon EPfP EWes EWoo GMaP LRHS MHer MNrw MRav NBir NGdn NRHS NSti NWsh SMad SPeP SPoG SRms WCAu WFar WSpi
'Little Carlow' (*cordifolium* hybrid) ♀H7 Widely available
'Little Dorrit' (*cordifolium* hybrid) ECtt NWsh
(Newstars Series) 'Newstars Fantasy' MAvo
- 'Newstars Glory' WFar
'Nicholas' ECtt MACG WCot WFar
'Nineteen' MAvo
'Noreen' ECha MAvo MHCG
novae-angliae 'Abendsonne' SAko
- 'Alex Deamon' ELon WBrk
- 'Anabelle de Chazal' ECtt ELon WBrk WFar XLum
- 'Andenken an Alma Pötschke' Widely available
- 'Andenken an Paul Gerber' ♀H7 ECtt EHyd ELon EPfP IPot LRHS MAvo MNrw NLar NRHS SRGP XLum
- 'Augusta' ELon MACG NLar SPhx WBrk
- AUTUMN SNOW see *S. novae-angliae* 'Herbstschnee'
- 'Badsey Pink' ♀H7 WCot
- 'Barr's Blue' CMac EBee ECtt EHyd ELan ELon EPfP IPot LRHS MAvo MMuc NLar NRHS NWsh SCob SEND SPer SRms WBrk WCAu WSFF XLum
- 'Barr's Pink' CMac EBee ECtt EHyd ELan ELon EPfP LRHS MAvo MPie NRHS SRms WBrk WFar WSFF
- 'Barr's Purple' ♀H7 ECtt WBrk WCFE
- 'Barr's Violet' CDow ECtt MACG MAvo NSti SRms WBrk WCot WFar WHal
- 'Betel Nut' MAvo
- 'Bishop Colenso' EPPr LPla SPhx WBrk
- 'Blackheart' ELon
I - 'Brightness' WCot
- 'Brockamin' EPPr MNrw WBrk
- 'Brunswick' ♀H7 WFar
- 'Christopher Harbutt' LEdu
- 'Colwall Century' ♀H7 WBrk
- 'Colwall Constellation' ELon MAvo WBrk
- 'Colwall Galaxy' WBrk
- 'Colwall Orbit' ECtt ELon WBrk
- 'Connie' MNrw
- 'Constanze' EBee ECtt ELon MAvo
- 'Crimson Beauty' ECtt ELon MAvo MHCG MHer MNrw SAko WBor WBrk WFar
- 'Dapper Tapper' ECtt ELon MAvo WCot
- 'Dark Desire' MNrw
- 'Denise' MAvo
- 'Early Bird' ELon
- 'Evensong' ECtt MPie WBrk
- 'Festival' WBrk
- 'Foxy Emily' ECtt MHCG WBrk
- 'Guido en Gezelle' ELon MAvo MNrw
- 'Harrington's Pink' Widely available
- 'Helen Picton' ♀H7 CDor CDow ECtt ELon EPPr LEdu LRHS MAvo MBrN MHer MPie MSpe NLar NWsh SBea SRms WBrk WFar WHoo
- 'Herbstflieder' EBee
§ - 'Herbstschnee' Widely available
- 'Hoo House' WHoo
- 'Ivy Patterson' **new** MAvo
- 'James' ♀H7 EPPr MAvo
- 'James Ritchie' ♀H7 CDow CTtf ECtt MCot WHoo
- 'John Davis' ♀H7 MNrw
- 'John Dickinson' WBrk
- 'Jon Baker' WBrk
- 'Kate Deamon' ECtt
- 'Kylie' ECtt EPPr LRHS LSRN MNrw MPie SPhx WBrk WCot WFar WMal
- 'Lachsglut' ♀H7 ELon EPPr LEdu NLar SAko WCot
- 'Little Bella' ECtt
- 'Lou Williams' CDow ECtt ELon MNrw NLar WFar
I - 'Lucida' MAvo SPhx SRms
- 'Lye End Beauty' CDor CDow ECtt ELon MAvo MHer MNrw MPie WBrk WCot WFar
- 'Mabelle' NDov
- 'Mandie's Choice' MAvo WCot
- 'Marina Wolkonsky' CDow CMiW ECtt ELon EWes IPot LEdu LPla MACG MNrw NLar SAko SPhx SRms WBrk WCot WFar WKif WMal
- 'Millennium Star' ECtt ELon WBrk
- 'Miss K.E. Mash' ECtt NLar SRGP WBrk WCAu WFar
- 'Mrs S.T. Wright' CTri ECtt EWes LEdu MBrN MNrw NWsh WBrk WFar XLum
- 'Mrs S.W. Stern' WBrk
- 'Nachtauge' SAko
- 'Naomi' MAvo WBrk
- 'Patricia' **new** MAvo
- 'Percy Picton' LEdu
- 'Pink Parfait' ECtt MACG MAvo NGdn SRms WBrk WCot WFar
- 'Pink Victor' CTtf EPPr SRms WFar
- 'Pontis Supreme' MAvo
- 'Pride of Rougham' ECtt EWes MAvo WBrk
- 'Primrose Upward' ECtt MNrw NDov NWsh SPhx WChS WCot
- 'Purple Cloud' ECtt ELon MHer NGdn WBrk WHal
I - 'Purple Dome' Widely available
- 'Quinton Menzies' ♀H7 ELon MAvo NLar
- 'Red Cloud' ECtt ELon LEdu MAvo MHer WBrk
- 'Rosa Sieger' ♀H7 ECtt ELon EPPr GMaP LEdu MAvo MNrw NGdn SBut SEdd WBrk WChS WFar WHoo WMal XLum
- 'Rose Williams' LEdu MAvo MPie WBrk
- 'Röter Stern' ECtt MPie WBrk
- 'Röter Turm' SAko
- 'Rougham Pink' WBrk
- 'Rougham Purple' EWes XLum
- 'Rougham Violet' WBrk
- 'Rubinschatz' EBee ECtt ELon IPot MAvo NLar NWsh SRms XLum
- 'Rudelsburg' CDow ECtt ELon IPot MAvo SHar WBrk
- 'Rudolph' ECtt EWes
- 'Saint Michael's' MAvo WBrk WFar

- 'Sayer's Croft' CDow ECtt ELon MAvo SRms WBrk WCot WFar WHoo
- 'Schneehügel' CDow
- SEPTEMBER RUBY see *S. novae-angliae* 'Septemberrubin'

§ - 'Septemberrubin' CMea ECtt ELan ELon EPPr EPfP GJos GQue IPot LEdu LPla MAvo MBel MMuc MRav NSti NWsh SEND SRms WCAu WFar WSpi WTyc XLum

- 'Treasure' ECtt EHyd ELon EPPr EWes SMrm SPhx SRGP WBrk
- 'Vibrant Dome'PBR EHyd ELon LRHS MNrw NLar NRHS SEdd
- 'Violet Dusk' ELon WBrk
- 'Violet Haze' CMea ELon WBrk
- 'Violetta' ECha ECtt EHyd ELon GMaP ILea IPot LRHS MAvo MNrw MPie NDov NRHS SPhx WBor WBrk WCAu WFar WKif
- 'W. Bowman' ECtt MNrw NLar WBrk
- 'Warm Throng' WCot
- 'Wineflower' MAvo MCot
- 'Wow' ELon SMrm

§ ***novi-belgii*** WHer

- 'Ada Ballard' CFis CMac EBee LRHS LSRN NGrd NRHS WFar
- 'Albanian' SRms
- 'Algar's Pride' WFar
- 'Alice Haslam' CMac EHyd ELan EPfP LRHS MSCN NLar NRHS SRGP SRms WCAu WFar XLum
- 'Angela Peel' EHyd
- 'Anita Webb' CDor CTtf NBir
- 'Anneke' EGrl NLar
- 'Apollo' EHyd LRHS MSCN NLar NRHS SCob SEdd WFar
- 'Apple Blossom' WFar
- 'Audrey' CDor CMac GMaP LSRN MBNS NGdn SRms WFar
- BAHAMAS ('Dasone') (Island Series) EHyd EPfP LRHS NRHS NWsh SCob SPoG SRms SWvt WCot
- BARBADOS ('Dastwo') (Island Series) CBod EHyd EPfP LRHS NLar NRHS SCob SPoG SWvt WCot WFar
- 'Beechwood Beacon' WFar
- 'Beechwood Challenger' MHCG MNrw MPie NWad
- 'Beechwood Charm' CTtf WFar XLum
- 'Beechwood Rival' CDor CTri
- 'Blauglut' WFar
- 'Blue Baby' CMac MPie
- 'Blue Bouquet' CTri SRms WFar
- 'Blue Gown' GQue
- 'Blue Lagoon' CDor CMea LSRN MACG WBrk WCAu XLum

I - 'Blue Moon' CDor EWTr WFar

- 'Blue Spire' SPhx
- 'Boningale White' MHCG NHol WFar
- 'Brigitte' CDor EWTr NLar
- 'Carnival' CMac ECtt EHyd
- 'Charles Wilson' CFis
- 'Chatterbox' CDor EHyd ELan EPfP LRHS MRav NRHS SRms WFar
- 'Chelwood' WFar
- 'Chequers' CBod MBNS MHer SGbt SRms WFar
- 'Christina' see *S. novi-belgii* 'Kristina'
- 'Cliff Lewis' WFar
- 'Climax Albus' see *S. laeve* 'White Climax'
- 'Coombe Rosemary' NLar WBor
- 'Countess of Dudley' CFis WFar
- 'Crimson Brocade' CDor EHyd ELan EPfP LRHS NLar NRHS SAko SCob SPoG SRms SWvt WFar
- 'Dandy' CMac EHyd ELan EPfP LRHS NBir NGdn NRHS SGbt SRms WFar WGwG
- 'Daniela' SRms WBrk WFar
- 'Davey's True Blue' CTri WFar XLum
- 'Dazzler' CDor WFar
- 'Diana' ECtt
- 'Dietgard' WFar
- 'Dolly' NBir SRms
- 'Dusky Maid' ELon WFar
- 'Elizabeth Hutton' SRGP WFar
- 'Erica' CElw
- 'Eva' ELon SRms
- 'Eventide' CTri LSRN XLum
- 'Faith' WFar
- 'Farncombe Lilac' MAvo
- 'Feckenham Rival' WMal
- 'Fellowship' ♀H6 CDor CTtf EAJP EBee ECtt EHyd ELon EPfP LEdu LRHS MMuc MNrw NLar NRHS SAko SEND SEdd SHar SRms SWvt WCAu WCot WFar XLum
- 'Flamingo' EHyd SRms WCAu
- 'Freda Ballard' ECtt EHyd GMaP LRHS NRHS WFar
- 'Freya' CElw LSRN SRms WSHC
- 'Fuldatal' WFar
- 'Gayborder Blue' WFar
- 'Gayborder Royal' WFar
- 'Grey Lady' WFar
- 'Gulliver' SRms WBrk WFar
- 'Gurney Slade' CDor WFar
- 'Harrison's Blue' CDor
- 'Heinz Richard' CFis ECha MHer NBir NGdn SRms
- 'Helen' ELon
- 'Helen Ballard' NBid SRms WFar
- 'Herbstgruss vom Bresserhof' EHyd LRHS NLar NRHS SAko WFar XSen
- 'Janet McMullen' SHar
- 'Jean' ELon SRms WFar
- 'Jeanette' SRms WFar
- 'Jenny' CBod CSBt ECtt EHyd ELan EPPr EPfP EWoo GMaP IPot LRHS LSRN LShi MRav NBir NGdn NHol NRHS SCob SGbt SMad SPer SRGP SRms SWvt WCAu WFar XLum
- 'Jugendstil' XLum
- 'Kassel' SRms WFar
- 'King of the Belgians' WFar

§ - 'Kristina' CRos ECha EHyd LRHS MNrw MRav NBir NRHS SDix SRGP WFar

- 'Lady Frances' SRms
- 'Lady in Blue' CRos CSBt EAJP ECtt EHyd ELan EPfP EWoo GWyn LEdu LRHS LShi MBNS MGos NGdn NGrd NRHS NWad SGbt SPer SPoG SRms SSut SWvt WCAu WFar WGwG XSen
- 'Lassie' NWsh SRms WFar
- 'Lawrence Chiswell' WFar
- 'Lisa Dawn' WFar
- 'Lisette' LEdu
- 'Little Boy Blue' CDor SRms XLum
- 'Little Man in Blue' CDor
- 'Little Ness' MNrw WFar WMal
- 'Little Pink Beauty' CCBP CRos ECtt EGrl EHyd ELan EPfP LRHS MBNS NGdn NGrd NHol NRHS NWad SPer SRGP SRms WCAu WFar
- 'Little Pink Lady' SRms WFar
- 'Little Pink Pyramid' SRms
- 'Madge Cato' SRms
- 'Marie Ann Neil' SRms

	- 'Marie Ballard'	CBod CDor CMac CRos CSBt CTtf EHyd GMaP GQue LEdu LRHS MHer MPie MRav NGdn NHol NLar NPer NRHS SBea SCob SGbt SPer SRms SWvt WCAu WFar XLum
	- 'Marie-Theres'	SAko
	- 'Marjorie'	LSRN XLum
	- 'Mauve Magic'	SRms WFar
	- 'Mistress Quickly'	ECtt WFar
	- 'Mittelmeer'	EHyd XLum
	- 'Mount Everest'	CDor
	- 'Nachtlicht'	SAko
	- 'Neron'	MNrw MPie NDov SHar SPhx WFar WMal
	- 'Norman's Jubilee'	EHyd EPfP NBir NRHS WFar
	- 'Pamela'	CTtf
	- 'Patricia Ballard' (d)	CBcs CBod CDor CMac CRos CSBt EBee EBou EHyd ELan EPfP GMaP LCro LOPS LRHS MHer NBir NGrd NLar NPer NRHS NWad SPer WCAu WFar
	- 'Percy Thrower'	CDor
	- 'Peter Chiswell'	SRms
	- 'Peter Harrison'	EHyd GMaP LRHS NBir NRHS XLum
	- 'Peter Pan'	SCob
	- 'Pink Buttons'	NDov
	- 'Pink Lace'	MBNS
	- 'Porzellan'	CBod CElw CMea ECtt LEdu MAvo MBNS MNrw NGdn NGrd NLar WCot WFar WHal WPGP
	- 'Pride of Colwall'	SRms
	- 'Priory Blush'	CDor SRms
	- 'Professor Anton Kippenberg'	EHyd ELan EPfP GMaP LRHS MNrw MRav NDov NGrd NLar NRHS SAko SPer SRms SWvt WFar XLum
	- 'Purple Dome'	CSBt CTtf ECha EGrl ELan LEdu LOPS LSRN MHer SBut SDix SHar SRkn WChS WFar
	- 'Purple Dream'	WFar
	- 'Ralph Picton'	WFar
	- 'Red Star'	SPhx
	- 'Red Sunset'	SRms
	- 'Rembrandt'	MArl NGdn
	- 'Remembrance'	CDor SRms WFar
	- 'Richness'	CTtf
	- 'Rose Bonnet'	EHyd SPlb WFar
	- 'Rosebud'	CDor
	- 'Rosenquartz'	NLar WFar
	- 'Rosenwichtel'	CDor SRms
	- 'Royal Ruby'	CBod CFis EBee ECtt EHyd IPot NLar SRms XLum
	- 'Rozika'	MNrw
	- 'Rufus'	NWsh WFar
	- 'Sam Banham'	MNrw WFar
	- SAMOA ('Dasthree') (Island Series)	EHyd EPfP LRHS LSou NLar NRHS SPoG SRms WCot
	- 'Sandford White Swan'	MHer WFar
	- 'Sarah Ballard'	NLar WFar
§	- 'Schneekissen'	ECtt EHyd ELan EPfP GKev GMaP LRHS LShi MBNS MHer NRHS SRms SWvt WFar XLum
	- 'Schneezicklein'	GBin GWyn
	- 'Schöne von Dietlikon'	CKno CSpe WFar XLum
	- 'Schoolgirl'	CTtf
	- 'Sheena'	WFar
	- SNOW CUSHION	see *S. novi-belgii* 'Schneekissen'
	- 'Snowdrift'	WGwG
	- 'Snowsprite'	CBod CSBt EHyd ELan EShb LRHS NLar NRHS SGbt SRms XLum
	- 'Sonata'	GMaP
	- STARLETTA BLUE ('Asflo Blue') **new**	NBir
	- 'Starlight'	CDor ECtt NLar WCAu WFar
	- 'Terry's Pride'	SRms WFar
	- 'The Archbishop'	ECtt
	- 'Thundercloud'	CDor
	- 'Timsbury'	CDor CTtf SRms
	- TONGA ('Dasfour') (Island Series)	EHyd EPfP LRHS NLar NRHS NWsh SCob SPoG SRms SWvt
	- 'Trudi Ann'	NBir
	- 'Vignem'	NSti
	- 'Waterperry'	WBrk
	- 'White Ladies'	CBcs CRos EHyd GMaP LCro LOPS LRHS MMuc MNrw NLar NRHS SCob WCAu XLum
	- 'White Swan'	ECtt
	- 'Winston S. Churchill'	CDor EAJP EHyd ELan EPfP GMaP LEdu LRHS MBel MHer MPie NRHS SPer SPlb SPoG SRGP WCAu WTor
	- 'Zwergenhimmel'	SAko
§	***oblongifolium***	EBlo LRHS NWsh XSen
§	- 'Fanny's'	ECtt NWad
	- 'October Skies'	EBee EWes MNrw SHar
	'Ochtendgloren' (*pilosum* var. *inglei* hybrid) ♀^{H4}	CDor CMea CTtf EBee ECtt ELon EPPr EWes MACG MHol MNrw NLar WHal WHoo WMal
§	'Oktoberlicht'	EHyd EPPr MNrw WHoo
§	***oolentangiense***	SPhx
	'Orchidee'	CMea ECtt EPri EShb EWes MAvo
	'Photograph' ♀^{H7}	CTtf ECtt EHyd EWes LEdu LRHS MPie MRav NRHS WPGP
§	***pilosum***	WCot WFar
§	- var. ***pringlei*** ♀^{H7}	ECha EWes NWad SMad
§	- - 'Monte Cassino'	CSBt EPfP GQue LPot LRHS MBNS NBro SPer SPhx SRms WCAu WMal WSpi XLum
	- - 'October Glory'	ECtt WFar
	'Pink Star'	CRos ECtt EHyd ELon GMaP LEdu LRHS MNrw MRav NRHS NSti SPhx WCAu WFar XLum
	'Pinwheel'	LEdu WCot
	'Pixie Dark Eye' (*ericoides* hybrid)	EBee ECtt SDix SRms WCot
	'Pixie Red Eye' (*ericoides* hybrid)	EBee ELon LEdu WCot WFar
	'Prairie Purple'	CDor ECha ECtt ELon SMHy SPhx WCot WFar WHoo WMal
	'Prairie Sky' **new**	SSal
	'Primrose Path'	CDor ECha ECtt LEdu MNrw SPhx SSal WBrk WCot WFar
§	***puniceum***	MMuc XLum
	'Purple Diamond' (Autumn Jewels Series)	SGBe WFar
	'Ringdove' (*ericoides* hybrid) ♀^{H7}	MAvo NSti SWvt WCot
	'Rose Crystal' (Autumn Jewels Series)	SGBe
	'Rose Glow'	EPPr
	'Rose Quartz' (Autumn Jewels Series)	NCou SGBe
	'Rose Queen'	MACG MMrt MNrw MPie NWsh SRms
	'Sea Spray'	WCot
§	***sericeum***	SPhx
	shortii	SPhx
	'Soft Lass'	WCot
	'Star of Chesters'	MAvo
	'Sunhelene'	EBee ECtt ELon WCot
	SUNPLUM ('Danasplum'PBR)	CTtf
	'Superstar'	MNrw SPhx WHoo WMal
§	***tradescantii***	MBNS NSti SMad WBrk WCot

'Treffpunkt' GBin MAvo MNrw SAko
turbinellum misapplied ♀H6 CFis ELon EPfP EWes LRHS MMuc NGdn SMHy SPhx SRkn SWvt
§ ***turbinellum*** Lindl. EBee EPfP EWTr LEdu NQui SSut WCot WPGP
- 'El Fin' MNrw
- hybrid CTtf GAbr SDix WSpi
'Vasterival' EWoo LEdu MHer MPie NDov SHar WCAu XLum
'Wood's Blue' EHyd LRHS NRHS
'Wood's Pink' CBod EHyd LRHS NRHS WCAu
'Wood's Purple' EHyd

Symphytum (*Boraginaceae*)

'Angela Whinfield' CMea LPla WMal
asperum CCBP ECha EPPr MRav NLar
* ***azureum*** CWCL EBee LPla MBel MNrw NChi WCAu
'Belsay Gold' NBid NBir SDix
'Bocking' see *S.* × *uplandicum* 'Bocking 4', 'Bocking 14'
bulbosum PAB 4886 LEdu
caucasicum ECha LEdu NLar NSti SPer SRms WWtn XLum
- 'Norwich Sky' CExl
cordatum EPPr LEdu MNrw WPGP
§ 'Goldsmith' (v) CMea EBee ECha ELan EPfP EWoo GKev LRHS MBriF MCot MHol NBid NBir NLar NPer SCob SGbt SPer SPoG WCAu WFar WWtn
grandiflorum CMac CTri GKev GPoy LEdu
- 'Sky-blue-pink' GJos
'Hidcote Blue' CBod CRos CTri ECha ECtt EHyd EMor EPPr EPfP LRHS MMuc NBro NRHS SEND SPer SPoG SRms WCav WGwG WPnP WWtn
§ 'Hidcote Pink' CBod CRos ECha ECtt EHyd EPPr LRHS LShi MMuc MNrw NBir NRHS NSti SEND SPer SRms WCAu WCav WFar WGwG WPnP WWtn XLum
'Hidcote Variegated' (v) CMac SRms
ibericum CAgr CBod CCBP ECha EGrI EHyd EMor GKev GMaP GPoy LRHS LShi MMuc NRHS NSti SEND SRms WGwG WWtn
- 'All Gold' EBee ECha EHyd LRHS LShi MNrw NRHS WFar
- 'Blaueglocken' ECha
- 'Gold in Spring' WFar
- 'Jubilee' see *S.* 'Goldsmith'
- 'Lilacinum' WHer
- 'Variegatum' see *S.* 'Goldsmith'
- 'Wisley Blue' CAgr CBcs CBod LRHS SCob WFar
'Lambrook Sunrise' CFis CMac NBro SRms WCot
'Langthorns Pink' EBee
officinale CAgr CHab EBee ENfk GJos GPoy GQue MHer MNHC NPer SPer SPoG SRms WCAu WHer WWild XAbr XLum
- var. ***ochroleucum*** WHer
orientale CCBP EBee EPPr GJos MBel MNrw
peregrinum see *S.* × *uplandicum*
'Romanian Red' SDix
'Roseum' see *S.* 'Hidcote Pink'
'Rubrum' CBod CTtf EHyd ELan EPfP EWes LRHS NBro NLar NRHS SPer WBor WCAu WWtn XLum
tuberosum CFis EPPr GPoy LEdu LPla MHer MMuc NGrd NWad WBor WCot WFar WHer WHil XAbr
§ × ***uplandicum*** CLau CTri GPoy MMuc SVic
- 'Axminster Gold' (v) CMea WCot
§ - 'Bocking 4' **new** CAgr
§ - 'Bocking 14' CAgr CBod CHby EOHP GAbr LCro LEdu LOPS MNHC NGrd SRms WSFF XLum
- 'Droitwich' (v) WCot
- 'Moorland Heather' CDor CSpe CTtf EAJP ECha LEdu LPla LRHS MBriF MHer MMrt MNrw MPie SPhx WMal WWFP
- 'Padworth Purple' **new** LEdu
- purple-flowered MMuc
- 'Variegatum' (v) CTtf ECtt EHyd ELan EWes LRHS NBir NGdn WAvo WSpi

Synadenium (*Euphorbiaceae*)

grantii 'Rubrum' EShb

Syncarpha (*Asteraceae*)

vestita SPlb

Syncolostemon (*Lamiaceae*)

'Candy Kisses' CBct WCot

Syneilesis (*Asteraceae*)

aconitifolia ESwi GEdr WCot WHal
- B&SWJ 879 LEdu WCru
palmata GEdr
- B&SWJ 14671 WCru
subglabrata ESwi
- B&SWJ 298 WCru
- NMWJ 14528 WCru
aff. ***tagawae*** B&SWJ 11191 WCot

Syngonium (*Araceae*)

'Pixie' CDoC

Synnotia see *Sparaxis*

Synthyris (*Plantaginaceae*)

missurica EBee GKev WFar
subsp. ***missurica***
- subsp. ***stellata*** CBod CMea EBee ECtt EHyd EPfP EPri EWes GAbr GBin GMaP LEdu LRHS MAvo MMrt MPie NBir NHpl NRHS NSti WHal WSHC

Synurus (*Asteraceae*)

excelsus **new** GGro

Syringa ✿ (*Oleaceae*)

afghanica misapplied see *S. protolaciniata*
BLOOMERANG DARK PURPLE ('Smsjbp7'PBR) CRos CWGN LCro LOPS LPar LSRN MAsh NLar SGol SPoG WSpi
BLOOMERANG PINK PERFUME see *S.* 'Pink Perfume'
BLOOMERANG PURPLE ('Penda') CRos LRHS NRHS
× ***chinensis*** EPfP
- 'Bicolor' WGob
- 'Saugeana' MBlu MMuc SPer XPic
× ***diversifolia*** MBlu
emodi 'Aurea' EPfP
- 'Aureovariegata' see *S. emodi* 'Variegata'
- 'Elegantissima' (v) CBcs CEnd CMac EBee ELan SPoG
§ - 'Variegata' (v) EHyd EMil EPfP LRHS NLar
× ***hyacinthiflora*** 'Anabel' (d) XPic
- 'Angel White' **new** XPic
- 'Buffon' **new** XPic
- 'California Rose' **new** XPic
- 'Clarke's Giant' SGol
- 'Dark Night' WGob XPic

- 'Esther Staley' ♀H6	EPfP LPar MRav WGob XPic
- 'Excel'	XPic
- 'Lavender Lady'	XPic
- MADAME NADJA N (d) new	XPic
- 'Maiden's Blush' ♀H6	EPfP SGol WGob XPic
§ - 'Mount Baker' new	XPic
- 'Pocahontas' ♀H6	WGob XPic
- SCHNEEWEISSCHEN	see *S.* × *hyacinthiflora* 'Mount Baker'
- 'Sweetheart' (d)	NOra WMat
JOSÉE ('Morjos 060f')	ELan ELon EPfP MAsh NLar SGol SWvt WFar WGob WLov XPic
× ***josiflexa***	CExl
- 'Agnes Smith'	CMac EHed LPar NLar SCob WSpi
- 'Bellicent' ♀H6	CBod CEnd CKel CMac CRos EHyd ELan EPfP LRHS MAsh MMuc MRav NLar NRHS SMad SNig SPer SPoG SRms SWvt WAvo WCFE WFar WLov WSpi
- 'James MacFarlane'	XPic
- 'Lynette'	XPic
- 'Redwine'	LRHS
§ - 'Royalty'	SCob XPic
josikaea	CAco CMCN CSBt NLar SPer WMat
- 'Oden'	WMat
komarowii	ESwi GGGa MGil
§ - subsp. ***reflexa***	EPfP MBlu NLar SLon SMad WPGP
§ × ***laciniata*** Mill.	CKel CTsd EBee EHed EHyd ELan EPfP LRHS MRav SPer WAvo WCFE WLov WPGP
'Lark Song'	NLar
meyeri	SVen
- (Flowerfesta Series) FLOWERFESTA PINK ('Anny200817'PBR)	LCro LOPS
- - FLOWERFESTA PURPLE ('Anny200809'PBR)	LCro LOPS
- - FLOWERFESTA WHITE ('Anny200810'PBR)	LCro LOPS
§ - 'Palibin' ♀H5	Widely available
microphylla	see *S. pubescens* subsp. *microphylla*
'Minuet'	CBcs LBuc SGol
'Miss Canada'	NLar SCob XPic
MISS JAPAN	EBee
oblata	CMCN
palibiniana misapplied	see *S. meyeri* 'Palibin'
patula misapplied	see *S. meyeri* 'Palibin'
patula (Palib.) Nakai	see *S. pubescens* subsp. *patula*
pekinensis	see *S. reticulata* subsp. *pekinensis*
× ***persica*** ♀H6	CExl CTri EPfP MGos MRav NLar NWea SLon SPer WFar WGob
- 'Alba' ♀H6	MRav WAvo WFar WGob
- var. ***laciniata***	see *S.* × *laciniata* Mill.
§ 'Pink Perfume'PBR	CRos EHyd ELon EPfP LCro LOPS LPar LRHS LSRN MAsh MTrO NRHS SGol SPoG WSpi XPic
pinnatifolia	CBcs CKel ELan GBin LRHS NLar SAko WCFE WPGP
× ***prestoniae*** 'Desdemona'	EHyd MMuc
- 'Elinor' ♀H6	CKel ELan EPfP LRHS MRav
- 'Hiawatha'	XPic
- 'Nocturne'	WFar
- 'Royalty'	see *S.* × *josiflexa* 'Royalty'
§ ***protolaciniata***	EShb IDee SGsty
pubescens subsp. ***julianae*** 'George Eastman'	MGos MRav
§ - subsp. ***microphylla***	CMea
- - 'Superba' ♀H6	Widely available
§ - subsp. ***patula***	CMac EHyd EPfP LRHS MMuc MRav NRHS SVen
- - 'Miss Kim' ♀H6	CBod CChe CKel CMCN CMac CSBt CTri EBee EHed ELan ELon EPfP EWTr IArd LSRN MAsh MGos MRav MSwo NHol NLar NOrn SCoo SNig SPoG SRkn SSta WFar WGob WLov
'Red Pixie'	CBod CDoC CKel CMac CRos EBee EHyd EMil EPfP LCro LOPS LRHS MAsh MGos NOrn NRHS SCoo SGsty SNig SRkn WGob XPic
reflexa	see *S. komarowii* subsp. *reflexa*
reticulata	CMCN EWTr MBlu
- 'Ivory Silk'	EBtc WMat WPGP
§ - subsp. ***pekinensis***	CMCN
- - 'Yellow Fragrance'	NLar
SUGAR PLUM FAIRY ('Bailsugar') (Fairytale Series)	NLar
× ***swegiflexa***	CExl XPic
tomentella	EBee SRms WCFE WPGP
- subsp. ***sweginzowii***	CBcs CWCL EHed EShb EWTr GKin NLar SNig SPer WBor WSpi
- - 'Superba'	SGol
- subsp. ***yunnanensis***	CExl GKev SBrt
velutina Kom.	see *S. pubescens* subsp. *patula*
villosa	SPlb
I - 'Aurea' new	LRHS
vulgaris	CAco EPfP LPar NWea
- 'Addie Tischler' (d) new	XPic
- var. ***alba***	LPar
- 'Alesha' new	XPic
- 'Amethyst'	CBod EPfP XPic
- 'Ametist 2' new	XPic
- 'Ami Schott' (d) new	XPic
§ - 'Andenken an Ludwig Späth' ♀H6	Widely available
- 'Anne Shiach' new	XPic
- 'Arthur William Paul' (d)	XPic
- 'Aucubifolia' (d/v)	WGob XPic
- 'Aurea'	MRav WAvo WFar
- 'Bad Frankenhausen' new	XPic
- BEAUTY OF MOSCOW	see *S. vulgaris* 'Krasavitsa Moskvy'
- 'Belle de Nancy' (d)	CBod CCCN CDoC ELan ELon GAbr IPap LPar MAsh MMuc MRav NOrn SEND SGol SGsty SWvt WGob XPic
- BLUE SKIES ('Monore') new	XPic
- 'Bogdan Khmelnitsckii' (d) new	XPic
- 'Boule Azurée' new	XPic
- 'Capitaine Perrault' (d) new	XPic
- CARPE DIEM	see *S. vulgaris* 'Evert de Gier'
- 'Charles Joly' (d) ♀H6	Widely available
- 'Comtesse d'Harcourt'	EPfP SPer WGob XPic
- 'Congo'	WGob XPic
- 'Dappled Dawn' (v)	MMrt
- 'Dark Koster'	WGob XPic
- 'Decaisne'	XPic
- DENTELLE D'ANJOU ('Mindent')	CDoC
- 'Diplomate' new	XPic
- 'Drushba' new	XPic
- 'Dwight D. Eisenhower'	WGob XPic
- 'Edmond Boissier' new	XPic
- 'Edward J. Gardner' (d) ♀H6	SEND XPic
- 'Émile Lemoine' (d) new	XPic
- 'Erzherzog Johann' new	XPic
- 'Etna'	WGob
- 'Étoile de Mai' (d) new	XPic
§ - 'Evert de Gier'PBR	CBcs CBod WSpi XPic
- 'Fałe Bałtyku' (d) new	XPic
- 'Firmament' ♀H6	MRav SEND SPer WGob WSpi XPic
- FRAU HOLLE new	LRHS

- 'G. J. Baardse'	EWTr XPic
- 'Galina Ulanova' **new**	XPic
- 'Gastello' **new**	XPic
- 'Général Pershing' Lemoine, 1924 (d)	LRHS WSpi XPic
- 'Gilbert' **new**	XPic
- 'Hope'	see *S. vulgaris* 'Nadezhda'
- 'Hugo de Vries'	XPic
- 'Indiya' **new**	XPic
- 'Jan van Tol' **new**	XPic
- 'Jeanne d'Arc' (d) **new**	XPic
- 'Katherine Havemeyer' (d) ♀H6	Widely available
- 'Königin Luise' **new**	XPic
§ - 'Krasavitsa Moskvy' (d) ♀H6	CCVT CDoC CTri CWCL ELon EPfP EWes LRHS MAsh MRav MTrO NLar NOra SGol WMat WSpi XPic
- 'Krasnaya Moskva' **new**	XPic
- 'La Tour d'Auvergne'	XPic
- 'Le Nôtre' (d) **new**	XPic
- 'Lebedushka' **new**	XPic
- 'Leonid Leonov' **new**	XPic
- 'Lila Wonder'PBR	CBod EPfP GAbr SPoG WGob XPic
- 'Louis van Houtte' **new**	XPic
- 'Lucie Baltet'	XPic
- 'Madame Antoine Buchner' (d)	LPar WSpi XPic
- 'Madame F. Morel' **new**	XPic
- 'Madame Felix' **new**	XPic
- 'Madame Florent Stepman'	CBod CMac CWCL LRHS WFar WGob WSpi XPic
- 'Madame Lemoine' (d) ♀H6	Widely available
- 'Marie Legraye' **new**	XPic
- 'Marshal Vasilevskii' (d) **new**	XPic
- 'Mechta' **new**	XPic
- 'Michel Buchner' (d)	CBcs CDoC CLnd ELan LMaj LRHS MBlu MGos NLar NOra SCob SCoo SPer WMat XPic
- 'Monique Lemoine' (d) **new**	XPic
- 'Montaigne' (d) **new**	XPic
- 'Mrs Edward Harding' (d) ♀H6	EPfP LRHS MRav NLar NWea WGob
- 'Mulatka' **new**	XPic
§ - 'Nadezhda' (d)	CBod EBee GAbr LPar LRHS WGob XPic
- 'Nebo Moskvy' (d) **new**	XPic
- 'Nevesta' **new**	XPic
- 'Olimpiada Kolesnikova' (d) **new**	XPic
- 'Olivier de Serres' (d)	XPic
- 'Pamyat' o Kolesnikove' (d) **new**	XPic
- 'Pat Pesata'	WGob
- 'Paul Thirion' (d)	CBod LRHS WGob XPic
- 'Pavlinka' (d)	XPic
- 'Perle von Stuttgart' **new**	LRHS XPic
- 'Polina Osipenko' (d) **new**	XPic
- 'Président Grévy' (d)	CBar CWCL EPfP MAsh SGol SPer SPoG XPic
- 'President Lincoln'	WGob XPic
- 'Président Poincaré' (d)	WGob
- 'Primrose' ♀H6	CBcs CCCN CMac EBee ELan EPfP IPap LRHS MAsh MGos MTrO NOra NOrn SCob SCoo SEND SGol SPer SPoG WGob WMat WSpi XPic
- 'Prince Wolkonsky' (d)	EBee ELan EPfP LRHS LSRN MAsh MGos MTrO SGsty SPer WFar WGob XPic
- 'Princesse Sturdza'	EPfP NOra XPic
- 'Professor Edmund Jankowski' **new**	XPic
- 'Professor Hoser'	WGob XPic
- 'Rochester'	XPic
- ROSE DE MOSCOU ('Minkarl'PBR)	SCob
- 'Ruhm von Horstenstein'	LPar XPic
- 'Rus' **new**	XPic
§ - 'Rustica' (d) **new**	XPic
- 'Saint Margaret'	WGob XPic
- 'Sarah Sands'	LRHS WGob XPic
- SCHNEEKÖNIGEN	see *S. vulgaris* 'Rustica'
- 'Sensation' ♀H6	Widely available
- 'Souvenir d'Alice Harding' (d) ♀H6	XPic
- 'Souvenir de Louis Spaeth'	see *S. vulgaris* 'Andenken an Ludwig Späth'
- 'Sovetskaya Arktika' (d) **new**	XPic
- 'Stefan Makowiecki' **new**	XPic
- 'Sumerki' **new**	XPic
- 'Svityazanka' **new**	XPic
- 'Tadeusz Kościuszko' (d) **new**	XPic
- 'Taras Bul'ba' (d) **new**	XPic
- variegated (v)	EWes
- variegated double (d/v)	WCot
- 'Vesper'	IArd XPic
- 'Victor Lemoine' (d)	WGob XPic
- 'Viviand-Morel' (d)	CMac
- 'Wedgewood Blue'	WGob XPic
- 'William Robinson' (d)	WGob
- 'Zarya Kommunizma' **new**	XPic
- 'Zashchitnikam Bresta' (d) **new**	XPic
- 'Zhemchuzhina' (d) **new**	XPic
- 'Znamya Lenina'	WSpi XPic
wolfii	EBtc GKev NLar

Syzygium (*Myrtaceae*)

paniculatum	CExl
zeylanicum	EShb

T

Tabernaemontana (*Apocynaceae*)

coronaria	see *T. divaricata*
§ ***divaricata***	CCCN WFib

Tacca (*Taccaceae*)

chantrieri	CCCN

Taccarum (*Araceae*)

weddellianum	WCot

Tacitus see *Graptopetalum*

Taenidia (*Apiaceae*)

integerrima	SPhx

Tagetes (*Asteraceae*)

'Cinnabar'	CSpe GBin
erecta	SCob SVic
- INCA I ORANGE (Inca I Series) ♀H2	LCro LOPS
- 'Taishan'	MBros
- 'Vanilla'	MBros
lemmonii	SDix

- 'Martin's Mutant'	SDix WCot
'Lemon Gem'	MBros
lucida	CSpe ENfk LEdu MHer SRms WJek
patula	SCob SVic
- 'Alumia Vanilla Cream' (Alumia Series)	CSpe
- Bonanza Series (d) ♀H2	LCro LOPS MBros
- - BONANZA BEE ('Pas2258') (d)	MBros
- - 'Bonanza Bolero' (d)	MBros
- - BONANZA ORANGE ('Pas91617') (d)	MBros
- - BONANZA YELLOW ('Pas2276') (d)	MBros
- 'Dainty Marietta' ♀H2	LCro LOPS
- DWARF DOUBLE MIXED (d)	LCro LOPS
- 'Fireball' (d) ♀H2	CSpe
- FRENCH FANCY (mixed) (d)	LCro LOPS
- 'Strawberry Blonde' (d)	MBros
tenuifolia 'Golden Gem'	LCro LOPS MBros
zypaquirensis B&SWJ 14840	WCru

Taiwania (*Cupressaceae*)

cryptomerioides	CAco IArd IDee SLim WPGP

Talbotia (*Velloziaceae*)

§ ***elegans***	SBrt

tamarillo see *Solanum betaceum*

tamarind see *Tamarindus indica*

Tamarindus (*Fabaceae*)

indica (F)	SPlb

Tamarix (*Tamaricaceae*)

gallica	NWea SArc SWeb
hampeana	SEND
'Hulsdonk White'^PBR	CBcs CCCN SPer
§ ***parviflora*** ♀H5	CMac EHyd EPfP LPar LRHS NRHS
pentandra	see *T. ramosissima*, *T. ramosissima* 'Rosea'
ramosissima	CBod CCCN CTri EBee EPfP LPar MAsh SGsty SLon SRms WSMil
- 'Pink Cascade' ♀H5	CBcs CBod CCCN CMac EBee ELan EPfP LCro LOPS MBlu MGos MRav SCob SEdd SGbt SNig SPer SPoG SWvt
§ - 'Rosea'	CBcs
§ - 'Rubra'	CBod EPfP LPar SCob SEND SEdd SPer
- 'Summer Glow'	see *T. ramosissima* 'Rubra'
tetrandra ♀H5	Widely available
- var. ***purpurea***	see *T. parviflora*

Tanacetum ✿ (*Asteraceae*)

§ ***argenteum***	MRav
- subsp. ***canum***	SLon
aureum	CKel
§ ***balsamita***	CBod CHby EBee EBou ENfk EPPr GJos GPoy MHer MMuc MNHC NGrd SEND SRms WHer WJek WSFF XAbr XLum
§ - subsp. ***balsamita***	GPoy GQue WJek
§ - subsp. ***balsamitoides***	CBod MHer SRms
- var. ***tanacetoides***	see *T. balsamita* subsp. *balsamita*
- ***tomentosum***	see *T. balsamita* subsp. *balsamitoides*
§ ***cinerariifolium***	CBod GPoy MNHC
§ ***coccineum***	SVic WFar
- 'Alfred'	MNrw
- 'Bees' Pink Delight'	LRHS
- 'Duro'	EHyd LRHS NRHS
- 'Eileen May Robinson'	LRHS SGbt WGwG
- 'H.M. Pike'	EBee
- 'Laureen' **new**	WNPC
- 'Laurin'	EBlo ECtt EHyd LRHS MHol NRHS
- Robinson's crimson-flowered	EHyd LRHS NRHS
- - giant-flowered	EHyd LRHS NRHS SRms
- - pink-flowered	CBod EAJP EBee EBou EHyd ELan EPfP GMaP LRHS MHol SCob XLum
- - red-flowered	CBod CSBt EAJP EBou EHyd ELan EPfP GMaP GWyn LRHS MHol SCob SPlb SVic SWvt XLum
- - rose-flowered	CSBt EWTr
- 'Snow Cloud'	CBod ECtt LRHS
- 'Vanessa'	MNrw
§ ***corymbosum***	EBee EHyd NLar WCot
- 'Bukke'	LEdu
- 'Festtafel'	LEdu LPla
densum	WCFE
- subsp. ***amani***	CKel ECha EHyd GMaP SEND XSen
§ ***haradjanii***	EBou SGro WKif
macrophyllum misapplied	see *Achillea grandifolia* Friv.
§ ***macrophyllum*** (Waldst. & Kit.) Sch.Bip.	EBee ECtt EPPr GWyn SPhx WBor
- 'Cream Klenza'	WCot
niveum	ECha SDix WCot XSen
- 'Jackpot'	ELan EWes SBls SHar SWvt WHil
§ ***parthenium***	CBod CCBP CHab CHby ENfk GPoy GQue LCro LOPS MHer MNHC NPer SRms SVic WFar WHer XAbr XLum
- 'Aureum'	CBod CTtf EBou ECha ELan EMor ENfk EWes EWhm GPoy MHer MNHC SPer SPlb SRms SWvt WCot WFar WHer WHil XLum
- double white-flowered (d)	CTtf NPer SRms
- 'Golden Ball'	WFar
- 'Golden Moss'	XLum
- 'Magic Lime Green'	MNrw WFar
- 'Malmesbury'	WHer
- 'Plenum' (d)	MNrw
§ - 'Rowallane' (d)	MMuc SEND WCot
- 'Selma Star' (d)	MNrw WFar WHer
- 'Sissinghurst White'	see *T. parthenium* 'Rowallane'
- 'White Bonnet' (d)	WHer
poteriifolium	EBlo EHyd LRHS NRHS
ptarmiciflorum 'Silver Feather'	SRms SVen
RADIANT DEEP PINK ('Tntadp') **new**	MHol WNPC
RADIANT LIGHT PINK ('Tntalp') **new**	WNPC
* ***tommansii***	EHyd
vulgare	CCBP CHab CHby ECha ECtt ENfk GBin GJos GPoy GQue GWyn IRos LCro LOPS MACG MHer MNHC NGrd NMir SRms SVic WFar WSFF XAbr XSen
- 'All Gold'	MBriF SMad SRms
- var. ***crispum***	EBee ENfk MRav SMad SRms WFar
- 'Gold Sticks'	CBod
- 'Golden Fleece'	CSpe ECtt EWes LEdu SDix WCot
- 'Isla Gold' (v)	CDor ECtt EWes LEdu MBriF MHer MMuc NBid SEND SMrm WCAu WCot WFar
- 'Silver Lace' (v)	EBee WFar

Tanakaea (*Saxifragaceae*)

radicans	WSHC

tangelo see *Citrus* × *aurantium* Tangelo Group

tangerine see *Citrus reticulata* Tangerine Group

tangor see *Citrus* × *aurantium* Tangor Group

Taraxacum (*Asteraceae*)

faeroense	NPoe WCot
leucanthum **new**	GGro
officinale agg.	CHab
pseudoroseum	GGro NPoe WFar
rubrifolium	WFar

tarragon see *Artemisia dracunculus*

Tasmannia (*Winteraceae*)

§ ***lanceolata***	Widely available
- (f)	EHed SPer
- (m)	SPer
- 'Red Spice'	EPfP LRHS LSRN MPkF SEle
- 'Suzette' (v)	MBlu SRms

Taxodium ✿ (*Cupressaceae*)

ascendens 'Nutans'	see *T. distichum* var. *imbricarium* 'Nutans'
distichum	Widely available
- 'Cascade Falls'	CAco LRHS MBlu MTrO NOra SLim
- var. ***imbricarium***	CAco CMCN LRHS
§ - - 'Nutans'	CAco CBcs EPfP IArd MBlu MTrO SLim WHwl WMat
- 'Little Leaf'	SLim
- 'Little Twister'	SLim
- 'Minaret'	MBlu
* - 'Pendulum'	IDee LMaj
- 'Pévé Minaret'	CMen LRHS MGil NOra SArc SGol SLim
- 'Pévé Yellow'	MBlu SLim
- 'Schloss Herten'	SLim
- 'Secrest'	MBlu
- SHAWNEE BRAVE ('Mickelson')	MBlu SLim
mucronatum	CAco CExl
- NJM 09.037	WPGP

Taxus ✿ (*Taxaceae*)

baccata 🏆H7	Widely available
- 'Aldenham Gold'	CKen
- 'Amersfoort'	CAco NLar
- 'Argentea Minor'	see *T. baccata* 'Dwarf White'
- Aurea Group	ELan NWea SRms
I - 'Aureomarginata' (v)	CBcs MAsh SWvt
- 'Autumn Shades'	LRHS NLar
- 'Barabits' Express' **new**	CAco
- 'Bence' **new**	CAco
- 'Black Rod' **new**	CKen
- 'Corleys Coppertip'	CKen ELan MRav NLar
- 'Cristata'	CKen MBlu NLar
- 'David'	CAco EPfP IArd LRHS MGos NLar SCoo SLim SMad SPoG SWvt
- 'Dorothea'	NLar
- 'Dovastoniana' (m or f)	CAco NLar NWea SMad
- 'Dovastonii Aurea' (m or f/v)	CAco CBcs GKin MBlu NLar SGol SRms
§ - 'Dwarf White' (v)	NLar
- 'Elegantissima' (f/v)	EPfP LMaj NWea SCoo SLim SPoG
§ - 'Fastigiata' (f) 🏆H7	CAco CBcs CBod CMac CSBt CTri ELan EPfP LPar LRHS MGos MRav MSwo MTrO NOra NOrn NWea SCob SCoo SGol SGsty SPer SPoG SRms SWeb SWvt SavN WMat WSpi WTSh
- Fastigiata Aurea Group	CAco EPfP GQue IArd LMaj LPar LRHS MAsh MGil MGos NLar NOrn SArc SCob SGol SGsty SRms SWeb
- 'Fastigiata Aureomarginata' (m/v) 🏆H7	CMac CSBt CTri EPfP LBee LRHS MGos MSwo SCoo SLim SLon SPer SPoG SWvt WHwl WTSh
- 'Fastigiata Robusta' (f)	CAco CSBt ELan EPfP LRHS MAsh MGos MTrO NLar SCoo SGsty SLim SPoG WMat
- 'Globus' **new**	CAco
- 'Goldener Zwerg'	MBlu
- 'Gracilis Pendula'	SMad
- 'Graciosa'	NLar
- 'Grayswood Hill'	WFar
- 'Great Column'	MBlu
- 'Green Column'	NLar
- 'Green Diamond'	MBlu NLar
- 'Hibernica'	see *T. baccata* 'Fastigiata'
- 'Icicle' 🏆H7	CAco LRHS MAsh NHol NLar SLim
- 'Itsy Bitsy'	CKen
- 'Ivory Tower'	CAco CKen LRHS NHol NLar SLim
- 'Jack's Gold'	NLar
- 'Klitzeklein'	CKen NLar
- 'Lakatos'	CAco
- 'Luca'[PBR]	NLar
- 'Lutea' (f)	CAco SLim
- 'Micro'	CKen MAsh NLar
- 'Nutans'	CKen
- 'Overeynderi'	CAco
- 'Pendula'	CAco
- 'Pygmaea'	CKen
- 'Renke's Kleiner Grüner' **new**	LRHS
- 'Repandens' (f) 🏆H7	CAco IArd LRHS SavN WFar WSpi
I - 'Repens Aurea' (v) 🏆H7	CMac EPfP SCoo SLim SRms WFar WSpi
- 'Rushmore'	NLar
- 'Semperaurea' (m) 🏆H7	CBcs CMac LBuc LPar LRHS MAsh NLar NWea SCoo SGol SLim SPoG WSpi
- 'Standishii' (f) 🏆H7	CBcs CBrac CEme CKen CMac CSBt ELan EPfP GKin IArd LBee LRHS MAsh MGos MRav NHol NLar NOra NOrn NWea SCoo SLim SPoG SWvt WMat
- 'Stove Pipe'	CKen
- 'Summergold' (v)	CBrac ELan LRHS MAsh MRav NBir NLar SCoo SGsty WSpi
- 'Washingtonii' (v)	LPar
- 'Zöld' **new**	CAco
cuspidata	CAco CMen
- 'Aurescens' (v)	CKen
- 'Minuet'	CKen
- 'Silver Queen'	CAco SLim
× ***media*** 'Brownii'	CAco
- 'Hicksii' (f)	CAco LBuc LMaj NWea SGol SGsty
- 'Hillii'	CAco LBuc SGsty
- 'Nixe'	SLim
- 'Tymon'[PBR] **new**	NLar
- 'Viridis'	CAco
wallichiana	CAco IDee

tayberry see *Rubus* Tayberry Group; see also AGM Fruit Section

Tecoma (*Bignoniaceae*)

capensis 🏆H1c	CRHN SVen
- 'Lutea'	EShb

- yellow-flowered WLov
ricasoliana see *Podranea ricasoliana*

Tecomanthe (*Bignoniaceae*)

speciosa CRHN

Tecomaria see *Tecoma*

Tecophilaea (*Tecophilaeaceae*)

cyanocrocus 🏆H3 CBor EHyd EPot GKev LRHS NDry NRHS NRog
- 'Leichtlinii' 🏆H3 CAvo CBor EHyd EPot GKev LRHS NDry NRHS NRog SDeJ
- 'Purpurea' see *T. cyanocrocus* 'Violacea'
- Storm Cloud Group EPot GKev
§ - 'Violacea' CAvo CBor EHyd EPot GKev LRHS NDry NRHS NRog
violiflora NRog

Tectona (*Verbenaceae*)

grandis EBee

Teesdalia (*Brassicaceae*)

nudicaulis **new** SPhx

Telekia (*Asteraceae*)

§ ***speciosa*** CMac CSpe EBee EHyd EPfP GAbr GJos GLog LEdu LRHS NBro NChi NGBl NLar NRHS NSti SBls SDix SEND SPlb WBor WBrk WCAu WHoo WSMil

Telesonix see *Boykinia*

Teline see *Genista*

Tellima (*Saxifragaceae*)

grandiflora Widely available
- 'Bob's Choice' WCot
- 'Delphine' (v) EPPr MBriF WCot XLum
- 'Forest Frost' CBod CFis CMac EBee EHyd ELan EMor EPPr EPfP EShb LRHS MBNS MBel MBriF MPnt NLar NRHS SWvt WCAu WCot
- Odorata Group ECha WCot
- 'Purpurea' see *T. grandiflora* Rubra Group
- 'Purpurteppich' ECha EHyd EPPr EPfP GPSL LRHS MPnt MRav NRHS SWvt WCot WPnP
§ - Rubra Group CBod CBro CMac CTri CTtf ECha EHyd ELan EPfP EWoo GMaP GQue LPot LRHS MBriF NChi NLar NPer NSti SCob SPer SPlb SRms SWvt WCAu WCot WFar WHoo
- 'Silver Select' EPPr

Telopea (*Proteaceae*)

'Braidwood Brilliant' XSte
§ 'Bridal Gown'PBR CCCN
'Emperor's Torch' LRHS XSte
oreades LRHS SPlb
SHADY LADY CRIMSON ('T90101'PBR) CCCN XSte
SHADY LADY YELLOW CCCN XSte
speciosissima CCCN LRHS SPlb
- 'Red Embers' XSte
truncata CCCN SPlb
white-flowered **new** XSte

Temu see *Blepharocalyx*

Tephroseris (*Asteraceae*)

integrifolia subsp. ***capitata*** GEdr SPlb

Ternstroemia (*Pentaphylacaceae*)

chapaensis WWJ 11918 WCru
gymnanthera WCru
kwangtungensis FMWJ 13402 WCru
luteoflora FMWJ 13360 WCru

Tetracentron (*Trochodendraceae*)

§ ***sinense*** CBcs CMCN EPfP ESwi IArd MBlu WPGP
- WJC 13818 from the Himalaya WCru
- var. ***himalense*** see *T. sinense*

Tetradium (*Rutaceae*)

§ ***daniellii*** CBcs CMCN EBee ELan EPfP ESwi IArd LEdu LPar SAko SEND SPtp WGob WMat
- from Korea WPGP
§ - Hupehense Group CMCN MCoo NLar
fraxinifolium PAB 9101 LEdu
- WJC 13750 WCru
aff. ***fraxinifolium*** WWJ 11615 WCru
glabrifolium IArd
- B&SWJ 6882 WCru
- CWJ 12364 WCru
ruticarpum MBlu WPGP
- B&SWJ 3541 WCru

Tetragonolobus see *Lotus*

Tetraneuris (*Asteraceae*)

§ ***grandiflora*** GKev SPlb
scaposa EPot

Tetrapanax ✿ (*Araliaceae*)

§ ***papyrifer*** 🏆H3 CDTJ CDoC ELan ESwi MPie SDix SEND SVen WLov
- B&SWJ 7135 WCru
- 'Empress' WCru
- 'Meifeng' WCru
- 'Rex' Widely available
- 'Steroidal Giant' CDTJ

Tetrapathaea see *Passiflora*

Tetrastigma (*Vitaceae*)

obtectum CCCN CRHN CTsd CWit EShb EWld SEND

Teucrium (*Lamiaceae*)

* ***ackermannii*** 🏆H5 CMea EPot GKev LRHS MHer MHol NCou SGro WAbe WHoo WIce WMal WPGP XSen XSte
* ***armenum*** EBou
aroanium EDAr EPot GEdr XSen
asiaticum XSen
botrys MHer
capitatum EDAr
chamaedrys misapplied see *T.* × *lucidrys*
chamaedrys L. Widely available
- f. ***albiflora*** CCBP ECha ELan EWes WSpi
- 'Nanum' GMaP
- 'Rose' EBou SRms
- 'Schneeflocke' XSen

- 'Spring Gold' LRHS
aff. ***chamaedrys*** MGil NPol SEdd
§ ***creticum*** SPhx
flavum CSde EBee EPPr XSen
fruticans Widely available
- 'Agadir' XSen
- 'Azureum' ♀H3 CBcs CBod CCBP CCoa CDoC CKel CSde EBee EHyd ELan EPfP LRHS LSRN MRav SBrt SCob SEND SIvy SMad SNig SPer SPoG SRkn SRms SWvt WKif WSMil XSen
I - 'Azureum Compactum' SCob
- 'Compactum' CBod CDoC CKel EBee ELan LRHS SLon SPer SPoG SWvt WAvo WCFE WPGP WSpi
- 'Drysdale' CCoa CDoC CKel CSBt EHyd LRHS SWvt
hircanicum CCBP CElw EBee EBou ECha EGrI EHyd ELan LRHS LSRN MMuc MNrw NBir NWad SEND SPhx SRkn XSen
- PAB 13.341 LEdu
- 'Paradise Delight' ECtt GWyn
- 'Purple Tails' CBod CChe CSpe CTsd CWCL EBee ELan EMor EPfP GBee MHol MRav NBir NGrd SRms SSal WFar
§ × ***lucidrys*** Widely available
- 'Chedglow' CNat
- 'Lucky Gold'PBR SPoG SRms
lucidum SLon
marum CTri LRHS SBrt SRms WJek XSen
massiliense misapplied see *T.* × *lucidrys*
montanum XSen
parviflorum EDAr
pyrenaicum ♀H7 CMea EPot EWes GEdr SGro
scorodonia CBod CCBP CHab MHer NLar NMir SRms WHer WJek XSen
- 'Binsted Gold' NSti
- 'Crispum' CCBP CKel EHyd EMor LEdu LRHS MGil MHer MNHC NBro NLar NRHS SPer SRms WGrn WJek WKif
- 'Crispum Marginatum' (v) EBee EBou ECha EPPr LEdu LSou MRav WFar
subspinosum CMea EDAr EPot LRHS WHoo XSen XSte
§ ***viscidum*** 'Lemon and Lime' (v) NSti

Thalia (*Marantaceae*)

dealbata CBen ECha EWat LLWG WMAq XLum

Thalictrum (*Ranunculaceae*)

CC 4576 CExl
from Afghanistan see *T. isopyroides*
actaeifolium MBel
- B&SWJ 4664 WCru
- B&SWJ 6310 WCru
- var. ***brevistylum*** B&SWJ 8819 LEdu WCru
- compact B&SWJ 4946 WCru
- 'Perfume Star' CPar ECtt ILea LEdu MMrt SCob WSpi XSte
adiantifolium see *T. minus* 'Adiantifolium'
alpinum EPPr NGBl WFar
angustifolium see *T. lucidum*
'Anne'PBR CDor CKno CWCL EBee ECha ECtt EMor EWTr ILea IPot LRHS MAvo MBel MBriF MHol MNrw NDov NGBl NLar SEdd SMad SPeP SPoG WCAu WCot WPnP WSpi
aquilegiifolium Widely available
- 'Album' CMea EBee ECha EHyd EMor EPfP GBin GMaP LRHS MACG MBel MCot NBid NRHS SEND SPer SPhx SWvt WCAu WFar WSpi
- var. ***intermedium*** B&SWJ 10965 WCru
- 'Purpureum' NLar NQui
- var. ***sibiricum*** B&SWJ 11007 WCru
- 'Small Thundercloud' SMHy
- 'Thundercloud' Widely available
- 'White Cloud' NFav
'Black Stockings' ♀H7 Widely available
calabricum NLar
chelidonii HWJK 2216 WCru
coreanum see *T. ichangense*
cultratum EBee EHyd EPfP LRHS NRHS
dasycarpum EPPr SMHy SPhx WCot WPnP
§ ***delavayi*** Widely available
- BWJ 7800 WCru
- BWJ 7903 WCru
- var. ***acuminatum*** MBel
- - BWJ 7535 WCru
- - BWJ 7971 WCru
- 'Album' Widely available
- 'Ankum' ♀H7 CRos EBee EHyd IPot LRHS MMrt MNrw NLar NRHS
- var. ***decorum*** CElw CSpe MBel WCot WCru WPGP
- - BWJ 7770 WCru
- - CD&R 2135 ESwi
- - var. decorum CExl
- 'Gold Laced' EBee ECtt NLar
- 'Hewitt's Double' (d) Widely available
- 'Hinkley' CMiW ECtt IPot LRHS MNrw NLar SMad WSpi
- var. ***mucronatum*** MBel WCru
- - DJHC 473 WCru
- purple-stemmed BWJ 7748 WCru
diffusiflorum EBee LRHS MMrt WAbe WCru WSHC
dipterocarpum misapplied see *T. delavayi*
dipterocarpum Franch. CMac CRos EHyd LRHS NRHS XLum
'Elin' ♀H7 Widely available
fendleri GBin
filamentosum CSpe MBel WCot
- B&SWJ 777 WCru
- B&SWJ 4145 WCru
finetii misapplied ECha LRHS
flavum CBod CHab CMac EBee EWld NBro NMir WFar WShi
- 'Chollerton' see *T. isopyroides*
§ - subsp. ***glaucum*** Widely available
- - 'Ruth Lynden-Bell' ♀H7 CBod MHol SPoG WCot WHoo
- - 'Silver Sparkler' (v) WCot
- - 'True Blue' SGbt
- 'Illuminator' CDor CElw CTri EHyd EShb LRHS MArl MRav NLar NRHS WCot WFar
grandiflorum GEdr
honanense BWJ 7962 WCru
§ ***ichangense*** CSpe EBee ECtt EHyd EPri GAbr GEdr LEdu MBel NWad SPad WCot
- B&SWJ 8203 WCru
- 'Evening Star' (v) ECtt SMad WHil
- var. ***minus*** 'Chinese Chintz' WCru
- 'Purple Marble' CWGN LEdu WCot WSpi
§ ***isopyroides*** CRos EBee EHyd EMor ESwi GKev GKin LEdu LRHS MBel MHid MHol MRav NRHS NWad SHar WCot WHil
javanicum B&SWJ 9506 WCru

- PAB 9431 LEdu WPGP
- var. ***puberulum*** B&SWJ 6770 WCru
johnstonii B&SWJ 9127 WCru
kiusianum CBod CMiW EBee ECha EHed ELan EMor EPfP EWes GEdr GMaP LRHS MBel NBir NGBl NHpl NLar NSla SMad SWvt WAbe WCot WFar WPnP
- Kew form WSHC
koreanum see *T. ichangense*
'Little Pinkie' (Censation Series) **new** MMrt
§ ***lucidum*** CBod CElw CExl CSpe EBee ECtt EHyd EShb GBin LEdu MHol MMuc MPie NGBl NLar NQui NSti SEND SPhx WCot WPnP
minus EHyd LEdu SEND XAbr
§ - 'Adiantifolium' ESwi MBel MRav NGdn SHar SRms WSpi XLum
- var. ***hypoleucum*** B&SWJ 8634 WCru
- subsp. ***kemense*** EBee
- var. ***sipellatum*** B&SWJ 5051 WCru
morisonii CRos EHyd LRHS NRHS
(Nimbus Series) NIMBUS PINK ('Tntnp') CBod LEdu LRHS MBel SMad
- NIMBUS WHITE ('Tntnw') **new** MBel NSti SMad SPad
'Nishiki' GEdr WFar
omeiense BWJ 8049 WCru
orientale EHyd
osmundifolium WCru
petaloideum LRHS SPhx
platycarpum B&SWJ 2261 WCru
podocarpum B&SWJ 14297 WCru
polygamum see *T. pubescens* Pursh
przewalskii WCru
§ ***pubescens*** Pursh EBee ECha EHyd GJos GMaP LRHS MAvo NDov NLar NRHS SHar SPhx
punctatum ESwi
- B&SWJ 1272 WCru
'Purplelicious' CBor ILea NLar SMad
ramosum MBel
- BWJ 8126 WCru
reniforme LEdu
- B&SWJ 13969 WCru
- GWJ 9311 WCru
- HWJK 2403 WCru
- WJC 13761 WCru
rochebruneanum ♀H7 Widely available
- 'Lavender Mist' LSun SPtp
rubescens B&SWJ 10006 WCru
rugosum CRos EHyd LRHS NRHS
sachalinense RBS 0279 EPPr NLar
shensiense CExl
simplex var. ***brevipes*** B&SWJ 4794 WCru
speciosissimum see *T. flavum* subsp. *glaucum*
* ***sphaerostachyum*** CElw EHyd EPPr EPfP EShb EWoo GAbr GPSL LEdu LRHS MNrw MPie NDov NRHS SPeP WHal
'Splendide' Widely available
SPLENDIDE WHITE ('Fr21034'PBR) ♀H7 Widely available
squarrosum EBee
tenuisubulatum BWJ 7929 WCru
tuberiferum var. ***yakusimense*** B&SWJ 6094 WCru
tuberosum CBor CElw CMea CMiW CSpe EPot NDov SHar WAbe WCot
- 'Rosy Hardy' WCot
tubiferum B&SWJ 10999 WCru
'Tukker Princess' ♀H7 EBee ECtt EWhm ILea NDov NLar SMad WCot
uchiyamae EAJP EBee ESwi EWld GKev WCot WPGP
'Ulrike' **new** SMHy
urbainii B&SWJ 7085 WCru
- 'Taiwan Baika' GBin
'Yubari Mountains' WFar
'Yulia' **new** MHol
yunnanense WCru

Thamnocalamus (*Poaceae*)

crassinodus 'Gosainkund' CDTJ MWht
- 'Kew Beauty' ♀H3 CDTJ EPfP MBrN MWht WCot WPGP
- 'Langtang' CBdn CDTJ MWht WPGP
- 'Merlyn' CDTJ EPfP MWht
falconeri see *Himalayacalamus falconeri*
spathaceus misapplied see *Fargesia murielae*
spathiflorus subsp. ***nepalensis*** CBdn MWht

Thamnochortus (*Restionaceae*)

bachmannii XSte
cinereus CPbh XSte
fruticosus CPbh
insignis ♀H3 CPbh MPkF SPlb
lucens SPlb
punctatus **new** LRHS
rigidus CCCN CTrC

Thapsia (*Apiaceae*)

decipiens see *Melanoselinum decipiens*
villosa B&SWJ 14014 WCru

Thaspium (*Apiaceae*)

trifoliatum SPhx

Thea see *Camellia*

Thelypteris (*Thelypteridaceae*)

kunthii CLAP EBee LEdu WCot
ovata var. ***lindheimeri*** CBdn EHyd LRHS NRHS
palustris EBee EShb NBir NBro NLar SRms WFib WPnP XLum
phegopteris see *Phegopteris connectilis*

Theobroma (*Malvaceae*)

cacao CTsd

Thermopsis (*Fabaceae*)

sp. MHol
caroliniana see *T. villosa*
chinensis CRos EBee EHyd ELan EPfP GAbr LPla LRHS MHer MNrw NRHS SBls SPad
fabacea see *T. lupinoides*
lanceolata EBee EHyd EPfP EWld LRHS NQui NRHS SHar WCot WFar
§ ***lupinoides*** CDor ECha SRms
macrophylla EBee
mollis CExl NBid
montana LRHS MPie
- var. ***montana*** CBod CWCL EBee EHyd ELan EPfP GBee GMaP LRHS MBel MMuc NBir NGBl NGrd NRHS NSti NWad SEND SGbt SPer

– – NNS 99-480	WCot
§ ***villosa***	EHyd LPla MRav NGdn NLar SSal

Therorhodion see *Rhododendron*

Thladiantha (*Cucurbitaceae*)

dubia	EBee SBrt SDix SMrm WCot

Thlaspi (*Brassicaceae*)

sp.	NGdn
biebersteinii	see *Pachyphragma macrophyllum*

Thryptomene (*Myrtaceae*)

baeckeacea	CCCN

Thuja ✿ (*Cupressaceae*)

'Extra Gold'	see *T. plicata* 'Irish Gold'
§ ***koraiensis***	NLar
occidentalis	GPoy NWea SWeb
– 'Amber Glow'	CAco CBrac CKen CSBt MAsh NHol NLar NWad SCoo SLim SPoG SRms
– 'Anniek'PBR	CKen LRHS SCoo SPoG
– Aurea Group	CBrac
– 'Bateman Broom'	CKen
– 'Beaufort' (v)	CKen
– 'Brabant' 🏆H7	GDam LPar NLar NWea SCoo SGsty SLim WMou
– 'Brobeck's Tower' 🏆H7	CKen EPfP NLar SLim
– 'Caespitosa'	CKen
– 'Cuprea'	CKen
– 'Danica' 🏆H7	CBrac CMac GKin LCro LOPS LPar MAsh NWea SCoo SLim SPoG SRms WCFE
– 'Danica Gold'	SLim
– 'Degroot's Spire'	CKen ELan LRHS NLar SGsty SLim
– 'Douglasii Aurea' (v)	CKen
– EMERALD	see *T. occidentalis* 'Smaragd'
– 'Ericoides'	SRms
– 'Filiformis'	SLim
– 'Filips Magic Moment'PBR	SPoG
– FIRE CHIEF ('Congabe'PBR)	CKen EPfP LPar LRHS NLar SCoo SLim SPoG
– 'Gold Drop'	CKen
– 'Golden Anne'PBR	LRHS SPoG
– 'Golden Brabant'PBR **new**	LRHS
– 'Golden Globe'	LPar LSRN SCoo SLim
– GOLDEN SMARAGD ('Janed Gold'PBR)	EPfP LRHS LSRN NLar SCoo SLim SPoG
– 'Golden Tuffet' 🏆H7	CKen CMea ELan GKin LBee MAsh NWad SCoo SLim SPoG
– 'Hetz Midget' 🏆H7	GKin NWad SCoo SLim SPlb WFar
– 'Holmstrup' 🏆H7	CBod CBrac CMac MAsh SRms
– 'Jantar'PBR	LRHS NLar SGsty SLim SPoG
– 'Konfettii' (v)	SLim SPoG
– 'Linesville'	CKen
– 'Little Gem'	SRms
– 'Maria Wn'PBR	CKen
– 'Meineke's Zwerg' (v)	CKen
– 'Miky'	LRHS
– 'Milleri'	CKen
– 'Mirjam'PBR (v)	CKen
– 'Mr Bowling Ball'	LRHS NLar SLim
– 'Ohlendorffii'	CKen
I – 'Pygmaea'	CKen
– 'Pyramidalis Aurea'	SCob SGsty
– 'Recurva Nana'	NWad
– 'Rheingold' 🏆H7	CAco CBcs CBod CBrac CMac CSBt ELan GKin LBee LRHS MAsh MGos MMuc NHol NWea SCoo SEND SLim SPer SPlb SPoG SRms WCFE WFar
§ – 'Smaragd' 🏆H7	CBrac CCVT CSBt ELan EPfP GDam LBuc LCro LOPS LPar LRHS MAsh MGos NLar NOrn NWea SCoo SEWo SGol SGsty SLim SPoG SWeb SWvt WMou
* – 'Smaragd Variegated' (v)	CKen MAsh
– 'Smokey'	CKen
– 'Starstruck'	SPoG
§ – 'Stolwijk' (v)	SLim
– 'Sunkist' 🏆H7	CBod CBrac CKen CMac MAsh SCoo SRms WFar
– 'Teddy'	EPfP LBee LRHS MAsh NHol NLar NWad SCoo SPoG
– 'Tiny Tim'	CMac LPar SGsty SLim SVic
– 'Trompenburg'	CBod
– 'Wansdyke Silver' (v)	CMac SLim
– 'Wareana'	CMac
– 'Waterfield'	NWad
– 'White Smaragd' (v)	SCoo SLim
– 'Yellow Ribbon'	CBod CKen CSBt SGsty SLim SRms
orientalis	see *Platycladus orientalis*
plicata	CBcs CBrac CCVT CMac ELan EPfP IPap LMaj LPar NWea SCob SPer WMou WTSh
– 'Atrovirens' 🏆H6	CBrac ELan LBee LBuc LCro LOPS LRHS MAsh MGos MHed NWea SCob SCoo SEND SEWo SGol SGsty SLim SRms SWvt WAvo WMat WMou
– 'Aurea' 🏆H6	MAsh SLim SRms
– 'Can-can' (v)	CBrac
– 'Collyer's Gold'	SRms
– 'Copper Kettle'	CBod CKen GKin SLim
– 'Cuprea'	CKen
– 'Doone Valley'	CKen NWad
– 'Excelsa'	LMaj WMou
– 'Gelderland' 🏆H6	ELan EPfP SCoo SWeb
– GOLDY ('4ever'PBR)	LRHS NLar SCoo SGsty SLim SPoG
§ – 'Irish Gold' (v)	CMac LRHS
– 'Little Boy'PBR **new**	CBod
– 'Martin'	CBrac SGsty SRms SWvt
– 'Rogersii' 🏆H6	CBrac CKen CMac MAsh NHol SCoo SPoG SRms
– 'Semperaurescens' (v)	CMac
– 'Stolwijk's Gold'	see *T. occidentalis* 'Stolwijk'
– 'Stoneham Gold' 🏆H6	CBrac CMac GKin MAsh MGos SRms WCFE
– VERIGOLD ('Courtapli')	MMuc SEND
– 'Whipcord' 🏆H6	CBcs CKen ELan EPfP LRHS MMuc NHol NLar SCoo SLim SPoG
– 'Winter Pink' (v)	CKen
– 'Zebrina' (v) 🏆H6	CBcs CBrac CMCN CMac ELan EPfP MAsh MGos MMuc NLar NWea SCob SCoo SEND SLim SPer SPoG SWvt WAvo
standishii	GDam

Thujopsis (*Cupressaceae*)

dolabrata 🏆H6	CAco CBcs CBrac LRHS MMuc NLar SWvt WFar
– 'Aurea' (v)	CKen LRHS
– 'Laetevirens'	see *T. dolabrata* 'Nana'
§ – 'Nana'	CAco CKen CMac LRHS NLar SCoo SRms
– 'Solar Flare'	LRHS NLar
– 'Variegata' (v)	CMac GKin NLar SRms
koraiensis (Nakai) hort.	see *Thuja koraiensis*

Thunbergia ✿ (*Acanthaceae*)

alata	SPoG
– 'African Sunset'	CCht CSpe EShb

- 'Lemon Queen' SWvt
- 'Orange Beauty' CCht SWvt
- TANGERINE SLICE A-PEEL ('Dl1501') new WHil

* ***arborea*** CCCN

battiscombei CCCN

coccinea CCCN

- B&SWJ 7166 WCru

erecta CCCN EShb

fragrans GWJ 9441 ESwi WCru

grandiflora Υ^{H1b} CCCN WFib WSFF

- 'Alba' CCCN

gregorii Υ^{H1b} CCCN CSpe EShb WFib

laurifolia B&SWJ 7166 WCru

'Moonglow' CCCN

mysorensis Υ^{H1b} WFib

natalensis CCCN EShb

'Orange Wonder' CCCN

Thymbra (*Lamiaceae*)

capitata GJos XSen

spicata SPhx

thyme, caraway see *Thymus herba-barona*

thyme, garden see *Thymus vulgaris*

thyme, lemon see *Thymus citriodorus*

thyme, wild see *Thymus serpyllum*

Thymus ✿ (*Lamiaceae*)

from Turkey EWes LEdu SPhx

§ 'Alan Bloom' CRos EHyd LRHS NRHS

'Albus' ENfk

'Anderson's Gold' see *T. pulegioides* 'Bertram Anderson'

azoricus see *T. caespititius*

'Bressingham' CBod CMea CTri EBou ECtt EHyd EWhm GAbr GMaP GQue LCro LOPS LRHS MBow MHer MNHC NRHS SPlb SRms WIce

'Caborn Wine and Roses' CCBP ENfk SRms WFar WJek

§ ***caespititius*** GPoy MHer NRya SGro SPlb SRms WAbe WJek

caespitosus see *T. praecox* subsp. *praecox*

camphoratus ENfk EWes GArf MBros NHpl SEdi SPhx WAbe WFar WJek

- 'Derry' CSpe

§ ***carnosus*** Boiss. XSen

'Carol Ann' (v) ENfk EWes MNHC SRms

CASCATA LEMONADE new ENfk

ciliatus CBod XSen

cilicicus misapplied see *T. caespititius*

cilicicus ambig. MNHC SRms

cilicicus Boiss. & Bail. WAbe

citriodorus misapplied see *T.* 'Culinary Lemon'

citriodorus ambig. CTsd GQue SPhx SRms SVic XLum

citriodorus (Pers.) Schreb. CLau LEdu

- 'Archer's Gold' see *T. pulegioides* 'Archer's Gold'
- 'Aureus' see *T. pulegioides* 'Aureus'
- 'Bertram Anderson' see *T. pulegioides* 'Bertram Anderson'
- 'Silver Posie' see *T.* 'Silver Posie'

'Coccineus' see *T.* Coccineus Group

§ Coccineus Group Υ^{H5} CBod CKel CTri EBou ECha ECtt ECul ELan ENfk EWoo GMaP LCro LOPS LRHS MHer MNHC NHpl NRya SPer SPhx SPoG SRms WAbe WCav WFar WHoo WIce WJek XSen

- 'Atropurpureus' Schleipfer see *T.* 'Purple Beauty'

§ - 'Purple Beauty' ECtt EHyd EPot LRHS MHer NRHS SRms WHoo XSen

§ - 'Red Elf' GAbr MHer NSla

'Coccineus Major' CMea EHyd LRHS NRHS SRms

'Creeping Lemon' misapplied see *T. pulegioides* 'Kurt'

§ 'Culinary Lemon' CBod CHby CLau ENfk GPoy LCro LOPS MBow MBrN MHer MNHC MPri SEdi SSut WJek XLum XSen

'Dartmoor' WJek

'Dillington' ENfk

doerfleri XSen

'Doone Valley' (v) CBod CCBP CMea CRos CTri EBou ECha ECul EHyd ELan ENfk EPfP EWhm EWoo LRHS MAsh MHer MNHC NBir NRHS SCob SPer SPhx SPlb SPoG SRms SRot WCav WFar WIce

drucei see *T. polytrichus* A. Kern. ex Borbás subsp. *britannicus*

'Duftkissen'^{PBR} XSen

'E.B.Anderson' see *T. pulegioides* 'Bertram Anderson'

× ***faustinoi*** CLau

'Fragrantissimus' CLau EBou ENfk EWhm GJos GPoy MHer MNHC SPhx SPlb WJek

'Golden King' (v) ECha ELan ENfk LSRN MAsh MHer SRms

'Golden Lemon' misapplied see *T. pulegioides* 'Aureus'

'Golden Lemon' (v) WJek

'Golden Queen' (v) CBod LRHS SRms WFar

§ 'Hartington Silver' (v) CMea CRos CTri EBou ECha ECtt EHyd ENfk EPot EWes GArf GKev LRHS MHer NHpl NRHS SLee SPlb SPoG SRms SRot WCav WJek

herba-barona CBod CCBP CLau CMea EBou ENfk GPoy GQue MHer MNHC SRms WFar WJek

- ***citrata*** see *T. herba-barona* 'Lemon-scented'

§ - 'Lemon-scented' ECha GPoy LEdu MHer SRms WJek XSen

'Highland Cream' see *T.* 'Hartington Silver'

hirsutus CKel

§ 'Iden' CBod WJek

'Jekka' CBod CLau EWhm LCro LOPS MHer MNHC SRms WHoo WJek

'Jekka's Autumn Pink' WJek

'Jekka's Rosy Carpet' WJek

'Kurt' see *T. pulegioides* 'Kurt'

'Lammefjord' XSen

'Lavender Sea' EWes

'Lemon Caraway' see *T. herba-barona* 'Lemon-scented'

'Lemon Curd' CLau ENfk MNHC NHol SPlb SPoG SRms WJek

* 'Lemon Variegated' (v) ENfk EPfP EWhm LCro LOPS MNHC SPer SPoG

'Lilac Time' ECtt ENfk EWes MHer SPlb SRms WJek

'Lime' LEdu WFar

longicaulis ECha MHer SAng SRms

'Magic Carpet' WJek

marschallianus see *T. pannonicus*

mastichina SPhx XSen

- 'Didi' MHer

membranaceus WAbe

micans see *T. caespititius*

minus see *Calamintha nepeta*

neiceffii CKel CMea ECha

nitens XSen

odoratissimus SPhx

'Orange' CBod LEdu SEdi SRms WFar

§ ORANGE SPICE ('Tm95') XSen

§	***pannonicus***	MHer
	- PAB 9021	LEdu
	'Peter Davis'	CBod CLau EHyd ENfk LCro LOPS NBir SPoG SRms WAbe WFar WIce WJek WTor XSen
§	'Pinewood'	MHer WFar WJek XSen
	'Pink Ripple'	CBod CLau CMea ECtt ENfk EWes EWhm LEdu MHer MNHC SRms WHal WHoo WJek
	polytrichus misapplied	see *T. praecox*
	polytrichus A. Kern. ex Borbás	WWild
§	- subsp. ***britannicus***	CKel CTri EBou ECha EWhm GBin GMaP GPoy LEdu LOPS MBNS MHer MNHC NBir NBro SPhx SPlb SRms WJek XLum XSen
§	- - 'Thomas's White' 🏆H5	CTri
	'Porlock'	CBod CLau CTri EPfP MHer MNHC SRms WHoo WJek
§	***praecox***	EWhm GJos MHer
	- 'Albiflorus'	EWoo MRav XSen
	- subsp. ***arcticus***	see *T. polytrichus* A. Kern. ex Borbás subsp. *britannicus*
	- - 'Albus'	see *T. polytrichus* subsp. *britannicus* 'Thomas's White'
§	- subsp. ***praecox***	CTri GAbr
	prostrate	CBod
	'Provence'	XSen
	pulegioides	CBod CCBP CHby CTri EBou ENfk GPoy LRHS MBow MHer NHpl SRms SRot WFar WJek WSFF XAbr
§	- 'Archer's Gold'	CCBP CRos ECtt EHyd ENfk EPfP EPot GAbr LRHS LSRN MAsh MHer MNHC MRav NBir NHol NHpl NRHS SCob SRms WCav WFar
§	- 'Aureus' 🏆H5	ENfk GMaP LCro LOPS MAsh SPer SPlb SRms WHoo
§	- 'Bertram Anderson' 🏆H5	CBod CMea EBou ECha ENfk EPfP GMaP LShi MAsh MHer NBir NRya SPer SPoG SRms WCav WHoo WIce XSen
	- 'Foxley' (v)	CBod CCBP CLau ECul ENfk EPfP EWhm GMaP LRHS MHer MNHC SPlb SPoG SRms WFar WJek
	- 'Golden Dwarf'	WFar
§	- 'Goldentime'	GQue
§	- 'Kurt'	CLau ENfk LEdu MHer SRms WJek
	- 'Sir John Lawes'	MHer
	- 'Tabor'	CBod CLau ENfk EWhm MNHC SRms WGwG
	'Rainbow Falls' (v)	EPfP SEdi SRms WFar
	'Rasta' (v)	MHer
	'Redstart'	CBod ECha ECtt ENfk EPot LEdu MHer SRms WJek
	'Ruby Glow'	ECtt ENfk EWes MHer NBir
	serpyllum ambig.	SVic WFar XLum
	serpyllum L.	GJos LBuc SPlb SRms
	- var. ***albus***	CRos ECha EHyd GAbr GMaP GPoy GQue LRHS MNHC NRHS SPer SRms SRot WCav WFar WHoo
	- 'Albus Variegatus'	see *T.* 'Hartington Silver'
	- 'Amadé'	XSen
	- 'Annie Hall'	CRos CSma EHyd EPfP EPot LRHS MAsh MHer MNHC NRHS SRms WCFE WJek
	- 'Atropurpureus'	see *T.* (Coccineus Group) 'Purple Beauty'
	- ***coccineus*** 'Minor' misapplied	see *T.* Coccineus Group
	- 'Conwy Rose'	WAbe
§	- 'Desborough'	MHer
	- 'East Lodge'	MHer MNHC SRms
	- 'Elfin'	ECtt EWes ITim MRav NSla SPlb SRms SRot WAbe XSen
	- 'Goldstream' (v)	CMea CRos EBou EHyd ENfk LRHS MHer NRHS SLee SPlb SRms
	- 'Iden'	see *T.* 'Iden'
	- 'Minimalist'	see *T. serpyllum* 'Minor'
	- 'Minimus'	see *T. serpyllum* 'Minor'
§	- 'Minor'	CMea CRos CTri EBou ECha ECtt EHyd ENfk LCro LOPS LRHS MHer MNHC NRHS NSla SLee SPlb SRms SRot WAbe WFar WHoo
	- 'Minus'	see *T. serpyllum* 'Minor'
	- 'Pink Chintz' 🏆H5	CCBP CRos EBou ECha ECtt ECul EHyd ENfk EPfP EPot EWhm EWoo GMaP GPoy LCro LEdu LOPS LRHS MHer MNHC NRHS NRya SPer SPhx SPlb SPoG SRms WFar WIce WJek
	- 'Purple Beauty'	see *T.* (Coccineus Group) 'Purple Beauty'
	- 'Red Carpet'	CBod ECtt GAbr SRms WFar
	- 'Red Elf'	see *T.* (Coccineus Group) 'Red Elf'
	- 'Russetings'	CBod EBou ECtt ENfk EPfP GKev LCro LOPS MHer MNHC SDix SPoG SRms WCav WFar
	- 'September'	MHer
	- 'Snowdrift'	CCBP CMea ECtt ECul EPfP EWoo GKev LCro LOPS MHer MNHC SPlb SRms WCFE WFar WIce
	- 'Variegatus'	see *T.* 'Hartington Silver'
	- 'Vey'	CRos CSma EHyd EWes LRHS MHer NRHS SRms
	- 'Wirral White'	XSen
	'Silver King' (v)	ENfk
§	'Silver Posie'	Widely available
	'Silver Queen' (v) 🏆H5	CBcs EBou ECha ELan EMor ENfk EPfP EWhm EWoo GMaP LRHS LShi MNHC NHol SPer SPhx SPlb SRms SVic WCav WJek
	'Sparkling Bright' **new**	ENfk
	striatus	LEdu
§	***vulgaris***	Widely available
	- 'Aureus' hort.	see *T. pulegioides* 'Goldentime'
*	- 'Compactus'	CLau ENfk GPoy MHer MNHC MRav SPhx SRms WFar WJek XSen
	- 'Corbière'	XAbr
	- 'Deutsche Auslese'	see *T. vulgaris*
	- English, winter	SRms
	- French	see *T. vulgaris*
	- 'Lucy'	MHer
	- 'Pinewood'	see *T.* 'Pinewood'
	zygis	XSen

Tiarella ✿ (*Saxifragaceae*)

'Angel Wings' (Fox Series) 🏆H6	MPnt NSti WNPC
'Appalachian Trail' (Happy Trails Series)	CBcs ECha EMor MAvo MPnt NCou NWad SHeu
'Black Snowflake'	MPnt SHeu
'Black Velvet'	MPnt SHeu
'Braveheart'	MPnt SHeu
'Butter and Sugar'	MPnt
'Butterfly Wings'	MPnt
'Candy Striper'	MPnt SHeu
'Cascade Creeper'PBR	LRHS LSou MPnt NWad SHeu WNPC
collina	see *T. wherryi*
cordifolia 🏆H5	CBcs CMac CTri EBee ECha ELan EPfP EWoo GAbr GMaP LPar LPot LRHS MCot MGos MPnt MRav NBir NDov NRHS SCob SPer SRms SWvt WCAu WHoo XLum

- 'Glossy'	MPnt
- 'Milk Chocolate'	MPnt
- 'Oakleaf'	MPnt NBro SHeu WCAu
- 'Rosalie'	see × *Heucherella alba* 'Rosalie'
- 'Running Tapestry'	MPnt SHeu
'Crow Feather'PBR	MPnt NWad SHeu
'Cygnet'	CDor MPnt SHeu
'Dunvegan'	MPnt
'Elizabeth Oliver'	MPnt
'Emerald Ellie' (Fox Series)	CBod MPnt WNPC
'Fairy's Footsteps'	SHeu
'Happy Trails'PBR (Happy Trails Series)	MPnt NWad SHeu WNPC
'Inkblot'	LRHS MPnt NBro SHeu
'Iron Butterfly'PBR (v)	CBod CDor CMac CPla EBee ECha EPfP EWoo GMaP LRHS LSRN MBel MPnt MRav SCob SEdd SGbt SHeu SPer SPoG SRms WHoo
'Iron Cross'	SPlb
'Jeepers Creepers'PBR	CBod LRHS MPnt NDov NWad SHeu WNPC
'Martha Oliver'	MPnt
'Mint Chocolate'	EHyd ELan MPnt NBir NGdn NLar SHeu SWvt
'Moorgrün'	EPPr SHeu
MORNING STAR ('Tntia042')	MPnt SHeu SRkn
'Mystic Mist'PBR (v)	CDor CWGN ECtt MPnt NWad SCoo SHeu SPoG WNPC
'Neon Lights'PBR	MPnt NBir NWad SHeu SWvt WNPC
§ 'Ninja'	EHyd MPnt NBir SCob SWvt
'Oregon Trail' (Happy Trails Series)	MNrw MPnt NWad SHeu WNPC
'Pacific Crest'PBR (Happy Trails Series)	EBee MPnt NWad SHeu WNPC
'Pink Bouquet'	CBod CMac CSpe ELan EMor LRHS MACG MBel MPnt NBro NLar SCob SHeu WFar WPnP
'Pink Brushes'PBR	MPnt SHeu
'Pink Skyrocket'PBR ♀H6	CBod CDor ELan EMor EPau EPfP EWoo LRHS LSRN LSou MAsh MBel MPnt NBir NGdn NHol NWad SCoo SEdd SHeu SMad SPer SPoG SWvt WCot WNPC WPnP
'Pinwheel'	MPnt
'Pirate's Patch'PBR	MPnt SHeu
polyphylla	MACG MPnt SHeu WCru
- 'Baoxing Pink'	MPnt WCru
- 'Filigran'	EPfP GQue MPnt NHol NWad SHar SHeu
'Raspberry Sundae' (Fox Series) ♀H6	LRHS MPnt WNPC
'Running Tiger'	LRHS MPnt
'Sea Foam'	MPnt SHeu
'Simsalabim'	MPnt
'Skeleton Key'	MPnt
'Skid's Variegated' (v)	MPnt SHeu SPoG SWvt
'Spanish Cross'	MPnt SHeu
'Special Star' (Heucheraholics Series)	SHeu
'Spring Symphony'PBR ♀H6	CDor CRos EHyd ELan EMor EPfP EShb GDam GMaP GQue GWyn LCro LOPS LRHS MAsh MBel MPnt NPer NRHS NWad SCob SCoo SHar SHeu SPoG WCav WNPC WSHC
STARBURST ('Tntia041'PBR)	MPnt NWad SHeu
'Sugar and Spice'PBR	CWGN EHyd EPfP GPSL LRHS MPnt NDov NLar NRHS NWad SHeu WCAu WNPC
'Sunset Ridge'PBR (Happy Trails Series)	EBee MPnt NWad SHeu WNPC
SYLVAN LACE ('Tntiasl') (American Trial Series)	MPnt SHeu WNPC
'Tiger Stripe'	EBee LRHS MPnt NBro SHeu
'Timbuktu'	MPnt SHeu
trifoliata	MPnt MRav
- var. ***unifoliata***	MPnt
'Viking Ship'	see × *Heucherella* 'Viking Ship'
§ ***wherryi*** ♀H5	CBcs EBee EHyd ELan EMor EPfP LPot MACG MBel MPnt NBir NBro SBls SCob SPer SPlb SWvt WCAu WPnP XLum
- 'Bronze Beauty'	MPnt SHeu
- 'Green Velvet'	ECha MPnt SHeu
- 'Heronswood Mist' (v)	SHeu SWvt
- 'Pink Foam'	SHeu

Tibouchina (*Melastomataceae*)

grandifolia	CCCN CRHN
grossa B&SWJ 10758	WCru
heteromalla	CCCN
organensis	CBcs CBod CCCN EGrI EHed SEdd SEle SHeu SIvy SPoG SWvt
paratropica	CBod CCCN CRHN MGil SIvy WCot
semidecandra misapplied	see *T. urvilleana*
§ ***urvilleana*** ♀H2	CBcs CBct CBod CCCN CEnd CPla CSBt CTsd EBak EGrI EMdy SDix SPalm SPer SRkn SWvt
- 'Compacta'	CCCN
- 'Edwardsii' ♀H2	CRHN SAdn WCot
- variegated (v)	CBcs CCCN CKel SPalm SPer SWvt WCot

Tigridia (*Iridaceae*)

immaculata B&SWJ 10393	WCru
§ ***orthantha***	CPla
- 'Red-Hot Tiger'	CBod CSpe EBee WCot WCru WSHC
pavonia	CExl EShb SDeJ WSHC
- 'Alba'	CSpe WSHC
- 'Alba Grandiflora'	GKev SDeJ SDir
- 'Aurea'	GKev SDir
- 'Canariensis'	GKev SDeJ SDir
- 'Lilacea'	CPla GKev SDeJ SDir WSHC
- 'Speciosa'	GKev SDeJ SDir
van-houttei	GKev

Tilia ✿ (*Malvaceae*)

americana	CLnd CMCN
- AMERICAN SENTRY ('McKSentry') **new**	IPap
- 'Redmond'	MBlu
amurensis	CMCN
- from Korea	WPGP
argentea	see *T. tomentosa*
begoniifolia	see *T. dasystyla* subsp. *caucasica*
callidonta	WPGP
§ ***caroliniana*** subsp. ***heterophylla***	CMCN EBee EPfP MBlu WPGP
chinensis	CMCN WPGP
- F 30558	WPGP
chingiana	CMCN EBee WPGP
concinna	WPGP
cordata	Widely available
- 'Dainty Leaf'	CAco
- 'Green Globe'	LMaj
- 'Greenspire' ♀H6	CArg CCVT CLnd EBar EPfP IPap LMaj LPar MRav MTrO NOrn NWea SCob SEWo SGsty SWeb WMat WMou
- 'Len Parvin'	EBee WPGP
- 'Rancho'	LPar

	- 'Winter Orange' ♀H6	CBcs CBod CEnd EBee ELan EPfP LRHS MBlu MNic MSwo MTrO SCoo SEWo WMat
	dasystyla	CMCN
§	- subsp. ***caucasica***	CMCN EBee WPGP
	- - A&L 16	WPGP
	- - NJM 13.029	WPGP
	endochrysea	WPGP
	× ***euchlora***	CArg CCVT CLnd CMCN EBee EPfP LMaj NRog NWea SCob SEWo SPer WMat
§	× ***europaea***	CBcs EWTr LPar MMuc NOrn SEND
	- 'Pallida'	CLnd LMaj LPar MBlu NRog NWea
	- 'Wratislaviensis' ♀H6	EBee EBtc MBlu
	- 'Zwarte Linde'	NRog
§	'Harold Hillier'	CMCN MBlu WPGP
	henryana	CBcs CEnd CLnd CMCN EBee EPfP IArd IDee MBlu MMuc SCob SEND WLov WMat WMou WPGP
	- 'Arnold Select'	MTrO NWea WPGP
	- 'Bluebell'	MBlu
	- 'Kerdalo'	WPGP
	'Hillieri'	see *T.* 'Harold Hillier'
	insularis misapplied	see *T. japonica*, *T. japonica* 'Ernest Wilson'
§	***japonica***	CMCN EBee EPfP WPGP
	- 'Ernest Wilson' ♀H6	CMCN MBlu
	- large-leaved, from China	WPGP
	kiusiana	CBcs CMCN MBlu WPGP
	mandshurica	CMCN WPGP
	maximowicziana	CMCN EPfP MBlu WPGP
	mexicana	EBee WPGP
	- CD&R 1318	WPGP
	miqueliana	CMCN EBee MBlu
	× ***moltkei***	CMCN EBee IArd WPGP
	mongolica	CBcs CMCN EPfP MBlu WMou WPGP
	- 'Buda' **new**	WPGP
	- 'Harvest Gold'	CBcs MBlu
	monticola	see *T. caroliniana* subsp. *heterophylla*
	nobilis KR 226	WPGP
	oliveri	CBcs CMCN EBee MBlu WPGP
	aff. ***oliveri*** HRS 2808	WPGP
	paucicostata	IArd WPGP
	platyphyllos	CAgr CCVT CHab CLnd CMCN CSBt CTri EPfP EWTr IPap LBuc LPar MMuc MTrO NRog NWea SCob SCoo SEND SPer WMat WMou WTSh
	- 'Aurea'	MBlu WMat
	- 'Corallina'	see *T. platyphyllos* 'Rubra'
	- 'Laciniata'	CMCN MBlu
§	- 'Rubra' ♀H6	CCVT CLnd EBar NWea SCob SEWo
	- 'Tortuosa'	LMaj MBlu WMou
	× ***stellata***	WPGP
§	***tomentosa***	CAco CLnd CMCN MMuc NRog NWea SCoo SEND
	- 'Brabant' ♀H6	EPfP LMaj LPar SCob
	- 'Petiolaris' ♀H6	CArg CBod CCVT CEnd CLnd CMCN ELan EPfP MBlu MSwo NRog NWea SCob SPer WMou
	- 'Silver Globe'	LPar
	tuan	WPGP
	- var. ***chenmoui***	CMCN EBtc EPfP MBlu WPGP
I	'Varsaviensis'	WPGP
	× ***vulgaris***	see *T.* × *europaea*

Tillaea see *Crassula*

Tillandsia (*Bromeliaceae*)

	abdita	NCft
	aeranthos	LWei NCft
	- var. ***alba***	NCft
	- 'Bronze'	NCft
	- 'Miniata'	LWei NCft
	- 'Minuette'	NCft
	- purple-flowered	NCft
	- var. ***rosea***	NCft
	aeranthos × ***stricta***	NCft
	aizoides	NCft
	albertiana	LWei NCft
	albertiana × ***argentina*** **new**	NCft
	albida	LWei NCft SPlb
	andicola	NCft
	andreana	NCft
	araujei	NCft
	arequitae	NCft
	argentea ♀H1c	LCro LOPS LWei NCft
	argentina	NCft
	arhiza **new**	NCft
	ariza-juliae	NCft
	bagua-grandensis	NCft
	baileyi	NCft
*	- var. ***vivipara***	NCft
	baileyi × ***ionantha***	LWei NCft
	balbisiana	LWei NCft
	balsasensis	NCft
	bandensis	LWei NCft
	bartramii	LWei NCft
	bella **new**	NCft
	bergeri	LWei NCft SChr SPlb
	brachycaulos	NCft
	- var. ***multiflora***	LWei NCft
	brachycaulos × ***concolor***	NCft
	brachycaulos × ***schiedeana***	NCft
	brachycaulos × ***streptophylla***	NCft
	brachycaulos × ***xerographica***	NCft
	bryoides	LWei NCft
	bulbosa	LWei NCft SPlb
	- 'Gigante'	NCft
	butzii	LWei NCft
	- var. ***roseiflora***	NCft
	cacticola	LWei NCft
	cacticola × ***purpurea***	NCft
	caerulea	LWei NCft
	caerulea × ***straminea***	NCft
	'Califano'	NCft
	caliginosa	NCft
	capillaris	NCft
	- f. ***incana***	NCft
	- f. ***virescens***	NCft
	capitata	NCft
	- 'Domingensis'	NCft
	- 'Peach'	LWei NCft
	- red-leaved	NCft
	caput-medusae	LWei NCft
	caput-medusae × ***flabellata***	NCft
	cardenasii	NCft
	caulescens	NCft
	caulescens × ***tenuifolia***	NCft
	cauligera	NCft
	chaetophylla	LWei NCft
	chartacea **new**	NCft
	chiapensis	NCft
	chusgonensis	NCft
	circinnatoides	NCft

	cocoensis	NCft
	compressa	NCft
	concolor	LWei NCft
	concolor* × *streptophylla	NCft
	'Cotton Candy'	NCft
	crocata	NCft
	- 'Copper Penny'	NCft
	- 'Copper Penny' × ***albertiana***	NCft
	- 'Copper Penny' × ***duratii***	NCft
	crocata* × *mallemontii	NCft
	crocata* × *usneoides	NCft
	'Curly Slim' new	NCft
	cyanea	LCro LOPS LWei NCft
	delicata	NCft
	diaguitensis	LWei NCft
	disticha	LWei NCft
	duratii	LWei NCft
	dyeriana 🏆H1c	NCft
	edithae	NCft
	ehlersiana	NCft
	elongata	NCft
	'Eric Knobloch'	NCft
	espinosae	NCft
	exserta	NCft
	exserta* × *juncea	NCft
	extensa new	NCft
	fasciculata	LWei NCft
	'Feather Duster'	NCft
	festucoides	LWei NCft
	filifolia	NCft
	flabellata 🏆H1c	LWei NCft
	flavobracteata	NCft
	flexuosa	NCft
	floribunda	LWei NCft
	× ***floridana***	NCft
	fresnilloensis	LWei NCft
	fuchsii var. ***fuchsii***	NCft
	- f. ***gracilis***	LWei NCft
	funckiana	LWei NCft SPlb
	- var. ***recurvifolia***	NCft
	funebris	NCft
	gardneri	LWei NCft
	geminiflora	NCft
	geminiflora* × *recurvifolia	NCft
	glabrior	NCft
	'Gordon C'	NCft
	grao-mogolensis	NCft
	hammeri	NCft
	harrisii	NCft
	'Heather's Blush'	NCft
	heteromorpha	LWei NCft
	hondurensis	NCft
	'Houston'	LWei
	'Houston Enano'	NCft
	humilis	NCft
	- var. ***simplex***	NCft
	incarnata	NCft
	intermedia	NCft
	ionantha	LWei NCft
*	- 'Fuego'	LWei NCft
	- 'Haselnuss'	NCft
	- var. ***ionantha***	NCft
	- - 'Druid'	NCft
	- 'Peach'	LWei NCft
	- 'Ron'	NCft
I	- 'Rosea'	LWei NCft
	- 'Rubra'	LWei NCft
	- var. ***scaposa***	see *T. kolbii*
	- 'Silver'	LWei NCft
§	- var. ***stricta***	NCft
	- var. ***vanhyningii***	NCft
	- 'Variegata'	NCft
	ionantha* × *schiedeana	NCft
	ixioides	NCft
	ixioides* × *reichenbachii new	NCft
	'Jackie Loinaz'	NCft
	jonesii	NCft
	jucunda	NCft
	juncea	LWei NCft
	kammii	LWei NCft
	karwinskyana	NCft
	'Kashkin'	NCft
	kautskyi	NCft
	'Kimberly'	NCft
§	***kolbii***	LWei NCft
	latifolia	LWei NCft
	- var. ***divaricata***	NCft
	- 'Enano Latifolia'	NCft
	- var. ***latifolia***	NCft
	lautneri	LWei
	leiboldiana	LWei NCft
	leonamiana	LWei NCft
	lepidosepela	NCft
	loliacea	LWei NCft
	lorentziana	LWei NCft
	magnusiana	CDoC LWei NCft
	mallemontii	LWei NCft
	marconae	LWei NCft
	'Maria Teresa'	NCft
§	***matudae***	NCft
	mauryana	NCft
	mereliana	NCft
	mima var. ***chiletensis***	NCft
	minutiflora new	NCft
	mitlaensis	NCft
	montana	NCft
	myosura	LWei NCft
	'Mystic Burgundy'	NCft
	'Mystic Flame'	NCft
	'Mystic Haze'	NCft
	'Mystic Rainbow'	NCft
	'Mystic Trumpet'	NCft
	nana	NCft
	neglecta	LWei NCft
I	- 'Rubra'	LWei NCft
	nolleriana new	NCft
	oaxacana	LWei NCft
	paleacea	LWei NCft
	- var. ***apurimacensis***	NCft
	- 'Enano Paleacea'	NCft
	paleacea* × *tectorum	NCft
	pardoi	NCft
	paucifolia	NCft
	pedicellata	NCft
	plagiotropica	LWei NCft
	pohliana	LWei NCft
	× ***polita***	NCft
	polystachia	LWei NCft
	pruinosa	LWei NCft
	- 'Columbia'	NCft
	pseudobaileyi	LWei NCft
	pseudosetacea	LWei NCft
	pueblensis	LWei NCft
	punctulata	LWei NCft
	purpurea	NCft
	- 'Shooting Star'	NCft
	queroensis new	NCft
	× ***rectifolia***	LWei NCft
	recurvata	LWei NCft

	recurvifolia	NCft
	recurvifolia* × *gardneri **new**	NCft
	'Redy'	NCft
	reichenbachii	LWei NCft
	retorta	LWei NCft
	riohondoensis	NCft
	schatzlii	NCft
	schiedeana	LWei NCft
	- 'Major'	LWei NCft
I	- 'Minor'	NCft
	schreiteri	NCft
	schusteri **new**	NCft
	seideliana	LWei NCft
	seleriana	LWei NCft SPlb
	setacea **new**	LWei
	setiformis	LWei NCft
	simulata **new**	NCft
	sphaerocephala	NCft
	spiralipetala	NCft
	sprengeliana	NCft
	stellifera	NCft
	straminea	LWei NCft
	streptocarpa	LWei NCft
	streptophylla	LWei NCft
	stricta	LWei
	- var. ***albifolia***	NCft
I	- 'Amethyst'	NCft
	- 'Grey'	NCft
	- 'Hard Leaf'	NCft
	- var. ***stricta***	NCft
	sucrei	NCft
	tectorum	LWei NCft
	- caulescent	NCft
*	- var. ***filifoliata***	NCft
	- 'Snow' **new**	LWei
	tenuifolia	LWei NCft
	- blue-flowered	NCft
	- bronze-leaved	NCft
I	- 'Minima'	LWei NCft
	- var. ***tenuifolia***	LWei NCft
	- var. ***vaginata***	NCft
	- white-flowered	NCft
	toropiensis **new**	NCft
	tricholepis	LWei NCft
	tricolor	LWei NCft
	- var. ***melanocrater***	LWei NCft
	'Twisted Tim'	NCft
	usneoides	CDoC LWei NCft SHmp SPlb WSFF
	utriculata subsp. ***pringlei***	NCft
	variabilis	NCft
	velutina	CDoC LWei NCft
	'Wonga' **new**	NCft
	xerographica	CDoC LWei NCft
	xiphioides	NCft
	zecheri	NCft
	- var. ***cafayatensis***	LWei NCft

Tinantia (*Commelinaceae*)

	pringlei	GEdr LEdu MNrw MPie SBrt SDys WPGP
	- AIM 77	EBee MNrw WCot
	- variegated (v)	WCot

Titanopsis (*Aizoaceae*)

	calcarea ♀H1c	CCCN SSim
	fulleri	SSim

Titanotrichum (*Gesneriaceae*)

	oldhamii	GEdr MVil XSte

Tithonia (*Asteraceae*)

	rotundifolia	SVic
	- 'Fiesta del Sol' **new**	SSal
	- 'Torch'	CSpe SSal
	'Torchlight'	SPhx

Tofieldia (*Tofieldiaceae*)

	coccinea	GArf GEdr WCot WCru
	furusei	GEdr

Tolmiea (*Saxifragaceae*)

	menziesii	CBod CMac GGro MCot XLum
	- 'Cool Gold'PBR **new**	GMaP
	- 'Goldsplash'	see *T. menziesii* 'Taff's Gold'
	- 'Maculata'	see *T. menziesii* 'Taff's Gold'
§	- 'Taff's Gold' (v)	CBod SPlb XLum
	- 'Variegata'	see *T. menziesii* 'Taff's Gold'

tomatoes see AGM Vegetables Section

Toona (*Meliaceae*)

§	***sinensis***	CAgr CBcs CLnd EBee ELan EPfP LEdu MTrO MVil NWea SEND WPGP
	- 'Flamingo' (v)	CKel CRos EHed EHyd ELan EPfP ESwi LCro LMil LOPS LPar LRHS MAsh MPkF MTrO NLar NRHS NWea SChF SGol SPoG SWvt WCot WMat XSte
	- 'Lise'	CMCN

Torenia (*Linderniaceae*)

	(Moon Series) PURPLE MOON ('Dantopur')	MBros
	- ROSE MOON ('Dantoromoon')	MBros
	- YELLOW MOON ('Danmoon20'PBR)	MBros
	Summer Wave Series	CCCN

Torilis (*Apiaceae*)

	japonica	SPhx

Torreya (*Taxaceae*)

	californica	CAco CMCN
	nucifera	CBcs IDee

Townsendia (*Asteraceae*)

§	***alpigena*** var. ***alpigena***	GKev
	eximia	GKev
	formosa	NHpl
	hookeri	GArf GKev
	incana	GEdr
	minima **new**	GKev
	montana	see *T. alpigena* var. *alpigena*
	parryi	GKev
	scapigera	GEdr
	spathulata	SPlb

Toxicodendron (*Anacardiaceae*)

§	***orientale*** B&SWJ 3656	WCru
	- large-leaved B&SWJ 10884	WCru
§	***radicans***	GPoy
§	***succedaneum***	CDTJ
	- NJM 10.154	WPGP
§	***vernicifluum***	NLar

Trachelium (*Campanulaceae*)

§	***asperuloides***	SPlb WAbe
	caeruleum 'Black Knight'	CSpe WCot

Trachelospermum ✿ (*Apocynaceae*)

	from Nanjing, China	EShb
§	***asiaticum*** 🏆H4	Widely available
	- 'Avonbank'	WAvo
	- 'Bella' **new**	CCCN
	- 'Bredon'	WAvo
	- 'Copper Tips'	MGil WAvo
	- 'Golden Memories'	CBcs CBod CExl CMac CRHN CRos CWCL CWGN EBee EHyd ELan ELon EPfP LRHS LSRN MRav NLar NRHS SIvy SLon SNig SPoG SRms SWvt WCot
	- 'Goshiki' (v)	EShb SEle
	- 'Kulu Chirimen'	WCot
	- 'Ōgon-nishiki' (v)	CCCN EHyd LRHS SEle SMad SPoG WFar
	- 'Pink Showers'	CBcs CMac CWCL CWGN EPfP LRHS MHtn SCoo SNig XSte
	- 'Summer Sunset'	CBcs ELan ELon EShb MGos SGol SRms WCot
	- 'Theta'	LRHS WCot WFar WLov WPGP XSte
	'Chameleon'	ELan SMad
	'Christabel Bielenberg'	WSpi
	jasminoides 🏆H4	Widely available
	- 'Major'	CMac CWCL EBee ELan MAsh MGil SRms
§	- var. ***pubescens*** 'Japonicum'	CRHN EHyd LRHS SLon SNig SPoG WBor
	- STAR OF TOSCANA ('Selbra'PBR)	CBod CCCN CRos CWGN ECtt EHyd EPfP ETod EWTr IDee LCro LOPS LPar LRHS NLar NRHS SGsty SPer SPoG
	- 'Tricolor' (v)	LRHS SEle SGol SGsty SWvt WFar
	- 'Variegatum' (v) 🏆H4	Widely available
	- 'Waterwheel'	CBcs CBod CMac CSde CWCL ELan ELon EShb NLar SMad SWvt WLov
	- 'White Wings'	LRHS SCoo
	- 'Wilsonii'	CExl CMac CRos ELan ELon EPfP EShb LRHS LSRN MGil MRav NLar SAdn SEND SNig SPer SPoG SWvt WAvo WCot WPGP WTyc
	majus misapplied	see *T. jasminoides* var. *pubescens* 'Japonicum'
	majus Nakai	see *T. asiaticum*

Trachycarpus ✿ (*Arecaceae*)

	from Manipur	CPHo
§	***fortunei*** 🏆H5	Widely available
	fortunei* × *wagnerianus	EOli SWeb
	latisectus	CPHo
	nanus* × *wagnerianus	SChr
	princeps	CBrP CPHo
	takil ambig.	CPHo WSMil
	ukhrulensis	LEdu
	- NJM 13.085	WPGP
	wagnerianus 🏆H5	CBcs CBrP CCCN CDTJ CExl CPHo CTsd ETod LPar LRHS SArc SChr SPalm WPGP WSMil XSte

Trachymene (*Apiaceae*)

coerulea	CSpe SPhx

Trachystemon (*Boraginaceae*)

orientalis	CCBP CDor CExl CMac EBee ECha EGrI EPfP EWTr ILea LEdu LRHS LShi MAvo MCot MHol MMuc MNrw MRav NBid NLar NWad WBrk WCot WCru WHer WHil WPGP WPnP XLum

Tradescantia (*Commelinaceae*)

	albiflora	see *T. fluminensis*
	× ***andersoniana*** W. Ludwig & Rohw.	see *T.* Andersoniana Group
§	Andersoniana Group	EGrI ESwi WWtn
	- 'Angelic Charm' (Charm Series)	ECtt
	- 'Baby Doll'	XLum
	- 'Baerbel'	XLum
	- 'Bilberry Ice'	CDor CMac CWCL EAJP ECtt EHyd EPfP EWTr GMaP LRHS LSun MTin NBir NBro NGBl NGdn NLar NRHS SBea SCob SGbt SWvt WGwG WWtn XLum
	- 'Blanca'	WWtn
	- 'Blue and Gold'	CBcs CPla CRos ECtt EHyd ELon EPfP EWhm LRHS MRav NCou NRHS NSti SEdd WCot WGrn WHil
	- 'Blue Spider'	MAsh
	- 'Blue Stone'	CDor CKel CMea ECha ECtt EGrI EWld LRHS MAvo MRav SRkn SRms WHoo XLum
	- 'Bridal Veil'	SChr WDib
	- 'Caerulea Plena'	see *T. virginiana* 'Caerulea Plena'
	- CARMINE GLOW	see *T.* (Andersoniana Group) 'Karminglut'
	- 'Charlotte'	CDor ECha ECtt EHyd ELan LRHS NBro NGdn NLar NRHS WWtn XLum
	- 'Concord Grape' 🏆H6	CBod CMac CMea ECtt EGrI EHyd ELan EPfP EWoo GBee GMaP LRHS LSun MAvo MGos NBro NChi NGdn NRHS NSti SGbt SPer WCAu WFar WGwG WHoo WKif XLum
	- 'Domaine de Courson'	ECtt XLum
	- 'Euridice'	EWTr MBel
	- 'In the Navy'	NLar
	- 'Innocence'	CDor CNor CSBt CTri EAJP ECha ECtt EHyd ELan EPfP GMaP GWyn LRHS MBel NBir NGdn NRHS NSti SCob SGbt SPer SWvt WGwG XLum
	- 'Iris Prichard'	EAJP EBee GMaP NLar
	- 'Isis'	EBee ECtt EHyd ELan EPfP EWoo GMaP LRHS MRav NBir NGdn NRHS SGbt SPer SWvt WGwG WKif
	- 'J.C. Weguelin'	EGrI NBir SRms WCAu XLum
§	- 'Karminglut'	ECtt GLog GMaP LShi NBir NGdn WHoo XLum
	- 'Leonora'	EPfP MBel NLar SCob XLum
	- 'Little Doll'	CDor ECtt EPfP LRHS NBro NLar NRHS XLum
	- 'Little White Doll'	ECtt
	- 'Mac's Double' (d)	EBee
	- 'Melissa'	XLum
	- 'Osprey'	CBcs CBod CDor ECha ECtt EGrI EHyd ELan EWoo LRHS LShi MBel MRav NGdn NRHS NSti SPer SRms WCAu WGwG WHoo WKif XLum
	- 'Pauline'	MRav NBir NLar XLum
	- 'Perinne's Pink'	EBlo EHyd LRHS NRHS NSti WCAu
	- 'Pink Chablis'	CBod ECtt EHyd EPfP LRHS NBro NLar NRHS SPeP XLum
	- 'Pink Spider'	MAsh
	- 'Purewell Giant'	CMac CTri EBlo EHyd LRHS NBro NLar NRHS SWvt WKif
	- 'Purple Dome'	ECtt EHyd EPfP GMaP LRHS MAvo MRav NBir NBro NGBl NGdn NRHS SPoG
	- 'Red Grape'	CTtf EHyd LRHS NRHS NSti SCob XLum

- 'Rubra'	EGrI SRms XLum
- 'Satin Doll'PBR	ECtt
- 'Sunshine Charm'PBR (Charm Series)	EHyd LRHS NLar NRHS WHil
- 'Sweet Kate'	CBod CMac ECtt LRHS NBro NLar NRHS SGbt SPoG SRms WSMil XLum
- 'Sylvana'	EBee
- 'Valour'	CSBt EBee EHyd LRHS NRHS
- 'Zwanenburg Blue'	ECha ECtt EHyd ELan LRHS NLar NRHS SPlb SPoG XLum
'Angel Eyes'	EBee
bracteata	SBrt
canaliculata	see *T. ohiensis*
§ ***cerinthoides*** 'Variegata' (v) 𝕐H1c	EShb
crassifolia F&M 258	WPGP
§ ***fluminensis***	SChr WDib
§ - 'Aurea' 𝕐H1c	EShb SChr
- 'Maiden's Blush' (v)	CSpe EShb MBNS SPlb SVen
- 'Quicksilver' (v) 𝕐H1c	EShb NGBl
'Green Hill'	LCro LOPS
§ ***ohiensis***	SBrt
pallida 𝕐H1c	EShb WSMil
- 'Biltmore Bimbo' **new**	EShb
- 'Kartuz Giant'	EShb MPie WCot
- 'Pale Puma'	EShb
§ - 'Purpurea' 𝕐H3	CBcs EOHP EShb NGBl SPlb SSal
pendula	see *T. zebrina*
'Purple Sabre'	see *T. pallida* 'Purpurea'
purpurea	see *T. pallida* 'Purpurea'
sillamontana 𝕐H3	EShb MPie SChr
I - 'Variegata' (v)	EShb
spathacea	EShb
- 'Versicolor'	EShb
tricolor	see *T. zebrina*
virginiana	NChi
- 'Alba'	CMac SRms
* - 'Brevicaulis'	ECha NBro
§ - 'Caerulea Plena' (d)	MRav NLar XLum
- 'Rubra'	SPlb
§ ***zebrina*** 𝕐H1c	CDoC EShb SSal
- ***pendula***	see *T. zebrina*
- 'Purpusii' 𝕐H1c	EShb WDib
- 'Quadricolor' (v) 𝕐H1c	CDoC EShb

Tragopogon (*Asteraceae*)

crocifolius	CSpe LRHS SPhx
porrifolius	CFis LRHS MCot NGBl SBls SDix SPhx SVic WCot WSFF WTre
- 'Mammoth' **new**	EPPr
pratensis	NMir
- subsp. ***orientalis*** **new**	LRHS

Trautvetteria (*Ranunculaceae*)

carolinensis	ESwi EWes MBel WHil WSHC
- var. ***japonica***	GEdr WCru
- - B&SWJ 10861	WCru
- var. ***occidentalis***	EBee LEdu WCru WFar WPGP

Triadica (*Euphorbiaceae*)

sebifera	MBlu WPGP
- CWJ 12819	WCru

Trichodiadema (*Aizoaceae*)

densum 𝕐H1c	SSim
intonsum	SPlb
mirabile	SAll

Trichopetalum (*Asparagaceae*)

§ ***plumosum***	CBro

Tricuspidaria see *Crinodendron*

Tricyrtis (*Liliaceae*)

B&SWJ 3229 from Taiwan	WCru
'Abdane'	GKev
'Adbane'	CLAP ELan EWes WGwG
affinis B&SWJ 2804	WCru
- B&SWJ 5645	WCru
- B&SWJ 6182	WCru
- B&SWJ 11169	WCru
- B&SWJ 11442	WCru
- 'Early Bird'	WCru
'Amanagowa'	CLAP
bakeri	see *T. latifolia*
'Blue Wonder'	CBod LBuc LRHS MCot SPer WWtn XLum
dilatata	see *T. macropoda*
'Empress'	CBct CDor CExl CLAP EWes GMaP LPot LRHS LSou MAvo NLar NWad SCob SEdd SRkn WWtn
flava	EHyd
formosana	CAvo CTri ECha ELan EWoo GKev GLog GMaP ILea LRHS MCot MNrw SCob SDys SRms WAvo WKif
- B&SWJ 355	WCru
- B&SWJ 3073	WCru
- B&SWJ 3616	CExl WCru
- B&SWJ 3712	WCru
- B&SWJ 6741	WCru
- B&SWJ 6970	WCru
- RWJ 10109	WCru
- 'Dark Beauty'	CBod CCBP CDor CExl CLAP ECtt EGrI ELan EWTr LCro MAvo MHol MPnt WCAu WFar WTyc
- 'Emperor' (v)	ESwi
- 'Gilt Edge' (v)	CBct CExl ECtt ELan ELon LPot LSou MNrw NWad SWvt WFar WSMil WTre
- f. ***glandosa*** B&SWJ 7084	WCru
- aff. f. ***glandosa*** 'Blu-Shing Toad'	ESwi MAvo WCru
- var. ***grandiflora*** 'Long-Jen Violet'	WFar
- - 'W-Ho-ping Toad'	WCru
- 'Kestrel' (v)	CBct ESwi WCot WFar
- 'Purple Beauty'	XSte
- 'Samurai' (v)	EBee EWes MCot WSHC
- 'Seiryu'	EBee MBel
- 'Shelley's'	CLAP
- 'Small Wonder'	LEdu WCru
- 'Spotted Toad'	LEdu WCru
§ - Stolonifera Group	CAvo CBcs CDor CMac EHyd ELan EPfP EShb LRHS MCot NRHS NWad SHar
- - B&SWJ 7046	WCru
- 'Taiwan Toad'	CExl
- 'Taroko Toad'	WCru
- 'Tiny Toad'	WCru
- 'Variegata' (v)	LEdu NBir SRms WCru
- 'Velvet Toad'	WCru WFar
§ ***hirta***	CBcs CBod CDor CMac CMiW CTri EBee EGrI EHyd EMor EWTr GKev ILea LCro LOPS LRHS MCot MPie NBro NChi NHol NRHS SBls SCob SCoo SDix SGbt SPlb SWvt WSHC
- B&SWJ 5971	WCru
- B&SWJ 11182	WCru
- B&SWJ 11227	WCru

- 'Alba'	CMac GArf WAvo
- 'Albomarginata' (v)	CBod CMac EBee EHyd EWhm LRHS NRHS NSti SPoG SWvt WFar WGwG WWtn
- 'Doctor Hiraos' new	IPot
- 'Golden Gleam'	WCot
- var. ***masamunei***	WCru
- 'Matsukaze'	CExl EWes
- 'Miyazaki'	CMac ECtt EWld GKev GPSL IPot LRHS MACG MHer MNrw NRHS NSti SPoG WCAu WSHC WWtn XLum
- 'Taiwan Atrianne'	CDor CLAP ECtt EHyd ELan EMor ESwi GPSL LRHS MBNS MNrw NRHS NWad SGbt SPoG WCAu WWtn XSte
- 'Variegata' (v)	CTri EBee EHyd EWes GKev LRHS NRHS WCot
Hototogisu	CExl CRos EAJP EBee ECtt EHyd ELan ESwi LRHS MHer NHol NLar NRHS SPoG WWtn
ishiiana	CTtf EBee WCot WCru WSHC
- var. ***surugensis***	GKev LEdu WCru WFar
japonica	see *T. hirta*
'Kohaku'	EBee GKev
lasiocarpa	ESwi LEdu XLum
- B&SWJ 3635	CExl WCru
- B&SWJ 6861	WCru
- B&SWJ 7013	WCru
- 'Royal Toad'	WCru
§ ***latifolia***	EHyd GKev LEdu WCru WFar
- 'Saffron'	WCru
'Lightning Strike' (v)	CDor ECtt ESwi WCot WFar
'Lilac Towers'	LRHS
macrantha	GAbr GKev WCru WSHC
§ - subsp. ***macranthopsis***	CBct CDor CExl EBee MNrw WCot WCru
- - 'Juro' (d)	WCru
macranthopsis	see *T. macrantha* subsp. *macranthopsis*
* ***macrocarpa***	NChi XLum
macropoda	ILea LEdu LRHS
- B&SWJ 1271 from Korea	WCru
- B&SWJ 5013	WCru
- B&SWJ 5556	WCru
- B&SWJ 5847 from Japan	WCru
- B&SWJ 6209	WCru
- B&SWJ 8700	WCru
- B&SWJ 8829 from Korea	WCru
maculata PAB 3188	LEdu
'Momoyama'	WFar
'Moonlight Treasure' PBR	CExl NHol WCot
nana 'Karasuba'	WFar
ohsumiensis	CMiW ECha
- 'Fukurin-fu' (v)	WCot WFar
perfoliata	LEdu WCru
- 'Spring Shine' (v)	WCru
pilosa	GKev LEdu
PINK FRECKLES ('Innotripf' PBR)	CBct CChe CDoC CDor CLAP ELon EPot ESwi GDam LSou NCou SWvt XSte
'Raspberry Mousse'	CWCL MCot
ravenii B&SWJ 3229	WCru
- RWJ 10012	WCru
setouchiensis	WCru
'Shimone'	CExl
'Sinonome'	EBee MNrw
stolonifera	see *T. formosana* Stolonifera Group
suzukii RWJ 10111	WCru
'Taipei Silk' PBR	CBod CLAP LOPS SPad WWtn
'Tojen'	CLAP CRos ECtt ELon EPfP EWes GPSL LRHS MACG MNrw NLar NRHS WCAu WWtn
'White Towers'	CAvo CBro CExl CLAP ECtt EHyd ELan EWoo LPot LRHS MBel MRav NRHS NSti SGbt SRms WCAu WFar WSHC WWtn XLum

Trifolium (*Fabaceae*)

'Angel Clover Chocolate' new	MBNS
arvense	SPhx
badium	SPhx
barnebyi	WAbe
dubium	SPhx SPre
fragiferum	NAts
fucatum	SPhx
- var. ***virescens***	SPhx
incarnatum	CSpe GJos SPhx
jokerstii	SPhx
macrocephalum	EBee
montanum	SPhx
ochroleucon	CDor CTtf EAJP EBee ECtt ELon EWTr GBin GMaP ILea LEdu LPot MACG MBel MCot MHol MPie SBls SBut SEdd SHar SPhx WCAu WFar WPGP
pannonicum	CMea MACG MNrw SPhx
pratense	CHab MHer NMir SPhx SRms SVic WSFF WWild
- 'Dolly North'	see *T. pratense* 'Susan Smith'
- 'Ice Cool'	see *T. repens* 'Green Ice'
§ - 'Susan Smith' (v)	CCCN EBee EPfP ILea
purpureum	SPhx
repens	LCro LOPS SPhx SVic WSFF
- DARK DEBBIE ('Trifpot001' PBR)	LEdu
- 'Dragon's Blood'	CMea EPPr GWyn LEdu LPot MPie SPer WPGP
- 'Estelle' PBR	LEdu
- 'Gold Net'	see *T. pratense* 'Susan Smith'
§ - 'Green Ice'	NSti WFar
- 'Harlequin' (v)	WCot
- 'Isabella' PBR	LEdu WFar WPGP
- 'Pentaphyllum'	see *T. repens* 'Quinquefolium'
- 'Purpurascens'	EHyd EPfP GQue MAsh MBNS MHer MPie NGrd SPoG WFar
§ - 'Purpurascens Quadrifolium'	CMea ECha EPau EWes GAbr GWyn LEdu MCot NFav NMir NPer SPer SPlb WFar WTor
§ - 'Quinquefolium'	XLum
- 'Saint Patrick'	CNat
- 'Tetraphyllum Purpureum'	see *T. repens* 'Purpurascens Quadrifolium'
- 'Wheatfen'	CNat LEdu NDov NPer
- 'William'	WCot WFar
rubens	Widely available
- 'Drama'	ELon LEdu MNrw WPGP
- 'Frosty Feathers'	CDor CFis CSpe EPPr MAvo SBls WNPC
- 'Peach Pink'	CDor CSpe ELon EPPr MMrt SHar SPhx WCot
- 'Red Feathers'	CSpe ELon EPPr EWes GQue LSun MACG MBel MHol SBls SHar SMad
trichocephalum	EBee EPPr MACG MNrw SPhx
willdenovii	SPhx

Trigonella (*Fabaceae*)

foenum-graecum	SPhx SVic WSFF XAbr

Trillidium see *Trillium*

Trillium ✿ (*Melanthiaceae*)

	albidum 🏆H5	EBee EHyd EPot EWld GEdr GKev MNrw NRHS
	amabile	GEdr
	angustipetalum	GEdr
	apetalon	GEdr
	camschatcense	CExl GEdr GKev
	- 'Nemuro'	GEdr
§	***catesbyi***	CExl EBee GEdr GKev ILea MNrw NChi NWad SDir
	cernuum	GKev
	chloropetalum	CBro CElw EHyd GEdr LRHS NRHS NWad
§	- var. ***giganteum*** 🏆H5	CExl EGrI GArf GBin GKev LEdu NHar NHpl NSla
	- - EBG form	GRum
	- var. ***rubrum***	see *T. chloropetalum* var. *giganteum*
	- white-flowered	GKev
	cuneatum	CBcs CExl CMiW CWCL EHyd GAbr GEdr GKev GWyn LEdu MNrw NBir NChi NHol NHpl NRHS NWad SDeJ SDir WFar WPGP WPnP
	erectum 🏆H5	Widely available
	- f. ***albiflorum***	CMea ECha EHyd GKev LRHS MNrw NRHS NWad
	- red-flowered	GKev
	erectum* × *flexipes	EBee GKev MNrw NBir
	flexipes	CWCL EHyd EPot GEdr GKev ILea MNrw NHol NHpl NWad
	- 'Harvington Dusky Pink'	EHyd LRHS NRHS
	- 'Harvington Select'	EBee EHyd LRHS NRHS
	govanianum	GKev
	grandiflorum 🏆H5	Widely available
	- 'Jenny Rhodes'	LEdu
	- pale pink-flowered	EHyd NRHS
	- f. ***polymerum*** 'Flore Pleno' (d)	CBro EHyd GArf GEdr LRHS NHar NHpl NRHS SDir
	- - 'Snowbunting' (d)	EHyd EWes GKev LEdu WThu
	- f. ***roseum***	EHyd GEdr GKev MNrw NRHS
	- white-flowered	MAvo
	kurabayashii	CExl EBee EGrI EHyd EPot EWld GEdr GKev MNrw NRHS WPGP
	luteum 🏆H5	CBcs CExl CMiW EBee EGrI EHyd EPfP GAbr GArf GEdr GKev GMaP ILea LCro LEdu LOPS MNrw MSCN NChi NHol NHpl NRHS NWad SDeJ SDir WPnP
	maculatum	GKev
	nivale	GEdr GKev WThu
	ovatum	GKev
	- f. ***hibbersonii***	GEdr GKev
	- 'Roy Elliott'	CExl
	parviflorum	GEdr GKev MNrw
	pusillum	CExl EGrI GEdr GKev ILea MNrw NHol NHpl
	recurvatum	CBcs CWCL EBee EGrI GEdr GKev ILea LEdu MVil NChi NHol NHpl NWad WPnP
	rivale 🏆H4	CExl GEdr GKev
	- Purple Heart Group	GEdr
	rugelii	EBee EWes GEdr GKev MNrw WSHC
	- Askival hybrids	MNrw
	rugelii* × *vaseyi	EWes MNrw
	sessile	CExl CWCL EGrI EPot GEdr GKev GPSL GWyn MAvo MNrw NBir NChi NWad SDeJ SDix WKif WPnP WShi
	- 'Rubrum'	see *T. chloropetalum* var. *giganteum*
	simile	EBee EHyd GKev LEdu MNrw NHpl NRHS
	smallii	GEdr
	stylosum	see *T. catesbyi*
	sulcatum	CExl EBee EHyd GAbr GEdr GKev LEdu LRHS MNrw NHpl NRHS WSHC
	taiwanense B&SWJ 3411	WCru
	tschonoskii	GEdr
	undulatum	MNrw
	vaseyi	EBee EHyd EWes GAbr GEdr GKev MNrw NRHS SDir
	viridescens	GEdr GKev

Trinia (*Apiaceae*)

	glauca	SPhx

Triosteum (*Caprifoliaceae*)

	erythrocarpum	GKev LEdu SMad
	himalayanum	EWld GKev NBid WPnP WSHC
	- B&SWJ 7907	ESwi
	- BWJ 7907	WCru
	pinnatifidum	EBee GGro GKev MMrt

Tripleurospermum (*Asteraceae*)

§	***maritimum***	WHer

Tripogandra (*Commelinaceae*)

	serrulata 'Purple Scimitars'	EShb

Tripolium (*Asteraceae*)

§	***pannonicum***	CEls WHer

Tripsacum (*Poaceae*)

	dactyloides	EPPr

Tripterospermum (*Gentianaceae*)

	japonicum	GEdr

Tripterygium (*Celastraceae*)

	doianum B&SWJ 11467	WCru
	aff. ***doianum*** CWJ 12852	WCru
	regelii	CBcs
	- B&SWJ 5453	WCru
	- B&SWJ 8666 from Korea	WCru
	- B&SWJ 10921	WCru
	wilfordii	EBee LEdu
	- BWJ 7852 from China	WCru
	- NJM 11.029 from China	WPGP
	- NMWJ 14466 from Taiwan	WCru
	- WWJ 12009	WCru

Tristagma (*Alliaceae*)

	nivale	EBee
	patagonicum **new**	GKev

Triteleia (*Asparagaceae*)

	'4U'	NRog
	'Aquarius'	CBor EGrI ERCP NRog
	bridgesii	NRog
	californica	see *Brodiaea californica*
	clementina **new**	NRog
§	'Corrina'	CAvo EBee EPot ERCP GKev NRog
	'Crystal Pink'	SDeJ
	'Double Touch' (d)	NRog SDeJ WCot
	'Foxy'	CAvo CTtf EPot GKev MNrw NRog
	grandiflora	WCot
	hendersonii	GKev
	hyacinthina	NRog WCot
	- NNS 06-560	WCot
	- blue-flowered **new**	NRog

- white-flowered	NRog
ixioides var. ***scabra***	NRog
- 'Splendens'	CBor GKev NRog
- 'Starlight'	CTri NRog SDeJ
§ ***laxa***	ECha EGrI
- from Butte County, California **new**	NRog
- 'Allure'	NRog
- dwarf **new**	NRog
- from Mount Diablo, California **new**	NRog
§ - 'Koningin Fabiola'	CTtf EGrI EShb GKev MNrw NBir NRog SDeJ SDix WCot WHil
- QUEEN FABIOLA	see *T. laxa* 'Koningin Fabiola'
lemmoniae	GKev
lilacina	NRog
§ ***peduncularis***	GKev NRog WCot
'Phantasio' (d)	GKev
'Rosy' (d)	CBor GKev
'Rudy'	CAvo CBro CMea CTtf CWCL ERCP GKev MMrt MNrw NRog SDeJ WCot WHil
'Silver Queen'	EPot ERCP GKev NRog SDeJ WCot
'Twilight'	GKev NRog
uniflora	see *Ipheion uniflorum*
'White Cloud'	CAvo CBor GKev

Trithrinax (*Arecaceae*)

brasiliensis	SPalm
campestris	CBrP SPalm

Tritoma see *Kniphofia*

Tritonia (*Iridaceae*)

crocata $\mathbb{Y}^{H3}$	GKev NRog
- 'Baby Doll'	LEdu NRog
- 'Duchess' **new**	NRog
- 'Serendipity'	EPri
- 'Tangerine'	NRog
deusta	CPbh EPri GKev
- subsp. ***miniata***	NRog
disticha	EGrI SMad SPlb
§ - subsp. ***rubrolucens***	Widely available
dubia	NRog
flabellifolia	NRog
gladiolaris	EPri LEdu NRog
- 'Parvifolia'	GKev
laxifolia	EGrI EPot GKev
pallida	SPlb
parvula	NRog
rosea	see *T. disticha* subsp. *rubrolucens*
securigera	NRog
- subsp. ***watermeyeri***	GKev
squalida	EPri

Trochocarpa (*Ericaceae*)

clarkei	WThu
gunnii	WThu
thymifolia	WThu
- white-flowered	WThu

Trochodendron (*Trochodendraceae*)

aralioides	CBcs CTsd EPfP GArf GKin LPar LRHS LShi MBlu MGos MMuc NLar SAko SDix SLon SPer SSta WPGP XSte
- B&SWJ 1651 from Taiwan	WCru
- B&SWJ 6080 from Japan	WCru
- CWJ 12357 from Taiwan	WCru
- RWJ 9845 from Taiwan	WCru
- from Taiwan	CDTJ WPGP

Trollius (*Ranunculaceae*)

ACE 1187	CExl
acaulis	EWes GAbr
altaicus	EHyd ELan LRHS NRHS
asiaticus	GKev
buddae	CBod CWCL MNrw MRav
§ ***chinensis***	ECha GKev GWyn
- 'Golden Queen' $\mathbb{Y}^{H7}$	Widely available
- 'Imperial Orange'	GWyn
- 'Morning Sun'	ELan EPfP LRHS SPad WPnP
- orange-flowered	GKev
× ***cultorum*** 'Alabaster'	Widely available
- 'Baudirektor Linne'	MRav NGdn
- 'Byrne's Giant'	ECtt GBin
- 'Canary Bird'	NGdn SRms WSpi
- 'Cheddar'	see *T. × cultorum* 'Taleggio'
- 'Earliest of All'	CWCL GBin NGdn NLar WSHC WSpi
- 'Etna'	NLar
§ - 'Feuertroll'	ECha ECtt MRav NGdn NLar WSpi
- FIREGLOBE	see *T. × cultorum* 'Feuertroll'
- 'Golden Cup'	GWyn NBir NGdn
- 'Goldquelle' $\mathbb{Y}^{H7}$	EBee GBin GWyn
- 'Goliath'	GWyn NLar
- 'Helios'	ECha
- 'Lemon Queen'	CBod CMiW CWat ECtt EHyd EPfP EWTr GKev GMaP GWyn LRHS MBel MRav NLar NQui SCob SPer SRms WWtn
- 'New Moon'	CBcs CDor CRos CSpe EBlo EHyd EMor EPfP EShb GBin GWyn LLWG LRHS MBNS NChi NQui NRHS SBls SPoG WHoo WSHC WWtn
- 'Orange Crest'	ELon EPfP NLar WWtn
- 'Orange Globe'	GMaP
- 'Orange Princess' $\mathbb{Y}^{H7}$	CDor CWat EHyd GWyn LCro LOPS LRHS NBro NLar NRHS SPer SRms
- 'Orange Queen'	SWvt
- 'Prichard's Giant'	ELon NBro WCFE WSpi
§ - 'Superbus' $\mathbb{Y}^{H7}$	CBod EHyd ELon EPfP GMaP GWyn MHol NGdn NLar SPer WFar WPnP WWtn
- 'T. Smith'	ECtt NBro
§ - 'Taleggio'	CTtf CWCL EBlo EHyd ELan EWTr GMaP LRHS MRav NBro NLar NRHS SPoG SRms SWvt WCav WNPC WPnP
'Dancing Flame'	CMac EHyd EMor EPfP LCro LOPS LRHS NLar NRHS SHar SPoG SRms WNPC
europaeus	CTtf CWCL EBee ECha EHyd ELan EPfP EWoo GBin GDam GWyn LEdu LLWG LRHS MACG MHol MRav NGdn NGrd NMir NRHS NSti SCob SRms WShi
- SDR 6306	GKev
- subsp. ***europaeus***	WFar
- 'Golden Globe'	WCav
- 'Lemon Supreme'	EBee EHyd ELan EMor EPfP GKev MACG NRHS WWtn
- 'Superbus'	see *T. × cultorum* 'Superbus'
farreri	GKev
- var. ***farreri***	EBee GKev
- var. ***major*** SDR 2713	GKev
hondoensis	NLar
ircuticus	EMor GJos GKev
laxus 'Albiflorus'	CExl EBee GBin GEdr
ledebourii misapplied	see *T. chinensis*
macropetalus	GKev
pumilus	CRos EBlo ECha LRHS NLar NRHS SPer WIce

	- ACE 1818	CExl MHer
	vaginatus	EBee GJos
	yunnanensis ♀^{H6}	CRos EBee EHyd EPfP GBin LRHS NRHS
	- orange-flowered	CExl GKev
§	- var. ***yunnanensis***	EBee

Tropaeolum (*Tropaeolaceae*)

	azureum	CCCN CExl MVil
	brachyceras	CCCN GKev MVil
	ciliatum	CCCN EWld GKev MVil NBid WCot WCru WPGP
	hookerianum	CExl
	- subsp. ***austropurpureum***	CExl
	incisum	CCCN GKev
	majus	ENfk GPoy SVic
	- Alaska Series (v) ♀^{H3}	ENfk LCro LOPS MNHC
	- 'Banana Split'	CCCN MPri SCob
	- 'Black Velvet' (Tom Thumb Series)	LCro LOPS
	- 'Blue Pepe'	CLau
§	- 'Darjeeling Double' (d) ♀^{H3}	EPPr
	- 'Darjeeling Gold'	see *T. majus* 'Darjeeling Double'
	- 'Empress of India'	CLau LCro LOPS MNHC
	- 'Hermine Grashoff' (d)	CSpe EPPr
	- Jewel Series	ENfk
	- 'Ladybird' (Ladybird Series)	SCob
	- 'Margaret Long' (d)	CSpe EPPr
	- 'Milkmaid'	SCob
	- 'Red Wonder'	CCCN MPri WCot
	- 'Strawberry Ice'	CLau
	- 'Sunset Pink'	CLau
	- 'Tip Top Alaska Salmon' (Tip Top Alaska Series) (v)	LOPS
	- Tom Thumb Series	MNHC
	- Whirlybird Series ♀^{H3}	LCro LOPS
	pentaphyllum	CExl CRHN GKev
	polyphyllum ♀^{H3}	CBor CCCN CWCL EBee EPot NBir SMHy
	sessilifolium	EBee
	smithii	WPGP
	speciosum ♀^{H5}	Widely available
	tricolor ♀^{H2}	CAvo CBor CCCN CRHN CWCL GKev SDir WCot
	tuberosum	CAgr CAvo CEnd GKev GPoy SDeJ SPoG WKor
	- var. ***lineomaculatum*** 'Ken Aslet' ♀^{H3}	CBcs CBor CCCN CSpe ECha EHyd ELan EPfP EPot GAbr GKev LEdu SPer WFar

Trozelia (*Solanaceae*)

§	***grandiflora***	CCCN SEND

Tsuga ✿ (*Pinaceae*)

	canadensis	CAco EPfP LMaj MMuc NWea
	- 'Abbott's Dwarf'	CKen NHol
§	- 'Abbott's Pygmy'	CKen
	- 'Bacon Cristate'	CKen
	- 'Beehive'	NLar
	- 'Betty Rose' (v)	CKen
	- 'Birkett's White'	CKen
	- 'Brandley'	CKen LRHS
§	- 'Branklyn'	CKen WCFE
	- 'Cappy's Choice'	CKen
	- 'Cinnamonea'	CKen
	- 'Coffin'	CKen
	- 'Cole's Prostrate' ♀^{H7}	CAco CKen LRHS MAsh NLar
	- 'Creamey' (v)	CKen
	- 'Curley'	CKen
	- 'Curtis Ideal'	CKen
	- 'Dr Hornbeck'	see *T. canadensis* 'Hornbeck'
	- 'Essex'	CKen MGil
*	- 'Everitt's Dense Leaf'	CKen
	- 'Everitt's Golden'	CKen
	- 'Fantana'	MAsh NHol
	- 'Gentsch White' (v)	LPar
	- 'Hedgehog'	NLar
§	- 'Hornbeck'	CKen
	- 'Horsford'	CKen
	- 'Horstmann' No 1	CKen
	- 'Hussii'	CKen NHol
	- 'Jacqueline Verkade'	CKen MAsh NLar
	- 'Jeddeloh' ♀^{H7}	LPar MAsh NHol NLar SCob
	- 'Jervis'	CKen NHol NWad
	- 'Julianne'	CKen
	- 'Little Joe'	CKen NLar
I	- 'Lutea'	CKen
	- 'Many Cones'	CKen
	- 'Minima'	CKen
	- 'Minuta' ♀^{H7}	CKen NHol WAbe
	- 'Palomino'	CKen
	- 'Pendula' ♀^{H7}	CKen LRHS MAsh
	- 'Pincushion'	CKen
	- 'Prostrata'	see *T. canadensis* 'Branklyn'
	- 'Pygmaea'	see *T. canadensis* 'Abbott's Pygmy'
	- 'Rugg's Washington Dwarf'	CKen
	- 'Snowflake'	CKen
	- 'Stewart's Gem'	CKen
	- 'Verkade Petite'	CKen
	- 'Verkade Recurved'	CKen
	- 'Von Helms' Dwarf'	CKen
	- 'Warnham'	CKen
	caroliniana 'La Bar Weeping'	CKen
	- 'Planting Fields Broom'	CKen
	chinensis	CKen
	diversifolia 'Gotelli'	CKen
	dumosa	CKen
	heterophylla ♀^{H6}	CAco CBcs CCVT EPfP GJos IPap MMuc NWea SEWo WFar WMou WTSh
	- 'Iron Springs'	CKen NLar
	- 'Laursen's Column'	CKen
	- 'Thorsens Weeping'	CKen NLar
	menziesii	see *Pseudotsuga menziesii*
	mertensiana 'Blue Star'	CAco CKen
	- 'Elizabeth'	CKen
	- 'Glauca'	CKen
I	- 'Glauca Nana'	CKen
I	- 'Horstmann'	CKen
I	- 'Nana Pendula' **new**	CKen
	- 'Quartz Mountain'	CKen
	sieboldii 'Baldwin'	CKen
	- 'Green Ball'	CKen NLar
	- 'Honeywell Estate'	CKen
	- 'Nana'	CKen

Tuberaria (*Cistaceae*)

	lignosa	WAbe

Tulbaghia ✿ (*Alliaceae*)

	acutiloba	CAvo LEdu NHoy
	alliacea	EPri LEdu NHoy WCot
*	***allioides***	CBro
	'Cally White' **new**	LEdu
	capensis	LEdu NBir WAvo
	capensis* × *violacea	NHoy
	'Cariad'	LEdu
	cernua CD&R 199	EBee LEdu
	- hybrid	EPri
§	***coddii***	MHer

cominsii CExl EPri LEdu SGro
cominsii* × *violacea CAvo CExl EPri WHoo
'Cosmic' CTtf EBee EPPr EPri LEdu NHoy SMHy
'Dark Beauty' NHoy
'Elaine Ann' NHoy
'Fairy Snow' LEdu WCot
'Fairy Star' CCht CWGN ELan EPri EShb LEdu NHoy SMHy WABo WCot
'Fairy Star Mk II' SMHy
fragrans see *T. simmleri*
- 'Alba' SDeJ
'Hazel' LEdu MHer NHoy
'John May's Special' EShb LEdu NHoy SMHy WCot WHoo
leucantha ♀H2 EPri GKev LEdu NHoy
- H&B 11996 LEdu
ludwigiana MHer
maritima see *T. violacea* var. *maritima*
Marwood seedling LEdu MHer
montana CBor EBee LEdu MPie NHoy SPlb
'Moshoeshoe' LEdu NHoy WPGP
'Moya' GKev
natalensis ♀H2 CBro GKev
- B&V 421 EPri
- clone 2 pink-flowered B&V 421 LEdu
- pink-flowered LPla
'Purple Eye' ♀H2 CBro CCht CDoC EBee ELan EPPr GBin LEdu LRHS LSou NHoy SCoo SGBe SPoG WABo WCot WNPC WSMil XSte
'Scented Beauty' NHoy
§ ***simmleri*** ♀H3 EPri EWes LEdu SDeJ
- 'Cheryl Renshaw' WCot
'Snow White' LEdu WCot
verdoorniae LEdu
violacea ♀H3 CAvo CBcs CBod CBro CCBP CKno CSpe ECha EGrI ELan EPfP EPri ERCP EWoo GKev LEdu NHoy SEND SEdd SPlb SSut WCFE WPnP WTre WTyc XSen
* - 'Alba' EBee EGrI EPri EShb GKev MHer NHoy WCFE WKif WPnP XSen
- 'Dissect White' NHoy SAng
I - 'Fine Form' CKno
- 'Harry Hay' SMHy
- 'John Rider' EPri NHoy SBls
* - var. ***maritima*** CBor EShb LEdu MHer NHoy
- 'Pallida' CAvo CBro EBee LEdu NHoy
- 'Peppermint Garlic' LEdu
- var. ***robustior*** ECha EWes NHoy
- 'Seren' LEdu
§ - 'Silver Lace' (v) ♀H3 Widely available
- 'Variegata' see *T. violacea* 'Silver Lace'
white-flowered NHoy

Tulipa ✿ (Liliaceae)

(4) CArg
'Abba' (2) CArg NRog SDeJ
'Abigail' (11) NRog
'Absalon' (9) GKev SDir
'Abu Hassan' (3) ERCP NRog SDeJ WPhe
acuminata (15) ERCP GKev NRog SDeJ SPhx WCot WShi
'Ad Rem' (4) ♀H6 NRog SDeJ WPhe
'Ad Rem's Beauty' (4) **new** NRog
'Affaire' (3) GKev LHWs WPhe
'African King' (3) **new** LHWs
aitchisonii see *T. clusiana*
'Akebono' (11) GKev NRog SDeJ SDir
'Akita' (6) NRog
'Aladdin' (6) CArg GKev LCro LOPS NRog SDeJ WPhe
'Aladdin's Record' (6) NRog SDeJ SDir
'Alba Regalis' (1) GKev SDir
'Albert Heijn' (13) GKev NRog SDeJ
ALBION STAR ('Mieke Telkamp') (13) CArg NRog SDeJ
'Aleppo' (7) SDeJ SDir
'Alfred Cortot' (12) ♀H6 SDeJ
'Algarve' (3) WPhe
'Ali Baba' (14) ♀H6 NRog WPhe
'Alibi' (3) GKev SDeJ
altaica (15) ♀H6 NRog
amabilis see *T. hoogiana*
'Amazing Grace' (2) ERCP LHWs WPhe
'Amazing Parrot' (10) **new** ERCP LHWs
'Amazone' (3) **new** NRog
'American Dream' (4) NRog SDir WPhe
'American Eagle' (7) SDeJ
anadroma (15) **new** GKev
'Ancilla' (12) ♀H6 GKev NRog SDeJ WShi
'André Rieu' (5) LCro LOPS
'Angélique' (11) ♀H6 CAvo EPfP ERCP GKev LCro LOPS NBir NRog SDeJ SPer WPhe
'Angels Wish' (5) ♀H6 CAvo NRog SDeJ SDir WPhe
'Annie Schilder' (3) CAvo ERCP NRog
'Antoinette'PBR (5) CAvo GKev LCro LOPS NRog SDeJ
'Antraciet' (11) ERCP LCro LOPS WPhe
'Apeldoorn' (4) CArg GKev LCro LOPS NRog SDeJ
'Apeldoorn's Elite' (4) ♀H6 NRog SDeJ
'Apricona' (3) LHWs SPhx
'Apricot Beauty' (1) ♀H6 ERCP LCro LOPS NBir NRog SDeJ
'Apricot Delight' (4) GKev
'Apricot Emperor' (13) GKev NRog SDeJ SDir
'Apricot Foxx' (3) CArg GKev LHWs NRog SDeJ
'Apricot Impression'PBR (4) ERCP LCro LOPS NRog
'Apricot Jewel' see *T. linifolia* (Batalinii Group) 'Apricot Jewel'
'Apricot Parrot' (10) ♀H6 ERCP GKev NRog SDeJ
'Aquilla' (11) SDeJ
'Arabian Beauty' (3) LCro LOPS
'Arabian Mystery' (3) GKev NHol SDeJ
'Aria Card' (7) SDeJ
'Arie Hoek' (3) **new** NRog
'Armani' (3) **new** CAvo NRog
armena (15) GKev NRog
- var. ***armena*** NRog
'Armscote' (7) **new** NRog
'Artist' (8) ♀H6 CAvo ERCP GKev NRog SDeJ SDir WPhe
'Atlantis' (5) CArg ERCP NRog SDeJ WPhe
'Attila' (3) NRog
aucheriana (15) ♀H5 EPot GKev NRog
australis (15) GKev NRog
'Authority' (14) **new** NRog
'Auxerre' (7) WPhe
'Avenue' (3) WPhe
'Aveyron' (11) GKev
'Avignon' (5) GKev NRog SDeJ
aximensis (15) EPot GKev
'Baby Blue' (3) **new** NRog
'Ballade' (6) ♀H6 ERCP GKev LCro LOPS NRog SDeJ WPhe
BALLADE DREAM see *T.* 'Sonnet'
'Ballade Lady' (6) **new** NRog
'Ballerina' (6) ♀H6 CArg CAvo CMea EPfP ERCP GKev LCro LOPS NRog SDeJ SPer WPhe
'Banja Luka' (4) NRog SDeJ
'Barbados' (7) SDeJ WPhe
'Barcelona' (3) ♀H6 CAvo ERCP GKev LCro LOPS NRog

'Baronesse' (5)	SDeJ
'Bastogne' (3)	NRog
'Bastogne Parrot' (10)	NRog
batalinii	see *T. linifolia* Batalinii Group
'Beau Monde' (3) 🏆H6	NRog SDeJ
'Beauty of Apeldoorn' (4)	NRog
'Beauty of Spring' (4)	GKev LHWs
'Beauty Queen' (1)	NRog SDeJ
'Beethoven's Memory' (19)	NRog
'Belicia' (2)	GKev NRog SDir WPhe
'Bell Song' (7)	NRog
'Bellona' (3)	SDeJ
'Berlioz' (12)	SDeJ
'Bestseller' (1)	GKev NRog SDeJ
§ ***biflora*** (15)	EPot ERCP GKev NRog SDeJ
- var. ***major*** (15)	GKev
bifloriformis (15)	NRog
I - 'Maxima' (15)	NRog
- 'Starlight' (15) 🏆H6	GKev NRog
'Big Chief' (4) 🏆H6	NRog
'Big Smile' (5)	GKev
binutans (15) **new**	NRog
'Black Hero' (11)	ERCP GKev LCro LOPS NRog SDeJ
'Black Jewel' (7)	ERCP GKev NRog SDeJ WPhe
'Black Parrot' (10) 🏆H6	CArg CAvo EPfP ERCP GKev LCro LOPS NRog SDeJ WPhe
'Black Swan' (5)	SDeJ
'Blackjack' (3)	NRog
'Bleu Aimable' (5)	ERCP GKev NRog SDeJ
'Blue Beauty' (3)	GKev LCro LOPS
'Blue Diamond' (11)	CArg CAvo ERCP LCro NRog SDeJ WPhe
'Blue Heron' (7) 🏆H6	ERCP GKev LCro LOPS MCot NRog SDeJ
'Blue Parrot' (10)	CArg ERCP GKev LCro LOPS NRog SDeJ
'Blue Ribbon' (3)	LCro LOPS NRog
'Blue Spectacle' (11)	GKev
'Blue Wow' (11)	LCro LOPS
BLUEBERRY RIPPLE	see *T.* 'Zurel'
'Blumex Favourite'PBR (10)	LCro LOPS
'Blushing Beauty' (5)	SDeJ
'Blushing Bride' (5)	SDeJ
'Blushing Girl' (5)	SDeJ
'Blushing Lady' (5)	MCot
'Boa Vista' (11)	ERCP
'Border Legend' (13)	GKev NRog
'Bourbon Street'PBR (3) **new**	LHWs
'Boutade' (14)	NPer
'Brest' (7)	WPhe
'Brooklyn' (11)	GKev NPer
'Brown Sugar' (3)	CAvo ERCP LCro LHWs LOPS NRog WPhe
'Brownie' (2) **new**	ERCP
'Bruine Wimpel' (5)	LCro LOPS
'Buddy' (14)	NRog
'Budlight' (6)	LHWs WPhe
'Bulldog' (7)	SDeJ
'Burgundy' (6)	ERCP GKev LCro LOPS NRog SDeJ SDir SPer
'Burgundy Lace' (7)	GKev LCro LOPS NRog SDeJ
'Burning Heart' (4) 🏆H6	CArg NRog SDeJ
butkovii (15)	GKev NRog
'Buttercup' (14)	SDeJ
'Café Noir' (5)	ERCP LCro LHWs LOPS NHol
'Cairo' (3)	CAvo ERCP
'Calgary' (3) 🏆H6	CAvo LCro LOPS NRog SDeJ WPhe
'Calgary Flames' (3) 🏆H6	CAvo
'Calypso' (14) 🏆H6	CRos EHyd LRHS NRHS
'Camargue' (5)	NRog SDeJ
'Canasta' (7) 🏆H6	LRHS NRog SDeJ WPhe

'Candela' (13) 🏆H6	LRHS NRog SDeJ
'Candy Apple Delight' (4)	NRog
'Candy Club' (5)	NRog SDeJ
'Candy Prince'PBR (1)	CArg CRos EHyd ERCP LRHS NRHS NRog SDeJ WPhe
'Canova' (7)	SDeJ
'Cap d'Or' (14)	NRog
'Cape Cod' (14)	CAvo NRog SDeJ
'Cape Town' (1) 🏆H6	SDeJ WPhe
'Caractère' (3)	CArg
'Caravelle' (5)	ERCP GKev MCot SDeJ
'Cardinal Mindszenty' (2)	EHyd ERCP SDeJ
'Caribbean Parrot' (10)	LHWs WPhe
carinata (15)	NRog
'Carnaval de Nice' (11/v) 🏆H6	ERCP LCro LOPS NRog SDeJ WPhe
'Carnaval de Rio' (3)	MBros NRog
'Carrousel' (7)	NRog SDeJ
'Cartouche' (11)	NRog SDeJ WPhe
'Casa Grande' (14) 🏆H6	LCro
'Casablanca' (11)	NRog
'Cassini' (3)	SDeJ
'Catherina' (5)	GKev LCro LHWs LOPS
§ ***celsiana*** (15)	NRog
'Chansonnette' (3)	ERCP GKev NRog
'Charmeur'PBR (3)	NRog SDeJ
'Charming Beauty' (11)	GKev
'Charming Lady' (11)	ERCP NRog
'Cherry Delight' (4)	GKev
'China Lady' (14)	SDeJ
'China Pink' (6) 🏆H6	CAvo ERCP GKev LCro LOPS NRog SDeJ WPhe
'China Town' (8) 🏆H6	ERCP GKev LCro LOPS NRog SDeJ
'Chopin' (12)	NHol
'Christmas Dream' (1)	NRog SDeJ
'Christmas Marvel' (1)	NRog SDeJ
'Christmas Orange' (1)	WPhe
'Christmas Pearl' (1)	WPhe
'Christmas Sweet' (1)	CArg
chrysantha	see *T. montana*
'Cilesta' (2)	GKev
'Cistula' (6)	NRog SDeJ
'City of Vancouver' (5)	CAvo SDeJ
'Claudia' (6)	CArg NRog SDeJ WPhe
'Clearwater'PBR (5)	SDeJ
'Cleveland' (3)	WPhe
'Cloud Nine' (5)	NRog
§ ***clusiana*** (15)	ERCP GKev LHWs NRog
- f. ***cashmeriana*** (15)	NRog
- var. ***chrysantha*** (15) 🏆H6	CExl EHyd GKev LRHS NRHS NRog WShi
- - 'Tubergen's Gem' (15)	EPot GKev LHWs NRog WPhe
- 'Cynthia' (15) 🏆H6	CAvo EPot GKev MPie NRog SDeJ SPhx WPhe WShi
- 'Mountains Pride' (15) **new**	NRog
- 'Sheila' (15)	GKev NRog SPhx
§ - var. ***stellata*** (15) 🏆H6	GKev NRog
'Colour Parade' (14) **new**	NRog
'Columbine' (5)	GKev
'Compostella' (14)	NRog
'Concerto' (13)	GKev NPer NRog SDeJ
'Continental' (3)	GKev
'Cool Crystal' (7)	NRog WPhe
'Coors' (14) 🏆H6 **new**	NRog
'Copper Image' (11)	ERCP LHWs SPhx WPhe
'Coquette' (1)	SDeJ
'Corona' (12)	CAvo NRog SDeJ
'Corsage' (14) 🏆H6	SDeJ
'Cortina' (9)	SDeJ
'Couleur Cardinal' (3)	CAvo CRos EHyd ERCP GKev LCro LOPS LRHS NRHS NRog SDeJ

'Cream Cocktail' (4)	MCot
'Creme Lizard' (10) **new**	NRog
'Crème Upstar' (11)	ERCP GKev LCro LOPS NRog SDeJ WPhe
'Crystal Star' (7)	CArg
'Cum Laude' (5)	SDeJ
'Cummins' (7)	ERCP LCro LOPS NRog WPhe
'Curly Sue' (7)	ERCP MCot NRog
'Cutie Honey' (6)	WPhe
'Czaar Peter' (14) ♀H6	NPer NRog SDeJ WPhe
'Dance' (13)	NRog SDeJ
'Danceline' (11)	GKev LHWs
'Darwisnow' (3)	GKev
dasystemon (15)	GKev
- from Tajikstan (15) **new**	NRog
dasystemonoides (15)	NRog
'Davenport' (7)	ERCP NRog
'David Teniers' (2)	ERCP NRog SDeJ
'Daydream' (4) ♀H6	CArg GKev NRog SDeJ SPer
'Daytona' (7)	NRog
'Dazzling Sensation' (11/d/v) **new**	LHWs
'Deirdre' (8)	NRog
'Denmark'PBR (3) **new**	NRog
'Diana' (1)	CArg
'Diantha' (14)	NRog
didieri misapplied	see *T. passeriniana*
'Doberman' (3) **new**	MMrt
'Doll's Minuet' (8)	ERCP LCro LOPS NRog SPer
'Don Quichotte' (3) ♀H6	ERCP LCro LOPS NRog SDeJ
'Donauperle' (14)	SDeJ
'Donna Bella' (14)	SDeJ
'Dordogne' (5) ♀H6	NRog SDeJ
'Double Dazzle' (2)	SDir
'Double Focus' (11) **new**	NRog
'Double Red Riding Hood' (14/v)	NRog SDeJ
'Double Touch' (11) **new**	GKev
'Dow Jones'PBR (3)	WPhe
'Dragon King' (3)	SDeJ
'Dream Touch' (11)	LCro LHWs LOPS WPhe
'Dreamland' (5) ♀H6	SDeJ
'Drumline' (11) ♀H6 **new**	NRog
dubia	GKev
- 'Beldersai' (15)	NRog
'Duc van Tol Red and Yellow' (1)	GKev SDir
'Duc van Tol Rose' (1)	SDir
'Duc van Tol Violet' (1)	GKev
'Dynasty' (3)	NRog
'Early Glory' (3)	LCro LOPS
'Early Harvest' (12) ♀H6	GKev NRog SDeJ
'Easter Surprise' (14) ♀H6	GKev NRog SDeJ
'Ego Parrot' (10)	LCro LOPS
eichleri	see *T. undulatifolia*
'Electra' (5)	NHol
'Elegant Lady' (6)	GKev MCot NRog SDeJ
'Elizabeth Arden' (4)	GKev NRog
'Esperanto' (8/v) ♀H6	NPer NRog SDeJ WPhe
'Esta Bonita'PBR (3)	WPhe
'Estella Rijnveld' (10)	ERCP GKev LCro LOPS NRog SDeJ
'Eternal Flame' (2)	LCro LOPS NRog WCot
'Evergreen' (3)	ERCP GKev LCro LHWs LOPS WPhe
'Exotic Emperor' (13)	CAvo LCro LHWs LOPS MCot NRog SDeJ WPhe
'Fabio' (7)	CRos EHyd LRHS NRHS
'Fancy Frills' (7) ♀H6	ERCP GKev NRog SDeJ
'Fancy Parrot' (10)	SDeJ
'Fantasy' (10) ♀H6	NRog
'Fashion' (12)	SDeJ
ferganica (15)	NRog WCot

	'Fidelio' (3) ♀H6	SDeJ
	'Finola' (11)	GKev LCro LOPS WPhe
	'Fire Wings' (6)	LHWs
	'Firework' (6)	CAvo WPhe
	'Flair' (1)	CRos EHyd LRHS NRHS NRog SDeJ
	'Flamenco' (7)	NRog SDeJ
	'Flaming Evita'PBR (2)	SDeJ
	'Flaming Flag' (3)	CAvo GKev LCro LOPS
	'Flaming Parrot' (10)	ERCP GKev LCro LOPS NRog SDeJ
I	'Flaming Purissima' (13)	CAvo GKev NRog SDeJ WPhe
	'Flaming Springgreen' (8)	ERCP GKev LCro LOPS NRog SDeJ SPer WPhe
	'Flash Point'PBR (2)	WPhe
	'Flashback' (10)	WPhe
	'Florijn Chic' (6)	LHWs
	'Florosa' (8)	ERCP LCro LOPS NRog SDeJ
	'Flower Power' (10)	GKev NRog
	'Fly Away' (6)	CAvo NRog WPhe
	'Fontainebleau' (3)	ERCP NRog SDeJ
	fosteriana (13)	SVic
	'Foxtrot'PBR (2) ♀H6	CAvo ERCP GKev NRog SDeJ
	'Foxy Foxtrot' (2)	NRog SDeJ WPhe
	'Françoise' (3)	NRog SDeJ
	'Frank Graham' (3) **new**	LHWs
	'Franz Léhar' (12)	NRog SDeJ
	'Freedom Flame' (3) **new**	LHWs
	'Fringed Elegance' (7) ♀H6	LCro LOPS
	'Fringed Family' (7)	SDeJ
	'Fritz Kreisler' (12)	SDeJ
	'Für Elise' (14)	GKev NRog SDeJ
	'Gabriella' (3)	NRog
	'Gaiety' (12)	SDeJ
	'Garden Party' (3)	SDeJ
	'Gavota' (3) ♀H6	NHol NRog SDeJ WPhe
	'Generaal de Wet' (1)	LCro LOPS SDeJ
	'Gerbrand Kieft' (11) ♀H6	ERCP GKev
	gesneriana (15)	GKev SVic WCot
	'Gipsy Love' (7)	SDeJ
	'Girlfriend' (15)	NRog
	'Giuseppe Verdi' (12)	CRos EHyd LRHS NRHS NRog
	'Global Desire' (2) **new**	GKev
	'Glück' (12) ♀H6	NRog
	'Golden Apeldoorn' (4)	CArg GKev LCro LOPS NRog SDeJ
	'Golden Artist' (8)	GKev LCro LOPS NRog SDeJ
	'Golden Emperor' (13)	GKev NRog SDeJ
	'Golden Melody' (3)	SDeJ
	'Golden Nizza' (11)	NRog
	'Golden Oxford' (4)	NRog
	'Goldwest' (14)	NRog SDeJ
	'Gordon Cooper' (4)	SDeJ
	'Goudstuk' (12)	NRog
	'Grand Perfection'PBR (3) ♀H6	CAvo LCro LOPS SDeJ
	'Green Eyes' (8)	SDeJ
	'Green River' (8)	SDeJ
	'Green Valley' (8) **new**	NRog
	'Green Wave' (10)	ERCP LCro LOPS MBros NRog SDeJ WPhe
	'Greenstar' (6)	CAvo ERCP GKev LHWs WPhe
	greigii (14)	NRog
	grengiolensis (15)	GKev NRog
	'Greuze' (5)	LCro LOPS
	'Groenland' (8)	CAvo GKev LCro LOPS NRog SDeJ WPhe
	'Guus Papendrecht' (3)	NRog
	'Gwen'PBR (3)	LHWs
	hageri (15)	GKev NRog
	- 'Splendens' (15)	GKev NRog SDeJ SPhx
	'Hakuun' (4)	NRog SDir
	'Hamilton' (7)	NRog SDeJ WPhe
	'Hans Dietrich Genscher' (3)	NRog

	'Happy Generation' (3)	GKev LCro LOPS
	'Happy Hour' (7)	ERCP
	'Harvest Moon' (3) **new**	LHWs
	'Hatsuzakura' (4) **new**	NRog
	'Havran' (3)	CAvo ERCP LCro LOPS NRog WPhe
	'Heart's Delight' (12)	CArg GKev NRog SDeJ
	'Heart's Desire' (3)	WPhe
	'Helmar' (3) 𝕐H6	NRog SDeJ WPhe
	'Hemisphere' (3)	CArg CAvo GKev LHWs LRHS NRog SDeJ
	'Hermitage' (3)	ERCP NRog
	heweri (15)	EPot GKev NRog
	hissarica (15)	NRog
	'Hocus Pocus' (5)	SDeJ
	'Holland Baby' (2)	SDeJ
	'Holland Beauty'PBR (3)	MCot
	'Holland Chic' (6)	NRog SDeJ
	'Holland Queen'PBR (3)	NRog SDeJ WPhe
	'Hollands Glorie' (4)	SDeJ
	'Honeymoon' (7)	CAvo LCro LHWs LOPS WPhe
	'Honky Tonk' (15) 𝕐H6	CAvo GKev LCro LOPS NRog WPhe
§	***hoogiana*** (15)	GKev NRog
	'Horizon'PBR (11) **new**	NRog
	'Hotpants' (3)	CAvo NRog
§	***humilis*** (15)	CRos EHyd GKev LRHS NRHS NRog SDeJ WShi
I	- 'Alba' (15) **new**	NRog
	- 'China Carol' (15)	GKev NRog SDeJ
	- 'Eastern Star' (15)	GKev NRog
§	- 'Lilliput' (15)	CRos EHyd EPot LRHS NRHS NRog
	- 'Magenta Queen' (15)	NRog
	- 'Odalisque' (15)	EHyd EPot GKev LRHS NRHS NRog
	- 'Persian Pearl' (15)	CAvo EPot ERCP GKev LCro LOPS LRHS NRog SDeJ WPhe WTor
*	- 'Pink Charm' (15)	NRog
	- var. ***pulchella*** Albocaerulea Oculata Group (15)	EPot ERCP LCro LOPS NRog
	- 'Rosea' (15)	GKev NRog
I	- 'Rosea Coerulea Oculata' (15)	NRog
	- 'Tête-à-tête' (15)	NRog
§	- Violacea Group (15)	CRos EHyd LRHS NRHS
	- - black base (15)	EPot ERCP GKev NRog
	- - yellow base (15)	EPot GKev NRog
	hungarica	GKev
	'Ice Age' (11)	WPhe
	'Ice Cream' (11)	ERCP LCro LOPS NRog SDeJ WPhe
	'Ice Stick' (12)	NRog SDeJ
	'Ice Wing' (6)	GKev
	'Île de France' (5)	ERCP LCro LOPS NRog SDeJ
	iliensis (15)	EPot GKev NRog
	INDELAND	ERCP
	'Indian Velvet' (5)	LCro LOPS
	ingens (15)	NRog
	'Innuendo' (3)	EHyd NRog SPer
	'Insulinde' (9)	GKev
	'Inzell' (3)	GKev
	'Irene Parrot' (10)	SDeJ
	'Isaak Chic' (6) **new**	LHWs
	'Istanbul' (6) **new**	LHWs
	'Ivory Floradale' (4) 𝕐H6	NRog SDeJ
	'Jackpot' (3)	SPer
	'Jacqueline' (6)	LCro LOPS
	'James Wild' (5) **new**	GKev
	'Jan Reus' (3)	CAvo ERCP LCro LOPS NRog WPhe
	'Jazz' (6)	ERCP
	'Jeantine' (12)	NRog
	'Jimmy' (3)	LRHS
	'Joanne Woodward' (14) **new**	NRog
	'Johann Strauss' (12)	CArg CAvo NRog SPer
	'Juan' (13) 𝕐H6	NRog
	'Jumbo Beauty' (5)	GKev SDeJ
	kaufmanniana (12)	GKev
§	'Kees Nelis' (3)	NRog
	'Keizerskroon' (1)	SDeJ
	'Kikomachi' (3)	CRos EHyd LRHS NRHS
	'Kingsblood' (5) 𝕐H6	ERCP NRog SDeJ
	kolpakowskiana (15) 𝕐H6	EPot ERCP GKev NRog WShi
	kurdica (15)	NRog
	- purple-flowered (15)	NRog
	'La Belle Époque' (2)	CAvo CKel ERCP GKev LCro LHWs LOPS NRog SDeJ WPhe
	'La Courtine' (5)	NRog
	'Labrador' (7)	SPer WPhe
	'Lac van Rijn' (1)	GKev
*	'Lady Diana' (14)	NRog
	'Lady Jane' (15) 𝕐H6	EPfP NRog SPhx WPhe WShi
	'Lalibela' (4)	GKev LCro LOPS
	'Lambada' (7) 𝕐H6	CAvo NRog SDeJ WPhe
	lanata (15)	GKev NRog WCot
	'Lasting Love' (3)	WPhe
	'Latvian Gold' (15)	GKev NRog
	'Leen van der Mark' (3)	NRog WPhe
	'Lemon Flight' (7)	WPhe
	'Lemon Giant' (14)	GKev
	'Libretto Parrot' (10)	SDeJ
	'Light and Dreamy' (4)	ERCP GKev LCro LHWs LOPS NRog SDeJ
	'Lilac Crystal' (7)	LCro LOPS
	'Lilac Perfection' (11)	ERCP NRog SDeJ
	'Lilac Time' (6)	SDir
	'Lilac Wonder'	see *T. saxatilis* (Bakeri Group) 'Lilac Wonder'
	'Lilliput'	see *T. humilis* 'Lilliput'
	'Lilyfire' (6)	NRog SDeJ
	'Lilyrosa' (6)	NRog
	'Lingerie' (7)	SDeJ
	linifolia (15) 𝕐H5	CAvo EPot ERCP GKev LHWs NRog SDeJ SPhx WPhe WShi
§	- Batalinii Group (15) 𝕐H5	GKev NRog
§	- - 'Apricot Jewel' (15)	EPot NRog
	- - 'Bright Gem' (15) 𝕐H5	EPot GKev NPer NRog SPhx WHoo WPhe
	- - 'Bronze Charm' (15)	CAvo EGrI EPot GKev NRog SDeJ WTor
	- - 'Red Gem' (15)	GKev NRog WCot
	- - 'Red Hunter' (15) 𝕐H5	ERCP LRHS NRog SDeJ
	- - 'Salmon Gem' (15)	CAvo SPer
	- - 'Salmon Jewel' (15)	GKev NRog
	- - 'Yellow Jewel' (15)	GKev NRog WShi
§	- Maximowiczii Group (15)	GKev NRog
	'Lion King' (7)	SDeJ
	'Lipgloss' (3)	NHol
	'Little Beauty' (15) 𝕐H6	CAvo CMea CRos EGrI EHyd EPot GKev LCro LOPS LRHS NRHS NRog SDeJ SPer SPhx WCot WHoo WPhe
	'Little Princess' (15) 𝕐H6	CAvo CRos EHyd EPot GKev LRHS NRHS NRog SDeJ SPhx
	'Little Star' (15) 𝕐H6	CMea GKev NRog SPhx
	'Long Lady' (5)	MCot NRog SDeJ
	'Love Song' (12)	NRog SDeJ
	'Lovely Surprise' (14)	SDeJ
	'Lucky Parrot' (10) **new**	NRog
§	'Lustige Witwe' (3)	SDeJ
	'Mabel' (9)	GKev
	'Macarena' (6) **new**	NRog
	'Madalyn' (6) **new**	CAvo
§	'Madame Lefeber' (13)	GKev LCro LOPS NRog SDeJ
	'Magic Lavender' (3)	GKev LHWs NRog

'Mango Charm' (3)	LHWs SDeJ
'March of Time' (14)	NRog
'Margarita' (2)	GKev LCro LOPS WPhe
'Marie José' (14)	SDeJ
'Mariette' (6)	GKev MCot NRog SDeJ
'Marilyn' (6)	ERCP GKev NRog SDeJ
marjolletii (15)	GKev
'Mary Ann' (14)	NRog
'Mascotte' (7)	NRog WPhe
'Master Peace' (7) **new**	LHWs
'Match' (3)	LCro LOPS
'Matchmaker' (3)	WPhe
'Matchpoint' (7/d)	SDeJ
'Maureen' (5) ♀H6	ERCP LCro LOPS NRog SDeJ
mauritiana 'Cindy' (15)	NRog
maximowiczii	see *T. linifolia* Maximowiczii Group
'Maytime' (6)	LCro LOPS NRog SDeJ
'Maytime Design' (6) **new**	NRog
'Melody d'Amour' (5)	GKev
'Menton' (5) ♀H6	ERCP LCro LOPS NRog SDeJ WPhe
'Menton Exotic' (11)	ERCP LCro LOPS
'Merlot' (6)	CAvo ERCP LCro LOPS MBros WPhe
'Merry Christmas' (1)	NRog
MERRY WIDOW	see *T.* 'Lustige Witwe'
'Miskodeed' (14)	NRog SDeJ
'Miss Elegance' (3)	SDir
'Mistress' (3)	CAvo ERCP LCro LOPS NRog
'Mistress Mystic' (3)	ERCP
'Mona Lisa' (6)	SDeJ
'Mondial'^{PBR} (2)	LCro LOPS NRog WPhe
'Moneymaker' (6) ♀H6	ERCP
'Monsella' (2)	NRog WPhe
§ ***montana*** (15)	EPot GKev NRog SPhx WCot
- yellow-flowered (15)	NRog
'Monte Carlo' (2) ♀H6	CArg NRog SDeJ SDir
'Monte Orange' (2)	WPhe
'Montreux' (2)	SDir
'Moulin Rouge' (3) **new**	NRog
'Mount Tacoma' (11)	ERCP GKev LCro LOPS NRog SDeJ
'Mr Van der Hoef' (2)	SDeJ
'Mrs John T. Scheepers' (5)	SDeJ
'Muriel' (10)	ERCP NRog
'Muriel Roze' (10) **new**	LHWs
'Murillo' (2)	NRog
'Mysterious Parrot' (10)	ERCP
'Mystic van Eijk'^{PBR} (4)	ERCP
'Nachtwacht' (2)	LHWs
'National Velvet' (3)	EPfP ERCP GKev LCro LOPS SPhx
'Negrita' (3)	CArg CAvo ERCP GKev LCro LOPS MCot NRog SDeJ SDir WPhe
neustruevae (15)	GKev NRog
'New Design' (3/v)	LCro LOPS NRog
'New Santa' (7)	LHWs WPhe
'Nicholas Heyek' (3)	LCro
'Night Club' (5)	CAvo ERCP
'Nightrider' (8)	LCro LOPS MCot NRog SDeJ WPhe
'Ollioules' (4) ♀H6	NRog SDeJ
'Olympic Flame' (4) ♀H6	LCro LOPS NRog SDeJ
'Orange Bouquet' (3) ♀H6	NRog SDeJ
'Orange Brilliant' (13)	GKev LCro LOPS
'Orange Emperor' (13) ♀H6	CAvo ERCP GKev MCot NRog SDeJ
'Orange Favourite' (10)	ERCP GKev NRog
'Orange Juice' (3)	WPhe
'Orange Princess' (11) ♀H6	CAvo EHyd ERCP GKev LCro LOPS NRog SDeJ SDir WPhe
'Orange Sun'	see *T.* 'Oranjezon'
'Orange Toronto' (14)	NRog
'Oranje Nassau' (2) ♀H6	EHyd
§ 'Oranjezon' (4) ♀H6	ERCP NRog
'Oratorio' (14) ♀H6	NRog SDeJ
'Oriental Beauty' (14) ♀H6	NRog
orithyioides (15)	NRog
orphanidea (15)	GKev NRog
- 'Flava' (15)	CMea ERCP GKev NRog
§ - Whittallii Group (15) ♀H6	CAvo ERCP GKev NRog SDeJ SPhx WCot WShi
'Oscar' (3)	NHol
ostrowskiana (15)	NRog
'Oviedo' (7) **new**	NRog
'Oxford' (4) ♀H6	NRog
'Pacific Pearl' (7) **new**	CAvo
'Page Polka' (3)	SDeJ
'Pallada' (3)	LCro LOPS
'Parrot King' (10)	NRog SDeJ
§ ***passeriniana*** (15)	GKev NRog
'Passionale' (3) ♀H6	LCro LOPS NRog SDeJ WPhe
'Paul Scherer' (3) ♀H6	CAvo EPfP ERCP GKev LCro LOPS MMrt NRog SDeJ WPhe
'Peach Blossom' (2)	CArg EHyd LCro LOPS LRHS NRHS NRog SDeJ
Peacock Group	SDeJ
'Peppermintstick' (15) ♀H6	CAvo ERCP GKev MPie NRog SDeJ SPhx
'Perestroyka' (5)	ERCP SDeJ
persica	see *T. celsiana*
'Picture' (5)	ERCP SDeJ
'Pieter de Leur' (6)	CAvo LCro LOPS
'Pimpernel' (8/v)	SDeJ
'Pink Diamond' (5)	ERCP GKev MBros NHol SDeJ SDir
'Pink Dwarf' (12)	NRog SDeJ
'Pink Impression' (4) ♀H6	CArg LCro LOPS NRog SDeJ
'Pink Ribbon' (3) **new**	NRog
'Pink Sensation' (14)	SDeJ
'Pink Star' (11)	ERCP
'Pinocchio' (14)	CArg CRos EHyd GKev LRHS NRHS NRog SDeJ WPhe
'Pirand' (13) ♀H6	NRog SDeJ
'Pittsburg' (3)	LCro LOPS
'Plaisir' (14) ♀H6	NRog
'Playtime' (6) **new**	NRog
'Poco Loco' (13)	GKev NRog SDeJ
polychroma	see *T. biflora*
praestans (15)	GKev LRHS NRog WShi
- 'Bloemenlust' (15)	NRog
- 'Fusilier' (15) ♀H6	CExl GKev NRog SDeJ
- 'Moondance' (15)	NRog
- 'Red Sun' (15)	NRog
- 'Shogun' (15)	EGrl ERCP GKev NRog SDeJ
- 'Unicum' (15/v)	ERCP LRHS NRog SDeJ SDir
- 'Van Tubergen's Variety' (15)	GKev NPer NRog
- 'Yari' (15)	NRog
- 'Zwanenburg Variety' (15)	GKev NRog
'Pretty Princess' (3)	CRos ERCP LRHS SDeJ WPhe
'Princeps' (13)	NRog SDeJ
'Princesse Charmante' (14) ♀H6	LCro LOPS NRog
'Prinses Irene' (3) ♀H6	CArg CAvo CMea CRos EHyd ERCP GKev LCro LOPS LRHS NBir NHol NRHS NRog SDeJ WPhe
'Prinses Margriet' (3)	ERCP NRog WPhe
'Professor Röntgen' (10)	ERCP LCro LOPS NRog SDeJ
pulchella humilis	see *T. humilis*
§ 'Purissima' (13) ♀H6	CAvo EPfP GKev LCro LOPS LRHS NRog SDeJ SPer WPhe
'Purissima Design' (13) **new**	NRog
'Purple Bouquet' (3)	SDeJ
'Purple Doll' (6)	LCro LOPS
'Purple Dream' (6)	LCro LOPS MCot NRog SDeJ
'Purple Flag' (3)	LCro LOPS
'Purple Peony' (2)	ERCP

	'Purple Prince' (5) **new**	LRHS
I	'Purple Prince' (1)	CArg EHyd LCro LOPS NRHS NRog SDeJ WPhe
	'Purple Tower' (7)	ERCP NRog
	'Quebec' (14)	NRog SDeJ
	'Queen of Marvel' (2)	NRog SDeJ
	'Queen of Night' (5)	CArg CAvo CMea EPfP ERCP GKev LCro LOPS MBros MCot NBir NRog SDeJ SDir SPer WPhe
	'Queensday' (11)	SDeJ
	'Queensland' (7)	NRog WPhe
	'Rai' (10)	SDeJ
	'Real Time' (7)	WPhe
	'Recreado' (5)	ERCP NRog SDeJ
	'Red Emperor'	see *T.* 'Madame Lefeber'
	'Red Georgette' (5) ♀H6	GKev NBir NRog SDeJ
	'Red Hat' (7) ♀H6	LCro LOPS
	'Red Impression'PBR (4) ♀H6	LCro LOPS NRog
	'Red Princess' (11) ♀H6	ERCP LRHS NRog WPhe
	'Red Revival' (1)	GKev
	'Red Riding Hood' (14) ♀H6	CArg CAvo CRos EHyd EPfP GKev LCro LOPS LRHS NBir NRHS NRog SDeJ SPer
	'Red Rover' (3)	LCro LOPS
	'Red Shine' (6) ♀H6	ERCP LCro LOPS NRog SDeJ
	'Red Springgreen' (8)	GKev LCro LOPS NRog SDeJ
	'Red Wing' (7) ♀H6	SDeJ
	'Redwood' (14)	SDeJ
	regelii (15)	NRog
	'Rems Favourite' (3)	LCro LOPS NRog SDeJ WPhe
	'Renown' (5)	NRog SDeJ
	'Request' (3)	ERCP GKev
	'Ringo'	see *T.* 'Kees Nelis'
	'Rob Verlinden' (14) **new**	SPer
	'Robassa' (13)	NRog
	'Robinho'PBR (11)	GKev
	'Rockery Master' (14)	NRog
	'Rococo' (10)	CAvo ERCP LCro LOPS LRHS NRog SDeJ SDir WPhe
	'Roi du Midi' (5)	NRog SDeJ
	'Ronaldo' (3)	ERCP GKev LCro LOPS NRog
	'Rosalie' (3)	ERCP NRog SDeJ
	'Rosy Dream' (13)	SDeJ
	'Royal Acres' (2)	LRHS
	'Royal Anthos' (14)	NRog SDeJ
	'Royal Celebration' (6) **new**	SPer
	'Royal Virgin' (3)	ERCP
	'Salmon Impression' (4)	NRog SDeJ
	'Sanne' (3) ♀H6	CAvo ERCP SDeJ WPhe
	'Santander' (7)	SDeJ
	'Sapporo' (6)	ERCP LCro LOPS
	saracenica (15)	GKev
	saxatilis (15)	GKev LCro LOPS NRog SDeJ
§	- Bakeri Group (15)	SEND
§	- - 'Lilac Wonder' (15) ♀H6	CAvo CExl EPot ERCP LCro LOPS NPer NRog SDeJ SDir SPhx WShi
	'Scarlet Baby' (12)	NRog WPhe
	'Scarlet Verona' (2) **new**	LRHS
	schrenkii (15)	EPot ERCP GKev NRog WShi
	'Seadov' (3) ♀H6	LCro LOPS LRHS NRog SDeJ SPer
	'Seattle' (6)	ERCP
	'Secret Perfume' (2) **new**	LHWs
	'Sensual Touch' (7) ♀H6	LHWs NRog SDeJ WPhe
	'Shakespeare' (12)	NRog SDeJ
	'Shirley' (3)	CAvo ERCP GKev LCro LOPS NRog SDeJ
	'Shirley Double' (11) **new**	LHWs
	'Shirley Dream' (3)	SDeJ
	'Showtime' (14)	SDeJ
	'Showwinner' (12) ♀H6	GKev MBros NHol NRog SDeJ

	'Silk Road' (2)	GKev
	'Silver Parrot' (10)	WPhe
	'Silverstream' (4)	GKev NRog
	'Slawa'PBR (3)	CAvo LCro LOPS
	'Snow Crystal' (11)	WPhe
	'Snow Parrot' (10)	ERCP
	'Snow Valley' (7)	ERCP
	sogdiana (15)	GKev NRog
	'Solar Wind' (15) **new**	NRog
	'Solva' (13) **new**	NRog
	'Sombrero' (14) **new**	NRog
§	'Sonnet' (6)	NRog SDeJ
	'Sorbet' (5) ♀H6	GKev NRog SDeJ
	sosnowskyi (15)	GKev
	sprengeri (15) ♀H6	CAvo CBro CExl CSpe ECha ERCP GKev ITim NRog WHal
	- Trotter's form (15)	GKev WCot
	'Spring Green' (8) ♀H6	CArg CAvo EPfP ERCP GKev LCro LOPS MCot NRog SDeJ SPhx WPhe
	'Spryng' (3) ♀H6	LHWs SDeJ
	'Spryng Break' (3) **new**	LHWs
	'Spryng Tide' (3) **new**	LHWs
	'Starfighter' (7)	SDeJ
	stellata	see *T. clusiana* var. *stellata*
	'Stresa' (12) ♀H6	CRos EHyd GKev LRHS NRHS NRog SDeJ
	'Striped Bellona' (3)	NRog
	'Strong Gold' (3) ♀H6	NRog SDeJ WPhe
	'Stunning Apricot' (5)	GKev LCro LOPS
	subpraestans (15)	NRog
	'Suncatcher' (3)	SDeJ
	'Sundowner' (11) **new**	LHWs
	'Sunny Prince'PBR (1)	CAvo NRog SDeJ WPhe
	'Super Parrot' (10)	WPhe
	'Survivor' (5)	SDeJ
	'Swan Wings' (7)	ERCP GKev LCro LOPS NRog SDeJ
	'Sweet Desire' (2)	SDeJ
	'Sweet Impression' (4)	ERCP NRog
	'Sweet Lady' (14)	LRHS NRog SDeJ
	'Sweet Love' (3) **new**	NRog
	'Sweetheart' (13)	GKev LCro LOPS MCot NRog SDeJ WPhe
	sylvestris (15)	CAvo EPot ERCP GKev LCro LOPS NBir NRog SDeJ SPhx WCot WShi
	'Synaeda Amor' (3)	LCro LOPS NRog SPer
	'Synaeda King' (6) ♀H6	NRog
	systola (15)	GKev NRog
	'Tabledance' (11) **new**	LRHS
	'Taco' (15)	NRog WPhe
	'Tarafa' (14)	SDeJ
	tarda (15) ♀H6	CAvo CExl CRos EHyd EPfP ERCP GKev LCro LOPS LRHS NRHS NRog SDeJ SPhx WPhe WShi
	- 'Kashka-Su' (15) **new**	NRog
	'Temple of Beauty' (5) ♀H6	GKev NRog SDeJ
	tetraphylla (15)	NRog
	'Texas Flame' (10)	GKev NRog SDeJ
	'Texas Gold' (10)	NRog SDeJ
	'The Edge' (2) **new**	LRHS
	'The First' (12)	GKev NRog
	'The Lizard' (9)	GKev SDir
	'Tinka' (15) ♀H6	GKev NRog
	'Tiny Timo' (15)	ERCP NRog
	'Tom Pouce' (3)	LCro LOPS NRog WPhe
	'Toplips' (11)	SDeJ
	'Topparrot' (10)	SDeJ
	'Toronto' (14) ♀H6	NRog SDeJ
	'Toronto Double' (2)	NRog SDeJ
	'Toyota' (5)	SDeJ
	'Très Chic' (6)	CAvo EPfP LCro LOPS NRog SPer

'Tricolored Beauty' (8) NRog
'Tropical Dream' (3) NRog
tschimganica (15) NRog WCot
- red-flowered GKev
- yellow-flowered GKev
tubergeniana NRog
'Keukenhof' (15)
turkestanica (15) ♀H5 CAvo CExl EHyd EPot ERCP GKev LRHS MBros NPer NRHS NRog SDeJ WHoo WShi
- 'Dshizak' (15) **new** NRog
'Turkish Delight' (14) NPer
'Typhoon' (3) NRog
'Uncle Tom' (11) ERCP GKev NRog SDeJ WPhe
§ ***undulatifolia*** (15) GKev NRog WCot
- 'Clare Benedict' (15) NRog
- 'Excelsa' (15) NRog
'Unique de France'PBR (3) CAvo NRog
'United States' (14) ♀H6 NPer
urumiensis (15) ♀H5 EPot ERCP GKev NRog SDeJ SPhx
'Valentine' (3) SDeJ
'Valery Gergiev' (7) ERCP NRog SDeJ
'Van der Neer' (1) NRog SDeJ
'Van Eijk'PBR (4) GKev
'Vanilla Cream' (14) NRog SDeJ
'Vaya con Dios' (7) **new** LHWs
'Verona' (2) LRHS NRog SDeJ WPhe
'Véronique Sanson' (3) ERCP LCro LOPS NRog SDeJ
'Victoria's Secret' (3) GKev LHWs SPer
'Viking' (2) LRHS WPhe
'Vincent van Gogh' (7) ♀H6 LHWs
'Violet Beauty' (5) LCro LOPS SDeJ WPhe
'Violet Bird' (8) CAvo GKev LCro LOPS SDeJ SDir
'Virichic' (8) ERCP GKev LCro LOPS MCot NRog WPhe
'Viridiflora' (8) SVic
vvedenskyi (15) EPot NRog
- 'Tangerine Beauty' (15) ♀H6 GKev NRog
'Wallflower' (5) NRog
'Warbler' (7) NRog SDeJ
'Washington' (3) LCro LOPS NRog
'Weber's Parrot' (10) LCro LOPS MCot
'Wedding Gift' (11) SDeJ
'Weisse Berliner' (3) NRog
'West Point' (6) LCro LOPS NRog SDeJ WPhe
'Whispering Dream' (3) LHWs WPhe
'White Dream' (3) CArg GKev LCro LOPS NRog SDeJ SPer
'White Emperor' see *T.* 'Purissima'
'White Liberstar' (3) ERCP
'White Marvel' (3) EHyd NRog
'White Parrot' (10) CAvo ERCP GKev LCro LOPS MCot NRog SDeJ
'White Prince' (1) GKev WPhe
'White Triumphator' (6) ♀H6 CArg CAvo CMea ERCP GKev LCro LOPS MCot NBir NRog SDeJ SPhx WPhe
whittallii see *T. orphanidea* Whittallii Group
'Wildhof' (3) ♀H6 NRog
§ 'Willem van Oranje' (2) LRHS NRog SDeJ
'Willemsoord' (2) EHyd NRog SDeJ
WILLIAM OF ORANGE see *T.* 'Willem van Oranje'
wilsoniana see *T. montana*
'Wisley' (5) ♀H6 LCro LOPS
'World Expression' (5) ♀H6 NRog SDeJ
'World Friendship' (3) GKev LHWs SPer
'World Peace'PBR (4) LCro LOPS
'World's Favourite' (4) ♀H6 NRog
'Wow' (11) ERCP
'Yellow Flight' (3) NRog SDeJ
'Yellow Pompenette'PBR (11) ♀H6 SDeJ
I 'Yellow Purissima' (13) ♀H6 NRog SDir
'Yellow Spider' (11) WPhe
'Yellow Springgreen' (8) ERCP NRog SDeJ SDir
'Yellow Sun' (10) WPhe
'Yellow Wave' (4) NRog
'Yoko Parrot' (10) SDeJ
'Yokohama' (3) NRog SDeJ
'Yonina' (6) CArg GKev LCro LOPS NRog SDeJ
'Zampa' (14) ♀H6 NRog
'Zombie' (13) NRog
§ 'Zurel' (3) CArg ERCP GKev SDir

tummelberry see *Rubus* 'Tummelberry'

Tunica see *Petrorhagia*

Tupistra (*Asparagaceae*)

aurantiaca GEdr GGro LEdu WPGP
- B&SWJ 2267 WCot WCru
- B&SWJ 2401 WCru
chinensis 'Eco China Ruffles' WCot
grandistigma WCot
- B&SWJ 11773 WCru
jinshanensis WCot
urotepala HWJ 562 WCru
wattii B&SWJ 8297 WCru

turnip see AGM Vegetables Section

Turpinia (*Staphyleaceae*)

ternata CWJ 12360 WCru

Tussilago (*Asteraceae*)

farfara GPoy MHer WHer WSFF

Tweedia (*Apocynaceae*)

§ ***coerulea*** ♀H1c CBcs CCCN CDTJ CSpe SChF SGro SIvy SPad SPer SWvt WSFF

Typha (*Typhaceae*)

angustifolia CBen CPud CWat LLWG NPer SPlb
latifolia CBen CPud CWat LLWG NBir NMir NPer SVic WMAq XLum
- 'Variegata' (v) CWat LLWG MWts WMAq
§ ***laxmannii*** CBen LLWG WPnP XLum
lugdunensis MWts
minima CBen CPud CWat EWat LLWG MWts NPer WMAq WPnP XLum
shuttleworthii CBen LLWG
stenophylla see *T. laxmannii*

Typhonium (*Araceae*)

giganteum SBrt WCot
horsfieldii MPie
roxburghii EBee WFar

U

ugli see *Citrus* × *aurantium* (Tangelo Group) 'Ugli'

Ugni ✿ (*Myrtaceae*)

candollei SVen
§ ***molinae*** Widely available
- PAB 1347 SBrt
- 'Big Burning Pink' LEdu

- 'Butterball'	CBcs CBod CDoC CKel CTrC EBee EPfP LEdu LRHS SPoG SWvt
- 'Flambeau' (v)	CAgr CBcs CBod CDoC CEme CExl CKel CMac CSde CTrC EBee EHyd ELan EPfP EShb LEdu LRHS MAsh MGil NLar NRHS SEle SIvy SLon SPoG SRms SWvt WPav
- 'Ka-Pow'	CBod CCCN CDoC CTrC LCro LRHS MHtn SPad WPGP WTyc
- 'Miss Green' **new**	SBrt
- orange-leaved	WJek
- 'Variegata' (v)	LEdu WJek
- 'Villarica Strawberry'	LEdu WPGP

Ulex (*Fabaceae*)

europaeus	CBcs CCVT CHab CMac CTri ELan ELon EPfP GQue LBuc MGil MGos MMuc NWea SCob SEWo SPer WKor
§ - 'Flore Pleno' (d) 🏆H6	CBcs CBod CCoa CDoC CMac CSBt CSde ELan ELon EPfP IArd MBlu NWea SCob SDix SPer WFar WHer
- 'Irish Double' (d)	NLar
- 'Plenus'	see *U. europaeus* 'Flore Pleno'

Ulmus ✿ (*Ulmaceae*)

americana 'Princeton'	SCob
× ***androssowii***	WPGP
bergmanniana	WPGP
changii	WPGP
chenmoui	IArd IDee WPGP
'Clusius' **new**	LPar
'Columella'	LPar SAko WPGP
davidiana	WPGP
- var. ***davidiana***	WPGP
- var. ***japonica***	WPGP
- - 'Prospector'	WPGP
'Dodoens'	LPar MBlu SCob
'Frontier'	SGol WPGP
§ ***glabra***	CAco EPfP IPap LPar MGos NRog NWea WTSh
- 'Camperdownii'	CBod CMac ELan SGsty WMou
- 'Lutescens'	CDoC NOra WMat
harbinensis	WPGP
§ × ***hollandica*** 'Dampieri Aurea' 🏆H7	ELan ELon EPfP LBuc LPar MAsh MBlu MRav NLar NOrn NRog NWea SPoG WMat
- 'Jacqueline Hillier'	CMac CSpe EBee ELan LMaj LPar LRHS MMuc NLar SEND SGBe SGol WFar WLov
- 'Wredei'	see *U.* × *hollandica* 'Dampieri Aurea'
'Homestead'	WPGP
laevis	WPGP
lamellosa **new**	WPGP
'Lobel'	CCVT LPar SCob
LUTÈCE ('Nanguen')	MTrO
× ***mesocarpa***	WPGP
minor	MGos NWea
- 'Dampieri Aurea'	see *U.* × *hollandica* 'Dampieri Aurea'
- var. ***suberosa*** **new**	CAco
montana	see *U. glabra*
parvifolia	CAco CMCN CMen EShb WPGP
- 'Geisha' (v)	ELan NLar
- 'Hallelujah' **new**	WPGP
§ - 'Hokkaido'	EWes NLar WAbe
- var. ***lanceolata*** **new**	WPGP
- 'Pygmaea'	see *U. parvifolia* 'Hokkaido'
- 'Sagei' **new**	NLar
- 'Yatsubusa'	MRav WPGP
procera	MGos WSFF
- 'Argenteovariegata' (v)	NLar
prunifolia	WPGP
pumila 'Beijing Gold'	ELan NLar
'Regal'	WPGP
'Sapporo Autumn Gold'	CCVT MRav
szechuanica	WPGP
uyematsui	SMad WPGP
VADA ('Wanoux'[PBR])	SGol
villosa	EBee WPGP

Umbellularia (*Lauraceae*)

californica	CMCN NLar

Umbilicus (*Crassulaceae*)

§ ***oppositifolius*** 🏆H5	CBod CElw CTri ECha EDAr EHyd ELan EPfP GAbr GEdr GKev GLog LPot LRHS MRav NBid NRHS NSla SPlb SRms SRot WFar WHoo WKif WSHC XLum
- 'Jane's Reverse' (v)	WCot
§ - 'Jim's Pride' (v)	ECha EWes GKev GPSL MHer MRav NFav NHpl NPer NWad SPlb SRms WFar WSHC
rupestris	SChr SPhx WHer WShi

Uncinia (*Cyperaceae*)

* ***cyparissias*** from Chile	NBir
egmontiana	CBod CPla EBee EHyd EPfP LShi NWad WGrn
rubra	CBod CChe CEnd CRos CSBt EBee EHyd ELan EPfP EShb GMaP LRHS MGos MRav NRHS NSti NWad SPad SPlb SPoG WChS WFar
§ - 'Belinda's Find'[PBR]	CBod CKno CPla EBee EHyd ELan LRHS MAsh MBNS MPri NLar SCoo SPoG SRms WPnP XSte
- EVERFLAME	see *U. rubra* 'Belinda's Find'
uncinata	CBcs ECha EGrl SDix
* - ***rubra***	CDoC CKno MAsh MBow SCob SRms SWvt

Uniola (*Poaceae*)

latifolia	see *Chasmanthium latifolium*

Urginea (*Asparagaceae*)

maritima	see *Charybdis maritima*

Urospermum (*Asteraceae*)

dalechampii	CCCN

Urtica (*Urticaceae*)

dioica 'Bradfield Purpler'	CNat
- 'Chedglow 2' (v)	CNat
- 'Good as Gold'	CNat

Utricularia (*Lentibulariaceae*)

alpina	SHmp
bisquamata	SHmp
- 'Betty's Bay' 🏆H2	CHew
calycifida	SHmp
dichotoma	CHew
geminiloba	CHew
lateriflora	CHew
livida 🏆H2	CHew SHmp
longifolia	SHmp
microcalyx	CHew
nephrophylla	CHew
parthenopipes	CHew
paulineae	CHew
praelonga	CHew SHmp
prehensilis	CHew

reniformis CHew SHmp
sandersonii ♀H2 CHew SHmp
tricolor CHew SHmp
uniflora CHew

Uvularia (*Colchicaceae*)

grandiflora ♀H6 Widely available
- gold-leaved CMiW
- 'Lynda Windsor' LEdu NHsp WSHC
- var. ***pallida*** CBct CMiW CRos CTtf EBee ECha EHed EMor EPPr EPfP EPot GBin GEdr GKev IBlr ILea LEdu LRHS MRav NHsp NLar NRHS WCru WFar
- 'Susie Lewis' WCru

grandiflora × perfoliata CMiW NBir
perfoliata CExl EBee ECha EMor EPPr EPfP EPot GKev IBlr LEdu MRav NBir NChi NHpl NLar SPlb WCru WFar
- tall EPPr

sessilifolia CExl CMiW EHyd EMor EPfP GKev LEdu LRHS MMrt NHsp NLar NRHS WCru
- 'Cobblewood Gold' (v) EPPr LEdu WCru WFar

V

Vaccaria (*Caryophyllaceae*)

§ ***hispanica*** SPhx

Vaccinium ✿ (*Ericaceae*)

arctostaphylos SWvt
'Berkeley' (F) CAgr CCCN CEnd GKin MBlu SEdi SGsty SPre WLea
BLUE DESSERT (F) **new** LRHS
BLUE SUEDE ('Th-682') (F) CBcs CMac LCro LOPS LRHS NLar NRHS XSte
'Bluejay' (F) CRos EHyd ELan LRHS MAsh NRHS NRog SCoo SEdi SLon SPoG WLea
'Blueray' (F) GKin
'Brigitta' (F) CEnd CTrh EPom NRHS NRog SBdl SCoo SPoG SPre WLea
chaetothrix WAbe WThu
'Chandler' (F) CAgr CArg CDoC CEnd CMac CTrh EPom GKin LCro LOPS LRHS MTrO SEdi SKee SSFr
consanguineum B&SWJ 10486 WCru
corymbosum (F) CBcs MNHC SCoo SSta
- 'Aurora'PBR (F) CTrh
- 'Blauweiss-Goldtraube' (F) CAgr CMac CSBt ELan EPfP GKin MAsh NLar NRog SCoo SPoG SVic WLea WTSh
- 'Blue Duke' (F) LSRN
- 'Blue Pearl' (F) CMac
- 'Blue Sapphire' (F) LCro LOPS
- 'Bluecrop' (F) Widely available
- 'Bluegold' (F) CRos EHyd LCro LOPS LRHS MAsh NRHS SCoo SPoG
- 'Bluetta' (F) CAgr CTri ELan SCoo SPoG
- 'Collins' (F) SBdl
- 'Darrow' (F) CAgr MTrO NRHS WMat
- 'Dixie' (F) CSBt NLar
- 'Duke' (F) ♀H6 CArg CDoC CTrh ELan EPfP EPom LCro LOPS MCoo MGos NRog NWea SCoo SPre SRkn SSFr
- 'Elliott' (F) CMac LRHS LSRN XSte
- 'Grover' (F) SEdi
- 'Hardyblue' (F) CAgr
- 'Hortblue Petite'PBR (F) SBdl SVic
- 'Huron'PBR (F) CTrh
- 'Jersey' (F) CAgr CEnd CRos EHyd EPfP LRHS MAsh MGos NRHS NRog SCoo SEdi SPer SPoG SVic
- 'Legacy' (F) NRHS
- 'Liberty'PBR (F) CTrh EPfP MTrO SBdl
- 'Nelson' (F) SCoo
- 'Nui' (F) CEnd EPom LSRN MRav
- 'Patriot' (F) CAgr CEnd CRos CSBt CTrh EHyd ELan EPom GDam GKin LBuc LRHS MGos MPri MRav MTrO NLar NRHS NRog SCoo SPer SPre SSFr WLea WMat XSte
- 'Polaris' (F) CEnd
- 'Reka' (F) CAgr NPer
- 'Spartan' (F) ♀H6 CDoC CMac CTrh EPom LCro LOPS LRHS LSRN MGos SKee
- 'Stanley' (F) CRos EHyd EPfP LRHS NRHS SPoG
- 'Toro' (F) SPre
- YELLOBERRY BLUE ('Andval1601') (F) LCro

crassifolium subsp. ***sempervirens*** 'Well's Delight' (F) EHyd LRHS MAsh
cylindraceum ♀H4 CBcs CEnd EBee NLar SSta
delavayi GArf LRHS MAsh SSta WThu
dunalianum var. ***caudatifolium*** B&SWJ 1716 WCru
- - NMWJ 14558 WCru
- var. ***megaphyllum*** HWJ 515 WCru

'Earliblue' (F) CAgr CSBt CTrh GKin LBuc NRHS NWea SPer SPoG WLea WMat
floribundum CRos EHyd GArf LRHS MAsh
glaucoalbum ♀H5 CMac EBee EGrl EHyd LRHS MAsh MBlu MRav NRHS SPoG
'Goldtraube 71' MAsh NRog SEdi
griffithianum SSta
'Herbert' (F) CAgr CTrh EPom LBuc SEdi
macrocarpon (F) CRos EHyd ELan LRHS MAsh NRHS SPre SRms WKor XAbr
- 'Early Black' (F) ELan EPom GKin IDee LBuc NRog SVic WTSh
- 'Hamilton' EPot GArf WThu
- 'Howes' (F) NRog
- 'Langlois' (F) NLar
- 'McFarlin' (F) NRog
- 'Olson's Honkers' (F) CAgr
- 'Pilgrim' (F) CAgr CSBt LCro LEdu LOPS MAsh NRog SPoG WMat
- 'Red Star' (F) CTrh
- 'Stevens' (F) CAgr NRog

moupinense LRHS MAsh WThu
myrtillus CAgr EPom GPoy SVic WKor XAbr
'Northblue' (F) ELan
'Northland' (F) CSBt EPfP EPom MAsh MRav MTrO NLar NRHS NRog SCoo SPoG WMat
nummularia GRum NLar WAbe WThu
'Osorno' (F) CTrh
ovatum (F) CBcs CMac GKin WThu
- 'Pacific Spear' (F) SVic
- 'Thundercloud' (F) EHyd EPfP LRHS MAsh NRHS SSta

§ ***oxycoccos*** (F) CAgr GPoy MCoo WThu
'Ozarkblue' (F) EPom LCro LOPS NRHS SEdi
palustre see *V. oxycoccos*
§ 'Pink Lemonade' (F) CRos ELan EPom LCro LOPS LRHS MHtn MPri NRHS NRog SBdl SEdi SPer SPoG SSFr

'Pink Sapphire'	see *V.* 'Pink Lemonade'
praestans	GArf
randaiense B&SWJ 14601 **new**	WCru
retusum	WThu
'Rubel' (F)	NRHS
sikkimense	GArf
'Spring Surprise'	WAbe WThu
'Sunshine Blue' (F)	CAgr CEnd CTrh EHyd ELan EPom LBuc LRHS MTrO SPoG SSFr
'Tophat' (F)	CCCN LEdu
vitis-idaea	EPfP EWes GPoy SVic WKor
- 'Compactum'	EWes
- FIREBALLS ('Lirome'PBR) (F) **new**	NRog
- 'Ida'	LBuc
- Koralle Group ♀H5	CAgr EPot GArf GKin NLar NRog NWad
- 'Leucocarpa'	NLar
- subsp. ***minus***	GEdr NLar NWad
- MISS CHERRY ('Meliro'PBR) (F) **new**	NRog
- 'Red Candy'PBR	LCro LOPS LRHS
- 'Red Pearl'	CSBt EPom MAsh NRog

Vachellia (*Leguminosae*)

§ ***karroo***	CDTJ SPlb

Vagaria (*Amaryllidaceae*)

parviflora	GKev

Valeriana (*Caprifoliaceae*)

'Alba'	see *Centranthus ruber* 'Albus'
alliariifolia	GQue MSpe NBro SPhx
- PAB 3001	LEdu WPGP
arizonica	EBou
'Coccinea'	see *Centranthus ruber*
dioica	LLWG
fauriei	GGro
hardwickii PAB 8999	LEdu
jatamansi	GPoy SRms
- PAB 6846	LEdu WPGP
montana	CTtf GGro LEdu MMuc NBro NRya SPhx SRms
officinalis	Widely available
- 'Chiri Fu' (v) **new**	WCot
- subsp. ***sambucifolia***	EPPr MNrw MSpe SHar
phu **new**	EGrI
- 'Aurea'	CBod CCBP CDor CHby CMac EBee ECha EGrI EHyd ELan EPfP GKin GQue LRHS MBriF MPie MRav NBid NBir NBro NLar NSti SPer SPoG SRms WCAu WWtn
pyrenaica	CKel EBee ECha EPPr GGro LEdu LRHS MBriF MMuc MNrw MPie SDix SEND SHar SPhx SPtp WCot WHrl
wallrothii	WCot

Valerianella (*Caprifoliaceae*)

§ ***locusta***	CBod GPoy SVic
- 'Medaillon' ♀H3	LCro LOPS
olitoria	see *V. locusta*

Vallea (*Elaeocarpaceae*)

stipularis	CTsd IArd IDee SBrt

Vallisneria (*Hydrocharitaceae*)

spiralis	LLWG

Vallota see *Cyrtanthus*

Vancouveria (*Berberidaceae*)

chrysantha	CExl ECha EPPr EPfP GEdr GLog NRya WFar WPGP
hexandra	CExl CMac EBee ECha EMor EPPr EPfP GEdr GKev GLog ILea LEdu LRHS NBir NSti SPlb WCru WPGP
planipetala	GEdr WCru

Vania see *Thlaspi*

Vasconcellea (*Caricaceae*)

§ ***pubescens***	CDTJ SPlb

Vellozia (*Velloziaceae*)

elegans	see *Talbotia elegans*

Veltheimia ✿ (*Asparagaceae*)

§ ***bracteata*** ♀H2	CPla EPri GKev NRog SGro SRms
- cream-flowered **new**	NRog
- deep pink-flowered **new**	NRog
- 'Lemon Flame'	GKev NRog
- 'Rosalba' **new**	NRog
- yellow-flowered	NRog
§ ***capensis*** ♀H2	NRog
viridifolia misapplied	see *V. capensis*
viridifolia Jacq.	see *V. bracteata*

× *Venidioarctotis* see *Arctotis*

Venidium see *Arctotis*

Veratrum (*Melanthiaceae*)

album ♀H7	EBee ECha EMor GEdr GJos GKev GPoy ILea MNrw MRav NBid WCot WCru WPGP WSHC
- PAB 537	LEdu
- 'Auvergne White'	EBee LEdu MNrw
- var. ***flavum***	LPla MNrw SPhx WCot WCru
- - 'Primrose Warburg'	GEdr
- subsp. ***lobelianum***	LEdu
- 'Lorna's Green' ♀H7	MAvo MNrw WCot
californicum ♀H3	CBct EBee ECha LEdu LPla MNrw NBid WCru WPGP WSHC WWFP
formosanum	EBee GEdr MNrw WCot WSHC
- B&SWJ 1575	WCru
- RWJ 9806	WCru
grandiflorum B&SWJ 4416	WCru
longebracteatum	WCru
maackii	EBee ECha GArf MNrw SMad
- B&SWJ 5875	WCru
- green-flowered	LEdu MNrw
- var. ***japonicum***	GKev MNrw
- var. ***maackii***	MNrw
nigrum ♀H6	CBct EBee ECha EHyd EWoo GEdr GKev GMaP ILea LEdu MMrt MNrw MRav NBid NBir SEdd SMad SPhx SPlb WCot WCru WMal WSHC
- B&SWJ 4450 from South Korea	WCru
schindleri	GEdr MNrw
- B&SWJ 4068	WCru
viride	EBee EWes LEdu MNrw NBid WCot WCru

Verbascum (*Scrophulariaceae*)

'Apricot Sunset'	SPhx
'Arctic Summer'	see *V. bombyciferum* 'Polarsommer'
arcturus	SVen

	'Argentina'	WHer
	blattaria	NBir SBut WHer
	- f. ***albiflorum***	CSpe EAJP LRHS NDov NGBl SPhx SPlb WHer
	- 'White Blush' **new**	LShi
	'Blue Lagoon'	CWGN SCob
§	***bombyciferum***	ECha ELan GMaP LRHS NGBl SCob SPhx SRms
*	- 'Arctic Snow'	SPoG
§	- 'Polarsommer'	CSpe EPfP LRHS NBir SPer
	- 'Silver Lining'	NPer
	'Broussa'	see *V. bombyciferum*
	'Buttercup'	EHyd
	'Camelot'	EHyd
	'Caribbean Crush'	CRos ECtt EHyd ELan GWyn LRHS MBNS SGBe SPer SPoG WSpi
	chaixii	CBod ECha EPPr MArl MMrt NBir SDix WFar
	- 'Album'	Widely available
	- 'Sixteen Candles'	CBod NLar WFar
	- 'Wedding Candles'	ELan EPfP GWyn NGdn SBls SPtp WFar
	'Cherry Helen'PBR	EBee LCro LOPS LRHS MBNS NLar SCob
	'Christo's Yellow Lightning' ♀H6	CBod EBee ECha ECtt GBin LRHS MAvo SDix SEdd SPoG WCot
	'Clementine'	CBcs ECtt EPPr EPfP LCro LOPS SCob SPhx WFar WHil
	'Coneyhill Yellow'	EPPr
	(Cotswold Group) 'Cotswold Beauty'	CBod ECtt EHyd EPfP EWoo GMaP LRHS MRav NDov NGdn NRHS SCob SHar SPer WCAu WCav WHoo
	- 'Cotswold Queen'	CBod ECtt EHyd EPPr EPfP LCro LOPS LRHS MMrt MRav NDov NRHS SCob SCoo SHar SPer SWvt WCAu WSpi
	- 'Gainsborough' ♀H6	CBod CDor ECha ECtt EPfP EWTr EWoo GDam GMaP LCro LOPS LRHS MArl MRav NLar NRHS SCob SGbt SPer SPoG SWvt WCAu WGwG WSpi
	- 'Mont Blanc'	LRHS NRHS
	- 'Pink Domino' ♀H6	CBod ECtt EHyd EPPr EPfP EWhm GMaP LCro LOPS LRHS MCot MHer MHol MRav NDov NRHS SCob SPer SWvt WSpi
	- 'Royal Highland'	CBod CNor EBee ECtt EHyd EPfP LRHS MBNS NRHS SWvt WHoo
	- 'White Domino'	SPer WSpi
	'Cotswold King'	see *V. creticum*
§	***creticum***	CSpe CTtf SCob WCot
	'Dark Eyes'PBR	CBod CWGN ECtt LRHS NHpl NLar SCoo SGBe
	dumulosum ♀H4	EPot WAbe
	epixanthinum ♀H5	EBee GJos
	'Firedance'	CBcs ECtt EHyd EPfP GBin LRHS MHer MHol NGBl NRHS SHar WCAu
	'Golden Wings' ♀H4	WAbe
	'Guinevere'	EHyd
	'Helen Johnson'	CBod CWCL ECtt EHyd LRHS MGos MRav NLar NRHS SCob SCoo SGbt SPer SWvt WSpi
	'Honey Dijon'	MBros SPad
	× ***hybridum*** 'Banana Custard'	EHyd EPfP NGBl WSpi
	- 'Copper Rose'	EHyd EPfP
	- 'Snow Maiden'	CTri EPfP LShi SBut
	- 'Wega'	NLar
	'Jackie'	ECtt EHyd LRHS SGBe
	'Jackie in Pink'	LRHS

	'Jackie in Spots' **new**	LRHS
	'Jackie in Yellow'PBR	LRHS
	'Jester'	EBee ECtt MBNS SCob SPoG WSpi
	'June Johnson'	ECtt EHyd LRHS NRHS
	'Kynaston'	CBcs ECtt EHyd EPfP EWoo LRHS NRHS SGbt
	'Lavender Lass'	LRHS NLar WSpi
	'Letitia' ♀H4	EBee EHyd EPot EWes LRHS NRHS SWvt WAbe
	longifolium var. ***pannosum***	see *V. olympicum*
	lychnitis	GJos NGBl SPhx
	'Megan's Mauve'	WSpi
	'Merlin'PBR	ECtt EHyd EPfP LRHS NDov NRHS SGbt
	nigrum	CHab GJos LShi NGdn NLar SCob SPhx
	- var. ***album***	GJos NGdn NLar WSpi
§	***olympicum***	CBcs CBee CBod EHyd ELan EPfP GJos LRHS MArl NGBl NRHS SCob SDix SRms WCAu WCot
	- f. ***album*** **new**	EAJP
	'Petra'	LRHS SPhx
	phlomoides	SPhx
	phoeniceum	CBcs CSBt ELan EPfP GJos NBro SCob SPlb SPoG WFar WSpi
*	- 'Album'	CSpe GJos SCob
	- 'Antique Rose'	MACG
	- 'Flush of White'	CBod CDor EPfP LRHS MACG NGBl NGdn NLar SBls SBut SCob WFar
	- 'Rosetta'	CBod EPfP GWyn MCot NGBl WFar
	- 'Violetta'	CBod CSpe CTsd EAJP EPPr EPfP EWTr GMaP GQue LCro LOPS LRHS LShi MCot MHol NGBl NGdn SBls SBut SGbt SPer SPhx WCAu WCFE WFar
	'Pink Kisses'	CRos EHyd LRHS NRHS SGBe
	'Pink Petticoats'	LRHS NLar
	'Plum Smokey'PBR	CBod ECtt LRHS NEoE
	'Primrose Path'	EHyd EPfP MBNS NLar SCoo SGBe
	pyramidatum	EBee SPhx
	'Queen of Hearts'	EHyd
	'Raspberry Ripple'	GWyn MRav
	roripifolium	SPhx
	'Rosie'	ECtt NHpl
	'Southern Charm'	EPfP GJos MACG NQui SCob
	'Sugar Plum'PBR	ECtt LCro LOPS LRHS SGBe WCAu
	'Temptress Purple'	SCoo
	thapsus	CHab EBou ENfk GJos GPoy GQue MArl MBow MNHC NBir NMir SPhx SRms
	'Tropic Sun' ♀H5	SPhx WHoo
	'Ventnor Giant'	SVen
	'Wessex'	EHyd

Verbena (Verbenaceae)

	(G)	see *Glandularia*
	Aztec Series	see *Glandularia* Aztec Series
§	***bonariensis*** ♀H4	Widely available
	- 'Little One'	CBod ECha EPPr GBin MAsh SHar
	- 'Lollipop'PBR	Widely available
	brasiliensis misapplied	see *V. bonariensis*
	chamaedrifolia	see *Glandularia peruviana*
	hastata	CBod CRos CSpe EBee ECtt EGrI EHyd EPfP LEdu LRHS MArl MNrw NLar NRHS NSti SCob SEdd SEle SPhx SPlb SRms SWvt WCav WFar XLum
*	- 'Alba'	CSpe EPfP LRHS MBel NLar NSti SCob WFar WMal XLum

- 'Blue Spires'	CBod CCBP CNor CTtf EPfP IPot LRHS MNHC
- f. ***rosea***	CElw CSpe CTtf EGrI EHyd ELan EPfP LCro LEdu LOPS MNrw MRav NBir NDov NSti SBls SCob SDix SMad SPer SPhx WCAu WFar WMal WSHC XLum
- - 'Pink Spires'	CBod EPfP IPot MNHC MPie SPeP
- 'White Spires'	CBod GQue SBls
lasiostachys	EBee
macdougalii	CPla
- 'Lavender Spires'	ECha EPPr GBin LRHS NDov SHar SPhx SRms WMal WTre
officinalis	CCBP EBee ENfk GJos GPoy MHer MNHC NAts SRms WHer WSFF XAbr
- var. ***grandiflora*** 'Bampton'	Widely available
Quartz Series	see *Glandularia* Quartz Series
§ ***rigida*** ♀H3	Widely available
- f. ***lilacina*** 'Lilac Haze'	CMac EPfP
- - 'Polaris'	CMea EAJP EBee ECha EHyd ELan ELon EPfP EShb GWyn LRHS LSRN MAsh NRHS SCob SPer WMal
- 'Santos'	MHer
scabridoglandulosa	see *Junellia succulentifolia*
serpyllifolia	see *Junellia micrantha*
stricta	CBod EBee EPPr LRHS NLar SPhx
venosa	see *V. rigida*

Verbesina (*Asteraceae*)

alternifolia	CPla EBee SDix
- 'Goldstrahl'	EPPr WFar

Vernicia (*Euphorbiaceae*)

fordii	SPlb

Vernonia (*Asteraceae*)

angustifolia	SPhx
angustifolia* × *missurica	WCot
§ ***arkansana***	CBod EBee ECha ECtt EHyd EWes LEdu LPla LRHS NLar NRHS SDix SMHy SPhx WFar
- 'Alba'	EBee ECtt
- 'Betty Blindeman'	MNrw
- 'Mammuth' ♀H7	CKno CMiW EBee ECha ECtt ELon EShb EWTr EWes EWoo ILea IPot LEdu LRHS MHol MNrw SDix SEdd SMad SPeP SPhx SPoG WCot WTor
baldwinii	EBee LRHS SPhx
crinita	see *V. arkansana*
fasciculata	EWes LRHS MHol MRav NLar SPhx WCot
gigantea	EWes MMuc MNrw NLar SMad
glauca	SPhx WCot
lettermannii new	CSpe SPhx
- 'Iron Butterfly'	EBee SMad WHil
missurica	LEdu LRHS SPhx
noveboracensis	EAJP EBee EWhm ILea NLar SBls SBut SMad WCAu XLum
- 'Albiflora'	EPPr EWes
- 'White Lightning'	EBee ECha EPPr ILea SDix WHil

Veronica (*Plantaginaceae*)

allionii	GKev
aphylla new	GKev
armena	EWes MHer SGro WAbe XSen
(Atomic Ray Series) 'Atomic Hot Pink Ray'	SCob WFar
- 'Atomic Pink-White Ray'	SCob
- 'Atomic Red Ray'	NGBl SCob
- 'Atomic Silvery Pink Ray'	NLar
- 'Atomic Sky Ray'PBR	NLar SCob
§ ***austriaca***	EWTr WCav
- dark blue-flowered	NChi
- var. ***dubia***	see *V. prostrata*
- 'Ionian Skies'	CMea EBou ECtt GBin LEdu NWad SPer WIce WKif WSHC
§ - subsp. ***teucrium***	EBee MHol SRms
- - 'Blue Fountain'	EHyd
- - 'Crater Lake Blue' ♀H6	CDor CTri EBee ECha ECtt EHyd ELan EPfP EWoo GWyn LRHS MArl MAvo MBel MHol MRav NChi SPhx SPlb SRms SWvt WCAu WChS WCot WFar WGwG WKif
- - 'Kapitän'	ECtt EHyd LRHS NGdn NRHS WFar
- - 'Knallblau'	MNrw NDov WFar
- - 'Royal Blue' ♀H6	CCBP CRos EBee EHyd EPfP GBee GMaP LRHS MAsh MHol NRHS NSti SRms WFar WKif XLum XSen
'Baby Blue'PBR	EPfP
'Baby Doll'PBR	LSou SCob SPoG
beccabunga	CBen CHab CPud CWat EWat GPoy LLWG MWts NPer SPhx WMAq WSFF WSpi
'Bergen's Blue'	NLar SHar WSHC
BLUE BOUQUET	see *V. longifolia* 'Blaubündel'
'Blue Indigo'	MNrw NGdn
'Blue Spire'	WSpi
bombycina	WAbe
- subsp. ***bolkardaghensis***	WAbe
bonarota	see *Paederota bonarota*
caespitosa subsp. ***caespitosa***	EPot WAbe
candida	see *V. spicata* subsp. *incana*
× ***cantiana*** 'Kentish Pink'	EBee WCFE WFar XLum
chamaedrys	NMir XLum
CHRISTY ('Henslerone'PBR)	ECtt EPfP LBuc MHol
cinerea ♀H5	SBrt WSHC XSen
dabneyi	SBut
DARK BLUE MOODY BLUES ('Novaverblu')	CBod ELan
'Dark Martje'	NLar
'Darwin's Blue'	NLar
'Ellen Mae'	ECtt EGrI EPPr EWes MNrw WCAu WCot
'Eveline'PBR	ECtt EPfP NDov NHpl NLar SPer
exaltata (d)	NChi WSpi
'Fairytale'PBR	LRHS LSou NGdn NRHS
'Fantasy'	WGoo
filiformis	XLum
formosa	see *Parahebe formosa*
§ ***fruticans***	GJos
gentianoides	Widely available
- 'Alba'	CMea LEdu
- 'Barbara Sherwood' ♀H7	CRos EBlo EHyd EWTr LRHS NGdn NRHS WBrk WFar
- 'Blue Streak'	XLum
- 'Little Blues'	EAJP ECha EDAr GKev LSun
- 'Maihimmel'	WCAu
- 'Mountain Breeze'	EHyd EPfP LBuc LRHS NRHS SCoo SHar SPoG WFar
- 'Nana'	NBro
- 'Pallida'	EWoo GKev LPot MMuc MRav SCob SPlb XLum
- 'Robusta'	CBod EHyd EPPr GMaP GWyn LRHS NGdn WFar
- 'Tissington White'	CBod CChe CRos CTtf EAJP EBee EHyd ELan EPfP GMaP LEdu LRHS MCot MHol MPie MSpe NBir NBro NGdn NLar NRHS NWad SCoo SHar SPoG SRms WBrk WCAu WFar WGwG

	- 'Variegata' (v)	CBod EBee ECha EHyd ELan GMaP GWyn LRHS MRav NBir NWad SPer WGwG
	'Giles van Hees'	SEdd
	grandis	EBee LShi MMuc NLar SEND WFar XLum
	incana	see *V. spicata* subsp. *incana*
	'Inspire Blue'	CRos LBuc LPot LRHS MPnt NRHS WHil
	'Inspire Pink'	CRos EHyd LRHS MPnt NBir NRHS WHil
	kellereri	see *V. spicata*
	kiusiana	CMea EBee EBlo ECtt NLar NWad
*	- subsp. ***japonica*** new	LRHS
	liwanensis	EPot MNrw XSen
	longifolia	CBee CMac CSBt ECha EGrI MBel MSpe NSti XLum
	- 'Alba'	CBod ELan MArl MMuc SBut XLum
	- 'Antarctica'	EBee
	- 'Blaubart'	XLum
§	- 'Blaubündel'	EHyd ELan NGdn NRHS
	- 'Blauer Sommer'	EHyd EPfP LRHS LSou NGdn
§	- 'Blauriesin'	ELan EPfP GMaP GWyn MCot MMrt NLar NSti SAko SPer SRms WSpi
	- BLUE GIANTESS	see *V. longifolia* 'Blauriesin'
	- 'Blue John'	ECtt EPfP MPie NDov NLar NSti
	- blue-flowered	CBod SBls SBut
	- 'Charlotte'[PBR] (v)	CBod CChe CDor CWGN EBee ECha ECtt EMor EWTr GMaP GWyn LCro LOPS MBel MHol MSCN NDov NGBl NLar SEdd SHar SPer SPoG WCot WTyc
	- 'Charming Pink'	CDor LRHS MAvo NDov SAko
	- 'Christa'[PBR]	ECtt
	- 'Fascination'	ECtt MSCN NEoE NGdn
	- FIRST CHOICE ('Allchoice'[PBR])	LSou NLar
	- FIRST GLORY ('Alllord'[PBR])	CBod CMea CPla ELan LRHS LSou NLar NRHS SPad WHil
	- FIRST LADY ('Alllady'[PBR])	CBod ECtt ELan EPfP LRHS LSou MAsh NFav NLar NRHS WHil WTor
	- 'Foerster's Blue'	see *V. longifolia* 'Blauriesin'
	- 'Incarnata'	EHyd
	- 'Lila Karina'	GJos
	- 'Lilac Fantasy'	MAvo MRav NSti
	- 'Marietta'[PBR]	CBod CCBP CDor CRos ECtt EHyd EWTr EWoo LCro LOPS LRHS MAvo MHol NDov NLar NRHS SEdd SPer SPoG SRms WCot WHoo WPnP WTyc
	- 'Melanie White'	EWoo MAvo SPer WHil WPnP
	- 'Pacific Ocean'[PBR]	NLar
	- 'Pink Eveline'[PBR]	CBod EBee ECtt ELan EPfP LRHS MBros MHol NDov NGdn
	- pink-flowered	CBod CMac SBls SBut
	- 'Schneeriesin'	EBee ECha ECtt EHyd EPfP GBin GMaP LRHS MRav NBir NLar NRHS SAko SPer
	lyallii	see *Parahebe lyallii*
	'Martje'	SMrm XLum
	MAUVE MOODY BLUES ('Novavermau') (Moody Blues Series)	CBod ELan LRHS WHil
	× ***media*** 'Can Can'[PBR]	NDov
	- FIRST KISS ('Allkiss'[PBR])	ELan NLar
	- FIRST LOVE ('Alllove')	CMea ECtt EHyd ELan EPfP LRHS LSou MMrt MPri MSCN NFav NGdn NLar NRHS SCob SPad SRms WHil
	- FIRST MATCH ('Allvglove'[PBR])	NLar
	- FIRST MEMORY ('Allv1461'[PBR])	ELan NLar WTor

	montana 'Corinne Tremaine' (v)	SRms
	officinalis	GJos XLum
	oltensis	EPot SPlb WAbe
	orientalis subsp. ***orientalis***	EPot
	ornata	SEdd
	'Pacific Ocean'	ECtt NLar
	pectinata	ECtt
	peduncularis 'Oxford Blue'	see *V. umbrosa* 'Georgia Blue'
	perfoliata	see *Parahebe perfoliata*
	petraea 'Madame Mercier'	EBou XLum
	'Pink Damask'	ECtt ELan ELon EPfP EWTr GMaP MCot MRav MSpe NDov NGdn NLar SCob SRms WHoo
	'Pink Harmony'	CBod NGBl
	PINK MOODY BLUES ('Novaverpin') (Moody Blues Series)	CBod ELan WHil
	(Plumosa Series) PLUMOSA AMETHYST PLUME	ECtt MSCN WFar
	- PLUMOSA BLUE PLUME	MHol
	- PLUMOSA LAVENDER PLUME	CWGN
	prenja	see *V. austriaca*
§	***prostrata*** ♀[H5]	CBod CMea CSpe CTri ECtt EPfP GEdr GJos GKev NHol SLee SRms WHoo WIce
	- 'Aztec Gold'[PBR]	CMac
§	- 'Blauspiegel'	SRot
	- 'Blue Sheen'	ECtt EHyd EPfP LRHS NBir NRHS
	- GOLDWELL ('Verbrig') (v)	EBee ECtt WFar
	- 'Lavender Mist'	EHyd LRHS NRHS
	- 'Lilac Time'	CRos EBou ECtt EHyd GKev LLWG LRHS NBir NHol NRHS SLee SRms WFar WIce WTor
	- 'Little Nell'	ECtt
	- 'Loddon Blue'	SRms WCot
	- 'Minor' new	NSla
	- 'Mrs Holt'	CRos EBou ECtt EHyd LRHS MHer NBir NLar NRHS NWad SRms
	- 'Nana'	EBou ECtt EPot EWes
	- 'Nestor'	CTri SRms XLum
	- 'Rhapsody in Blue'	CRos EHyd LRHS NRHS SRms
	- 'Rosea'	SRot
	- 'Spode Blue' ♀[H5]	CBod CMac CMea CRos CTri ECtt EHyd GKev GQue GWyn LRHS MHer NRHS SLee SPoG SRms
	- 'Trehane'	CBod CPla EBou ECtt EHyd EPfP LRHS LShi MAsh MHer NRHS NRya NWad SPlb SPoG SRms SRot WFar WIce
	'Purpleicious Harmony'[PBR]	CBod EBee ELan LRHS MBel SCob SPer WHil
	repens	NEoE SPlb
	'Rosalinde'	NGdn
	'Royal Pink'	MRav NLar
	rupestris	see *V. prostrata*
	saturejoides	SRms
	saxatilis	see *V. fruticans*
	schmidtiana 'Nana'	GKev
	selleri	see *V. wormskjoldii*
	'Shirley Blue' ♀[H6]	EGrI ELan EPfP EWTr LCro LOPS LPot LSRN MHer MHol MMuc SPer SPhx SRGP SRms WCAu WCFE WSpi
	SKY BLUE MOODY BLUES ('Novaversky') (Moody Blues Series)	CBod WHil

§ ***spicata***	EBee EHyd ELan EPfP GJos LBuc LRHS LSun MBow MRav NRHS SCob SRms WBrk WFar WShi XLum
- 'Alba'	CBcs EPfP GJos LRHS MRav NLar SCob WFar XLum
§ - 'Erika'	ECtt NBir NGdn
§ - 'Glory'PBR	CBcs CBod CDor CWGN EBee EHyd ELan LRHS LSou MMrt MSCN NLar NRHS SCob SCoo SMrm SPer SPoG
- 'Heidekind'	CBar CMea EBee EBou ECha ELan EPot GKev GMaP LLWG NBir NGdn SAng SRms SRot WCAu WCav WHoo WIce XLum
- subsp. ***hybrida***	WHer
I - - 'Elaine's Form'	WCot
§ - 'Icicle'	EBee SCob WCAu
§ - subsp. ***incana*** ♀H4	EBou EPPr EPfP MMuc SPlb SRms
- - 'Nana'	NBir SRms
- - 'Silver Carpet'	EHyd LRHS MBel MRav SPer WGwG WSpi
- 'Nana Blauteppich'	EHyd NLar
§ - subsp. ***orchidea***	SRms
- 'Pink Goblin'	EHyd ELan
- 'Pink Marshmallow'	CBod NLar SRkn
- 'Pink Panther'PBR	WCot
- 'Pink Passion' **new**	SCoo
- RED FOX	see *V. spicata* 'Rotfuchs'
- 'Rocket Power Blue'	LRHS
- 'Rocket Power Pink' **new**	LRHS
- 'Romiley Purple'	EBee SPer WSpi
- 'Rosalind'	NLar
- ***rosea***	see *V. spicata* 'Erika'
§ - 'Rotfuchs'	CBcs CRos EAJP ECtt EHyd ELan ELon EPfP GWyn LCro LOPS LRHS MACG MBow MHer MRav NBid NBir NGdn NRHS SAng SCob SPer SPoG SRms WCAu WCFE
- 'Royal Candles'	see *V. spicata* 'Glory'
- 'Sightseeing'	GJos NBir SRms
- subsp. ***spicata*** 'Nana'	XSen
- 'Total Eclipse'PBR	ELan
- 'Twilight'PBR	ECtt SCob
- 'Ulster Blue Dwarf'	CRos EBee EHyd EPfP GMaP LRHS MAvo NGdn NRHS SAng SCob WCAu XLum
- VERSPI ('Bubblegum Candles') **new**	SPad WNPC
- YOUNIQUE BABY RED ('Versbabyred')	EPfP
- YOUNIQUE BABY WHITE ('Versbabywhite')	EPfP MBNS
stelleri	see *V. wormskjoldii*
'Summer Breeze'	NBro
'Sunny Border Blue'	EBee GWyn NLar
surculosa	XSen
teucrium	see *V. austriaca* subsp. *teucrium*
§ ***umbrosa*** 'Georgia Blue' ♀H5	Widely available
urticifolia	SBrt
virginica	see *Veronicastrum virginicum*
'White Icicle'	see *V. spicata* 'Icicle'
WHITE MOODY BLUES ('Novaverwhi') (Moody Blues Series)	CBod WHil
whitleyi	MMuc
§ ***wormskjoldii***	EBou GKev LPot MBrN SLee SRms

Veronicastrum ✿ (*Plantaginaceae*)

'Adoration'	CBod CSpe EBee ECtt ELon EPPr IPot LCro LOPS LRHS LSun MACG MBel NDov NLar SMHy SMad SPhx SRkn STPC WCot WFar WSpi
axillare	GGro
brunonianum	WSHC
japonicum var. ***australe*** B&SWJ 11009	WCru
latifolium	WCot
- BWJ 8158	EPPr ESwi NWad WCot WCru WSHC
'Red Arrows'	Widely available
sibiricum	CBar CKno CRos ECha EHyd EPfP EShb LRHS LShi MMuc NRHS SEND SHar SRms WSpi XLum
- BWJ 6352	WCru WFar
- 'Kobaltkaars'	LPla SMHy
- var. ***yezoense***	WFar
- - RBS 0290	EPPr WFar
villosulum	EWes NBro WSHC XLum
§ ***virginicum***	CKno CTri EBee ECtt EPfP GPoy LRHS NBir NLar SBut SRms WChS WFar WSpi XLum
- 'Album' ♀H7	Widely available
- 'Apollo'	Widely available
- 'Challenger'PBR	CBor NDov NLar WSpi
- 'Cupid'	CBod CDor CWCL EBee ECtt ELon EMor EPfP EWes GBin GMaP ILea LEdu LRHS MNrw NDov NLar SHar STPC WFar WSpi
- 'Diane'	CDor EAJP EBee ECha ECtt ELon EMor EPPr EPfP EWhm GMaP ILea IPot LEdu LRHS MAvo MCot NDov NLar SCob SHar SPhx SWvt WCAu WSpi
- 'Du Jardin'	LEdu LPla
- 'Erica'	Widely available
- 'Fascination'	Widely available
- var. ***incarnatum***	see *V. virginicum* f. *roseum*
- 'Lavendelturm' ♀H7	Widely available
- 'Pointed Finger'	CMea GMaP LEdu LRHS NLar SPhx
§ - f. ***roseum***	CMea ECha EHyd ELan EMor EPPr GMaP GQue LRHS MACG MRav NBro NDov SGbt SPhx SWvt WBor WChS WHrl WKif WSpi XLum
- - 'Pink Glow'	Widely available
- 'Spring Dew'	EBee EWTr EWoo ILea LRHS MNrw NBid NEoE NGBl NLar SPhx WCAu WSpi
- 'Temptation'	EBee EPPr GMaP ILea IPot LEdu LPla LRHS MAvo MRav NBro NEoE NLar SPhx WPGP

Vesalea (*Caprifoliaceae*)

§ ***floribunda*** ♀H4	CBcs CBod CExl CKel CMac CSde ECre EGrl EHyd ELan ELon EPfP LRHS MAsh MGil MGos MRav NLar SBrt SGbt SPer SPoG SRms WCot

Vestia (*Solanaceae*)

§ ***foetida***	CBcs CCCN CExl CMac CPla CTsd EHyd ELan EWld LRHS MGil MNrw NSti SBrt SEND WHil WPav
lycioides	see *V. foetida*

Viburnum ✿ (*Adoxaceae*)

NJM 11.008	WPGP
acerifolium	NWad
alnifolium	see *V. lantanoides*
atrocyaneum	CExl CJun EBee NWad SBrt WFar
- B&SWJ 7272	EPfP WCru
- HIRD 113	WPGP

betulifolium	CBcs CExl CJun CMCN EBee EGrI ELan EPfP EWes GKev GKin MMuc SAko WPGP
- f. ***aurantiacum***	CJun
- 'Hohuanshan'	SSta WCru
bitchiuense	CJun
× ***bodnantense***	CTri EBee WFar
- 'Charles Lamont' ♀H6	Widely available
- 'Dawn' ♀H6	Widely available
- 'Deben' ♀H6	EGrI EPfP NLar SCob SPer
brachyandrum B&SWJ 5784	WCru
bracteatum	NLar
buddlejifolium	CMac EBee EBtc EPfP EWes LRHS MMuc WCru
× ***burkwoodii***	Widely available
- 'Anne Russell'	Widely available
- 'Chenaultii'	MRav
- 'Compact Beauty'	CJun WLov WSpi
- 'Conoy'	ELon MAsh WLov
- 'Fulbrook'	EHyd EPfP LEdu LRHS MAsh SSta
- 'Mohawk' ♀H6	CDoC CEnd CJun CRos EHed EHyd ELon EPfP LRHS MAsh MGos MRav NLar NOrn NRHS SCoo SWvt WLov WSpi
- 'Park Farm Hybrid' ♀H6	CDoC CExl CKel CMac CRos CTri EBee EGrI ELan ELon EPfP LEdu LRHS MAsh MGos MRav NHol NLar SPer SPoG SRms SSta SWvt WHwl WKif WSpi
calvum	CExl
aff. ***calvum*** WWJ 12012	EBee WCru
× ***carlcephalum*** ♀H6	Widely available
- 'Cayuga' ♀H5	LPar MAsh WLov WSpi
carlesii	CBcs CBod CBrac CCVT CDoC CMac CTri EGrI ELon EPfP GKin LSRN LSou MBlu MGos MRav MSwo SCob SGol SPer SRms SavN WFar
- B&SWJ 8838	WCru
- 'Aurora' ♀H6	Widely available
- 'Charis'	CJun WKif WPGP
- 'Compactum'	CJun MAsh SSta WLov
- 'Diana' ♀H6	CEnd CJun CKel CMac CRos EBee EHyd ELon EMil EPfP LRHS LSRN MAsh MBlu NLar SPer SPoG SSta WLov WPGP WSpi
- 'Marlou'	CJun
cassinoides	CJun EBee
'Chesapeake'	EWes MMrt MMuc SEND
chingii	CJun WCru
cinnamomifolium ♀H5	CBcs CExl EHyd ELan EPfP LMaj LRHS NFav NLar SBrt SEND SLon SPer SPoG WCot WSpi
cf. ***cinnamomifolium*** new	EHed
costaricanum B&SWJ 10477	WCru
cotinifolium	CExl GKev
- CC 4541	CExl NLar
cylindricum	EHyd EPfP LEdu SBrt WCru WLov WPav
- B&SWJ 6479 from Thailand	WCru
- B&SWJ 7239	WCru
- B&SWJ 9719 from Vietnam	WCru
- HWJCM 434 from Nepal	WCru
- from Vietnam	IKel
- 'Chino-Crûg'	WCru
davidii ♀H5	Widely available
- (f)	CBcs CMac CSBt ELan EPfP MAsh SGbt SPer SPoG SRms WCFE
- (m)	CBcs CMac CSBt ELan EPfP SGbt SPer SPoG SRms
- 'Angustifolium'	CEnd CJun EBee NLar
dentatum	EBtc
- BLUE MUFFIN ('Christom')	CBcs EBee EHed ELan SGol
- 'Moonglow'	NLar
- 'Morton'	SSta
- PATHFINDER ('Patzam')	SSta
- var. ***pubescens*** 'Longifolium'	SSta
- 'White and Blue'	NLar
dilatatum	EBtc
- B&SWJ 5844	WCru
- B&SWJ 8734	WCru
- B&SWJ 10830	WCru
- PAB 6831	LEdu
- 'Asian Beauty'	SSta
- CARDINAL CANDY	see *V. dilatatum* 'Henneke'
§ - 'Henneke'	SSta
- 'Iroquois'	SSta
- 'Michael Dodge'	EPfP MBlu
erosum B&SWJ 8735	WCru
- B&SWJ 8893	WCru
- B&SWJ 11083	WCru
erubescens	CJun EPfP NLar
- HWJK 2163	WCru
- VdL 4122	WPGP
- var. ***gracilipes***	CJun EHed
- 'Milke Danda' new	WPGP
- 'Ward van Teylingen'	NLar
'Eskimo' ♀H5	CBcs CBod CCVT CEnd CKel CMac CRos CSBt EBee EHyd ELan EPfP LRHS MAsh MBNS MBlu MGos NOrn SAko SCoo SGol SPoG SRms SSta SWvt SavN
fansipanense B&SWJ 8302	WCru
- KWJ 12239	WCru
§ ***farreri*** ♀H6	CBcs CBod CMCN CSBt EBee EGrI ELan EPfP EWTr LBuc LEdu LRHS LSRN MGos MMuc MRav MSwo NLar NWea SGol SPer SWvt SavN WHwl
- 'Album'	see *V. farreri* 'Candidissimum'
§ - 'Candidissimum'	CExl CKel CMac EBee ELan EPfP LRHS LSRN MMuc MRav NLar SCoo SGol SPer SPoG SRms SWvt WHwl WLov
- 'December Dwarf'	CJun EPfP NLar SCoo
- 'Farrer's Pink'	CExl CJun NLar
- 'Nanum'	CJun CMac EHyd EPfP MAsh MBrN MRav WAvo WCot WHwl WLov
foetidum	LEdu
- var. ***rectangulatum*** B&SWJ 1888	WCru
- - B&SWJ 3451	WCru
fordiae new	SPtp
formosanum CWJ 12460	WCru
fragrans Bunge	see *V. farreri*
'Fragrant Cloud'	SWvt
furcatum ♀H6	EPfP GKin NLar SAko WLov
- B&SWJ 5939	WCru
- B&SWJ 10880	WCru
× ***globosum*** 'Jermyns Globe'	CJun CMac MRav NLar SEND SGol SLon SPoG WFar
grandiflorum	CJun EPfP NLar
- 'De Oirsprong'	NLar
harryanum	CBod CSBt CTsd EBtc EPfP NLar WCru WLov WPGP
henryi	CJun EPfP WCFE
× ***hillieri*** 'Winton' ♀H6	CBcs CBod CJun CKel CMac CRos EBee EHyd EPfP IArd LRHS LSRN MGos MMrt NLar NRHS SChF SGol SLon SPoG WFar WPGP WSpi

	hoanglienense	EBee EPfP
	- B&SWJ 8281	WCru
	- HWJ 934	WCru
	- KWJ 12283	WCru
	- PAB 7833	LEdu
	hupehense MF 93087	SSta
	ichangense	CJun NLar
	japonicum	CExl EBee EPfP
	- B&SWJ 5968	WCru
	× ***juddii***	Widely available
	kansuense	CExl
	- BWJ 7737	WCru
	koreanum B&SWJ 4231	WCru
	lantana	CBrac CCVT CHab CLnd CMac CTri ELan EPfP EShb EWTr LBuc MNic NWea SCob SEWo SPer SVic WMat WMou WTSh
	- 'Aureum'	EPfP MAsh MBlu NLar
	- var. ***discolor***	NLar
	- 'Mohican'	NLar
	- 'Variegatum' (v)	ELan
	- 'Xanthocarpum'	SWvt WFar
§	***lantanoides***	SSta
	aff. ***lautum*** B&SWJ 10290	WCru
	'Le Bois Marquis'[PBR]	CDoC CDow CRos EHed EHyd EPfP EShb LCro LOPS LRHS LSRN MAsh MGos SGol SGsty SPoG
	lentago	CMac EPfP LMaj
	luzonicum B&SWJ 3637	WCru
	- var. ***formosanum*** B&SWJ 3585	WCru
	- var. ***oblongum***	EBee
	- - B&SWJ 3549	WCru
	- var. ***sinuatum*** B&SWJ 4009	WCru
	macrocephalum	SLon SSta WPGP
	- 'Sterile'	SSta
	mariesii	see *V. plicatum* f. *tomentosum* 'Mariesii'
	mullaha B&SWJ 2251A	WCru
	- GWJ 9227	WCru
	aff. ***mullaha*** GWJ 9388	WCru
	nervosum HWJK 2241	WCru
	- HWJK 2373	WCru
	nudum BRANDYWINE ('Bulk')	EPfP SSta WPGP
	- 'Pink Beauty'	CJun CKel CRos EHed EHyd EPfP LCro LOPS LRHS LSRN MMrt NRHS SAng SChF SGol SGsty SPoG SSta SWvt WFar WGob WPGP WSpi
	- 'Winterthur'	CJun SSta
	odoratissimum misapplied	see *V. japonicum*, *V. odoratissimum* var. *arboricola*, *V. odoratissimum* var. *awabuki*
	odoratissimum Ker Gawl.	CKel EBee
	- RWJ 10046	WCru
	- var. ***arboricola*** B&SWJ 3052	WCru
	- - B&SWJ 3397	WCru
	- - B&SWJ 6913	WCru
§	- var. ***awabuki***	CBod CExl EGrI EPfP LRHS MBlu MGos SEND SGol SPer WCot
	- - B&SWJ 8404	ESwi WCru
	- - B&SWJ 11374 from Wabuka, Japan	WCru
	- - 'Emerald Lustre'	CBcs WFar
	aff. ***odoratissimum*** B&SWJ 3913 from the Philippines	WCru
	oliganthum 'Kyo Kanzashi'	WPGP
	opulus	Widely available
§	- var. ***americanum***	LRHS NLar WKor
	- - 'Phillips'	CAgr
	- - 'Wentworth'	CAgr
	- 'Amy's Magic Gold'	NLar
	- 'Apricot'	NLar
	- 'Aureum'	CMac EHed ELan EPfP LRHS MAsh MGil MGos MMuc MRav NLar SPer SPoG WCFE
	- var. ***calvescens*** B&SWJ 10544	WCru
	- 'Compactum' ♀H6	Widely available
	- 'Fructuluteo'	CMCN SGol
*	- 'Harvest Gold'	SCoo SGol
	- 'Lady Marmalade'	NLar
	- 'Nanum'	EPfP EShb GBin MRav NFav NLar NWad
	- 'Notcutt's Variety' ♀H6	MAsh WLov
	- 'Park Harvest'	CKel EBee EHyd LRHS MAsh NLar SWvt
§	- 'Roseum' ♀H6	Widely available
	- 'Sterile'	see *V. opulus* 'Roseum'
*	- 'Sterile Compactum'	SWvt
	- 'Sylvie'	NLar
	- 'Xanthocarpum' ♀H6	CBcs CBod CExl CKel CMac CRos EBee EHyd ELan EPfP EShb GBin LRHS MAsh MGos MMuc MRav MSwo NLar SCob SGol SLon SPer SPoG SRms SWvt WFar WSpi
	parvifolium	EPfP NLar
	- B&SWJ 3375	WCru
	- B&SWJ 6768	WCru
	phlebotrichum B&SWJ 11058	WCru
	- B&SWJ 11470	WCru
	pichinchense B&SWJ 10660	WCru
	plicatum	SCob
	- 'Nanum'	see *V. plicatum* f. *tomentosum* 'Nanum Semperflorens'
§	- f. ***plicatum***	SChF
	- - 'Grandiflorum'	CBcs CCCN CKel CMac EPfP LRHS NLar SPer SPoG WCFE
	- - 'Mary Milton'	CJun EHed ELan IArd NLar SSta
	- - NEWPORT ('Newzam')	CKel
	- - 'Pink Sensation'	CJun GBin NLar
	- - 'Popcorn' ♀H6	CDoC CExl CJun CKel CMac CRos EHyd ELan EPfP EShb LPar LRHS LSRN MAsh MMrt NHol NLar SGol SPoG SSta WLov
	- - 'Rosace'	EHyd EPfP LRHS MBlu NLar NRHS SAko
	- - 'Rotundifolium'	IArd MAsh MGos MRav WFar
	- 'Sterile'	see *V. plicatum* f. *plicatum*
§	- f. ***tomentosum***	MTrO SGol SPoG
	- - 'Cascade' ♀H6	CJun CKel EHed ELan LRHS SAko WSpi
	- - 'Dart's Red Robin'	ECtt MAsh
	- - 'Elizabeth Bullivant'	EHyd LRHS NRHS
	- - KILIMANJARO ('Jww1'[PBR])	CBod CDoC CRos EBee EHyd ELan EPfP GBin LCro LOPS LRHS LSRN MBlu MGos MThu MTrO NLar NRHS SCob SGol SPer SPoG WHwl WSpi
	- - KILIMANJARO SUNRISE ('Jww5')	CBcs CBod CRos EHed EHyd EPfP LCro LOPS LPar LRHS MGos MPkF NLar NRHS SCoo SEdd SGsty SPer WHwl
	- - 'Lanarth'	CBcs CBod CCCN CDoC CExl CMac CRos CSBt CTri EBee EHed EHyd ELan EPfP LRHS LSRN MAsh MBlu MGos NLar SCoo SGbt SGol SGsty SPer SWvt WSpi
§	- - 'Mariesii' ♀H6	Widely available

	- - 'Molly Schroeder'	NLar SSta
§	- - 'Nanum Semperflorens'	CBcs CMCN CMac CMea EHed EHyd EPfP ERom EShb LRHS MGos NLar NRHS SGol SPoG WFar WLov
	- - 'Pink Beauty' ♀H6	Widely available
	- - 'Saint Keverne'	GKin
	- - 'Shasta'	CJun CKel CMCN EHed EPfP LRHS NLar SGol WFar WSpi
	- - 'Shoshoni'	CKel NLar SGol WPGP WSpi
	- - 'Summer Snowflake' ♀H6	CBar CCCN CEnd CKel CRos CWGN EHyd ELan EPfP EShb LRHS MAsh MSwo NLar NRHS SGol SPer SPoG WFar WHwl
	- 'Watanabe'	see *V. plicatum* f. *tomentosum* 'Nanum Semperflorens'
	'Pragense' ♀H6	CBcs CJun CMCN EGrI EPfP LRHS NHol NLar SPer
	propinquum	WFar
	- CWJ 12395	WCru
	- CWJ 12426	WCru
	- var. ***propinquum*** Guiz 222	WPGP
	prunifolium	EBtc SGol WCru
	- 'Mrs Henry's Large'	CJun NLar
	× ***rhytidophylloides***	CEnd
	- 'Alleghany'	NLar
	- DART'S DUKE ('Interduke')	WCFE
	- 'Willowwood'	CKel EHyd ELan LRHS MAsh MGos NLar SCob SGsty
	rhytidophyllum	CBcs CKel CMac EBee EPfP LMaj LPar LRHS MGos MMuc MSwo NLar NWea SAdn SArc SCob SEND SGol SPer SRms SWvt WCFE WSFF
	- 'Roseum'	CExl SWvt
	- 'Wisley Pink'	MAsh
	sambucinum	EBee
	- HWJ 838	WCru
	- var. ***tomentosum*** HWJ 733	WCru
	sargentii B&SWJ 8695	WCru
	- 'Onondaga' ♀H6	Widely available
	semperflorens	see *V. plicatum* f. *tomentosum* 'Nanum Semperflorens'
§	***setigerum***	EPfP IArd IDee NLar SPtp WLov
	- BWJ 8409	WCru
	sieboldii	EBtc
	- B&SWJ 2837	WCru
	- CWJ 12808	WCru
	subalpinum	EPfP NLar
	taitoense CWJ 12406	WCru
	taiwanianum B&SWJ 3009	WCru
	- CWJ 12467	WCru
	theiferum	see *V. setigerum*
	tinoides B&SWJ 10612	WCru
	tinus	Widely available
I	- 'Compactum'	SWvt
	- 'Eve Price' ♀H4	Widely available
	- 'French White' ♀H4	CBod CBrac CCCN CDoC CKel CMac EBee ELan EPfP EWTr LCro LOPS LRHS MRav NLar SCoo SLim SNig SRms SWvt
	- 'Gwenllian' ♀H4	Widely available
	- 'Israel'	EShb MBNS
	- 'Ladybird'	CDoC CKel
	- 'Lisarose'PBR	CBar CBcs CBod CDoC CEnd EBee EPfP LCro LOPS LPar LSRN MAsh MGos NLar SPoG SWvt WSpi
	- 'Lucidum'	CBcs CCoa CSde EPfP LMaj LPar NLar SGol SGsty
	- 'Lucidum Variegatum' (v)	CMac
*	- 'Macrophyllum'	EPfP NLar SWvt
	- 'Peter's Purple'	CRos EHyd EPfP LRHS NRHS SPoG
	- 'Purpureum'	CBcs CBod CKel CSBt EBee ELon EPfP LPar MAsh MGos MSwo NLar SCoo SPer WFar
	- SPIRIT ('Anvi'PBR)	CBod CEnd CRos CSBt EHyd ELan EPfP LRHS MAsh NEoE NLar NRHS NWad SCoo SPoG SWeb SWvt
	- 'Spring Bouquet'	MAsh
	- subsp. ***subcordatum***	see *V. treleasei*
	- 'Variegatum' (v)	CBod CMac EBee EHyd ELan EPfP LRHS MAsh NLar NPol NRHS SCob SGol SPoG SRms SWvt SavN WFar WLov
	tomentosum	see *V. plicatum* f. *tomentosum*
§	***treleasei*** B&SWJ 12544	WCru
	trilobum	see *V. opulus* var. *americanum*
	triphyllum B&SWJ 10757	WCru
	- B&SWJ 14298	WCru
	utile	LRHS WThu
	aff. ***venustum*** B&SWJ 10477	WCru
	wrightii	EPfP IArd IDee MRav
	- B&SWJ 5871	WCru
	- 'Hessei'	WLov
	- var. ***stipellatum*** B&SWJ 5856	WCru
	- - B&SWJ 8780A	WCru

Vicia (*Fabaceae*)

americana	EBee
benghalensis	SPhx
cracca	CHab MBow NMir SPhx WSFF
nigricans subsp. ***gigantica***	SBrt
sativa	CHab

Vigna (*Fabaceae*)

radiata	SVic

Villaresia see *Citronella*

Vinca (*Apocynaceae*)

	difformis	CBod CDor CFis CTri ECha IDee LPla SDix SPer SRms WAvo WHer XLum
	- 'Alba'	CCBP
	- Greystone form	CExl EPPr SEND
	- 'Jenny Pym'	CChe CDor CExl CMac CRos EBee ECha EPfP EWes EWld LRHS MBNS NLar SEND SIvy SPoG SRms WAvo
	- 'Ruby Baker'	CDoC CKel EPPr EPfP EWes LRHS NChi SPoG WAvo WFar
	- subsp. ***sardoa***	CBod ECha EHyd EPPr EPfP EWes WCot WFar
	- 'Snowmound'	CBod CSBt LRHS MRav NLar SPoG SWvt WAvo
	herbacea RCB UA 21	WCot
	'Hidcote Purple'	see *V. major* var. *oxyloba*
	major	CBcs CBod CBrac CSBt ELan EShb GPoy GWyn LBuc LCro LPar LPot LRHS MAsh MGos MSwo NPol NWea SCob SGbt SGol SPer SRms WFar XLum XSen
	- 'Alba'	CMac
	- subsp. ***balcanica***	XLum
	- 'Elegantissima'	see *V. major* 'Variegata'
	- subsp. ***hirsuta*** misapplied	see *V. major* var. *oxyloba*
§	- subsp. ***hirsuta*** (Boiss.) Stearn	CMac WCot XLum
§	- 'Maculata' (v)	CBcs CSBt EShb GWyn MSwo SEND SGol SPer SPoG SWvt WAvo
§	- var. ***oxyloba***	CBod CCBP CExl CFis CKel CTri ECha ELan EPPr EPfP EPri EWld

		LPla LPot LRHS MRav SRms WAvo WHer
	- var. ***pubescens***	see *V. major* subsp. *hirsuta* (Boiss.) Stearn
	- 'Surrey Marble'	see *V. major* 'Maculata'
§	- 'Variegata' (v) ♀H6	Widely available
	- 'Wojo's Jem' (v)	CMac CRos EHyd ELan EPfP EWes LRHS MGos NLar NRHS SCob SWvt WAvo WCot
	minor	CBar CBcs CBod CDoC CSBt EHyd ELan GAbr GBin GKin GPoy GQue LCro LOPS MAsh MGos NWea SCob SVic WFar XLum
	- f. ***alba***	CBcs CBod CDoC CMac CRos ECha EPPr EPfP GJos LCro LOPS LRHS LSRN MAsh NLar NRHS NWea SCob SGBe SGol SPer SVic WCot WFar XLum XSen
§	- - 'Alba Variegata' (v)	CBar CBrac CExl LSRN NEoE NWad SRms WCot WFar WHoo
	- 'Alba Aureovariegata'	see *V. minor* f. *alba* 'Alba Variegata'
	- f. ***alba*** 'Elisa'	GWyn NLar
	- - 'Gertrude Jekyll'	Widely available
	- 'Anna'	NLar
§	- 'Argenteovariegata' (v) ♀H6	CBcs CBod CBrac CDoC CDor CMac CSBt CTri ECha EHyd ELan ELon EPfP GArf LRHS MGos MMuc MSwo NChi NRHS SCob SGol SPer SRms WFar
§	- 'Atropurpurea' ♀H6	Widely available
§	- 'Aureovariegata' (v)	CBcs CMac EBee ELan EPPr EPfP GAbr MGos MRav NWea SGol SPer SPlb
§	- 'Azurea Flore Pleno' (d) ♀H6	CDoC CKel CMac CRos CTri ECha EPPr EPfP GQue LRHS LShi MRav NChi NLar NRHS SPer SPoG SRms SWvt WFar WHoo XLum
	- 'Blue and Gold' (v)	EPPr
	- 'Blue Drift'	EWes MSwo
	- 'Bowles's Blue'	see *V. minor* 'Bowles's Variety'
	- 'Bowles's Purple'	GMaP NCou SPer
§	- 'Bowles's Variety' ♀H6	Widely available
	- 'Burgundy'	SRms
	- 'Caerulea Plena'	see *V. minor* 'Azurea Flore Pleno'
	- 'Dartington Star'	see *V. major* var. *oxyloba*
	- 'Double Burgundy'	see *V. minor* 'Multiplex'
	- 'Evelyne'PBR (v)	WFar
	- 'Flower Power'	EPPr NLar
§	- 'Grüner Teppich'	SGol WFar
	- 'Halstenbek'	XLum
	- 'Illumination' (v)	Widely available
	- 'La Grave'	see *V. minor* 'Bowles's Variety'
	- 'Marie'	EPPr NLar XSen
	- 'Mrs Betty James' (d)	EPPr WCot
§	- 'Multiplex' (d)	EPPr LBuc MSwo SGol SRms
	- 'Purpurea'	see *V. minor* 'Atropurpurea'
	- 'Ralph Shugert' (v) ♀H6	CBod CDoC CDor CExl CKel CMac CRos EHyd ELan ELon EPPr EPfP EWes EWoo GJos LCro LOPS LRHS MAsh MGos MPri NLar NRHS SCob SCoo SGBe SGol SPoG SRms WFar
	- 'Rubra'	see *V. minor* 'Atropurpurea'
	- 'Silver Service' (d/v)	WFar
	- 'Snowdrift'	EPPr
	- 'Temptation' (d)	CBod WTyc
	- 'Variegata'	see *V. minor* 'Argenteovariegata'
	- 'Variegata Aurea'	see *V. minor* 'Aureovariegata'
	- 'White Power'	EPPr EWes

Vincetoxicum (*Apocynaceae*)

cretaceum PAB 3432	LEdu
forrestii	CExl
fuscatum	EBee
hirundinaria	EBee EPPr GPoy WCot WHil
- HPA 1358 **new**	GGro
nigrum	EBee NChi WCot
yellow-flowered W/O 7287 **new**	GGro

Viola ✿ (*Violaceae*)

	'Abigail' (Vtta)	LRHS WFar
	'Ada Segre' (Vt)	CGro
	'Admiral Avellan'	see *V.* 'Amiral Avellan'
	'Admiration' (Va)	WGoo
	adunca var. ***minor***	see *V. labradorica* ambig.
	'Alethia' (Va)	GAbr SDys WGoo
	'Alice Kate' (Va)	WGoo
	'Alice Witter' (Vt)	CGro SHar
*	'Alison' (Va)	WGoo
	altaica	SPlb
	'Amelia' (Va)	WGoo
§	'Amiral Avellan' (Vt)	CDor CGro
	'Amy' (Va)	EVic
	'Andy Pandy' (Va) **new**	LRHS
	'Annaleisia' (Vt)	CGro
	'Annette Ross' (Va)	GWyn WGoo
I	'Annie' (Vt)	CGro
	'Ardross Gem' (Va)	GArf LShi MNrw WGoo
	arenaria	see *V. rupestris*
	arvensis	CHab
	'Ashvale Blue' (dPVt)	CGro
	'Aspasia' (Va) ♀H5	GWyn MAsh WGoo
	'Avril Lawson' (Va)	GKev SHar WGoo
	'Barbara' (Va)	ECtt WGoo
	'Baroness de Rothschild' misapplied	see *V.* 'Baronne Alice de Rothschild'
	'Baroness de Rothschild' ambig. (Vt)	CGro WHer
§	'Baronne Alice de Rothschild' (Vt)	CDor SHar
	'Beatrice' (Vtta)	WGoo
	'Becky Groves' (Vt)	CGro
	'Beetroot' (Vt)	CGro
§	'Belmont Blue' (C)	CSpe CTri ELon EWes GBin GKev GMaP LCro LOPS MAsh MHol MRav NBir SCob SHar SPer SPhx WCAu WFar WGoo WSpi
§	***bertolonii***	WGoo
	'Beshlie' (Va) ♀H5	WGoo
*	***betonicifolia albescens***	GGro
	biflora	EPPr EWld LShi MNrw
	'Blackout'PBR (C)	ECtt
	'Blue Butterfly' (C)	GWyn MHol
	'Blue Carpet' (Va)	EHyd
	'Blue Ice' (Va)	LRHS WFar
	'Blue Moon' (C)	LShi MAsh WGoo
	BLUE MOON ('Smev1') (Celestial Series) (Va)	GWyn
	'Blue Moonlight' (C)	MHer MNrw MPie
	'Blue Sails' (Va)	EVic
	'Blue Tit' (Va)	ECtt
	(Bonnie Lassies Series) BONNIE LASSIES EMMA (Va)	CRos LRHS
	- BONNIE LASSIES SARAH (Va)	CRos LRHS MHer
	'Bonny' (Va)	EVic
	'Bo-Peep' (Va) **new**	LRHS
	'Boughton Blue'	see *V.* 'Belmont Blue'
	'Bournemouth Gem' (Vt)	CDor CGro
§	'Bowles's Black' (T)	CPla CSpe EPfP EShb MNHC NBro SRms

	brevistipulata var. ***hidakana***	GEdr GKev WFar
	- var. ***laciniata***	GEdr
	'Bruneau' (dVt)	ECtt WCot WFar
	bubanii	GKev
	'Budgie' (Va) **new**	LRHS
	'Burncoose Yellow' (Va)	WGoo
	'Buttercup' (Vtta)	ECtt GWyn MHol SDys SPoG WGoo
	'Butterpat' (C)	MAsh NDov SHar WFar WGoo
	'Candy' (Vt)	CGro EBee WFar
	canina	EMor NBro
	'Carol' (Vt)	CGro WFar
	'Catalina'	CGro
	chaerophylloides 'Beni-zuru'	GGro
§	- var. ***sieboldiana***	GGro SBrt
	'Charles W. Groves'	see *V.* 'Charles William Groves', *V.* 'Charles Winston Groves'
	'Charles William Groves' (Vt)	CGro WFar
	'Charles Winston Groves' (Vt)	CGro WFar
	'Charlotte' (Va)	GWyn WGoo
	'Chloe' (Vtta)	CGro
	'Christie's Wedding' (Vt)	CGro WFar
	'Christmas' (Vt)	CGro WFar
	'Citronella' (Va) **new**	LRHS
	'Clementina' (Va) Υ^{H5}	MRav WGoo
	'Cleo' (Va)	GWyn
	'Clive Farrell' (Vt)	MNrw
	'Clive Groves' (Vt)	CDor CGro
	'Cockatoo' (Va) **new**	LRHS
	'Coeur d'Alsace' (Vt)	CGro CLAP EBee ECtt GMaP IPot NLar SHar SRms WFar WHal XLum
	'Colette' (Va)	WGoo
	'Colombine' (Vt)	CGro MAsh
	'Columbine' (Va)	CBod CDor CRos CTtf ECtt EHyd EPfP GWyn LRHS LShi MBow MCot MHer MRav NDov NRHS SPoG WCav WFar WGoo WTor
§	'Conte di Brazza' (dPVt)	NLar SHar WHer
	'Copperfield' (P)	EHyd
	'Cordelia' (Vt)	CDor LShi
	cornuta Υ^{H5}	CDor CElw GKev GWyn LRHS MBow MNrw NBir NBro SCob SHar SRms SSut WFar WGoo WHoo
	- Alba Group (C) Υ^{H5}	Widely available
	- 'Alba Minor' (C)	EPfP EWes LRHS LShi NBro NDov SPhx WFar
	- 'Blaue von Paris' (C)	GWyn
	- blue-flowered	MHer
	- 'Brimstone' (C)	LShi MHol
	- 'Cleopatra' (C)	MHol MNrw MPie
	- 'Clouded Yellow' (C)	GWyn MHol MNrw WFar
	- 'Cream Gem' (C)	MHol WFar
	- 'Deltini Honey Bee' (Deltini Series) (C)	MBros
	- 'Gypsy Moth' (C)	GAbr GWyn LShi MHol
	- 'Icy But Spicy' (C)	GWyn MAsh MHol MRav NDov WFar WGoo
	- Lilacina Group (C)	ECha
	- 'Maiden's Blush' (C)	MHol WFar
	- 'Minor' (C)	CMea EPfP LShi MAsh NBro WGoo
	- 'Netta Statham' (C)	MHol WGoo
	- 'Pale Apollo' (C)	MHol WFar
	- Purpurea Group (C)	ECha
	- 'Spider' (C)	GWyn MAsh MHol MNrw MPie SDys WFar WGoo
	- 'Swallowtail' (C)	GWyn MHol
	- 'Ulla' (C)	WHer
	- 'Victoria's Blush' (C)	CDor CElw CSpe EWTr GAbr GBin GMaP MAsh MBel MHol NDov SHar WGoo
	- 'Violacea' (C)	MHol MPie
	corsica	CMea CSpe SPhx
	'Covent Garden' (Vt)	CGro WFar
	'Crepuscle' (Vt)	WFar
§	***cucullata*** Υ^{H5}	SRms
§	- 'Alba' (Vt)	CBro CGro NBir SRms
*	- 'Striata Alba' (Vt)	NBro
	'Curlylocks'	ECtt
	'Cuty' (Va)	LRHS
	'Czar'	see *V.* 'The Czar'
§	'Czar Bleu' (Vt)	CGro
	'Daisy Smith' (Va)	WGoo
	'Danielle Molly'	WGoo
	'Dawn' (Vtta)	CBod CDor CMea ECtt EPfP EWoo GWyn MCot NLar SPoG WFar WGoo WTor
	'Delicia' (Vtta)	GWyn NDov WGoo
	'Des Charentes' (Vt)	CGro
	'Desdemona' (Va)	GKev GWyn WGoo
	'Devon Cream' (Va)	WGoo
	'Diana Groves' (Vt)	CGro WFar
	'Dick o' the Hills' (Vt)	CDor CGro WFar
	dissecta var. ***sieboldiana***	see *V. chaerophylloides* var. *sieboldiana*
	'Donau' (Vt)	CGro WCot WFar
	'Doreen' (Vt)	WFar
	'Double White' (dVt)	CGro WHer
	douglasii	SBrt
	dubyana	GKev
	'Duchesse de Parme' (dPVt)	CGro GMaP NLar SRms WHer
	'D'Udine' (dPVt)	CGro ECtt SRms WCot WFar WHer
	'E.A. Bowles'	see *V.* 'Bowles's Black'
	'Eastgrove Blue Scented' (C)	SDys WFar WGoo WMal
	'Eastgrove Ice Blue' (C)	WGoo
	eizanensis	GGro
	'Elaine Quin' (Va)	ECtt GWyn NLar SPoG WGoo WKif
§	***elatior***	EPPr MNrw
	'Eliza May Groves' (Vt)	CGro
	'Elizabeth Bailes' (Vt)	CDor
	'Elizabeth Lee' (Vt)	WCot
	'Elliot Adam' (Va)	WGoo
	'Elworthy Velvet' (Va)	CElw
	'Emperor Magenta Red'	EMor SVic
	erecta	see *V. elatior*
	'Eris' (Va)	WGoo
	'Etain' (Va)	CBod CRos CTsd ECtt EHyd ELan EPfP GWyn IPot LRHS MHol NLar NRHS SCob SPoG WFar WGoo
	'Fabiola' (Vtta)	GAbr
*	'Fantasy'	WGoo
	'Fee Jalucine' (dVt)	CGro
	'Fiona' (Va)	GAbr MCot SGro WGoo
	'Fiona Lawrenson' (Va)	WGoo
	'Floella' (Va) **new**	LRHS
	'Florence' (Va)	GWyn WGoo
	'Flossy' (Va) **new**	LRHS
	'Flower Girl' (Va) **new**	LShi
	'Foxbrook Cream' (C)	MAsh WGoo
	'Francesca' (Va)	WGoo
	'Freckles'	see *V. sororia* 'Freckles'
	'Fred Morey' (Vt)	CDor CGro
	glabella	GGro SBrt
	'Gladys Findlay' (Va)	WGoo
	'Glanmore' (Vt)	WCot WFar
*	'Glenda'	WGoo
	'Glenholme' (Vt)	GAbr GWyn LShi WMal
	'Gloire de Verdun' (PVt)	CGro
	'Governor Herrick' (Vt)	CGro ECtt WCot WFar

	gracilis 'Lutea'	CElw
	– 'Major'	WGoo
	'Green Goddess'[PBR] (P)	CBod
	'Grovemount Blue' (C)	CMea
§	***grypoceras*** var. ***exilis***	EPPr
	'Gustav Wermig' (C)	MHol WGoo
	hancockii	SPtp
	'Hannah May' (Va) **new**	LRHS
	'Heartthrob' (v)	CBod ECtt GEdr MNrw NFav NHpl SPeP SPoG WHil WNPC
§	***hederacea***	CBod CExl CTsd EWoo GGro GKev GQue GWyn SRms WFar
§	'Helen Mount' (T)	GWyn
	'Helena' (Va)	GWyn WGoo
	'Hespera' (Va)	WGoo
	heterophylla subsp. ***epirota***	see *V. bertolonii*
	'Holdgate'	WGoo
	'Hopleys White' (PVt)	CGro
	'Hudsons Blue'	CElw MNrw
	'Huntercombe Purple' (Va) ♀H5	CRos EHyd LRHS NBir NRHS WFar WGoo WHal
	'Iden Gem' (Va)	ECtt WGoo
	'Inverurie Beauty' (Va) ♀H5	GAbr GBin GMaP GWyn MHer SDys WGoo WKif
	'Irish Elegance'	see *V.* 'Sulfurea'
	'Irish Molly' (Va)	CBod ECtt ELan EPfP EShb GKev GWyn MAsh MCot SPoG WFar WGoo WIce WTor
	'Isabel'	SRms WGoo
	'Isabella' (Vt)	CGro EBee LRHS WFar
	'Isobel'	MAsh
	'Ivory Queen' (Va)	GAbr GWyn MHer MRav WFar WGoo
	'Jack Sampson' (Vt)	EBee
	'Jackanapes' (Va) ♀H5	CBod EBee ECtt ELan GWyn LRHS LShi MAsh NLar SPoG WGoo WTor
	'Janet' (Va)	GWyn LSRN SDys SPoG
	'Janette' (Va)	WGoo
	'Jean Jeannie' (Va)	GWyn NDov WFar WGoo
	'Jeannie Bellew' (Va)	ECtt WGoo
	'Jennifer Andrews' (Va)	GWyn LShi SGro WGoo
	'Joanna' (Va)	WGoo
	'John Raddenbury' (Vt)	CGro
	'Johnny Jump Up'	see *V.* 'Helen Mount'
	jooi	EPfP
	'Josephine' (Vt)	CGro
	'Josie' (Va)	GWyn SGro WGoo
	'Joyce Mary Paul' (Vt)	CGro
	'Judy Goring' (Va)	ECtt WMal
	'Julian' (Va)	ECtt GAbr GWyn WGoo
	'Jupiter' (Va)	GWyn WCot
	kamtschadalorum **new**	WFar
	'Kerry Girl' (Vt)	CGro WFar
	'Kim' (Vt)	CGro
	'Kitten'	LShi MHol SDys WFar WGoo
	'Kitty White' (Va)	GWyn SDys
§	'Königin Charlotte' (Vt)	CBod CGro EHyd EMor EPfP GMaP LRHS LSou MHer NLar SRms WCAu WCot
	koreana	see *V. grypoceras* var. *exilis*
	labradorica misapplied	see *V. riviniana* Purpurea Group
	– ***purpurea***	see *V. riviniana* Purpurea Group
§	***labradorica*** ambig.	CTri EWTr GWyn NHpl WCAu WHer
	'Lady Hume Campbell' (dPVt)	CGro WHer
	'Lady Jane' (Vt)	CGro
	'Lavender Lady' (Vt)	CGro
	'Lavender Lights' (Vt) **new**	CDor
	'Lees Blue' (Vt)	CGro WFar
	'Lees Peachy Pink' (Vt)	CGro MNrw
	'Letitia' (Va)	MAsh MNrw
	'Lianne' (Vt)	CGro SRms WCot
	'Lincoln Cathedral' (Va) **new**	LRHS
	'Lindsay'	WGoo
	'Lisa Tanner' (Va)	GWyn WGoo
	'Little David' (Vtta) ♀H5	CTri ECtt LShi MCot NDov WGoo
	'Lord Plunket' (Va)	WGoo
	'Lorna Cawthorne' (C)	SDys WGoo
	'Louisa' (Va)	GAbr GWyn WGoo
	'Lucy' (Va)	MAsh
§	***lutea***	GKev LShi SBut SHar WGoo
	– subsp. ***elegans***	see *V. lutea*
	'Luxonne' (Vt)	CGro
	'Lydia Groves' (Vt)	CDor CGro SRms WCot WFar
	'Lydia's Legacy' (Vt)	CGro
	'Mabel' (Va) **new**	LRHS
	'Madame Armandine Pagès' (Vt)	CGro
	'Madeleine Mary Groves' (Vt)	CGro
	'Maggie Mott' (Va) ♀H5	ECtt GArf GWyn MAsh MCot MRav WFar WGoo
	'Magic' (C)	NDov WGoo
	mandshurica f. ***albiflora***	SBrt
	– 'Fuji Dawn' (v)	GWyn LShi WCot
	'Margaret' (Va)	ECtt WGoo
	'Marie Rose' (Vt)	WFar
	'Marie-Louise' (dPVt)	CGro GWyn
I	'Mars'	WSpi
	'Martin' (Va) ♀H5	CBod CMea ECha ECtt EWoo GMaP GWyn LRHS LSRN MAsh MCot NDov SPoG WFar WGoo
	'Martini' (Va) **new**	LRHS
	'Mary Mouse'	WGoo
	'Marylyn' (Va)	LRHS WFar
	'Mauve Haze' (Va)	WGoo
	'Mauve Radiance' (Va)	WGoo
	'May Mott' (Va)	WGoo
	'Mayfly' (Va)	ECtt
	'Melinda' (Vtta)	WGoo
	'Mercury' (Va)	WGoo
	'Michelle' (Va) **new**	LRHS
	'Midnight' (Va)	LRHS
	MINIOLA HEART AQUA **new**	LRHS
	MINIOLA HEART GOLD **new**	LRHS
	MINIOLA HEART ICE BLUE **new**	LRHS
	MINIOLA HEART PURPLE **new**	LRHS
	Miracle Series (Vt)	EWTr
	– 'Miracle Bride White' (Vt)	WFar
	– 'Miracle Classy (Vt)	MHol WFar
	– 'Miracle Ice White' (Vt)	NLar
	– 'Miracle Intense Blue' (Vt)	WFar
	'Miss Brookes' (Va)	WGoo
	'Misty Guy' (Vtta)	MAsh
	'Molly Sanderson' (Va) ♀H5	CRos EAJP ECha ECtt EHyd ELan EPfP GWyn LRHS LShi MAsh MBow MBros MCot MHer NLar NRHS SCob SPer SPlb SPoG SRms WCav WFar WGoo
	'Moonlight' (Va) ♀H5	CRos EHyd ELan LRHS NRHS WGoo
	'Morwenna' (Va)	ECtt GWyn MAsh MCot NDov WGoo
	'Mrs Lancaster' (Va)	CBod ECtt ELan EWoo GWyn LSRN LShi MCot NLar NWad SPoG SSut WFar WGoo WHil WTor
	'Mrs Pinehurst' (Vt)	CGro GWyn SRms
	'Mrs R. Barton' (Vt)	CDor CGro SRms WHil
	'Myfawnny' (Va)	CRos EHyd LRHS NDov NRHS WFar WGoo WSpi
	'Neapolitan'	see *V.* 'Pallida Plena'

	nephrophylla **new**	GGro
	'Netta Statham'	see *V.* 'Belmont Blue'
	'Nora' (Va)	ECtt NDov WFar WGoo
	'Norah Leigh' (Va)	WGoo
	NORTHERN LIGHTS ('Smev4') (Celestial Series) (Va) **new**	EPfP
	odorata (Vt)	CBcs CBod CDor CGro CHab CTsd EBee EBou EWTr GPoy GQue LCro LPot LRHS MBow MRav NGrd NMir SEND SRms SVic WBor WCAu WJek
	- 'Alba' (Vt)	CDor CGro CLAP CTsd EBee ELan EPfP GQue LEdu MHer SEND SRms WCAu WFar
	- 'Amelia Violet Groves Stork' (Vt) **new**	CGro
	- 'Amethyst Witch' (Vt)	CGro WFar
	- apricot-flowered	see *V.* 'Sulfurea'
	- 'Bethan Davies' (dVt)	WCot
	- 'Carol Lockton' (Vt)	CGro EBee WFar
	- 'Christopher William Groves' (Vt)	CGro
	- 'Copper Pennies' (Vt)	CGro
	- 'Cyclops' (Vt)	CGro
	- 'Dawnie' (Vt)	CGro EBee
	- deep violet-flowered (Vt)	SPtp
	- 'Ellie' (Vt)	WFar
	- 'Empress Augusta' (Vt)	CGro
	- 'Explorateur Dybowski' (Vt)	CGro
	- 'Frederick Peter Groves Stork' (Vt) **new**	CGro
	- 'Hungarian Beauty' (Vt)	EBee LCro LOPS
	- 'Ivy Thirza Groves' (Vt) **new**	CGro
	- 'Katy' (Vt)	CLAP
	- 'King of Violets' (dVt)	ECtt SHar
	- 'Lees Ivory' (Vt)	CGro
	- 'Little Plum' (Vt)	CGro
	- 'Melanie' (Vt)	CDor CGro CLAP MNrw
	- 'Mrs R.O. Barlow' (Vt)	CLAP WSHC
	- 'Piddle Pink' (Vt)	CGro
	- pink-flowered	see *V. odorata* Rosea Group
	- 'Princess Thirza' (Vt)	CGro
	- ***rosea***	see *V. odorata* Rosea Group
§	- Rosea Group (Vt)	CBod CDor MRav SEND SRms WCot
	- 'Sulphurea'	see *V.* 'Sulfurea'
	- 'Vin d'André Thorp' (Vt)	CGro ECtt
I	- 'Violett Charm' (Vt)	WCot
	'Olive Edwards' (Va)	WGoo
	'Orchid Pink' (Vt)	CGro GMaP MNrw
	orientalis	GEdr
§	'Pallida Plena' (dPVt)	CGro WHer
	palustris	EWat NLar WHer WShi
	'Pamela Zambra' (Vt)	CGro SHar WSHC
	'Panola Beaconsfield' (Panola Series)	SCob
	papilionacea	see *V. sororia*
	'Parchment' (Vt)	CGro EBee GWyn
	'Parme de Toulouse' (dPVt)	CGro EBee GWyn NLar WHer XLum
	'Pasha' (Va)	GWyn
	'Pat Creasy' (Va)	NDov WGoo
	'Pat Kavanagh' (C)	MAsh WGoo
	'Patience'	WGoo
	'Patricia Lillington' (Va)	GWyn
	pedata	MPie WAbe
	- 'Bicolor' (Vt)	WAbe
	pedatifida white-flowered	EPot GEdr
	'Perle Rose' (Vt)	CGro SHar
	'Petra' (Vtta)	GWyn WGoo
	phalacrocarpa	SBrt

	'Pickering Blue' (Va)	WGoo
	pinnata	CTri SBrt
	'Primrose Dame' (Va)	ECtt WGoo
	'Primrose Pixie' (Va)	WGoo
	'Prince Henry' (T)	MNHC
	'Princess Diana' (Vt)	EBee
	'Princess of Prussia' (Vt)	CGro
	'Princess of Wales'	see *V.* 'Princesse de Galles'
§	'Princesse de Galles' (Vt)	CGro CTri
	'Prunella' (Va)	LRHS LShi WFar
§	***pubescens*** var. ***eriocarpa***	SRms
	QUEEN CHARLOTTE	see *V.* 'Königin Charlotte'
	'Raven' (Va)	WGoo
	'Rebecca' (Vtta)	CDor CPla CRos ECtt EHyd ELan EPfP EShb GKev GWyn LRHS LSRN MAsh MBel MBow MBros MCot MHer MHol NBir NDov NLar NRHS SPoG WCav WFar WGoo WHer
	'Rebecca Cawthorne' (C)	MHol
	'Red Charm' (Vt)	CGro WCav
	'Red Giant' (Vt)	CGro MPie
	'Red Lion' (Vt)	CGro
	'Reine des Blanches' (dVt)	ECtt LEdu SRms
	'Reine des Neiges' (Vt)	CBod CDor CGro EMor EWTr LShi LSou
	reniforme	see *V. hederacea*
	riviniana	GJos GQue MBow WHer WSFF WShi
§	- Purpurea Group	CBcs CBod CDor CMac EBee ECha EPfP EWes EWoo GMaP LPot LRHS MHer MPie MRav NBir NDov NRya NSti SPer SPhx SPlb SRms WFar WJek
	- 'Rosea'	WJek
	- white-flowered	EWes
	'Roscastle Black' (Va)	CBod CMea CSma GBee GWyn MAsh NDov WGoo WSpi
	'Rose Marie' (Va)	LRHS WFar
	'Rosy Rayne' (Va)	LRHS LShi WFar
	'Royal Elk' (Vt)	CGro
	'Royal Robe' (Vt)	CGro
	'Royal Wedding' (Vt) **new**	CGro
	'Rubra' (Vt)	EPfP XLum
§	***rupestris***	GGro
*	- ***rosea***	CTri WHer
	sagittata	LPot
	'Saint Helena' (Vt)	CGro
	'Sally' (Vtta)	CGro
	'Sea Horse' **new**	LShi
	selkirkii Pursh ex Goldie	WThu
	- 'Variegata' (v)	GGro
	septentrionalis	see *V. sororia*
	'Sherbet Dip' (Va)	WGoo
	'Showgirl' (Va)	LRHS WFar
	'Silver Lining' (Va) **new**	LRHS
	'Silver Samurai' (Vt)	WCot
	'Skylark' (Va)	LRHS WFar
	'Smugglers' Moon' (Va)	GWyn LShi WGoo
	'Sophie' (Vtta)	WGoo
	Sorbet Series (Va)	LCro LOPS MBros MPri
	- SORBET BLACK DELIGHT IMPROVED ('Pas211779') (Va)	MBros
	- SORBET XP T&M Mix (Va)	MBros
	- SORBET YELLOW FROST (Va)	LCro LOPS
§	***sororia***	ECha GWyn MNrw NBir NBro SCob SPhx
*	- 'Albiflora' (Vt) ♀H6	CTtf EPfP EWTr EWoo GPSL LEdu LRHS LSun MBriF MRav NLar SBea SCob SPhx WJek

	- 'Dark Freckles' (Vt)	CGro EBee NLar NRya WFar
§	- 'Freckles' (Vt)	CBro CMac CSBt CTri CTtf EBee ECha ECtt EMor EPfP GKev LEdu LSun MAsh MBow MBriF MRav MSCN NBir NHpl NLar NRya SCob SPhx SPlb SRkn WCAu WCav WFar WSHC
	- 'Hungarian Beauty' (Vt)	GBin
	- 'Priceana' (Vt)	LEdu MPie MRav NBir SHar SPlb WCot
	- 'Sorority Sisters' (mixed) (Vt)	SVic
	- 'Speckles' (Vt/v)	WCot
	- 'Sweet Emma' (Vt)	SPhx
*	'Spencer's Cottage' (Vt)	WGoo
	'Steyning' (Va)	WGoo
	stojanowii	WIce
§	'Sulfurea' (Vt)	CDor CLAP EBou EMor EPfP LShi MBriF MRav WCot
	'Sulfurea' lemon-flowered (Vt)	WFar
	'Sultan' (Vt)	CDor
	'Summer Showers' (Va) **new**	LRHS
	'Sundowner' (Va)	ECtt
	'Sunny Jim' (Va)	EVic
	'Sunshine' (Va)	WFar
	'Susan Chilcott' (Vt)	CGro
	'Susanne Lucas' (Vt)	CGro
	'Susie' (Va)	GWyn MHol WFar WGoo
	'Swanley White'	see *V.* 'Conte di Brazza'
	'Sweetheart' (Va)	EVic
	'Sybil' (SP)	WGoo
	TEARDROPS MIXED (P)	LCro LOPS
	'Teardrops Yesterday, Today, Tomorrow'	LCro LOPS
	'Thalia' (Vtta)	GWyn
§	'The Czar' (Vt)	CTtf SHar
	'Tiger Eyes' (Va)	MBow SPoG
	'Titania' (Va)	EBee
	'Tom Tit' (Va)	ECtt WGoo
	'Tony Venison' (C/v)	CBod ELon GWyn NLar WFar
	tricolor	CBod CHab ENfk EPfP EWhm GJos GPoy LCro LOPS MHer MNHC NGrd SPhx SRms WWild XAbr
	- 'Sawyer's Black'	ENfk WJek
	vaginata	GEdr
	verecunda	GGro
	- B&SWJ 604a	WCru
§	- var. ***yakusimana***	WThu
	'Victoria Cawthorne' (C)	MAsh MHol NDov WFar WGoo
	'Virginia' (Va)	GWyn WGoo
	'Vita' (Va)	ECtt GAbr SRms WFar WGoo WMal
	'Wasp' (Va)	ECtt
	'White Ladies'	see *V. cucullata* 'Alba'
	'White Pearl' (Va)	LShi WGoo
	'White Perfection' (C)	GWyn
	'White Swan' (Va)	MAsh WFar
	'Winifred Jones' (Va)	GKev WGoo
	'Winnie' (Va)	LRHS WFar
	'Winona Cawthorne' (C)	MHol
	'Wisley White'	CRos GBin LRHS MBel MHol
	× ***wittrockiana***	SVic XAbr
	- COASTAL SUNRISE MIXED (P)	LCro LOPS
	- Cool Wave Series (P)	LCro LOPS
	- 'Joker Light Blue' (Joker Series) (P)	LCro LOPS
	- Matrix Series (P)	MBros MPri
	- - MATRIX CASSIS (P)	MBros
	- - MATRIX CLEAR YELLOW (P)	MBros
	- - MATRIX MIDNIGHT GLOW ('Pas12374') (P)	SCob
	- - MATRIX MORPHEUS (P)	MBros SCob
	- - MATRIX RED BLOTCH (P)	MBros
	- - MATRIX SUNRISE (P)	MBros
	- - MATRIX YELLOW BLOTCH (P)	MBros
	'Woodlands Cream' (Va)	GWyn WGoo
	'Woodlands Lilac' (Va)	WGoo
	yakusimana	see *V. verecunda* var. *yakusimana*
	'Yellowtail' (Va) **new**	GAbr
	'Zara' (Va)	WGoo
	'Zoe' (Vtta)	ECtt EPfP GWyn MAsh SPoG WFar WGoo

Viscaria (*Caryophyllaceae*)

	vulgaris	see *Lychnis viscaria*

Visnaga (*Apiaceae*)

§	***daucoides***	CHby CSpe EPfP EWoo LRHS MNHC SPhx SRms WHal
	- 'Green Mist'	LCro LOPS MAvo SBut

Vitaliana (*Primulaceae*)

§	***primuliflora***	GArf GKev NRya NSla
	- subsp. ***assoana***	EPot
	- subsp. ***cinerea***	EPot GKev
	- subsp. ***praetutiana***	GKev NWad

Vitex (*Lamiaceae*)

	agnus-castus	CAgr CBcs CCht CLau CMCN CSde EBee EHed EPri EShb EWTr GPoy LPar LRHS MGil MMrt MRav NLar SLon SPer WCFE WJek XAbr XSen
	- f. ***alba***	CRos EHyd LRHS MBlu NRHS SPoG XSen
	- - PAB 9281	LEdu
	- - 'Silver Spire'	EBee ELan EPfP SRms WPGP
	- BLUE DIDDLEY ('Smvacbd') **new**	LRHS
	- f. ***latifolia*** ♀H4	CCBP CKel CRos ECre EHed EHyd ELan EPfP LEdu LRHS LSRN MGos MHer NLar NRHS SEND SEdd SGsty SPoG WLov WPGP
	chinensis	see *V. negundo* var. *heterophylla*
	incisa	see *V. negundo* var. *heterophylla*
	negundo	LEdu
	- var. ***cannabifolia*** **new**	XSen
§	- var. ***heterophylla***	EWes XSen

Vitis ✿ (*Vitaceae*)

	'Abundante' (F)	WSuV
	'Alden' (O/B)	WSuV
	'Amandin' (G/W)	WSuV
	amurensis	CDoC EPfP WSpi
	- B&SWJ 4138	WCru
	- B&SWJ 4299	WCru
	'Atlantis' (O/W)	WSuV
§	'Aurore' (W)	CAgr WSuV
	'Autumn Royal'	LRHS MTrO NRog
	'Baco Noir' (O/B)	CAgr WSuV
	'Bianca' (O/W)	LPar NRog SSFr WSuV
	BLACK HAMBURGH	see *V. vinifera* 'Schiava Grossa'
*	'Black Strawberry' (B)	CAgr MTrO WSuV
§	'Boskoop Glory' (O/B) ♀H5	CMac ELan LBuc MBros SBdl SCoo WSuV
	'Brant' (O/B) ♀H5	Widely available
	'Brilliant' (B)	WSuV
	'Buffalo' (B)	WSuV
	'Cabernet Cortis' (B)	WSuV
	californica (F)	NLar
	'Canadice' (O/R/S)	WSuV
	'Cascade'	see *V.* SEIBEL 13053

'Castel 19637' (B)	WSuV
'Chambourcin' (B)	WSuV
CLARET CLOAK ('Frovit') ♀H5	CBcs ELan EPfP GBin LRHS LSRN MBlu NLar NRHS SCoo SPer WLov WSpi
coignetiae ♀H5	Widely available
- B&SWJ 4550 from Korea	WCru
- B&SWJ 4744	WCru
- B&SWJ 8553 from Korea	WCru
- B&SWJ 10882 from Japan	WCru
- B&SWJ 10908 from Japan	WCru
- var. ***glabrescens*** B&SWJ 8537	WCru
- Sunningdale form	NLar
'Dalkauer' (W)	WSuV
'Dutch Black' (O/B)	WSuV
'Edwards No 1' (O/W)	WSuV
'Eger Csillaga' (O/W)	WSuV
'Einset' (B/S)	WSuV
ficifolia	see *V. thunbergii*
flexuosa B&SWJ 5568	WCru
- B&SWJ 6304	WCru
- var. ***choii*** B&SWJ 4101	WCru
- var. ***parvifolia*** B&SWJ 1946	WCru
'Fragola' (O/R)	CAgr CMac CTri ECha EHyd ELan EPfP EPom LCro LOPS LRHS MAsh MRav NLar NRog SCoo SPoG SRms WMat WSpi WSuV
'Gagarin Blue' (O/B)	CAgr EPom SVen WSuV
'Glenora' (F/B/S)	CAgr WSuV
'Hecker' (O/W)	WSuV
henryana	see *Parthenocissus henryana*
'Himrod' (O/W/S)	CCCN ELan NRog WSuV
'Horizon' (O/W)	WSuV
inconstans	see *Parthenocissus tricuspidata*
'Interlaken' (O/W/S)	CAgr WSuV
'Johanniter' (W)	SPre WSuV
'Kempsey Black' (O/B)	CAgr WSuV
'Kozmapalme Muscatoly' (O/W)	WSuV
'Kuibishevski' (O/R)	WSuV
'Kyoho' (B)	WSuV
LANDOT 244 (O/B)	WSuV
LANDOT 3217 (O/B)	WSuV
'L'Arcadie Blanche' (W)	WSuV
'Léon Millot' (O/G/B)	CAgr CSBt LSRN WSuV
'Lucy Kuhlman' (B)	WSuV
'Maréchal Foch' (O/B)	WSuV
'Maréchal Joffre' (O/R)	CAgr WSuV
'Mars' (O/B/S)	WSuV
'Merzling' (O/W)	WSuV
'Munson R.W.' (O/R)	WSuV
'Muscat Bleu' (O/B)	CBod CCCN EPom LRHS MTrO NLar NRog SKee SPoG SSFr WMat WSuV
'Nero'PBR (O/O)	CAgr
'New York Muscat' (O/B) ♀H5	WSuV
'New York Seedless' (O/W/S)	WSuV
'Niagara' (O/W)	WSuV
'Niederother Monschrebe' (O/R)	WSuV
OBERLIN 595 (O/B)	WSuV
'Orion' (O/W)	CBod WSuV
'Paletina' (O/W)	SEdi WSuV
'Perdin' (O/W)	WSuV
'Phönix' (O/W)	CAgr CCCN EHyd EPom LBuc LCro LOPS LRHS LSRN MAsh MGos MTrO NRHS NRog SCoo SKee SPer SPoG SPre SSFr SVic WMat WSuV
piasezkii var. ***pagnuccii***	WCru

* 'Pink Strawberry' (O)	WSuV
'Pirovano 14' (O/B)	WSuV
§ 'Plantet' (O/B)	WSuV
'Poloske Muscat' (W)	CCCN EPom NLar NRog WMat WSuV
pulchra	WCru
purpurea 'Spetchley Park' (O/B)	CAgr WHwl WSuV
quinquefolia	see *Parthenocissus quinquefolia*
'Ramdas' (O/W)	WSuV
RAVAT 51 (O/W)	WSuV
'Rayon d'Or' (O/W)	WSuV
'Regent'PBR (O/B)	CAgr CCCN CTri EPom LCro LOPS LRHS MCoo MGos MTrO NLar NRog SKee SPer SPoG SPre SVic WMat WSuV
'Reliance' (O/R/S)	CAgr WSuV
'Rembrant' (R)	CAgr WSuV
riparia	NLar
'Romulus' (O/G/W/S)	WSuV
'Rondo' (O/B)	CAgr NRog SPre SVic WMat WSuV
'Saturn' (O/R/S)	CAgr WSuV
'Schuyler' (O/B)	CAgr LPar WSuV
SEIBEL (F)	EHyd NRHS
SEIBEL 5279	see *V.* 'Aurore'
SEIBEL 5409 (W)	WSuV
SEIBEL 5455	see *V.* 'Plantet'
SEIBEL 7053 (R)	WSuV
SEIBEL 9549 (R)	WSuV
§ SEIBEL 13053 (O/B)	CMac CRos EHyd LRHS MAsh NRHS SRms WSuV
SEIBEL 138315 (R)	WSuV
'Seneca' (W)	WSuV
'Serena' (O/W)	WSuV
§ 'Seyval Blanc' (O/W)	CAgr MAsh NRog SVic WSuV
SEYVE VILLARD ambig.	EHyd LRHS NPer
SEYVE VILLARD 5276	see *V.* 'Seyval Blanc'
SEYVE VILLARD 12.375	see *V.* 'Villard Blanc'
SEYVE VILLARD 20.473 (F)	NPer
'Sirius' (B)	WSuV
'Solaris' (O/W)	NLar NRog WMat WSuV
'Sovereign Coronation' (B/S) new	WSuV
'Stauffer' (O/W)	WSuV
'Suffolk Seedless' (B/S)	WSuV
SUPERIOR SEEDLESS ('Sugraone') new	CBod
'Tereshkova' (O/B)	CAgr WSuV
'Thornton' (O/S)	WSuV
§ ***thunbergii*** B&SWJ 4702	WCru
'Triomphe d'Alsace' (O/B)	CAgr CSBt NPer WSuV
'Trollhaugen' (O/B/S)	WSuV
'Trollinger'	see *V. vinifera* 'Schiava Grossa'
'Vanessa' (O/R/S)	EPom SPer SVic WSuV
'Venus' (O/B/S)	LRHS SVic
§ 'Villard Blanc' (O/W)	WSuV
vinifera	LRHS SGsty SWeb
- 'Abouriou' (O/B)	WSuV
- 'Acolon' (O/B)	WSuV
- 'Adelheidtraube' (O/W)	WSuV
- 'Albalonga' (W)	WSuV
§ - 'Alicante' (G/B)	CBcs WSuV
- 'Augusta Louise' (O/W)	WSuV
- 'Auxerrois' (O/W)	WSuV
- 'Bacchus' (O/W)	CAgr LBuc LRHS MTrO NLar NRog SCoo SVic WMat WSuV
- 'Baresana' (G/W)	SRms
- 'Beauty'	CAgr
- 'Black Alicante'	see *V. vinifera* 'Alicante'
- 'Black Frontignan' (G/O/B)	WSuV
- BLACK HAMBURGH	see *V. vinifera* 'Schiava Grossa'
- 'Black Monukka' (G/B/S)	WSuV

– 'Black Prince' (G/B)	CAgr WSuV
– 'Blue Portuguese'	see *V. vinifera* 'Portugieser'
§ – 'Bouvier' (W)	WSuV
– 'Bouviertraube'	see *V. vinifera* 'Bouvier'
– 'Buckland Sweetwater' (G/W)	WSuV
– 'Cabernet Sauvignon' (O/B)	CRos EHyd LRHS MAsh MGos NPer NRHS SVic WSuV
– 'Cardinal' (O/R)	WSuV
– 'Carla' (O/R)	WSuV
– 'Centennial' (O/N/S)	WSuV
– 'Chardonnay' (O/W)	CAgr CCCN CDoC CRos EHyd LRHS LSRN MAsh NPer NRog SPre SVic WSuV
§ – 'Chasselas' (G/O/W)	EHyd LRHS NRog WSuV
– 'Chasselas de Fontainebleau' (G/O/W)	SVic
– 'Chasselas d'Or'	see *V. vinifera* 'Chasselas'
– 'Chasselas Rosé' (G/R)	CAgr NRog WSuV
– 'Chasselas Rosé Royal' (O/R)	CCCN SVic
– 'Chasselas Vibert' (G/W)	WSuV
– 'Chenin Blanc' (O/W)	SVic WSuV
– 'Ciotat' (F)	EShb MRav WSuV
– 'Cot Précoce de Tours' (O/B)	WSuV
– 'Crimson Seedless' (R/S)	CBod WSuV
– 'Csabagyöngye' (O/W)	WSuV
– 'Dattier de Beyrouth' (G/W)	WSuV
– 'Dattier Saint Vallier' (O/W)	SVic WSuV
– 'Dolcetto' (O/B)	WSuV
– 'Dornfelder' (O/R)	CCCN MTrO NLar NRog SCoo SPoG SVic WMat WSuV
– 'Dunkelfelder' (O/R)	WSuV
– 'Ehrenfelser' (O/W)	WSuV
– 'Elbling' (O/W)	WSuV
– 'Exalta' (G/W/S)	CCCN WSuV
– 'Excelsior' (W)	WSuV
– 'Faber' (O/W)	WSuV
– 'Fiesta' (W/S)	WSuV
– 'Findling' (W)	WSuV
– 'Flame' (R/S)	CAgr MTrO SPer SVic WMat
– 'Flame Red' (O/D)	CCCN EPom
– 'Flame Seedless' (G/O/R/S)	CMac EPom NRog SSFr WSuV
– 'Forta' (O/W)	WSuV
– 'Foster's Seedling' (G/W)	WSuV
– 'Freisamer' (O/W)	WSuV
– 'Frühburgunder' (O/B)	WSuV
– 'Gamay Hâtif des Vosges' (B)	WSuV
– 'Gamay Noir' (O/B)	SVic WSuV
– Gamay Teinturier Group (O/B)	WSuV
§ – 'Garnacha Tinta'	SVic
– 'Gewürztraminer' (O/R)	EHyd LRHS MAsh NRHS SVic WSuV
– 'Glory of Boskoop'	see *V.* 'Boskoop Glory'
– 'Golden Chasselas'	see *V. vinifera* 'Chasselas'
– 'Goldriesling' (O/W)	WSuV
– 'Grenache'	see *V. vinifera* 'Garnacha Tinta'
– 'Gros Colmar' (G/B)	WSuV
– 'Grüner Veltliner' (O/W)	WSuV
– 'Gutenborner' (O/W)	WSuV
– 'Helfensteiner' (O/R)	WSuV
– 'Huxelrebe' (O/W)	SVic WSuV
– 'Incana' (O/B)	EBee ELon EPfP LRHS MRav SVen WCFE WCot WPGP
– 'Irsay Olivér' (O/W)	WSuV
– 'Italia' (O/W)	SWeb
– 'Juliaumsrebe' (O/W)	WSuV

– 'Kanzler' (O/W)	WSuV
– 'Kerner' (O/W)	WSuV
– 'Kernling' (F)	WSuV
– 'King's Ruby' (F/S)	WSuV
– 'Lakemont' (O/W/S)	CAgr CCCN CDoC CMac CTri EHyd ELan EPfP EPom LEdu LRHS MGos MTrO NLar NRHS NRog SCoo SEdi SKee SPoG SPre SSFr SVic WMat WSuV
– 'Lival' (O/B)	WSuV
– 'Macabeo'	see *V. vinifera* 'Viura'
– 'Madeleine Angevine' (O/W)	CAgr CRos EHyd LRHS LSRN MAsh NPer NRHS NRog SPoG SVen SVic WSuV
– 'Madeleine Céline' (B)	WSuV
– 'Madeleine Royale' (G/W)	WSuV
– 'Madeleine Silvaner' (O/W)	CRos CSBt EHyd LRHS MAsh NPer NRHS SPoG WSuV
– 'Madresfield Court' (G/B)	WSuV
– 'Merlot' (G/B)	EHyd EPfP LRHS NRHS SVic WSuV
§ – 'Meunier' (B)	SVic WSuV
– 'Mireille' (F)	WSuV
– 'Morio Muscat' (O/W)	WSuV
§ – 'Müller-Thurgau' (O/W)	LRHS LSRN MAsh NRog SPoG SVic WSuV
– 'Muscat Blanc à Petits Grains' (O/W)	SWvt
– 'Muscat de Lierval' (O/B)	WSuV
– 'Muscat de Saumur' (O/W)	WSuV
– 'Muscat Hamburg' (G/B)	CRos LRHS LSRN MAsh SGsty SWvt WSuV
– 'Muscat of Alexandria' (G/W)	CBcs CCCN CMac CRHN CRos CTri EHyd LRHS MRav NRHS NRog SRms SVic WMat
– 'Muscat Ottonel' (O/W)	WSuV
– 'Muscat Saint Laurent' (W)	WSuV
– 'Nebbiolo' (O/B)	WSuV
– 'No 69' (W)	WSuV
– 'Noblessa' (W)	WSuV
– 'Noir Hâtif de Marseille' (O/B)	WSuV
– 'Olive Blanche' (O/W)	WSuV
– 'Optima' (O/W)	WSuV
– 'Ora' (O/W/S)	LRHS WSuV
– 'Ortega' (O/W)	CCCN NRog WSuV
– 'Parellada' (W)	SVic
– 'Perle' (O/W)	WSuV
– 'Perlette' (O/W/S)	CCCN EPom WSuV
– 'Petit Rouge' (R)	WSuV
– 'Picurka' (O/W/S)	SVic
– 'Pinot Blanc' (O/W)	CCCN EHyd LCro LOPS LRHS MAsh SVic WSuV
– 'Pinot Gris' (O/B)	SVic WSuV
– 'Pinot Noir' (O/B)	CCCN SVic WSuV
§ – 'Portugieser' (O/B)	WSuV
– 'Précoce de Bousquet' (O/W)	WSuV
– 'Précoce de Malingre' (O/W)	CAgr
– 'Prima' (O/B)	WSuV
– 'Primavis Frontignan' (G/W)	WSuV
– 'Purpurea' (O/B) 🏆H5	Widely available
– 'Queen of Esther' (B)	WSuV
– 'Regner' (O/W)	WSuV
– 'Reichensteiner' (O/G/W)	CAgr NRog SVic WSuV
– 'Rhea' (G/O/R)	SVic
– 'Riesling' (O/W)	CCCN EHyd LRHS MAsh SVic WSuV
– RIESLING-SILVANER	see *V. vinifera* 'Müller-Thurgau'
– 'Rotberger' (O/G/B)	WSuV
– 'Royal Muscadine' (G/O/W)	WMat WSuV

- 'Saint Laurent' (G/O/W) SVic WSuV
- 'Sauvignon Blanc' (O/W) CCCN EHyd LRHS NRHS SVic WSuV
- 'Scheurebe' (O/W) WSuV
§ - 'Schiava Grossa' (G/B/D) CBcs CBod CDoC CMac CRHN CSBt CTri EHyd EPfP EPom LRHS LSRN MAsh MRav MTrO NPer NRHS NRog SPer SPoG SPre SVic SWvt WMat WSuV
- 'Schönburger' (O/W) SVic WSuV
- 'Schwarzriesling' see *V. vinifera* 'Meunier'
- 'Sémillon' (G/O/W) EHyd LRHS LSRN MAsh SVic
- 'Senator' (O/W) WSuV
- 'Septimer' (O/W) WSuV
- 'Shiraz' (B) WSuV
- 'Siegerrebe' (O/W/D) CAgr EHyd LRHS MAsh NPer NRog SPoG SVic WSuV
- 'Silvaner' (O/W) WSuV
- 'Spetchley Red' (O/B) ♀H5 CBod CRHN MNrw WAvo WCot WCru WLov WMou WPGP WSpi
- strawberry grape see *V.* 'Fragola'
- 'Suffolk Red' (G/R/S) SVic
§ - 'Sultana' (W/S) CAgr NRog WSuV
- 'Syrah' (G/B) SVic
- 'Tempranillo' SVic
- 'Theresa' (O/W) WSuV
- 'Thompson Seedless' see *V. vinifera* 'Sultana'
* - 'Triomphe' (O/B) SVic
- 'Triomphrebe' (W) WSuV
- 'Valvin Muscat' **new** NRog
- 'Verdejo' SVic
§ - 'Viura' SVic
- 'Vroege van der Laan' (O/W) NLar SRms
- 'White Muscat' (W) **new** WSuV
- 'Wrotham Pinot' (O/B) WSuV
- 'Würzer' (O/W) WSuV
- 'Zweigeltrebe' (O/B) WSuV
* 'White Strawberry' (O/W) WSuV
'Zalagyöngye' (W) CAgr WSuV

Volutaria (*Asteraceae*)

muricata CSpe

Vriesea (*Bromeliaceae*)

'Astrid' ♀H1b NCft
correia-arauji **new** NCft
delicatula **new** NCft
fosteriana 'Red Chestnut' **new** NCft
gigantea 'Nova' NCft
hieroglyphica NCft
saundersii NCft
splendens ♀H1a NCft SPlb

W

Wachendorfia (*Haemodoraceae*)

multiflora CPbh
thyrsiflora CBcs CCht CDoC CExl CTsd EBee IKel LEdu SVen WCFE WPGP

Wahlenbergia (*Campanulaceae*)

congesta NWad
gloriosa EPot WAbe
hederacea GArf
pumilio see *Edraianthus pumilio*
serpyllifolia see *Edraianthus serpyllifolius*

Waldsteinia (*Rosaceae*)

fragarioides GKev
geoides EPPr GKev LRHS MGil MMuc NEoE XLum
ternata Widely available
§ - 'Mozaick' (v) EBee EPPr EShb NBir NFav
- 'Variegata' see *W. ternata* 'Mozaick'

walnut, black see *Juglans nigra*

walnut, common see *Juglans regia*

Wasabia (*Brassicaceae*)

wasabi see *Eutrema japonicum*

Washingtonia (*Arecaceae*)

× ***filibusta*** CCCN SEND SPlb
robusta ERom IDee SPalm SPlb SWeb

Watsonia (*Iridaceae*)

aletroides CPbh SDeJ SVen
amatolae IBlr
angusta CBor CExl CPrp SPlb
ardernei see *W. borbonica* subsp. *ardernei* (Sander) Goldblatt 'Arderne's White'
'Ballyrogan Early Pink' IBlr
beatricis see *W. pillansii*
§ ***borbonica*** CPla
- subsp. ***ardernei*** misapplied see *W. borbonica* subsp. *ardernei* (Sander) Goldblatt 'Arderne's White'
§ - subsp. ***ardernei*** (Sander) Goldblatt 'Arderne's White' CExl EPri IBlr
- subsp. ***borbonica*** IBlr
- 'Peach Glow' EGrI EPri ERCP GKev SBls SDeJ SPeP WCFE
brevifolia see *W. laccata*
brick red-flowered LEdu
coccinea dwarf CPbh
'Curly Blooms' CPbh
'Dart Sea Trout' EBee EGrI
fourcadei ECre EGrI
fulgens LEdu
galpinii WCot
- lavender-flowered IBlr
- pink-flowered IBlr
I 'Gigantea' LRHS XSte
hybrid, burnt orange-flowered **new** CPbh
- dark pink-flowered **new** CPbh
- orange-flowered **new** CPbh
- peach-flowered CPbh
knysnana IBlr
§ ***laccata*** CPbh
lepida CPbh SPlb
marginata CPbh CPrp
marlothii WCot
meriana EBee EGrI GKev IBlr SDeJ WABo
- var. ***bulbillifera*** CPbh CPrp EBee ESwi GAbr IBlr WSHC
'Peachy Pink Orphan' EBee
§ ***pillansii*** CAbb CBcs CCCN CExl CPbh CPrp CSpe CTsd ECre EPfP EPri GBin ILea LEdu LRHS SGBe SVen XSte
- apricot-flowered CAbb CTsd LRHS
- peach-flowered CExl
- pink-flowered CExl CPrp
- red-flowered CExl
- salmon-flowered CSpe

- soft pink-flowered EPri
pink-flowered EBee
'Special Red' **new** CPbh
'Stanford Scarlet' CExl CPrp EBee ELon
'Tresco Dwarf Pink' CExl CPrp EBee EGrI LEdu LRHS WPGP XSte
Tresco hybrids CAbb CExl CPbh EPri ESwi SRkn
vanderspuyae CBcs CExl EGrI EPri
wilmaniae CExl CPrp IBlr WFar

Wattakaka see *Dregea*

Wedelia (*Asteraceae*)

trilobata see *Sphagneticola trilobata*

Weigela ✿ (*Caprifoliaceae*)

CC 1231 CExl
TCM 12-852 **new** SBrt
'Abel Carrière' CMac CTri ECtt LPot NWea SRms WCFE WFar WSpi
ALL SUMMER PEACH ('Slingpink') LCro LOPS
§ ALL SUMMER RED ('Slingco 1'PBR) CBod CEnd CRos CWGN EHyd EPfP LCro LOPS LRHS MAsh NLar NRHS SCob SPoG WSpi
'Avalanche' misapplied see *W.* 'Candida'
'Avant Garde' IDee MAsh WLov
BLACK AND WHITE ('Courtacad1'PBR) CBcs CBod CDoC CKel CRos CWGN EBee EHyd ELan EPfP LRHS LSRN MAsh NEoE NRHS SCob SEle SGol SPoG
'Boskoop Glory' SPer
§ BRIANT RUBIDOR ('Olympiade') (v) CBod CEnd CMac EHed EHyd MAsh MGos MMrt MMuc MRav NLar NQui SGol SPer SPlb SPoG WAvo WFar WSpi
'Bristol Ruby' Widely available
'Bristol Snowflake' CMac EHed EPfP MBlu MHer MSwo NLar SCob SLon SRms
§ 'Candida' CBrac CTri ELan MRav NLar SGol SGsty SPer WSpi
CAPPUCCINO ('Verweig 2'PBR) MBlu NLar SGol
CARNAVAL ('Courtalor') ♀H6 CBcs MRav SCob
'Chameleon' NEoE SGol
coraeensis ♀H6 CBcs CBod EPfP EWld MBlu MGil MMrt MNrw NLar SBrt WLov
CRIMSON KISSES see *W.* ALL SUMMER RED
decora B&SWJ 10834 WCru
EBONY AND IVORY ('Velda'PBR) CRos EHyd EPfP LCro LOPS LRHS NLar NRHS SGol
'Eva Rathke' LPar NLar NWea
'Evita' MBlu
floribunda B&SWJ 10831 WCru
florida CMac SavN
- B&SWJ 8439 WCru
* - 'Albovariegata' (v) CExl
- 'Alexandra'PBR ♀H6 CBod CDoC CExl CKel CRos CSBt EGrI EHyd ELan EMil EShb GKev LRHS LSRN MAsh MGos MRav NBro NLar SCob SEle SGBe SRkn SWvt WGrn
- 'Bicolor' CMac ELan
- 'Caricature' **new** SMad
- EYECATCHER ('Walweigeye') (v) MMrt
- 'Foliis Purpureis' CBar CBcs CBod CBrac CExl CMac ELan EPfP MAsh MGos MRav MSwo NLar NWea SGol SPer SPlb SRms SWvt WAvo WLov
- 'Gustave Malet' CMCN
- MAGICAL RAINBOW ('Kolmagira'PBR) CBod CRos EHyd LBuc LCro LOPS LRHS MAsh MMrt NEoE NRHS SCob SGol SPoG
- 'Milk and Honey' EHyd SCob
- MINOR BLACK ('Verweig 3'PBR) CKel EPfP LRHS MGos NBro NEoE NHol SCob SGol SPoG
- MONET ('Verweig'PBR) (v) CDoC CMac CRos EBee EHyd EPfP EShb LBuc LCro LOPS LRHS LSRN MAsh MGos MMrt NBro NHol NRHS SCob SGBe SGol SNig SPoG SRms
- MOULIN ROUGE ('Brigela'PBR) EHyd ELan EPfP LRHS MAsh MGos
- 'Pink Princess' EHyd LRHS MSwo
- RUBIGOLD see *W.* BRIANT RUBIDOR
- 'Versicolor' CExl LShi SLon SRms
- WINE AND ROSES see *W. florida* 'Alexandra'
- 'Wings of Fire'PBR EHyd EPfP ILea LBuc LPar LRHS NRHS
'Florida Variegata' (v) ♀H6 Widely available
'Gold Rush' NLar
'Golden Candy' NEoE SCob
hortensis CExl
- B&SWJ 10808 WCru
'Hulsdonk' NLar
japonica 'Dart's Colourdream' EHed EPfP EWes MMuc SEND SGol WGrn WPnP
- 'Variegated Dart's Colourdream' (v) ELon
'Jean's Gold' MBlu MRav
'Kosteriana Variegata' (v) CDoC CKel CSBt EBee EHyd EPfP LRHS MAsh SEle SRms
'Little Red Robin' CBod NEoE SCob WFar
'Looymansii Aurea' CBrac CExl CTri ELan EPfP NLar SGol SPer SRms WFar
LUCIFER ('Courtared') WSpi
maximowiczii CExl
§ ***middendorffiana*** Widely available
- 'Mango' CRos EHyd LCro LOPS LRHS NRHS
'Minuet' CRos MRav MSwo NEoE SGol
'Mont-Blanc' MAsh MMrt
NAIN ROUGE ('Courtanin') CTri NLar
'Nana Variegata' (v) CExl EHyd ELon EPfP LCro LRHS NLar NRHS WFar
NAOMI CAMPBELL ('Bokrashine'PBR) EGrI SGol
'Newport Red' see *W.* 'Vanicek'
PINK POPPET ('Plangen'PBR) CBod CEnd CRos CSBt EHyd ELan EPfP LRHS LSRN MAsh MGos NLar NRHS SCob SCoo SGBe SPoG SRkn SWvt
praecox B&SWJ 8705 WCru
'Praecox Variegata' (v) ♀H6 CMac CRos CTri EHyd EPfP LRHS MAsh MRav NBir NRHS SDix SPer SPoG SRms WCFE
'Red Prince' ♀H6 CDoC EBee EPfP GArf LPar LRHS MAsh MSwo NLar SCob SGol
RUBIDOR see *W.* BRIANT RUBIDOR
RUBIGOLD see *W.* BRIANT RUBIDOR
'Ruby Anniversary' CBod EHyd SGBe SLon
'Ruby Queen'PBR CMac
'Rumba' CMac
sessilifolia see *Diervilla sessilifolia*
'Snowflake' SRms
subsessilis B&SWJ 1056 WCru
- B&SWJ 4206 WCru
'Suzanne' (v) EPPr MAsh
'Tango' MAsh NEoE WAvo WFar
§ 'Vanicek' CBrac NWea SCob
'Victoria' CMac EPfP MGos MSwo NBir SGol SPer

WHITE LIGHTNING ('Wf-2009') (v) — NEoE

Weldenia (*Commelinaceae*)

candida — GEdr IBlr NHar SChF WCot

Westringia (*Lamiaceae*)

brevifolia — CCCN CSde SVen
eremicola blue-flowered **new** — CTsd
§ ***fruticosa*** ♀H1c — CBcs CBod CCCN CSde CTsd SRms SVen
- 'Smokie' (v) — CCCN
- 'Variegata' (v) — CCCN CPbh CSde SRms SVen
longifolia — CCCN
rosmariniformis — see *W. fruticosa*
'Wynyabbie Gem' — CAbb CBod CCCN CKel EHyd EPPr SEND SPoG SVen WLov

whitecurrant see *Ribes rubrum* (W); see also AGM Fruit Section

Wigandia (*Boraginaceae*)

caracasana — CTsd

Wikstroemia (*Thymelaeaceae*)

gemmata — see *Daphne gemmata*

wineberry see *Rubus phoenicolasius*

Wisteria (*Fabaceae*)

'Betty's Dwarf Blue' — NLar
§ ***brachybotrys*** — LRHS MTrO SWeb WSpi
§ - f. ***albiflora*** 'Shiro-kapitan' ♀H6 — Widely available
- 'Okayama' ♀H6 — CDoC CKel CRos EHyd EMil EPfP LRHS MGos MTrO NRHS SGsty SLau SPer SWeb WMat
- 'Showa-beni' ♀H6 — CAco CBod CEnd CKel CRHN CRos CTri CWGN EHyd EMil EPfP LRHS MGil MGos MTrO NLar NRHS SCoo SEND SGsty SLau SNig SPoG SWeb WHwl WLov WPGP WSpi
'Burford' — see *W.* × *valderi* 'Burford'
floribunda — CBcs CBrac CRHN MTrO SEWo SGol SWeb
- B&SWJ 12748 from South Korea — WCru
- f. ***alba*** 'Shiro-noda' ♀H6 — Widely available
- BLACK DRAGON — see *W. floribunda* 'Kokuryū'
- blue-flowered — WLov
§ - 'Domino' ♀H6 — Widely available
- 'Ed's Blue Dragon' (d) — EBee
- 'Eranthema' — see *W.* × *valderi* 'Eranthema'
- f. ***floribunda*** — SWeb
- 'Fragrantissima' — see *W. sinensis* var. *sinensis* f. *alba* 'Jako'
- 'Geisha' — CBcs CEnd CKel CRos CWCL EHyd ELon EPfP LRHS NRHS SEND SNig SRms WHwl WPGP
- 'Golden Dragon' — SWeb
- 'Harlequin' — CBcs CBod CRos CWCL EBee EHyd ELon LRHS SEND WLov
- 'Hon-beni' — see *W. floribunda* 'Rosea'
- 'Honey Bee Pink' — see *W. floribunda* 'Rosea'
- 'Issai Perfect' — CRos EHyd LRHS LSRN NLar SCoo SLon
- 'Issai-naga' — NLar
- 'Jakohn-fuji' — see *W. sinensis* var. *sinensis* f. *alba* 'Jako'
- 'Kimono' ♀H5 — CBod LRHS SLau WHwl
§ - 'Kokuryū' ♀H6 — CBcs CDoC CEnd CRos CWCL EGrI EMil EPfP GBin MAsh MTrO NLar NOrn SCob SGsty SLau SNig SPoG WLov WSpi
§ - 'Kuchi-beni' — CBcs CBod CEnd CRHN CRos CWCL ELan LCro LOPS LRHS LSRN MGos MRav NHol NLar SCob SEND SLau SMad SPer SPoG SRms
- 'Lawrence' ♀H6 — CBcs CEnd CMac CRos CWCL CWGN EWTr LRHS MGos NLar SCoo SLau SPoG
- 'Lipstick' — see *W. floribunda* 'Kuchi-beni'
- 'Loder's Purple' **new** — SLau
- 'Longissima' — see *W. floribunda* f. *multijuga* 'Kyushaku'
- 'Longissima Alba' — see *W. floribunda* f. *alba* 'Shiro-noda'
- 'Macrobotrys' — see *W. floribunda* f. *multijuga* 'Kyushaku'
- 'Magenta' — EHyd LRHS
- f. ***microphylla*** — WPGP
- 'Mon-nishiki' (v) — WCot
§ - f. ***multijuga*** ♀H6 — Widely available
- - 'Cascade' — CBcs LRHS WSpi
§ - - 'Kyushaku' — SLau
- MURASAKI-NAGA — see *W. floribunda* 'Purple Patches'
- 'Nana Richin's Purple' — CEnd EHyd
- 'Peaches and Cream' — see *W. floribunda* 'Kuchi-beni'
- 'Pink Ice' — see *W. floribunda* 'Rosea'
§ - 'Purple Patches' — WSpi
- REINDEER — see *W. sinensis* var. *sinensis* f. *alba* 'Jako'
- 'Rolvenden Bronze' — SLau
§ - 'Rosea' ♀H6 — Widely available
- 'Royal Purple' — see *W. floribunda* 'Kokuryu'
- 'Russelliana' — see *W. floribunda* 'Kokuryu'
- 'Strella' **new** — NLar
- 'Variegata' (v) — CWGN
- 'Violacea Plena' — see *W. floribunda* 'Yae-kokuryu'
- 'Yae-kokuryu' (d) ♀H6 — Widely available
× ***formosa*** — CEnd LCro LOPS SLau
- 'Caroline' — Widely available
- 'Domino' — see *W. floribunda* 'Domino'
- 'Issai' Wada *pro parte* — see *W. floribunda* 'Domino'
- 'Ivy Hatch' — WPGP
- 'Kokuryu' — see *W. floribunda* 'Kokuryū'
- 'Yae-kokuryū' — see *W. floribunda* 'Yae-kokuryū'
frutescens — CDoC EPfP
- 'Alba' — see *W. frutescens* 'Nivea'
- 'Amethyst Falls'[PBR] — CBcs CBod CEnd CRos CTsd CWGN ELan EShb IArd LBuc LCro LOPS LRHS LSRN MGos SCoo SGsty SLon SPoG WLov WTyc
- 'Longwood Purple' — CRos CWCL EHyd LRHS NRHS SNig
- var. ***macrostachya*** 'Aunt Dee' — CWGN NLar
- - 'Blue Moon' — IPot WSpi
- - 'Clara Mack' — CWGN WSpi
§ - 'Nivea' — EHyd LRHS NRHS
Kapitan-fuji — see *W. brachybotrys*
sinensis — Widely available
- 'Amethyst' ♀H6 — CArg CBcs CDoC CEnd CRos EGrI EHyd EPfP LCro LOPS LRHS LSRN MAsh MGil MGos NRHS SCob SLau SPer SWeb WSpi
- 'Consequa' — see *W. sinensis* 'Prolific'
- 'Cooke's Special' — see *W. sinensis* 'Prolific'
- 'Oosthoek's Variety' — see *W. sinensis* 'Prolific'
I - 'Pink Ice' — EWTr MAsh SRms
- 'Prematura' — see *W. floribunda* 'Domino'
- 'Prematura Alba' — see *W. brachybotrys* f. *albiflora* 'Shiro-kapitan'

§ - 'Prolific' 🏆H6 — Widely available
- 'Rosea' — EPfP LMaj LSRN SWvt
- 'Shiro-kapitan' — see *W. brachybotrys* f. *albiflora* 'Shiro-kapitan'
- var. ***sinensis*** f. ***alba*** — CBcs CBod CDoC CKel CMen CRos EHyd ELan EPfP ERom EWTr LCro LOPS LRHS LSRN MAsh MGil MGos MSwo NRHS SCob SCoo SLau SPer SPoG SRms SWeb WFar

§ - - - 'Jako' 🏆H6 — CEnd NHol NLar
- 'Texas Purple' **new** — NLar

'Tiverton' — LRHS

× ***valderi*** — CDoC CRos CWCL LPar MAsh NOrn SGsty SNig SWeb WLov
- 'Burford' 🏆H6 — CEnd CKel CMac CRos CWCL CWGN EBee EHyd EMil EPfP LPar LRHS LSRN MAsh MGos MNHC MTrO NLar NOrn SCoo SEND SLau SRms WHwl WLov WMat WPGP WSpi

§ - 'Eranthema' **new** — SLau
- 'Hocker Edge' — SLau
- 'Lavender Lace' — CBcs EHyd EPfP LRHS LSRN MAsh NLar SCob SLau

§ - 'Murasaki-kapitan' — CEnd CMac CTri CWCL CWGN EHyd EMil EPfP LRHS MGil SEND SLau

venusta — see *W. brachybotrys* f. *albiflora* 'Shiro-kapitan'
- 'Alba' — see *W. brachybotrys* f. *albiflora* 'Shiro-kapitan'
- var. ***violacea*** misapplied — see *W.* × *valderi* 'Murasaki-kapitan'

Withania (*Solanaceae*)

sinensis BWJ 8093 — WCru

somnifera — GPoy XAbr

Wittsteinia (*Alseuosmiaceae*)

vacciniacea — GEdr WCru

Wollemia (*Araucariaceae*)

nobilis — CDTJ ELan EPfP ESwi GBin IKel LPar LRHS MGos NPoe NWea SArc WBor

Woodsia (*Woodsiaceae*)

obtusa — CDTJ CLAP CWCL EBee EHyd EMor EPfP NBro SPoG SRms SRot WCot XLum

polystichoides — SRms

Woodwardia (*Blechnaceae*)

from Emei Shan, China — CLAP

fimbriata 🏆H3 — Widely available

orientalis — CLAP EHed EHyd ESwi LEdu LRHS MAsh NRHS WFib
- var. ***formosana*** — LEdu SPlb
- - B&SWJ 6865 — ESwi WCru

prolifera 🏆H3 — CBdn CKel SPlb WPGP

radicans 🏆H3 — EShb EWes LEdu WFib

unigemmata 🏆H4 — CBdn CLAP EFer EHed EHyd EPfP EShb EWes LEdu LRHS NRHS SPlb WAbe WFib WPGP

virginica — CLAP EHyd

Worcesterberry see *Ribes* 'Worcesterberry'

Wulfenia (*Plantaginaceae*)

amherstiana — GEdr LEdu

baldaccii — EBee GKev SBrt

carinthiaca — EBee GArf GEdr GKev LEdu NBir NLar WCot XLum
- 'Alba' — GEdr GKev

× ***schwarzii*** — CDor CMiW EBee LEdu WSHC

Wurmbea (*Colchicaceae*)

§ ***stricta*** — WCot

Wyethia (*Asteraceae*)

amplexicaulis — EAJP GEdr

angustifolia — SBrt

helianthoides — CPla

mollis B&SWJ 14067 — WCru

X

Xanthisma (*Asteraceae*)

§ ***coloradoense*** — NSla WHil

Xanthoceras (*Sapindaceae*)

sorbifolium 🏆H7 — CAgr CBcs CMCN EBee ELan EPfP LRHS MBlu MGil MVil NLar SBrt SPoG WSpi

Xanthocyparis (*Cupressaceae*)

§ ***nootkatensis*** — CAco MAsh
- 'Aurea' — CAco
- 'Boyko's Sundown' — NLar
- 'Flaming Arrow' — NLar
- 'Glauca' — CAco

I - 'Gloria Polonica' (v) — NLar
- 'Golden Waterfall' — NLar
- 'Green Arrow' 🏆H7 — CAco CKen MTrO SLim WMat
- 'Jubilee' — SLim WCFE WMat
- 'Kanada' — SLim
- 'Moon Shot' — SLim
- 'Pendula' 🏆H7 — CAco CCVT CEme CKen ELan EPfP MAsh MBlu MTrO NWea

I - 'Pendula Aurea' **new** — CAco
- 'Sparkling Arrow' — NLar
- 'Strict Weeper' — CKen NLar SLim

vietnamensis — LRHS WPGP

Xanthorhiza (*Ranunculaceae*)

simplicissima — CBcs EPfP LEdu MGil NLar WCot WPGP

Xanthorrhoea (*Xanthorrhoeaceae*)

australis — SPlb

fulva — SPlb

glauca — CCCN

johnsonii — SPlb

preisii — CTsd SPlb

Xerochrysum (*Asteraceae*)

§ ***bracteatum*** — SVen

§ - 'Coco' — CSpe

§ - 'Dargan Hill Monarch' — CSpe SRms
- 'King Fireball' — CSpe
- 'Nevada Orange' **new** — LRHS
- 'Nevada Red' **new** — LRHS

Xeronema (*Xeronemataceae*)

callistemon — CBrP CCCN

Xerophyta (*Velloziaceae*)

retinervis — SPlb

Xylorhiza see *Machaeranthera*

Y

Ypsilandra (*Melanthiaceae*)

cavaleriei	CExl GEdr GGro WCot WFar
thibetica	CBct CExl CMil CTtf EBee EPfP ESwi GEdr GGro GKev LEdu MNrw SMad WCot WCru WSHC

Yucca ✿ (*Asparagaceae*)

aloifolia	CCCN CDTJ SArc SPlb
- 'Purpurea'	LRHS
angustifolia	see *Y. glauca*
arizonica	CDTJ
baccata	CAgr CCCN CDoC SPlb XSen
campestris	CDTJ XSen
carnerosana	CDTJ
cernua	WCot
constricta	CDTJ
decipiens	XSen
§ ***elata***	CCCN XSen
§ ***elephantipes*** ♀H2	CDTJ LCro LOPS SEND
- 'Jewel' (v)	EPfP SEND
- 'Puck' (v)	SEND
- variegated (v)	EBee SEND
faxoniana	CDTJ SPlb
filamentosa	CBcs CCCN CEme CKel CMac CTri EBee EHyd ELan EPfP LCro LOPS LRHS LSun MGos MSwo SCob SEND SIvy SPer SPlb SRms WSMil XSen
- 'Bright Edge' (v) ♀H4	CBcs CBod CBrac CMac CTri ELan ELon EPfP LCro LOPS LSRN MRav MSwo SGol SWvt WSMil
- 'Color Guard' (v) ♀H5	CBod CTsd EHyd EPfP LRHS SIvy SPalm SPeP SPoG WSMil
- 'Garland's Gold' (v)	CBcs CCCN
- 'Variegata' (v)	CBcs SRms WSMil
filifera	SPlb
flaccida	XSen
- 'Golden Sword' (v) ♀H4	CBcs CBrac CEme CMac EBee ELan EPfP GMaP LRHS LSRN MGos MSwo SCob SRms SWvt WFar
- 'Ivory' ♀H5	ELan ELon GBin GMaP LSRN MRav NLar SRms
× ***floribunda***	SArc
§ ***glauca***	SPlb SPtp WCot XSen
gloriosa ♀H5	CBcs CMac CTri ERom GKev LPar SArc SCob SEND SGsty SPer SPlb SWeb SWvt WFar
- 'Aureovariegata'	see *Y. gloriosa* 'Variegata'
- BRIGHT STAR ('Walbristar'PBR) (v) ♀H5	XSte
§ - 'Variegata' (v) ♀H5	CBcs CBod CDoC CKel CMac CSBt EGrI ELan ELon EPfP GMaP LRHS MAsh NRHS SArc SCob SEND SIvy SPer SPlb SPoG SRms SWeb SWvt WCFE
guatemalensis	see *Y. elephantipes*
harrimaniae	WCot
linearis	see *Y. thompsoniana*
mexicana	CDTJ
mixtecana	XSen
queretaroensis	CDTJ
recurvifolia ♀H5	SArc
- BANANA SPLIT ('Monca') (v)	WCot
- 'Gold Stream' (v)	WCot
rigida	CDTJ XSen
rostrata	CCCN CDTJ EOli ETod SArc SPalm SPlb SWeb WSMil XSen XSte
- 'Sapphire Skies'	CMac
rupicola	WCot XSen
schottii	EShb
§ ***thompsoniana***	CDTJ XSen
torreyi	CDTJ
'Vittorio Emanuele II'	SMad
whipplei	CBcs CCCN ELan EPfP LRHS SPtp WPGP XSen

Yushania (*Poaceae*)

KR 7698	MWht
§ ***anceps***	CAgr CBcs CExl MMuc MWht SEND
- 'Pitt White'	CAgr CBdn CExl MWht
chungii	CBdn CExl MWht
maculata	CAgr CBdn CExl ELon MWht
§ ***maling***	CExl
Yunnan 5	CExl MWht

Z

Zabelia (*Caprifoliaceae*)

§ ***triflora***	CExl EPfP MBlu NLar SEND WGob WPGP
§ ***umbellata*** new	SBrt

Zaluzianskya (*Scrophulariaceae*)

JCA 15665	WAbe
capensis 'Midnight Candy'	SBls
elongata	SPlb
microsiphon	SPlb
ovata	CPbh CTtf CWCL EPfP EPot EWld GBin GKev LCro LOPS LRHS LShi MHer NSla SPlb SPoG WFar WIce
- 'Orange Eye'	CPbh ELan EWes GKev NHpl NSla WIce
- 'Star Balsam'	CBod LRHS MCot
pulvinata	SPlb
'Semonkong'	SWvt

Zamia (*Zamiaceae*)

furfuracea	SPlb
pumila	SPlb

Zamioculcas (*Araceae*)

zamiifolia	CCCN CDoC LCro LOPS
- RAVEN ('Dowon'PBR)	CDoC LCro LOPS

Zantedeschia (*Araceae*)

§ ***aethiopica***	Widely available
- 'Apple Court Babe'	ELon
- 'Childsiana'	CRos EBee EBlo EHyd LRHS NRHS
- 'Crowborough' ♀H4	Widely available
- 'Flamingo'PBR	CDoC CDor
- 'Flamingo Beauty' new	LHWs
- 'Glencoe'	CBct CBod EBee ECtt ESwi GAbr MAvo MHol NWad SMad SPad WBrk WCot WFar WHwl WPGP WSHC WTyc
- 'Glow'	CExl CMac ECtt WAvo
- 'Green Goddess' ♀H4	Widely available
- 'Little Gem'	SMad
- 'Luzon Lovely'	ESwi WCru WFar

– 'Marshmallow'	CBod CPud ECtt EHyd EPfP LRHS MAsh NRHS WAvo WFar WGwG WHwl
– 'Mr Martin'	CCCN ECtt ELon SWvt WCot WFar
– 'Pershore Fantasia' (v)	CDTJ CExl WAvo WCot WFar WHwl
– 'Pink Mist'	LHWs
– 'Spotted Giant'	CDTJ
– 'White Gnome'	WCot WFar
– 'White Sail'	CBod ECtt EHyd LRHS NGdn NRHS WGwG
albomaculata	GKev SPlb WPGP
'Allure'[PBR]	GKev
'Anneke'	CCCN SDeJ
'Ascari'[PBR]	CCCN
'Auckland'[PBR]	SDeJ
'Black Art' **new**	LHWs
'Black Berry' **new**	LHWs
'Black Magic'	CCCN CMac GKev SChr
'Black Star'	see *Z.* 'Edge of Night'
'Cameo'	CCCN SDeJ
'Candy Art' **new**	LHWs
'Cantor'[PBR]	CRos EHyd LHWs LRHS NRHS
(Captain Series) 'Captain Memphis'[PBR] **new**	LHWs
– 'Captain Murano'[PBR]	SPoG
– 'Captain Prado'[PBR]	CRos EHyd LRHS NRHS SPoG
– 'Captain Romance'[PBR]	GKev LCro LHWs LOPS
– 'Captain Rosette'[PBR] **new**	LHWs
– 'Captain Tendens'[PBR]	SDeJ
– 'Captain Trinity'[PBR] **new**	LHWs
– 'Captain Ventura'[PBR] **new**	LHWs
'Chianti'	SDeJ
'Crystal Blush'	SDeJ
'Crystal Clear' **new**	CBod
§ 'Edge of Night'	CBcs CCCN SDeJ
'Festival'[PBR]	SRms
'Flame'	CBcs CCCN GKev MSCN
'Garnet Glow'	CBod LCro LOPS MHol
'Golden Nugget'	CRos LRHS
'Goliath' **new**	WPGP
'Helen O'Connor'	CExl
'Hercules'	ESwi
'Hot Shot'	WMal
jucunda	GKev
'Kiwi Blush'	CBod CBro CCCN CDoC CDor CExl CKel CPud CSpe ECtt EHyd ELan ELon EPfP EWoo LRHS NRHS WCot WFar WGwG
'Lime Lady'	ECha
'Mango'	EPri SRms
'Memories'[PBR]	LRHS
'Mercedes'[PBR]	CRos EHyd LRHS NRHS
'Morning Queen' **new**	CBod
'Mozart'	CCCN SDeJ
'Nightlife'[PBR]	CBod SRms
'Odessa'[PBR]	LCro LOPS MSCN WTyc
'Philomena'	EHyd
'Picasso'[PBR]	CBcs CBod CCCN GKev MSCN SDeJ
'Pink Persuasion'	GKev
'Pot of Gold'	GKev
'Red Alert'[PBR]	EHyd GKev MSCN
'Red Sox'[PBR]	CCCN SDeJ
rehmannii ♀H1c	GKev SDeJ SRms
'San Remo'[PBR]	LRHS
'Sapporo'[PBR]	EHyd
'Schwarzwalder'[PBR]	GKev
'Siberia'[PBR]	LRHS
'Summer Sun'[PBR]	EHyd LRHS
'White Flirt'[PBR]	EHyd
'White Giant'	EPri EWat MAvo
'Yellow Queen'	CBod MSCN

Zanthorhiza see *Xanthorhiza*

Zanthoxylum (*Rutaceae*)

acanthopodium GWJ 9287	WCru
– PAB 8760	LEdu
– WJC 13653	WCru
aff. ***acanthopodium*** WJC 13795	WCru
ailanthoides	CDTJ
– B&SWJ 11115 from Japan	WCru
– B&SWJ 11394 from Japan	WCru
– from Taiwan	WPGP
– f. ***inermis*** RWJ 10048	WCru
americanum	ELan ESwi
armatum	CAgr
– B&SWJ 12753	WCru
– CWJ 12824	WCru
– FMWJ 13091	WCru
– NJM 11.080	WPGP
– PAB 8902	LEdu
bungeanum	NLar
– BWJ 8040	ESwi WCru
coreanum	NLar
dissitum FMWJ 13498	WCru
fauriei B&SWJ 11080	WCru
aff. ***fauriei*** B&SWJ 11371	WCru
– B&SWJ 11523	WCru
* ***giraldii***	EBee
laetum FMWJ 13175	WCru
myriacanthum B&SWJ 11844	WCru
oxyphyllum	CMCN IKel
– GWJ 9428	WCru
– HWJK 2131	WCru
piperitum	CAgr CBcs ELan GPoy LEdu SPtp WJek WPGP
– B&SWJ 11377	WCru
– B&SWJ 14677	WCru
– var. ***inerme***	WPGP
– purple-leaved	CBcs CDTJ CExl LEdu WPGP
scandens	SPlb
schinifolium	CAgr
– B&SWJ 8593	WCru
– B&SWJ 11080	WCru
– B&SWJ 11391	WCru
– B&SWJ 14654	WCru
simulans	CAgr CBcs CExl ESwi LCro LEdu LOPS MBlu MVil SBrt SPtp WJek WPGP
stenophyllum	CMCN
tomentellum B&SWJ 13903	WCru
aff. ***yuanjiangense*** FMWJ 13498	WCru

Zauschneria (*Onagraceae*)

arizonica	see *Z. californica* subsp. *latifolia*
§ ***californica***	MBrN SLon SWvt WKif XLum
– 'Albiflora'	ECha
§ – 'Dublin' ♀H4	CBar CBcs CBod CKel CMea EBee ECha ECtt EHyd EPfP LRHS LSRN MGil NRHS SEND SLee SPlb SPoG SRms SWvt WAbe WCFE WCav WHoo WIce WKif WLov WSHC XLum
– 'Ed Carman'	ECha ECtt MGil WLov WMal
* – subsp. ***garrettii***	SDys XLum
– 'Glasnevin'	see *Z. californica* 'Dublin'
§ – subsp. ***latifolia***	XLum
§ – subsp. ***mexicana***	SRms

- 'Olbrich Silver'	ECha WAbe WKif WMal XSen
- 'Solidarity Pink'	WAbe
- 'Western Hills' ♀^{H4}	CFis ECha EPfP EWld LRHS MHer MMuc MRav SEND SPhx SRms SWvt WPGP XLum
§ ***cana***	ECha XSen
I 'Pumilio'	EPot MHer
§ ***septentrionalis***	WAbe

Zea (*Poaceae*)

mays 'Variegata' (v)	CSpe

Zebrina see *Tradescantia*

Zelkova ✿ (*Ulmaceae*)

abelicea	CBcs CMCN LRHS MBlu
carpinifolia	CMCN WPGP
- PAB 13.047	LEdu
- NJM 13.014 from Azerbaijan	WPGP
- NJM 13.016 from Azerbaijan	WPGP
'Kiwi Sunset'	MTrO WMat
serrata ♀^{H6}	CAco CBcs CCVT CMCN CMen CTsd EBee EGrI ELan EShb GQue IPap LMaj LPar MGos MMuc MVil NWea SEND
- B&SWJ 8491 from Korea	WCru
- 'Burgundy Fall' **new**	MBlu
- 'Goblin'	MBlu NLar
- GREEN VASE ('Flekova')	LMaj MBlu
- 'Green Veil'	IDee
- 'Kiwi Sunset'^{PBR}	EBee ELan MGos SPoG
- 'Musashino'	ESwi SGol
- 'Ogon'	MBlu SGol
- 'Urban Ruby'	LMaj
- 'Variegata' (v)	CJun MBlu NLar SGol
sicula	WPGP
- 'Ciranna' **new**	LRHS
× ***verschaffeltii***	CMCN IArd MBlu

Zenobia (*Ericaceae*)

pulverulenta	CBcs CDoC CMac EHyd ELan MAsh MBlu MGil MGos SLon
- 'Blue Sky'	CBcs CMCN CRos EHyd EPfP IDee LRHS MAsh MBlu MGos MPkF NLar SPer SPoG WPGP XSte
- 'Misty Blue'	ELan
- f. ***nitida***	CMac
- 'Raspberry Ripple'	CBcs EHyd ELan LRHS MAsh NLar NRHS SPoG

Zephyranthes (*Amaryllidaceae*)

candida	CBor CBro EBee EHyd EPot EShb EWld GKev LRHS NRHS SChF SDeJ WAvo WCFE
citrina	CBor CExl GKev SDeJ
drummondii	CBor
'Krakatau'	WCot
La Bufa Rosa Group	CExl WCot
robusta	see *Habranthus robustus*
rosea	CBor GKev SDeJ

Zigadenus (*Melanthiaceae*)

elegans	CRos EBee EDAr EHyd EPri GAbr LEdu LPla LRHS MHer NRHS SBls SLon WFar WSHC
nuttallii	GKev

Zingiber ✿ (*Zingiberaceae*)

clarkei	CTsd
mioga	CAgr CLau CSpe CTsd ELan GPoy LEdu LRHS SBls SChr SHor SPlb SPtp SRms WPGP XSte
- 'Crûg's Zing'	LEdu SBrt WCru WPGP
- 'Dancing Crane' (v)	CMac ESwi LEdu SRms WPGP
- 'White Feather'	LEdu MAvo WPGP
officinale	GPoy SPlb SPre

Zinnia (*Asteraceae*)

DAHLIA-FLOWERED MIXED	LCro LOPS
elegans	SVic
- (Benary's Giant Series) 'Benary's Giant Lime'	CSpe
- - 'Benary's Giant Scarlet' ♀^{H2}	CSpe
- 'Macarenia' (d) **new**	SSal
- (Queen Series) 'Queen Lime Orange' (d) **new**	CSpe
- - 'Queen Lime Red' (d) ♀^{H2}	CSpe
- - 'Queen Orange' (d) **new**	SSal
haageana AZTEC SUNSET (mixed) (d) **new**	SSal
marylandica Zahara Series **new**	MBros
- - ZAHARA FIRE ('Pas719124') **new**	CSpe
- - ZAHARA RED ('Pas1118265')	SCob
- - ZAHARA STARLIGHT ROSE ('Pas719128')	SCob
- - ZAHARA YELLOW IMPROVED ('Pas951086')	SCob
Oklahoma Series ♀^{H2}	LCro LOPS
'Red Spider'	CSpe CTtf

Zizia (*Apiaceae*)

aptera	SPhx WSHC
aurea	LPla LRHS MBriF MNrw SPhx WSHC XLum

Ziziphus (*Rhamnaceae*)

§ ***jujuba*** (F)	CBcs CKel MBlu
- 'Lang' (F)	CAgr
- 'Li' (F)	CAgr
sativa	see *Z. jujuba*

Zosima (*Apiaceae*)

absinthifolia	WCot

III
RHS AWARD OF GARDEN MERIT
FRUIT

Award of Garden Merit Fruit

This is a directory of fruit offered by nurseries participating in *RHS Plant Finder 2019* that have been awarded an RHS Award of Garden Merit (AGM). It does not represent a complete list of AGM fruit.

Entries are accompanied by a short description and the relevant **hardiness rating** for the UK (see p.39 for an explanation of these). The figures to the left of the rating indicate the year of the award. Cultivars particularly suitable for culinary use are flagged **(C)**, while **(D)** denotes dessert fruit.

Cultivation

All fruits are best grown in sheltered sites, with protection from spring frosts and cold winds. Brief guidance is given below on suitability for different locations, rootstocks, pollination and storage.

Location

Most of the **apple** cultivars listed here succeed all over the country, including the north of England. Those which have been found to be particularly successful in higher-rainfall and colder areas are **marked with an asterisk**; this is also used to highlight other fruits that have been found to be successful in northern regions. **Pears** crop best in sheltered warm situations; in the more exposed areas and northern counties, some pears will benefit from the protection of walls. **Plums** are susceptible to spring frosts and also need warm summers to ripen fully. Only early ripening plums can be relied upon in the shorter season of northern counties.

Currants, **gooseberries**, **raspberries** and **berry fruits** are generally satisfactory in most parts of the country, but cold winds at flowering time can be a problem. **Strawberries** can be grown all over the country, but will need some protection in exposed sites and from spring frosts. **Blueberries** are hardy plants but require light, well-drained, moisture-retentive, acid soil (pH 4.0–5.5).

Figs can crop satisfactorily in sheltered, warm situations in southern England. In northerly areas they will need protection such as a south-facing wall, or to be grown under glass or in polytunnels.

Pollination

Most tree fruits need to be pollinated by another tree of the same kind growing reasonably close by, which flowers at approximately the same time. Flowering groups are given in descriptions; for good pollination, choose cultivars from the same group, though those from adjacent groups will also serve as pollinators. **Apples** and **pears** listed as triploid are poor pollinators and require a normal (i.e. diploid) pollinator to set fruit. Gardeners should be aware that this diploid pollinator will not itself set fruit unless pollinated by another diploid tree. Many *Malus* species and crab apples, such as 'Golden Hornet' and 'Evereste', are also a good source of pollen for dessert and culinary apples. A number of the **plums** listed are self-fertile or partly self-fertile and will produce crops without a pollinator, but a pollinator is needed for all other plums. **Cherries** listed as self-fertile will crop without a pollinator, but otherwise cherries need a pollinator. Soft fruits are self-fertile, except that **blueberries** may need a pollinator.

Rootstocks

All tree fruits are grafted onto rootstocks of varying vigour. Choice of rootstock will determine the ultimate size of the tree and hence needs to be borne in mind when selecting new trees for the garden. For example, **apple trees** on 'M9' rootstock are suitable for small gardens, while those on 'M25' will produce large, standard trees. The size of the tree will also be determined by the vigour of the cultivar. It is often advisable to obtain a very vigorous cultivar, for example 'Bramley's Seedling', on a more dwarfing stock. **Apples** are available on 'M27' (very dwarfing), 'M9' (dwarfing), 'M26' (semi-dwarfing), 'MM 106' (semi-vigorous), and 'M25' (vigorous) rootstocks. **Pears** are available on 'Quince C' (dwarfing), 'Quince A' (semi-vigorous), 'BA 29' (semi-vigorous) and seedling pear (vigorous) rootstocks. Some pear cultivars are incompatible with a quince rootstock and these are sold with a pear interstock (usually 'Beurré Hardy'). **Plums** are available on 'Pixy' (semi-dwarfing) and 'Saint Julien A' (semi-vigorous) rootstocks; cherries on 'Tabel' (very dwarfing), 'Gisela 5' (dwarfing), and 'Colt' (semi-vigorous).

Storage

Early **apples** and **pears** will not store, but many more of the apple and pear cultivars listed will store to Christmas and some to the spring. This calls for good storage conditions, i.e. a cool, dark, frost-free place that is not subject to fluctuating temperatures. Often this can be achieved in sheds and garages, but in general centrally heated houses are not suitable for long-term storage.

Apple (*Malus domestica*)

98 H6 **'Alkmene'** (D)
Pollination group 2. Aromatic, Cox-like flavour. Good, regular crops; some resistance to scab and mildew. Season: late Sept.–late Oct.
CAgr LPar NOra NRog SBdl SKee

'American Mother' *see* 'Mother'

93 H6 **'Arthur Turner'** (C)
Pollination group 3. Flavoursome cooker. Large, golden exhibition fruit. Good, regular crops; prone to mildew; some resistance to scab. Striking deep pink blossom, for which an Award of Merit was given in 1945. Season: Sept.–Nov.
CArg CCVT CHab CTri EPom LBuc MTrO NOra NRog NWea SBdl SKee SSFr WJas WMat

93 H6 **'Ashmead's Kernel'** (D)
Pollination group 4. Intense fruit-drop flavour. Cropping erratic; prone to bitter pit. Season: Dec.–Feb.
CAgr CArg CBod CEnd CHab CLnd CRos CSBt CTri EPfP EPom LBuc LRHS MRav MTrO NOra NRog NWea SBdl SEdi SKee SLim SLon SSFT SSFr SVic WJas WMat WWct

93 H6 **'Belle de Boskoop'** (C/D)
Triploid. Pollination group 3. Needs little or no extra sugar when cooked; mellows to brisk eating apple. Good, regular crops; very vigorous tree. Season: Oct.–Apr.; keeps well.*
CAgr CEnd CHab NOra NRog NWea SBdl SKee

93 H6 **'Blenheim Orange'** (C/D)
Triploid. Pollination group 3. Characteristic nutty flavour. Use early for cooking. Some resistance to mildew; very vigorous tree; partial tip-bearer; light crops. Season (C): from late Sept. (D): Oct.–Dec. / Jan.*
CAgr CArg CBod CCVT CHab CLnd CSBt CTri ELan EPfP EPom IArd LBuc LEdu LRHS MRav MTrO NOra NRHS NRog SBdl SCob SEdi SEND SEWo SGbt SKee SPer SSFr SVic WJas WMat WWct

93 H6 **'Bramley's Seedling'** (C)
Triploid. Pollination group 3. Cooks to very sharp, savoury purée; retains acidity to spring. Heavy crops; prone to bitter pit and scab; partial tip-bearer; can bear fruit parthenocarpically; tendency to be biennial if over-cropped; blossom susceptible to frost. Very vigorous tree. Season: Nov.–Mar.; stores well.*
CAgr CArg CBcs CBod CCVT CEnd CLnd CMac CRos CSBt CTri EBee ELan EPfP EPom EWTr GDam GKin IPap LBuc LEdu LMaj LPar LRHS LSRN MGos MMuc MPri MRav MTrO NLar NOra NRHS NRog NWea SBdl SCob SEdi SEND SEWo SKee SLim SPer SRms SSFr SSFT SVic SWvt WJas WMat WWct

93 H6 **'Charles Ross'** (C/D)
Pollination group 3. Quite rich flavour; needs no sugar when cooked. Handsome exhibition fruit. Good, regular crops; hardy tree; some resistance to scab. Season: Oct.–Dec.*
CAgr CArg CCVT CEnd CHab CLnd CMac CSBt CTri EPom IArd LBuc LPar LSRN MAsh MRav MTrO NOra NRog NWea SBdl SCob SEWo SKee SLim SSFT SSFr WJas WMat WWct

14 H6 **'Christmas Pippin'** (D)
Pollination group 3. Medium vigour; upright spreading habit; good, regular crops. Medium-sized apple of attractive appearance, flushed with colour over yellow background with some russet; crisp, juicy, sweet flesh with rich sweet sharp flavour, developing aromatic quality. Well-flavoured, good quality apple.
CArg CBod CEnd CRos CTri EBee ELan EPom LBuc LCro LRHS MCoo MTrO NLar NOra NRHS SGbt SSFr WMat

93 H6 **'Discovery'** (D)
Pollination group 3. Bright red, crisp, juicy; keeps longer than most earlies. Ornamental tree. Good, regular crops; partial tip-bearer; good resistance to scab and mildew. Season: mid Aug.–Sept.*
CAgr CArg CBcs CCVT CDoC CLnd CMac CSBt CTri EBee EPfP EPom EWTr GBin GKin IPap LBuc LMaj LPar LRHS MGos MPri MRav MTrO NLar NOra NRog NWea SBdl SCob SCoo SEdi SGbt SKee SLim SPer SSFr SSFT SVic WJas WMat WWct

93 H6 **'Dummellor's Seedling'** (C)
Pollination group 4. Also sold as 'Dumelow's Seedling'. Cooks to well-flavoured, juicy purée; retains acidity to spring. Good, regular crops, but fruit can be small for a cooker. Season: Nov.–Apr.*
CHab NOra NRog SBdl SKee

93 H6 **'Edward VII'** (C)
Pollination group 6. Cooks to well-flavoured purée, not as acidic as 'Bramley's Seedling'. Large, regular, exhibition fruit. Deep pink blossom; flowers very late so escapes frosts; needs late-flowering pollinator. Good, regular crops; resistant to scab; some resistance to mildew. Season: Dec.–Apr.*
CHab NOra NRog SBdl SKee WMat WWct

93 H6 **'Egremont Russet'** (D)
Pollination group 2. Characteristic nutty flavour. Good, regular crops; fruit resistant to scab, but prone to leaf scab; very prone to bitter pit and woolly aphids. Season: Oct.–Dec.*
CAgr CArg CBod CCVT CEnd CHab CLnd CMac CRos CSBt CTri EBee ELan EPfP EPom EWTr LBuc LEdu LPar LRHS MAsh MGos MMuc MPri MTrO NLar NOra NRog NWea SBdl SEdi SEND SEWo SKee SLim SPer SRms SSFr SSFT WJas WMat WWct

93 H6 **'Ellison's Orange'** (D)
Pollination group 4. Rich, aniseed flavour. Good, regular crops; some resistance to scab, but susceptible to canker. Season: late Sept.–late Oct.
CAgr CArg CEnd CHab CLnd CMac CSBt CTri EPfP EPom LBuc LRHS MMuc MTrO NOra NRog NWea SBdl SEdi SEND SGbt SKee SLon SPer SRms SSFr SVic SWeb WJas WMat WWct

93 H6 **'Elstar'** (D)
Pollination group 3. Intense flavour, honeyed, crisp. Heavy regular crops. Season: late Oct.–Dec.
CBod CCVT CLnd EPom LPar NOra SBdl SEdi SKee

93 H6 **'Emneth Early'** (C)
Pollination group 3. Codlin type, cooking to fluffy purée; needs hardly any sugar. Heavy but biennial crops; needs thinning for size. Some resistance to scab and mildew. Season: Aug.–Sept.*
CAgr CArg CHab NOra NRog SBdl SEdi WMat WWct

'Epicure' *see* 'Laxton's Epicure'

93 H6 **'Fiesta'** (D)
Pollination group 3. Aromatic, Cox-like flavour. Heavy, regular crops; frost-resistant blossom; less prone to disease than Cox, but can be susceptible to scab and develop canker on some sites. Season: Oct.–Dec. / Jan.*
CAgr CArg CBod CCVT CDoC CEnd CMac CTri EBee EPfP EPom EWTr LBuc LPar LRHS MAsh MCoo MGos MMuc MPri MRav MTrO NLar NOra NRog NWea SBdl SCoo SEdi SEND SEWo SKee SLim SPer SPoG SRms SSFr WJas WMat WWct

'Fortune' *see* 'Laxton's Fortune'

93 H6 **'Golden Noble'** (C)
Pollination group 4. Cooks to a well-flavoured purée, not as acidic as 'Bramley's Seedling'. Attractive blossom. Good, regular crops; partial tip-bearer; some scab and mildew resistance. Season: Oct.–Dec. and longer.
CAgr CTri IArd NOra NRog SBdl SKee

93 H6 **'Greensleeves'** (D)
Pollination group 3. Crisp, brisk, becoming sweeter. Very precocious and heavy, regular crops; needs thinning for good fruit size. Can be susceptible to scab. Season: late Sept.–Oct.; short season once picked.
CAgr CArg CMac CTri ELan EPfP EPom LPar MAsh MGos MMuc MTrO NOra NRog NWea SBdl SEND SEdi SKee SLim SPer SSFT SSFr WJas WMat WWct

93 H6 **'Grenadier'** (C)
Pollination group 3. Cooks to sharp purée. Heavy, regular crops; good disease resistance. Season: Aug.–Sept.*
CAgr CArg CHab CLnd CTri EPom MGos MMuc MTrO NOra NRog NWea SBdl SEND SEdi SKee SLon SPer SSFT SSFr WJas WMat

14 H6 **'Howgate Wonder'** (C)
Pollination group 3. Very large, late-season, heavy-cropping apple with a very mild flavour. Vigorous; fruit yellow-green flushed with red. Partially self-fertile.
CAgr CArg CBod CCVT CDoC CHab CLnd CSBt CTri EPfP EPom GDam LBuc MMuc MTrO NOra NRog NWea SBdl SEdi SKee SPer SSFr SVic WJas WMat WWct

93 H6 **'James Grieve'** (C/D)
Pollination group 3. Savoury, crisp to melting flesh; when cooked keeps shape, with juicy, delicate flavour. Good, regular crops; fruit bruises easily. Prone to scab, canker; resistant to mildew; requires well-drained soil. Season: Sept.–Oct. and longer.*
CAgr CArg CBcs CBod CCVT CDoC CEnd CHab CLnd CMac CRos CSBt CTri EBee EPfP EPom EWTr GDam LBuc LMaj LRHS LSRN MAsh MGos MMuc MPri MRav MTrO NLar NOra NRHS NRog NWea SBdl SCob SCoo SEdi SEND SEWo SGbt SKee SLim SPer SRms SSFr SSFT SVic SWvt WJas WMat WTSh WWct

93 H6 **'Jonagold'** (D)
Triploid. Pollination group 3. Attractive, crisp, honeyed taste; large fruit. Heavy, regular crops; prone to canker. Fruit can be poorly coloured, but many more colourful sports exist. Vigorous. Season: Nov.–Jan. / Feb.; stores well.
CArg CLnd CTri ELan EPom IArd IPap LMaj LRHS NOra NRog SBdl SEdi SGsty SKee SPer SSFr WWct

93 H6 **'Jupiter'** (D)
Triploid. Pollination group 3. Cox-like flavour, but sharper. Heavy crops, but biennial if allowed to over-crop; fruit can be heavily russetted. Vigorous. Season: late Oct.–Jan.*
CAgr CArg CBod CSBt CTri EPfP LSRN MRav MTrO NLar NOra NRog NWea SBdl SEdi SKee SLon SSFr WJas WMat

93 H6 **'Kidd's Orange Red'** (D)
Pollination group 3. Very attractive; rich aromatic, perfumed taste. Good, regular crops; fruit prone to coarse russet. Season: Nov.–Jan.
CAgr CArg CBod CEnd CLnd CMac CRos CTri EBee EPfP EPom LBuc LRHS MTrO NOra NRog NWea SKee SLon SSFr WMat WWct

93 H6 **'King of the Pippins'** (C/D)
Pollination group 5. Well ripened, good flavour. Cooked, keeps shape, flavoursome; suited to open tarts, etc. Heavy, regular crops; upright habit; good resistance to disease; keeps well. Season: Oct.–Dec.; can store to Feb.*
CArg CHab CLnd CTri EPom LBuc MTrO NOra SBdl SKee SVic

93 H6 **'King Russet'** (D)
Pollination group 3. Russetted form of 'King of the Pippins'. Improved eating quality; good distinct russet flavour. Not as heavy cropping. Season: Oct.–Dec.
SBdl

93 H6 **'Lane's Prince Albert'** (C)
Pollination group 3. Cooks to brisk purée, not as acidic as 'Bramley's Seedling'. Large fruit. Good, regular crops; fruit easily bruised. Resistant to scab; very prone to mildew; prone to canker on all but very well-drained soils. Season: Nov.–Mar.; stores well.*
CAgr CArg CBod CEnd CHab CLnd CSBt CTri EPfP LRHS MGos MRav MTrO NOra NRog NWea SBdl SCoo SEdi SSFr SVic SWeb WMat

93 H6 **'Laxton's Epicure'** (D)
Pollination group 3. Delicate, aromatic, Cox-like flavour. Heavy, regular crops; needs thinning for size; prone to bitter pit, canker. Season: late Aug.–Sept. Awarded as 'Epicure'.*
CAgr CBod CEnd CHab CTri NRog SBdl SKee

93 H6 **'Laxton's Fortune'** (D)
Pollination group 3. Sweet, lightly aromatic flavour; needs to colour well for good quality. Good crops, but tendency to be biennial. Fruit bruises easily, can be poorly coloured. Prone to canker, good resistance to scab. Season: Sept.–Oct. Awarded as 'Fortune'.
CArg CHab CMac CSBt CTri IArd MTrO NOra NRog SBdl SEdi SKee SSFr WMat WWct

14 H6 **'Limelight'** (D)
Pollination group 3. Crisp and refreshing; heavy-cropping.
CArg CBod CDoC EBee MAsh MCoo MTrO NLar NOra NRog NWea SBdl SCoo SKee SSFT SSFr WMat

93 H6 **'Lord Lambourne'** (D)
Pollination group 2. Sweet, juicy, attractive flavour. Skin can become greasy when stored. Good, regular crops. Partial tip-bearer; resistant to mildew. Season: late Sept.–Nov.*
CAgr CArg CEnd CHab CLnd CMac CSBt CTri ELan EPom LSRN MAsh MGos MTrO NOra NRog SBdl SEdi SKee SLon SPer SSFr WJas WMat WWct

93 H6 **'Mother'** (D)
Pollination group 5. Sweet, perfumed, distinctive flavour. Crops can be erratic, light; good resistance to scab and mildew. Also sold as 'American Mother'. Season: Oct.–Dec.*
CAgr CEnd CLnd CTri SBdl SKee SSFr

93 H6 **'Peasgood's Nonsuch'** (C/D)
Pollination group 3. Cooks to sweet, delicately flavoured purée; needs no or little extra sugar. Exhibition apple with large, handsome regular shape. Good, regular crops; resistance to mildew and red spider; moderate resistance to scab. Season: late Sept.–Dec.
CAgr CArg CHab EPom IArd LSRN MAsh MTrO NOra NRog SBdl SKee SLon WMat

93 H6 **'Pixie'** (D)
Pollination group 4. Intensely aromatic, Cox-like flavour, but sharper and firmer-fleshed. Good to heavy crops, but small fruit unless thinned. Very reliable and easy to grow. Season: Dec.–Mar.*
CDoC CLnd CSBt EPom LRHS MPri MTrO NOra NRog SBdl SKee SLon WWct

14 H6 **'Red Falstaff'** (D)
Pollination group 3. Late-season, heavy-cropping sport of 'Falstaff' with a fruity flavour and crisp, juicy flesh. Self-fertile and moderately vigorous. Skin flushed with orange-red when ripe. Season: Nov.–Jan.
CAgr CArg CBod CCVT CDoC CEnd CMac CTri EPfP GKin LBuc LRHS LSRN MAsh MTrO NLar NOra NRHS NRog SBdl SCoo SEWo SGbt SKee SLim SLon SPoG SSFT WMat WWct

93 H6 **'Ribston Pippin'** (D)
Triploid. Pollination group 2. Intense, rich, aromatic flavour; more acidity and more robust than Cox. Good, regular crops; resistant to scab; prone to mildew and canker. Season: Oct.–Jan.
CArg CTri LBuc MRav MTrO NOra NRog NWea SBdl SKee SLon SSFr WJas WMat WWct

93 H6 **'Rosemary Russet'** (D)
Pollination group 3. Sweet-sharp acid drop taste, resembling 'Ashmead's Kernel'. Crops good, regular; vigorous tree with upright habit. Season: Nov. / Dec.–Mar.
CAgr CArg CHab ELan NOra NRog SBdl SKee SLon SSFr WMat WWct

93 H6 **'Saint Edmund's Pippin'** (D)
Pollination group 2. Very attractive; richly flavoured when fully ripe. Good, regular crops; fruit bruises easily. Prone to mildew. Season: late Sept.–Oct. AGM reconfirmed 2017.*
CHab ELan EPfP MTrO NOra NRog NWea SKee SSFr

14 H6 **'Santana'** (D)
Pollination group 4. Medium to quite vigorous tree, with upright spreading habit. Good to heavy crop, with low susceptibility to scab. Midseason apple; picking early September and keeping well. Bright red flushed; sweet, crisp, juicy flesh; good flavour.
LPar NOra SBdl WMat

09 H6 **'Scrumptious'** (D)
Pollination group 3. Regular cropper, good fruit size, attractive ornamental fruit. Good tree habit; easily managed. A good dessert apple: sweet, good flavour, crisp, juicy.
CAgr CArg CCVT CDoC CMac CRos CSBt CTri EBee ELan EPfP EPom LBuc LCro LOPS LRHS LSRN MAsh MGos MTrO NLar NOra NRHS NRog NWea SBdl SCoo SEWo SGbt SKee SLim SLon SPer SPoG SSFr SSFT WJas WMat

93 H6 **'Sunset'** (D)
Pollination group 3. Aromatic, like small early Cox, but sharper. Heavy, regular crops, but small fruit. Resistant to scab; prone to mildew and canker. Season: Oct.–Dec.
CAgr CArg CBod CCVT CDoC CEnd CHab CLnd CMac CSBt CTri EBee EPfP EPom GKin LBuc LRHS LSRN MRav MTrO NOra NRog NWea SBdl SCoo SEdi SKee SLim SLon SPer SSFr SSFT SVic WJas WMat WWct

14 H6 **'Topaz'** (D)
Pollination group 4. Medium vigour, with upright spreading habit. Good crop, with resistance to scab; late season, picking in early / mid October. Medium-sized; red flushed over a yellow background; crisp, juicy flesh, sweet-sharp taste; mellows with keeping.
LPar MTrO NOra SBdl SKee

93 H6 **'Warner's King'** (C)
Triploid. Pollination group 2. Cooks to well-flavoured purée; not as acidic as 'Bramley's Seedling'. Attractive, deep pink blossom. Heavy, regular crops; fruit can be very large. Prone to bitter pit. Vigorous. Season: late Sept.–Dec.
CTri MTrO NOra NRog SBdl SKee

93 H6 **'Winston'** (D)
Pollination group 4. Aromatic and rich. Good, regular crops; fruit can be rather small; good disease resistance. Season: Dec.–Apr.; keeps well.*
CAgr CBod CCVT CMac CTri LPar NRog SBdl SKee SRms SVic SWeb WWct

93 H6 **'Worcester Pearmain'** (D)
Pollination group 3. Intense strawberry flavour when well-ripened and scarlet. Tip-bearer; heavy, regular crops. Resistant to mildew; some susceptibility to canker. Season: late Sept.–Oct.
CAgr CArg CBcs CCVT CHab CLnd CMac CSBt CTri EBee EPfP EPom LBuc LRHS MAsh MMuc MRav MTrO NOra NRog NWea SBdl SCoo SEdi SEND SEWo SKee SLim SPer SSFr WJas WMat WWct

Blackberry (*Rubus fruticosus* agg.)

Season extends from late July to early September.

93 H6 **'Loch Ness'**
Large, well-flavoured berries. Thornless; heavy-cropping; moderate vigour; hardy. Good resistance to purple blotch and botrytis, but prone to downy mildew. Reconfirmed after trial 2015.
CAgr CArg CHab CMac CRos EHyd EPom IArd LCro LOPS LRHS LSRN NRHS NRog NWea SCoo SKee SPer SSFr SVic

15 H6 **'Loch Tay'**
No spines; has a good blackberry flavour and shiny fruit. Healthy but not too vigorous, producing good replacement canes. Early.
CArg CHab CMac CRos EHyd EPom LRHS NRHS NRog SPoG

Blackcurrant (*Ribes nigrum*)

Season extends from early July to mid August.

95 H6 **'Ben Connan'**
Large fruit; medium long strigs. Heavy crops; compact habit. Good resistance to mildew, leaf-curling midge. Season: early. Reconfirmed after trial 2012.
CAgr CMac CRos CSBt EHyd EPfP EPom GDam LBuc LCro LEdu LOPS LRHS LSRN MAsh MGos MNHC MTrO NLar NRHS NRog NWea SBdl SCoo SEND SGbt SKee SPer SPoG SRms SSFr SWvt WMat

12 H6 **'Big Ben'**
Fairly vigorous medium-sized bush, flowering early to midseason. Fruit large and easy to pick. Good yields, showing resistance to mildew and leaf spot. Fresh fruit flavour pleasant to quite sweet; rich when cooked. Good all-round cultivar.
CArg CRos EBee EHyd EPfP EPom LBuc LCro LOPS LRHS LSRN MTrO NRHS SBdl SGbt SKee SPer SPoG WMat

Blueberry (*Vaccinium corymbosum*)

Blueberries begin to ripen mid July and continue to late August.

03 H6 **'Duke'** (D)
Good flavour, medium to large fruit. Crops well; easy to grow. Flowers late; good for frost-prone sites; partly self-fertile. Season: early.
CArg CDoC CTrh ELan EPfP EPom LCro LOPS MCoo MGos NRog NWea SCoo SPre SRkn SSFr

03 H6 **'Spartan'** (D)
Excellent flavour; medium-sized fruit. Quite good crops; not self-fertile. Vigorous; upright habit. Good autumn colour. Season: early–mid.
CDoC CMac CTrh EPom LCro LOPS LRHS LSRN MGos SKee

Cherry (morello) (*Prunus cerasus*)

93 H6 **'Morello'** (C)
Dark red, acid cherry; excellent for preserves, tarts, etc. Regular, good crops; very attractive in blossom; self-fertile. Crops on north-facing site. Season: late July–early Aug.
CAgr CArg CBod CCVT CDoC CLnd CMac CSBt CTri CTsd ELan EPfP EPom EWTr GDam IPap LBuc LCro LOPS LRHS LSRN MGos MMuc MPri MTrO NLar NOra NRog SBdl SEdi SEND SEWo SGbt SKee SLim SPer SSFr SSFT SVic SWvt WJas WMat

Cherry (sweet) (*Prunus avium*)

14 H6 **'Kordia'** (D)
Pollination group 5. Mid to late season; large to very large, true black cherry; bold appearance; excellent rich flavour. Spreading habit; can show some bare wood; medium vigour. Heavy, reliable crops; easy to grow. Not self-fertile; usually pollinated by 'Regina' or 'Sylvia' in commercial orchards; can also be pollinated by 'Summer Sun', 'Stella' (early bloom only). Blossom can be a little frost-sensitive. Good garden cherry.
CArg EPom LMaj LPar MTrO NOra SBdl SKee SSFr WMat WWct

14 H6 **'Lapins'**
Pollination group 4. Mid to late season; large, dark red cherry; very good flavour. Upright habit; medium vigour. Heavy, reliable crops. All-round excellent cherry; self-fertile.
CAgr CArg CBod CLnd EPfP EPom LMaj LPar MRav NLar NOra NWea SEdi SGsty SKee SSFT SSFr WJas WMat WWct

95 H6 **'Merchant'** (D)
Pollination group 3. Early black cherry; well-flavoured. Regular crops. Pollination: universal donor, but not self-fertile. Season: early July. Reconfirmed 2014.
MTrO NOra NRog SBdl SEdi SKee SSFT SSFr WMat WWct

14 H6 **'Penny'**
Pollination group 4. Mid to late season; dark red, very large, meaty cherry; excellent flavour. Upright spreading habit; medium vigour; prone to some bare wood. Crops well and regularly on Gisela 5; bred for UK conditions. Not self-fertile; pollinated by late to midseason cultivars, e.g. 'Summer Sun', 'Skeena', 'Regina'; needs sufficient pollination to ensure heavy crops.
CAgr CArg CTri EPom MTrO NOra NRog SKee WMat WWct

93 H6 **'Stella'**
Pollination group 4. Black cherry; large, rich, high quality. Heavy, regular crops; self-fertile. Prone to splitting in wet weather. Season: late July. Reconfirmed 2014.
CAgr CArg CDoC CEnd CHab CLnd CMac CRos CSBt CTri ELan EPfP EPom EWTr IPap LBuc LCro LOPS LPar LRHS MAsh MGos MMuc MRav NLar NOra NRHS NRog NWea SBdl SCoo SEdi SEND SEWo SGbt SKee SLim SPer SPoG SSFr SSFT SVic SWvt WJas WMat WTSh WWct

04 H6 **'Summer Sun'** (D)
Pollination group 4. Late (July). Produces firm, well-flavoured, red to black fruit. Very good crops. Some resistance to bacterial canker. Attractive, upright, spreading habit; moderate vigour. Not self-fertile. Reconfirmed 2014.
CAgr CArg CLnd CMac CTri EPom LBuc MAsh MGos MTrO NLar NOra NRog SBdl SCoo SKee SLim SPoG SSFT SSFr WMat WWct

14 H6 **'Sweetheart'**
Pollination group 4. Dark red cherry; latest of the season. Good flavour; very firm fruit. Medium vigour, upright spreading habit. Heavy, regular crops; fruits moderate size. Slightly prone to canker and brown rot. Only late-season self-fertile cultivar available. Prolific blossom, making a tree exceptionally pretty in the spring. Sets dense clusters of fruits, which can be prone to botrytis / brown rot.
CAgr CArg CLnd CTri EPom LCro LMaj LOPS LPar LRHS LSRN MAsh MTrO NOra NRHS NRog NWea SCoo SEWo SKee SLim SPoG SVic WMat

Damson (*Prunus insititia*)

00 H6 **'Farleigh Damson'** (C)
Pollination group 4. Excellent flavour. Regular, heavy crops. Blossom shows some resistance to frost. Season: late Aug.

CAgr CArg CDoC CHab EPfP EPom EWTr LBuc LEdu MTrO NLar NOra NRog NWea SEdi SKee SPer SVic WJas WMat WWct

98 H6 **'Prune Damson'** (C)
Pollination group 4. Larger fruits than 'Farleigh Damson', but typical damson flavour. Regular, good crops. Season: late Aug.
CAgr CArg CHab CLnd CMac CTri EBee EPfP EPom LBuc LCro LRHS MMuc MTrO NLar NOra NRog NWea SEND SEWo SGbt SKee SPer SSFr WJas WMat WWct

Fig (*Ficus carica*)

93 H4 **'Brown Turkey'** (D)
Fruits regularly in the open in southern England and in many parts of the Midlands and East Anglia in a warm position. For good crop, root restriction advisable. Season: mid Aug.–mid Sept., depending on site.
CAgr CBcs CBod CBrac CCCN CCVT CDoC CJun CKel CLnd CMac CPla CRHN CRos CSBt CTri CTsd EBee EHyd ELan EPfP EPom ETod EWTr IPap LBuc LCro LEdu LOPS LRHS LSRN MAsh MBlu MBros MGos MHer MHtn MMuc MNHC MRav MTrO NGKo NLar NOra NPer NRHS NRog NWea SBls SCoo SEND SEWo SGBe SGol SGsty SKee SLim SMad SNig SPer SPlb SPoG SPre SRms SSFT SSta SVen SVic SWeb SWvt WAvo WFar WLea WLov WMat WMou WPGP WTSh XSen

Gooseberry (*Ribes uva-crispa*)

Season extends from early June to mid August. For culinary use, pick from early June. For ripe fruit pick from early July.

93 H6 **'Careless'** (C/D)
Green fruit. Reliable, good crops. Good for tarts, jam, etc. Prone to mildew. Season: mid.
CSBt CTri EPom LSRN MAsh MGos NRog SCoo SEdi SPer WMat

94 H6 **'Greenfinch'** (C/D)
Green fruit; compact bush. Some resistance to mildew and leaf spot. Season: mid.
CAgr

93 H6 **'Invicta'** (C/D)
Green fruit; quite good flavour. Heavy crops; very vigorous; spreading habit; large thorns. Some resistance to mildew. Young shoots can be damaged on exposed site. Season: mid; slightly earlier than 'Careless'. Main use culinary.
CAgr CDoC CMac CRos CSBt CTri EHyd EMil EPfP EPom GBin LBuc LCro LOPS LRHS LSRN MAsh MGos MMuc MNHC MPri MTrO NLar NRHS NRog NWea SBdl SCoo SEdi SEND SKee SPer SPoG SRms SSFr SVic SWvt WMat

93 H6 **'Leveller'** (C/D)
Large, yellow fruit; good dessert quality. Season: mid to late.
MCoo NRog NWea SEdi SPer

93 H6 **'Whinham's Industry'** (C/D)
Red fruit; quite good dessert quality. Heavy, reliable crops. Very susceptible to mildew. Season: mid.
ELan LBuc LSRN MGos MMuc MPri NRog SEND SEdi SPer SRms

Grape (*Vitis*)

04 H5 **'Boskoop Glory'** (D)
Black grape. Good outdoor vine for the amateur, both dessert and wine; crops reliably; disease-resistant. Moderately good flavour, but better than many shop-bought grapes. Awarded as 'Gloire de Boskoop'.
CMac ELan LBuc MBros SBdl SCoo WSuV

04 H5 **'New York Muscat'** (D)
Black grape. A good dessert Muscat with blackcurrant flavour. Disease-resistant. Best when grown on a warm site or wall.
WSuV

Hazelnut (*Corylus maxima*)

14 H6 **'Gunslebert'**
Good-sized nut; kernel fills the shell; very few blanks. Excellent flavour; very tasty. Midseason. Regular, good crops; nuts held as large clusters of four nuts. Medium vigour tree; moderate amount of suckering. Pollinated by 'Kentish Cob', 'Cosford'. Good tree habit, with a natural goblet shape and exceptionally attractive with prolific catkins making it also an ornamental tree. A mainstay of Kent nut production. Reliable, hardy hazel nut, easy to grow in a garden situation; productive and ornamental; requires a pollinator.
CCVT CMac CTri MTrO NOra SBdl SPoG SRms SSFr WMat

14 H6 **'Kentish Cob'**
Good-sized nut; kernel fills the shell; very few blanks. Excellent flavour; rich and meaty. Early season, cropping before the squirrels become active. Regular, good crops. Medium vigour tree; moderate amount of suckering. Pollinated by 'Gunslebert', 'Cosford', 'Hall's Giant' ('Merveille de Bollwiller'). The main cultivar of commercial nut plantations in Kent. Reliable hazel nut, easy to grow in a garden situation; needs a pollinator.
CAgr CBcs CSBt CTri EBee ELan EPfP EPom IArd LBuc LRHS MCoo MTrO NLar NOrn NRog NWea SBdl SEdi SEWo SKee SLim SPer SPoG SRms SSFr SSFT SVic SWvt WMat WMou

Loganberry (*Rubus × loganobaccus*)

93 H5 **'Ly 654'** (C)
Large, dark fruit; distinctive flavour; good crops. Thornless. Season: July.
CRos CSBt EHyd EPom LBuc LRHS NRHS NRog SPer SSFr SVic

Medlar (*Mespilus germanica*)

17 H6 **'Iranian'**
Compact bushy tree with small leaves and bunches of fruit. Fruit ripens early, so can be picked before they fall off. Fruit can be eaten off the tree. Has a pleasant taste with a good balance of sweetness and acidity.
CAgr SKee

14 H6 **'Nottingham'**
Mid-sized fruit with good flavour for eating fresh as well as for jelly-making. Good acid–sweetness balance. Very productive, with very open eye. Has potential for splitting and allowing rot to enter. Reconfirmed 2017.
CAgr CArg CBcs CCVT CDoC CEnd CHab CTri EBee ELan EPfP EPom LBuc LRHS MAsh MGos MMuc MTrO NOra NRog NWea SCoo SEdi SEND SEWo SKee SLim SPer SPoG SSFr SSFT SVic WJas WMat

Pear (*Pyrus communis*)

93 H6 **'Beth'** (D)
Pollination group 4. Attractive; good quality and flavour. Small fruit. Heavy, regular crops. Season: mid / late Aug.–early Sept.; short season once picked.
CAgr CArg CBod CDoC CHab CLnd CMac CSBt CTri CTsd EBee EPfP EPom EWTr IArd LBuc MAsh MGos MPri MTrO NLar NOra NRog SBdl SCoo SEdi SEWo SGbt SKee SLim SPer SSFr SSFT WMat WWct

93 H6 **'Beurré Hardy'** (D)
Pollination group 3. Very melting and fragrant with rose-water perfume. Good, regular crops. Very hardy, vigorous tree; slow to bear; resistant to scab. Season: Nov.–Dec.*
CAgr CArg CCVT CMac CSBt CTri ELan EPfP EPom IArd IPap LMaj MCoo MTrO NOra NRog NWea SBdl SEND SEdi SGsty SKee SPer SSFT SSFr WMat WWct

06 H6 **'Beurré Superfin'** (D)
Pollination group 3. An excellent September-cropping cultivar for the amateur gardener, with a lovely cinnamon-russet colour and an exquisite flavour. Gives a good, consistent yield and is not over-vigorous. Midseason.
MTrO SBdl SKee SSFr

93 H6 **'Concorde'** (D)
Pollination group 4. Sweet, buttery, fragrant flavour, similar to 'Conference', but superior. Heavy, regular crops; frost-tolerant blossom. Young trees very precocious. Season: late Oct. / Nov.–Dec.
CAgr CArg CBod CCVT CDoC CMac CRos CSBt CTri EBee ELan EPfP EPom IArd LBuc LCro LOPS LRHS LSRN MAsh MGos MPri MRav MTrO NLar NOra NRog NWea SBdl SCoo SEdi SEWo SGbt SKee SLim SPer SPoG SPre SSFr SSFT SVic WJas WMat WWct

93 H6 **'Conference'** (D)
Pollination group 3. Sweet, buttery, quite rich taste. Heavy, regular crops. Can produce fruits without pollinators, but resulting fruits often misshapen. Season: Oct.–Nov. / Dec.*
CAgr CArg CBcs CBod CCVT CDoC CLnd CMac CRos CSBt CTri CTsd EBee ELan EPfP EPom EWTr GBin IPap LBuc LCro LEdu LMaj LOPS LPar LRHS LSRN MAsh MGos MMuc MPri MRav MTrO NLar NOra NRHS NRog NWea SBdl SCoo SEdi SEND SEWo SGbt SGsty SKee SLim SPer SPoG SSFr SVic SWvt WJas WMat WTSh WWct

93 H6 **'Doyenné du Comice'** (D)
Pollination group 4. Very rich flavour; very juicy, buttery, perfumed. Excellent quality, but moderate crops, although older trees more regular. Vigorous tree; prone to scab. Season: Nov.–Dec. Not compatible with 'Onward'.
CAgr CArg CBcs CBod CCVT CHab CLnd CMac CSBt CTri EBee ELan EPfP EPom EWTr IArd LBuc LCro LOPS LRHS MMuc MPri MRav MTrO NLar NOra NRog NWea SBdl SCoo SEdi SEND SEWo SKee SLim SPer SSFr SVic WJas WMat WTSh WWct

06 H6 **'Gorham'** (D)
Pollination group 4. A beautiful green pear with a good covering of russet. Has an excellent flavour; a good reliable cropper and is readily available. Late.
CAgr MTrO NOra SBdl SKee SSFT SSFr WMat

93 H6 **'Joséphine de Malines'** (D)
Pollination group 3. Very rich, buttery and perfumed. Crops good, reliable, but needs warm site. Fruit easily bruised. Tip-bearer; resistant to scab. Season: Nov.–Dec. / Jan.
CAgr IArd MTrO NOra SBdl SKee

Plum (*Prunus domestica*)

00 H5 **'Blue Rock'** (C/D)
Pollination group 1. Quite well-flavoured blue plum. Regular, good crops; not self-fertile. Neat tree. Season: mid Aug.
SKee

95 H5 **'Blue Tit'** (C/D)
Pollination group 5. Pleasant flavour; blue plum. Regular, good crops. Self-fertile. Season: mid Aug.
CAgr CBod EPom MMuc NOra NRog SEND SKee SSFr WMat WWct

98 H5 **'Cambridge Gage'** (D)
Pollination group 4. Honeysweet excellent greengage quality. Reasonably regular crops in favourable situations. Partly self-fertile. Season: mid Aug.
CAgr CArg CBod CCVT CEnd CHab CLnd CMac CTri EBee EPfP EPom EWTr LCro LRHS LSRN MAsh MMuc MTrO NOra NRog SBdl SCoo SEdi SEND SEWo SKee SLim SPer SSFr SSFT WJas WMat WWct

93 H6 **'Czar'** (C/D)
Pollination group 3. Well-flavoured; early blue plum; used for jam but also moderate eating quality. Heavy, regular crops. Self-fertile. Season: mid Aug.
CAgr CArg CCVT CDoC CEnd CHab CLnd CMac CSBt CTri ELan EPfP EPom EWTr IPap LBuc LCro LOPS LPar LRHS MAsh MCoo MGos MMuc MPri MTrO NLar NOra NRog NWea SBdl SEdi SEND SEWo SKee SLim SPer SPoG SSFr SSFT SVic SWvt WMat WWct

14 H5 **'Haganta'** (D)
Pollination group 3. Large dark blue plum, late-ripening, with good consistent crop; juicy, sweet; sugary; and stone almost free; good flavour.
CAgr MTrO NOra WMat

93 H5 **'Imperial Gage'** (C/D)
Pollination group 2. Gage quality but not as rich as 'Cambridge Gage'. Regular crops. Partly self-fertile. Season: mid Aug.
CAgr CArg CLnd CMac CSBt CTri EPom EWTr LRHS MMuc MTrO NOra NRog SEND SKee SPer SSFT SSFr WMat

94 H5 **'Jefferson'** (D)
Pollination group 1. Yellow flushed with red; rich, gage quality. Moderate, regular crops. Not self-fertile. Season: mid to late Aug.
CAgr CArg CHab CLnd MTrO NOra NRog SKee SSFr SVic WMat

00 H6 **'Mallard'** (D)
Pollination group 1. Medium-sized red plum; quite good flavour. Good, regular crops. Moderate vigour; not self-fertile. Season: mid–late Aug.
NOra SKee WMat

93 H5 **'Marjorie's Seedling'** (C)
Pollination group 5. Late blue plum. Good for jam. Reliable good crops; vigorous, upright habit. Self-fertile. Season: late Sept.–early Oct.
CAgr CArg CBod CCVT CDoC CEnd CHab CLnd CMac CSBt CTri EPfP EPom LBuc LCro LOPS LRHS LSRN MAsh MGos MMuc MPri MTrO NLar NOra NRog NWea SBdl SCoo SEdi SEND SKee SLim SPer SSFr SSFT WJas WMat WWct

95 H6 **'Opal'** (D)
Pollination group 3. Small purple plum; good flavour. Reliable, heavy crops; needs thinning. Partly self-fertile. Blossom buds very prone to bird damage. Season: early–mid Aug.
CAgr CArg CBod CCVT CMac CRos CTri EBee ELan EPfP EPom LBuc LCro LMaj LOPS LPar LRHS LSRN MAsh MGos MMuc MTrO NLar NOra NRog NWea SBdl SCoo SEdi SEND SGbt SKee SLim SPer SSFr SSFT WMat WTSh WWct

93 H5 **'Oullins Gage'** (D)
Pollination group 4. Large, yellow flushed with pink. Not typical gage quality, but quite rich. Heavy, regular crops. Partly self-fertile. Season: mid Aug.
CAgr CArg CCVT CLnd CMac CSBt CTri ELan EPfP EPom LBuc LCro LEdu LOPS LRHS MGos MMuc MPri MRav MTrO NOra NRog SBdl SEdi SEND SEWo SKee SPer SPoG SSFr SSFT SVic SWvt WJas WMat WWct

14 H5 **'Purple Pershore'** (C)
Pollination group 3. Good flavour; reliable good crops.
CAgr CHab CTri IArd NOra NRog SKee WMat WWct

95 H5 **'Valor'** (C/D)
Pollination group 2. Blue, medium-sized plum. Good quality. Moderately good, regular crops. Not self-fertile. Season: late Aug.
LPar NOra NRog SKee

93 H5 **'Victoria'** (C/D)
Pollination group 3. Red plum; reasonable to good eating quality; excellent for bottling, jam and tarts. Heavy, regular crops. Self-fertile. Season: mid to late Aug.
CAgr CArg CCVT CDoC CHab CLnd CMac CRos CSBt CTri CTsd EBee ELan EPfP EPom EWTr GDam GKin IArd IPap LBuc LCro LEdu LMaj LOPS LPar LRHS LSRN MAsh MGos MMuc MPri MRav MTrO NLar NOra NRHS NRog NWea SBdl SCoo SEdi SEND SEWo SKee SLim SPer SPoG SSFr SSFT SVic SWvt WJas WMat WTSh WWct

Quince (*Cydonia oblonga*)

17 H5 **'Serbian Gold'**
Good resistance to leaf blight, and said to be fireblight-resistant. A compact tree for modern gardens, with a small leaf and pretty flowers. Consistently good cropper, with roundish fruit; quite acidic when eaten raw. Good jelly-making quince.

CMac EBee EPom GQue LRHS MTrO NLar NOra NRog SKee SSFT WMat

Raspberry (*Rubus idaeus*)

Raspberries crop from late June to early August. Autumn primocanes from late July to early October.

09 H6 **'All Gold'**
Autumn-cropping. Yellow- / golden-fruited; needs to be left to ripen well before the flavour is fully tasted. Yield generally peaking at the end of August and early September. An upright habit with easy-to-manage cane.
CDoC CMac EPfP EPom NLar NRog SCoo SPer SRms SVic WMat

93 H6 **'Autumn Bliss'** (D)
Autumn-cropping. Primocane-fruiting (fruiting on current season's canes). Excellent flavour; large fruit. Good crops. Resistant to aphid vectors of virus disease and phytophthora root rot. Season: crops late July to early Oct. Reconfirmed after trial 2009.
CAgr CDoC CMac CRos CSBt CTri EBee EHyd ELan EPfP EPom GDam LBuc LCro LEdu LOPS LRHS LSRN MAsh MGos MNHC MPri NLar NRHS NRog NWea SBdl SCoo SEdi SEWo SGbt SKee SPer SPoG SRms SSFr SVic WMat

00 H6 **'Glen Ample'** (D)
Summer-cropping. Large fruit, excellent flavour. Recommended for freezing. Heavy crops; spine-free canes. Resistant to main aphid vector of virus disease; some tolerance to phytophthora root rot; some susceptibility to leaf and bud mite. Season: mid. Reconfirmed after trial 2009.
CAgr CArg CMac CRos CSBt CTri EBee EHyd ELan EPfP EPom LBuc LCro LOPS LRHS LSRN MAsh MCoo MNHC NLar NRHS NRog NWea SBdl SCoo SEdi SEWo SGbt SKee SPer SPoG SRms SSFr SVic WMat

09 H6 **'Glen Magna'** (D)
Summer-cropping. A very vigorous cultivar with long, strong fruiting laterals. It has large fruit with a good flavour. Yields high with a long cropping season.
CAgr CArg CSBt MAsh MPri SCoo SEdi SKee SRms

09 H6 **'Joan J'**
Autumn-cropping. Easy to grow and pick; upright habit; good berry size.
CArg CMac EPom LBuc LSRN NRog SBdl SPer SRms SSFr

93 H6 **'Leo'** (D)
Large firm fruit; excellent flavour. Good crops. Very long laterals. Season: late.
CSBt LCro LOPS MAsh NRog SCoo SKee SRms SSFr

93 H6 **'Malling Admiral'** (D)
Summer-cropping. Good quality; medium to large, attractive fruit. Consistent, moderate to good crops; tall canes; withstands wet conditions, but laterals easily damaged in exposed sites. Good disease resistance. Season: mid to late. Reconfirmed after trial 2009.
CSBt CTri EPom LSRN MAsh NRog NWea SCoo SKee SPer

93 H6 **'Malling Jewel'** (D)
Summer-cropping. Good flavour and crops. Season: early to mid. Reconfirmed after trial 2009.
CAgr CArg CDoC CSBt CTri EPfP EPom LBuc LSRN MAsh MPri NRog NWea SEdi SKee SPer SRms

09 H6 **'Polka'**
Autumn-cropping. Early flush of fruit with good berry size and appearance; good upright habit with medium vigorous cane growth.
CArg CDoC CRos EHyd EPfP EPom LBuc LCro LOPS LRHS LSRN MAsh MCoo MRav NRHS NRog SBdl SCoo SKee SPer SRms SSFr WMat

09 H6 **'Tulameen'**
Summer-cropping. Outstanding cultivar, with strong cane growth and upright habit. Spine-free and easily handled, with exceptional fruit quality and high yield. Less prone to pest and disease than other varieties.
CAgr CArg CDoC CSBt EBee EHyd ELan EPfP EPom LBuc LCro LOPS LPar LRHS LSRN MAsh NRHS NRog NWea SBdl SCoo SEWo SEdi SKee SPer SPoG SRms SSFr SVic WMat

Redcurrant (*Ribes rubrum*)

Redcurrants crop from mid July to early September.

93 H6 **'Jonkheer van Tets'** (C)
Large, handsome fruit; long strigs. Heavy crops. Season: early.
CAgr CDoC CRos CSBt EHyd EPfP EPom IArd LRHS LSRN MAsh MCoo MPri NLar NRHS NWea SBdl SCoo SEND SEdi SGbt SKee SPer SRms SSFr WMat

93 H6 **'Red Lake'** (C)
Good quality medium to large fruit; cropping on long trusses. Prone to wind damage in exposed sites; in summer prune early. Season: mid to late.
CAgr CTri ELan EPfP EPom LBuc LEdu MGos MPri NLar NRog SEdi SKee SPer SPoG SRms SSFr WMat

93 H6 **'Stanza'** (C)
Medium-sized fruit; good quality. Compact habit; heavy crops. Season: mid to late.
CAgr NRog SEND

Strawberry (*Fragaria × ananassa*)

In an early season, strawberries begin to crop mid June; in a late season, mid to late June.

06 H6 **'Alice'** (D)
A good consistent cropper, with a high percentage of mid to large, bright orange-red, sweet, juicy fruit. Scored well in taste tests and performed well at different geographical locations (Stafford, Kent, Dundee) in HDC trials. Has good resistance to verticillium wilt; very useful to home gardener. Mid to late season.
CAgr CMac EPom

93 H6 **'Cambridge Favourite'** (D)
Good flavour; medium size, but rather soft berries. Moderate crops; excellent resistance to disease. Good runner production. Season: mid.
CAgr CArg CMac CRos CSBt CTri EHyd EMil EPfP EPom GDam GQue LBuc LCro LOPS LRHS MGos MPri NRHS NRog SEdi SPlb

18 H6 **'Finesse'** (D)
Good yields of bright fruit with good size and good flavour.
NRHS NRog

18 H6 **'Florence'** (D)
Bright dark red berries of good size; late main season fruit with consistent good flavour.
CAgr CArg CRos CSBt CTri EHyd EPom LBuc LRHS NRHS NRog SPer

94 H6 **'Hapil'** (D)
Large glossy berries; good flavour. Heavy crops; vigorous. Susceptible to verticillium wilt. Season: early / mid. Reconfirmed after trial 2004.
EPfP EPom GDam LBuc NRog

93 H6 **'Honeoye'** (D)
Excellent flavour. Heavy crops; susceptible to verticillium wilt. Season: early. Reconfirmed after trial 2004.
CAgr CArg CMac CSBt EPfP EPom GDam LBuc LCro LEdu LOPS LRHS NRog SPer

18 H6 **'Malling Centenary'** (D)
Large bright red berries with consistently good flavour.
EPom LRHS NRog

94 H6 **'Pegasus'** (D)
Good flavour; quite soft flesh. Good disease resistance; tolerance to verticillium wilt. Season: mid. Reconfirmed after trial 2004 and 2006.
CAgr CRos CSBt EHyd EPfP EPom LRHS NRHS

94 H6 **'Rhapsody'** (D)
Good flavour; medium to large berries. Resistant red core; some resistance to verticillium wilt and mildew. Season: late. Reconfirmed after trial 2006.
CRos EHyd LRHS LSRN NRHS

95 H6 **'Symphony'** (D)
Good flavour; bright, firm berries. Vigorous; good resistance to red core; susceptible to mildew. Good runner production. Season: mid to late. Reconfirmed after trial 2006.
CAgr CRos EHyd EPfP EPom LBuc LRHS LSRN NRHS SCoo

18 H6 **'Vibrant'** (D)
Early fruit; best June bearer; attractive dark berry with good flavour.
EPom NRog

Tayberry (*Rubus*)

93 H5 **'Tayberry'**
Distinctive flavour. Larger fruit; heavier crops than loganberry. Excellent for cooking, freezing, jam, etc. Season: July. Reconfirmed 2015.
CDoC SCoo

Walnut (*Juglans regia*)

15 H6 **'Franquette'**
Old French variety, known since 19th century; received the designation *appellation d'origine contrôlée* in 1938 as 'Noix de Grenoble' and in 2002 as 'Noix du Perigord'; remains a main market walnut of France; long recommended for planting in UK. Tree upright with rounded crown; moderate vigour; late-leafing; tolerates disease. Good, regular crops; reliable and productive. Nuts easily husked; quite soft shell, and can be cracked with fingers; well-sealed and well-filled nut; medium size, long, oval shape. Flavour excellent. Season: quite late / late. Pollinated by 'Meylanaise', 'Ronde de Montignac', 'Fernette'; reported partially self-fertile.
CAgr MTrO NOra WMat

15 H6 **'Lara'**
French cultivar; seedling of American cultivar 'Payne'. One of the main cultivars of modern walnut plantations. Good habit, making broad spreading tree, but not very vigorous; quite early leafing out; lateral bearing; good disease resistance. Good, regular crops; reliable and productive. Nuts easily husked; medium to quite large, globose; well-sealed, well-filled; well-flavoured as fresh nut and as dried nut. Season: early. Pollinated by 'Franquette', 'Meylanaise' and 'Ronde de Montignac'.
CAgr NOra WMat

Whitecurrant (*Ribes rubrum*)

93 H6 **'White Grape'** (D/C)
Attractive, translucent berries; good flavour. Season: mid July.
CTri LEdu NRog

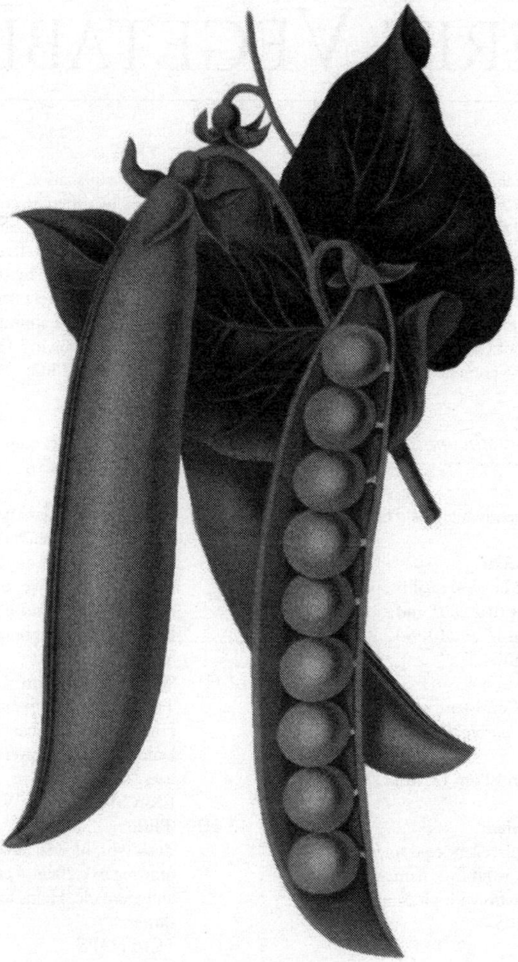

IV

RHS AWARD OF GARDEN MERIT
VEGETABLES

Award of Garden Merit Vegetables

This is a directory of vegetables offered by nurseries participating in *RHS Plant Finder 2019* that have been awarded an RHS Award of Garden Merit (AGM). It does not represent a complete list of AGM vegetables.

Entries are accompanied by a short description and the relevant hardiness rating for the UK. **Hardiness ratings** are explained on p.39. The figures to the left of the rating indicate the year the Award of Garden Merit was made.

Vegetables present some nomenclatural peculiarities that may require explanation. Cultivars that are repeatedly raised by different growers, while retaining their essential characteristics, can become recognisably different. These strains are referred to as maintenances and are often distinguished by the use of **maintenance names** which exist separately from the cultivar name. Here maintenance names appear after the cultivar name separated by a dash following The Vegetable Seed (England) Regulations 2002.

Asparagus (*Asparagus officinalis*)

01 H4 **'Backlim'**
F_1 hybrid; consistently high yield of large spears.
EPom

93 H4 **'Connover's Colossal'**
Early; heavy yield of good quality spears. Reconfirmed after trial 2001 and 2012.
CTsd EKin ELan LCro LOPS LSRN MCtn MNHC NRob SVic

01 H4 **'Gijnlim'**
F_1 hybrid; early. Consistently high yield of mid green spears with purple tips. Reconfirmed after trial 2012.
CRos EDel EKin EPom LCro LOPS LRHS NRob

12 H5 **'Guelph Millennium'**
Bred in Canada. Excellent cold tolerance. Lateness helps to avoid frost damage. Sound yield of slender stems with pleasing flavour.
EPom LCro LOPS

Aubergine (*Solanum melongena*)

95 H1c **'Bonica'**
F_1 hybrid. Early-cropping, good quality, attractive glossy black fruits are a good size. Plants are tall, but also strong and vigorous. Reconfirmed after trial 2008.
MCtn

Basil (*Ocimum basilicum*)

12 H1c **'Aroma 2'**
Standard Genovese type. Lovely aroma, good disease resistance, quite tall.
LCro LOPS MCtn

12 H1c **'Lemonade'**
Compact, even plant growing to c.30cm. Aromatic with a sherbet-lemon scent and taste. Fine leaves: keeled as young foliage. Flowers are white, and attractive to bees. Plants hold well and show good disease and weather resistance. Previously listed as basil (× *africanum*).
SRms

12 H1c **'Mrs Burns' Lemon'**
Tall, upright, neat habit, growing to c.60cm. Fine, mid green leaves, aromatic and intensely lemon-scented. Flowers white, and attractive to bees.
EKin MCtn SRms WJek

12 H1c **'Pluto'**
Bush type, of small, even, dome-shaped habit, growing to c.20cm. Leaves are fine, mid green and aromatic. Holds form well and slow to flower.
LCro LOPS

Beans

Broad beans (*Vicia faba*)

95 H5 **'Aguadulce'**
Dark green foliage, showing some variability. Long pods; the highest yielding in the trial. November sown. May also be sold as 'Aquadulce'.
CHby

93 H5 **'Aquadulce Claudia'**
Not too tall; a good compact plant. An early crop when spring sown, but can also be sown in

November. One of the most reliable cultivars for overwintering. Reconfirmed after trial 1999, 2011.
EKin LCro LOPS MBros MCtn NRob

11 H3 **'De Monica'**
Short pods; well filled. Good ratio of seed to pod; excellent cropping.
EKin MCtn SVic

93 H3 **'Express'**
Quick to mature, with well-filled pods. Spring sown.
EKin MCtn

11 H3 **'Giant Exhibition Longpod'**
Smooth, slender pods of good length; long cropping period.
EKin LRHS MCtn NRHS NRob

93 H3 **'Imperial Green Longpod'**
Green-seeded, with long smooth pods; good green colour and flavour; particularly good for freezing. Spring sown. Reconfirmed after trial 1999, 2011.
EKin LCro LOPS MCtn

99 H3 **'Masterpiece Green Longpod'**
Slender, well-filled pods; stands well; good green colour and flavour; suitable for freezing; spring sown; reconfirmed after trial 2011.
EDel EKin LCro LOPS

11 H3 **'Robin Hood'**
Green-seeded; 3–5 seeds per pod. Good yield. Dwarf cultivar, ideal for containers and small gardens.
MCtn

11 H3 **'Suprifin'**
Pale green pods of mid size; pleasant taste. Early-cropping.
LCro LOPS

93 H3 **'The Sutton'**
Dwarf compact plants, with nice flavour; ideal for smaller gardens or containers and windy situations. Spring sown. Reconfirmed after trial 1999, 2011.
EKin LCro LOPS NRob SVic

99 H4 **'Witkiem' – Manita**
Traditional 'Witkiem' type; sets well. Good early yield, with uniform pods; spring sown; reconfirmed after trial 2011.
CHby EKin

CLIMBING FRENCH BEANS (*Phaseolus vulgaris*)

00 H2 **'Cobra'**
Very high early yield; long, fleshy, round; very attractive; reconfirmed after trial 2008.
CHby EKin LCro LOPS MCtn NRob

93 H2 **'Eva'**
Very early. Long straight fleshy pods, wider-podded than other round varieties. Reconfirmed after trial 2000 and 2008.
CHby

08 H2 **'Golden Gate'**
Good crop of golden, fleshy, flat pods with a sweet, fresh flavour.
CHby LCro LOPS

93 H2 **'Hunter'**
Attractive long flat stringless pods. Slow to show seed development. Reconfirmed after trial 2000 and 2008.
EKin MCtn NRob

08 H2 **'Limka'**
Consistently high yields of good quality, flat, light green pods with a good flavour.
CHby

DWARF FRENCH BEANS (*Phaseolus vulgaris*)

93 H2 **'Annabel'**
Dark green colour, compact habit, fine foliage, tender fleshy tasting pods. Reconfirmed after trial 1996 and 2010.
EKin MCtn

01 H2 **'Safari'**
Short, slim, mid green, round, attractive pods. Low yields.
EKin LCro LOPS LRHS MCtn NRHS

93 H2 **'Sprite'**
Heavy yield, with long, dark green pods on compact bushy plants.
EHyd EKin LCro LOPS LRHS MCtn NRHS

10 H2 **'Stanley'**
Mid to dark green colour; tender and sweet. Taller plant. Uniform and picks over long period.
MCtn

96 H2 **'The Prince'**
Excellent yield; straight pale green pods.
EKin NRob

RUNNER BEANS (*Phaseolus coccineus*)

06 H2 **'Benchmaster'**
Long, fairly straight beans, good yield; reconfirmed after trial 2013.
EKin LCro LOPS MBros

06 H2 **'Celebration'**
High yield of attractive, straight, smooth, good quality, fleshy pods with good colour and flavour. Flowers are a decorative pink. Reconfirmed after trial 2013, 2017.
EKin

13 H2 **'Firestorm'**
Hybrid of runner and French bean parentage. Excellent yield, slender, straight, smooth-skinned, fleshy pods. Self-setting. Reconfirmed after trial 2017.
EDel EKin LCro LOPS MCtn

93 H2 **'Liberty'**
Very long pods; a popular show variety.
NRob

13 H2 **'Moonlight'**
Hybrid of runner and French bean parentage; grown commercially. Very high yielding. Easy to pick; leaves pedicel behind on picking. Smooth, straight, fleshy pods, with good length and nice colour. Self-setting. Reconfirmed after trial 2017.
EHyd EKin LCro LOPS LRHS MCtn NRHS

99 H2 **'Red Rum'**
Good early and late yield; slim, straight, stringless pods of medium length. Reconfirmed after trial 2006, 2013.
EKin

06 H2 **'St George'**
Bicolour variety; prized for ornamental value. Some French bean parentage. Popular commercial variety; easy to pick, leaving pedicel behind. Slender beans, straight, pale green. Reconfirmed after trial 2013, 2017.
CHby

99 H2 **'White Lady'**
Late; very fleshy pods. Reconfirmed after trial 2006, 2013.
CHby EKin LCro LOPS LRHS MBros MCtn NRHS

BEETROOT (*Beta vulgaris*)

05 H3 **'Alto'**
F_1 hybrid; early. Cylindrical, uniform, smooth round red roots with very good internal colour and good long shape. Potential to bulk up well. Reconfirmed after trial 2016.
EKin

93 H3 **'Boltardy'**
Open-pollinated; round red root; good bolting resistance.
EKin LCro LOPS MBros MCtn SVic

16 H3 **'Bona'**
Open-pollinated; round red root; even size with very smooth skin.
MCtn

93 H3 **'Forono'**
Open-pollinated. Cylindrical, with fairly smooth skins and long red roots of moderate uniformity; good internal colour. Slow to bulk up. Reconfirmed after trial 2005.
EKin

93 H3 **'Pablo'**
F_1 hybrid; very early. Uniform round red roots with very smooth skins. Appears to have good bolting resistance. Widely used as a show cultivar. Reconfirmed after trial 2001, 2005 and 2016.
EHyd EKin LRHS MCtn NRHS NRob

01 H3 **'Red Ace'**
F_1 hybrid; uniform round red roots with good flesh colour and no rings. Reconfirmed after trial 2016.
EKin NRob

05 H3 **'Solo'**
F_1 hybrid. Round to slightly flattened shape. Bulks up well; smooth roots of good internal colour. Reconfirmed after trial 2016.
LCro LOPS

93 H3 **'Wodan'**
F_1 hybrid with round, slightly flattened shape. Smooth roots; good internal colour. Bulks up well. Reconfirmed after trial 2005, 2016.
EKin

BORECOLE OR CURLY KALE (*Brassica oleracea* Acephala Group)

15 H5 **'Black Magic'**
A new selection of 'Cavolo Nero', with very dark green, strap-leaved type with small blisters. Good yield.
MCtn

99 H5 **'Redbor'**
F_1 hybrid. Tall, uniform plants with open habit; strongly curled purple-green leaves. Good salad leaf, with ornamental value too. Winters well. Reconfirmed after trial 2015.
EDel EKin LCro LOPS NRob

93 H5 **'Winterbor'**
F_1 hybrid. Tall plants with finely curled blue-green leaves; winters well. Developed from (but superior to) 'Westland Winter'. Reconfirmed after trial 1999, 2015.
EKin MCtn

BROCCOLI (*Brassica oleracea* Italica Group)

SEE UNDER CALABRESE FOR CALABRESE BROCCOLI

PURPLE SPROUTING

13 H5 **'Cardinal'**
Tidy upright plants, some variability in height, as expected for open-pollinated cultivars. Dense spears of deep purple. Good for late crop.
EKin

95 H5 **'Claret'**
F_1 hybrid. Very tall; heavy yield of dark purple spears from March through April. Reconfirmed after trial 2013.
EDel LCro LOPS NRHS

13 H5 **'Mendocino'**
Sturdy vigorous plants, with large, attractive deep purple spears of good quality.
EDel

03 H4 **'Red Admiral'**
Early, yielding well with good quality secondaries. Good colour and long stems. Performs better if sown later and grown to produce hardier plants. Reconfirmed after trial 2013.
EDel LCro LOPS

95 H5 **'Red Arrow'**
Early to midseason; long cropping period. Good winter hardiness; bushy, vigorous plants. Reconfirmed after trial 2003, 2013.
MCtn

BRUSSELS SPROUTS (*Brassica oleracea* Gemmifera Group)

15 H5 **'Brodie'**
Clean buttons, developing unevenly; mild taste when cooked.
LCro LOPS

99 H5 **'Cascade'**
F_1 hybrid; late. Smooth, clean, well-spaced, fairly round sprouts. Uniform plants which stand and yield well.
EKin LCro LOPS

15 H4 **'Crispus'**
Early to midseason. Clubroot-resistant; nice colour, with mild, slightly nutty taste when cooked.
EKin

15 H5 **'Doric'**
Tall plants, with sparse large buttons. Slightly bitter, with slight aftertaste when cooked.
EDel

93 H5 **'Igor'**
F_1 hybrid. Mid to late season; attractive, vigorous, uniform plants producing well-spaced, solid, round, mid green sprouts. Reconfirmed after trial 2006.
NRob

15 H4 **'Marte'**
Tall plants with sprouts well spaced. Buttons quite round; good size; nice and dense. Not bitter, even uncooked.
EKin

06 H4 **'Maximus'**
F_1 hybrid; early to mid season. Leading commercial variety; uniform plants, producing a good crop of mid to dark green, smooth, solid sprouts, slightly sweet and crunchy after cooking. Reconfirmed after trial 2015.
EKin LCro

06 H5 **'Petrus'**
F_1; late season. Tall, vigorous plants that stand well. Good crop of clean, round, dark green sprouts; well-spaced and easy to pick.
EDel

CABBAGE (*Brassica oleracea* Capitata Group)

EARLY RED, NON-STORING – SEPTEMBER TO OCTOBER

96 H3 **'Rookie'**
F_1 hybrid; early. Round to slightly flat heads.
LCro LOPS

AUTUMN – SEPTEMBER TO NOVEMBER

09 H3 **'Buscaro'**
F_1 hybrid. Attractive dark red, oval-round, well-filled heads. Very short core, with petioles that are not too thick. Stands well.
EDel

09 H3 **'Minicole'**
F_1 hybrid. Good early autumn cultivar with attractive round heads.
EHyd LRHS NRHS NRob

09 H3 **'Red Jewel'**
F_1 hybrid. Attractive, solid, round-headed red cabbage with upright foliage and a short core. Could be grown at a closer spacing.
NRob

SAVOY – SEPTEMBER TO MARCH

01 H5 **'Tundra'**
F_1 hybrid; dark green, slightly blistered leaf; heads solid and attractive. Sweet-tasting; overwinters well. Reconfirmed after trial 2007.
EKin LCro LOPS MCtn

01 H5 **'Wintessa'**
F_1 hybrid; late. Dark green well-blistered leaves, with uniform well-filled heads of good quality and flavour. Plants stand well.
EKin

JANUARY KING – NOVEMBER TO MARCH

08 H5 **'Deadon'**
Uniform, attractive 'January King' type with a flattened round head.
EDel EKin

08 H5 **'January King 3'**
Open-pollinated. Attractive heads that develop a good colour. Good yield and long spread of cut.
EKin MCtn

98 H4 **'Noelle'**
F_1 hybrid; flat, round, heads; dark green leaves with good purple colouring. Winters well. Previously listed as 'Holly'. Reconfirmed after trial 2009 for September–November cropping.
LCro LOPS

WINTER HYBRID – NOVEMBER TO MARCH

08 H3 **'Kilaton'**
Late-season large white cabbage with claimed resistance to club-root.
EDel EKin

SPRING

11 H5 **'Advantage'**
Good heart. Compact, uniform, with little bolting.
MCtn

93 H5 **'Duncan'**
F_1 hybrid. Mid to dark green uniform heads

with well-closed bases. A good early yield; compact neat habit; plants heart slowly to produce small, solid, well-filled heads. Reconfirmed after trial 2001, 2011 as spring greens and hearted cabbage.
EDel LRHS NRHS

11 H5 **'Spring Hero'**
Distinctive round-headed spring cabbage for overwintering. Large, dense ball-shaped heads. Blue-grey, rugose leaves. Showing excellent winter survival.
EKin

Summer – June to August

16 H2 **'Cabbice'**
Hybrid; Japanese flat cabbage. Sweet, heavy and dense, with good flavour.
EKin

04 H2 **'Candisa'**
F_1 hybrid; early. Uniform, medium green, well-filled heads, with short core. Reconfirmed after trial 2016.
EKin

16 H2 **'Caraflex'**
Hybrid; early sweetheart type. Quite big for the garden, but capable of making smaller heads.
EDel EKin LCro LOPS

98 H2 **'Elisa'**
F_1 hybrid; early. Compact round heads with bright green glossy leaves. Reconfirmed after trial 2016.
EDel

02 H2 **'Hispi'**
F_1 hybrid; early. Smooth, pointed, dark green outer leaves, with good uniformity and well-filled heart.
CHby LCro LOPS NRHS NRob

93 H2 **'Stonehead'**
F_1 hybrid; late. Uniform, round, mid green heads. Stands well. Also useful for cropping into the autumn from later planting. Reconfirmed after trial 2016.
EKin LRHS MBros NRHS NRob

Calabrese broccoli (*Brassica oleracea* Italica Group)

03 H3 **'Belstar'**
F_1 hybrid; May sown. Mid to late season; uniform medium-sized plants, with attractive heads and medium to small buds.
EKin

07 H3 **'Green Magic'**
Autumn-cropping; very good yield of slightly domed, good-sized heads with small beads. Known to make good side-shoots. Reconfirmed after trial 2013.
EKin MCtn

13 H2 **'Ironman'**
Domed larger heads of tight blue-green buds; healthy foliage.
EDel EKin

03 H3 **'Kabuki'**
F_1 hybrid; May sown; early. Short, compact plants, producing a good crop of medium green, deep, well-rounded heads with uniform buds. Average yield of medium-sized secondaries, produced 3 to 5 weeks after the primary heads. Could be closely spaced to produce baby heads. Reconfirmed after trial 2007, 2013.
EHyd LRHS MCtn NRHS

13 H2 **'Marathon'**
Dome-shaped heads, uniform, mid-size, held high.
EKin LCro LOPS LRHS NRHS

Carrot (*Daucus carota*)

99 H3 **'Adelaide'**
F_1 hybrid; very early. Good weight and colour; sweet-flavoured; quickly forms very smooth, stump-ended roots; almost coreless; fine tops. Ideal for successional sowings and early sowing in frames. Reconfirmed after trial 2006 and 2010 as early, suitable for containers.
EKin LCro LOPS

06 H3 **'Amsterdam Forcing 3'**
Open-pollinated. Relatively smooth with good flesh and core colour; bulks up well. Strong foliage that does not grow too tall.
EKin MCtn

14 H3 **'Deep Purple'**
Purple skin and flesh, with tapered roots and pleasant flavour; reasonable uniformity of crop.
MCtn

05 H5 **'Eskimo'**
F_1 hybrid; medium-length, smooth roots with good colour. Useful size, well-filled. Grows with crowns at or below ground level, so very little crown discoloration. Good overwintering cultivar. Reconfirmed after trial 2014.
EKin LCro LOPS MBros MCtn

99 H3 **'Flyaway'**
F_1 hybrid. Maincrop; medium-length, well-filled, stump-ended roots with good flesh and core colour. Good strong tops. Partial resistance (i.e. lack of attraction) to carrot flies. Reconfirmed after trial 2006.
EKin LCro LOPS MCtn

99 H3 **'Maestro'**
F_1 hybrid. Best lifted before Christmas. Blunt, smooth-skinned, medium to slim, fairly well-filled roots, uniform in size and shape. Mid to pale internal colour with some green shoulders. Widely grown by organic carrot

growers. Reconfirmed after trial 2005, 2014.
LCro LOPS

10 H3 **'Marion'**
Early to mature; uniform crop of slightly tapered roots with good weight. Smooth skin, deep orange flesh and good core colour. Suitable for containers.
EKin

99 H3 **'Nairobi'**
F_1 hybrid; second early / early maincrop. Strong tops, with uniform, broader-shouldered, cylindrical, stump-ended roots. Heavy yields. Reconfirmed after trial 2006, 2014.
EKin

93 H3 **'Napoli'**
F_1 hybrid, very early maturing. Slightly tapering; good weight. Smooth skin, core and flesh deep orange. Strong tops for easy pulling; quick to bulk up. Ideal for successional sowings and early sowing in frames. Reconfirmed after trial 2010 as early, suitable for containers.
EKin

06 H3 **'Primo'**
Hybrid; flavoursome crop of good weight. Smooth skin, deep orange colour, with low core–flesh ratio. Reconfirmed after trial 2010 as early, suitable for containers.
LCro LOPS

14 H3 **'Romance'**
Longer, early-maturing 'Nantes' type, though resembling 'Berlicum'. Smooth skin, no splitting, dense texture, good colour.
MCtn

05 H4 **'Sugarsnax 54'**
F_1 hybrid. Very long, smooth, 'Imperator' type with roots of good internal colour. Suited to deep, light soils. Commercially used, cut into short lengths and sold as pre-packed baton carrots.
EKin MCtn

05 H3 **'Sweet Candle'**
F_1 hybrid; short, blunt, quite smooth, well-filled, uniform roots. Good internal colour. Reconfirmed after trial 2014.
EKin LCro LOPS NRob

14 H3 **'Tozresis'**
A 'Nantes' type. Bred for intermediate carrot fly resistance. Smooth skin, good uniformity, well-stumped root, good colour, nice flavour. Previously listed as 'Resistafly'.
MCtn SVic

CAULIFLOWER (*Brassica oleracea* Botrytis Group)

Coloured and Romanesco

05 H3 **'Graffiti'**
F_1 hybrid. Small to medium, high quality, solid curds of a very attractive amethyst colour. The colour fades a little if boiled, and is retained better if steamed. The raw curds have a good flavour and would be a colourful addition to a salad or dish of crudités. Midseason. Reconfirmed after trial 2006.
EDel EKin LRHS NRHS SVic

05 H3 **'Veronica'**
F_1 hybrid; appetising light green Romanesco type. Uniform good-sized, solid, well-shaped heads.
EDel EKin

Autumn heading – September to November

15 H3 **'Boris'**
Good, deep, round curd.
EKin

15 H3 **'Clapton'**
Neat, well-covered variety, with lovely curds and good upright habit.
EDel EKin

02 H3 **'Moby Dick'**
F_1 hybrid; early with a short cropping period; uniform, very deep, heavy curds. Good width. Reconfirmed after trial 2015.
LCro LOPS

Summer heading – June to mid July

97 H3 **'Fargo'**
F_1 hybrid; late. Deep, white, well-protected curds.
EKin

06 H3 **'Flamenco'**
Hybrid; midseason to late. Very high quality, large to medium-sized, white, solid curds with good depth.
NRob

97 H3 **'Nautilus'**
F_1 hybrid; late. Vigorous plants with deep, white, well-protected curds of excellent quality.
LRHS NRHS

Summer or autumn heading

06 H3 **'Aviron'**
Hybrid; late. High quality, well-protected, large to medium-sized solid, white heads. Reconfirmed after trial for autumn heading 2015.
EKin

Winter for spring heading, maturing from March to May

05 H5 **'Aalsmeer'**
Open-pollinated cultivar; early midseason. Produces medium to small, cream-coloured, slightly lumpy, well-protected curds that have a good depth. This cultivar produced several multiple heads and side-shoots, many of usable quality.
EKin NRob

97 H5 **'Jerome'**
F_1 hybrid; early midseason. Vigorous plant, producing good quality, well-covered curds. Curds well-rounded, medium to small and cream-coloured. Reconfirmed after trial 2005.
EDel

CELERIAC (*Apium graveolens* var. *rapaceum*)

00 H4 **'Prinz'**
Smooth, deep, white-skinned; small to medium, flattened and round; compact plant with healthy foliage. Reconfirmed after trial 2011.
CHby EDel EKin LCro LOPS MCtn SVic

CELERY (*Apium graveolens* var. *dulce*)

93 H2 **'Celebrity'**
Self-blanching, fairly short plants, with ribbed petioles and good flavour. Reconfirmed after trial 2001.
LRHS MCtn NRHS

93 H4 **'Giant Pink' – Mammoth Pink**
Pink-tinged, green variety for blanching or earthing up; solid stems.
NRob

94 H2 **'Victoria'**
F_1 hybrid. Tall, well-filled plants with medium-green, smooth, fleshy petioles. Widely used for commercial crops. Reconfirmed after trial 2005.
EDel EKin MBros

CHARD (*Beta vulgaris* subsp. *cicla* var. *flavescens*)

00 H3 BRIGHT LIGHTS
Good colourful mix, including reds, yellows and whites; very ornamental and decorative.
CHby EHyd LRHS NRHS NRob SVic

00 H3 **'Bright Yellow'**
Bright golden-yellow petioles and mid green puckered leaf; uniform; sweet taste; reconfirmed after trial 2011.
MCtn NRob

11 H3 **'Canary Yellow'**
Green leaves and yellow stem; healthy blister-type attractive glossy leaf. Even stock. Taste is not bitter. No bolting in either sowing during trial.
NRob

00 H3 **'Fordhook Giant'**
Attractive shiny light green, puckered leaf with white stem and long succulent broad white petioles; old blister-leaf chard type.
EKin MCtn NRob

00 H3 **'Rhubarb Chard'**
Dark green leaves and red stem; vigorous but uniform; blister-type leaf; reconfirmed after trial 2011.
EKin LCro LOPS MBros MCtn NRob SVic

CHICORY (*Cichorium intybus*)

RADICCHIO

02 H5 **'Palla Rossa'**
Medium to large heads; well-filled red hearts; fairly uniform. No bolting.
CHby MCtn SRms

SUGAR LOAF

02 H5 **'Pan di Zucchero'**
Uniform plants with medium to large frames and dark green outer leaves. Hearts blanch well.
CHby

CHILLI PEPPER (*Capsicum annuum*)

06 H1c **'Apache'**
Decorative, growing to 45cm; does well in both large and small pots. Produces large crop of small, juicy, hot peppers that ripen from bright green to red and are held outwards from the stems. Reconfirmed after trial 2013.
CCCN CRos EHyd EKin LRHS MBros MPri NRHS NRob SPre

13 H1c **'Basket of Fire'**
Multi-branched, open habit, height to c.25cm. Numerous upright fruits, maturing through cream, lemon, yellow and orange to red.
CRos EDel EHyd EKin NRHS SPre SVic

13 H1c **'Bolivian Rainbow'**
Compact plant, height c.32 cm, with mid green foliage. Stumpy, broad-based fruit held erect. Fruit ripening cream through orange to red.
SVic

06 H1c **'Caribbean Antillais'**
Quite small, blocky, bright red fruits; aromatic and very hot, of a type widely used in South American and Caribbean cooking. Later-cropping, best sown in January and given a higher temperature to germinate.
SVic

06 H1c **'Demon Red'**
A small, ornamental plant, starred with white flowers, producing an abundant crop of tiny upward-pointing fruits that mature to dark, bright red. Fruits are hot and used in Thai cooking. Reconfirmed after trial 2013.
CRos EHyd EKin LRHS MCtn NRHS SPre SVic

06 H1c **'Etna'**
Attractive bunches of erect, shiny peppers that mature from bright mid green to red, carried on compact plants that are suitable for growing in pots. Large crop of very hot peppers.
CRos EHyd LRHS MCtn NRHS

06 H1c **'Filius Blue'**
Attractive, highly ornamental plants. The young leaves are mid green, becoming very dark green with a purple flush; the plants are covered with purple, orange and bright red fruits that are spicy and hot.
NRob

06 H1c **'Fresno'**
Fairly short, upright-growing plants; very productive. The conical fruits ripen from light green to deep scarlet red, with medium thick flesh that is very hot.
LRHS NRHS

13 H1c **'Hot Thai'**
Bushy yet compact habit, height to 25cm. Dainty dark green foliage. Small, hot fruits (1.5cm in length, and 1cm wide), held erect. Ideal for a windowsill.
CRos EHyd LRHS NRHS

06 H1c **'Hungarian Hot Wax'**
Conical fruits ripening from pale yellow to bright red; medium hot; very good for frying, stuffing and using in salads. One of the easiest to grow. Suitable for growing in pots.
CHby EKin LCro LOPS MCtn NRob SVic

13 H1c **'Krakatoa'**
Compact, bushy plant, with dark green foliage; height c.20cm. Erect clusters of glossy fruit, 3cm long, and 1cm across the base.
CRos EHyd LRHS NRHS

13 H1c **'Loco'**
Bushy plant, height c.25 cm, cascading habit which looks especially attractive in a basket or container. Numerous oblong fruit, c.2cm long, held erect above the foliage. Ripening purple to red.
CRos EHyd LRHS NRHS

14 H1c **'Pot Black'**
Upright plant with branching habit; height c.36cm. Stem, foliage, fruit very dark purple. Fruit blocky in shape, held erect above the foliage. Interesting and unusual variety.
EDel SVic

06 H1c **'Prairie Fire'**
Very attractive, short (20cm high), spreading plants covered in a mass of very small, very hot, upright peppers that ripen from white, through yellow and orange, to red. Compact and multibranched plant; ideal for pots or a windowsill. Reconfirmed after trial 2013.
CCCN CRos EHyd LCro LOPS LRHS NRHS NRob SVic

06 H1c **'Super Chili'**
Ornamental plants; well suited to growing in pots. Produces a high yield of very hot, thin-walled fruits that are held upright and ripen from light green to orange-red.
EDel SPre SVic

14 H1c **'Treasure's Red'**
Compact multi-branched plant, with dark green foliage, height c.26 cm. Glossy, conical fruit held in erect clusters. Maturing cream, through orange to red.
LRHS

06 H1c **'Tricolor Variegatum'**
Ornamental foliage an attractive mid green, splashed cream and purple. Small fruits mature from purple, through orange to red. Plants 70cm high with a rather spreading habit, but can be pruned to shape.
NRob

CHINESE CABBAGE (*Brassica rapa* Pekinensis Group)

03 H3 **'Yuki'**
Barrel-shaped. Medium green, slightly savoyed outer leaves; very short internal stem; medium-sized heavy head; well-blanched.
EKin MCtn

CORIANDER (*Coriandrum sativum*)

14 H2 **'Calypso'**
Vigorous, bushy strong growth; holds well; good leaf yield. Ideal size for the home gardener.
EKin MCtn

14 H2 **'Confetti'**
Neat and clean, with distinct fern-like look; uniform. Ideal for smaller gardens.
EKin LCro LOPS MCtn

14 H2 **'Cruiser'**
A compact plant, with big leaves.
EDel

CORNSALAD (*Valerianella locusta*)

94 H3 **'Medaillon'**
Slow-growing, short, thick-leaved under frames.
LCro LOPS

COURGETTE (*Cucurbita pepo*)

93 H2 **'Defender'**
F_1 hybrid. A high yield of medium-sized, slender, very lightly flecked fruits.
EKin LCro LOPS MCtn

93 H2 **'Early Gem'**
F_1 hybrid; a high yield of slender, lightly speckled fruits. Easy to see on the plant.
EKin MCtn

13 H2 **'Orelia'**
Upright plant, producing a good yield of yellow fruits. Vigorous plants, showing good mildew resistance.
EKin

13 H2 **'Patio Star'**
Compact plant, ideal for small space or container. No mildew. Glossy, dark green fruits.
EDel

07 H2 **'Romanesco'**
Distinctive, heavily ribbed fruits that hold their flowers. Popular in Italy; the flowers are used for stuffing. Semi-trailing plants; good yield.
EDel LCro LOPS

Cucumber (*Cucumis sativus*)

02 H1c **'Carmen'**
F_1 hybrid; standard length, dark green, slightly ribbed fruits. Reconfirmed after trial 2009.
EKin NRob

09 H1c **'Cucino'**
Smooth, small, dark green, uniform fruits with good flavour and texture. Highly productive.
NRHS SVic

09 H1c **'Emilie'**
Useful mid-length fruits with attractive dark green colour and good flavour.
LCro LOPS

95 H2 **'Marketmore'**
Good yield of short, attractive, dark green fruits. Grown in the open garden. Reconfirmed after trial 2001.
CHby EDel EKin MCtn

09 H1c **'Mini Munch'**
Highly productive plants producing abundant small, crunchy, shiny-skinned fruits with good flavour.
EKin

Endive (*Cichorium endivia*)

96 H3 **'Pancalieri'**
Very strong cut-leaf type. Does not blanch well.
CHby EKin MCtn

Florence fennel (*Foeniculum vulgare* var. *azoricum*)

96 H2 **'Fino'**
Quick-maturing. Medium large, round, very uniform bulbs of excellent quality.
EKin MCtn NRob

05 H2 **'Orion'**
F_1 hybrid; vigorous foliage; attractive, medium to large bulbs with a good shape, with few side shoots and clean, with a bright white colour.
EKin

Garlic (*Allium sativum* var. *ophioscorodon*)

04 H4 **'Early Wight'**
Very early crop (during May); good fat cloves. Hard neck; best used immediately after harvest.
NRob

04 H4 **'Germidour'**
Late-maturing, virus-free selection. Soft necks; well-packed, purple-skinned cloves.
EDel NRob

04 H4 **'Solent White'**
Late. Soft neck; many purple-skinned, very attractive cloves, with appealing bouquet; high yield; keeps beyond Christmas (up to March). Also performed well at Harlow Carr.
EKin LCro LOPS NRob

Kohlrabi (*Brassica oleracea* Gongylodes Group)

06 H3 **'Kolibri'**
Hybrid; uniform crop of purple, decorative bulbs with crisp flesh and good flavour. Medium-sized tops.
EDel

97 H3 **'Quickstar'**
F_1 hybrid. Uniform crop of juicy, tender bulbs with a mild flavour. Medium-sized tops. Reconfirmed after trial 2006.
LRHS MCtn NRHS

Leek (*Allium porrum*)

Autumn & early winter

00 H4 **'Jolant' (Swiss Giant Group)**
For December cropping; high yield; medium to dark green flags; long, solid shafts with little bulbing and very few bolters. Low levels of rust infection. Has a long season and peels nicely. Reconfirmed after trial 2002, 2015.
EKin MCtn NRob

00 H4 **'Mammoth Blanch'**
A show variety suitable for December sowing. Early-maturing, with high yields of well-shaped leeks with pale green flags, long, heavy shafts and no bolters.
EKin NRob

00 H4 **'Pancho'**
Good early yield of medium long, mid green, solid shafts with only slight bulbing. Little rust; fast-growing.
LCro LOPS

Winter hardy

09 H5 **'Blauwgroene Winter' – Atlanta**
Good open-pollinated cultivar. Dark blue-green, erect flags, with healthy foliage. Medium length of blanch.
EKin

09 H5 **'Blauwgroene Winter' – Bandit**
Good open-pollinated cultivar. Dark blue-green flags; reasonable length of blanch.
EDel EKin MCtn

15 H5 **'Lancaster'**
Hybrid; lovely leek, dark green and upright; really uniform.
NRob

02 H5 **'Mammoth Pot'**
Uniform, with whole stem blanched and light green flag. High December yield. A good short garden plant.
EKin NRob

02 H5 **'Oarsman'**
F_1 hybrid; erect plant, with very straight shank, uniform, smooth; flag leaf clean. Good yield. Reconfirmed after trial 2015.
EKin LCro LOPS MCtn

Lettuce (*Lactuca sativa*)

Butterhead

97 H2 **'Clarion'**
Open heads, with pale to mid green leaves. Reconfirmed after trial 2002
LCro LOPS

Cos

12 H2 **'Chartwell'**
Neat, mid-size green Cos; dense, crisp heart.
EKin

07 H2 **'Chatsworth'**
Medium-sized with rugose leaves; dense hearts make a good weight and have a good blanch. Very good flavour.
LCro LOPS

93 H2 **'Little Gem'**
Small solid heads with mid green, medium-blistered leaves. Reconfirmed after trial 1999, 2007, 2012.
CHby CRos EHyd EKin LCro LOPS LRHS MBros MCtn NRHS NRob

99 H2 **'Little Leprechaun'**
Semi-Cos with dark red leaves.
NRob

93 H2 **'Lobjoit's Green Cos'**
Large, rather open heads, with relatively smooth mid green leaves. Reconfirmed after trial 1999.
EKin NRob SVic

12 H2 **'Maureen'**
Uniform crop, with mid green leaves. One of the most popular commercial 'Gem' varieties.
EDel EKin

99 H2 **'Parris Island Cos'**
Vigorous with pale green uniform heads; reconfirmed after trial 2007.
EKin

00 H2 **'Winter Density'**
Semi-Cos with leafy, erect habit; dark green, very uniform. Reconfirmed after trial 2007, 2012.
EDel EKin LCro LOPS MCtn NRob

Crisphead

01 H2 **'Robinson'**
Medium to large frame, good quality solid hearts; reconfirmed after trial 2014.
NRob

03 H2 **'Sioux'**
Smooth leaves, large frame, with a green heart and outer leaves tipped red. Slow to bolt.
LCro LOPS

Leafy

95 H2 **'Black-seeded Simpson Improved'**
Yellow-green leaves with frilled edges. Cos-like in growth.
MCtn

95 H2 **'Catalogna'**
Strong-growing oak-leaved type. Light green slightly blistered leaves.
MCtn SVic

95 H2 **'Cocarde'**
Large oak-leaved type, with bronze green-tinged leaves.
EDel

95 H2 **'New Red Fire'**
Large, with puckered light bronze outer leaves.
EKin MCtn

95 H2 **'Salad Bowl'**
Large open-hearted plants with light green frilled leaves.
CHby EKin LCro LOPS LRHS MCtn NRHS NRob

Mangetout see under Peas

Marrow (*Cucurbita pepo*)

97 H2 **'Tiger Cross'**
F_1 hybrid. High yield of pale-striped fruits.
EKin LCro LOPS LRHS MCtn NRHS SVic

Melon (*Cucumis melo*)

09 H1c **'Alvaro'**
Big crop; attractive pale green skins with dark green stripes and salmon-orange flesh. Good flavour.
EDel

09 H1c **'Emir'**
Good crop of netted Charentais-type fruits with orange flesh; H2 for outdoor use.
EKin LCro LOPS MCtn

Onion (*Allium* species)

From sets

93 H3 **'Centurion'**
F_1 hybrid. Flattened globe-shaped bulbs with straw-coloured skins of good thickness.

Reconfirmed after trial 2002, 2013.
NRob

13 H3 **'Rumba'**
Uniform crop; large bulb size, globe-shaped, with brown skin. Stores well.
EKin NRob

02 H3 **'Sturon'**
Very good yield of globe-shaped, slightly high-shouldered bulbs, with good yellow-brown skins. Reconfirmed after trial 2002, 2013.
CHby EKin LCro LOPS NRob

02 H3 **'Stuttgarter'**
High yield, well shaped, deep bulb, good skin.
EKin LCro LOPS NRob

93 H3 **'Turbo'**
Globe-shaped to slightly conical bulbs with brown skins. Some skin splitting. Reconfirmed after trial 2013.
NRob

MAINCROP

93 H3 **'Golden Bear'**
F_1 hybrid; early. Thin-skinned, high-shouldered bulbs; do not store well.
MCtn NRob

RED, GLOBE, FROM SEED AND SETS

05 H3 **'Red Baron'**
High yield of attractive, dark-skinned, globe-shaped bulbs with good internal colour. Plants in the trial grown from seed produced a higher yield and bolder bulbs than those grown from sets. Reconfirmed after trial 2013.
CHby EKin LCro LOPS LRHS MCtn NRHS NRob

05 H3 **'Redspark'**
Attractive globe-shaped, uniform, medium-sized bulbs with tight, dark skins and good internal colour.
EDel

SALAD

04 H4 **'Guardsman'**
F_1 hybrid: cross between *A. fistulosum* and *A. cepa*. Medium to dark green leaves. Very vigorous; well-blanched with some bulbing. Also performed well at Harlow Carr.
MCtn

96 H3 **'Ishikura'**
Strong-growing; long-stemmed; non-bulbing.
MCtn

17 H4 **'Matrix'**
Very even, with very thick roots and good flavour; has a kick.
EDel

04 H3 **'Parade'**
Very straight, strong-growing, uniform plants with good length of blanch; non-builbing; slow to bolt. Also performed well at Harlow Carr.
EDel

93 H4 **'White Lisbon'**
Medium-green leaves with good length of blanch. Good for early and successional sowing. Reconfirmed after trial 2004.
CHby CRos EHyd EKin LCro LOPS LRHS MBros MCtn NRHS NRob SVic

93 H4 **'Winter White Bunching'**
Strong-growing with dark green leaves. Overwinters well.
EKin

SHALLOT

01 H3 **'Golden Gourmet'**
Well-shaped, good size; high yield.
EKin LCro LOPS NRob SVic

01 H3 **'Longor'**
Good yield and shape; also suitable for exhibition.
LCro LOPS NRob

01 H3 **'Matador'**
F_1 hybrid; thick skins, and good yield.
EDel EKin LRHS MCtn NRHS SVic

93 H3 **'Santé'**
Attractive, reddish brown, uniform bulbs with smooth skins. Plant a month later than others to avoid bolting.
NRob

PAK CHOI (*Brassica rapa* Chinensis Group)

10 H3 **'Baraku'**
Good germination rate. Little bolting. Compact and uniform, attractive dark green leaf and petiole. Good size for cooking.
MCtn

10 H3 **'Red Choi'**
Good germination rate. Very little bolting. Stands well. Attractive purple leaves and tender green stem. Good hearting, uniform clean, healthy crop. Ideal size for cooking.
EDel EKin

PARSLEY (*Petroselinum crispum*)

97 H6 **'Bravour'**
A reliable cropper; good stalks, well curled.
MHer

97 H4 **'Curlina'**
Compact and uniform; tightly curled.
LCro LOPS

93 H6 **'Moss Curled'**
Aromatic, deeply cut, tightly curled leaves and small umbels of yellow-green flowers in summer.
CHby EHyd EKin LRHS MCtn NRHS NRob SRms

PARSNIP (*Pastinaca sativa*)

01 H5 **'Gladiator'**
F_1 hybrid; very smooth skin, good potential yield, uniform shape, shallow lenticels. Reconfirmed after trial 2009.
EHyd EKin LCro LOPS LRHS MCtn NRHS

PEAS (*Pisum sativum*)

93 H2 **'Hurst Green Shaft'**
Maincrop; heavy yield of dark green, medium-length, pointed pods. Excellent taste, with good number of peas per pod. Nicely progressive yield. Reconfirmed after trial 1998, 2005, 2017.
EKin LCro LOPS MCtn

05 H2 **'Jaguar'**
Early maincrop; heavy crop of mainly double pods per node. Medium-length pods have an average of seven peas per pod, with good flavour.
MCtn

97 H2 **'Kelvedon Wonder'**
Early maincrop. Long, dark green pods, with an average of 7 to 8 peas per pod. Reconfirmed after trial 2004, 2005.
EDel EKin LCro LOPS MBros MCtn NRob

05 H2 **'Serge'**
Maincrop; semi-leafless plants produce a heavy crop of easy-to-pick pods. Medium-length pods have an average of ten peas per pod, with good flavour.
EKin MBros MCtn

98 H2 **'Show Perfection'**
Maincrop; an exhibition pea, very tall with long dark green pods. A high yield over a long period.
NRob

MANGETOUT

00 H2 **'Delikata'**
Tall, with similar pods to 'Oregon Sugar Pod'. A shade earlier and carries a heavy crop. Pods soon form strings if not picked regularly. Mildew- and fusarium-resistant.
LCro LOPS

09 H2 **'Oregon Giant'**
Clean, healthy, mid-height plants. Attractive broad, mid-green pods.
EKin

SUGARSNAP

00 H2 **'Cascadia'**
Dwarf habit, producing very fleshy, crisp, sweet pods, which remain tender and sweet over a longer period than many snaps. Heavy crops over a long picking season. Reconfirmed after trial 2009.
LCro LOPS

00 H2 **'Delikett'**
Dwarf habit. Young, dark green pods stringless but soon form strings; become fleshier and sweeter with age. Very well cropped and a long season of picking. Reconfirmed after trial 2009.
EKin MCtn NRob

00 H2 **'Sugar Ann'**
Medium height. Early to crop and gives a good yield of juicy, sweet pods. Good flavour. Reconfirmed after trial 2009.
CHby EKin

00 H2 SUGAR DWARF SWEET GREEN (**'Norli'**)
Medium height. About the earliest to mature and a heavy cropper, but over a short period and so requires successional sowing. Medium height plants; good for garden use. Reconfirmed after trial 2009.
CHby MCtn

POTATOES (*Solanum tuberosum*)

FIRST EARLY

98 H2 **'Accent'**
A super-tasting new potato, with pale creamy yellow waxy flesh. Eelworm and common scab resistance.
EKin NRob

98 H2 **'Foremost'**
Originally 'Suttons Foremost'. Ever popular new potato with slightly waxy, firm, white, good-flavoured flesh that does not discolour or disintegrate on cooking.
EKin NRob

07 H2 **'Orla'**
Can also be used as a second early and maincrop. Good yield of round to oval creamy white tubers; flesh slightly waxy with good flavour. Popular with organic gardeners.
EDel NRob

98 H2 **'Red Duke of York'**
Oval red sport of 'Duke of York' with moist pale yellow flesh of superb flavour. Excellent roasted, but a good all-rounder as tubers bulk up quickly if left to mature as a late second early.
EDel EKin LCro LOPS NRob

07 H2 **'Vivaldi'**
Can be left to bulk up as summer baker. Good yield of oval, pale yellow, smooth-skinned tubers with creamy flesh.
EKin LCro LOPS NRob

98 H2 **'Winston'**
Bulks up quickly to produce large, even-shaped tubers. Creamy moist flesh of excellent flavour which does not discolour on cooking.
EKin NRob

Second early

98 H2 **'British Queen'**
Heavy and uniform crop of white-skinned and floury-textured tubers of delicious flavour for all cooking purposes.
EDel NRob

98 H2 **'Charlotte'**
Long oval variety producing yellow-skinned and waxy tubers with creamy yellow flesh of first-class flavour either hot or cold. Reconfirmed after trial 2013 as early for container use.
EDel EKin LCro LOPS NRob

98 H2 **'Kondor'**
Large pale red-skinned oval tubers with tasty, almost waxy, yellow flesh. Very high yields. Excellent for baking.
NRob

98 H2 **'Lady Christl'**
Bulks up very quickly and is almost a first early. Long oval, shallow-eyed, pale yellow-skinned and creamy flesh which remains firm on cooking. Eelworm-resistant. Reconfirmed after trial 2007; also in 2013 after trial as early for container use.
EKin NRob

98 H2 **'Nadine'**
Exceptionally smooth skin and shallow eyes. Cream flesh with a moist, waxy texture that does not discolour and remains firm on cooking. Heavy uniform yields; scab-free. An exhibitor's favourite. Reconfirmed after trial 2017.
EKin NRob

Early in containers

13 H2 **'Casablanca'**
Clean crop, white flesh, uniform size.
EDel EKin LCro LOPS NRob

13 H2 **'Maris Bard'**
White flesh, thin skin, good flavour and texture; fairly uniform crop.
EDel EKin NRob

13 H2 **'Sharpe's Express'**
Heritage variety; white skin, uniform crop size. Slightly waxy, good flavour.
NRob

Early maincrop

13 H2 **'Jazzy'**
Attractive, oval, uniform crop. Yellow skin and flesh, waxy tubers with sweet taste.
EKin NRob

93 H2 **'Maxine'**
Large, smooth, pale red-skinned tubers with white waxy flesh. Uniform tubers so also recommended for exhibitors. Eelworm-resistant. Reconfirmed after trial 1998.
NRob

93 H2 **'Picasso'**
One of the heaviest croppers with creamy skin and striking bright red eyes. Waxy fine-flavoured flesh, particularly when boiled. Eelworm-resistant and good resistance to common scab. Reconfirmed after trial 1998, 2014.
NRob

Maincrop

14 H2 **'Desiree'**
Red skin, light yellow flesh, oval tubers; reliable, and still the world's most popular red.
EDel LCro LOPS

14 H2 **'Maris Piper'**
Cream skin, cream flesh, oval tubers; a massive favourite with gardeners.
LCro LOPS

14 H2 **'Sarpo Mira'**
Red skin, white flesh, oval tubers; still the leading blight benchmark.
EDel LCro LOPS

Salad

98 H2 **'Charlotte'**
Long oval variety producing yellow-skinned and waxy tubers with creamy yellow flesh of first-class flavour either hot or cold. Reconfirmed after trial 2013 as early for container use.
EDel EKin LCro LOPS NRob

03 H2 **'Pink Fir Apple'**
Late main crop. Very vigorous plants; elongated, knobbly tubers; good flavour.
EDel EKin LCro LOPS NRob SVic

03 H2 **'Ratte'**
Early main crop. Oval tubers, waxy, cream flesh; good flavour.
NRob

Radish (*Raphanus sativus*)

13 H2 **'Escala'**
Hybrid. Globe-shaped, bright cherry-red, with thin tap root; not pithy. Very uniform crop.
LCro LOPS

08 H2 **'Lunar'**
Very uniform crop of solid, round, white roots that are crunchy, juicy and have a mild flavour. No pithiness. Tops are short with leaves that are almost entire. Also sold as 'Ping Pong'.
LCro LOPS

08 H2 **'Pink Beauty'**
Attractive, shiny pink roots. Crunchy texture and good, sweet flavour. No pithiness.
LCro LOPS MCtn

96 H2 **'Scarlet Globe'**
Round medium to large red roots.
EKin

96 H2 **'Sparkler'**
Slightly flattened round roots. Unique colour split: red upper with white lower skin. Reconfirmed after trial 2013.
CHby EKin MCtn

Rhubarb (*Rheum × hybridum*)

03 H5 **'Fulton's Strawberry Surprise'**
Maincrop. Very attractive bright red colour. Strong plant, but not too vigorous for the garden.
CDoC

03 H5 **'Grandad's Favorite'**
First early. Vigorous plants, high yield, thick, fairly sweet stem, bright colour, good leaf to stem ratio. Suitable for showing.
CRos EBlo EHyd LRHS NRHS

03 H5 **'Hawke's Champagne'**
Second early. Compact plants; high yield potential. Attractive, bright red, medium-length, uniform stems.
WCot

12 H5 **'Raspberry Red'**
First early. High quality rich red stalks. Crops heavily and reliably.
CDoC CMac CRos EPfP EPom LCro LOPS NRHS SPoG

03 H5 **'Timperley Early'**
First early. Thick stems, early, high yield. Bred for forcing; performs very well outside, but even better colour when forced.
DoC CMac CRos CSBt CTri EBee EHyd EKin ELan EMil EPfP EPom LCro LEdu LOPS LRHS LSRN MAsh MGos MPri MRav NLar NRHS NRob NRog SCoo SEdi SKee SLim SPer SPoG WMat

Shallot see under Onions

Spinach (*Spinacia oleracea*)

08 H2 **'Amazon'**
F_1 hybrid; resistant to mildew races 1–10. Vigorous plants that bulk well; leaves are large, round and a good glossy dark green.
MCtn SVic

00 H2 **'Matador'**
F_1 hybrid. Thick, dark green, upright leaf.
EKin

00 H2 **'Medania'**
Open-pollinated; resistant to mildew races 1 and 3. Good yield from slower-growing plants that are slow to bolt. Slightly blistered, large round leaves. Reconfirmed after trial 2008.
EKin MCtn

08 H2 **'Missouri'**
F_1 hybrid; resistant to mildew races 1–10. Heavy yield of bright, medium green leaves with an upright habit.
EKin LCro LOPS

Spinach Beet (*Beta vulgaris* subsp. *cicla* var. *cicla*)

00 H4 **'Perpetual Spinach'**
Mid to pale green with fairly soft texture, medium vigour; uniform; stable and clean; flat leaf with good green petiole; reconfirmed after trial 2011.
CHby EDel EKin LCro LRHS MBros MCtn NRHS NRob SVic

Squashes (*Cucurbita* species)

Butternut

08 H2 **'Harrier'**
Early crop of small to medium-sized, bell-shaped fruits, with a small seed cavity.
EDel LCro LOPS

08 H2 **'Hunter'**
A very high yield of uniformly small to medium, long pear-shaped fruits with a small seed cavity. Early ripening with orange-gold flesh.
EKin MCtn NRob SVic

Summer

06 H2 **'Eight Ball'**
Good yield of round, green fruits; easy to see and pick from the compact, upright plants.
SVic

06 H2 **'Geode'**
Early and heavy crop of uniform, round, mid to pale green, marbled fruits with smallish blossom end scar. Clean, healthy plants.
LRHS NRHS

06 H2 **'Satellite'**
Hybrid; smaller, compact plants produce an early and prolific crop. Oval fruits are an attractive, vibrant dark green.
EDel

06 H2 **'Sunburst'**
Hybrid; attractive yellow, scallop-shaped fruits. Used for baby veg; best harvested when small (5–6cm diameter).
EDel NRob

Winter

11 H2 **'Crown Prince'**
Large fruits, with blue-grey skin and excellent storage quality. Popular, reliable variety. Fruits have high flesh content, of deep orange colour and excellent flavour.
CHby EKin MCtn NRob SVic

11 H2 **'Harlequin'**
High sugar cultivar. Decorative ridged fruits, striped yellow, gold and green; mid-sized with a

typical diameter 10–13cm. Good yield per plant and excellent storage quality. Plant has a semi-bush habit. Firm flesh of smooth texture and sweet flavour.
EDel SVic

11 H2 **'Honey Bear'**
High sugar variety. Dark green, mini-acorn-shaped fruits of uniform size, typically 8–10cm in diameter. Sweet flavour; ideal size for baking whole. Compact, bushy habit, giving a reasonable yield of fruits, with excellent storage qualities. Plant demonstrates good resistance to powdery mildew.
MCtn

11 H2 **'Kabocha' large-fruited**
Dark green flattened fruit, typically 15 to 17cm in diameter. Good storage. Flesh is thick, sweet and smooth. Ideal for desserts.
SVic

11 H2 **'Sweet Dumpling'**
Original sweet dumpling type. Uniform crop of small fruit, approximately 9 to 10cm in diameter; ridged, cream-coloured with green stripes and mottling; sweetly flavoured orange flesh. Trailing habit, producing a good yield of fruits with excellent storage quality.
CHby EKin MCtn NRob

SUGARSNAP SEE UNDER PEAS

SWEET CORN (*Zea mays*)

03 H2 **'Earlibird'**
F_1 hybrid; 2nd early supersweet. Uniform cobs; good vigour. Reconfirmed after trial 2009, 2016.
EKin MCtn

03 H2 **'Lark'**
F_1 hybrid; 2nd early extra tender sweet. High yield of well-filled cobs with very sweet, clean flavour. Reconfirmed after trial 2009, 2016; among the first to be harvested in the trial.
EDel EKin LCro LOPS MCtn SVic

03 H2 **'Mainstay'**
F_1 hybrid; maincrop supersweet. Vigorous plants, reliable crop, well-filled cobs.
MBros

09 H2 **'Mirai 003'**
Early; uniform, small, exceptionally sweet cobs.
LCro LOPS

03 H2 **'Swift'**
F_1 hybrid; early extra tender sweet. High yield of cobs with excellent eating quality. Good sweet flavour and tender kernels. Very popular variety. Thin pericarp is prone to damage. Reconfirmed after trial 2009, 2016; among the first to be harvested.
EKin LCro LOPS MCtn

SWEET PEPPER (*Capsicum annuum* var. *annuum* Grossum Group)

05 H1c **'Corno di Toro Rosso'**
Open-pollinated; later-cropping. Long, horn-shaped, very fleshy fruits that have a good flavour. Maturing from pale green to bright red. Big fruits, huge yield. Reconfirmed after trial 2016.
CHby LCro LOPS MCtn

16 H1c **'Demetra'**
Hybrid. Medium cone, uniform fruits, maturing from light green to red. Very high yields. Attractive and vigorous.
EKin

05 H1c **'Friggitello'**
Open-pollinated; productive plants with small, long, slim, pointed fruits. Ripening from mid green to red; the versatile sweet-flavoured fruits have the appearance of a hot pepper and are also suitable for stirfry and pickling.
MCtn

05 H1c **'Mohawk'**
F_1 hybrid. Medium-sized, blocky, bell-shaped fruits that ripen from dark green to bright yellow / orange; good flavour. Dwarf-growing plants are well suited to growing in pots. Reconfirmed after trial 2016.
CRos EHyd EKin LRHS MBros NRHS

05 H1c **'Redskin'**
F_1 hybrid; small to medium, blocky, bell-shaped fruits that ripen from dark green to a glossy, dark red. Compact plants give a high yield and are well suited to growing in pots. Original windowsill pepper. Reconfirmed after trial 2016.
CRos EHyd EKin LCro LOPS LRHS NRHS

05 H1c **'Topepo Rosso'**
Open-pollinated; productive, early-cropping plants. Medium-sized, beef tomato shape that is good for stuffing. Attractive fruits mature from dark green to bright red and have a good flavour.
MCtn

TOMATOES (*Solanum lycopersicum*)

97 H1c **'Alicante'**
Good shape; heavy crop of attractive fruits which ripen well. Very reliable and productive; early to mature; sweet flavour. H2 for outdoor use.
CRos EHyd EKin LCro LOPS LRHS MBros NRHS NRob

13 H1c **'Elegance'**
Strong plants producing high yield of large fruits. Trusses of 8–10 flavoursome fruits.
LRHS

97 H1c **'Golden Sunrise'**
Later-maturing; small yellow fruits.
EKin LCro LOPS LRHS MBros MCtn NRHS NRob SVic

93 H1c **'Outdoor Girl'**
Early. Round red fruits with good flavour.
CRos EHyd LCro LOPS LRHS MCtn NRHS NRob SVic

93 H1c **'Shirley'**
F_1 hybrid; fairly early. Uniform trusses; nice round red fruit of medium size and average flavour. Reconfirmed after trial 1997.
CRos EDel EHyd EKin LRHS MBros NRHS NRob SVic

93 H1c **'Tigerella'**
Interesting attractive striped fruit with quite good flavour; reconfirmed after trial 1997. H2 for outdoor use.
CHby EDel EKin LRHS MCtn NRob SVic

93 H1c **'Yellow Perfection'**
Indeterminate, uniform, round, pale, yellow fruit. H2 for outdoor use.
EKin

Beefsteak

14 H1c **'Beefmaster'**
Multilocular; large fruit; deeply ribbed; light, smooth taste, good yield.
EKin

03 H1c **'Costoluto Fiorentino'**
High yield; medium-sized, attractive bright red, highly ribbed, succulent fruit with good flavour.
LCro LOPS MCtn

14 H1c **'Gigantomo'**
Irregular-shaped heavy fruit; light but pleasant flavour; good yield.
EKin NRob

03 H1c **'Marmande'**
High yield; large, bright red, attractive fruits, with solid flesh and good flavour.
CHby EKin MCtn

14 H1c **'Orange Wellington'**
Pleasing flavour; orange-golden fruit; smooth skin; cat-faced but not too deep; good yield.
EKin

14 H1c **'Supersteak'**
Multilocular; smooth skin; good-sized fruit; nice taste, good yield.
CRos EHyd LRHS NRHS

14 H1c **'Tomande'**
Multilocular; smooth skin; good-sized fruit; light taste, good yield.
LCro LOPS

Cherry

07 H1c **'Apero'**
Good yield of oval fruits on compact trusses.
MCtn

07 H1c **'Cherrola'**
High yield, with attractive fruit well spaced on long trusses. Good flavour; not too fleshy inside. Reconfirmed after trial 2017.
LCro LOPS

17 H1c **'Rosella'**
Very high yield, with nice size and good taste.
LCro LOPS

07 H1c **'Sakura'**
High yield; very bright fruits carried on long trusses; very sweet flavour.
EDel

98 H1c **'Sun Baby'**
Good trusses of uniform, attractive, yellow fruits. H2 for outdoor use.
MCtn

07 H1c **'Sungold'**
Good yield of attractive round golden-orange fruits. Good flavour.
CHby CRos EDel EHyd EKin LCro LOPS LRHS MCtn NRHS NRob SVic

98 H1c **'Sweet Million'**
F_1 hybrid. Long open trusses of sweet, round, bright red fruits; good yield. Reconfirmed after trial 2017.
CRos EDel EHyd LRHS MBros MCtn NRHS NRob

Plum

04 H1c **'Ildi'**
Vigorous, indeterminate plants; heavy crop of small, attractive, yellow, plum-shaped fruit.
EKin LCro LOPS

04 H1c **'Sweet Olive'**
F_1 hybrid; very early. Very high yield from vigorous, healthy, determinate plants. Small, red, round to plum-shaped fruits, a little difficult to pick, but of good flavour.
MCtn

Turnip (*Brassica rapa* Rapifera Group)

04 H3 **'Oasis'**
Good early crop of conical white roots.
MCtn

04 H3 **'Primera'**
Uniform crop of flat-shaped roots with purple top and attractive smooth skin. Good internal flesh.
EHyd LRHS NRHS

93 H3 **'Tokyo Cross'**
F_1 hybrid; early. Uniform, medium size, smooth, round, pure white, shiny roots; reconfirmed after trial 1997 and 2004.
LCro LOPS

Sharing
your
passion
for plants

V
PLANTS FOR POLLINATORS

RHS PLANTS FOR POLLINATORS

Subspecies and cultivars of plants listed here are also **Plants for Pollinators**, except for those that provide significantly reduced floral resources (i.e. pollen and nectar). This includes most doubles.

Key to codes: T tree S shrub C climber **B** bulb / corm A annual **Bi** biennial H herbaceous perennial † denotes an archaeophyte (a naturalised plant introduced before 1500)

WILDFLOWERS

SHORT GRASS (UP TO 15CM)

Ajuga reptans bugle	H
Bellis perennis daisy	H
Campanula rotundifolia common harebell	H
Hippocrepis comosa horseshoe vetch	H
Lotus corniculatus bird's foot trefoil	H
Potentilla anserina silverweed	H
Potentilla erecta tormentil	H
Potentilla reptans creeping cinquefoil	H
Primula veris common cowslip	H
Prunella vulgaris selfheal	H
Ranunculus repens creeping buttercup	H
Sanguisorba minor salad burnet	H
Taraxacum officinale dandelion	H
Thymus polytrichus wild thyme	H
Thymus pulegioides large thyme	H
Trifolium pratense red clover	H
Trifolium repens white clover	H
Veronica chamaedrys germander speedwell	H

HEDGES, SHRUB BORDERS AND WOODLAND EDGES

Acer campestre field maple	S or T
Alliaria petiolata garlic mustard	Bi
Allium ursinum ramsons	B
Aquilegia vulgaris columbine	H
Ballota nigra black horehound	H
Berberis vulgaris barberry †	S
Bryonia dioica white bryony	H/C
Buxus sempervirens common box	S
Campanula trachelium nettle-leaved bellflower	H
Clematis vitalba old man's beard, traveller's joy	C
Clinopodium vulgare wild basil	H
Cornus sanguinea common dogwood	S
Crataegus monogyna common hawthorn	S or T
Cytisus scoparius common broom	S
Digitalis purpurea common foxglove	Bi
Euonymus europaeus spindle	S
Ficaria verna subsp. *verna* lesser celandine	H
Fragaria vesca wild strawberry	H
Frangula alnus alder buckthorn	S
Galium mollugo hedge bedstraw	H
Galium odoratum sweet woodruff	H
Galium verum lady's bedstraw	H
Geranium robertianum herb robert	A/Bi
Geum urbanum wood avens	H
Hedera helix common ivy	C
Helleborus foetidus stinking hellebore	H
Hyacinthoides non-scripta bluebell	B
Hylotelephium telephium orpine	H
Ilex aquifolium common holly	T
Lamium album white deadnettle	H
Lamium galeobdolon yellow archangel	H
Ligustrum vulgare wild privet	S
Lonicera periclymenum common honeysuckle	C
Malus sylvestris crab apple	T
Malva sylvestris common mallow	H
Myosotis sylvatica wood forget-me-not	H
Primula vulgaris primrose	H
Prunus avium wild cherry, gean	T
Prunus padus bird cherry	T
Prunus spinosa blackthorn, sloe	S
Rhamnus cathartica purging buckthorn	S
Rosa species rose	S
Rubus fruticosus blackberry	S
Salix caprea goat willow (male forms best)	S
Salix cinerea subsp. *oleifolia* grey willow (male forms best)	S
Sanicula europaea sanicle	H
Silene dioica red campion	H
Silene latifolia subsp. *alba* white campion	H
Smyrnium olusatrum alexanders †	Bi
Sorbus aria common whitebeam	T
Sorbus aucuparia rowan, mountain ash	T

Sorbus torminalis wild service tree T
Stachys officinalis betony H
Stellaria holostea greater stitchwort H
Symphytum officinale common comfrey H
Teucrium scorodonia wood sage H
Tilia cordata small-leaved lime T
Viburnum lantana common wayfaring tree S
Viburnum opulus guelder rose S
Vicia cracca common tufted vetch H
Vicia sativa common vetch H

Disturbed Ground

Agrostemma githago corncockle † A
Anchusa arvensis bugloss † A
Anthemis arvensis corn chamomile † A
Anthemis cotula stinking chamomile † A
Centaurea cyanus cornflower † A
Cichorium intybus chicory † H
Dipsacus fullonum common teasel Bi
Echium vulgare viper's bugloss Bi
Glebionis segetum corn marigold † A
Iberis amara wild candytuft A
Lamium amplexicaule henbit deadnettle † A
Matricaria recutita scented mayweed † A
Mentha arvensis corn mint H
Myosotis arvensis field forget-me-not † A/H
Onopordum acanthium cotton thistle † Bi
Papaver dubium long-headed poppy † A
Papaver rhoeas common poppy † A
Sinapis arvensis charlock † A
Sonchus arvensis perennial sowthistle H
Tussilago farfara coltsfoot H
Verbascum thapsus great mullein Bi

Flower Beds

Calluna vulgaris heather, ling excl. bud-blooming cultivars S
Erica ciliaris Dorset heath S
Erica cinerea bell heather S
Erica tetralix cross-leaved heath S

Long Grass (above 50cm)

Arctium minus lesser burdock Bi
Carduus crispus welted thistle Bi
Carduus nutans musk thistle Bi
Chamaenerion angustifolium rosebay willowherb H
Cirsium arvense creeping thistle H
Cirsium vulgare spear thistle Bi
Conopodium majus pignut H
Cynoglossum officinale hound's tongue H
Daucus carota wild carrot Bi
Geranium pratense meadow cranesbill H
Heracleum sphondylium hogweed Bi
Hypericum perforatum perforate St John's wort H
Knautia arvensis field scabious H
Lathyrus pratensis meadow vetchling H
Pastinaca sativa wild parsnip Bi
Succisa pratensis devil's bit scabious H
Tanacetum vulgare tansy † H
Thalictrum flavum meadow rue H
Tragopogon pratensis goat's beard Bi
Verbascum nigrum dark mullein Bi/H

Medium Height Grass (up to 50cm)

Achillea millefolium common yarrow H
Achillea ptarmica sneezewort H
Agrimonia eupatoria agrimony H
Anthyllis vulneraria kidney vetch H
Armeria maritima thrift, sea pink H
Blackstonia perfoliata yellowwort A
Campanula glomerata clustered bellflower H
Centaurea nigra common knapweed, hardheads H
Centaurea scabiosa greater knapweed H
Centaurium erythraea common centaury Bi
Echium vulgare viper's bugloss Bi
Erigeron acris blue fleabane A/H
Filipendula vulgaris dropwort H
Helianthemum nummularium common rockrose H
Hypochaeris radicata cat's ear H
Inula conyzae ploughman's spikenard H
Leontodon hispidus rough hawkbit H
Leucanthemum vulgare ox-eye daisy H
Linaria vulgaris common toadflax H
Malva moschata musk mallow H
Ononis repens common restharrow H
Origanum vulgare wild marjoram H
Pilosella officinarum mouse-ear hawkweed H
Ranunculus acris meadow buttercup H
Ranunculus bulbosus bulbous buttercup H
Reseda lutea wild mignonette Bi/H
Rhinanthus minor yellow rattle A
Scabiosa spp. A/H
Scorzoneroides autumnalis autumn hawkbit H
Silene vulgaris bladder campion H
Solidago virgaurea goldenrod H

Ponds, Pond Margins & Wet Soils

Alisma plantago-aquatica water plantain H
Angelica sylvestris wild angelica Bi
Butomus umbellatus flowering rush H
Caltha palustris marsh marigold H
Cardamine pratensis cuckoo flower, lady's smock H
Cirsium dissectum meadow thistle H
Epilobium hirsutum great willowherb H
Eupatorium cannabinum hemp agrimony H
Filipendula ulmaria meadowsweet H
Galium palustre marsh bedstraw H
Geum rivale water avens H
Hypericum tetrapterum square-stalked St John's wort H

Iris pseudacorus yellow iris H
Lotus pedunculatus greater bird's-foot trefoil H
Lychnis flos-cuculi ragged robin H
Lycopus europaeus gypsywort H
Lysimachia nummularia creeping Jenny H
Lysimachia vulgaris yellow loosestrife H
Lythrum salicaria purple loosestrife H
Mentha aquatica water mint H
Menyanthes trifoliata bogbean H
Myosotis scorpioides water forget-me-not H
Nasturtium officinale common watercress H
Nuphar lutea yellow waterlily H
Nymphaea alba white waterlily H
Oenanthe aquatica fine-leaved water dropwort A/Bi
Oenanthe crocata hemlock water dropwort H
Persicaria amphibia amphibious bistort H
Persicaria bistorta common bistort H
Polemonium caeruleum Jacob's ladder H
Pulicaria dysenterica common fleabane H
Ranunculus aquatilis common water crowfoot A/H
Ranunculus flammula lesser spearwort H
Ranunculus fluitans river water crowfoot H
Ranunculus lingua greater spearwort H
Ranunculus sceleratus celery-leaved buttercup A
Sagittaria sagittifolia arrowhead H
Sanguisorba officinalis great burnet H
Scrophularia auriculata water figwort H
Scutellaria galericulata common skullcap H
Stachys palustris marsh woundwort H
Valeriana officinalis common valerian H
Veronica beccabunga brooklime H

Shingle – Gravel Garden

Cakile maritima sea rocket A
Crambe maritima sea kale H
Crithmum maritimum rock samphire H
Eryngium maritimum sea holly H
Glaucium flavum yellow horned poppy Bi/H
Sedum acre biting stonecrop H
Sedum album white stonecrop † H
Silene uniflora sea campion H

Garden Plants

Winter (nov – feb)

Clematis cirrhosa Spanish traveller's joy C
Crocus species crocus (winter-flowering) B
Eranthis hyemalis winter aconite B
× *Fatshedera lizei* tree ivy S
Galanthus nivalis common snowdrop B
Helleborus species and hybrids hellebore (winter-flowering) H
Lonicera × *purpusii* Purpus honeysuckle S
Mahonia species Oregon grape S
Salix aegyptiaca musk willow S
Sarcococca confusa sweet box S
Sarcococca hookeriana sweet box S
Viburnum tinus laurustinus S

Spring (mar – may)

Acer campestre Native plant; field maple S or T
Acer platanoides Norway maple T
Acer pseudoplatanus sycamore T
Acer saccharum sugar maple T
Aesculus hippocastanum horse chestnut T
Ajuga reptans Native plant; bugle H
Arabis alpina subsp. *caucasica* alpine rock cress H
Armeria juniperifolia juniper-leaved thrift H
Aubrieta species aubretia H
Aurinia saxatilis gold dust H
Berberis darwinii Darwin's barberry S
Berberis thunbergii Japanese barberry S
Bergenia species elephant ear H
Buxus sempervirens Native plant; common box S
Caltha palustris Native plant; marsh marigold H
Ceanothus species California lilac S
Cercis siliquastrum Judas tree T
Chaenomeles species Japanese quince S
Cornus mas Cornelian cherry S
Cotoneaster conspicuus Tibetan cotoneaster S
Crataegus monogyna Native plant; common hawthorn S or T
Crocus species crocus (spring-flowering) B
Doronicum × *excelsum* leopard's bane H
Enkianthus campanulatus redvein enkianthus S
Erica carnea alpine heath S
Erica × *darleyensis* Darley Dale heath S
Erysimum species wallflower Bi or H
Euphorbia amygdaloides Native plant; wood spurge H
Euphorbia characias Mediterranean spurge H
Euphorbia cyparissias cypress spurge H
Euphorbia epithymoides cushion spurge H
Euphorbia × *martini* Martin's spurge S
Euphorbia nicaeensis Nice spurge H
Geranium species cranesbill H
Geum rivale Native plant; water avens H
Hebe species hebe S
Helleborus species & hybrids hellebore (spring-flowering) H
Iberis saxatilis alpine candytuft H
Iberis sempervirens perennial candytuft H
Ilex aquifolium Native plant; common holly T
Lamium maculatum spotted dead nettle H
Lunaria annua honesty Bi
Mahonia species Oregon grape (spring-flowering) S
Malus baccata Siberian crab T
Malus domestica edible apple T

Malus floribunda Japanese crab T
Malus hupehensis Hupeh crab T
Malus sargentii Sargent's crab apple T
Mespilus germanica common medlar T
Muscari armeniacum Armenian grape hyacinth B
Nectaroscordum species honey garlic B
Ornithogalum umbellatum common star of Bethlehem B
Pieris formosa lily-of-the-valley bush S
Pieris japonica lily-of-the-valley bush S
Primula veris Native plant; common cowslip H
Primula vulgaris Native plant; primrose H
Prunus avium Native plant; wild & edible cherries T
Prunus domestica wild & edible plums T
Prunus dulcis almond T
Prunus incisa 'Kojo-no-mai' cherry 'Kojo-no-mai' S
Prunus insititia damson T
Prunus laurocerasus cherry laurel S
Prunus mume Japanese apricot T
Prunus padus Native plant; bird cherry T
Prunus pendula f. *ascendens* 'Rosea' flowering cherry T
Prunus persica peach T
Prunus spinosa Native plant; blackthorn S
Prunus tenella dwarf Russian almond S
Prunus × yedoensis flowering cherry T
Pulmonaria species lungwort H
Pyrus communis pear T
Ribes nigrum blackcurrant S
Ribes rubrum Native plant; common redcurrant S
Ribes sanguineum flowering currant S
Salix caprea Native plant; goat willow (male form only) S or T
Salix hastata 'Wehrhahnii' halberd willow 'Wehrhahnii' S
Salix lanata Native plant; woolly willow (male form only) S
Skimmia japonica skimmia S
Smyrnium olusatrum Native plant; alexanders † Bi
Stachyurus chinensis stachyurus S
Stachyurus praecox stachyurus S
Vaccinium corymbosum blueberry S

Summer (June – Aug)

Achillea species yarrow H
Actaea japonica baneberry H
Aesculus indica Indian horse chestnut (resistant to leaf-mining moth) T
Aesculus parviflora bottlebrush buckeye S
Agastache species giant hyssop H
Ageratum houstonianum flossflower A
Alcea rosea hollyhock Bi
Allium species ornamental and edibles (when allowed to flower) B
Alstroemeria species Peruvian lily H
Amberboa moschata sweet sultan A
Amsonia tabernaemontana eastern bluestar H
Anchusa azurea large blue alkanet A
Anchusa capensis Cape alkanet A
Angelica archangelica angelica Bi
Angelica gigas purple angelica Bi
Angelica sylvestris Native plant; wild angelica Bi
Anthemis tinctoria dyer's chamomile H
Antirrhinum majus snapdragon A or H
Aquilegia species columbine H
Arabis allionii Siberian wallflower H
Argemone platyceras crested poppy A or H
Armeria maritima Native plant; thrift H
Aruncus dioicus goat's beard (male form only) H
Asparagus officinalis common asparagus H
Astrantia major greater masterwort H
Borago officinalis borage A
Brachyglottis (Dunedin Group) 'Sunshine' brachyglottis 'Sunshine' S
Brachyglottis monroi Monro's ragwort S
Buddleja davidii butterfly bush S
Buddleja globosa orange ball tree S
Buphthalmum salicifolium yellow ox-eye H
Bupleurum fruticosum shrubby hare's ear S
Calamintha nepeta Native plant; lesser calamint H
Calendula officinalis common marigold A
Callicarpa bodinieri var. *giraldii* beautyberry S
Callistephus chinensis China aster A
Calluna vulgaris Native plant; heather S
Campanula carpatica tussock bellflower H
Campanula glomerata Native plant; clustered bellflower H
Campanula lactiflora milky bellflower H
Campanula latifolia Native plant; giant bellflower H
Campanula medium Canterbury bells Bi
Campanula persicifolia peach-leaved bellflower H
Campsis radicans trumpet honeysuckle C
Caryopteris × clandonensis caryopteris S
Catalpa bignonioides Indian bean tree T
Catananche caerulea blue cupidone H
Centaurea atropurpurea purple knapweed H
Centaurea cyanus cornflower † A
Centaurea dealbata mealy centaury H
Centaurea macrocephala giant knapweed H
Centaurea montana perennial cornflower H
Centaurea nigra Native plant; common knapweed H
Centaurea scabiosa Native plant; greater knapweed H
Centranthus ruber red valerian H
Centratherum punctatum Manaos beauty A
Cerinthe major 'Purpurascens' honeywort 'Purpurascens' A
Cirsium rivulare 'Atropurpureum' purple plume thistle H
Clarkia unguiculata butterfly flower A
Clematis vitalba Native plant; old man's beard, traveller's joy C
Cleome hassleriana spider flower A
Consolida ajacis giant larkspur A
Convolvulus tricolor dwarf morning glory C/A
Coreopsis species tickseed H or A

Cornus alba red-barked dogwood S
Cosmos species cosmos A
Crambe cordifolia greater sea kale H
Crataegus monogyna Native plant; common hawthorn S or T
Cucurbita pepo marrow, courgette A
Cuphea ignea cigar flower A
Cynara cardunculus including Scolymus Group globe artichoke and cardoon H
Cynoglossum amabile Chinese forget-me-not H
Dahlia species dahlia H
Delosperma floribundum ice plant H
Delphinium elatum candle larkspur H
Dianthus barbatus sweet william Bi
Dictamnus albus dittany H
Digitalis species foxglove Bi
Dipsacus fullonum Native plant; common teasel Bi
Echinacea purpurea purple coneflower H
Echinops species globe thistle H
Echium vulgare Native plant; viper's bugloss A
Elaeagnus angustifolia oleaster S
Erica cinerea Native plant; bell heather S
Erica erigena Irish heath S
Erica vagans Native plant; Cornish heath S
Erigeron species fleabane H
Eriophyllum lanatum golden yarrow H
Eryngium alpinum alpine eryngo H
Eryngium giganteum Miss Willmott's ghost Bi
Eryngium planum blue eryngo H
Eryngium × *tripartitum* eryngo H
Erysimum species wallflower H or S
Escallonia species escallonia S
Eschscholzia californica California poppy A
Eupatorium cannabinum Native plant; hemp agrimony H
Eupatorium maculatum Joe Pye weed H
Euphorbia cornigera horned spurge H
Euphorbia donii euphorbia H
Euphorbia sarawschanica Zeravshan spurge H
Ferula communis giant fennel H
Foeniculum vulgare common fennel † H
Fragaria × *ananassa* garden strawberry H
Fuchsia species fuchsia – hardy types S
Gaillardia × *grandiflora* blanket flower H
Gaura lindheimeri white gaura H
Geranium pratense Native plant; meadow cranesbill H
Geranium species cranesbill (summer-flowering) H
Geum species avens (summer-flowering) H
Gilia capitata blue thimble flower A
Glebionis segetum corn marigold † A
Gypsophila elegans annual baby's breath A
Hebe species hebe S
Helenium species Helen's flower H
Helianthus annuus common sunflower excl. pollen-free cultivars A
Helianthus debilis cucumberleaf sunflower A
Heliopsis helianthoides smooth ox-eye H
Heliotropium arborescens common heliotrope A
Heracleum sphondylium Native plant; hogweed Bi
Hesperis matronalis dame's violet H
Hydrangea anomala subsp. *petiolaris* climbing hydrangea C
Hydrangea paniculata paniculate hydrangea (only cultivars with many fertile flowers, e.g. 'Kyushu', 'Big Ben', 'Floribunda', 'Brussels Lace') S
Hylotelephium spectabile & hybrids ice plant H
Hylotelephium telephium Native plant; orpine H
Hyssopus officinalis hyssop S
Iberis amara Native plant; wild candytuft A
Ilex aquifolium Native plant; common holly T
Inula species harvest daisy H
Jasminum officinale common jasmine C
Kalmia latifolia mountain laurel S
Knautia arvensis Native plant; field scabious H
Knautia macedonica Macedonian scabious H
Koelreuteria paniculata pride of India T
Lathyrus latifolius broad-leaved everlasting pea H
Laurus nobilis bay tree S
Lavandula angustifolia English lavender S
Lavandula × *intermedia* lavandin S
Lavandula stoechas French lavender S
Lavatera olbia tree lavatera S
Lavatera trimestris annual lavatera A
Leucanthemum × *superbum* Shasta daisy H
Leucanthemum vulgare Native plant; ox-eye daisy H
Liatris spicata button snakewort H
Ligustrum ovalifolium garden privet S
Ligustrum sinense Chinese privet S
Limnanthes douglasii poached egg flower A
Limonium platyphyllum broad-leaved statice H
Linaria maroccana annual toadflax A
Linaria purpurea purple toadflax H
Lobularia maritima sweet alyssum A
Lonicera periclymenum Native plant; common honeysuckle C
Lychnis coronaria rose campion Bi or H
Lychnis flos-cuculi Native plant; ragged robin H
Lysimachia vulgaris Native plant; yellow loosestrife H
Lythrum salicaria Native plant; purple loosestrife H
Lythrum virgatum wand loosestrife H
Malope trifida large-flowered mallow wort A
Malva alcea greater musk mallow H
Malva moschata Native plant; musk mallow H
Matthiola incana hoary stock Bi
Mentha aquatica Native plant; water mint H
Mentha spicata spearmint H
Monarda didyma bergamot H
Myosotis species forget-me-not Bi
Nemophila menziesii baby blue eyes A
Nepeta species catmint H
Nicotiana alata flowering tobacco A
Nicotiana langsdorffii Langsdorff's tobacco A
Nicotiana sylvestris flowering tobacco Bi
Nigella damascena love-in-a-mist A
Nigella hispanica Spanish fennel flower A

Oenothera species evening primrose Bi
Olearia species daisy bush S
Onopordum acanthium cotton thistle Bi
Origanum orites pot marjoram S
Origanum 'Rosenkuppel' marjoram 'Rosenkuppel' H
Origanum vulgare Native plant; oregano, wild marjoram H
Paeonia species peony H
Papaver orientale oriental poppy H
Papaver rhoeas Native plant; common poppy † A
Parthenocissus tricuspidata Boston ivy C
Penstemon species beard-tongue T
Perovskia atriplicifolia Russian sage S
Persicaria amplexicaulis red bistort H
Persicaria bistorta Native plant; common bistort H
Phacelia campanularia Californian bluebell A
Phacelia tanacetifolia fiddleneck A
Phaseolus coccineus scarlet runner bean A
Phlomis species sage S
Phlox paniculata perennial phlox H
Photinia davidiana stranvaesia S
Phuopsis stylosa Caucasian crosswort H
Pileostegia viburnoides climbing hydrangea C
Polemonium caeruleum Native plant; Jacob's ladder H
Potentilla species cinquefoil H or S
Prostanthera cuneata alpine mint bush S
Ptelea trifoliata hop tree S
Pyracantha species firethorn S
Reseda odorata garden mignonette A
Ridolfia segetum false fennel A
Robinia pseudoacacia false acacia T
Rosa species rose S
Rosmarinus officinalis rosemary S
Rubus fruticosus agg. Native plant; blackberry S
Rubus idaeus Native plant; common raspberry S
Rudbeckia species coneflower H or A
Salvia species sage A or H
Sanvitalia procumbens creeping zinnia A
Scabiosa spp. A/H
Sidalcea malviflora checkerbloom H
Solidago species goldenrod H
Sorbus aria Native plant; common whitebeam T
Sorbus aucuparia Native plant; mountain ash, rowan T
Spiraea japonica Japanese spiraea S
Stachys byzantina lamb's ear H
Stachys macrantha big sage H
Stokesia laevis Stokes' aster H
Symphoricarpos albus snowberry S
Tagetes patula French marigold A
Tamarix ramosissima tamarisk S
Tanacetum coccineum pyrethrum H
Tanacetum vulgare Native plant; tansy † H
Telekia speciosa yellow ox-eye H
Tetradium daniellii bee-bee tree T
Teucrium chamaedrys Native plant; wall germander H
Thymus species thyme S
Tilia × *europaea* common lime T
Tilia maximowicziana lime T
Tilia oliveri lime T
Tilia platyphyllos Native plant; broad-leaved lime T
Tithonia rotundifolia Mexican sunflower A
Trachymene coerulea blue lace flower A
Trollius species globeflower H
Tropaeolum majus garden nasturtium A
Verbascum species mullein Bi
Verbena bonariensis purple top H
Verbena rigida slender vervain A
Veronica longifolia garden speedwell H
Veronica spicata Native plant; spiked speedwell H
Veronicastrum virginicum Culver's root H
Viburnum lantana Native plant; common wayfaring tree S
Viburnum opulus Native plant; guelder rose S
Vicia faba broad bean A
Weigela florida weigelia S
Zauschneria californica Californian fuchsia S
Zinnia elegans youth and old age A

Autumn (Sept – Oct)

Aconitum carmichaelii Carmichael's monk's hood H
Actaea simplex simple-stemmed bugbane H
Anemone hupehensis Chinese anemone H
Anemone × *hybrida* Japanese anemone H
Arbutus unedo strawberry tree S or T
Campanula poscharskyana trailing bellflower H
Ceratostigma plumbaginoides hardy blue-flowered leadwort H
Chrysanthemum species & hybrids chrysanthemum H
Clematis heracleifolia tube clematis C
Colchicum species autumn crocus B
Crocus species crocus (autumn-flowering types) B
Dahlia species & hybrids dahlia H
Elaeagnus pungens silverthorn S
Elaeagnus × *submacrophylla* Ebbinge's silverberry S
Fatsia japonica Japanese aralia S
Hedera colchica Persian ivy C
Hedera helix Native plant; common ivy C
Helianthus × *laetiflorus* perennial sunflower H
Leucanthemella serotina autumn ox-eye H
Machaeranthera tanacetifolia tansy-leaf aster A
Salvia species sage (autumn-flowering types) H
Symphyotrichum species and hybrids Michaelmas daisy H
Tilia henryana Henry's lime (one of the last to flower) T

RHS membership
Start your year of gardening inspiration
Join today and enjoy:
• Free, personalised gardening advice from RHS experts
• Free days out at our four RHS Gardens and more than 200 RHS Partner Gardens
• The Garden monthly magazine, worth £59
• Members' Days and savings for RHS Flower Shows
Visit rhs.org.uk/join or call 020 3176 5820
RHS
Inspiring everyone to grow
RHS Registered Charity No. 222879/SC038262
Image: RHS / Jason Ingram

VI
NURSERIES

Nursery Codes and Symbols

The first letter of each nursery code represents the area of the country in which the nursery is situated.

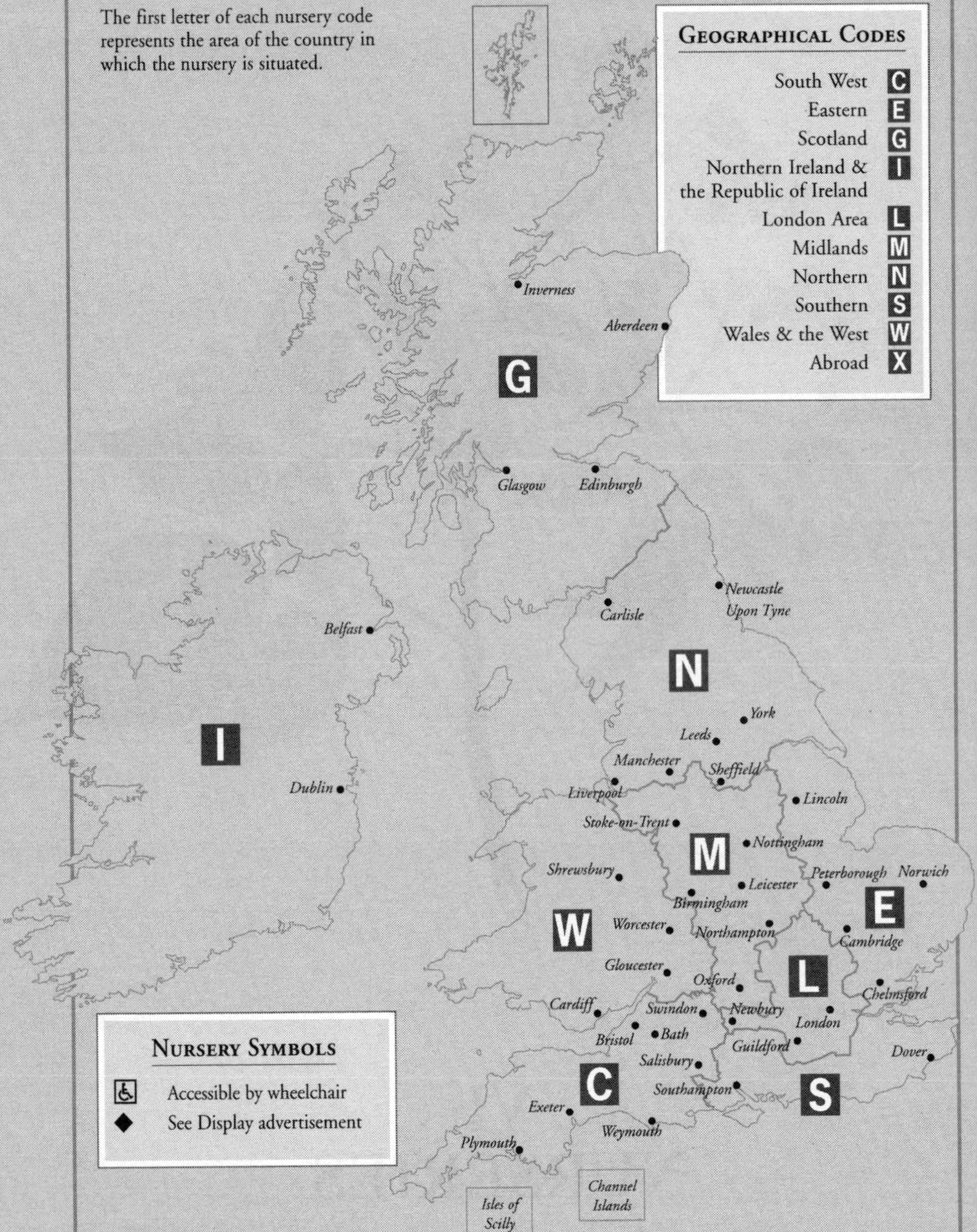

Geographical Codes

South West	C
Eastern	E
Scotland	G
Northern Ireland & the Republic of Ireland	I
London Area	L
Midlands	M
Northern	N
Southern	S
Wales & the West	W
Abroad	X

Nursery Symbols

- ♿ Accessible by wheelchair
- ◆ See Display advertisement

USING THE NURSERY LISTINGS

Your main reference from the Plant Directory is the Nursery Details by Code listing, which includes all relevant information for each nursery in order of nursery code. The Nursery Index by Name is an alphabetical list for those who know a nursery's name but not its code and wish to check its details in the main list.

1 NURSERY DETAILS BY CODE

Once you have found your plant in the Plant Directory, turn to this list to find out the name, address, opening times and other details of the nurseries whose codes accompany the plant.

KEY
♿ Accessible by wheelchair ◆ See Display advertisement

ESwi **SWINES MEADOW FARM NURSERY** ♿ ◆

A geographical code is followed by three or four letters reflecting the nursery's name

47 Towngate East, Market Deeping,
Peterborough, Lincolnshire, PE6 8LQ
Ⓣ 07432 627766
Ⓔ rareplants@me.com
Ⓦ www.swinesmeadowfarmnursery.co.uk
Contact: Colin Ward
Opening Times: 0900-1600 Mon-Sat, 1000-1600 Sun. Closed Jan-Feb except by appt. only.
Min Mail Order UK: £10.00
Min Mail Order EU: £10.00
Credit Cards: All major debit/credit cards except American Express
Specialities: Hardy exotics, tree ferns, bamboos & *Hostas*. Wollemi pine stockist. Many specialities available in small quantities only.
Notes: Delivers to shows. Wheelchair accessible.
OS Grid Ref: TF150113

A brief summary of the plants available

Other information about the nursery

The Ordnance Survey national grid reference for use with OS maps

2 NURSERY INDEX BY NAME

If you are looking for a particular nursery, use this alphabetical index to find it, note its code and then turn to the Nursery Details by Code listing for full information.

Sunnyside Nursery	LSun
Sussex Fruit Trees	SSFT
Swallows Nursery	MSwo
Swines Meadow Farm Nursery	ESwi
T. D. Thursfield	MThu
Taylors Clematis Nursery	**NTay**
Thorncroft Clematis Ltd	ETho
Thuya Alpine Nursery	WThu

How to Use the Nursery Listings

The details given for each nursery have been compiled from information supplied to us in answer to a questionnaire. In some case, because of space constraints, the entries have been abbreviated.

Nurseries are not charged for their entries and inclusion in no way implies a value judgement.

Nursery Details by Code (p.866)

Each nursery is allocated a code, for example GPoy. The first letter of each code indicates the region of the British Isles in which the nursery is situated. In this example G = Scotland. The remaining three or four letters reflect the nursery's name, in this case Poyntzfield Herb Nursery.

In this listing, nurseries are given in alphabetical order of code for quick referral from the Plant Directory. All of the nurseries' details, such as addresses, opening times, etc will be found in this index.

Opening Times

These are published as submitted. It is always advisable, especially if travelling a long distance, to double-check with the nursery before setting out.

Mail Order

Many nurseries offer a mail order service. This is often restricted to certain times of the year or to particular genera. Please check the **Notes** section of the nursery entry for restrictions or special conditions.

In some instances the mail order service extends throughout the European Union. Where this is the case, the minimum charge to the EU will be noted. If this is "Nmc" ("no minimum charge") please note that to send even one plant may involve the nursery in substantial postage and packaging costs. Some nurseries may not be prepared to send tender or bulky plants.

Where a nursery offers a mail order only service, this will be noted under **Opening Times** in the nursery entry. Many nurseries offer a mail order online service with some only operating in this way.

Export

This refers to mail order beyond the EU and indicates nurseries that are prepared to consider this. There is usually a substantial minimum charge and, in addition, all the costs of phytosanitary certificates and Customs have to be met by the purchaser.

Catalogue Cost

Only a small number of nurseries now offer a printed catalogue. Some may not charge or may ask for stamps to bear the cost of postage. If plant lists are available in an electronic format, some nurseries have indicated that they will email them to enquirers.

The majority of nurseries now publish their catalogues only on the internet as this is more cost-effective than producing a printed copy and enables them to reflect stock changes throughout the year.

Specialities

This is where nurseries list the plants or genera in which they specialise and any National Collections that they hold. Please note that some nurseries may charge an entry fee to visit a National Collection. Charges may also be levied to visit any garden to which the nursery is attached.

Nurseries also indicate here if they only have small quantities of individual plants available for sale or if they will propagate to order.

Notes

This section contains: information on restrictions to mail order or export; whether payment in euros is accepted; whether nurseries deliver to shows; details of partial wheelchair access; the nursery site address if this differs from the office address; and any other non-horticultural or general information.

Wheelchair Access ♿

Nurseries are asked to indicate if their premises are suitable for wheelchair users.

We use the wheelchair symbol for those nurseries that tell us their site is fully accessible. Where only partial or restricted access is offered, this is stated in the **Notes** section of the nursery's details and the nursery is not marked with the symbol.

Please note that wheelchair access does not necessarily relate to any gardens to which the nursery may be attached.

The assessment of ease of access is entirely the responsibility of the individual nursery.

Delivers to Shows

Many nurseries will deliver pre-ordered plants to flower shows for collection by customers. Contact the nursery for details of shows that they will be attending.

Payment in Euros

A number of UK nurseries will accept payment in euros. You should check with the nursery concerned before making such a payment, as some will only accept cash and some only cheques, whilst others will expect the purchaser to pay bank charges.

OS Grid Ref

Nurseries are also encouraged to provide their Ordnance Survey national grid reference for use with OS Land Ranger Series maps.

Nursery Index by Name

An alphabetical index of nurseries is included (p.950). Nurseries new to the book and those making a re-entry are shown in embolden type.

Deleted Nurseries

Every year some nurseries ask to be removed from the book. This may be a temporary measure because, for example, they are relocating or because their plant stocks are low due to adverse growing conditions, or it may be permanent following closure, sale, retirement or a change in the way they trade.

Some nurseries miss the deadline for submissions and may ask to re-enter the book in the following edition. Other nurseries do not respond at all and, as we have no current information on their trading status, they are not included in the book.

We recommend that you use the latest edition of the *RHS Plant Finder*

Nursery Details by Code

Please note that all these nurseries are listed in alphabetical order by their code. All nurseries are listed in alphabetical order by their name in the **Nursery Index by Name** on page 950.

South West

CAbb **Abbotsbury Sub-Tropical Gardens**
♿
Abbotsbury, Nr Weymouth, Dorset, DT3 4LA
Ⓣ (01305) 871344
Ⓕ (01305) 871344
Ⓔ info@abbotsburygardens.co.uk
Ⓦ www.abbotsbury-tourism.co.uk/gardens/
Contact: David Sutton
Opening Times: 1000-1800 daily, mid Mar-1st Nov. 1000-1500, Nov-mid Mar.
Credit Cards: Access, Visa, Mastercard, Switch
Specialities: Less common & tender shrubs incl. palms, tree ferns, bamboos & plants from Australia, New Zealand & S. Africa.
Notes: Mail order of some plants is possible upon request, please phone/email for details & a quotation. Wheelchair accessible.

CAco **Acorn Trees and Shrubs**
Hilltown Farm, Rackenford, Tiverton, Devon, EX16 8DX
Ⓣ (01884) 881633
Ⓜ 07976 807510
Ⓔ goakey101@gmail.com
Ⓦ www.acorntreesandshrubs.co.uk
Contact: Grahame Oakey
Opening Times: By appt. only.
Min Mail Order UK: £100.00
Min Mail Order EU: £150.00
Cat. Cost: Full plant listing available by email only.
Credit Cards: All major credit/debit cards
Specialities: Specialist in conifers, particularly long-needled varieties such as *Pinus montezumae* (several cvs), *holfordiana*, *schwerinii*, *pseodostrobus*, *palustris* & other short-needled varieties. Stock subject to availability.
Notes: Seedling to specimen sizes up to 35yrs old. Enviable collection of short-needled *Pinus parviflora* cvs. Also sell broadleaves and rhododendrons. The conifer collection is one of the most diverse for sale within the UK, with more than 500 species/cvs. Also sells wholesale. Wheelchair accessible (except toilet).
OS Grid Ref: SS852051

CAgr **Agroforestry Research Trust**
46 Hunters Moon, Dartington, Totnes, Devon, TQ9 6JT
Ⓣ (01803) 840776
Ⓕ (01803) 840776
Ⓔ mail@agroforestry.co.uk
Ⓦ www.agroforestry.co.uk
Contact: Martin Crawford
Opening Times: Not open. Mail order only.
Min Mail Order UK: Nmc
Min Mail Order EU: Nmc
Cat. Cost: 4 × 1st class.
Credit Cards: All major credit/debit cards
Specialities: Top & soft fruit, nut trees including *Castanea*, *Corylus*, *Juglans*, *Pinus*. Also seeds. Some plants in small quantities only.
Notes: Euro accepted.

CArg **Ashridge Nurseries**
Grove Cross Barn, Castle Cary, Somerset, BA7 7NJ
Ⓣ (01963) 359444
Ⓕ (01963) 359445
Ⓔ support@ashridgetrees.co.uk
Ⓦ www.ashridgetrees.co.uk
Contact: Rose Hurst
Opening Times: Not open. Mail order only.
Min Mail Order UK: £20.00
Credit Cards: MasterCard, Visa
Specialities: Trees, hedging. Fruit trees & soft fruit. Roses, lavender, climbers & bulbs.

CAvo **Avon Bulbs**
Burnt House Farm, Mid-Lambrook, South Petherton, Somerset, TA13 5HE
Ⓣ (01460) 242177/(01460) 249060

Ⓔ info@avonbulbs.co.uk
Ⓦ www.avonbulbs.co.uk
Contact: Chris Ireland-Jones
Opening Times: Mail order only.
Min Mail Order UK: Nmc
Min Mail Order EU: Nmc
Cat. Cost: 4 × 2nd class.
Credit Cards: All major credit/debit cards
Specialities: Specialise in named snowdrops, some are only available in small quantities, both 'in the green' in the spring, and as dormant bulbs in the early autumn.
Notes: Can deliver to some shows. A mail-order nursery but pre-booked orders can be collected by prior arrangement.
OS Grid Ref: ST422187

CBar **Barters Plant Centre & Nursery** ♿
Chapmanslade, Westbury, Wiltshire, BA13 4AL
Ⓣ (01373) 832694
Ⓕ (01373) 832677
Ⓔ plantcentre@barters.co.uk
Ⓦ www.barters.co.uk
Contact: Andrew Stone
Opening Times: 0900-1700 Mon-Sat, Mar-Oct. 0900-1630 Mon-Sat, Nov-Feb. 1000-1600 Sun (closed Sun Jul-Nov & Jan-Feb).
Cat. Cost: Online only.
Credit Cards: All major debit/credit cards except American Express
Specialities: Wide range of shrubs, herbaceous perennials, container trees, ferns, seasonal bedding plants, ornamental grasses & climbers. Hedging, fruit trees, roses & seasonal bare-root trees and native hedging plants.
Notes: Also sells wholesale. Wheelchair accessible.
OS Grid Ref: ST830480

CBcs **Burncoose Nurseries** ♿
Gwennap, Redruth, Cornwall, TR16 6BJ
Ⓣ (01209) 860316
Ⓔ info@burncoose.co.uk
Ⓦ www.burncoose.co.uk
Contact: C. H. Williams
Opening Times: 0830-1700 Mon-Sat & 1100-1600 Sun.
Min Mail Order UK: Nmc
Min Mail Order EU: Individual quotations for EU sales
Cat. Cost: Free.
Credit Cards: Visa, MasterCard, Maestro, American Express
Specialities: Extensive range of over 3500 ornamental trees & shrubs and herbaceous. Rare & unusual *Magnolia*, *Rhododendron*. Conservatory plants. 30 acre garden.
Notes: Also sells wholesale. Delivers to shows. Wheelchair accessible. Click and collect available. Many care articles and videos to be found on website.
OS Grid Ref: SW742395

CBct **Barracott Plants** ♿
Old Orchard, Calstock Road, Gunnislake, Cornwall, PL18 9AA
Ⓣ (01822) 832234
Ⓜ 07811 207186
Ⓔ gandt@barracottplants.co.uk
Ⓦ www.barracottplants.co.uk
Contact: Geoff & Thelma Turner
Opening Times: 0900-1700 Thu & Fri, Mar-end Sep. Other times by appt.
Min Mail Order UK: £20.00
Credit Cards: Paypal
Specialities: Herbaceous plants: shade-loving, foliage & form. *Acanthus*, *Aspidistra*, *Astrantia*, *Begonia*, *Bergenia*, *Convallaria*, *Disporum*, *Liriope*, *Maianthemum*, *Polygonatum*, *Roscoea*, *Schefflera*, *Trillium* & *Uvularia*.
Notes: Also sells wholesale. Delivers to shows. Euro accepted. Wheelchair accessible.
OS Grid Ref: SX436702

CBdn **Bowden Hostas**
Sales Office, Bowdens Nursery Ltd, Bowden Place, Sticklepath, Devon, EX20 2NL
Ⓣ (01837) 840989
Ⓔ sales@bowdenhostas.com/tim@bowdenhostas.com
Ⓦ www.bowdenhostas.com
Contact: Tim Penrose
Opening Times: 1000-1600 Mon-Sat, Apr-Sep. Oct-Mar, please ring before travelling.
Min Mail Order UK: Nmc
Min Mail Order EU: Nmc
Cat. Cost: Free.
Credit Cards: Visa, Access, EuroCard, Switch
Specialities: *Hosta*, ferns, bamboos, *Agapanthus*. National Plant Collection of Hostas (Halcyon and sports) and *Agapanthus* (Pine Cottage hybrids).
Notes: Also sells wholesale. Exports beyond EU.
OS Grid Ref: SX640940

CBee **Bee Happy Plants & Seeds**
Lakehayes Nursery, South Chard, Somerset, TA20 2NZ
Ⓣ (01460) 221929
Ⓜ 07976 949893
Ⓔ info@beehappyplants.co.uk
Ⓦ www.beehappyplants.co.uk/
Contact: Sarah Holdsworth
Opening Times: By appt. only.

C

Min Mail Order UK: Nmc
Min Mail Order EU: £10.00
Cat. Cost: Online only.
Credit Cards: All major credit/debit cards
Specialities: *Leptospermum scoparium.*
Notes: Specialist in wild species plants suitable for bees and other pollinators. Also sells wholesale. Delivers to shows.
OS Grid Ref: ST325550

CBen **BENNETTS WATER GARDENS** ♿
Putton Lane, Chickerell, Weymouth, Dorset, DT3 4AF
Ⓣ (01305) 785150
Ⓔ orders@waterlily.co.uk
Ⓦ www.shop.waterlily.co.uk
Contact: James Bennett
Opening Times: 1000-1600 Apr-Sep, Sun-Fri.
Min Mail Order UK: Nmc
Min Mail Order EU: Nmc
Credit Cards: Visa, MasterCard, JCB, Maestro
Specialities: National Plant Collection of *Nymphaea* (hardy water lilies).
Notes: Bare root plants available by mail order. Pre-potted plants available in store. Wheelchair accessible.
OS Grid Ref: SY650797

CBgR **BEGGAR'S ROOST PLANTS**
Lilstock, Bridgwater, Somerset, TA5 1SU
Ⓣ (01278) 741519
Ⓔ ro@lilstock.eclipse.co.uk
Contact: Lady Rosemary FitzGerald
Opening Times: Not open. Mail order only.
Min Mail Order UK: £10.00
Min Mail Order EU: £15.00
Cat. Cost: 3 × large 2nd class.
Credit Cards: None
Specialities: *Hemerocallis* (incl. heritage) grown in British conditions.
Notes: Mail order for speciality *Hemerocallis*. Ask for list. Euro accepted.
OS Grid Ref: ST168450

CBod **BODMIN NURSERY** ♿
Laveddon Mill, Laninval Hill, Bodmin, Cornwall, PL30 5JU
Ⓣ (01208) 72837
Ⓕ (01208) 76491
Ⓔ sales@bodminnursery.co.uk
Ⓦ www.bodminnursery.co.uk
Contact: Mark Lawlor
Opening Times: 0900-1700 Mon-Sat. 1000-1600 Sun.
Credit Cards: All major credit/debit cards
Specialities: Herbs, herbaceous & grasses, hardy geraniums & coastal plants. Interesting shrubs, fruit & ornamental trees.
Notes: Wheelchair accessible.
OS Grid Ref: SX053659

CBor **BORDER ALPINES**
Chasty Court, Chasty, Holsworthy, Devon, EX22 6NA
Ⓣ (01409) 253654
Ⓜ 07841 021557
Ⓔ borderalpines@btinternet.com
Ⓦ www.borderalpines.co.uk
Contact: Janette Lowe
Opening Times: By appt. only
Min Mail Order UK: Nmc
Min Mail Order EU: Nmc
Cat. Cost: Online only.
Credit Cards: None
Specialities: Alpines, dwarf herbaceous & specimen acers. A family-run nursery, selling a range of British-grown alpines, dwarf herbaceous and other hardy perennial plants. Experienced growers and breeders for over 30 years.
Notes: Delivers to shows.

CBrac **BRACKENDALE NURSERIES** ♿
Horton Road, Three Legged Cross, Wimborne, Dorset, BH21 6SD
Ⓣ (01202) 822349
Ⓔ info@brackendalenurseries.co.uk
Ⓦ www.brackendalenurseries.co.uk
Contact: Nicola Stainer
Opening Times: Opening times are subject to seasonal change, please see our website for current opening hours.
Credit Cards: All major credit/debit cards
Specialities: Wide range of plants, especially shrubs, conifers and hedging. Established specimen-sized shrubs and native, ornamental and fruit trees available. Acid loving *Azalea*, *Camellia* & *Rhododendron* together with coastal favourites.
Notes: Wheelchair accessible.

CBro **BROADLEIGH GARDENS** ♿
Bishops Hull, Taunton, Somerset, TA4 1AE
Ⓣ (01823) 286231
Ⓔ info@broadleighbulbs.co.uk
Ⓦ www.broadleighbulbs.co.uk
Contact: Christine Skelmesdale
Opening Times: 0900-1600 Mon-Fri for viewing only (charity donation). Orders may be collected if notice given.
Min Mail Order UK: Nmc
Min Mail Order EU: Nmc
Cat. Cost: 2 × 1st class.
Credit Cards: All major credit/debit cards
Specialities: Jan catalogue for bulbs in growth & herbaceous woodland plants. Extensive list

of *Agapanthus* and other South African bulbs. June: dwarf & unusual bulbs. National Plant Collection of Alec Grey hybrid daffodils.
Notes: Display garden and nursery open. Euro accepted as cash payment only. Wheelchair accessible.
OS Grid Ref: ST195251

CBrP **Brooklands Plants**
25 Treves Road, Dorchester, Dorset, DT1 2HE
Ⓣ (01305) 265846
Ⓔ cycads@btinternet.com
Ⓦ http://www.botanicalgardenphotography.com/brooklands-plants.html
Contact: Ian Watt
Opening Times: By appt. only for collection of plants.
Min Mail Order UK: £50.00 + p&p
Cat. Cost: Online only.
Credit Cards: None
Specialities: *Encephalartos, Dioon, Macrozamia* & *Cycas.*
Notes: Fern and Cycad nursery that also specialises in hardy palms, unusual conifers, plants from New Zealand and plants for the terrarium, including mosses. Generally only small/young specimens available. Some species available in small quantites only. Mail order available on small plants only. Euro accepted.
OS Grid Ref: SY682897

CCal **Calamazag Nursery**
St Martins, Looe, Cornwall, PL13 1NX
Ⓜ 07958 167096
Ⓔ calamazagnursery@gmail.com
Ⓦ www.calamazagnursery.co.uk
Contact: Stephen & Benedicte Jenkinson
Opening Times: Not open, mail order only.
Min Mail Order UK: £5.00
Min Mail Order EU: £15.00
Cat. Cost: Online only.
Credit Cards: All major credit/debit cards
Specialities: Wide range of hardy *Dianthus* including Heritage and Species varieties. Wide selection of hardy *Sempervivum*. Plants sold in 10.5cm pots ready to be grown on. (Pls note these are NOT plug plants and cannot be planted directly outside).

CCBP **CB Plants**
Lower Severalls Nursery, Crewkerne, Somerset, TA18 7NX
Ⓜ 07851 468430
Ⓔ cbplantsinfo@gmail.com
Ⓦ www.cbplants.co.uk
Contact: Catherine Bond
Opening Times: 1000-1700 Wed-Sat. Early Mar-End Sept.
Min Mail Order UK: £5.00 + p&p
Credit Cards: All major debit/credit cards except American Express
Specialities: Nectar-rich hardy perennials herbs and wild flowers all grown peat-free. Available in small quantities only.
Notes: Small nursery situated just off the A30, half a mile east of Crewkerne.

CCCN **Cross Common Nursery**
The Lizard, Helston, Cornwall, TR12 7PD
Ⓣ (01326) 290722/290668
Ⓔ info@crosscommonnursery.co.uk
Ⓦ www.crosscommonnursery.co.uk
Contact: Kevin Bosustow
Opening Times: 1000-1700 7 days, Apr, May & Jun. Reduced hours Mar, Jul, Aug & Sep, please phone for opening times.
Min Mail Order UK: Nmc
Cat. Cost: Online only.
Credit Cards: All major debit/credit cards except American Express
Specialities: Tropical/sub-tropical, coastal plants & conservatory plants. Wide range of citrus trees.
Notes: The most southerly nursery in England, offering a wide range of unusual plants & shrubs. Some plants available in small quantities only.
OS Grid Ref: SW704116

CChe **Cherry Tree Nursery** ♿
(Sheltered Work Opportunities Project), off New Road Roundabout, Northbourne, Bournemouth, Dorset, BH10 7DA
Ⓣ (01202) 593537
Ⓔ contactus@cherrytreenursery.org.uk
Ⓦ www.cherrytreenursery.org.uk
Contact: Stephen Jailler
Opening Times: 0830-1530 Mon-Fri, 0900-1500 Sat, Apr-Sep & 0900-1300 Sat, Oct-Mar. 1000-1500 Sun, Mar-Oct.
Credit Cards: All major debit/credit cards except American Express
Specialities: Hardy shrubs, perennials, climbers, grasses & bamboos.
Notes: A registered charity providing work for adults with severe and enduring mental illness. Also sells wholesale. Wheelchair accessible.
OS Grid Ref: SZ083965

CCht **Chestnut Nursery** ♿
(Sheltered Work Opportunities Project)
75 Kingland Road, Poole, Dorset, BH15 1TN
Ⓣ (01202) 685999
Ⓔ info@chestnutnursery.org.uk

C

Ⓦ www.chestnutnursery.org.uk
Contact: Andrew Verreck
Opening Times: 0800-1600 Mon-Fri. 1000-1600 Sat (Mar-Nov) & 1000-1500 Sat (Nov-Xmas). 1000-1500 Sun (Mar-Sep).
Credit Cards: All major credit/debit cards
Specialities: Wide selection of herbaceous perennials, evergreen shrubs, ornamental grasses, annual bedding and southern hemisphere exotics.
Notes: A registered charity providing work for adults with severe and enduring mental illness. Wheelchair accessible.
OS Grid Ref: SZ018909

CCoa **Coastal Hedging**
Marsh Lane Nursery, West Charleton, Kingsbridge, Devon, TQ7 2AQ
Ⓣ (01548) 531734
Ⓜ 07775 201 595
Ⓔ info@coastalhedging.co.uk
Ⓦ www.coastalhedging.co.uk
Contact: William Hornby
Opening Times: By appt. only
Min Mail Order UK: £6.95
Cat. Cost: Online only.
Credit Cards: All major credit/debit cards
Specialities: *Griselina*, *Elaeagnus*, *Olearia*.
Notes: Euro accepted.
OS Grid Ref: SX752425

CCVT **Chew Valley Trees Ltd** ♿
Chew Road, Winford, Bristol, BS40 8HJ
Ⓣ (01275) 333752
Ⓔ simon@chewvalleytrees.co.uk
Ⓦ www.chewvalleytrees.co.uk
Contact: Wendy Downer
Opening Times: 0800-1700 Mon-Fri all year. 0800-1630 Sat. Closed Sun. Closed B/hols & Sat Jul & Aug.
Min Mail Order UK: Nmc
Cat. Cost: Free.
Credit Cards: All major credit/debit cards
Specialities: Native British & ornamental trees, shrubs, fruit trees & hedging.
Notes: Also sells wholesale. Wheelchair accessible.
OS Grid Ref: ST558635

CDoC **Duchy of Cornwall**
Cott Road, Lostwithiel, Cornwall, PL22 0HW
Ⓣ (01208) 872668
Ⓕ (01208) 871809
Ⓔ sales@duchyofcornwallnursery.co.uk
Ⓦ www.duchyofcornwallnursery.co.uk
Contact: Nicky Hill
Opening Times: 0900-1700 Mon-Sat, 1000-1700 Sun.
Credit Cards: All major credit/debit cards
Specialities: Large range of garden plants including trees, shrubs, roses, perennials, fruit and conservatory plants.
Notes: Nursery partially accessible to wheelchair users.
OS Grid Ref: SX112614

CDor **Dorset Perennials**
Berkeley Perennials, Holnest, Sherborne, Dorset, DT9 5PR
Ⓣ (01963) 210643
Ⓕ (01963) 210643
Ⓔ sales@dorsetperennials.co.uk
Ⓦ www.dorsetperennials.co.uk
Contact: Dawn & Martin Preston
Opening Times: Open for collections only. Please check with nursery first.
Min Mail Order UK: Nmc
Cat. Cost: Online only.
Credit Cards: All major credit/debit cards
Specialities: An eclectic mix of hardy perennials grown. Plants for herbaceous borders & cottage gardens with a good mix of oddities to tempt the discerning.
Notes: All plants available via website. Delivers to shows.
OS Grid Ref: ST662090

CDow **Downside Nurseries** ♿
143 Upper Westwood, Bradford-on-Avon, Wiltshire, BA15 2DE
Ⓣ (01225) 862392
Ⓕ (01225) 862392
Ⓔ info@downsidenurseries.co.uk
Ⓦ www.downsidenurseries.co.uk
Contact: Lorraine Young
Opening Times: 0900-1700 7 days.
Cat. Cost: Not available.
Credit Cards: All major credit/debit cards
Specialities: Herbaceous perennials, also shrubs, roses, trees & seasonal bedding.
Notes: Traditional family-run retail working nursery set over three acres. Unrivalled choice of quality plants, trees and bedding stock, much of which is grown on site. Wheelchair accessible. Local delivery available on request.
OS Grid Ref: ST805104

CDTJ **Desert to Jungle** ♿
Henlade Garden Nursery, Lower Henlade, Taunton, Somerset, TA3 5NB
Ⓣ (01823) 443701
Ⓜ 07969 652547
Ⓔ plants@deserttojungle.com
Ⓦ www.deserttojungle.com
Contact: Rob Gudge
Opening Times: 1000-1700 Mon, Tue &

Thu-Sun (closed Wed), 1st Mar-31st Oct. Thu, Fri & Sat only Nov-Feb. Opening times may vary during RHS shows, so please phone to check.
Min Mail Order UK: Nmc
Cat. Cost: Online only.
Credit Cards: All major credit/debit cards
Specialities: Exotic-looking plants giving a desert or jungle effect in the garden. Incl. *Agave*, *Canna*, aroids, succulents, ferns, tree ferns & bamboos.
Notes: Nursery shares drive with Mount Somerset Hotel. Also sells wholesale. Delivers to shows. Wheelchair accessible.
OS Grid Ref: ST273232

CEls **Elsworth Herbs**
Farthingwood, Broadway, Sidmouth, Devon, EX10 8HS
Ⓣ (01395) 578689
Ⓔ john.twibell@btinternet.com
Contact: Drs J. D. & J. M. Twibell
Opening Times: By appt. only.
Min Mail Order UK: £10.00
Cat. Cost: By email only.
Credit Cards: None
Specialities: National Plant Collection (Scientific & Reference) of *Artemisia*. Stock available in small quantities only. Orders may require propagation from Collection material, for which we are the primary reference source. Native coastal plants
Notes: Mail order only on small scale in exceptional circumstances. Partially accessible for wheelchairs.
OS Grid Ref: SY119881

CElw **Elworthy Cottage Plants** ♿
Elworthy Cottage, Elworthy, Nr Lydeard St Lawrence, Taunton, Somerset, TA4 3PX
Ⓣ (01984) 656427
Ⓔ mike@elworthy-cottage.co.uk
Ⓦ www.elworthy-cottage.co.uk
Contact: Mrs J. M. Spiller
Opening Times: By appt. only Apr-Sept & Feb for Galanthus. Open for NGS days.
Credit Cards: None
Specialities: Unusual herbaceous plants esp. *Galanthus*, hardy *Geranium*, *Geum*, *Crocosmia*, *Epimedium*, *Monarda*, *Pulmonaria* & *Viola*. Some varieties only available in small quantities. *Galanthus* available by mail order in Feb.
Notes: Nursery on B3188, 5 miles north of Wiveliscombe, in centre of Elworthy village. Delivers to shows. Wheelchair accessible. Mail order for Galanthus only.
OS Grid Ref: ST084349

CEme **Emerald Plants**
85 Regal Walk, Bridgwater, Somerset, TA6 4FL
Ⓜ 07909 118470
Ⓔ sales@emeraldplants.co.uk
Ⓦ http://www.emeraldplants.co.uk/
Contact: Olly
Opening Times: Not open, mail order only
Credit Cards: All major credit/debit cards
Specialities: Shrubs, perennials, bamboos, conifers, ferns, climbers and more.
Notes: Large range of garden plants available to order 24hrs a day from our online garden centre, including over 1000 varieties in stock online at any given time. Also sells wholesale.

CEnd **Endsleigh Gardens Nursery**
Milton Abbot, Tavistock, Devon, PL19 0PG
Ⓣ (01822) 870235
Ⓕ (01822) 870513
Ⓔ info@endsleigh-gardens.com
Ⓦ www.endsleighgardens.co.uk
Contact: Adrian Steele
Opening Times: 0800-1700 Mon-Sat. 1000-1600 Sun.
Min Mail Order UK: Nmc
Credit Cards: Visa, Access, Switch, MasterCard
Specialities: Choice & unusual trees & shrubs incl. *Acer*, alpines, bamboos, climbers, conifers, *Cornus*, heathers, old apple & cherry varieties, *Rosa*, *Wisteria*. Grafting service. Modern fruit trees, soft fruit and good selection of perennials.
Notes: Wheelchair accessible (but no disabled toilets).
OS Grid Ref: SX398780

CExl **Exclusive Plants Nursery**
Tretawn, High Cross, Constantine, Falmouth, Cornwall, TR11 5RE
Ⓣ (01326) 341496
Ⓜ 07775 811385
Ⓕ (01326) 341496
Ⓔ info@exclusiveplants.com
Ⓦ www.exclusiveplants.com
Contact: Paul Bonavia
Opening Times: W/ends or by appt. only.
Min Mail Order UK: Nmc
Min Mail Order EU: £25.00
Cat. Cost: 2 × 1st class.
Credit Cards: All major credit/debit cards
Specialities: A plantsperson's nursery, offering rare & unusual plants from around the world. Also new introductions & the best forms of our better known plants.
Notes: Euro accepted.
OS Grid Ref: SW175131

C

CFis **MARGERY FISH PLANT NURSERY**
East Lambrook Manor Gardens, Silver Street, East Lambrook, South Petherton, Somerset, TA13 5HH
Ⓣ (01460) 240328
Ⓜ 07710 484745
Ⓔ enquiries@eastlambrook.com
Ⓦ www.eastlambrook.com
Contact: Ellie Hanscomb
Opening Times: 1000-1700 Tue-Sat, Feb-Oct, plus B/hol Mons & Sun Feb, May-Jul. Nov-Jan by appt.
Credit Cards: All major credit/debit cards
Specialities: Cottage garden plants and interesting perennials including hardy *Geranium*, snowdrops and plants propagated from East Lambrook Manor Gardens. Stock available in small quantities only. Major collection of hardy geraniums in garden.
Notes: Partial wheelchair access.
OS Grid Ref: ST431188

CFoA **FORDE ABBEY NURSERY** ♿
Forde Abbey, Chard, Somerset, TA20 4LU
Ⓣ (01460) 220231
Ⓔ info@fordeabbey.co.uk
Ⓦ www.fordeabbey.co.uk
Contact: Tom Wild
Opening Times: 1000-1700 1st Mar-31st Oct 7 days
Credit Cards: All major debit/credit cards except American Express
Specialities: Many unusual perennials.
Notes: Wheelchair accessible

CFoP **FOXPLANTS** ♿
2 Old Park Cottages, Woodbury Lane, Devon, Axminster, Devon, EX13 5TL
Ⓜ 07928 805985
Ⓔ jo_fox2@hotmail.com
Ⓦ www.foxplants.com
Contact: Jo Fox
Opening Times: See website.
Min Mail Order UK: £20.00
Cat. Cost: Online only.
Specialities: Independant nursery specialising in *Salvia* and unusual herbaceous perennials.
Notes: All salvias grown by Foxplants are from seed or cuttings collected by reputable plant finders and enthusiasts. Also sells wholesale. Delivers to shows. Wheelchair accessible.

CFst **FOREST EDGE NURSERIES (THE HEATHER GARDEN)**
Verwood Road, Woodlands, Wimborne, Dorset, BH21 8LJ
Ⓣ (01202) 824387
Ⓕ (01202) 829564
Ⓔ info@theheathergarden.co.uk
Ⓦ www.theheathergarden.co.uk
Contact: David Edge
Opening Times: 0900-1630 Mon. Collection available by arrangement on other days.
Min Mail Order UK: £8.95
Cat. Cost: £2.00.
Credit Cards: Paypal
Specialities: Heathers incl. *Calluna, Erica, Daboecia.*
Notes: Also sells wholesale. Euro accepted.

CGrG **GRACELANDS GARDEN**
443 Fishponds Road, Fishponds, Bristol, BS16 3AP
Ⓣ 07508 649863
Ⓔ info@gracelandsgarden.garden
Ⓦ https://www.gracelands.garden
Contact: Tim Barton
Opening Times: By appt. only
Min Mail Order UK: £4.99
Credit Cards: MasterCard, Visa
Notes: Micro-nursery

CGro **C W GROVES & SON LTD** ♿
West Bay Road, Bridport, Dorset, DT6 4BA
Ⓣ (01308) 422654
Ⓔ garden@grovesnurseries.co.uk :becky@grovesnurseries.co.uk
Ⓦ www.grovesnurseries.co.uk
Contact: Becky Groves
Opening Times: 0800-1700 Mon-Sat, 10.00-16.00 Sun.
Min Mail Order UK: Nmc
Min Mail Order EU: £15.00 + p&p
Cat. Cost: Free.
Credit Cards: Visa, Switch, MasterCard
Specialities: Established in 1866, a family run garden centre with nursery on site specialising in *Viola odorata*, Parma violets & roses.
Notes: Mainly violets, roses, herbs, soft fruit & grapevines by mail order. Main violet display at nursery in Feb, Mar & Apr. Will export violet seeds only beyond EU. Wheelchair accessible.
OS Grid Ref: SY466918

CHab **HABITAT AID LTD**
Hookgate Cottage, South Brewham, Somerset, BA10 0LQ
Ⓣ (01749) 812355
Ⓔ info@habitataid.co.uk
Ⓦ www.habitataid.co.uk
Contact: Nick Mann
Opening Times: Not open. Mail order only.
Min Mail Order UK: £50.00, incl. p&p
Credit Cards: All major credit/debit cards
Specialities: British trees, wildflowers and

C

seeds. Local provenance seed mixes. Native aquatic plants. Ornamental trees for bees. Heritage fruit trees.
Notes: Also sells wholesale. Delivers to shows.

CHby **The Herbary**
161 Chapel Street, Horningsham, Warminster, Wiltshire, BA12 7LU
Ⓣ (01985) 844442
Ⓔ info@beansandherbs.co.uk
Ⓦ www.beansandherbs.co.uk
Contact: Pippa Rosen
Opening Times: May-Sep strictly by appt. only.
Min Mail Order UK: Nmc
Min Mail Order EU: Nmc
Cat. Cost: Online only.
Credit Cards: None
Specialities: Culinary, medicinal & aromatic herbs organically grown in small quantities.
Notes: Mail order for seed only. All year for organic vegetable, flower, bean & herb seed. Also sells wholesale.
OS Grid Ref: ST812414

CHew **Hewitt-Cooper Carnivorous Plants**
The Homestead, Glastonbury Road, West Pennard, Somerset, BA6 8NN
Ⓜ 07702 190518
Ⓔ sales@hccarnivorousplants.co.uk
Ⓦ www.hccarnivorousplants.co.uk
Contact: Nigel Hewitt-Cooper
Opening Times: Not open.
Min Mail Order UK: Nmc
Min Mail Order EU: Nmc
Cat. Cost: Online only.
Credit Cards: All major credit/debit cards
Specialities: Carnivorous plants.
Notes: Mail order all year. Euro accepted. Delivers to shows.

CHVG **Hidden Valley Gardens** ♿
Treesmill, Par, Cornwall, PL24 2TU
Ⓣ (01208) 873225
Ⓜ 07966 230222
Ⓔ hiddenvalleygardens@yahoo.co.uk
Ⓦ www.hiddenvalleygardens.co.uk
Contact: Tricia Howard
Opening Times: 1000-1800 Thu-Mon (closed Tue & Wed), 20th Mar-15th Oct.
Credit Cards: All major debit/credit cards except American Express
Specialities: Cottage garden plants, *Dahlia* & many perennials which can be seen growing in the garden.
Notes: Some stock available in small quantities only. Display garden (opening times same as nursery). Please phone for directions. Euro accepted. Wheelchair accessible.
OS Grid Ref: SX094567

CJun **Junker's Nursery**
Higher Cobhay, Milverton, Somerset, TA4 1NJ
Ⓣ (01823) 400075
Ⓔ karan@junker.co.uk
Ⓦ www.junker.co.uk
Contact: Karan Junker
Opening Times: Strictly by appt. only. Email nursery for directions (do not rely on Sat Nav).
Min Mail Order UK: Nmc
Min Mail Order EU: Nmc
Cat. Cost: Free list available by email.
Credit Cards: None
Specialities: Unusual shrubs & trees incl. *Acer palmatum*, *Betula*, *Cornus*, *Daphne*, *Magnolia*, deciduous *Euonymus*, *Ilex*, *Liquidambar* & *Parrotia* cvs. Mature plants available. Small quantities only of some hard to propagate plants, esp. daphnes.
Notes: Extensive planted areas show how the plants look growing in "real world" conditions. Propagate & grow all own plants. Increasing number grown naturally in open ground, incl. larger sizes and younger plants in pots. Limited wheelchair access.

CKel **Kelways Plants Ltd** ♿
Barrymore Farm, Picts Hill, Langport, Somerset, TA10 9EZ
Ⓣ (01458) 250521
Ⓜ 07515 525230
Ⓔ sales@kelways.co.uk
Ⓦ www.kelways.co.uk
Contact: Andy Martin
Opening Times: 0900-1700 Mon-Sat, 0930-1600 Sun.
Min Mail Order UK: Nmc
Cat. Cost: Online only.
Credit Cards: Paypal
Specialities: *Paeonia*, *Iris*, *Rosa*, *Clematis*, *Dicksonia*, *Cyathea*, tree ferns, herbaceous perennials & shrubs.
Notes: Contract growing & plant sourcing service. Coffee Shop. Also sells wholesale. Euro accepted. Wheelchair accessible.
OS Grid Ref: ST434273

CKen **Kenwith Conifer Nursery (Gordon Haddow)** ♿
Blinsham, Off A3124 only, Beaford, Winkleigh, Devon, EX19 8NT
Ⓣ (01805) 603274
Ⓔ info@kenwithconifernursery.co.uk
Ⓦ www.kenwithconifernursery.co.uk

C

Contact: Gordon Haddow
Opening Times: 1000-1630 Tue-Sat all year. Closed all B/hols. If travelling a long distance, please phone previous day to ensure nursery will be open.
Min Mail Order UK: £20 + p&p
Cat. Cost: Online only.
Credit Cards: Visa, MasterCard
Specialities: All conifer genera. Grafting a speciality.
Notes: Wheelchair accessible.
OS Grid Ref: SS518160

CKno **Knoll Gardens** ♿
Hampreston, Wimborne, Dorset, BH21 7ND
Ⓣ (01202) 873931
Ⓕ (01202) 870842
Ⓔ enquiries@knollgardens.co.uk
Ⓦ www.knollgardens.co.uk
Contact: N. R. Lucas
Opening Times: 1000-1700 Tue-Sat, Feb-Dec. Open B/hol Mons. See website.
Min Mail Order UK: Nmc
Min Mail Order EU: Nmc
Cat. Cost: None.
Credit Cards: Visa, MasterCard
Specialities: Grasses (main specialism). Flowering perennials. National Plant Collection of *Pennisetum*.
Notes: Also sells wholesale. Wheelchair accessible.

CLAP **Long Acre Plants** ♿
South Marsh, Charlton Musgrove, Wincanton, Somerset, BA9 8EX
Ⓣ (01963) 32802
Ⓕ (01963) 32802
Ⓔ info@longacreplants.co.uk
Ⓦ www.plantsforshade.co.uk
Contact: Nigel Rowland
Opening Times: By appt. only.
Min Mail Order UK: £12.00 + p&p
Min Mail Order EU: £30
Cat. Cost: Catalogue available online.
Credit Cards: MasterCard, Visa, Maestro
Specialities: Ferns, woodland bulbs & perennials. Marginal/bog plants. Specialise in plants for shade, carrying a wide range of unusual and tough shade tolerant perennials and ferns.
Notes: Mail order online. Wheelchair accessible. Delivers to shows.

CLau **The Edible Garden Nursery**
Moorland Barn, Whiddon Down, Okehampton, Devon, EX20 2QL
Ⓣ (01647) 400301
Ⓜ 07905 518666
Ⓔ ediblegardennursery@gmail.com
Ⓦ www.theediblegardennursery.co.uk
Contact: Chris Seagon
Opening Times: 1000-1700 Apr-Oct.
Min Mail Order UK: £9.95
Cat. Cost: Online only.
Credit Cards: All major credit/debit cards, Paypal
Specialities: Edible plants.
Notes: Everything grown is edible in some way. All plants are peat, chemical and pesticide free. Also sells wholesale. Delivers to shows (payment in advance).

CLnd **Landford Trees**
Landford Lodge, Landford, Salisbury, Wiltshire, SP5 2EH
Ⓣ (01794) 390808
Ⓔ trees@landfordtrees.co.uk
Ⓦ www.landfordtrees.co.uk
Contact: C. D. Pilkington
Opening Times: 0800-1700 Mon-Thu, 0800-1530 Fri.
Cat. Cost: Free.
Credit Cards: All major debit/credit cards except American Express
Specialities: Deciduous ornamental trees.
Notes: Also sells wholesale.
OS Grid Ref: SU247201

CLoc **C S Lockyer (Fuchsias)** ◆
Lansbury, 70 Henfield Road, Coalpit Heath, Bristol, BS36 2UZ
Ⓣ (01454) 772219
Ⓕ (01454) 772219
Ⓔ mary@lockyerfuchsias.co.uk
Ⓦ www.lockyerfuchsias.co.uk
Contact: Mary Lockyer
Opening Times: 1000-1300, 1430-1700 most days, please telephone first.
Min Mail Order UK: 6 plants + p&p
Min Mail Order EU: £12.00 + p&p
Cat. Cost: 4 × 1st class or online.
Credit Cards: All major credit/debit cards
Specialities: *Fuchsia*.
Notes: Many open days & coach parties. Also sells wholesale. Exports beyond EU. Euro accepted. Delivers to shows. Partial wheelchair access.

CMac **Mac Pennys Nurseries**
154 Burley Road, Bransgore, Christchurch, Dorset, BH23 8DB
Ⓣ (01425) 672348
Ⓔ office@macpennys.co.uk
Ⓦ www.macpennys.co.uk
Contact: T. & V. Lowndes & S. Lowndes
Opening Times: 0900-1700 Mon-Sat, 1000-

1700 Sun & B/hols. Closed Xmas to New Year.
Min Mail Order UK: Nmc
Cat. Cost: A4 sae with 4 × 1st class.
Credit Cards: All major debit/credit cards except American Express
Specialities: Wide range of plants, available in small quantities only.
Notes: Mail order available Oct-Feb incl. UK only. Also sells wholesale. Nursery partially accessible for wheelchairs.

CMCN **MALLET COURT NURSERY** ♿
Marshway, Curry Mallet, Taunton, Somerset, TA3 6SZ
Ⓣ (01823) 481493
Ⓜ 07713 091521
Ⓕ (01823) 481009
Ⓔ malletcourtnursery@btinternet.com
Ⓦ www.malletcourt.co.uk
Contact: J. G. S. & P. M. E. Harris F.L.S.
Opening Times: 0930-1700 Mon-Fri summer, 0930-1600 winter. Sat & Sun by appt.
Min Mail Order UK: Nmc
Min Mail Order EU: Nmc
Cat. Cost: £1.50.
Credit Cards: All major credit/debit cards
Specialities: Maples, oaks, *Magnolia*, hollies & other rare and unusual plants including those from China & South Korea.
Notes: Mail order throughout the year. Also sells wholesale. Exports beyond EU. Euro accepted. Wheelchair accessible.

CMea **THE MEAD NURSERY** ♿
Brokerswood, Nr Westbury, Wiltshire, BA13 4EG
Ⓣ (01373) 859990
Ⓔ info@themeadnursery.co.uk
Ⓦ www.themeadnursery.co.uk
Contact: Steve & Emma Lewis-Dale
Opening Times: 0900-1700 Wed-Sat & B/hol Mons, 1200-1700 Sun, 1st Feb-10th Oct. Closed Easter Sun.
Cat. Cost: 4 × 2nd class.
Credit Cards: All major credit/debit cards
Specialities: Perennials, alpines, pot-grown bulbs and grasses.
Notes: Wheelchair accessible.
OS Grid Ref: ST833517

CMen **MENDIP BONSAI STUDIO**
Byways, Back Lane, Downside, Shepton Mallet, Somerset, BA4 4JR
Ⓣ (01749) 344274
Ⓜ 07711 205806
Ⓔ john@mendipbonsai.co.uk
Ⓦ www.mendipbonsai.co.uk
Contact: John Trott
Opening Times: By appt. only. Mail order Oct-Mar.
Min Mail Order UK: £15.00
Cat. Cost: Workshop lists available.
Credit Cards: All major credit/debit cards
Specialities: Bonsai, potensai. Many plants available in small numbers only. Can propagate to order. Young trees for garden or bonsai culture. Many rare & unusual ferns from Japan for 'accent' use and gardens (very limited numbers).
Notes: Talks & lectures on bonsai. Stockist of most bonsai pots, related bonsai sundries & large range of bronze figurines. Mail orders despatched late Mar-early Apr, late Sep-Oct. Delivers to shows by arrangement.

CMHG **MARWOOD HILL GARDENS** ♿
Marwood, Barnstaple, Devon, EX31 4EB
Ⓣ (01271) 342528
Ⓕ (01271) 342528
Ⓔ info@marwoodhillgarden.co.uk
Ⓦ www.marwoodhillgarden.co.uk
Contact: Mrs P. Stout
Opening Times: 1100-1630 7 days. Closed Nov-Mar.
Min Mail Order UK: £15.00 + p&p
Cat. Cost: Please see website.
Credit Cards: All major credit/debit cards
Specialities: National Collection of *Astilbe*. Large range always in stock.
Notes: Mail order for *Astilbe* only. Wheelchair accessible.
OS Grid Ref: SS545375

CMil **MILL COTTAGE PLANTS** ♿
Henley Mill, Henley Lane, Wookey, Somerset, BA5 1AW
Ⓣ (01749) 676966
Ⓜ 07851 698759
Ⓔ millcottageplants@gmail.com
Ⓦ www.millcottageplants.co.uk
Contact: Sally Gregson
Opening Times: By appt. only.
Min Mail Order UK: Nmc
Min Mail Order EU: £25.00 + p&p
Cat. Cost: Online only.
Credit Cards: All major credit/debit cards
Specialities: Rare *Hydrangea serrata* cvs, *H. aspera* cvs, *Epimedium*, shade & damp-loving plants.
Notes: Please telephone for directions. Euro accepted. Wheelchair accessible.

CMiW **MILLWOOD PLANTS**
Millwoods, Colleton Mills, Umberleigh, Nr Chulmleigh, Devon, EX37 9ET

Ⓜ 07756 515084
Ⓔ millwoodplants@mail.com
Ⓦ www.millwoodplants.com
Contact: Gary Buckingham
Opening Times: 1000-1700 Mon-Thu Mar-Sept
Specialities: Hardy herbaceous perennials for woodland gardens and shade. Old fashioned roses.
Notes: Hardy, unusual & authentic plants. Traditional propagation methods retain colour, size & hardiness. Exhibits at shows all year. See website for details. Nursery postcode for Sat Nav is EX37 9ES. Delivers to shows.
OS Grid Ref: SS65882

CNat **Natural Selection**
1 Station Cottages, Hullavington, Chippenham, Wiltshire, SN14 6ET
Ⓜ 07800 583999
Ⓔ martin@worldmutation.demon.co.uk
Contact: Martin Barber
Opening Times: Please phone for details
Min Mail Order UK: £9.00 + p&p
Min Mail Order EU: Nmc
Cat. Cost: 1 × 2nd class.
Credit Cards: None
Specialities: Unusual British natives & others. Also seed. Only available in small quantities.
Notes: Euro accepted.

CNMi **Newport Mills Nursery**
Wrantage, Taunton, Somerset, TA3 6DJ
Ⓣ (01823) 490231
Ⓔ john@newportmillsnursery.net
Ⓦ www.newportmillsnursery.net
Contact: John Barrington
Opening Times: Not open. Mail order only.
Min Mail Order UK: Nmc free p&p
Min Mail Order EU: Nmc EU postal rate per order
Cat. Cost: Free.
Credit Cards: All major credit/debit cards
Specialities: *Delphinium elatum* hybrids. English scented perpetual flowering carnations. *Dianthus*. Pinks: Exhibition, Modern & Old World.
Notes: Mail order Apr-Sep for young delphiniums in 7cm pots. Euro accepted.
OS Grid Ref: ST318234

CNor **Northbrook Nursery** ♿
47 Northbrook Road, Broadstone, Dorset, BH18 8HD
Ⓣ (01202) 695256
Ⓔ marg@northbrooknursery.co.uk
Ⓦ www.northbrooknursery.co.uk
Contact: Margaret Bailey
Opening Times: 1000-1600 Thu & Fri end Apr-end Sept.
Min Mail Order UK: Nmc
Credit Cards: Paypal
Specialities: Perennials. Plants available in small quantities only.
Notes: Delivers to shows. Wheelchair accessible.
OS Grid Ref: SZ001947

CPar **Parks Perennials**
242 Wallisdown Road, Wallisdown, Bournemouth, Dorset, BH10 4HZ
Ⓣ (01202) 524464
Ⓜ 07977 878546
Ⓔ parks.perennials@ntlworld.com
Contact: S. Parks
Opening Times: Apr-Oct most days, please telephone first.
Credit Cards: All major credit/debit cards
Specialities: Hardy herbaceous perennials.
Notes: Delivers to shows.

CPbh **Penberth Plants**
St Buryan, Penzance, Cornwall, TR19 6HJ
Ⓣ (01736) 810978
Ⓔ info@penberthplants.co.uk
Ⓦ www.penberthplants.co.uk
Contact: Jeff Rowe
Opening Times: Not open. Mail order.
Min Mail Order UK: Nmc
Min Mail Order EU: Nmc
Cat. Cost: Online only.
Credit Cards: All major credit/debit cards
Specialities: *Protea*, *Restio*, succulents and other unusual plants.
Notes: Sells at RHS shows. Open days throughout the year, check website or contact nursery for dates. Card payment accepted at shows. Mail order through website only. Delivers to shows.

CPhi **Alan Phipps Cacti**
62 Samuel White Road, Hanham, Bristol, BS15 3LX
Ⓣ (0117) 9607591
Ⓦ www.cactus-mall.com/alan-phipps/index.html
Contact: A. Phipps
Opening Times: 1000-1700 but prior phone call essential to ensure a greeting.
Min Mail Order UK: £5.00 + p&p
Min Mail Order EU: £20.00 + p&p
Cat. Cost: Sae or 2 × IRC (EC only).
Credit Cards: None
Specialities: *Mammillaria*, *Astrophytum* & *Ariocarpus*. Species & varieties will change with times. Ample quantities exist in spring.

Limited range of *Agave*.
Notes: Specimen-size plants not available by mail order.
OS Grid Ref: ST644717

CPHo **The Palm House**
8 North Street, Ottery St Mary, Devon, EX11 1DR
Ⓣ (01404) 815450
Ⓜ 07815 673397
Ⓔ george@thepalmhouse.co.uk
Ⓦ www.thepalmhouse.co.uk
Contact: George Gregory
Opening Times: Open by appt. only.
Cat. Cost: 2 × 1st class.
Credit Cards: Paypal
Specialities: Palms.
Notes: Also sells wholesale.
OS Grid Ref: SY098955

CPla **Plant World Gardens and Nurseries**
St Marychurch Road, Newton Abbot, Devon, TQ12 4SE
Ⓣ (01803) 872939
Ⓕ (01803) 875018
Ⓔ raybrown@plant-world-seeds.com
Ⓦ www.plant-world-seeds.com
Contact: Doug De Val
Opening Times: 0930-1700 7 days a week, Apr-Oct.
Min Mail Order UK: Nmc
Min Mail Order EU: Nmc
Cat. Cost: Free.
Credit Cards: Visa, Access, EuroCard, MasterCard
Specialities: Alpines, perennials, small shrubs, succulents, herbaceous & patio plants.
Notes: Four acre garden planted as map of the world (entry charge applies). Mail order for seed only (no mail order for plants). Also sells wholesale. Exports beyond EU. Partial wheelchair access (nursery & café only).
OS Grid Ref: SX893693

CPne **Pine Cottage Plants** ♿
Sales Office, Bowdens Nursery Ltd, Bowden Place, Sticklepath, Devon, EX20 2NL
Ⓣ (01837) 840989
Ⓔ sales@bowdenhostas.com
Ⓦ www.bowdenhostas.com
Contact: Tim Penrose
Opening Times: 1000-1600 Apr-Sep. Oct-Mar Please telephone nursery before travelling.
Min Mail Order UK: Nmc
Min Mail Order EU: Nmc
Cat. Cost: Free.
Credit Cards: Maestro, MasterCard, Visa
Specialities: National Plant Collection of *Agapanthus* (Pine Cottage cvs).
Notes: Mail order *Agapanthus*. Wheelchair accessible.
OS Grid Ref: SX642940

CPrp **ProperPlants.com**
Penknight, Edgcumbe Road, Lostwithiel, Cornwall, PL22 0JD
Ⓣ (01208) 872291
Ⓔ sarahwilks52@gmail.com
Ⓦ www.agapanthus-plants.co.uk
Contact: Sarah Wilks
Opening Times: By appt. only. Please telephone or email first.
Min Mail Order UK: Nmc
Min Mail Order EU: Nmc
Credit Cards: All major credit/debit cards
Specialities: *Agapanthus* & *Crocosmia*.
Notes: Also sells wholesale. Exports beyond EU. Delivers to shows.
OS Grid Ref: SX093596

CPud **Puddleplants**
The Barn, Cwmceiliog Fawr, Taliaris, Llandeilo, Carmarthenshire, SA19 7NL
Ⓣ (01558) 615056
Ⓔ sonia@puddleplants.co.uk
Ⓦ www.puddleplants.co.uk
Contact: David Thomas
Opening Times: Not open, online only
Min Mail Order UK: Nmc
Cat. Cost: Online only.
Credit Cards: All major credit/debit cards
Specialities: Marginal, bog garden, oxygenating and pond plants. A range of native aquatic plants to the UK available.
Notes: On-line nursery retailing to the public and trade, specialising in British native pond and bog garden plants. Also have a very good selection of ornamentals, including irises (both pond and bog), and water lilies. Deliver anywhere in the UK all year around via 24 hour courier. Euro accepted.

CQua **R and A Scamp Quality Daffodils**
49 Mongleath Road, Falmouth, Cornwall, TR11 4PN
Ⓣ (01326) 317959
Ⓜ 07826 067175
Ⓔ amscamp@qualitydaffodils.com
Ⓦ www.qualitydaffodils.com
Contact: Adrian Scamp
Opening Times: Not open. Mail order only. Viewing by appt. only.
Min Mail Order UK: Nmc
Min Mail Order EU: Nmc
Cat. Cost: 4 × 1st class.

C

Credit Cards: All major credit/debit cards
Specialities: *Narcissus* hybrids & species. Some stocks have less than 100 bulbs.
Notes: Euro accepted.

CRea **REALLY WILD FLOWERS**
H V Horticulture Ltd, Heather Cottage, 23 New Close, Bourton, Gillingham, Dorset, SP8 5DL
Ⓣ (01747) 416376
Ⓔ info@reallywildflowers.co.uk
Ⓦ www.reallywildflowers.co.uk
Contact: Grahame Dixie
Opening Times: Not open. Mail order & online only.
Min Mail Order UK: £10 + p&p
Cat. Cost: 3 × 1st class.
Credit Cards: All major debit/credit cards except American Express
Specialities: Native wild flowers for grasslands, woodlands & wetlands. Seeds & bulbs. Hedge plants & trees. Soil analysis services.
Notes: Credit card payment accepted for online orders only. Also sells wholesale.

CRHN **ROSELAND HOUSE NURSERY**
Chacewater, Truro, Cornwall, TR4 8QB
Ⓣ (01872) 560451
Ⓔ clematis@roselandhouse.co.uk
Ⓦ www.roselandhouse.co.uk
Contact: Charlie Pridham
Opening Times: 1300-1700 Tue & Wed, Apr-Sep. Other times by appt.
Min Mail Order UK: Nmc
Min Mail Order EU: Nmc
Cat. Cost: Online only.
Credit Cards: All major credit/debit cards
Specialities: Climbing & conservatory plants. National Plant Collections of *Clematis viticella* & *Lapageria rosea*. Named *Lapageria* in short supply but occasionally available.
Notes: Garden open to the public. Delivers to shows.
OS Grid Ref: SW752445

CRos **ROSEMOOR PLANT CENTRE (RHS)** ♿ ◆
RHS Garden Rosemoor, Torrington, Devon, EX38 8PH
Ⓣ (01805) 626824
Ⓔ rosemooradmin@rhs.org.uk
Ⓦ www.rhs.org.uk/rosemoor
Contact: Plant Centre Team
Opening Times: 1000-1800 Mon-Sat, 1130-1730 Sun, Apr-Sep (summer). 1000-1700 Mon-Sat, 1030-1630 Sun, Oct-Mar (winter). Closed Easter Sun & Xmas Day.
Credit Cards: All major credit/debit cards
Specialities: Wide range of shrubs, herbaceous perennials, roses, climbers, alpines & seasonal plants, reflecting the diversity of planting in the garden. Displays themed by colour, position and season, also highlighting plants with the RHS Award of Garden Merit.
Notes: Plant centre attached to RHS Garden Rosemoor. Free entry to Plant Centre, Gift Shop & Restaurant. Accept HTA & RHS vouchers (paper only). Broad range of plants, including many varieties seen growing at RHS Garden Rosemoor. Wheelchair accessible.
OS Grid Ref: SS500176

CSBt **ST BRIDGET NURSERIES LTD** ♿
Old Rydon Lane, Exeter, Devon, EX2 7JY
Ⓣ (01392) 873672
Ⓕ (01392) 876710
Ⓔ sales@stbridgetnurseries.co.uk
Ⓦ www.stbridgetnurseries.co.uk
Contact: Sales Dept
Opening Times: 0900-1700 Mon-Sat, 1030-1630 Sun. Closed Xmas Day, Boxing Day, New Year's Day & Easter Sun.
Min Mail Order UK: Nmc
Cat. Cost: Free.
Credit Cards: All major credit/debit cards
Specialities: General nursery propagating a wide range of top quality plants, with two retail garden centres near Exeter. Founded 1925.
Notes: Mail order available, please contact for prices & carriage charges. Also sells wholesale. Wheelchair accessible.
OS Grid Ref: SX955905

CSde **SEASIDE PLANTS**
Marsh Lane Nursery, West Charleton, Kingsbridge, Devon, TQ7 2AQ
Ⓜ 07775 201595
Ⓔ info@seasideplants.co.uk
Ⓦ www.seasideplants.co.uk
Contact: Michael Hornby
Opening Times: Not open. By appt. only.
Min Mail Order UK: Nmc
Min Mail Order EU: Nmc
Cat. Cost: Online only.
Credit Cards: All major credit/debit cards
Specialities: Wide range, esp. coastal plants, *Elaeagnus*, *Euonymus*, *Fuchsia*, grasses, *Griselinia*, *Hydrangea*, *Olearia* & *Pittosporum*.
Notes: Euro accepted.

CSgt **STRETE GATE CAMELLIAS**
17 Seymour Drive, Torquay, Devon, TQ2 8PY
Ⓣ (01803) 770710
Ⓜ 07964 824673

Ⓔ plants@stretegatecamellias.co.uk
Ⓦ www.stretegatecamellias.co.uk
Contact: Jeremy Wilson
Opening Times: Nursery not open to public, but plant collection can be arranged.
Min Mail Order UK: Nmc
Specialities: Growing around 500 varieties of *Camellia*, some in small numbers.
Notes: Nursery is not open to the public and is at a different address, but orders can be collected. Delivers to shows. Also sells wholesale.
OS Grid Ref: SX833455

CSma **Plants for Small Gardens**
Goosegate, Bridford, Exeter, Devon, EX6 7LW
Ⓜ 07845 793582
Ⓔ sales@plantsforsmallgardens.co.uk
Ⓦ www.plantsforsmallgardens.co.uk
Contact: Sue Hearnden
Opening Times: Not open. Mail order online only.
Min Mail Order UK: £15.00
Cat. Cost: Online only.
Credit Cards: Paypal
Specialities: Dwarf hardy, rockery and alpine plants, all grown on our nursery in Devon. Range to suit all types of gardeners from *Aubrieta* & *Helianthemum* to more specialist plants such as kabschia saxifrages & *Meconopsis*. Good range of hardy geraniums.
Notes: Delivers to shows.

CSpe **Special Plants**
Hill Farm Barn, Greenways Lane, Cold Ashton, Chippenham, Wiltshire, SN14 8LA
Ⓣ (01225) 891686
Ⓔ derry@specialplants.net
Ⓦ www.specialplants.net
Contact: Derry Watkins
Opening Times: 1000-1700 7 days Mar-Oct. Other times please ring first to check.
Min Mail Order UK: £10.00 + p&p
Cat. Cost: Free.
Credit Cards: All major credit/debit cards
Specialities: Tender perennials, *Pelargonium*, *Salvia*, hardy geraniums, *Anemone*, *Papaver* Umbels & grasses. Many varieties propagated in small numbers only. Seeds.
Notes: Mail order Sep-Mar only. Delivers to shows.
OS Grid Ref: ST749726

CSta **Staddon Farm Nurseries** ♿
Staddon Road, Holsworthy, Devon, EX22 6NH
Ⓜ 07547 711189
Ⓔ penny@pennysprimulas.co.uk
Ⓦ www.pennysprimulas.co.uk
Contact: Penny Jones
Opening Times: By appt. only.
Min Mail Order UK: Nmc
Min Mail Order EU: Nmc
Cat. Cost: Online only.
Credit Cards: All major credit/debit cards
Specialities: *Primula*. National Plant Collection of *Primula sieboldii* Japanese cvs. Modest collection of *Epimedium*, ferns and other Asiatic Primulas.
Notes: Exports beyond EU. Delivers to shows. Euro accepted. Wheelchair accessible.
OS Grid Ref: SS359031

CSto **Stone Lane Gardens**
Chagford, Newton Abbot, Devon, PL20 7BW
Ⓣ (01647) 231311
Ⓔ admin@stonelanegardens.com
Ⓦ www.stonelanegardens.com
Contact: Paul Bartlett
Opening Times: 0930-dusk during tree-lifting season. Please phone for appt. all other times
Min Mail Order UK: £9.95
Min Mail Order EU: £40.00
Cat. Cost: £2.50.
Credit Cards: All major credit/debit cards, Paypal
Specialities: National Plant Collections (scientific status) of *Betula* & *Alnus*,
Notes: Charity devoted to public education through the conservation and distribution of Birch and Alder. Exports beyond EU.
OS Grid Ref: SX709908

CTrC **Trevena Cross Nurseries** ♿
Breage, Helston, Cornwall, TR13 9PY
Ⓣ (01736) 763880
Ⓕ (01736) 762828
Ⓔ sales@trevenacross.co.uk
Ⓦ www.trevenacross.co.uk
Contact: Graham Jeffery
Opening Times: 0900-1700 Mon-Sat, 1030-1630 Sun.
Min Mail Order UK: Nmc
Credit Cards: All major credit/debit cards
Specialities: Southern Hemisphere plants and plants for windy or exposed sites. Restionaceae, Proteaceae.
Notes: Family owned business operating as a garden centre and growing most stock on site. Garden kitchen café offering daily coffee and lunches. Wheelchair accessible.

CTrh **Trehane Nursery** ♿
Stapehill Road, Hampreston, Wimborne, Dorset, BH21 7ND
Ⓣ (01202) 873490

Ⓔ office@trehanenursery.co.uk
Ⓦ www.trehanenursery.co.uk
Contact: Lorraine Keets
Opening Times: 0830-1630 Mon-Fri all year (excl. Xmas & New Year). 1000-1600 Sat in spring & by appt.
Min Mail Order UK: Nmc
Min Mail Order EU: Nmc
Cat. Cost: Free.
Credit Cards: All major credit/debit cards
Specialities: Extensive range of *Camellia* species, cultivars & hybrids. Many new introductions. Blueberries.
Notes: Wheelchair accessible.
OS Grid Ref: SU059000

CTri **Triscombe Nurseries** ♿ ◆
West Bagborough, Nr Taunton, Somerset, TA4 3HG
Ⓣ (01984) 618267
Ⓔ info@triscombenurseries.co.uk
Ⓦ www.triscombenurseries.co.uk
Contact: S. Parkman
Opening Times: 0900-1730 Mon-Sat.
Min Mail Order UK: Nmc
Cat. Cost: 1 × 1st class.
Credit Cards: None
Specialities: Trees, shrubs, roses, fruit, *Clematis*, herbaceous & rock plants.
Notes: Wheelchair accessible.

CTsd **Treseders Nursery** ♿
Wallcottage Nursery, Lockengate, St. Austell, Cornwall, PL26 8RU
Ⓣ (01208) 832234
Ⓔ Treseders@btconnect.com
Ⓦ www.treseders.co.uk
Contact: James Treseder
Opening Times: 0900-1700 daily, except Wed 1000-1600 Sun.
Min Mail Order UK: Nmc
Min Mail Order EU: Nmc
Cat. Cost: Online or by email only.
Credit Cards: All major credit/debit cards
Specialities: A wide range of choice & unusual plants grown in peat-free compost. Establishing collection of *Prostanthera*.
Notes: Plants sometimes only available in small quantities. Enquiries welcome. Delivers to shows. Wheelchair accessible.
OS Grid Ref: SX034618

CTtf **Triffids**
The Nursery, Withy Lane, Oakhill, Radstock, Somerset, BA3 5SE
Ⓣ (01749) 840561
Ⓜ 07779 868133
Ⓔ jackietriffids@hotmail.co.uk
Contact: Jackie Williams
Opening Times: By appt. only. Please phone for details
Credit Cards: All major credit/debit cards
Specialities: Traditional & unusual perennials, plants for shade, potted bulbs, galanthus, geums, epimediums, wildflowers.
Notes: Plants available at plant fairs and shows. Delivers to shows.

CWat **The Water Garden** ♿
Hinton Parva, Swindon, Wiltshire, SN4 0DH
Ⓣ (01793) 790558
Ⓔ ben@thewatergarden.co.uk
Ⓦ www.thewatergarden.co.uk
Contact: Ben Newman
Opening Times: 1000-1700 Wed-Sun.
Min Mail Order UK: £10.00 + p&p
Cat. Cost: 4 × 1st class.
Credit Cards: Visa, Access, Switch
Specialities: Waterlilies, marginal & moisture plants, oxygenators & alpines.
Notes: Also sells wholesale. Wheelchair accessible.

CWCL **Westcountry Nurseries (North Devon) Ltd**
Donkey Meadow, Woolsery, Devon, EX39 5QH
Ⓣ (01237) 431111
Ⓔ info@westcountrylupins.co.uk
Ⓦ www.westcountry-nurseries.co.uk
Contact: Sarah Conibear
Opening Times: Mon-Fri, open for collection of plant orders by appointment ONLY. Please ring beforehand 1000-1530 weekdays only, closed w/ends.
Min Mail Order UK: Nmc
Cat. Cost: 2 × 1st class + A5 sae for full colour cat.
Credit Cards: All major credit/debit cards
Specialities: *Lupinus*, *Lewisia*, *Helleborus*, *Clematis*, cyclamen, select perennials, grasses, ferns & climbers. National Plant Collection of Lupins.
Notes: Delivers to shows.
OS Grid Ref: SS351219

CWGN **Walled Garden Nursery** ♿
Brinkworth House, Brinkworth, Nr Malmesbury, Wiltshire, SN15 5DF
Ⓜ 07921 436863
Ⓔ sales@clematis-nursery.co.uk
Ⓦ www.clematis-nursery.co.uk
Contact: Fraser Wescott
Opening Times: 1000-1700 Mon-Sat, 1000-1600 Sun Mar-Oct. 1030-dusk Mon-Fri, Nov & Feb. Closed Dec & Jan.

Min Mail Order UK: £15.00
Credit Cards: All major credit/debit cards
Specialities: *Clematis* & climbers, with a selection of unusual perennials & shrubs.
Notes: Mail order UK mainland only. Wheelchair accessible.
OS Grid Ref: SU002849

CWGr **National Dahlia Collection**
Varfell Farm, Long Rock, Penzance, Cornwall, TR20 8AQ
Ⓣ (01736) 339276
Ⓜ 07753 959856
Ⓔ info@nationaldahliacollection.co.uk
Ⓦ www.nationaldahliacollection.co.uk
Contact: Louise Danks
Opening Times: Garden open in summer. See website or contact nursery for details.
Min Mail Order UK: Nmc
Min Mail Order EU: Nmc
Cat. Cost: Online. Contact nursery for hard copy.
Credit Cards: All major debit/credit cards except American Express
Specialities: National Plant Collection of *Dahlia*. 1600 plus cvs.
Notes: See website for plant availability. Also sells wholesale. Partial wheelchair access.

CWit **Withleigh Nurseries**
Withleigh, Tiverton, Devon, EX16 8JG
Ⓣ (01884) 253351
Ⓜ 07854 691040
Ⓔ withleigh@aol.com
Ⓦ www.withleighnurseries.co.uk
Contact: Terry Watling
Opening Times: 0900-1700 Tue-Sat (summer) 1000-1600 Tue-Sun (winter)
Credit Cards: All major credit/debit cards
Specialities: Shrubs & herbaceous.

Eastern

EACa **Alpine Campanulas (Bellflower Nursery)**
Ⓜ 07879 644958
Ⓔ sue@bellflowernursery.co.uk
Ⓦ www.bellflowernursery.co.uk
Contact: Sue Wooster
Opening Times: Not open.
Min Mail Order UK: £10.00
Cat. Cost: Online only.
Credit Cards: None
Specialities: *Campanula*. National Plant Collection of Alpine Campanula. Most stock in small numbers only.
Notes: Hardy plant nursery & National Plant Collection. Garden design service. A wide selection of plants available at The Leaping Hare Country Store at RHS Partner Garden Wyken Hall, Stanton, Suffolk IP31 2DW.

EAJP **A & J Plants**
Chappel Road, Great Tey, Colchester, Essex, CO6 1JR
Ⓣ (01206) 212124
Ⓕ (01206) 212124
Ⓔ mail@aandjplants.com
Ⓦ www.aandjplants.com
Contact: Jackie Rhodes
Opening Times: Not open. Mail order only. Orders can be collected from nursery by prior arrangement.
Min Mail Order UK: Nmc
Specialities: Wide variety of choice perennials and ornamental grasses propagated on the nursery, some in small quantities.
Notes: Plant Centre at Marks Hall Garden (CO6 1TG) stocked with seasonal selection of perennials & grasses. Also sells wholesale. Delivers to shows.

EBak **B & H M Baker** ♿
Bourne Brook Nurseries, Greenstead Green, Halstead, Essex, CO9 1RB
Ⓣ (01787) 476369
Contact: Clive Baker
Opening Times: 0800-1600 Mon-Fri, 0900-1200 & 1400-1600 Sat & Sun, Mar-Jun.
Cat. Cost: 2 × 1st class + 33p.
Credit Cards: All major credit/debit cards
Specialities: *Fuchsia* & conservatory plants.
Notes: Also sells wholesale. Wheelchair accessible.

EBar **Barcham Trees PLC**
Eye Hill Drove, Ely, Cambridgeshire, CB7 5XF
Ⓣ (01353) 720950
Ⓔ info@barchamtrees.co.uk
Ⓦ www.barcham.co.uk
Opening Times: Office hours 0900-1730 Mon-Fri. Nursery visits by appt. only.
Min Mail Order UK: Nmc
Min Mail Order EU: Nmc
Cat. Cost: £20.00.
Credit Cards: All major debit/credit cards except American Express
Specialities: Large grower of containerised trees. 478 varieties available, from 10-12cm to 40cm girth.
Notes: As trees range from 3-8 metres all are despatched on lorries rather than through the mailing service. Also sells wholesale. Exports beyond EU. Delivers to shows. Euro accepted.

E

EBee **Beeches Nursery** ♿
Crown Hill, Ashdon, Saffron Walden, Essex, CB10 2HB
Ⓣ (01799) 584362
Ⓔ sales@beechesnursery.co.uk
Ⓦ www.beechesnursery.co.uk
Contact: Alan Bidwell / Philip Seymour
Opening Times: 0830-1700 Mon-Sat, 0930-1630 Sun & B/hols.
Min Mail Order UK: £15.00
Min Mail Order EU: £20.00
Cat. Cost: Online.
Credit Cards: All major credit/debit cards
Specialities: Herbaceous specialists & extensive range of other garden worthy plants. Rarities available in limited numbers only.
Notes: Orders accepted throughout the year. No trees or very large shrubs by mail order, selected trees can be dispatched direct from our grower. Wheelchair accessible.
OS Grid Ref: TL586420

EBlo **Bressingham Gardens Nursery**
Foggy Bottom, Bressingham, Diss, Norfolk, IP22 2AB
Ⓣ (01379) 688282
Ⓕ (01379) 687227
Ⓔ info@bressinghamgardens.com
Ⓦ https://www.thebressinghamgardens.com/shop/
Contact: Adrian Bloom
Opening Times: (Office) 0830-1630 Mon-Fri. Mail order only.
Min Mail Order UK: £6.95 + p&p
Credit Cards: All major debit/credit cards except American Express
Specialities: Perennials and grasses, many from The Bressingham Gardens' extensive collection raised by Alan Bloom.
Notes: Mail order only. Exports beyond EU. Also sells wholesale.

EBls **Peter Beales Roses** ♿ ◆
London Road, Attleborough, Norfolk, NR17 1AY
Ⓣ (01953) 454707
Ⓔ support@peterbealesroses.com
Ⓦ www.classicroses.co.uk
Contact: Tina Limmer
Opening Times: 0900-1700 Mon-Sat, 1000-1600 Sun & B/hols. Closed 25th Dec-2nd Jan.
Min Mail Order UK: Nmc
Min Mail Order EU: Nmc
Cat. Cost: £5.00 outside UK.
Credit Cards: All major debit/credit cards except American Express
Specialities: Large range of perennials, shrubs, *Clematis*, climbers, ornamental trees, fruit, summer & winter bedding. National Plant Collection of Species roses.
Notes: Display garden, open all year round (free entry). Agent for Classic Garden Element iron work. Also sells wholesale. Exports beyond EU. New wildlife garden. East Anglia's Finest Plant, Craft & Food Fair 4th May 2019, Rose Festival 22-23 Jun 2019. Wheelchair accessible.
OS Grid Ref: TM026929

EBou **Boundary Nursery**
Colne Road, Bluntisham, Huntington, Cambridgeshire, PE28 3LU
Ⓣ (01487) 842611
Ⓔ herbsandalpines@gmail.com
Ⓦ https://boundarynursery.co.uk/
Contact: Peter Reason
Opening Times: By appt. only
Min Mail Order UK: Nmc
Credit Cards: All major credit/debit cards
Specialities: Range of rockery plants, ground-cover plants, drought-tolerant plants, shade tolerant plants, ones for clay soil, bee and butterfly pollinator friendly plants and ones for coastal regions.
Notes: Offers a range of alpines, perennials, herbs and ornamental grasses for all areas of the garden.
OS Grid Ref: TL369752

EBtc **Botanica**
Chantry Farm, Campsea Ashe, Wickham Market, Suffolk, IP13 0PZ
Ⓣ (01728) 747113
Ⓜ 07887 423964
Ⓔ sales@botanica.org.uk
Ⓦ www.botanicaplantnursery.co.uk
Contact: Daniel Everett
Opening Times: 0900-1700 Mon-Fri (0900-1600 in winter), 1030-1600 w/ends. Closed w/ends Jul-Aug.
Min Mail Order UK: £30 + p&p
Cat. Cost: Online only.
Credit Cards: All major debit/credit cards except American Express
Specialities: Range of rare & unusual hardy plants. All stock is English, grown at our nursery and in non-peat based compost.
Notes: Also sells wholesale.
OS Grid Ref: TM328550

ECha **The Beth Chatto Gardens** ♿
Elmstead Market, Colchester, Essex, CO7 7DB
Ⓣ (01206) 822007
Ⓕ (01206) 825933

Ⓔ dave@bethchatto.co.uk
Ⓦ www.bethchatto.co.uk
Contact: David Ward
Opening Times: 1000-1700 Mon-Sun 1st Mar-31st Oct. 0900-1600 Mon-Sun, Nov-end Feb.
Min Mail Order UK: Nmc
Min Mail Order EU: Ask for details
Cat. Cost: Online only.
Credit Cards: All major debit/credit cards except American Express
Specialities: Predominantly herbaceous perennials, grasses & ferns. Many unusual for special situations.
Notes: Delivers to Shows. Wheelchair accessible. Border design service.
OS Grid Ref: TM069238

ECnt **Cants of Colchester Ltd**
Nayland Road, Mile End, Colchester, Essex, CO4 5HA
Ⓣ (01206) 844008
Ⓕ (01206) 855371
Ⓔ enquiries@cantsroses.co.uk
Ⓦ www.cantsroses.co.uk
Contact: Angela Pawsey
Opening Times: 0900-1300, 1400-1630 Mon-Fri. Sat varied, please phone first. Sun closed.
Min Mail Order UK: Nmc
Min Mail Order EU: Nmc
Cat. Cost: Free.
Credit Cards: Visa, MasterCard, Delta, Maestro
Specialities: Roses.
Notes: Celebrated 250 years of being rose specialists in 2015. Bare-root mail order end Oct-end Mar, containers Apr-Oct. Limited bare-root exports beyond EU and worldwide, depending on regulations. Partial wheelchair access.

ECre **Creake Plant Centre** ♿
Leicester Road, South Creake, Fakenham, Norfolk, NR21 9PW
Ⓣ (01328) 823018
Ⓜ 07760 762499
Ⓕ (01328) 823018
Ⓔ trevor-harrison@btconnect.com
Ⓦ www.creakeplantcentre.co.uk
Contact: Mr T. Harrison
Opening Times: 1000-1300 & 1400-1730 7 days excl. Xmas.
Credit Cards: All major credit/debit cards
Specialities: Unusual shrubs, herbaceous, conservatory plants, old roses, Hellebores. Some plants only available in small quantities.
Notes: Delivers to shows. Wheelchair accessible.
OS Grid Ref: TF864353

ECtt **Cottage Nurseries** ♿
Thoresthorpe, Alford, Lincolnshire, LN13 0HX
Ⓣ (01507) 466968
Ⓔ bill@cottagenurseries.net
Ⓦ www.cottagenurseries.net
Contact: W. H. Denbigh
Opening Times: 0900-1700 7 days 1st Mar-31st Oct. 1000-1500 Nov-Feb. Closed 1st Dec-6th Jan.
Min Mail Order UK: £20.00
Cat. Cost: Online only.
Credit Cards: Visa, MasterCard, Maestro
Specialities: Hardy perennials. Wide general range.
Notes: Wheelchair accessible.
OS Grid Ref: TF461776

ECul **John Cullen Gardens Ltd**
Eagle Lodge, Archers Lane, Algarkirk, Lincolnshire, PE20 2AG
Ⓣ (01205) 460567
Ⓜ 07931 634933
Ⓔ design@johncullengardens.com
Ⓦ www.johncullengardens.com
Contact: John Cullen
Opening Times: Not open, online only
Specialities: Scented plants, plants for pollinators, herbs, shrubs & bulbs.
Notes: A wide selection of plants from shrubs to perennials, bulbs & herbs. Delivers to shows.

EDAr **D'Arcy & Everest**
Meadowsweet Nursery, Pidley Sheep Lane (B1040), Pidley, Cambridgeshire, PE28 3FL
Ⓣ (01480) 463570
Ⓕ (01480) 466042
Ⓔ info@darcyeverest.co.uk
Ⓦ www.darcyeverest.co.uk
Contact: Luke Whiting
Opening Times: Open on selected days, please see website/contact nursery for dates. Also for nursery tour dates (bookable in advance only). Coach parties welcome by appt. Closed Oct-Feb.
Cat. Cost: None available.
Credit Cards: All major credit/debit cards
Specialities: Alpines, perennials & sempervivums.
Notes: Delivers to shows.
OS Grid Ref: TL338762

EDel **Delfland Nurseries Ltd** ♿
Benwick Road, Doddington, March, Cambridgeshire, PE15 0TU
Ⓣ (01354) 740553
Ⓕ (01354) 741200
Ⓔ info@delfland.co.uk
Ⓦ www.organicplants.co.uk

E

Contact: Jill Vaughan
Opening Times: 0900-1600 Mon-Sat 1000-1600 Sun Apr-Oct. 0900-1600 Mon-Fri 0900-1300 Sat Nov-Mar
Min Mail Order UK: £6.95
Cat. Cost: Free.
Credit Cards: All major debit/credit cards except American Express
Specialities: Vegetable, bedding & container plants.
Notes: Mail order and retail organic & peat-free from stock (mainly veg. plants) or to order (for large orders). Retail bedding & container plants not organic or peat-free. Also sells wholesale. Wheelchair accessible.
OS Grid Ref: TL386908

EFer **The Fern Nursery** ♿
Grimsby Road, Binbrook, Lincolnshire, LN8 6DH
Ⓣ (01472) 398092
Ⓔ rtimm@fernnursery.co.uk
Ⓦ www.fernnursery.co.uk
Contact: R. N. Timm
Opening Times: 0900-1600 Fri, Sat & Sun Apr-Oct or by appt.
Min Mail Order UK: Nmc
Min Mail Order EU: Nmc
Cat. Cost: Online only.
Credit Cards: All major credit/debit cards
Specialities: Ferns.
Notes: Display garden. Only plants in the mail order part of the catalogue can be sent mail order. Also sells wholesale. Euro accepted. Wheelchair accessible.
OS Grid Ref: TF212942

EFly **The Fly Trap Plants** ♿
Cookes Road, Thurton, Norwich, Norfolk, NR14 6AE
Ⓣ (01508) 480348
Ⓜ 07769 256556
Ⓔ sales@tftplants.co.uk
Ⓦ www.tftplants.co.uk
Contact: Pauline Steward
Opening Times: By appt. only.
Min Mail Order UK: Nmc
Cat. Cost: 1 × 1st class sae.
Credit Cards: Paypal
Specialities: All kinds of carnivorous plants, from *Sarracenia*, *Drosera*, *Pinguicula*, to *Utricularia* aquatic plants.
Notes: Delivers to shows. Euro accepted. Wheelchair accessible.

EGren **Grenville Nurseries** ♿
Cow Watering Lane, Writtle, Chelmsford, Essex, CM1 3SB
Ⓣ (01245) 420400
Ⓕ (01245) 420400
Ⓔ info@grenvillenurseries.co.uk
Ⓦ www.grenvillenurseries.co.uk
Contact: Charlie Lauman
Opening Times: 0830-1730 Mon-Thu. 0830-1900 Fri. 0900-1700 Sat. 1000-1700 Sun.
Cat. Cost: Online only.
Credit Cards: All major credit/debit cards
Specialities: Trees, shrubs, herbaceous ferns, climbers, grasses and bamboo. Seasonal bareroot and rootball hedging and trees. Bulbs available in large quantities.
Notes: Leading plant nursery open to both the public and trade. Growers of seasonal bedding and herbaceous plants. Also stock seasonal bareroot and rootball hedging and trees and bulbs. Also sells wholesale. Wheelchair accessible.

EGrI **Green Island Gardens**
Park Road, Ardleigh, Colchester, Essex, CO7 7SP
Ⓣ (01206) 230455
Ⓔ info@greenislandgardens.co.uk
Ⓦ www.greenislandgardens.co.uk
Contact: Fiona Edmond
Opening Times: 10th Jan-30th Nov
Credit Cards: All major credit/debit cards
Specialities: Acers, camellias and autumn-flowering camellias, cornus, hydrangeas, hamamelis, dwarf rhododendrons.
Notes: Large selection of acers & camellias (incl. autumn-flowering camellias). Unusual trees & shrubs, all seen growing in the gardens.
OS Grid Ref: TM056273

EHDe **Harper & Debbage**
33 The Ridgeway, Norwich, Norfolk, NR1 4ND
Ⓣ (01603) 708104
Ⓜ 07889 679444
Ⓔ info@harperanddebbage.co.uk
Ⓦ www.harperanddebbage.co.uk
Contact: Kristopher Harper
Opening Times: By appt. only. Plant collection by appt. only.
Min Mail Order UK: NMC
Cat. Cost: Online only.
Credit Cards: All major credit/debit cards
Specialities: *Fuchsia*. National Plant Collection of *Fuchsia* introduced by James Lye.
Notes: Sells by mail order. Attends some shows (contact nursery for details). Delivers to shows.
OS Grid Ref: TG248096

EHed **HEDGEHOG PLANTS AND GARDENS** ♿
Risby Barns, South Street, Bury St Edmunds, Suffolk, IP28 6QU
Ⓣ (01284) 811055
Ⓔ info@theinterestingplantnursery.co.uk
Ⓦ www.theinterestingplantnursery.co.uk
Contact: Simon or Jay McWilliams
Opening Times: 1000-1700 Mon-Sat 1000-1600 Sun Closed Mon from Oct-end Feb
Specialities: *Cornus, Viburnum, Epimedium* and other shrubs and shade-loving plants.
Notes: If you are travelling any distance, please call ahead to check plant availability. Wheelchair accessible, plenty of parking available. Delivers to shows. Please check website for details.
OS Grid Ref: TL796662

EHyd **HYDE HALL PLANT CENTRE (RHS)** ♿ ◆
RHS Garden Hyde Hall, Rettendon Common, Chelmsford, Essex, CM3 8ET
Ⓣ (01245) 402113
Ⓔ benmansfield@rhs.org.uk
Ⓦ www.rhs.org.uk
Contact: Ben Mansfield
Opening Times: 0930-1600 Mon-Sat, 1000-1600 Sun, Nov-Feb. 0930-1800 Mon-Sat, 1100 -1700 Sun, Mar-Oct. Closed Xmas Day & Easter Sun.
Credit Cards: All major credit/debit cards
Notes: Wheelchair accessible.

EIri **IRISESONLINE**
Slade Cottage, Petts Lane, Little Walden, Essex, CB10 1XH
Ⓣ (01799) 526294
Ⓔ enquiries@sladecottageirisesonline.co.uk
Ⓦ www.sladecottageirisesonline.co.uk
Contact: Clare Kneen
Opening Times: By appt. only.
Min Mail Order UK: Nmc
Cat. Cost: Online only.
Credit Cards: None
Specialities: *Iris*. Some varieties available in small quantities only.
Notes: Small family-run nursery. Delivers to shows.
OS Grid Ref: TL546416

EKin **E W KING & CO. LTD (KINGS SEEDS)**
Monks Farm, Pantling Lane, Coggeshall Road, Kelvedon, Essex, CO5 9PG
Ⓣ (01376) 570000
Ⓕ (01376) 571189
Ⓔ info@kingsseeds.com
Ⓦ www.kingsseeds.com
Contact: Andrew Tokely
Min Mail Order UK: Nmc
Min Mail Order EU: Nmc
Cat. Cost: Free.
Credit Cards: All major credit/debit cards
Specialities: Vegetable, flower, grass, sweet pea and pea & bean seeds, incl. many hybrid & unusual items.
Notes: Incorporating Suffolk Herbs. Also sells wholesale. Exports beyond the EU.

ELan **LANGTHORNS PLANTERY** ♿
High Cross Lane West, Little Canfield, Dunmow, Essex, CM6 1TD
Ⓣ (01371) 872611
Ⓔ info@langthorns.com
Ⓦ www.langthorns.com
Contact: E. Cannon
Opening Times: 0830-1800 Apr-end June. 0900-1730 or dusk (if earlier) 7 days. Closed Xmas fortnight.
Min Mail Order UK: £20.00
Cat. Cost: Online only.
Credit Cards: Visa, Access, Switch, MasterCard, Delta
Specialities: Wide general range with many unusual plants.
Notes: Mail order any plant under 4ft tall. Wheelchair accessible.
OS Grid Ref: TL592204

ELon **LONG HOUSE PLANTS** ♿
The Long House, Church Road, Noak Hill, Romford, Essex, RM4 1LD
Ⓣ (01708) 371719
Ⓔ tim@longhouse-plants.co.uk
Ⓦ www.longhouse-plants.co.uk
Contact: Tim Carter
Opening Times: 1000-1700 Fri, Sat & B/hols, 1000-1600 Sun, beginning Mar-end Sep, or by appt.
Credit Cards: All major credit/debit cards
Specialities: Choice trees, shrubs, herbaceous perennials & ferns. Many unusual varieties incl. *Agapanthus, Aster, Camellia, Hemerocallis, Iris sibirica, Kniphofia, Phlox* & *Symphyotrichum*. Some only available in small quantities.
Notes: Wheelchair accessible. Disabled toilet. See website for garden open days.
OS Grid Ref: TQ554194

EMac **FIRECREST TREES & SHRUBS NURSERY** ♿
Hall Road, Little Bealings, Woodbridge, Suffolk, IP13 6LG
Ⓣ (01473) 625937
Ⓕ (01473) 625937
Ⓔ firecrest98@tiscali.co.uk

E

Ⓦ www.firecrest.org.uk
Opening Times: 0900-1500 Tue-Fri, 0900-1200 Sat.
Credit Cards: None
Specialities: Trees & shrubs. Japanese maples. Bare-root hedging.
Notes: Also sells wholesale. Bareroot mail order only. Euro accepted. Wheelchair accessible.

EMal **Marshall's Malmaisons** ♿
Hullwood Barn, Shelley, Ipswich, Suffolk, IP7 5RE
Ⓣ (01473) 822400
Ⓜ 07768 454875
Ⓔ jim@malmaisons.plus.com
Contact: J. M. Marshall/Sarah Cook
Opening Times: By appt. only.
Min Mail Order UK: £33.00 incl. p&p
Min Mail Order EU: £36.00 incl. p&p
Cat. Cost: 1st class sae.
Credit Cards: None
Specialities: National Plant Collection of Malmaison carnations, perpetual flowering carnations (pre 1970) & Cedirc Morris Irises. *Iris* stock only available in small quantities.
Notes: Also sells wholesale. Wheelchair accessible.
OS Grid Ref: TM006394

EMdy **Mandy Plants** ♿
(office) 4 Stevens Road, Little Snoring, Norfolk, NR21 0GZ
Ⓣ (01328) 878144
Ⓜ 07432 112245
Ⓔ enquiries@mandyplants.com
Ⓦ www.mandyplants.com
Contact: Liz Spanton
Opening Times: By appt. only.
Min Mail Order UK: Nmc
Min Mail Order EU: £25.00
Credit Cards: Paypal, All major credit/debit cards
Specialities: *Mandevilla*, *Dipladenia*, *Lantana* & other tender perennials.
Notes: Nursery is at Little Snoring, Norfolk. Also sells wholesale. Delivers to shows. Wheelchair accessible.

EMic **Mickfield Hostas** ♿
The Poplars, Wetheringsett Road, Mickfield, Stowmarket, Suffolk, IP14 5LH
Ⓣ (01449) 711576
Ⓕ (01449) 711576
Ⓔ mickfieldhostas@btconnect.com
Ⓦ www.mickfieldhostas.co.uk
Contact: Mr & Mrs R. L. C. Milton
Opening Times: 1000-1600 Fri to Mon (Closed Tue-Thu) during May and June. All other times by appt. Check website for latest information
Min Mail Order UK: Nmc
Min Mail Order EU: Nmc
Cat. Cost: Online only.
Credit Cards: All major debit/credit cards except American Express
Specialities: National Plant Collection of *Hosta* containing over 2000 varieties. Waiting list for rarities & some limited quantity plants only available at nursery. Will divide parent plants for collectors if feasible. Expect to pay more for root divisions of mature plants.
Notes: See website for details of cvs held & latest availability. Delivers to shows. Wheelchair accessible. Gardens under development.
OS Grid Ref: TM136619

EMil **Mill Race Garden Centre** ♿
New Road, Aldham, Colchester, Essex, CO6 3QT
Ⓣ (01206) 242521
Ⓔ PlantDesk@swallowaquatics.co.uk
Ⓦ www.millracegardencentre.co.uk
Contact: Annette Bayliss
Opening Times: 0900-1730 Mon-Sat, 1000-1630 Sun.
Min Mail Order UK: £9.00
Credit Cards: All major credit/debit cards
Specialities: Stock available in small quantities only.
Notes: Trees & large shrubs not sent by mail order. Wheelchair accessible.
OS Grid Ref: TL918268

EMor **Moore and Moore Plants** ♿
London Road, Billericay, Essex, CM12 9HR
Ⓜ 07799 865946
Ⓔ contact@mooreandmooreplants.co.uk
Ⓦ www.mooreandmooreplants.co.uk
Contact: Lynne Moore
Opening Times: By appt. only.
Min Mail Order UK: £15.00
Cat. Cost: Online only.
Credit Cards: All major credit/debit cards
Specialities: Specialists in plants for shady places. Great selection of plants that attract pollinating insects. Most plants available in small quantities only.
Notes: See website or contact nursery for details of Open Days. Delivers to shows. Wheelchair accessible.

ENfk **Norfolk Herbs** ♿
Blackberry Farm, Dillington, Dereham, Norfolk, NR19 2QD

Ⓣ (01362) 860812
Ⓕ (01362) 860812
Ⓔ info@norfolkherbs.co.uk
Ⓦ www.norfolkherbs.co.uk
Contact: Rosemary or Oliver Clifton-Sprigg
Opening Times: 0900-1700 Mon-Sat Mar 1st-Sept 30th. 1000-1600 Fri & Sat Oct 1st-Feb 28th. Closed Sundays & Dec 24th-Jan 31st. At all other times please contact nursery.
Min Mail Order UK: £8.39
Cat. Cost: 2 × 2nd class.
Credit Cards: All major credit/debit cards
Specialities: Established 1986. Growers & suppliers of naturally raised culinary, medicinal & aromatic herb plants, *Salvias*, Bay trees & scented *pelargoniums*.
Notes: Sells from nursery, online & at local shows. A founding member of Norfolk Nursery Network. Also sells wholesale. Delivers to shows. Wheelchair accessible.
OS Grid Ref: TF967150

ENor NORFOLK LAVENDER ♿
Caley Mill, Heacham, King's Lynn, Norfolk, PE31 7JE
Ⓣ (01485) 570384
Ⓜ 07787 550286
Ⓕ (01485) 571176
Ⓔ info@norfolk-lavender.co.uk
Ⓦ www.norfolk-lavender.co.uk
Contact: Shelley Eagle
Opening Times: 0900-1700 7 days, Apr-Oct. 0900-1600 7 days, Nov-Mar.
Min Mail Order UK: Nmc
Cat. Cost: Free.
Credit Cards: All major debit/credit cards except American Express
Specialities: National Plant Collection of *Lavandula*, sect. *L. dentata* & *L. pterostoechas*.
Notes: Wheelchair accessible.
OS Grid Ref: TF685368

EOHP OLD HALL PLANTS
1 The Old Hall, Barsham, Beccles, Suffolk, NR34 8HB
Ⓣ (01502) 717475
Ⓔ info@oldhallplants.co.uk
Ⓦ www.oldhallplants.co.uk
Contact: Janet Elliott
Opening Times: By appt. only. Please telephone first.
Min Mail Order UK: Nmc
Min Mail Order EU: Nmc
Cat. Cost: 4 × 1st class.
Specialities: House plants. Some plants available in small quantities.
Notes: Partial wheelchair access.
OS Grid Ref: TM396904

EOli THE NORFOLK OLIVE TREE COMPANY ♿
61-63 Riverside Road, Norwich, Norfolk, NR1 1SR
Ⓜ 07766 730893
Ⓔ thenorfolkolivetreecompany@gmail.com
Ⓦ www.thenorfolkolivetreecompany.co.uk
Contact: Antonia Smith
Opening Times: Wed-Sun winter. Mon-Sun summer.
Min Mail Order UK: £2.95
Min Mail Order EU: £50.00
Credit Cards: All major credit/debit cards
Specialities: We specialise in the *Arbequina*, *Picual* and *Gordal* Olive Tree.
Notes: We specialise in hardy exotics and Mediteranean plants. Euro accepted. Delivers to shows. Wheelchair accessible.

EPau PAUGERS PLANTS LTD
Bury Road, Depden, Bury St Edmunds, Suffolk, IP29 4BU
Ⓣ (01284) 850527
Ⓔ enquiries@paugers-plants.co.uk
Ⓦ www.paugers-plants.co.uk
Contact: Geraldine Arnold
Opening Times: 0900-1730 Wed-Sat, 1000-1700 Sun & B/hols, 1st Mar-30th Nov.
Min Mail Order UK: Nmc
Credit Cards: All major credit/debit cards
Specialities: Hardy shrubs & perennials in large or small quantities.
Notes: Also sells wholesale.
OS Grid Ref: TL783568

EPfP THE PLACE FOR PLANTS ♿
East Bergholt Place, East Bergholt, Suffolk, CO7 6UP
Ⓣ (01206) 299224
Ⓕ (01206) 299229
Ⓔ sales@placeforplants.co.uk
Ⓦ www.placeforplants.co.uk
Contact: Sara Eley
Opening Times: 1000-1700 (or dusk if earlier) 7 days. Closed Easter Sun & Christmas B/hol.
Min Mail Order UK: Nmc
Cat. Cost: Online only.
Credit Cards: All major credit/debit cards
Specialities: Wide range of specialist & popular plants. National Collection of deciduous *Euonymus*. 20 acre mature garden with free access to RHS members Apr-Sept excluding Sundays.
Notes: Mail order. Delivers to shows. Euro accepted. Wheelchair accessible.

EPom POMONA FRUITS LTD
Pomona House, 12 Third Avenue, Walton-on-the-Naze, Essex, CO14 8JU

Ⓣ (01255) 440410
Ⓕ (01255) 440420
Ⓔ Info@PomonaFruits.co.uk
Ⓦ www.PomonaFruits.co.uk
Contact: Ming Yang/Claire Higgins
Opening Times: Not open. Mail order only.
Min Mail Order UK: Nmc
Cat. Cost: Free.
Credit Cards: All major credit/debit cards
Specialities: Fruit stock.

EPot **POTTERTONS NURSERY** ♿
Moortown Road, Nettleton, Caistor, Lincolnshire, LN7 6HX
Ⓣ (01472) 851714
Ⓔ sales@pottertons.co.uk
Ⓦ www.pottertons.co.uk
Contact: Robert Potterton
Opening Times: 1000-1500 Tue-Fri, Mar-Oct.
Min Mail Order UK: Nmc
Min Mail Order EU: Nmc
Cat. Cost: £2.00 in stamps.
Credit Cards: MasterCard, Visa
Specialities: Alpines, dwarf bulbs & woodland plants.
Notes: Talks given nationally & internationally to garden clubs & societies. Group nursery tours by arrangement. Delivers to shows. Euro accepted. Wheelchair accessible.
OS Grid Ref: TA091001

EPPr **THE PLANTSMAN'S PREFERENCE** ♿
Church Road, South Lopham, Diss, Norfolk, IP22 2LW
Ⓣ (01379) 710810
Ⓜ 07799 855559
Ⓔ tim@plantpref.co.uk
Ⓦ www.plantpref.co.uk
Contact: Tim Fuller
Opening Times: 0930-1700 Fri, Sat & Sun Mar-Oct. Other times by appt.
Min Mail Order UK: Nmc
Min Mail Order EU: Nmc
Cat. Cost: Online only.
Credit Cards: All major credit/debit cards
Specialities: Hardy geraniums & ornamental grasses. Unusual & interesting perennials incl. shade/woodland. Some choice shrubs esp. *Caprifoliaceae*. National Plant Collection of *Molinia*.
Notes: Mail order all year except Xmas-New Year. Delivers to shows. Wheelchair accessible. Switch to Peat-free compost in progress.
OS Grid Ref: TM041819

EPri **PRIORY PLANTS** ♿
1 Covey Cottages, Hintlesham, Nr Ipswich, Suffolk, IP8 3NY
Ⓣ (01473) 652656
Ⓜ 07798 627618
Ⓕ (01473) 652656
Ⓔ sue.mann3@btinternet.com
Contact: Sue Mann
Opening Times: By appt. only. Please ring first to avoid disappointment.
Min Mail Order UK: Nmc
Min Mail Order EU: Nmc
Cat. Cost: Online only.
Credit Cards: None
Specialities: Cottage garden perennials, as well as increasing range of South African plants. *Agapanthus, Astrantia, Dierama, Dietes, Eucomis*, Siberian *Iris, Kniphofia, Nerine, Tritonia, Tulbaghia* & *Watsonia*.
Notes: Sells at plant fairs & agricultural shows. Also sells wholesale. Exports beyond EU. Delivers to shows. Wheelchair accessible.
OS Grid Ref: TM070448

EPts **POTASH NURSERY LTD** ♿
Cow Green, Bacton, Stowmarket, Suffolk, IP14 4HJ
Ⓣ (01449) 781671
Ⓔ enquiries@potashnursery.co.uk
Ⓦ www.potashnursery.co.uk
Contact: M. W. Clare
Opening Times: Not open except for collection of pre-ordered plants by appt. only.
Min Mail Order UK: £24.90
Cat. Cost: 1 × 1st class.
Credit Cards: Visa, Delta, MasterCard
Specialities: *Fuchsia*.
Notes: Peat free. Delivers to shows. Wheelchair accessible.
OS Grid Ref: TM055656

ERCP **ROSE COTTAGE PLANTS**
Bay Tree Farm, Epping Green, Essex, CM16 6PU
Ⓣ (01992) 573775
Ⓔ anne@rosecottageplants.co.uk
Ⓦ www.rosecottageplants.co.uk
Contact: Anne & Jack Barnard
Opening Times: Most Fridays Mar-Oct. Also by appt. & for special events. See website for details.
Min Mail Order UK: Nmc
Min Mail Order EU: £20.00
Cat. Cost: Online only.
Credit Cards: All major debit/credit cards except American Express
Specialities: Hardy bulbs & dahlias.
Notes: Mail order for Dahlia tubers and hardy bulbs. Delivers to shows.
OS Grid Ref: TL435053

ERom **THE ROMANTIC GARDEN** ♿
The Street, Swannington, Norwich, Norfolk, NR9 5NW
Ⓣ (01603) 261488
Ⓜ 07802 722072
Ⓕ (01603) 864231
Ⓔ enquiries@romantic-garden-nursery.co.uk
Ⓦ www.romantic-garden-nursery.co.uk
Contact: John Powles
Opening Times: 1000-1700 Mon-Sat incl. B/hol Mons.
Min Mail Order UK: £5.00 + p&p
Min Mail Order EU: £30.00 + p&p
Cat. Cost: 6 × 1st class.
Credit Cards: All major credit/debit cards
Specialities: Conservatory. *Buxus* topiary, ornamental standards, large specimens. Hedging. Topiary
Notes: Exports beyond EU. Wheelchair accessible. Also sells wholesale.

ESgI **SEAGATE IRISES** ♿
A17 Long Sutton By-Pass, Long Sutton, Lincolnshire, PE12 9RX
Ⓣ (01406) 364028
Ⓜ 07766 862603
Ⓔ sales@irises.co.uk
Ⓦ www.irises.co.uk
Contact: Chris Davey
Opening Times: 1000-1700 daily Apr-Oct
Min Mail Order UK: £20.00 + p&p
Cat. Cost: £3.50 + p&p.
Credit Cards: Paypal
Specialities: Different types of *Iris*, bearded, beardless & species hybrids with about 800+ varieties, both historic & modern. Plants available in pots & bareroot in lifting season. Some only available in small quantities. A growing selection of choice perennials.
Notes: Wheelchair accessible.
OS Grid Ref: TF437218

EShb **SHRUBLAND PARK NURSERIES**
Maltings Farm, Whatfield Road, Elmsett, Ipswich, Suffolk, IP7 6LZ
Ⓣ (01473) 657012
Ⓜ 07890 527744
Ⓔ gill@shrublandparknurseries.co.uk
Ⓦ www.shrublandparknurseries.co.uk
Contact: Gill & Catherine Stitt
Opening Times: See website or contact nursery.
Min Mail Order UK: Nmc
Min Mail Order EU: Nmc
Credit Cards: All major credit/debit cards, Paypal
Specialities: Conservatory plants, succulents, hardy perennials, climbers, shrubs, ferns & grasses. Some more unusual plants may be in short supply.
Notes: Please check before visiting that nursery is open & that any plants you require are in stock. Delivers to shows.
OS Grid Ref: TM052466

ESMi **STRAIGHT MILE NURSERY GARDENS** ♿
Ongar Road, Pilgrims Hatch, Brentwood, Essex, CM15 9SA
Ⓣ (01277) 374439
Ⓔ info@straightmile.net
Ⓦ www.straightmile.net
Contact: David Sisley
Opening Times: 1000-1700 7 days (but closed some Weds, phone first.)
Min Mail Order UK: Nmc
Cat. Cost: Epimedium catalogue only.
Credit Cards: All major debit/credit cards except American Express
Specialities: General nursery stock. Japanese maples, *Epimedium*. Some in small quantities only. Mail order *Epimedium* only.
Notes: Delivers to shows. Wheelchair accessible.
OS Grid Ref: TQ571964

EStr **STRICTLY DAYLILIES**
2 Primes Corner, Histon, Cambridgeshire, CB24 9AG
Ⓣ (01223) 236239
Ⓜ 07765 236880
Ⓔ info@strictlydaylilies.com
Ⓦ www.strictlydaylilies.com
Contact: Paula & Chris Dyason
Opening Times: Mail order only.
Min Mail Order UK: Nmc
Min Mail Order EU: Nmc
Cat. Cost: No charge.
Credit Cards: All major credit/debit cards
Specialities: *Hemerocallis*. Some stock available in small quantities only. National Collection of *Hemerocallis* (post 2014 hybrid registrations).
Notes: Open gardens Fri-Sun in Jul, please phone for confirmation. Also sells wholesale. Exports beyond EU. Delivers to shows. Euro accepted.

ESty **STYLE ROSES** ♿
(office/Admin) Highworth, 56 Spalding Road, Holbeach, Spalding, Lincolnshire, PE12 7HG
Ⓣ (01406) 424089
Ⓜ 07760 626750/07780 860415
Ⓕ (01406) 490006
Ⓔ mail@styleroses.co.uk
Ⓦ www.styleroses.co.uk

E

Contact: Margaret Styles
Opening Times: 0900-1700 Mon-Fri at Nursery address only, other times by appt. Rose Field Jun-Oct.
Min Mail Order UK: Nmc
Min Mail Order EU: Nmc
Cat. Cost: Free in UK.
Credit Cards: MasterCard, Visa
Specialities: Standard & Bush garden roses sold bareroot, order from July and available for dispatch from November to March only. Potted roses available all year round. Mail order and collection service.
Notes: Nursery at Cackle Hill Farm, Boston Road North, Holbeach, Spalding, Lincolnshire, PE12 8AG. Bush roses av mail order mainland UK all year, Std roses as bare-root Nov-Mar. Potted roses by collection/ shows all year. Export to EU Nov-Mar. Also sells wholesale. Delivers to shows. Wheelchair accessible

ESwi **SWINES MEADOW FARM NURSERY** ♿ ◆
47 Towngate East, Market Deeping, Peterborough, Lincolnshire, PE6 8LQ
Ⓣ 07432 627766
Ⓔ rareplants@me.com
Ⓦ www.swinesmeadowfarmnursery.co.uk
Contact: Colin Ward
Opening Times: 0900-1600 Mon-Sat, 1000-1600 Sun. Closed Jan-Feb except by appt. only.
Min Mail Order UK: £10.00
Min Mail Order EU: £10.00
Credit Cards: All major debit/credit cards except American Express
Specialities: Hardy exotics, tree ferns, bamboos & *Hostas*. Wollemi pine stockist. Many specialities available in small quantities only.
Notes: Delivers to shows. Wheelchair accessible.
OS Grid Ref: TF150113

ETho **THORNCROFT CLEMATIS LTD** ♿
The Lings, Reymerston, Norwich, Norfolk, NR9 4QG
Ⓣ (01953) 850407
Ⓔ sales@thorncroftclematis.co.uk
Ⓦ www.thorncroftclematis.co.uk
Contact: Peter Skeggs-Gooch
Opening Times: Mail order only. Telephones answered 1000-1600 Mon-Fri.
Min Mail Order UK: £7.99
Min Mail Order EU: £20.00
Cat. Cost: £3.50.
Credit Cards: All major credit/debit cards
Specialities: *Clematis.*
Notes: Supply, by mail order, mature garden-ready Clematis plants 2 years +. Diverse range from all over the world including unusual & popular varieties. Excellent customer service & advice as well as quality plants. Delivers to shows. Wheelchair accessible.
OS Grid Ref: TG039062

ETod **TODD'S BOTANICS**
Ⓣ (01376) 561212
Ⓔ info@toddsbotanics.co.uk
Ⓦ www.toddsbotanics.co.uk
Contact: Emma Macdonald
Opening Times: Not open, mail order only
Min Mail Order UK: Nmc
Credit Cards: All major debit/credit cards except American Express
Specialities: Specialists in Olives, *Canna*, *Blechnum*, *Cyathea* & *Dicksonia*. Hold a range of tall bearded *Iris* grown in large quantities.
Notes: Website mail order sales but also sells through the larger RHS shows such as Chelsea, Hampton Court and Tatton Park. Larger plants can be pre-ordered and collected from shows, subject to availability. Also sells wholesale. Euro accepted.

ETWh **TREVOR WHITE OLD FASHIONED ROSES**
Bennetts Brier, 59, The Street, Felthorpe, Norwich, Norfolk, NR10 4AB
Ⓣ (01603) 755135
Ⓕ (01603) 755135
Ⓔ sales@trevorwhiteroses.co.uk
Ⓦ www.trevorwhiteroses.co.uk
Contact: Trevor White
Opening Times: 0900-1630 Mon-Fri (office)
Min Mail Order UK: One plant + p&p
Min Mail Order EU: One plant + p&p
Credit Cards: All major credit/debit cards
Specialities: Old, shrub, climbing and rambling roses.
Notes: Specialist grower of roses for over 30 years. All plants grown by us and available via the website. Unique collection of ancient and modern varieties for all types of garden. Bare root plants are top quality and lifted to order (not stored). Some varieties available potted (all in peat-free compost).

EVic **VICTORIAN VIOLAS**
85 Fulmar Road, Lincoln, Lincolnshire, LN6 0RX
Ⓣ (01522) 686343
Ⓔ victorianviolas@gmail.com
Ⓦ www.victorianviolas.co.uk
Contact: Robert Chapman
Opening Times: Not open. Mail order only.

Min Mail Order UK: Nmc
Cat. Cost: Online only.
Credit Cards: None
Specialities: Hardy perennial violas (summer flowering). Named cultivars.
Notes: BACS payments accepted. Also sells wholesale.

EWat **Water Garden Plants**
Beck View, Chequers Road, Gresham, Norwich, Norfolk, NR11 8RQ
Ⓣ (01263) 577627
Ⓔ sales@watergardenplants.co.uk
Ⓦ www.watergardenplants.co.uk
Contact: Anna Robinson
Opening Times: Mail order only.
Min Mail Order UK: Nmc
Min Mail Order EU: Nmc
Cat. Cost: Online.
Credit Cards: All major credit/debit cards
Specialities: Range of water garden plants: water lilies, floating plants, oxygenating plants, marginals, marsh plants. Some stock in small quantities.
OS Grid Ref: TQ585995

EWes **West Acre Gardens** ♿
Tumbleyhill Road, West Acre, King's Lynn, Norfolk, PE32 1UJ
Ⓣ (01760) 755562
Ⓔ info@westacregardens.co.uk
Ⓦ www.westacregardens.co.uk
Contact: J. J. Tuite
Opening Times: 1000-1700 7 days 1st Feb-30th Nov. Other times by appt.
Credit Cards: Visa, MasterCard, Delta, Switch
Specialities: Very wide selection of herbaceous & other garden plants incl. *Rhodohypoxis*, *Primula auricula* & *Galanthus*.
Notes: Delivers to shows. Wheelchair accessible.
OS Grid Ref: TF792182

EWhm **Waltham Herbs**
Willow Vale Nursery, North Kelsey Road, Caistor, Lincolnshire, LN7 6SF
Ⓣ (01472) 859481
Ⓜ 07949 883091
Ⓕ (01472) 859481
Ⓔ angelasach2@aol.com
Ⓦ www.waltham-herbs.co.uk
Contact: Steve Penney
Opening Times: By appt. only.
Min Mail Order UK: £3.00
Credit Cards: All major credit/debit cards
Specialities: Herbs, lavenders and perennials, also some shrubs. Peat-free and pesticide-free.
Notes: For open days, see website or contact nursery. Delivers to shows.
OS Grid Ref: TA401509

EWld **Woodlands**
Peppin Lane, Fotherby, Louth, Lincolnshire, LN11 0UW
Ⓣ (01507) 603586
Ⓔ annbobarmstrong@btinternet.com
Ⓦ www.woodlandsplants.co.uk
Contact: Ann Armstrong
Opening Times: Very flexible, year round. Always open Wednedsay afternoons May-Aug.
Min Mail Order UK: Nmc
Min Mail Order EU: Nmc
Credit Cards: None
Specialities: Small but interesting range of unusual plants, esp. woodland, *Codonopsis* and *Salvia*, all grown on the nursery in limited quantity. National Plant Collection of *Codonopsis*.
Notes: Mature garden, art gallery & refreshments. Euro accepted.
OS Grid Ref: TF322918

EWoo **Woottens of Wenhaston** ♿
The Iris Field, Hall Road, Wenhaston, Suffolk, IP19 9HF
Ⓣ (01502) 478258
Ⓜ 07802 507693
Ⓕ (01502) 478888
Ⓔ info@woottensplants.co.uk
Ⓦ https://www.woottensplants.com/
Contact: Lucinda Skinner
Opening Times: 1000-1600 every Sat Mar-Oct open to the public. Nursery Office 0900-1700 Mon-Fri.
Min Mail Order UK: £7.50
Min Mail Order EU: £25.00
Cat. Cost: Online only.
Credit Cards: All major debit/credit cards except American Express
Specialities: *Pelargonium*, *Hemerocallis*, *Auricula*, *Iris* and hardy *Geranium*.
Notes: Suffolk based plant nursery specialising in *Iris*, *Auricula*, *Pleargonium* and *Hemerocallis* as well as many other herbaceous perennials. Our mail order service runs throughout the year and the nursery is open to the public every Saturday from Mar-Oct and select events. Specialist event days throughout the year. Delivers to shows. Wheelchair accessible.
OS Grid Ref: TM429747

EWTr **Walnut Tree Garden Nursery**
Flymoor Lane, Rocklands, Attleborough, Norfolk, NR17 1BP
Ⓣ (01953) 488163

E

Ⓔ info@wtgn.co.uk
Ⓦ www.wtgn.co.uk
Contact: Jim Paine & Clare Billington
Opening Times: 0900-1700 Wed-Sun 1st Feb-31st Oct or by appt.
Min Mail Order UK: £20.00
Cat. Cost: Online.
Credit Cards: All major credit/debit cards
Specialities: Flowering dogwood: *Cornus florida*, *C. kousa* & *C. nuttalli* cvs. Crab apple (*Malus*) cvs.
Notes: Delivers to shows.
OS Grid Ref: TL978973

Scotland

GAbr **Abriachan Nurseries**
Loch Ness Side, Inverness, Inverness-shire, IV3 8LA
Ⓣ (01463) 861232
Ⓔ info@lochnessgarden.com
Ⓦ www.lochnessgarden.com
Contact: Mr & Mrs D. Davidson
Opening Times: 0900-1900 daily (dusk if earlier) Feb-Nov.
Min Mail Order UK: Nmc
Cat. Cost: 4 × 1st class.
Credit Cards: All major credit/debit cards
Specialities: Herbaceous perennials, old-fashioned *Primula*, *Helianthemum*, hardy Geraniums, *Sempervivum* & *Primula auricula*.
Notes: Delivers to shows. Partial wheelchair access (to nursery only).
OS Grid Ref: NH571347

GArf **Ardfearn Nursery** ♿
Bunchrew, Inverness, Highland, IV3 8RH
Ⓣ (01463) 243250
Ⓜ 07770 887299
Ⓕ (01463) 711713
Ⓔ ardfearn@gmail.com
Ⓦ www.ardfearn-nursery.co.uk/
Contact: Alasdair Sutherland
Opening Times: 0900-1700 Mon-Fri. W/ends by appt.
Min Mail Order UK: Nmc
Min Mail Order EU: Nmc
Cat. Cost: Online.
Credit Cards: All major credit/debit cards
Specialities: Extensive selection of alpines & woodland plants, including *Ericaceae*, *Primulaceae*, trilliums & celmisias. Many Asiatic and Southern Hemisphere varieties available.
Notes: Specialist grower of alpines and hardy plants in the Scottish Highlands. Famous for alpines but also grow shrubs, perennials and climbers. Many unusual varieties. Friendly, expert advice. Attend Scottish Rock Garden Club shows. Mail order primarily for Alpines only. Wheelchair accessible. Delivers to shows.
OS Grid Ref: NH604461

GBee **Beeches Cottage Nursery**
Near Hawksland, Lesmahagow, South Lanarkshire, ML11 9PY
Ⓣ (01555) 893369
Ⓜ 07930 343131
Ⓔ thebeeches.nursery@talktalk.net
Ⓦ www.beechescottage.co.uk
Contact: Margaret & Steven Harrison
Opening Times: 1000-1630 Wed-Sun Apr-Sep.
Credit Cards: None
Specialities: Traditional & unusual hardy cottage garden perennials which can be seen growing in display gardens at 850ft.
Notes: Group visits by arrangement. Partial wheelchair access.
OS Grid Ref: NS837403

GBin **Binny Plants** ♿
Binny Estate, Ecclesmachan Road, Near Broxburn, West Lothian, EH52 6NL
Ⓣ (01506) 858931
Ⓜ 07753 626117
Ⓔ contact@binnyplants.com
Ⓦ www.binnyplants.com
Contact: Billy Carruthers & David Wong
Opening Times: 1000-1700 7 days. Closed over Christmas & New Year.
Min Mail Order UK: Nmc
Min Mail Order EU: Nmc
Cat. Cost: 4 × 1st class.
Credit Cards: Visa, MasterCard, EuroCard, Maestro
Specialities: Over 250 varieties of *Paeonia*, plus a good range of herbaceous perennials, grasses & ferns incl. *Astilbe*, *Bergenia*, *Geranium*, *Molinia*, *Persicaria* & *Iris*.
Notes: Also sells wholesale. Exports beyond the EU. Delivers to shows. Wheelchair accessible.
OS Grid Ref: NT050732

GCro **Croft 16 Daffodils**
16 Midtown of Inverasdale, Poolewe, Ross-shire, IV22 2LW
Ⓣ (01445) 781717
Ⓔ sales@croft16daffodils.co.uk
Ⓦ www.croft16daffodils.co.uk
Contact: Duncan & Kate Donald
Opening Times: Not open. Mail order only.

Min Mail Order UK: Nmc
Min Mail Order EU: Nmc
Cat. Cost: Online only.
Credit Cards: Paypal
Specialities: National Plant Collection of *Narcissus* bred pre-1930. Some stocks only available in small quantities. A waiting list for *desiderata* is in operation.
Notes: Please order by mid-May for delivery in the same year. Orders unfulfilled in one season will take priority the following year, if then available. Customers outside the EU should contact nursery.
OS Grid Ref: NG822851

GDam **Damhead Nursery Ltd** ♿
Damhead Farm, Lothianburn, Edinburgh, Midlothian, EH10 7DZ
Ⓣ (0131) 445 4698
Ⓔ enquiries@damheadnursery.co.uk
Ⓦ www.damheadnursery.co.uk
Contact: Sue Gray
Opening Times: 0800-1630 Mon-Fri
Credit Cards: All major credit/debit cards
Specialities: Hardy plants for Scottish gardens.
Notes: Also sells wholesale. Wheelchair accessible.

GEdr **Edrom Nurseries**
Coldingham, Eyemouth, Berwickshire, TD14 5TZ
Ⓣ (01890) 771386
Ⓕ (01890) 771387
Ⓔ mail@edrom-nurseries.co.uk
Ⓦ www.edrom-nurseries.co.uk
Contact: Mr Terry Hunt
Opening Times: 0900-1700 Thu, Fri, Sat & Mon (closed Tue & Wed), 1000-1600 Sun.
Min Mail Order UK: Nmc
Min Mail Order EU: Nmc
Cat. Cost: Free.
Credit Cards: All major credit/debit cards
Specialities: *Epimedium*, *Gentiana*, *Primula*, *Meconopsis*, *Rhodohypoxis*, *Trillium*, *Hepatica* & Japanese *Saxifraga*.
Notes: Delivers to shows.
OS Grid Ref: NT873663

GFgr **Firgrove Plants**
21 South Main Street, Wigtown, Newton Stewart, Dumfries and Galloway, DG8 9EH
Ⓣ (01988) 402054
Ⓜ 07749 314394
Ⓔ jenny.mackinnon@virgin.net
Ⓦ http://firgrovehouseleeks.zohosites.eu/
Contact: Jenny MacKinnon
Opening Times: Not open. Mail order only.
Min Mail Order UK: £11.00
Cat. Cost: Sae.
Credit Cards: None
Specialities: Wide range of houseleeks in small quantities.
Notes: Houseleeks by mail order Apr-Sept.

GGGa **Glendoick Gardens Ltd**
Glendoick, Perth, Perthshire, PH2 7NS
Ⓣ (01738) 860205
Ⓔ gardencentre@glendoick.com
Ⓦ www.glendoick.com
Contact: Kenneth Cox
Opening Times: Nursery not open to the public. Garden centre open 0900-1730 (summer), 0900-1700 (winter) 7 days. Gardens open Apr & May, details on website or contact nursery for details.
Min Mail Order UK: £250.00
Min Mail Order EU: £500.00
Credit Cards: All major debit/credit cards except American Express
Specialities: Rhododendrons, azaleas, other ericaceous plants, & *Meconopsis*. Plants from wild seed. Most but not all plants available at garden centre. Three National Plant Collections.
Notes: Wheelchair access to Garden Centre.

GGro **Growild Nursery**
Loganhill Farm, Cumnock, East Ayrshire, KA18 3BX
Ⓔ info@growildnursery.co.uk
Ⓦ www.growildnursery.co.uk
Contact: Lisa Wesley & Andrew Blackwood
Opening Times: Not open, mail order only
Min Mail Order UK: Nmc
Min Mail Order EU: Nmc
Cat. Cost: Online only.
Credit Cards: Paypal
Specialities: Grow rare and unusual species plants, in particular hardy perennials from Japan, China and the Himalayas. A large selection of woodland plants, begonias, hardy impatiens, persicaria, violas & salvias as well as rarely grown UK wildflowers that attract pollinating insects.
Notes: No peat-based products are used in the nursery. No chemicals or animal-derived products are used on our plants and only seaweed fertilser is used.

GJos **Jo's Garden Enterprise** ♿
Easter Balmungle Farm, Eathie Road, by Rosemarkie, Ross-shire, IV10 8SL
Ⓣ (01381) 621006
Ⓔ jos_garden_enterprise@hotmail.co.uk/anne.chance@ukonline.co.uk

Contact: Joanna Chance
Opening Times: 1000 to dusk, 7 days.
Cat. Cost: None.
Credit Cards: None
Specialities: Alpines & herbaceous perennials. Selection of native wild flowers.
Notes: Wheelchair accessible.
OS Grid Ref: NH600742

G

GKev **Kevock Garden Plants**
Kevock Road, Lasswade, Midlothian, EH18 1HX
Ⓣ (0131) 454 0660
Ⓔ info@kevockgarden.co.uk
Ⓦ www.kevockgarden.co.uk
Contact: Elea Strang
Opening Times: Mail order only.
Min Mail Order UK: £30.00
Min Mail Order EU: £30.00
Cat. Cost: 2 × 2nd class.
Credit Cards: All major credit/debit cards
Specialities: Chinese and Himalayan plants. *Trillium*, *Daphne*, *Paeonia*, *Primula*, *Meconopsis*, *Iris*, woodland plants, alpine plants, rock plants, marginal and bog plants, bulbs, Chinese and Himalayan trees and shrubs, *Sorbus*, *Rhododendron*.
Notes: We only sell by mail order as we are a nursery and so we are not open to the public. Please purchase plants by mail order or from plant stalls at the shows we attend. Delivers to shows. Also sells wholesale.

GKin **Kinlochlaich Garden Plant Centre**
c/o Blarchasgaig, Appin, Argyll, PA38 4BB
Ⓜ 07881 525754
Ⓔ fiona@kinlochlaich.plus.com
Ⓦ www.kinlochlaichgardencentre.co.uk
Contact: Fiona Hutchison
Opening Times: 1000-1700 Mar-mid Oct, 1000-1500 or by appt. mid-Oct-Feb.
Credit Cards: All major credit/debit cards
Specialities: Hardy shrubs, trees, azaleas, perennials. Also Gulf Stream plants such as *Tropaeolum*, *Embothrium*, *Eucryphia*, *Drymis* & more. Good selection of hardy seaside plants.
Notes: Does not offer mail order but will post where possible. Limited wheelchair access (gravel paths), wheelchair accessible toilet.

GLet **Letham Plants**
11a Letham Mains Holdings, Haddington, East Lothian, EH41 4NW
Ⓣ (01620) 822350
Ⓜ 07842 211712
Ⓔ lethamplants@hotmail.co.uk
Ⓦ www.letham-plants.co.uk
Contact: Caroline Samuel
Opening Times: By appt. only.
Min Mail Order UK: Nmc
Min Mail Order EU: Nmc
Cat. Cost: Online only.
Credit Cards: All major credit/debit cards
Specialities: *Astrantia*, *Dicentra*.
Notes: Also sells wholesale. Delivers to shows. Euro accepted.
OS Grid Ref: NT487730

GLog **Logie Steading Plants** ♿
Logie Steading, Dunphail, Forres, Moray, IV36 2QN
Ⓣ (01309) 611222 or 611278
Ⓕ (01309) 611300
Ⓔ panny@logie.co.uk
Ⓦ www.logie.co.uk
Contact: Mrs Panny Laing
Opening Times: 1000-1700 hours, 7 days, Feb-Xmas.
Credit Cards: All major credit/debit cards
Specialities: Unusual hardy plants, grown in Scotland for Scottish gardens. Large range of hardy geraniums, bold herbaceous plants, grasses & marginal plants, trees and shrubs
Notes: Logie House Garden open every day. Café, farm shop, art gallery, second-hand books, antiques, whisky & wine, river walk, heritage centre. Wheelchair accessible (except river walk).
OS Grid Ref: NJ006504

GMaP **Macplants** ♿
Berrybank Nursery, 5 Boggs Holdings, Pencaitland, East Lothian, EH34 5BA
Ⓣ (01875) 341179
Ⓔ sales@macplants.co.uk
Ⓦ www.macplants.co.uk
Contact: Gavin McNaughton
Opening Times: 1030-1700 7 days, Mar-end Sep. 1030-1600 Mon-Fri, Oct. Closed Nov-end Feb except by appt.
Min Mail Order UK: Nmc
Cat. Cost: 4 × 2nd class.
Credit Cards: MasterCard, Switch, Visa
Specialities: Herbaceous perennials, alpines, hardy ferns & grasses. *Meconopsis*. National Collection of *Sanguisorba*.
Notes: Also sells wholesale. Delivers to shows. Wheelchair accessible.
OS Grid Ref: NT447703

GPer **Perthshire Heathers**
Starr Farm, Cupar, Fife, KY15 4NP
Ⓜ 07734 175937

Ⓔ irene@perthshireheathers.com
Ⓦ www.perthshireheathers.com
Contact: Irene Lang
Min Mail Order UK: Nmc
Specialities: Heathers.
Notes: Mail order for small orders only.

GPoy **Poyntzfield Herb Nursery** ♿
Nr Balblair, Black Isle, Dingwall, Ross-shire, IV7 8LX
Ⓣ (01381) 610352. Phone between 1200-1300 & 1800-1900 Mon-Fri 1200-1300 Sat
Ⓔ info@poyntzfieldherbs.co.uk
Ⓦ www.poyntzfieldherbs.co.uk
Contact: Duncan Ross
Opening Times: 1300-1700 Mon-Sat 1st Mar-30th Sep, 1300-1700 Sun May-Aug.
Min Mail Order UK: £10.00 + p&p
Min Mail Order EU: £20.00 + p&p
Cat. Cost: 4 × 1st class.
Credit Cards: All major credit/debit cards
Specialities: Over 400 popular, unusual & rare herbs esp. medicinal. Also seeds.
Notes: Mail order operates in the spring & autumn. Exports beyond the EU. Wheelchair accessible.
OS Grid Ref: NH711642

GPSL **Plants, Shoots and Leaves**
Dovecot Bungalow, Haddington, East Lothian, EH41 4HA
Ⓣ (01620) 823536
Ⓜ 07885 444241
Ⓔ karen.leys@btinternet.com
Ⓦ www.plantsshootsandleaves.co.uk
Contact: Karen Payne
Opening Times: 1000-1700 1st Apr-1st Oct. Closed Mon. Please phone first. Nursery may be closed when we are attending shows.
Min Mail Order UK: £3.50
Min Mail Order EU: £6.60
Cat. Cost: Online only.
Credit Cards: All major credit/debit cards
Specialities: *Epimedium*. Hardy geraniums. Perennials and some shrubs. Some available in small quantities only.
Notes: Delivers to shows. Euro accepted. Partial wheelchair accessible.
OS Grid Ref: NT500730

GQue **Quercus Garden Plants Ltd**
Whitmuir Farm, Lamancha, West Linton, Scottish Borders, EH46 7BB
Ⓣ (01968) 660708
Ⓔ rona@quercusgardenplants.co.uk
Ⓦ www.quercusgardenplants.co.uk
Contact: Rona Dodds
Opening Times: 1000-1700 Wed-Sun.
Cat. Cost: Online only.
Credit Cards: All major credit/debit cards
Specialities: Tough plants for Scottish gardens. Wide range of plants, including old favourites and many unusual varieties of herbaceous perennials, grasses, trees, shrubs & plants for shade, wet ground and other challenging garden area suited to growing in exposed gardens.
Notes: Plants grown at 850ft above sea level, making them tough and well acclimatised to Scottish growing conditions. Majority of plants propagated on site and grown on for at least one season. Display gardens show customers what can be grown in these challenging conditions.
OS Grid Ref: NT192512

GRum **Rumbling Bridge Nursery**
Briglands Estate, Rumbling Bridge, Kinross, Perth and Kinross, KY13 0PS
Ⓣ (01577) 840160
Ⓔ hello@rumblingbridgenursery.co.uk
Ⓦ www.rumblingbridgenursery.co.uk
Contact: Graeme Butler
Opening Times: By appt. only, all year.
Min Mail Order UK: Nmc
Min Mail Order EU: £50.00
Cat. Cost: Online only.
Specialities: Alpines, woodland plants, dwarf shrubs, dwarf ericaceous, *Cyclamen*, *Primula auricula* cultivars.
Notes: All plants grown in peat-free compost, except ericaceous shrubs. Mail order to the public all year round. Also accept pre-booked groups for visits (Pls call to arrange). Delivers to shows. Partially wheelchair accessible to sales area.

GWyn **Wyndford Farm Plants Ltd**
Wyndford Farm, Ecclesmachan, West Lothian, EH52 6NW
Ⓜ 07871 496732
Ⓔ info@wyndfordfarmplants.com
Ⓦ www.wyndfordfarmplants.com
Contact: Adam Fleming
Opening Times: 1000-1700 Apr-Oct 7 days or by appt.
Min Mail Order UK: Nmc
Cat. Cost: Online only.
Credit Cards: All major credit/debit cards
Specialities: Large range of perennials & shrubs, incl. large collection of *Primula sieboldii* and *Viola*.
Notes: Also sells wholesale. Delivers to shows.
OS Grid Ref: NT059731

N. IRELAND & REPUBLIC

IArd **ARDCARNE GARDEN CENTRE** ♿
Ardcarne, Boyle, Co. Roscommon, F52 RY61, Ireland
Ⓣ +353 (7196) 67091
Ⓕ +353 (7196) 67341
Ⓔ info@ardcarne.ie
Ⓦ www.ardcarne.ie
Contact: James Wickham, Mary Frances Dwyer, Kirsty Ainge
Opening Times: 0900-1800 Mon-Sat, 1300-1800 Sun & B/hols.
Credit Cards: Access, Visa, Mastercard, Switch, American Express
Specialities: Native & unusual trees, choice perennials, roses, plants for coastal areas, fruit trees, incl. heritage Irish apple trees, vegetable plants, specimen plants & semi-mature trees. Wide general range.
Notes: Café. Groups & tours welcome. Ample free parking. Garden design & landscape service available. Euro accepted. Wheelchair accessible.

IBal **BALI-HAI MAIL ORDER NURSERY**
42 Largy Road, Carnlough, Ballymena, Co. Antrim, N. Ireland, BT44 0EZ
Ⓣ (028) 2888 5289
Ⓜ 07708 257164
Ⓔ balihainursery@btinternet.com
Ⓦ www.mailorderplants4me.com
Contact: Mrs M. E. Scroggy
Opening Times: Mon-Sat by appt. only.
Min Mail Order UK: Nmc
Min Mail Order EU: Nmc
Cat. Cost: Online only.
Credit Cards: All major credit/debit cards
Specialities: National Collection of *Hosta* and *Agapanthus*, part planted in 1.5 acres, open to the public by appt. *Crocosmia*, *Rhodohypoxis*, tree ferns & other perennials. Hostas grown to order.
Notes: Also sells wholesale. Export beyond EU restricted to bare-root perennials, no grasses. Euro accepted.
OS Grid Ref: D287184

IBlr **BALLYROGAN NURSERIES** ♿
The Grange, Ballyrogan, Newtownards, Co. Down, N. Ireland, BT23 4SD
Ⓣ (028) 9181 0451 (evenings)
Ⓔ gary.dunlop@btinternet.com
Contact: Gary Dunlop
Opening Times: By appt. only
Min Mail Order UK: £10.00 + p&p
Min Mail Order EU: £20.00 + p&p
Cat. Cost: 1 x 2nd class stamp or by email.
Credit Cards: None
Specialities: Choice herbaceous. *Agapanthus*, *Crocosmia*, *Rodgersia*, *Dierama*, *Erythronium*, *Roscoea* & *Watsonia*.
Notes: Also sells wholesale. Euro accepted. Wheelchair accessible.

IDee **DEELISH GARDEN CENTRE**
Deelish, Skibbereen, Co. Cork, P81FD34, Ireland
Ⓣ +353 (28) 21374
Ⓕ +353 (28) 21374
Ⓔ sales@deelish.ie
Ⓦ www.deelish.ie
Contact: Bill & Rain Chase
Opening Times: 1000-1800 Mon-Sat, 1400-1800 Sun.
Min Mail Order UK: Nmc
Min Mail Order EU: Nmc
Credit Cards: Visa, MasterCard, Access, Paypal
Specialities: Unusual plants for the mild coastal climate of Ireland. Conservatory plants. Sole Irish agents for Chase Organic Seeds.
Notes: No mail order outside Ireland & UK. Euro accepted.

IDic **COLIN DICKSON T/A DICKSON NURSERIES**
50 Milecross Road, Newtownards, Co. Down, N. Ireland, BT23 4SR
Ⓣ 07821 922204
Ⓔ mail@dickson-roses.co.uk
Ⓦ www.dickson-roses.co.uk
Contact: Colin Dickson
Opening Times: 0800-1430 Mon-Thu. 0800-1230 Fri. Closed w/ends
Min Mail Order UK: Nmc
Min Mail Order EU: £25.00 + p&p
Cat. Cost: Free.
Credit Cards: None
Specialities: Roses esp. modern Dickson varieties. Limited selection, check website or contact nursery. Most varieties available in small quantities only.
Notes: Also sells wholesale.

IKel **KELLS BAY HOUSE AND GARDENS**
Kells, Cahersiveen, Kerry, V23 EP48, Ireland
Ⓣ +353 (66) 947 7975
Ⓜ +353 (87) 7776666
Ⓔ billy@kellsbay.ie
Ⓦ www.kellsbay.ie
Contact: Billy Alexander
Opening Times: Gardens are open all year round from 0900 to dusk. Nursery is open daily, but we advise you to contact us in

advance of a visit as we are not always there.
Cat. Cost: By email free of charge.
Credit Cards: All major credit/debit cards
Specialities: We specialise in Southern Hemisphere ferns, especially the genera *Blechnum*, *Cyathea*, *Dicksonia*, *Doodia* and *Lophosoria*.
Notes: The Kells Bay Gardens Plant Centre is an enthusiast-owned nursery that specialises in the import of Tree Ferns and other rare and unusual exotics from around the world. Delivers to shows.

ILea **LEAMORE NURSERY**
Cronroe, Ashford, Co. Wicklow, A67 Y681, Ireland
Ⓣ +353 (87) 227 8850
Ⓔ info@leamorenursery.com
Ⓦ www.leamorenursery.com
Contact: Phil Havercroft
Opening Times: Not open.
Min Mail Order UK: €25
Min Mail Order EU: €25
Cat. Cost: Online only.
Credit Cards: All major credit/debit cards
Specialities: *Paeonia* & other perennials. Most items in large quantities. Itoh peonies & some more unusual items only available in small quantities.
Notes: Bare-root peonies supplied in autumn, available to order from Jul (on website). Founding members of the Irish Specialist Nursery Association (ISNA). Also sells wholesale. Delivers to shows. Sterling & Euro accepted.

IPap **PAPERVALE TREES**
48 Old Newry Road, Rathfriland, Newry, County Down, N. Ireland, BT34 5BQ
Ⓣ (02830) 850059
Ⓜ 07753 117837
Ⓔ info@papervaletrees.com
Ⓦ www.papervaletrees.com
Contact: Jonathan Jackson
Opening Times: Mon-Fri by appt. only 0800-1800 Sat
Min Mail Order UK: Nmc
Min Mail Order EU: Nmc
Cat. Cost: Available online.
Credit Cards: All major credit/debit cards
Specialities: Almost 300 varieties of home-grown containerised trees grown in peat-free compost.
Notes: Based at the foothills of the Mourne mountains, Papervale Trees produces almost 300 species and cultivars of 'Home Grown' trees. Our range includes many hard to find varieties as well as traditional garden favourites, all grown in peat-free compost. Also sells wholesale. Delivers to shows.
OS Grid Ref: SB231884

IPot **THE POTTING SHED**
Bolinaspick, Camolin, Enniscorthy, Co. Wexford, Y21 TD93, Ireland
Ⓣ +353 (5393) 83629
Ⓔ susan@camolinpottingshed.com
Ⓦ www.camolinpottingshed.com
Contact: Susan Carrick
Opening Times: 1300-1700 Thu-Fri 29th Mar-6th Sep, other times by prior arrangement.
Min Mail Order UK: Nmc
Min Mail Order EU: Nmc
Cat. Cost: 3 × 1st class.
Credit Cards: MasterCard, Visa, American Express
Specialities: Grow a wide range of unusual, hard to find & new introductions of herbaceous perennials, ornamental grasses *Clematis* and *Wisteria*.
Notes: Member of the Irish Specialist Nursery Assoc. (ISNA). Orders outside Ireland can only be delivered by courier, charges at cost. Delivers to shows. Euro accepted. Wheelchair accessible.

IRos **ROS BAN WILDLIFE GARDEN** ♿
Common, Raphoe, Co. Donegal, F93 HH0X, Ireland
Ⓣ +353 (74) 91 45336
Ⓜ +353 (8608) 05214
Ⓔ Rosbangarden@gmail.com
Contact: Ann Kavanagh
Opening Times: Garden open, morning to evening, Easter to Sep.
Credit Cards: None
Notes: Plants available in season from the garden. Please check plant availability with nursery before travelling. Euro accepted. Wheelchair accessible.

ITim **TIMPANY NURSERIES & GARDENS** ♿
77 Magheratimpany Road, Ballynahinch, Co. Down, N. Ireland, BT24 8PA
Ⓣ (028) 9756 2812
Ⓜ 07711 428477
Ⓔ s.tindall@btconnect.com
Ⓦ www.timpanynurseries.com
Contact: Susan Tindall
Opening Times: 1000-1730 Tue-Sat, Sun by appt.
Min Mail Order UK: £40.00 + p&p
Min Mail Order EU: £40.00 + p&p
Cat. Cost: £3.50.

Credit Cards: All major debit/credit cards except American Express
Specialities: *Androsace, Cassiope, Celmisia, Cyclamen, Dianthus, Galanthus, Meconopsis, Hosta, Primula, Primula auricula, Rhodohypoxis* & *Saxifraga*.
Notes: Delivers to shows. Wheelchair accessible.

LONDON AREA

L

LAma **JACQUES AMAND INTERNATIONAL LTD** ♿
The Nurseries, 145 Clamp Hill, Stanmore, Middlesex, HA7 3JS
Ⓣ (0208) 420 7110
Ⓕ (0208) 954 6784
Ⓔ bulbs@jacquesamand.co.uk
Ⓦ www.jacquesamandintl.com
Contact: Stuart Chapman
Opening Times: 0900-1700 Mon-Fri, 1000-1600 Sat.
Min Mail Order UK: Nmc
Min Mail Order EU: Nmc
Cat. Cost: 1 × 1st class.
Credit Cards: All major credit/debit cards
Specialities: Rare and unusual species bulbs esp. *Arisaema, Fritillaria, Trillium*, tulips.
Notes: Also sells wholesale. Exports beyond EU. Delivers to shows. Euro accepted. Wheelchair accessible.
OS Grid Ref: TQ154919

LAyl **AYLETT NURSERIES LTD** ♿
North Orbital Road, St Albans, Hertfordshire, AL2 1DH
Ⓣ (01727) 822255
Ⓕ (01727) 823024
Ⓔ info@aylettnurseries.co.uk
Ⓦ www.aylettnurseries.co.uk
Contact: Julie Aylett
Opening Times: 0830-1730 Mon-Fri, 0830-1700 Sat, 1030-1630 Sun.
Cat. Cost: Free.
Credit Cards: All major credit/debit cards
Specialities: *Dahlia*. 2-acre trial ground and garden adjacent to garden centre.
Notes: Wheelchair accessible.
OS Grid Ref: TL169049

LBee **BEECHCROFT NURSERY** ♿ ◆
127 Reigate Road, Ewell, Surrey, KT17 3DE
Ⓣ (020) 8393 4265
Ⓕ (020) 8393 4265
Ⓔ enquiries@beechcroft-nursery.co.uk
Ⓦ www.beechcroft-nursery.co.uk
Contact: C. Kimber
Opening Times: 1000-1600 Mon-Sat, 1000-1400 Sun & B/hols. Closed Xmas-New Year week.
Credit Cards: All major credit/debit cards
Specialities: Conifers.
Notes: Wheelchair accessible.

LBuc **BUCKINGHAM NURSERIES** ♿
14 Tingewick Road, Buckingham, Buckinghamshire, MK18 4AE
Ⓣ (01280) 822133
Ⓕ (01280) 815491
Ⓔ web-enquiries@hedging.co.uk
Ⓦ www.buckingham-nurseries.co.uk
Contact: R. J. & P. L. Brown
Opening Times: 0830-1730 (1800 in summer) Mon-Sat, 1000-1600 Sun.
Min Mail Order UK: Nmc
Min Mail Order EU: Nmc
Cat. Cost: Free.
Credit Cards: Visa, MasterCard, Maestro
Specialities: Bare-rooted and container grown hedging. Fruit trees, soft fruit, trees, shrubs, herbaceous perennials, alpines, grasses & ferns.
Notes: Garden centre with a large range of container grown plants, many unusual. Well stocked shop and restaurant. Wheelchair accessible.
OS Grid Ref: SP676333

LCro **CROCUS.CO.UK**
Nursery Court, London Road, Windlesham, Surrey, GU20 6LQ
Ⓣ (01344) 578000
Ⓔ customerservices@crocus.co.uk/john.hiorns@crocus.co.uk
Ⓦ www.crocus.co.uk
Contact: Customer Care Team
Opening Times: Mail order only. Order lines open 24hrs, 7 days. Nursery has several Open Days a year, see website or phone for details.
Min Mail Order UK: Nmc + delivery charges
Cat. Cost: Free.
Credit Cards: All major debit/credit cards except American Express
Specialities: Large general nursery. Perennials, shrubs, climbers, roses, bulbs, ferns, grasses, herbs & house plants.
Notes: Also sells wholesale.

LEdu **EDULIS** ♿
(office) 1 Flowers Piece, Ashampstead, Reading, Berkshire, RG8 8SG
Ⓣ (01635) 578113
Ⓜ 07802 812781
Ⓔ edulisnursery@gmail.com
Ⓦ www.edulis.co.uk
Contact: Paul Barney

Opening Times: 1000-1600 Tue & Wed, & by appt. Apr-Oct. Nov-Mar by appt. only. See website or contact nursery for Open Days.
Min Mail Order UK: £20.00 + p&p
Min Mail Order EU: £30.00 + p&p
Cat. Cost: Online only.
Credit Cards: All major debit/credit cards except American Express
Specialities: Unusual edibles, architectural plants, permaculture plants & many of our own collections.
Notes: Nursery is at The Walled Garden, Tidmarsh Lane, Pangbourne, RG8 8HT. Also sells wholesale. Delivers to shows. Euro accepted. Wheelchair accessible.
OS Grid Ref: SU615747

LHGe **The Hardy Geranium Nursery**
PO Box 1543, Guildford, Surrey, GU11 9HT
Ⓣ (0208) 1444050
Ⓔ info@hardygeraniumnursery.co.uk
Ⓦ https://hardygeraniumnursery.co.uk/
Contact: Suzie Dewey
Opening Times: Not open, mail order only
Credit Cards: All major credit/debit cards
Specialities: Specialise in hardy geraniums, holding over 100 different cultivars in stock at the height of the growing season.
Notes: This nursery is not open to the public. Mail order, online nursery only. Website open 24 hours a day, 7 days a week.

LHkn **R Harkness & Co. Ltd**
The Rose Gardens, Cambridge Road, Hitchin, Herts, SG4 0JT
Ⓣ (01462) 420402
Ⓔ harkness@roses.co.uk
Ⓦ www.roses.co.uk
Contact: Philip Harkness
Opening Times: 0900-1700 Mon-Fri (Office). 1000-1600 daily during spring/ summer Mon-Fri only during winter (Rose Shop).
Min Mail Order UK: £2.95
Min Mail Order EU: Nmc
Cat. Cost: Free.
Credit Cards: American Express, Visa, Access, Switch, Delta
Specialities: Roses.
Notes: Also sells wholesale. Delivers to shows.

LHom **Home Farm Plants**
Home Farm, Shantock Lane, Bovingdon, Hertfordshire, HP3 0NG
Ⓜ 07773 798068
Ⓔ homefarmplants@gmail.com
Ⓦ www.homefarmplants.co.uk
Contact: Graham Austin
Opening Times: 0900-1730 Fri & Sat, 1000-1600 Sun, viewing by appt. only Mon-Thu, 1st Apr-end Oct (subject to weather conditions).
Cat. Cost: 1st class sae for list.
Credit Cards: All major debit/credit cards except American Express
Specialities: *Delphinium elatum* (over 60 varieties). Hardy perennials. Show area of 200+ delphiniums (contact nursery for flowering times). Some varieties only available in small quantities.
Notes: If travelling, please contact nursery to confirm plant availability. Delivers to shows. Limited wheelchair access.

LHWs **H W Hyde and Son**
The Nursery, New Road, Ruscombe, Reading, Berkshire, RG10 9LN
Ⓣ (0118) 9340011
Ⓜ 07557 530845
Ⓕ (0118) 934 4552
Ⓔ info@hwhyde.co.uk
Ⓦ www.hwhyde.co.uk
Contact: Richard
Opening Times: 1000-1600 By appt.
Min Mail Order UK: £3.25
Min Mail Order EU: £13.50
Cat. Cost: £2.00.
Credit Cards: All major credit/debit cards
Specialities: Bulbous plants including Lilies, *Narcissus*, Tulips and *Zantedeschia*, plus *Dahlia* and hardy *Alstroemeria*.
Notes: Family run business started in 1926 by Herbert William Hyde, currently run by his 3 Grandchildren, Sarah, Richard and Elizabeth. Exports beyond EU. Also sells wholesale. Delivers to shows.

LLWG **Lilies Water Gardens** ♿
Broad Lane, Newdigate, Surrey, RH5 5AT
Ⓣ (01306) 631064
Ⓜ 07801 166244
Ⓔ mail@lilieswatergardens.co.uk
Ⓦ www.lilieswatergardens.co.uk
Contact: Simon Harman
Opening Times: 0900-1700 Thu-Sat, Mar-Aug. By appt. only Sep-Feb.
Min Mail Order UK: Nmc
Min Mail Order EU: Nmc
Cat. Cost: Online only.
Credit Cards: All major credit/debit cards
Specialities: A range of water lilies, moist perennials, bog-garden, pond, marginal & oxygenating plants for all types of water features. Alpine plants, rushes and grasses
Notes: Flat rate £6.50 UK delivery charge. Wheelchair accessible.

L

LMaj **Majestic Trees**
Chequers Meadow, Chequers Hill (Junc 9, M1), Flamstead, St Albans, Hertfordshire, AL3 8ET
Ⓣ (01582) 843881
Ⓕ (01582) 843882
Ⓔ info@majestictrees.co.uk
Ⓦ www.majestictrees.co.uk
Contact: Andy Miles
Opening Times: 0830-1700 Mon-Fri. 1000-1600 Sat, Nov-Feb, 1000-1700 Sat, Mar-Oct. Closed Sun, B/hols, Xmas through New Year.
Credit Cards: MasterCard, Visa, Switch, Maestro
Specialities: Semi-mature & mature containerised trees primarily grown in AirPots from 50ltr to 5000 ltr.
Notes: Also sells wholesale. Delivers to shows. Euro accepted. Disabled access by golf buggy can be arranged by appt. Wheelchair access to building.
OS Grid Ref: TL081081

LMil **Millais Nurseries** ♿
Crosswater Farm, Crosswater Lane, Churt, Farnham, Surrey, GU10 2JN
Ⓣ (01252) 792698
Ⓔ sales@rhododendrons.co.uk
Ⓦ www.rhododendrons.co.uk
Contact: David Millais
Opening Times: 1000-1700 Mon-Fri all year. Please phone or see website for additional weekend opening in spring.
Min Mail Order UK: Nmc
Min Mail Order EU: Nmc
Cat. Cost: Free list on request. Full catalogue online.
Credit Cards: All major credit/debit cards
Specialities: Rhododendrons, azaleas, magnolias, camellias & acers. Garden open in spring.
Notes: Mail order all year. Also sells wholesale. Wheelchair accessible.
OS Grid Ref: SU856397

LOPS **RHS Plant Shop: RHSplants.co.uk** ◆
Nursery Court, London Road, Windlesham, Surrey, GU20 6LQ
Ⓣ (01344) 578822
Ⓔ customerservices@rhsplants.co.uk/john.hiorns@rhsplants.co.uk
Ⓦ www.rhsplants.co.uk
Contact: Customer Care Team
Opening Times: Not open. Mail order online only.
Min Mail Order UK: Nmc
Credit Cards: All major debit/credit cards except American Express
Notes: Large range of plants, including a substantial range of RHS AGM plants.

LPar **Paramount Plants & Gardens Ltd**
131 Theobalds Park Road, Crews Hill, Enfield, London, EN2 9BH
Ⓣ (0208) 367 8809
Ⓜ 07802 952517
Ⓔ info@paramountplants.co.uk
Ⓦ https://www.paramountplants.co.uk/
Contact: Paula Sheehan
Opening Times: On-line store open 24/7.
Min Mail Order UK: Nmc
Min Mail Order EU: Nmc
Credit Cards: All major credit/debit cards
Specialities: While we stock a good cross section of all plants in a wide range of sizes, our specialist areas are mature hedging, mature trees including Japanese *Acers* and Conifers, topiary including unique cloud trees, Mediteranean plants such as Olive trees and hardy tropical plants such as Chusan Palms.
Notes: Established over 25 years ago, Paramount Plants & Gardens is a family-run online retailer of mature trees, plants and hedging, with well over 1,000 plants in our ever-growing collection. Based in Crews Hill, North London, we deliver our plants, no matter the size, throughout the entire UK. Delivers to shows.

LPla **The Plant Specialist** ♿
7 Whitefield Lane, Great Missenden, Buckinghamshire, HP16 0BH
Ⓣ (01494) 866650
Ⓔ enquire@theplantspecialist.co.uk
Ⓦ www.theplantspecialist.co.uk
Contact: Sean Walter
Opening Times: 1000-1700 Wed-Sat, 1000-1600 Sun, Apr-Oct. 1000-1600 B/hol Mon.
Credit Cards: All major credit/debit cards
Specialities: Herbaceous perennials, grasses, half-hardy perennials, bulbs.
Notes: Wheelchair accessible. Delivers to shows.

LPmr **Primrose Hall Peonies**
Toddington Road, Westoning, Bedford, Bedfordshire, MK45 5AH
Ⓣ (01525) 878924
Ⓕ (01525) 878924
Ⓔ customerservice@primrosehall.co.uk
Ⓦ www.primrosehallpeonies.co.uk
Contact: Tracy Gibbon
Opening Times: 0930-1600 Mon-Fri. Please note we are often in the nursery and cannot answer the phone, an email will usually be more reliable.

Min Mail Order UK: Nmc
Min Mail Order EU: Nmc
Credit Cards: All major credit/debit cards
Specialities: National Collection of *Itoh* hybrids.
Notes: Also sells wholesale. Delivers to shows. Euro accepted.

LPot **Potash Plants** ♿
Potash Nursery, Drayton Parslow, Milton Keynes, Buckinghamshire, MK17 0JE
Ⓣ (01296) 720578
Ⓜ 07778 398808
Ⓕ (01296) 720578
Ⓔ info@potashplants.co.uk
Ⓦ www.potashplants.co.uk
Contact: Gill Gallon
Opening Times: 0900-1730 Mon-Sat. 1030-1630 Sun.
Cat. Cost: Online.
Credit Cards: All major debit/credit cards except American Express
Specialities: Wide range of traditional and unusual hardy perennials, grasses, trees & shrubs. Some available in small quantities only.
Notes: Nursery on B4032 mid-way between Aylesbury and Milton Keynes. Also sells wholesale. Delivers to shows. Wheelchair accessible.
OS Grid Ref: SP834279

LRHS **Wisley Plant Centre (RHS)** ♿ ◆
RHS Garden, Wisley, Woking, Surrey, GU23 6QB
Ⓣ (01483) 211113
Ⓔ wisleyplantcentre@RHS.org.uk
Ⓦ www.rhs.org.uk/wisleyplantcentre
Contact: Wisley Plant Centre
Opening Times: 0900-1700 Mon-Sat, Oct-Feb. 0900-1800 Mon-Sat, Mar-Sep. 1100-1700 Sun all year, browsing from 1030.
Credit Cards: All major credit/debit cards
Specialities: Over 10,000 plants, many rare or unusual, reflecting the plantings in the RHS flagship garden at Wisley. New for 2019 a range of heathers to reflect the newly replanted National Heather Collection. Also houseplants, bedding plants, bulbs & seed potatoes, plus a range of garden sundries and gifts.
Notes: Plants subject to seasonal availability. A further range of plants is available online via www.rhsplants.co.uk. Wheelchair accessible.

LShi **Shire Plants**
The Paddock, Buckingham Road, Gawcott, Buckinghamshire, MK18 1TN
Ⓣ (01280) 817800
Ⓔ enquiries@shireplants.co.uk
Ⓦ https://shireplants.co.uk
Contact: Matt Killick
Opening Times: Please see website for opening times. Collection of orders welcome by arrangement.
Cat. Cost: Online only.
Credit Cards: All major credit/debit cards
Specialities: Unusual and rare plants. A wide range of Old Fashioned Pinks (*Dianthus*) and Perennial Tufted Violas.
Notes: Traditional plant nursery offering a growing range of plants, many of which are not widely available. A mix of heritage varieties, new discoveries and familiar favourites.
OS Grid Ref: SP685322

LSou **Southon Plants** ♿
Mutton Hill, Dormansland, Lingfield, Surrey, RH7 6NP
Ⓣ (01342) 870150
Ⓔ lyn@southon-plants.co.uk
Ⓦ www.southon-plants.co.uk
Contact: Lyn Southon
Opening Times: See website or telephone for up-to-date opening hours.
Cat. Cost: Online only.
Credit Cards: All major credit/debit cards
Specialities: New & unusual hardy & tender perennials, specialising in *Agapanthus* (over 30 varieties), & *Heuchera* (over 30 varieties). Many new varieties for tender perennials/patio plants.
Notes: Wheelchair accessible.

LSRN **Spring Reach Nursery** ♿
Long Reach, Ockham, Guildford, Surrey, GU23 6PG
Ⓣ (01483) 284769
Ⓜ 07884 432666
Ⓕ (01483) 284769
Ⓔ info@springreachnursery.co.uk
Ⓦ www.springreachnursery.co.uk
Contact: Nick & Lissa Hourhan
Opening Times: 7 days. 1000-1700 Mon-Sat, 1030-1630 Sun. Open B/hols. Closed 23rd Dec-2nd Jan.
Min Mail Order UK: Nmc
Min Mail Order EU: Nmc
Credit Cards: All major credit/debit cards
Specialities: Shrubs, evergreen climbers, *Clematis*, perennials, roses, grasses, ferns, bamboos, trees, hedging, soft fruit & top fruit. Plants for chalk & clay. Deer & rabbit proof plants. Specimen & acid-loving plants.
Notes: Please ring for mail order details.

Also sells wholesale. Delivers to shows. Wheelchair accessible.

LSun **Sunnyside Nursery**
Upper Allotments, New Road, Northchurch, Hertfordshire, HP4 1NJ
Ⓜ 07743 552154
Ⓔ philsmith2004@yahoo.co.uk
Contact: Philip Smith
Opening Times: 0900-1700 Mon-Fri summer. Closed Sat, Sun & B/hols. 1000-1600 Tue-Fri winter. 10 or more shows during the season. Please contact the nursery for details.
Cat. Cost: Availability list on request.
Credit Cards: All major credit/debit cards
Specialities: Hardy perennials, alpines & ornamental grasses. Some plants available in small quantities only.
Notes: Please phone for stock availability & updates. Trade discounts available with orders of £100 & free local deliveries.

M

LSvl **Savill Gardens Visitor Centre** ♿
Wick Lane, Englefield Green, Egham, Surrey, TW20 0UU
Ⓣ (01784) 485401
Ⓔ veronique.serre@thecrownestate.co.uk
Ⓦ www.windsorgreatpark.co.uk
Contact: Veronique Serre
Opening Times: 0930-1800 (summer), 0930-1630 (winter).
Credit Cards: All major debit/credit cards except American Express
Specialities: Plants available in small numbers only.
Notes: Wheelchair accessible.

LTop **Topiary Arts**
(office) Vine Cottage, Newbury Road, Hermitage, Thatcham, Berkshire, RG18 9TB
Ⓣ (01635) 202878
Ⓜ 07775 602704
Ⓔ jcb@topiaryarts.com
Ⓦ www.topiaryarts.com
Contact: James Crebbin-Bailey
Opening Times: By appt. only.
Min Mail Order UK: £30
Cat. Cost: Free.
Credit Cards: Paypal
Specialities: Topiary. Many individual sculptural pieces.
Notes: Nursery is at Walled Garden, Copped Hall, Upshire, Epping, Essex CM16 5HS. Field stock area. English grown plants. Also sells wholesale. Delivers to shows. Additional nursery in Hermitage, Berkshire. Please contact office for appointment to view.

LWei **Weird Plants by Gill**
59 Wintringham Way, Purley On Thames, Reading, Berkshire, RG8 8BH
Ⓣ 07478 930030
Ⓔ weirdplantsbygill@gmail.com
Ⓦ gillsweirdplants.co.uk/
Contact: Gill Passman
Specialities: *Tillandsia*
Notes: Over 10 years experience growing and selling Airplants (Tillandsia). Also sells wholesale. Delivers to shows.

Midlands

MACG **Ashdale Cottage Garden Plants**
204 Lambley Lane, Gedling, Nottingham, Nottinghamshire, NG4 4PB
Ⓣ (0115) 8457864
Ⓔ info@ashdale-nursery.co.uk
Ⓦ www.ashdale-nursery.co.uk
Contact: Mick and Dani
Opening Times: 0900-1700 Mon-Sat, 1000-1600 Sun, Mar-Oct
Credit Cards: All major credit/debit cards
Specialities: Wide range of rare and unusual herbaceous perennials.
Notes: Hardy perennials & classic cottage garden plants.
OS Grid Ref: SK622443

MArl **Arley Hall Nursery** ♿
Estate Office, Arley Hall & Gardens, Northwich, Cheshire, CW9 6NA
Ⓣ (01565) 777479
Ⓔ arleyhallplantnursery@gmail.com
Ⓦ www.arleyhallandgardens.com
Contact: Rob Groom
Opening Times: 1000-1730 Mon-Sun 1st Mar-31st Oct.
Cat. Cost: 4 × 1st class.
Credit Cards: All major credit/debit cards
Specialities: Wide range of herbaceous incl. many unusual varieties, some in small quantities. Wide range of unusual pelargoniums.
Notes: Nursery is beside car park at Arley Hall Gardens. Wheelchair accessible.
OS Grid Ref: SJ673808

MAsh **Ashwood Nurseries Ltd** ♿
Ashwood Lower Lane, Ashwood, Kingswinford, West Midlands, DY6 0AE
Ⓣ (01384) 401996
Ⓕ (01384) 401108
Ⓔ info@ashwoodnurseries.com
Ⓦ www.ashwoodnurseries.com
Contact: Karrina Gilbert & Steve Lampitt
Opening Times: 0900-1700 Mon-Sat &

0930-1700 Sun, excl. Xmas & Boxing Day.
Min Mail Order UK: Nmc
Min Mail Order EU: Nmc
Cat. Cost: 4 × 1st class.
Credit Cards: All major credit/debit cards
Specialities: Large range of hardy plants, shrubs & dwarf conifers. Roses, alpines & herbaceous plants. Also specialises in *auriculas*, *Cyclamen*, *Galanthus*, hellebores, *Hepatica*, *Hydrangea* & *Salvia*. National Plant Collection of *Lewisia*.
Notes: Tea room overlooking display garden. Ample parking. Regular events. Groups by appt. to visit private garden. Wheelchair accessible.
OS Grid Ref: SO865879

MAvo **Avondale Nursery** ♿
(office) 3 Avondale Road, Earlsdon, West Midlands, CV5 6DZ
Ⓣ (024) 766 73662
Ⓜ 07979 093096
Ⓔ enquiries@avondalenursery.co.uk
Ⓦ www.avondalenursery.co.uk
Contact: Brian Ellis
Opening Times: 1000-1230, 1400-1700 Mon-Sat, 1030-1630 Sun, Mar-Sep. Other times by appt.
Cat. Cost: 4 × 1st class.
Credit Cards: All major credit/debit cards
Specialities: Rare & unusual perennials esp. asters, *Eryngium*, *Geranium*, *Geum*, *Crocosmia*, *Sanguisorba* & grasses. National Plant Collections of *Symphyotrichum novae-angliae*, *Anemone nemorosa* & *Sanguisorba*.
Notes: Nursery is at Russell's Nursery, Mill Hill, Baginton, near Coventry CV8 3AG. Display garden open. Groups welcome. Wheelchair accessible.
OS Grid Ref: SP339751

MBel **Bluebell Cottage Nursery** ♿
Lodge Lane, Dutton, Cheshire, WA4 4HP
Ⓣ (01928) 713718
Ⓔ info@bluebellcottage.co.uk
Ⓦ www.bluebellcottage.co.uk
Contact: Sue Beesley
Opening Times: 1000-1700 Wed-Sun & B/hols, 1st Apr-end Sep. By appt. only outside these dates.
Min Mail Order UK: £4.95 (based on weight)
Cat. Cost: Online only.
Credit Cards: All major credit/debit cards
Specialities: *Achillea*, *Anthemis*, *Brunnera*, *Centaurea*, *Echinacea*, *Geranium*, *Geum*, *Lychnis*, *Persicaria*, *Potentilla*, *Sanguisorba*, *Thalictrum* & ornamental grasses. Some items stocked in small quantities.
Notes: Mail order available all year round. Peat-free. No neonicotinoid pesticides used. Plants are fully established, ready to plant out in 9cm (3 pots). RHS Partner Garden open Apr-Sep. Refreshments available. Delivers to shows. Wheelchair accessible.
OS Grid Ref: SJ586779

MBlu **Bluebell Arboretum & Nursery** ♿
Annwell Lane, Smisby, Nr Ashby de la Zouch, Derbyshire, LE65 2TA
Ⓣ (01530) 413700
Ⓔ sales@bluebellnursery.com
Ⓦ www.bluebellnursery.com
Contact: Robert & Suzette Vernon
Opening Times: 0900-1700 Mon-Sat & 1030-1630 Sun, Mar-Oct. 0900-1600 Mon-Sat (not Sun) Nov-Feb. Closed 24th Dec-1st Jan incl. & Easter Sun.
Min Mail Order UK: £8.95
Min Mail Order EU: Nmc
Cat. Cost: £1.50 + 3 × 1st class.
Credit Cards: Visa, Access, Switch, MasterCard
Specialities: Specialists in rare & unusual plants. Uncommon trees & shrubs. Rare *Acer*, *Betula*, *Cornus*, *Fagus*, *Magnolia*, *Liquidambar*, *Quercus* & *Tilia*. Woody climbers.
Notes: 9-acre woodland garden & arboretum surrounds nursery. RHS partner garden. Guide dogs only. Working nursery, so wear appropriate clothing & sturdy footwear if visiting. Delivers to shows. Wheelchair accessible but pls call first if weather wet.
OS Grid Ref: SK344187

MBNS **Barnsdale Gardens** ♿
Exton Avenue, Exton, Oakham, Rutland, LE15 8AH
Ⓣ (01572) 813200
Ⓔ info@barnsdalegardens.co.uk
Ⓦ www.barnsdalegardens.co.uk
Contact: Nick Hamilton
Opening Times: 0900-1700 Mar-May & Sep-Oct, 0900-1900 Jun-Aug, 1000-1600 Nov-Feb, 7 days. Closed 24th & 25th Dec.
Min Mail Order UK: Nmc
Min Mail Order EU: Nmc
Cat. Cost: Online only.
Credit Cards: All major credit/debit cards
Specialities: Wide range of choice & unusual garden plants but specialising in perennials.
Notes: Mail order from website or by telephone ordering only. Delivers to Gardeners' World Live flower show. Wheelchair accessible.
OS Grid Ref: SK912108

MBow **Fawside Farm Nursery**
Fawside Farm, Longnor, Buxton, Derbyshire, SK17 0RA
Ⓜ 07919 556425
Ⓔ julie.norfolk@acorncapital.co.uk
Ⓦ www.Fawsidefarmnursery.com
Contact: Julie Norfolk
Opening Times: By appt. only
Min Mail Order UK: £25.00
Cat. Cost: Online.
Credit Cards: Paypal
Specialities: Bee-friendly hardy perennials, British wildflowers and herbs. It is a small nursery so does not have large numbers of all the varieties. Large orders can be grown by arrangement.
Notes: The nursery is situated 1,000ft above sea level in the Pennines and we aim to grow hardy species of plants to survive in these conditions as well as being wildlife friendly. We use peat-free compost, use organic growing methods & recycle our pots. Visitors very welcome, please call to arrange a visit. Also sells wholesale.

M

MBriF **Bridge Farm Plants**
Bridge Farm, Main Road, Lower Hartshay, Derbyshire, DE5 3RP
Ⓣ (01773) 742848
Ⓜ 07812 350132
Ⓔ alisonfarnsworth@btinternet.com
Contact: Alison Farnsworth
Opening Times: By appt. only.
Specialities: Herbaceous perennials and bulbs.
Notes: Interesting range, including half-hardy and tender. Most in small quantities only. Delivers to shows.

MBrN **Bridge Nursery** ♿
Tomlow Road, Napton-on-the-Hill, Nr Rugby, Warwickshire, CV47 8HX
Ⓣ (01926) 812737
Ⓔ philipemartino@gmail.com
Ⓦ www.Bridge-Nursery.co.uk
Contact: Christine Dakin & Philip Martino
Opening Times: 1000-1600 Sat, Sun & B/hol Mons Mar-Oct. Other times by appt.
Min Mail Order UK: £10.00
Cat. Cost: Online only.
Credit Cards: All major credit/debit cards
Specialities: Ornamental grasses, sedges & bamboos. Also range of shrubs & perennials. Display garden.
Notes: Limited range available by mail order, please check with nursery. Also sells wholesale. Euro accepted. Wheelchair accessible.
OS Grid Ref: SP463625

MBros **Brookside Nursery** ♿
School Lane, Hints, Tamworth, Staffordshire, B78 3DW
Ⓣ (0333) 335 6789
Ⓔ info@brooksidenursery.co.uk
Ⓦ www.brooksidenursery.co.uk
Contact: James Thomas
Opening Times: 0900-1700 Mon-Sat, 1000-1600 Sun 1st Mar-31st Oct. Closed 1st Nov-28th Feb. Office & Customer Services Mon-Fri 0900-1700 all year.
Cat. Cost: Free. Postal and Online.
Credit Cards: All major credit/debit cards
Specialities: *Begonia, Lobelia, Petunia, Geranium.*
Notes: Producer of bedding and hanging basket plants. Veg & perennials sold as young plug plants and bare root plants for mail order and as finished plants for collection from the nursery. Also sells wholesale. Wheelchair accessible.

MCms **Chrysanthemums Direct**
Holmes Chapel Road, Over Peover, Knutsford, Cheshire, WA16 9RA
Ⓣ (0800) 046 7443
Ⓜ 07977 312 593
Ⓔ sales@chrysanthemumsdirect.co.uk
Ⓦ www.chrysanthemumsdirect.co.uk
Contact: Martyn Flint
Opening Times: Not open. Mail order only.
Min Mail Order UK: Nmc
Min Mail Order EU: Nmc
Cat. Cost: 4 × 1st class.
Credit Cards: All major credit/debit cards
Specialities: Chrysanthemum. Young plants grown to order. Delivery within 21 days.
Notes: Delivers to shows.

MCoo **Cool Temperate**
(office) 45 Stamford Street, Awsworth, Nottinghamshire, NG16 2QL
Ⓣ 07952 019376
Ⓔ phil.corbett@cooltemperate.co.uk
Ⓦ www.cooltemperate.co.uk
Contact: Phil Corbett
Opening Times: 0900-1700 7 days. Please ring/write first.
Min Mail Order UK: Nmc
Cat. Cost: Online or via email.
Credit Cards: None
Specialities: Tree fruit, soft fruit, nitrogen-fixers, hedging, own-root fruit trees. Many species available in small quantities only.
Notes: Nursery at Newton's Lane, Cossall, Notts NG16 2YH.
OS Grid Ref: SK473433

MCor **Cornovium Snowdrops**
Woodlands, Nant Lane, Selattyn, Oswestry, Shropshire, SY10 7HA
Ⓣ (01691) 655824
Ⓜ 07496 042724
Ⓔ cornoviumsnowdrops@gmail.com
Ⓦ www.cornoviumsnowdrops.co.uk
Contact: Jane Rowlinson
Opening Times: Not open. Mail order only.
Min Mail Order UK: Nmc
Min Mail Order EU: Nmc
Cat. Cost: Online only.
Credit Cards: Paypal
Specialities: We grow and breed *Galanthus* species and cultivars, *Erythronium* and other bulbs. Some of our named bulbs are available in limited numbers only.
Notes: We offer in the green snowdrops from the 1st Jan every year on our website to our UK and EU customers. Additionally, we offer dormant bulbs during the summer months. We also supply dormant bulbs to the US every summer, please see our website for more details. Exports beyond EU.

MCot **Coton Manor Garden**
Guilsborough, Northampton, Northamptonshire, NN6 8RQ
Ⓣ (01604) 740219
Ⓔ pasleytyler@cotonmanor.co.uk
Ⓦ www.cotonmanor.co.uk
Contact: Caroline Tait
Opening Times: 1200-1730 Tue-Sat, 1st Apr-27th Sep. Also Sun Apr, May & B/hol w/ends. Other times in working hours by appt.
Cat. Cost: Online only.
Credit Cards: All major credit/debit cards
Specialities: Wide-range of herbaceous perennials (1200+ varieties), some available in small quantities only. Also many tender perennials & selected shrubs.
Notes: Garden open. Tea rooms. Garden school. Partial wheelchair access.
OS Grid Ref: SP675715

MCtn **Chiltern Seeds Ltd**
Crowmarsh Battle Barns, 114 Preston Crowmarsh, Wallingford, Oxfordshire, OX10 6SL
Ⓣ (01491) 824675
Ⓔ info@chilternseeds.co.uk
Ⓦ www.chilternseeds.co.uk
Contact: Any member of staff
Opening Times: Mail order only. Normal office hours, Mon-Fri.
Min Mail Order UK: Nmc
Min Mail Order EU: Nmc
Cat. Cost: Free.
Credit Cards: All major debit/credit cards except American Express
Specialities: Large selection of wild flowers, trees, shrubs, cacti, annuals, houseplants, vegetables & herbs.
Notes: Exports beyond EU. Customer's responsibility to ensure no restrictions & special import requirements apply.

MDon **Donington Nurseries Ltd** ♿
Kings Mills, Park Lane, Castle Donington, Derbyshire, DE74 2RS
Ⓣ (01332) 853004
Ⓕ (01332) 853793
Ⓔ sales@doningtonnurseries.co.uk
Ⓦ www.doningtonnurseries.co.uk
Contact: Rebecca
Opening Times: 0900-1700 Mon-Sat, 1000-1600 Sun. Closed Thu Nov-Feb. Closed Christmas and New Year.
Cat. Cost: None.
Credit Cards: All major credit/debit cards
Specialities: Home grown Laurel (*Prunus*) hedging. Large range of ornamental plants, subject to seasonal availability, please phone ahead of your visit to check stocks.
Notes: A traditional plant based nursery with a large number of trees, shrubs and other plants. Home grown perennials ans seasonal bedding. Delivery available locally, Derby, Notts, Leics charges apply. Wheelchair accessible.
OS Grid Ref: SK421273

MEch **Echium World**
The Walled Garden, Thoresby Park, Nr Ollerton, Nottinghamshire, NG22 9EP
Ⓜ 07957 602073
Ⓔ echiumworld@gmail.com
Ⓦ www.echiumworld.co.uk
Contact: Linda Heywood
Opening Times: Thu, Sat & Sun from 16th Mar 2019 (Closed July). Other times by appointment.
Min Mail Order UK: £9.95
Credit Cards: Paypal
Specialities: The Echium Garden & Plant nursery occupies a corner of the old Victorian walled garden at Thoresby Park, Nottinghamshire, currently under renovation. Showcasing over 35 varieties of *Echium* including the giant tree Echium, *Echium*pinanana that grows to over 5 metres tall. Plant & Seed sales. Please call or email to arrange order collection. See website for further information.
Notes: *Echium* including rare & endangered species. Varieties on display in planting schemes throughout the Echium Garden.

Suppliers of *Echium* plants and seeds for wildlife gardens. Plants grown onsite. National Collection of *Echium* species & cvs from the Macaronesian Islands.
OS Grid Ref: SK626665

MFry **Fryer's Roses and Garden Centre** ♿
Manchester Road, Knutsford, Cheshire, WA16 0SX
Ⓣ (01565) 755455
Ⓔ webenquiries@bluediamond.gg
Ⓦ www.fryers-roses.co.uk
Contact: Jill Kerr
Opening Times: 0900-1800 Mon-Sat & 1030-1630 Sun.
Min Mail Order UK: £6.50 (bare root)
Min Mail Order EU: Contact nursery
Cat. Cost: Free.
Credit Cards: All major debit/credit cards except American Express
Specialities: Stocks over 250 varieties of roses. New roses usually launched at RHS Hampton Court Palace Flower Show. Bare root roses available for sale from Nov-Mar, potted roses available all year round.
Notes: Talks held throughout the year, contact nursery for information. Group bookings available. Exports beyond EU. Wheelchair accessible.
OS Grid Ref: SJ738803

MGil **John Gillies** ♿
at Russell's Garden Centre, Mill Hill, Baginton, Warwickshire, CV8 3AG
Ⓜ 07546 064961
Ⓔ enquiries@gilliesrareplants.com
Ⓦ www.gilliesrareplants.com
Contact: John Gillies
Opening Times: 1000-1700 Wed, Thu, Fri & Sat, 1030-1630 Sun 1st Mar-30th Sep. Closed Mon & Tue. Closed Easter Sun. Open Bank Holiday Mons. 1000-1600 Sat. 1030-1600 Sun 1st Oct-30th Nov Oct-Nov. Other times by appt.
Cat. Cost: Online only.
Credit Cards: All major credit/debit cards
Specialities: Offer a range of choice & rare plants of all types.
Notes: Please contact nursery before visiting to ensure plant you require is currently in stock. Wheelchair accessible.
OS Grid Ref: SP337750

MGos **Goscote Nurseries Ltd** ♿
Syston Road, Cossington, Leicestershire, LE7 4UZ
Ⓣ (01509) 812121
Ⓔ sales@goscote.co.uk
Ⓦ www.goscote.co.uk
Contact: James Toone
Opening Times: 7 days, all year round (Not Xmas to New Year).
Cat. Cost: Online only.
Credit Cards: Visa, Access, MasterCard, Delta, Switch
Specialities: Japanese maples, rhododendrons & azaleas, *Magnolia*, *Camellia*, *Pieris* & other *Ericaceae*. Ornamental trees & shrubs, conifers, fruit, heathers, alpines, roses, *Clematis* & unusual climbers.
Notes: Design & landscaping service available. Café & show garden. Also sells wholesale. Wheelchair accessible.
OS Grid Ref: SK602130

MHCG **Hill Close Gardens** ♿
Bread and Meat Close, Warwick, Warwickshire, CV34 6HF
Ⓣ (01926) 493339
Ⓜ 07533 401934
Ⓔ headgardener@hcgt.org.uk
Ⓦ www.hillclosegardens.com
Contact: Gary Leaver
Opening Times: 1100-1700 7 days, Apr-Oct. 1100-1600 Mon-Fri only, Nov-Mar.
Cat. Cost: 2 × 1st class or online.
Credit Cards: All major credit/debit cards
Specialities: Hold dispersed National Plant Collection of hardy *Chrysanthemum*. Also specialise in *Symphyotrichum* (asters) & *Galanthus*.
Notes: Small retail nursery attached to heritage garden which is open to the public. Wheelchair accessible.
OS Grid Ref: SP277647

MHed **Hedgexpress** ♿
Buckland Road, Bampton, Oxfordshire, OX18 2AA
Ⓣ (01993) 850979
Ⓔ sales@hedgexpress.co.uk
Ⓦ www.hedgexpress.co.uk
Contact: Gavin Stevens
Opening Times: 0900-1600 Mon-Fri.
Min Mail Order UK: £100
Cat. Cost: Online only.
Credit Cards: All major credit/debit cards, Paypal
Specialities: Hedging & lavenders.
Notes: Also sells wholesale. Wheelchair accessible.
OS Grid Ref: SP322024

MHer **The Herb Nursery** ♿
Thistleton, Oakham, Rutland, LE15 7RE
Ⓣ (01572) 767658
Ⓔ info@herbnursery.co.uk

Ⓦ www.herbnursery.co.uk
Contact: Peter & Christine Bench
Opening Times: 0900-1700 Mon-Sat, incl. b/hols 1000-1600 Sun. Closed Xmas until 1st Feb.
Cat. Cost: Free with A5 sae.
Credit Cards: All major credit/debit cards
Specialities: Herbs, wild flowers, cottage garden plants and a range of alpines. Large collections of *Pelargonium, Thymus, Mentha, Lavandula* and *Salvia.*
Notes: Open garden weekend 15th and 16th June (see website for details). Five acres of nursery, gardens and woodland not normally open to the public. Refreshments available. Proceeds to village church repairs and maintenance. Delivers to shows. Wheelchair accessible.

MHid **HIDDEN PARADISE PLANTS** ♿
7 Lumber Lane, Burtonwood, Newton-le-Willows, Warrington, Cheshire, WA5 4AS
Ⓣ (01925) 229100
Ⓔ timothyatkinson@msn.com
Ⓦ www.sound-garden-designs.co.uk
Contact: Tim Atkinson
Opening Times: By appt. only.
Min Mail Order UK: Nmc
Cat. Cost: 2 × 1st class.
Credit Cards: None
Specialities: Species *Rhododendron, Hedychium, Cautleya.*
Notes: Delivers to shows. Wheelchair accessible.
OS Grid Ref: SJ948901

MHol **HOLLIES FARM PLANT CENTRE**
Uppertown, Bonsall, Nr Matlock, Derbyshire, DE4 2AW
Ⓣ (01629) 822734
Ⓔ rbrt.wells@gmail.com
Ⓦ www.holliesfarmplantcentre.co.uk
Contact: Robert or Linda Wells
Opening Times: 0900-1700 every day except Wed.
Credit Cards: All major credit/debit cards
Specialities: Range of rare & unusual herbaceous perennials.
Notes: Garden designers welcome.

MHost **NORTH STAFFORDSHIRE HOSTAS**
6 Spinney Close, Endon, Stoke-on-Trent, Staffordshire, ST9 9BP
Ⓣ (01782) 502345 (after 6pm)
Ⓜ 07837 581109
Ⓔ robert.e.barlow@btopenworld.com
Ⓦ www.northstaffordshirehostas.co.uk
Contact: Robert Barlow
Opening Times: By appt. only
Min Mail Order UK: £20.00
Cat. Cost: Online only.
Specialities: *Hosta, Geum, Carex, Hemerocallis* & ferns. All plants available in small quantities only.
Notes: Mail order only. 2019 Open Days 18 May, 29 June & 24 August 1000-1700. Plants sold at shows and fairs during the year, including RHS Tatton Park. Aim is to develop their *Hosta* collection to 450 plus cultivars. Delivers to shows.

MHtn **HINTONS NURSERY** ♿
Coventry Road, Guy's Cliffe, Warwick, Warwickshire, CV34 5FJ
Ⓣ (01926) 492273
Ⓔ info@hintonsnursery.co.uk
Ⓦ www.hintonsnursery.co.uk
Contact: Sarah Ridgeway
Opening Times: 0900-1600 Mon-Sat, 1000-1630 Sun Apr-Jun. 0900-1600 Mon-Sat, 1000-1600 Sun Jul-Mar.
Min Mail Order UK: Nmc
Credit Cards: All major debit/credit cards except American Express
Specialities: Specialise in fruit (soft fruit & trees) and veg. Nearly 200 varieties of veg plants ready to plant out. Also offer more unusual fruit such as Chilean guava, honeyberries, worcesterberries, *Aronia* and pluots.
Notes: Grow & sell all types of plant from alpines, herbs, aquatics, herbaceous, shrubs and climbers to trees, ferns, bamboos & roses in a range of sizes. Plug plants for summer bedding available in spring. Also sells wholesale. Wheelchair accessible.
OS Grid Ref: SP289636

Midl **MIDDLETON NURSERIES**
Coppice Lane, Middleton, Tamworth, Staffordshire, B78 2BT
Ⓣ (0121) 3084077
Ⓔ sales@middletonnurseries.co.uk
Ⓦ www.middletonnurseries.co.uk
Contact: John Zako
Opening Times: By appointment only. Online store.
Min Mail Order UK: £5.00
Cat. Cost: Online.
Credit Cards: All major credit/debit cards
Specialities: We specialise in growing *Salvia* which are all available to purchase at our Online store. Our collections can also be purchased at all the RHS shows.
Notes: Middleton Nurseries are located in the village of Middleton in Staffordshire and have been growing plants since 1975. We are

M

dedicated to growing new & unusual perennials, specialising in the *Salvia* species. We attend the RHS shows up and down the country. We also have our Online store. Delivers to shows. Also sells wholesale.

MJac JACKSON'S NURSERIES
72 Main Street, Clifton Campville, Nr Tamworth, Staffordshire, B79 0AP
Ⓣ (01827) 373307
Ⓔ jacksonsnurseries.fuchsias@gmail.com
Contact: N. Jackson
Opening Times: 0900-1800 Mon & Wed-Sat, 1000-1700 Sun.
Cat. Cost: 2 × 1st class.
Credit Cards: None
Specialities: *Fuchsia.*
Notes: Also sells wholesale.

MLod LODGE FARM PLANTS & WILDFLOWERS ♿
Lodge Farm, Case Lane, Fiveways, Hatton, Warwickshire, CV35 7JD
Ⓣ (07977) 631368
Ⓔ lodgefarmplants@btinternet.com
Ⓦ www.lodgefarm-plants.com
Contact: Jan Cook
Opening Times: 1100-1600 everyday.
Min Mail Order UK: Nmc
Cat. Cost: Availability list online.
Credit Cards: All major credit/debit cards
Specialities: Espaliers, fan trained, stepovers and cordons. All rootstocks. All UK grown.
Notes: Fruit trees, native trees, ornamental trees, hedging and wildflowers. Euro accepted. Wheelchair accessible.
OS Grid Ref: SP223700

MMrt MORTON NURSERIES LTD ♿
Mansfield Road, Morton, Retford, Nottinghamshire, DN22 8HE
Ⓣ (01777) 702530
Ⓜ 07940 434398
Ⓔ enquiries@morton-nurseries.com
Ⓦ www.morton-nurseries.co.uk
Contact: Gill McMaster
Opening Times: 1000-1600 Mon-Fri, 1400-1700 Sat & Sun.
Min Mail Order UK: £5.00 + p&p
Credit Cards: All major credit/debit cards
Specialities: Shrubs & perennials.
Notes: Delivers to shows. Wheelchair accessible.
OS Grid Ref: SK671794

MMuc MUCKLESTONE NURSERIES
Rock Lane, Mucklestone, Nr Market Drayton, Shropshire, TF9 4FA
Ⓣ (01630) 674284
Ⓜ 07714 241667
Ⓕ (07929) 178751
Ⓔ info@botanyplants.co.uk
Ⓦ www.botanyplants.co.uk
Contact: William & Louise Friend
Opening Times: 0930-1700 (or dusk) Wed, Fri, Sat May-Aug. Pls check website
Min Mail Order UK: Nmc
Cat. Cost: Online.
Credit Cards: All major credit/debit cards
Specialities: A range of trees and plants for acid & damp soils. Also grow complementary range for dry, chalk & coast at our Kent nursery. Extensive grounds showing plants in situ. Small numbers only of each variety available.
Notes: Please send plant requests by email or contact Louise Friend on 07714 241667 to discuss orders & availability. Plants listed under nursery code SEND (in Kent) can be ordered for collection from Mucklestone or sent/delivered direct. Tours & talks by arrangement.
OS Grid Ref: SJ728373

MNHC THE NATIONAL HERB CENTRE ♿
Banbury Road, Warmington, Nr Banbury, Oxfordshire, OX17 1DF
Ⓣ (01295) 690999
Ⓕ (01295) 690034
Ⓔ info@herbcentre.co.uk
Ⓦ www.herbcentre.co.uk
Contact: Plant Centre Staff
Opening Times: 0900-1730 Mon-Sat, 1030-1700 Sun.
Min Mail Order UK: Nmc
Credit Cards: All major credit/debit cards
Specialities: Herbs, culinary & medicinal. Extensive selection of rosemary, thyme & lavender in particular.
Notes: Next day delivery UK mainland only, signature required. Carriage charge of £10.00 for orders valued up to £50, more for larger orders. Wheelchair accessible.
OS Grid Ref: SP413471

MNic NICHOLSON NURSERIES LIMITED ♿
The Park, North Aston, Bicester, Oxfordshire, OX25 6HL
Ⓣ (01869) 340342
Ⓔ plantsales@nicholsonsgb.com
Ⓦ www.nicholsonsgb.com
Contact: Merlin Brooke-Little
Opening Times: 0730-1630 Mon-Fri, 0830-1630 Sat & Bank Holidays. Closed Sundays.
Cat. Cost: Free.
Credit Cards: All major credit/debit cards
Specialities: We specialise in container-grown native hedging species such as hawthorn,

spindle, hazel, privet etc., and grow our own *Quercus ilex* hedging, stilted and feathered.
Notes: A family-run Plant Centre and Nursery, established in 1979. We grow native hedging plants and curate a stunning selection of plants in our Plant Centre: many either grown ourselves or UK sourced. Specialising in ornamental, specimen trees, shrubs and native hedging. Also sells wholesale. Wheelchair accessible.
OS Grid Ref: SP475287

MNrw **Norwell Nurseries & Gardens** ♿
Woodhouse Road, Norwell, Newark, Nottinghamshire, NG23 6JX
Ⓣ (01636) 636337
Ⓔ wardha@aol.com
Ⓦ www.norwellnurseries.co.uk
Contact: Dr Andrew Ward
Opening Times: 1000-1700 Mon, Wed-Fri & Sun (Wed-Mon May & Jun). By appt. Aug & 23rd Oct-1st Mar.
Min Mail Order UK: £20.00 + p&p
Min Mail Order EU: £40.00
Cat. Cost: 3 × 1st class or online.
Credit Cards: None
Specialities: Large collection of 2500+ unusual herbaceous perennials esp., hardy geraniums, *Geum*, pond & bog plants, cottage garden plants, *Hemerocallis*, grasses, *Trillium* & woodland plants. National Plant Collection of hardy *Chrysanthemum* & *Astrantia*.
Notes: One acre garden & tea room. Talks given and garden tours. Hardy Plant Society names as within top 60 perennial gardens. Also sells wholesale. Delivers to shows. Wheelchair accessible.
OS Grid Ref: SK767616

MPhe **Phedar Nursery**
42 Bunkers Hill, Romiley, Stockport, Cheshire, SK6 3DS
Ⓣ (0161) 430 3772
Ⓔ mclewin@phedar.com
Ⓦ www.phedar.com
Contact: Will McLewin
Opening Times: Frequent but irregular. Please phone to arrange appt.
Min Mail Order UK: Nmc
Min Mail Order EU: Nmc
Cat. Cost: Online or write for printed version.
Credit Cards: None
Specialities: Species *Helleborus*, *Paeonia*. Limited stock of some rare items.
Notes: Also sells wholesale. Exports beyond EU subject to destination & on an ad hoc basis only. Please contact nursery for details. Euro accepted.
OS Grid Ref: SJ936897

MPie **Piecemeal Plants** ♿
Whatton House Gardens, Nr Kegworth, Loughborough, Leicestershire, LE12 5BG
Ⓣ (01509) 672056
Ⓜ 07950 757444
Ⓔ nursery@piecemealplants.co.uk
Ⓦ www.piecemealplants.co.uk
Contact: Mary Thomas
Opening Times: 1300-1630 (longer hours in summer) Thu & Fri, early Apr-mid Sep. 1300-1700 Suns May. For further details, telephone, see website or follow on Facebook. Also open by appt. all year.
Cat. Cost: Online only.
Credit Cards: All major credit/debit cards
Specialities: Wide range of quality, hardy herbaceous perennials. Unusual varieties & cottage garden favourites. Most in small quantities. Limited selection of shrubs, flowering bulbs, half hardy & tender plants.
Notes: Nursery located at entrance to Whatton House Gardens, behind House. Access via main gate on A6 between Kegworth and Hathern. Parking in front of house. Delivers to shows (mainly Midlands specialist Plant Fairs). Wheelchair accessible. Gardens also open (see website).
OS Grid Ref: SK494242

MPkF **Packhorse Farm Nursery** ♿
Sandyford House, Lant Lane, Tansley, Matlock, Derbyshire, DE4 5FW
Ⓣ (01629) 57206
Ⓜ 07974 095752
Ⓕ (01629) 57206
Contact: Hilton W. Haynes
Opening Times: 1000-1500 Tue & Wed, 1st Mar-30th Sept. Other times by appt. only.
Cat. Cost: 2 × 1st class for plant list.
Credit Cards: None
Specialities: *Acer*, rare stock is limited in supply. Other more unusual hardy shrubs, trees & conifers.
Notes: Delivers to shows. Wheelchair accessible.
OS Grid Ref: SK322617

MPnt **Plantagogo.com**
Jubilee Cottage Nursery, Snape Lane, Englesea Brook, Crewe, Cheshire, CW2 5QN
Ⓣ (01270) 820335
Ⓜ 07713 518271
Ⓔ info@plantagogo.com
Ⓦ www.plantagogo.com
Contact: Vicky & Richard Fox

M

Opening Times: By appt. only. Also open days (no appt. required): 1000-1600 5-7 Apr, 22-23 Jun, 20-22 Sep 2019.
Min Mail Order UK: £9.95
Min Mail Order EU: Price on application
Cat. Cost: Online only.
Credit Cards: All major credit/debit cards
Specialities: Large selection of perennials. Plants listed in the book available in good quantities. Others not listed available from our collections on request. National Plant Collections of *Heuchera*, *Heucherella* & *Tiarella*.
Notes: Open days throughout the year (see opening times). Also sells wholesale (small amounts). Homemade cake & coffee/tea daily. Delivers to shows. Limited wheelchair access.
OS Grid Ref: SJ750516

M

MPri **Primrose Cottage Nursery** ♿
Altrincham Road, Styal, Wilmslow, Cheshire, SK9 4JE
Ⓜ 07798 754457
Ⓔ info@primrosecottagenursery.co.uk
Ⓦ www.primrosecottagenursery.co.uk
Contact: Caroline Dumville
Opening Times: 0930-1630 Mon-Sat, 1000-1630 Sun (summer). 0930-1600 Mon-Sat, 1000-1600 Sun (winter).
Credit Cards: All major credit/debit cards
Specialities: Perennials, herbs, patio & hanging basket plants, always lots of new & unusual varieties. Shrubs, roses, ornamental trees, fruit trees, soft fruit bushes, bedding & vegetable plants.
Notes: In Styal Village, close to National Trust Quarry Bank Mill and estate. Village café next door to nursery. Wheelchair accessible.

MPtr **Petrichor Bulb Specialists**
369/371 Stockport Road, Thelwall, Warrington, Cheshire, WA4 2TP
Ⓣ (01925) 730992
Ⓜ 07500 937363
Ⓔ info@bulbspecialists.co.uk
Ⓦ www.bulbspecialists.co.uk
Contact: Bert Blankers
Opening Times: By appt. only.
Specialities: Our main crops are *Allium*, *Agapanthus*, *Camassia*, *Fritilaria*, *Scilla peruviana*, *Ornithogalum saundersiae*, and *Eucomis*.
Notes: We sell bulbs and bulbous plants in season. Delivers to shows. Also sells wholesale.

MRav **Ravensthorpe Nursery** ♿
6 East Haddon Road, Ravensthorpe, Northamptonshire, NN6 8ES
Ⓣ (01604) 770548
Ⓔ ravensthorpenursery@hotmail.com
Contact: Jean & Richard Wiseman
Opening Times: 1000-1800 (or dusk if earlier) Wed-Sat. B/hol Mons in May.
Min Mail Order UK: Nmc
Credit Cards: Visa, MasterCard
Specialities: Huge range of perennials, shrubs & trees with numerous unusual varieties, many of which can be seen growing in the display garden. Some plants only available as dug from garden during the lifting season.
Notes: Search & delivery service for large orders, winter months only. Wheelchair accessible.
OS Grid Ref: SP665699

MSCN **Stonyford Cottage Nursery** ♿
Stonyford Lane, Cuddington, Northwich, Cheshire, CW8 2TF
Ⓣ (01606) 888970/888128 (answerphone)
Ⓔ stonyfordcottage@yahoo.co.uk
Ⓦ www.stonyfordcottagenursery.co.uk
Contact: Andrew Overland
Opening Times: 1000-1700 Tue-Sat & B/hol Mons 1st Feb-31st Oct.
Min Mail Order UK: Nmc
Min Mail Order EU: Nmc
Cat. Cost: None.
Credit Cards: All major credit/debit cards
Specialities: Wide range of herbaceous perennials, *Iris*, hardy *Geranium*, moisture-loving & bog plants. *Sempervivum*, *Paeonia*, candelabra *Primula*.
Notes: Also sells wholesale. Wheelchair accessible.
OS Grid Ref: SJ580710

MSpe **SpecialPerennials.com**
Ⓜ 07716 990695
Ⓔ plants@specialperennials.com
Ⓦ www.specialperennials.com
Contact: Janet & Martin Blow
Opening Times: Not open. Strictly no visitors. Mail order and at Plant Hunters' Fairs only.
Min Mail Order UK: Nmc
Cat. Cost: Online only.
Credit Cards: Paypal
Specialities: *Helenium*, *Phlox*, *Salva* and other herbaceous plants for summer colour. All plants in fairly small numbers. Plants are propagated here with a few exceptions (e.g. PVR).
Notes: Small nursery growing garden worthy plants. Featured on Gardeners' World in 2014. See our website for a list of plant fairs attended where we can bring orders. Delivers to shows (orders delivered to plant fairs free of p&p charge).

MSwo **SWALLOWS NURSERY** ♿
Mixbury, Brackley, Northamptonshire, NN13 5RR
Ⓣ (01280) 847721
Ⓔ enq@swallowsnursery.co.uk
Ⓦ www.swallowsnursery.co.uk
Contact: Chris Swallow
Opening Times: 0900-1300 & 1400-1700 (earlier in winter) Mon-Fri, 0900-1300 Sat.
Min Mail Order UK: £19.50
Cat. Cost: 3 × 1st class (plus phone number).
Credit Cards: All major credit/debit cards
Specialities: Growing a wide range, particularly shrubs, climbers, trees & roses.
Notes: Trees not for mail order unless part of larger order. Nursery transport used where possible, esp. for trees. Also sells wholesale. Wheelchair accessible.
OS Grid Ref: SP607336

MThu **T. D. THURSFIELD**
Kerry Hill Nurseries, Eaves Lane, Bucknall, Stoke-on-Trent, Staffordshire, ST2 8NA
Ⓣ (01782) 302498
Ⓜ 07977 464363
Ⓔ tdthursfield@aol.com
Ⓦ www.tdthursfield.co.uk
Contact: Susan Thursfield
Opening Times: 0900-1730 Mon-Fri, 0930-1630 Sat, 1000-1600 Sun.
Credit Cards: All major debit/credit cards except American Express
Specialities: Broad selection of hardy nursery stock.
Notes: Traditional family nursery founded in the 1930s. Also sells wholesale. Delivers to shows. Wheelchair access to main sales areas.

MTin **THE TINY PLANT COMPANY**
25 Owley Wood Road, Weaverham, Cheshire, CW8 3LF
Ⓣ (01606) 851146
Ⓔ thetinyplantco@hotmail.com
Ⓦ www.tinyplantcompany.co.uk
Contact: Matt Wood
Opening Times: Not open. Mail order only.
Min Mail Order UK: £3.00
Cat. Cost: Online only.
Credit Cards: All major credit/debit cards
Specialities: Newly-opened small nursery. All plants available in very small quantities only.
Notes: Delivers to shows.

MTrO **TREES ONLINE**
ICAM Ltd, c/o Emerald Accountancy Services, 3rd Floor, Staveley Hall, Staveley Hall Drive, Chesterfield, Derbyshire, S43 3TN
Ⓣ (0800) 0431057
Ⓜ 07904 179772
Ⓔ info@trees-online.co.uk
Ⓦ https://www.trees-online.co.uk
Contact: Alan Russell
Opening Times: Online business only.
Credit Cards: All major credit/debit cards
Specialities: Wide range of ornamental and fruit trees.
Notes: An online tree supplier covering ornamental, bare root, artificial, hedging, fruit and memorial urns with trees. Free UK mainland delivery and 3 year limited tree warranty. Delivers to shows. Also sells wholesale.

MVil **VILLAGE PLANTS NURSERY LTD** ♿
7 Bosden Fold Road, Hazel Grove, Stockport, Manchester, Cheshire, SK7 4LQ
Ⓣ (0161) 4569009
Ⓔ info@kevinpratt.co.uk
Ⓦ www.kevinpratt.co.uk
Contact: Kevin Pratt
Opening Times: 0900-1600 Mon, Thu, Fri, Sat 1000-1600 Sun Closed Tue & Wed
Min Mail Order UK: £10.00
Cat. Cost: Online only.
Credit Cards: All major credit/debit cards
Specialities: Propagation of rare shrubs
Notes: Small nursery run from home. Many trees and shrubs not widely available and many rare plants only available in small quantities. Plantman's collection of rare, woody plants. Seasonal bedding and hanging baskets. Always phone first before travelling from a distance. Wheelchair accessible.

MWht **WHITELEA NURSERY** ♿
Whitelea Lane, Tansley, Matlock, Derbyshire, DE4 5FL
Ⓣ (01629) 55010
Ⓕ (01629) 55010
Ⓔ sales@uk-bamboos.co.uk
Ⓦ www.uk-bamboos.co.uk
Contact: David Wilson
Opening Times: By appt.
Min Mail Order UK: Nmc
Cat. Cost: Online only. Price list available 2 × 1st class.
Credit Cards: None
Specialities: Bamboos. Substantial quantities of 45 species/cvs of bamboo, remainder stocked in small numbers only. Limited stocks of grasses, trees & shrubs.
Notes: Mail order limited by carrier restrictions, please contact nursery or see website for details. Also sells wholesale. Wheelchair accessible.
OS Grid Ref: SK325603

M

MWts **Waterside Nursery**
Sharnford, Leicestershire,
Ⓣ (01455) 273730
Ⓜ 07931 557082
Ⓔ info@watersidenursery.co.uk
Ⓦ www.watersidenursery.co.uk
Contact: Linda Smith
Opening Times: Mail order only.
Min Mail Order UK: Nmc
Cat. Cost: Online only.
Credit Cards: All major credit/debit cards
Specialities: Aquatics, marginal pond plants, miniature waterlilies, water lilies, submerged oxygenating plants, bog garden plants & moisture-loving plants.

N

Northern

NAbi **Abi and Tom's Garden Plants** ♿
Halecat Nurseries, Witherslack, Grange Over Sands, Cumbria, LA11 6RT
Ⓣ (015395) 52946
Ⓔ info@halecatplants.co.uk
Ⓦ www.abiandtom.co.uk
Contact: Abi Attwood
Opening Times: 1000-1700 7 days Mar-Oct. See website for late autumn/winter opening times
Cat. Cost: Online.
Credit Cards: All major credit/debit cards
Specialities: Range of cottage garden herbaceous perennials that are easy to propagate and grow in the changeable Cumbrian climate.
Notes: Our one acre nursery, plant centre and garden is a fusion of traditional horticulture with a modern approach to displaying and growing the plant material. The full range of perennials can be seen growing in our inspiring nursery borders. A true gardener's paradise. Wheelchair accessible.
OS Grid Ref: SD433838

NAts **Natural Surroundings**
Bayfield, Nr Glandford, Holt, Norfolk, NR25 7JN
Ⓣ (01263) 711091
Ⓔ wildlife@naturalsurroundings.info
Ⓦ www.naturalsurroundings.info
Contact: Anne Harrap
Opening Times: 1000-1700 7 days May-Sep. 1000-1600 Tue-Sun Oct-Mar. Open B/hol Mons.
Credit Cards: All major debit/credit cards except American Express
Specialities: British wild flowers, native trees, shrubs and cottage garden plants, plus a selection of unusual hardy perennials. Also seed.
Notes: Propagate & grow in peat-free compost. Plants available in limited quantities. Wildlife-friendly demonstration gardens and semi-natural meadows open to the public (small charge). Group visits by arrangement; talks to clubs and societies in Norfolk.
OS Grid Ref: TG047407

NBid **Bide-A-Wee Cottage Gardens** ♿
Stanton, Netherwitton, Morpeth, Northumberland, NE65 8PR
Ⓣ (01670) 772004
Ⓜ 07484 637216
Ⓕ (01670) 772004
Ⓔ info@bideawee.co.uk
Ⓦ www.bideawee.co.uk
Contact: Mark Robson
Opening Times: 1330-1700 Sat & Wed, 20th Apr-14th Sept 2019. Group visits at other times, except Sun.
Min Mail Order UK: £28.00
Cat. Cost: Online only.
Credit Cards: All major credit/debit cards
Specialities: Unusual herbaceous perennials, *Agapanthus*, *Primula*, ferns, grasses. National Plant Collection of *Centaurea*.
Notes: Wheelchair accessible.
OS Grid Ref: NZ132900

NBir **Birkheads Secret Gardens & Nursery**
Birkheads Lane, Sunniside, Gateshead, Tyne & Wear, NE16 5EL
Ⓣ (01207) 232262
Ⓜ 07778 447920
Ⓔ birkheadsnursery@gmail.com
Ⓦ www.birkheadssecretgardens.co.uk
Contact: Christine Liddle
Opening Times: 1100-1700 Sat and Sun & 1000-1700 Wed-Fri in summer. Closed Mon & Tue. (Pre-booked coach groups Tue only). Open B/hol Mons. Pls check website for spring & winter opening.
Credit Cards: All major credit/debit cards
Specialities: Hardy herbaceous perennials, grasses, hardy bulbs. Herbs. *Allium*, *Euphorbia*, *Galanthus*, *Geranium*, *Primula*, *Sedum* & *Rodgersia*.
Notes: RHS Partner Garden. Gardens are on a sloping site so wheelchair access is limited to the nursery & coffee shop, please ring for special access directions. Coffee shop closes 30 mins before the gardens.
OS Grid Ref: NZ220569

NBro **Brownthwaite Hardy Plants** ♿
Fell Yeat, Casterton, Kirkby Lonsdale, Lancashire, LA6 2JW

Ⓣ (015242) 71340 (after 1800 hours).
Ⓦ www.hardyplantsofcumbria.co.uk
Contact: Chris Benson
Opening Times: 1000-1700 1st Apr-20th Sep.
Min Mail Order UK: Nmc
Cat. Cost: 3 × 1st for fern list.
Credit Cards: None
Specialities: Herbaceous perennials and hardy ferns incl. *Athyrium*, *Dryopteris*, *Polystichum*, *Hosta*, *Primula*, *Hydrangea paniculata* & *Hydrangea serrata* varieties.
Notes: Follow brown signs from A65 between Kirkby Lonsdale & Cowan Bridge. Mail order for ferns. Delivers to shows. Wheelchair accessible.
OS Grid Ref: SD632794

NCft **Craftyplants**
(office) 21 Woodgreen Drive, Radcliffe, Lancashire, M26 1BF
Ⓣ (0161) 820 8606
Ⓜ 07742 783631
Ⓔ sales@craftyplants.co.uk
Ⓦ www.craftyplants.co.uk
Contact: Graham Sigsworth
Opening Times: Mail order only. Not open except for nursery Open Days (see website or phone for details).
Min Mail Order UK: Nmc
Min Mail Order EU: Nmc
Cat. Cost: Online. Printed list available on request.
Credit Cards: All major debit/credit cards except American Express
Specialities: *Tillandsia*.
Notes: Nursery at Eezitill, Startley Nook, Preston PR4 4XW. Also sells wholesale. Delivers to shows. Euro accepted.

NChi **Chipchase Castle Nursery** ♿
Chipchase Castle, Wark, Hexham, Northumberland, NE48 3NT
Ⓜ 07575 714002
Ⓔ chipchaseplants@aim.com
Ⓦ www.chipchasenursery.com
Contact: Mark Cummings
Opening Times: 1000-1600 Thu-Sun & B/hol Mons, 1st Apr (or Easter if earlier) to end Aug.
Min Mail Order UK: £10.00
Credit Cards: All major credit/debit cards
Specialities: Rare & unusual herbaceous esp. *Pulmonaria*, *Geum*, *Geranium* (100+), *Potentilla*, *Vinca* & *Primula*. Some plants only available in small quantities.
Notes: Delivers to shows. Suitable for accompanied wheelchair users.
OS Grid Ref: NY880758

NCou **Courtyard Planters** ♿
9 Westgate, Otley, West Yorkshire, LS21 3AT
Ⓣ (01943) 462390
Ⓔ katie@courtyardplanters.co.uk
Ⓦ www.courtyardplanters.co.uk
Contact: Katie Burnett
Opening Times: 0930-1700 Tue-Sat. Closed Jan.
Cat. Cost: Online only.
Credit Cards: All major debit/credit cards except American Express
Specialities: Perennials. Plants for heavy clay soils. Peat free.
Notes: Gardening classes & workshops. Also sells wholesale. Wheelchair accessible.
OS Grid Ref: SE201455

NDal **Daleside Nurseries Ltd** ♿
Ripon Road, Killinghall, Harrogate, North Yorkshire, HG3 2AY
Ⓣ (01423) 506450
Ⓕ (01423) 527872
Ⓔ contact@dalesidenurseries.co.uk
Ⓦ www.dalesidenurseries.co.uk
Contact: Any Member of Staff
Opening Times: 0830-1700 Mon-Sat, 1030-1630 Sun. winter hours: 0830-1600 Mon-Sat (closed Sun) Jan & 0830-1630 Mon-Sat, 1030-1630 Sun, Feb.
Cat. Cost: Online only.
Credit Cards: All major debit/credit cards except American Express
Specialities: Many plants & trees not generally available. Container-grown fruit trees: apples, pears & soft fruit. Container-grown trees. Conifers, *Clematis* & hardy perennials.
Notes: Wheelchair accessible.
OS Grid Ref: SE287590

NDav **Dave Parkinson Plants**
4 West Bank, Carlton, Goole, East Yorkshire, DN14 9PZ
Ⓣ (01405) 860693
Ⓦ www.daveparkinsonplants.co.uk
Contact: Mary Parkinson
Opening Times: Not open. Mail order only.
Min Mail Order UK: £12 + p&p
Min Mail Order EU: Nmc
Cat. Cost: 1st class stamp.
Credit Cards: None
Specialities: Hardy orchids. Terrestrial South African *Disa* orchids, species & hybrids.
Notes: Sells at RHS & Orchid Shows and by mail order. Exports beyond EU. Delivers to shows.

N

NDov **Dove Cottage Nursery & Garden** ♿
Shibden Hall Road, Halifax, West Yorkshire, HX3 9XA
Ⓣ (01422) 203553
Ⓔ info@dovecottagenursery.co.uk
Ⓦ www.dovecottagenursery.co.uk
Contact: Stephen & Kim Rogers
Opening Times: 1000-1700 Thu-Sat, 4th Apr-28th Sep. Pls check website or phone before travelling.
Cat. Cost: £3.00.
Credit Cards: All major credit/debit cards
Specialities: Herbaceous perennials & selected grasses, many displayed in adjoining naturalistic garden.
Notes: Wheelchair accessible.
OS Grid Ref: SE115256

NDro **Drointon Nurseries** ♿
Plaster Pitts, Norton Conyers, Ripon, North Yorkshire, HG4 5EF
Ⓣ (01765) 641849
Ⓜ 07909 971529
Ⓔ info@auricula-plants.co.uk
Ⓦ www.auricula-plants.co.uk
Contact: Robin & Annabel Graham
Opening Times: Open days in spring, otherwise by appt. only.
Min Mail Order UK: Nmc
Min Mail Order EU: Nmc
Cat. Cost: 4 × 1st class.
Credit Cards: All major credit/debit cards
Specialities: *Primula auricula*. More than 1150 cvs of show, alpine, double & border auriculas. Limited stock of any one cultivar. National Plant Collection of *Primula auricula* (borders).
Notes: Also sells wholesale. Exports beyond EU. Delivers to shows. Wheelchair accessible.
OS Grid Ref: SE315753

NDry **Dryad Nursery**
130 Prince Rupert Drive, Tockwith, York, North Yorkshire, YO26 7PU
Ⓣ (01423) 358791
Ⓔ dryadnursery@gmail.com
Ⓦ www.dryad-home.co.uk
Contact: Anne Wright
Opening Times: Not open, mail order only.
Min Mail Order UK: £5.50
Min Mail Order EU: £8.70
Cat. Cost: Online only.
Credit Cards: Paypal
Specialities: Miniature and species *Narcissus*, *Galanthus*, wood anemones, *Hepatica* and other small bulbs.
Notes: Grower and breeder of miniature daffodils, snowdrops and hepaticas. Holder of large collection of wood anemones. All plants available in limited numbers and from seasonal lists only. Exports beyond EU. All our plants are propagated at the nursery, or by Brian Duncan in Ireland.

NEoE **East of Eden Nursery** ♿
Ainstable, Carlisle, Cumbria, CA4 9QN
Ⓣ (01768) 896604
Ⓜ 07788 142969
Ⓔ roger@east-of-eden-nursery.co.uk
Ⓦ www.east-of-eden-nursery.co.uk
Contact: Roger Proud
Opening Times: Mar-Nov. Days & times variable, so please phone or email before calling.
Min Mail Order UK: £10.00
Credit Cards: All major credit/debit cards
Specialities: Interesting & unusual shrubs, perennials & alpines, esp. astilbes & geums with over 60 new *Geum* cvs, bred & raised on nursery.
Notes: Delivers to shows. Wheelchair accessible.
OS Grid Ref: NY467504

NFav **Perennial Favourites Ltd** ♿
East Park View, Blyth, Northumberland, NE24 3AY
Ⓣ (01670) 540653
Ⓜ 07805 607128
Ⓔ gardener@perennialfavourites.co.uk
Ⓦ www.perennialfavourites.co.uk
Contact: Adam Greenwold
Opening Times: 0730-1700 7 days, Apr-Oct. 0900-1600 Mon-Sat, (closed Sun) Nov-Mar.
Credit Cards: All major credit/debit cards
Specialities: Specialising in hardy herbaceous perennials, but also supplying alpines and shrubs with a bent for surviving on the north sea coast.
Notes: Perennial and alpine nursery, seaside plants. Wheelchair accessible. Also sells wholesale.
OS Grid Ref: NZ320812

NGBl **Garden Blooms**
Fieldgate, Mill Field Road, Fishlake, Doncaster, Yorkshire, DN7 5GH
Ⓣ (01302) 288145
Ⓔ info@gardenblooms.co.uk
Ⓦ www.gardenblooms.co.uk
Contact: Liz Webster
Opening Times: Open by appt. or on Open Days. Contact nursery for details.
Min Mail Order UK: Nmc
Cat. Cost: Online only.

Credit Cards: All major credit/debit cards
Specialities: Hardy & tender perennials, especially *Rudbeckia*, & small range of conservatory/house plants. Some plants available in small quantities only.
Notes: Delivers to shows. Credit card payments not taken over the phone.
OS Grid Ref: SE659148

NGdn **GARDEN HOUSE NURSERY** ♿
The Square, Dalston, Carlisle, Cumbria, CA5 7LL
Ⓣ (01228) 710297
Ⓜ 07595 219082
Ⓔ stephickso@hotmail.co.uk
Ⓦ www.gardenhousenursery.co.uk
Contact: Stephen Hickson
Opening Times: 0930-1700 Mon-Fri, 1000-1630 Sat-Sun, mid-Mar to Oct. Oct please ring if visiting at w/ends.
Cat. Cost: Plant list online only.
Credit Cards: All major credit/debit cards
Specialities: *Geranium, Hosta, Hemerocallis, Iris*, grasses, *Brunnera, Pulmonaria* & *Aconitum*.
Notes: Also sells wholesale. Wheelchair accessible.
OS Grid Ref: NY369503

NGKo **GREENKOOS**
16 Elm Grove, Droylsdon, Greater Manchester, M43 6LP
Ⓣ (0161) 612 5705
Ⓜ 07806 893816
Ⓔ keeflong@hotmail.com
Ⓦ http://www.greenkoos.co.uk/
Contact: Keith Long
Opening Times: By appt. only
Min Mail Order UK: £20.00
Cat. Cost: Online only.
Credit Cards: All major credit/debit cards
Specialities: Exotic and architectural plants including Brugmansia, *Lochroma, Canna*, Aroids and *Eucomis*. Also grow and sell a wide range of trees, shrubs, perennials, ferns, bonsai and medicinal plants.
Notes: Plant nursery based in Manchester, best known for their *Brugmansia*. No online shop available yet. Please phone or email nursery for orders or details of plant fairs attended. Delivers to shows.

NGrd **GARDENER'S COTTAGE PLANTS**
Gardener's Cottage, Bingfield, Newcastle-upon-Tyne, Tyne and Wear, NE19 2LE
Ⓣ (01434) 672594
Ⓜ 07500 895052
Ⓔ andrew@gcplants.co.uk
Ⓦ www.gcplants.co.uk
Contact: Andrew Davenport
Opening Times: 1000-1700 Fri-Sat, May-Oct incl.
Min Mail Order UK: £20.00
Min Mail Order EU: £20.00
Credit Cards: None
Specialities: Perennials, herbs and wildflowers. The nursery runs on sustainable and organic principles whereby all plants sold are propagated on site in peat-free composts and reycled pots.
Notes: Also sells at plant fairs. Contact nursery for details.

NHal **HALLS OF HEDDON**
West Heddon Nurseries, Heddon-on-the-Wall, Northumberland, NE15 0JS
Ⓣ (01661) 852445
Ⓕ (01661) 852398
Ⓔ enquiry@hallsofheddon.co.uk
Ⓦ www.hallsofheddon.co.uk
Contact: David Hall
Opening Times: 0900-1700 Mon-Sat 1000-1700 Sun.
Min Mail Order UK: £10.00
Min Mail Order EU: £35.00
Cat. Cost: 3 × 2nd class.
Credit Cards: MasterCard, Visa, Switch, Delta
Specialities: *Chrysanthemum* & *Dahlia*.
Notes: Also sells wholesale.
OS Grid Ref: NZ122679

NHar **HARTSIDE NURSERY GARDEN**
Penrith Road, Alston, Cumbria, CA9 3BL
Ⓣ (01434) 381372
Ⓕ (01434) 381372
Ⓔ enquiries@plantswithaltitude.co.uk
Ⓦ www.plantswithaltitude.co.uk
Contact: Mr Neil Huntley
Opening Times: 1130-1630 Tue-Fri & 1230-1600 Sat, Sun & B/hols, Mar-Jun. 1130-1630 Tue-Fri, Jul-Oct. Other times by appt. only.
Min Mail Order UK: Nmc
Min Mail Order EU: £50.00 + p&p
Cat. Cost: 4 × 1st class.
Credit Cards: All major credit/debit cards
Specialities: *Primula*, including Asiatic, petiolaris, European species and forms of *P. allionii*. *Saxifrages*, autumn flowering gentians, erythoniums, roscoeas, trilliums.
Notes: If visiting our nursery we strongly advise checking our opening hours, especially during busy periods and in adverse weather conditions. Pls check website for latest news. Delivers to shows.
OS Grid Ref: NY708447

NHaw **The Hawthornes Nursery** ♿
Marsh Road, Hesketh Bank, Nr Preston, Lancashire, PR4 6XT
Ⓣ (01772) 812379
Ⓔ richardhaw@talktalk.net
Ⓦ www.hawthornes-nursery.co.uk
Contact: Irene & Richard Hodson
Opening Times: 0900-1800 7 days, Mar-Jun & Thu-Sun, July-Oct. Gardens open for NGS.
Min Mail Order UK: £10.00
Min Mail Order EU: Nmc
Credit Cards: None
Specialities: *Clematis*. National Plant Collection of *Clematis viticella*.
Notes: Exports beyond EU. Euro accepted. Wheelchair accessible.

N

NHol **Holden Clough Nursery** ♿
Holden, Bolton-by-Bowland, Nr Clitheroe, Lancashire, BB7 4PF
Ⓣ (01200) 447447
Ⓔ info@holdencloughnursery.co.uk
Ⓦ www.holdencloughnursery.com
Contact: Kate Lawson
Opening Times: 0900-1700 Mon-Sat, 1030-1630 Sun, incl. B/hols. Closed Xmas Day & Boxing Day.
Min Mail Order UK: Nmc
Min Mail Order EU: Nmc
Cat. Cost: 2 × 1st class.
Credit Cards: All major credit/debit cards
Specialities: Large general list incl. perennials, esp. *Crocosmia*, shrubs, dwarf conifers, alpines, heathers, grasses & ferns.
Notes: Seasonal mail order on some items. Also sells wholesale on some items. Exports beyond EU. Delivers to shows. Wheelchair accessible.
OS Grid Ref: SD773496

NHoy **Hoyland Plant Centre**
Market Street, Hoyland, Barnsley, South Yorkshire, S74 0ET
Ⓣ (01226) 744466
Ⓜ 07717 182169
Ⓕ (01226) 744466
Ⓔ hoylandplantcentre@btconnect.com
Ⓦ www.somethingforthegarden.co.uk
Contact: Steven Hickman
Opening Times: Open by appt. only.
Min Mail Order UK: Nmc
Min Mail Order EU: Nmc
Cat. Cost: Free online.
Credit Cards: All major credit/debit cards
Specialities: National Plant Collections of *Agapanthus* & *Tulbaghia*. Also holds a large collection of *Clivia* & *Nerine*.
Notes: Sells mail order or at major flower shows. Also sells wholesale. Exports beyond EU. Delivers to shows. Euro accepted. Top of the nursery and glasshouse accessible for most wheelchairs.
OS Grid Ref: SE372010

NHpl **Harperley Hall Farm Nurseries** ♿
Harperley, Stanley, Co. Durham, DH9 9UB
Ⓣ (01207) 233318
Ⓜ 07944 644126
Ⓔ enquiries@harperleyhallfarmnurseries.co.uk
Ⓦ www.harperleyhallfarmnurseries.co.uk
Contact: Gary McDermott
Opening Times: 7 days Mar-Oct
Min Mail Order UK: Nmc
Min Mail Order EU: Nmc
Credit Cards: All major credit/debit cards
Specialities: Growers of a wide range of alpine & woodland plants, incl. *Meconopsis* & *Primula*, many of which are rare or unusual.
Notes: Also sells wholesale. Delivers to shows. Euro accepted. Wheelchair accessible.

NHsp **Hare Spring Cottage Plants**
Church Orchard, Church Wind, Alne, York, Yorkshire, YO61 1RX
Ⓜ 07792 376805
Ⓔ stella@harespringcottageplants.co.uk
Ⓦ www.harespringcottageplants.co.uk
Contact: Stella Exley
Opening Times: By appt. only
Min Mail Order UK: Nmc
Min Mail Order EU: Nmc
Cat. Cost: Online only.
Credit Cards: All major debit/credit cards except American Express
Specialities: *Camassia*, *Uvularia* & *Sidalcea*. National Plant Collection of *Camassia*. Some specialist plants available in small quantities only.
Notes: Sells at & delivers to specialist plant fairs. Talks to specialist groups & societies by arrangement. See website for Open Days Also sells wholesale. Delivers to shows. Euro accepted. Pls call nursery to discuss accessibility requirements.

NJRG **JRG Dahlias**
22 Summerville Road, Milnthorpe, Cumbria, LA7 7DF
Ⓣ (01539) 562691
Ⓔ jack@jrg-dahlias.co.uk
Ⓦ www.jrg-dahlias.co.uk
Contact: Jack Gott
Opening Times: By appt. only.
Min Mail Order UK: £10.00 + p&p
Min Mail Order EU: Price with order
Cat. Cost: Sae: 110mm × 220mm, 2nd class.

Credit Cards: Paypal
Specialities: *Dahlia*. Some available in small quantities only.
Notes: Delivers to shows.

NLAp **Laneside Hardy Orchid Nursery** ♿
74 Croston Road, Garstang, Lancashire, PR3 1HR
Ⓣ (01995) 605537
Ⓜ 07946 659661
Ⓔ jcrhutch@aol.com
Ⓦ www.lanesidehardyorchids.co.uk
Contact: Jeff Hutchings
Opening Times: Not open, mail order only.
Min Mail Order UK: Nmc
Min Mail Order EU: Nmc
Credit Cards: All major credit/debit cards
Specialities: Wide range of hardy, terrestrial orchids for the garden, meadow and alpine house.
Notes: Sales via shows and online shop. Delivers to shows. Exports beyond EU. Wheelchair accessible.

NLar **Larch Cottage Nurseries** ♿ ◆
Melkinthorpe, Penrith, Cumbria, CA10 2DR
Ⓣ (01931) 712404
Ⓔ plants@larchcottage.co.uk
Ⓦ www.larchcottage.co.uk
Contact: Peter & Joanne Stott
Opening Times: Daily from 1000-1700 (or dusk in winter), all year. excl Xmas, Boxing Day & New Year's Day.
Min Mail Order UK: £20.00 + p&p
Credit Cards: All major credit/debit cards
Specialities: Comprehensive plant collection in unique garden setting. Rare & unusual plants, particularly shrubs, trees, perennials, dwarf conifers & Japanese maples. *Acer*, *Hamamelis*, *Magnolia* & *Cornus kousa* cvs. Old-fashioned roses, bamboo & alpines.
Notes: Terraced restaurant, art gallery and shop open everyday. RHS partner gardens open Wed-Sun throughout the summer. Please check website for details. Wheelchair accessible.
OS Grid Ref: NY315602

NMen **Mendle Nursery** ♿
Holme, Scunthorpe, North Lincolnshire, DN16 3RF
Ⓣ (01724) 850864
Ⓔ ann.earnshaw@tiscali.co.uk
Ⓦ www.mendlenursery.co.uk
Contact: Mrs A. Earnshaw
Opening Times: 1000-1600 Tue-Sun.
Min Mail Order UK: Nmc
Min Mail Order EU: Nmc
Credit Cards: Paypal
Specialities: *Jovibarba*, *Saxifraga* & *Sempervivum*.
Notes: Wheelchair accessible.
OS Grid Ref: SE925070

NMir **Mires Beck Nursery** ♿
Low Mill Lane, North Cave, Brough, East Riding, Yorkshire, HU15 2NR
Ⓣ (01430) 421543
Ⓕ (01430) 421543
Ⓔ sales@miresbeck.co.uk
Ⓦ www.miresbeck.co.uk
Contact: Sue Hewitt
Opening Times: 1000-1600 7 days, 1st Mar-30th Sep. 1000-1600 Mon-Fri, 1st Oct-30th Apr.
Min Mail Order UK: Nmc
Credit Cards: All major debit/credit cards except American Express
Specialities: Wildflower plants of Yorkshire provenance.
Notes: Mail order for wildflower plants & plugs only. Also sells wholesale. Wheelchair accessible.
OS Grid Ref: SE889316

NNor **Norcroft Nurseries** ♿
19, Carlton Gardens, Stanwix, Carlisle, Cumbria, CA3 9NR
Ⓣ (01228) 597681
Ⓜ 07887 781555
Ⓔ info@norcroftnurseries.co.uk
Ⓦ www.norcroftnurseries.co.uk
Contact: Keith Bell
Opening Times: By appt. only
Min Mail Order UK: Nmc
Cat. Cost: 2 × 2nd class.
Credit Cards: None
Specialities: *Hosta*
Notes: Also sells wholesale. Euro accepted. Wheelchair accessible. Visits by appointment only, please ring nursery for to arrange.
OS Grid Ref: NY397572

NOra **Orange Pippin Ltd**
(office) 33 Algarth Rise, Pocklington, York, Yorkshire, YO42 2HX
Ⓣ (01759) 392007
Ⓔ trees@orangepippin.com
Ⓦ www.orangepippintrees.co.uk
Contact: Maureen Borrie
Opening Times: Not open. Mail order online only.
Min Mail Order UK: Nmc
Min Mail Order EU: Nmc
Cat. Cost: Online only.
Credit Cards: MasterCard, Visa

Specialities: Wide range of fruit trees & ornamentals, incl. traditional & modern varieties. Wide choice of rootstocks & tree forms.
Notes: Fruit tree expert available most days. See website for ornamental tree www.pippintrees.co.uk. Order online all year round, deliveries from Aug-Apr. Exports beyond EU (to USA).

NOrn **Ornamental Trees Ltd**
The Nursery Office, Farnley Hall Estate, Farnley, West Yorkshire, LS21 2QF
Ⓣ (01943) 660870
Ⓔ sales@ornamental-trees.co.uk
Ⓦ www.ornamental-trees.co.uk
Contact: Nigel Coultas
Opening Times: Mail order only. 0800-1800 Mon-Fri, 0900-1200 Sat.
Min Mail Order UK: Nmc
Cat. Cost: Online only.
Credit Cards: MasterCard, Visa
Specialities: Specialise in ornamental and fruit trees, including mature trees.
Notes: Delivers to shows.

NPer **Perry's Plants** ♿
The River Garden, Sleights, Whitby, North Yorkshire, YO21 1RR
Ⓜ 07879 498623
Ⓔ richardperry008@hotmail.co.uk
Ⓦ www.perrysplants.co.uk
Contact: Sharon & Richard Perry
Opening Times: 1000-1700 mid-March to Oct.
Cat. Cost: None published.
Credit Cards: None
Specialities: *Lavatera*, *Malva*, *Erysimum*, *Euphorbia*, *Anthemis*, *Osteospermum* & *Hebe*. Uncommon hardy & container plants & aquatic plants.
Notes: Euro accepted. Wheelchair accessible.
OS Grid Ref: NZ869082

NPnk **Primrose Bank** ♿
Redroofs, Dauby Lane, Kexby, York, Yorkshire, YO41 5LH
Ⓣ (01759) 380220
Ⓜ 07774 944447
Ⓔ suegoodwill@yahoo.co.uk
Ⓦ www.primrosebank.co.uk
Contact: Sue Goodwill
Opening Times: 1000-1700 Thu-Sat Pls telephone for opening times July-Oct
Min Mail Order UK: Nmc
Credit Cards: All major credit/debit cards
Specialities: *Hydrangea*, *Galanthus*, *Primula*.
Notes: Delivers to shows. Wheelchair accessible.
OS Grid Ref: SE696508

NPoe **Poets Cottage Shrub Nursery** ♿
Lealholm, Whitby, North Yorkshire, YO21 2AQ
Ⓣ (01947) 897424
Ⓜ 07813 252303
Ⓔ enquiries@poetscottage.co.uk
Ⓦ www.poetscottage.co.uk
Contact: Ilona J. McGivern
Opening Times: 1300-1530 Feb, 0900-1700 Mar-Christmas, 7 days. Closed Jan.
Credit Cards: All major debit/credit cards except American Express
Specialities: Conifers, pines, trees, shrubs, herbaceous, alpines, herbs & *Acer*.
Notes: Wheelchair accessible.

NPol **Polemonium Plantery** ♿
28 Sunnyside, Trimdon Grange, Co. Durham, TS29 6HF
Ⓣ (01429) 881529
Ⓔ dandd@polemonium.co.uk
Ⓦ www.polemonium.co.uk
Contact: David or Dianne Nichol-Brown
Opening Times: By appt. only or see website
Min Mail Order UK: £10.00
Cat. Cost: 3 × 1st class.
Credit Cards: All major credit/debit cards, Paypal
Specialities: National Plant Collections of *Polemonium*, *Collomia*, *Gilia*, *Fragaria vesca*, *Leptodactylon* (*Polemoniaceae*) & *Hakonechloa*.
Notes: Also sells wholesale. Delivers to shows. Wheelchair accessible.
OS Grid Ref: NZ369353

NQui **Quiet Corner Plants**
(office) 20 Grove Road, Brandon, Co. Durham, DH7 8AW
Ⓜ 07932 159204
Ⓔ hal@uwclub.net
Ⓦ www.quietcornerplants.co.uk
Contact: Howard Leslie
Opening Times: By appt. only
Min Mail Order UK: Nmc
Cat. Cost: Online only.
Credit Cards: All major credit/debit cards
Specialities: Hardy herbaceous & shrubby perennials, incl. small quantities of lesser known and harder to find plants.
Notes: Nursery is at Misty Blue Farm, Rock Road, Kirk Merrington, Co. Durham, DL16 7HJ. Also sells wholesale. Delivers to shows.

NRHS **Harlow Carr Plant Centre (RHS)** ◆
RHS Garden Harlow Carr, Crag Lane, Harlow Carr, Harrogate, North Yorkshire, HG3 1QB
Ⓣ (01423) 724666

Ⓕ (01423) 569521
Ⓔ nigeleaton@rhs.org.uk
Ⓦ www.rhs.org.uk
Contact: Nigel Eaton
Opening Times: 0930-1700 Mon-Sun.
Specialities: Wide general range, particularly alpines.
Notes: Programme of free plant events throughout the year. Please ring or check website for details. Customer ordering system for plants which need to be collected from the plant centre (no mail order).

NRib **Ribblesdale Nurseries** ♿
Newsham Hall Lane, Preston, Lancashire, PR4 0AS
Ⓣ (01772) 863081
Ⓔ philsd@btinternet.com
Ⓦ www.ribblesdalenurseries.co.uk
Contact: Angela Dunnett
Opening Times: 0900-1700 Mon-Sat 1030-16.30 Sun
Credit Cards: All major credit/debit cards
Specialities: Trees, shrubs & perennials. Conifers, hedging, alpines, fruit, climbers, herbs, aquatics, ferns & wildflowers. Own grown plants in peat-free compost.
Notes: Wheelchair accessible.
OS Grid Ref: SD515351

NRob **W Robinson & Son (Seeds & Plants) Ltd** ♿
Sunny Bank, Forton, Nr Preston, Lancashire, PR3 0BN
Ⓣ (01524) 791210
Ⓕ (01524) 791933
Ⓔ info@mammothonion.co.uk
Ⓦ www.mammothonion.co.uk
Contact: Miss Robinson
Opening Times: 1000-1600 7 days Mar-Jun, 0800-1700 Mon-Fri Jul-Feb.
Min Mail Order UK: £2.75
Min Mail Order EU: £4.75
Cat. Cost: Free.
Credit Cards: All major credit/debit cards
Specialities: Mammoth vegetable seed. Onions, leeks, tomatoes & beans. Range of vegetable plants in the spring.
Notes: Also sells wholesale. Exports beyond EU. Delivers to shows. Euro accepted. Wheelchair accessible.

NRog **R V Roger Ltd** ♿
The Nurseries, Pickering, North Yorkshire, YO18 7JW
Ⓣ (01751) 472226
Ⓔ sales@rvroger.co.uk
Ⓦ www.rvroger.co.uk
Contact: Ian Roger
Opening Times: 0800-1700 Mon-Sat 1000-1600 Sun
Min Mail Order UK: Nmc
Min Mail Order EU: Nmc
Cat. Cost: £1.00.
Credit Cards: All major credit/debit cards
Specialities: Holders of National Collection of *Erythronium*.
Notes: Third generation family-owned business, established in 1913 growing hardy stock at the foot of the North York Moors. Also sells wholesale. Wheelchair accessible. Exports beyond EU.
OS Grid Ref: SE801827

NRush **Rushrose Nursery**
Berwick Road, Wooler, Northumberland, NE71 6AJ
Ⓣ (01668) 281348
Ⓕ (01668) 932001
Ⓔ info@rushrose.co.uk
Ⓦ www.rushrose.co.uk
Contact: Amy O'Rourke
Opening Times: By appt. only via email.
Min Mail Order UK: £3.00
Min Mail Order EU: £3.00
Cat. Cost: N/A.
Credit Cards: All major credit/debit cards
Specialities: *Helianthemum*.
Notes: Please see website for up to date stock availability. Exports beyond EU. Also sells wholesale.

NRya **Ryal Nursery** ♿
East Farm Cottage, Ryal, Northumberland, NE20 0SA
Ⓣ (01661) 886562
Ⓔ ruthhadden@btinternet.com
Contact: R. Hadden
Opening Times: Mar-Jul by appt., please telephone in advance.
Cat. Cost: Sae.
Credit Cards: None
Specialities: Alpine & woodland plants, mainly available in small quantities only. Nat. Collection of *Primula marginata*.
Notes: Also sells wholesale. Delivers to shows. Wheelchair accessible.
OS Grid Ref: NZ015744

NSla **Slack Top Alpine Nursery**
Alpine House, 22A Slack Top, Hebden Bridge, West Yorkshire, HX7 7HA
Ⓣ (01422) 845348
Ⓜ 07392 856395
Ⓔ enquiries@slacktopnurseries.co.uk
Ⓦ www.slacktopnurseries.co.uk

Contact: Michael & Allison Mitchell
Opening Times: 1000-1700 Fri-Sun, Mar-Aug & B/hols. Other times by appt.
Min Mail Order UK: £20.00
Min Mail Order EU: £50.00
Cat. Cost: 2 × 1st class A5 sae or online.
Credit Cards: All major credit/debit cards
Specialities: Alpine, rockery & woodland plants.
Notes: Talks given to gardening clubs & other groups by appt. Delivers to shows. Euro accepted. Partial wheelchair access. (Some areas of garden inaccessible.)
OS Grid Ref: SD977286

N

NSti **STILLINGFLEET LODGE NURSERIES** ♿
Stewart Lane, Stillingfleet, York, YO19 6HP
Ⓣ (01904) 728506
Ⓔ info@stillingfleetlodgenurseries.co.uk
Ⓦ www.stillingfleetlodgenurseries.co.uk
Contact: Vanessa Cook
Opening Times: 1300-1700 Wed & Fri, 1st Apr-30th Sep. 1300-1700 1st & 3rd Sat & Sun in each month.
Cat. Cost: Online only.
Credit Cards: All major credit/debit cards
Specialities: Foliage & unusual perennials. Hardy geraniums, *Pulmonaria*, variegated plants & grasses.
Notes: Wheelchair accessible.

NSue **SUE PROCTOR PLANTS** ♿
69 Ings Mill Avenue, Clayton West, Huddersfield, West Yorkshire, HD8 9QG
Ⓣ (01484) 866189
Ⓜ 07917 006636
Ⓔ hostas@sueproctorplants.co.uk
Ⓦ www.sueproctorplants.com
Contact: Sue Proctor
Opening Times: By appt. only. Please telephone first.
Min Mail Order UK: £3.50
Cat. Cost: 1st class sae.
Credit Cards: All major credit/debit cards
Specialities: *Hosta*, miniature *Hosta*.
Notes: Wheelchair accessible.
OS Grid Ref: SE256110

NSum **SUMMERDALE GARDEN NURSERY**
Summerdale House, Cow Brow, Lupton, Carnforth, Cumbria, LA6 1PE
Ⓣ (01539) 567210
Ⓔ summerdale@btinternet.com
Ⓦ www.summerdalegardenplants.co.uk
Contact: Gail Sheals
Opening Times: 1100-1630 Mar to end of August.
Min Mail Order UK: £20.00
Cat. Cost: Online only.
Credit Cards: None
Specialities: Shade-loving perennials. *Primula*, including *P. auricula* cultivars.
Notes: Mail order for primulas only. Delivers to shows.
OS Grid Ref: SD545819

NTay **TAYLORS CLEMATIS NURSERY** ♿
Sutton Road, Sutton, Nr Askern, Doncaster, South Yorkshire, DN6 9JZ
Ⓣ (01302) 700716
Ⓜ 07793 201808
Ⓔ info@taylorsclematis.co.uk
Ⓦ www.taylorsclematis.co.uk
Contact: Chris Cocks
Opening Times: Open by appt. only.
Min Mail Order UK: Nmc
Min Mail Order EU: Nmc
Cat. Cost: £1.00.
Credit Cards: All major credit/debit cards
Specialities: *Clematis* (over 400 varieties).
Notes: Largest selection of *Clematis* in the UK. Nursery is open by appointment only. Delivers to shows. Wheelchair accessible.
OS Grid Ref: SE552122

NTPC **TREE PEONY COMPANY**
Willow Cottage, Rillington, Malton, North Yorkshire, YO17 8JU
Ⓣ (01944) 758280
Ⓔ info@treepeony.co.uk
Ⓦ www.treepeony.co.uk
Contact: Thelma Scruton, Roger Scruton
Min Mail Order UK: £15.00
Min Mail Order EU: Nmc
Cat. Cost: None.
Credit Cards: None
Specialities: Tree peonies. *Paeonia suffruticosa*, *P.* Gansu Group, *P. rockii*.
Notes: Also sells wholesale. Euro accepted. Delivers to shows.

NWad **WADDOW LODGE GARDEN** ♿
Clitheroe Road, Waddington, Clitheroe, Lancashire, BB7 3HQ
Ⓣ (01200) 429145
Ⓔ peterfoleyhcn@hotmail.co.uk
Ⓦ www.gardentalks.co.uk
Contact: Peter Foley
Opening Times: By appt. only all year. Also open under NGS (May and July) once again in 2020.
Min Mail Order UK: Nmc
Min Mail Order EU: Nmc
Cat. Cost: Online only.
Credit Cards: None
Specialities: An ever-developing plantsman's

garden with an interesting plant collection. Some plants may only be available in small numbers.
Notes: Open for group visits by appt. (incl. evenings). Wheelchair accessible.
OS Grid Ref: SD732434

NWea **Weasdale Nurseries Ltd**
Newbiggin on Lune, Kirkby Stephen, Cumbria, CA17 4LX
Ⓣ (015396) 23246
Ⓕ (015396) 23277
Ⓔ sales@weasdale.com
Ⓦ www.weasdale.com
Contact: Andrew Forsyth
Opening Times: 0830-1730 Mon-Fri (closed for lunch 13.00-14.00). Closed w/ends & B/hols.
Min Mail Order UK: Nmc
Min Mail Order EU: Nmc
Cat. Cost: Free.
Credit Cards: All major credit/debit cards
Specialities: Hardy forest trees, hedging, broadleaved & conifers. Specimen trees & shrubs grown at 850ft (260m) elevation. Some rarer plants grown in small batches, so availability can't be guaranteed. Peat-free.
Notes: Mail order a speciality. Mail order Nov-Apr only. Also sells wholesale to VAT registered customers.

NWsh **Westshores Nurseries**
82 West Street, Winterton, Scunthorpe, Lincolnshire, DN15 9QF
Ⓣ (01724) 733940
Ⓜ 07875 732535
Ⓔ westshnur@aol.com
Ⓦ www.westshores.co.uk
Contact: Gail & John Summerfield
Opening Times: By appt. only
Min Mail Order UK: £15.00
Min Mail Order EU: £15.00
Cat. Cost: Online only.
Credit Cards: All major credit/debit cards
Specialities: Ornamental grasses, autumn flowering perennials & scented pelargoniums.
Notes: Wide selection of talks for gardening clubs and Hardy Plant Society groups located up to 130 miles (or 3 hours) away in one direction.
OS Grid Ref: SE927187

Southern

SAdn **Ashdown Forest Garden Centre & Nursery** ♿
Duddleswell, Ashdown Forest, East Sussex, TN22 3JP
Ⓣ (01825) 712300
Ⓔ info@ashdownforestgardencentre.co.uk
Ⓦ www.ashdownforestgardencentre.co.uk
Contact: Victoria Falletti
Opening Times: 0900-1700 winter, 0900-1700 summer. Greenfingers Café open 0930-1700.
Min Mail Order UK: Nmc
Credit Cards: All major credit/debit cards
Specialities: *Lapageria*, *Fuchsia*, conservatory climbers, unusual shrubs. Available in small quantities only.
Notes: Wheelchair accessible.
OS Grid Ref: TQ468283

SAko **Akorn and Oake**
18 Twyford Avenue, Southampton, Hampshire, SO15 5NP
Ⓣ (023) 8034 4040
Ⓜ 07973 149404
Ⓔ stefan.rau@hotmail.co.uk
Contact: Stefan Rau
Opening Times: Open by appt. only.
Specialities: *Saxifraga*.
Notes: Delivers to shows.

SAll **Allwoods (Hassocks) Ltd**
London Road, Hassocks, West Sussex, BN6 9NA
Ⓣ (01273) 844229
Ⓔ info@allwoods.net
Ⓦ www.allwoods.net
Contact: David & Emma James
Opening Times: Office 0900-1630 Mon-Fri. Answer machine all other times. Office is closed B/hols and Xmas-New Year. Visits by prior appt. only.
Min Mail Order UK: Nmc
Min Mail Order EU: Nmc
Cat. Cost: £1.00.
Credit Cards: All major debit/credit cards except American Express, Paypal
Specialities: Large collection of *Dianthus*. Unusual & collectors' geraniums & pelargoniums. *Fuchsia* & other garden plants. Wide range of interesting succulents British grown direct from our Sussex nursery.
Notes: All listed varieties available as plugs but choice varies depending on time of year. Please phone before travelling to avoid disappointment &/or to ensure order is ready for collection. Also sells wholesale.

SAls **Alstroemeria Select**
Dingley Dell, Toddington Road, Westoning, Bedfordshire, MK45 5AH
Ⓣ (01525) 878924
Ⓔ customerservice@alstroemeriaselect.co.uk

Ⓦ www.alstroemeriaselect.co.uk
Contact: Sarah Castleman
Opening Times: 0900-1600 Mon-Fri. We are often in the nursery so do email with queries if no answer on telephone.
Min Mail Order UK: Nmc
Min Mail Order EU: Nmc
Credit Cards: All major credit/debit cards
Specialities: Around 120 varieties of *Alstroemeria*.
Notes: Small, family run nursery growing and supplying stock. Not open to the public but plants can be collected by prior arrangement. Also sells wholesale. Delivers to shows.

SAng **Angharad Pike Gardener and Plants** ♿
Old Workshop, St Peters Road, Hayling Island, Hampshire, PO11 0RX
Ⓣ (02392) 468036
Ⓜ 07753 225670
Ⓔ angharad.pike@gmail.com
Ⓦ www.angharadpike.com
Contact: Angharad Pike
Opening Times: Please see website for opening times.
Credit Cards: All major credit/debit cards, American Express
Notes: All plants listed are available to view in the gardens at The Old Workshop. Plants can be pre-ordered for collection at any of the Open Gardens we are attending. Plants are sold in one-litre pots, grown in peat-free compost. All our plants are British grown. Wheelchair accessible.
OS Grid Ref: SU731037

SApu **Apuldram Roses**
Crouchers Farm, 163 Birdham Road, Apuldram, Chichester, West Sussex, PO20 7EQ
Ⓣ (01243) 785769
Ⓔ enquiries@apuldramroses.co.uk
Ⓦ www.apuldramroses.co.uk
Contact: Elizabeth Sawday
Opening Times: Winter 1000-1600 Mon to Fri & 1000 -1300 Sat. Summer 1000-1700 Mon-Fri & 1000-1600 Sat.
Min Mail Order UK: £10.00
Min Mail Order EU: £10.00
Cat. Cost: N/A.
Credit Cards: All major credit/debit cards,
Specialities: Roses.
Notes: Specialist rose grower. Euro accepted.

SArc **Architectural Plants Ltd** ♿
Stane Street, North Heath, Pulborough, West Sussex, RH20 1DJ
Ⓣ (01798) 879213
Ⓔ enquiries@architecturalplants.com
Ⓦ www.architecturalplants.com
Contact: Sophie Pett-Gallacher
Opening Times: Nursery 0900-1700 Mon-Sat & B/hols. Closed Sun. Café 1000-1600 Mon-Sat
Cat. Cost: Free.
Credit Cards: All major debit/credit cards except American Express
Specialities: Architectural plants & hardy exotics esp. rare evergreen & seaside exotics, spiky plants, yuccas/agaves, climbers, evergreen trees and shrubs, topiary & bamboos.
Notes: Café & shop. Also sells wholesale. Delivers to shows. Wheelchair accessible (& available on site).
OS Grid Ref: TQ192262

SavN **Savin Nurseries**
Hillside Road, Stondon, Bedfordshire, SG16 6LP
Ⓣ (01462) 850680
Ⓔ savinbase@hotmail.co.uk
Ⓦ www.savinnurseries.co.uk
Contact: Darryl Savin
Opening Times: 0830-1745 Mon-Fri, 0830-1700 Sat, 1000-1600 Sun (winter)
Credit Cards: All major debit/credit cards except American Express
Specialities: Bonsai, bedding, house plants, acers, perennials, olives.
Notes: Family run nursery growing their own bedding plants, shrubs, perennials and small trees.

SBdl **Grow at Brogdale** ♿
Brogdale Farm, Brogdale Road, Faversham, Kent, ME13 8XZ
Ⓣ (01795) 531888
Ⓕ (01795) 531710
Ⓔ fruit@brogdaleonline.co.uk
Ⓦ https://www.brogdaleonline.co.uk
Contact: Donna Cooper
Opening Times: 1000-1600 Mon-Sun
Min Mail Order UK: Nmc
Min Mail Order EU: Nmc
Cat. Cost: £4.95.
Credit Cards: All major credit/debit cards
Specialities: Rare and heritage varieties of apple, pear, cherry, plum and nuts.
Notes: Fruit trees grafted by hand from the trees in the National Fruit Collection, with rare and heritage varieties being our specialism. Exports beyond EU. Euro accepted. Also sells wholesale. Wheelchair accessible.
OS Grid Ref: TR006505

SBea **BEAN PLACE NURSERY**
Watersfield, Bletchenden Road, Headcorn, Kent, TN27 9JB
Ⓜ 07841 484822
Ⓔ info@beanplace.co.uk
Ⓦ www.beanplace.co.uk
Contact: Timothy Waters
Opening Times: By appt. only.
Min Mail Order UK: £5.95
Cat. Cost: Online.
Credit Cards: None
Specialities: Ornamental grasses, herbaceous perennials & cottage garden plants.
Notes: Growers of hardy herbaceous perennials, bearded iris, ornamental grasses and hardy garden ferns. Delivers to shows.

SBls **BLACKSTEM PLANTS**
Shepherds Lodge, Clay Hill Road, Lamberhurst, Kent, TN3 8LT
Ⓣ (07973) 129102
Ⓔ info@blackstemplants.co.uk
Ⓦ www.blackstemplants.co.uk
Contact: Carole Lamond
Opening Times: 1000-1600 Mar-Oct By appt. only
Credit Cards: All major credit/debit cards, Paypal
Specialities: Wildlife-friendly plants
Notes: All plants grown onsite. Please call before visiting. Plants also sold at plant fairs and other seasonal events. Delivers to shows.
OS Grid Ref: TQ652368

SBrt **BRIGHTON PLANTS** ♿
New Hall Lane, Small Dole, Sussex, BN5 9YJ
Ⓜ 07955 744802
Ⓔ brighton.plants@gmail.com
Ⓦ www.brightonplants.blogspot.com
Contact: Steve Law
Opening Times: Open by appt. only. Please email/phone before visiting.
Min Mail Order UK: Nmc
Min Mail Order EU: Nmc
Cat. Cost: 4 × 1st class.
Credit Cards: None
Specialities: Hardy herbaceous and woody plants. Drought-tolerant plants.
Notes: Delivers to shows. Euro accepted. Wheelchair accessible.
OS Grid Ref: TQ208132

SBut **BUTTERFLY COTTAGE GARDEN PLANTS** ♿
office, 55 Middle Brook Street, Winchester, Hampshire, SO23 8DQ
Ⓣ (01962) 621882
Ⓜ 07962 869105
Ⓔ andrew.ward203@ntlworld.com
Ⓦ www.butterflycottageplants.co.uk
Contact: Andy Ward
Opening Times: Open Mar-Sep 1000-1700 Thu, Fri and most Sats. (Please telephone for Sat opening times)
Min Mail Order UK: Nmc
Cat. Cost: Online only.
Credit Cards: All major credit/debit cards
Specialities: Growing perennials to attract a variety of pollinators, including many garden-worthy natives. Limited numbers of each variety as all grown at nursery. Order early to avoid disappointment.
Notes: Nursery is at Cheriton Village, Alresford, Hants SO24 0PW. See website for directions. Please check plant availability before travelling long journeys. Wheelchair accessible. Delivers to shows.

SCam **CAMELLIA GROVE NURSERY** ♿
Market Garden, Lower Beeding, Horsham, West Sussex, RH13 6PP
Ⓣ (01403) 891412
Ⓔ lp@hortic.com
Ⓦ www.camellia-grove.com
Contact: Chris Loder
Opening Times: 1000-1600 Mon-Sat, please phone first so we can give you our undivided attention.
Min Mail Order UK: Nmc
Min Mail Order EU: Nmc
Cat. Cost: Please enquire.
Credit Cards: All major debit/credit cards except American Express
Specialities: *Camellia japonica*, *C. williamsii*, *C. sasanqua* & *C. reticulata*, from the purest white to richest red flowers.
Notes: Also sells wholesale. Exports beyond EU. Delivers to shows. Euro accepted. Wheelchair accessible.
OS Grid Ref: TQ221255

SChF **CHARLESHURST FARM NURSERY**
Loxwood Road, Plaistow, Billingshurst, West Sussex, RH14 0NY
Ⓣ (01403) 752273
Ⓜ 07736 522788
Ⓔ info@charleshurstplants.co.uk
Ⓦ www.charleshurstplants.co.uk
Contact: Clive Mellor
Opening Times: Normally 0900-1730 Fri, Sat, Sun, Feb-Oct, but please ring before travelling.
Min Mail Order UK: Nmc
Min Mail Order EU: Nmc
Cat. Cost: Online only.
Credit Cards: All major credit/debit cards

Specialities: Shrubs including some more unusual species. Good range of Daphnes & Japanese maples.
Notes: Delivers to shows. Euro accepted.
OS Grid Ref: TQ015308

SChr **JOHN CHURCHER**
47 Grove Avenue, Portchester, Fareham, Hampshire, PO16 9EZ
Ⓣ (023) 9232 6740
Ⓜ 07717 495861
Ⓔ johnchurcher47@btinternet.com
Contact: John Churcher
Opening Times: By appt. only. Please phone or email.
Min Mail Order UK: Nmc
Min Mail Order EU: Nmc
Credit Cards: None
Specialities: Hardy exotics for the Mediterranean-style garden, incl. palms, tree ferns, *Musa*, hedychiums, cycads, *Agave*, *Aloe*, *Opuntia* & echiums. Stock available in small quantities only.
OS Grid Ref: SU614047

SCit **THE CITRUS CENTRE** ♿
West Mare Lane, Pulborough, West Sussex, RH20 2EA
Ⓣ (01798) 872786
Ⓔ enquiries@citruscentre.co.uk
Ⓦ www.citruscentre.co.uk
Contact: Amanda & Chris Dennis
Opening Times: 0930-1600 Tue-Sat. Phone or check website for Xmas & B/hol opening times.
Min Mail Order UK: Nmc
Min Mail Order EU: Nmc
Cat. Cost: Online.
Credit Cards: Visa, MasterCard
Specialities: *Citrus* & *Citrus* relatives.
Notes: Wheelchair accessible.

SCmr **CROMAR NURSERY** ♿
39 Livesey Street, Wateringbury, Maidstone, Kent, ME18 5BQ
Ⓣ (01622) 812380
Ⓔ CromarNursery@aol.com
Ⓦ www.cromarnursery.co.uk
Contact: Martin
Opening Times: w/ends incl. B/hols. Please phone or email to check opening times.
Min Mail Order UK: Nmc
Min Mail Order EU: Nmc
Cat. Cost: 2 × 1st class.
Credit Cards: All major credit/debit cards
Specialities: Ornamental & fruit trees.
Notes: Wheelchair accessible.
OS Grid Ref: TQ697547

SCob **COBLANDS ONLINE**
Coblands Sevenoaks Plant Centre, Dryhill Lane, Sundridge, Sevenoaks, Kent, TN14 6AA
Ⓣ (01452) 742445
Ⓔ customerservice@coblands.co.uk
Ⓦ www.coblands.co.uk
Contact: Hannah
Opening Times: 0830-1700 Mon-Fri.
Min Mail Order UK: Nmc
Min Mail Order EU: Nmc
Credit Cards: All major credit/debit cards
Specialities: Wide range of shrubs & established specimen plants. Herbaceous perennials incl. many new varieties. Wide range of shrubs and established specimen plants.
Notes: Also sells wholesale. Free delivery on online orders over £40.
OS Grid Ref: TQ586487

SCoo **COOLING'S NURSERIES LTD** ♿
Rushmore Hill, Knockholt, Sevenoaks, Kent, TN14 7NN
Ⓣ (01959) 532269
Ⓕ (01959) 534092
Ⓔ Plantfinder@coolings.co.uk
Ⓦ www.coolings.co.uk
Contact: Mark Reeve or Garry Norris
Opening Times: 0900-1700 Mon-Sat & 0900-1630 Sun.
Min Mail Order UK: Nmc
Credit Cards: All major debit/credit cards except American Express
Specialities: Large range of perennials, conifers & bedding plants. Many unusual shrubs & trees. Third generation family business.
Notes: Display garden. Coffee shop. Wheelchair accessible.
OS Grid Ref: TK477610

SDay **A LA CARTE DAYLILIES**
Little Hermitage, St Catherine's Down, Ventnor, Isle of Wight, PO38 2PD
Ⓣ (01983) 730512
Ⓔ andy.hyjack@googlemail.com:jan.hyjack@gmail.com
Ⓦ www.alacartedaylilies.co.uk
Contact: Jan & Andy Wyers
Opening Times: Mail order only. Open by appt. only. Difficult to find on an unmade private road, phone/email for directions.
Min Mail Order UK: Nmc
Min Mail Order EU: Nmc
Cat. Cost: 3 × 1st class.
Credit Cards: None
Specialities: *Hemerocallis*. National Plant Collection of miniature & small flowered

Hemerocallis & large flowered *Hemerocallis* (post-1960 award-winning cvs).
Notes: Euro accepted.
OS Grid Ref: SZ499787

SDeJ **P. de Jager & Sons Ltd** ♿ ◆
Church Farm, Ulcombe, Maidstone, Kent, ME17 1DN
Ⓣ (01622) 840229
Ⓕ (01622) 844073
Ⓔ flowerbulbs@dejager.co.uk
Ⓦ www.dejager.co.uk
Contact: George Clowes
Opening Times: Mail order only. Orders taken from 0900-1700 Mon-Fri.
Min Mail Order UK: Nmc
Min Mail Order EU: Nmc
Cat. Cost: Free.
Credit Cards: All major credit/debit cards
Specialities: Wide range of all flower bulbs.
Notes: Also sells wholesale. Exports beyond EU. Euro accepted. Wheelchair accessible.

SDir **Direct Bulbs**
Mault-Ley, 6, Hillside Close, Teg Down, Winchester, Hampshire, SO22 5LW
Ⓣ (01962) 840038
Ⓜ 07766 517703
Ⓔ tim.woodland@btconnect.com
Ⓦ www.directbulbs.co.uk
Contact: Tim Woodland
Opening Times: Mail order only
Min Mail Order UK: £6.00
Min Mail Order EU: £20.00
Credit Cards: All major credit/debit cards
Specialities: Bulbs.
Notes: Also sells wholesale. Suppliers of spring and summer flowering bulbs.

SDix **Great Dixter Nurseries** ♿
Dixter Road, Northiam, Rye, East Sussex, TN31 6PH
Ⓣ (01797) 254044
Ⓔ nursery@greatdixter.co.uk
Ⓦ www.greatdixter.co.uk
Contact: Michael Morphy
Opening Times: 0900-1700 Mon-Sat, 10.00-1700 Sun Apr-end Oct. 0900-1230 & 1330-1630 Mon-Fri, 0900-1230 Sat. Sun closed Nov-end Mar.
Min Mail Order UK: Nmc
Min Mail Order EU: Nmc
Cat. Cost: £1.00.
Credit Cards: All major credit/debit cards
Specialities: *Clematis*, shrubs and plants. Gardens open.
Notes: Usual and unusual shrubs and perennials. Mail order October to end of March. Wheelchair accessible.
OS Grid Ref: TQ821251

SDow **Downderry Nursery** ♿
Pillar Box Lane, Hadlow, Nr Tonbridge, Kent, TN11 9SW
Ⓣ (01732) 810081
Ⓔ info@downderry-nursery.co.uk
Ⓦ www.downderry-nursery.co.uk
Contact: Dr Simon Charlesworth
Opening Times: 1000-1700 Thu-Sun, 2nd May-29th Sep & B/hols. Other times by appt.
Min Mail Order UK: Nmc
Min Mail Order EU: Nmc
Cat. Cost: Free.
Credit Cards: Delta, MasterCard, Maestro, Visa
Specialities: National Plant Collections of *Lavandula* and *Rosmarinus*.
Notes: Wheelchair accessible.
OS Grid Ref: TQ625521

SDys **Dysons Nurseries** ♿
Great Comp Garden, Platt, Sevenoaks, Kent, TN15 8QS
Ⓣ (01732) 885094
Ⓜ 07887 997663
Ⓔ dysonsorders@greatcompgarden.co.uk
Ⓦ www.dysonsalvias.com
Contact: William T. Dyson
Opening Times: 1100-1700 7 days 1st Apr-31st Oct. Other times by appt.
Cat. Cost: Online only.
Credit Cards: All major credit/debit cards
Specialities: Salvias & an eclectic range of choice and uncommon plants.
Notes: Delivers to shows. Wheelchair accessible.

SEdd **Eddington House Nursery**
Eddington Road, Nettlestone/Seaview, Isle of Wight, Hampshire, PO34 5EF
Ⓜ 07837 589478
Ⓔ info@eddingtonhousenursery.co.uk
Ⓦ www.eddingtonhousenursery.co.uk
Contact: Ian Chadwick
Opening Times: 1000-1700 Mon-Sat (Closed Sun). Closed end Nov-end Jan except by appt.
Min Mail Order UK: Nmc
Cat. Cost: Online only.
Credit Cards: All major credit/debit cards
Specialities: *Salvia*, *Hydrangea*, perennials & dry garden plants planted in display gardens which are being developed. We aim to increase our range of succulents in this coming year. Some rare plants, we only sell a few of each season, need to be propagated to order.
Notes: Home to the Isle of Wight Rare Plant

Fair featuring many specialist nurseries, plant groups and related organisations speakers, café, live band and open gardens. See website for plant availability. Some plants are grown as stock plants and can be grown to order.
OS Grid Ref: SZ626900

SEdi **Edibleculture** ♿
The Horticultural Unit, The Abbey School, London Road, Faversham, Kent, ME13 8RZ
Ⓣ (01795) 537662
Ⓔ info@edibleculture.co.uk
Ⓦ www.edibleculture.co.uk
Contact: Chris or David
Opening Times: 0900-1700 Mon-Sat 1000-1600 Sun, Mar-Jan. Jan-Feb by appt. only but telephone/email orders taken.
Cat. Cost: online only.
Credit Cards: All major credit/debit cards
Specialities: Herbs, vegetables, fruit trees and soft fruit, herbaceous perennials, hedgerow plants.
Notes: Focus on interesting plants grown sustainably. Specialists in establishing and maintaining orchards. Also sells wholesale. Wheechair accessible.

S

SEle **Eleplants Nursery**
32 Framfield Road, Uckfield, East Sussex, TN22 5AH
Ⓜ 07810 660109
Ⓔ eleplantsnursery@talk21.com
Ⓦ www.eleplantsnursery.co.uk
Contact: Martin Batchelor
Opening Times: Not open. By appt. only.
Min Mail Order UK: Nmc
Min Mail Order EU: Nmc
Credit Cards: All major credit/debit cards, Paypal
Specialities: Shrubs.
Notes: Exports beyond EU. Delivers to shows.

SEND **East Northdown Nurseries** ♿
George Hill Road (B2052), Margate, Kent, CT10 3BN
Ⓣ (01843) 862060
Ⓜ 07714 241667
Ⓔ info@botanyplants.co.uk
Ⓦ www.botanyplants.co.uk
Contact: Louise & William Friend
Opening Times: 0900-1700 7 days, all year except Sun in winter. Closed Xmas week.
Min Mail Order UK: Nmc
Cat. Cost: Online only.
Credit Cards: All major credit/debit cards
Specialities: Chalk & coast-loving plants. Specimen shrubs & bamboos available. Complementary range of plants for damp/acid conditions available to order from our Mucklestone Nursery (MMuc). Collection of rare Mediterranean plants.
Notes: Tea room & gardens. Close to Botany Bay. Lectures given to gardening groups in Kent. Garden tours by appt. See website or contact nursery for full list & details. Wheelchair accessible.
OS Grid Ref: TR383702

SEsH **Essentially Hops**
Chalkpit Farm, Adisham Road, Bekesbourne, Canterbury, Kent, CT4 5EU
Ⓣ (01227) 830666
Ⓔ shop@essentiallyhops.co.uk
Ⓦ http://www.essentiallyhops.co.uk
Contact: Ashley
Opening Times: 0900-1700 Mon-Sat
Credit Cards: Visa, MasterCard
Specialities: Over 40 varieties of hops including English, foreign, dwarf and ornamental varieties.
Notes: Hop plants for sale. Also specialise in growing hop garlands (bines/vines) for traditional home decoration. Some hops grown on the farm are supplied to brewers and hop plants and growing equipment are available from the shop and online. Also sells wholesale.

SEWo **English Woodlands** ♿
Burrow Nursery, Herrings Lane, Cross-in-Hand, Heathfield, East Sussex, TN21 0UG
Ⓣ (01435) 862992
Ⓔ sales@englishwoodlands.com
Ⓦ www.englishwoodlands.com
Opening Times: 0800-1700 Mon-Fri. 0800-1600 Sat. Closed Sun & B/hols.
Min Mail Order UK: £25.00
Cat. Cost: Free.
Credit Cards: All major debit/credit cards except American Express
Specialities: Trees, shrubs, hedging. Please telephone to check plant availability before visiting.
Notes: Also sells wholesale. Wheelchair accessible.
OS Grid Ref: TQ567222

SFai **Fairweather's Garden Centre** ♿
High Street, Beaulieu, Hampshire, SO42 7YB
Ⓣ (01590) 612307
Ⓔ info@fairweathers.co.uk
Ⓦ www.fairweathers.co.uk
Contact: Sue Greaves
Opening Times: 0900-1700 7 days.
Min Mail Order UK: Nmc
Credit Cards: Visa, MasterCard

Specialities: *Agapanthus* & *Lavandula*.
Notes: Wheelchair accessible.

SGBe **Garden Beauty**
Hook Lane, Southampton, Hampshire, SO31 9HH
Ⓣ (01489) 550830
Ⓕ (01489) 660630
Ⓔ sales@gardenbeauty.co.uk
Ⓦ https://www.gardenbeauty.co.uk/
Contact: Stephanie Hansen
Opening Times: Not open, mail order only
Min Mail Order UK: £4.99
Cat. Cost: Online only.
Credit Cards: All major credit/debit cards
Specialities: Hebes, shrubs, perennials, grasses. Specimen plants also available.
Notes: Offer a range of new, rare and unusual plants grown at their nurseries in Southampton, as well as old favourites. Varieties are chosen to perform well in gardens with many having the RHS AGM. Continually testing and introducing new varieties. Standard delivery charge of £4.99 per order. See website for further details.

SGbt **Gilbert's Nursery** ♿
Dandy's Ford Lane, Sherfield English, Romsey, Hampshire, SO51 6DT
Ⓣ (01794) 322566
Ⓔ gilbertsnursery@aol.com
Ⓦ www.gilbertsnursery.co.uk
Contact: Nick Gilbert
Opening Times: 0900-1700 Tue-Sat, 10.00-16.30 Sun, all year round. *Dahlia* field open from 2nd week Aug to 2nd week Oct.
Min Mail Order UK: Nmc
Min Mail Order EU: Nmc
Cat. Cost: 2 × 1st class.
Credit Cards: All major debit/credit cards except American Express
Specialities: *Dahlia*. Proper plant nursery with many unusual plants & staff happy to share their knowledge & help with plant selection.
Notes: *Dahlia* field with over 400 cvs on view (grass pathways). See above for opening times or go to www.gilbertsdahlias.co.uk. Tea room. Delivers to shows. Wheelchair accessible.

SGol **Golden Hill Nurseries** ♿
Lordsfield, Goudhurst Road, Marden, Kent, TN12 9LT
Ⓣ (01622) 833218
Ⓜ 07826 523655
Ⓔ enquiries@goldenhillplants.com
Ⓦ www.goldenhillplants.com
Contact: Roger Butler
Opening Times: 0900-1700 Mon-Sat, 1st Mar-31st Oct. 0900-1600 Mon-Sat, 1st Nov-28th Feb. 1100-1600 Sun from 3rd Sun in Feb-end Nov.
Min Mail Order UK: Nmc
Cat. Cost: Online only.
Credit Cards: All major credit/debit cards
Specialities: *Hydrangea*, *Chaenomeles*, *Camellia* & *Viburnum*. Specimen trees & shrubs, ground cover and hedging.
Notes: Also sells wholesale. Euro accepted. Wheelchair accessible. Delivers to shows.

SGro **Growing Delights**
Address not publishable. Pls ring for details or look on website.
Ⓜ 07874 678175
Ⓔ growingdelights@gmail.com
Ⓦ www.growingdelights.co.uk
Contact: Lesley Baker
Opening Times: Not open.
Min Mail Order UK: £15 + p&p
Min Mail Order EU: £15+ p&p
Cat. Cost: Online only.
Credit Cards: Paypal
Specialities: Unusual plants, alpines & drought-tolerant plants. Plants to attract bees & butterflies. A small nursery so only able to supply small quantities.
Notes: Almost entirely growing peat-free. A small nursery only able to supply plants in small quantities. Mail order mostly for small plants only. No mail order sent Dec-Jan. Plants can be collected by arrangement and from sales & shows. Delivers to shows if attending.

SGsty **Garden Style Plant Centre** ♿
Farnham Road, Holt Pound, Farnham, Hampshire, GU10 4LD
Ⓣ (01420) 521092
Ⓔ sales@gardenstyle.co.uk
Ⓦ www.gardenstyle.co.uk
Contact: Elizabeth Nightingale
Opening Times: 0900-1730 Mon-Sat, 1030-1630 Sun.
Credit Cards: All major credit/debit cards
Specialities: Bamboo, climbers, conifers, hedging, evergreen & deciduous shrubs, fruit & ornamental trees, topiary.
Notes: Suppliers of larger plants to enhance your garden since 1991. Also sells wholesale. Delivers to shows. Wheelchair accessible.
OS Grid Ref: SU810429

SHaC **Hart Canna** ♿
Lincluden Nursery, Shaftesbury Road, Bisley, Woking, Surrey, GU24 9EN
Ⓣ (01252) 514421

Ⓜ 07762 950000
Ⓔ sales@hartcanna.com
Ⓦ www.hartcanna.co.uk
Contact: Keith Hayward
Opening Times: By appt. only
Min Mail Order UK: Nmc
Min Mail Order EU: Nmc
Cat. Cost: Online only.
Credit Cards: All major credit/debit cards
Specialities: *Canna*. National Plant Collection of *Canna*.
Notes: Also sells wholesale. Euro accepted. Delivers to shows. Wheelchair accessible.

SHar **Hardy's Cottage Garden Plants** ♿
Priory Lane Nursery, Freefolk Priors, Whitchurch, Hampshire, RG28 7FA
Ⓣ (01256) 896533
Ⓔ info@hardysplants.co.uk
Ⓦ www.hardysplants.co.uk
Contact: Rosemary Hardy
Opening Times: 1000-1700 7 days, 1st Mar-30th Sep. 1000-1600 Mon-Fri, Oct. 1000-1500 Mon-Fri, 1st Nov-28th Feb. Closed 23rd Dec-4th Jan.
Min Mail Order UK: Nmc
Cat. Cost: Online only.
Credit Cards: Visa, Access, Electron, Switch, Solo
Specialities: Wide range of herbaceous perennials incl. *Achillea, Gaura, Geum, Geranium, Hemerocallis, Heuchera, Lathryus vernus, Paeonia, Penstemon* & *Salvia*.
Notes: Accepts HTA Gift Tokens. Offers trade discount. Delivers to shows. Wheelchair accessible.

SHeu **Heucheraholics** ♿
Boldre Nurseries, Southampton Road, Lymington, Hampshire, SO41 8ND
Ⓣ (01590) 670581
Ⓜ 07973 291062
Ⓔ jooles.heucheraholics@gmail.com
Ⓦ www.heucheraholics.co.uk
Contact: Julie Burton/Sean Atkinson
Opening Times: By appt. only (except Open Days) Please phone for details
Min Mail Order UK: Nmc
Min Mail Order EU: Please contact nursery to discuss
Cat. Cost: Online only.
Credit Cards: All major credit/debit cards, Paypal
Specialities: *Heuchera, Heucherella, Pulmonaria, Tiarella.*
Notes: Working nursery in the New Forest. Toilet facilities. Well-behaved dogs welcome. See website or contact nursery for details of open days. Visits by groups can be arranged, please contact nursery for details. See website for Open Days. Delivers to shows. Wheelchair accessible.
OS Grid Ref: SZ310934

SHmp **Hampshire Carnivorous Plants**
Stroudwood Nursery, Stroudwood Lane, Lower Upham, Southampton, Hampshire, SO32 1HG
Ⓣ (023) 8047 3314
Ⓜ 07703 258296
Ⓕ (023) 8047 3314
Ⓔ sales@hantsflytrap.com
Ⓦ www.hantsflytrap.com
Contact: Matthew Soper
Opening Times: By appt. only.
Min Mail Order UK: Nmc
Min Mail Order EU: £50.00 + p&p
Credit Cards: All major credit/debit cards
Specialities: Carnivorous plants esp. *Cephalotus, Darlingtonia, Dionaea, Drosera, Heliamphora, Nepenthes, Pinguicula, Sarracenia* & *Utricularia.*
Notes: Also sells wholesale. Exports beyond EU. Delivers to shows. Euro accepted. Partial wheelchair access.
OS Grid Ref: SU514091

SHor **The Plant Centre at Hortus Loci**
Hound Green, Hook, Hampshire, RG27 8LQ
Ⓣ (01189) 326487
Ⓔ enquiries@hlpantcentre.co.uk/robin.wallis@hortusloci.co.uk
Ⓦ http://hlplantcentre.co.uk/
Contact: Adam Hawkins
Notes: Also sells wholesale.

SHyH **Hydrangea Haven** ♿
Market Garden, Lower Beeding, West Sussex, RH13 6PP
Ⓣ (01403) 891412
Ⓔ lp@hortic.com
Ⓦ www.hydrangea-haven.com
Contact: Chris Loder
Opening Times: 1000-1600 Mon-Sat, please phone first.
Min Mail Order UK: Nmc
Min Mail Order EU: Nmc
Cat. Cost: Please enquire.
Credit Cards: All major debit/credit cards except American Express
Specialities: *Hydrangea*: mophead, lacecap & panicle. *Agapanthus.*
Notes: Also sells wholesale. Exports beyond EU. Delivers to shows. Euro accepted. Wheelchair accessible.
OS Grid Ref: TQ221255

SIri **Iris of Sissinghurst**
Roughlands Farm, Goudhurst Road, Marden, Kent, TN12 9NH
Ⓣ (01622) 831511
Ⓔ orders@irisofsissinghurst.com
Ⓦ www.irisofsissinghurst.com
Contact: Sue Marshall
Opening Times: Contact nursery or see website for opening times.
Min Mail Order UK: Nmc
Min Mail Order EU: Nmc
Cat. Cost: Online only.
Credit Cards: None
Specialities: *Iris*, short, intermediate & tall bearded, *ensata*, *sibirica* & many species.
Notes: Euro accepted. Delivers to shows (pre-ordered plants).
OS Grid Ref: TQ735437

SIvy **Ivy Hatch Plant Supplies**
Coach Road, Ivy Hatch, Kent, TN15 0PE
Ⓜ 07769 604468
Ⓔ debs@ivyhatchplantsupplies.co.uk
Ⓦ www.ivyhatchplantsupplies.co.uk
Contact: Debs Ednie
Opening Times: By appt. only.
Min Mail Order UK: £5.00
Min Mail Order EU: £10.00
Cat. Cost: None.
Credit Cards: Paypal
Specialities: Hardy salvias and succulents including *Echeveria*. Good variety of *Aeonium* and a range of tropical plants.
Notes: Sole supplier for The World Garden Nursery, Lullingstone Castle. Unusual varieties. Limited stock, can source/grow to order. Also sells wholesale. Full range avail. by mail order or at The World Garden Nursery, Lullingstone, Kent. Exports beyond EU (restrictions apply).

SJap **The Japanese Garden Centre** ♿
Addlestead Road, East Peckham, Kent, TN12 5DP
Ⓣ (01622) 872403
Ⓔ info@buildajapanesegarden.com
Ⓦ www.buildajapanesegarden.com
Contact: Mark
Opening Times: 1000-1600 7 days
Credit Cards: MasterCard, Visa
Specialities: Japanese plants
Notes: Established in 1993 to cater solely for the provision of plants and materials suitable for Japanese gardens in the UK. Plants stocked range from small plants to specimen trees. Also sells wholesale. Wheelchair accessible.
OS Grid Ref: TQ662485

SKee **Keepers Nursery**
Gallants Court, Gallants Lane, East Farleigh, Maidstone, Kent, ME15 0LE
Ⓣ (01622) 326465
Ⓔ sales@keepers-nursery.co.uk
Ⓦ www.keepers-nursery.co.uk
Contact: Hamid Habibi
Opening Times: Limited number of open days & for collection of order by arrangement.
Min Mail Order UK: Nmc
Cat. Cost: Online only.
Credit Cards: Visa, MasterCard, Switch, Maestro
Specialities: A very large range of old & rare as well as modern fruit tree varieties. Soft fruit plants & nut trees.

SKin **Kings Barn Trees**
Wheler Stables, Welford Road, Husbands Bosworth, Leicestershire, LE17 6JL
Ⓜ 07815 189350
Ⓔ sales@kingsbarntrees.co.uk
Ⓦ www.kingsbarntrees.co.uk
Contact: Annetta Toolan
Opening Times: Not open. Mail order via website only.
Min Mail Order UK: £3.00
Min Mail Order EU: £9.95
Cat. Cost: Online only.
Credit Cards: All major credit/debit cards
Specialities: Grow containerised trees, specialising in *Eucalyptus*. *Eucalyptus* available in small quantities only.

SLau **The Laurels Nursery**
Benenden, Cranbrook, Kent, TN17 4JU
Ⓣ (01580) 240463
Ⓦ www.thelaurelsnursery.co.uk
Contact: Peter or Sylvia Kellett
Opening Times: 0800-1600 Wed-Fri, 0900-1200 Sat, Sun by appt. only.
Min Mail Order UK: £30
Cat. Cost: Free.
Credit Cards: All major credit/debit cards
Specialities: Open ground & container ornamental trees, shrubs & climbers especially birch, beech *Wisteria* & *Acer palmatum* varieties.
Notes: Mail order of small *Wisteria* only. Also sells wholesale. Delivers to shows. Partly accessible for wheelchairs.
OS Grid Ref: TQ815313

SLBF **Little Brook Fuchsias** ♿
Ash Green Lane West, Ash Green, Nr Aldershot, Hampshire, GU12 6HL
Ⓣ (01252) 329731
Ⓜ 07817 272361

Ⓔ carol@littlebrookfuchsias.co.uk
Ⓦ www.littlebrookfuchsias.co.uk
Contact: Carol Gubler
Opening Times: 1000-1700 Wed-Sun, 1st Jan-28th Jun.
Cat. Cost: 70p + sae.
Credit Cards: All major credit/debit cards
Specialities: Fuchsias, old & new.
Notes: Nursery located off White Lane in Ash Green. Wheelchair accessible.
OS Grid Ref: SU901496

SLdr **LODER PLANTS** ♿
Market Garden, Long Hill, Lower Beeding, West Sussex, RH13 6PP
Ⓣ (01403) 891412
Ⓔ sales@rhododendrons.com
Ⓦ www.rhododendrons.com
Contact: Chris Loder
Opening Times: 1000-1600 Mon-Sat, please telephone first.
Min Mail Order UK: Nmc
Min Mail Order EU: Nmc
Cat. Cost: Please enquire.
Credit Cards: All major debit/credit cards except American Express
Specialities: Rhododendrons & azaleas in all sizes. Some in very limited quantities only. *Agapanthus*.
Notes: Also sells wholesale. Exports beyond EU. Delivers to shows. Euro accepted. Wheelchair accessible.
OS Grid Ref: TQ221255

SLee **LEESA'S NOT JUST ALPINES**
101c First Avenue, Batchmere, Birdham, Chichester, West Sussex, PO20 7LQ
Ⓜ 07900 815636
Ⓔ leesasnotjustalpines@gmail.com
Ⓦ www.leesasalpines.co.uk
Contact: Leesa Barrett
Opening Times: Open by appt. only. Please call for other Open Day event information.
Specialities: Alpines and perennials.
Notes: Small nursery growing a good selection of garden worthy alpine and rock garden plants. A range of cottage garden perennials also available. Also sells wholesale. Delivers to shows.

SLim **LIME CROSS NURSERY** ♿
Herstmonceux, Hailsham, East Sussex, BN27 4RS
Ⓣ (01323) 833229
Ⓔ info@limecross.co.uk
Ⓦ www.limecross.co.uk
Contact: Vicky Tate, Anita Green
Opening Times: 0830-1700 Mon-Sat & 1000-1700 Sun.
Min Mail Order UK: Nmc
Min Mail Order EU: £50.00
Cat. Cost: Online only.
Credit Cards: All major credit/debit cards
Specialities: Conifers, trees & shrubs, climbers.
Notes: Wheelchair accessible.
OS Grid Ref: TQ642125

SLon **LONGSTOCK PARK NURSERY** ♿
Longstock, Stockbridge, Hampshire, SO20 6EH
Ⓣ (01264) 810894
Ⓕ (01264) 810924
Ⓔ longstock.park.nursery@waitrose.co.uk
Ⓦ www.leckfordestate.co.uk
Contact: Mark Pitman
Opening Times: 0900-1730 Mon-Sat, 1000-1600 Sun. Closed 25th-27th Dec & 1st Jan.
Min Mail Order UK: £15.00
Credit Cards: All major credit/debit cards
Specialities: A wide range, over 2000 varieties of hardy trees (ornamental and fruiting), shrubs, perennials, climbers, aquatics & ferns. Extensive collection of *Penstemon*. National Plant Collections of *Buddleja* & *Clematis viticella*.
Notes: Farm shop and café on same site as nursery. Wheelchair accessible.
OS Grid Ref: SU365389

SMad **MADRONA NURSERY** ♿
Pluckley Road, Bethersden, Kent, TN26 3EG
Ⓣ (01233) 820100
Ⓔ madrona@hotmail.co.uk
Ⓦ www.madrona.co.uk
Contact: Liam Mackenzie
Opening Times: 1000-1700 Sat, Mon & Tue, 1300-1700 Sun. 16th Mar-29th Oct. Other times by appt.
Cat. Cost: Free.
Credit Cards: All major credit/debit cards
Specialities: Unusual shrubs, conifers & perennials. *Eryngium*, *Colletia*.
Notes: Delivers to shows. Euro accepted. Wheelchair accessible.
OS Grid Ref: TQ918419

SMea **MEADOWGATE NURSERY**
Street End Lane, Sidlesham, Chichester, West Sussex, PO20 7RG
Ⓣ (01243) 641997
Ⓜ 07736 523262
Ⓔ info@meadowgatenursery.co.uk
Ⓦ www.meadowgatenursery.co.uk
Contact: David Allen
Opening Times: 1000-1700 Sat-Thu.

Min Mail Order UK: Nmc
Credit Cards: All major credit/debit cards
Specialities: Ornamental grasses.
Notes: Also sells wholesale. Delivers to shows.
OS Grid Ref: SZ854994

SMHy **MARCHANTS HARDY PLANTS** ♿
2 Marchants Cottages, Mill Lane, Laughton, East Sussex, BN8 6AJ
Ⓣ (01323) 811737
Ⓔ graham@marchantsplants.plus.com
Ⓦ www.marchantshardyplants.co.uk
Contact: Graham Gough
Opening Times: 0930-1730 Wed-Sat, Mar to Oct 2018.
Cat. Cost: 3 × 2nd class.
Credit Cards: Visa, MasterCard
Specialities: Uncommon herbaceous perennials. *Agapanthus*, choice grasses, *Galanthus*, *Miscanthus*, *Molinia*.
Notes: Euro accepted. Wheelchair accessible.
OS Grid Ref: TQ506119

SMor **MOREHAVENS**
Stocks Lane, Meonstoke, Hampshire, SO32 3NQ
Ⓣ (01489) 878501
Ⓔ morehavens@camomilelawns.co.uk
Ⓦ www.camomilelawns.co.uk
Contact: E. Clements
Opening Times: Mail order direct to you only. Open for pre-arranged collection.
Min Mail Order UK: £21.00
Min Mail Order EU: £21.00 + p&p
Cat. Cost: Free.
Credit Cards: All major credit/debit cards, Paypal
Specialities: *Chamaemelum nobile* 'Treneague' & *Chamaemelum nobile* dwarf.
Notes: Also sells wholesale.

SMrm **MERRIMENTS GARDENS** ♿
Hawkhurst Road, Hurst Green, East Sussex, TN19 7RA
Ⓣ (01580) 860666
Ⓕ (01580) 860324
Ⓔ info@merriments.co.uk
Ⓦ www.merriments.co.uk
Contact: Imogen Stephens
Opening Times: 0900-1700 Mon-Sat, 1000-1630 Sun.
Cat. Cost: Online only.
Credit Cards: Visa, Access, American Express
Specialities: Specialist in perennials. Extensive range of unusual perennials, tender perennials, grasses & annuals. Also large selection of roses & seasonal shrubs. 4-acre show garden.
Notes: Wheelchair accessible.

SNig **NIGHTINGALE NURSERY** ♿
Gardeners Lane, East Wellow, Romsey, Hampshire, SO51 6AD
Ⓣ (02380) 814350
Ⓔ gfnightingale4@gmail.com
Ⓦ www.nightingalenursery.co.uk
Contact: Graham Farmiloe
Opening Times: 0800-1700 Mon-Fri & open 7 days from mid-Mar to mid-Jun. 0800-1630 winter.
Cat. Cost: Free via email.
Credit Cards: All major debit/credit cards except American Express
Specialities: *Clematis*. Also climbers, wall shrubs, herbaceous, seasonal bedding & hanging baskets.
Notes: Also sells wholesale. Wheelchair accessible.

SPad **PADDOCK PLANTS**
The Paddock, Upper Toothill Road, Rownhams, Southampton, Hampshire, SO16 8AL
Ⓣ (02380) 739912
Ⓜ 07763 386717
Ⓔ rob@paddockplants.co.uk
Ⓦ https://paddockplants.co.uk
Contact: Rob & Joanna Courtney
Opening Times: By appt. only. Please telephone in advance.
Min Mail Order UK: £5.00
Cat. Cost: Online only.
Credit Cards: All major credit/debit cards
Specialities: A family-run nursery offering an interesting range of perennials, grasses, ferns & shrubs, incl. some more unusual varieties or plants new to the UK market. All plants are grown in a peat-free medium. Some varieties grown in small quantities.
Notes: Local delivery by our own transport. Courier delivery throughout UK. Delivers to shows.
OS Grid Ref: SU383177

SPalm **PALMS-EXOTICS LTD**
Abbots Farm, Canada Road, West Wellow, Romsey, Hampshire, SO51 6DE
Ⓣ (01794) 278356
Ⓜ 07809 123164
Ⓔ palmsexotics@icloud.com
Ⓦ Palms-exotics.co.uk
Contact: Michelle Alice Carr
Credit Cards: Paypal, All major credit/debit cards
Specialities: Palms, banana, ginger, colocasia, bamboo, grasses, perennials & shrubs.
Notes: Family nursery growing a range of exotic plants, many grown from seed or plugs.

S

Larger palms sourced from our own and selected nurseries in Spain.

SPeP **PEAKE PERENNIALS** ♿
Shaftesbury Road, Child Okeford, Dorset, DT11 8EQ
Ⓣ (01202) 244510
Ⓜ 07708 872918
Ⓔ helen@peakeperennials.co.uk
Ⓦ www.peakeperennials.co.uk
Contact: Helen Day
Opening Times: 0900-1700 Wed-Fri (Mon-Tue by prior arrangement), 1000-1600 Sat, Sun & Bank Holidays. Nov-Dec 0900-1600, Closed January.
Credit Cards: All major credit/debit cards
Specialities: Specialising in tall & unusual herbaceous perennials & grasses. Also increasing stock range of popular perennials with a twist. Reservation service for out of stock plants. Local delivery. Range of landscaping perennials.
Notes: For details of special events we attend please telephone or check website for details. Register on the website for regular news on events and plants. Wheelchair accessible. Delivers to shows.

SPer **PERRYHILL NURSERIES LTD** ♿
Edenbridge Road, Hartfield, East Sussex, TN7 4JP
Ⓣ (01892) 770377
Ⓔ sales@perryhillnurseries.co.uk
Ⓦ www.perryhillnurseries.co.uk
Contact: P. J. Chapman
Opening Times: 0900-1700 7 days, 1st Mar-31st Oct. 0900-1630, 1st Nov-28th Feb.
Min Mail Order UK: Nmc
Cat. Cost: Online only.
Credit Cards: Maestro, Visa, Access, MasterCard
Specialities: Wide range of trees, shrubs, perennials, roses, fruit trees & soft fruit. Unusual & rare plants may be available in small quantities.
Notes: Mail order despatch depends on size & weight of plants. Wheelchair accessible.
OS Grid Ref: TQ480375

SPet **PETTET'S NURSERY** ♿
Drainless Road, Eastry, Sandwich, Kent, CT13 0EA
Ⓣ (01304) 613869
Ⓜ 07940 337520
Ⓕ (01304) 613869
Ⓔ pettets.nursery@btconnect.com
Ⓦ www.pettetsnursery.co.uk
Contact: Terry Pettet
Opening Times: 1000-1600 Tue-Sun, Mar-Oct. Closed Mon (except B/hol). Closed Nov-Feb.
Min Mail Order UK: £12.00
Cat. Cost: Online only.
Credit Cards: None
Specialities: *Pelargonium*: scented-leaf, decorative regal, unique, angel.
Notes: Delivers to shows. Wheelchair accessible.

SPhx **PHOENIX PERENNIAL PLANTS**
Paice Lane, Medstead, Alton, Hampshire, GU34 5PR
Ⓣ (01420) 560695
Ⓜ 07909 528191
Ⓔ marina@phoenixperennialplants.co.uk
Ⓦ www.phoenixperennialplants.co.uk
Contact: Marina Christopher
Opening Times: By appt. only.
Credit Cards: All major credit/debit cards
Specialities: Perennials, many uncommon & hardy, selected for beneficial insects particularly pollinators. *Agastache*, *Centaurea*, *Salvia*, *Sanguisorba*, *Sedum*, *Thalictrum*, *Verbascum*, bulbs, prairie plants, umbellifers & late-flowering perennials.
Notes: Also sells wholesale. Delivers to shows.
OS Grid Ref: SU657362

SPlb **PLANTBASE** ♿
Sleepers Stile Road, Cousley Wood, Wadhurst, East Sussex, TN5 6QX
Ⓣ (01892) 785599
Ⓜ 07967 601064
Ⓔ plantbaseuk@gmail.com
Ⓦ www.plantbase.co.uk
Contact: Graham Blunt
Opening Times: 1000-1700 7 days all year (appt. advisable).
Min Mail Order UK: Nmc
Min Mail Order EU: Nmc
Cat. Cost: Online only.
Credit Cards: All major credit/debit cards
Specialities: Wide range of alpines, perennials, shrubs, climbers, waterside plants, herbs, Australasian, South African & South American plants in particular. Some available in small quantities only.
Notes: Delivers to shows. Euro accepted. Wheelchair accessible.

SPoG **THE POTTED GARDEN NURSERY** ♿
Ashford Road, Bearsted, Maidstone, Kent, ME14 4NH
Ⓣ (01622) 737801
Ⓔ markreeve@coolings.co.uk
Ⓦ www.thepottedgarden.co.uk

S

Contact: Mark Reeve
Opening Times: 0900-1730 (dusk in winter), 7 days. Xmas/New Year period opening times on website or answerphone.
Credit Cards: All major credit/debit cards
Notes: Mail order not available. Wheelchair accessible.
OS Grid Ref: TQ810550

SPre **Plants4Presents ◆**
The Glasshouses, Fletching Common, Newick, Lewes, East Sussex, BN8 4JJ
Ⓣ (01825) 721162
Ⓔ plants@4presents.co.uk
Ⓦ www.plants4presents.co.uk
Contact: Emily Rae
Opening Times: Not open. Mail order only.
Min Mail Order UK: Nmc
Cat. Cost: Online only.
Credit Cards: All major credit/debit cards
Specialities: Well-established nursery offering a range of unusual flowering and fruiting plants, incl. citrus trees.
Notes: Delivers to shows.

SPtp **PlantsToplant.com**
Paragon Plants, Fromefield, Ratley Lane, Awbridge, Romsey, Hampshire, SO51 0HN
Ⓣ (01794) 341123
Ⓔ info@plantstoplant.com
Ⓦ www.plantstoplant.com
Contact: David West
Opening Times: Not open. Mail order only.
Min Mail Order UK: Nmc
Cat. Cost: Online only.
Credit Cards: All major credit/debit cards, Paypal
Specialities: Rare & hard to find special garden plants of all types. *Cotoneaster* a speciality.
Notes: Mail order only through website or ebay. Orders can be collected by appt. only.

SPVi **Pineview Plants**
Pineview, 19 Windmill Hill, Wrotham Heath, Sevenoaks, Kent, TN15 7SU
Ⓣ (01732) 882945
Ⓜ 07736 420016
Ⓔ colin@pineviewplants.co.uk
Ⓦ www.pineviewplants.co.uk
Contact: Colin Moat
Opening Times: By appt. only
Min Mail Order UK: £15.00 + p&p
Cat. Cost: Online only.
Credit Cards: All major credit/debit cards
Specialities: Shade loving plants including *Epimedium, Actaea, Roscoea, Sanguisorba, Thalictrum*. Wide range of ferns and herbaceous perennials.
Notes: The majority of plants are propagated on site and many are only available in small quantities. Delivers to shows, see list on website.

SRGP **Rosie's Garden Plants**
Fieldview Cottage, Pratling Street, Aylesford, Kent, ME20 7DG
Ⓣ (01622) 715777
Ⓜ 07740 696277
Ⓕ (01622) 715777
Ⓔ jcaviolet@aol.com
Ⓦ www.rosiesgardenplants.biz
Contact: Jacqueline Aviolet
Opening Times: Not open. Mail order only.
Min Mail Order UK: Nmc
Min Mail Order EU: Nmc
Cat. Cost: Online only.
Credit Cards: None
Specialities: Hardy *Geranium, Symphyotrichum* & *Aster*, Herbs & Roses.
Notes: Some species & varieties available in small quantities. Exports beyond EU.

SRiv **River Garden Nurseries**
Troutbeck, Otford, Sevenoaks, Kent, TN14 5PH
Ⓣ (07717) 277175
Ⓔ box@river-garden.co.uk
Ⓦ www.river-garden.co.uk
Contact: Jenny Alban Davies
Opening Times: By appt. only.
Min Mail Order UK: £10.00 + p&p
Min Mail Order EU: £50.00 + p&p
Cat. Cost: Online only.
Credit Cards: None
Specialities: *Buxus* species & cultivars. *Buxus* topiary.
Notes: Also sells wholesale. Delivers to shows.
OS Grid Ref: TQ523593

SRkn **Rapkyns Nursery**
Street End Lane, Broad Oak, Heathfield, East Sussex, TN21 8UB
Ⓣ (01825) 830065
Ⓜ 07771 916933
Ⓔ rapkynsnursery@hotmail.com
Ⓦ www.rapkynsnursery.co.uk
Contact: Steven Moore
Opening Times: 1000-1700 Tue, Thu & Fri, Mar-Oct incl. or by appt.
Min Mail Order UK: Nmc
Min Mail Order EU: Nmc
Cat. Cost: Online only.
Credit Cards: All major credit/debit cards
Specialities: Unusual shrubs, perennials & climbers including asters, geraniums,

S

penstemons & grasses. New collections of *Crocosmia, Anemone, Heuchera, Heucherella, Phlox, Coreopsis* & *Helleborus*. Extensive range of salvias.
Notes: Nursery next door to Scotsford Farm, TN21 8UB. Mail order Sep-Apr incl. Also sells wholesale. Delivers to shows.
OS Grid Ref: TQ604248

SRms **Rumsey Gardens** ♿
117 Drift Road, Clanfield, Waterlooville, Hampshire, PO8 0PD
Ⓣ (02392) 593367
Ⓔ info@rumsey-gardens.co.uk
Ⓦ www.rumsey-gardens.co.uk
Contact: Mrs M. A. Giles
Opening Times: 0900-1700 Mon-Sat & 1000-1600 Sun & B/hols. Closed Xmas to New Year B/hol.
Min Mail Order UK: £15.00
Cat. Cost: Online only.
Credit Cards: Visa, MasterCard
Specialities: Wide general range. Herbaceous, alpines, heathers & ferns. National & International Plant Collection of *Cotoneaster*.
Notes: Wheelchair accessible.

S

SRot **Rotherview Nursery** ♿
Ivyhouse Lane, Three Oaks, Hastings, East Sussex, TN35 4NP
Ⓣ (01424) 756228
Ⓔ rotherview@btinternet.com
Ⓦ www.rotherview.com
Contact: Wendy Bates
Opening Times: 1000-1600
Min Mail Order UK: £10.00
Min Mail Order EU: Nmc
Cat. Cost: 6 × 1st class.
Credit Cards: All major credit/debit cards
Specialities: *Camellia*, alpines and ferns.
Notes: Rotherview Nursery and Coghurst Camellias are on the same site. Delivers to shows. Euro accepted. Wheelchair accessible.

SSal **The Salutation Nursery** ♿
The Salutation, Knightrider Street, Sandwich, Kent, CT13 9EW
Ⓣ (01304) 619919
Ⓜ 07843 961813
Ⓔ enquiries@the-salutation.com: thesalutationnursery@hotmail.com
Ⓦ www.the-salutation.com
Contact: Steven
Opening Times: 1000-1700 daily.
Cat. Cost: £2.00.
Credit Cards: All major credit/debit cards
Specialities: National Collection *Plectranthus*. National Collection of dark leaf *Dahlia*.
Notes: Traditional nursery specialising in perennials, exotic, plus an eclectic mix of other plants for sale, with garden open to the public 7 days a week. Exports beyond EU. Delivers to shows. Wheelchair accessible.
OS Grid Ref: TR333581

SSea **Seale Rose Garden**
Seale Nurseries, Seale Lane, Seale, Farnham, Surrey, GU10 1LD
Ⓣ (01252) 782410
Ⓔ catherine@sealenurseries.demon.co.uk
Ⓦ www.sealenurseries.co.uk
Contact: David & Catherine May
Opening Times: Please phone for details
Credit Cards: Visa, Access, Delta, MasterCard
Specialities: Roses & *Pelargonium*. Some varieties in short supply, please phone first.
Notes: Opening times vary according to season. Please telephone for details.
OS Grid Ref: SU887477

SSem **Sempervivums By Post**
Ⓔ sempervivumsbypost@gmail.com
Ⓦ www.sempervivumsbypost.co.uk
Contact: Becky Scott
Opening Times: Not open
Min Mail Order UK: £15.00 + postage
Credit Cards: All major credit/debit cards
Specialities: *Sempervivums*. A selection of cacti and other succulents.
Notes: Our nursery was established in 1981. In early 2018, we started a specialised internet shop to sell *Sempervivums* by post to anywhere in the UK. The first year response has been fantastic. We offer the best varieties, the best quality plants, at the best prices, plus a genuine first-class service.

SSFr **Southern Fruit Trees** ♿
The Old Grain Dryer Corner, Blackmoor, Hampshire, GU33 6BP
Ⓣ (01420) 488822
Ⓜ 07811 253530
Ⓔ neil@southernfruittrees.co.uk
Ⓦ www.southernfruittrees.co.uk
Contact: Neil Smith
Opening Times: 0900-1600 7 days, Nov-May. 0900-1600 Fri & Sat only Sept-Oct. Webshop open all year around.
Min Mail Order UK: Nmc
Cat. Cost: Free.
Credit Cards: All major credit/debit cards
Specialities: Over 200 varieties of fruit trees, mostly home-grown, incl. bush, half-standard, cordon espalier and fan-trained fruit.
Notes: Wheelchair accessible.
OS Grid Ref: SU778335

SSFT **Sussex Fruit Trees**
Hook Farm, Nettlesworth Lane, Heathfield, East Sussex, TN21 9EN
Ⓜ 07745 379526
Ⓔ mark@sussexfruittrees.co.uk
Ⓦ www.sussexfruittrees.co.uk
Contact: Mark Piper
Opening Times: 0800-1700 7 days.
Specialities: Grows & sells a wide range of fruit trees on various rootstocks. Some Sussex apple tree cultivars.
Notes: Also provides delivery, planting, pruning, grafting, orchard maintenance & tree sundries. Delivers to shows (pre-ordered plants).

SSien **Sienna Hosta**
Knap Hill Nursery, Barrs Lane, Knaphill, Surrey, GU21 2JW
Ⓣ (01483) 663160
Ⓔ nursery@siennahosta.co.uk
Ⓦ www.siennahosta.co.uk
Contact: Ollie
Opening Times: Not open. Mail order only.
Min Mail Order UK: £5.00
Credit Cards: All major credit/debit cards
Specialities: *Hosta* growers with over 30 years' experience. Over 800 varieties held within the collection with many available to order via our website. Availability may vary throughout the season.
Notes: Orders sent 1st class Royal Mail all year round. We aim to send out orders placed before 12pm Mon-Thu on the same day. Orders placed Fri-Sun will be sent on Mon.

SSim **Simply Succulents**
(office) 5 Galliard Street, Sandwich, Kent, CT13 9BG
Ⓜ 07548 947357
Ⓔ simplysucculents@gmx.co.uk
Ⓦ www.simplysucculents.co.uk
Contact: John Chandler
Opening Times: Not open. Mail order online only.
Min Mail Order UK: Nmc
Cat. Cost: Online only.
Specialities: Succulents for home, garden & containers.
Notes: Online sales only.

SSta **Starborough Nursery** ♿
Starborough Road, Marsh Green, Edenbridge, Kent, TN8 5RB
Ⓣ (01732) 865614
Ⓔ starborough@hotmail.co.uk
Contact: Sales
Opening Times: 0900-1600 Thu, Fri & Sat. Closed Jan, Jul & Aug or open by appt. only. Please phone first if travelling.
Credit Cards: Visa, Access
Specialities: Rare & unusual shrubs esp. *Daphne*, *Acer*, rhododendrons & azaleas, *Magnolia* & *Nyssa*. Some plants only available in larger sizes.
Notes: Deliveries can be made at cost. Planting & landscaping services available. Wheelchair accessible.

SSut **Dan Sutton**
(office) 142 Hawks Road, Hailsham, East Sussex, BN27 1NA
Ⓣ (01323) 845270
Ⓜ 07772 869645
Ⓔ suttonnursery@gmail.com
Ⓦ www.suttonnursery.co.uk
Contact: Dan Sutton
Opening Times: By appt. only.
Min Mail Order UK: £5.80
Cat. Cost: Online only.
Credit Cards: Paypal
Specialities: Herbaceous perennials, bulbs/corms, incl. *Crocosima*, grasses, specimen bamboos, *Fargesia robusta*, *F. scabrida* & *Borinda boliana*. Coastal and drought-tolerant plants.
Notes: Nursery at Park Wood Farmhouse, Upper Dicker, Hailsham, BN27 3QL. Landscape design. Also sells wholesale. Delivers to shows (pre-ordered plants),

STPC **The Plant Company** ♿
Rose Barn, Coolham Road, West Chiltington, Pulborough, West Sussex, RH20 2LH
Ⓣ (01403) 740100
Ⓔ sales@theplantco.co.uk
Ⓦ www.theplantco.co.uk
Contact: Tim Ricketts
Opening Times: 0900-1730 Mon-Fri.
Min Mail Order UK: £8.95
Cat. Cost: Online only.
Credit Cards: All major debit/credit cards except American Express
Specialities: A range of herbaceous, shrubs and grasses.
Notes: Also sells wholesale. Delivers to shows. Wheelchair accessible.
OS Grid Ref: TQ111196

SVen **Ventnor Botanic Garden** ♿
Undercliff Drive, Ventnor, Isle of Wight, PO38 1UL
Ⓣ (01983) 855397
Ⓔ sales@botanic.co.uk
Ⓦ www.botanic.co.uk
Contact: Chris Kidd

S

Opening Times: 1000-1700 7 days, all year.
Min Mail Order UK: Nmc
Min Mail Order EU: Nmc
Credit Cards: All major debit/credit cards except American Express
Specialities: Coastal, drought-tolerant, Mediterranean & southern hemisphere plants. Rare & esoteric half-hardy trees, shrubs & perennials. National Plant Collection of hardy & half-hardy *Puya*.
Notes: Also sells wholesale. Wheelchair accessible.
OS Grid Ref: SZ548768

SVic **VICTORIANA NURSERY GARDENS** ♿
Challock, Ashford, Kent, TN25 4DG
Ⓣ (01233) 740529
Ⓔ help@victoriananursery.co.uk
Ⓦ www.victoriananursery.co.uk
Contact: Serena Shirley
Opening Times: 0930-1615 (or dusk if sooner) Mon-Fri, 1030-1500 (or dusk if sooner) Sat.
Min Mail Order UK: Nmc
Cat. Cost: Free by post or online.
Credit Cards: All major credit/debit cards
Specialities: Heritage & unusual vegetable plants, seeds, fruit trees & bushes. Specialist grower of chillies & tomatoes, with annual tasting days. Also 600+ varieties of *Fuchsia*.
Notes: Also sells wholesale. Wheelchair accessible.
OS Grid Ref: TR018501

SWeb **WEB GARDEN CENTRE**
Meadow Farm, Sway Road, Tiptoe, Lymington, Hampshire, SO41 6FR
Ⓣ (01590) 637443
Ⓜ 07786 064018
Ⓔ info@webgardencentre.com
Ⓦ www.webgardencentre.com
Contact: Shaun
Opening Times: By appt. only. Pls telephone to arrange.
Min Mail Order UK: Nmc
Min Mail Order EU: Nmc
Cat. Cost: Online only.
Credit Cards: All major credit/debit cards
Specialities: Web Garden Centre specialise in specimen, ornamental and architectural plants, all forms of topiary and evergreen screening plants.
Notes: Web Garden Centre are an online nursery supplying plants daily at great prices throughout the United Kingdom. Next day delivery available. Euro accepted. Also sells wholesale.
OS Grid Ref: SZ263971

SWvt **WOLVERTON PLANTS LTD** ♿
Wolverton Common, Tadley, Hampshire, RG26 5RU
Ⓣ (01635) 298453
Ⓜ 07880 971397
Ⓔ plantranch2000@hotmail.com
Contact: Julian Jones
Opening Times: 0900-1700 (or dusk Nov-Feb), 7 days. Closed Xmas/New Year.
Credit Cards: All major credit/debit cards
Specialities: Wide range of herbaceous perennials & shrubs grown on a commercial scale for the public.
Notes: Horticultural club visits welcome by prior arrangement. Able to source plants for the public and Garden Designers. Also sells wholesale. Euro accepted. Wheelchair accessible.
OS Grid Ref: SU555589

WALES AND THE WEST

WAbe **ABERCONWY NURSERY**
Graig, Glan Conwy, Conwy, LL28 5TL
Ⓣ (01492) 580875
Ⓔ enquiries@aberconwynursery.co.uk
Ⓦ www.aberconwynursery.co.uk
Contact: Tim Lever
Opening Times: 1000-1600 Tue-Fri Mar-Sep incl. Other times by appt.
Cat. Cost: 2 × 2nd class.
Credit Cards: Visa, MasterCard
Specialities: Alpines, including specialist varieties, esp. gentians, dionysias, dwarf *Dianthus*, *Primula*, *Saxifraga* & dwarf ericaceous plants. Some choice shrubs & woodland plants incl. smaller ferns.
Notes: Delivers to shows.
OS Grid Ref: SH799744

WABo **ATLANTIC BOTANIC** ♿
Whitegates, Moor Lane, Braunton, Devon, EX33 2NU
Ⓣ (01271) 816225
Ⓜ 07989 444461
Ⓔ atlanticbotanic@live.co.uk
Ⓦ www.atlanticbotanic.co.uk
Contact: Kay Tudor
Opening Times: See website.
Min Mail Order UK: At cost
Credit Cards: All major credit/debit cards
Specialities: *Agapanthus*.
Notes: Wheelchair accessible. Delivers to shows.
OS Grid Ref: SS467362

WAln **L. A. ALLEN**
Windy Ridge, Llandrindod Wells, Powys, LD1 5NY
Ⓔ elandem80@gmail.com

Contact: Les Allen
Opening Times: Mail order. Open by appt. only
Min Mail Order UK: Nmc
Min Mail Order EU: Nmc
Cat. Cost: 6 × 1st class.
Credit Cards: None
Specialities: All sections of *Primula auricula*: alpine auricula, show-edged, show-self, doubles, show-stripe. Surplus plants from private collection so available in small quantities. Occasionally only 1 or 2 available of some cvs.
Notes: Also sells wholesale.

WAvo **PERSHORE COLLEGE GARDEN CENTRE & NURSERY** ♿
Avonbank, Pershore, Worcestershire, WR10 3JP
Ⓣ (01386) 551177
Ⓔ pershorenurseries@wcg.ac.uk
Ⓦ www.wcg.ac.uk/plantcentre
Contact: Josh Egan-Wyer
Opening Times: 0900-1700 Mon-Sat 1000-1630 Sun (0900-1630 Mon-Sat 1030-1600 Sun in winter)
Credit Cards: All major debit/credit cards except American Express
Specialities: Extensive range of shrubs, perennials and good garden plants incl. National Plant Collections of *Penstemon* (pre-1995 cvs) & *Philadelphus* cvs. Several college raised.
Notes: Also sells wholesale. Wheelchair accessible.
OS Grid Ref: SO957447

WBor **BORDERVALE PLANTS** ♿
Nantyderi, Sandy Lane, Ystradowen, Cowbridge, Vale of Glamorgan, CF71 7SX
Ⓣ (01446) 774036
Ⓔ bordervaleplants@gmail.com
Ⓦ www.bordervale.co.uk
Contact: Claire E. Jenkins
Opening Times: 1000-1700 Fri-Sun & B/hols Mid Mar-Mid Sep. Often open Mon-Thu. Please check or make an appt. any day if travelling some distance.
Min Mail Order UK: £20.00 + p&p
Cat. Cost: 3 × 1st class.
Specialities: Unusual herbaceous perennials, trees, shrubs & roses, as well as cottage garden plants, many displayed in the 2-acre garden.
Notes: Mail order available for smaller items, subject to season. Garden open mid-May to mid-Sep when nursery open. Also open for NGS. See website or contact nursery for details. Delivers to shows. Wheelchair accessible.
OS Grid Ref: ST022776

WBrk **BROCKAMIN PLANTS** ♿
Brockamin, Old Hills, Callow End, Worcestershire, WR2 4TQ
Ⓣ (01905) 830370
Ⓔ stone.brockamin@btinternet.com
Contact: Margaret Stone
Opening Times: By appt. only.
Credit Cards: None
Specialities: National Plant Collections of *Symphyotrichum novae-angliae*, *Geranium sanguineum*, *G. macrorrhizum* & *G.* × *cantabrigiense*. Plants available in small quantities only.
Notes: Wheelchair accessible.
OS Grid Ref: SO830488

WCAu **CLAIRE AUSTIN HARDY PLANTS**
White Hopton Farm, Wern Lane, Sarn, Newtown, Powys, SY16 4EN
Ⓣ (01686) 670342
Ⓔ enquiries@claireaustin-hardyplants.co.uk
Ⓦ www.claireaustin-hardyplants.co.uk
Contact: Claire Austin
Opening Times: Mail order only. Open by appointment for the NGS.
Min Mail Order UK: Nmc
Min Mail Order EU: Nmc
Cat. Cost: Free, UK only.
Credit Cards: MasterCard, Visa, Switch
Specialities: *Paeonia*, *Iris*, *Hemerocallis* & hardy plants. National Plant Collections of Bearded *Iris*.

WCav **CAVES FOLLY NURSERIES** ♿
Evendine Lane, Colwall, Malvern, Worcestershire, WR13 6DX
Ⓣ (01684) 540631
Ⓜ 07918 649276
Ⓔ bridget@cavesfolly.com
Ⓦ www.cavesfolly.com
Contact: Bridget Evans
Opening Times: 1000-1700 Thu-Sat Mar-Nov. Other times By appt.
Min Mail Order UK: £6.00
Cat. Cost: Free.
Credit Cards: All major credit/debit cards
Specialities: Organically grown perennials and alpines.
Notes: Nursery has grown plants in peat free organic compost for 30 yrs+. Certified by the Soil Association. Majority of plants grown from their own seed, division or cuttings. Also sells wholesale. Delivers to shows. Wheelchair accessible.
OS Grid Ref: SO751114

WCFE **CHARLES F ELLIS**
Oak Piece Nurseries, Stanway Road, Stanton, Nr Broadway, Worcestershire, WR12 7NQ
Ⓣ (01386) 584077
Ⓔ ellisplants@cooptel.net
Contact: Charles Ellis
Opening Times: By appt.only.
Min Mail Order UK: £15.00
Credit Cards: None
Specialities: Wide range of shrubs, conifers, climbers & perennials, some unusual. All available in small quantities only. A few specimen sizes (but not for mail order).

WChS **CHICKENSTREET**
1-3 The Stanyards, Gobowen, Oswestry, Shropshire, SY11 4NG
Ⓣ (01691) 657178
Ⓔ enquiry@chickenstreet.co.uk
Ⓦ www.chickenstreet.co.uk
Contact: Jill Cawthray
Opening Times: Mail Order only
Min Mail Order UK: £4.95
Cat. Cost: On-line catalogue only.
Specialities: A good selection of grasses and easy care perennials that associate well in naturalistic plantings. Combinations for sunny, shady or boggy areas with emphasis on plants for polinators and wildlife.
Notes: Plants are propagated by ourselves and therefore stock may vary throughout the year. Generally plants are only sent out during the growing season between early March and November. Delivers to shows.

WCot **COTSWOLD GARDEN FLOWERS**
Sands Lane, Badsey, Evesham, Worcestershire, WR11 7EZ
Ⓣ nursery: (01386) 833849 or mail order: (01386) 422829
Ⓕ nursery: (01386) 49844
Ⓔ info@cgf.net
Ⓦ www.cgf.net
Contact: Bob Brown
Opening Times: 0900-1730 Mon-Fri &1000-1730 Sat & Sun, Mar-Sep. W/ends Oct-Feb by appt. only
Min Mail Order UK: Nmc
Min Mail Order EU: Nmc
Cat. Cost: Free.
Credit Cards: All major debit/credit cards except American Express
Specialities: A very wide range of easy to grow & unusual perennials.
Notes: Delivers to shows. Euro accepted. Limited wheelchair access.
OS Grid Ref: SP077426

WCra **CRANESBILL NURSERY**
1 Waverley Road, Mossley Estate, Bloxwich, Walsall, West Midlands, WS3 2SW
Ⓣ (01684) 770733
Ⓜ 07500 600205
Ⓔ gary@cranesbillnursery.com
Ⓦ www.cranesbillnursery.com
Contact: Gary Carroll
Opening Times: Mail order only. Not open to the public. Collections by appt. only.
Min Mail Order UK: Nmc
Min Mail Order EU: £25.00
Cat. Cost: Free.
Credit Cards: All major credit/debit cards
Specialities: Hardy geraniums, Approx 200 varieties in stock. Can supply large quantities with 6-8 weeks notice. Please contact nursery for further details.
Notes: Cranesbill Nursery is the longest established UK specialist in Hardy Geraniums. Most of our stock is listed on the website when available, however we do also have limited stock of some unusual geraniums, so always ask.
OS Grid Ref: SO940378

WCru **CRÛG FARM PLANTS** ♿
Griffith's Crossing, Caernarfon, Gwynedd, LL55 1TU
Ⓣ (01248) 670232
Ⓜ 07774 980842
Ⓔ mailorder@crug-farm.co.uk
Ⓦ www.mailorder.crug-farm.co.uk
Contact: B. and S. Wynn-Jones
Opening Times: 0930-1630 Thu-Sat, 1st Sat in Apr to 4th Sat in Sep. Or Mon-Fri by appt. all year.
Min Mail Order UK: Nmc
Min Mail Order EU: Nmc
Cat. Cost: Online only.
Credit Cards: All major credit/debit cards
Specialities: Mostly self, wild collected new introductions from Asia, Americas & southern Europe. Especially *Araliaceae*, *Asparagaceae*, shade tolerant perennials & shrubs. Unusual or rare trees, shrubs, herbaceous & bulbous. Many supplied bare-rooted when dormant.
Notes: Delivery by overnight carrier for UK & Ireland. Courier for rest of EU or dedicated vehicle for large orders. Delivers to shows. Wheelchair accessible.
OS Grid Ref: SH509652

WDib **DIBLEYS NURSERIES** ♿ ◆
Llanelidan, Ruthin, Denbighshire, LL15 2LG
Ⓣ (01978) 790677
Ⓕ (01978) 790668
Ⓔ info@dibleys.com

Ⓦ www.dibleys.com
Contact: R. Dibley
Opening Times: 1000-1700 Mon-Sat (closed Sun), Apr-Aug. 1000-1700 Mon-Fri, Mar, Sep & Oct.
Min Mail Order UK: Nmc
Min Mail Order EU: Nmc
Cat. Cost: Free.
Credit Cards: Visa, Access, Switch, Electron, Solo
Specialities: *Streptocarpus*, *Columnea*, *Solenostemon*, *Saintpaulia* & other gesneriads & *Begonia*. National Plant Collections of *Streptocarpus*, *Saintpaulia* & *Petrocosmea*.
Notes: Also sells wholesale. Euro accepted. Delivers to shows. Wheelchair accessible.

WFar **FARMYARD NURSERIES**
Dol Llan Road, Llandysul, Carmarthenshire, SA44 4RL
Ⓣ (01559) 363389
Ⓜ 01267 220259
Ⓔ sales@farmyardnurseries.co.uk
Ⓦ www.farmyardnurseries.co.uk
Contact: Richard Bramley
Opening Times: 0900-1700 7 days, excl. Xmas Day, Boxing Day & New Year's Day.
Min Mail Order UK: 3 plants
Min Mail Order EU: 3 plants
Credit Cards: Visa, Switch, MasterCard
Specialities: Large range of home grown shrubs & herbaceous perennials, incl. trees, shrubs, climbers, alpines, conifers & bedding plants. National Collection of *Primula sieboldii* and *Sarracenia*.
Notes: Additionally sells from shop/yard in Carmarthen. Also sells wholesale. Partial wheelchair access (not garden or some areas of the nursery).
OS Grid Ref: SN421406

WFib **FIBREX NURSERIES LTD** ♿
Honeybourne Road, Pebworth, Stratford-on-Avon, Warwickshire, CV37 8XP
Ⓣ (01789) 720788
Ⓔ sales@fibrex.co.uk
Ⓦ www.fibrex.co.uk
Contact: Heather Godard-Key
Opening Times: 0900-1700 Mon-Fri, 1st Mar-30th Aug. 0900-1600 Mon-Fri, 2nd Sep-28th Feb. 1030-1600 Sat & Sun, 6th Apr-30th Jun. Closed last week Dec & 1st week Jan. Closed Easter Sun & Aug B/hol Mon.
Min Mail Order UK: £10.00 + p&p
Min Mail Order EU: £20.00 + p&p
Cat. Cost: 3 × 1st class.
Credit Cards: MasterCard, Visa, Maestro
Specialities: *Hedera*, ferns, *Pelargonium*, named tuberous begonias, *Hibiscus rosa-sinensis* cvs, hardy geraniums. National Plant Collections of *Pelargonium* & *Hedera*. Plant collections subject to time of year, please check by phone.
Notes: Also sells wholesale. Delivers to shows. Wheelchair accessible.
OS Grid Ref: SP133458

WGob **THE GOBBETT NURSERY**
Farlow, Kidderminster, Worcestershire, DY14 8TD
Ⓣ (01746) 718647
Ⓔ chris.link59@gmail.com
Ⓦ www.thegobbettnursery.co.uk
Contact: C. H. Link
Opening Times: By appt. only.
Credit Cards: None
Specialities: *Syringa* & *Cornus*, *Iris sibirica*, *Iris ensata*.
Notes: Delivers to shows.
OS Grid Ref: SO648811

WGoo **WILDEGOOSE NURSERY** ♿
The Walled Garden, Lower Millichope, Munslow, Craven Arms, Shropshire, SY7 9HE
Ⓣ (01584) 841890
Ⓜ 07798 628762
Ⓔ office@wildegoosenursery.co.uk
Ⓦ www.wildegoosenursery.co.uk
Contact: Laura Willgoss
Opening Times: 1000-1630 Fri-Sun, 30th Mar-13th Oct 2019.
Min Mail Order UK: Nmc
Min Mail Order EU: Nmc
Cat. Cost: 1st class sae.
Credit Cards: All major credit/debit cards
Specialities: *Viola*, incl. stock from Bouts Cottage Nursery. Herbaceous perennials & grasses. Some varieties propagated in small quantities.
Notes: Delivers to shows. Wheelchair accessible. Site is on a slope with gravel paths.

WGrf **GRAFTON NURSERY**
Worcester Road, Grafton Flyford, Worcester, Worcestershire, WR7 4PW
Ⓣ 07515 261511
Ⓔ office@hardy-eucalyptus.com
Ⓦ www.hardy-eucalyptus.com
Contact: Steve Hilary
Opening Times: Not open. Please order online or phone to arrange a suitable time.
Min Mail Order UK: £10.00
Min Mail Order EU: £35.00
Credit Cards: All major credit/debit cards
Specialities: *Eucalyptus*
Notes: Specialise in a range of eucalyptus

suitable for growing in UK gardens, incl. a selection of smaller growing varieties ideal for modern town gardens. Also sell more vigorous varieties for flower arranging, foliage and firewood production. Also sells wholesale. Delivers to shows.

WGrn **Green's Leaves** ♿
36 Ford House Road, Newent, Gloucestershire, GL18 1LQ
Ⓣ (01531) 820154
Ⓜ 07890 413036
Ⓔ r.paul.green@hotmail.co.uk
Ⓦ www.greensleavesnursery.co.uk
Contact: Paul Green
Opening Times: By appt. only. Please phone to arrange collection of orders from house (nursery site not open).
Min Mail Order UK: £10.00 + p&p
Cat. Cost: Online only.
Credit Cards: None
Specialities: Range of rare & choice shrubs, also some perennials. Ornamental grasses & sedges. Coloured foliage plants.
Notes: Delivers to shows. Wheelchair accessible.
OS Grid Ref: SO732273

W

WGwG **Gwynfor Growers**
Gwynfor, Pontgarreg, Llangrannog, Llandysul, Ceredigion, SA44 6AU
Ⓣ (01239) 654151
Ⓔ info@gwynfor.co.uk
Ⓦ www.gwynfor.co.uk
Contact: S. & A. Hipkin
Opening Times: By appt. only. For additional opening times please see website.
Min Mail Order UK: Nmc
Cat. Cost: Online only.
Credit Cards: All major credit/debit cards, Paypal
Specialities: National Plant Collection of *Rosmarinus* cvs. Specialist supplier of Welsh fruit trees. Classic & contemporary plants grown organically & peat-free. Some plants available in small quantities only. Rarities propagated to order.
Notes: Plants also available at local farmers' markets, plant fairs & some NGS Open Gardens. Delivers to shows.
OS Grid Ref: SN331536

WHal **Hall Farm Nursery**
Vicarage Lane, Kinnerley, Nr Oswestry, Shropshire, SY10 8DH
Ⓣ (01691) 682135
Ⓔ info@hallfarmnursery.co.uk
Ⓦ www.hallfarmnursery.co.uk
Contact: Christine & Nic Ffoulkes Jones
Opening Times: 1000-1700 Fri & Sat, 1st Mar-14th Sep.
Cat. Cost: Online only.
Credit Cards: Visa, MasterCard, Electron, Maestro
Specialities: Wide range of herbaceous perennials including woodland plants, ornamental grasses & herbs.
Notes: Partial wheelchair access.
OS Grid Ref: SJ333209

WHCr **Hergest Croft Gardens**
Hergest Estate Office, Ridgebourne Road, Kington, Herefordshire, HR5 3EG
Ⓣ (01544) 230160
Ⓜ 07968 435627
Ⓔ gardens@hergest.co.uk
Ⓦ www.hergest.co.uk
Contact: Stephen Lloyd
Opening Times: 1200-1730 7 days, Apr-Oct.
Credit Cards: All major credit/debit cards
Specialities: *Acer, Betula* & unusual woody plants.
Notes: Limited wheelchair access.
OS Grid Ref: SO286567

WHer **The Herb Garden & Historical Plant Nursery**
Frondeg, Gilfachreda, New Quay, Ceredigion, SA45 9SP
Ⓣ (01545) 580893
Ⓜ 07840 106956
Ⓔ corinnetremaine@gmail.com
Ⓦ www.historicalplants.co.uk
Contact: Corinne Tremaine
Opening Times: By appt. only.
Min Mail Order UK: Nmc
Min Mail Order EU: Nmc
Cat. Cost: Online only.
Credit Cards: None
Specialities: Rare herbs, rare natives & wild flowers; rare & unusual & historical perennials, old roses, heritage pinks & Parma violets.

WHil **Hillview Hardy Plants** ♿
(off B4176), Worfield, Nr Bridgnorth, Shropshire, WV15 5NT
Ⓣ (01746) 716454
Ⓜ 07974 391608
Ⓔ hillview@onetel.net
Ⓦ www.hillviewhardyplants.com
Contact: Ingrid, John & Sarah Millington
Opening Times: 1000-1700 Mon-Sat, Mar-mid Oct. At other times, please phone first.
Min Mail Order UK: Nmc
Min Mail Order EU: £20.00 + p&p

Cat. Cost: Online only.
Credit Cards: All major credit/debit cards
Specialities: Choice herbaceous perennials incl. *Acanthus*, *Albuca*, *Aquilegia*, *Primula auricula*, *Eucomis*, *Ixia*, South African bulbs. National Plant Collections of *Acanthus* & *Albuca*.
Notes: Also sells wholesale. Exports beyond EU. Delivers to shows. Euro accepted. Wheelchair accessible.
OS Grid Ref: SO772969

WHoo **Hoo House Nursery**
Hoo House, Gloucester Road, Tewkesbury, Gloucestershire, GL20 7DA
Ⓣ (01684) 293389
Ⓕ (01684) 293389
Ⓔ nursery@hoohouse.co.uk
Ⓦ www.hoohouse.co.uk
Contact: Julie & Robin Ritchie
Opening Times: 1000-1700 Mon-Sat, 1100-1700 Sun. Please ring to check Nov-Jan.
Cat. Cost: 3 × 1st class.
Credit Cards: All major credit/debit cards
Specialities: Wide range of herbaceous & alpines grown peat-free. Aster, *Cyclamen*, *Geranium*, *Penstemon*, *Saxifraga* & many later-flowering varieties.
Notes: Also sells wholesale. Partially wheelchair accessible.
OS Grid Ref: SO893293

WHrl **Harrells Hardy Plants**
(office) 15 Coxlea Close, Evesham, Worcestershire, WR11 4JS
Ⓣ (01386) 443077
Ⓜ 07799 577120/07733 446606
Ⓔ mail@harrellshardyplants.co.uk
Ⓦ www.harrellshardyplants.co.uk
Contact: Liz Nicklin & Kate Phillips
Opening Times: By appt. only. Please telephone.
Min Mail Order UK: Nmc
Min Mail Order EU: Nmc
Cat. Cost: Online plant list.
Credit Cards: None
Specialities: Display gardens showcase wide range of hardy perennials, esp. *Hemerocallis* & grasses.
Notes: Nursery located off Rudge Rd, Evesham. Please phone for directions or see website. Exports beyond EU. Partial wheelchair access.
OS Grid Ref: SP033443

WHwl **Howle Hill Nursery** ♿ ◆
Watersedge, Howle Hill, Ross-on-Wye, Herefordshire, HR9 5SP
Ⓣ (01989) 567726
Ⓜ 07961 570409
Ⓔ andy@howlehillnursery.co.uk:enquiries@howlehillnursery.co.uk
Ⓦ www.howlehillnursery.co.uk
Contact: Andy Houghton
Opening Times: 0900-1700 Mon-Fri. 0900-1600 Sat during spring/summer.
Min Mail Order UK: £25
Min Mail Order EU: £25
Cat. Cost: No catalogue at present.
Credit Cards: All major credit/debit cards
Specialities: We grow a wide and varied selection of plants from a 2Ltr pot up to 750Ltr semi-mature trees. We usually grow between 150-200 varieties of Japanese Maples.
Notes: Also sells wholesale. Euro accepted. Wheelchair accessible. We have now opened a purpose built plant centre at Leaf Creative, Ross Road, Huntley, Gloucester, GL19 3EX. Delivers to shows.
OS Grid Ref: SO604892

WIce **Ice Alpines** ♿
Lye Head Road, Bewdley, Worcestershire, DY12 2UW
Ⓣ (01299) 269219
Ⓕ (01562) 510003
Ⓔ icealpines@googlemail.com
Ⓦ www.icealpines.co.uk
Contact: Mark Lagomarsino
Opening Times: Mail order. Open by appt. only.
Min Mail Order UK: Nmc
Min Mail Order EU: £18
Credit Cards: All major credit/debit cards
Specialities: British grown alpine & rockery plants.
Notes: Delivers to shows. Wheelchair accessible.

WJas **Paul Jasper Trees**
The Lighthouse (office only), Bridge Street, Leominster, Herefordshire, HR6 8DX
Ⓔ jaspertreescouk@aol.com
Ⓦ www.jaspertrees.co.uk
Contact: Paul Jasper
Opening Times: Not open. Mail order only.
Min Mail Order UK: £25.00 + p&p
Cat. Cost: Online only.
Credit Cards: All major credit/debit cards
Specialities: Many unusual varieties of *Malus domestica* & *Prunus*.
Notes: Full range of fruit & ornamental trees. 100+ modern & traditional fruit tree varieties. 100 ornamental tree varieties, direct from the grower. Less popular varieties available in small quantities only. See website for details. Also sells wholesale.

WJek **Jekka's Herb Farm** ♿
Rose Cottage, Shellards Lane, Alveston, Bristol, South Gloucestershire, BS35 3SY
Ⓣ (01454) 418878
Ⓔ sales@jekkasherbfarm.com
Ⓦ www.jekkasherbfarm.com
Contact: Jekka McVicar
Opening Times: Open on specific days only. Please check website or contact nursery for dates.
Min Mail Order UK: £10.00
Min Mail Order EU: £18.00
Cat. Cost: Online only.
Credit Cards: Visa, MasterCard, Delta, Maestro
Specialities: Specialist herb farm with a herbetum containing over 300 culinary herbs. The collection contains herbs from all around the world.
Notes: Wheelchair accessible.

WKif **Kiftsgate Court Gardens** ♿
Kiftsgate Court, Chipping Camden, Gloucestershire, GL55 6LN
Ⓣ (01386) 438777
Ⓕ (01386) 438777
Ⓔ anne@kiftsgate.co.uk
Ⓦ www.kiftsgate.co.uk
Contact: Mrs J. Chambers
Opening Times: 1200-1800 Sat-Wed, May, Jun & Jul. 1400-1800 Sat-Wed, Aug. 1400-1800 Sun, Mon & Wed, Apr & Sep.
Credit Cards: All major debit/credit cards except American Express
Specialities: Small range of unusual plants.
Notes: Wheelchair accessible.
OS Grid Ref: SP170430

WKor **Kore Wild Fruit Nursery**
Bridport House, Cilcennin, Lampeter, Ceredigion, SA48 8RL
Ⓣ (01570) 470439
Ⓔ info@korewildfruitnursery.co.uk
Ⓦ www.korewildfruitnursery.co.uk
Contact: Coral Guppy
Opening Times: Mail order only.
Min Mail Order UK: Nmc
Min Mail Order EU: Nmc
Cat. Cost: Free.
Credit Cards: All major credit/debit cards
Specialities: Range of mainly hardy trees, shrubs and perennials that produce edible fruit and some perennial veg. Unusual plants for indoors. Exotic and native species available.
Notes: Ideal for a range of uses, aspects and soil types. All plants propagated on site in 7cm pots and sold when 1 to 3 years old. Plants available all year round. Customers can arrange to collect.

WLav **The Lavender Garden**
Ashcroft Nurseries, Nr Ozleworth, Kingscote, Tetbury, Gloucestershire, GL8 8YF
Ⓣ (01453) 860356
Ⓜ 07837 582943
Ⓔ andrew007bullock@aol.com
Ⓦ www.thelavenderg.co.uk
Contact: Andrew Bullock
Opening Times: 1100-1700 Sat & Sun. Weekdays variable, please phone. 1st Nov-1st Mar by appt. only.
Min Mail Order UK: £10.00 + p&p
Min Mail Order EU: £20.00 + p&p
Cat. Cost: Online only.
Credit Cards: All major credit/debit cards
Specialities: *Lavandula*, *Buddleja*, plants to attract butterflies. Herbs, wildflowers. National Plant Collection of *Buddleja*.
Notes: Also sells wholesale. Delivers to shows. Limited wheelchair access.
OS Grid Ref: ST798948

WLea **Leaf Creative Design Ltd** ♿
Huntley Plant Centre, Ross Road, Huntley, Gloucestershire, GL19 3EX
Ⓣ (01452) 830837
Ⓔ enquiries@leafcreative.co.uk
Ⓦ www.leafcreative.co.uk
Contact: Neil Evans
Opening Times: 0900-1700 Mon-Sat, 1000-1600 Sun.
Min Mail Order UK: £5.00
Min Mail Order EU: £50.00
Credit Cards: All major credit/debit cards
Notes: Wheelchair accessible. Delivers to shows.
OS Grid Ref: SO713194

WLov **Lovegroves**
The Old Chapel, Pendock, Gloucestershire, GL19 3PG
Ⓣ (01531) 650918
Ⓜ 07973 331142
Ⓔ clare@plants-paradise.co.uk
Ⓦ www.plants-paradise.co.uk
Contact: Clare Lovegrove
Opening Times: Mail order.
Min Mail Order UK: Nmc
Cat. Cost: Available by email or download from website only.
Credit Cards: All major credit/debit cards
Specialities: Interesting selection of trees, shrubs, ferns and climbers; many of which are rare or unusual. All grown in peat-free compost.
Notes: Traditional plant nursery, producing an inspiring collection of desirable trees and shrubs grown in the UK. Collection of plants by prior arrangement. Delivers to shows.
OS Grid Ref: SO786326

WMal **Malcolm Allison Nurseries**
79 Byron Road, St Mark's, Cheltenham, Gloucestershire, GL51 7EY
Ⓣ (01242) 256349
Ⓜ 07817 730509
Ⓔ majallison2000@yahoo.com
Ⓦ http://www.malcolmallisonplants.com
Contact: Malcolm Allison
Opening Times: By appt. only
Credit Cards: Paypal
Specialities: Drought tolerant perennials, cultivars of *Nerine sarniensis*.
Notes: Wide range of hardy and half-hardy herbaceous plants, many available only in small quantities.
OS Grid Ref: SO914286

WMAq **Merebrook Water Plants**
Kingfisher Barn, Merebrook Farm, Hanley Swan, Worcestershire, WR8 0DX
Ⓣ (01684) 310950
Ⓜ 07876 777066
Ⓔ enquiries@pondplants.co.uk
Ⓦ www.pondplants.co.uk
Contact: Roger Kings
Opening Times: Not open. Mail order only.
Min Mail Order UK: Nmc
Min Mail Order EU: £25.00
Cat. Cost: Online only.
Credit Cards: All major credit/debit cards
Specialities: Hardy *Nymphaea*, Louisiana irises & other aquatic plants. International Waterlily & Water Gardening Soc. accredited collection.
Notes: Full range of pond plants including water lilies, marginal and deeper marginal plants, oxygenating plants, wetland and bog plants and moisture-loving plants.
OS Grid Ref: SO802425

WMat **The Tree Shop at Frank P. Matthews Ltd** ♿
Berrington Court, Tenbury Wells, Worcestershire, WR15 8TH
Ⓣ (01584) 812800
Ⓕ (01584) 811830
Ⓔ treeshop@fpmatthews.co.uk
Ⓦ www.frankpmatthews.com
Contact: Steve Grosvenor
Opening Times: 0730-1700 Mon-Fri
Cat. Cost: 4 × 1st class.
Credit Cards: All major credit/debit cards
Specialities: Fruit & deciduous ornamental trees.
Notes: Also sells wholesale. Wheelchair accessible.
OS Grid Ref: SO571676

WMil **Anne Milner**
Meadow House, Baunton, Cirencester, Gloucestershire, GL7 7BB
Ⓣ (01285) 643731
Ⓔ anne.milner@btinternet.com
Ⓦ www.blissiris.co.uk
Contact: Anne Milner
Opening Times: By appt. only.
Min Mail Order UK: Nmc
Min Mail Order EU: Nmc
Cat. Cost: 50p (UK) £1.00 (EU) to cover postage.
Credit Cards: None
Specialities: National Plant Collection of *Iris* (A. J. Bliss introductions). Available in small quantities only.
Notes: Euro accepted. Delivers to some shows, check with nursery.

WMon **National Plant Collection of Monarda** ♿
Glyn Bach, Pont Hywel, Efailwen, Pembrokeshire, SA66 7JP
Ⓣ (01994) 419104
Ⓜ 07828 199303
Ⓔ carole_whittaker@hotmail.com
Ⓦ www.glynbachgardens.co.uk
Contact: Carole Whittaker
Opening Times: Open by appt. & May-Oct for collection of orders only.
Min Mail Order UK: Nmc
Min Mail Order EU: Nmc
Cat. Cost: Online only.
Credit Cards: None
Specialities: National Plant Collection of *Monarda*. Limited stock available.
Notes: Gardens open under Plant Heritage and by appt. Talks given. If travelling some distance please contact nursery to check plant availability. Wheelchair accessible.
OS Grid Ref: SN132275

WMou **Mount Pleasant Trees Ltd** ♿
Rockhampton, Berkeley, Gloucestershire, GL13 9DU
Ⓣ (01454) 260348
Ⓔ info@mountpleasanttrees.com
Ⓦ www.mountpleasanttrees.com
Contact: Tom Locke & Elizabeth Murphy
Opening Times: 0830-1630 Mon-Fri, 0830-1230 Sat, Oct-Apr.
Cat. Cost: Free.
Credit Cards: All major credit/debit cards
Specialities: Wide range of trees for forestry, hedging, woodlands & gardens esp. *Populus*, *Salix*, *Tilia* & *Quercus*.
Notes: Mail order available for plants under 1m in height, quotes on request, p&p quoted

on individual basis. Also sells wholesale. Wheelchair accessible.
OS Grid Ref: ST654929

WNHG **NEW HOPE GARDENS** ♿
(office) The Old Chapel, Cefn Einion, Nr Bishops Castle, Shropshire, SY9 5LF
Ⓣ Office: (01588) 630750
Ⓔ markwzenick@aol.com
Ⓦ www.newhopegardens.com
Contact: Mark Zenick
Opening Times: Open W/ends: 1200-1700 Sat & Sun, 29th/30th Jun; 6th/7th, 13th/14th, 20th/21st, 27th/28th Jul, & 3rd/4th Aug or by appt.
Min Mail Order UK: Nmc
Min Mail Order EU: Nmc
Cat. Cost: Online only. Plant list on request.
Credit Cards: All major credit/debit cards
Specialities: American bred, British grown, *Hemerocallis*. Ships bare-rooted plants. Daylily plants are growing and for sale at New Hope Gardens, Colebatch Farm, Shropshire on Open w/ends.
Notes: Wheelchair accessible.
OS Grid Ref: SO872317

W

WNPC **NEWENT PLANT CENTRE** ♿
Little Verzons Farm, Hereford Road, Ledbury, Herefordshire, HR8 2PZ
Ⓣ (01531) 670121
Ⓔ markmoir999@btinternet.com
Ⓦ www.newentplantcentre.co.uk
Contact: Mark Moir
Opening Times: 0900-1700 Mon-Sat, 1000-1600 Sun.
Credit Cards: All major credit/debit cards
Specialities: Extensive range of *Heuchera* & *Euphorbia*. Herbaceous perennials, climbers, shrubs, trees, alpines, herbs, roses & fruit.
Notes: Coffee shop & deli on site. Delivers to shows. Wheelchair accessible.
OS Grid Ref: SO665395

WOld **OLD COURT NURSERIES**
Colwall, Nr Malvern, Worcestershire, WR13 6QE
Ⓣ (01684) 540416
Ⓜ 07971 522891
Ⓔ oldcourtnurseries@btinternet.com
Ⓦ www.autumnasters.co.uk
Contact: Paul, Meriel or Helen Picton
Opening Times: 1400-1700 Wed-Sat, May-Aug. 1100-1700 Wed-Sun, Aug. 1100-1700 7 days, 1st week Sep-20th Oct. Also by appt. May to Oct.
Min Mail Order UK: Nmc
Min Mail Order EU: Nmc
Cat. Cost: Free.
Credit Cards: All major debit/credit cards except American Express
Specialities: National Plant Collection of Michaelmas Daisies. Herbaceous perennials.
Notes: Mail order sent in spring only. Display garden open Aug-Oct, plus some early season open days. See website or contact nursery for further information.
OS Grid Ref: SO759430

WPav **PAVIOUR AND DAVIES PLANTS** ♿
(office) Dame School, Castle Street, Wigmore, Herefordshire, HR6 9UA
Ⓣ (01568) 770005
Ⓜ 07966 580812
Ⓔ markpaviour@gmail.com
Ⓦ www.paviouranddaviesplants.co.uk
Contact: Mark Paviour
Opening Times: By appt. only.
Min Mail Order UK: Nmc
Cat. Cost: Online.
Credit Cards: None
Specialities: Plants of Chilean and Argentinian origin together with a selection of unusual plants from Australasia. All plants propagated and grown on site. National Plant Collection of *Azara*. Some plants only available in small numbers.
Notes: Groups welcome by appt. Talks given by arrangement. Delivers to shows. Wheelchair accessible.
OS Grid Ref: SO429556

WPGP **PAN-GLOBAL PLANTS** ♿
The Walled Garden, Frampton Court, Frampton-on-Severn, Gloucestershire, GL2 7EX
Ⓣ (01452) 741641
Ⓜ 07801 275138
Ⓔ info@panglobalplants.com
Ⓦ www.panglobalplants.com
Contact: Nick Macer
Opening Times: 1100-1700 Wed-Sun 1st Feb-31st Oct. Also B/hols. Closed 2nd Sun in Sep. Winter months by appt. please telephone first.
Min Mail Order UK: £25.00
Min Mail Order EU: £35.00
Cat. Cost: 4 × 1st class.
Credit Cards: Maestro, MasterCard, Visa, Solo, Delta
Specialities: Serious plantsman's nursery offering a wide selection of rare & desirable trees, shrubs, herbaceous, bamboos, exotics, climbers, ferns etc. Specialities incl. *Magnolia*, *Hydrangea*, *Tilia*, *Betula*, *Sorbus*, *Bamboo* & *Agavaceae*.

Notes: Wheelchair accessible.
OS Grid Ref: SO750080

WPhe **Pheasant Acre Plants ◆**
3 Pheasant Walk, Pen-y-Fai, Bridgend, Mid Glamorgan, CF31 4DU
Ⓣ (01656) 664086
Ⓜ 07816 236462
Ⓔ sales@pheasantacreplants.co.uk
Ⓦ www.pheasantacreplants.co.uk
Contact: Rob Evans
Opening Times: By appt. only.
Min Mail Order UK: Nmc
Min Mail Order EU: Nmc
Cat. Cost: £1.00.
Credit Cards: All major credit/debit cards
Specialities: Bulbous. Ornamental. *Gladiolus.*
Notes: Open Days throughout the year. Delivers to shows. Euro accepted.

WPnP **Penlan Perennials ♿**
Landre, Drefach, Llanybydder, Ceredigion, SA40 9YD
Ⓣ (01570) 480097
Ⓜ 07984 880241
Ⓔ info@penlanperennials.co.uk
Ⓦ www.penlanperennials.co.uk
Contact: Graham & Julie Moore
Opening Times: Open for collection of orders & by appt.
Min Mail Order UK: Nmc
Min Mail Order EU: Nmc
Cat. Cost: Online only.
Credit Cards: All major credit/debit cards
Specialities: Aquatic, marginal & bog plants. Shade-loving & woodland perennials, ferns, hardy geraniums & shrubs, all grown organically in peat-free compost.
Notes: Mail order all year, next day delivery. Secure online web ordering. Also sells wholesale. Euro accepted. Delivers to shows. Wheelchair accessible.
OS Grid Ref: SN500464

WRou **Roualeyn Nurseries**
Trefriw, Conwy, LL27 0SX
Ⓣ (01492) 640548
Ⓔ roualeynnursery@btinternet.com
Ⓦ www.roualeynfuchsias.co.uk
Contact: Colin Jones
Opening Times: 1000-1600 Sat & Sun only 2nd Mar-30th June
Min Mail Order UK: £15.00
Cat. Cost: 2 x 1st class sae.
Credit Cards: All major credit/debit cards
Specialities: Fuchsias
Notes: Orders may be collected from any of the flower shows listed in current catalogue. Delivers to shows.
OS Grid Ref: SH632778

WSFF **Saith Ffynnon Wildlife Plants ♿**
Downing Road, Whitford, Holywell, Flintshire, CH8 9EN
Ⓣ (01352) 711198
Ⓜ 07979 603846
Ⓕ (01352) 716777
Ⓔ Jan@7wells.org
Ⓦ www.7wells.co.uk
Contact: Jan Miller
Opening Times: By appt. only.
Min Mail Order UK: Nmc
Min Mail Order EU: Nmc
Cat. Cost: 2 × 1st class (list only) or full catalogue online.
Credit Cards: All major credit/debit cards
Specialities: Plants and seeds to attract bees, butterflies & other wildlife. Natural dye plants. National Plant Collection of *Eupatorium*. Stock available in small quantities unless ordered well in advance.
Notes: Percentage of profits go to conservation. Credit cards accepted via website only. Also sells wholesale. Euro accepted. Wheelchair accessible.
OS Grid Ref: SJ154775

WSHC **Stone House Cottage Nurseries ♿**
Church Lane, Stone, Nr Kidderminster, Worcestershire, DY10 4BG
Ⓜ 07817 921146
Ⓔ louisa@shcn.co.uk
Ⓦ www.shcn.co.uk
Contact: L. N. Arbuthnott
Opening Times: 1000-1700 Wed-Sat, early Apr-late Aug
Credit Cards: All major credit/debit cards
Specialities: Small general range esp. wall shrubs, climbers & unusual plants.
Notes: Wheelchair accessible.
OS Grid Ref: SO863750

WShi **Shipton Bulbs**
Y Felin, Henllan Amgoed, Whitland, Carmarthenshire, SA34 0SL
Ⓣ (01994) 240637
Ⓕ (01994) 240637
Ⓔ admin@shiptonbulbs.co.uk
Ⓦ www.shiptonbulbs.co.uk
Contact: Astra Shipton
Opening Times: By appt. only.
Min Mail Order UK: Nmc
Min Mail Order EU: Nmc
Cat. Cost: Sae.
Credit Cards: All major credit/debit cards
Specialities: Native British bulbs. Bulbs &

plants for naturalising.
Notes: Also sells wholesale. Euro accepted.
OS Grid Ref: SN188207

WSMil **South Milton Plant Nursery** ♿
South Milton, Kingsbridge, South Devon, TQ7 3JP
Ⓣ (01548) 561081
Ⓜ 07936 279762
Ⓔ info@southmiltonnursery.co.uk
Ⓦ www.southmiltonnursery.co.uk
Contact: Theo Cooper
Opening Times: 1000-1700 Wed-Sun Feb-Oct. 1000-1500 Wed-Sat Nov-Dec. Closed all of Jan and Mon & Tue all year.
Cat. Cost: Online.
Credit Cards: Paypal
Specialities: *Echium*
Notes: Also sells wholesale. Wheelchair accessible.
OS Grid Ref: SX691427

W

WSpi **Spinneywell Nursery**
Spinneywell Farm, Waterlane, Oakridge, Stroud, Gloucestershire, GL6 7PH
Ⓣ (01452) 770092
Ⓜ 07879 133046
Ⓔ info@spinneywell.co.uk
Ⓦ www.plantproviders.co.uk
Contact: Wendy Asher
Opening Times: 0900-1700 Wed-Sat Mar-Oct, otherwise by prior appt. only. Pls telephone before travelling. Also advertised Open Days & weekend events. Check website or contact nursery for details.
Min Mail Order UK: £10.00 + p&p
Min Mail Order EU: £30.00 + p&p
Cat. Cost: Online only.
Credit Cards: All major credit/debit cards
Specialities: *Buxus*, *Daphne*, *Euphorbia*, Ferns, Grasses, *Hellebore*, Hardy geraniums, unusual shrubs *Taxus* (Yew) and Topiary.
Notes: Plant sourcing service available. Mail order and organised collections/deliveries only. Also sells wholesale.
OS Grid Ref: SO921044

WSSs **Shropshire Sarracenias** ♿
Beaufort, Coppice Drive, Wrockwardine Wood, Telford, Shropshire, TF2 7BP
Ⓣ (01952) 612452
Ⓔ mike@carnivorousplants.uk.com
Ⓦ www.carnivorousplants.uk.com
Contact: Mike King
Opening Times: By appt. only.
Min Mail Order UK: Nmc
Min Mail Order EU: Nmc
Cat. Cost: 2 × 1st class.
Credit Cards: Paypal
Specialities: *Sarracenia*. *Dionaea muscipula* & forms. Some stock available in small quantities only. National Plant Collections of *Sarracenia* & *Dionaea*.
Notes: Exports beyond EU. Delivers to shows. Euro accepted. Wheelchair accessible.
OS Grid Ref: SJ689085

WSuV **Sunnybank Vine Nursery (National Vine Collection)**
Cwm Barn, King Street, Ewyas Harold, Rowlestone, Herefordshire, HR2 OEE
Ⓣ (01981) 240256
Ⓔ Sarah@sunnybankvines.co.uk
Ⓦ www.sunnybankvines.co.uk
Contact: Sarah Bell
Opening Times: Not open. Open day annually, see website for details
Min Mail Order UK: £15.00 incl. p&p
Min Mail Order EU: £23.00 incl. p&p
Cat. Cost: Online only.
Credit Cards: None
Specialities: Vines. National Plant Collection of *Vitis vinifera* (hardy, incl. dessert & wine). Small quantities of 60-70 varieties available as rooted plants, the entire collection usually available as bare wood cuttings for own propagation depending upon wood ripening this season.
Notes: Open day once a year advertised on both nursery & Plant Heritage websites. Exports beyond EU by arrangement.

WThu **Thuya Alpine Nursery**
Glebelands, Hartpury, Gloucestershire, GL19 3BW
Ⓣ (01452) 700548 (ring between 1900-2100 hours)
Ⓜ 07435 419667
Contact: S. W. Bond
Opening Times: 1000-dusk Sat & B/hols. 1100-dusk Sun, Weekdays appt. advised.
Min Mail Order UK: £7.00 + p&p
Min Mail Order EU: £14.00 + p&p
Cat. Cost: 4 × 2nd class.
Credit Cards: None
Specialities: Wide and changing range including rarities, available in small quantities only.
Notes: Will deliver plants to AGS shows only. Partial wheelchair access.

WTor **Tortworth Plants Ltd**
Old Lodge Farm, Tortworth, Wotton-under-Edge, Gloucestershire, GL12 8HF
Ⓣ (01454) 260020
Ⓕ (01454) 260020
Ⓔ info@tortworthplants.co.uk
Ⓦ www.tortworthplants.co.uk

Contact: Rebecca Flint or Tim Hancock
Opening Times: By appt. only.
Min Mail Order UK: Nmc
Cat. Cost: Online or 2 × 1st for plant list.
Credit Cards: All major credit/debit cards
Specialities: Herbaceous perennials & alpines, incl. the more unusual.
Notes: Also sells wholesale. Partial wheelchair access. Delivers to shows.

WTre **WALLED GARDEN TREBERFYDD**
Llangasty, Brecon, Powys, LD3 7PX
Ⓣ (01874) 730169
Ⓜ 07711 222700
Ⓔ alison@walledgardentreberfydd.com
Ⓦ www.walledgardentreberfydd.com
Contact: Alison Sparshatt
Opening Times: 1000-1700 daily, Apr-Oct. For Nov-Mar opening times see website or contact nursery.
Cat. Cost: Online only.
Credit Cards: All major credit/debit cards
Specialities: Old-fashioned plant nursery in a walled Victorian kitchen garden. Hardy plants grown in Wales which are structural, unusual, herbal or fragrant. Special emphasis on herbs & perennial vegetables. Many varieties propagated in small quantities only.
Notes: Events & workshops throughout the year. Contact nursery for details.
OS Grid Ref: SO128255

WTSh **TREE SHOP LTD**
Unit 16, Harts Barn, Monmouth Road, Longhope, Gloucestershire, GL17 0QD
Ⓣ (01452) 832100
Ⓕ (01452) 831273
Ⓔ office@tree-shop.co.uk
Ⓦ www.tree-shop.co.uk
Contact: Helen Conneely & Lorraine Organ
Opening Times: By appt. only 0830-1600 Mon-Fri. Please phone first.
Min Mail Order UK: Nmc
Cat. Cost: Free.
Credit Cards: All major debit/credit cards except American Express
Specialities: Trees, hedging, shrubs.
OS Grid Ref: SO679185

WTyc **TY CWM NURSERY**
Penfordd, Llanybydder, Ceredigon, SA40 9XE
Ⓣ (01570) 480655
Ⓔ helenwarrington@hotmail.co.uk
Ⓦ www.tycwmnursery.co.uk
Contact: Helen Warrington
Opening Times: 1000-1800 1st Apr-30th Sep, Tue-Sun. Closed Mon. 1st Oct-31st Mar by appt. only.
Min Mail Order UK: Nmc
Min Mail Order EU: Nmc
Cat. Cost: Online only.
Credit Cards: All major credit/debit cards
Specialities: Carnivorous plants & unusual perennials including a good selection for shade. Also sell shrubs, climbers, bedding, fruit and veg plants. Many rare items not listed available in small quantities.
Notes: Partial wheelchair access. Delivers to shows.

WViv **VIV MARSH POSTAL PLANTS**
Hunkington Nurseries, Walford Heath, Shrewsbury, Shropshire, SY4 2HT
Ⓣ (01939) 291475
Ⓔ mail@postalplants.co.uk
Ⓦ www.postalplants.co.uk
Contact: Mr Viv Marsh
Opening Times: Open 2 w/ends a year. Please phone or see website for details.
Min Mail Order UK: £30.00
Min Mail Order EU: £30.00
Cat. Cost: Free.
Credit Cards: All major credit/debit cards
Specialities: Specialists in *Alstroemeria* and tall bearded *Iris*. National Plant Collection of *Alstroemeria*, viewing by appt.
Notes: Partial wheelchair access (to tunnels. No disabled toilet).
OS Grid Ref: SJ445197

WWct **WALCOT ORGANIC NURSERY**
Walcot Lane, Drakes Broughton, Pershore, Worcestershire, WR10 2AL
Ⓣ (01905) 841587
Ⓜ 07780 547983
Ⓔ enquiries@walcotnursery.co.uk
Ⓦ www.walcotnursery.co.uk
Contact: Kevin O'Neill
Opening Times: 0800-1700 Mon-Fri. 1000-1300 Sat. Sat only Nov-Mar.
Min Mail Order UK: £16.00
Cat. Cost: Free.
Credit Cards: All major credit/debit cards
Specialities: Growers of Organic fruit trees, apples, plums, damsons, pears, cherries, quinces & crab apples on different rootstocks. Supplied bare-rooted while dormant from late November until end of March.
Notes: Also sells wholesale. Nursery buildings accessible for wheelchairs.
OS Grid Ref: SO944461

WWFP **WHITEHALL FARMHOUSE PLANTS**
Sevenhampton, Cheltenham, Gloucestershire, GL54 5TL
Ⓣ (01242) 820772

Ⓜ 07711 021034
Ⓔ victoria@wfplants.co.uk
Ⓦ www.wfplants.co.uk
Contact: Victoria Logue
Opening Times: By appt. only.
Min Mail Order UK: Nmc
Credit Cards: None
Notes: A very small nursery producing some interesting & easy hardy perennials for the garden. Most plants held in very small quantities only.
OS Grid Ref: SP018229

WWild **THE WILD FLOWER NURSERY**
Hackett Farm, Reynalton, Kilgetty, Pembrokeshire, SA68 0XN
Ⓜ 07854 845014
Ⓔ info@thewildflowernursery.co.uk
Ⓦ www.thewildflowernursery.co.uk
Contact: Lindsey Jones
Opening Times: Open by appt. only.
Min Mail Order UK: £4.99
Cat. Cost: Online only.
Credit Cards: All major credit/debit cards
Specialities: British wild flower plants.
Notes: Sells online only.

X

WWtn **WESTONBURY MILL WATER GARDEN** ♿
Pembridge, Herefordshire, HR6 9HZ
Ⓣ (01544) 388650
Ⓕ (01544) 388650
Ⓔ westonburymillnursery@gmail.com
Ⓦ www.westonburymillwatergardens.com
Contact: Richard Pim
Opening Times: 1100-1700 daily, 1st Apr-30th Sep. By appt. only at other times & to arrange collection. Please contact nursery for orders outside open season.
Specialities: Range of herbaceous plants with special emphasis on plants for the water garden & bog areas. Plants available in small quantities. Seasonal availability varies as stock sells out. Contact nursery to confirm availability before travelling.
Notes: Café. Wheelchair accessible.

ABROAD

XAbr **ABRIHERBS**
La Gigude, Soulatgé, Aude, 11330, France
Ⓣ +33 (685) 651155
Ⓕ +33 (685) 651155
Ⓔ abriherbs@gmail.com
Contact: Cassy
Opening Times: By appt. only.
Min Mail Order UK: Nmc
Min Mail Order EU: Nmc
Cat. Cost: Sae for free plant list.
Specialities: Natural medicinal and rare plants.
Notes: Mostly pure species offered. Natural methods of production with no use of chemicals. Also sells wholesale. Euro accepted.

XBar **BARNHAVEN PRIMROSES**
Keranguiner, Plestin-les-grèves, Brittany, 22310 France
Ⓣ +33 (2) 9635 6841
Ⓜ +33 (6) 06623687
Ⓔ info@barnhaven.com
Ⓦ www.barnhaven.com
Contact: Rob and Jodie Mitchell
Opening Times: 1400-1700 Feb-May. For visits outside this period, please phone first.
Min Mail Order UK: Nmc
Min Mail Order EU: Nmc
Credit Cards: Visa, MasterCard, Paypal
Specialities: *Primula.* French National Plant Collection of Barnhaven *Primula* hybrids. Certified collection of *Primula auricula* cvs. Old-fashioned and double primroses. Large collection of Asiatic and Alpine *Primula.* Seeds & plants available worldwide.
Notes: Exports beyond EU. Euro & sterling accepted. Delivers to shows.

XFro **FROSCH EXCLUSIVE PERENNIALS**
Ziegelstadelweg 5a, Dietramszell, 83623 Germany
Ⓣ +49 (8027) 9049974
Ⓜ +49 172 8422050
Ⓕ +49 (8027) 904 9975
Ⓔ info@cypripedium.de
Ⓦ www.cypripedium.de
Contact: Michael Weinert
Opening Times: Not open. Mail order only. Orders taken between 0700-2200 hours.
Min Mail Order UK: £350.00 + p&p
Min Mail Order EU: £350.00 + p&p
Cat. Cost: Online only.
Credit Cards: None
Specialities: *Cypripedium* hybrids. Hardy orchids.
Notes: Also sells wholesale. Exports beyond EU. Euro accepted.

XLum **ATELIER DU VÉGÉTAL**
Ferme Miane, 25 route du libraire, 24100 Bergerac, France
Ⓣ +33 (5) 5357 6215
Ⓔ contact@atelierduvegetal.com
Ⓦ www.atelierduvegetal.com
Contact: Jordi & Amélie Tura
Opening Times: 0800-1730 Mon-Sat. Closed Sun.
Min Mail Order UK: Nmc
Min Mail Order EU: Nmc

Cat. Cost: Online only.
Credit Cards: Visa, MasterCard, Paypal
Specialities: Hardy perennials. Grasses. Plants for dry gardens. Large collection of *Geranium*, *Aster*, *Acanthus*, *Miscanthus*.
Notes: Also sells wholesale. Exports beyond EU. Delivers to shows. Euro accepted.

XPic **Piccoplant Mikrovermehrungen GmbH**
Brokhauser Weg 75, Oldenburg, 26129 Germany
Ⓣ +49 (0) 441 96980-0
Ⓕ +49 (0) 441 96980-10
Ⓔ anmeldung@piccoplant.de
Ⓦ www.piccoplant.de
Contact: Elke Haase
Specialities: Around 500 varieties of *Syringa* and 200 of *Rhododendron*.
Notes: Fifteen hectare nursery offering a broad range of woody ornamental plants. Exports beyond EU. Euro accepted. Also sells wholesale.

XSen **GAEC Senteurs Du Quercy** ♿
Mas de Fraysse, Escamps, Lot, 46230, France
Ⓣ +33 (5) 652 10162
Ⓔ contact@senteursduquercy.com
Ⓦ www.senteursduquercy.com
Contact: Frédéric Prévot
Opening Times: 1400-1800 spring & summer (excl. Aug). Other times, incl. Aug by appt.
Min Mail Order UK: Nmc
Min Mail Order EU: Nmc
Cat. Cost: €5.00.
Specialities: *Salvia*, *Iris*, *Phlomis*, *Teucrium*, *Lavandula* and drought tolerant plants. French National Plant Collection of *Salvia* species.
Notes: Euro accepted. Delivers to shows. Wheelchair accessible.

XSte **Pépinières Stervinou**
1, Lieu-Dit Kerguelen, Guipronvel, Milizac-Guipronvel, 29290, France
Ⓣ +33 (0) 298 07 28 00
Ⓕ +33 (0) 298 07 20 99
Ⓔ contact@stervinou.fr
Ⓦ www.stervinou.fr
Contact: Yves Stervinou
Min Mail Order UK: €45.00
Min Mail Order EU: €45.00
Cat. Cost: Online only.
Credit Cards: MasterCard, Visa
Specialities: We specialise in ericaceous plants such as *Camelia* (200 varieties), *Rhododendron* (100 varieties), *Magnolia*, *Michelias*, Japanese and Chinese *Azalea*. Other specialities include our large collection of unusual shrubs (*Restio*, *Protea* etc.) and perennials (*Watsonia*, *Agapanthus* etc.).
Notes: Our family-run nursery has been operating in Brittany, France since 1944. We produce a wide variety of high-quality plants for sale to garden centres and nurseries, but also to numerous individual collectors. Also sells wholesale.

Nursery Index by Name

Nurseries that are included in the *RHS Plant Finder* for the first time this year (or have been reintroduced after a significant absence) are marked in **bold type**.

Full details of the nurseries will be found in **Nursery Details by Code** on page 866. For a key to the geographical codes, see the start of **Nurseries**.

A & J Plants	EAJP
A La Carte Daylilies	SDay
Abbotsbury Sub-Tropical Gardens	CAbb
Aberconwy Nursery	WAbe
Abi and Tom's Garden Plants	**NAbi**
Abriachan Nurseries	GAbr
Abriherbs	XAbr
Acorn Trees and Shrubs	**CAco**
Agroforestry Research Trust	CAgr
Akorn and Oake	SAko
Alan Phipps Cacti	CPhi
Allwoods (Hassocks) Ltd	SAll
Alpine Campanulas (Bellflower Nursery)	EACa
Alstroemeria Select	**SAlS**
Angharad Pike Gardener and Plants	**SAng**
Anne Milner	WMil
Apuldram Roses	SApu
Architectural Plants Ltd	SArc
Ardcarne Garden Centre	IArd
Ardfearn Nursery	**GArf**
Arley Hall Nursery	MArl
Ashdale Cottage Garden Plants	**MACG**
Ashdown Forest Garden Centre & Nursery	SAdn
Ashridge Nurseries	CArg
Ashwood Nurseries Ltd	MAsh
Atelier du Végétal	XLum
Atlantic Botanic	WABo
Avon Bulbs	CAvo
Avondale Nursery	MAvo
Aylett Nurseries Ltd	LAyl
B & H M Baker	EBak
Bali-Hai Mail Order Nursery	IBal
Ballyrogan Nurseries	IBlr
Barcham Trees PLC	EBar
Barnhaven Primroses	XBar
Barnsdale Gardens	MBNS
Barracott Plants	CBct
Barters Plant Centre & Nursery	CBar
Bean Place Nursery	**SBea**
Bee Happy Plants & Seeds	CBee
Beechcroft Nursery	LBee
Beeches Cottage Nursery	GBee
Beeches Nursery	EBee
Beggar's Roost Plants	CBgR
Bennetts Water Gardens	CBen
Beth Chatto Gardens, The	ECha
Bide-A-Wee Cottage Gardens	NBid
Binny Plants	GBin
Birkheads Secret Gardens & Nursery	NBir
Blackstem Plants	**SBls**
Bluebell Arboretum & Nursery	MBlu
Bluebell Cottage Nursery	MBel
Bodmin Nursery	CBod
Border Alpines	CBor
Bordervale Plants	WBor
Botanica	EBtc
Boundary Nursery	EBou
Bowden Hostas	CBdn
Brackendale Nurseries	CBrac
Bressingham Gardens Nursery	**EBlo**
Bridge Farm Plants	MBriF
Bridge Nursery	MBrN
Brighton Plants	SBrt
Broadleigh Gardens	CBro
Brockamin Plants	WBrk
Brooklands Plants	CBrP
Brookside Nursery	MBros
Brownthwaite Hardy Plants	NBro
Buckingham Nurseries	LBuc
Burncoose Nurseries	CBcs
Butterfly Cottage Garden Plants	SBut
C S Lockyer (Fuchsias)	CLoc
C W Groves & Son Ltd	CGro
Calamazag Nursery	CCal
Camellia Grove Nursery	SCam
Cants of Colchester Ltd	ECnt
Caves Folly Nurseries	WCav
CB Plants	CCBP
Charles F Ellis	WCFE
Charleshurst Farm Nursery	SChF

Cherry Tree Nursery	CChe
Chestnut Nursery (Sheltered Work Opportunities Project)	CCht
Chew Valley Trees Ltd	CCVT
ChickenStreet	**WChS**
Chiltern Seeds Ltd	MCtn
Chipchase Castle Nursery	NChi
Chrysanthemums Direct	MCms
Citrus Centre, The	SCit
Claire Austin Hardy Plants	WCAu
Coastal Hedging	CCoa
Coblands Online	SCob
Colin Dickson t/a Dickson Nurseries	IDic
Cool Temperate	MCoo
Cooling's Nurseries Ltd	SCoo
Cornovium Snowdrops	**MCor**
Coton Manor Garden	MCot
Cotswold Garden Flowers	WCot
Cottage Nurseries	ECtt
Courtyard Planters	NCou
Craftyplants	NCft
Cranesbill Nursery	WCra
Creake Plant Centre	ECre
Crocus.co.uk	LCro
Croft 16 Daffodils	GCro
Cromar Nursery	SCmr
Cross Common Nursery	CCCN
Crûg Farm Plants	WCru
Daleside Nurseries Ltd	NDal
Damhead Nursery Ltd	**GDam**
Dan Sutton	SSut
D'Arcy & Everest	EDAr
Dave Parkinson Plants	NDav
Deelish Garden Centre	IDee
Delfland Nurseries Ltd	**EDel**
Desert to Jungle	CDTJ
Dibleys Nurseries	WDib
Direct Bulbs	SDir
Donington Nurseries Ltd	MDon
Dorset Perennials	CDor
Dove Cottage Nursery & Garden	NDov
Downderry Nursery	SDow
Downside Nurseries	CDow
Drointon Nurseries	NDro
Dryad Nursery	NDry
Duchy of Cornwall	CDoC
Dysons Nurseries	SDys
E W King & Co. Ltd. (Kings Seeds)	EKin
East Northdown Nurseries	SEND
East of Eden Nursery	NEoE
Echium World	MEch
Eddington House Nursery	SEdd
Edible Garden Nursery, The	CLau
Edibleculture	SEdi
Edrom Nurseries	GEdr
Edulis	LEdu
Eleplants Nursery	SEle
Elsworth Herbs	CEls
Elworthy Cottage Plants	CElw
Emerald Plants	**CEme**
Endsleigh Gardens Nursery	CEnd
English Woodlands	SEWo
Essentially Hops	**SEsH**
Exclusive Plants Nursery	CExl
Fairweather's Garden Centre	SFai
Farmyard Nurseries	WFar
Fawside Farm Nursery	MBow
Fern Nursery, The	EFer
Fibrex Nurseries Ltd	WFib
Firecrest Trees & Shrubs Nursery	EMac
Firgrove Plants	GFgr
Fly Trap Plants, The	EFly
Forde Abbey Nursery	**CFoA**
Forest Edge Nurseries (The Heather Garden)	CFst
Foxplants	CFoP
Frosch Exclusive Perennials	XFro
Fryer's Roses and Garden Centre	MFry
GAEC Senteurs Du Quercy	XSen
Garden Beauty	**SGBe**
Garden Blooms	NGBl
Garden House Nursery	NGdn
Garden Style Plant Centre	SGsty
Gardener's Cottage Plants	NGrd
Gilbert's Nursery	SGbt
Glendoick Gardens Ltd	GGGa
Gobbett Nursery, The	WGob
Golden Hill Nurseries	SGol
Goscote Nurseries Ltd	MGos
Gracelands Garden	**CGrG**
Grafton Nursery	**WGrf**
Great Dixter Nurseries	SDix
Green Island Gardens	**EGrI**
Greenkoos	NGKo
Green's Leaves	WGrn
Grenville Nurseries	EGren
Grow at Brogdale	**SBdl**
Growild Nursery	**GGro**
Growing Delights	SGro
Gwynfor Growers	WGwG
H W Hyde and Son	**LHWs**
Habitat Aid Ltd.	CHab
Hall Farm Nursery	WHal
Halls of Heddon	NHal
Hampshire Carnivorous Plants	SHmp
Hardy Geranium Nursery, The	**LHGe**
Hardy's Cottage Garden Plants	SHar
Hare Spring Cottage Plants	NHsp
Harlow Carr Plant Centre (RHS)	NRHS
Harper & Debbage	EHDe
Harperley Hall Farm Nurseries	NHpl
Harrells Hardy Plants	WHrl
Hart Canna	SHaC
Hartside Nursery Garden	NHar
Hawthornes Nursery, The	NHaw

Hedgehog Plants and Gardens **EHed**
Hedgexpress MHed
Herb Garden & Historical Plant Nursery, The WHer
Herb Nursery, The MHer
Herbary, The CHby
Hergest Croft Gardens WHCr
Heucheraholics SHeu
Hewitt-Cooper Carnivorous Plants Chew
Hidden Paradise Plants MHid
Hidden Valley Gardens CHVG
Hill Close Gardens MHCG
Hillview Hardy Plants WHil
Hintons Nursery MHtn
Holden Clough Nursery NHol
Hollies Farm Plant Centre MHol
Home Farm Plants LHom
Hoo House Nursery WHoo
Howle Hill Nursery WHwl
Hoyland Plant Centre NHoy
Hyde Hall Plant Centre (RHS) EHyd
Hydrangea Haven SHyH
Ice Alpines WIce
Iris of Sissinghurst SIri
Irisesonline EIri
Ivy Hatch Plant Supplies SIvy
Jackson's Nurseries MJac
Jacques Amand International Ltd **LAma**
Japanese Garden Centre, The **SJap**
Jekka's Herb Farm WJek
John Churcher SChr
John Cullen Gardens Ltd ECul
John Gillies MGil
Jo's Garden Enterprise GJos
JRG Dahlias NJRG
Junker's Nursery CJun
Keepers Nursery SKee
Kells Bay House and Gardens **IKel**
Kelways Plants Ltd **CKel**
Kenwith Conifer Nursery (Gordon Haddow) CKen
Kevock Garden Plants GKev
Kiftsgate Court Gardens WKif
Kings Barn Trees SKin
Kinlochlaich Garden Plant Centre GKin
Knoll Gardens CKno
Kore Wild Fruit Nursery WKor
L. A. Allen WAln
Landford Trees CLnd
Laneside Hardy Orchid Nursery **NLAp**
Langthorns Plantery ELan
Larch Cottage Nurseries NLar
Laurels Nursery, The SLau
Lavender Garden, The WLav
Leaf Creative Design Ltd **WLea**
Leamore Nursery ILea
Leesa's not just Alpines **SLee**
Letham Plants GLet
Lilies Water Gardens LLWG
Lime Cross Nursery SLim
Little Brook Fuchsias SLBF
Loder Plants SLdr
Lodge Farm Plants & Wildflowers MLod
Logie Steading Plants GLog
Long Acre Plants CLAP
Long House Plants ELon
Longstock Park Nursery SLon
Lovegroves WLov
Mac Pennys Nurseries CMac
Macplants GMaP
Madrona Nursery SMad
Majestic Trees LMaj
Malcolm Allison Nurseries WMal
Mallet Court Nursery CMCN
Mandy Plants EMdy
Marchants Hardy Plants SMHy
Margery Fish Plant Nursery CFis
Marshall's Malmaisons EMal
Marwood Hill Gardens **CMHG**
Mead Nursery, The CMea
Meadowgate Nursery SMea
Mendip Bonsai Studio CMen
Mendle Nursery NMen
Merebrook Water Plants WMAq
Merriments Gardens **SMrm**
Mickfield Hostas EMic
Middleton Nurseries **Midl**
Mill Cottage Plants CMil
Mill Race Garden Centre EMil
Millais Nurseries LMil
Millwood Plants CMiW
Mires Beck Nursery NMir
Moore and Moore Plants EMor
Morehavens SMor
Morton Nurseries Ltd MMrt
Mount Pleasant Trees Ltd WMou
Mucklestone Nurseries MMuc
National Dahlia Collection CWGr
National Herb Centre, The MNHC
National Plant Collection of Monarda WMon
Natural Selection CNat
Natural Surroundings NAts
New Hope Gardens WNHG
Newent Plant Centre WNPC
Newport Mills Nursery CNMi
Nicholson Nurseries Limited **MNic**
Nightingale Nursery SNig
Norcroft Nurseries NNor
Norfolk Herbs ENfk
Norfolk Lavender ENor
Norfolk Olive Tree Company, The **EOli**
North Staffordshire Hostas MHost
Northbrook Nursery CNor
Norwell Nurseries & Gardens MNrw

Old Court Nurseries	WOld
Old Hall Plants	EOHP
Orange Pippin Ltd	NOra
Ornamental Trees Ltd	NOrn
P. de Jager & Sons Ltd	SDeJ
Packhorse Farm Nursery	MPkF
Paddock Plants	SPad
Palm House, The	CPHo
Palms-Exotics Ltd	SPalm
Pan-Global Plants	WPGP
Papervale Trees	**IPap**
Paramount Plants & Gardens Ltd	**LPar**
Parks Perennials	CPar
Paugers Plants Ltd	EPau
Paul Jasper Trees	WJas
Paviour and Davies Plants	WPav
Peake Perennials	SPeP
Penberth Plants	CPbh
Penlan Perennials	WPnP
Pépinières Stervinou	**XSte**
Perennial Favourites Ltd	**NFav**
Perryhill Nurseries Ltd	SPer
Perry's Plants	NPer
Pershore College Garden Centre & Nursery	WAvo
Perthshire Heathers	GPer
Peter Beales Roses	EBls
Petrichor Bulb Specialists	**MPtr**
Pettet's Nursery	SPet
Pheasant Acre Plants	WPhe
Phedar Nursery	MPhe
Phoenix Perennial Plants	SPhx
Piccoplant Mikrovermehrungen GmbH	**XPic**
Piecemeal Plants	MPie
Pine Cottage Plants	CPne
Pineview Plants	SPVi
Place for Plants, The	EPfP
Plant Centre at Hortus Loci, The	**SHor**
Plant Company, The	STPC
Plant Specialist, The	LPla
Plant World Gardens and Nurseries	CPla
Plantagogo.com	MPnt
Plantbase	SPlb
Plants for Small Gardens	CSma
Plants, Shoots and Leaves	GPSL
Plants4Presents	SPre
Plantsman's Preference, The	EPPr
PlantsToplant.com	SPtp
Poets Cottage Shrub Nursery	NPoe
Polemonium Plantery	NPol
Pomona Fruits Ltd	EPom
Potash Nursery Ltd	EPts
Potash Plants	LPot
Potted Garden Nursery, The	SPoG
Pottertons Nursery	EPot
Potting Shed, The	IPot
Poyntzfield Herb Nursery	GPoy
Primrose Bank	NPnk
Primrose Cottage Nursery	MPri
Primrose Hall Peonies	**LPmr**
Priory Plants	EPri
ProperPlants.com	CPrp
Puddleplants	**CPud**
Quercus Garden Plants Ltd	GQue
Quiet Corner Plants	NQui
R and A Scamp Quality Daffodils	CQua
R Harkness & Co. Ltd.	**LHkn**
R V Roger Ltd	**NRog**
Rapkyns Nursery	SRkn
Ravensthorpe Nursery	MRav
Really Wild Flowers	CRea
RHS Plant Shop: RHSplants.co.uk	LOPS
Ribblesdale Nurseries	NRib
River Garden Nurseries	SRiv
Romantic Garden, The	**ERom**
Ros Ban Wildlife Garden	IRos
Rose Cottage Plants	ERCP
Roseland House Nursery	CRHN
Rosemoor Plant Centre (RHS)	CRos
Rosie's Garden Plants	**SRGP**
Rotherview Nursery	**SRot**
Roualeyn Nurseries	**WRou**
Rumbling Bridge Nursery	GRum
Rumsey Gardens	SRms
Rushrose Nursery	NRush
Ryal Nursery	NRya
Saith Ffynnon Wildlife Plants	WSFF
Salutation Nursery, The	**SSal**
Savill Gardens Visitor Centre	LSvl
Savin Nurseries	SavN
Seagate Irises	**ESgI**
Seale Rose Garden	SSea
Seaside Plants	CSde
Sempervivums By Post	**SSem**
Shipton Bulbs	WShi
Shire Plants	**LShi**
Shropshire Sarracenias	WSSs
Shrubland Park Nurseries	EShb
Sienna Hosta	SSien
Simply Succulents	SSim
Slack Top Alpine Nursery	NSla
South Milton Plant Nursery	WSMil
Southern Fruit Trees	SSFr
Southon Plants	LSou
Special Plants	CSpe
SpecialPerennials.com	MSpe
Spinneywell Nursery	WSpi
Spring Reach Nursery	LSRN
St Bridget Nurseries Ltd	CSBt
Staddon Farm Nurseries	CSta
Starborough Nursery	SSta
Stillingfleet Lodge Nurseries	NSti
Stone House Cottage Nurseries	WSHC
Stone Lane Gardens	**CSto**
Stonyford Cottage Nursery	MSCN

Straight Mile Nursery Gardens ESMi
Strete Gate Camellias CSgt
Strictly Daylilies EStr
Style Roses ESty
Sue Proctor Plants NSue
Summerdale Garden Nursery NSum
Sunnybank Vine Nursery (National Vine Collection) WSuV
Sunnyside Nursery LSun
Sussex Fruit Trees SSFT
Swallows Nursery MSwo
Swines Meadow Farm Nursery ESwi
T. D. Thursfield MThu
Taylors Clematis Nursery NTay
Thorncroft Clematis Ltd ETho
Thuya Alpine Nursery WThu
Timpany Nurseries & Gardens ITim
Tiny Plant Company, The MTin
Todd's Botanics ETod
Topiary Arts LTop
Tortworth Plants Ltd WTor
Tree Peony Company NTPC
Tree Shop at Frank P. Matthews Ltd, The WMat
Tree Shop Ltd WTSh
Trees Online MTrO
Trehane Nursery CTrh
Treseders Nursery CTsd
Trevena Cross Nurseries CTrC
Trevor White Old Fashioned Roses ETWh
Triffids CTtf
Triscombe Nurseries CTri
Ty Cwm Nursery WTyc
Ventnor Botanic Garden SVen
Victorian Violas EVic
Victoriana Nursery Gardens SVic
Village Plants Nursery Ltd MVil
Viv Marsh Postal Plants WViv
W Robinson & Son (Seeds & Plants) Ltd NRob
Waddow Lodge Garden NWad
Walcot Organic Nursery WWct
Walled Garden Nursery CWGN
Walled Garden Treberfydd WTre
Walnut Tree Garden Nursery EWTr
Waltham Herbs EWhm
Water Garden Plants EWat
Water Garden, The CWat
Waterside Nursery MWts
Weasdale Nurseries Ltd. NWea
Web Garden Centre SWeb
Weird Plants by Gill LWei
West Acre Gardens EWes
Westcountry Nurseries (North Devon) Ltd CWCL
Westonbury Mill Water Garden WWtn
Westshores Nurseries NWsh
Whitehall Farmhouse Plants WWFP
Whitelea Nursery MWht
Wild Flower Nursery, The WWild
Wildegoose Nursery WGoo
Wisley Plant Centre (RHS) LRHS
Withleigh Nurseries CWit
Wolverton Plants Ltd SWvt
Woodlands EWld
Woottens of Wenhaston EWoo
Wyndford Farm Plants Ltd GWyn

INDEX OF ADVERTISERS

A

Alpine Garden Society, The 4

B

Beechcroft Nurseries & Garden Centre 32
Big Plant Nursery 956
Birchfleet Nurseries 957

D

David Austin Roses 24
Deacon's Nursery 957
Dibleys Nurseries 957
Dingle Nursery & Garden 31

G

Greenhouse People, The IBC

H

Hardy Plant Society 959
HotBin Composting IFC
Howle Hill Nursery 956

J

Jelitto Perennial Seeds 31

L

Larch Cottage Nurseries 32
Lockyer C S 957

P

Patio Black Spot Removal Co, The 3
P de Jager & Sons Ltd 957
Peter Beales Roses 32
Pheasant Acre Plants 24
Plant Heritage 960
Plants4Presents 957
Plantsman, The 852

R

RHS membership 860
RHS Monographs 955
RHS Shops and Plant Centres 6
RHS Plants Online 23

S

Sheen Botanical Labels Limited 31
Swines Meadow Garden Centre 957

T

Triscombe Nurseries 956